Prospects Postgraduate Directory 2013/14

WE BRING YOU MORE THAN 55,000 POSTGRAD COURSES AND RESEARCH OPPORTUNITIES IN THE UK AND IRELAND

Prospects Postgraduate Directory tells you everything you need to know about becoming a postgraduate student. It shows you how to find a postgraduate course and where the courses are, and explains what it's like to do one.

The editorial section at the start of the directory (page 6) gets to grips with the key issues that face prospective postgraduates, including job prospects, fees and funding,

university league tables, and what to ask postgraduate recruiters.

The UK and Ireland's leading postgraduate course and research providers showcase their opportunities in the profile section, beginning on page 21. This section is designed to help you make an informed choice about which university to attend.

We also bring you more than 55,000

postgraduate courses and research opportunities available in the UK and Ireland. This section begins on page 77. You can search these programmes in more depth, and contact course providers directly, at *www.prospects.ac.uk/findcourses*

You can also search the UK's biggest database of postgraduate funding at *www.prospects.ac.uk/funding*

Graduate Prospects is owned by, and gifts its profits to, the registered charity HECSU, an agency of UUK and GuildHE. HECSU supports the work of higher education careers services in the UK and Ireland, commissions and funds high-quality research and gives financial support to the organisation AGCAS (Association of Graduate Careers Advisory Services). Graduate Prospects publishes the Prospects series of graduate recruitment and postgraduate study publications and provides online careers and postgraduate course information via the UK's official graduate recruitment site, *Prospects.ac.uk*

Published by Graduate Prospects Ltd, Prospects House, Booth Street East, Manchester M13 9EP UK · 00 44 161 277 5200 · *www.prospects.ac.uk*
Publisher Fateha Khalik F.Khalik@prospects.ac.uk Produced by Graham Allchurch and Luke Berté · Advertising sales Robyn Benjamin, Emma Fowler, Jennifer Nicholls, Heather Reynolds, Simon Rust, Alison Smith, Becky Stevens, Leanne Watts · postgrad@prospects.ac.uk · 00 44 161 277 5200
Prospects Postgraduate Directory 2013/14 ©2013 Graduate Prospects Ltd · Company Registration NO: 2626618 · ISBN 978-1-84016-183-0 · ISSN 1471-8510

FSC
www.fsc.org
MIX
Paper from responsible sources
FSC® C006032

ISBN 978-1-84016-183-0

3011010363

9 781840 161830

My Prospects

It is now even easier to stay on top
of your hunt for a job or postgraduate
course with Prospects' personalised service

What is My Prospects?

My Prospects is a personalised
environment, delivering careers
advice, jobs and training
opportunities specifically
tailored to your preferences.

Create an account

Go to *prospects.ac.uk/myprospects*
to register.

Select your preferences

Tell us what types of jobs you're
interested in and where you're
willing to work so that we only
send you relevant jobs
and courses.

Your favourites

Researching jobs and courses
on prospects.ac.uk? Why not save
them to your favourites and apply
when you're ready.

Career Planner

If you're struggling with what
to do next then My Prospects
can help you to decide. You need
to answer a number of questions
based on four key areas:

What am I able to do?
What skills do I have?
What motivates me?
What do I want out of a job?

You will then be matched to the
most relevant occupations for
you. These may be roles you've
already considered, or entirely
new opportunities you've never
thought of before. You'll also
see current vacancies on offer
in these areas.

Explore your dashboard

An essential tool for managing
your career, where you'll find your
favourite jobs and courses. Other
suitable opportunities will also
appear automatically.

Your applications

Jobs you've applied for through
your My Prospects account
are saved here. Use this
as a reference point to help
you prepare for any interviews.

Get social

Browse career events in your
area, have your say in our latest
poll and join in the conversation
with our social media feeds.

Get more from Prospects

Prospects.ac.uk is the UK's official graduate careers and postgraduate study website. It contains the UK's official postgraduate study database as well as comprehensive information on postgraduate funding and guidance on issues such as postgraduate qualifications, applications and studying abroad

Search more than 55,000 postgraduate taught courses and research opportunities at
www.prospects.ac.uk/findcourses
The UK's official postgraduate course database contains all the information in this directory plus course descriptions, contact information, a breakdown of each programme's aims, assessment methods and the way in which it is delivered. Further information on the institution, such as tuition fees and the number of postgraduate students is also provided. Each entry provides a direct email address and link to the postgraduate course provider so you can contact them yourself.

Apply directly to your chosen institution through
www.prospects.ac.uk/findcourses
The majority of the courses held online at *www.prospects.ac.uk/findcourses* offer the opportunity to apply online.

Register with My Prospects and get postgraduate course information and the latest job vacancies via email or text

Search hundreds of postgraduate funding opportunities
at *www.prospects.ac.uk/funding*
Prospects provides a comprehensive guide to all aspects of postgraduate funding, complete with links to funding bodies and advice on how to secure the best funding for your course.

Focus your career at
www.prospects.ac.uk/myprospects_login.htm
Register with My Prospects and you can benefit from our email services. Get postgraduate course information and the latest job vacancies via email or text. Sign up for our newsletter and digital magazine and receive information on postgraduate courses, higher education news, practical advice on job applications and career strategy, as well as the latest job adverts. Not sure where to start? By joining My Prospects you gain access to Prospects Career Planner, a great tool which examines your key skills and interests to determine what jobs will suit you.

International students
For information on services available to international students visit *www.prospects.ac.uk/postgraduate_study_in_the_uk.htm*

Marine Biology
Course details

1 University name
University of Aberdeen

Department
School of Biological Sciences

Course title
Marine Biology

2 Qualification, duration, mode
PhD 36FT 60PT * MPhil 24FT 42PT * MSc by research 12FT 24PT

Points of entry
October

3 Entry requirements
Minimum Second Class honours degree in relevant discipline

4 Funding
Research Councils, charitable trusts (Wellcome, Leverhulme), various sponsorships.

5 International student info
Some PhD programmes may be available allowing students to undertake the majority of their studies off-campus, e.g. carrying out fieldwork in their home country.

6 Course description
The School of Biological Sciences is at the forefront of international biological research. Our research ranges from the arctic to the tropics, from molecular biology to community ecology, and involves both marine and terrestrial ecosystems.

7 Contact name
Senior Postgraduate Secretary

Telephone
+44(0)1244 272686

Fax
+44(0)1244 272703

Email
graduateschoolBSPR-clsm@abdn.ac.uk

Web
www.abdn.ac.uk/clsm/graduateschool

8 Apply online
Apply online

WHAT A POSTGRADUATE DATABASE ENTRY TELLS YOU

1 What the course is called and where it is offered

2 Name of the qualification, how long it takes and how it is delivered – e.g. distance learning, modular

3 What qualifications you need to get on the course

4 Available financial support. This may refer to one of the Research Councils, or to institutional scholarships and awards. Often it will tell you that most students on the course are self-funded

5 This section provides information specifically relevant to students from outside the UK and usually states the minimum English language qualification required

6 A summary of what the course offers and how it is put together

7 Contact information plus an email link to the course provider. You can find institutions' contact details in the Higher Education Institutions section at the back of this directory

8 The option to apply online for the course direct to the institution

What's inside?

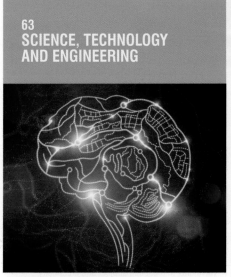

63 SCIENCE, TECHNOLOGY AND ENGINEERING

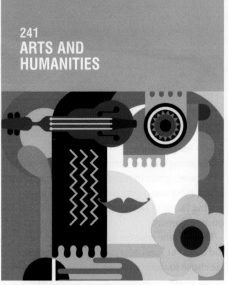

241 ARTS AND HUMANITIES

Section sponsored by:
BPP UNIVERSITY COLLEGE

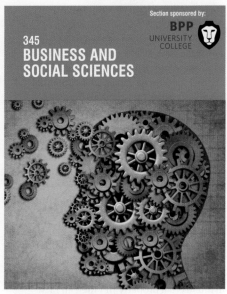

345 BUSINESS AND SOCIAL SCIENCES

Why become a postgraduate?

Further study lets you follow your passions, develop specialist knowledge and improve your job prospects. However, you need to weigh up the pros and cons to ensure it's the right choice for you

If you're considering postgraduate study you'll find a huge range of degree programmes available in the UK, with more than 55,000 courses listed in Prospects' postgraduate database alone.

Regardless of the subject you choose to take on you need to make sure that you're studying for the right reasons.

Increase your employability

Whether you want to gain entry into a particular job, move up the career ladder or start out in a new industry, studying at postgraduate level can improve your prospects.

'From a professional perspective, a postgraduate degree can be a valuable addition to your CV if it is undertaken for reasons that can be explained to potential employers,' says Tracy Bussoli from The Careers Group at the University of London.

For example, someone with an engineering degree might do a Masters in sustainable energy to develop the specific knowledge and skills required to work in the solar industry, while an art graduate might take a Masters in museum or gallery management if they want to go down that particular route.

Developing an area of specialisation through postgraduate study is a popular way of forging a career. For instance, if you have a law background and want to specialise in intellectual property (IP) then an LLM in IP might be one way to gain these skills. Before specialising, research where there are skills shortages in the industry by speaking to employers and make sure that your chosen course will fill those gaps. However, don't opt for the most lucrative career just for the sake of it – you need to make sure you love the subject you study.

Networking is a great way to find opportunities to progress your career. Postgraduate study can help to build contacts by liaising with people who have similar interests, such as your peers and your supervisor. Add experts from industry into the mix – now that most institutions offer work placements with employers and guest lectures from professionals – and you could be one step closer to gaining work experience or even a job.

'A postgraduate degree can help you to tap into relevant networks by meeting employers

at presentations, working on projects pertinent to employers or doing internships that relate to specific sectors,' explains Tracy.

Study for pleasure

While many students embark on further study with career goals in mind, for some enjoyment of a subject and a curiosity to find out more is a big factor in persuading them to stay on at university.

This was the case for Jakob Whitfield, who did a PhD at The University of Manchester. He chose to study a degree that was unrelated to his undergraduate course and the job he was doing at the time.

'A friend had seen a Masters and PhD place advertised and called me to say that she thought it was perfect for me. The position was for a joint project with a museum looking at the history of gas turbines.'

Although Jakob had no qualifications in this area, it was a topic that interested him. He called the department and explained the relevant experience he did have, which included some knowledge of museums and museum management.

'My prospective supervisor invited me to the department for a chat, which was positive and I applied for the position. I was then invited to a formal interview and was lucky enough to get a place.'

If you're considering postgraduate study you need to make sure you have the funds to support yourself. Jakob was fortunate enough to have the freedom to take up something that he loved and secure funding.

'I'm happy that I did the PhD, as it taught me a lot about myself and gave me the chance to spend three years doing something I love.'

Gain transferable skills

As well as furthering your career, postgraduate study gives you the chance to prepare for the world of work. For example, doing a research course such as a PhD will enhance your analytical, motivational and self-management skills, all of which are valuable attributes whatever you decide to do after your studies.

Such research courses can seem counter-intuitive, as sometimes the research topic appears to be very specific and not always transferable to the workplace. However, by recording and producing your own research, transferable skills are developed, which are highly valued by employers.

Doing postgraduate study because you lack other ideas or because you don't want to enter the working world is unlikely to turn out well. So, while there are lots of good reasons to commit to spending more time in the classroom, there are also a number of reasons it might not be for you.

Do you want to spend money on additional education if you don't need to? You could be gaining a year's paid work experience rather than studying for a postgraduate degree if it's not essential in helping you to succeed in your future career. Make these decisions early, investigate funding options and be clear about your reasons for continuing your studies.

If you decide that postgraduate study is for you, go for it. It offers a unique opportunity to expand your skills and puts you in a great position from which to embark on your dream career. Get in there now and reap the awards.

INSIDE VIEW

Dr Holly Prescott is a recruitment adviser at the University of Birmingham. She discusses her views on postgraduate study

The benefits of postgraduate study vary depending on the subject areas. For instance, if you decide you want a career change or want to train in a profession for which your undergraduate degree did not directly prepare you, further study can help you change direction.

Postgraduate study also helps to develop your critical thinking and keep your cerebral muscles exercised, as well as allowing you to dip back into the world of education if you have spent a period of time in a professional environment.

A postgraduate degree, especially a PhD, will provide you with an intellectual challenge and will also give you time to devote to one particular subject or research area – a luxury rarely afforded in the world of work.

Postgraduate study gives you the chance to expand your CV and your personal development, so that you come out of your postgraduate course with transferable skills and experience as well as an academic qualification. Aim to graduate from your postgraduate degree not only knowing your subject better, but knowing yourself better too.

STUDENT VIEW

Josephine Cadwallader-Thornewill currently studies the MSc Sustainability of the Built Environment at the University of Brighton. She talks about the benefits of postgraduate study

I didn't feel like my undergraduate degree prepared me enough for working in my desired industry. The job specifications that appealed to me and the roles I wanted to apply for required me to be much more knowledgeable, so I chose the course because the modules covered information gaps that I need to fill if I am going to start a career in the environment and renewable industries.

The advantages of further study far outweigh the disadvantages. You get a great education with more support and interaction from lecturers, plus

you have the opportunity to stay at university for another year and to take advantage of the unique lifestyle that comes with it. What's more, you eventually get to a point where you can call yourself a specialist in a subject.

To fully comprehend all of the intricacies of a subject and to be able to debate the significance of various issues within your subject with peers is something quite special and very attractive to employers.

After three years of juggling student finance and part-time jobs, the prospect of a salary is the light at the end of the tunnel. It's really important to remember that spending this extra year in further study is a financial investment in yourself.

How to... choose the right course

If you're continuing your studies, it's vital that you pick the right qualification and so preparation and research are essential

There are many different courses and programmes in any field of study, as anyone who searches through this directory or online at *Prospects.ac.uk* will discover.

But, depending on your goals and ambitions, not all of them will be relevant for your specific aims. Courses with similar titles do not necessarily have the same content or recruit students from the same undergraduate degrees. So where do you start when shortlisting potential courses?

Think carefully

It's essential that you are absolutely sure that the subject you have chosen and the courses for which you are planning on applying for are right for you.

Don't just do it for the sake of it – postgraduate study is intense and for the most part discipline and a love of the subject is required to succeed. What's more, it's an investment of time and money, which it'd be better not to waste.

Natalie Laing graduated from the University of Liverpool with a degree in psychology. After working in various administrative roles she wanted a new challenge and decided to do a Postgraduate Certificate in Education (PGCE).

'There were a number of reasons why I thought doing a PGCE would be beneficial to me. Teaching is fast paced and there is barely enough time to eat, let alone clock watch. You are in a position to be incredibly influential and make a real difference to children's lives. It could also prove to be a very useful qualification if at some point I decided to spend some time in another country.'

Natalie believes that further study in any capacity is a great advantage to your career, but she sounds a note of caution.

'Other than the fact it enhances your CV, you will also learn new skills, make great friends and potentially great contacts. I would, however, think carefully about the course to which you apply.'

Natalie advises prospective postgraduates to look at the university itself, what the course offers in comparison to others and what your career options are.

....

'It's nice to be regarded as having the potential for further study, but make sure it fits into your longer-term plans too'

'Get some experience of the role you hope to obtain before you commit to a course so that you can be confident it's the right career for you. Also, consider your chances of gaining employment within the sector – what roles are available within your area? Is it likely you would have to move or commute and, if so, is that something you want? Look carefully at the financial side – would you be entitled to receive a bursary or would there be a chance of gaining sponsorship from a company?'

Know your reasons for studying

Postgraduate courses such as teaching, law, social work, nursing, medicine, clinical

psychology and town planning open professional doors that would otherwise be locked firmly shut.

While the logic of taking courses like the PGCE is clear, there can be a mixture of reasons for choosing other postgraduate options. If the course is relevant to future career aims, it could help you to stand out from the crowd of other graduates.

Postgraduates on any career-oriented or conversion course must decide if they truly want to work in that specific profession. Research can obviously help make this decision easier, as can using Prospects' career planner tool *(www.prospects.ac.uk/myprospects_planner_login)* to find out what jobs would suit your personality and ambitions.

On the other hand, many people embark on postgraduate study simply due to their love of a subject and a desire to contribute to the research around a topic, rather than being driven completely by their career goals.

Fine tune your skills

Angela Kilpatrick studied English Language and Linguistics with Theatre Studies at the University of Central Lancashire (UCLan) before working as a research assistant.

Realising she would need a postgraduate qualification in order to progress her career;

she is now studying the Master of Research (MRes) in Educational Linguistics at UCLan.

'The nature of my subject discipline allows me to develop a multitude of subject-specific and transferable skills. It's an area applicable to a number of careers, particularly those where excellent communication skills and analytical skills are required.

'Having a degree is not enough in this economic climate and obtaining one is almost obligatory. With the increase of degree holders saturating the labour market, it's become important to go one step further. A Masters allows you to fine tune your skills and acquire specialist knowledge.'

Angela asserts the importance of choosing the correct course based on her own experiences of indecision.

'Make sure the course you choose is right for you. I started a taught Masters and soon found it wasn't quite what I was expecting. It was a costly mistake to make. I'm much happier now that I am on a course that suits my interests, and is directly applicable to my career. It helps to improve your motivation and dedication to the course, which is important as studying at postgraduate level is not easy.

'You need to enjoy what you're studying so that you can fully immerse yourself and apply your energies. Before you sign up, find out about the course content, approaches to teaching and learning, and assessment process.'

Get a feel for the university

Postgraduate recruitment adviser at the University of Birmingham Dr Holly Prescott recommends attending university open days and meeting representatives at fairs. 'It's the only way to get a feel for the university – see yourself there, think about whether you would fit in and, most importantly, whether the course on offer is suited to your needs.

'Research the interests of staff at the university and ask about the modules and research areas that will be available to you. Then consider whether these meet your interests, motivations and aims.

'If you're currently studying, consult your lecturers and tutors; if you want to do a PhD, they are likely to know who is prominent in a certain research area, where they are currently working and how you might arrange a meeting with them. Don't just do postgraduate study because your current tutors tell you that you should, though. It's nice to be regarded as having the potential for further study, but make sure it fits into your longer-term plans too.'

QUALIFICATIONS: WHAT'S ON OFFER?

Find out more about the types of postgraduate programmes available...

At postgraduate level, study opportunities fall into two main areas: taught and research.

Taught Masters

These usually last for 12 months and are either vocationally based or involve a detailed study of a particular aspect of your field. The qualification gained depends on the area of study:

- Masters of Arts (MA) courses cover arts, business and social sciences
- Masters of Science (MSc) programmes are awarded for study in science and technology, as well as some social science and business courses
- Master of Business Administration (MBA) programmes are the most well-known qualifications for business, but cost considerably more than other courses

Other disciplines may have their own specific taught Masters qualifications.

Research Masters

These degrees focus on students producing original material and independent thought and often last for a year if taken full time. Students will have little to no in-class teaching and will be expected to work on their own. A Master of Research (MRes) is the next step up from an undergraduate degree, with many students continuing their academic research into doctoral programmes such as a PhD.

Combined Masters

Such programmes are offered at many universities and require students to complete a combination of taught modules, independent research and, in some cases, placements.

Different modes of study

An increasing number of students are starting to realise that a full-time postgraduate course might not fit in with their lifestyles. As a result, they're taking advantage of the different modes of study on offer, such as part-time, distance learning and blended learning options. For more information on the modes of study available, turn to page 11.

KEY QUESTIONS

Do course leaders have expertise in my research area?

Has this course helped recent graduates to enter their chosen profession?

Does the course provide close links with industry professionals and enable me to make contacts?

Can I afford the course fees and cost of living?

Am I happy to live where my university is based?

How many places are there on the course? What is the student-staff ratio?

Is there any specialist funding available if I take this course at this university?

How good are the facilities, student resources and IT departments?

Will I need any other qualifications to get a job after my postgraduate degree?

University league tables

Popular among would-be undergraduates choosing their first degree, but are university league tables helpful to prospective postgraduates?

Choosing between similar courses at different universities is more art than science. For prospective undergraduates, help is available in university league tables that use different data sets, surveys and studies to work out the institutions that perform best in each subject area.

As a result, league tables are often one of the most popular resources for those trying to find their perfect course and university. However, at postgraduate level it's much more complicated than that.

Subjective weightings

The *Financial Times* publishes a number of different international rankings that could come in useful for those interested in further study in business. These include a global ranking of Master of Business Administration (MBA) courses, a table for European business schools, and a list of the top providers of Masters in management programmes.

Found online at *http://rankings.ft.com/businessschoolrankings/rankings*, the tables provide a range of information such as the average salary of alumni three years after graduation, the difference in salary prior to the course and afterwards, and the number of graduates in employment.

Data for the tables is collected using two surveys: one for alumni and one for the institutions themselves. In addition, the news source's research ranking, which is calculated according to the number of articles published in internationally recognised academic and practitioner journals, contributes to the final ranking.

However, the component items of information here are given subjective weightings to produce overall rankings, meaning these tables are, of course, by no means official.

In addition, they rely on the opinions of alumni, which are also subjective. One MBA might have been perfect for one student, but what if that same MBA, which is ranked at number one, doesn't cover the topics that you're interested in? Is it still 'the best' MBA?

Open to criticism

For those considering a postgraduate qualification outside of the discipline of business, the *Guardian* has tables on universities' taught postgraduate courses – mainly Masters – at *www.guardian.co.uk/education/series/postgraduate-subject-tables-2013*

These tables provide some key pieces of information on university departments' expenditure per student, completion rate and student-staff ratio, among others.

However, the biggest snag with the tables becomes clear with a look at American studies – only one university is shown for the subject, while in reality there are many more that offer the programme, as you will see in this publication. A check on other courses fares much better, but the information is not comprehensive.

In addition, it's important to note that these are not tables in the traditional sense, as the institutions are listed in alphabetical order, rather than being ranked.

The final place prospective postgraduates could look when deciding on a course is the league tables produced for potential undergraduates. Although not intended for postgrads, the information provided could give you a bit of extra insight into a university's potential strengths or weaknesses in a particular discipline. Examples of such tables include the Complete University Guide, *The Times'* Good University Guide, the QS World University Rankings and the *Guardian's* university league tables.

That said, these are open to criticism in the same way that the *Financial Times'* tables are. This is why there is so much debate over what is the best university across the board or for a particular subject.

....

'These tables provide some key pieces of information on university departments' expenditure per student, completion rate and student-staff ratio, among others'

Holly Higgins, who studied an MA in eighteenth century studies and is a researcher at the Higher Education Careers Service Unit (HECSU), says, 'I avoided looking at the league tables published in newspapers when I was choosing where to study for my postgraduate degree because they aren't official, they rarely agree, and they weren't looking at the kinds of issues I was interested in.

'I wanted to find out about course content, departments' specialist fields, lecturers' research interests, training opportunities, the postgraduate community, and so on; none of these are covered by league tables.'

Holly goes on to state how the best way to get a feel for the reputation of an institution or particular course among employers, academics or previous graduates is to do your own research and find out what people think yourself.

So, if you're considering postgraduate study and are yet to decide on a course or university, feel free to glean as much useful contextual information from these postgraduate university tables as possible. However, make sure you add your own research – based on your specific goals – into the mix and don't solely rely on the tables when making your final decision.

Modes of study

Choosing a postgraduate course can be difficult at the best of times, but things can get more confusing when you consider the different study options on offer. Let us help you decide which type of study is best for you...

Full-time study

This is the most common form of postgraduate study and allows you to study intensively for the duration of the course. The exact meaning of 'full time' will differ from programme to programme and university to university. For example, it could mean 9am to 5pm every weekday, or it could mean differing contact and research hours every week.

However the full-time course is set up, it will allow you to achieve your chosen qualification in the shortest possible time compared to other modes of study.

Part-time study

Another popular choice, part-time study is typically aimed at students who have to juggle work or family commitments as well as their degree. It also tends to attract those considering changing careers.

It will take longer for you to complete a course of this kind and you may find you're not as immersed in university life as those on full-time programmes, but it will give you more flexibility.

For most part-time courses, the days and times you need to be at university will be set in stone and won't change. Teaching could take place in the daytime or the evening.

However, sometimes this isn't the case and your tuition days may change, which can make things difficult for those in full-time employment to get sufficient time off for their studies.

BLENDED LEARNING

This is a method of study in which face-to-face classroom time is combined with online learning.

This means that as well as providing students with contact time with lecturers, private tutors and fellow students, they also get increased flexibility from being able to work from home.

Other benefits of this mode of study include reducing travel costs and developing independent learning skills.

BLOCK MODE LEARNING

A relatively new method of study, block mode helps students who want to study part time but are affected by not being able to plan time off from employment.

This involves modules being taught in full over a fixed period of time (usually five days at a time), allowing students to look at their timetable, see which weeks they will be in university, and book the relevant time off.

The number of learning blocks planned for a course will depend on the number of modules taken. The blocks only take into account face-to-face contact time with lecturers, so you will be expected to revise, research and complete assignments in your own time.

DISTANCE LEARNING

If you want to study a postgraduate course but your location or other commitments are such that travelling to university for your learning would be inconvenient, distance learning could be an option for you.

This mode of study involves learning exclusively from home, or another location of your choice. While that may sound like a disadvantage, distance learning courses have developed significantly since first being introduced.

Students still get a personal tutor, who they can communicate with throughout the course and from who they receive regular and comprehensive feedback on their work.

Work is similar to a regular postgraduate course, with assignments taking the form of essays, short tests, projects, dissertations, projects or presentations. Assignments are either tutor marked or computer marked.

All the resources you need to complete your studies are provided, often in a variety of platforms, from print and eBooks to DVDs and online videos.

In addition, you can take as long as you like to complete your course and, in some cases, even dedicate more time to your studies in one year than the next.

How to... apply for postgraduate study

Once you've narrowed down your choices it's time to take the plunge and apply. However, this can sometimes be a complicated and time-consuming process. Let us help you maximise your chances of success...

In the last academic year, 568,505 people were studying for a part- or full-time postgraduate degree in the UK.

The majority of these students chose medicine, business or education-related degrees, but even in these popular subjects there's an abundance of programmes to choose from. Dig a bit deeper and you'll find courses covering almost every topic you can imagine across arts and humanities; business; social sciences; teaching and education; and science, engineering, technology and mathematics (STEM).

With so many courses on offer the process of choosing the right one and then applying to get onto the programme can be daunting, but there are ways to make it efficient and stress free.

Investigate

'The best way to feel confident that you've made a great choice is to visit the universities you are considering, speak to the tutors and check out whether the location will suit you. Especially if you want to be near to particular business or industrial sectors that may offer placements or internships,' says Alisa Quinn from the student recruitment and enquiries department at Middlesex University.

Postgraduate study attracts people for many reasons. Students may wish to achieve a professional qualification or further their interest in a particular subject area. Professor Anthony Woodman, pro vice-chancellor of research and enterprise at the University of West London, thinks students should already have a clear picture in their minds of the purpose of their studies. 'Know why you wish to undertake postgraduate study. For example: for personal development; for salary enhancement; if it's required to retain a job; or if it will support a change in career.'

Wherever possible, visit your shortlisted universities and research how current students rate their study experience in your chosen subject. Be sure to search social networks such as Facebook for course-specific pages or groups for useful feedback.

If you're still unsure about things once you've carried out your own research, contact each of your shortlisted universities to obtain further information and ask any unresolved questions. Don't be afraid to continue your investigations until you feel confident about your choices, as studying at postgraduate level is a big commitment.

Alisa thinks that further study depends on strong student-teacher relationships. 'The academics teaching you will be central to your success, so learning more about them is a good use of your time. What are their specialisms? What are they researching and what industry experience do they have?'

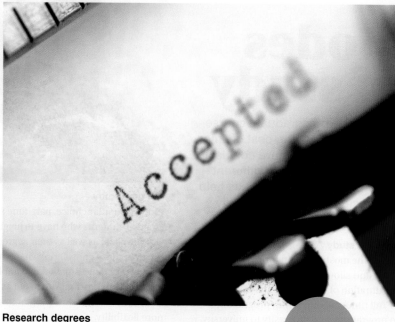

Research degrees

There is no single body that covers all postgraduate admissions. Each university will have alternative application procedures and deadlines so it's important to make a note of closing dates and then apply as soon as you can. It's worth noting that, unlike the UCAS application system for undergraduate schemes, you can apply to as many universities and courses as you like.

If you're applying for a research degree, you are advised to make contact with your chosen institution before submitting an application in order to check whether or not the university has the specialist staff required to supervise your proposed research.

'We recommend that potential research students try and identify a suitable supervisor at university before applying. They can explore department research pages, or look at the potential research scholarships that are advertised,' says Dr Mark Skippen, senior postgraduate recruitment officer at Swansea University.

Higher expectations

If applying for a research degree, it's important to act like you are applying for a graduate job rather than sticking to the same principles for previous higher education applications. 'Your application form and behaviour should be professional. Remember, a university will view you as a professional graduate and therefore has higher expectations than when students apply to join undergraduate programmes,' stresses Professor Woodman.

Universities will also be impressed with an application outlining a student's ability to self-motivate and work in their own time. Professor Woodman adds, 'Provide evidence to show that you will be capable of independent study and workload management; postgraduate study places high emphasis on self learning.'

Most courses – research and taught – require students to apply directly to the institution using an online application form through the university's website.

FIVE KEY POINTS

Be as professional as possible throughout the entire process

....

Carry out thorough research and create a refined shortlist

....

Visit your shortlisted universities

....

Check social media and gather student feedback on courses

....

Apply early to avoid missing out

However, for some courses there are different application processes. For instance, those wishing to gain a postgraduate certificate in education (PGCE) or complete School-Centred Initial Teacher Training (SCITT) are required to submit an application through the Graduate Teacher Training Registry (GTTR). Practice-based music courses at UK conservatoires are another example; applications are made through the Conservatoires UK Admissions Service.

As part of your application you will need to show supporting evidence, as well as provide references, in order to back up your credentials. It's generally a requirement that you provide testimonials from former lecturers or course leaders who've helped to guide your learning. 'Most universities will require academic transcripts and references from your previous studies,' advises Steven Holdcroft, head of admissions and recruitment at the University of Kent.

Funding and finance

Universities will ask how you intend to finance your study when you apply. Departments need to know how many of their applicants are seeking nomination for funding awards and how many are competing for other public funding. If no funding is available through the department, you must state your most likely means of paying for your course (if you have any). You don't need to have established a definitive source at this point.

....

'Provide evidence to show that you will be capable of independent study and workload management'

Although your sources of funding don't need to be confirmed at the application stage, it's important to start planning how you will support yourself financially as soon as possible. Dr Skippen advises students to apply for as much funding as possible. 'There are numerous organisations that offer scholarships, grants or awards for postgraduate study. In order to maximise your chances of success, you should start your research early and apply to as many organisations as you are eligible for.'

Most students fund postgraduate study through a variety of means, including: Professional and Career Development Loans (PCDLs); Research Council grants; part-time work and scholarships and bursaries.

However, there are avenues that many forget to explore, which Professor Woodman highlights. 'Don't forget family and friends for financial support, they are often more willing to help than expected.'

With some early decision making and careful planning, applying for postgraduate study might not be as difficult as you once anticipated.

Dr Manny Ling is a lecturer on the MA Design: Multimedia and Graphics programme at the University of Sunderland...

Research as much as you can about the programme via the internet and brochures. Then, you should visit the institution and ask questions that have not been answered during your research. These might include: What are the tutors like? What is their expertise? What resources does the course have? How many students are on the course? What are the contact hours?

Find out what the university can offer you and, if you are applying for a research degree, make your research proposal applicable to the institution for which you are applying.

If you are applying to more than one university, don't do a standard proposal letter and just change the name of the institution – make sure you tailor it specifically for that university, just like if you were applying for a job.

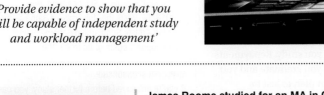

STUDENT VIEW

James Roome studied for an MA in Creative Writing at Manchester Metropolitan University (MMU)...

When I applied for my MA, I only applied to one course due to geographical and work-related restrictions – MMU was the only institution which offered a part-time course structured around my full-time job.

The MA Creative Writing required submission of a portfolio of work, poetry in my case, accompanied by a cover letter/personal statement, followed by a relatively informal telephone interview.

At postgraduate level, it's not all about your academic achievements, particularly if you've spent time out of university in work following the completion of your undergraduate course.

It's important not to be put off if you don't have the standard qualifications you feel would be required to gain entry onto such a course. For example, my creative writing MA contemporaries came from a range of backgrounds – many had spent a long time out of the world of academia before deciding to apply. Just because you've been out in the wilderness for 20 years, it doesn't mean you'll struggle to get onto an MA course, particularly in a subject like creative writing, where it's far more about your skills in writing than it is your academic qualifications.

How to... fund further study

The cost of postgraduate study is often one of the biggest obstacles for prospective students, but you could find that's taken care of if you get your finances in order and do your research into the funding available

Finding a place on a course is the simple part of postgraduate study. The hard part is working out a way to pay for your course fees on top of supporting yourself financially. Because of this, it's vital that you put funding near the top of your list of priorities and try to secure some as early as possible.

Research Council grants

The biggest source of funding available to universities to support postgraduate students on a research course is the UK's seven Research Councils. They cover disciplines from arts and humanities to science and technology and everything in between. Around 6,000 studentships are awarded to universities by the councils each year. Those fortunate enough to be awarded a studentship receive a stipend that normally covers tuition fees and contributes to the cost of living. For 2013/14, this will be worth a minimum of £13,726.

As universities and research institutions continue to deal with funding cuts, the number of studentships has declined in recent years and no Research Council funding will be available to students taking taught postgraduate programmes in 2013/14.

Applications must be submitted to university departments and not directly to the Research Councils. Make sure you ask your university about the availability of Research Council funding in its departments and schools.

Professional and Career Development Loans

As the number of postgraduates in the UK grows, but the amount of Research Council

funding declines, more and more students are finding that they have to look elsewhere if they are to fund their studies.

Student and professional loans can be taken out from most of the major banks in one form or another, and the most notable are Professional and Career Development Loans (PCDLs), offered by Barclays and The Co-operative.

With PCDLs, the banks agree to lend students a fixed amount between £300 and £10,000, with the interest paid by the Skills Funding Agency while you study. Repayments begin one month after you graduate and you can organise a payment plan to last for between one and five years.

There are restrictions to the type of course you can take when funding it with a PCDL. Barclays and The Co-operative will only approve the loan if you are enrolled on an approved vocational course and are unable to meet the costs of taking the course yourself. Students who apply for part-time courses may find that the banks are only willing to cover the cost of tuition fees, expecting you to be able to work to cover your living costs.

'Many charitable organisations offer grants and bursaries to students who meet eligibility criteria'

FURTHER FUNDING

UNIVERSITY FUNDING

Visit your university's finance department to discuss any funding opportunities that may be available and specific to you based on your course and circumstances. For example, Keele University is offering a bursary for UK/European Union students with exceptional academic qualifications who enrol on the MSc Chemical Science programme in 2013/14, while the University of Bath has the Talented Athlete Scholarship Scheme, which offers support costs of up to £3,000.

EMPLOYER SPONSORSHIP

If you're employed before further study, you can sometimes persuade your employer to pay for your course if you can show how it will be beneficial to the business. If they agree, you may have to sign an agreement keeping you at the company for a specific period of time. Some programmes are costly and your employer will want a return on their investment rather than see you go to work elsewhere upon graduation.

DISABILITY FUNDING

You may be entitled to support through the Disabled Students' Allowance (DSA). Postgraduates receive the payment in one lump sum to help with disability-related costs. Students with disabilities, mental health conditions or learning difficulties are eligible. Courses must be full time and last for one year.

The banks pay the course fees directly to your university, so it's important that you apply well in advance of starting your postgraduate course. It can take up to three months for a loan to be approved, and even longer in busy periods around September and October. You can only apply to one bank at a time, but if you do get turned down by the first you can then turn your attention to the other.

Bursaries and scholarships

If you don't secure university funding or can't afford a loan, all is not lost. Many charitable organisations offer grants and bursaries to students who meet eligibility criteria. Some are available to large numbers of people but others apply to just a few.

Take, for example, the grants offered by the Royal Society. It provides numerous grant schemes for science students, such as the University Research Fellowship. This is for outstanding scientists in the early stages of a research career and provides a basic salary and research costs worth up to £37,555 in the first year.

Another example of potential funding is the Emerging Excellence Awards, offered by the Musicians Benevolent Fund. Awards are available to UK musicians with a long-term vision. Applicants must be aged between 18-30, need financial help and have a musical talent. Grants usually range from £500 to £1,500, but can sometimes be larger.

There are many students likely to be chasing this 'free' money and so it's easy to become

disheartened if it's not possible to secure funding. The key is to research what's available as thoroughly as possible and apply early. Competition for Research Council funding will be competitive, so look for charities and foundations that specialise in your chosen subject and be aware that many of them have strict criteria.

Working part time

While course fees, living costs and study materials can take up the majority of your budget, it's how you find the extra money that can make the difference. Many postgraduates will opt to get part-time jobs to help fund their studies, and universities are a good source of employment. Departments often take on postgraduates as research or teaching assistants for undergraduate courses, paying

around £10 per hour. Universities also provide part-time work in student unions and libraries, with flexible hours to fit around your study.

Furthermore, students who get into financial difficulty while studying may be able to receive help from their university. The Access to Learning Fund, or Hardship Fund, provides emergency loans to students having money trouble. Funds are distributed at the university's discretion and are likely to go to students who are hit with unexpected costs or are experiencing delays in receiving their PCDL. Payments do not need to be repaid but are only made to students in severe financial difficulties.

For more information, visit *www.prospects.ac.uk/ funding_ postgraduate_study.htm*

STUDENT VIEW

Natalie Cureton is studying for a PhD in Human Development at The University of Manchester after gaining funding from the Biotechnology and Biological Sciences Research Council (BBSRC)

My funding has been provided by the BBSRC through its new Doctoral Training Partnership (DTP). This funding covers my tuition fees, along with an annual allowance for research materials and a stipend.

The DTP is a new initiative by the BBSRC, which aims to provide multidisciplinary challenges for students with backgrounds in and including: bioscience; biomedical; mathematical and physical sciences with a focus on interdisciplinary training; enabling new ways of working and the development of niche skills.

The DTP also allows PhD students to participate in a three-month professional internship placement. This is in an area independent of your research project which allows you to gain a perspective of different career pathways and postgraduate employability.

I also gained President's Doctoral Scholarship Award status and this provides me with an extra £1,000 per year directly from The University of Manchester.

I found out about which projects were receiving funding by visiting *www.findaphd.com* This website provides details of all postgraduate courses

throughout the UK and how these courses may be funded. The University of Manchester also offers additional funding through scholarships, which may be applied for directly.

My funding body provides me with a set amount of money each year to put towards laboratory equipment and materials. This funding has allowed me to buy reagents and the equipment necessary to complete my research, manage my project more effectively and plan with more efficiency. I have also been able to travel to a number of conferences across the UK, which has helped me develop my presentation and poster skills.

Without funding I wouldn't have been able to afford the tuition fees for the four years of my PhD. Equally, without the personal financial support provided by my stipend I wouldn't be able to afford to study full time. Funding has made my PhD possible, as it takes up so much time that it'd be very difficult to work part time.

The student experience

Hear from current and past postgraduates as they provide the lowdown on further study and what it takes to succeed at this level

James Chandler achieved an MA in Political Economy at The University of Manchester

The current economic situation in the UK informed my thinking a lot and I was really keen to try and gain some understanding of it. In addition, I was always open to the idea of pursuing a Masters degree and reasoned that studying political economy would give me a rudimentary understanding of economics and also build on the knowledge I gained studying politics at undergraduate level.

In principle I want to keep learning and feel that pursuing a PhD will serve these interests best. Ideally I would like to work at a university as a researcher and reason that the most viable way of doing this is studying for a PhD.

The research skills that I have acquired over the course of my Masters will provide a good foundation for PhD research, which will in turn

further develop these research skills and hopefully put me in a good position to work as a researcher. If you genuinely believe a Masters is necessary to pursue your ambitions then it is something you should definitely consider. It is a challenging but rewarding experience that allows you to develop a real understanding of your chosen subject.

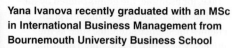

I'd also only recommend it to people who are willing to devote themselves to something that doesn't result in an immediate pay off and instead see it as an investment in their future – the benefits of which will probably only be realised in the long term.

Yana Ivanova recently graduated with an MSc in International Business Management from Bournemouth University Business School

I chose to take the Masters in International Business Management as I wanted to improve my competitiveness as a potential employee for a global company.

The structure of the course enabled me to both work as part of a team, while also having the opportunity to focus on individual assignments. Group work was a key element in sharing ideas and learning from others, enabling personal development and creativity.

At the same time, working on individual projects provided me with an opportunity to explore areas of personal interest within management.

I think that one of the best aspects of the course was being a part of an international, multicultural team. This experience has brought a better understanding of the uniqueness of different cultures and enabled me to practise my communication and leadership skills.

Postgraduate degrees are more intense, and in most cases require students to have existing knowledge of a subject. This makes studying for a postgraduate degree challenging, yet very exciting. As for the social part of the course, I have made many new friends from around the world who I wouldn't have met otherwise.

Ashton Kelly is studying for a Postgraduate Certificate in Education (PGCE) at the University of Sheffield

What I enjoy most about my course is the opportunity to work with young people. The PGCE at Sheffield involves two placements in secondary schools, as well as an initial placement in a primary school.

As an aspiring teacher, working with young people is something I love doing and my course is centred on that – meaning I get to do something I love while gaining a valuable qualification. Furthermore, I've made lots of new friends who are

in the same position as me, providing me with the support that I feel is a vital part of postgraduate study.

My advice for students considering postgraduate study would be to make sure you're certain it's the right thing for you to do. It's a fantastic experience, but it's expensive and it's tough.

The economy at the moment means that postgraduate study seems like a good option if you want to gain an extra qualification that will give you an advantage in the job market. This is true to an extent but you've got to weigh up the advantages against the costs.

You have to feel passionately about what you are studying as a postgraduate, and if you don't have that passion then you won't be able to succeed at your course.

Meriel Hodgson-Teall is currently studying for a Graduate Diploma in Law (GDL) at The University of Law

Having studied history at undergraduate level, I wanted my next move to be either to go straight into a job or to do something that would give a marketable skill and clear direction, especially as further study is so expensive.

Thinking about my general interests and experience, I decided that law was something that was relevant to all of them and so started to look more specifically at the legal sector.

This style of learning has been a complete contrast to what I had grown used to at university, where I mainly had one-on-ones and two-on-ones with tutors and other students.

At The University of Law, there is a great deal of emphasis on how well you can function in a group and work with others. This has been particularly beneficial as, in addition to studying the law, I feel that I'm gaining skills which are relevant to the 'real world' and will be useful in any job.

For other students considering starting the GDL, I would urge them to think carefully about whether this is the career they want as job applications for lawyers start early and are incredibly competitive.

Also, try to do something law-related before starting. This experience doesn't need to be monumental – it could be a vacation placement, shadowing or volunteering for the Citizens Advice Bureau – but it does need to be enough for you to be sure in yourself that law is something you want to pursue.

Rachael Camp has recently graduated from the London College of Communication with an MA in Graphic Design

Postgraduate study is not something to be taken lightly and it isn't for everyone, as it places a big demand on your time and social commitments. A full-time course is the equivalent to a full-time job, and then some. I worked alongside the course to fund it myself, but I found this a juggling act at times.

If you plan to work while you study, even if it is just part time, opt for a part-time course in order to get the most out of your experience.

Consider how you will finance your postgraduate study before you apply, as it is expensive. I took out a Professional and Career Development Loan (PCDL) and worked at the same time, although I was restricted to working less than 30 hours per week as part of my loan agreement.

Lesley Robinson is studying for a PhD in History at Northumbria University

I completed an MRes in Historical Research first, which gave me a great insight into what it was like to complete research more independently. I thoroughly enjoyed doing my Masters, so, having well and truly caught the research bug, I decided to continue with postgraduate education and start a PhD.

Think hard about why you would like to take a postgraduate degree – don't embark on postgraduate study simply because you are not sure what else to do. While studying for a PhD is extremely rewarding and enjoyable, it is equally very challenging and requires a lot of self-motivation. If your heart isn't truly in it then you may find it difficult to devote to it the time and dedication required.

If you do decide to start a postgraduate degree, I would advise that you use the flexibility of a PhD

schedule to develop other valuable skills: attend conferences; organise conferences if you get the opportunity; and network with other postgraduates in your field. By getting involved in your department and the wider postgraduate community in this way you will find the experience a lot more enjoyable and rewarding.

Heidi Yeandle is currently studying for a PhD in Literature at Swansea University. The focus of her thesis is novelist, journalist and poet Angela Carter

As part of my role as a PhD student, I plan and lead seminars for first- and second-year undergraduate students, mark assessments and attend conferences, where I present papers on the progress of my research.

While the teaching provides me with essential experience for my desired career path, the enjoyment of discussing ideas with students also reinforces the idea that working in an academic environment, both teaching and researching, is ideal for me. The extra money is, of course, a great bonus.

I hope this combination of researching, teaching, marking and presenting will help me reach my goal of having a career in academia.

My advice for those considering postgraduate study is to do it. It provides you with the opportunity to expand on your knowledge in your chosen field, and to contribute your original research to this area.

My biggest tip, though, is to apply for funding. It is time consuming, but bursaries and scholarships are available, so apply for any funding you can from councils, organisations and charities. This could enable you to pursue a career in a subject you love.

London College of Communication

A pioneering world leader in postgraduate media and design education, London College of Communication (LCC) is at the cutting edge of new thinking and developments with innovation and the articulation of ideas central to the LCC experience...

LCC is industry focused and you will be taught by an inspiring community of experienced academics, technical experts and leading specialist practitioners.

Industry and alumni

Our tutors are highly engaged with their profession and so students benefit from their industry contacts. Often, our postgraduates are commissioned to work on live projects for major companies such as Nike, National Trust, BFI and Nokia. They go on to lead and inform the creative industries of their generation and include award-winning filmmakers, journalists, broadcasters, designers and photographers.

Alumni of the School of Media are working around the world from Hollywood to Bollywood; from the National Gallery to the Elevator Gallery; from the BBC to Al Jazeera. Some work in large corporations, some are freelancers and others work in academic sectors or go on to further study.

And with more than equal success, the School of Design's alumni are well known for having gone on to found some of the world's leading design agencies such as Pentagram, BBH and M&C Saatchi.

The visible word

A one day conference at the Design Museum exploring current issues in typographic design

Design by Sthuthi Ramesh

Award-winning media

Many iconic designers started their careers at the College, including: Tom Eckersley and Neville Brody, Dave King famed for his *Time Out* covers, David Hillman, who redesigned the *Guardian*, Simon Clowes, an Emmy-award winning film and TV graphics designer and Lynda Brockbank, known for her design that aspires to societal change.

Get hands on

LCC is well known for its practice-based approach. We believe you should get your hands dirty and we see first-hand how creative skills flourish in our outstanding technical facilities, studios and spaces. These include photographic and television studios, darkrooms, galleries, sound design and interactive media and animation suites, broadcast and printing studios, and newsrooms.

In addition to our great resources for hands-on experimentation and research, the College is home to the Kubrick, Knightly and Eckersley Archives, offering an invaluable teaching, learning and research base.

Specialists in media and design

Postgraduate media students are challenged to explore and navigate new creative directions that have the potential to reshape and impact on ways of communicating, seeing and representing the world. We have one of the largest media schools in Europe and its success lies within its ethos of 'learn by doing'.

Students have recently won prestigious awards such as: the Converse/Dazed Emerging Artists award; the Taylor Wessing Portrait Prize; the Magenta Flash Forward Emerging Photographers award; the World Press Photo Daily Life Singles category; Young Lions, Cannes; D&AD UK and The One Show New York.

Leading professionals often act as associate lecturers or give specialist classes or talks. The school also hosts the prestigious, annual Hugh Cudlipp lecture and award and previous speakers have included: Jon Snow; Lionel Barber; Michael Grade; Paul Dacre and Alastair Campbell.

Our postgraduate design provision builds on LCC's long-standing design heritage and it's this, together with a commitment to remain at the forefront of developments in industry that gives our programmes their world-class reputation. Expert course provision in typography, printing, graphics, spatial design, and interaction shape the School of Design's curriculum, in which traditional skills such as drawing and craft meet the latest digital advances.

Learning is about intellectual engagement, discovery, interaction and change, and the school is constantly exploring opportunities for interdisciplinary and hybrid approaches to design. Course tutors encourage students to engage with the contribution they will make to the social, cultural and economic wellbeing of wider communities through their practice.

Love London life

Located on a single site in the centre of London, renowned for its concentration of key media and design companies, LCC is well positioned to open doors to the creative industries. These may include: student internships; mentorships; and work opportunities. The city is the powerhouse of the UK's creative sector with one in three of the country's creative jobs based here.

We are also on the doorstep of renowned galleries and cultural institutions such as Tate Modern, the Design Museum, BFI and South Bank and nearby there are innovative artists' communities to tap into around Shoreditch, Hoxton and Brick Lane.

With around 5,000 students across more than 40 courses, LCC is a melting pot of diverse backgrounds, attitudes and interests that makes for original collaborations – and a great social scene. To help students to reach their personal, creative and professional potential, our student services team will help you to organise essential aspects of living and studying in the city.

We ask our students to throw themselves into London and college life, and say, 'If you see something happening you like, join it; if you can't see it, find it; and if it's not there, start it'.

The world's creative community

LCC is a vital part of the largest creative community in the world, as one of six colleges that make up the celebrated network of University of the Arts London.

'It was the professional reputations of the tutors and visiting tutors and the way they treat you as a person rather than a student that contributed to my decision to study at LCC.'
Edward Thompson, MA Photojournalism and Documentary Photography

Hands on learning

WHERE WILL IT LEAD?

Ruth Patterson graduated from The University of Manchester with an LLB. She then studied the Legal Practice Course at BPP Law School, converting it into an LLM in Professional Legal Practice. She now works as a solicitor at Herbert Smith Freehills LLP

Why did you choose these courses and institutions?

I chose to complete the Legal Practice Course (LPC) at BPP because I wanted to pursue a career as a practising solicitor – after my law degree the LPC was the next logical step to enable me to do this. I chose BPP Law School because it has an excellent reputation as a leading provider of this postgraduate course.

I studied on the City LPC consortium, which consists of classes made up of the trainees from several firms being taught together, which was a great way to get to know colleagues at other law firms who I might work alongside in future transactions. BPP has a great reputation for legal studies and I was impressed with the level of teaching I received on the LPC.

After graduating from the LPC with distinction in July 2009, I decided to undertake three months of further study to convert this qualification into a Masters (LLM). I wrote two dissertations and completed my LLM in January 2010. I chose to undertake this course with BPP as they allowed me to add on modules to my existing LPC qualification in order to complete the LLM, rather than having to complete a full, separate course – a great initiative to help students gain further qualifications.

Did the institutions have good links with industry?

BPP has excellent links with a lot of law firms and legal institutions, but I already had my training contract with Herbert Smith Freehills LLP when I started at BPP.

What does your job involve?

As a solicitor in the finance division at Herbert Smith Freehills LLP, where I qualified in March 2012, the majority of my role is divided between debt-restructuring work, real-estate financing transactions and general banking.

With restructuring work, I get involved with debt and equity-

restructurings of large international corporates which are often widely reported in the media and usually involve a whole team of advisers from lawyers to financial advisers, brokers and accountants, so the transactions tend to be very complicated and time-pressured due to the difficult financial position of the companies.

My job involves analysing and drafting legal documents such as loan agreements and security documents in order to implement a financing or a restructuring. These documents can be quite complex when a transaction involves different levels of debt, such as senior debt and mezzanine debt in the same transaction where the lenders have different rights, or where there are a large number of lenders in a syndicate who make the negotiation and agreement process more difficult.

The work I do involves liaising closely with auditors, accountants and financial advisers to make sure our clients' debt is structured in the most efficient way for tax and

I thought I knew everything there was to know about going to art galleries, but this Masters has made me rethink everything

accounting reasons as well as being structured in a legally sound manner, in order to allow our clients to move forward with their businesses as successfully as possible.

My job can involve liaising with the client on a daily basis to implement the transaction, often holding their hand throughout what can be a stressful process, and also being the link between all of the different advisers.

What advice would you give to other students hoping to break into this career?

It's important to study hard so that you learn as much as possible and achieve good grades – competition for a career in law is very tough.

I'd also advise students to gain as much practical experience as possible through work experience, internships and vacation schemes. Not only do these look great on your CV and give you things to talk about at interview, they also show your enthusiasm for the career and your endeavours to gain useful experience. This is what will help set you apart from your competition.

What are your plans for the future?

I am currently enjoying my role as a qualified solicitor in a global law firm and the challenges this presents, so I am looking forward to gaining more experience on market-leading transactions and expanding my skills as I progress in this career.

University profiles

The following pages feature profiles of specific higher education institutions in the UK and Ireland offering quality postgraduate taught and research opportunities. Browse this section to gain an insight into universities that may excel in your required subject areas, have facilities that suit your needs, or offer funded postgraduate places

GOING TO APPLY? MENTION PROSPECTS' ADVICE ON YOUR APPLICATION

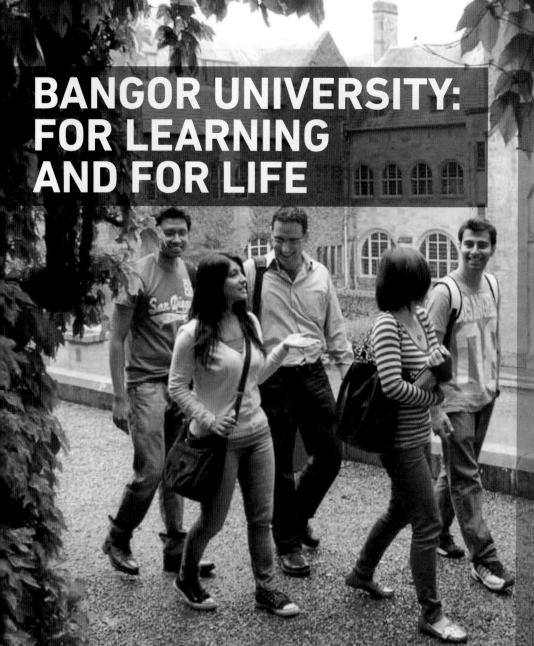

University of Bedfordshire

Our world-leading research is everything you would expect from a modern university. And our research-led culture means that you have the opportunity to learn from, and work alongside, leading experts in the field who are investigating real-world issues

POSTGRADUATE STUDY

Coupled with the fact that 90% of graduates go into employment or further study within six months of graduating, it's clear that Bedfordshire is a university that's serious about enhancing students' knowledge and career development. Add in a great location – only 30 minutes from central London by train – and it's easy to see why so many choose Bedfordshire.

INVESTING IN YOUR FUTURE

As part of a major investment programme, a brand-new Postgraduate and Continuing Professional Development Centre opened its doors in 2013. This bespoke facility offers:

- innovative learning spaces;
- two Harvard-style lecture theatres;
- free Wi-Fi;
- social areas including a postgraduate lounge and games room.

This new building, located at our Luton campus, also offers dedicated space for postgraduate research students, alongside board rooms and conference rooms to emulate the modern business environment.

Kristine Anaska, an MSc Investment and Finance student says: 'My class and I are really excited to have our own space. The PG Centre has fantastic, spacious rooms and the IT support is great. It facilitates our studies very well.'

www.beds.ac.uk/pgstudy
admission@beds.ac.uk
twitter.com/uobpg
facebook.com/unibeds

POSTGRADUATE FUNDING

We offer a variety of scholarships to support your studies. Terms and conditions apply. Visit *http://uob.cc/pgfunding*

PRACTICAL HANDS-ON EXPERIENCE

Our Student Internship Scheme provides paid placements in local or national companies, alongside your studies: *http://uob.cc/pginternships*

DISCOVER FOR YOURSELF

Find out what we can offer you by coming along to one of our postgraduate open events. Visit: *http://uob.cc/postgrad-event*

STAY INFORMED

See what it's really like to study at Bedfordshire by subscribing to our monthly award-winning e-zine *Postgraduate Life.* Visit *http://uob.cc/signup*

Your essential guide to funding postgraduate study

Postgraduate Funding Guide

Available from your university careers service,
graduate fair or visit us online

www.prospects.ac.uk/funding

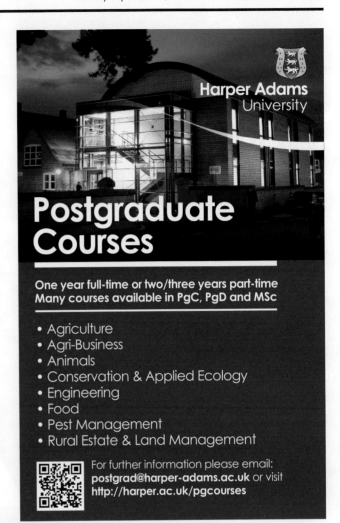

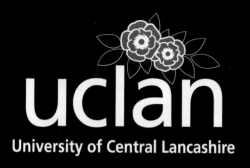

University of Central Lancashire

Professor Joe Howe

Find your postgraduate inspiration at UCLan

At UCLan, we're always pushing the boundaries of research and sharing this knowledge with our postgraduate students.

For example, Professor Joe Howe, a world-renowned expert on environmental planning, management and procurement issues, leads strategic partnerships with BAE Systems and the National Nuclear Laboratory, as well as advising Government bodies and NGOs.

Choose from our diverse range of full and part-time postgraduate programmes and research degrees, and learn from some of the most innovative thinkers on the planet.

Visit www.uclan.ac.uk/pg or call 01772 830656

Innovative thinking for the real world

City University London, a leading global university located in the heart of London

City University London is committed to academic excellence, focused on business and the professions and proud of its education, research and enterprise.

Ranked in the top five per cent of universities in the world*, we have one of the highest proportions of graduate students of any university in the UK – over forty per cent of our students are studying at postgraduate level and we are the largest provider in the United Kingdom of taught postgraduate courses in the disciplines of Journalism; Speech, Language and Communication Science; and Law.**

We are renowned for the employability of our graduates. Successfully combining academic and professional studies, the majority of our students gain a professional as well as an academic award.

Our research in 15 subject areas is of a quality comparable with the very best in the world according to the most recent Research Assessment Exercise (RAE).

As the University for business and the professions we maintain close links with many businesses both at home and internationally; our industry connections feed directly into our research and your education. Actively involved in pioneering research, we continue to break new ground in academic thought and study. This ensures our courses are relevant, up-to-date and help students to enhance their employment prospects.

* *Times Higher Education* World University Rankings 2012/13
** *The Guardian* Postgraduate Tables 2013

We currently offer opportunities for postgraduate study in the following areas:

Accounting
Actuarial Science
Business & Management
Computing
Creative Practice and Enterprise
Creative Writing
Cultural Management
Economics
Engineering
Finance
Health Management, Policy and Research
Insurance and Risk Management
International Politics
Journalism
Language and Communication Science
Law
Library and Information Science
MBA
Midwifery
Music
Nursing
Optometry
Psychology
Publishing
Radiography
Shipping and Energy
Sociology
Translation

www.city.ac.uk

Email enquiries
enquiries@city.ac.uk

Telephone enquiries
+44 (0)20 7040 5060

CITY UNIVERSITY LONDON

EST 1894

www.city.ac.uk
enquiries@city.ac.uk
twitter.com/CityUniLondon
www.facebook.com/cityuniversitylondon

City is a leading international university and the only university in London to be both committed to academic excellence and focused on business and the professions. With six academic Schools, City offers higher education across a range of subjects in business, law, health sciences, engineering, mathematical sciences, informatics, social sciences, and the arts including journalism and music

City has one of the highest proportions of international and graduate students of any university in the UK with more than 40% of City students studying at postgraduate level. Combining academic and professional studies, the majority of students gain a professional and an academic award.

ACADEMIC EXCELLENCE

City is a special place. With skill and dedication, we have been delivering education, research and enterprise that transforms the lives of our students, our community and the world for more than 100 years. We are proud of our position among the top 5% of universities in the world (Times Higher Education World Rankings 2012/13).

EMPLOYMENT PROSPECTS

We have exceptional links with business and the professions, with many of our courses accredited by professional bodies, ensuring they are relevant and enhance students' employment prospects. City is ranked 9th in the UK for graduate-level jobs (*The Sunday Times University Guide 2012*).

Our students benefit from our close ties with some of the major London employers and our Career and Skills Development Service provides specialist careers advice and workshops to help with effective applications, successful interviews and presentation skills.

UNBEATABLE LOCATION

City is located in Islington in central London, close to the capital's leading financial, legal, media and medical institutions. Both professionally and personally, our students have the opportunity to benefit from all that London has to offer.

RESEARCH

Research informs our education and our students learn from those who are themselves learning as they develop their subjects. City has around 1,500 full and part-time academic staff and about 600 PhD students. The research in which they engage – in diverse areas from climate change to healthcare to economic theory – benefits large sections of society in the UK and overseas. In the government's latest Research Assessment Exercise (RAE), our research in 15 subject areas was rated as amongst the best in the world. We receive funding for our research from the government, industry and the professions, within the UK and internationally.

THE CITY GRADUATE SCHOOL

The City Graduate School provides a focus for the university's research degrees provision and the skills development of its research degree students. The Graduate School works to strengthen the university's research student community, support research skills training, provide opportunities for our research students to interact with other students and senior academic staff across the university and meet the wider needs of our research student body.

ESSENTIAL INFORMATION

COURSES

We offer a range of subjects across:
- the arts (including journalism and music)
- business
- engineering
- health sciences
- informatics
- law
- mathematical sciences
- social sciences

ENTRY REQUIREMENTS

Applicants for all postgraduate degrees should hold a university honours degree or equivalent qualification in an appropriate subject. If you don't hold an honours degree or equivalent but have suitable experience and/or professional qualifications, you may still be accepted for a Masters or postgraduate diploma at the discretion of the university.

FINANCIAL SUPPORT

Postgraduate study at City is an affordable option for students from wide-ranging backgrounds. Many sources of funding exist, including scholarships, studentships and professional development loans.

ACCOMMODATION

Some accommodation is available for postgraduate students. Our new and refurbished halls of residence have private, modern study bedrooms and communal living spaces.

UNIVERSITY OF EDINBURGH
Business School

OUR STUDENTS COME FROM OVER 27 COUNTRIES

DYNAMIC THINKING, ACADEMIC RIGOUR, GLOBAL REPUTATION

CONNECTS YOU WITH LEADING PRACTITIONERS

EDINBURGH

ONE OF THE WORLD'S LEADING FINANCIAL AND CULTURAL CAPITALS

THE EDINBURGH MBA

OUR UNIVERSITY DATES BACK TO 1582

The Edinburgh MBA.
Set your sights on a global experience.

Attracting an international cohort, you'll be part of a truly global experience. The Edinburgh MBA delivers a rigorous curriculum focused on leadership, innovation and best practice, incorporating extensive opportunities to connect with a vibrant and influential business community at the heart of Scotland's historic financial capital.

The University of Edinburgh Business School shares in an educational heritage that stretches back more than 400 years.

Our history, reputation and location ensures that the experience you can expect is one of the world's best.

If you'd like to join a thoughtful, ambitious and diverse group of like-minded business people, immersing yourself in our comprehensive approach to leadership, visit our website and hear what our graduates have to say.

Take a closer look, visit
www.business-school.ed.ac.uk/mba

Got a smartphone?

Scan this QR code to visit the Business School's MBA page.

EFMD
EQUIS
ACCREDITED

Accredited by
Association of MBAs

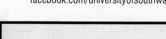

www.southwales.ac.uk/postgraduate
enquiries@southwales.ac.uk
twitter.com/unisouthwales
facebook.com/universityofsouthwales

At the University of South Wales, our students benefit from superb courses, facilities and support, as well as our excellent reputation as a major university for jobs with employers. You can find our graduates all over the world, building strong careers and making a difference

COURSES

As one of the largest universities in the UK, we offer an exceptional range of subjects and courses at every level – from Postgraduate Certificate to PhD. Many of our courses have part-time study options, while others are available through distance learning or 'block' format. The university has extensive e-learning facilities for you to access information whenever it suits you. You'll find award-winning support to help you along the way too – we won the 2012 Times Higher Award for Outstanding Support for Students.

EMPLOYABILITY

Employability is at the heart of everything we do, with teaching informed by what happens in the real world. We are dedicated to professional, employment-focused education. Our range of higher-level qualifications can help you take the next step in your career and improve your employment prospects. You'll have every opportunity to apply what you learn – whether it's through case studies, a project based in industry or your workplace, or a field course.

ACCREDITATIONS

To give that extra seal of approval, many courses are accredited by leading professional bodies in their respective sectors, such as the Chartered Institute of Logistics and Transport (CILT) and the British Psychological Society (BPS). Our

students are taught by leading academics in their field – for example our staff includes prize-winning poets, Olympic psychologists and an ESA Space Ambassador. Our links with industry and business are hard to beat too – we work with leaders such as Microsoft and the BBC, plus British Airways has chosen us as their sole university partner for aircraft maintenance training.

RESEARCH

Our staff are actively involved in research, so you will be taught by lecturers who are national and international experts in their fields. We also ensure that our research is relevant to the real world and influences decision makers. This means that our courses contain the latest thinking and developments, giving your university education an added distinction.

INVESTMENT

As part of our commitment to excellence, we have heavily invested in state-of-the-art facilities across our campuses to ensure you get the best possible learning experience. Wherever you look, you will find industry-standard equipment. From simulated hospital wards and scenes of crime, to an aircraft hangar and green screen TV studios, you will gain essential skills using some of the best facilities in the UK.

Scholarships are available for UK and EU students at the time of production on selected courses. For full terms and conditions, visit our website:
www.southwales.ac.uk/money

The University of South Wales is a registered charity. Registration No. 1140312

ESSENTIAL INFORMATION

LOCATION
The university has campuses throughout South Wales, in Cardiff, Newport and Pontypridd. Our locations mean you can enjoy everything the region has to offer – city life and culture, stunning beaches and breathtaking countryside.

START DATES
Many of our courses start in February as well as September, to give you added flexibility.

FEES AND FUNDING
To support you during your studies, we offer postgraduate scholarships on many of our courses.* Our Student Money Team can help you with all money-related enquiries, from information about bursaries and scholarships to budgeting tips. Visit our money pages for more information *www.southwales.ac.uk/money*

OPEN EVENINGS
We hold open evenings throughout the year, which are a great way to find out whether postgraduate study is right for you. You can discuss your options with academics and get professional career and money advice. Simply visit our website to find out more and book your place at an event.

CONTACT DETAILS
University of South Wales
Pontypridd CF37 1DL
UK Tel: 08455 194 787
Overseas Tel: +44 (0)1443 654 450

Goldsmiths
UNIVERSITY OF LONDON

www.gold.ac.uk
course-info@gold.ac.uk
twitter.com/myGoldsmiths
facebook.com/GoldsmithsUoL

A CREATIVE POWERHOUSE

Championing research-rich degrees that provoke thought, stretch the imagination and tap into tomorrow's world, at Goldsmiths we're asking the questions that matter now in subjects as diverse as the arts and humanities, social sciences, cultural studies, computing, and entrepreneurial business and management. We are a community defined by its people: innovative in spirit, analytical in approach and open to all.

A RICH ACADEMIC HERITAGE

We blend academic rigour with creative insight. Founded in 1891, and part of the University of London since 1904, we've a rich academic history but we're also known for our creative approach. We also keep good company. As part of the prestigious 1994 Group of UK research-led universities, from the moment you enrol you'll be part of a powerful legacy of learning.

PERSONAL CONTACT WITH LEADING ACADEMICS

You'll be taught by and will debate with the best in the field: the people who write the books that appear on reading lists across the country. They include the digital journalists, social workers and computer programmers working in today's industries, bringing with them the experience of professional practice, and the researchers who are carrying out pioneering developments in areas as diverse as infant recognition and the anthropology of gambling.

WE PUT YOUR FUTURE FIRST

With 1,400 students currently accessing work placements, and interdisciplinary programmes that reflect and respond to contemporary concerns and current practice, from the moment you join us we'll be helping you shape your career. You'll also benefit from our global links and will have the opportunity to develop a network of contacts who could enhance your professional prospects.

SMALL CAMPUS COMMUNITY

We are small but mighty – a close-knit community that comes from every corner of the world, which makes for a diverse learning experience. We're based on a single-site campus within London's vibrant New Cross, but we're also just minutes from the heart of this great global city, home to major cultural landmarks.

SUPPORT TO SUCCEED

At Goldsmiths you can be whoever who you want to be. We nurture individual talent, providing a safe and supportive environment to grow academically and personally. We also champion the bold. Our former students reflect Goldsmiths' brand of magic across the world and are shaping the socio-cultural landscape on a global scale.

GRADUATE PROFILE

Mouthanna, award-winning film and television editor

MA Filmmaking, 2010

'The Goldsmiths name is recognised nationally and internationally, and many job offers I received were based on the fact that I had undertaken a Masters degree at Goldsmiths. Since graduating, I've edited short and feature films, documentaries, promos and television shows which have been broadcast on international channels and screened at major film festivals, and won awards and accolades.'

ESSENTIAL INFORMATION

World top 100 university for arts and humanities (QS World University Rankings 2012).

Voted one of the UK's top creative universities by students (Which? University 2012).

For fees and funding information, visit *www.gold.ac.uk/pg/fees-funding*

Over 1,200 places in Goldsmiths accommodation within walking distance of the campus: *www.gold.ac.uk/accommodation*

Regular open days and postgraduate information evenings: *www.gold.ac.uk/open-days*

Single-site campus with purpose-built Grade II-listed buildings, large college green and extensive library.

Our Graduate School is open 24/7 and provides support, materials and resources for all our postgraduate students: *www.gold.ac.uk/graduate-school*

40% of our students study at postgraduate level and one-fifth of our students are from overseas.

Vibrant, urban and affordable location in London travelcard zone 2, with extensive transport links to the rest of the city *www.gold.ac.uk/student-life*

Access to central University of London facilities, including Senate House Library in Bloomsbury with over 1 million volumes.

Former students include Blur's Graham Coxon and Alex James, Damian Hirst, Lucian Freud, Anthony Gormley, Mary Quant, James Blake, Steve McQueen and David Tattersall.

Our alumni accolades include BAFTA, Emmy and Olivier awards, Mercury Music Prize nominations and six Turner Prizes *www.gold.ac.uk/about/alumni*

Middlesex University London

Middlesex University teaches 40,000 students on courses at campuses in London, Dubai, Mauritius and Malta and with prestigious academic partners across the world. We have a reputation for the highest quality teaching, research that makes a real difference to people's lives and a practical, innovative approach to working with businesses to develop staff potential and provide solutions to business issues.

CAREER FOCUSED COURSES

All of our postgraduate courses are developed and structured with the goal of enabling you to develop professionally in the UK or overseas. Our courses are accredited by professional bodies and we work closely with employers to ensure our courses are aligned with industry needs and provide you with the opportunity to connect with the professional world.

STUDENT FACILITIES

We have invested more than £180million into our campuses and facilities in recent years. Our Art, Design and Media building, The Grove, is home to an extensive range of studios and workshops giving you access to the latest technology and traditional art, design and media processes to push the boundaries of creative possibilities. For scientists we offer state-of-the-art labs and technology centres and for law and business-minded students our professional links provide real-world case studies and expert industry speakers.

TAUGHT COURSES

Middlesex offers taught courses in Art and Design, Biomedical Sciences, Business and Management, Complementary Health, Computing Science, Criminology, Economics, Engineering, Environment and Development, Finance, Health, Interpreting and Translation Studies, Law, Media and Writing, Music and Theatre Arts, Nursing, Midwifery and Health, Project Management, Psychology, Social Sciences, Sport and Exercise Science, Teaching and Education, and Work Based Learning.

RESEARCH PROGRAMMES

As a leading international university, Middlesex University is committed to excellence in research and the discovery of new knowledge as a core element of our mission. Our schools and research centres are acknowledged by the Research Assessment Exercise (RAE) as being of an international standard across a number of departments.

www.mdx.ac.uk/postgraduate
enquiries@mdx.ac.uk
twitter.com/MiddlesexUni
facebook.com/MiddlesexUniversity

WANT TO KNOW MORE?
You can find out more about postgraduate study at Middlesex University by visiting,
www.mdx.ac.uk/postgraduate

FINANCIAL SUPPORT
You can find out more about support for our postgraduate students by visiting,
www.mdx.ac.uk/pggeneral

FEES
Tuition fees for postgraduate courses vary depending on the course. For details, please visit our website
www.mdx.ac.uk/pgfees

CONTACT DETAILS
Tel: +44 (0)20 8411 5555

160 inspiring career options at your fingertips.

If you're looking to boost your employability, enhance your qualifications or simply want a new challenge, then we can help you reach your potential. We're passionate about working closely with industry and have strong links with major regional, national and global employers. With over 160 postgraduate options to choose from, many accredited by leading professional bodies, we're confident that we'll have the right one for you. At Leeds Metropolitan you will have access to fantastic facilities, industry experts and key employers. It's an exciting opportunity to take control of your future.

Find out more at courses.leedsmet.ac.uk

LEEDS
METROPOLITAN
UNIVERSITY

Find Out More

LSE
THE LONDON SCHOOL OF ECONOMICS AND POLITICAL SCIENCE ■

lse.ac.uk
twitter.com/LSE_Recruitment
facebook.com/lseps

The London School of Economics and Political Science (LSE) is the world's leading dedicated social science institution. Founded in 1895, the School enjoys a global reputation for academic excellence and cutting edge research. In the most recent national Research Assessment Exercise (RAE) LSE had the highest percentage of world-leading research of any university in the United Kingdom

ABOUT LSE

All LSE's teaching and research is undertaken from a social science perspective, giving the institution a unique approach to otherwise common fields. LSE academics are at the forefront of developments in the social sciences and their expertise is called upon by governments, businesses and media around the globe. More than 40% of its academic staff, and 69% of LSE's students originate from outside the UK, ensuring that LSE's education is truly international, both in and out of the classroom.

LSE's location in the heart of London is fundamental to its identity. It enjoys an easy interchange of ideas with the external environment – Westminster, the City, the Law Courts and the media are all on the School's doorstep.

London is an exciting, vibrant and colourful city. Whatever your interests or appetite you will find something to suit your palate and pocket in this truly international capital. Whether you are into art, architecture, dance, film, music or theatre, sport, shopping or even green spaces and the great outdoors, London really does have it all. Major attractions such as Theatreland, the West End, the Royal Opera House and the British Library and Museum are all within walking distance of the School.

The School has one of the most prestigious public events programmes in the world. Leading figures from all walks of life have spoken at LSE, including Aung San Suu Kyi, Kofi Annan, Nelson Mandela, His Holiness the Dalai Lama, Amartya Sen, Bill Clinton, Bill Gates, David Cameron, George Soros and Boris Johnson.

POSTGRADUATE STUDY

LSE offers over 140 taught Masters programmes across 30 departments or institutes. As a 'laboratory of the social sciences', the School's academic profile spans a wide range of disciplines, from accounting to law, management to urbanisation.

Postgraduate research degrees (MPhil/PhD) are offered by all LSE departments and institutes. Students are invited to submit applications that complement the academic interests of the School's staff.

EMPLOYMENT PROSPECTS

LSE graduates are in great demand and can be found in senior positions around the world. LSE alumni and former staff include 16 Nobel Prize winners in Economics, Peace or Literature, and 35 past or present Heads of State.

HOW TO APPLY

Applications can be submitted online from mid-October in the year prior to entry and are considered on a rolling basis until all the available places are filled.

ESSENTIAL INFORMATION

USUAL ENTRY REQUIREMENTS
Applicants for a taught Masters degree should offer a first or 2:1 class honours undergraduate degree from a UK university or a non-UK equivalent in a subject appropriate to the programme to be followed. Research degree applicants are normally expected to have a UK taught master's degree with a merit or a non-UK equivalent in a subject appropriate to the research to be undertaken.

DURATION
The majority of full-time taught Masters degrees last for 12 months but some programmes are 24 months. A full-time research degree takes 3-4 years to complete and consists of both taught courses and primary research leading to a 100,000 word thesis.

FINANCIAL SUPPORT
LSE makes available over £10million in scholarships each year to its graduate students. Awards range from a contribution to tuition fees to full coverage of all expenses and are usually awarded to students from a certain country or region, or to students on a specific degree programme.

CONTACT DETAILS
Student Recruitment Office, Tower 3, Houghton Street, London WC2A 2AE
Tel: +44 (0)20 7955 6613
lse.ac.uk

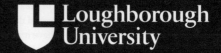

MANCHESTER 1824
The University of Manchester

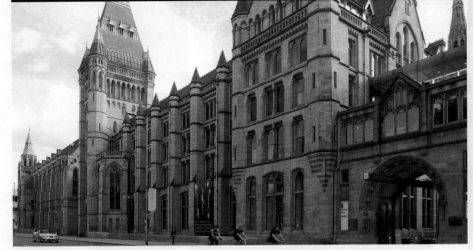

The University of Manchester is one of Britain's most famous and forward-thinking universities with a rich heritage stretching back 180 years and an exciting agenda for the future. Many major advances of the 20th century began in the university's laboratories, including the birth of the computer, the splitting of the atom and the founding principles of modern economics

Today, research remains at the heart of The University of Manchester, placing it at the forefront of the search for solutions to some of the world's most pressing problems, using strong collaborative links with industry and public services.

RESEARCH EXCELLENCE

According to the 2008 Research Assessment Exercise, Manchester is ranked third behind only Oxford and Cambridge in terms of research power, with 65% of its research activity judged to be world-leading or internationally excellent.

The University has 22 academic schools and hundreds of specialist research groups, each undertaking pioneering multi-disciplinary teaching and research. These span across our four faculties of Engineering and Physical Sciences, Humanities, Life Sciences, and Medical and Human Sciences. Whether you are studying for a taught postgraduate award or a research degree, you will be directly involved in cutting-edge research at the highest level.

The University of Manchester has consistently high rankings in UK and worldwide league tables, such as the influential Academic Ranking of World Universities conducted by Shanghai Jiao Tong University. According to the 2012 Shanghai Jiao Tong World Ranking, we are ranked 40th in the world, seventh in Europe and fifth in the UK.

FACILITIES AND RESOURCES

As part of our vibrant community of over 10,000 postgraduates, you will have access to one of the best-resourced academic libraries in the UK and one of the largest and most advanced academic IT services in Europe.

The newly opened Alan Gilbert Learning Commons offers a flexible, ultramodern and stimulating space in which to relax and learn. Cutting-edge IT facilities, a host of student-centred activities and various learning support services are all available within its walls. The iconic £30million building was developed in full consultation with representatives from the students' union and designed specifically to support the learning needs of the 21st century student.

EMPLOYMENT PROSPECTS

The University of Manchester not only gives you a postgraduate qualification which is globally recognised, but also provides access to a careers service which has been consistently voted the best in the UK, offering:

- unrivalled access to employers, both on campus and through recruitment events;
- support from careers professionals with specialist training in working with postgraduates;
- training and development opportunities during your degree to ensure you stand out from the crowd when seeking employment.

FUNDING

As well as receiving among the highest number of Research Council grants of any UK university, The University of Manchester has considerable funds available within its schools and faculties. These allow the university to offer a substantial number of funding opportunities for students undertaking postgraduate study across all disciplines. For more information visit **www.manchester.ac.uk/postgraduate/funding/**

FOUR REASONS TO CHOOSE THE UNIVERSITY OF MANCHESTER FOR POSTGRADUATE STUDY

COURSES
As the UK's largest single site university, we offer one of the UK's broadest ranges of degree programmes. This is particularly valuable for our postgraduates, whose specialist areas of knowledge at the cutting edge of research often transcend traditional discipline boundaries.

WORLD-LEADING FACILITIES
A total of £1billion will be invested in campus facilities over the next ten years, £700million of which will be delivered in the next six years. Facilities will include a new engineering campus, new centres for the law, business and medical schools, as well as a major refurbishment of the university library and students' union.

RESEARCHER SKILLS TRAINING
The University of Manchester is committed to training its postgraduate students to the highest level, equipping them with the skills needed for a career inside and outside of academia. Each faculty offers a comprehensive skills training and development programme.

ACCOMMODATION
Manchester offers more spaces in university-managed accommodation than virtually any other university in the country, giving an extensive range of choice, including some postgraduate-only residences. Students looking for private accommodation benefit from advice from Manchester Student Homes, which advertise university-approved private housing.

FIND OUT FOR YOURSELF
Don't just take our word for it – come and see for yourself at our postgraduate open day on Wednesday 27 November 2013, or come and meet us at one of the postgraduate study fairs taking place throughout the year in various locations: **www.manchester.ac.uk/postgraduate/opendays**

Postgraduate study
An investment in your future

mmu.ac.uk/postgrad

There are many reasons to study for your postgraduate qualification at Manchester Metropolitan University. Postgraduate study gives you a competitive edge and can improve your career prospects and long term earning potential.

Manchester
Metropolitan
University

Professionally focused courses

We offer over 500 professionally relevant postgraduate courses, recognised by more than 70 professional bodies and associations. Coupled with our close links with businesses and employers, we ensure that our courses are relevant to today's professional working environment.

World-leading research

We have a strong research profile and we pride ourselves on conducting world-class, relevant research which informs curriculum development, shapes business and professional practice and influences policy making, both nationally and internationally. The University is research rich with many of its research themes rated as world leading or internationally excellent.

Experts in the field

We have over 4,000 staff at the University, all committed to sharing their passion for their subject. This includes many award winning academics at the forefront of their professional fields with established networks in their sectors.

A Big Investment in World-class facilities

An exciting investment programme in excess of £350m is due for completion in 2014, providing state-of-the-art, environmentally sustainable buildings and facilities to create one of the best teaching and research universities in the UK. Our programme of investment, which started seven years ago, has been funded entirely from University resources to create an outstanding, inspiring and sustainable environment for learning and teaching.

Our new £75m Business School and Student Hub is already open.

Dedicated support

As a postgraduate student, you will have access to comprehensive and dedicated student support services from teams including Careers and Employability, Learner Development and Financial Support.

The UK's most popular student city

Manchester is one of the most extensive higher education centres in Europe and undoubtedly the most popular city for students in the UK. Our central campus is situated close to Manchester's city centre, with three more campus locations in other parts of the city. In addition, we have a campus in Crewe, 36 miles from Manchester city centre, with outstanding sporting facilities, a lively Students Union and easy access to nearby towns.

Wide choice of courses

Within the North-West we have perhaps the widest range of postgraduate study options; from part-time to full-time, short courses to CPD, Masters of Arts/Science and longer term Research and PhD opportunities across many subject areas, such as:

- Accounting, Finance and Economics
- Acting, Performance and Music
- Art, Design and Architecture
- Biology and Healthcare Science
- Business and Management
- Computing, Mathematics and Digital Technology
- Education, Early Years, Youth and Community
- Exercise and Sports Science
- Food and Nutrition
- Geography and Environment
- Health, Psychology and Social Care
- Hospitality, Tourism, Leisure and Events Management
- Humanities and Social Science
- Law
- Marketing, PR and Communications
- Psychology and Social Work
- Science and Engineering
- Sport Management

Visit us

We hold postgraduate course fairs four times a year in September, November, March and May and have many more opportunities during the year to visit us and speak to us.

Why not visit us to find out about our facilities and studying a postgraduate course at university? Come

INNOVATION COMES FROM TAKING CHANCES

OXFORD BROOKES UNIVERSITY

TO FIND OUT MORE about our wide range of programmes and scholarships available, visit our website and come to a **postgraduate fair**.

tde.bz/ tde-prospects

Technology, Design and Environment courses at Oxford Brookes University have an **international reputation for excellence**. We understand that innovation comes from being able to take risks in a supportive environment and we embrace new technologies and encourage experimentation, playful trial and error and academic curiosity. The results are seen in our very strong student satisfaction statistics, research rankings and graduate destinations. We work closely with our graduates'

future employers and marketplaces, and appreciate that we are part of a world with a voracious appetite for new and exciting creative ideas welded to solid business acumen.

Our schools and departments provide specialist and interdisciplinary teaching, research and knowledge transfer across a wide range of postgraduate programmes from **architecture**, **arts** and **urban design** through to **media technology**, **mechanical engineering** and **construction**.

It is a particularly good time for teachers to take our **MSc or PGDip in Computing** to take advantage of the government's push for computer science in the classroom.

We hope you will join us in developing your discipline within a twenty first century context of technological development and interdisciplinary innovation.

The blueprint for postgraduate success

Everything you need to make the right postgraduate choice

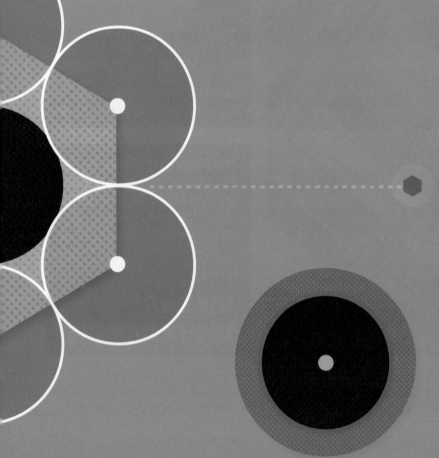

Prospects Postgrad Magazine

The University of Nottingham

UNITED KINGDOM · CHINA · MALAYSIA

www.nottingham.ac.uk/pgstudy
postgraduate-enquiries@nottingham.ac.uk
twitter.com/UniofNottingham
facebook.com/TheUniofNottingham

Described as the 'nearest Britain has to a truly global university'*, The University of Nottingham has campuses in the UK, China and Malaysia, links with institutions and employers around the world and students from more than 150 countries. A member of the Russell Group, Nottingham is internationally recognised for groundbreaking research and quality teaching and attracts world-class academics and students. With a programme of development for all research students, an award-winning Careers and Employability Service, business support facilities for entrepreneurial students and a dedicated Graduate School, the Nottingham postgraduate experience is invaluable. We offer a global learning experience that will prepare you for the international jobs market

RESEARCH AT NOTTINGHAM

Nottingham coordinates research on some of the most pressing human concerns and global challenges. Our total research portfolio is worth more than £300million. This funds more than 2,300 research projects. We also have over 200 industrial sponsors of research.

The Research Assessment Exercise 2008 ranked Nottingham 7th in the UK in terms of research power with more than 90% of our research judged to be of international quality. Our postgraduate students play a key role in this success. You will benefit from working with pioneering researchers in cutting-edge facilities and will be encouraged to gain teaching experience, present papers at conferences worldwide, and publish your work. If any inventions arise from your research, our Technology Transfer Team has the expertise to assess their viability and help you develop them commercially.

TEACHING EXCELLENCE

We have an outstanding reputation for the quality of our teaching and consistently perform well in independent reviews. We offer more than 360 postgraduate taught courses including Masters, PGDip and PGCert programmes, many of which can be pursued full or part time, and some by distance learning. Our courses will equip you with a thorough understanding of your subject and vital transferable skills.

FACILITIES AND RESOURCES

We provide state-of-the-art teaching and research facilities, as well as first-rate leisure and sporting provision across all of our campuses.

Postgraduate students receive membership of the Graduate School and can take advantage of its impressive Researcher Development Programme, funding opportunities and busy social calendar. Our student support services provide information and advice on academic and personal issues. The students' union is home to more than 200 clubs and societies and is one of the most active in the UK, and the Postgraduate Students' Association provides specialised support and events for postgraduates.

CAREER DEVELOPMENT

Nottingham is the 2nd university in the UK most targeted by leading graduate employers. **

Our award-winning careers and employability service runs more than 250 recruitment events, one-to-one careers guidance sessions, CV sessions and lots more. After you graduate, you will have access to the service for life. If you are interested in starting your own business, the university's EnterpriseLab offers advice and support.

ESSENTIAL INFORMATION

USUAL ENTRY REQUIREMENTS
Taught Masters: honours degree at 2:2 or above; PhD: honours degree at 2:1 or above (or international equivalents).

FEES
Fees vary. For a full table, visit *www.nottingham.ac.uk/fees*

FUNDING
We offer a range of postgraduate funding opportunities. Visit *www.nottingham.ac.uk/graduateschool/ funding* and *www.nottingham.ac.uk/pgstudy/funding*

DOCTORAL TRAINING CENTRES
Nottingham leads on or is involved in a range of Doctoral Training Centres all offering fully funded PhD opportunities: *www.nottingham.ac.uk/dtc*

ACCOMMODATION
We guarantee all postgraduate students university-arranged accommodation for the first year of study, providing you accept your course place and return your accommodation application by 1 August of your year of study.

VISITING US
You are welcome to visit us at any time – just contact us. You can also visit our Postgraduate Virtual Open Day: *www.nottingham.ac.uk/dtc*

* *The Times Good University Guide 2013*

** High Fliers Research – The Graduate Market in 2013

SUCCEED WITH PLYMOUTH UNIVERSITY

www.plymouth.ac.uk/postgraduate
admissions@plymouth.ac.uk
twitter.com/PlymUni
facebook.com/plymouthuni

Winner of the Queen's Anniversary Prize for Higher and Further Education, Plymouth University is a friendly and vibrant community which has recently earned a place in the top 10 modern UK universities in the world. The university has a strong record of excellence, enterprise and innovation across its teaching and research activities and is distinguished by its long-term engagement with employers and the local community

An essential aspect of Plymouth University's lively, enterprising culture is our growing community of postgraduate students. Whether you choose a taught Masters programme, or undertake a research degree or professional Doctorate, you will be supported and supervised by staff who are international experts in their field. Their breadth and depth of knowledge means they are well placed to help you plan towards your future career and give advice based on genuine experience.

WORLD-RENOWNED RESEARCH

With an international reputation for the quality of our research in many diverse fields, Plymouth University is one of the leading research universities in the South West. Plymouth is ranked in the top 50 research universities in the UK and has showed the greatest improvement in research performance (Research Assessment Exercise, 2008).

The results of the latest RAE showed the majority of areas submitted by the university included world-leading research, achieving the highest rating possible. Overall, 80% of the research was judged as being of international repute, which means that our students can be taught by, and work alongside world-class experts.

Our research informs our teaching and impacts on student learning, encouraging students to engage with cutting edge research and become creative, highly employable graduates through engagement with research-active staff who are involved with solving real-world problems.

EMPLOYABILITY

After graduating with a postgraduate degree from Plymouth University, a number of different career opportunities will be opened up to you, increasing your likelihood of finding meaningful employment. The university has a higher-than-average employment rate for postgraduate students, with 84% of full-time and 93% of part-time students employed within six months of completing their studies.

LOCATION & FACILITIES

With more than £300million invested in long-term campus development, Plymouth University is dedicated to enhancing students' experience in living and learning. The campus is well established right in the heart of the city, meaning everything you could possibly need is right on your doorstep. Whatever your preference – whether perusing museums and galleries, shopping in the West Country's most popular shopping centre, riding on the moors, exploring the internationally acclaimed Eden Project, or windsurfing from a spectacular coast – Devon and Cornwall will cater for your taste.

'Plymouth University provides excellent facilities for study, supportive members of staff, and a perfect environment to learn.'

Jonathan Harvey, MSc Social Research

ESSENTIAL INFORMATION

KEY SUBJECT AREAS

We offer a range of postgraduate programmes across:

- architecture, building and construction
- art, design, media and performance
- business and management
- computing, mathematics and statistics
- earth, geography and environment
- education and teaching
- engineering
- English and humanities
- hospitality and tourism
- law and social science
- life sciences
- marine and maritime
- medicine, dentistry, health and social work
- psychology

FEES AND FUNDING

Course fees vary by subject. For more information on this and available funding opportunities, visit *www.plymouth.ac.uk/money*

Current and former students should enquire about our 10% alumni fee reduction.

CONTACT DETAILS

Admissions Office
Plymouth University
Drake Circus
Plymouth
Devon
PL4 8AA
T: +44 (0)1752 585858

Find your postgraduate future with us

Join one of the top 1% of universities worldwide and you are promised a dynamic and stimulating learning environment, at the forefront of global research.

- Over £8 million in postgraduate research studentships and bursaries available

- Masters and research programmes across a broad range of disciplines

- State-of-the-art facilities located on a stunning parkland campus

- Vibrant postgraduate community with students from over 130 countries

Visit our website for further information
www.reading.ac.uk/pg

SETTING THE FOUNDATION FOR AN INTERNATIONAL CAREER

BENEFIT FROM

– Access to competitive scholarships
– Completing your degree in one year full-time or in two years part-time
– Accredited work placements[1]
– A convenient Central London location
– A dually recognised degree in both the UK & the US[2]

– MBA
– MA Art History & Visual Culture
– MA Visual Arts Management & Curating
– MA International Relations
– MA International Development
– MA International Conflict & Security Studies
– MSc International Management: Entrepreneurship
– MSc International Management: Event Management

RICHMOND
THE AMERICAN INTERNATIONAL
UNIVERSITY
IN LONDON

+44 (0)20 8332 9000
ma@richmond.ac.uk
www.richmond.ac.uk/postgraduate

[1] *Work placements are subject to grades and references.* [2] *Some of our programmes hold dual recognition in the UK and the US.*

REGENT'S
UNIVERSITY LONDON

www.regents.ac.uk
exrel@regents.ac.uk
twitter.com/regentscollege
facebook.com/EFLondon

Regent's University London offers an unrivalled setting for higher education. Our main campus in Regent's Park enjoys beautiful, tranquil surroundings while being just minutes away from all that central London has to offer. As a charity, we are committed to promoting social benefit. We continually reinvest our profits to improve the university environment and put resources back into student education

TAUGHT POSTGRADUATE STUDY

Regent's offers both British and American postgraduate programmes in a wide range of fields, including business and management, finance, the humanities, the creative arts, and social sciences.

Our highly qualified faculty have many years of work experience in industry and are on hand to guide and support you as you progress in your academic career. To simulate the professional workplace, there is a careful balance between individual and group work, lectures with theory and practical seminars and workshops.

PROFESSIONALISM AND EMPLOYABILITY

We aim to develop our students as global citizens, equipped with the essential skills and experience to sustain exciting, rewarding careers in their chosen fields.

The high-quality teaching environment produces graduates who are internationally aware, innovative and employable. We emphasise the practical application of academic learning, offering diverse opportunities for students to develop their skills, both inside and outside the classroom.

Our graduates go on to build successful international careers in a range of industries as well as becoming entrepreneurs, starting their own companies, or returning to ensure the continuing success of family businesses.

LONDON ADVANTAGE

With mellow red-brick buildings set in 11 acres of private garden, our Regent's Park campus is a safe, secluded haven in which to live and study.

A short walk away, our Marylebone campus sits in a lively historic area, known for its up-market boutiques and cafés.

Excellent transport links make it easy to get around. We are close to central London tube stations, 10 minutes by underground from the Eurostar and less than one hour's travel from London airports. Our campuses are close to the City of London and the West End, with easy access to London's excellent theatres, galleries and museums, as well as major sporting and entertainment venues.

At Regent's University, London is our classroom. Whether you plan to study business or one of the arts, you will find that London's culture and commerce form an important part of the Regent's experience.

A TRULY INTERNATIONAL COMMUNITY

At Regent's you will find one of the most diverse educational communities in the United Kingdom.

With classmates from all corners of the world, our 4,500 students have unparalleled opportunities to make international friends and build global professional networks for the future. International experience is an increasingly important part of student education.

Most of our degree programmes have an international focus, led by staff who have trained, worked and taught across the world.

ESSENTIAL INFORMATION

USUAL ENTRY REQUIREMENTS
Bachelors degree with a minimum of a 2:2.

DURATION/START DATE
Courses start in September and January each year and programmes run from 12 to 16 months.

PROFESSIONAL ACCREDITATION
Most of our programmes are recognised by the Chartered Management Institute (CMI), giving graduates full CMI membership, providing recognition and endorsement from the UK's prestigious, professional body for managers and leaders.

WANT TO KNOW MORE?
Check our website for open evening dates or contact us to book a personal consultation.

FEES
All students pay the same tuition fees, regardless of nationality, course fees start at £14,975.

'Regent's taught me how to challenge established positions and gave me a new, international perspective.'
Joanna Marcinak, Bulgaria, MSc Global Banking & Finance

University of St Andrews

600 YEARS

SCOTLAND'S FIRST UNIVERSITY

St Andrews is Scotland's oldest university, having an academic tradition reaching back almost six centuries. It is the third oldest university in the English-speaking world after Oxford and Cambridge. The town provides a stunning location for students who want to engage in high-level academic study. The university is very diverse; students representing more than 120 nationalities are currently studying there.

RANKINGS PERFORMANCE

St Andrews performs well in many of the high-profile ranking lists compiled on university data. Recent highlights include:

- 4th in the UK by *The Guardian University Guide 2013*;
- 5th in the UK by *The Sunday Times 2013*;
- the QS World Rankings (2012/13), which placed St Andrews at 93rd overall;
- the Times Higher Education World University rankings for 'Arts and Humanities'; 34th in the world;
- the Leiden Rankings for scientific research output (April 2013); 47th in the world.

With 92% of academic staff submitted for consideration in the last Research Assessment Exercise (RAE 2008), the university is one of the most research-intensive universities in the UK.

SCHOLARSHIPS

A range of scholarships is available for both undergraduate and postgraduate students. Many of the awards are based on financial need but the majority are awarded for academic excellence. Full details are available from the university website.

SETTLING IN AND NETWORKING

The university is not a campus institution; it is integrated very closely with the local town. Although some postgraduate students are only in St Andrews for one year, they become part of both a thriving student environment and the dynamic local community. It doesn't take long for anyone to settle in or make friends.

The students' union has more than 140 affiliated societies, and approximately 60 sports clubs exist too, available to all students. The size and diversity of the university means that the networking possibilities that exist, both inside and outside the labs and lecture halls, are second to none.

www.st-andrews.ac.uk
pgrecruitment@st-andrews.ac.uk
twitter.com/univofstandrews
facebook.com/univofstandrews

COURSES
The University of St Andrews has c.1,800 postgraduates studying both postgraduate taught and research programmes.

SUPPORT
Information on the support provided by the University of St Andrews Careers Centre can be found at *www.st-andrews.ac.uk/careers*

OPEN DAYS
Prospective students can arrange to visit the university at *www.st-andrews. ac.uk/admissions/pg/visiting*

CONTACT DETAILS
University of St Andrews, St Katherine's West, 16 The Score, St Andrews, Fife, KY16 9AX
Tel: 01334 463325

Swansea University
Prifysgol Abertawe

www.swansea.ac.uk/postgraduate
postgraduate.admissions@swansea.ac.uk
twitter.com/SwanseaUni
facebook.com/swanseauniversity

Swansea University is a world-class, research-intensive institution with collaborative industry links that are among the best in the UK. Situated in stunning parkland overlooking a sandy beach, we've been equipping students for exceptional personal and professional achievement since 1920. We believe that postgraduate study should be about nurturing the creativity, innovation, and high-level skills necessary for a successful future, and that it should always be inspirational

FUNDING

The university invests significantly in postgraduate study each year, with research studentships and Masters scholarships available across all academic subject areas. Visit *www.swansea.ac.uk/postgraduate/scholarships* for details.

At least £5million of postgraduate scholarships and bursaries are available each year. For regular scholarship updates follow us at *twitter.com/SwanseaPostgrad* and on *facebook.com/SwanseaPostgrad*

EMPLOYABILITY

As one of the UK's leading universities for collaborative research with industry, Swansea is able to offer vocationally relevant programmes which give students the knowledge and skills employers demand. Our students have the opportunity to carry out industry-linked research projects and undertake work placements.

Organisations that have supported the university's research activities include: BUPA Foundation; Cancer Research UK; GlaxoSmithKline; Hewlett Packard; Rolls-Royce PLC; Tata Steel; and the World Health Organisation.

LOCATION

The postgraduate experience at Swansea goes beyond research and teaching excellence: our students enjoy a spectacular seafront campus, whilst the culturally rich city is home to the SA1 Swansea Waterfront development and the tallest building in Wales. The area is perfect for outdoor pursuits with the Gower Peninsula – the UK's first Area of Outstanding Natural Beauty – ideal for surfing, canoeing and mountain biking.

FACILITIES

We have postgraduate accommodation and can also support your search for private sector accommodation through our own letting agency. Our main library has the longest opening hours of any university library in Wales, more than 450 PCs, and a postgraduate study area.

We are serious about promoting sport for all, whatever your level. Our facilities include: the Wales National Pool; a double sports hall; astro pitches; an indoor and outdoor running track; fitness and power gyms; spin studios; and physiotherapy facilities. Our Beach and Watersports Centre offers activities such as beach volleyball, kayaking and kite surfing.

ESSENTIAL INFORMATION

RESEARCH
£33million – Value of research grants awarded to the University in 2011/12.

47.5% – Research rated as world-leading or internationally excellent (RAE 2008).

TEACHING
120 – Number of taught Masters programmes to choose from.

5 stars – Swansea University has been awarded a 5-star rating for its teaching quality (QS Stars).

POSTGRADUATE OPEN DAYS
We hold postgraduate open days in November, March and June each year. Find out more about visiting us at *www.swansea.ac.uk/postgraduate/open days*

SUBJECT AREAS
We offer postgraduate taught and research degrees in:
- ageing studies
- American studies
- biosciences
- business
- classics, ancient history and Egyptology
- computer science
- criminal justice and criminology
- Cymraeg/Welsh
- economics
- engineering
- English
- geography
- health and social sciences
- history
- law
- mathematics
- media studies
- medicine
- modern languages and translation
- nursing
- physics
- politics, international relations and development studies
- psychology
- sports and exercise science
- war and society

 University of
ULSTER

PhD and MRes Studentships
2014/2015

The University invites applications for admission to full-time research studies commencing in September 2014. Studentships will be available for selected applicants*.

Research supervision leading to the degree of Doctor of Philosophy (PhD) is offered in the following Research Institutes:

Science, Engineering and Information Technology

Biomedical Sciences, Built Environment, Computer Science, Engineering, Environmental Sciences, Nursing and Health Research, Psychology

Social Sciences

Business and Management, Research in Social Sciences, Sports and Exercise Sciences, Transitional Justice (Law)

Arts and Humanities

Art and Design, Arts and Humanities, Irish and Celtic Studies, Media Research

Master of Research (MRes)

A one-year full-time programme leading to the award of Master of Research is offered in the Faculties of Arts and Life and Health Sciences. Awards may be available for selected applicants.

How to Apply

To be considered for entry, applicants should hold, or expect to hold by 15 August 2014 a first or upper second class honours degree in a subject relevant to the proposed research topic. Application materials and specific project details are available on the University web site at **http://research.ulster.ac.uk/info/status/studentopp.html** Applications must be submitted using the University online admission system www.ulster.ac.uk/applyonline .

The closing date for the receipt of applications for full-time study and associated awards will be advertised in January/February 2014.

Interviews will form part of the selection process and are likely to be held during April 2014.

* Awards may be directed to some areas in preference to others on the basis of the number and quality of applications received and the University's strategic approach to the support of research activity.

For further information, contact:
Hazel Campbell, Research Office
e: **researchstudent@ulster.ac.uk** t: **+44 (0)28 7012 4729**
www.ulster.ac.uk/researchstudy

UNIVERSITY OF WEST LONDON
Connected.

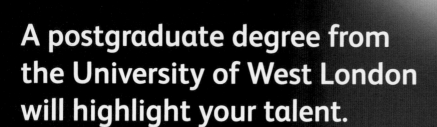

A postgraduate degree from the University of West London will highlight your talent.

The University of West London offers a diverse range of postgraduate courses, many with options for full-time and part-time study, both in daytimes and evenings giving you flexibility to develop your education around other commitments.

A variety of courses are available from all eight of our schools:

- College of Nursing, Midwifery and Healthcare
- Ealing Law School
- Ealing School of Art, Design and Media
- London College of Music
- London School of Hospitality and Tourism
- School of Computing and Technology
- School of Psychology, Social Work and Human Sciences
- The Business School

Find out more at uwl.ac.uk/prospects

THE UNIVERSITY OF WINCHESTER

Enhance your career, follow your passion for knowledge

Postgraduate study at the University of Winchester

What's on offer

- A learning experience that targets your career ambitions, enhances your employability and deepens your knowledge

- Research activity at national and international levels of excellence

- Innovative and forward thinking teaching with scholars at the forefront of their fields

- A dynamic and social campus, located in the heart of Winchester, an hour away from London.

Contact us

Tel: 01962 827234

Email: course.enquiries@winchester.ac.uk

 Facebook.com/universityofwinchester

 Twitter:@_UOW

www.winchester.ac.uk

We've got your career covered

Pick up our guides to graduate jobs and postgraduate study at your university careers service or graduate fair.

Postgrad

Issue 2 – Spring 2014

Choose your course

Work Experience & Internships

2013/14

www.prosp

Your guide to shaping your future

...stg

...1 – Autumn 2

...lore

...options

A comprehe
of graduat

Postgraduate Directory

2013/14

Find your perfect postgraduate course

Law

2013/14

www.prospects.ac.uk/la

Helping your legal career take shape

Prospects

View digital editions and keep up with the latest opportunities online

www.prospects.ac.uk

Science, technology and engineering

GOING TO APPLY? MENTION PROSPECTS' ADVICE ON YOUR APPLICATION

This section includes articles and profiles specifically relating to the science, technology and engineering subject areas. There are student and graduate case studies, advice from an expert in the field and features on new and popular courses. Browse the following pages to gain a greater understanding of your chosen subject field and hear from other people who have been in a similar position

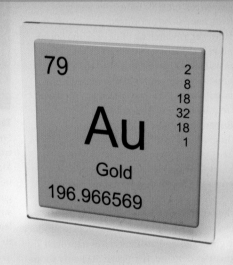

Cultivate a career with STEM

With an economy that's struggling to get back on track, the UK needs highly skilled postgraduates in science, technology, engineering and maths (STEM) subjects now more than ever…

STEM subjects have always been popular among postgraduates looking to increase their knowledge in their area of expertise and build up the skills necessary to work in industry.

Nowadays, though, the demand for STEM postgraduates is much higher as a result of the economic backdrop. In the government's 2011 Plan for Growth, which outlined the strategy of bringing growth back to the UK economy, it was suggested that advanced manufacturing, life sciences, creative industries and green energy need to be prioritised.

However, research by think tank the Social Market Foundation (SMF) recently suggested this will require an extra 40,000 UK STEM graduates every year to fill the 100,000-plus graduate-level jobs the economy is predicted to require on an annual basis.

Robert Beahan from the Institute of Engineering and Technology (IET) agrees, stating that without a highly skilled and knowledgeable workforce it will not be possible to generate economic growth through these sectors.

'It is vital that higher education in the UK has a strong STEM sector and is able to produce the graduates and postgraduates high-tech industries demand. IET research clearly shows a desire by employers to recruit new staff, but that they are struggling to find the right people.'

So, it's clear that there is a huge STEM skills gap to fill in the country. And that's where postgraduate study comes in, helping graduates develop their expertise so that they can produce work of the highest quality and drive innovation and growth.

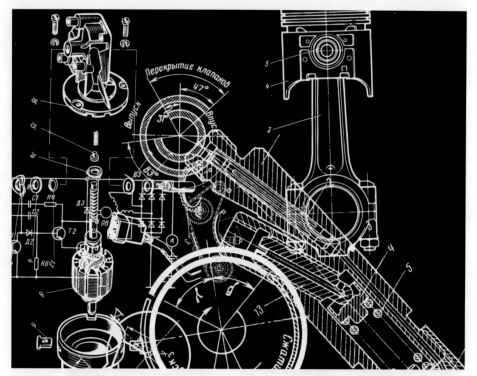

Taught or research?

Postgraduate study and research is a well-trodden path in the scientific subjects. Taught Masters allow students to narrow down their field of study, and translate the knowledge gained at undergraduate level into a career, such as engineering. This type of scientific learning is known as 'applied' study, as opposed to the 'pure' science you may have studied at undergraduate level, which involves experimentation and the study of the laws that govern objects and forces and do not necessary lead directly into a specific job role.

The scientific subjects have a clear path of learning from undergraduate level through to Masters and then PhD level. It is typically easier to secure funding in this area compared to many others. However, prospective students need to be aware that research can take many years of dedication to come to fruition.

Professor Visakan Kadirkamanathan, head of the department of automatic control and systems engineering at the University of Sheffield says, 'A taught postgraduate course in a STEM subject will help you to specialise in a topic of your choice and while you learn something new that excites you it will also give you a competitive edge in today's demanding job market'.

'You will discover and create something new that will have an impact in your discipline and that has the potential to transform society'

A career in scientific research can be based in either industry or academia. Many students aim for the better-paid roles at large companies and, while PhD qualifications make such career moves more likely, they can never be taken for granted. A minimum of three years of individual study can be a hard slog and a genuine interest in the topic is a must. However, it's not without reason that the scientific researcher is seen as the archetypal postgraduate.

Professor Kadirkamanathan explains, 'A PhD in a STEM subject will enable you to pursue a subject that you are passionate about in great depth. You will discover and create something new that will have an impact in your discipline and that has the potential to transform society.'

Engineering

Making up a significant part of STEM courses, engineering and all its branches of study remain extremely popular at postgraduate level.

Postgraduate options in engineering depend on what undergraduate qualification you have completed. Some undergraduates take a Masters of Engineering (MEng) for their first degree. This is a longer degree course than the Bachelor of Engineering (BEng), typically taking four years in England and five years in Scotland. It qualifies graduates to the minimum educational standard required to become a chartered engineer.

There are a few MSc courses available to BEng graduates who wish to gain chartered status, but MSc postgraduates normally work towards a specialism in a given field. For example, MSc programmes can turn marine engineers into submarine designers, or mechanical engineering graduates into automotive engineers. They also allow graduates to concentrate on an advanced topic, such as structural integrity within construction engineering.

Engineering research programmes typically come in two forms: the PhD and the Engineering Doctorate (EngD). Both qualifications involve a research project, but the EngD is distinguished by having close collaboration with an industrial sponsor, meaning that students spend up to 75% of their time working and researching in industry.

You may also, however, come across some engineering-related MSc by Research courses, as well as Master of Research (MRes) or MPhil programmes, which are often treated as a preliminary stage for a PhD but are higher education qualifications in their own right.

Computing
One rapidly growing STEM subject is computing, which is a central part of everyday life and has a huge influence on the business world. As a result, demand for bonafide computing experts is high in pretty much every industry which makes up the UK economy.

The IT sector is renowned for having excellent in-house training and consequently many graduates opt to go straight into employment as opposed to taking up postgraduate study. However, those who do look to take further study often find themselves at the centre of cutting-edge research into the latest computing trends. Most taught courses enable students to explore niche areas

in depth, allowing them to become specialists in topics such as artificial intelligence (AI) and software engineering.

Another reason to consider postgraduate study in computing is the ability to take conversion courses, of which many are on offer. These allow graduates of other disciplines to acquire an MSc in Computer Science, for example, and the skills they need to start a career in the industry, regardless of what they studied for their first degree.

Medicine
Undergraduate degrees in medicine take a long time to complete – usually between five and six years. After this, all newly qualified medical graduates must enrol on the Foundation Programme for two years, after which they can register with the General Medical Council and practise medicine unsupervised.

Despite the length of time it takes to become a doctor in the first place, medicine-related postgraduate degrees are still very popular.

A whole host of programmes and subjects are covered by UK universities, from the more general Doctor of Medicine (MD) Doctorate to courses focusing on anaesthetics, cardiology, dental sciences, gastroenterology, oncology, paediatrics, and more. Many allow you to drill down even further within that area and specialise in subjects that are yet more niche.

In the field of medicine, the sole aim is to provide the best possible care for the patients who require it. And this is obviously often a matter of life and death. That being the case, it makes perfect sense for qualified doctors to want to continue learning, continue improving and continue to merit one of the most difficult and well-respected occupations that exists.

STUDENT VIEW

Peter Thain is undertaking a PhD in Clinical Biomechanics at the University of Hertfordshire

Alongside my attention to detail and need to understand how things work, I have always had an inquisitive mind and a thirst for knowledge. During the final year of my undergraduate degree in sports therapy I became captivated by the research I was conducting for my dissertation, and it quickly became apparent that there was a gap in the literature that I believed I could explore. As a result, I decided to initially pursue a research Masters.

As the year progressed, I developed new ideas about future research and my supervisor encouraged me to convert onto a PhD pathway. Initially I was undecided, but when there was an accompanying offer of lecturing hours on the sports therapy and sport and exercise science undergraduate programmes, I decided I would accept the offer and continue onto the PhD.

Postgraduate study differs depending on the course you sign up for. I have friends who have completed taught programmes of study and they say it resembles an undergraduate programme with lectures, practicals and seminars.

As far as a research degree is concerned, I can tell you that it is far removed from an undergraduate course. With research you have no teaching at all, just yourself and one topic. As a result, I strongly believe you have to be very motivated to complete a PhD. On a full-time PhD you have a progression report every 12 months, which outlines the work completed to date and the proposed research for the next phase. This is effectively the only deadline.

The research process is not generally a smooth ride, and there will inevitably be times of difficulty, but in the end it is very rewarding.

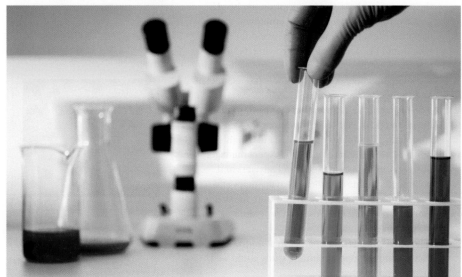

Fishy business

AQUACULTURE IS THE WORLD'S FASTEST GROWING FOOD-PRODUCING SECTOR. BUT WHAT IS IT? AND HOW CAN A POSTGRADUATE DEGREE HELP YOUR CHANCES OF A CAREER IN THE INDUSTRY?

Upon hearing the term aquaculture, you would be forgiven for thinking it is a fan club of a cheesy 90s Scandinavian pop outfit with a penchant for iconic children's figurines.

The truth is that outside the world of agriculture the practice is not widely recognised or understood. Aquaculture – often simply called fish farming or aquafarming – is the raising and selling of fish and other seafood on a commercial basis.

According to the United Nations' Food and Agriculture Organization (FAO), it is responsible for producing almost half of all of the world's food fish – over 65 million tonnes every year – and is worth some £77billion a year.

Fish farming courses

Students taking an aquaculture postgraduate programme are usually marine biology, biology and environmental science graduates with an interest in marine living resources for aquatic food production and marine biotechnology.

Taught and research aquaculture-related courses are offered by universities across the UK, although the majority are unsurprisingly situated on the coast.

Among those are the MSc Aquatic Biosciences and Resource Management at the University of Exeter; the MSc Aquaculture Enterprise and Technology at Newcastle University; and a number of courses at the Institute of Aquaculture at the University of Stirling.

On these programmes students could learn about everything from biodiversity and ecosystem management to environmental law, marketing and molecular toxicology.

Educated staff required

Dr Neil Hazon, course director of the MSc in Sustainable Aquaculture by online distance learning at the University of St Andrews, explains how a postgraduate course can benefit those looking for a career in the industry.

'Aquaculture faces many challenges over the next few years to be economically, socially and environmentally sustainable and will require highly educated, trained and experienced staff to achieve these goals,' he says.

Professor Simon Davies, course leader of the MSc Sustainable Aquaculture Systems at Plymouth University, adds, 'Training to the level of Masters in multi-disciplinary fields is required to provide sustainable solutions to the production of suitable feeds; control diseases; and optimise the production, health and welfare of farmed species to meet growing consumer demand'.

In addition, Professor Davies notes how governance and regulation has become a central topic in aquaculture Masters courses in recent years. There are some environmental and ethical concerns about the practice – for example overcrowding and the spread of disease among farmed fish – which aquafarmers aim to eliminate, and it's important for postgraduates to learn about how this can be improved.

'The environmental impact of aquaculture is an issue and the socioeconomic and governance aspects are addressed on the MSc Sustainable Aquaculture Systems. There are major technical and scientific innovations currently being developed and these are central to the course in Plymouth,' Professor Davies says.

Fastest-growing sector

Aquaculture is the fastest-growing sector of agri-business in the world. According to the FAO, the global demand for aquatic food products is expected to continue to increase. The organisation predicts that global aquaculture production will have to reach a huge 80 million tonnes by 2050 if it is to maintain the current level of fish consumption per head.

As a result, there are plenty of employment opportunities on offer across the world for those who would like a career in the growing industry.

Some examples of roles in the sector include: site manager; hatchery scientist; aquatic lab technician; and aquaculture analyst.

Speaking of the job prospects for postgraduates he has taught at Plymouth, Professor Davies comments, 'Graduates of our MSc Sustainable Aquaculture Systems course can expect managerial positions, or to become technical advisers and policy consultants to government agencies and commercial organisations. In addition, many often embark on related PhD research programmes in specialised fields.'

If you're considering a career in a unique and exciting industry, postgraduate study could well help you on your way.

AQUACULTURE IN NUMBERS

£77billion
The total value of the global industry

65 million tonnes
The current production per year

1 million tonnes
Aquaculture production as recently as 1950

80 million tonnes
Projected production in 2050 to keep pace with demand

89%
The proportion of global aquaculture production in the Asia-Pacific region

8%
Average growth rate of the industry per year for the past ten years

School of ENGINEERING AND DESIGN

PG taught courses are offered in:

- **Advanced Electronic and Electrical Engineering MSc** full-time
- **Advanced Engineering Design MSc** full-time and part-time
- **Advanced Manufacturing Systems MSc** full-time and distance learning
- **Advanced Mechanical Engineering MSc** full-time
- **Advanced Multimedia Design and 3D Technologies MSc** full-time and part-time
- **Aerospace Engineering MSc** full-time
- **Automotive and Motorsport Engineering MSc** full-time
- **Biomedical Engineering MSc** full-time
- **Building Services Engineering MSc** full-time and distance learning
- **Building Services Engineering Management MSc** distance learning
- **Building Services Engineering with Sustainable Energy MSc** full-time and distance learning
- **Computer Communication Networks MSc** full-time
- **Design and Branding Strategy/Strategy and Innovation MA** full-time
- **Digital Design and Branding MSc** full-time
- **Embedded Systems MSc – Multimedia Communications / Signal Processing** full-time
- **Engineering Management MSc** full-time and distance learning
- **Integrated Product Design MSc** full-time
- **Packaging Technology Management MSc** full-time and distance learning
- **Project and Infrastucture Management MSc** full-time
- **Renewable Energy Engineering MSc** full-time
- **Structural Integrity MSc** full-time
- **Sustainable Electrical Power MSc** full-time and part-time
- **Sustainable Energy: Technologies and Management MSc** full-time
- **Water Engineering MSc** full-time
- **Wireless Communication Systems MSc** full-time

For further information and application form contact:

PG courses: Marketing Office
Telephone +44 (0)1895 265814
Email sed-pg-admissions@brunel.ac.uk
Web www.brunel.ac.uk/sed/postgradute-study

Research: Research Office
Telephone +44 (0)1895 266876
Email sed-research@brunel.ac.uk
Web www.brunel.ac.uk/sed/research

For information on student study experiences view the spotlight newsletters at **www.brunel.ac.uk/sed**

7879 240613

Brunel
UNIVERSITY
L O N D O N

Enhance your career with Postgraduate Study

The only UK University with official accreditation for both computer games technology and computer arts
Scotland's leading university for its environmental science research, and leading modern university for law and psychology research (RAE 2008)

Postgraduate Subject Areas

- Biotechnology • Computer Games Technology •
- Counselling • Digital Forensics • Energy and Environment • Energy Industry Economics •
- Ethical Hacking • Finance • Food • Human Resource Management • Information Technology •
- Intelligence and Security • Management •
- MBA (Executive-style) • Oil and Gas Accounting •
- Oil and Gas Finance • Oil and Gas Management •
- Psychology • Renewable Bio-Energy

abertay.ac.uk
sro@abertay.ac.uk

The University of Abertay Dundee is a charity registered in Scotland, No. SC016040

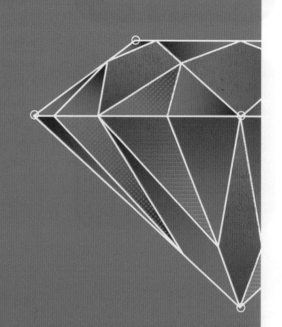

CASE STUDY

Erin Michno is studying for the Masters by Research in Computer Games Technology at Abertay University

Why did you choose this course and institution?

I moved to Scotland from New York State after looking at computer games technology degree courses around the world. Abertay appealed to me because it focuses on hands-on development for current gaming platforms – even the maths classes are centred on games.

All five academic schools at Abertay participate in the Masters by Research programme, so there's a huge range of specialist areas to choose from. This includes everything from business and innovation to psychology, nursing and exercise science.

Tell us a bit more about the course...

My Masters by Research degree is focused on computer games technology, which for me means creating tools relevant to improving how art is created and added to games, from a programmatical standpoint. This involves researching the integration of procedural content from a mathematical basis as well as from a user experience.

Many of the generation techniques I'm researching are rooted in computational geometry, but my research also looks at a practical, functional element as well. I'm very fortunate to have the freedom to research something so important to me personally while receiving great support from lecturers also working in this field.

Did you secure funding for your studies?

I've received several academic-based scholarships through Abertay, including an overseas student award. The recruitment office and student support in general has been a great help in finding information on funding sources.

What facilities are available at the institution?

Abertay has great facilities for game development students, from computer labs with industry-standard software to the Prototyping Studio for young companies, where many graduates and current students, including myself, start

up a company or find work placements through the talent pool.

Also, with the university working so closely with companies such as Sony and its PlayStation First programme, students get access to PlayStation 3 and PlayStation Vita development kits just like professional games studios.

What are the main differences between undergraduate and postgraduate life?

As I've moved through the different stages at Abertay, there has been progressively more academic and intellectual freedom to explore my own interests. This really started with our undergraduate third-year project, where we developed a game for the PlayStation 3, and that's continued right through into postgraduate life.

My first few years as an undergrad gave me the skills I needed to investigate research areas I am interested in more deeply. Now the focus is on taking what I learned as an undergraduate and applying that to my own research work, with the emphasis very much on me leading the direction of this with the help of my supervisors. It's a big challenge, but a very exciting one.

Also, having the opportunity to spend a summer working as a researcher on a lecturer's project really helped the transition to postgraduate life. We built an affordable motion-control system for film production studios, and that's now being used by

There has been progressively more academic and intellectual freedom to explore my own interests

20th Century Fox in producing blockbuster Hollywood movies.

How has the course helped you prepare for employment?

The Masters by Research has allowed me to really specialise in a key interest of mine: graphics programming and creating tools for all game developers. Being able to work closely with leading experts in this area has been a great help to my professional development – and the skills I'm learning are directly impacting on the work I do at Quartic Llama, the game development studio I've co-founded while doing my postgraduate research.

What advice would you give to other students considering taking this course?

Focus on what you're really interested in – being able to specialise your research really allows you to follow your passion. Becoming an expert in that area with a flexible Masters by Research can have a real impact on developing a career in that area, whether it's working for somebody else or building your own business.

What are your plans for after you graduate?

I'll continue working with Quartic Llama, which is preparing to finish two titles. The company has been fortunate enough to work with some exciting partners, including National Museums Scotland and the National Theatre of Scotland. Now we're looking at how we transfer that experience into releasing our own original games, hopefully for millions of people around the world to play and enjoy.

CASE STUDY

Jaz Rabadia graduated from City University London with an MSc Energy, Environmental Technology and Economics. She now works as an energy manager at multi-channel retailer Debenhams

Why did you decide to take a postgraduate course?

I took the MSc Energy, Environmental Technology and Economics after a BEng in Mechanical Engineering to gain more specialist knowledge in my chosen field and pursue my passion for a career in the energy and environment sector.

The course also allowed me to study part time, so I could gain valuable work experience in the field while studying. The postgraduate course proved a great stepping stone from undergraduate studies to working life.

What did your course involve?

I loved how varied my course was. We would often get great speakers from industry to lead modules and give us first-hand insights into the challenges they face on a daily basis.

My course involved a lot of group debates, individual written assessments, presentations and a dissertation. There were lots of opportunities to pick the brains of the academic staff and industry speakers.

Did you take up further study immediately after your first degree?

Yes. After taking energy management and renewable energy modules in my mechanical engineering degree, I knew then that I wanted to learn more in this area, so it was an easy decision to make. I found it worked well for me to go straight onto the postgraduate course as I was quite familiar with university life; I knew the academic staff and the university really well so it made the transition a lot smoother.

How did postgraduate life differ from undergraduate life?

The postgraduate course consisted of a real mix of students, some of them fresh undergraduates, some mature students already working in the industry and taking the course as part of their professional development.

Postgraduate study required more independent learning, greater drive and good time-management skills,

as for me it meant juggling university with a full-time job.

What does your job involve?

I'm now an energy manager at Debenhams, a leading international retailer. My responsibilities include producing and maintaining the company's energy policy; implementing energy-reduction projects; purchasing and negotiating contracts for electricity, gas and water; ensuring compliance against energy legislation; and engaging employees in energy-awareness best practice.

How did your studies prepare you for this career?

In my role, I put into practice all the skills I learned at university, such as writing compelling business cases, undertaking financial appraisals of energy technologies, working in teams, managing stakeholders and developing leadership skills. My studies not only gave me the academic

I knew the academic staff and the university really well so it made the transition a lot smoother

foundations I need to succeed in my role but also the behavioural skills required.

What advice would you give to others considering further study?

It's important that your further studies complement your career choice. It's very competitive in the job market and a relevant postgraduate degree can give you an edge against other applicants. I certainly found that it makes heads turn.

A postgraduate degree can be completed at any stage in your career, so it's important to time it well; often employers will sponsor employees to complete a degree as part of their training and professional development if it's required for the job.

What did you enjoy most about your time at City University London?

I made some great friends, not only among the student population but also the academic staff. City University London supported me through the very early stages of my career and provided me with great networking opportunities.

It was through the university that I joined the Energy Institute, and I've gone from being a graduate member to being the youngest member to be awarded chartered energy manager status. I was also highly commended as energy manager of the year in 2012 and was a finalist in the Asian Women of Achievement awards in the Young Achiever category.

The university is in a great central London location, has brilliant facilities – particularly in the School of Engineering and Mathematical Sciences – and is one of the top universities for graduate and postgraduate employment.

The academic staff are highly knowledgeable and there are lots of opportunities to get involved in the many research projects the university is carrying out. I proudly endorse the university and would recommend it to anyone considering a postgraduate degree.

Constructing careers

If you're interested in building a lasting legacy and helping to create and improve the environment in which we live, a postgraduate course in civil engineering could be for you

One of the oldest forms of engineering, civil engineering is at the heart of our everyday lives, and yet we take its work for granted. In fact, according to the Institute of Civil Engineers (ICE), the discipline is so important to society that you wouldn't be able to get through your Monday morning routine without it.

'You clean your teeth using the running water in your bathroom. Have a cup of tea or coffee. You travel to work on a finely constructed network of roads or on a train or underground system. You park your car or grab another cup of coffee at the train station before heading to the office. You might even walk through an underpass or over a bridge before finally settling at your desk. None of this would have been possible without civil engineers,' the ICE explains on its website.

Civil engineers are involved with the design, development and construction of projects in the built and natural environment. They ensure the safe and timely completion of everything from stadiums and train stations to bridges, roads and railways.

Chartered status

At undergraduate level, the most common civil engineering courses are either the Bachelor of Education (BEng) or Master of Engineering (MEng) programmes.

Taking between four and five years to complete, MEng courses are the most direct route to achieving the academic requirements for chartered engineer (CEng) status, an important benchmark of competence that is highly valued by employers.

Although BEng courses allow graduates to move into work earlier than MEng students, and the grades required are lower, three-to-four-year BEng courses do not provide students with the requirements for CEng status.

That's where postgraduate study comes in – if you've opted for a BEng or one of the BSc engineering courses on offer, it gives you the chance to further develop your expertise and satisfy the criteria for that coveted CEng status.

A range of courses

There are multiple facets to civil engineering, and that's reflected in the range of courses on offer at UK institutions.

For example, you might want to study a course on anything from structural integrity or environmental engineering to the built environment. Or you may wish to enrol on a generic civil engineering course.

Dr Amer Ali, senior lecturer in civil engineering at London South Bank University (LSBU) and director of the institution's MSc Civil Engineering course, explains how having a selection of programmes to choose from can benefit students of the discipline.

'While our MSc Civil Engineering is a broad-based course covering the areas of structures, geotechnics, water engineering, transportation and asset management, the other two MSc courses we offer in this area – structural engineering and transport engineering and planning – are specialised. However, all are designed to enhance the knowledge and skills of engineers and other construction and transportation industry professionals.'

Job prospects

The construction sector has suffered significantly as a result of the recession, leading to building projects being shelved and companies' output dipping.

This has been particularly worrying as figures show that every £1 spent on construction actually generates £2.84 for the economy. However, the government realises the importance of boosting construction output, as underlined by its £310billion National Infrastructure Plan, which aims to increase growth and the number of jobs in the sector.

As a result, those entering the industry over the next few years could find a range of employment opportunities available to them.

Dr Ali explains, 'Employment prospects for graduates of these courses are very good, especially in view of the upturn in new infrastructure projects in the UK and overseas.'

Commenting on the destination of graduates from LSBU's civil engineering course, he adds, 'Successful students enter into a variety of positions within the construction industry, ranging from working in a design office, with contractors and in local authorities'.

If you want to make the world's built environment safer, more efficient and more beautiful, and ensure Monday mornings continue to run without a hitch, a postgraduate degree in civil engineering could be right up your street.

WHAT DO CIVIL ENGINEERS DO?

Civil engineers are responsible for designing, developing, constructing and maintaining a range of structures, including:

- roads;
- bridges;
- tunnels;
- stadiums;
- dams;
- airports;
- water treatment facilities;
- sewage and power plants;
- railways and train stations.

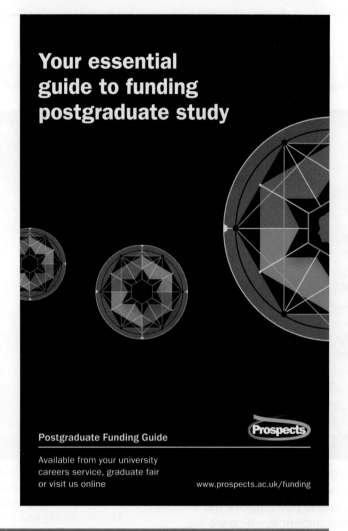
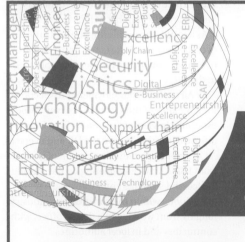

CASE STUDY

Alberto Berardi from Macerata, a small town in central Italy, is currently studying for a PhD in Pharmaceutical Development of Virus-like Particles Expressed in Plants at the University of East Anglia (UEA)

What inspired you to study for a postgraduate degree?

I really enjoyed the last year of project work (drug delivery) during my Masters and decided to carry on with my research.

Tell us about your PhD and why you chose to study your particular project at UEA…

My PhD is the result of collaboration between the School of Pharmacy at UEA and the John Innes Centre, an independent, international centre of excellence in plant science and microbiology. The project focuses on the development of plant-based oral vaccines.

My decision to study at UEA was based on feedback from colleagues already studying here. Furthermore, UEA is considered a prestigious university in my home country. I was offered the opportunity to work for a PhD while the research was at an early stage, and the prospect of working in a completely new area like this, rather than following up on an ongoing project, was really exciting. I also relished the idea of working in an interdisciplinary topic, covering areas of drug delivery, plant biology, biochemistry and biology of the gastrointestinal tract.

What do you really enjoy about your PhD?

What I like most is the opportunity to work both independently and develop my own ideas within the research group. I can also count on my supervisors' experience whenever I need it. Another aspect I particularly appreciate about my research group is the friendly interaction I have with the other PhD students and supervisors – whenever I need a word of support or a friendly chat I know they are there for me.

Has your programme met your expectations?

I am really satisfied with my PhD programme. Alongside working on my own project in the lab, I really enjoy helping my supervisor in laboratory demonstrations and workshops – this has given

me hands-on work experience, as well as an insight into the teaching aspect of being a scientist.

I appreciate the immense support I receive from my supervisors in my development as a postgraduate student. They have opened up opportunities for me to attend conferences whenever I like.

I have made use of the professional development opportunities organised by the Science Graduate School, the School of Pharmacy and Norwich Research Park.

How do you rate the research facilities at UEA?

UEA research laboratories are equipped with a variety of top-class facilities that have given me and my colleagues lots of possibilities when planning and developing almost any kind of experimental method we come up with. This wide range of facilities makes our work original and unique in our own fields.

What I like most is the opportunity to work both independently and develop my own ideas within the research group

What advice would you give to new students considering postgraduate study?

If I were able to make my choice again, I would definitely choose UEA. I think UEA offers a truly unique opportunity to do research in a vibrant and stimulating multicultural environment, using state-of-the-art facilities while working alongside highly renowned scientists.

On a personal note UEA is a great, sociable place to work and live. In addition, I love using the Sportspark and have had many enjoyable nights at the campus bars. It's a unique, welcoming environment.

What are your plans for the future?

After my PhD I would like to carry on with research. Whether in university or industry, I would like to find a position in which I will still be able to develop research using my own ideas, and hopefully avoid any job that falls into a routine.

How do you believe your degree programme is helping you fulfil these plans?

This degree programme is teaching me to think, and develop my research, independently. I think this will be a very important tool to achieve my goals both in my career and in my personal life. Moreover, I think that this experience gained in the scientific field is really solid and based on the use of the most up-to-date methods, making my colleagues and myself very strong candidates for relevant positions in industry or academia.

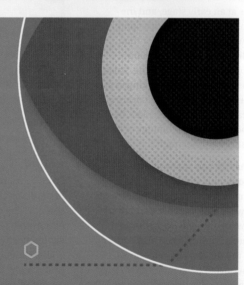

CASE STUDY

Kimberley Tucker-Hood is studying for a PhD in Atmosphere, Oceans and Climate at the University of Reading

Why this course and why the University of Reading?

When I was halfway through my undergraduate degree, I decided I wanted to go into research in the field of meteorology. I spent hours checking course listings and potential university prospectuses, and it turned out that the University of Reading has the only dedicated meteorology department in the country. It's a world-renowned department, too – very active in research and boasting several Nobel Prize winners.

The university itself has some beautiful campuses renowned for their green space, while Reading is ideally situated for travelling, being so close to London and to major airports and train stations.

What are the main differences between undergraduate and postgraduate study?

A PhD is all about you, the student, taking a step into the unknown and doing independent research. Although there's the option of taking Masters modules in topics you might need to help you, there's no set list of things to do. You need to be motivated and disciplined, especially when the university's great outdoors beckon.

My time is my own to allocate as I see fit – I don't have to attend lectures, although I do have a lot more meetings. The university offers postgraduates opportunities to get involved in things like demonstrating and invigilating exams – positions of increased responsibility that pay very well. There are also no set holidays, apart from things like Christmas and Easter, so I can take a week off and it doesn't make much difference. It is harder to visualise the end goal, though, since the days can easily blend into one.

How are you funding your studies?

My PhD is funded by a grant from the National Environmental Research Council. As it is a CASE study, I also get additional funding from the Met Office. This means I have a maximum of four years to complete my PhD.

What facilities for postgraduates does the university offer?

Every PhD student gets a desk and computer in an office with other PhD students, with access 24/7, including all printing, copying and library facilities. The graduate school has extra computers and hosts events to encourage PhD students to take part in university life. It also provides the Reading Researcher Development Programme (RRDP) of training sessions and development workshops for Doctoral researchers.

My department provides funding for each student to attend one conference and one summer school – I'm going to America and Hungary this year. There are also daily seminars and presentations about research others are doing – an excellent way of keeping up to date with current work. We also have the annual Met pantomime, *Met's Got Talent* show, summer BBQ and departmental nights out, arranged by PhD students as a way of interacting with the whole department.

As the university has many halls of residence, all first-year PhD students are offered a place in halls.

How have your studies and the university prepared you for employment?

The PhD itself is very useful for employment if you're

A PhD is all about you, the student, taking a step into the unknown and doing independent research

planning a career in research, as it demonstrates you've picked up the essential skills.

The RRDP courses are really useful, covering things like giving presentations and project management – essential when you're employed as a researcher. The careers advice service offers CV and skills workshops and the students' union has a JobShop that arranges part-time employment in local businesses, providing experience and some extra money.

What advice would you give to someone considering the same course?

Do your homework before applying – ask lecturers for advice, visit the institutions and speak to as many people studying there as you can. PhDs are hard work and you need to be sure that's what you want.

Remember that each university has its own application and interview system. In the meteorology department at Reading, I sent in a generic application and they then provided a list of topics for which they had funding, before conducting 'interview speed dates' to match project supervisors up with potential students.

Also, allow plenty of time for the application process – it took me three months just to get my personal statement up to scratch!

What are your plans?

As I'm only in my first year, I haven't thought too much about what I'm going to do. The university often employs people who have completed their PhDs here, or another option is the Met Office, or perhaps even working abroad.

Helping your legal career take shape

Training contracts, vacation schemes, further study and alternative careers

Prospects Law

Available from your university careers service, graduate fair or visit us online

www.prospects.ac.uk/law

Science, technology and engineering
Course and research opportunities

This section sets out every UK and Ireland postgraduate opportunity in the area of science, technology and engineering. Use the following pages to browse the taught courses and research opportunities at each institution. The listings are divided into subject chapters which are subsequently divided into related subject areas.

Taught courses and research opportunities are listed separately, each entry containing university name, course name, mode of study and type of study information. Please see the full A-Z index of all subjects in this publication on page 557. Further details of each course can be found at *www.prospects.ac.uk/findcourses*

SCIENCE, TECHNOLOGY AND ENGINEERING SUBJECT CHAPTERS LIST

Agricultural sciences

Agricultural sciences
Taught Courses

Aberystwyth University
Green Biotechnology and Innovation .... MSc 12FT

Anglia Ruskin University
Sustainability: Working for Positive Change....MSc 12FT 24-30PT

Bangor University
Agricultural Systems................................ PhD by taught 36FT 60PT/
MPhil 24FT 36PT
Agroforestry...... MSc 12FT 24PT/PhD by taught 36FT 60PT/MPhil
24FT 36PT
Agroforestry .... MSc 12FT
Environmental Forestry .... MSc 12FT
Forestry (Distance Learning)...................... MSc 36DL/PGDip 24DL/
PGCert 12DL
Sustainable Forest and Nature Management (SUFONAMA)
(Erasmus Mundus course)... MSc 24FT

Cranfield University
Agricultural and Environmental Engineering .... MSc(Res) 12FT
24-36PT

University of East Anglia
Plant Genetics & Crop Improvement .... MSc 12FT 24PT
Sustainable Agriculture and Food Security...................... MSc 12FT

Heriot-Watt University
Food Science and Nutrition..........MSc 12FT 24PT/PGDip 9FT 21PT
Food Science, Safety and Health .... MSc 12FT 24PT 24-84DL/
PGDip 9FT 21PT 24-84DL

Newcastle University
Agricultural and Environmental Science .... MSc 12FT
Food and Rural Development Research .... MSc 12FT 24PT
Medicinal Plants and Functional Foods .... MSc 12FT

University of Nottingham
Agrifood .... MSc 24PT/PGCert 21PT/PGDip 21PT
Crop Improvement ....MSc 12FT 24PT/PGDip 9FT 24PT
Plant Genetic Manipulation .... MSc 12FT 24PT

Royal Agricultural University
Advanced Farm Management....MBA 15FT 24PT/MBA 36PT/MBA
48PT
Climate Change and Development.......................... MSc 12FT 24PT
Agriculture .... PGDip 12FT 24PT
International Food and Agribusiness .... MBA 15FT

Natural Resource Management .... MSc 12FT 24PT
Organic Agricultural Systems................................. MSc 12FT 24PT
Sustainable Agricultural Systems .... MSc 12FT 24PT
Sustainable Agriculture and Food Security............. MSc 15FT 24PT
Sustainable Rural Tourism.. MSc 12FT 24PT
Sustainable Soil Management.................................. MSc 12FT 24PT

Schumacher College
Sustainable Horticulture and Food Production .... MSc 12FT

Swansea University
Aquatic Ecology and Conservation .... MRes 12FT 24-36PT

Agricultural sciences
Research Courses

Aberystwyth University
IBERS - Rural Sciences (MPhil) .... MPhil 12FT 24PT

Bangor University
Agricultural Systems.................... MPhil 24FT 36PT/PhD 36FT 60PT
Agroforestry.................................. MPhil 24FT 36PT/PhD 36FT 60PT
Environmental and Soil Science ....MPhil 24FT 36PT/
PhD 36FT 60PT
Forest Ecology and Management........MPhil 24FT 36PT/PhD 36FT
60PT

Cranfield University
Agricultural and Environmental Engineering ....MPhil 24FT 96PT/
PhD 36FT 96PT/MSc by research 12FT 24-60PT

University of Greenwich
Agricultural and Food Sciences..... MPhil 18 - 36FT 30 - 48PT/PhD
33 - 60FT 45 - 72PT
Natural Resources by Research ....MSc by research 12FT 24PT

Harper Adams University
Crop Protection ....MPhil 24FT/PhD 36FT
Precision Farming (MRes is Subject to Validation)...... MRes 12FT/
MPhil 24FT/PhD 38FT

University of Nottingham
Agricultural and Environmental Sciences ....PhD 36FT

Oxford Brookes University
Biological Sciences - Spatial Ecology and Land Use........................
PhD 24-60FT 36-72PT/MPhil 24-36FT 36-48PT

University of Oxford
International Development Centre.................................. DPhil 48FT

Royal Agricultural University
Sustainable Agricultural Development ....PhD 33FT 45PT/MPhil
18FT 30PT

Swansea University
Aquatic Biology...MSc by research 12FT 24PT
Sustainable Aquaculture and Fisheries ....MRes 12FT 24PT
Sustainable Resources...................................MSc by research 12FT

Agriculture
Taught Courses

Aberystwyth University
Green Biotechnology and Innovation .... MSc 12FT

Bangor University
Agricultural Systems................................ PhD by taught 36FT 60PT/
MPhil 24FT 36PT
Agroforestry...... MSc 12FT 24PT/PhD by taught 36FT 60PT/MPhil
24FT 36PT
Agroforestry .... MSc 12FT
Environmental Forestry .... MSc 12FT
Forestry (Distance Learning)...................... MSc 36DL/PGDip 24DL/
PGCert 12DL
Sustainable Forest and Nature Management (SUFONAMA)
(Erasmus Mundus course)... MSc 24FT

Cardiff Metropolitan University
Food Technology for Industry ....MSc 24-60DL

University of Chester
Sustainability for Community and Business ....MSc 12FT 24PT/
PGDip 12FT 24PT/PGCert 12FT 12-24PT

University of East Anglia
Agriculture and Rural Development.......................... MA 12FT 24PT
Sustainable Agriculture and Food Security...................... MSc 12FT

Edge Hill University
Sustainable Production...MSc 12-24DL

University of Edinburgh
Management of Bioeconomy, Innovation and Governance... MSc
12FT 24PT

University of Exeter
Applied Ecology.. MSc 12FT
Food Security and Sustainable Agriculture............. MSc 12FT 24PT

Harper Adams University
Dairy Business Management /subject to validation... PGCert 6FT
12PT/PGDip 6FT 12PT/MSc 6FT 12PT
Farm and Agri-business Management ....MSc 12FT 48PT/PGDip
12FT 48PT/PGCert 6FT 48PT
International Agri-business and Food Chain Management... MSc
12FT 48PT/PGDip 12FT 48PT/PGCert 6FT 48PT
Poultry Business Management /subject to validation ....
PGCert 6FT 48PT/MSc 6FT 12PT/PGDip 6FT 12PT
Sustainable Agriculture ....MSc 12FT 48PT/PGDip 12FT 48PT/
PGCert 6FT 48PT

Heriot-Watt University
Food Science and Nutrition..........MSc 12FT 24PT/PGDip 9FT 21PT
Food Science, Safety and Health .... MSc 12FT 24PT 24-84DL/
PGDip 9FT 21PT 24-84DL

Lancaster University
(Research) International Masters in Sustainable Agriculture and
Food Security .... MSc(Res) 21FT
Sustainable Agriculture and Food Security............. MSc 12FT 24PT

Newcastle University
Medicinal Plants and Functional Foods .... MSc 12FT
Organic Farming and Food Production Systems.............. MSc 12FT

University of Nottingham
Global Food Security (MRes)................................... MRes 12FT 36PT

University of Reading
Agricultural Development Economics .... MSc 12FT 24PT
Agricultural Economics .... MSc 12FT 24PT
Agriculture and Development .... MSc 12FT 24PT
Applied Development Studies .... MSc 12FT 24PT

Royal Agricultural University
Advanced Farm Management....MBA 15FT 24PT/MBA 36PT/MBA
48PT

Royal Veterinary College
Intensive Livestock Health and Production .... PGCert 12-36DL

Schumacher College
Sustainable Horticulture and Food Production .... MSc 12FT

Scotland's Rural College
Applied Poultry Science .... MSc 27DL/PGDip 18DL
Organic Farming .... MSc 36DL/PGDip 24DL

Swansea University
Aquatic Ecology and Conservation .... MRes 12FT 24-36PT

University of Ulster
Agri-food Business Development..........................MSc 12FT 26PT/
PGDip 9FT 21PT

Writtle College
Livestock Production Science ....MSc 12FT/PGDip 8FT/PGCert 4FT

New courses added every week at Prospects.ac.uk/findcourses

Find postgraduate funding at Prospects.ac.uk/funding

Jobs, study and advice at Prospects.ac.uk/agriculture

Agricultural sciences

Agriculture
Research Courses

Bangor University
Agricultural Systems.................... MPhil 24FT 36PT/PhD 36FT 60PT
Agroforestry................................ MPhil 24FT 36PT/PhD 36FT 60PT
Forest Ecology and Management........MPhil 24FT 36PT/PhD 36FT 60PT

Coventry University
Sustainable Agriculture .... MSc by research 12FT 24-36PT

University of Greenwich
Natural Resources by Research ....MSc by research 12FT 24PT

Harper Adams University
Agri-Environment...MPhil 24FT/PhD 38FT
Precision Farming (MRes is Subject to Validation)...... MRes 12FT/MPhil 24FT/PhD 38FT
Renewable Resources.....................................DPhil 24FT/PhD 38FT
Rural Affairs Management...............................MPhil 24FT/PhD 38FT

University of Hertfordshire
Agriculture and the Environment .... PhD 36FT 72PT/MRes 12FT 24PT

Newcastle University
Agriculture .... PhD 36FT 72PT/MPhil 12FT 24PT

Oxford Brookes University
Biological Sciences - Spatial Ecology and Land Use ....
PhD 24-60FT 36-72PT/MPhil 24-36FT 36-48PT

Swansea University
Sustainable Aquaculture and Fisheries ....MRes 12FT 24PT
Sustainable Resources....................................MSc by research 12FT

Writtle College
Agriculture ..... MSc by research 12FT 24PT/MPhil 24FT 48PT/PhD 36FT 72PT

Crop science
Taught Courses

Aberystwyth University
Green Biotechnology and Innovation .... MSc 12FT

Bangor University
Agricultural Systems................................ PhD by taught 36FT 60PT/MPhil 24FT 36PT

University of Cambridge
Bioscience Enterprise .... MPhil 10FT
Human Evolutionary Studies.................................... MPhil 11FT

University of Dundee
Crops for the Future (MRes)...................................MRes 12FT

University of East Anglia
Agriculture and Rural Development........................ MA 12FT 24PT
Plant Genetics & Crop Improvement .... MSc 12FT 24PT

University of East London
Biotechnology .... MSc 12FT 24PT/PGDip 8FT 16PT/PGCert 4FT 8PT
Biotechnology and Management ....MSc 12FT 24PT/PGDip 8FT 16PT/PGCert 4FT 8PT

University of Exeter
Food Security and Sustainable Agriculture............MSc 12FT 24PT

University of Glasgow
Crop Biotechnology .... MSc 12FT

Harper Adams University
Sustainable Agriculture ....MSc 12FT 48PT/PGDip 12FT 48PT/PGCert 6FT 48PT

Heriot-Watt University
Brewing and Distilling...................MSc 12FT 24PT/PGDip 9FT 21PT

University of Nottingham
Crop Biotechnology and Entrepreneurship ....MSc 12FT 24PT
Crop Improvement........................MSc 12FT 24PT/PGDip 9FT 24PT
Sustainable Bioenergy ....MSc 12FT 36PT

Schumacher College
Sustainable Horticulture and Food Production .... MSc 12FT

University of Warwick
Sustainable Crop Production: Agronomy for the 21st Century.....
MSc 12FT 36PT

Writtle College
Arable Crop Production..MSc 12FT 24PT
Horticulture (Crop Production) ....MSc 12FT 24-36PT/PGDip 8FT 20-36PT/PGCert 4FT 16-36PT

Crop science
Research Courses

Bangor University
Agricultural Systems.................... MPhil 24FT 36PT/PhD 36FT 60PT

Coventry University
Crop Improvement by Molecular Biotechnology MSc by research 12FT 24-36PT

Harper Adams University
Engineering..MPhil 24FT/PhD 38FT

Heriot-Watt University
International Centre for Brewing and Distilling (ICBD)..................
PhD 36FT 48PT/MPhil 24FT

University of Nottingham
Biorenewables and Bioprocessing Group ...PhD 36FT 48PT/MPhil 24FT 36PT
Plant and Crop Sciences...PhD 36FT 72PT/MPhil 24FT 48PT/MRes 12FT 24PT

Swansea University
Biomathematics ....MSc by research 12FT 24PT
Environmental Sustainability..............MSc by research 12FT 24PT
Sustainable Resources....................................MSc by research 12FT

University of the Highlands and Islands
Agriculture: Agronomy .... PhD 36FT 72PT/MPhil 24FT 48PT

University of Warwick
Plant and Environmental Sciences.............. PhD 36FT/MPhil 24FT/MSc by research 12FT

Fish farming
Taught Courses

University of Central Lancashire
Carbon and Resource Management....MSc 12FT 24PT/PGDip 9FT 18PT/PGCert 6FT 12PT

University of Glasgow
Aquatic System Science ....MSc 12FT 24PT/PGDip 8FT 16PT

Heriot-Watt University
Marine Biodiversity and Biotechnology .....MSc 12FT 24PT/PGDip 9FT 21PT
Marine Resource Management (MRM) .... MSc 12FT 24PT

King's College London
Aquatic Resource Management .... MSc 12FT

Newcastle University
Aquaculture Enterprise and Technology ....MSc 12FT 24PT

Plymouth University
Sustainable Aquaculture Systems ....MSc 12FT 24PT

Queen Mary, University of London
Aquatic Ecology by Research ....MSc 12FT 24PT
Environmental Science: Integrated Management of Freshwater
Environments ....MSc 12FT 24-36PT

University of Southampton
Freshwater Sciences ....MRes 12FT

University of St Andrews
Ecosystem-based Management of Marine Systems ....MRes 12FT
Sustainable Aquaculture . MSc 12FT 24PT/PGDip 9FT 24PT 24DL/Cert 12DL

University of Stirling
Aquaculture: Sustainable Aquaculture .... MSc 12FT
Aquatic Pathobiology .... PGCert 4FT/PGDip 11FT/MSc 12FT

Swansea University
Aquatic Ecology and Conservation .... MRes 12FT 24-36PT

UCL - University College London
Aquatic Science .... MSc 12FT

Fish farming
Research Courses

University of Hull
Aquatic Ecology and Resource Management........PhD 36FT 60PT/MPhil 24FT 36PT/MSc by research 12FT 24PT
Fisheries ....PhD 36FT/MSc by research 12FT

University of Roehampton
Ecology .... PhD 24-48FT 36-60PT/MPhil 21-36FT 33-48PT

University of Stirling
Aquaculture Research .... PhD 36FT/MPhil 24FT

Swansea University
Aquatic Biology......................................MSc by research 12FT 24PT
Sustainable Aquaculture and Fisheries ....MRes 12FT 24PT

Forestry science
Taught Courses

University of Aberdeen
Forestry ....MSc 12FT 24PT/PGDip 9FT
Management Economics and International Relations .MSc 12FT/PGDip 9FT/PGCert 6FT

Bangor University
Agroforestry...... MSc 12FT 24PT/PhD by taught 36FT 60PT/MPhil 24FT 36PT
Agroforestry... MSc 12FT
Environmental Forestry .... MSc 12FT
Forest Ecology and Management......... PhD by taught 36FT 60PT/MPhil 24FT 36PT
Forestry (Distance Learning with International Commonwealth
Scholarship) .... MSc 12DL
Forestry (Distance Learning)MSc 36DL/PGDip 24DL/PGCert 12DL
Forestry and Environmental Management degrees
(TRANSFOR-M).. MSc 24FT

Sustainable Forest and Nature Management (SUFONAMA)
(Erasmus Mundus course)... MSc 24FT
Sustainable Tropical Forestry (SUTROFOR) (Erasmus Mundus
course)... MSc 24FT
Tropical Ecosystems ..PhD by taught 36FT 60PT/MPhil 24FT 36PT
Tropical Frorestry .... MSc 36FT/PGDip 24FT/PGCert 12FT

University of Cumbria
Forest Ecosystem Management .... MSc 12FT 24PT/GradDip 6FT 12PT/GradCert 3FT 6PT

University of Glasgow
Landscape Monitoring & Mapping.................. MSc 12FT 24-36PT/PGDip 9FT 18-21PT
Landscape: Integrated Research and Practice.......MSc 12FT 24PT/PGDip 9FT 18PT

Harper Adams University
Conservation & Forest Protection......MSc 12FT 24PT/PGDip 12FT 24PT/PGCert 12FT 24PT

Manchester Metropolitan University
Conservation Biology....................................MSc 12FT 24-60PT

University of Southampton
Ecological and Environmental Sciences..........................MRes 12FT

Swansea University
Environmental Biology: Conservation and Resource
Management... MSc 12FT 36PT

Forestry science
Research Courses

Bangor University
Agroforestry.................................. MPhil 24FT 36PT/PhD 36FT 60PT
Forest Ecology and Management........MPhil 24FT 36PT/PhD 36FT 60PT

University of Roehampton
Ecology .... PhD 24-48FT 36-60PT/MPhil 21-36FT 33-48PT

Swansea University
Environmental Conservation...............MSc by research 12FT 24PT
Sustainable Resources....................................MSc by research 12FT

Horticultural studies
Taught Courses

University of Glasgow
Landscape Monitoring & Mapping.................. MSc 12FT 24-36PT/PGDip 9FT 18-21PT
Landscape: Integrated Research and Practice.......MSc 12FT 24PT/PGDip 9FT 18PT

Harper Adams University
Integrated Pest Management.MSc 12FT 24PT/PGDip 12FT 24PT/PGCert 12FT 24PT

Newcastle University
Agricultural and Environmental Science .... MSc 12FT

Schumacher College
Sustainable Horticulture and Food Production .... MSc 12FT

Writtle College
Horticulture (Crop Production) ....MSc 12FT 24-36PT/PGDip 8FT 20-36PT/PGCert 4FT 16-36PT
Landscape Management MSc 12FT 24-36PT/PGDip 8FT 20-36PT/PGCert 4FT 16-36PT
Postharvest Technology.MSc 12FT 24 -36PT/PGDip 8FT 20-36PT/PGCert 4FT 16-36PT

Rural development
Taught Courses

University of Aberdeen
Sustainable Rural Development..............................MSc 12FT 24PT/PGDip 9FT 18PT

Aberystwyth University
Food & Water Security ....MSc 12FT 24PT/PGDip 9FT 18PT

University of Chester
Regeneration for Practitioners.....MA 12FT 24 - 72PT/PGDip 12FT 24 - 60PT/PGCert 12FT 12 - 36PT
Sustainability for Community and Business.........MSc 12FT 24PT/PGDip 12FT 24PT/PGCert 12FT 12-24PT

University of Cumbria
Sustainable Uplands................. MSc 12FT 24PT/GradDip 6FT 12PT/GradCert 3FT 6PT

University College Dublin
Development Studies................... MSc 15FT 24PT/HDip 12FT 24PT

University of East Anglia
Agriculture and Rural Development......................... MA 12FT 24PT
Environment and International Development ......MSc 12FT 24PT

Edinburgh Napier University
International Human Resource Management.................. MSc 12FT

University of Exeter
Food Security and Sustainable Agriculture............MSc 12FT 24PT

University of Gloucestershire
Sustainable Environments............................ MSc 12FT 24PT 18DL/PGDip 9FT 20PT 12DL/PGCert 4FT 8PT 6DL

Agricultural sciences

Harper Adams University
Farm and Agri-business Management ....MSc 12FT 48PT/PGDip 12FT 48PT/PGCert 6FT 48PT
International Agri-business and Food Chain Management... MSc 12FT 48PT/PGDip 12FT 48PT/PGCert 6FT 48PT
Rural Estate and Land Management ....MSc 12FT 48PT/PGDip 12FT 48PT/PGCert 6FT 48PT

University of Kent
Conservation and Rural Development ....MSc 12FT 24PT

Leeds Metropolitan University
International Political Economy...MA 12FT

London Metropolitan University
Planning and Sustainable Communities.................MSc 12FT 24PT

London School of Economics and Political Science (LSE)
Development Studies..MSc 12FT 24PT

University of Manchester
International Development: Economics and Management of Rural Development ....MSc 12FT 24PT

Newcastle University
Food and Rural Development Research ....MSc 12FT 24PT

University of Oxford
Development Studies .... MPhil 36FT

Queen's University Belfast
Leadership for Sustainable Rural Development .... MSc 12FT
Urban and Rural Design.................................MSc 12FT/PGDip 12FT

University of Reading
Agricultural Development Economics ....MSc 12FT 24PT
Agricultural Economics ....MSc 12FT 24PT
Agriculture and Development ....MSc 12FT 24PT
Applied Development Studies ....MSc 12FT 24PT
Communication for Innovation and Development .... MSc 12FT 24PT
Rural Land and Business Management .... MSc 12FT
Social Development and Sustainable Livelihoods ....MA 12FT

Royal Agricultural University
International Rural Development ....MSc 15FT 24PT

University of Salford
Real Estate Development ....MSc 12FT 28DL/PGDip 8FT 20DL

Schumacher College
Sustainable Horticulture and Food Production ....MSc 12FT

Sheffield Hallam University
Sustainable Communities and Environments ....MSc 12-18FT 24-36PT

University of Sheffield
Planning and Development ....MA 12FT

Staffordshire University
Regeneration .... MA 12FT 24PT

University of Sussex
Innovation and Sustainability for International Development ..... MSc 12FT 24PT

University of the Highlands and Islands
Managing Sustainable Rural Development...........MSc 24FT 36PT/PGDip 12FT 24PT/PGCert 12FT 24PT

UCL - University College London
Anthropology, Environment and Development ....MSc 12FT 24PT

University of Worcester
Sustainable Development Advocacy (Professional Practice) ...MA 12FT 36PT

Rural development
Research Courses

Aberystwyth University
IBERS - Rural Sciences (PhD)......................................PhD 36FT 60PT

Coventry University
Rural Change .... MSc by research 12FT 24-36PT

University College Dublin
Development Studies................. PhD 36FT/MLitt by research 24FT

University of Dundee
Non-Graduating Research in Natural Resources Law, Policy and Management (6 months or more) ....Non-Grad 1-5FT
Town and Regional Planning (MPhil) .... MPhil 24FT

University of East Anglia
International Development: Economic Development ....PhD 36FT 72PT/MPhil 24FT 48PT
International Development: Social DevelopmentPhD 36FT 72PT/MPhil 24FT 48PT
International Development: Sustainable Development................PhD 36FT 72PT/MPhil 24FT 48PT

University of Gloucestershire
Countryside and Community...
PhD 30-48FT 48-84PT/MPhil 18-36FT 30-60PT/MSc by research 12-24FT 18-36PT/MA by research 12-24FT 18-36PT

Harper Adams University
Precision Farming (MRes is Subject to Validation)...... MRes 12FT/MPhil 24FT/PhD 38FT

Rural Affairs Management.............................MPhil 24FT/PhD 38FT

London School of Economics and Political Science (LSE)
Development Studies.......................... PhD 36-48FT/MPhil 36-48FT

University of the Highlands and Islands
Sustainability Studies... MPhil 24FT 48PT/PhD 36FT 72PT/MSc by research 12FT 24PT

Soil science
Taught Courses

Bangor University
Agroforestry...... MSc 12FT 24PT/PhD by taught 36FT 60PT/MPhil 24FT 36PT
Agroforestry... MSc 12FT
Ecology .... MRes 12FT
Environmental Forestry .... MSc 12FT
Forestry (Distance Learning with International Commonwealth Scholarship) ....MSc 12DL
Forestry (Distance Learning)..................... MSc 36DL/PGDip 24DL/PGCert 12DL
Natural Sciences .... MRes 12FT
Sustainable Forest and Nature Management (SUFONAMA) (Erasmus Mundus course)... MSc 24FT
Sustainable Tropical Forestry (SUTROFOR) (Erasmus Mundus course)... MSc 24FT
Tropical Frorestry .... MSc 36FT/PGDip 24PT/PGCert 12PT

University of Edinburgh
Soils and Sustainability... MSc 12FT

University of Greenwich
Science (Open)....................................MSc 12FT 24-36FT

Harper Adams University
Integrated Pest Management.MSc 12FT 24PT/PGDip 12FT 24PT/PGCert 12FT 24PT

Soil and Water Management ..MSc 12FT 48PT/PGDip 12FT 48PT/PGCert 6FT 48PT

Imperial College London
Soil Mechanics and Engineering Seismology.........MSc 12FT 24FT
Soil Mechanics and Environmental Geotechnics..MSc 12FT 24FT
Soil Mechanics, also with Business Management or Sustainable Development..MSc 12FT 24FT

University of Nottingham
Sustainable Bioenergy ....MSc 12FT 36FT

University of Reading
Environmental Management ....MSc 12FT 24PT
Geoarchaeology .... MSc 12FT 24PT/PGDip 12FT 24PT

Schumacher College
Sustainable Horticulture and Food Production ....MSc 12FT

Soil science
Research Courses

Bangor University
Agricultural Systems.................... MPhil 24FT 36PT/PhD 36FT 60PT
Agroforestry.................................... MPhil 24FT 36PT/PhD 36FT 60PT
Ecology ....MRes 12FT
Environmental and Soil Science ....MPhil 24FT 36PT/PhD 36FT 60PT
Forest Ecology and Management........MPhil 24FT 36PT/PhD 36FT 60PT
Natural Sciences ....MRes 12FT
Tropical Ecosystems .... MPhil 24FT 36PT/PhD 36FT 60PT

Harper Adams University
Soil and Water Management ... MRes 12FT/MPhil 24FT/PhD 38FT

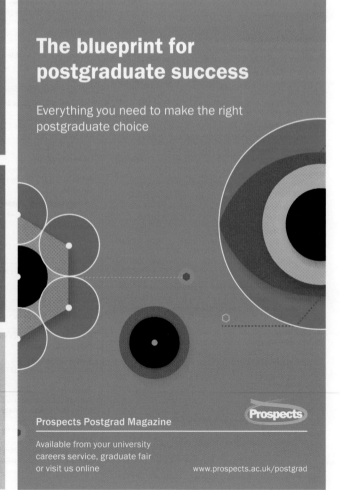

Animal care and veterinary care

Animal behaviour
Taught Courses

Anglia Ruskin University
Animal Behaviour: Applications for Conservation.......... MSc 12FT 24PT

Bangor University
Natural Sciences .... MRes 12FT

University of Edinburgh
Applied Animal Behaviour and Animal Welfare.... MSc 12FT 24PT

University of Exeter
Animal Behaviour.................... MSc 12FT 24PT
Applied Ecology.................... MSc 12FT
Biosciences.................... MSc(Res) 12FT 36PT

National University of Ireland Galway
Applied Behaviour Analysis .... PGDip 12FT/MA 24FT

University of Glasgow
Animal Welfare Science, Ethics & Law.......... MSc 12FT/PGDip 9FT

University of Kent
Conservation and Primate Behaviour .... MSc 12FT 24PT
Endangered Species Recovery .... PGDip 5FT
Evolution and Human Behaviour (taught jointly with the School of Psychology) .... MSc 12FT 24PT

University of Lincoln
Clinical Animal Behaviour.................... MSc 12FT 24PT

Manchester Metropolitan University
Animal Behaviour.................... MSc 12FT 24-60PT
Zoo Conservation Biology.................... MSc 12FT 24-60PT

Newcastle University
Applied Animal Behaviour and Welfare .....MSc 12FT 24PT/PGDip 12FT 24PT

University of Nottingham
Behaviour Change.................... PGCert 12-36PT

Queen's University Belfast
Animal Behaviour and Welfare............ MSc 12FT 24PT/PGDip 7FT

University of Reading
Species Identification and Survey Skills .... MSc 12FT
Wildlife Management and Conservation .... MSc 12FT

University of Roehampton
Primate Biology, Behaviour and Conservation.............. MRes 12FT

Royal Veterinary College
IIntensive Livestock Health and Production ....MSc 24-60DL PGCert 12-36DL
Veterinary Education .... MSc 24-60PT
Veterinary Education .... PGCert 6-24DL PGCert 6-24PT PGDip 24-60PT
Veterinary Epidemiology and Public Health by Distance Learning 24-60DL/PGDip 24-60DL/PGCert 12-60DL
Veterinary Epidemiology .... MSc 24PT
Wild Animal Biology .... MSc 12FT PGDip 8FT
Wild Animal Health .... PGDip 8FT

University of Salford
Wildlife Documentary Production .... MA 12FT

Scotland's Rural College
Applied Poultry Science .... MSc 27DL/PGDip 18DL

University of Southampton
Companion Animal Behaviour Counselling.........MSc 24PT/PGDip 48PT
MRes Wildlife Conservation.................... MRes 12FT

University of St Andrews
Behavioural and Neural Sciences.................... MPhil 12FT 24PT

Animal behaviour
Research Courses

Bangor University
Natural Sciences .... MRes 12FT

University of Exeter
Biosciences......PhD 36FT 72PT/MPhil 24FT 48PT/MSc by research 12FT 36PT

Harper Adams University
Animal Health, Behaviour and Welfare.......MPhil 24FT/PhD 38FT

University of Lincoln
Animal Behaviour and Welfare..... PhD 24FT 48PT/MPhil 12-33FT 24-60PT

Newcastle University
Animal Behaviour.................... MRes 12FT

University of Nottingham
Animal Behaviour.................... MRes 12FT
Animal Behaviour & Ecology Research Group......PhD 36FT 72PT/MPhil 24FT 48PT
Animal Population Heath and Welfare........PhD 36FT 72PT/MPhil 24FT 48PT

Swansea University
Animal Movement Science ....MSc by research 12FT 24PT
Mathematical Ecology ....MSc by research 12FT 24PT

Animal care and veterinary science
Taught Courses

Aberystwyth University
Animal Science.................... MSc 12FT 24PT
Equine Reproduction and Stud Management .... PGCert 6FT 12PT
Equine Science .... MSc 12FT 24PT
Livestock Science .... MSc 12FT 24PT

Anglia Ruskin University
Animal Behaviour: Applications for Conservation.......... MSc 12FT 24PT
Applied Wildlife Conservation .... MSc 24PT

University of Birmingham
Physiotherapy (pre-registration) .... MSc 24FT

University of Edinburgh
Animal Biosciences .... MSc 12FT/PGDip 9FT
Animal Breeding and Genetics .... MSc 12FT 24PT/PGDip 9FT
Applied Animal Behaviour and Animal Welfare.... MSc 12FT 24PT
Equine Science .... MSc 36DL
Veterinary Science.................... MVetSci 12FT

University of Exeter
Anthrozoology.................... MA 12FT 24PT 24DL

University of Glasgow
Animal Welfare Science, Ethics & Law.......... MSc 12FT/PGDip 9FT
Quantitative Methods in Biodiversity, Conservation and Epidemiology.................... MSc 12FT/PGDip 9FT
Veterinary Public Health.................... MVPH 12FT 24-36PT

Harper Adams University
Veterinary Nursing....... MSc 12FT 24PT/PGCert 12FT 24PT/PGDip 12FT 24PT
Veterinary Physiotherapy.......... MSc 12FT 48PT/PGDip 12FT 48PT

University of Lincoln
Clinical Animal Behaviour.................... MSc 12FT 24PT

Liverpool School of Tropical Medicine
Veterinary Parasitology.................... MSc 12FT/PGDip 8FT

University of Liverpool
Bovine Reproduction .... PGDip 12FT 24PT

London School of Hygiene and Tropical Medicine
Veterinary Epidemiology.................... MSc 12FT 24PT

Manchester Metropolitan University
Animal Behaviour.................... MSc 12FT 24-60PT

Newcastle University
Applied Animal Behaviour and Welfare .....MSc 12FT 24PT/PGDip 12FT 24PT
Aquaculture Enterprise and Technology .... MSc 12FT 24PT

University of Northampton
Animal Physiotherapy.................... MSc 12FT 24PT
Animal Welfare .... MSc 12FT 24PT/PGDip 12PT
Equine Behaviour and Welfare .... MSc 12FT 24PT/PGDip 12PT

Nottingham Trent University
Equine Health and Welfare....... MSc 12FT 24PT/MRes 12FT 24PT/PGDip 12FT 24PT

Queen's University Belfast
Animal Behaviour and Welfare............ MSc 12FT 24PT/PGDip 7FT

Royal Agricultural University
Applied Equine Science.................... MSc 18FT 24PT

Royal Veterinary College
Certificate of Advanced Veterinary Practice .... CertAVP 240DL
Control of Infectious Diseases in Animals .... MSc 24PT
Livestock Health and Production by Distance Learning.......... MSc 24-60DL/PGDip 24-60DL/PGCert 12-60DL
Veterinary Education ....MSc 24-60PT PGCert 6-24DL PGCert 6-24PT PGDip 24-60PT
Veterinary Epidemiology and Public Health by Distance Learning ....MSc 24-60DL/PGDip 24-60DL/PGCert 12-60DL
Veterinary Epidemiology.................... MSc 12FT MSc 24PT
Wild Animal Health .... MSc 12FT

University of Salford
Wildlife Documentary Production .... MA 12FT

Scotland's Rural College
Applied Poultry Science .... MSc 27DL/PGDip 18DL

University of Southampton
MRes Wildlife Conservation.................... MRes 12FT

University of Stirling
Aquaculture: Sustainable Aquaculture .... MSc 12FT
Aquatic Pathobiology.............. PGCert 4FT/PGDip 11FT/MSc 12FT

University of the West of England, Bristol
Equine Business Management .... MA 18FT
Equine Science .... MSc 18FT
Veterinary Physiotherapy.................... MSc 36PT

University of Wolverhampton
Computer Aided Design for Construction.............. MSc 12FT 24PT

Writtle College
Animal Health Science....MSc 12FT 24-36PT/PGDip 8FT 20-36PT/PGCert 4FT 16-36PT
Animal Welfare and Conservation .... MSc 12FT 24-36PT/PGDip 8FT 20-36PT/PGCert 4FT 16-36PT
Applied Equine Science...MSc 12FT 24-36PT/PGDip 8FT 20-36PT/PGCert 5FT 16-36PT

Animal care and veterinary science
Research Courses

Aberystwyth University
IBERS - Rural Sciences (MPhil) .... MPhil 12FT 24PT PhD 36FT 60PT

Anglia Ruskin University
Equine Research Anglia... MPhil 18 - 36FT 30-48PT/PhD 24 - 60FT 30 - 48PT

University of Bristol
Veterinary Science.............. PhD 36FT 48PT/MSc by research 12FT

University of Cambridge
Animal Health.................... PhD 36FT/MPhil 12FT

University of Edinburgh
Animal Genomics & Disease Resistance (Veterinary Science)....... PhD 36FT
Animal Health & Welfare.................... PhD 36FT
Pathophysiology of Pain & Animal Welfare (Veterinary Medicine).................... PhD 36FT
Royal (Dick) School of Veterinary Studies..............PhD 36FT 72PT/MSc by research 12FT
Veterinary Medicine ......PhD 36FT 72PT/MPhil 24FT 48PT/MSc by research 12FT 24PT
Veterinary Science (M.Vet.Sci) .... M.Vet.Sci 12FT
Veterinary Studies (Pathology/Clinical/Infectious Diseases)..PhD 36FT 72PT

Harper Adams University
Animal Health, Behaviour and Welfare.......MPhil 24FT/PhD 38FT

University of Lincoln
Animal Behaviour and Welfare..... PhD 24FT 48PT/MPhil 12-33FT 24-60PT

Liverpool School of Tropical Medicine
Veterinary Parasitology.................... PhD/MPhil/MIHR

University of Liverpool
Infection and Global Health (Veterinary)....MPhil 12FT/PhD 36FT
Musculoskeletal Biology (Veterinary) .... MPhil 12FT/PhD 36FT/MD 24FT
Obesity and Endocrinology (Veterinary) ... MPhil 12FT/PhD 36FT/MD 24FT
One Health (Veterinary)......MPhil 12-48FT 24-72PT/PhD 24-48FT 48-84PT

University of Nottingham
Animal Behaviour & Ecology Research Group......PhD 36FT 72PT/MPhil 24FT 48PT
Animal Infection and Immunity.................... PhD 36FT 72PT/MPhil 24FT 48PT
Animal Sciences.......PhD 36FT 72PT/MPhil 24FT 48PT/MRes 12FT 24PT
Comparative Medicine.................... PhD 36FT

Royal Agricultural University
Equine Studies.................... MPhil 18FT 30PT/PhD 33FT 45PT

Royal Veterinary College
PhD Opportunities at the Royal Veterinary College .... PhD 36-48FT 48-72PT

University of Sheffield
Infection, Inflammation and Immunity.......PhD 36FT 72PT/MPhil 24FT 48PT

Animal nutrition
Taught Courses

Aberystwyth University
Animal Science.................... MSc 12FT 24PT
Livestock Science .... MSc 12FT 24PT

University of Edinburgh
Applied Animal Behaviour and Animal Welfare.... MSc 12FT 24PT

University of Glasgow
Animal Welfare Science, Ethics & Law.......... MSc 12FT/PGDip 9FT

Harper Adams University
Ruminant Nutrition ......PGCert 12FT 24PT/MSc 12FT 24PT/PGDip 12FT 24PT

Newcastle University
Aquaculture Enterprise and Technology .... MSc 12FT 24PT

University of Roehampton
Clinical Nutrition .... PGCert 6FT 24PT 24DL

Royal Veterinary College
Veterinary Education - MSc (P/T).................... MSc 24-60PT
Veterinary Education - PGCert (DL).................... PGCert 6-24DL
Veterinary Education - PGCert (P/T) .... PGCert 6-24PT
Veterinary Education - PGDip (P/T).................... PGDip 24-60PT
Veterinary Epidemiology and Public Health by Distance Learning ....MSc 24-60DL/PGDip 24-60DL/PGCert 12-60DL
Veterinary Epidemiology- MSc (P/T).................... MSc 24PT
Wild Animal Biology - MSc (F/T).................... MSc 12FT
Wild Animal Biology - PGCert (F/T).................... PGDip 8FT
Wild Animal Health - PGCert (F/T).................... PGDip 8FT

Animal care and veterinary care

University of Salford
Wildlife Documentary Production .... MA 12FT

Scotland's Rural College
Applied Poultry Science .... MSc 27DL/PGDip 18DL

University of Southampton
MRes Wildlife Conservation .... MRes 12FT

University of Stirling
Aquaculture: Sustainable Aquaculture .... MSc 12FT
Aquatic Pathobiology .... PGCert 4FT/PGDip 11FT/MSc 12FT

University of Ulster
Food Regulatory Affairs (Veterinary Public Health) .. PGDip 15DL/MSc 24DL

Animal nutrition
Research Courses

Aberystwyth University
IBERS - Biological Sciences (MPhil) .... MPhil 12FT 24PT
IBERS - Biological Sciences (PhD) .... PhD 36FT 60PT
IBERS - Rural Sciences (MPhil) .... MPhil 12FT 24PT
IBERS - Rural Sciences (PhD) .... PhD 36FT 60PT

University of Edinburgh
Animal Health & Welfare .... PhD 36FT

Harper Adams University
Animal Nutrition .... MPhil 24FT/PhD 38FT

University of Nottingham
Animal Population Heath and Welfare .... PhD 36FT 72PT/MPhil 24FT 48PT

Veterinary sciences
Taught Courses

Coventry University
Diplomacy, Law and Global Change .... MA 12FT 24-30PT

University of Edinburgh
Animal Biosciences .... MSc 12FT/PGDip 9FT
Animal Breeding and Genetics .... MSc 12FT 24PT/PGDip 9FT
Applied Animal Behaviour and Animal Welfare .... MSc 12FT 24PT
Conservation Medicine MVetSci 36DL/PGDip 24DL/PGCert 12DL
Equine Science .... MSc 36DL
International Animal Health .... MSc 36DL/PGCert 12DL/PGDip 24DL
International Animal Welfare, Ethics and Law .. MSc 36DL/PGDip 24DL/PGCert 12DL
Veterinary Science .... MVetSci 12FT

University of Glasgow
Environmental Science, Technology & Society (Dumfries Campus) .... MSc 12FT 24PT

Harper Adams University
Veterinary Nursing .... MSc 12FT 24PT/PGCert 12FT 24PT/PGDip 12FT 24PT
Veterinary Pharmacy ... MSc 12FT 48PT/PGDip 12FT 48PT/PGCert 12FT 24PT
Veterinary Physiotherapy .... MSc 12FT 48PT/PGDip 12FT 48PT

University of Liverpool
Veterinary Science .... MSc 12FT 24PT

London School of Hygiene and Tropical Medicine
Veterinary Epidemiology .... MSc 12FT 24PT

Newcastle University
Applied Animal Behaviour and Welfare ..... MSc 12FT 24PT/PGDip 12FT 24PT

University of Nottingham
Small Animal Rehabilitation Certificate .... PGCert 12FT 24DL
Veterinary Medicine .... PGCert 12FT/MVM 36FT/DVM 36FT
Veterinary Science .... MRes 12FT 24PT
Veterinary Surgery .... PGCert 24FT/DVS 36FT/MVS 36FT

Queen's University Belfast
Animal Behaviour and Welfare .... MSc 12FT 24PT/PGDip 7FT

University of Reading
Species Identification and Survey Skills .... MSc 12FT

Royal Veterinary College
Certificate of Advanced Veterinary Practice .... CertAVP 240DL
Control of Infectious Diseases in Animals .... MSc 12FT MSc 24PT
Intensive Livestock Health and Production .... MSc 24-60DL
Intensive Livestock Health and Production .... PGCert 12-36DL
One Health (Infectious Diseases) .... PGDip 8FT
Veterinary Education - PG Associate ..... PG Associateship 6-24PT
Veterinary Education .... MSc 24-60PT
Veterinary Education .... PGCert 6-24DL
PGCert 6-24PT PGDip 24-60PT
Veterinary Epidemiology and Public Health by Distance Learning MSc 24-60DL/PGDip 24-60DL/PGCert 12-60DL
Veterinary Epidemiology- MSc (P/T) .... MSc 24PT
Wild Animal Biology - MSc (F/T) .... MSc 12FT
Wild Animal Biology - PGCert (F/T) .... PGDip 8FT
Wild Animal Health - PGCert (F/T) .... PGDip 8FT

Scotland's Rural College
Applied Poultry Science .... MSc 27DL/PGDip 18DL

University of Stirling
Aquatic Veterinary Studies ...... PGCert 4FT/PGDip 11FT/MSc 12FT

University of Ulster
Veterinary Public Health .... PGCert 8DL

Veterinary sciences
Research Courses

University of Aberdeen
Translational Medicine ... PhD 36FT/MPhil 24FT/MD 24FT/ChM by research 24FT

Aberystwyth University
IBERS - Biological Sciences (MPhil) ...... MPhil 12FT 24PT PhD 36FT 60PT

University of Cambridge
Veterinary Medicine .... PhD 36FT
Veterinary Science .... MPhil 12FT

University of Edinburgh
Animal Genomics & Disease Resistance (Veterinary Science) PhD 36FT
Animal Health & Welfare .... PhD 36FT
Epidemiology of Infectious Disease (Veterinary Science) .... PhD 36FT
Host Pathogen Interactions in Infectious Disease (Veterinary Medicine) .... PhD 36FT
Neuroscience and Neurodegenerative Diseases (Veterinary Medicine) .... PhD 36FT
Royal (Dick) School of Veterinary Studies .... PhD 36FT 72PT/MSc by research 12FT
Veterinary Medicine ...... PhD 36FT 72PT/MPhil 24FT 48PT/MSc by research 12FT 24PT
Veterinary Science (M.Vet.Sci) .... M.Vet.Sci 12FT
Veterinary Studies (Pathology/Clinical/Infectious Diseases) .. PhD 36FT 72PT

University of Glasgow
Veterinary Medicine .... PhD 48FT 60PT/MVM by research 12FT 24PT/MSc by research 12FT

University of Liverpool
Veterinary Epidemiology .... MPhil 12-48FT 48-72PT/PhD 24-48FT 48-84PT
Veterinary Immunology ...... MPhil 12-48FT 24-72PT/PhD 24-48FT 48-84PT
Veterinary Microbiology ..... MPhil 12-48FT 24-72PT/PhD 24-48FT 48-84PT
Veterinary Parasitology .... PhD 24-48FT 48-84PT/MPhil 12-48FT 48-72PT
Veterinary Pathology .... MPhil 12-48FT 24-72PT/PhD 24-48FT 48-84PT
Veterinary Virology .... MPhil 12-48FT 24-72PT/PhD 24-48FT 48-84PT

University of Nottingham
Comparative Medicine .... PhD 36FT
Veterinary Educational Development .... PhD 36FT
Veterinary Science .... MRes 12FT 24PT

Robert Gordon University
Aberdeen Business School ... PhD 12FT 36PT 36DL/MSc(Res) 12FT 36PT 36DL

Royal Veterinary College
Master of Research .... MRes 12FT 24-36PT

Zoology
Taught Courses

University of Aberdeen
Applied Marine and Fisheries Ecology:Concepts and Practices for Ecosystem-Based Management .... MRes 12FT/MSc 12FT/PGDip 9FT

Aberystwyth University
Animal Science .... MSc 12FT 24PT

Anglia Ruskin University
Animal Behaviour: Applications for Conservation .... MSc 12FT 24PT
Applied Wildlife Conservation .... MSc 24PT

Bangor University
Natural Sciences .... MRes 12FT

University of Chester
Applied Wildlife Conservation .... PGCert 12FT 12 - 36PT
Applied Wildlife Forensics .... PGCert 12FT 12 - 36PT
Conservation in Practice .... PGCert 12FT 12 - 36PT
Wildlife Conservation .... MSc 12FT 24PT/PGDip 12FT 24PT/PGCert 12FT 12-24PT

University College Cork
Applied Science (Marine Biology) .... MSc 12FT

University of Derby
Conservation Biology .... MSc 12FT 36PT

Edinburgh Napier University
Wildlife Biology and Conservation ... MSc 12FT 24-48PT 24-48DL/PGDip 9FT 18-36PT 18-36DL/PGCert 6FT 12-24PT 12-24DL

University of Exeter
Anthrozoology .... MA 12FT 24PT 24DL
Bioarchaeology .... MSc 12FT 24PT

University of Glasgow
Animal Welfare Science, Ethics & Law .... MSc 12FT/PGDip 9FT
Marine System Science .... MSc 12FT 24PT/PGDip 8FT 16PT

Harper Adams University
Entomology .. MSc 12FT 24PT/MRes 12FT 24PT/PGDip 12FT 24PT/PGCert 12FT 24PT

Heriot-Watt University
Marine Spatial Planning .... MSc 12FT 24PT/PGDip 9FT

Imperial College London
Conservation Science .... MSc 12FT
Integrative Mammalian Biology .... MRes 12FT

University of Kent
Conservation and International Wildlife Trade ...... MSc 12FT 24PT
Conservation and Primate Behaviour .... MSc 12FT 24PT
Endangered Species Recovery .... PGDip 5FT

King's College London
Analytical Science for Industry .... MSc 12FT 24PT

Lancaster University
Biomedical Science (by research) .... MSc 12FT 24PT

Leeds Metropolitan University
Biomedical Sciences .... MSc 12FT unknownPT

University of Leeds
Biological Identification and Conservation .... MSc 12FT 24PT

London School of Economics and Political Science (LSE)
Anthropology and Development Management .... MSc 12FT 24PT

Manchester Metropolitan University
Biomedical Science featuring Exercise and Health options ... MSc 12FT 24-36PT
Zoo Conservation Biology .... MSc 12FT 24-60PT

Newcastle University
Ecological Consultancy .... MSc 12FT

Oxford Brookes University
Primate Conservation ...... MSc 12FT 24PT/PGDip 8FT 16PT 16DL/PGCert 8PT

Plymouth University
Zoo Conservation Biology .... MSc 12FT 24PT/PGDip 9FT 18PT

University of Portsmouth
Applied Aquatic Biology .... MSc 12FT 24PT

Queen's University Belfast
Ecological Management and Conservation Biology .... MSc 12FT 24PT/PGDip 9FT

University of Reading
Species Identification and Survey Skills .... MSc 12FT
Wildlife Management and Conservation .... MSc 12FT

University of Roehampton
Primate Biology, Behaviour and Conservation .... MRes 12FT

Royal Veterinary College
Wild Animal Biology - MSc (F/T) .... MSc 12FT
Wild Animal Biology - PGCert (F/T) .... PGDip 8FT
Wild Animal Health - PGCert (F/T) .... PGDip 8FT

University of Salford
Wildlife Documentary Production .... MA 12FT

University of Southampton
Biodiversity and Conservation .... MSc 12FT 27PT
MRes Wildlife Conservation .... MRes 12FT

University of St Andrews
Ecosystem-based Management of Marine Systems .... MRes 12FT
Marine Mammal Science .... MRes 12FT

Staffordshire University
Ecology and Conservation .... MSc 15FT
Invertebrate Ecology and Conservation ...... MSc 15FT/PGDip 15FT
Urban Ecology and Conservation .... MSc 15FT

University of Stirling
Marine Biotechnology .... MSc 12FT 24PT/PGDip 9FT

Swansea University
Aquatic Ecology and Conservation .... MRes 12FT 24-36PT

UCL - University College London
Biodiversity, Evolution and Conservation MRes .... MRes 12FT

Writtle College
Animal Welfare and Conservation .... MSc 12FT 24-36PT/PGDip 8FT 20-36PT/PGCert 4FT 16-36PT

Zoology
Research Courses

University of Aberdeen
Biological Science .... MSc by research 12FT/MPhil 24FT/PhD 36FT
Ecology .... PhD 36FT/MPhil 24FT/MSc by research 12FT
Environmental Science ..... PhD 36FT/MPhil 24FT/MSc by research 12FT
Marine BiologyPhD 36FT 60PT/MPhil 24FT 42PT/MSc by research 12FT 24PT

Animal care and veterinary care

Plant Science...PhD 36FT 60PT/MPhil 24FT 42PT/MSc by research 12FT 24PT

Zoology .... PhD 36FT/MPhil 24FT/MSc by research 12FT

Aberystwyth University
IBERS - Rural Sciences (MPhil) .... MPhil 12FT 24PT PhD 36FT 60PT

Bangor University
Natural Sciences .... MRes 12FT

University of Cambridge
Biological Anthropological Science.................................. MPhil 10FT
Zoology .... PhD 36/48FT/MPhil 12FT

University of Central Lancashire
Biological and Biomedical Sciences....PhD 48FT 84PT/MPhil 36FT 60PT/MSc by research 24FT 36PT/MD 48PT

University of Edinburgh
Molecular Plant Sciences... PhD 36FT 72PT

University of Gloucestershire
Biological Sciences .... PhD 30-48FT

Imperial College London
Biological Sciences ....PhD/MPhil

University of Lincoln
Animal Behaviour and Welfare..... PhD 24FT 48PT/MPhil 12-33FT 24-60PT

University of Manchester
Animal Biology.................PhD 36-48FT 72-96PT/MPhil 12FT 24PT

Newcastle University
Engineering & Science in the Marine Environment ......Integrated PhD 36FT
Marine Sciences .... PhD 36FT 72PT/MPhil 12FT 24PT

University of Nottingham
Animal Sciences ....PhD 36FT 72PT/MPhil 24FT 48PT/MRes 12FT 24PT

Molecular Evolution..MRes 12FT

University of Oxford
Zoology .... DPhil 48FT/MSc by research 24FT

Queen's University Belfast
Ecology, Evolution, Behaviour and Environmental Economics ......
PhD 36FT 72PT/MPhil 24FT 48PT

University of Roehampton
Ecology.................. PhD 24-48FT 36-60PT/MPhil 21-36FT 33-48PT

University of Sheffield
Animal and Plant Sciences......... PhD 36FT 72PT/MPhil 24FT 48PT

Swansea University
Animal Movement Science ....MSc by research 12FT 24FT

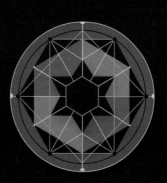

Biology and life sciences

Anatomy and physiology
Taught Courses

University of Aberdeen
Molecular Nutrition .... MSc 12FT/PGDip 9FT/PGDip 4FT

Bangor University
Advanced Clinical Practice .... MSc 12FT 24 - 60PT/PGDip 9FT
Applied Sport Science .... MA 12FT 36PT MSc 12FT 36PT
Applied Sport Science (Outdoor Activities) .... MA 12FT 36PT
Applied Sport Science and Outdoor Activities .... MSc 12FT 36PT
Applied Sport and Exercise Physiology .... MA 12FT 36PT MSc 12FT 36PT/PGDip 8FT
Applied Sport and Exercise Psychology . MA 12FT 36PT MSc 12FT 36PT
Exercise Rehabilitation .... MA 12FT 36PT MSc 12FT 36PT
Sport and Exercise Physiology .... MRes 12FT 36PT
Sport and Exercise Psychology ... MRes 12FT 36PT MSc 12FT 36PT
Sport and Exercise Sciences .... MRes 12FT 36PT

University of Bath
Developmental Biology MRes .... MRes 12FT

University of Bedfordshire
Clinical Exercise Physiology .. MSc 12FT/PGCert 12FT/PGDip 12FT
Molecular and Cellular Exercise Physiology .... MSc 12FT

University of Birmingham
Exercise and Sport (Sciences) .... MSc 12FT 24PT
Functional and Clinical Anatomy .... MSc 24PT

Bournemouth University
Osteoarchaeology .... MSc 12FT 24PT

University of Brighton
Applied Exercise Physiology ..... MSc 12FT 24PT/PGDip 12FT 24PT/PGCert 12FT 24PT

Canterbury Christ Church University
Clinical Reporting (Appendicular and Axial Skeleton) .... PGCert 18PT/PGDip 36PT/MSc 54PT

University of Central Lancashire
Dance and Somatic Well-being .... MA 24PT/PGDip 24PT/PGCert 24PT
Osteoarchaeology: Techniques and Data Analysis .... MSc 12FT
Physiotherapy Professional Practice .... MSc 12FT up to 60PT
Sport and Exercise Biomechanics .... MSc 12FT 24PT/PGDip 12FT 24PT
Sport and Exercise Physiology .. MSc 12FT 24PT/PGDip 12FT 24PT
Sport and Exercise Psychology .. MSc 12FT 24PT/PGDip 9FT 24PT/PGCert 9FT 24PT
Sport and Exercise Science .... MSc 12FT 24PT/PGDip 12FT 24PT
Sports Therapy .... MSc 18FT 36PT/PGDip 18FT 24PT
Sports Therapy Professional Practice .... MSc up to 24FT

University of Chester
Sports Sciences (with named pathways) ..... MA 12FT 24PT/PGDip 12FT 24PT/PGCert 12FT 12-24PT

University of Chichester
Sport and Exercise Physiology .... MSc 11FT 22+PT
Sport and Exercise Psychology .... MSc 12-15FT 24-36PT

University of Dundee
Anatomy and Advanced Forensic Anthropology .... MSc 12FT
Forensic Art (MSc full time) .... MSc 12FT
Human Anatomy .... MSc 12FT
Motion Analysis .... MSc 12FT 24PT 24DL
Non-Graduating Taught Postgraduate in College of Life Sciences PG module variableFT
Sports and Biomechanical Medicine (MSc Full time in-house) ..... MSc 12FT
Sports and Biomechanical Medicine (MSc Part time with externally arranged project) .... MSc 24PT
Sports and Biomechanical Medicine (MSc Part time with in-house project) .... MSc 24PT

University of East London
Medical Physiology MSc MSc 12FT 24PT/PGDip 8FT 16PT/PGCert 4FT 8PT

University of Edinburgh
Human Anatomy .... MSc 12FT
Human Osteoarchaeology .... MSc 12FT 24PT
Internal Medicine (online distance learning) .... MSc 36DL/PGCert 12DL/Diploma 24DL
Osteoarchaeology .... MSc 12FT 24PT
Regenerative Medicine: Industrial and Clinical Delivery .... MSc 12FT
Surgical Sciences .... MSc 36DL/Diploma 24DL/Cert 12DL
Transfusion, Transplanting and Tissue Banking .... MSc 36PT

University of Exeter
Bioarchaeology .... MSc 12FT 24PT

University of Glasgow
Clinical Radiation Physics .... MSc(MedSci) 12FT
Medical Visualisation & Human Anatomy .... MSc 12FT

Keele University
Cell and Tissue Engineering .... MSc 12FT 24PT

King's College London
Human & Applied Physiology .... MSc 12FT
Space Physiology & Health .... MSc 12FT

Loughborough University
Human Biology .... MRes 12FT 24PT/PGDip 9FT 20PT

Manchester Metropolitan University
Clinical Physiology .... MSc 24-36PT
Human Movement Science in Health and Disease .... MSc 12FT 24-36PT

Northumbria University
Clinical Exercise Physiology .... MSc 12FT 36PT

University of Nottingham
Integrated Physiology in Health and Disease .... MSc 12FT
Sensory Science .... PGCert 48PT

Queen's University Belfast
Clinical Anatomy ...... MSc 12FT TBCPT/PGDip 12FT TBCPT/PGCert 12FT TBCPT

University of Roehampton
Sport and Exercise Physiology .... MSc 12FT 24-48PT

University of Salford
Trauma and Orthopaedics .... MSc 12FT 36PT/PGDip 8FT 24PT/PGCert 4FT 9PT
Upper Limb Orthopaedics .... PGCert 12PT

Sheffield Hallam University
Pathological Sciences .... MSc 12FT 24PT

University of Sheffield
Clinical Neurology .... MSc 12FT
Diagnostic Oral Pathology .... MMedSci 12FT
Integrative Physiology and Pharmacology .... MSc 12FT
Stem Cell and Regenerative Medicine .... MSc 12FT

University of Southampton
MSc Physiotherapy .... MSc 24FT

St Mary's University College, Twickenham
Applied Sport and Exercise Physiology .... MA 12FT 24PT/PGDip 12PT/PGCert 12PT

Staffordshire University
Applied Sport and Exercise Science .... PGCert 12FT 7DL/PGDip 14DL/MSc 24DL
Postgraduate Certificate in Musculoskeletal Diagnosis ..... PGCert 9PT

Trinity College Dublin - the University of Dublin
Molecular Pathology .... MSc 24PT

UCL - University College London
Biology of Vision .... MSc 12FT
Musculoskeletal Science. MSc 24FT 24-60PT/PGDip 9FT 18-45PT/PGCert 3FT
Musculoskeletal Science (by Distance Learning) MSc 12FT/PGDip 9FT 24-60PT/PGCert 3FT

University of Warwick
Evidence Based Musculoskeletal Care: Managing Lower Limb Pain .... PGA 12PT
Evidence Based Musculoskeletal Care: Managing Neck and Back Pain .... PGA 12PT
Evidence Based Musculoskeletal Care: Managing Upper Limb Pain .... PGA 12PT
Health Sciences: Trauma and Orthopaedic Surgery .... MSc 24-96PT
Obesity and Eating Disorders in Diabetes PGA 12PT/CPDmod 1PT

Anatomy and physiology
Research Courses

University of Aberdeen
Cell and Developmental Biology .... PhD 36FT/MPhil 24FT/MSc by research 12FT
Pathology .... PhD 36FT/MPhil 24FT/MSc by research 12FT
Physiology .... PhD 36FT/MPhil 24FT/MSc by research 12FT

Bangor University
Biological Sciences .... MPhil 12FT/PhD 24-36FT
Sport, Health and Exercise Sciences .... MPhil 12FT/PhD 36FT

Barts and the London School of Medicine and Dentistry
Morbid Anatomy and Histopathology .... PhD/MPhil

University of Birmingham
Exercise and Sport Sciences MRes .... MRes 12FT
Neurophysiology .... PhD 36FT 72PT/MPhil 12FT 24PT
Physiology .... PhD 36FT 72PT/MPhil 12FT 24PT

University of Bristol
Centre for Comparative and Clinical Anatomy .... PhD 36-48FT 72-96PT
Physiology and Pharmacology ... PhD 36FT 72PT/MSc by research 12FT

University of Cambridge
Pathology .... PhD 36FT 60PT
Physiology .... PhD 36FT 60PT

Cardiff University
Drug Delivery and Microbiology .... PhD 36FT/MPhil 24FT
Pathophysiology and Repair .... MPhil 24FT 24-36PT/PhD 36-48FT 60PT/MD 24FT 36PT

University of Chichester
Centre for Sports Science, Physical Education and Recreation Studies .... PhD 36-48FT 84PT/MPhil 24-36FT 84PT

Coventry University
Applied Physiology .... MSc by research 12FT 24-36PT
Clinical Physiology .... MSc by research 12FT 24-36PT
Exercise Physiology .... MSc by research 12FT 24-36PT

University of Dundee
Life Sciences .... PhD 48FT
Life Sciences .... MPhil 24FT MSc by research 12FT
Life Sciences - A/Star Dundee Programme (4 year PhD) PhD 48FT
Life Sciences - EMBL Joint Programme (PhD) .... PhD 36FT
Life Sciences - Wellcome Programme (PhD) .... PhD 48FT

University of Edinburgh
Internal Medicine .... PhD 36FT
Pathology .... PhD 36FT 72PT/MPhil 24FT/MSc by research 12FT 24PT
Regenerative Medicine .... MPhil 24FT 48PT/PhD 36FT 72PT

Imperial College London
Musculoskeletal ...... MSc by research 12FT 36PT/MBBS 12FT 36PT

University of Kent
Cell Biology ..... MSc by research 12FT 24PT/MPhil 24FT 36PT/PhD 36FT 60PT

King's College London
Human & Aerospace Physiological Sciences, Centre for (CHAPS). MPhil 36FT 48-72PT/PhD 36FT 48-72PT

University of Leeds
Computational Biology of the Heart .... PhD 36+FT/MPhil 24FT/MSc by research 12FT

University of Leicester
Department of Cell Physiology and Pharmacology .... PhD 36FT/MRes 12FT

University of Liverpool
Cellular and Molecular Physiology MPhil 12FT 48-72PT/PhD 36FT 48-84PT/MD 24-72FT
Musculoskeletal Biology (Medicine) ..... PhD 36FT/MPhil 12-48FT/MD 60FT
Pathology .... PhD 24-48FT 48-84PT/MPhil 12-48FT 24-72PT/MD 24-72FT
Pathophysiology .... MPhil 12FT 24PT/PhD 36FT/MD 12FT 24PT
Physiology (Ph.D.) .... MPhil 12FT 24PT/PhD 36FT

Loughborough University
Human Biology .... PhD 36FT 60PT/MPhil 24FT 36PT
Masters of Research in Psychology, Human Biology .... MRes 12FT 24PT/PGDipRes 9FT 18PT

University of Manchester
Physiology .... PhD 36-48FT 72-96PT/MPhil 12FT 24PT

Nottingham Trent University
Cell Biology .... MRes 12FT 24PT

University of Nottingham
Cell Biology .... MRes 12FT
Cell Signalling .... PhD 36FT 72PT/MPhil 24FT 48PT/MRes 12FT/DM 36FT 72PT
Integrative Cardiovascular and Metabolic Physiology and Pharmacology . PhD 36FT 72PT/MPhil 24FT 48PT/DM 36FT 72PT/MRes 12FT 24PT
Otorhinolaryngology and Head and Neck Surgery .. PhD 36-48FT/DM 24FT
Wolfson Centre for Stem Cells, Tissue Engineering and Modelling (STEM) .... PhD 24-36FT 48-72PT/MPhil 12-24FT 24-48PT

University of Oxford
Pathology .... DPhil 48FT/MSc by research 24FT
Physiology, Anatomy and Genetics ... DPhil 48FT/MSc by research 24-36FT

University of Sheffield
Health and Related Research ..... PhD 36FT 72PT/MPhil 24FT 48PT
Musculoskeletal Science .... PhD 36FT 72PT/MPhil 24FT 48PT

St George's, University of London
Clinical Developmental Sciences .... PhD 36FT 84PT/MPhil 24FT 48PT/MDRes 24PT

UCL - University College London
Cell and Developmental Biology ....
Orthopaedics and Musculo-Skeletal Science .... PhD 36FT 60PT/MD(Res) 24FT 24PT
Pathology .... PhD 36FT 60PT/MD(Res) 24FT 24PT
Physiology .... PhD 36FT 60PT/PhD 48FT

Astrobiology
Research Courses

University of Nottingham
Magnetic Resonance .... PhD 36FT 72PT/MPhil 24FT 48PT/MRes 12FT

The Open University
Astrobiology and Habits for Life PhD 36FT 72PT variableDL/MPhil 15FT 24PT variableDL

Biology and life sciences

Biochemistry
Taught Courses

Bangor University
Analytical Chemistry .... MSc 12FT/Diploma 9FT
Chemistry .... MRes 12FT
Environmental Chemistry .... MSc 12FT/PGDip 9FT
Marine Biology .... MSc 12FT 24-36PT/PGDip 9FT
Molecular Biology with Biotechnology .... MSc 12FT
Natural Sciences .... MRes 12FT
Physical Oceanography .... MSc 12FT 24-36PT/PGDip 9FT

University of Bristol
Biomedical Engineering .... MSc 12FT

Cardiff University
Chemical Biology .... MSc 12FT 36PT

University of Central Lancashire
Pharmaceutical Biotechnology .... MSc 12FT

University of East Anglia
Chemical Sciences .... GradDip 12FT
Molecular Medicine .... MSc 12FT

University of Edinburgh
Biomedical Sciences (Life Sciences) .... MSc(Res) 12FT
Medicinal & Biological Chemistry .... MSc 12FT

University of Exeter
Biosciences .... MSc(Res) 12FT 36PT

Glasgow Caledonian University
Biomedical Science .... MSc 24PT/PGDip 24PT/PGCert 12PT
Pharmacology .... MSc 12FT

Heriot-Watt University
Biotechnology .... MSc 12FT 24PT/PGDip 9FT 20PT

Imperial College London
Molecular and Cellular Biosciences .... MRes 12FT

King's College London
Molecular Biophysics .... MRes 12FT

Leeds Metropolitan University
Applied Biomedical Sciences Research .... MSc 12FT
Integrated Masters Biomedical Sciences .... MBIOMS 48FT
Microbiology & Biotechnology .... MSc 12FT 24PT
Sport and Exercise Nutrition ... MSc 12FT 24PT/PGDip 12FT 24PT/PGCert 4FT 12PT
Sport and Exercise Physiology .. MSc 12FT 24PT/PGCert 4FT 12PT/PGDip 12FT 24PT
Toxicology Sciences .... MSc 12FT 24PT

University of Leicester
Cancer Cell and Molecular Biology .... MSc 12FT

University of Liverpool
Advanced Chemical Sciences (Organic and Biomolecular Chemistry) .... MSc 12FT

University of Manchester
Biochemistry .... MSc 12FT
Clinical Biochemistry .... MSc 12FT

Newcastle University
Bioinformatics .... MSc 12FT
Synthetic Biology .... MSc 12FT

Northumbria University
Biotechnology .... MSc 16FT 30PT

Nottingham Trent University
Biomedical Science .... MSc 12FT 24PT
Biotechnology .... MSc 12FT 24PT
Applied Biosciences .... MSc(Res) 12FT 24PT
Biotechnology .... MSc(Res) 12FT 24PT

University of Nottingham
Industrial Physical Biochemistry .... MRes 12FT 24PT

The Open University
Medicinal Chemistry .... MSc variableDL/PGDip variableDL

Queen's University Belfast
Chemical Biology .... MSc 12FT

Sheffield Hallam University
Advanced Professional Development .... MSc VAFT/PGDip VAFT/PGCert VAFT
Biomedical Sciences .... MSc 12FT 24PT/PGDip 8FT 16PT/PGCert 4FT 8PT
Biotechnology .... MSc 12FT 24PT/PGDip 8FT 16PT/PGCert 4FT 8PT

St George's, University of London
Biomedical Science .... MRes 12FT

University of Strathclyde
Medical Devices .... MSc 12FT/PGDip 9FT

University of Surrey
Clinical Biochemistry .... MSc 12FT 24PT

Trinity College Dublin - the University of Dublin
Bioengineering .... MSc 12FT
Clinical Chemistry .... MSc 24PT

UCL - University College London
Biochemical Engineering .... MSc 12FT/PGDip 9FT
Biomedical Sciences .... MSc 12FT 24PT
Biosciences .... MRes 12FT
Drug Design .... MSc 12FT/PGDip 9FT
Nanotechnology and Regenerative Medicine .... MSc 12FT 24PT
Organic Chemistry: Drug Discovery .... MRes 12FT
Synthetic Biology .... MRes 12FT
Systems Biology .... MRes 12FT

University of Warwick
Mathematical Biology and Biophysical ChemistryMSc 12FT 24PT

University of Westminster
Clinical Chemistry .... MSc 12FT

Biochemistry
Research Courses

Bangor University
Biological Sciences .... MPhil 12FT/PhD 24-36FT
Chemistry .... PhD 36FT
Chemistry .... MPhil 24FT
Chemistry .... MRes 12FT
Natural Sciences .... MRes 12FT
Ocean Sciences .... MPhil 24FT/PhD 36FT

Barts and the London School of Medicine and Dentistry
Biochemistry .... PhD 36FT 48PT
Department of Clinical Biochemistry .... PhD/MPhil

University of Bath
Biology and Biochemistry PhD .... PhD 24-48FT 36-72PT/MRes 12-36FT 24-48PT

University of Birmingham
Biosciences PhD / Msc by (Research) MSc by research 12FT 24PT/PhD 36FT 72PT

University of Bristol
Biochemistry .... PhD 36FT 72PT/MSc by research 12FT 24PT

University of Cambridge
Biochemistry .... PhD 36FT 60PT/MPhil 9FT
Clinical Biochemistry .... PhD 36FT/MPhil 12FT

Cardiff University
Chemical Biology .... PhD 36FT/MPhil 12FT

University of Dundee
Life Sciences (4 year PhD) .... PhD 48FT
Life Sciences (MPhil) .... MPhil 24FT
Life Sciences (MSc by research) .... MSc by research 12FT
Life Sciences - A/Star Dundee Programme (4 year PhD) .... PhD 48FT
Life Sciences - EMBL Joint Programme (PhD) .... PhD 36FT
Life Sciences - Wellcome Programme (PhD) .... PhD 48FT

University of Edinburgh
Clinical Biochemistry ..... PhD 36FT 72PT/MPhil 24FT 36PT/MSc by research 12FT 24PT

University of Essex
Biochemistry .... PhD 36FT 72PT/MPhil 24FT 48PT/MSc by research 12FT 24PT
Chemical Biology .... PhD 36FT 72PT/MPhil 24FT 48PT/MSc by research 12FT 24PT

University of Exeter
Biosciences ...... PhD 36FT 72PT/MPhil 24FT 48PT/MSc by research 12FT 36PT

University of Glasgow
Biochemistry and Molecular Biology .... PhD 36FT/MSc by research 12FT

Imperial College London
Chemical Biology of Health and Disease ..... MRes 12FT/PhD 36FT
Department of Biochemistry .... PhD/MPhil

University of Kent
Biochemistry ... PhD 36FT 60PT/MPhil 24FT 36PT/MSc by research 12FT 24PT

King's College London
Cell & Molecular Biophysics, Randall Division of .... PhD 36FT 48-72PT/MPhil 36FT 48-72PT/MD 36FT 48-72PT

University of Leeds
Biochemistry and Molecular Biology .... PhD 36+FT/MPhil 24FT/MSc by research 12FT
Centre for Self-Organising Molecular Systems .... PhD 36+FT/MPhil 24+FT/MSc by research 12FT

University of Leicester
Research in Biochemistry .... PhD 36-48FT 72-96PT/MRes 12FT

University of Liverpool
Advanced Chemical Sciences (Organic and Biomolecular Chemistry) .... MRes 12FT
Biological Sciences (Structural and Chemical Biology) .... MPhil 12-48FT 24-72PT/PhD 24-48FT 48-84PT

University of Manchester
Biochemistry .... PhD 36-48FT 72-96PT/MPhil 12FT 24PT
Biological Chemistry .... PhD 36-48FT 72-96PT/MPhil 12FT 24PT

Newcastle University
Biological Sciences .... PhD 36FT 72PT/MPhil 12FT 24PT
Biomedicine .... MPhil 12FT 24PT/PhD 36FT 72PT/MD 24FT 48PT
Biotechnology .... MPhil 12FT 24PT/PhD 36FT 72PT
Biotechnology and Business Enterprise .... MRes 12FT
Nanomedicine .... MRes 12FT
Systems Biology .... MRes 12FT

University of Nottingham
Biochemistry and Cell Biology .. PhD 36FT 72PT/MPhil 24FT 48PT/MRes 12FT/DM 36FT 72PT
Industrial Physical Biochemistry .... MRes 12FT 24PT
Molecular and Cellular Science PhD 36FT 72PT/MPhil 24FT 48PT/MRes 12FT

Oxford Brookes University
Biological Sciences - Biofilm Development MPhil/PhD .... PhD 24-60FT 36-72PT/MPhil 24-36FT 36-48PT
Biological Sciences - Bioprocess Research MPhil/PhD .... PhD 24-60FT 36-72PT/MPhil 24-36FT 36-48PT
Biological Sciences - Cell Systems Modelling MPhil/PhD .... PhD 24-60FT 36-72PT/MPhil 24-36FT 36-48PT
Biological Sciences - Environmental Ecology MPhil/PhD .... PhD 24-60FT 36-72PT/MPhil 24-36FT 36-48PT
Biological Sciences - Evolutionary Developmental Biology MPhil/PhD .... PhD 24-60FT 36-72PT/MPhil 24-36FT 36-48PT
Biological Sciences - Invertebrate Ecology and Biogeography MPhil/PhD .... PhD 24-60FT 36-72PT/MPhil 24-36FT 36-48PT
Biological Sciences - Plant Cell Biology ...... PhD 24-60FT 36-72PT/MPhil 24-36FT 36-48PT
Biological Sciences - Spatial Ecology and Land Use .... PhD 24-60FT 36-72PT/MPhil 24-36FT 36-48PT
Biological and Biomedical Science MPhil/PhD ..... PhD 36FT 48PT/MPhil 24FT 36PT

University of Oxford
Biochemistry .... DPhil 48FT/MSc by research 24FT
Biochemistry .... DPhil 48FT
Chromosome and Developmental Biology .... DPhil 48FT
Structural Biology .... DPhil 48FT
Systems Biology .... DPhil 48FT

School of Pharmacy, University of London
Pharmaceutical and Biological Chemistry .... PhD 36FT 60PT

University of Strathclyde
Drug Delivery Systems .... MRes 12FT 24PT
Drug Delivery Systems with International Placement .... MRes 12FT 24PT
Drug Discovery .... MRes 12FT

University of Surrey
Biochemistry, Toxicology, Neuropharmacology, Chronobiology, Apoptosis .... PhD 36FT 48PT/MPhil 24FT 36PT

University of Sussex
Biochemistry .... PhD 24-48FT 36-72PT/MPhil 12-36FT 24-48PT

Teesside University
Applied Sciences .... PhD 24-60FT 36-72PT/MPhil 18FT 30PT/DProf 36PT/MProf by research 30PT

University of the Highlands and Islands
Genetics and Biochemistry .... PhD 36FT 72PT/MPhil 24FT 36PT

UCL - University College London
Biomedical Research .... PhD 36FT 60PT

University of Warwick
Mathematical Biology and Biophysical Chemistry .... MSc 11FT 22PT/PhD 48FT 96PT

Biodiversity
Taught Courses

Anglia Ruskin University
Applied Wildlife Conservation .... MSc 24PT

Bangor University
Biodiversity Conservation .... PhD by taught 36FT 60PT/MPhil 24FT 36PT
Conservation and Land Management .... MSc 12FT/PGDip 9FT
Ecology .... MRes 12FT
Marine Biology .... MSc 12FT 24-36PT/PGDip 9FT
Marine Environmental Protection .... MSc 12FT 24-36PT
Natural Sciences .... MRes 12FT
Physical Oceanography .... MSc 12FT 24-36PT/PGDip 9FT

Bournemouth University
Biodiversity Conservation .... MSc 12FT 24PT

Cranfield University
Applied Bioinformatics .... MSc 12FT 24PT

University of Derby
Conservation Biology .... MSc 12FT 36PT

University of East Anglia
Environmental Sciences .... MSc 12FT 24PT

Edinburgh Napier University
Wildlife Biology and Conservation ... MSc 12FT 24-48PT 24-48DL/PGDip 9FT 18-36PT 18-36DL/PGCert 6FT 12-24PT 12-24DL

University of Edinburgh
Biodiversity and Taxonomy of Plants .... MSc 12FT/PGDip 9FT
Biodiversity, Wildlife & Ecosystem Health (online distance learning) ... MSc 36PT 36DL/PGDip 24PT 24DL/PGCert 12PT 12DL
Ecosystem Services .... MSc 12FT 24-36PT

University of Exeter
Conservation and Biodiversity .... MSc 12FT

Biology and life sciences

University of Glasgow
Animal Welfare Science, Ethics & Law .... MSc 12FT/PGDip 9FT
Quantitative Methods in Biodiversity, Conservation and Epidemiology .... MSc 12FT/PGDip 9FT

University of Greenwich
Natural Resources .... MSc 12FT 24PT/PGDip 12FT 24PT

Heriot-Watt University
Climate Change: Managing The Marine Environment.. MSc 12FT 24PT/PGDip 9FT 21PT
Marine Biodiversity and Biotechnology ..... MSc 12FT 24PT/PGDip 9FT 21PT

University of Hertfordshire
Environmental Management .... MSc 12-15FT 24-60PT/PGDip 12FT 18-48PT/PGCert 12FT 18-48PT

Imperial College London
Advanced Methods in Taxonomy and Biodiversity .... MSc 12FT/DIC 12FT
MRes Biodiversity, Informatics and Genomics .... MRes 12FT

University of Kent
Agri-Environmental Economics and Policy .... MSc 12FT 24PT
Conservation Biology .... MSc 12FT 24PT
Conservation Project Management .... MSc 12FT 24PT
Conservation and Business .... MSc 12FT 24PT
Environmental Anthropology .... MA 12FT 24PT/MSc 12FT 24PT
Ethnobotany .... MSc 12FT 24PT

University of Leeds
Biodiversity and Conservation .... MSc 12FT 24PT
Biological Identification and Conservation .... MSc 12FT 24PT

Nottingham Trent University
Biodiversity Conservation .... MSc 12FT 24PT/MRes 12FT 24PT/PGDip 12FT 24PT/PGCert 12FT 24PT
Endangered Species Recovery and Conservation . MSc 12FT 24PT/MRes 12FT 24PT
Human Security and Environmental Change .... MA 12FT 24PT/PGDip 9FT 18PT/PGCert 9FT

Oxford Brookes University
Conservation Ecology .... MSc 12FT 24PT/PGDip 8FT 20PT/PGCert 8FT 8PT

University of Oxford
Biodiversity, Conservation & Management .... MSc 12FT
Geography and the Environment .... MPhil 24FT

Plymouth University
Marine Biology .... MRes 12FT 24PT

University of Reading
Plant Diversity .... MSc 12FT 24PT
Species Identification and Survey Skills .... MSc 12FT
Wildlife Management and Conservation .... MSc 12FT

University of Salford
Wildlife Documentary Production .... MA 12FT

Schumacher College
Holistic Science .... MSc 12FT

University of Southampton
Biodiversity and Conservation .... MSc 12FT 27PT

Staffordshire University
Invertebrate Ecology and Conservation ...... MSc 15FT/PGDip 15FT

Swansea University
Aquatic Ecology and Conservation .... MRes 12FT 24-36PT

Trinity College Dublin - the University of Dublin
Biodiversity and Conservation .... MSc 12FT

UCL - University College London
Biodiversity, Evolution and Conservation MRes .... MRes 12FT

University of Warwick
MBA Global Energy .... MBA 36PT

Biodiversity
Research Courses

Aberystwyth University
IBERS - Environmental Science .... MPhil 12FT 24PT. PhD 36FT 60PT

Anglia Ruskin University
Animal and Environmental .... PhD 24-60FT 36-72PT

Bangor University
Biodiversity Conservation .... MPhil 24FT 36PT/PhD 36FT 60PT
Ecology .... MRes 12FT
Natural Sciences .... MRes 12FT
Ocean Sciences .... MPhil 24FT/PhD 36FT
Tropical Ecosystems .... MPhil 24FT 36PT/PhD 36FT 60PT

University of East Anglia
Copy of Environmental Sciences: Geosciences and Natural Hazards .... PhD 36FT 72PT/MPhil 24FT 48PT
Environmental Sciences: Climate, Ocean and Atmospheric Sciences .... PhD 36FT 72PT/MPhil 24FT 48PT
Environmental Sciences: Resources, Sustainability and Governance .... PhD 36FT 72PT/MPhil 24FT 48PT

University of Greenwich
Natural Resources by Research .... MSc by research 12FT 24PT

University of Kent
Biodiversity Management .... PhD 36FT 60PT/MSc by research 12FT 24PT

Nottingham Trent University
Environmental Biology .... MRes 12FT 24PT

The Open University
Biodiversity and Conservation .... PhD 36FT 72PT variableDL/MPhil 15FT 24PT variableDL

University of Oxford
Geography and the Environment...... DPhil 48FT/MSc by research 24FT

Queen's University Belfast
Environmental Change .... PhD 36FT 72PT/MPhil 24FT 48PT

Swansea University
Aquatic Biology .... MSc by research 12FT 24PT

Biology and life sciences
Taught Courses

Aberystwyth University
Green Biotechnology and Innovation .... MSc 12FT
Managing the Environment .... MSc 12FT 24PT/PGDip 9FT 18PT

Anglia Ruskin University
Animal Behaviour: Applications for Conservation .... MSc 12FT 24PT
Applied Wildlife Conservation .... MSc 24PT
Biomedical Science .... MSc 36 - 60DL
Biotechnology .... MSc 12FT 24PT
Forensic Science .... MSc 12 - 15FT 24 - 30PT
Sustainability: Working for Positive Change .... MSc 12FT 24-30PT

Anglo-European College of Chiropractic
Chiropractic .... MSc 30DL/PGDip 24DL/PGCert 12DL
Medical Ultrasound .... MSc 36PT

Bangor University
Ecology .... MRes 12FT
Marine Biology .... MSc 12FT 24-36PT/PGDip 9FT
Marine Environmental Protection .... MSc 12FT 24-36PT
Medical Molecular Biology with Genetics .... MSc 12-24FT
Natural Sciences .... MRes 12FT
Physical Oceanography .... MSc 12FT 24-36PT/PGDip 9FT

University of Bath
Biosciences .... MRes 12FT
Biosciences .... MSc 12FT
Developmental Biology .... MRes 12FT
Developmental Biology .... MSc 12FT
Evolutionary Biology .... MRes 12FT
Evolutionary Biology .... MSc 12FT
Medical BioSciences .... MSc 12FT
Protein Structure and Function .... MSc 12FT
Regenerative Medicine .... MRes 12FT

Birkbeck, University of London
Analytical Bioscience .... MSc 12FT 24 - 60PT/PGDip 12FT 24 - 60PT
Bioinformatics with Systems Biology .... MRes 12FT 24PT
Bioinformatics with Systems Biology .... MSc 12FT 24PT
Health and Disease .... MSc 24PT
Microbiology .... MRes 12FT
Microbiology .... MSc 24PT
Principles of Protein Structure .... PGCert 12DL
Protein Crystallography .... PGCert 12DL
Structural Biology .... MRes 12FT
Structural Molecular Biology .... MSc 24-36PT 24-36DL/PGDip 24PT 24DL
Techniques in Structural Molecular Biology .... PGCert 12DL

University of Birmingham
Applied and Petroleum Micropalaeontology .... MSc 12FT
Mathematics and Computing in Biology and Medicine MSc 12FT

Bournemouth University
Applied Sciences by Research .... MSc 12FT 24PT

University of Brighton
Bioscience .... MRes 12FT 24PT

University of Bristol
Palaeobiology .... MSc 12FT 24 - 36PT

Brunel University
Medicine, Bioscience and Society .... MSc 12FT 30PT

University of Cambridge
Computational Biology .... MPhil 11FT
Public Health .... MPhil 12FT

Cardiff University
Biophotonics .... MSc 12FT 24PT

University of Central Lancashire
Allied Health Practice .... MSc up to 60PT
Allied Health Practice; MSc Allied Health Practice (Occupational Therapy) .... MSc 36PT/PGDip 24PT/PGCert 12PT
Biomedical Science .... MSc 12FT
Cancer Biology and Therapy .... MSc 12FT
Non-Surgical Facial Aesthetics for Registered Healthcare Professionals .... MSc 36PT/PGDip 24PT

University of Chester
Applied Wildlife Conservation .... PGCert 12FT 12 - 36PT
Applied Wildlife Forensics .... PGCert 12FT 12 - 36PT
Biomedical Sciences.. MSc 12FT 24 - 48PT/PGDip 12FT 24 - 48PT/PGCert 12FT 12 - 24PT
Conservation in Practice .... PGCert 12FT 12 - 36PT
Wildlife Conservation .... MSc 12FT 24PT/PGDip 12FT 24PT/PGCert 12FT 12-24PT

University College Cork
Applied Science (Marine Biology) .... MSc 12FT
Biomedical Sciences .... MSc 24PT

University of Cumbria
Conservation Biology .... MSc 12FT min 24PT/GradDip 6FT min 12PT/GradCert 3FT min 6PT

University of Derby
Conservation Biology .... MSc 12FT 36PT

University of Dundee
Anatomy and Advanced Forensic Anthropology .... MSc 12FT
Cancer Biology .... MRes 12FT

University of East Anglia
Plant Genetics & Crop Improvement .... MSc 12FT 24PT

University of East London
Bioscience .... MRes 12FT 24PT
Bioscience .... MSc 12FT 24PT/PGDip 8FT 16PT/PGCert 4FT 8PT

Edinburgh Napier University
Biomedical Science .... MSc 12FT 24PT/PGDip 9FT 18PT/PGCert 6FT 12PT

University of Edinburgh
Animal Breeding and Genetics .... MSc 12FT 24PT/PGDip 9FT
Biodiversity and Taxonomy of Plants .... MSc 12FT/PGDip 9FT
Bioelectronics and Biosensors .... MSc 12FT
Bioinformatics .... MSc 12FT/PGDip 9FT
Biomechanics .... MSc 12FT
Biomedical Sciences (Life Sciences) .... MSc(Res) 12FT
Biotechnology .... MSc 12FT/PGDip 9FT
Cardiovascular Biology .... MSc(Res) 12FT
Drug Discovery & Translational Biology .... MSc 12FT/PGDip 9FT
Ecosystem Services .... MSc 12FT 24-36PT
Evolutionary Genetics .... MSc 12FT 24PT/PGDip 9FT
Forensic Anthropology .... MSc 12FT 24PT
Human Cognitive Neuropsychology .... MSc 12FT 24PT
Human Complex Trait Genetics .... MSc 12FT 24PT/PGDip 9FT
Medicinal & Biological Chemistry .... MSc 12FT
Next Generation Drug Discovery (Online Distance Learning) .... MSc 72DL/PG Professional Development 48DL/PGCert 24DL/PGDip 48DL
Reproductive Sciences .... MSc(Res) 12FT
Systems and Synthetic Biology .... MSc 12FT

University of Essex
Biomedical Science .... MSc 12FT 24PT
Biotechnology .... MSc 12FT
Environmental Governance: the Natural World, Science and Society .... MSc 12FT 24PT/MA 12FT 24PT
Environmental Resource Management .... MSc 12FT 24PT
Marine Biology .... MSc 12FT
Molecular Medicine .... MSc 12FT
Natural Environment and Society .... MSc 12FT

University of Exeter
Bioarchaeology .... MSc 12FT 24PT
Biosciences .... MSc(Res) 12FT 36PT
Conservation and Biodiversity .... MSc 12FT
Evolutionary and Behavioural Ecology .... MSc 12FT
History and Philosophy of Biology .... MA 12FT 24PT

Glasgow Caledonian University
Biomedical Science .... MSc 24PT/PGDip 24PT/PGCert 12PT
Biomolecular and Biomedical Sciences .... MSc 12FT
Clinical Microbiology .... MSc 12FT
Food Bioscience .... MSc 12FT
Life Sciences - Biological and Biomedical Sciences/Psychology/Vision Sciences .... MRes 12FT

University of Glasgow
Evolutionary Biology & Systematics .... MRes 12FT/PGDip 9FT
Physics: Life Sciences .... MSc 12FT

University of Greenwich
Biomedical Sciences .... MSc 12FT 24PT/PGDip 12FT 24PT

Heriot-Watt University
Applied Mathematical Sciences with Biological and Ecological Modelling .... MSc 12FT 24-84PT/PGDip 9FT 15-48PT
Biotechnology .... MSc 12FT 24PT/PGDip 9FT 20PT
Food Science and Nutrition .... MSc 12FT 24PT/PGDip 9FT 21PT

University of Hertfordshire
Environmental Management .... MSc 12-15FT 24-60PT/PGDip 12FT 18-48PT/PGCert 12FT 18-48PT

University of Huddersfield
Analytical Bioscience .... MSc 12FT 24-48PT

Imperial College London
Bioinformatics and Theoretical Systems Biology .... MSc 12FT
Biosystematics .... MSc(Res) 12FT/DIC 12FT
Clinical Cytology .... MSc 24PT

Biology and life sciences

Integrative Mammalian Biology......MRes 12FT
Systems and Synthetic Biology......MRes 12FT
Quantitative Biology......MSc 12FT
Reproductive and Developmental Biology......MSc 12FT
Structural Molecular Biology......MRes 12FT

Keele University
European Scientific Research Training......MRes 12FT 12BM

University of Kent
Biosciences......GradDip 12FT
Cancer Biology......PGDip 12FT 24PT/MSc 12FT 24PT
Conservation Biology......MSc 12FT 24PT
Graduate Diploma in Biosciences......GradDip 12FT
Reproductive Medicine: Science and Ethics......MSc 12FT 24PT

Leeds Metropolitan University
Microbiology & Biotechnology......MSc 12FT 24PT

University of Leeds
Bioscience......MSc 12FT
Infection and Immunity......MSc 12FT

University of Lincoln
Biotechnology......MSc 12FT

Liverpool Hope University
Education & Biology......MA 36PT

Liverpool School of Tropical Medicine
Biology & Control of Parasites & Disease Vectors......MSc 12FT/PGDip 8FT/PGCert 4FT
Molecular Biology of Parasites & Disease Vectors......MSc 12FT/PGDip 8FT

University of Liverpool
Advanced Biological Sciences......MSc 12FT

London School of Hygiene and Tropical Medicine
Clinical Trials (by Distance Learning)......MSc 24 - 60DL/PGDip 12 - 60DL/PGCert 12-60DL
Control of Infectious Diseases......MSc 12FT 24PT
Demography & Health......MSc 12FT 24PT
Epidemiology......MSc 12FT 24PT
Epidemiology (by Distance Learning)......MSc 24 - 60DL/PGDip 12 - 60DL/PGCert 12-60DL
Global Mental Health......MSc 12FT 24PT
Health Policy, Planning and Financing......MSc 12FT 24PT
Immunology of Infectious Diseases......MSc 12FT 24PT
Infectious Diseases (by Distance Learning)......24 - 60DL/PGDip 12 - 60DL/PGCert 12-60DL
Medical Microbiology......MSc 12FT 24PT
Medical Parasitology......MSc 12FT 24PT
Medical Statistics......MSc 12FT 24PT
Molecular Biology of Infectious Diseases......MSc 12FT 24PT
Nutrition for Global Health......MSc 12FT 24PT
One Health......MSc 12FT 24PT
Public Health......MSc 12FT 24PT
Public Health (Environment & Health)......MSc 12FT 24PT
Public Health (Health Economics)......MSc 12FT 24PT
Public Health (Health Promotion)......MSc 12FT 24PT
Public Health (Health Services Management)......MSc 12FT 24PT
Public Health (Health Services Research)......MSc 12FT 24PT
Public Health (Public Health)......MSc 12FT 24PT
Public Health (by Distance Learning)......MSc 24 - 60DL/PGDip 12 - 60DL/PGCert 12-60DL
Public Health for Eye Care......MSc 12FT 24PT
Public Health in Developing Countries......MSc 12FT 24PT
Reproductive & Sexual Health Research......MSc 12FT 24PT
Tropical Medicine & International Health......MSc 12FT 24PT
Veterinary Epidemiology......MSc 12FT 24PT

Manchester Metropolitan University
Animal Behaviour......MSc 12FT 24-60PT
Biological Recording......MSc 24-36PT
Biomedical Science......MSc 12FT 30PT
Biomedical Science (general route)......MSc 12FT 24-36PT
Conservation Biology......MSc 12FT 24-60PT
Conservation Genetics......MSc 12FT 24PT

University of Manchester
Biological Sciences......MRes 12FT
Developmental Biology......MSc 12FT
Integrative Biology......MRes 12FT
Molecular Parasitology and Vector Biology......MSc 12FT 24PT

Newcastle University
Biomedical Engineering......MSc 12FT
Ecological Consultancy......MSc 12FT
Environmental Consultancy......MSc 12FT 48PT
Neuroinformatics......MSc 12FT
Synthetic Biology......MSc 12FT

Nottingham Trent University
Biomedical Science......MSc 12FT 24PT
Biotechnology......MSc 12FT 24PT
Research Applied Biosciences......MSc(Res) 12FT 24PT
Research Biotechnology......MSc(Res) 12FT 24PT
Research Cancer Biology......MSc(Res) 12FT 24PT
Research Ecology......MSc(Res) 12FT 24PT
Research Microbiology......MSc(Res) 12FT 24PT
Research Molecular Cell Biology......MSc(Res) 12FT 24PT
Molecular Biology......MRes 12FT 24PT
Molecular Cell Biology......MSc 12FT 24PT
Pharmacology......MRes 12FT 24PT

University of Nottingham
Advanced Geonomic and Proteomic Sciences......MRes 12FT
Mathematical Medicine and Biology......MSc 12FT
Sensory Science......PGCert 48PT
Techniques in Developmental Biology......MRes 12FT

The Open University
Professional Science......MSc variableDL
Science......MSc variableDL

Plymouth University
Biomedical Science......MSc 12FT 24PT
Marine Biology......MRes 12FT 24PT

University of Portsmouth
Applied Aquatic Biology......MSc 12FT 24PT
Science......MRes 12FT 24PT

Queen's University Belfast
Computational Biology......MSc 12FT
Ecological Management and Conservation Biology......MSc 12FT 24PT/PGDip 9FT
Molecular Biology and Biotechnology......MSc 12FT 24PT

University of Reading
Biometry......MSc 12FT 24PT
Plant Diversity......MSc 12FT 24PT

Robert Gordon University
Clinical Biomechanics......MSc 12FT
Instrumental Analytical Sciences: DNA Analysis, Proteomics and Metabolomics......MSc 12FT 36PT/PGDip 9FT 24PT
Instrumental Analytical Sciences: Oilfield Chemicals ... MSc 12FT 36PT/PGDip 9FT 24PT/PGCert 4FT 12PT

Royal Agricultural University
Fisheries and Aquaculture Management......MSc 12FT 24PT

Royal Holloway, University of London
Biological Sciences Research......MSc 12FT 24PT

Royal Veterinary College
Veterinary Education - PG Associate (PT)......PG Associateship 6-24PT

University Campus Suffolk
MSc Regenerative Medicine......MSc 12FT

University of Salford
Analytical Biosciences and Drug Design......MSc 12FT 36PT/PGDip 8FT 24PT
Environmental and Public Health......MSc 12FT 24-36PT/PGDip 8FT 24PT
Molecular Parasitology and Vector Biology......MSc 12FT 24PT/PGDip 9FT

Sheffield Hallam University
Biomedical Sciences......MSc 12FT 24PT/PGDip 8FT 16PT/PGCert 4FT 8PT
Biotechnology......MSc 12FT 24PT/PGDip 8FT 16PT/PGCert 4FT 8PT
Pathological Sciences......MSc 12FT 24PT

University of Sheffield
Biological and Bioprocess Engineering......MSc(Eng) 12FT
Mechanistic Biology......MSc 12FT
Molecular Medicine......MSc 12FT
Molecular and Cellular Basis of Disease......MSc 12FT
Reproductive and Developmental Medicine......MSc 12FT

University of Southampton
Chemistry by Research......MSc 12FT
Vertebrate Palaeontology......MRes 12FT 18PT
Marine Resource Management......MSc 12FT

University of St Andrews
Environmental Biology (collab)......MRes 12FT
Environmental Biology Conversion for Mathematical, Physical & Molecular Sciences (collab)......MRes 12FT

St George's, University of London
Biomedical Science......MRes 12FT

Staffordshire University
Clinical Biomechanics and Diabetes......PGCert 12PT
Clinical Biomechanics and Pain Management in the Lower limb......PGCert 12PT
Ecology and Conservation......MSc 15FT
Forensic Science via Distance Learning......MSc 12-18FT 12/36DL/PGDip 12-18FT
Invertebrate Ecology and Conservation......MSc 15FT/PGDip 15FT
Molecular Biology for Health Professionals......PGDip 20DL
Molecular Biology via Distance Learning......PGCert 12DL/PGDip 24DL/MSc 12-36DL
Urban Ecology and Conservation......MSc 15FT

University of Stirling
Aquaculture: Sustainable Aquaculture (Named Degree Outcomes)......MSc 12FT/PGDip 9FT/PGCert 6FT
Conservation and Sustainability......MSc 12FT 27PT/PGDip 9FT 21PT
Marine Biotechnology......MSc 12FT 24PT/PGDip 9FT

Teesside University
Health & Social Care Sciences (Generic Pathway)......MSc 18FT 36PT
Health & Social Care Sciences (Public Health)......MSc 18FT 36PT
Neurological Rehabilitation......PGCert 12PT

University of Ulster
Professional Practice......PGDip 24FT/MSc 36FT
Stem Cell Biology......PGCert 9DL/PGDip 12-20DL
Systems Biology......PGCert 9DL

UCL - University College London
Biochemical Engineering......MSc 12FT/PGDip 9FT
Biology of Vision......MSc 12FT
Biomedical Sciences......MSc 12FT 24PT
Biosciences......MRes 12FT
Cell and Gene Therapy......MSc 12FT 24-60PT/PGDip 9FT 24-60PT/PGDip 3FT 6-24PT
Modelling Biological Complexity......MRes 12FT
Molecular Measurement in Medicine......MSc 12FT
Molecular Modelling......MSc 12FT 36PT
Molecular Modelling and Materials Science......MRes 12FT 24PT
Neurology for Clinical Trainees......MSc 24-48PT
Synthetic Biology......MRes 12FT
Systems Biology......MRes 12FT

University of Warwick
Environmental Bioscience in a Changing ClimateMSc 12FT 24PT/PGDip 12FT 24PT
Systems Biology......MSc 11FT 22PT

University of Westminster
Cellular Pathology......MSc 12FT
Life Sciences Postgraduate Modules - Biosciences......Individual modules 6-12PT
Life Sciences Postgraduate Modules - Intergrated Health......Individual modules 6-12PT

University of Wolverhampton
Computational Bioinformatics......MSc 12FT 24PT
Doctor of Biomedical Science......DSc by taught 36PT
Medical Biotechnology......MSc 12FT 24PT

University of York
Bioscience Technology......MSc 12FT
Computational Biology......MRes 12FT
Ecology and Environmental Management......MRes 12FT

Biology and life sciences
Research Courses

University of Aberdeen
Biological Science......MSc by research 12FT/MPhil 24FT/PhD 36FT
Environmental Science......PhD 36FT/MPhil 24FT/MSc by research 12FT

Aberystwyth University
IBERS - Biological Sciences......MPhil 12FT 24PT
IBERS - Biological Sciences......PhD 36FT 60PT
IBERS - Environmental Science......MPhil 12FT 24PT
IBERS - Environmental Science......PhD 36FT 60PT

Anglia Ruskin University
Animal and Environmental......PhD 24-60FT 36-72PT
Cellular Pathology and Molecular Genetics......PhD 24 - 60FT 36 - 72PT
Professional Doctorate in Science and Technology......DProf 60DL

Bangor University
Biological Sciences......MPhil 12FT/PhD 24-36FT
Ecology......MRes 12FT
Natural Sciences......MRes 12FT
Ocean Sciences......MPhil 24FT/PhD 36FT

Barts and the London School of Medicine and Dentistry ......
Rheumatology/Bone and Joint Research Unit......PhD

University of Bath
Protein Structure & Function......MRes 12FT

University of Bedfordshire
Biology..MA by research 12FT 24PT/MSc by research 12FT 24PT/MPhil 24FT/PhD 36FT

Birkbeck, University of London
Biological Sciences......PhD 36-48FT 48-84PT/MPhil 24FT 36PT

University of Birmingham
Biosciences......MSc by research 12FT 24PT/PhD 36FT 72PT
Earth Sciences......PhD 36FT 72PT/MPhil 24FT 48PT

University of Bristol
Biological Sciences......PhD 36FT 72PT/MSc by research 12FT 24PT

Brunel University
Biology......PhD/MPhil

University of Buckingham
Anthropology......MA by research 12FT
Bioinformatics......MSc by research 12FT
Clinical Science......MSc by research 36FT
Diabetes, Obesity and Metabolic Disease.DPhil 36FT 72PT/MPhil 24FT 48PT

University of Cambridge
Biological Science......MPhil 12FT
Developmental Biology......MPhil 12FT/PhD 36FT

Biology and life sciences

Epidemiology..PhD 36FT
Human Evolutionary Studies.................................... MPhil 11FT
Molecular Biology ....PhD 36FT

Canterbury Christ Church University
Biological Sciences .... MPhil 24FT 48PT/PhD 36FT 60PT

Cardiff University
Biosciences..MRes 12FT

University of Central Lancashire
Biological and Biomedical.........PhD 48FT 84PT/MPhil 36FT 60PT/
MSc by research 24FT 36PT/MD 48PT
Biological and Biomedical Sciences....PhD 48FT 84PT/MPhil 36FT
60PT/MSc by research 24FT 36PT/MD 48PT

University of Chester
Higher Degrees by Research .... MPhil 12 - 48FT 24 - 72PT/PhD
24 - 48FT 48 - 84PT

University of Dundee
Life Sciences.........................PhD 36FT PhD 48FT MPhil 24FT
MSc by research 12FT
Life Sciences - A/Star Dundee Programme ....PhD 48FT
Life Sciences - EMBL Joint Programme (PhD) ....PhD 36FT
Life Sciences - Wellcome Programme (PhD) ....PhD 48FT

Durham University
Biological and Biomedical Sciences........... PhD 36FT 72PT/MSc by
research 12FT 24PT

University of East Anglia
Biological Sciences ....PhD 36FT/MPhil 24FT/MSc by
research 12FT

University of East London
Research Programmes..PhD/MPhil

University of Edinburgh
Cardiovascular (Msc by Research) ....MSc by research 12FT 24PT
Cardiovascular Research............. PhD 36FT 48PT/MPhil 24FT 36PT
Cell Biology.. PhD 36FT 72PT
Evolutionary Biology..PhD 36FT 72PT
Genomics and Pathway Biology ....MSc by research 12FT
Immunology & Infection Research ....PhD 36FT 72PT
Infectious Diseases ....MSc by research 12FT
Informatics: Institute for Adaptive & Neural Computation... MSc
by research 12FT 24PT/PhD 36FT 72PT/MPhil 24FT 48PT
Informatics: Life Sciences Institute............................ PhD 36FT 72PT
Molecular Plant Sciences ....PhD 36FT 72PT
Neuroscience.........PhD 36FT 72PT/MSc by research 12FT 24PT
Pathology.........PhD 36FT 72PT/MPhil 24FT/MSc by research 12FT
24PT
Population Health Sciences PhD 36FT 72PT/MPhil 24FT 48PT/MSc
by research 12FT 24PT
Reproductive & Developmental Science ....PhD 36FT
Reproductive Biology.................. PhD 36FT 72PT/MPhil 24FT 36PT
Reproductive Biology ....MSc by research 12FT

University of Essex
Biochemistry....................PhD 36FT 72PT/MPhil 24FT 48PT/MSc by
research 12FT 24PT
Bioinformatics.................PhD 36FT 72PT/MPhil 24FT 48PT/MSc by
research 12FT 24PT
Biological Sciences.........PhD 36FT 72PT/MPhil 24FT 48PT/MSc by
research 12FT 24PT
Biological Sciences: Immunology........PhD 36FT 72PT/MPhil 24FT
48PT/MSc by research 12FT 24PT
Biostatistics.....PhD 36FT 72PT/MPhil 24FT 48PT/MSc by research
12FT 24PT
Cell and Molecular Biology ....PhD 36FT 72PT/
MPhil 24FT 48PT/MSc by research 12FT 24PT
Chemical Biology...........PhD 36FT 72PT/MPhil 24FT 48PT/MSc by
research 12FT 24PT
Environmental Governance ......PhD 36FT 72PT/MPhil 24FT 48PT/
MSc by research 12FT 24PT
Environmental Sciences...........PhD 36FT 72PT/MPhil 24FT 48PT/
MSc by research 12FT 24PT
Marine Biology PhD 36FT 72PT/MPhil 24FT 48PT/MSc by research
12FT 24PT
Mathematical Biology...PhD 36FT 72PT/MPhil 24FT 48PT/MSc by
research 12FT 24PT
Microbiology...PhD 36FT 72PT/MPhil 24FT 48PT/MSc by research
12FT 24PT
Molecular Medicine ....PhD 36FT 72PT/MPhil 24FT 48PT/MSc by
research 12FT 24PT
Sports and Exercise Medicine...PhD 36FT 72PT/MPhil 24FT 48PT/
MSc by research 12FT 24PT
Sports and Exercise Psychology ....PhD 36FT 72PT/
MPhil 24FT 48PT/MSc by research 12FT 24PT
Sports and Exercise Science ......PhD 36FT 72PT/MPhil 24FT 48PT/
MSc by research 12FT 24PT

University of Exeter
Biosciences......PhD 36FT 72PT/MPhil 24FT 48PT/MSc by research
12FT 36PT
Sociology ....PhD 36FT 72PT 72DL/MPhil 24FT 48PT 48DL

National University of Ireland Galway
College of Science.... PhD 48FT 72PT/MSc by research 24FT 48PT/
Structured PhD 48FT

Glasgow Caledonian University
Biological and Biomedical Sciences/Psychology/Vision Sciences ..
....MRes 12FT
School of Life Sciences...............................MPhil 24FT/PhD 48FT

University of Glasgow
Environmental and Evolutionary Biology............PhD 36FT/MSc by
research 12FT

University of Gloucestershire
Biological Sciences .... PhD 30-48FT

University of Greenwich
Chemical and Life Sciences .... MSc by research 12FT 24-36PT

University of Hertfordshire
Biological and Neural Computation ...PhD 36FT 72PT/MPhil 24FT
48PT/MRes 12FT 24PT

University of Huddersfield
Department of Chemical and Biological Sciences PhD 36FT 60PT/
MPhil 30FT 60PT

University of Hull
Biological Sciences .... PhD 36FT 60PT/MSc by research 12FT 24PT

Imperial College London
Biological Sciences ....PhD/MPhil
Biological Sciences ....PhD/MPhil
Biological Sciences ....PhD/MPhil
Biological Sciences ....PhD/MPhil
Clinical Sciences Centre .... PhD 48FT 72PT
Department of Biology ....PhD/MPhil
Metabolic Medicine..PhD

University of Kent
Genetics .... MSc by research 12FT 24PT/MPhil 24FT 36PT/
PhD 36FT 60PT

King's College London
Age-Related Diseases (Wolfson Centre for) PhD 36-48FT 48-72PT/
MPhil 36-48FT 36-48PT/MDS by research 36-48FT 36-48PT
Cell & Molecular Biophysics, Randall Division of ....PhD 36FT
48-72PT/MPhil 36FT 48-72PT/MD 36FT 48-72PT
Transplantation Immunology & Mucosal Biology .... MPhil 48FT
72PT/PhD 48FT 72PT

Lancaster University
Biological Sciences .... PhD 36FT 72PT/MPhil 24FT 36PT
Biomedical and Life Sciences..... PhD 36FT 48PT/MPhil 24FT 36PT

University of Leeds
Biology ....PhD 36+FT/MPhil 24FT/MSc by research 12FT
Biomedical Sciences........PhD 36+FT/MPhil 24FT/MSc by research
12FT
Membrane Biophysics and Biotechnology ....PhD 36+FT/MPhil
24FT/MSc by research 12FT
Plant-Sciences ....PhD 36+FT/MPhil 24FT/MSc by research 12FT

University of Leicester
Department of Biology- Research .... PhD 36FT/MPhil 24FT/
MSc by research 12FT

University of Lincoln
Biochemistry and Molecular Biology ......MSc(Res) 12-36FT/MPhil
12-36FT/PhD 12-36FT
Biology ....MSc(Res) 12-36FT/MPhil 12-36FT/PhD 12-36FT
Biomedical and Medical Science ....MPhil 18FT 30PT/
PhD 33FT 60PT
Ecology ....MSc(Res) 12-36FT/MPhil 12-36FT/PhD 12-36FT
Forensic Science ..... MSc by research 12FT 24PT/MPhil 18FT 36PT/
PhD 33FT 60PT
Microbiology........MSc(Res) 12-36FT/MPhil 12-36FT/PhD 12-36FT
Nutrition ....MSc(Res) 12-36FT/MPhil 12-36FT/PhD 12-36FT
Zoology ....MSc(Res) 12-36FT/MPhil 12-36FT/PhD 36FT

University of Liverpool
Advanced Biological Sciences.......................................MRes 12FT
Biological Sciences (Biochemistry and Cell Biology)............. MPhil
12-24FT 48-72PT/PhD 24-48FT 48-72PT
Biological Sciences (Evolution, Ecology and Behaviour)....... MPhil
12-24FT 24-72PT/PhD 24-48FT 48-84PT
Biological Sciences (Functional and Comparative Genomics) ....
MPhil 12-48FT 24-72PT/PhD 24-48FT 48-84PT
Biological Sciences (Plant Sciences).........MPhil 12-48FT 24-72PT/
PhD 24-48FT 48-84PT

London School of Hygiene and Tropical Medicine
Infectious & Tropical Diseases (Research)....DrPH 42FT 42PT/PhD
42FT 42PT/MPhil 12FT 12PT
Public Health & Policy (Research).........DrPH 42FT 42PT/PhD 42FT
42PT/MPhil 12FT 12PT

University of Manchester
Adaptive Organismal Biology......................PhD 36-48FT 72-96PT/
MPhil 12FT 24PT
Cell Biology.........................PhD 36-48FT 72-96PT/MPhil 12FT 24PT
Cell Matrix Research........PhD 36-48FT 72-96PT/MPhil 12FT 24PT
Channels and Transporters...... PhD 36-48FT 72-96PT/MPhil 12FT
24PT
Developmental Biology ....PhD 36-48FT 72-96PT/
MPhil 12FT 24PT
Evolutionary Biology........PhD 36-48FT 72-96PT/MPhil 12FT 24PT
Gene Expression ....PhD 36-48FT 72-96PT/MPhil 12FT 24PT
Membrane Trafficking.....PhD 36-48FT 72-96PT/MPhil 12FT 24PT

Organelle Function ....PhD 36-48FT 72-96PT/MPhil 12FT 24PT
Stem Cell Research...........PhD 36-48FT 72-96PT/MPhil 12FT 24PT
Structural Biology............PhD 36-48FT 72-96PT/MPhil 12FT 24PT
Systems Biology............................ MPhil 12FT 24PT/PhD 36FT 72PT

Newcastle University
Biological Sciences .... PhD 36FT 72PT/MPhil 12FT 24PT
Biomedicine.......MPhil 12FT 24PT/PhD 36FT 72PT/MD 24FT 48PT
Biopharmaceutical Process Development .... EngD 48FT
Biotechnology ....MPhil 12FT 24PT/PhD 36FT 72PT
Biotechnology and Business Enterprise ....MRes 12FT
Evolution and Human Behaviour ....MRes 12FT
Immunobiology...MRes 12FT
Molecular Microbiology...MRes 12FT
Systems Biology...MRes 12FT

Northumbria University
Biomedical Sciences ....DProf 24-48PT

Nottingham Trent University
Cancer Biology..MRes 12FT 24PT
Cell Biology...MRes 12FT 24PT
Environmental Biology.......................................MRes 12FT 24PT
School of Biosciences .... PhD 36FT 48PT/MPhil 24FT 36PT

University of Nottingham
Animal Behaviour and Ecology ....MPhil 24FT/PhD 36FT
Biological Systems..MRes 12FT
Biology .... PhD 24FT/MRes 12FT 24PT
Conservation Biology...MRes 12FT
Developmental Biology ....MRes 12FT
Evolutionary Biology..MRes 12FT 24PT
Fungal Biology & Genetics Group.......PhD 36FT 72PT/MPhil 24FT
48PT
Molecular and Cellular Science PhD 36FT 72PT/MPhil 24FT 48PT/
MRes 12FT
Parasite Biology and Immunogenetics .... PhD 36FT/MPhil 24FT
PhD and MPhil Biology research opportunities... MPhil 24FT/PhD
36FT
Reproductive Biology................... PhD 36FT 72PT/MPhil 24FT 48PT
Techniques in Development Biology ....MRes 12FT 24PT

The Open University
Biomedical Sciences PhD 36FT 72PT variableDL/MPhil 15FT 24PT
Ecosystems and Biodiversity .....PhD 36FT 72PT variableDL/MPhil
15FT 24PT
STEM Education and engagement .... PhD 36FT 72PT variableDL

Oxford Brookes University
Biological Sciences - Biofilm Development.............................
PhD 24-60FT 36-72PT/MPhil 24-36FT 36-48PT
Biological Sciences - Bioprocess Research..............................
PhD 24-60FT 36-72PT/MPhil 24-36FT 36-48PT
Biological Sciences - Cell Systems Modelling............. PhD 24-60FT
36-72PT/MPhil 24-36FT 36-48PT
Biological Sciences - Environmental Ecology .... PhD 24-60FT
36-72PT/MPhil 24-36FT 36-48PT
Biological Sciences - Evolutionary Developmental Biology
MPhil/.................... PhD 24-60FT 36-72PT/MPhil 24-36FT 36-48PT
Biological Sciences - Invertebrate Ecology and Biogeography
.... PhD 24-60FT 36-72PT/MPhil 24-36FT 36-48PT
Biological Sciences - Plant Cell Biology ..... PhD 24-60FT 36-72PT/
MPhil 24-36FT 36-48PT
Biological Sciences - Spatial Ecology and Land Use.......................
PhD 24-60FT 36-72PT/MPhil 24-36FT 36-48PT
Biological and Biomedical Science .....PhD 36FT 48PT/MPhil 24FT
36PT
Health & Biomedical Sciences - Glycobiology and Cancer .....PhD
24-60FT 36-72PT/MPhil 24-36FT 36-48PT
Health & Biomedical Sciences - Human Health & Performance
Research Group ... PhD 24-60FT 36-72PT/MPhil 24-36FT 36-48PT
Health & Biomedical Sciences - Molecular Neuroscience ......PhD
24-60FT 36-72PT/MPhil 24-36FT 36-48PT
Health and Biomedical Sciences - Cell Biology of Trypanosomes ..
.... PhD 24-60FT 36-72PT/MPhil 24-36FT 36-48PT
Health and Biomedical Sciences - Cell Systems Modelling .....PhD
24-60FT 36-72PT/MPhil 24-36FT 36-48PT
Health and Biomedical Sciences - Chromatin and Non-coding ....
PhD 24-60FT 36-72PT/MPhil 24-36FT 36-48PT
Health and Biomedical Sciences - Genomic Instability ....PhD
24-60FT 36-72PT/MPhil 24-36FT 36-48PT
Health and Biomedical Sciences - Insect Virology & Protein
Expression .... PhD 24-60FT 36-72PT/MPhil 24-36FT 36-48PT
Health and Biomedical Sciences - Movement Science ....PhD
24-60FT 36-72PT/MPhil 24-36FT 36-48PT
Health and Biomedical Sciences - Peptide Transport ....MPhil/
PhD 36-60FT 48-72PT/PhD 24-60FT 36-72PT/MPhil 24-36FT
36-48PT
Health and Biomedical Sciences - The Functional Food Centre ....
PhD 24-60FT 36-72PT/MPhil 24-36FT 36-48PT

University of Oxford
Biochemistry................................. DPhil 48FT/MSc by research 24FT
Chemical Biology.......................................DPhil 48FT/MSc(Res) 24FT
Chromosome and Developmental Biology..................... DPhil 48FT
Clinical Laboratory Sciences .... DPhil 48FT/MSc by
research 24-36FT
Life Sciences Interface Doctoral Training Centre .... DPhil 48FT
Musculoskeletal Sciences.......... DPhil 48FT/MSc by research 24FT
Pathology...................................... DPhil 48FT/MSc by research 24FT

Biology and life sciences

Structural Biology .... DPhil 48FT
Systems Biology .... DPhil 48FT

Plymouth University
School of Biomedical and Biological Sciences .... PhD 36FT 72PT/MPhil 24FT 36PT

University of Portsmouth
Biological Sciences .... MPhil 24FT 48PT/PhD 36FT 72PT

Queen Mary, University of London
School of Biological Sciences..... PhD 36FT 48PT/MPhil 24FT 36PT

Queen's University Belfast
Biomolecular Processes .... PhD 36FT 72PT/MPhil 24FT 48PT
Ecology, Evolution, Behaviour and Environmental EconomicsPhD 36FT 72PT/MPhil 24FT 48PT
Molecular Biosciences .... PhD 36FT 72PT/MPhil 24FT 48PT

University of Roehampton
Life Sciences .... PhD 24-36FT 36-48PT/MPhil 24-36FT 36-48PT

Royal Holloway, University of London
Biology .... MPhil 24FT/PhD 36FT

Royal Veterinary College
Master of Research .... MRes 12FT 24-36PT
PhD Opportunities at the Royal Veterinary College .... PhD 36-48FT 48-72PT

University of Salford
Biosciences .... PhD 36FT/MSc by research 12FT

University of Southampton
Biological Sciences .... PhD 36FT 72PT
School of Biological Sciences: Cellular and Molecular Biology...... PhD 36FT 72PT
School of Biological Sciences: Ecology and the Environment .... PhD 36FT 72PT
School of Biological Sciences: Neurosciences .... PhD 36FT 72PT

University of St Andrews
Biology .... PhD 36-48FT 72-96PT/MPhil 12-24FT 24-48PT

St George's, University of London
Cellular and Molecular Medicine .... PhD 36FT 72PT/MPhil 24FT 48PT/MD(Res) 24 minFT 48 minPT

Staffordshire University
Biology Division .... PhD 72PT/MPhil 72PT

University of Strathclyde
Pharmacy and Biomedical Sciences - Research .... PhD 36FT 48PT/MPhil 12FT 24PT/MRes 12FT/DPharm 36FT

University of Surrey
Pharmacology, Neuropharmacology, Chronobiology .... MPhil 24FT 36PT/PhD 36FT 48PT

University of Sussex
Biology .... PhD 24-48FT 36-72PT/MPhil 12-36FT 24-48PT

Swansea University
Biological Sciences .... PhD 36FT 60PT/MPhil 12FT 24PT
Sustainable Aquaculture and Fisheries .... MRes 12FT 24PT

University of Ulster
Biomedical Sciences .... PhD 36FT 72PT/MPhil 24FT 48PT

UCL - University College London
Biology .... PhD 36FT 60PT
Biomedical Research .... PhD 36FT 60PT
Cell and Developmental Biology ....
Neurology .... PhD 36FT 60PT/MD(Res) 24FT 24PT

University of Warwick
Biological Sciences .... PhD 36FT 48PT/MPhil 18FT 34PT/MSc by research 12FT 18PT
Biological Sciences .... PhD 36FT 48PT/MPhil 12FT 18PT MSc by research 12FT 18PT
Systems Biology .... PhD 36FT

University of the West of Scotland
Department of Biological Sciences .... PhD/MPhil
Department of Biological Sciences .... PhD/MPhil

University of the West of England, Bristol
Faculty of Health and Life Sciences .... PhD FT
School of Life Sciences .... PhD FT

University of Westminster
Life Sciences .... MPhil 18-36FT 30-60PT

University of Worcester
Biological Sciences .... PhD 48FT 70PT/MPhil 24FT 48PT
Biology .... MRes 12FT 24PT

University of York
Biology .... PhD 36FT/MPhil 24FT/MSc by research 12FT

Biotechnology
Taught Courses

University of Aberdeen
Biotechnology .... MBA 12FT
Cell and Molecular Systems Biology.... MSc 12FT 24PT/PGDip 9FT 18PT
Medical Biotechnology (with Bio-Business)MSc 12FT/PGDip 9FT/MRes 12FT

University of Abertay Dundee
Biotechnology .... MSc 12FT 24PT/PGDip 9FT 18PT
Food Biotechnology .... MSc 12FT/PGDip 9FT
Medical Biotechnology .... MSc 12FT
Renewable Bio-Energy .... MSc 12FT

Aberystwyth University
Green Biotechnology and Innovation .... MSc 12FT

Anglia Ruskin University
Biotechnology .... MSc 12FT 24PT

Bangor University
Molecular Biology with Biotechnology .... MSc 12FT

University of Bath
Protein Structure and Function MRes .... MSc 12FT

University of Bedfordshire
Biotechnology .... MSc 12FT 36PT

University of Birmingham
Mathematics and Computing in Biology and Medicine........ MSc 12FT
Molecular Biotechnology .... MSc 12FT
Translational Medicine: Interdisciplinary Biomedical Technologies .... MSc 12FT
Translational Medicine: Interdisciplinary Biomedical Technologies .... MSc 12FT

University of Bristol
Stem Cells and Regeneration .... MSc 12-24DL/PGDip 12-24DL/PGCert 12-24DL

University of Cambridge
Computational Biology .... MPhil 11FT

Cardiff University
Tissue Engineering .... MSc 12FT

University of Central Lancashire
Pharmaceutical Biotechnology .... MSc 12FT

University of Chester
Biomedical Sciences .... MSc 12FT 24 - 48PT/PGDip 12FT 24 - 48PT/PGCert 12FT 12 - 24PT

University College Cork
Applied Science (Biotechnology) .... MSc 12FT

Cranfield University
Analytical BiotechnologyMSc 12FT 24-36PT/PGDip 9FT 24-36PT/PGCert 6FT 24-36PT
Medical Technology Regulatory Affairs .... MSc 24-60PT/PGDip 24-48PT/PGCert 36PT

De Montfort University
Pharmaceutical Biotechnology .... MSc 12FT 24PT

University of East Anglia
Biotechnology for a Sustainable Future .... MSc 12FT
Molecular Medicine .... MSc 12FT

University of East London
Biotechnology .... MSc 12FT 24PT/PGDip 8FT 16PT/PGCert 4FT 8PT
Biotechnology and Management .... MSc 12FT 24PT/PGDip 8FT 16PT/PGCert 4FT 8PT

Edinburgh Napier University
Biotechnology ..... MSc 12FT 24-36PT/PGDip 9FT 18-27PT/PGCert 6FT 12-18PT

University of Edinburgh
Bioelectronics and Biosensors .... MSc 12FT
Biomechanics .... MSc 12FT
Biotechnology .... MSc 12FT/PGDip 9FT
Regenerative Medicine: Industrial and Clinical Delivery........ MSc 12FT

University of Essex
Biotechnology .... MSc 12FT
Biotechnology with English for Academic Purposes .... Diploma 9FT

University of Exeter
Biotechnology and Enterprise .... MSc 12FT

National University of Ireland Galway
Biotechnology .... MSc 12FT 24PT

Glasgow Caledonian University
Biotechnology .... MSc 12FT
Biotechnology with Business .... MSc 12FT

University of Glasgow
Biotechnology .... MSc 12FT
Crop Biotechnology .... MSc 12FT

University of Greenwich
Biotechnology .... MSc 12FT 24PT

Heriot-Watt University
Biotechnology .... MSc 12FT 24PT/PGDip 9FT 20PT
Marine Biodiversity and Biotechnology ..... MSc 12FT 24PT/PGDip 9FT 21PT

University of Hertfordshire
Biotechnology .... MSc 12-16FT/PGCert 12-16FT/PGDip 12-16FT

Imperial College London
Advanced Chemical Engineering with Biotechnology... MSc 12FT
Bioimaging Sciences .... MRes 12FT
Molecular Plant and Microbial Sciences .... MRes 12FT

University of Kent
Biosciences .... GradDip 12FT
Biotechnology and Bioengineering .... MSc 12FT 24PT
Drug Design .... MSc 12FT

Kingston University
Biotechnology .... MSc 12FT 24PT

Leeds Metropolitan University
Microbiology & Biotechnology .... MSc 12FT 24PT

University of Leeds
Bionanotechnology.. MSc 12FT 24PT/Diploma 12FT 24PT/PGCert 12FT 24PT
Biotechnology .... MSc 12FT

Manchester Metropolitan University
Science, Technology, Engineering and Maths (STEM) .... MSc 24-72PT

University of Manchester
ACS: Digital Biology .... MSc 12FT
Biotechnology .... MSc 12FT 60PT/PGDip 9FT 24PT/PGCert 6FT 12PT
Biotechnology and Enterprise .... MSc 12FT

Newcastle University
Industrial and Commercial Biotechnology .... MSc 12FT

Northumbria University
Biotechnology .... MSc 16FT 30PT

Nottingham Trent University
Biotechnology .... MSc 12FT 24PT

University of Nottingham
Applied Biopharmaceutical Biotechnology and Entrepreneurship .... MSc 12FT 24PT
Cancer Immunology and Biotechnology .... MSc 12FT
Crop Biotechnology and Entrepreneurship .... MSc 12FT 24PT
Research Methods Science and Technology Studies .... MA 12FT 24PT
Stem Cell Technology .... MSc 12FT

Oxford Brookes University
Biotechnology .... MSc 12FT 24PT/PGDip 8FT 20PT
Biotechnology with Business ..... MSc 12FT 24PT/PGDip 8FT 20PT

Robert Gordon University
Clinical Biomechanics .... MSc 12FT

University of Salford
Biotechnology .... MSc 12FT 24 - 36PT/PGDip 8FT 24PT

Sheffield Hallam University
Biotechnology .. MSc 12FT 24PT/PGDip 8FT 16PT/PGCert 4FT 8PT
Pharmacology and Biotechnology .... MSc 12FT 24PT

University of Sheffield
Biological and Bioprocess Engineering .... MSc(Eng) 12FT
Mechanistic Biology .... MSc 12FT
Microbrewing .... MSc 12FT/PGDip 9FT/PGCert 6FT
Prosthodontics .... DClinDent 36FT
Stem Cell and Regenerative Medicine .... MSc 12FT
Translational Oncology .... MSc(Res) 12FT

Staffordshire University
Clinical Biomechanics and Diabetes .... PGCert 12PT
Clinical Biomechanics and Pain Management in the Lower limb... .... PGCert 12PT

University of Stirling
Marine Biotechnology .... MSc 12FT 24PT/PGDip 9FT

University of Sussex
Genetic Manipulation and Molecular Cell Biology........ MSc 12FT

Teesside University
Biotechnology .... MSc 12 or 16FT 24PT/PGDip 8 or 12FT

University of Ulster
Biotechnology .... MSc 12FT/PGDip 9FT/PGCert 4FT

UCL - University College London
Cell and Gene Therapy .... MSc 12FT 24-60PT/PGDip 9FT 24-60PT/PGDip 3FT 6-24PT

University of Warwick
Biotechnology, Bioprocessing and Business Management.... MSc 12FT

University of the West of England, Bristol
Biosensing Technology - MSc by Research .... MSc 12FT 24PT
Molecular Biotechnology .... MSc 12FT 24PT

University of Westminster
Environmental Biotechnology .... MSc 12FT 24PT
Medical Biotechnology .... MSc 12FT 24PT

University of Wolverhampton
Applied Microbiology and Biotechnology .... MSc 12FT 24PT

University of York
Bioscience Technology .... MSc 12FT

Biology and life sciences

Biotechnology
Research Courses

University of Aberdeen
Molecular and Cell Biology .... PhD 36FT/MPhil 24FT/MSc by research 12FT

University of Bath
Protein Structure & Function .... MRes 12FT

University of Cambridge
Biotechnology .... PhD 36FT
Stem Cell Research .... PhD 36FT 60PT

Coventry University
Crop Improvement by Molecular Biotechnology MSc by research 12FT 24-36PT

University of Edinburgh
Regenerative Medicine .... MPhil 24FT 48PT/PhD 36FT 72PT
Stem Cell Research .... PhD 36FT 72PT

University of Hertfordshire
Biotechnology, Microbiology and Molecular Biology ..... PhD 36FT 72PT/MPhil 24FT 48PT/MRes 12FT 24PT

Imperial College London
Department of Biochemistry .... PhD/MPhil

University of Kent
Cell Biology..... MSc by research 12FT 24PT/MPhil 24FT 36PT/PhD 36FT 60PT

University of Leeds
Membrane Biophysics and Biotechnology .... PhD 36+FT/MPhil 24FT/MSc by research 12FT

University of Manchester
Biotechnology .... PhD 36-48FT 72-96PT/MPhil 12FT 24PT
Biotechnology and Enterprise .... PhD 42FT

Newcastle University
Biosciences .... MRes 12FT
Biotechnology .... MPhil 12FT 24PT/PhD 36FT 72PT
Biotechnology and Business Enterprise .... MRes 12FT
Stem Cells and Regenerative Medicine .... MRes 12FT

Nottingham Trent University
Cell Biology .... MRes 12FT 24PT

University of Nottingham
Cell Biology .... MRes 12FT
Cell Signalling.. PhD 36FT 72PT/MPhil 24FT 48PT/MRes 12FT/DM 36FT 72PT
Microbial Biotechnology .... MRes 12FT
Stem Cell Biology .... MRes 12FT
Wolfson Centre for Stem Cells, Tissue Engineering and Modelling (STEM) .... PhD 24-36FT 48-72PT/MPhil 12-24FT 24-48PT

University of Sheffield
Molecular Biology and Biotechnology .... PhD 36FT 72PT/MPhil 24FT 48PT

University of Southampton
School of Health Professions and Rehabilitation Sciences.. MPhil 36FT 60PT/PhD 36FT 60PT

Swansea University
Bioprocess Engineering .... MSc by research 12FT 24PT

Botany and plant science
Taught Courses

University of Aberdeen
Environmental Microbiology .... MSc 12FT/PGDip 9FT
Soil Science .... MSc 12FT/PGDip 9FT

Aberystwyth University
Green Biotechnology and Innovation .... MSc 12FT

Bangor University
Ecology .... MRes 12FT
Environmental and Soil Science .... PhD by taught 36FT 60PT/MPhil 24FT 36PT
Natural Sciences .... MRes 12FT

University of Bath
Molecular Plant Sciences .... MRes 12FT MSc 12FT

University of Derby
Conservation Biology .... MSc 12FT 36PT

University of East Anglia
Plant Genetics & Crop Improvement .... MSc 12FT 24PT

University of Edinburgh
Biodiversity and Taxonomy of Plants .... MSc 12FT/PGDip 9FT

University of Exeter
Biosciences .... MSc(Res) 12FT 36PT

University of Glasgow
Plant Science .... MRes 12FT 36PT/PGDip 9FT

Harper Adams University
Entomology..MSc 12FT 24PT/MRes 12FT 24PT/PGDip 12FT 24PT/PGCert 12FT 24PT
Integrated Pest Management.MSc 12FT 24PT/PGDip 12FT 24PT/PGCert 12FT 24PT

Imperial College London
Molecular Plant and Microbial Sciences .... MRes 12FT

University of Kent
Conservation and Plant Science .... MSc 12FT 24PT
Ethnobotany .... MSc 12FT 24PT

King's College London
Molecular Biophysics .... MRes 12FT

Lancaster University
Plant Sciences (by research) .... MSc(Res) 12FT 24PT

University of Leeds
Plant Science and Biotechnology .... MSc 12FT

University of Manchester
Plant Sciences .... MSc 12FT

Northumbria University
Microbiology .... MSc 12FT 24PT

University of Nottingham
Plant Genetic Manipulation .... MSc 12FT 24PT

University of Reading
Plant Diversity .... MSc 12FT 24PT
Species Identification and Survey Skills .... MSc 12FT
Wildlife Management and Conservation .... MSc 12FT

Royal Veterinary College
Wild Animal Biology .... MSc 12FT
Wild Animal Biology .... PGDip 8FT
Wild Animal Health .... PGDip 8FT

Botany and plant science
Research Courses

University of Aberdeen
Environmental Science..... PhD 36FT/MPhil 24FT/MSc by research 12FT

Bangor University
Biological Sciences .... MPhil 12FT/PhD 24-36FT
Ecology .... MRes 12FT
Natural Sciences .... MRes 12FT

University of Bath
Biology and Biochemistry ... PhD 24-48FT 36-72PT/MRes 12-36FT 24-48PT

University of Cambridge
Plant Sciences .... PhD 36FT

University of Exeter
Biosciences...... PhD 36FT 72PT/MPhil 24FT 48PT/MSc by research 12FT 36PT

University of Gloucestershire
Biological Sciences .... PhD 30-48FT

Heriot-Watt University
International Centre for Brewing and Distilling (ICBD).. PhD 36FT 48PT/MPhil 24FT

Imperial College London
Biological Sciences .... PhD/MPhil

University of Leeds
Plant-Sciences .... PhD 36+FT/MPhil 24FT/MSc by research 12FT

University of Liverpool
Biological Sciences (Plant Sciences) .... MPhil 12-48FT 24-72PT/PhD 24-48FT 48-84PT

University of Manchester
Plant Sciences .... PhD 36-48FT 72-96PT/MPhil 12FT 24PT

Nottingham Trent University
Environmental Biology .... MRes 12FT 24PT

University of Nottingham
Fungal Biology .... MRes 12FT
Fungal Biology & Genetics Group....... PhD 36FT 72PT/MPhil 24FT 48PT
Plant and Crop Sciences... PhD 36FT 72PT/MPhil 24FT 48PT/MRes 12FT 24PT

Oxford Brookes University
Biological Sciences - Biofilm Development .... PhD 24-60FT 36-72PT/MPhil 24-36FT 36-48PT
Biological Sciences - Cell Systems Modelling .... PhD 24-60FT 36-72PT/MPhil 24-36FT 36-48PT
Biological Sciences - Plant Cell Biology ..... PhD 24-60FT 36-72PT/MPhil 24-36FT 36-48PT

University of Oxford
Plant Sciences .... DPhil 48FT/MSc by research 24FT

University of Sheffield
Animal and Plant Sciences .... PhD 36FT 72PT/MPhil 24FT 48PT

Swansea University
Environmental Conservation .... MSc by research 12FT 24PT

University of Warwick
Plant and Environmental Sciences .... PhD 36FT/MPhil 24FT/MSc by research 12FT

Forensics
Taught Courses

Anglia Ruskin University
Forensic Science .... MSc 12 - 15FT 24 - 30PT

Bournemouth University
Forensic Osteology .... MSc 12FT 24PT
Forensic Toxicology by Research .... MSc 12FT 24PT

University of Central Lancashire
Criminal Investigation .... MSc 12PT
DNA Profiling .... MSc 12FT 24PT
Document Analysis .... MSc 12FT 24PT
Fire Investigation .... MSc 12FT/PGDip 9FT/PGCert 6FT
Fire Scene Investigation .... MSc 24-36PT
Forensic Anthropology..... MSc 12FT/PGDip 6FT 12PT/PGCert 3FT 6PT
Forensic Medicine and Bioethics .... MSc 36PT/PGDip 24PT
Forensic Psychology .... MSc 12FT 24PT/PGDip 9FT 24PT/PGCert 9FT 24PT
Forensic Toxicology .... MSc 12FT
Forensic and Legal Medicine........ LLM 36PT/MA 36PT/PGDip 24PT

Cranfield University
Safety and Accident Investigation - Air Transport .... MSc 24-36PT
Safety and Accident Investigation - Rail... MSc 36PT/PGDip 36PT/PGCert 36PT

Cranfield University, Shrivenham
Forensic Archaeology and Anthropology .... MSc 12FT 60PT
Forensic Ballistics .... MSc 12FT 60PT/PGDip 12FT 60PT/PGCert 12FT 60PT
Forensic Engineering and Science .... MSc 12FT 60PT/PGDip 7FT 36PT/PGCert 7FT 36PT
Forensic Explosives and Explosion Investigation .MSc 12FT 60PT/PGDip 12FT 60PT/PGCert 12FT 60PT
Forensic Investigation .... MSc 12FT 60PT/PGDip 12FT 60PT/PGCert 12FT 60PT

University of Dundee
Anatomy and Advanced Forensic Anthropology .... MSc 12FT
Forensic Art .... MSc 12FT
Forensic Art .... MSc 48PT
Forensic Custody Nursing .... GradCert 12FT
Forensic Facial Identification .... MSc 12FT
Forensic Medicine .... MFM 12FT
Forensic Odontology .... MFOdont 12FT
Forensic Toxicology .... MFTox 12FT

University of East Anglia
Forensic Linguistics and Translation .... MA 12FT 24PT

University of Edinburgh
Forensic Anthropology .... MSc 12FT 24PT

University of Glasgow
Forensic Toxicology .... MSc(MedSci) 12FT

University of Huddersfield
Forensic Podiatry .... PGCert 18-24BM

University of Hull
Analytical and Forensic Chemistry .... MSc 12FT

University of Kent
Forensic Science .... GradDip 12FT/MSc 12FT

King's College London
Forensic Mental Health............. MSc 12FT 24PT/PGDip 12FT 24PT
Forensic Science .... MSc 12FT/MRes 15FT

Kingston University
Forensic Analysis .... MSc 12FT

University of Leicester
Forensic Science and Criminal Justice .... MSc 24-27DL

London Metropolitan University
Forensic Science .... MSc 12FT 24PT

London South Bank University
Forensic Science .... MSc 12FT 24PT

University of Manchester
Biomedical and Forensic Studies in Egyptology .... MSc 12FT 24PT

Northumbria University
Forensic Science .... MSc 12FT 36PT

Nottingham Trent University
Forensic Science and Technology .... MSc 12FT 24PT

Queen Mary, University of London
Forensic Medical Sciences .... MSc 12FT 24-60PT

Sheffield Hallam University
Forensic Accounting .... MSc 12FT 24PT
Forensic Engineering .... MSc 12FT 24PT
Forensic Science .... MSc 12FT 24PT

University of South Wales
Analytical and Forensic Science .... MSc 24FT

Staffordshire University
Forensic Science via Distance Learning..... MSc 12-18FT 12/36DL/PGDip 12-18FT

University of Strathclyde
Forensic Science .... MSc 12FT/PGDip 9FT/PGCert 9FT

Biology and life sciences

Swansea University
Applied Analytical Science (LCMS).....MSc 12FT 36PT/PGDip 12FT 36PT

Teesside University
Criminal Investigation.....MSc 12FT 24PT
Forensic Radiography.....PGCert 12PT 12DL MSc 36PT 36DL
Forensic Science.....MSc 12 or 16FT 24PT

UCL - University College London
Crime Analysis (by Distance Learning).....PGCert 12-24PT
Crime Prevention and Community Safety.....PGCert 9FT/PGDip 9FT 18-45PT
Crime and Forensic Science.....MSc 12FT

University of the West of England, Bristol
Advanced Forensic Analysis.....MSc 12FT 24PT

University of Wolverhampton
Fire Scene Investigation.....MSc 12FT 24PT
Forensic Genetics and Human Identification.....MSc 12FT 24PT
Forensic Mark Comparison in collaboration with West Midlands Police.....MSc 12FT 24PT

Forensics
Research Courses

University of Central Lancashire
Forensic and Investigative Science.....PhD 48FT 84PT/MPhil 36FT 60PT/MD 48PT/MSc by research 24FT 36PT

University of Dundee
Forensic Medicine.....MPhil 24FT
Forensic Medicine.....MSc by research 12FT PhD 36FT

University of Lincoln
Forensic Science.....MSc by research 12FT 24PT/MPhil 18FT 36PT/PhD 33FT 60PT

Teesside University
Forensic Science.....PhD 24FT 36PT/MPhil 18FT 30PT

UCL - University College London
Crime Science.....PhD 36FT 60PT

Genetics
Taught Courses

University of Aberdeen
Medical Biotechnology (with Bio-Business).....MSc 12FT/PGDip 9FT/MRes 12FT
Medical Molecular Genetics.....MSc 12FT/PGDip 9FT
Molecular Biology.....MRes 16-24FT

Bangor University
Medical Molecular Biology with Genetics.....MSc 12-24FT
Medical Sciences.....MRes 12FT 24PT/PGCert 3FT 15PT

University of Bath
Medical BioSciences MSc.....MSc 12FT

University of Cambridge
Human Evolutionary Studies.....MPhil 11FT

Cardiff University
Genetic Counselling.....MSc 24FT

University of Central Lancashire
DNA Profiling.....MSc 12FT 24PT
Forensic & Conservation Genetics.....MSc 12FT 24PT

University of East Anglia
Computational Biology.....MSc 12FT/MSc 24PT/MSc 48PT
Molecular Medicine.....MSc 12FT
Plant Genetics & Crop Improvement.....MSc 12FT 24PT

Edinburgh Napier University
Biotechnology.....MSc 12FT 24-36PT/PGDip 9FT 18-27PT/PGCert 6FT 12-18PT

University of Edinburgh
Animal Breeding and Genetics.....MSc 12FT 24PT/PGDip 9FT
Evolutionary Genetics.....MSc 12FT 24PT/PGDip 9FT
Human Complex Trait Genetics.....MSc 12FT 24PT/PGDip 9FT
Quantitative Genetics and Genome Analysis.....MSc 12FT/PGDip 9FT

Glasgow Caledonian University
Biotechnology.....MSc 12FT

University of Glasgow
Biotechnology.....MSc 12FT
Medical Genetics.....MSc(MedSci) 12FT 24PT

Imperial College London
Bioinformatics and Theoretical Systems Biology.....MSc 12FT
Human Molecular Genetics.....MSc 12FT

King's College London
Genes, Environment & Development.....MSc 12FT

University of Leicester
Molecular Genetics.....MSc 12FT/PGDip 9FT/PGCert 4FT

Liverpool School of Tropical Medicine
Molecular Biology of Parasites & Disease Vectors.....MSc 12FT/PGDip 8FT

London Metropolitan University
Medical Genetics.....MSc 12FT 24PT

University of Manchester
Genetic Medicine.....MRes 12FT

Newcastle University
Medical Genetics.....MRes 12FT

University of Nottingham
Molecular Genetics.....MRes 12FT
Molecular Genetics and Diagnostics.....MSc 12FT

Plymouth University
Genetic Healthcare.....PGCert 24FT 24PT

Queen Mary, University of London
Molecular Pathology and Genomics.....MSc 12FT 24PT/PGDip 12FT 24PT 12/24DL

Sheffield Hallam University
Genes and Proteins in Disease.....MSc 12FT 24PT/PGDip 8FT/PGCert 4FT/MSc 36PT

University of Sussex
Genetic Manipulation and Molecular Cell Biology.....MSc 12FT

UCL - University College London
Cell and Gene Therapy.....MSc 12FT 24-60PT/PGDip 9FT 24-60PT/PGDip 3FT 6-24PT
Genetics of Human Disease.....MSc 12FT
Haemaglobinopathy (by Distance Learning).....MSc 12FT 24PT/PGDip 9FT 18PT/PGCert 4FT 8PT
Prenatal Genetics and Fetal Medicine.....MSc 12FT 24PT

University of Warwick
Obesity and Eating Disorders in Diabetes.....PGA 12PT/CPDmod 1PT

University of Westminster
Environmental Biotechnology.....MSc 12FT 24PT

University of Wolverhampton
Forensic Genetics and Human Identification.....MSc 12FT 24PT

Genetics
Research Courses

University of Aberdeen
Biological Science.....MSc by research 12FT/MPhil 24FT/PhD 36FT

Anglia Ruskin University
Cellular Pathology and Molecular Genetics.....PhD 24 - 60FT 36 - 72PT

Bangor University
Biological Sciences.....MPhil 12FT/PhD 24-36FT

Barts and the London School of Medicine and Dentistry
Experimental Pathology.....PhD

University of Birmingham
Clinical and Molecular Genetics.....PhD 36FT 72PT/MSc by research 12FT 24PT/MD 24PT

University of Cambridge
Genetics.....PhD 36FT/MPhil 12FT
Medical Genetics.....PhD 36FT/MPhil 12FT

University of Dundee
Life Sciences.....PhD 48FT
Life Sciences.....MPhil 24FT
Life Sciences.....MSc by research 12FT
Life Sciences - A/Star Dundee Programme (4 year PhD).....PhD 48FT
Life Sciences - EMBL Joint Programme.....PhD 36FT
Life Sciences - Wellcome Programme.....PhD 48FT

University of Edinburgh
Animal Genomics & Disease Resistance (Veterinary Science)PhD 36FT
Cell Biology.....PhD 36FT 72PT
Evolutionary Biology.....PhD 36FT 72PT
Genomics and Pathway Biology.....MSc by research 12FT
Pathology.....PhD 36FT 72PT/MPhil 24FT/MSc by research 12FT 24PT
Stem Cell Research.....PhD 36FT 72PT

University of Glasgow
Molecular Genetics.....PhD 36FT/MSc by research 12FT

University of Kent
Genetics MSc by research 12FT 24PT/MPhil 24FT 36PT/PhD 36FT 60PT

King's College London
Genetics & Molecular Medicine (Research Division).....PhD 36-48FT/MPhil 36-48FT

University of Leeds
Institute of Medical and Biological Engineering.....PhD 36+FT/MPhil 24FT

University of Leicester
Genetics.....PhD 36FT/MPhil 12FT

University of Manchester
Genetics.....PhD 36-48FT 72-96PT/MPhil 12FT 24PT

Newcastle University
Genetics.....PhD 36FT 72PT/MD 24FT 48PT/MPhil 12FT 24PT

University of Nottingham
Advanced Genomic and Proteomic Sciences MRes (with Nottingham Trent University).....MRes 12FT
Comparative Genomics.....MRes 12FT
Conservation Biology.....MRes 12FT
Developmental Biology.....MRes 12FT
Developmental Genetics and Gene Control.....PhD 36FT 72PT/MPhil 24FT 48PT
Evolutionary Biology.....MRes 12FT 24PT
Fungal Biology.....MRes 12FT
Fungal Biology & Genetics Group.....PhD 36FT 72PT/MPhil 24FT 48PT
Genetics.....MRes 12FT
Human Genetics Research Group.....PhD 36FT 72PT/MPhil 24FT 48PT
Human Molecular Genetics.....MRes 12FT
Molecular Genetics.....MRes 12FT
Parasite Biology and Immunogenetics.....PhD 36FT/MPhil 24FT
Population Genetics.....MRes 12FT
Population and Evolutionary genetics Research Group.....PhD 36-72FT/MPhil 24-48FT

Oxford Brookes University
Health and Biomedical Sciences - Chromatin and Non-coding RNA.....PhD 24-60FT 36-72PT/MPhil 24-36FT 36-48PT
Health and Biomedical Sciences - Genomic Instability.....PhD 24-60FT 36-72PT/MPhil 24-36FT 36-48PT
Health and Biomedical Sciences - Insect Virology & Protein Expression.....PhD 24-60FT 36-72PT/MPhil 24-36FT 36-48PT

University of Oxford
Cardiovascular Medicine.....DPhil 48FT/MSc by research 24FT
Chromosome and Developmental Biology.....DPhil 48FT
Genomic Medicine and Statistics.....DPhil 48FT
Life Sciences Interface Doctoral Training Centre.....DPhil 48FT
Physiology, Anatomy and Genetics... DPhil 48FT/MSc by research 24-36FT

Royal Veterinary College
PhD Opportunities at the Royal Veterinary College . PhD 36-48FT 48-72PT

St George's, University of London
Clinical Developmental Sciences.....PhD 36FT 84PT/MPhil 24FT 48PT/MDRes 24PT

University of the Highlands and Islands
Genetics and Biochemistry.....PhD 36FT 72PT/MPhil 24FT 36PT

UCL - University College London
Genetics, Evolution and Environment.....PhD 36FT 60PT

Haematology
Taught Courses

Bangor University
Medical Molecular Biology with Genetics.....MSc 12-24FT

University of Bristol
Transfusion and Transplantation Sciences.....MSc 12FT 36PT/PGCert 12FT 36PT/PGDip 12FT 36PT

University of Edinburgh
Transfusion, Transplanting and Tissue Banking.....MSc 36PT

University of Essex
Biomedical Science.....MSc 12FT 24PT

Leeds Metropolitan University
Biomedical Sciences.....MSc 12FT unknownPT

London Metropolitan University
Blood Science.....MSc 12FT 24PT

Middlesex University
Biomedical Science (Haematology and Transfusion Science).....MSc 12FT 24PT

UCL - University College London
Haemaglobinopathy (by Distance Learning).....MSc 12FT 24PT/PGDip 9FT 18PT/PGCert 4FT 8PT

University of Westminster
Haematology.....MSc 12FT

University of York
Haematopathology.....MSc 24PT/PGCert 24PT/PGDip 24PT

Haematology
Research Courses

Barts and the London School of Medicine and Dentistry
Department of Haematology.....PhD/MPhil

University of Cambridge
Haematology.....PhD 36FT

University of Dundee
Life Sciences.....PhD 48FT MPhil 24FT MSc by research 12FT
Life Sciences - A/Star Dundee Programme (4 year PhD) PhD 48FT
Life Sciences - EMBL Joint Programme.....PhD 36FT
Life Sciences - Wellcome Programme.....PhD 48FT

University of Liverpool
Haematology and Leukaemia.....MPhil 12FT/PhD 36FT/MD 60FT

Biology and life sciences

Histology
Taught Courses

Bangor University
Medical Molecular Biology with Genetics .... MSc 12-24FT

Barts and the London School of Medicine and Dentistry
Experimental Oral Pathology .... MSc 12FT

Cardiff University
Wound Healing and Tissue Repair . MSc 36-60PT 36-60DL/PGDip 36-60PT 36-60DL

University of Edinburgh
Transfusion, Transplanting and Tissue Banking .... MSc 36PT

UCL - University College London
Cell and Gene Therapy ....MSc 12FT 24-60PT/PGDip 9FT 24-60PT/PGDip 3FT 6-24PT

Histology
Research Courses

Barts and the London School of Medicine and Dentistry
Mineralised Tissue Research .... PhD/MPhil
Morbid Anatomy and Histopathology .... PhD/MPhil

University of Birmingham
Tissue Injury and Repair .... PhD 36FT/MPhil 12FT

University of Cambridge
Brain Repair .... PhD 36FT

Imperial College London
Histochemistry .... PhD
Histopathology .... PhD

Nottingham Trent University
Cell Biology .... MRes 12FT 24PT

University of Nottingham
Cell Signalling.. PhD 36FT 72PT/MPhil 24FT 48PT/MRes 12FT/DM 36FT 72PT
Drug Delivery and Tissue Engineering .... PhD 36FT 72PT
Wolfson Centre for Stem Cells, Tissue Engineering and Modelling (STEM) .... PhD 24-36FT 48-72PT/MPhil 12-24FT 24-48PT

St George's, University of London
Cellular and Molecular Medicine ....PhD 36FT 72PT/MPhil 24FT 48PT/MD(Res) 24 minFT 48 minPT

Immunology
Taught Courses

University of Aberdeen
Medical Biotechnology (with Bio-Business)MSc 12FT/PGDip 9FT/MRes 12FT
Molecular and Cellular Immunology...........MSc 12FT/PGDip 9FT/PGCert 6FT

Bangor University
Medical Molecular Biology with Genetics .... MSc 12-24FT

University of Birmingham
Immunology and Immunotherapy .... MSc 12FT

Cardiff Metropolitan University
Biomedical Science ...... MSc 12FT 24PT/PGDip 12FT 24PT/PGCert 12FT 12PT

University of Dundee
Advanced Practice (Infection: Diseases, Prevention & Control) .... MSc 36DL

University of East London
Biomedical Immunology MSc ... MSc 12FT 24PT/PGDip 8FT 16PT/PGCert 4FT 8PT

Imperial College London
Certificate of Advanced Study in Allergy/MSc in Allergy .... MSc(MedSci) -FT 24-36PT 24-36DL/AdvCert -FT 9PT 9DL
Immunology .... MSc 12FT

King's College London
Immunology .... MSc 12FT
Translational Cancer Medicine .... MRes 12FT 24PT

Leeds Metropolitan University
Integrated Masters Biomedical Sciences .... MBIOMS 48FT

University of Leeds
Infection and Immunity .... MSc 12FT

University of Leicester
Infection and Immunity .... MSc 12FT/Diploma 12FT

Liverpool John Moores University ....
Virology...............MSc 24-60DL/PGDip 24-60DL/PGCert 24-60DL/

Liverpool School of Tropical Medicine
Biology & Control of Parasites & Disease Vectors ....MSc 12FT/PGDip 8FT/PGCert 4FT

University of Manchester
Medical Mycology ... MSc 12FT 60PT/PGDip 9FT 48PT/PGCert 5FT 36PT
Medical Virology .... MSc 12FT 24PT/PGDip 9FT 24PT

University of Nottingham
Cancer Immunology and Biotechnology .... MSc 12FT
Immunology and Allergy .... MSc 12FT 24PT
Microbiology and Immunology .... MSc 12FT

University of Oxford
Integrated Immunology .... MSc 12FT/PGDip (must be pre-registered for DPhil to apply) 6FT

Sheffield Hallam University
Biomedical Basis of Disease....... MSc 12FT 36PT/PGDip 8FT 24PT/PGCert 4FT 12PT
Genes and Proteins in Disease........... MSc 12FT 24PT/PGDip 8FT/PGCert 4FT/MSc 36PT

University of Southampton
Allergy ....MSc 12-36PT/PGDip 12-24PT/PGCert 12PT

Swansea University
Infection Prevention and Control .... PGCert 12PT

UCL - University College London
Infection and Immunity..MSc 12FT 24-60PT/PGDip 9FT 24-60PT/PGCert 3FT 6-24PT

Immunology
Research Courses

University of Aberdeen
Immunology ....PhD 36FT/MPhil 24FT/MSc by research 12FT

Aberystwyth University
IBERS - Biological Sciences .... MPhil 12FT 24PT

Barts and the London School of Medicine and Dentistry
Department of Immunology .... PhD/MPhil

University of Birmingham
Immunity and Infection..... PhD 36FT 72PT/MSc by research 12FT 24PT/MD 24PT

Cardiff University
Infection and Immunity .... PhD 36-48FT/MPhil 12FT

University of Edinburgh
Immunology & Infection Research .... PhD 36FT 72PT
Infection and Immunity... PhD 36FT/MPhil 24FT/MSc by research 12FT

University of Glasgow
Immunology, Infection & Inflammation ....PhD 36FT 60PT/MD 24FT 48PT/MMedSci by research 12FT 24PT
Infection and Immunity................PhD 36FT/MSc by research 12FT

Imperial College London
Biomedical Research (Microbial Pathogenesis) .... MRes 12FT
Immunology .... PhD/MSc by research 12FT

King's College London
Immunology, Infection and Inflammatory Disease (DIID) (Research Division)...........PhD 36FT 48-72PT/MPhil 36FT 48-72PT
Transplantation Immunology & Mucosal Biology....... MPhil 48FT 72PT/PhD 48FT 72PT

University of Leicester
Infection, Immunity and InflammationPhD 36 - 48FT 72PT/MPhil 24FT 36PT/MSc by research 12FT/MD 24FT

University of Liverpool
Immunology ....PhD 24-48FT 48-84PT/MPhil 12-48FT 24-72PT/MD 24-72FT
Infection and Global Health (Medical) MPhil 12FT/PhD 36FT/MD 24FT
Infection and Immunity................ MPhil 12FT/PhD 36FT/MD 24FT

University of Manchester
Immunology .... PhD 36-48FT 72-96PT/MPhil 12FT 24PT

Newcastle University
Immunobiology .... MRes 12FT

University of Nottingham
Immunology .... MPhil 24FT/PhD 36FT/DM 24FT
Parasite Biology and Immunogenetics .... PhD 36FT/MPhil 24FT

Oxford Brookes University
Health and Biomedical Sciences - Insect Virology & Protein Expression .... PhD 24-60FT 36-72PT/MPhil 24-36FT 36-48PT

University of Oxford
Clinical Neurosciences ....DPhil 48FT/MSc by research 24-36FT
Infection, Immunology and Translational Medicine .... DPhil 48FT

Queen's University Belfast
Infection and Immunity...... PhD 36FT 72PT/MD 24FT 48PT/MPhil 24FT 48PT

University of Sheffield
Cardiovascular Science................ PhD 36FT 72PT/MPhil 24FT 48PT
Infection, Inflammation and Immunity.......PhD 36FT 72PT/MPhil 24FT 48PT

UCL - University College London
Infection and Immunity .... PhD 36FT 60PT

Microbiology
Taught Courses

University of Aberdeen
Medical Molecular Microbiology..........MSc 12FT 24PT/PGDip 9FT

Aberystwyth University
Green Biotechnology and Innovation .... MSc 12FT

Bangor University
Molecular Biology with Biotechnology .... MSc 12FT

Barts and the London School of Medicine and Dentistry
Clinical Microbiology.................. MSc 12FT 24PT/PGDip 12FT 24PT
Experimental Oral Pathology .... MSc 12FT

University of Bath
Molecular Microbiology .... MRes 12FT MSc 12FT
Molecular Plant Sciences .... MRes 12FT MSc 12FT

Birkbeck, University of London
Microbiology .... MRes 12FT MSc 24PT

University of Birmingham
Microbiology and Infection .... MSc 12-24FT

University of Central Lancashire
Biomedical Science .... MSc 12FT
Cancer Biology and Therapy .... MSc 12FT

University College Cork
Food Microbiology .... MSc 24FT

University of Dundee
Advanced Practice (Infection: Diseases, Prevention & Control) ... MSc 36DL

University of East London
Molecular Medical Microbiology ....MSc 12FT 24PT/PGDip 8FT 16PT/PGCert 4FT 8PT

University of Exeter
Biosciences .... MSc(Res) 12FT 36PT

National University of Ireland Galway
Microbiology .... PGDip 12FT

Glasgow Caledonian University
Clinical Microbiology .... MSc 12FT

Heriot-Watt University
Biotechnology ....MSc 12FT 24PT/PGDip 9FT 20PT
Food Science and Nutrition..........MSc 12FT 24PT/PGDip 9FT 21PT
Food Science, Safety and Health .... MSc 12FT 24PT 24-84DL/PGDip 9FT 21PT 24-84DL

Imperial College London
Biomedical Research: Microbial Pathogensis.................. MRes 12FT
Molecular Biology and Pathology of Viruses .... MSc 12FT

Leeds Metropolitan University
Microbiology & Biotechnology .... MSc 12FT 24PT

Liverpool School of Tropical Medicine
Medical Microbiology..................MSc 12FT/PGDip 8FT/PGCert 4FT
Molecular Biology of Parasites & Disease Vectors.........MSc 12FT/PGDip 8FT

University of Liverpool
Biology and Control of Parasites and Disease Vectors..MSc 12FT/PGDip 6FT/PGCert 3FT

London School of Hygiene and Tropical Medicine
Medical Microbiology .... MSc 12FT 24PT
Medical Parasitology .... MSc 12FT 24PT

University of Manchester
Medical Microbiology............. MSc 12FT 24-36PT/PGDip 9FT 24PT
Medical Mycology ... MSc 12FT 60PT/PGDip 9FT 48PT/PGCert 5FT 36PT

Middlesex University
Biomedical Science (Medical Microbiology)........... MSc 12FT 24PT

Northumbria University
Microbiology .... MSc 12FT 24PT

Nottingham Trent University
Research Microbiology .... MSc(Res) 12FT 24PT
Microbial Bioinformatics .... CPD 1FT
Molecular Biology .... MRes 12FT 24PT
Molecular Cell Biology .... MSc 12FT 24PT

University of Nottingham
Clinical Microbiology .... MSc 12FT
Microbiology and Immunology .... MSc 12FT
Molecular Medical Microbiology .... MSc 12FT

Plymouth University
Marine Biology .... MRes 12FT 24PT

Queen Mary, University of London
Clinical Microbiology .... MSc 12FT 24PT/PGDip 12PT

University of Reading
Food Science .... MSc 12FT 24PT
Food Technology - Quality Assurance .... MSc 12FT

University of Salford
Molecular Parasitology and Vector Biology...........MSc 12FT 24PT/PGDip 9FT

University of Sheffield
Molecular Medicine .... MSc 12FT
Molecular and Cellular Basis of Disease .... MSc 12FT

University of Surrey
Medical Microbiology (Part-time) .... MSc 24PT
Medical Microbiology (Research) .... MSc 24FT

University of Sussex
Genetic Manipulation and Molecular Cell Biology......... MSc 12FT

Biology and life sciences

Swansea University
Infection Prevention and Control .... PGCert 12PT

University of the Highlands and Islands
Medical Device Decontamination...MSc 12PT 12DL/PGDip 12PT/PGCert 12PT

UCL - University College London
Medical Bacteriology (by Distance Learning)...MSc 24FT 24-60PT
Medical Mycology .... MSc 36-60PT/PGDip 36-60PT
Molecular Measurement in Medicine .... MSc 12FT
Molecular Modelling .... MSc 12FT 36PT
Molecular Modelling and Materials Science .... MRes 12FT 24PT

University of Westminster
Applied Microbiology and Biotechnology .... MSc 12FT 24PT
Medical Microbiology .... MSc 12FT/MSc 12FT

University of Wolverhampton
Applied Microbiology and Biotechnology .... MSc 12FT 24PT

University of Worcester
Airborne Infectious Agents and Allergens. .... MSc 12FT 24PT

Microbiology
Research Courses

University of Aberdeen
Microbiology .... PhD 36FT/MSc by research 12FT/MPhil 24FT

Bangor University
Biological Sciences .... MPhil 12FT/PhD 24-36FT

Barts and the London School of Medicine and Dentistry
Department of Medical Microbiology and Virology ..... PhD/MPhil

Cardiff University
Organisms and Environment .. MPhil 24FT 24-36PT/PhD 36-48FT 60PT/MD 24FT 36PT

Cranfield University
Flow Cytometry for Rapid Analysis of Microbiological Water Quality .... MSc by research 12FT

University of Dundee
Non-Graduating Research in Medical School (6 months or more) Non-Grad 6-24FT
Non-Graduating Research in Medical School (less than 6 months) .... Non-Grad 1-5FT

University of Edinburgh
Medical Microbiology....PhD 36FT 72PT/MPhil 24FT 36PT/MSc by research 12FT 24PT

University of Essex
Microbiology...PhD 36FT 72PT/MPhil 24FT 48PT/MSc by research 12FT 24PT

University of Exeter
Biosciences......PhD 36FT 72PT/MPhil 24FT 48PT/MSc by research 12FT 36PT

University of Glasgow
Infection and Immunity .... PhD 36FT/MSc by research 12FT
Virology .... PhD 36FT/MSc by research 12FT

University of Hertfordshire
Biotechnology, Microbiology and Molecular Biology ..... PhD 36FT 72PT/MPhil 24FT 48PT/MRes 12FT 24PT

Imperial College London
Biomedical Research (Microbial Pathogenesis) .... MRes 12FT
Infectious Diseases and Microbiology .... PhD 36-48FT/MSc by research 10FT
Virology .... PhD 36PT

University of Kent
Microbiology...PhD 36FT 60PT/MPhil 24FT 36PT/MSc by research 12FT 24PT

King's College London
Immunology, Infection and Inflammatory Disease (DIID) (Research Division) .... PhD 36FT 48-72PT/MPhil 36FT 48-72PT

University of Leeds
Microbiology .... PhD 36+FT/MPhil 24FT/MSc by research 12FT

Liverpool School of Tropical Medicine
Molecular & Biochemical Parasitology .... PhD/MPhil/MIHR

University of Liverpool
Dental Microbiology .... MPhil 12FT/PhD 36FT/MD 60FT
Medical Microbiology .... PhD 12-48FT 48-84PT/MPhil 12-48FT 48-72PT/MD 12-72FT
Medical Parasitology .... MPhil 12-48FT 48-72PT/PhD 24-48FT 48-84PT/MD 24-72FT
Veterinary Microbiology ..... MPhil 12-48FT 24-72PT/PhD 24-48FT 48-84PT
Virology .... MPhil 12-48FT 24-48PT/PhD 24-72FT 48-84PT/MD 24-72FT

University of Manchester
Microbiology .... PhD 36-48FT 72-96PT/MPhil 12FT 24PT

Newcastle University
Microbiology .... MPhil 12FT 24PT/PhD 36FT 72PT
Molecular Microbiology .... MRes 12FT

Nottingham Trent University
Microbiology .... MRes 12FT 24PT

University of Nottingham
Bacteriology .... PhD 36FT 48PT/MPhil 24FT 36PT
Microbiology .... MRes 12FT
Molecular Microbiology .... MRes 12FT
Molecular Microbiology and Genome Dynamics Research Group .... PhD 36-72FT/MPhil 24-48FT
Parasite Biology and Immunogenetics .... PhD 36FT/MPhil 24FT
Parasitology .... MRes 12FT
Virology .... MPhil 12FT/PhD 24FT/DM 24FT

Oxford Brookes University
Health and Biomedical Sciences - Insect Virology & Protein Expression .... PhD 24-60FT 36-72PT/MPhil 24-36FT 36-48PT

University of Oxford
Pathology .... DPhil 48FT/MSc by research 24FT

Queen's University Belfast
Molecular Biosciences .... PhD 36FT 72PT/MPhil 24FT 48PT

University of Sheffield
Infection, Inflammation and Immunity .... PhD 36FT 72PT/MPhil 24FT 48PT

University of Surrey
Microbiology; Virology; Infection and Immunity .... MPhil 24FT 36PT/PhD 36FT 48PT

UCL - University College London
Medical Microbiology .... PhD 36FT 60PT
Virology .... PhD 36FT 60PT

Molecular biology
Taught Courses

University of Aberdeen
Cell and Molecular Systems Biology.... MSc 12FT 24PT/PGDip 9FT 18PT
Medical Biotechnology (with Bio-Business)MSc 12FT/PGDip 9FT/MRes 12FT
Medical Molecular Microbiology .... MSc 12FT 24PT/PGDip 9FT

Bangor University
Molecular Biology with Biotechnology .... MSc 12FT

Barts and the London School of Medicine and Dentistry
Experimental Oral Pathology .... MSc 12FT

University of Bath
Biosciences .... MRes 12FT
Medical BioSciences .... MSc 12FT

University of Bedfordshire
Molecular and Cellular Exercise Physiology .... MSc 12FT

Birkbeck, University of London
Analytical Bioscience .... MSc 12FT 24 - 60PT/PGDip 12FT 24 - 60PT
Principles of Protein Structure .... PGCert 12DL
Structural Biology .... MRes 12FT
Structural Molecular Biology. MSc 24-36PT 24-36DL/PGDip 24PT 24DL
Techniques in Structural Molecular Biology .... PGCert 12DL

University of Birmingham
Molecular Biotechnology .... MSc 12FT
Molecular and Cellular Biology .... MRes 12FT

University of Brighton
Bioscience .... MRes 12FT 24PT

University of Bristol
Stem Cells and Regeneration .... MSc 12-24DL/PGDip 12-24DL/PGCert 12-24DL

Brunel University
Molecular Medicine .... MSc 12FT 24PT
Molecular Medicine and Cancer Research .... MSc 12FT 24PT

Cardiff Metropolitan University
Biomedical Science ...... MSc 12FT 24PT/PGDip 12FT 24PT/PGCert 12FT 12PT

Cardiff University
Tissue Engineering .... MSc 12FT

University of Central Lancashire
Biomedical Science .... MSc 12FT
Cancer Biology and Therapy .... MSc 12FT

University of Chester
Human Nutrition .... MSc 12FT 24-48PT/PGDip 12FT 24-48PT/PGCert 12FT 12-24PT
Nutrition and Dietetics .... MSc 24FT/PGDip 24FT
Public Health Nutrition .... MSc 12FT 24 - 72PT/PGDip 12FT 24 - 60PT/PGCert 12FT 12 - 36PT

Cranfield University
Molecular Medicine .... MSc 12FT 36PT/PGDip 12FT 36PT

University of Derby
Conservation Biology .... MSc 12FT 36PT

Dublin Institute of Technology
Molecular Pathology .... MSc 12FT 24PT

University of Dundee
Oral Cancer .... MRes 12FT

University of East Anglia
Molecular Medicine .... MSc 12FT

Edinburgh Napier University
Pharmaceutical Science..MSc 12FT 24-36PT/PGDip 9FT 18-27PT/PGCert 6FT 12-18PT

University of Essex
Molecular Medicine .... MSc 12FT

Glasgow Caledonian University
Biomedical Science .... MSc 24PT/PGDip 24PT/PGCert 12PT
Biomolecular and Biomedical Sciences .... MSc 12FT

University of Glasgow
Applied Medical Science .... MSc 12FT
Crop Biotechnology .... MSc 12FT
Molecular Medicine .... MRes 12FT

University of Hertfordshire
Bioinformatics .... MSc 12FT/PGDip 12FT/PGCert 12FT
Biotechnology .... MSc 12-16FT/PGCert 12-16FT/PGDip 12-16FT
Molecular Biology .... MSc 12-16FT/PGDip 12-16FT/PGCert 12-16FT

University of Hull
Chemistry with Biological Chemistry .... MSc 12FT

Imperial College London
Biomedical Research: Microbial Pathogensis .... MRes 12FT
Biomedical Research: Personalised Healthcare .... MRes 12FT
Molecular Biology and Pathology of Viruses .... MSc 12FT
Molecular Medicine .... MSc 12FT
Structural Molecular Biology .... MRes 12FT

Keele University
Molecular Parasitology and Vector Biology .... MSc 12FT 24PT

University of Kent
Cancer Biology .... PGDip 12FT 24PT/MSc 12FT 24PT
Drug Design .... MSc 12FT
Reproductive Medicine: Science and Ethics .... MSc 12FT 24PT

King's College London
Biomedical & Molecular Sciences Research .... MSc 12FT
Molecular Biophysics .... MRes 12FT

University of Leeds
Chemical Biology .... MSc 12FT

University of Leicester
Cancer Cell and Molecular Biology .... MSc 12FT
Molecular Genetics .... MSc 12FT/PGDip 9FT/PGCert 4FT
Molecular Pathology and Toxicology.... MSc 12FT 24-36PT/PGDip 12FT

Liverpool School of Tropical Medicine
Molecular Biology of Parasites & Disease Vectors .... MSc 12FT/PGDip 8FT

University of Liverpool
Molecular Biology of Parasites and Disease Vectors ...... MSc 12FT

University of Manchester
Cancer Research and Molecular Biomedicine .... MSc 12FT
Cell Biology .... MSc 12FT

Newcastle University
Medical and Molecular Biosciences .... MRes 12FT

Northumbria University
Biotechnology .... MSc 16FT 30PT
Drug Design with Pharmaceutical Analysis .... MSc 12FT

Nottingham Trent University
Molecular Cell Biology .... MSc(Res) 12FT 24PT
Molecular Biology .... MRes 12FT 24PT
Molecular Cell Biology .... MSc 12FT 24PT

University of Nottingham
Advanced Geonomic and Proteomic Sciences .... MRes 12FT
Applied Biomolecular Technology for the Pharmaceutical, Biotechnology and Food Industries .... MSc 12FT 24PT
Molecular Genetics .... MRes 12FT
Molecular Genetics and Diagnostics .... MSc 12FT

Queen Mary, University of London
Molecular Pathology and Genomics .MSc 12FT 24PT/PGDip 12FT 24PT 12/24DL

University of Roehampton
Obesity: Risks and Prevention .... MSc 12FT 24PT
Obesity: Risks and Prevention .... PGCert 6FT 12PT
Obesity: Risks and Prevention .... PGDip 9FT 24PT

University of Sheffield
Bionanotechnology .... MSc(Eng) 12FT
Translational Oncology .... MSc(Res) 12FT
Mechanistic Biology .... MSc 12FT
Microbrewing .... MSc 12FT/PGDip 9FT/PGCert 6FT
Molecular Medicine .... MSc 12FT
Molecular and Cellular Basis of Disease .... MSc 12FT
Reproductive and Developmental Medicine .... MSc 12FT
Translational Neuroscience .... MSc 12FT

Staffordshire University
Molecular Biology for Health Professionals .... PGDip 20DL

University of Surrey
Clinical Biochemistry .... MSc 12FT 24PT

Biology and life sciences

University of Sussex
Genetic Manipulation and Molecular Cell Biology.......... MSc 12FT

Trinity College Dublin - the University of Dublin
Molecular Medicine ....MSc 12FT 24PT PGDip 12PT
Molecular Pathology..MSc 24PT

UCL - University College London
Molecular Measurement in Medicine........................ MSc 12FT
Molecular Medicine .... MSc 12FT
Molecular Modelling ....MSc 12FT 36PT
Molecular Modelling and Materials Science ....MRes 12FT 24PT

University of the West of England, Bristol
Molecular Biotechnology .... MSc 12FT 24PT

University of Westminster
Cellular Pathology .... MSc 12FT
Medical Biotechnology ....MSc 12FT 24PT
Medical Molecular Biology .... MSc 12FT
Molecular Biology in Medicine by Distance Learning
....PGCert 12DL

University of Wolverhampton
Molecular Biology with Bioinformatics...................MSc 12FT 24PT

Molecular biology
Research Courses

University of Aberdeen
Biological Science ....MSc by research 12FT/MPhil 24FT/PhD 36FT
Environmental Science..... PhD 36FT/MPhil 24FT/MSc by research 12FT
Molecular and Cell Biology ....PhD 36FT/MPhil 24FT/MSc by research 12FT

Aston University
Biomaterials and Bio-molecular Science Research Group ....PhD 36FT/MPhil 24FT

Bangor University
Biological Sciences ....MPhil 12FT/PhD 24-36FT

Barts and the London School of Medicine and Dentistry
Cell and Molecular Oral Biology ....PhD/MPhil
Mineralised Tissue Research...PhD/MPhil

University of Birmingham
Clinical and Molecular Genetics................................PhD 36FT 72PT/MSc by research 12FT 24PT/MD 24PT
Molecular Cell Biology................PhD 36FT 72PT/MPhil 12FT 24PT/MPhil(B) 12FT
Molecular and Cellular Biology..MRes 12FT

University of Brighton
MPhil/PhD in Pharmacy & Biomolecular Sciences... PhD 24-60FT 36-72PT/MPhil 18-36FT 30-48PT/DProf 48-72FT 48-72PT/PhD by publication 12FT
Pharmacy and Biomolecular Sciences Research........ PhD 24-60FT 30-72PT/MPhil 18-36FT 30-48PT

University of Bristol
Cellular and Molecular Medicine ....PhD 36FT 72PT/MSc by research 12FT 24PT

University of Buckingham
Diabetes, Obesity and Metabolic Disease........... DPhil 36FT 72PT/MPhil 24FT 48PT

University of Cambridge
Chemical Biology and Molecular Medicine ....PhD 48FT
Molecular Biology ....PhD 36FT

Cardiff University
Molecular Biosciences... MPhil 24FT 24-36PT/PhD 36-48FT 60PT/MD 24FT 36PT
Molecular and Experimental Medicine......PhD 36-48FT 84PT/MD 24FT 48PT
Visual Neuroscience and Molecular BiologyPhD 36FT/MPhil 24FT

Cranfield University
Molecular dynamics simulations of polylactic acid (PLA) biodegradable polymer...PhD 36FT

University of Dundee
Life Sciences ....PhD 48FT
Life Sciences ....MPhil 24FT
Life Sciences ....MSc by research 12FT
Life Sciences - A/Star Dundee Programme ....PhD 48FT
Life Sciences - EMBL Joint Programme ....PhD 36FT
Life Sciences - Wellcome Programme ....PhD 48FT

University of Edinburgh
Centre for Infectious Diseases .... PhD 36FT 72PT
Molecular Medicine .... PhD 36FT 72PT
Molecular Plant Sciences... PhD 36FT 72PT
Structural and Molecular Biology .... PhD 36FT 72PT

University of Essex
Cell and Molecular Biology ....PhD 36FT 72PT/MPhil 24FT 48PT/MSc by research 12FT 24PT
Molecular Medicine.......PhD 36FT 72PT/MPhil 24FT 48PT/MSc by research 12FT 24PT

University of Glasgow
Biochemistry and Molecular Biology ....PhD 36FT/MSc by research 12FT

Cancer Sciences and Molecular Pathology (including Surgery).....PhD 36FT 69PT/MD 24FT 48PT/MSc(MedSci) by research 12FT 24PT
Molecular Genetics ....PhD 36FT/MSc by research 12FT

University of Gloucestershire
Biological Sciences .... PhD 30-48FT

University of Hertfordshire
Biotechnology, Microbiology and Molecular Biology .....PhD 36FT 72PT/MPhil 24FT 48PT/MRes 12FT 24PT

Imperial College London
Biological Sciences ....PhD/MPhil

Keele University
Centre for Molecular Biomedicine ....PhD/MPhil

University of Kent
Cell Biology..... MSc by research 12FT 24PT/MPhil 24FT 36PT/PhD 36FT 60PT

King's College London
Cell & Molecular Biophysics, Randall Division of ....PhD 36FT 48-72PT/MPhil 36FT 48-72PT/MD 36FT 48-72PT
Genetics & Molecular Medicine (Research Division)PhD 36-48FT/MPhil 36-48FT

University of Leeds
Biochemistry and Molecular Biology .... PhD 36+FT/MPhil 24FT/MSc by research 12FT
Centre for Doctoral Training in Molecular-Scale Engineering........ Integrated PhD 48FT
Centre for Self-Organising Molecular Systems.............PhD 36+FT/MPhil 24+FT/MSc by research 12FT
Ion Channels, Transporters and Receptors..........PhD 36+FT/MPhil 24FT/MSc by research 12FT
Membrane Biophysics and Biotechnology ....PhD 36+FT/MPhil 24FT/MSc by research 12FT
Pathogen-host Interactions and Cell Biology.....PhD 36+FT/MPhil 24FT/MSc by research 12FT
Structural Molecular Biology.........PhD 36+FT/MPhil 24FT/MSc by research 12FT
The Molecular Basis of Biological Mechanisms............PhD 36+FT/MPhil 24FT/MSc by research 12FT

Liverpool John Moores University
Biomolecular Sciences Research Opportunities ...PhD 36FT 84PT/MPhil 36FT 84PT

University of Liverpool
Biological Sciences (Structural and Chemical Biology)......... MPhil 12-48FT 24-72PT/PhD 24-48FT 48-84PT
Cancer Biology.............MPhil 12FT 48PT/PhD 36FT 72PT/MD 60FT
Cancer Medicine ....MPhil 12FT 24-72PT/PhD 36FT 48-84PT/MD 12-72FT
Cellular and Molecular PhysiologyMPhil 12FT 48-72PT/PhD 36FT 48-84PT/MD 24-72FT
PancreatologyMPhil 12-48FT 24-72PT/PhD 24-48FT 48-84PT/MD 24-72FT
Pathology....... PhD 24-48FT 48-84PT/MPhil 12-48FT 24-72PT/MD 24-72FT

University of Manchester
Biological Physics.......PhD 36FT 72PT/MSc by research 12FT 24PT
Biomolecular Science ......PhD 36-48FT 72-96PT/MPhil 12FT 24PT
Molecular Biology ....PhD 36-48FT 72-96PT/MPhil 12FT 24PT
Molecular Cancer Studies............................ PhD 36-48FT 72-96PT/MPhil 12FT 24PT

Newcastle University
Biosciences.........PhD 36FT 72PT/MD 24FT 48PT/MPhil 12FT 24PT
Medical Sciences...MRes 12FT
Mitochondrial Biology and Medicine............................MRes 12FT
Molecular Microbiology ....MRes 12FT

Nottingham Trent University
Cell Biology...MRes 12FT 24PT

University of Nottingham
Cell Biology...MRes 12FT
Cell Biology and Imaging Research Group..PhD 36FT 72PT/MPhil 24FT 48PT/MRes 12FT
Microbial Biotechnology ....MRes 12FT
Molecular Biology ....MRes 12FT
Molecular Cell Biology ....MRes 12FT
Molecular Evolution...MRes 12FT
Molecular Genetics ....MRes 12FT
Molecular Microbiology ....MRes 12FT
Molecular Microbiology and Genome Dynamics Research Group PhD 36-72FT/MPhil 24-48FT
Molecular Neuroscience ....MRes 12FT
Molecular and Cellular Science PhD 36FT 72PT/MPhil 24FT 48PT/MRes 12FT
Neurobiology..MRes 12FT
Stem Cell Biology..MRes 12FT

Oxford Brookes University
Health and Biomedical Sciences - Cell Biology of Trypanosomes...
.... PhD 24-60FT 36-72PT/MPhil 24-36FT 36-48PT
Health and Biomedical Sciences - Cell Systems Modelling ....PhD 24-60FT 36-72PT/MPhil 24-36FT 36-48PT

University of Oxford
Cardiovascular Medicine .... DPhil 48FT/MSc by research 24FT

Plymouth University
Molecular Medicine...PhD 36FT

Queen Mary, University of London
Molecular and Cellular Biology (Medicine Related) ...... PhD 36FT/MPhil

Queen's University Belfast
Biomolecular Processes .... PhD 36FT 72PT/MPhil 24FT 48PT
Molecular Biosciences................ PhD 36FT 72PT/MPhil 24FT 48PT

University of Sheffield
Cardiovascular Science............ PhD 36FT 72PT/MPhil 24FT 48PT
Endocrinology and Reproduction........PhD 36FT 72PT/MPhil 24FT 48PT
Molecular Biology and Biotechnology ....PhD 36FT 72PT/MPhil 24FT 48PT

University of Southampton
School of Biological Sciences: Cellular and Molecular Biology......PhD 36FT 72PT

St George's, University of London
Cellular and Molecular Medicine ....PhD 36FT 72PT/MPhil 24FT 48PT/MD(Res) 24 minFT 48 minPT

University of Surrey
Biochemistry, Toxicology, Neuropharmacology, Chronobiology, Apoptosis... PhD 36FT 48PT/MPhil 24FT 36PT

Teesside University
Applied Sciences ...PhD 24-60FT 36-72PT/MPhil 18FT 30PT/DProf 36PT/MProf by research 30PT

UCL - University College London
Molecular Cell Biology...PhD 48FT
Structural and Molecular Biology .... PhD 36FT 60PT/PhD 48FT/MRes + PhD 48FT

University of Warwick
Mathematical Biology and Biophysical Chemistry......... MSc 11FT 22PT/PhD 48FT 96PT
Molecular Organisation and Assembly in Cells ..... PhD 36FT 72PT

Neuroscience
Taught Courses

Bangor University
Clinical and Functional Brain Imaging...........................PGCert 12PT
Neuroimaging .... MSc 12FT 24PT
Clinical and Functional Brain Imaging............................... PGCert 8PT
Psychological Research ..MSc 12FT 24PT/PGDip 8FT 16PT/PGCert 4FT 8PT
Psychology...........MA 12FT 24PT/PGDip 9FT 18PT/PGCert 4FT 8PT

Birkbeck, University of London
Cognition and Computation...........MSc 12FT 24PT/MA 12FT 24PT
Cognitive Neuroscience and Neuropsychology ....MSc 12FT 24PT/MA 12FT 24PT
Developmental Sciences..................MA 12FT 24PT/MSc 12FT 24PT
Educational Neuroscience...............MA 12FT 24PT/MSc 12FT 24PT
Functional Neuroimaging ....MRes 12FT 24PT

University of Birmingham
Clinical Neuropsychiatry...........MSc 12FT 24PT/PGDip 12FT 24PT/PGCert 12FT 24PT
Computational Neuroscience and Cognitive Robotics .. MSc 12FT

University of Bristol
Molecular Neuroscience ..... MSc 12FT 36PT/Diploma 7.5FT 36PT/Cert 3.5FT 36PT
Systems Neuroscience .... MRes 12FT

Brunel University
Functional Neuroimaging ....MSc 12FT 30PT
Neurorehabilitation..MSc 12FT 24PT

Cardiff University
Neuorehabilitation .... MSc 18FT 36-48PT/PGDip 12FT 24PT
Neuromusculoskeletal Physiotherapy .... MSc 36-48PT/PGDip 24PT

University of Central Lancashire
Advanced Stroke Practice ......MSc 36FT 60PT/PGDip 24PT/PGCert 12PT
Mental Health Practice (Including approved mental health professional training) ....MA 12-60PT/PGDip 12-60PT/PGCert 12PT

University of East London
Neurological Rehabilitation ....PGCert 5FT 12 - 36PT

University of Edinburgh
Cognition in Science and Society...............................MSc 12FT 24PT
Evolution of Language & Cognition ....MSc 12FT 24PT
Human Cognitive Neuropsychology ....MSc 12FT 24PT
Neuroimaging for Research ......MSc 72DL/Diploma 48DL/PGCert 24DL

National University of Ireland Galway
Neuropharmacology.. MSc 12FT

University of Glasgow
Brain Imaging..MSc 12FT
Brain Sciences: From Molecules to Mind..........................MSc 12FT

Biology and life sciences

Goldsmiths, University of London
Cognitive and Clinical Neuroscience .... MSc 12FT 24PT
The Science of Psychology, Genetics & Education .... MSc 12FT 24PT

Heriot-Watt University
Applied Psychology ....MSc 12FT 24-48PT/PGDip 9FT 15-48PT/PGCert 6FT 12-48PT
Engineering Psychology with Ergonomics .... MSc 12FT 24PT 24-84DL/PGDip 9FT 21PT 21-84DL/PGCert 6FT 18PT 18-84DL

Imperial College London
Experimental Neuroscience .... MRes 12FT

King's College London
Advanced Practice (Neuroscience Care) ....MSc 36-72PT/PGDip 24-72PT/PGCert 12-72PT
Biomedical Sciences & Scientific English ....GradDip 12FT
Clinical Neuroscience .... MSc 12FT 24PT
Neuroimaging .... MSc 12FT
Neuroscience .... MSc 12FT 24PT

Leeds Metropolitan University
Integrated Masters Biomedical Sciences ....MBIOMS 48FT

University of Manchester
Cognitive Brain Imaging .... MSc 12FT
Neuroscience .... MSc 12FT

Nottingham Trent University
Neuroscience ....MSc(Res) 12FT 24PT MSc 12FT 24PT

University of Nottingham
Translational Neuroimaging .... MSc 12FT 24PT

University of Oxford
Endovascular Neurosurgery (Interventional Neuroradiology) .... MSc 12FT
Neuroscience .... MSc 12FT

Queen Mary, University of London
Neuroscience and Translational Medicine .... MSc 12FT 24PT

University of Reading
Cognitive Neuroscience .... MSc 12FT 20-24PT/PGDip 8-12FT 20-24PT
Neuroscience of Language .... MSc 12FT 24PT

University of Roehampton
Clinical Neuroscience ....MSc 12FT 24PT PGCert 6FT 24PT

University of Sheffield
Cognitive Neuroscience and Human Neuroimaging ...... MSc(Res) 12FT
Cognitive and Computational Neuroscience .... MSc 12FT
Computational Intelligence and Robotics .... MSc 12FT
Translational Neuroscience .... MSc 12FT

University of St Andrews
Behavioural and Neural Sciences .... MPhil 12FT 24PT

University of Sussex
Cognitive Neuroscience .... MSc 12FT 24PT
Genetic Manipulation and Molecular Cell Biology .... MSc 12FT

Swansea University
Cognitive Neuroscience .... MSc 12FT 24PT

Trinity College Dublin - the University of Dublin
Cognitive Psychotherapy .... MSc 24PT PGDip 12PT
Neuroscience .... MSc 12FT

UCL - University College London
Advanced Neuroimaging .... MSc 12FT 24PT
Clinical Neuroscience .... MSc 12FT/PGDip 9FT
Cognitive Neuroscience .....MSc 12FT 24PT/PGDip 9FT MRes 12FT
Neuroscience .... MSc 12FT 24PT
Neuroscience, Language and Communication ...... MSc 12FT 24PT
Social Cognition: Research and Applications .... MSc 12FT 24PT

University of York
Cognitive Neuroscience .... MSc 12FT

Neuroscience
Research Courses

Anglia Ruskin University
Brain and Cognition ....PhD 24-60FT 36-72PT

Aston University
Neurosciences Research Institute .... PhD 36FT/MPhil 12FT
Optometry and Vision Science.. PhD 36FT 60PT/MPhil 24FT 48PT

Bangor University
Doctorate by Research .... PhD 36FT/MPhil 24FT

Barts and the London School of Medicine and Dentistry
Department of Neurosurgery .... PhD/MPhil/MD

University of Birmingham
Neurophysiology .... PhD 36FT 72PT/MPhil 12FT 24PT

University of Cambridge
Anaesthesia ....PhD 36FT
Brain Sciences .... PhD 36FT 60PT
Cognition and Brain Sciences .... PhD 36FT 60PT
Neurosurgery ....PhD 36FT

Cardiff University
Neuroscience.. MPhil 24FT 24-36PT/PhD 36-48FT 60PT/MD 24FT 36PT
Psychological Medicine and Clinical Neurosciences ..... PhD 36FT/MPhil 36FT/MD 36FT
Visual Neuroscience and Molecular BiologyPhD 36FT/MPhil 24FT

University of Dundee
Psychology .... MPhil 24FT

University of Edinburgh
Clinical Neurosciences .... PhD 36FT 72PT
Neuroinformatics ....MSc by research 12FT
Neuroinformatics & Computational Neuroscience Doctoral Training Centre (DTC) ....MSc by research 12FT
Neuroscience ....PhD 36FT 72PT/MSc by research 12FT 24PT
Neuroscience and Neurodegenerative Diseases (Veterinary Medicine) ....PhD 36FT

University of Glasgow
Clinical Neurosciences .... PhD 36FT 60PT/MD 24FT 48PT/MSc(MedSci) by research 12FT 24PT
Neuroscience and Biomedical Systems ....PhD 36FT/MSc by research 12FT

University of Hertfordshire
Biological and Neural Computation ...PhD 36FT 72PT/MPhil 24FT 48PT/MRes 12FT 24PT

Imperial College London
Neuroscience and Psychological Medicine ......PhD/MPhil/MSc by research 12FT

King's College London
Clinical Neuroscience .... PhD 36FT 72PT/MPhil 36FT 72PT
MRC Centre for Developmental Neurobiology .... PhD 36-48FT 48-72PT/MPhil 36-48FT 48-72PT
Neuroimaging .... MPhil 36FT 72PT/PhD 36FT 72PT
Neuroscience .... PhD 36FT 72PT/MPhil 36FT 72PT

University of Leeds
Neuroscience ....PhD 36+FT/MPhil 24FT/MSc by research 12FT

University of Manchester
Integrative Neurobiology and Behaviour .. PhD 36-48FT 72-96PT/MPhil 12FT 24PT
Molecular and Cellular Neuroscience .... PhD 36-48FT 72-96PT/MPhil 12FT 24PT
Neuroscience ....PhD 36-48FT 72-96PT/MPhil 12FT 24PT
Systems Neuroscience ....PhD 36-48FT 72-96PT/MPhil 12FT 24PT

Newcastle University
Neuroscience .....PhD 36FT 72PT/MD 24FT 48PT/MPhil 12FT 24PT MRes 12FT

University of Nottingham
Behavioural Neuroscience .... PhD 36FT 72PT/MPhil 24FT 48PT
Biological Systems .... MRes 12FT
Cognition and Cognitive Neuroscience ....PhD 36FT 72PT/MPhil 24FT 48PT
Molecular Neuroscience .... MRes 12FT
Neurobiology .... MRes 12FT
Neuroscience ....PhD 36FT/MRes 12FT

The Open University
Neuroscience and behaviour .....PhD 36FT 72PT variableDL/MPhil 15FT 24PT variableDL

Oxford Brookes University
Health & Biomedical Sciences - Molecular Neuroscience ....PhD 24-60FT 36-72PT/MPhil 24-36FT 36-48PT

University of Oxford
Neuroscience .... DPhil 48FT

Plymouth University
Brain ....MPhil 24FT/PhD 36FT

Queen Mary, University of London
Neuroscience ....PhD 36FT

University of Sheffield
Motor Neurone Disease ....PhD 36FT
Neuroscience .... PhD 36FT 72PT/MPhil 24FT 48PT

University of Southampton
School of Biological Sciences: Neurosciences .... PhD 36FT 72PT

University of Strathclyde
Neuroscience .... MRes 12FT

University of Surrey
Pharmacology, Neuropharmacology, Chronobiology .... MPhil 24FT 36PT/PhD 36FT 48PT

University of Sussex
Neuroscience .... PhD 24-48FT 36-72PT/MPhil 12-36FT 24-48PT

UCL - University College London
Biomedical Research .... PhD 36FT 60PT
Cognitive Neuroscience .... PhD 36FT 60PT
Cognitive, Perceptual and Brain Sciences .... PhD 36FT 60PT
Computational Neuroscience .... PhD 48FT
Neuroscience ....PhD 48FT/PhD 36FT 60PT

Podiatry
Taught Courses

University of Brighton
Podiatry ....MSc 12 - 24FT 24 - 72PT/PGDip 12 - 24FT 24 - 48PT/PGCert 12FT 24PT
Podiatry and Education ....MSc 12 - 24FT 24 - 72PT/PGCert 12FT 24PT/PGDip 12 - 24FT 24 - 48PT
Podiatry and Management .... MSc 12 - 24FT 24 - 72PT/PGCert 12FT 24PT/PGDip 12 - 24FT 24 - 48PT
Podiatry with Clinical Biomechanics .... MSc 12-24FT 12-72PT/PGDip 12-24FT 12-48PT/PGCert 12FT 24PT
Podiatry with Diabetes ......MSc 12-24FT 24-72PT/PGDip 12-24FT 24-48PT/PGCert 12FT 24PT
Podiatry with Rheumatology .... MSc 12-24FT 24-72PT/PGDip 12-24FT 24-48PT/PGCert 12FT 24PT
Principles of Podiatric Surgery .... MSc 12-24FT 24-72PT/PGDip 12-24FT 24-48PT/PGCert 12FT 24PT

Cardiff Metropolitan University
Musculoskeletal Studies (Lower Limb) ..... MSc 36PT/PGDip 36PT/PGCert 36PT

University of Dundee
Advanced Practice (Clinical Governance) ....MSc 36DL

University of East London
Podiatric Medicine ....MSc 12FT 24-72PT

Glasgow Caledonian University
Podiatric Medicine .... MSc 12FT
Podiatry .... MSc 12FT
Theory of Podiatric Medicine ....MSc 12-24FT 12-72PT
Theory of Podiatric Surgery ....MSc 12-24FT 12-72PT

University of Huddersfield
Forensic Podiatry ....PGCert 18-24BM
Multi Disciplinary Care of High Risk Patients ....PGCert 24PT
Musculoskeletal Management of the Lower Limb ... PGDip 24BM
Podiatry .... MSc 36PT
Theory of Podiatric Surgery .... MSc 36BM

University of Northampton
Advanced Podiatry .... MSc 12FT 36PT/PGDip 24PT

Queen Margaret University, Edinburgh
Podiatric Medicine .... PGCert 36-60PT/PGDip 36-60PT/MSc 36-60PT
Podiatry .... MSc 36PT
Theory of Podiatric Surgery .... MSc 36PT

Staffordshire University
Clinical Podiatric Biomechanics .... PGCert 9PT/PGDip 15PT/MSc 36PT

University of Warwick
Diabetes and the Foot .... PGA 12PT/CPDMod 1PT

Podiatry
Research Courses

University of Southampton
School of Health Professions and Rehabilitation Sciences .. MPhil 36FT 60PT/PhD 36FT 60PT

Toxicology
Taught Courses

University of Birmingham
Toxicology .... MSc 12FT/PGDip 9FT

Bournemouth University
Forensic Toxicology by Research .... MSc 12FT 24PT

Cardiff Metropolitan University
Biomedical Science ...... MSc 12FT 24PT/PGDip 12FT 24PT/PGCert 12FT 12PT

Cardiff University
Medical Toxicology ....MSc 24DL/PGDip 24DL/PGCert 12DL

University of Central Lancashire
Forensic Toxicology .... MSc 12FT

Cranfield University
Toxicology and Epidemiology ......MSc 12FT 36PT/PGDip 9FT 36PT

University of Dundee
Forensic Toxicology (MFTox) ....MFTox 12FT

University of East London
Toxicology MSc .... MSc 12FT 24PT/PGDip 8FT 16PT/PGCert 4FT 8PT

University of Edinburgh
Drug Discovery & Translational Biology .... MSc 12FT/PGDip 9FT

National University of Ireland Galway
Toxicology .... MSc 12FT

Glasgow Caledonian University
Life Sciences - Biological and Biomedical Sciences/Psychology/Vision Sciences .... MRes 12FT

University of Glasgow
Forensic Toxicology ....MSc(MedSci) 12FT

Biology and life sciences

Heriot-Watt University
Marine Biodiversity and Biotechnology .....MSc 12FT 24PT/PGDip 9FT 21PT

King's College London
Analytical Toxicology.. MSc 12FT
Biopharmaceuticals..MSc 12FT 24PT

Lancaster University
Environmental and Biochemical Toxicology........... MSc 12FT 24PT

Leeds Metropolitan University
Applied Biomedical Sciences Research .... MSc 12FT
Biomedical Sciences...MSc 12FT unknownPT
Toxicology Sciences...MSc 12FT 24PT

University of Leicester
Molecular Pathology and Toxicology.... MSc 12FT 24-36PT/PGDip 12FT

Newcastle University
Synthetic Biology.. MSc 12FT

Robert Gordon University
Instrumental Analytical Sciences: Drug Analysis and
Toxicology...MSc 12FT 36PT

University of Stirling
Marine Biotechnology............................MSc 12FT 24PT/PGDip 9FT

University of Strathclyde
Forensic Science............................MSc 12FT/PGDip 9FT/PGCert 9FT

University of Surrey
Applied Toxicology .... MSc 36-60PT
Genetic Toxicology and Environmental Mutagenesis.........MSc 24
-72PT
Toxicology... MSc 12FT

UCL - University College London
Synthetic Biology...MRes 12FT

Toxicology
Research Courses

University of Aberdeen
Environmental Science..... PhD 36FT/MPhil 24FT/MSc by research 12FT
Molecular and Cell Biology .... PhD 36FT/MPhil 24FT/MSc by research 12FT

Bangor University
Biological Sciences ....MPhil 12FT/PhD 24-36FT

University of Birmingham
Molecular and Mechanistic Toxicology............................MRes 12FT

Cranfield University
Pesticides in Groundwater...........................MSc by research 12FT

University of Dundee
Forensic Medicine (MPhil)..........MPhil 24FT MSc by research 12FT

University of Manchester
Toxicology...........................PhD 36-48FT 72-96PT/MPhil 12FT 24PT

Newcastle University
Toxicology...MRes 12FT

University of Nottingham
Molecular Toxicology..................... PhD 36FT 72PT/MPhil 24FT 48PT
Molecular and Cellular Science PhD 36FT 72PT/MPhil 24FT 48PT/
MRes 12FT
Toxicology..MRes 12FT

University of Surrey
Biochemistry, Toxicology, Neuropharmacology, Chronobiology,
Apoptosis.. PhD 36FT 48PT/MPhil 24FT 36FT

Zoology
Taught Courses

University of Aberdeen
Applied Marine and Fisheries Ecology: Concepts and Practices
for Ecosystem-Based Management............. MRes 12FT/MSc 12FT/
PGDip 9FT
Design Anthropology ....MSc 12FT 24PT/PGDip 9FT 18PT
People and the Environment.. MSc 12FT 24PT

Aberystwyth University
Animal Science... MSc 12FT 24PT
Managing the Environment ....MSc 12FT 24PT/PGDip 9FT 18PT

Anglia Ruskin University
Animal Behaviour: Applications for Conservation MSc 12FT 24PT

Applied Wildlife Conservation .... MSc 24PT

Bangor University
Natural Sciences .... MRes 12FT

University of Chester
Applied Wildlife Conservation ....PGCert 12FT 12 - 36PT
Applied Wildlife Forensics ....PGCert 12FT 12 - 36PT
Conservation in Practice ....PGCert 12FT 12 - 36PT
Wildlife Conservation.. MSc 12FT 24PT/PGDip 12FT 24PT/PGCert
12FT 12-24PT

University College Cork
Applied Science (Marine Biology).. MSc 12FT

University of Derby
Conservation Biology...MSc 12FT 36PT

Edinburgh Napier University
Wildlife Biology and Conservation...MSc 12FT 24-48PT 24-48DL/
PGDip 9FT 18-36PT 18-36DL/PGCert 6FT 12-24PT 12-24DL

University of Exeter
Anthrozoology ....MA 12FT 24PT 24DL
Bioarchaeology ....MSc 12FT 24PT

University of Glasgow
Animal Welfare Science, Ethics & Law .... MSc 12FT/PGDip 9FT
Marine System Science ....MSc 12FT 24PT/PGDip 8FT 16PT

Harper Adams University
Entomology..MSc 12FT 24PT/MRes 12FT 24PT/PGDip 12FT 24PT/
PGCert 12FT 24PT

Heriot-Watt University
Marine Spatial Planning........................ MSc 12FT 24PT/PGDip 9FT

Imperial College London
Conservation Science .... MSc 12FT
Integrative Mammalian Biology................................MRes 12FT

University of Kent
Conservation and International Wildlife Trade......MSc 12FT 24PT
Conservation and Primate Behaviour ....MSc 12FT 24PT
Endangered Species Recovery ....PGDip 5FT

King's College London
Analytical Science for Industry ....MSc 12FT 24PT

Lancaster University
Biomedical Science (by research) ....MSc 12FT 24PT

Leeds Metropolitan University
Biomedical Sciences..MSc 12FT unknownPT

University of Leeds
Biological Identification and Conservation.............MSc 12FT 24PT

London School of Economics and Political Science (LSE)
Anthropology and Development Management....MSc 12FT 24PT

Manchester Metropolitan University
Biomedical Science featuring Exercise and Health options ... MSc
12FT 24-36PT
Zoo Conservation Biology.................................MSc 12FT 24-60PT

Newcastle University
Ecological Consultancy .... MSc 12FT

Oxford Brookes University
Primate Conservation ...... MSc 12FT 24PT/PGDip 8FT 16PT 16DL/
PGCert 8PT

Plymouth University
Zoo Conservation Biology.............MSc 12FT 24PT/PGDip 9FT 18PT

University of Portsmouth
Applied Aquatic Biology ....MSc 12FT 24PT

Queen's University Belfast
Ecological Management and Conservation Biology....... MSc 12FT
24PT/PGDip 9FT

University of Reading
Species Identification and Survey Skills ....MSc 12FT
Wildlife Management and Conservation .... MSc 12FT

University of Roehampton
Primate Biology, Behaviour and Conservation...............MRes 12FT

Royal Veterinary College
Wild Animal Biology ....MSc 12FT PGDip 8FT
Wild Animal Health - PGCert ....PGDip 8FT

University of Salford
Wildlife Documentary Production ....MA 12FT

University of Southampton
Biodiversity and Conservation ....MSc 12FT 27PT

Wildlife Conservation...MRes 12FT

University of St Andrews
Ecosystem-based Management of Marine Systems .... MRes 12FT
Marine Mammal Science...MRes 12FT

Staffordshire University
Ecology and Conservation .... MSc 15FT
Invertebrate Ecology and Conservation......MSc 15FT/PGDip 15FT
Urban Ecology and Conservation ....MSc 15FT

University of Stirling
Marine Biotechnology............................MSc 12FT 24PT/PGDip 9FT

Swansea University
Aquatic Ecology and Conservation .... MRes 12FT 24-36PT

UCL - University College London
Biodiversity, Evolution and Conservation.......................MRes 12FT

Writtle College
Animal Welfare and Conservation .... MSc 12FT 24-36PT/
PGDip 8FT 20-36PT/PGCert 4FT 16-36PT

Zoology
Research Courses

University of Aberdeen
Biological Science ....MSc by research 12FT/MPhil 24FT/PhD 36FT
Ecology ....PhD 36FT/MPhil 24FT/MSc by research 12FT
Environmental Science.....PhD 36FT/MPhil 24FT/MSc by research
12FT
Marine BiologyPhD 36FT 60PT/MPhil 24FT 42PT/MSc by research
12FT 24PT
Plant Science...PhD 36FT 60PT/MPhil 24FT 42PT/MSc by research
12FT 24PT
Zoology ....PhD 36FT/MPhil 24FT/MSc by research 12FT

Aberystwyth University
IBERS - Rural Sciences ....MPhil 12FT 24PT PhD 36FT 60PT

Bangor University
Natural Sciences .... MRes 12FT

University of Cambridge
Biological Anthropological Science................................... MPhil 10FT
Zoology .... PhD 36/48FT/MPhil 12FT

University of Central Lancashire
Biological and Biomedical Sciences....PhD 48FT 84PT/MPhil 36FT
60PT/MSc by research 24FT 36PT/MD 48PT

University of Edinburgh
Molecular Plant Sciences.. PhD 36FT 72PT

University of Gloucestershire
Biological Sciences .... PhD 30-48FT

Imperial College London
Biological Sciences ....PhD/MPhil

University of Lincoln
Animal Behaviour and Welfare..... PhD 24FT 48PT/MPhil 12-33FT
24-60PT

University of Manchester
Animal Biology.................PhD 36-48FT 72-96PT/MPhil 12FT 24PT

Newcastle University
Engineering & Science in the Marine Environment......Integrated
PhD 36FT
Marine Sciences .... PhD 36FT 72PT/MPhil 12FT 24PT

University of Nottingham
Animal Sciences.......PhD 36FT 72PT/MPhil 24FT 48PT/MRes 12FT
24PT
Molecular Evolution...MRes 12FT

University of Oxford
Zoology ....DPhil 48FT/MSc by research 24FT

Queen's University Belfast
Ecology, Evolution, Behaviour and Environmental Economics
.... PhD 36FT 72PT/MPhil 24FT 48PT

University of Roehampton
Ecology .... PhD 24-48FT 36-60PT/MPhil 21-36FT 33-48PT

University of Sheffield
Animal and Plant Sciences......... PhD 36FT 72PT/MPhil 24FT 48PT

Swansea University
Animal Movement Science ....MSc by research 12FT 24PT

Chemical engineering

Biochemical engineering
Taught Courses

Bangor University
Analytical Chemistry ....MSc 12FT/Diploma 9FT
Chemistry ....MRes 12FT
Environmental Chemistry .... MSc 12FT/PGDip 9FT

University of Birmingham
Biochemical Engineering .... MSc 12FT 24PT
Chemical Biology and Biomedical Imaging .... MSc 12FT

University of Cambridge
Advanced Chemical Engineering.. MPhil 12FT

University of Edinburgh
Medicinal & Biological Chemistry.. MSc 12FT

Imperial College London
Molecular and Cellular Biosciences .... MRes 12FT

Newcastle University
Synthetic Biology... MSc 12FT

University of Sheffield
Biological and Bioprocess Engineering.....................MSc(Eng) 12FT

University of Strathclyde
Biomedical Sciences.. MSc 12FT/PGDip 9FT
Biotechnology .... MSc 12FT

UCL - University College London
Biochemical Engineering................................ MSc 12FT/PGDip 9FT
Nanotechnology and Regenerative Medicine........ MSc 12FT 24PT
Synthetic Biology...MRes 12FT
Systems Biology..MRes 12FT

Biochemical engineering
Research Courses

Bangor University
Chemistry.......................................PhD 36FT MRes 12FT MPhil 24PT

University of Birmingham
Neurophysiology .... PhD 36FT 72PT/MPhil 12FT 24PT

University of Dundee
Mechanical Engineering .... MPhil 24FT
Mechanical Engineering ....MSc by research 12FT

University of Exeter
Engineering.. EngD 48FT

University of Hertfordshire
Biological and Neural Computation ...PhD 36FT 72PT/MPhil 24FT
48PT/MRes 12FT 24PT

Newcastle University
Nanomedicine... MRes 12FT
Systems Biology.. MRes 12FT

University of Nottingham
Biorenewables and Bioprocessing Group ...PhD 36FT 48PT/MPhil
24FT 36PT

University of Oxford
Biochemistry................................. DPhil 48FT/MSc by research 24FT

University of Strathclyde
Biomedical Sciences...MRes 12FT 24PT
Drug Delivery Systems ....MRes 12FT 24PT
Drug Delivery Systems with International Placement ....
MRes 12FT 24PT
Drug Discovery .... MRes 12FT

Swansea University
Biochemical Engineering............. PhD 36FT 60PT/MPhil 12FT 24PT
Bioprocess Engineering.........................MSc by research 12FT 24PT

UCL - University College London
Biochemical Engineering .... PhD 36FT 60PT
Biochemical Engineering and Bioprocess Leadership.. EngD 48FT

Chemical engineering
Taught Courses

University of Aberdeen
Chemical Sciences..................... MSc 20FT/PGDip 12FT/PGCert 9FT

Bangor University
Analytical Chemistry ....MSc 12FT/Diploma 9FT
Chemistry ....MRes 12FT
Environmental Chemistry .... MSc 12FT/PGDip 9FT

University of Birmingham
Advanced Chemical Engineering....................... MSc 12FT 24-36PT/
PGDip 12FT 24-30PT
Efficient Fossil Energy Technologies ....MSc 12FT 24PT/
PGDip 12FT 24PT/PGCert 12FT 24PT

University of Cambridge
Advanced Chemical Engineering.. MPhil 12FT

Cardiff University
Catalysis ....MSc 12FT 36PT

University College Cork
Pharmaceutical Engineering ....MEngSci 24PT

University of Cumbria
The Research Process......................................PGCert 12 - 18PT

Heriot-Watt University
Sustainability Engineering......... MSc 12FT 24PT/PGDip 9FT 21PT/
PGCert 6FT 12PT

University of Hull
Petroleum, Oil and Gas: Chemical Engineering Management......
MSc 12FT
Petroleum, Oil and Gas: Chemical Engineering Technologies ....
MSc 12FT
REACH Management... PGCert 12FT 12DL

Imperial College London
Advanced Chemical Engineering....................................... MSc 12FT
Advanced Chemical Engineering with Biotechnology... MSc 12FT
Advanced Chemical Engineering with Process Systems
Engineering... MSc 12FT
Advanced Chemical Engineering with Structured Product
Engineering... MSc 12FT

University of Leeds
Chemical Engineering .... MSc 12FT
Chemical Process Research and Development .... MSc 12FT

University of Limerick
Chemical Engineering ....PGDip 12FT

University of Liverpool
Advanced Science (Chemical Sciences pathway) ....
MSc 12FT/PGDip 12FT/PGCert 12FT

Loughborough University
Advanced Chemical Engineering with Information Technology &
Management.....MSc 12FT 12-96PT/PGDip 12FT 24-96PT/PGCert
12FT 24-96PT
Advanced Process Engineering ....MSc 12FT 12-96PT

University of Manchester
Advanced Chemical Engineering..........MSc 12FT 60PT/PGDip 9FT
24PT/PGCert 6FT 12PT
Advanced Chemical Process Design ... MSc 12FT 60DL/PGDip 9FT
24DL/PGCert 6FT 12DL/Modular 60PT 60DL
Chemical Engineering with Design ..... MSc 12FT 60PT/PGDip 9FT
24PT/PGCert 6FT 12PT
Refinery Design and Operation......MSc 12FT 24-60DL/PGDip 9FT
24-60DL/PGCert 6FT 12-60DL/Modular 60PT 60DL

Newcastle University
Applied Process Control ....MSc 12FT/PGDip 9-12PT
Industrial Quality Technology .. MSc 12FT 72PT/PGDip 12FT 72PT
Materials Design and Engineering...........................MSc 12 or 24FT

Sustainable Chemical Engineering..............MSc 12FT/PGDip 12FT

University of Nottingham
Chemical Engineering .... MSc 12FT

The Open University
Engineering.............. MSc(Eng) 12-24DL/MEng variableDL/PGDip
variableDL

Staffordshire University
Professional Engineering...MSc 12-18FT

University of Strathclyde
Advanced Chemical and Process Engineering ....MSc 12FT/PGDip
9FT/PGCert 6FT
Chemical Technology and Management MSc 36DL/PGDip 24DL/
PGCert 12DL
Process Technology and Management ... MSc 36DL/PGDip 24DL/
PGCert 12DL
Sustainable Engineering: Chemical Processing....MSc 12FT 24PT/
PGDip 9FT 18PT/PGCert 6FT 12PT/MSc 12FT

University of Surrey
Process Systems Engineering .... MSc 12FT
Process and Environmental Systems Engineering.......... MSc 12FT

Swansea University
Chemical Engineering .... MSc 12FT

UCL - University College London
Chemical Process Engineering .... MSc 12FT

University of York
Green Chemistry and Sustainable Industrial Technology....... MSc
12FT 24-36PT

Chemical engineering
Research Courses

University of Aberdeen
Engineering... PhD 36FT/MPhil 24FT/MSc by research 12FT/EngD
36FT

Anglia Ruskin University
Engineering Analysis, Simulation and Tribology..... PhD 24 - 60FT
36 - 72PT
Investigative Chemistry Research Group .... MPhil 18 - 36FT
36 - 48PT/PhD 24 - 60FT 36 - 72PT

Bangor University
Chemistry.......................................PhD 36FT MRes 12FT MPhil 24PT

Chemical engineering

University of Bath
Chemical Engineering ....PhD 24-48FT 36-72PT/MPhil 12-36FT 24-48PT
Sustainable Chemical Technologies ....Integrated PhD 48FT

University of Birmingham
Chemical Engineering .... PhD 36FT/MSc by research 12FT 24PT
Chemical Engineering PhD with Integrated Study ....PhD 48FT
Formulation Engineering .... DEng 48FT

University of Bolton
Engineering Specialisms............. PhD 36FT 72PT/MPhil 18FT 36PT

University of Cambridge
Chemical Engineering ....PhD 36FT/MSc by research 12FT

Cranfield University
Characterisation of physicochemical properties of engineering
thermoplas..MSc by research 12FT

University of Edinburgh
Materials and Processes ....PhD 36FT 72PT/MPhil 24FT 48PT/
MSc by research 12FT 24PT

Heriot-Watt University
Chemical Engineering ....PhD 36FT 48PT/MPhil 24FT/MSc by
research 12FT
International Centre for Brewing and Distilling (ICBD) ..PhD 36FT 48PT/MPhil 24FT

Imperial College London
Chemical Engineering Research .... PhD 36FT 72PT

University of Leeds
Institute of Particle Science & Engineering ....PhD 36+FT/MPhil 24FT
Process, Research and Development ....Integrated PhD 48FT
Radiation research .... PhD 36+FT/MPhil 12+FT

University of Liverpool
Advanced Science (Chemical Sciences pathway) ....MRes 12FT

Loughborough University
Catalysis and Reaction Engineering ...PhD 36FT 60PT/MPhil 24FT 36PT
Separation and Purification Technology......PhD 36FT 60PT/MPhil 24FT 36PT

University of Manchester
Chemical Engineering .... MPhil 12FT 24PT/PhD 36FT 72PT
Chemical Engineering and Analytical Science ...MPhil 12FT 24PT/
PhD 36FT 72PT/Integrated PhD 48FT/EngD 48FT

Newcastle University
Chemical Engineering .... PhD 36FT 72PT/MPhil 12FT 24PT
Materials Engineering .... MPhil 12FT 24PT/PhD 36FT 72PT

Nottingham Trent University
Materials Science and Engineering .....MPhil 18FT 30PT/PhD 33FT 66PT

University of Nottingham
Chemical Engineering ....PhD 36FT
Fuel, energy and CO2 mitigation.........PhD 36FT 72PT/MPhil 24FT 48PT

Queen Mary, University of London
Engineering.. PhD 36FT/MPhil

Queen's University Belfast
Chemistry and Chemical Engineering....................PhD 36FT 72PT/
MPhil 24FT 48PT

University of Salford
Chemical Physics and Biomaterials ....PhD 36FT 60PT/MPhil 24FT 24PT/MRes 24FT 24PT/MSc by research 24FT 24PT
Institute for Materials ResearchPhD 36FT/MSc by research 12FT/
MPhil 12FT

University of Sheffield
Chemical and Process Engineering.....PhD 36FT 72PT/MPhil 24FT 48PT

University of Strathclyde
Chemical and Process Engineering - Research......PhD 36FT 72PT/
MPhil 12FT 24PT/MRes 12FT

Swansea University
Chemical Engineering ...PhD 36FT 60PT/MPhil 12FT 24PT/MSc by
research 12FT 24PT

Teesside University
Process Manufacturing and Design........... PhD 24- 60FT 36-72PT/
MPhil 18FT 30PT/DProf 36FT/MProf by research 30PT

UCL - University College London
Chemical Engineering ....PhD 36FT 60PT/EngD 48FT

University of Warwick
Engineering.... MSc by research 12FT 24PT/MPhil 24FT 36PT/PhD
36FT 60PT/EngD 60PT

University of the West of Scotland
Department of Chemistry and Chemical Engineering ....
PhD/MPhil

HVAC
Taught Courses

Middlesex University
Business Information Modelling Management (BIM) .....MSc 12 / 24DL

HVAC
Research Courses

University of Brighton
Engineering Research Division.......... PhD 24-60FT 36-72PT/MPhil 18-36FT 30-48PT

University of Manchester
Process Integration .... MPhil 12FT 24PT/PhD 36FT 72PT

Thermodynamics
Taught Courses

University of Aberdeen
Oil and Gas Law .... LLM 12FT 24PT

University of Central Lancashire
Wind Energy Engineering.............MSc 12FT 24PT/PGDip 9FT 24PT

Cranfield University
Aerospace Propulsion (Option of Thermal Power).......... MSc 12FT
Gas Turbine Technology (Option of Thermal Power MSc)....... MSc 12FT
Power, Propulsion and the Environment (Option of Thermal
Power) ....MSc 12FT/PGCert 12FT/PGDip 12FT
Rotating Machinery, Engineering and Management (Option of
Thermal Power MSc).. MSc 12FT
Thermal Power.. MSc 12FT

University of Glasgow
Aeronautical Engineering...MSc 12FT

King's College London
Air Power in the Modern World .... MA 24 - 72DL

Kingston University
Renewable Energy Engineering ....MSc 12FT 24PT

University of Manchester
Thermal Power and Fluid Engineering.............................MSc 12FT

Queen Mary, University of London
Aerospace Engineering ....MSc 12FT

University of Salford
Industrial and Commercial Combustion Engineering .MSc 36DL/
PGDip 12DL/PGCert 12DL

University of Strathclyde
Lean Six Sigma for Process Excellence ....MSc 12FT 24PT/
PGDip 9FT 18PT/PGCert 9FT 18PT

Thermodynamics
Research Courses

Anglia Ruskin University
Engineering Analysis, Simulation and Tribology ..... PhD 24 - 60FT 36 - 72PT

University of Glasgow
Aerospace Sciences ....PhD 36-48FT 60-72PT/MSc by research 12-24FT 24-36PT
Systems, Power and Energy ....PhD 36-48FT 60-72PT/MSc by
research 12-24FT 24-36PT

University of Leeds
Institute of Engineering Thermofluids, Surfaces and Interfaces ..
PhD 36+FT/MPhil 24FT

University of Nottingham
Thermofluids .... MRes 12FT

Chemistry

Analytical chemistry
Taught Courses

University of Aberdeen
Analytical Chemistry for Environmental Life Sciences . MSc 12FT/PGDip 9FT/PGCert 4FT

Bangor University
Analytical Chemistry .... MSc 12FT/Diploma 9FT
Chemistry .... MRes 12FT
Environmental Chemistry .... MSc 12FT/PGDip 9FT

Birkbeck, University of London
Analytical Chemistry (with specialisms) .... MSc 12FT 24-60PT/PGDip 12FT 24-60PT
Chemical Research .... MRes 12FT 24PT

University of Bradford
Analytical Sciences .... MSc 12FT 60PT/PGDip 12FT 60PT/PGCert 12FT 60PT

University of Central Lancashire
Instrumental Analysis .... MSc 12FT

University College Cork
Applied Science (Analysis Of Pharmaceutical Compounds)... MSc 12FT 24PT
Applied Science (Analytical Chemistry) .... PGDip 9FT 18PT MSc 12FT 24PT
Applied Science (Environmental Analytical Chemistry) MSc 12FT 24PT

Cranfield University
Analytical BiotechnologyMSc 12FT 24-36PT/PGDip 9FT 24-36PT/PGCert 6FT 24-36PT

Dublin Institute of Technology
Pharmaceutical Quality Assurance and BiotechnologyMSc 12FT/PGDip 9FT

University of East Anglia
Advanced Organic Chemistry .... MSc 12FT
Chemical Sciences .... GradDip 12FT

Edinburgh Napier University
Pharmaceutical Science .. MSc 12FT 24-36PT/PGDip 9FT 18-27PT/PGCert 6FT 12-18PT

University of Glasgow
Chemistry .... MSc 12FT

University of Huddersfield
Analytical Chemistry .... MSc 12FT 24-48PT

University of Hull
Analytical and Forensic Chemistry .... MSc 12FT

Kingston University
Analytical Chemistry .... MSc 12FT 24PT/PGCert 6FT 12PT
Analytical Chemistry with Management Studies. MSc 12FT 24PT
Pharmaceutical Analysis .... MSc 12FT 24PT

University of Liverpool
Advanced Science (Chemical Sciences pathway) .... MSc 12FT/PGDip 12FT/PGCert 12FT

Loughborough University
Analytical Chemistry .... MSc 12FT 24 - 60PT
Analytical Chemistry and Environmental Science .... MSc 12FT 24 - 60PT
Analytical and Pharmaceutical Science .... MSc 12FT 24 - 60PT

Nottingham Trent University
Analytical Chemistry .... MRes 12FT 24PT
Chemistry .... MSc 12/24FT 24PT
Pharmaceutical Analysis .... MRes 12FT 24PT

Queen's University Belfast
Chemical Biology .... MSc 12FT
Dating and Chronology .... MSc 12FT

University of Reading
Chemical Research .... PGDip 9FT 18PT MSc 12FT 24PT

Robert Gordon University
Instrumental Analytical Sciences: Oilfield Chemicals ... MSc 12FT 36PT/PGDip 9FT 24PT/PGCert 4FT 12PT

Sheffield Hallam University
Analytical Chemistry .... MSc 12FT 24PT/PGDip 8FT 16PT/PGCert 4FT 8PT

University of Sheffield
Health Economics and Decision Modelling .... MSc 12FT 24-36PT

University of Southampton
Instrumental Analytical Chemistry .... MSc 12FT

University of Strathclyde
Pharmaceutical Analysis .... MSc 12-24FT/PGDip 12-24FT
Pharmaceutical Quality and Good Manufacturing Practice .. MSc 27PT/PGDip 21PT

Swansea University
Applied Analytical Science (LCMS) ..... MSc 12FT 36PT/PGDip 12FT 36PT
Applied Liquid Chromatography Mass Spectrometry
.... PGCert 12FT 12PT

Trinity College Dublin - the University of Dublin
Pharmaceutical Analysis .... MSc 12FT 24PT

UCL - University College London
Chemical Research .... MSc 12FT 24PT

University of Warwick
Instrumental and Analytical Methods in Biological and Environmental Chemistry .... MSc 12FT 24-36PT

Analytical chemistry
Research Courses

Bangor University
Chemistry .... PhD 36FT MRes 12FT MPhil 24FT

University of Bath
Sustainable Chemical Technologies .... Integrated PhD 48FT

University of Bradford
Chemical and Forensic Sciences .... PhD 36-48FT 48-60PT/MPhil 12-24FT 24-48PT

Coventry University
Analytical Chemistry .... MSc by research 12FT 24-36PT

Keele University
Chemistry .... PhD 36FT 60PT/MPhil 12FT 24PT

University of Liverpool
Advanced Science MRes (Chemical Sciences pathway)MRes 12FT

Loughborough University
Separation and Purification Technology ...... PhD 36FT 60PT/MPhil 24FT 36PT

University of Manchester
Chemical Engineering and Analytical Science ... MPhil 12FT 24PT/PhD 36FT 72PT/Integrated PhD 48FT/EngD 48FT
Instrumentation .... PhD 36FT 72PT/MPhil 12FT 24PT

Newcastle University
Chemistry .... PhD 36FT 72PT/MPhil 12FT 24PT

University of Nottingham
Chemistry .... PhD 36FT 72PT/MPhil 24FT/MRes 12FT

The Open University
Cosmochemistry ...... PhD 36FT 72PT variableDL/MPhil 15FT 24PT variableDL

Plymouth University
Biogeochemistry and Environmental Analytical Chemistry Research Group (BEAch) .... MPhil 24FT/PhD 36FT

Queen's University Belfast
Chemistry and Chemical Engineering .... PhD 36FT 72PT/MPhil 24FT 48PT

Swansea University
Antimatter Physics .... MSc by research 12FT 24PT

Biochemistry
Taught Courses

Bangor University
Analytical Chemistry .... MSc 12FT/Diploma 9FT
Chemistry .... MRes 12FT
Environmental Chemistry .... MSc 12FT/PGDip 9FT
Marine Biology .... MSc 12FT 24-36PT/PGDip 9FT
Molecular Biology with Biotechnology .... MSc 12FT
Natural Sciences .... MRes 12FT
Physical Oceanography .... MSc 12FT 24-36PT/PGDip 9FT

University of Bristol
Biomedical Engineering .... MSc 12FT

Cardiff University
Chemical Biology .... MSc 12FT 36PT

University of Central Lancashire
Pharmaceutical Biotechnology .... MSc 12FT

University of East Anglia
Chemical Sciences .... GradDip 12FT
Molecular Medicine .... MSc 12FT

University of Edinburgh
Biomedical Sciences (Life Sciences) .... MSc(Res) 12FT
Medicinal & Biological Chemistry .... MSc 12FT

University of Exeter
Biosciences .... MSc(Res) 12FT 36PT

Glasgow Caledonian University
Biomedical Science .... MSc 24PT/PGDip 24PT/PGCert 12PT
Pharmacology .... MSc 12FT

Heriot-Watt University
Biotechnology .... MSc 12FT 24PT/PGDip 9FT 20PT

Imperial College London
Molecular and Cellular Biosciences .... MRes 12FT

King's College London
Molecular Biophysics .... MRes 12FT

Leeds Metropolitan University
Applied Biomedical Sciences Research .... MSc 12FT
Integrated Masters Biomedical Sciences .... MBIOMS 48FT
Microbiology & Biotechnology .... MSc 12FT 24PT
Sport and Exercise Nutrition ... MSc 12FT 24PT/PGDip 12FT 24PT/PGCert 4FT 12PT
Sport and Exercise Physiology.. MSc 12FT 24PT/PGCert 4FT 12PT/PGDip 12FT 24PT
Toxicology Sciences .... MSc 12FT 24PT

University of Leicester
Cancer Cell and Molecular Biology .... MSc 12FT

University of Liverpool
Advanced Chemical Sciences (Organic and Biomolecular Chemistry) .... MSc 12FT

University of Manchester
Biochemistry .... MSc 12FT
Clinical Biochemistry .... MSc 12FT

Newcastle University
Bioinformatics .... MSc 12FT
Synthetic Biology .... MSc 12FT

Northumbria University
Biotechnology .... MSc 16FT 30PT

Nottingham Trent University
Biomedical Science .... MSc 12FT 24PT
Biotechnology .... MSc 12FT 24PT
Applied Biosciences .... MSc(Res) 12FT 24PT
Biotechnology .... MSc(Res) 12FT 24PT

University of Nottingham
Industrial Physical Biochemistry .... MRes 12FT 24PT

The Open University
Medicinal Chemistry .... MSc variableDL/PGDip variableDL

Queen's University Belfast
Chemical Biology .... MSc 12FT

Sheffield Hallam University
Biomedical Sciences .... MSc 12FT 24PT/PGDip 8FT 16PT/PGCert 4FT 8PT
Biotechnology .. MSc 12FT 24PT/PGDip 8FT 16PT/PGCert 4FT 8PT

St George's, University of London
Biomedical Science .... MRes 12FT

University of Surrey
Clinical Biochemistry .... MSc 12FT 24PT

Trinity College Dublin - the University of Dublin
Bioengineering .... MSc 12FT
Clinical Chemistry .... MSc 24PT

UCL - University College London
Biochemical Engineering .... MSc 12FT/PGDip 9FT
Biomedical Sciences .... MSc 12FT 24PT
Biosciences .... MRes 12FT
Drug Design .... MSc 12FT/PGDip 9FT
Nanotechnology and Regenerative Medicine .... MSc 12FT 24PT
Organic Chemistry: Drug Discovery .... MRes 12FT
Synthetic Biology .... MRes 12FT
Systems Biology .... MRes 12FT

University of Warwick
Mathematical Biology and Biophysical Chemistry ....
MSc 12FT 24PT

University of Westminster
Clinical Chemistry .... MSc 12FT

Biochemistry
Research Courses

Bangor University
Biological Sciences .... MPhil 12FT/PhD 24-36FT
Chemistry .... PhD 36FT MPhil 24FT MRes 12FT
Natural Sciences .... MRes 12FT
Ocean Sciences .... MPhil 24FT/PhD 36FT

Barts and the London School of Medicine and Dentistry
Biochemistry .... PhD 36FT 48PT
Department of Clinical Biochemistry .... PhD/MPhil

University of Bath
Biology and Biochemistry ... PhD 24-48FT 36-72PT/MRes 12-36FT 24-48PT

University of Birmingham
Biosciences .... MSc by research 12FT 24PT/PhD 36FT 72PT

University of Bristol
Biochemistry .... PhD 36FT 72PT/MSc by research 12FT 24PT

University of Cambridge
Biochemistry .... PhD 36FT 60PT/MPhil 9FT
Clinical Biochemistry .... PhD 36FT/MPhil 12FT

Cardiff University
Chemical Biology .... PhD 36FT/MPhil 12FT

University of Dundee
Life Sciences .... PhD 48FT MPhil 24FT MSc by research 12FT
Life Sciences - A/Star Dundee Programme (4 year PhD) PhD 48FT
Life Sciences - EMBL Joint Programme (PhD) .... PhD 36FT
Life Sciences - Wellcome Programme (PhD) .... PhD 48FT

University of Edinburgh
Clinical Biochemistry ..... PhD 36FT 72PT/MPhil 24FT 36PT/MSc by research 12FT 24PT

Chemistry

University of Essex
Biochemistry...PhD 36FT 72PT/MPhil 24FT 48PT/MSc by research 12FT 24PT
Chemical Biology............PhD 36FT 72PT/MPhil 24FT 48PT/MSc by research 12FT 24PT

University of Exeter
Biosciences......PhD 36FT 72PT/MPhil 24FT 48PT/MSc by research 12FT 36PT

University of Glasgow
Biochemistry and Molecular Biology ....PhD 36FT/ MSc by research 12FT

Imperial College London
Chemical Biology of Health and Disease .....MRes 12FT/PhD 36FT
Department of Biochemistry ....PhD/MPhil

University of Kent
Biochemistry...PhD 36FT 60PT/MPhil 24FT 36PT/MSc by research 12FT 24PT

King's College London
Cell & Molecular Biophysics, Randall Division of ....PhD 36FT 48-72PT/MPhil 36FT 48-72PT/MD 36FT 48-72PT

University of Leeds
Biochemistry and Molecular Biology ....PhD 36+FT/MPhil 24FT/ MSc by research 12FT
Centre for Self-Organising Molecular Systems.............PhD 36+FT/ MPhil 24+FT/MSc by research 12FT

University of Leicester
Research in Biochemistry ....PhD 36-48FT 72-96PT/MRes 12FT

University of Liverpool
Advanced Chemical Sciences (Organic and Biomolecular Chemistry)..MRes 12FT
Biological Sciences (Structural and Chemical Biology)......... MPhil 12-48FT 24-72PT/PhD 24-48FT 48-84PT

University of Manchester
Biochemistry......................PhD 36-48FT 72-96PT/MPhil 12FT 24PT
Biological Chemistry........PhD 36-48FT 72-96PT/MPhil 12FT 24PT

Newcastle University
Biological Sciences .... PhD 36FT 72PT/MPhil 12FT 24PT
Biomedicine.......MPhil 12FT 24PT/PhD 36FT 72PT/MD 24FT 48PT
Biotechnology .... MPhil 12FT 24PT/PhD 36FT 72PT
Biotechnology and Business Enterprise ....MRes 12FT
Nanomedicine...MRes 12FT

Systems Biology..MRes 12FT

University of Nottingham
Biochemistry and Cell Biology..PhD 36FT 72PT/MPhil 24FT 48PT/ MRes 12FT/DM 36FT 72PT
Industrial Physical Biochemistry ....MRes 12FT 24PT
Molecular and Cellular Science PhD 36FT 72PT/MPhil 24FT 48PT/ MRes 12FT

Oxford Brookes University
Biological Sciences - Biofilm Development .... PhD 24-60FT 36-72PT/MPhil 24-36FT 36-48FT
Biological Sciences - Bioprocess Research................... PhD 24-60FT 36-72PT/MPhil 24-36FT 36-48FT
Biological Sciences - Cell Systems Modelling .... PhD 24-60FT 36-72PT/MPhil 24-36FT 36-48FT
Biological Sciences - Environmental Ecology .... PhD 24-60FT 36-72PT/MPhil 24-36FT 36-48FT
Biological Sciences - Evolutionary Developmental Biology ....PhD 24-60FT 36-72PT/MPhil 24-36FT 36-48FT
Biological Sciences - Invertebrate Ecology and Biogeography .... PhD 24-60FT 36-72PT/MPhil 24-36FT 36-48FT
Biological Sciences - Plant Cell Biology ..... PhD 24-60FT 36-72PT/ MPhil 24-36FT 36-48FT
Biological Sciences - Spatial Ecology and Land Use .... PhD 24-60FT 36-72PT/MPhil 24-36FT 36-48FT
Biological and Biomedical Science .....PhD 36FT 48PT/MPhil 24FT 36PT

University of Oxford
Biochemistry................................. DPhil 48FT/MSc by research 24FT
Chromosome and Developmental Biology.................... DPhil 48FT
Structural Biology... DPhil 48FT
Systems Biology.. DPhil 48FT

School of Pharmacy, University of London
Pharmaceutical and Biological Chemistry............. PhD 36FT 60PT

University of Strathclyde
Drug Delivery Systems ....MRes 12FT 24PT
Drug Delivery Systems with International Placement .... MRes 12FT 24PT
Drug Discovery ....MRes 12FT

University of Surrey
Biochemistry, Toxicology, Neuropharmacology, Chronobiology, Apoptosis.. PhD 36FT 48PT/MPhil 24FT 36PT

University of Sussex
Biochemistry......... PhD 24-48FT 36-72PT/MPhil 12-36FT 24-48PT

Teesside University
Applied Sciences...PhD 24-60FT 36-72PT/MPhil 18FT 30PT/DProf 36PT/MProf by research 30PT

University of the Highlands and Islands
Genetics and Biochemistry........ PhD 36FT 72PT/MPhil 24FT 36PT

UCL - University College London
Biomedical Research..................................... PhD 36FT 60PT

University of Warwick
Mathematical Biology and Biophysical Chemistry......... MSc 11FT 22PT/PhD 48FT 96PT

Chemistry
Taught Courses

University of Aberdeen
Analytical Chemistry for Environmental Life Sciences .MSc 12FT/ PGDip 9FT/PGCert 4FT

Anglia Ruskin University
Forensic Science...............................MSc 12 - 15FT 24 - 30PT

Anglo-European College of Chiropractic
Chiropractic............................MSc 30DL/PGDip 24DL/PGCert 12DL

Bangor University
Analytical Chemistry ....MSc 12FT/Diploma 9FT
Chemistry...MRes 12FT
Environmental Chemistry .... MSc 12FT/PGDip 9FT

University of Bath
Chemistry ....MRes 12FT
Sustainable Chemical Technologies PhD (Integrated) .... MRes 12FT

Birkbeck, University of London
Analytical Bioscience..MSc 12FT 24 - 60PT/PGDip 12FT 24 - 60PT
Analytical Chemistry (with specialisms) .... MSc 12FT 24-60PT/ PGDip 12FT 24-60PT
Chemical Research ....MRes 12FT 24PT

Bournemouth University
Applied Sciences by Research.......................... MSc 12FT 24PT

University of Brighton
Chemistry...MRes 12FT 24PT

University of Cambridge
Advanced Chemical Engineering...................................... MPhil 12FT

Cardiff University
Catalysis...MSc 12FT 36PT
Chemical Biology..MSc 12FT 36PT
Sustainable Chemistry..................................MSc 12FT 36PT

University of Central Lancashire
Instrumental Analysis .... MSc 12FT
Medicinal Chemistry .... MSc 12FT
Pharmaceutical Biotechnology.. MSc 12FT
Synthetic Organic Chemistry.. MSc 12FT

University College Cork
Applied Science (Analytical Chemistry)..................PGDip 9FT 18PT MSc 12FT 24PT
Applied Science (Environmental Analytical Chemistry).................. MSc 12FT 24PT

Durham University
Biophysical Sciences .... MSc 12FT

University of East Anglia
Advanced Organic Chemistry....................................... MSc 12FT
Chemical Sciences..GradDip 12FT

University of Edinburgh
Bioelectronics and Biosensors.. MSc 12FT
Carbon Capture & Storage...........................MSc 12FT 36PT
Materials Chemistry .... MSc 12FT
Medicinal & Biological Chemistry.................................... MSc 12FT

University of Glasgow
Chemistry .... MSc 12FT
Chemistry with Medicinal Chemistry .... MSc 12FT

University of Greenwich
Formulation Science ....MSc 12-24FT

University of Hertfordshire
Medicinal Chemistry ... MSc 12FT 24PT/PGDip 12FT 24PT/PGCert 12FT 24PT

University of Huddersfield
Analytical Chemistry ....MSc 12FT 24-48PT
Pharmaceutical and Analytical Science............MSc 12FT 24-48PT

University of Hull
Analytical and Forensic Chemistry.................................. MSc 12FT
Chemistry .... MSc 12FT
Chemistry with Biological Chemistry.............................. MSc 12FT
Chemistry with Nanotechnology .... MSc 12FT
REACH Management..PGCert 12FT 12DL

Imperial College London
Green Chemistry: Engineering, Energy and the Environment....... MRes 12FT

Chemistry

Chemical Biology of Crop Sustainability and Protection ...... MRes 12FT 24PT

King's College London
Analytical Science for Industry ...... MSc 12FT 24PT

University of Leeds
Chemical Biology ...... MSc 12FT
Polymers and Surface Coatings Science and Technology ...... MSc 12FT

University of Leicester
Cancer Chemistry ...... MSc 12FT
Chemical Research ...... MSc 12FT 24PT

University of Liverpool
Advanced Chemical Sciences (Nanoscale With Interfacial Science) ...... MSc 12FT
Advanced Chemical Sciences (Nanoscale With Materials Chemistry) ...... MSc 12FT
Advanced Chemical Sciences (Organic Chemistry With Catalysis) ...... MSc 12FT
Advanced Chemical Sciences (Organic and Biomolecular Chemistry) ...... MSc 12FT

London School of Hygiene and Tropical Medicine
Tropical Medicine & International Health ...... MSc 12FT 24PT

University of Manchester
Chemistry ...... MSc 12FT 24PT

Newcastle University
Environmental Consultancy ...... MSc 12FT 48PT

Nottingham Trent University
Chemistry ...... MSc 12/24FT 24PT
Pharmaceutical Analysis ...... MRes 12FT 24PT
Subject Knowledge Enhancement (SKE) Courses (Chemistry, Physics, Mathematics) ...... SKE 9FT

University of Nottingham
Chemistry ...... MSc(Res) 12FT

The Open University
Medicinal Chemistry ...... MSc variableDL/PGDip variableDL
Professional Science ...... MSc variableDL
Science ...... MSc variableDL

University of Oxford
Theoretical Chemistry ...... MSc 12FT

University of Portsmouth
Science ...... MRes 12FT 24PT
Science with Chemistry ...... PGCE (Postgraduate) 12FT/PGCE (Professional) 12FT

Queen Mary, University of London
Chemical Research ...... MSc 12FT 24PT

Queen's University Belfast
Chemical Biology ...... MSc 12FT
Chemical Research ...... MSc 12FT up to 36PT

University of Reading
Chemical Research ...... PGDip 9FT 18PT MSc 12FT 24PT
Food Science ...... MSc 12FT 24PT
Food Technology - Quality Assurance ...... MSc 12FT

University of Sheffield
Solid State Chemistry and its Applications ...... MSc(Eng) 12-24FT

University of Southampton
Chemistry by Research ...... MSc 12FT
Instrumental Analytical Chemistry ...... MSc 12FT

University of Strathclyde
Forensic Science ...... MSc 12FT/PGDip 9FT/PGCert 9FT
Medicinal Chemistry ...... MSc 12FT/PGDip 9FT

Swansea University
Applied Analytical Science (LCMS) ...... MSc 12FT 36PT/PGDip 12FT 36PT

Trinity College Dublin - the University of Dublin
Clinical Chemistry ...... MSc 24PT
Pharmaceutical Analysis ...... MSc 12FT 24PT

UCL - University College London
Chemical Research ...... MSc 12FT 24PT
Drug Design ...... MSc 12FT/PGDip 9FT

University of Warwick
Synthetic Chemistry ...... MSc 12FT 24PT

University of York
Computational Biology ...... MRes 12FT
Green Chemistry and Sustainable Industrial Technology ...... MSc 12FT 24-36PT

Chemistry
Research Courses

University of Aberdeen
Chemistry ...... PhD 36FT/MPhil 24FT/MSc by research 12FT

Anglia Ruskin University
Investigative Chemistry Research Group ...... MPhil 18 - 36FT 36 - 48PT/PhD 24 - 60FT 36 - 72PT
Science and Technology ...... DProf 60DL

Bangor University
Chemistry ...... PhD 36FT MPhil 24FT MRes 12FT

University of Bath
Chemistry ...... PhD 24-48FT 36-72PT/MPhil 12-36FT 24-48PT
Chemistry PhD (integrated)PhD 24-48FT 36-72PT/MPhil 12-36FT 24-48PT
Sustainable Chemical Technologies ...... Integrated PhD 48FT

University of Birmingham
Chemistry ...... PhD 36FT 72PT/MSc by research 12FT 24PT

University of Bristol
Chemistry ...... PhD 36FT 72PT/MSc by research 12FT 24PT
Synthetic Chemistry ...... PhD 48FT

University of Cambridge
Chemical Biology and Molecular Medicine ...... PhD 48FT
Chemistry ...... PhD 36FT 60PT
Chemistry ...... MPhil 12FT

Cardiff University
Chemical Biology ...... PhD 36FT/MPhil 12FT
Theoretical and Computational Chemistry ...... PhD 36FT/MPhil 12FT

Coventry University
Applied Chemistry ...... MPhil 12FT 36PT/PhD 12FT 36PT/MSc by research 12FT 24-36PT
Sonochemistry ...... MSc by research 12FT 24-36PT

Cranfield University, Shrivenham
Explosive Chemistry ...... PhD 36FT 48-72PT/MPhil 24FT 48-72PT

Durham University
Chemistry ...... PhD 36FT 48PT/MSc by research 12FT

University of East Anglia
Chemical Sciences ...... PhD 36FT 72PT/MPhil 24FT 48PT

University of Edinburgh
Chemistry ...... MPhil 24FT/PhD 36FT 72PT/MSc by research 12FT
Structural ChemistryPhD 36FT/MPhil 24FT/MSc by research 12FT

National University of Ireland Galway
College of Science ...... PhD 48FT 72PT/MSc by research 24FT 48PT/ Structured PhD 48FT

University of Glasgow
Chemistry ...... PhD 36FT/MSc by research 12FT

University of Greenwich
Chemical and Life Sciences ...... MSc by research 12FT 24-36PT
Chemical and Pharmaceutical Sciences - Research ...... MPhil 36FT 72PT/PhD 36FT 72PT

Heriot-Watt University
Chemistry ...... PhD 36FT 48PT/MPhil 24FT/MSc by research 12FT

University of Huddersfield
Department of Chemical and Biological SciencesPhD 36FT 60PT/ MPhil 30FT 60PT

University of Hull
Chemistry ...... PhD 36FT 60PT/MSc by research 12FT
Chemistry (New Route PhD) ...... PhD 48FT

Imperial College London
PhD in Chemistry ...... PhD 36FT/MPhil 24FT

Keele University
Chemistry ...... PhD 36FT 60PT/MPhil 12FT 24PT

University of Kent
Chemistry ...... PhD 36FT 60PT/MPhil 24FT 36PT/MSc by research 12FT 24PT

University of Leeds
Atmospheric and Climate Science ...... PhD 36FT 60PT 60DL/MPhil 24FT 48PT 48DL
School of Chemistry ...... PhD 36FT/MPhil 24FT/MSc by r esearch 12FT

University of Leicester
Department of Chemistry ...... PhD 36FT/MPhil 24FT

Liverpool John Moores University
Pharmacy and Chemistry ...... PhD 36FT 72PT/MPhil 24FT 48PT

University of Liverpool
Advanced Chemical Sciences (Nanoscale with Interfacial Science) ...... MRes 12FT
Advanced Chemical Sciences (Nanoscale with Materials Chemistry) ...... MRes 12FT
Chemistry ...... PhD 24-48FT 48-84PT/MPhil 12-48FT 48-84PT

University of Manchester
Chemistry ...... MEnt 12FT 24PT/EntD 48FT PhD 36-48FT 84PT/MPhil 12FT 24PT/MSc by research 12FT
Nonlinear and Liquid Crystals Physics ...... PhD 36FT 72PT/MSc by research 12FT 24PT
Physical Chemistry ...... PhD 36-48FT 72-96PT/MPhil 12FT 24PT
Theoretical Chemistry ...... PhD 36-48FT 72-96PT/MPhil 12FT 24PT

Newcastle University
Chemistry ...... PhD 36FT 72PT/MPhil 12FT 24PT

University of Nottingham
Chemistry ...... PhD 36FT 72PT/MPhil 24FT/MRes 12FT
Magnetic Resonance ...... PhD 36FT 72PT/MPhil 24FT 48PT/MRes 12FT

The Open University
Astrochemistry ...... MPhil 15FT 24PT variableDL/PhD 36FT 72PT variableDL
Cosmochemistry ...... PhD 36FT 72PT variableDL/MPhil 15FT 24PT variableDL
Medicinal chemistry and diagnostics ...... MPhil 15FT 24PT variableDL/PhD 36FT 72PT variableDL
STEM Education and engagement ...... PhD 36FT 72PT variableDL

University of Oxford
Biochemistry ...... DPhil 48FT/MSc by research 24FT DPhil 48FT
Chemical Biology ...... DPhil 48FT/MSc(Res) 24FT
Inorganic Chemistry ...... DPhil 36-48FT/MSc by research 24FT
Medicinal Chemistry for Cancer ...... DPhil 48FT
Physical and Theoretical Chemistry.. DPhil 48FT/MSc by research 24FT

Plymouth University
Biogeochemistry Research Centre ...... PhD 36FT 36-72PT/ MPhil 24FT 24-36PT

Queen Mary, University of London
Chemistry ...... PhD/MPhil
IRC in Biomedical Materials ...... PhD/MPhil

Queen's University Belfast
Chemistry and Chemical Engineering ...... PhD 36FT 72PT/ MPhil 24FT 48PT

University of Salford
Chemistry and Nanotechnology ...... PhD 36FT 60PT/MPhil 24FT 24PT/MRes 24FT 24PT/MSc by research 24FT 24PT
Institute for Materials ResearchPhD 36FT/MSc by research 12FT/ MPhil 12FT

University of Sheffield
Chemistry ...... PhD 36FT 72PT/MPhil 24FT 48PT
Engineering Materials: Integrated Studies...Integrated PhD 48FT

University of Southampton
Chemistry ...... PhD 36FT 72PT/MPhil 24FT 48PT

University of St Andrews
Chemistry ...... PhD 36-42FT 72-84PT/MPhil 12-24FT 24-48PT

University of Strathclyde
Pure and Applied Chemistry - Research ...... PhD 36FT 48PT/MPhil 12FT 24PT

University of Surrey
Chemistry ...... PhD 36FT 48PT/MPhil 24FT 36PT

University of Sussex
Chemistry Research Programme ...... PhD 24-48FT 36-72PT/MPhil 12-36FT 24-48PT

UCL - University College London
Chemistry ...... PhD 36FT 60PT

University of Warwick
Chemistry ...... PhD 36-48FT/MSc by research 12FT 24PT
Mathematical Biology and Biophysical Chemistry ...... MSc 11FT 22PT/PhD 48FT 96PT

University of the West of Scotland
Department of Chemistry and Chemical Engineering ...... PhD/ MPhil

University of York
Chemistry ...... PhD 36FT 72PT/MPhil 24FT 48PT/MSc by research 12FT 24PT

Colour science
Taught Courses

University of Glasgow
Chemistry ...... MSc 12FT

University of Leeds
Colour and Imaging Science ...... MSc 12FT/PGCert 12FT/ PGDip 12FT

Colour science
Research Courses

University of Leeds
Colour Chemistry ...... PhD 36+FT
Department of Colour and Polymer Chemistry ...... PhD 36+FT/ MPhil 12+FT/MSc by research 12FT

Crystals
Taught Courses

Birkbeck, University of London
Protein Crystallography ...... PGCert 12DL

Glasgow Caledonian University
Particulate Solids Handling ...... MSc 30DL/PGDip 30DL

Crystals
Research Courses

University of Manchester
Colloids, Crystals, Interfaces and Materials ...... MPhil 12FT 24PT/ PhD 36FT 72PT

Chemistry

The Open University
Atomic, Molecular and Optical Physics................ MPhil 15FT 24PT variableDL

Swansea University
Cold Atoms and Quantum Optics .... MSc by research 12FT 12-24PT

Inorganic chemistry
Taught Courses

Bangor University
Analytical Chemistry .... MSc 12FT/Diploma 9FT
Chemistry.. MRes 12FT
Environmental Chemistry .... MSc 12FT/PGDip 9FT

University of East Anglia
Chemical Sciences...GradDip 12FT

University of Glasgow
Chemistry with Medicinal Chemistry .... MSc 12FT

University of Reading
Chemical Research .... PGDip 9FT 18PT MSc 12FT 24PT

UCL - University College London
Organic Chemistry: Drug Discovery................................. MRes 12FT

Inorganic chemistry
Research Courses

Bangor University
Chemistry...................... MPhil 24FT PhD 36FT MRes 12FT

Cardiff University
Inorganic Chemistry ....PhD 36FT/MPhil 12FT

University of Manchester
Inorganic Chemistry ....PhD 36-48FT 72-96PT/MPhil 12FT 24PT

University of Oxford
Inorganic Chemistry ....DPhil 36-48FT/MSc by research 24FT

Materials chemistry
Taught Courses

Bangor University
Analytical Chemistry .... MSc 12FT/Diploma 9FT
Chemistry.. MRes 12FT
Environmental Chemistry .... MSc 12FT/PGDip 9FT

University of Birmingham
Materials for Sustainable Energy Technologies...MRes 12FT 24PT

University of Bristol
Advanced Composites.. MSc 12FT

University of Cambridge
MASt in Materials Science .... MASt 9FT

University of Edinburgh
Materials Chemistry .... MSc 12FT

Glasgow Caledonian University
Particulate Solids Handling .... MSc 30DL/PGDip 30DL

University of Glasgow
Chemistry... MSc 12FT
Chemistry with Medicinal Chemistry .... MSc 12FT

Heriot-Watt University
Materials for Sustainable and Renewable Energies .... MSc 12FT 24PT/PGDip 9FT 21PT/PGCert 6FT 12PT

University of Liverpool
Advanced Chemical Sciences (Nanoscale With Materials Chemistry).. MSc 12FT

Nottingham Trent University
Advanced Materials Engineering ....MRes 12FT 24PT

University of Reading
Chemical Research .... PGDip 9FT 18PT MSc 12FT 24PT

Royal College of Art
Ceramics and Glass ....MA 24FT

Sheffield Hallam University
Advanced Engineering Metals ....MSc 36PT/PGDip 24PT/PGCert 12PT
Advanced Materials Engineering ....MSc 12FT 36PT/PGDip 8FT 24PT/PGCert 4FT 12PT

University of Sheffield
Ceramic Science and Engineering .... MSc(Eng) 12-24FT
Solid State Chemistry and its Applications....... MSc(Eng) 12-24FT

University of Southampton
Chemistry by Research.. MSc 12FT

UCL - University College London
Molecular Modelling and Materials Science ....MRes 12FT 24PT

Materials chemistry
Research Courses

Aston University
Surface Science Research Group.................... PhD 36FT/MPhil 24FT

Bangor University
Chemistry .... PhD 36FT MRes 12FT MPhil 24FT

University of Bristol
Synthetic Chemistry ....PhD 48FT

Cardiff University
State and Solid Materials .... PhD 36FT/MPhil 12FT

University of Edinburgh
Structural ChemistryPhD 36FT/MPhil 24FT/MSc by research 12FT

University of Hull
Engineering - Design, Materials and Process Performance .....PhD 36FT 48PT/MPhil 24FT 36PT/MSc by research 12FT 24PT

Keele University
Chemistry .... PhD 36FT 60PT/MPhil 12FT 24PT

University of Leeds
Institute for Materials Research ....PhD 36+FT/MPhil 24FT
Institute of Engineering Thermofluids, Surfaces and Interfaces .. PhD 36+FT/MPhil 24FT

University of Liverpool
Advanced Chemical Sciences (Nanoscale with Materials Chemistry).. MRes 12FT

University of Manchester
Materials Chemistry ....PhD 36-48FT 72-96PT/MPhil 12FT 24PT

University of Nottingham
Biophysics and Surface Analysis..........PhD 36FT 72PT/MPhil 24FT 36PT/MRes 12FT

Queen Mary, University of London
Materials..................................... PhD/MPhil/MSc by research 12FT

Queen's University Belfast
Nanostructured Media .... PhD 36FT 72PT/MPhil 24FT 48PT

UCL - University College London
Molecular Modelling and Materials Simulation .... EngD 48FT

Molecular electronics
Taught Courses

Bangor University
Electronic Engineering .... MRes 12FT
Electronic Engineering (Bio-Electronics).......................... MRes 12FT
Electronic Engineering (Nanotechnology) .... MRes 12FT
Electronic Engineering (Organic Electronics) .... MRes 12FT
Electronic Engineering (Polymer Electronics)................. MRes 12FT

University of Westminster
Electronics ....MRes 12FT 24PT 24BM
Electronics (Evening Study)...MRes 24PT

Molecular electronics
Research Courses

Bangor University
Electrical Materials Science ....MPhil 24FT/PhD 36FT
Molecular Sensors......................................MPhil 24FT/PhD 24-36FT
Organic Electronics ....MPhil 24FT/PhD 36FT
Quantum Transport and Nanoelectronics ..MPhil 24FT/PhD 36FT

The Open University
Atomic, Molecular and Optical Physics................ MPhil 15FT 24PT variableDL
Fabrication .... PhD 36FT 72PT variableDL/MPhil 15FT 24PT variableDL

Organic chemistry
Taught Courses

Bangor University
Analytical Chemistry .... MSc 12FT/Diploma 9FT
Chemistry.. MRes 12FT
Environmental Chemistry .... MSc 12FT/PGDip 9FT

University of Bath
Chemistry for Drug Discovery .... MSc 12FT

University of Birmingham
MSc Drug Discovery and Medicinal Chemistry.....MSc 18FT 32PT/PGDip 12FT 24PT

University of Bradford
Drug Discovery .... MSc 12FT 24PT/PGDip 12FT 24PT

Cardiff University
Chemical Biology... MSc 12FT 36PT
Physical Organic Chemistry .... MSc 12FT 36PT

University of Central Lancashire
Carbon and Resource Management....MSc 12FT 24PT/PGDip 9FT 18PT/PGCert 6FT 12PT
Synthetic Organic Chemistry.. MSc 12FT

University College Cork
Applied Science (Analysis Of Pharmaceutical Compounds)... MSc 12FT 24PT

University of East Anglia
Advanced Organic Chemistry... MSc 12FT
Chemical Sciences...GradDip 12FT

University of Edinburgh
Medicinal & Biological Chemistry...................................... MSc 12FT

University of Glasgow
Chemistry.. MSc 12FT

Heriot-Watt University
Carbon Management.. MSc 12FT 24PT 24-84DL/PGDip 9FT 21PT 24-84DL

University of Liverpool
Advanced Chemical Sciences (Organic Chemistry With Catalysis).. MSc 12FT
Advanced Chemical Sciences (Organic and Biomolecular Chemistry)... MSc 12FT

Newcastle University
Synthetic Biology.. MSc 12FT

Nottingham Trent University
Chemistry.. MSc 12/24FT 24PT

Queen's University Belfast
Chemical Biology... MSc 12FT

University of Reading
Chemical Research .... PGDip 9FT 18PT MSc 12FT 24PT

University of Southampton
Chemistry by Research.. MSc 12FT

UCL - University College London
Chemical Research .... MSc 12FT 24PT
Drug Design .... MSc 12FT/PGDip 9FT
Organic Chemistry: Drug Discovery................................. MRes 12FT
Synthetic Biology... MRes 12FT
Systems Biology.. MRes 12FT

Organic chemistry
Research Courses

Bangor University
Chemistry.......................... PhD 36FT MRes 12FT MPhil 24FT

Cardiff University
Chemical Biology..PhD 36FT/MPhil 12FT
Organic Synthesis..PhD 36FT/MPhil 12FT
Physical Organic Chemistry ....PhD 36FT/MPhil 12FT

Coventry University
Pharmaceutical Synthesis .... MSc by research 12FT 24-36PT

Keele University
Chemistry .... PhD 36FT 60PT/MPhil 12FT 24PT

University of Leeds
Institute for Materials Research ....PhD 36+FT/MPhil 24FT

University of Liverpool
Advanced Chemical Sciences (Organic Chemistry with Catalysis)..MRes 12FT
Advanced Chemical Sciences (Organic and Biomolecular Chemistry)..MRes 12FT

University of Manchester
Biocatalysis .... MPhil 12FT 24PT/PhD 36FT 72PT
Organic Chemistry ....PhD 36-48FT 72-96PT/MPhil 12FT 24PT

Newcastle University
Chemistry .... PhD 36FT 72PT/MPhil 12FT 24PT
Systems Biology.. MRes 12FT

University of Nottingham
Chemistry ....PhD 36FT 72PT/MPhil 24FT/MRes 12FT

University of Oxford
Organic Chemistry ....DPhil 48FT/MSc by research 24-36FT 12-24PT

Queen's University Belfast
Chemistry and Chemical EngineeringPhD 36FT 72PT/MPhil 24FT 48PT

Swansea University
Biomathematics ....MSc by research 12FT 24PT

Civil engineering and construction

Civil engineering and construction
Taught Courses

Anglia Ruskin University
Civil Engineering........MSc 12FT 27PT
Conservation of Buildings........MSc 12FT 24 - 30PT
Construction Management........MSc 12FT 24-30PT
Sustainability: Working for Positive Change....MSc 12FT 24-30PT
Town Planning........MSc 12FT 24-30PT

Aston University
Professional Engineering........MSc(Eng) 24-60DL

University of Bath
Architectural Engineering: Environmental Design........ MSc 12FT 24PT/PGDip 9FT 18PT

University of Birmingham
Civil Engineering........MSc 12FT 24PT/PGDip 8FT 24PT

University of Bolton
Civil Engineering........MSc 36PT/PGDip 24PT/PGCert 12PT/MSc 12FT

Bournemouth University
Industrial Design........MA 12FT 24PT

University of Bradford
Civil and Structural Engineering........MSc 12-18PT MSc 12FT

University of Brighton
Civil Engineering........ MSc 12FT 24PT/PGCert 12FT 24PT/PGDip 12FT 24PT

Brunel University
Project and Infrastructure Management........MSc 12FT
Structural Integrity........MSc 12FT
Water Engineering........MSc 12FT

Cardiff University
Civil Engineering........MSc 12FT 24-36PT
Professional Engineering........MSc 12FT

City University London
Engineering-Modular.. MSc 12FT 24PT/PGDip 24PT/PGCert 24PT
Professional Civil Engineering........MSc 12FT 24PT

University College Cork
Information Technology in Architecture, Engineering and Construction........MEngSci 12FT 24PT

Coventry University
Civil Engineering........MSc 12FT 24-30PT
Civil and Structural Engineering........MSc 12FT 24-30PT

Cranfield University
Pre-Master's Course in Engineering Bridging course to MSc 10FT

University of Dundee
Civil Engineering........MSc 12FT

University of East Anglia
Energy Engineering with Environmental ManagementMSc 12FT/MSc 24PT/MSc 36PT/MSc 48PT

University of East London
Civil Engineering ..... MSc 12FT 24PT/PGDip 8FT 16PT/PGCert 4FT 8PT
Civil Engineering........PGDip 8FT 16PT/PGCert 4FT 8PT

Edinburgh Napier University
Advanced Materials Engineering........MSc 12FT 24PT
Advanced Structural Engineering ..MSc 12FT 24-36PT/PGDip 9FT 18PT/PGCert 6FT 12PT
Timber Engineering........MSc 12FT 36DL

University of Exeter
Advanced Civil Engineering........MSc 12FT
Applied Geotechnics........ MSc 12FT 36PT/PGDip 12FT 36PT
Engineering and Management........MSc 12FT
Minerals Engineering........MSc 12FT
Mining Engineering........MSc 12FT 24-36PT/PGDip 12FT 24-36PT
Surveying and Land/ Environmental Management....... MSc 12FT 24-36PT/PGDip 12FT 24-36PT

GCU London
Construction Management........MSc 12FT

University of Glasgow
Civil Engineering & Management........MSc 12FT

University of Greenwich
Building Engineering........MSc 12FT 24PT
Civil Engineering........MSc 12FT 24PT
Civil Engineering (International)........MSc 12FT 24PT

Heriot-Watt University
Civil Engineering and Construction Management........ MSc 12FT 24PT 24-84DL/PGDip 9FT 21PT 24-84DL/PGCert 6FT 12PT 24-84DL
Real Estate Investment and Finance...... MSc 12FT 24PT 24-84DL/PGDip 9FT 21PT 24-84DL

Kingston University
Civil Engineering........MSc 12FT 24PT
Management in Construction (Law)........MSc 24PT
Structural Design & Construction Management with Sustainability........MSc 12FT 24PT

Leeds Metropolitan University
Building Services Engineering........MSc 12FT 24PT
Civil Engineering........MSc 12FT 24PT

University of Leeds
Engineering Project Management........MSc(Eng) 12FT

University of Limerick
Advanced Materials........ PGDip 9FT/MSc 12FT

University of Lincoln ....
Construction Project Management........Diploma 12FT 36PT

University of Liverpool
Advanced Engineering Materials ......MSc(Eng) 12FT/PGDip 12FT/PGCert 12FT
Advanced Manufacturing Systems and Technology ....MSc(Eng) 12FT
Simulation in Aerospace Engineering........ MSc(Eng) 12FT 24PT
Sustainable Civil Engineering (Maritime)........ MSc 12FT
Sustainable Civil Engineering (Structural)........ MSc 12FT

London South Bank University
Civil Engineering........MSc 12FT MSc 24PT

Loughborough University
Energy Demand Studies........MRes 12FT 24PT
Infrastructure in Emergencies by Distance Learning........ PGCert 36PT 60DL
Transport........MSc 12FT 24-60PT

Newcastle University
Hydroinformatics........MSc 12FT 48PT

Northumbria University
Professional Engineering........MSc 36PT

Nottingham Trent University
Construction Management........MSc 12FT 24-60PT 24-60DL

University of Nottingham
Civil Engineering........MSc 12FT
Civil Engineering: Engineering Surveying........MSc 12FT
Civil Engineering: Environmental Fluid Mechanics........MSc 12FT
Civil Engineering: Geotechnical Engineering........MSc 12FT
Civil Engineering: Management........MSc 12FT
Civil Engineering: Pavement Engineering........MSc 12FT
Civil Engineering: Transportation........MSc 12FT
Energy Conversion and Management (Nottingham/ Ningbo) ....MSc 12FT MRes 12FT 24PT

Plymouth University
Civil Engineering........ MSc 12FT/PGDip 12FT/PGCert 6FT

University of Portsmouth
Civil Engineering........MSc 12FT 24PT
Civil Engineering with Environmental Engineering....... MSc 12FT 24PT
Civil Engineering with Geotechnical Engineering .... MSc 12FT 24PT

Queen's University Belfast
Advanced Concrete Technology.....MSc 24PT/PGDip 24PT/PGCert 24PT

Robert Gordon University
Construction Project Management.MSc 12FT 28-36PT 28-36DL/PGDip 9FT 18-24PT 18-24DL/PGCert 4FT 9-12PT 9-12DL

University of Salford
Construction Management........MSc 12FT 24DL/PGDip 8FT 16DL

Sheffield Hallam University
Advanced Design Engineering.. MSc 12FT 36PT/PGDip 8FT 24PT/PGCert 4FT 12PT
Construction Management........MSc 12FT 24-36PT

University of Sheffield
Architectural Engineering Design........MSc 12FT
Earthquake and Civil Engineering Dynamics........ MSc(Eng) 12FT 24PT

University of South Wales
Building Information Modelling and Sustainability....... MSc 12FT 36PT
Civil Engineering and Environmental Management...... MSc 12FT 36PT
Civil and Structural Engineering........MSc 12FT 36PT

University of Southampton
Civil and Environmental Engineering........MSc 12FT 24PT
Ecological and Environmental Sciences........MRes 12FT
Engineering for Development - Infrastructure, Water Supply and Sanitation........MSc 12FT 24PT/PGDip 9FT

Staffordshire University
Professional Engineering........MSc 12-18FT

University of Strathclyde
Civil Engineering........MSc 12FT
Environmental Engineering....... MSc 12FT 24PT/PGDip 9FT 18PT/PGCert 6FT 12PT
Environmental Entrepreneurship........MSc 12FT 24PT/PGDip 9FT 18PT/PGCert 6FT 12PT
Sustainable Engineering........ MSc 12FT 24PT/PGDip 9FT 18PT/PGCert 9FT 18PT

University of Surrey
Civil Engineering........ MSc 12FT 72PT 72DL

Swansea University
Civil Engineering........MSc 12FT 24-36PT
Computer Modelling and Finite Elements in Engineering Mechanics........MSc 12FT 36PT/PGDip 12FT

Teesside University
Civil Engineering........MSc 12 - 16FT 24PT/PGDip 8FT

Trinity College Dublin - the University of Dublin
Engineering (M.A.I.)........MAI 12FT

UCL - University College London
Civil Engineering........MSc 12FT
Civil Engineering Graduate Diploma........GradDip 9FT 60PT

University of West London
Civil and Environmental Engineering........MSc 12FT 24PT

University of Westminster
Construction Project Management........MSc 12FT 24PT

University of Wolverhampton
Civil Engineering........MSc 12FT 24PT/PGCert 12FT 24PT
Civil Engineering Management........ MSc 12FT 24PT/PGCert 12FT 24PT
Computer Aided Design for Construction........MSc 12FT 24PT
Construction Law and Dispute Resolution ..... MSc 12FT 24-36PT/PGCert 12FT 24PT
Construction Project Management........MSc 12FT 24PT/PGCert 12FT 24PT

Civil engineering and construction
Research Courses

University of Aberdeen
Engineering... PhD 36FT/MPhil 24FT/MSc by research 12FT/EngD 36FT

Anglia Ruskin University
Built Environment........MPhil 24 - 60FT 36 - 72PT

University of Bath
Architecture........ PhD 24-48FT 36-72PT/MPhil 12-36FT 24-48PT
Civil Engineering.. PhD 24-48FT 36-72PT/MPhil 12-36FT 24-48PT

University of Birmingham
Civil Engineering PhD/MPhil........PhD 36FT/MPhil 24FT

University of Bolton
Built Environment Specialisms....PhD 36FT 72PT/PhD (via MPhil) 36FT 72PT/MPhil 24FT 36PT
Engineering Specialisms........ PhD 36FT 72PT/MPhil 18FT 36PT

University of Bristol
Civil Engineering........PhD 36FT 72PT/MSc by research 12FT 24PT

University of Cambridge
Engineering........PhD 36FT 60PT/MPhil 12FT

City University London
Aeronautical, Automotive, Mechanical and Civil Engineering...... PhD/MPhil

Coventry University
Civil Engineering........ MSc by research 12FT 24-36PT
Disaster Relief and Development Engineering.....MSc by research 12FT 24-36PT

University of Dundee
Civil Engineering ......MPhil 24FT MSc by research 12FT PhD 36FT

University of Edinburgh
Infrastructure and the Environment ..PhD 36FT 72PT/MPhil 24FT 48PT/MSc by research 12FT 24PT

National University of Ireland Galway
College of Engineering & Informatics........PhD 48FT 72PT/MEngSci by research 24FT 48PT/MAppSci by research 24FT 48PT/MEng by research 24FT

University of Glasgow
Infrastructure and Environment (Civil, Structural & Environmental Engineering)........PhD 36-48FT 60-72PT/MSc by research 12-24FT 24-36PT

University of Greenwich
Architecture and Construction- Research ...PhD 36FT 72PT/MPhil 12 - 18FT 24 - 36PT
Engineering (by Research)........MSc by research 12FT 24PT

Heriot-Watt University
Civil Engineering........PhD 36FT/MPhil 12FT
Construction Management and Surveying ....PhD 36FT 48PT/MPhil 12FT 24PT

Imperial College London
Department of Civil and Environmental Engineering ....PhD

Kingston University
Management in Construction (Civil Engineering)........ MSc by research 12FT 24PT

Lancaster University
Engineering........ PhD 36FT 48PT/MPhil 24FT 36PT

University of Leeds
Pathogen Control Engineering Institute....PhD 36+FT/MPhil 24FT

Liverpool John Moores University
Engineering for the Built Environment........PhD/MPhil

Civil engineering and construction

University of Liverpool
Engineering...................................PhD 36FT/MPhil 12FT 24PT

London South Bank University
Faculty of Engineering, Science & the Built Environment.......PhD 36FT 60PT/MPhil 24FT 36PT

Loughborough University
Built Environment...PhD 36FT 60PT/MPhil 24FT 36PT/EngD 48FT
Civil Engineering......PhD 36FT 60PT/MPhil 24FT 36PT/EngD 48FT
Engineering... EngD 48FT

University of Manchester
Civil Engineering.............PhD 36FT 72PT/MPhil 12FT 24PT/MSc by research 12FT

Newcastle University
Civil Engineering (Environmental) ......PhD 36FT 72PT/MPhil 12FT 24PT
Civil Engineering (Geotechnical and Engineering Geology)...........MPhil 12FT 24PT/PhD 36FT 72PT
Civil Engineering (Structural).... MPhil 12FT 24PT/PhD 36FT 72PT
Civil Engineering (Transport)..... MPhil 12FT 24PT/PhD 36FT 72PT

Nottingham Trent University
Multidisciplinary Engineering... MPhil 18FT 30PT/PhD 33FT 66PT

University of Nottingham
Civil Engineering........................... PhD 36FT 72PT/MPhil 24FT 48PT

University of Oxford
Engineering Science.................. DPhil 48FT/MSc by research 24FT

Plymouth University
Structural Integrity ....PhD/MPhil

University of Portsmouth
Civil Engineering and Surveying...........................MPhil 24FT 48PT/PhD 36FT 72PT
Engineering .... MPhil 24FT 48PT/PhD 36FT 72PT

Queen Mary, University of London
Engineering...PhD 36FT/MPhil

Queen's University Belfast
Spatial and Environmental Planning..PhD 36FT 72PT/MPhil 24FT 48PT

University of Sheffield
Civil and Structural Engineering...............................PhD 36FT 72PT/MPhil 24FT 48PT
Civil and Structural Engineering: Integrated Studies....Integrated PhD 48FT

Southampton Solent University
Engineering and Construction Faculty...........................PhD/MPhil

University of Southampton
Coastal Engineering for Climate Change ....MRes 12FT 24PT
Doctorate by research ....PhD 36FT/MPhil 24FT

University of Strathclyde
Building Design and Management for Sustainability ....MRes 12FT 36PT
Civil and Environmental Engineering - Research .PhD 36FT 72PT/MPhil 12FT 24PT/MRes 12FT 24PT

Swansea University
Civil Engineering.............PhD 36FT 60PT/MPhil 12FT 24PT/MSc by research 12FT 24PT
Desalination and Water Re-Use...........MSc by research 12FT 24PT
Erasmus Mundus Simulation in Engineering and Entrepreneurship Development..............................PhD 36FT 72PT

University of Ulster
Built Environment....................... PhD 36FT 72PT/MPhil 24FT 48PT

UCL - University College London
Advanced Spatial Analysis ....PhD 36FT 60PT

University of Warwick
Engineering.... MSc by research 12FT 24PT/MPhil 24FT 36PT/PhD 36FT 60PT/EngD 36-48FT 60PT

University of the West of Scotland
Department of Civil, Structural and Environmental Engineering..PhD/MPhil

University of Westminster
Architecture and the Built Environment..MPhil 18-36FT 30-60PT

University of Wolverhampton
Built Environment Research Unit...........................PhD 36FT/MPhil

Construction engineering
Taught Courses

Birmingham City University
Integrated Design and Construction Management .... MSc 28PT

Brunel University
Building Services Engineering........................... MSc 12FT 36-60DL
Building Services Engineering Management.............MSc 36-60DL
Building Services Engineering with Sustainable Energy................ MSc 12FT 36-60DL

Building Services Engineering with Sustainable Energy
.... MSc 12FT 36-60DL

University of Central Lancashire
Wind Energy Engineering.............MSc 12FT 24PT/PGDip 9FT 24PT

Centre for Alternative Technology
Renewable Energy and the Built Environment.....MSc 18FT 30PT/PGCert 6FT 12PT/AdvPGDip 12FT 24PT

University College Cork
Information Technology in Architecture, Engineering and Construction..................................MEngSci 12FT 24PT

Cranfield University
Renewable Energy Technology ....MSc 12FT 24-60PT/PGDip 6FT 24PT/PGCert 5FT 24PT

University of Dundee
Renewable Energy and Sustainable Building in a Global Context .... MSc 12FT

Edinburgh Napier University
Advanced Materials Engineering ....MSc 12FT 24PT
Timber Engineering .... MSc 12FT 24-36PT/PGDip 9FT 24-36PT

GCU London
International Project Management (London).....MSc 12FT/PGDip 9FT
International Project Management (Oil and Gas)........... MSc 15FT

Heriot-Watt University
Building Conservation (Technology and Management)......... MSc 24-84DL/PGDip 24-84DL

Imperial College London
Concrete Structures, also with Business Management or Sustainable Development....................................MSc 12FT 21-33PT

Kingston University
Structural Design & Construction Management with Sustainability...MSc 12FT 24PT
Structural Design and Construction Management ....MSc 12FT 24PT

Leeds Metropolitan University
Advanced Engineering Management .... MSc 12FT 24PT/PGCert 12PT/PGDip 12FT 24PT

London South Bank University
Building Services Engineering (Flexible Learning)....MSc 24-48PT
Building Services Engineering ....MSc 12FT MSc 24PT

Loughborough University
Low Carbon Building Design and Modelling.. MSc 12FT 24-60PT/PGDip 12FT 24-60PT/PGCert 12FT 24-60PT
Low Energy Building Services Engineering .....MSc 12FT 24 - 60PT

Northumbria University
Pipeline Integrity Management ....PGCert 36DL
Renewable and Sustainable Energy Technologies...........................MSc 12 or 16FT

Queen's University Belfast
Advanced Concrete Technology.....MSc 24PT/PGDip 24PT/PGCert 24PT

University of Reading
Intelligent Buildings: Design, Construction and Management .... MSc 24PT
Project Management .... MSc 24PT

Sheffield Hallam University
Advanced Design Engineering .. MSc 12FT 36PT/PGDip 8FT 24PT/PGCert 4FT 12PT

University of Sheffield
Structural and Concrete Engineering............MSc(Eng) 12FT 24PT/Diploma 9FT 18PT/Cert 6FT 12PT

University of West London
Development and Management of Sustainable Built Environment...MSc 12FT 24PT

Construction engineering
Research Courses

University of Birmingham
Engineering, Sustainability and Resilience ....MRes 12FT

Cardiff University
Sustainable Engineering..PhD 36FT

University of Greenwich
Property/Construction by Research....MSc by research 12FT 24PT

University of Strathclyde
Building Design and Management for Sustainability ....MRes 12FT 36PT

Construction management
Taught Courses

Anglia Ruskin University
Construction Management ....MSc 12FT 24-30PT
Construction Project Management ....MSc 12FT 24-30PT

University of Bath
International Construction Management MSc 36DL/PGDip 24DL

Civil engineering and construction

Birmingham City University
Construction Project Management .....PGCert 4FT 8PT/PGDip 4FT 8PT/MSc 4FT 8PT
Integrated Design and Construction Management .... MSc 28PT

University of Birmingham
Construction Management ....MSc 12FT 24PT
Engineering Management....................................MSc 12FT 24-36PT

University of Bolton
Construction Management ....MSc 36PT/PGDip 24PT/ PGCert 12PT

University of Brighton
Construction Management .....MSc 12FT 24PT/PGDip 12FT 24PT/ PGCert 12FT 24PT
Project Management for Construction.......MSc 12FT 24PT/PGDip 12FT 24PT/PGCert 12FT 24PT

College of Estate Management
Real Estate and Construction Management ....MBA 36DL

University of Central Lancashire
Construction Management (Construction Economics)MSc 24DL/ PGDip 12DL/PGCert 6DL
Construction Management (Facilities Management)..MSc 24DL/ PGDip 12DL/PGCert 6DL
Construction Management (Project Management).....MSc 24DL/ PGDip 12DL/PGCert 6DL
Construction Project Management .....MSc 12FT 24PT/PGDip 6FT 12PT/PGCert 3FT 6PT
Management Studies .... DMS 18PT

University of Chester
Programme and Project Management .... MSc 12FT 24 - 48PT/ PGDip 12FT 24 - 48PT/PGCert 12FT 12 - 24PT

City University London
Construction Management .... MSc 12FT

Coventry University
Construction Management ....MSc 12FT 24-36PT

University of Cumbria
Management Studies........................ GradDip 24PT/GradCert 12PT

Edinburgh Napier University
Construction Project Management .MSc 12FT 24-36PT 12-60DL/ PGDip 9FT 18PT 12-60DL/PGCert 6FT 12PT
Timber Industry Management........................ MSc 12FT 36PT 36DL

University of Edinburgh
Architectural Project Management (Distance Learning)
....MSc 84DL

University of Exeter
Engineering and Management.. MSc 12FT

GCU London
Construction Economics..MSc 12FT 24PT
Construction Management .... MSc 12FT
International Project Management (London).....MSc 12FT/PGDip 9FT

Glasgow Caledonian University
Construction Management ..MSc 12FT 24PT 24-60DL/PGDip 7FT 14PT
Management..............MSc 12FT FlexiblePT/PGDip 9FT FlexiblePT/ PGCert 6FT FlexiblePT

University of Greenwich
Construction Management and Economics........... MSc 12FT 24PT

Heriot-Watt University
Construction Project Management....... MSc 12FT 24PT 24-84DL/ PGDip 9FT 21PT 24-84DL
Facilities Management (Dubai) .. MSc 12FT 24PT 24-84DL/PGDip 9FT 21PT

Kingston University
Management in Construction...................................MSc 12FT 24PT
Management in Construction (Law) .... MSc 24PT
Structural Design and Construction Management .... MSc 12FT 24PT

Leeds Metropolitan University
Advanced Engineering Management .... MSc 12FT 24PT/PGCert 12PT/PGDip 12FT 24PT

University of Leeds
International Construction Management and Engineering .... MSc(Eng) 12FT

Liverpool John Moores University
Construction Project Management ....MSc 12FT 24PT

London South Bank University
Construction Project Management ....MSc 12FT 24PT
Construction Project Management (Health Care)...........MSc 24PT

Loughborough University
Construction Business Management................MSc 12FT 24-60PT
Construction Management ....MSc 12FT 24-60PT
Construction Project Management....................MSc 12FT 24-60PT

Manchester Metropolitan University
Project Management..MSc 12FT 24PT

University of Manchester
Management of Projects: Construction Project Management .....
MSc 12FT 36PT

Newcastle University
Architectural Practice and Management .... PGDip 12PT

Northumbria University
Construction Project Management ...MSc 12FT 30PT/PGDip 12FT 24PT/PGCert 12FT 24PT
Project Management (Chalmers Dual Award)................ MSc 24FT
Project Management/Management de projets de construction a l'international - dual award .... MSc 15FT
Surveying/Construction programme - Building Surveying Pathway ....MSc 24DL
Surveying/Construction programme - Construction Pathway......
....MSc 24DL
Surveying/Construction programme - Housing Pathway....... MSc 24DL
Surveying/Construction programme - Quantity Surveying Pathway ....MSc 24DL
Surveying/Construction programme - Real Estate Pathway.. MSc 24DL

Nottingham Trent University
Construction Management ....MSc 12FT 24-60PT 24-60DL
Engineering Management..MSc 12FT 24PT
Project Management (Construction) ....MSc 24FT 24-60PT 24-60DL

Oxford Brookes University
Project Management in the Built Environment .... MSc 12FT 24DL/PGDip 9FT 21DL/PGCert 9FT 9DL

Plymouth University
Sustainable Construction...MSc 36PT 36DL

University of Portsmouth
Construction Project Management ....MSc 12FT 24PT
Property Development..MSc 12FT 24PT

Queen's University Belfast
Construction and Project Management/ Cionstruction and Project Management with Industrial Internship .... MSc 12FT 24-36PT/PGDip 9FT 18PT

University of Reading
Construction Management .... MSc 12FT
Intelligent Buildings: Design, Construction and Management .... MSc 24PT
Project Management .... MSc 24PT

Robert Gordon University
Construction Project Management .MSc 12FT 28-36PT 28-36DL/ PGDip 9FT 18-24PT 18-24DL/PGCert 4FT 9-12PT 9-12DL

University of Salford
Construction Management ....MSc 12FT 24DL/PGDip 8FT 16DL
Project Management in Construction MSc 12FT 28DL/PGDip 8FT 20DL/PGCert 4FT 8DL
Quantity Surveying (Mechanical and Electrical) .... MSc 12FT 28DL/PGDip 8FT 16DL

Sheffield Hallam University
Construction Management ....MSc 12FT 24-36FT

University of South Wales
Construction Project Management ....MSc 12FT 36PT

Teesside University
Engineering Management ....MSc 12-18FT 24PT/PGDip 8FT

Trinity College Dublin - the University of Dublin
Health and Safety in Construction .... PGDip 12PT

University of Ulster
Commercial Management in Construction.........PGCert 4FT 9PT/ PGDip 8FT 18PT/MSc 12FT 36PT
Construction Business and Project Management MSc 12FT 36PT/ PGDip 9FT 24PT/PGCert 9PT

UCL - University College London
Construction Economics and Management ... MSc 12FT 24-60PT/ PGDip 9FT

University of the West of England, Bristol
Construction Project Management ....MSc 12FT 28PT

University of Westminster
Building Information Management ....MSc 12FT 24PT

University of Wolverhampton
Construction Project Management .MSc 12FT 24PT/PGCert 12FT 24PT

Construction management
Research Courses

Anglia Ruskin University
Built Environment...DProf 60DL 60PT
Science and Technology...DProf 60DL

University of Birmingham
Engineering, Sustainability and Resilience ....MRes 12FT

University of Cambridge
Management Studies...PhD 36FT

Oxford Brookes University
Construction and Project Management Group .... PhD 24-60FT 36-72PT/MPhil 24-36FT 36-48PT

University of Strathclyde
Building Design and Management for Sustainability ....
MRes 12FT 36PT

Contaminated land
Taught Courses

Brunel University
Toxicology and Risk Assessment .... MSc 12FT 24PT

Cardiff University
Applied Environmental Geology .... MSc 12FT

Heriot-Watt University
Environmental Analysis and Assessment ....
MRes 12FT 24PT/PGDip 9FT 18PT/PGCert 9FT 18PT

Lancaster University
Contamination, Risk Assessment and Remediation ...... MSc 12FT 24PT
Environmental and Biochemical Toxicology...........MSc 12FT 24PT

University of Leeds
Hydrogeology ....MSc 12FT 24-48PT/PGDip 12FT 24-48PT

University of Portsmouth
Environmental Geology and Contamination ....MSc 12FT 24PT

University of Reading
Environmental Management ....MSc 12FT 24PT

University of Sheffield
Contaminant HydrogeologyMSc 12FT 24PT/PGDip 9FT 18PT/Cert 6FT 12PT

University of Ulster
Environmental Toxicology & Pollution Monitoring by e-Learning ....PGDip 24DL/MSc 36DL

Contaminated land
Research Courses

University of Nottingham
Contaminated Land Management ....MRes 24PT
Risk Analysis, Social Processes and Health ....MPhil 36FT/ PhD 24FT

Environmental engineering
Taught Courses

University of Abertay Dundee
Urban Water and Environmental Management ... MSc 12FT 24PT

Anglia Ruskin University
Business Management of Waste and Resources.......MSc 12-24DL

Bangor University
Environmental Management.. MBA 12FT
Rheolaeth Amgylcheddol Gynaliadwy (Sustainable Environmental Management)........MSc 12FT 24PT/MA 12FT 24PT

University of Brighton
Environmental Geology...........MSc 12FT 24PT/PGDip 12FT 24PT/ PGCert 12FT 24PT
Water and Environmental Management ...MSc 12FT 24PT/PGDip 12FT 24PT

University of Bristol
Water and Environmental Management ....MSc 12FT 24PT

University of Cambridge
Engineering for Sustainable Development....................MPhil 11FT
Fluid Flow in Industry and the Environment.................MPhil 11FT
Geographical Research...MPhil 12FT

Cardiff University
Geoenvironmental Engineering ....MSc 12FT 24-36PT
Hydro-environment Engineering ....MSc 12FT 24PT

University of Central Lancashire
Carbon and Resource Management....MSc 12FT 24PT/PGDip 9FT 18PT/PGCert 6FT 12PT
Sustainable Waste Management.......MSc 12FT 24PT/PGDip 12FT 24PT/PGCHE 4FT

Cranfield University
Agricultural and Environmental Engineering .... MSc(Res) 12FT 24-36PT
Environmental Engineering................................ MSc 12FT 24-60PT/ PGDip 6FT 24PT/PGCert 5FT 24PT/MTech 24FT
Environmental Risk Management .MSc 12FT 24-60PT/PGDip 6FT 24PT/PGCert 5FT 24PT
Waste and Resource Management....... MSc 12FT 24-60PT/PGDip 12FT 24PT/PGCert 12FT 24PT/MTech 24FT

De Montfort University
Environmental Technology and Management .... MSc 12FT

University of Derby
Sustainable Architecture and Healthy Environments .....MA 12FT

University of Dundee
Civil Engineering .... MSc 12FT
Concrete Engineering and Environmental Management ...... MSc 12FT

Civil engineering and construction

Spatial Planning with Environmental Assessment .... MSc 12FT

University of East Anglia
Energy Engineering with Environmental ManagementMSc 12FT/MSc 24PT/MSc 36PT/MSc 48PT

Edinburgh Napier University
Energy and Environmental Engineering................. MSc 12FT 36PT

University of Exeter
Advanced Civil Engineering .... MSc 12FT
Engineering and Management................................ MSc 12FT
Surveying and Land/ Environmental Management....... MSc 12FT 24-36PT/PGDip 12FT 24-36PT

GCU London
International Project Management (Oil and Gas).......... MSc 15FT

Glasgow Caledonian University
Energy and Environmental Management..MSc 12FT 24PT/PGDip 8FT 20PT/PGCert 4FT 8PT
Sustainable Energy Technology .... MSc 12FT 24PT
Waste Management.................... MSc 12FT 24PT/PGDip 8FT 20PT/PGCert 4FT 8PT

Heriot-Watt University
Sustainability Engineering......... MSc 12FT 24PT/PGDip 9FT 21PT/PGCert 6FT 12PT
Urban Strategies and Design.......MSc 12FT 24PT/PGDip 9FT 21PT

University of Hertfordshire
Water and Environmental Management ....MSc 12FT 24-60PT 24DL/PGDip 12FT 18-48PT 18DL/PGCert 12FT 18-48PT 18DL

Imperial College London
Environmental Engineering, also with Business Management or Sustainable Development.....................................MSc 12FT 24-36PT
General Structural Engineering...........................MSc 12FT 24-36PT
Systems Engineering and Innovation................................ MSc 24PT

University of Leeds
Environmental Engineering & Project Management .....MSc(Eng) 12FT
Water, Sanitation and Health Engineering.............MSc(Eng) 12FT

University of Leicester
Environmental Informatics..........MSc 12FT 24PT/PGDip 9FT 18PT

Loughborough University
Sustainable Engineering..MSc 12FT 96PT
Water and Environmental Management by Distance Learning.... MSc 96DL/PGDip 60DL/PGCert 36DL
Water and Waste Engineering ..MSc 12FT/PGDip 6FT/PGCert 3FT
Water and Waste Engineering by Distance Learning...MSc 96DL/PGDip 60DL/PGCert 36DL

Manchester Metropolitan University
Sustainable Aviation..MSc 12FT 12-36PT

University of Manchester
Renewable Energy and Clean Technology........................ MSc 12FT

Middlesex University
Environmental Pollution Control.............................. MSc 12FT 24PT

Newcastle University
Agricultural and Environmental Science.......................... MSc 12FT
Clean Technology.. MSc 12FT/PGDip 7FT
Environmental Engineering...................................... MSc 12FT 48PT
Environmental and Petroleum Geochemistry .... MSc 12FT 48PT
Offshore and Environmental Technology................MSc 12 or 24FT
Skills, Technology, Research and Management for the UK Water Sector (STREAM)..EngD by taught 48FT
Structural Engineering... MSc 12FT 48PT
Transport Planning and the Environment ....MSc 12FT 24-48PT

University of Northampton
International Wastes Management.................................MSc 24DL
Wastes Management................ MSc 12FT 24PT 36DL/PGDip 12PT

Nottingham Trent University
Structural Engineering with Management .... MSc 12FT 24PT
Structural Engineering with Materials .... MSc 12FT 24PT

University of Nottingham
Civil Engineering: Geotechnical Engineering.................. MSc 12FT
Engineering Surveying with Geographical Information Science .. MSc 12FT
Environmental Engineering.. MSc 12FT
Environmental and Resource Engineering........................ MSc 12FT

Plymouth University
Civil Engineering....................... MSc 12FT/PGDip 12FT/PGCert 6FT

University of Portsmouth
Civil Engineering with Environmental Engineering .... MSc 12FT 24PT

Queen's University Belfast
Advanced Concrete Technology.....MSc 24PT/PGDip 24PT/PGCert 24PT
Durability of Structures ....MSc 12FT 24PT/PGDip 12FT 24PT/PGCert 12FT 24PT
Environmental Engineering............................... MSc 12FT 24-36PT/PGDip 12FT 24PT
Environmental Planning... MSc 12FT

University of Reading
Renewable Energy ....MSc 12FT 24PT/PGDip 9FT 21PT

Robert Gordon University
Energy Management.... MSc 12FT 36DL/PGDip 8FT 24DL/PGCert 4FT 12DL
Energy and Sustainability ...MSc 42DL/PGDip 24DL/PGCert 12DL

University of Salford
Environmental Acoustics...MSc 12FT 28PT 28DL/PGDip 9FT 18PT 18DL

School of Oriental and African Studies - SOAS
Environmental Management................................MSc 12FT 24-36PT

Sheffield Hallam University
Built Environment.....MPhil 24FT 36PT/PhD by taught 24FT 60PT
Environmental Management.........................MSc 12-24FT 24-36PT
Environmental Management (International Resource and Climate Management)......................................MSc 12-18FT 24-36PT
Environmental Management (Wildlife and Landscape Conservation) ....MSc 12-18FT 24-36PT

University of Sheffield
Environmental Management of Urban Land and Water .... MSc 12FT 24PT/PGDip 9FT 18PT/PGCert 6FT 12PT
Structural and Concrete Engineering............MSc(Eng) 12FT 24PT/Diploma 9FT 18PT/Cert 6FT 12PT

University of Southampton
Civil and Environmental Engineering....................... MSc 12FT 24PT
Environmental Coastal Engineering......................... MSc 12FT 24PT
Environmental Monitoring and Assessment .... MSc 12FT 27PT
Freshwater Sciences .... MRes 12FT

University of Strathclyde
Environmental Engineering....... MSc 12FT 24PT/PGDip 9FT 18PT/PGCert 6FT 12PT
Environmental Entrepreneurship......... MSc 12FT 24PT/PGDip 9FT 18PT/PGCert 6FT 12PT
Environmental Health....MSc 12FT 24PT/PGDip 9FT 18PT/PGCert 6FT 12PT
Sustainability and Environmental Studies ....MSc 12FT 24PT/PGDip 9FT 18PT

University of Surrey
Process and Environmental Systems Engineering.......... MSc 12FT
Water and Environmental Engineering.................. MSc 12FT 72PT

Teesside University
Civil Engineering...............................MSc 12 - 16FT 24PT/PGDip 8FT
Energy and Environmental Management.........MSc 12-16FT 24PT

Trinity College Dublin - the University of Dublin
Engineering (Environmental/Structural & Geotechnics/Transport).. MSc 12FT 24PT
Environmental Engineering .... PGDip 12PT
Environmental Sciences.. MSc 12FT

UCL - University College London
Built Environment: Environmental Design and Engineering......... MSc 12FT 24-60PT/PGDip 9FT
Built Environment: Heritage Science ....MRes 12FT 24-60PT/PGCert 6FT
Energy Demand Studies ....MRes 12FT
Energy and Resources: Policy and Practice, Australia .... MSc 24FT 36-48PT
Environmental Systems Engineering....................... MSc 12FT 24PT

University of the West of Scotland
Waste Management with Environmental Management .... MSc 12FT 30PT/Diploma 9FT 20PT

University of Wolverhampton
Environmental Technology .... MSc 12FT 24PT

Environmental engineering
Research Courses

Bangor University
Agricultural Systems.................... MPhil 24FT 36PT/PhD 36FT 60PT
Renewable Materials.................... MPhil 24FT 36PT/PhD 36FT 60PT

University of Brighton
School of the Environment Research Division .... PhD 24-60FT 36-72PT/MPhil 18-36FT 30-48PT

Cranfield University
Agricultural and Environmental Engineering ....MPhil 24FT 96PT/PhD 36FT 96PT/MSc by research 12FT 24-60PT

University of Dundee
Civil Engineering ....MPhil 24FT MSc by research 12FT

Durham University
Earth Sciences ....PhD 36FT 72PT/MPhil 24FT 48PT/MSc by research 12FT 24PT

University of Glasgow
Infrastructure and Environment (Civil, Structural & Environmental Engineering)...........PhD 36-48FT 60-72PT/MSc by research 12-24FT 24-36PT

University of Greenwich
Engineering (by Research)....................MSc by research 12FT 24PT

Harper Adams University
Engineering...MPhil 24FT/PhD 38FT

University of Leeds
Energy and Resources Research Institute ....PhD 36+FT/MPhil 24FT
Low Carbon Technologies..................................Integrated PhD 48FT
Pathogen Control Engineering Institute....PhD 36+FT/MPhil 24FT

University of Liverpool
Engineering...PhD 36FT/MPhil 12FT 24PT

University of Manchester
Environmental Engineering....... PhD 36FT 72PT/MPhil 12FT 24PT

Newcastle University
Civil Engineering (Environmental) ......PhD 36FT 72PT/MPhil 12FT 24PT
Energy.. PhD 36FT 72PT/MPhil 12FT 24PT
Environmental Science............... MPhil 12FT 24PT/PhD 36FT 72PT
Integrated PhD 48FT

Nottingham Trent University
Applied Energy and Environmental Engineering .... MPhil 18FT 30PT/PhD 33FT 66PT

The Open University
Integrated Waste Systems .... PhD 36FT 72PT variableDL/MPhil 15FT 24PT variableDL

University of Sheffield
Civil and Structural Engineering: Integrated Studies....Integrated PhD 48FT
Environmental and Energy Engineering: Integrated Studies......... Integrated PhD 48FT

University of Southampton
Coastal Engineering for Climate Change ....MRes 12FT 24PT
Doctorate by research ....PhD 36FT/MPhil 24FT

University of Strathclyde
Building Design and Management for Sustainability .... MRes 12FT 36PT

University of Surrey
Sustainability for Engineering and Energy Systems (SEES) .. EngD 48FT

Swansea University
Environmental Management...................................MRes 12FT 24PT
Erasmus Mundus Simulation in Engineering and Entrepreneurship Development................................ PhD 36FT 72PT

UCL - University College London
Civil, Environmental and Geomatic Engineering .. PhD 36FT 60PT
Environmental Engineering Science................................ EngD 48FT

University of the West of Scotland
Department of Civil, Structural and Environmental Engineering...PhD/MPhil

Estate management
Taught Courses

University of Aberdeen
Urban Planning and Real Estate ....MSc 12FT/PGDip 12FT

University of Cambridge
Real Estate Finance .... MPhil 10FT

City University London
Real Estate.. MSc 9FT 18PT
Real Estate Investment .... MSc 9-12FT

Glasgow Caledonian University
Building Services Engineering...................................MSc 12FT 24PT
Real Estate Management ....MSc 12FT 24PT

University of Glasgow
Real Estate .... PGCert 12FT

University of Greenwich
Real Estate Development and Investment ....MSc 12FT 24PT

Heriot-Watt University
Housing and Real Estate........MSc 12FT 24PT 24-84DL/PGDip 9FT 18PT 18-84DL
Urban Studies/Housing/Planning Studies/Real Estate Research. MSc(Res) 12FT
Real Estate Management and Development .... MSc 12FT 24PT 24-84DL/PGDip 9FT 21PT 24-84DL
Real Estate and Planning.......MSc 12FT 24PT 24-84DL/PGDip 9FT 21PT 24-84DL

Kingston University
Real Estate...MSc 12-24FT 24-48PT

Northumbria University
International Real Estate Management .... MSc 12FT
Real Estate Management ....MSc 12FT 36PT
Surveying/Construction programme - Real Estate Pathway.. MSc 24DL

Nottingham Trent University
International Real Estate Investment and Finance........................... MSc 12FT 24PT

University of Reading
Corporate Real Estate ....MSc 24-72PT
Development Planning .... MSc 12FT 24PT/PGDip 12FT 24PT
Development Planning Research ......MSc 12FT 24PT/PGDip 12FT 24PT

Civil engineering and construction

Rural Land and Business Management .... MSc 12FT

Royal Agricultural University
International Real Estate .... MSc 12FT
Property Agency and Management.................................... MSc 12FT
Rural Estate Management .... MSc 12FT

University of Salford
Real Estate Development ....MSc 12FT 28DL/PGDip 8FT 20DL
Real Estate and Property Management......MSc 12FT 28DL/PGDip 8FT 20DL

Estate management
Research Courses

Anglia Ruskin University
Built Environment...DProf 60PT 60DL

Fire safety engineering
Taught Courses

University of Bradford
Integrated Emergency Management .... MA 32 - 60PT

University of Central Lancashire
Fire Investigation............................MSc 12FT/PGDip 9FT/PGCert 6FT
Fire Safety Engineering...MSc 12FT 24PT
Fire Scene Investigation...MSc 24-36PT
Fire and Rescue Service Management ....MSc 12FT 24PT

City University London
Analysis and Design of Structures for Fire, Blast and
Earthquakes............................. MSc 12FT 36PT/PGDip 8FT 12-36PT

Cranfield University, Shrivenham
Explosives Ordnance Engineering......MSc 12FT 60PT/PGDip 12FT 60PT
Forensic Explosives and Explosion Investigation .MSc 12FT 60PT/PGDip 12FT 60PT/PGCert 12FT 60PT

University of Edinburgh
Structural & Fire Safety Engineering................................... MSc 12FT

Glyndwr University
Fire Safety and Risk Management .. NEBOSH National Certificate 4PT

University of Leeds
Fire and Explosion Engineering..MSc 12FT

University of Salford
Industrial and Commercial Combustion Engineering .MSc 36DL/PGDip 12DL/PGCert 12DL

Swansea Metropolitan University
Non Destructive Testings and Evaluation ....MSc 12FT 24PT

Trinity College Dublin - the University of Dublin
Fire Safety Practice (Buildings and Other Structures) ....PGDip 12PT

University of Ulster
Fire Safety Engineering ....MSc 12FT 36PT/PGDip 9FT 24PT
Hydrogen Safety Engineering ....MSc 24-36DL/PGDip 24-36DL/PGCert 12-24DL

Fire safety engineering
Research Courses

University of Central Lancashire
Fire and Explosion Studies ....PhD 48FT 84PT/MPhil 36FT 60PT/MSc by research 24FT 36PT

Cranfield University, Shrivenham
Explosive Chemistry ....PhD 36FT 48-72PT/MPhil 24FT 48-72PT

Oxford Brookes University
Safety Technology ....PhD 24-60FT 36-72PT/MPhil 24-36FT 36-48PT

Geotechnical engineering
Taught Courses

University of Birmingham
Geotechnical Engineering.................... MSc 12FT 24-36PT/PGDip 8FT 16-24PT
Geotechnical Engineering and Management MSc 12FT 24-36PT/PGDip 8FT 16-24PT/PGCert 4FT 8PT

Cardiff University
Applied Environmental Geology .... MSc 12FT

University of Dundee
Geotechnical Engineering .... MSc 12FT

University of Edinburgh
GeoSciences (Individual Project) ....MSc(Res) 12FT 24PT
Petroleum Geoscience .... MSc 12FT

University of Exeter
Advanced Civil Engineering .... MSc 12FT
Applied Geotechnics....................MSc 12FT 36PT/PGDip 12FT 36PT

Heriot-Watt University
Environmental Analysis and Assessment .... MRes 12FT 24PT/PGDip 9FT 18PT/PGCert 9FT 18PT

Imperial College London
Engineering Geology for Ground Models, also with Business
Management or Sustainable Development...........MSc 12FT 24PT
General Structural Engineering ....MSc 12FT 24-36PT
Soil Mechanics and Environmental Geotechnics..MSc 12FT 24PT
Systems Engineering and Innovation................................MSc 24PT

University of Leeds
Engineering Geology ....MSc 12FT 12-48PT

Newcastle University
Engineering Geology ....MSc 12FT 48PT
Environmental Engineering ....MSc 12FT 48PT
Geotechnical Engineering................................MSc 12FT 48PT

University of Nottingham
Engineering Surveying with Geographical Information Science .. MSc 12FT

University of Portsmouth
Engineering Geology ....MSc 12FT 24PT

University of Sheffield
Osteoarchaeology ....MSc 12FT 24PT

University of Southampton
Environmental Monitoring and Assessment ....MSc 12FT 27PT

University of Sussex
Applied Geomorphology ....MSc 12FT 24PT

Teesside University
Civil Engineering...............MSc 12 - 16FT 24PT/PGDip 8FT

Trinity College Dublin - the University of Dublin
Engineering (Environmental/Structural & Geotechnics/Transport) ....MSc 12FT 24PT
Environmental Engineering .... PGDip 12PT
Highway and Geotechnical Engineering ....PGDip 12PT

Geotechnical engineering
Research Courses

City University London
Geotechnical Engineering Research Centre....................PhD/MPhil

Durham University
Earth Sciences ....PhD 36FT 72PT/MPhil 24FT 48PT/MSc by research 12FT 24PT

Newcastle University
Civil Engineering (Geotechnical and Engineering Geology)...........MPhil 12FT 24PT/PhD 36FT 72PT

Swansea University
Environmental Sustainability...............MSc by research 12FT 24PT

UCL - University College London
Environmental Engineering Science................................ EngD 48FT

Land and building surveying
Taught Courses

Anglia Ruskin University
Built Environment .... DProf by taught 60PT 60DL

College of Estate Management
Surveying.. MSc 40DL/PGDip 30DL

University of Central Lancashire
Building Conservation and Regeneration .... MSc 12FT 24-30PT/PGDip 6FT 12PT/PGCert 3FT 6PT
Building Services......MSc 12FT 30PT/PGDip 6FT 12PT/PGCert 3FT 6PT

Cranfield University
Integrated Landscape Ecology MSc 12FT 60PT/PGDip 12FT 60PT/PGCert 12FT 60PT
Land Reclamation and Restoration ....MSc 12FT 60PT/PGCert 12FT 60PT/PGDip 12FT 60PT

University of Exeter
Engineering and Management... MSc 12FT
Surveying and Land/ Environmental Management .... MSc 12FT 24-36PT/PGDip 12FT 24-36PT

University of Glasgow
Geomatics & Management .... MSc 12FT

Kingston University
Building Surveying ....MSc 12FT 24PT

London South Bank University
Quantity Surveying ....MSc 12FT MSc 24PT

Northumbria University
Real Estate Management ....MSc 12FT 36PT
Surveying (Minerals)...MSc 24DL

Nottingham Trent University
Building Surveying ....MSc 12FT 24PT

University of Salford
Accessibility and Inclusive Design............ MSc 32DL/PGDip 20DL/PGCert 8DL
Corporate Real Estate and Facilities Management.......MSc 28DL/PGDip 20DL/PGCert 8DL
Quantity Surveying........................MSc 12FT 28PT/PGDip 8FT 16PT
Quantity Surveying (Mechanical and Electrical) .MSc 12FT 28DL/PGDip 8FT 16DL

Sustainable Building Design...... MSc 12FT 28PT/PGDip 8FT 20PT/PGCert 4FT 8PT

University of St Andrews
Sustainable Development................................. MSc 12FT/PGDip 9FT

UCL - University College London
Environmental Modelling ....MSc 12FT 24PT
Mega Infrastructure Planning, Appraisal and Delivery ....MSc 12FT 24-60PT
Surveying...MSc 12FT 24PT

University of the West of England, Bristol
Building Surveying ....MSc 24FT 36PT

Land and building surveying
Research Courses

University of Aberdeen
Spatial Planning and Rural Surveying .... PhD 36FT/MPhil 24FT/MSc by research 12FT

Anglia Ruskin University
Built Environment...DProf 60PT 60DL

University of Glasgow
Geography and Geomatics .... PhD 36FT/MSc by research 12FT/PGDip by research 12FT/MRes 12FT

Newcastle University
Geomatics .... PhD 36FT 72PT/MPhil 12FT 24PT

University of Nottingham
Engineering and Surveying Space Geodesy...........PhD 36FT 72PT/MPhil 24FT 48PT

University of Portsmouth
Civil Engineering and Surveying...........................MPhil 24FT 48PT/PhD 36FT 72PT

UCL - University College London
Geomatic Engineering .... PhD 36FT 60PT

Mining engineering
Taught Courses

University of Exeter
Applied Geotechnics................... MSc 12FT 36PT/PGDip 12FT 36PT
Minerals Engineering .... MSc 12FT
Mining Engineering ....MSc 12FT 24-36PT/PGDip 12FT 24-36PT
Mining Geology .... MSc 12FT
Surveying and Land/ Environmental Management .... MSc 12FT 24-36PT/PGDip 12FT 24-36PT

Newcastle University
Geotechnical Engineering...MSc 12FT 48PT

Northumbria University
Surveying (Minerals)...MSc 24DL

The Open University
Engineering............... MSc(Eng) 12-24DL/MEng variableDL/PGDip variableDL

Robert Gordon University
Drilling and Well Engineering ....MSc 12FT 36DL/PGDip 9FT 24DL

Mining engineering
Research Courses

University of Exeter
Earth Resources............. MPhil 36FT 60PT/PhD 48FT 89PT/MSc by research 12FT 24PT
Engineering.. EngD 48FT
Geology.................. MSc by research 12FT 24PT/MPhil 36FT 60PT/PhD 48FT 84PT
Mining and Minerals Engineering.....MSc by research 12FT 24PT/MPhil 36FT 60PT/PhD 48FT 80PT

University of Greenwich
Engineering (by Research)....................MSc by research 12FT 24PT

University of Liverpool
Engineering..PhD 36FT/MPhil 12FT 24PT

Offshore engineering
Taught Courses

University of Aberdeen
Oil and Gas Engineering ....MSc 12FT 24PT
Renewable Energy..MSc 12FT/PGDip 9FT

Bangor University
Renewable Materials............................PhD by taught 36FT 60PT/MPhil 24FT 36PT

University of Cambridge
Energy Technology .... MPhil 12FT

University of Central Lancashire
Renewable Energy Engineering .... MSc 12FT 24PT/PGDip 24PT
Wind Energy Engineering.............MSc 12FT 24PT/PGDip 9FT 24PT

Cranfield University
Offshore and Ocean Technology with Offshore Materials
Engineering ....MSc 12FT 24-60PT/MTech 24FT/PGCert 5FT 24PT/PGDip 6FT 24PT

Civil engineering and construction

Offshore and Ocean Technology with Offshore Renewable Energy .... MSc 12FT 24-60PT/MTech 24FT/PGDip 6FT 24PT/PGCert 5FT 24PT

Offshore and Ocean Technology with Pipeline Engineering .... MSc 12FT 24-60PT/MTech 24FT/PGCert 5FT 24PT/PGDip 6FT 24PT

Offshore and Ocean Technology with Risk Management ...... MSc 12FT 24-60PT/MTech 24FT/PGDip 6FT 24PT/PGCert 5FT 24PT

Offshore and Ocean Technology with Subsea Engineering ... MSc 12FT 24-60PT/MTech 24FT/PGDip 6FT 24PT/PGCert 5FT 24PT

Edinburgh Napier University
Renewable Energy .... MSc 12FT 24PT

University of Exeter
Energy Policy .... MSc 12FT 24PT
Environment, Energy and Resilience .... MRes 12FT 24PT

Heriot-Watt University
Petroleum Geoscience (PetGeo) .... MSc 12FT
Renewable Energy Engineering .. MSc 12FT 24PT/PGDip 9FT 21PT
Reservoir Evaluation and Management .... MSc 12FT 24PT

University of Hull
Petroleum, Oil and Gas: Chemical Engineering Management MSc 12FT
Petroleum, Oil and Gas: Chemical Engineering Technologies MSc 12FT

Kingston University
Renewable Energy Engineering .... MSc 12FT 24PT

University of Leeds
Oilfield Corrosion Engineering .... MSc(Eng) 12FT

Liverpool John Moores University
Marine and Offshore Engineering MSc .... MSc 12FT 24PT/PGDip 9FT 18PT/PGCert 6FT 12PT/CPD 3-4FT 3-4PT

Newcastle University
Marine Structures and Integrity .... MSc 12 or 24FT
Marine and Offshore Power Systems .... MSc 12 or 24FT
Offshore Engineering .... MSc 12 or 24FT
Offshore and Environmental Technology .... MSc 12 or 24FT
Pipeline Engineering.... MSc 12FT 24PT/PGDip 12FT 24PT/PGCert 12FT 24PT
Subsea Engineering and Management .... MSc 12FT 24-36PT

Northumbria University
Renewable and Sustainable Energy Technologies .... MSc 12 or 16FT

University of Nottingham
Electrical Engineering for Sustainable and Renewable Energy ..... MSc 12FT/PGDip 9FT

Robert Gordon University
Energy Management .... MSc 12FT 36DL/PGDip 8FT 24DL/PGCert 4FT 12DL
Energy and Sustainability .. MSc 42DL/PGDip 24DL/PGCert 12DL
Offshore Renewables .... MSc 42DL
Subsea Engineering .... MSc 36DL

University of Salford
Petroleum and Gas Engineering .... MSc 12FT/PGDip 9FT

University of Strathclyde
Offshore Floating Systems .... MSc 12FT/PGDip 9FT
Ship and Offshore Structures .... MSc 12FT/PGDip 9FT
Ship and Offshore Technology .... MSc 24FT
Subsea Engineering .... MSc 12FT/PGDip 9FT
Sustainable Engineering: Marine Technology .... MSc 12FT/PGDip 9FT
Sustainable Engineering: Offshore Renewable Energy MSc 12FT/PGDip 9FT

Swansea University
Materials Engineering .... MSc 12FT 24-36PT

Teesside University
Energy and Environmental Management .... MSc 12-16FT 24PT

UCL - University College London
Energy Demand Studies .... MRes 12FT
Energy and Resources: Policy and Practice, Australia .... MSc 24FT 36-48PT

Offshore engineering
Research Courses

Cardiff University
Institute of Energy .... EngD 48FT/PhD 36FT/MPhil 12FT

University of Exeter
Environment, Energy and Resilience .. MPhil 36FT 60PT/PhD 36FT 84PT
Offshore Renewable Energy .... EngD 48FT
Renewable Energy MSc by research 12FT 24PT/MPhil 36FT 60PT/PhD 48FT 80PT

Heriot-Watt University
Petroleum Engineering .... PhD 36FT 48PT/MPhil 12-24FT 24PT

Newcastle University
Energy .... PhD 36FT 72PT/MPhil 12FT 24PT

UCL - University College London
Offshore Engineering .... PhD 36FT 60PT

Petroleum engineering
Taught Courses

University of Aberdeen
Hydrocarbon Exploration .... PGDip 9FT/MSc 12FT
Integrated Petroleum Geoscience .... MSc 12FT
Oil & Gas Chemistry .... MSc 12FT/PGDip 9FT/PGCert 4FT
Oil & Gas Structural Engineering .... MSc 36DL
Oil and Gas Enterprise Management .... MSc 12FT 24PT
Oil and Gas Law .... LLM 12FT 24PT
Pertroleum, Energy Economics and Finance .... MSc(Econ) 12FT

University of Birmingham
Applied and Petroleum Micropalaeontology .... MSc 12FT

University of Central Lancashire
Oil and Gas Operations Management .... MSc 12FT

Cranfield University
Flow Assurance for Oil and Gas Production ..... MSc 12FT 24-60PT

University of Derby
Applied Petroleum Geoscience MSc 4FT/PGDip 12FT 24PT/PGCert 3FT

University of Dundee
Energy Studies with Specialisation in Oil and Gas Economics ..... MSc 12FT
International Oil and Gas Management .... MBA 24DL
International Oil and Gas Management .... MBA 12FT
International Oil and Gas Management .... MSc 12FT
Managing in the Energy Industries .... MSc 12FT
Petroleum Law and Policy .... LLM 12FT/PGDip 9FT
Petroleum Law and Policy .... LLM 24-60DL

University of Edinburgh
GeoSciences (Individual Project) .... MSc(Res) 12FT 24PT
Petroleum Geoscience .... MSc 12FT

Glasgow Caledonian University
Master of Accounting (Oil and Gas Accounting) .... MAcc 12FT FlexiblePT

Heriot-Watt University
Petroleum Engineering .... MSc 12FT 21-84DL
Petroleum Geoscience (PetGeo) .... MSc 12FT
Reservoir Evaluation and Management .... MSc 12FT 24PT

University of Hull
Petroleum, Oil and Gas: Chemical Engineering Management ...... MSc 12FT
Petroleum, Oil and Gas: Chemical Engineering Technologies .... MSc 12FT

Imperial College London
Petroleum Engineering .... MSc 12FT
Petroleum Geophysics .... MSc 12FT
Petroleum Geoscience .... MSc 12FT

University of Leeds
Oilfield Corrosion Engineering .... MSc(Eng) 12FT

London South Bank University
Petroleum Engineering .... MSc 12FT 24PT

University of Manchester
Petroleum Exploration Geoscience .... MSc 12FT
Petroleum Geoscience for Reservoir Development and Production .... MSc 12FT

Middlesex University
MBA Oil and Gas .... MBA 24PT

Newcastle University
Environmental and Petroleum Geochemistry .... MSc 12FT 48PT
Petroleum Geochemistry .... MSc 12FT
Pipeline Engineering.... MSc 12FT 24PT/PGDip 12FT 24PT/PGCert 12FT 24PT

Robert Gordon University
Oil and Gas Engineering .... MSc 12FT 36DL/PGDip 9FT 24DL
Petroleum Production Engineering .... MSc 12FT 36DL/PGDip 9FT 24DL

Royal Holloway, University of London
Petroleum Geoscience (Tectonics) .... MSc 12FT 24-36PT

University of Salford
Gas Engineering and Management .... MSc 12FT/PGDip 9FT
Petroleum and Gas Engineering .... MSc 12FT/PGDip 9FT

University of Surrey
Petroleum Downstream Technology .... MSc 36FT up to 72PT
Petroleum Refining Systems Engineering .... MSc 12FT

Teesside University
Petroleum Engineering .... MSc 12 - 18FT 24PT/PGDip 8FT

Petroleum engineering
Research Courses

University of Aberdeen
Geology and Petroleum Geology ... PhD 36FT/MPhil 24FT/MSc by research 12FT

University of Dundee
Energy, Petroleum and Mineral Law and Policy... LLM by research 12FT
Energy, Petroleum and Mineral Law and Policy........... MPhil 24FT
Energy, Petroleum and Mineral Law and Policy .... MSc by research 12FT
Energy, Petroleum and Mineral Law and Policy ....PhD 36FT

Heriot-Watt University
Petroleum Engineering .... PhD 36FT 48PT/MPhil 12-24FT 24PT

University of Nottingham
Efficient Fossil Energy Technologies .... EngD 48FT
Fuel, energy and CO2 mitigation......... PhD 36FT 72PT/MPhil 24FT 48PT

Plymouth University
Petroleum and Environmental Geochemistry Research Group..... MPhil 24FT/PhD 36FT

Quantity surveying
Taught Courses

Glasgow Caledonian University
Quantity Surveying .... MSc 12FT 24PT 24DL/PGCert 9FT 18PT/PGDip 6FT 12PT

Heriot-Watt University
Quantity Surveying ...... MSc 12FT 24PT 24-84DL/PGDip 9FT 21PT 24-84DL

Kingston University
Quantity Surveying .... MSc 12FT 24PT

Liverpool John Moores University
Quantity, Surveying & Commercial Management .... MSc 12FT 24PT

London South Bank University
Quantity Surveying .... MSc 12FT MSc 24PT

Northumbria University
Surveying/Construction programme - Quantity Surveying Pathway .... MSc 24DL

Nottingham Trent University
Quantity Surveying .... MSc 12FT 24PT

University of Portsmouth
Quantity Surveying .... MSc 12FT 24PT

University of Salford
Quantity Surveying .... MSc 12FT 28PT/PGDip 8FT 16PT
Quantity Surveying (Mechanical and Electrical) .MSc 12FT 28DL/PGDip 8FT 16DL

University of the West of England, Bristol
Quantity Surveying .... MSc 36PT/GradDip 36PT

Quantity surveying
Research Courses

University of Nottingham
Engineering and Surveying Space Geodesy .... PhD 36FT 72PT/MPhil 24FT 48PT
Geospatial Science .... PhD 12-48FT

Quarry management
Taught Courses

University of Exeter
Mining Geology .... MSc 12FT

Structural engineering
Taught Courses

University of Birmingham
Civil Engineering .... MSc 12FT 24PT/PGDip 8FT 24PT

University of Bradford
Civil and Structural Engineering .... MSc 12-18PT

Brunel University
Project and Infrastructure Management .... MSc 12FT

Cardiff University
Structural Engineering .... MSc 12FT 24PT

City University London
Analysis and Design of Structures for Fire, Blast and Earthquakes .... MSc 12FT 36PT/PGDip 8FT 12-36PT
Civil Engineering Structures .... MSc 12FT 24-36PT

Coventry University
Civil and Structural Engineering .... MSc 12FT 24-30PT

University of Dundee
Concrete Engineering and Environmental Management ...... MSc 12FT
Structural Engineering .... MSc 12FT

University of East London
Structural Engineering .... MSc 12FT 24PT/PGDip 8FT 16PT/PGCert 4FT 8PT
Structural Engineering .... PGDip 8FT 16PT/PGCert 4FT 8PT

Edinburgh Napier University
Advanced Structural Engineering .. MSc 12FT 24-36PT/PGDip 9FT 18PT/PGCert 6FT 12PT

Civil engineering and construction

Mechanical Engineering..MSc 12FT 24PT

University of Edinburgh
Structural Engineering and Mechanics .... MSc 12FT 21-72PT/
PGDip 9FT 18-60PT

University of Exeter
Advanced Civil Engineering...MSc 12FT
Advanced Mechanical Engineering ....MSc 12FT

University of Glasgow
Structural Engineering & Mechanics ..MSc 12FT 24PT/PGDip 9FT
18PT

Heriot-Watt University
Civil Engineering (Distance Learning Only) ....MSc 24-84DL/
PGDip 24-84DL
Civil Engineering and Construction ManagementMSc 12FT 24PT
24-84DL/PGDip 9FT 21PT 24-84DL/PGCert 6FT 12PT 24-84DL
Structural and Foundation EngineeringMSc 12FT 24PT 24-84DL/
PGDip 9FT 21PT 24-84DL

Imperial College London
Earthquake Engineering...MSc 12FT 24-36PT
General Structural Engineering.....................MSc 12FT 24 or 36PT
Structural Steel Design, also with Business Management or
Sustainable Development......................................MSc 12FT 24-36PT
Systems Engineering and Innovation................................MSc 24PT

Kingston University
Structural Design & Construction Management with
Sustainability...MSc 12FT 24PT

University of Leeds
Structural Engineering.................................MSc(Eng) 12FT 24-60PT

University of Liverpool
Sustainable Civil Engineering (Structural).......................MSc 12FT

London South Bank University
Structural Engineering ....MSc 12FT MSc 36PT

Loughborough University
Infrastructure in Emergencies by Distance Learning.....................
PGCert 36PT 60DL

Manchester Metropolitan University
Mechanical Engineering...MSc 12FT 24PT

University of Manchester
Structural Engineering... MSc 12FT

Newcastle University
Structural Engineering.. MSc 12FT 48PT

Northumbria University
Pipeline Integrity Management ....PGCert 36DL

Nottingham Trent University
Structural Engineering with Management .... MSc 12FT 24PT
Structural Engineering with Materials ....MSc 12FT 24PT

University of Nottingham
Civil Engineering: Environmental Fluid Mechanics........ MSc 12FT
Civil Engineering: Geotechnical Engineering.................... MSc 12FT
Civil Engineering: Structural Engineering....................... MSc 12FT
Infrastructure .... MSc 12FT

Plymouth University
Civil Engineering........................ MSc 12FT/PGDip 12FT/PGCert 6FT

University of Portsmouth
Civil Engineering with Structural Engineering ...... MSc 12FT 24PT

Queen's University Belfast
Advanced Concrete Technology.....MSc 24PT/PGDip 24PT/PGCert
24PT
Durability of Structures ....MSc 12FT 24PT/PGDip 12FT 24PT/
PGCert 12FT 24PT

University of Salford
Structural Engineering...MSc 12FT 36PT/PGDip 9FT 24PT/PGCert
9FT 24PT

University of Sheffield
Advanced Mechanical Engineering ....MSc(Res) 12FT
Architectural Engineering Design .... MSc 12FT
Earthquake and Civil Engineering Dynamics ....
MSc(Eng) 12FT 24PT
Steel Construction. MSc(Eng) 12FT 24PT/PGDip 9FT 18PT/PGCert
6FT 12PT
Structural Engineering...... MSc(Eng) 12FT 24PT/PGDip 9FT 18PT/
PGCert 6FT 12PT
Structural and Concrete Engineering............MSc(Eng) 12FT 24PT/
Diploma 9FT 18PT/Cert 6FT 12PT

University of South Wales
Civil and Structural Engineering................................MSc 12FT 36PT

University of Strathclyde
Advanced Mechanical Engineering .....MSc 12FT 24PT/PGDip 9FT
18PT/PGCert 9FT 18PT
Environmental Engineering.......MSc 12FT 24PT/PGDip 9FT 18PT/
PGCert 6FT 12PT
Environmental Entrepreneurship.........MSc 12FT 24PT/PGDip 9FT
18PT/PGCert 6FT 12PT

University of Surrey
Bridge Engineering..MSc 12FT 72PT 72DL
Structural Engineering......................................MSc 12FT 72PT 72DL

Teesside University
Civil Engineering..............................MSc 12 - 16FT 24PT/PGDip 8FT

Trinity College Dublin - the University of Dublin
Engineering (Environmental/Structural & Geotechnics/
Transport)..MSc 12FT 24PT

University of Ulster
Infrastructure Engineering ....PGDip 8FT 16PT/MSc 12FT 36PT

UCL - University College London
Mega Infrastructure Planning, Appraisal and Delivery ....
MSc 12FT 24-60PT

Structural engineering
Research Courses

University of Bath
Innovative Structural Engineering .... MPhil 12FT

University of Birmingham
Civil Engineering ....PhD 36FT/MPhil 24FT

University of Bradford
Environmental and Infrastructure Engineering ...PhD 36FT 48PT/
MPhil 12FT 24PT

University of Edinburgh
Infrastructure and the Environment ..PhD 36FT 72PT/MPhil 24FT
48PT/MSc by research 12FT 24PT

University of Exeter
Engineering.. EngD 48FT

University of Glasgow
Infrastructure and Environment (Civil, Structural &
Environmental Engineering)............PhD 36-48FT 60-72PT/MSc by
research 12-24FT 24-36PT

University of Greenwich
Engineering (by Research).....................MSc by research 12FT 24PT

University of Leeds
Institute for Resilient Infrastructure ....PhD 36+FT/MPhil 24FT

University of Liverpool
Engineering ....PhD 36FT/MPhil 12FT 24PT

Newcastle University
Civil Engineering (Structural) .... MPhil 12FT 24PT/PhD 36FT 72PT

The Open University
Residual stress..........PhD 36FT 72PT variableDL/MPhil 15FT 24PT
variableDL

University of Salford
Stress Analysis..........PhD 36FT 60PT/MPhil 24FT 24PT/MRes 24FT
24PT/MSc by research 24FT 24PT

University of Sheffield
Civil and Structural Engineering...............................PhD 36FT 72PT/
MPhil 24FT 48FT
Civil and Structural Engineering: Integrated Studies....Integrated
PhD 48FT

University of Southampton
Doctorate by research ....PhD 36FT/MPhil 24FT

University of the West of Scotland
Department of Civil, Structural and Environmental
Engineering...PhD/MPhil

Transport infrastructure engineering
Taught Courses

Aston University
IT Project Management .... MSc 12FT

University of Birmingham
Road Management and Engineering ... MSc 12FT 24-36PT/PGDip
8FT 12PT

Brunel University
Project and Infrastructure Management .... MSc 12FT

Cardiff University
Transport and Planning .... MSc 12FT

City University London
Transport Strategy and Systems.........................MSc 12FT 24-30PT

Imperial College London
Transport, also with Business Management or Sustainable
Development..MSc 12FT 24-36PT

University of Leeds
Transport Planning and Engineering...... MSc(Eng) 12FT 24-36FT/
PGDip 9FT 18-24PT/PGCert 3FT 6-9PT
Transport Planning and the Environment ...... MSc 12FT 24-36PT/
PGDip 9FT 18-24PT/PGCert 3FT 6-9PT

Liverpool John Moores University
Port Management...MSc 12FT

London South Bank University
Transport Engineering and Planning.........................MSc 12FT 36PT

Loughborough University
Road and Vehicle Safety.. MSc 1FT 24PT

Newcastle University
Transport Planning and Engineering.................MSc 12FT 24-48PT

Transport Planning and Intelligent Transport Systems ....
MSc 12FT 24PT
Transport Planning and the Environment ....MSc 12FT 24-48PT

University of Nottingham
Civil Engineering: Transportation... MSc 12FT

University of Salford
Transport Engineering and Planning.........................MSc 12FT 36PT

Sheffield Hallam University
Transport Planning and Management....................MSc 12FT 36PT
Urban and Regional Planning (Transport)..............MSc 12FT 24PT

University of Southampton
Transportation Planning and Engineering.MSc 12FT 24PT/PGDip
12FT

University of Surrey
Transport Planning and Practice............................MSc 12FT 72PT

Trinity College Dublin - the University of Dublin
Engineering (Environmental/Structural & Geotechnics/
Transport)...MSc 12FT 24PT
Highway and Geotechnical Engineering .... PGDip 12PT

University of Ulster
Infrastructure Engineering ....PGDip 8FT 16PT/MSc 12FT 36PT

UCL - University College London
Transport ....MSc 12FT 24PT

University of Westminster
Transport Planning and Management....................MSc 12FT 24PT

Transport infrastructure engineering
Research Courses

University of East Anglia
Business, Accountability, Regulation and Development.................
PhD 36FT 72PT/MPhil 24FT 48PT

University of Exeter
Engineering.. EngD 48FT

University of Leeds
Institute for Resilient Infrastructure ....PhD 36+FT/MPhil 24FT

Newcastle University
Civil Engineering (Transport)..... MPhil 12FT 24PT/PhD 36FT 72PT

Oxford Brookes University
Intelligent Transport Systems .... PhD 24-60FT 36-72PT/MPhil
24-36FT 36-48PT

University of Southampton
Transport Knowledge and Systems Engineering .... EngD 48FT

UCL - University College London
Transport Studies ....PhD 36FT 60PT

Water resources engineering
Taught Courses

University of Abertay Dundee
Urban Water and Environmental Management ... MSc 12FT 24PT

Anglia Ruskin University
Business Management of Waste and Resources.......MSc 12-24DL

University of Birmingham
Hydrogeology .... MSc 12FT
River Environments and their Management..........MSc 12FT 24PT
Water Resources Technology and Management..MSc 12FT 24PT/
PGDip 9FT 24PT

University of Brighton
Water and Environmental Management ...MSc 12FT 24PT/PGDip
12FT 24PT

University of Bristol
Water and Environmental Management ....MSc 12FT 24PT

Brunel University
Water Engineering .... MSc 12FT

Cardiff University
Hydro-environment Engineering ....MSc 12FT 24PT

University of Central Lancashire
Carbon and Resource Management....MSc 12FT 24PT/PGDip 9FT
18PT/PGCert 6FT 12PT

University of Chester
Leadership and Management (Work Based and Integrative
Studies)............MA 24-72PT/MSc 24-72PT/PGDip 24-60PT/PGCert
12-36PT

Cranfield University
Community Water and Sanitation.................... MSc 12FT 24-60PT/
PGDip 6FT 24PT/PGCert 5FT 24PT/MTech 24FT
Environmental Water Management .... MSc 12FT 24-60PT/PGDip
6FT 24PT/PGCert 5FT 24PT/MTech 24FT
Waste and Resource Management...... MSc 12FT 24-60PT/PGDip
12FT 24PT/PGCert 12FT 24PT/MTech 24FT
Water and Wastewater Engineering .... MSc 12FT 24-60PT/PGDip
6FT 24PT/PGCert 5FT 24PT

University of Dundee
Catchment Hydrology & Management............................. MSc 12FT

Civil engineering and construction

International Mineral Resources Management (MBA by distance learning) ....MBA 18DL
International Mineral Resources Management .... MBA 12FT
Water Hazards, Risks & Resilience .... MSc 12FT
Water Law .... PGDip 18-60DL/PGCert 12-60DL/LLM 24-60DL

University of East Anglia
Environmental Assessment and Management ..... MSc 12FT 24PT
Water Security and International Development ... MSc 12FT 24PT

University of Exeter
Water Management .... MSc 12FT 24PT

Glasgow Caledonian University
Waste Management.....................MSc 12FT 24PT/PGDip 8FT 20PT/
PGCert 4FT 8PT

Heriot-Watt University
Environmental Analysis and Assessment .... MRes 12FT 24PT/
PGDip 9FT 18PT/PGCert 9FT 18PT
Marine Spatial Planning ....MSc 12FT 24PT/PGDip 9FT
Sustainable Urban Management........... MSc 12FT 24PT 24-84DL/
PGDip 9FT 21PT 24-84DL
Water Resources .... MSc 12FT 24PT 24-84DL/PGDip 9FT 21PT
24-84DL/PGCert 6FT 12PT 24-84DL

University of Hertfordshire
Water and Environmental Management ....MSc 12FT 24-60PT
24DL/PGDip 12FT 18-48PT 18DL/PGCert 12FT 18-48PT 18DL

Imperial College London
Environmental Engineering, also with Business Management or
Sustainable Development....................................MSc 12FT 24-36PT
Hydrology for Water Resource Management, also with Business
Management and Sustainable Dev...................MSc 12FT 24-36PT

Keele University
Urban Futures and Sustainable Communities.......MA 12FT 24PT/
PGDip 12FT 24PT/PGCert 12FT 24PT

King's College London
Water: Science and Governance.................................MSc 12FT 24PT

Lancaster University
Sustainable Water Management ....MSc 12FT 24PT

University of Leeds
Hydrogeology ....MSc 12FT 24-48PT/PGDip 12FT 24-48PT
Water, Sanitation and Health Engineering..............MSc(Eng) 12FT

Liverpool John Moores University
Water, Energy & the Environment ....MSc 12FT 24PT/
PGDip 24PT/PGCert 12PT

University of Liverpool
Marine Planning and Management ....MSc 12FT 24PT

Loughborough University
Water and Environmental Management ....MSc 12FT/PGDip 6FT/
PGCert 3FT
Water and Environmental Management by Distance Learning....
MSc 96DL/PGDip 60DL/PGCert 36DL
Water and Waste Engineering ..MSc 12FT/PGDip 6FT/PGCert 3FT
Water and Waste Engineering by Distance Learning...MSc 96DL/
PGDip 60DL/PGCert 36DL

Manchester Metropolitan University
Science, Technology, Engineering and Maths (STEM) .... MSc
24-72PT

Newcastle University
Environmental Engineering..MSc 12FT 48PT
Flood Risk Management....................MSc 36-60PT/PGDip 36-60PT
Hydrogeology and Water ManagementMSc 12FT 48PT 36-60DL/
PGDip 36-60DL
Hydroinformatics and Water Management (Euro Aquae)...... MSc
24FT
Hydrology and Climate Change.................................MSc 12FT 48PT
Skills, Technology, Research and Management for the UK Water
Sector (STREAM)..EngD by taught 48FT

University of Northampton
International Wastes Management ....MSc 24DL

University of Oxford
Water Science, Policy and Management .... MSc 12FT

Queen Mary, University of London
Environmental Science: Integrated Management of Freshwater
Environments ....MSc 12FT 24-36PT

University of Sheffield
Contaminant Hydrogeology.......................................MSc 12FT 24PT/
PGDip 9FT 18PT/Cert 6FT 12PT
Environmental Management of Urban Land and WaterMSc 12FT
24PT/PGDip 9FT 18PT/PGCert 6FT 12PT
Urban Water Engineering and Management........MSc 12FT 24PT/
PGDip 9FT 18PT/Cert 6FT 12PT

University of Southampton
Engineering for Development - Infrastructure, Water Supply and
Sanitation..MSc 12FT 24PT/PGDip 9FT
Freshwater Sciences ....MRes 12FT
Marine Resource Management ....MSc 12FT
Water Resources Management ....MSc 12FT 27PT

University of Strathclyde
Hydrogeology.............................MSc 12FT 24PT/PGDip 9FT 18PT
Offshore Floating Systems .... MSc 12FT/PGDip 9FT
Ship and Offshore Structures .... MSc 12FT/PGDip 9FT
Ship and Offshore Technology .... MSc 24FT
Sustainable Engineering: Marine Technology ....MSc 12FT/PGDip
9FT

Sustainable Engineering: Offshore Renewable Energy MSc 12FT/
PGDip 9FT

University of Surrey
Water Regulation and Management.......................MSc 12FT 72PT
Water and Environmental Engineering...................MSc 12FT 72PT

Trinity College Dublin - the University of Dublin
Environmental Engineering ....PGDip 12FT

UCL - University College London
Hydrographic Surveying .... MSc 12FT

Water resources engineering
Research Courses

Coventry University
Water Science.................................... MSc by research 12FT 24-36PT

Cranfield University
EngD Studentship: Disinfection Modelling for Water
Distribution Systems.. EngD 48FT
EngD Studentship: Process robustness tools in drinking water
treatment .... EngD 48FT
Land and Water Management PhD with Integrated Studies.........
Integrated PhD 48FT
MSc by Research - Changing practice in water and sanitation
technology introduction... MSc(Res) 12FT
Flow cytometry for rapid analysis of microbiological water
quality ....MSc by research 12FT
Pesticides in Groundwater............................MSc by research 12FT
Research Studentship - Drinking water distribution: elucidating
the chemistry ....MSc by research 12FT

University of Dundee
Water Law, Policy and Science (LLM by research) LLM by research
12FT

University of Exeter
Engineering... EngD 48FT

Newcastle University
Civil Engineering (Water Resources)...MPhil 12FT 24PT/PhD 36FT
72PT

The Open University
Integrated Waste Systems .... PhD 36FT 72PT variableDL/
MPhil 15FT 24PT variableDL

Swansea University
Desalination and Water Re-Use...........MSc by research 12FT 24PT
Sustainable Resources.....................................MSc by research 12FT

UCL - University College London
Environmental Engineering Science............................... EngD 48FT

Computer sciences and IT

Animation
Taught Courses

University of the Arts London - Central Saint Martins College of Art and Design
Character Animation .... MA 24FT

Bangor University
Advanced Visualization, Virtual Environments and Computer Animation .... MRes 12FT
Film and Visual Culture .... MRes 12FT 24PT

University of Bedfordshire
Computer Animation and Games Technology .... MSc 12FT 24-36PT

Arts University Bournemouth
Animation .... MA 12FT 24PT

University of Bradford
Advanced Computer Animation and Visual Effects .... MA 12FT 24PT/MSc 12FT 24PT
Computer Animation and Visual Effects .... MSc 12FT 24PT/MA 12FT 24PT
Visual Effects for Post-Production .... MSc 12FT 24PT

University of Bristol
Advanced Computing - Character Animation .... MSc 12FT 24PT

University of Central Lancashire
Animation .... MA 12FT/PGDip 12FT/PGCert 12FT

University for the Creative Arts
Animation .... MA 12FT 24PT
Graphic Storytelling and Comic Art .... MA 12FT 24PT

University of Derby
Visual Communication (Animation) .... MDes 48FT

University of Dundee
Animation and Visualisation .... MSc 12FT

University of East Anglia
Games Development .... MSc 12FT 24PT

University of Edinburgh
Animation .... MA 12FT/MFA 24FT
Digital Animation .... MSc(Res) 12FT 24PT

Glasgow School of Art
Animation .... PGCert 4FT/PGDip 8FT/MDes 12FT
Sound for the Moving Image.. PGCert 4FT/PGDip 8FT/MDes 12FT

University of Glasgow
Medical Visualisation & Human Anatomy .... MSc 12FT

Glyndwr University
Design Practice .... MA 12FT 24PT

University of Hertfordshire
Animation ....MA 12FT 24PT/PGDip 12FT 24PT/PGCert 12FT 24PT
Character Creation and Technical Effects.... MA 12FT 24PT/PGDip 12FT 24PT
Model Design and Model Effects .... MA 12FT 24PT/PGDip 12FT 24PT/PGCert 12FT 24PT
Two Dimensional Digital Animation .. MA 12FT 24PT/PGDip 12FT 24PT

University of Kent
Computer Animation .... MSc 12FT
Digital Visual Effects .... MSc 12FT/PGDip 12FT

Kingston University
Communication Design: Illustration .... MA 12FT 24PT

London Metropolitan University
Film and Animation .... MA 12FT

Nottingham Trent University
Puppetry and Digital Animation .... MA 12FT/PGDip 7FT/PGCert 4FT

Ravensbourne
Animation Futures .... MA 12FT 24PT
Applied Technologies, Rapid Prototyping and Digital Technologies .... MSc 12FT 24PT

Royal College of Art
Animation .... PhD by taught 72PT/MPhil 24FT 48PT/MA 24FT

University of Salford
Animation .... MA 12FT
Audio Production .... MSc 12FT 36PT
Professional Sound and Video Technology .... MSc 12FT 36PT/PGDip 9FT 24PT

Sheffield Hallam University
Animation and Special Effects .... MA 12FT 36PT
Animation for Computer Games .... MA 12FT 36PT

University of South Wales
Animation .... MA 12FT 24PT/MFA 24FT 36PT
Visual Effects .... MA 12FT 24PT

University of Sunderland
Animation and Design .... MA 12FT 24PT

Teesside University
Digital Character Animation MA 12FT 24-36PT/PGDip 8FT 24PT/PGCert 4FT 12PT

University of the West of England, Bristol
Animation .... MA 18FT 36PT/PGDip 12FT 24PT

University of Westminster
Design for Communication .... MA 12FT/MA 12FT

Animation
Research Courses

University of Kent
Cartoons and Caricature .... PhD 36FT 60PT/MPhil 24FT 36PT/MA by research 12FT 24PT

Royal College of Art
Animation .... PhD/MPhil/MA by research

Artificial intelligence and robotics
Taught Courses

University of Aberdeen
Artificial Intelligence .... MSc 12FT/PGDip 9FT

Aberystwyth University
Intelligent Autonomous Systems .... MSc 12FT 24PT/PGDip 9FT 18PT/PGCert 5FT 10PT
Intelligent Systems .... MSc 12FT 24PT/PGDip 9FT 21PT/PGCert 5FT 17PT

Anglia Ruskin University
Minimally Invasive & Robotic Surgery .... MCh 12FT 24PT

Bangor University
Computer Science with Artificial Intelligence .... MSc 12FT 24PT
Computer Science with Visualisation .... MSc 12FT 24PT
Electronic Engineering .... MRes 12FT

University of Birmingham
Computational Neuroscience and Cognitive Robotics .. MSc 12FT
Human Computer Interaction .... MSc 12FT
Natural Computation .... MRes 12FT
Robotics .... MSc 12FT

University of Bradford
Artificial Intelligence for Games .... MSc 12FT 24PT

University of Bristol
Advanced Computing (Machine Learning, Data Mining and High Performance Computing) .... MSc 12FT 24PT

Cardiff University
Computer Science .... MSc 12FT 36PT

De Montfort University
Intelligent Systems .... MSc 12FT 24-72PT 24-36DL/PGDip 8FT 24PT/PGCert 4FT 12PT
Intelligent Systems and Robotics ....MSc 12FT 24-72PT 24-36DL/PGDip 8FT 24PT/PGCert 4FT 12PT

University of Dundee
Business Intelligence .... MSc 12FT

University of East Anglia
Advanced Computing Science .... MSc 12FT 24PT
Computing Science .... MSc 12FT 24PT MRes 12FT
Games Development .... MSc 12FT 24PT

Edinburgh Napier University
Automation and control .... MSc 12FT

University of Edinburgh
Artificial Intelligence .... MSc 12FT 36PT

University of Essex
Computational Intelligence .... MSc 12FT 24PT
Computer Science .... MSc 12FT 24PT
Intelligent Systems and Robotics .... MSc 12FT 24PT

Heriot-Watt University
Advanced Internet Applications .... MSc 12FT 24PT/PGDip 9FT
Artificial Intelligence .... MSc 12FT 24PT/PGDip 9FT
Computer Services ManagementMSc 12FT 24PT/PGDip 9FT 21PT
Creative Software Systems .... MSc 12FT 24PT/PGDip 9FT 21PT
Information Technology (Business) ..... MSc 12FT 24PT/PGDip 9FT 21PT
Information Technology (Software Systems) .... MSc 12FT 24PT/PGDip 9FT 21PT
Smart Systems Integration .... MSc 24FT
Software Engineering .... MSc 12FT 24PT/PGDip 9FT 21PT

University of Hertfordshire
Artificial Intelligence with Robotics .... MSc 12-16FT

Imperial College London
Medical Robotics and Image Guided Intervention .... MRes 12FT

University of Kent
Advanced Computer Science (Computational Intelligence)... MSc 12FT 36PT

King's College London
Robotics .... MSc 12FT

University of Lincoln
Computer Science .... MSc 12FT 24PT

University of Liverpool
Information and Intelligence Engineering .... MSc(Eng) 12FT/PGDip 12FT

University of Manchester
ACS: Artificial Intelligence .... MSc 12FT 24PT
ACS: Semantic Technologies .... MSc 12FT

Newcastle University
Advanced Computer Science .... MSc 12FT 24PT

Nottingham Trent University
Engineering (Cybernetics and Communications).. MSc 12FT 24PT

University of Nottingham
Human Computer Interaction .... MSc 12FT 24-48PT

Plymouth University
Computer Science .... MSc 12FT 24PT MRes 12FT
Robotics .... MSc 12FT/MRes 12FT
Robotics Technology .... MSc 24FT

University of Reading
Cybernetics .... MSc 12FT 24PT
Systems Engineering .... MRes 12FT 24PT

University of Salford
Advanced Computer Science .... MSc 12FT 36PT/PGDip 6FT 24PT
Robotics and Automation .... MSc 12FT/PGDip 9FT

University of Sheffield
Computational Intelligence and Robotics .... MSc 12FT

University of St Andrews
Advanced Computer Science .... MSc 12FT 24PT
Artificial Intelligence .... MSc 12FT 24PT

University of Stirling
Advanced Computing .... MSc 12FT/PGDip 9FT/PGCert 9FT

University of Strathclyde
Advanced Computer Science .... MSc 12FT/PGDip 9FT

University of Sussex
Advanced Computer Science .... MSc 12FT 24PT
Evolutionary and Adaptive Systems .... MSc 12FT 24PT/PGDip 9FT 18PT
Intelligent Systems .... MSc 12FT 24PT

Teesside University
Advanced Computer Science .... MSc 12FT 36PT

University of Ulster
Computational Intelligence (Subject to approval) .... PGDip 9FT 18PT/MSc 12FT 36PT

UCL - University College London
Cognitive and Decision Sciences .... MSc 12FT 24PT
Computational Statistics and Machine Learning .... MSc 12FT
Machine Learning .... MSc 12FT

University of the West of England, Bristol
Advanced Engineering Robotics .... MSc 12FT
Robotics by Research .... MSc(Res) 12FT 24PT

University of York
Autonomous Robotics Engineering .... MSc 12FT
Computing .... MSc 12FT

Artificial intelligence and robotics
Research Courses

Aberystwyth University
Computer Science .... MPhil 12FT 24PT PhD 36FT 60PT

Aston University
Knowledge Engineering and Data Management Research Group .... PhD 36FT/MRes 12FT/MPhil 12FT

Bangor University
Artificial Intelligence and Intelligent Agents .... MPhil 24FT/PhD 36FT
Electrical Materials Science .... MPhil 24FT/PhD 36FT

University of Birmingham
Computer Science/Cognitive Science .... PhD 36FT/MSc by research 24FT
Natural Computation .... MRes 12FT

University of Bolton
Educational Organisations and Learning Technology Specialisms .... MPhil 18FT 30 - 36PT/PhD 36FT 60 - 72PT

City University London
Centre for Interactive Systems Research .... PhD/MPhil

University of Edinburgh
Artificial Intelligence .... MSc by research 12FT/MPhil 24FT/PhD 36FT
Informatics: Institute for Adaptive & Neural Computation... MSc by research 12FT 24PT/PhD 36FT 72PT/MPhil 24FT 48PT
Informatics: Institute for Computing Systems Architecture.......... MPhil 24FT 48PT/PhD 36FT 72PT/MSc by research 12FT 24PT
Informatics: Institute of Perception, Action & Behaviour ... MPhil 24FT 48PT/PhD 36FT 72PT/MSc by research 12FT 24PT
Institute for Communicating & Collaborative Systems .... hD 36FT 72PT/MPhil 24FT 48PT/MSc by research 12FT 24PT

University of Essex
Computer Science .... PhD 36FT 72PT/MPhil 24FT 48PT/MSc by research 12FT 24PT

University of Hertfordshire
Adaptive Systems .... PhD 36FT 72PT/MRes 12FT 24PT

Computer sciences and IT

University of Hull
Centre for Systems Studies .... PhD 36FT 60PT/MPhil 24FT 36PT

King's College London
Robotics .... MPhil 24FT 48PT/PhD 36FT 48-72PT

University of Leeds
Artificial Intelligence and Biological Systems ....PhD 36+FT/MPhil 24FT

University of Liverpool
Advanced Science (Computer Sciences pathway) (Artificial Intelligence)... MRes 12FT

The Open University
Complexity Science and Design.......... PhD 36FT 72PT variableDL/ MPhil 15FT 24PT variableDL
Mind, Meaning and Rationality.......... PhD 36FT 72PT variableDL/ MPhil 15FT 24PT variableDL

University of Salford
Centre for Robotics and Automation....................... PhD 36FT 60PT 48DL/MPhil 24FT 24PT 24DL/MSc by research 24FT 24PT 24DL/ MRes 24FT 24PT

Sheffield Hallam University
Communication and Computing Research Centre ... PhD 36-48FT 48-60PT/MPhil 24-36FT 48-60PT

University of Surrey
Mechatronics Systems and Robotics ..PhD 33FT 45PT/MPhil 21FT 33PT/EngD 48FT 60PT

Swansea University
Logic and Computation...MRes 12FT 24PT

Bioinformatics
Taught Courses

Bangor University
Electronic Engineering .... MRes 12FT
Electronic Engineering (Bio-Electronics)......................... MRes 12FT
Electronic Engineering (Organic Electronics) .... MRes 12FT

University of Bath
Protein Structure and Function .... MSc 12FT

Birkbeck, University of London
Analytical Bioscience ..MSc 12FT 24 - 60PT/PGDip 12FT 24 - 60PT
Bioinformatics with Systems Biology .... MSc 12FT 24PT MRes 12FT 24PT

University of Cambridge
Computational Biology.. MPhil 11FT

Cardiff University
Bioinformatics or Genetic Epidemiology and Bioinformatics....... MSc 12FT 24-48PT/PGDip 9FT/PGCert 9FT

University of Central Lancashire
Osteoarchaeology: Techniques and Data Analysis .... MSc 12FT

University College Cork
Applied Science (Bioinformatics with Systems Biology) .... MSc 12FT 24PT

Cranfield University
Applied Bioinformatics .... MSc 12FT 24PT
Nanomedicine................ MSc 12FT 24-36PT/PGDip 6-9FT 24-36PT

University of East Anglia
Computational Biology................... MSc 12FT/MSc 24PT/MSc 48PT
Molecular Medicine .... MSc 12FT

University of East London
Bioinformatics MSc....................MSc 12FT 24PT/PGDip 12FT 24PT/ PGCert 6FT 12PT

University of Edinburgh
Bioinformatics.. MSc 12FT/PGDip 9FT

University of Glasgow
Bioinformatics...MRes 12FT/PGDip 9FT

Heriot-Watt University
Biotechnology ....MSc 12FT 24PT/PGDip 9FT 20PT

University of Hertfordshire
Bioinformatics........................MSc 12FT/PGDip 12FT/PGCert 12FT

University of Hull
Molecular Medicine .... MSc 12FT

Imperial College London
Bioinformatics and Theoretical Systems Biology............ MSc 12FT
Biodiversity, Informatics and Genomics......................... MRes 12FT

King's College London
Bioinformatics... MSc 12FT
Molecular Biophysics..MRes 12FT

University of Leeds
Health Informatics .... MSc 12FT 24PT/PGDip 12FT 24PT/PGCert 12FT 12PT
Statistics .... MSc 12FT

University of Leicester
Advanced Computational Methods .... MSc 12FT/PGDip 9FT
Bioinformatics... MSc 12FT

University of Manchester
Bioinformatics and Systems Biology .... MSc 12FT

Newcastle University
Computational Systems Biology .... MSc 12FT

Nottingham Trent University
Bioinformatics...MRes 12FT MSc 12FT
Microbial Bioinformatics..CPD 1FT

University of Nottingham
Applied Bioinformatics .... MRes 12FT
Scientific Computation with Mathematical Medicine and Biology .... MSc 12FT

Queen's University Belfast
Computational Biology.. MSc 12FT

Robert Gordon University
Clinical Biomechanics.. MSc 12FT

Staffordshire University
Clinical Biomechanics and Diabetes............................PGCert 12PT
Clinical Biomechanics and Pain Management in the Lower limb ....PGCert 12PT

UCL - University College London
Statistics: Medical Statistics.................................MSc 12FT 24PT

University of Wolverhampton
Molecular Biology with Bioinformatics ....MSc 12FT 24PT

University of York
Computational Biology.. MRes 12FT
Post-Genomic Biology.. MRes 12FT

Bioinformatics
Research Courses

Bangor University
Electrical Materials Science ....MPhil 24FT/PhD 36FT
Organic Electronics ....MPhil 24FT/PhD 36FT

University of Bath
Protein Structure & Function MSc ....MRes 12FT

University of Buckingham
Bioinformatics..MSc by research 12FT

University of Cambridge
Bioinformatics..PhD 36FT

King's College London
Bioinformatics Research .... MPhil 24FT 36PT/PhD 36FT 48-72PT

University of Leeds
Bioinformatics........PhD 36+FT/MPhil 24FT/MSc by research 12FT

University of Leicester
Bioinformatics..MSc by research 12FT

University of Liverpool
Biostatistics............MPhil 12FT 24PT/PhD 36FT 48PT/MD 12-72FT
Post-Genomic Science .... MRes 12FT

University of Manchester
Bioinformatics...................PhD 36-48FT 72-96PT/MPhil 12FT 24PT

University of Nottingham
Bioinformatics..MRes 12FT
Biophysics and Surface Analysis..........PhD 36FT 72PT/MPhil 24FT 36PT/MRes 12FT

Oxford Brookes University
Health and Biomedical Sciences - Insect Virology & Protein Expression .... PhD 24-60FT 36-72PT/MPhil 24-36FT 36-48PT

University of Oxford
Genomic Medicine and Statistics.................................... DPhil 48FT

Swansea University
Biomathematics ....MSc by research 12FT 24PT

University of York
Post-Genomic Biology.. MRes 12FT

Business computing
Taught Courses

University of Aberdeen
Business Research ....MRes 12FT 24PT

Aston University
Information Systems and Business Analysis..........MSc 12FT 24PT

University of Bedfordshire
Business Information Systems.....................MSc 12-15FT 24-36PT
Information Systems and Business Management.......... MSc 12FT

Birkbeck, University of London
Business Technologies................ MSc 12FT 24PT/PGDip 12FT 24PT
Computing for the Financial Services .... MSc 24PT

Birmingham City University
Business Computing................. PGCert 4FT 10PT/PGDip 4FT 10PT/ MSc 4FT 10PT
IT for Strategic Management ....MSc 12/18FT

University of Birmingham
Digital Entrepreneurship...................................MSc 12FT 24PT

Brunel University
Business Intelligence and Social Media........................... MSc 12FT
Business Systems Integration (with SAP Technology) ... MSc 12FT 24PT
MSc Business Intelligence and Social Media................... MSc 12FT

Cardiff University
Computing and IT Management............................MSc 12FT 36PT
Computing and IT Management with Placement .... MSc 12FT

University of Central Lancashire
Computing ....MSc 12FT 24PT/PGDip 12PT/PGCert 6PT

University of Chester
Business and Information Technology (Work Based and Integrative Studies)...MA 24-72PT/MSc 24-72PT/PGDip 24-60PT/ PGCert 12-36PT

City University London
Business Systems Analysis and Design....................MSc 12FT 28PT

University College Cork
Business Information Systems.....................................MBS 12FT
Electronic Business...MBS 12FT
Information Systems for Business Performance ....MBS 12FT
Management Information and Managerial Accounting Systems MBS 15FT

Coventry University
Information Technology ....MSc 12FT 24-36PT 20DL/PGDip 8FT 16PT/PGCert 4FT 8PT
Information Technology for Management ..... MSc 12FT 24-36PT/ PGDip 8FT 16PT/PGCert 4FT 8PT
Management Information Systems ...... MSc 12FT 24-36PT 20DL/ PGDip 9FT 18PT

Cranfield University, Shrivenham
Information Capability Management......... MSc 12FT 48PT 48DL/ PGCert 5FT 24PT 18DL/PGDip 8FT 12PT 36DL

University of Cumbria
Computing and IT.........................PGDip 12PT/PGCert 12PT

De Montfort University
Business Intelligence Systems and Data Mining...MSc 12FT 36PT 24DL/PGDip 8FT 24PT/PGCert 4FT 12PT

University of Derby
Business and Payroll Management .... MSc 36PT
Information Technology..MSc 36PT 36DL

University of Dundee
Business Intelligence .... MSc 12FT
Computing with International Business .... MSc 12FT

University of East Anglia
Statistics ....MSc 12FT 24PT
Strategic Information Systems .... MSc 12FT

University of East London
Business Information Systems....................MSc 12FT 24PT/ PGDip 8FT 16PT/PGCert 4FT 8PT

Edinburgh Napier University
Business Information Technology........MSc 12FT 24PT/PGDip 9FT 18PT/PGCert 6FT 12PT
Strategic ICT Leadership .... MSc 24PT
Wealth Management...MSc 24-36DL

University of Essex
Financial Software Engineering...........................MSc 12FT 24PT

University of Exeter
Information Technology Management for Business...... MSc 12FT

National University of Ireland Galway
Business Information Systems.. MSc 12FT
Finance and Information Systems .... MSc 12FT
Technology Commercialisation ....:.......PGDip 12DL
Technology Management..MSc 24PT 24DL

Glasgow Caledonian University
Management of IT Innovation...................................... MSc 12FT

University of Gloucestershire
Information Technology Management (Top Up)...............MSc 6FT

University of Greenwich
Finance and Financial Information Systems..........MSc 12FT 24PT/ PGDip 12FT 24PT
Information Technology Management....................MBA 12FT 36PT

Heriot-Watt University
Information Technology (Business) .....MSc 12FT 24PT/PGDip 9FT 21PT

University of Hull
Business Technology Management....................................... MSc 12FT

Keele University
Finance and Information Technology...........MSc 12FT/PGDip 9FT/ PGCert 9FT

Kingston University
Business Information Technology...................................... MSc 12FT

Lancaster University
E-Business & Innovation................................. MSc 12FT/PGDip 9FT

Leeds Metropolitan University
Business (IPOS)... MA 12FT 60PT
Information & Technology.......MSc 12FT 24PT/PGDip 12FT 24PT/ PGCert 4FT 24PT

University of Leicester
Software Engineering for Financial Services ....MSc 12FT/ PGDip 9FT

Computer sciences and IT

University of Liverpool
E-Business Strategy and Systems.....MSc 12FT 24PT

London College UCK
Business Computing.....PGDip 12FT 24PT
Information Systems.....PGDip 12FT 24PT

London Metropolitan University
Information Technology.....MSc 12FT 24PT

London South Bank University
Business Administration.....MBA 12FT
Business Administration - Chinese Business Practice... MBA 12FT
Business Administration - Executive PT.....MBA 30PT
Certificate in Management.....CM 12PT
Charity Management - Blended.....ICSA Certificate 12PT
Enterprise Computing.....MSc 12FT 24PT
European Business.....Cert 12FT
Information Assurance.....MSc 12FT 24PT
Information Systems Management - PT.....MSc 24PT
Information Technology - FT.....MSc 15FT MSc 24PT
Public Administration.....MPA 28PT
Strategic Information Technology Management.....MSc 15FT
Web & Mobile Computing.....MSc 18FT

Loughborough University
Information Management and Business Technology.... MSc 12FT 24-60PT/PGDip 9FT 24-36PT/PGCert 6FT

Manchester Metropolitan University
Digital Business Management.....MSc 12FT
Financial Management.....MSc 12FT 24-36PT

University of Manchester
Information Systems - e-Business Technology.....MSc 12FT

Middlesex University
Business Information Modelling Management (BIM)..... MSc 12-24DL Business Information Systems Management...MA 12FT 24PT
Business Information Technology.....MSc 12FT 36PT
MBA Business Informatics.....MBA 24PT

University of Northampton
IT Service Management..MSc 12FT 24PT 24DL/PGDip 12PT 12DL

Northumbria University
Business with Information Management.....MSc 12FT

Nottingham Trent University
Internet and Enterprise Computing.....MSc 12FT 24PT

The Open University
Computing for Commerce and Industry ...MSc variableDL/PGDip variableDL
Technology Management.... MSc variableDL/PGCert variableDL/PGDip variableDL

Oxford Brookes University
E-Business.....MSc 12FT 24PT

University of Reading
Business Information Management.....MSc 12FT
Business Technology Consulting.....MSc 12FT
Informatics (MSc - Beijing)..... MSc 18FT 36PT/PGDip 9FT/PGCert 6FT
Information Management & Systems.....MSc 12FT 36PT/PGDip 9FT/PGCert 6FT

University of Roehampton
International Management with Information Systems..... MSc 12FT 24PT
International Management of Information Systems....PGDip 9FT 24PT

Royal Holloway, University of London
Business Information Systems.....MSc 12FT

Sheffield Hallam University
Enterprise Systems Professional (SAP).....MSc 12FT 36PT/PGDip 24PT/PGCert 12PT
Information Systems with SAP.....MBA 12FT 36PT

University of Sheffield
Information Systems (Professional Enhancement Programme)... MSc Up to 12FT 24-36PT/PGDip 9FT 18PT/PGCert 6FT 12PT

University of South Wales
Management and Development of International Financial Systems.....MSc 12FT

Southampton Solent University
Business Information Technology.....MSc 12FT 24PT

University of Southampton
Information Technology and Commerce.....LLM 12FT 24PT
Information Technology and Telecommunications Law..... LLM 24DL

Staffordshire University
Computing Solutions for Business via Distance Learning...... MSc 24-60FT/PGCert 24-60FT/PGDip 24-60FT
Computing Soluttions for Business.....MSc 12-18FT

University of Stirling
Business and Management.....MRes 12FT

University of Strathclyde
Business and Management.....MSc 12FT 30PT/PGDip 9FT 20PT

University of Sussex
Technology and Innovation Management.....MSc 12FT 24PT

Swansea University
Business Economics with Computing.....MSc 12FT

Teesside University
Applied Computing...MSc 12FT 24-36PT/PGDip 8FT 24PT/PGCert 4FT 12PT

University of Wales Trinity Saint David
Information Security Management.....MBA 12FT 24PT

University of Warwick
E-Business Management.....MSc 12FT 36PT
Information Systems Management & Innovation.....MSc 12FT

University of the West of Scotland
Management of eBusiness.....MSc 12FT/Diploma 12-24FT/Cert 12-24FT

University of Westminster
Business Information Systems.....MSc 12FT 24PT
Business Information Systems (evening study).....MSc 24PT
Business Intelligence and Analytics.....MSc 12FT 24-48PT

University of York
Statistics and Computational Finance.....MSc 11FT

Business computing
Research Courses

University of Bolton
Supply Chain, Business IT, Music and Creative Industries Management Specialisms..... MPhil 18FT 24 - 42PT/PhD 36FT 48 - 72PT

Cardiff University
Information Systems.....MRes 12FT

University of Chester
Business.....DBA 24-84PT

London Metropolitan University
Dept of Computing.....PhD Max 60FT Max 96PT/MPhil Max 36FT Max 54PT

London South Bank University
Faculty of Business, Computing & Information Management...... PhD 36FT 60PT/MPhil 24FT 36PT

Manchester Metropolitan University
Business Information Technology, Management Science, Policy Modelling......PhD 48FT 90PT/MPhil 36FT 72PT/MRes 12FT 24PT/MA or MSc by Research 18FT 36PT

The Open University
Technology Management.....PhD 36FT 72PT variableDL/MPhil 15FT 24PT variableDL

University of Salford
Information Systems Research Centre.....PhD/MPhil

University of Wales Trinity Saint David
Information Technology.....PhD 36FT 48-72PT/MPhil 12-36FT

Cheminformatics
Taught Courses

University of Bath
Sustainable Chemical Technologies PhD (Integrated)..... MRes 12FT

University College Cork
Pharmaceutical Engineering.....MEngSci 24PT

Queen's University Belfast
Chemical Biology.....MSc 12FT

University of Reading
Chemical Research.....PGDip 9FT 18PT MSc 12FT 24PT

UCL - University College London
Chemical Research.....MSc 12FT 24PT

Cheminformatics
Research Courses

University of Bath
Sustainable Chemical Technologies.....Integrated PhD 48FT

Loughborough University
Catalysis and Reaction Engineering ...PhD 36FT 60PT/MPhil 24FT 36PT

The Open University
Cosmochemistry......PhD 36FT 72PT variableDL/MPhil 15FT 24PT variableDL

Queen's University Belfast
Chemistry and Chemical Engineering.....PhD 36FT 72PT/MPhil 24FT 48PT

Computer aided design
Taught Courses

University of Aberdeen
Cloud Computing.....MSc 12FT 9PT/PGDip 9FT

University of the Arts London - London College of Fashion
Fashion: Creative Pattern Cutting For The Industry.... PGCert 3FT

Aston University
Product Design Enterprise.....MSc 12FT
Product Design Innovation.....MSc 12FT

Bangor University
Computer Science with Visualisation.....MSc 12FT 24PT

Birmingham City University
Enterprise Systems Management.....MSc 12/16FT 30PT
Integrated Design and Construction Management.....MSc 28PT

Bournemouth University
Design Engineering.....MSc 12FT/MSc 24-60PT
Product Design.....MSc 12FT/MSc 24-60PT
Product Design Management.....MA 12FT/MSc 24-60PT

University of Bristol
Advanced Computing - Character Animation.....MSc 12FT 24PT

Brunel University
Advanced Manufacturing Systems.....MSc 12FT 36-60DL

University of Cambridge
Advanced Computer Science.....MPhil 9FT

University of Central Lancashire
Computing.....MSc 12FT 24PT/PGDip 12PT/PGCert 6PT
Design.....MA 12-18FT 24-30PT/PGCert 12FT/PGDip 12FT
Games Design.....MA 12FT 24PT/PGDip 12FT/PGCert 12FT
Games Design by distance learning.....MA 12-36DL/PGCert 12-24DL/PGDip 12-24DL

Cranfield University
Computational Fluid Dynamics..MSc 12FT 24-36PT/PGCert 12FT 24-36PT/PGDip 12FT 24-36PT
Computational Software Techniques (Computer Aided Engineering).....MSc 12FT 24PT
Computational and Software Techniques in Engineering...... MSc 12FT 24-36PT

University for the Creative Arts
Design: Design Crafts.....MA 12FT 24PT
Design: Product Design.....MA 12FT 24PT

University of Cumbria
Computing and IT.....PGDip 12PT/PGCert 12PT

University of Derby
Mobile Device Software Development.....MSc 12FT 36PT
Visual Communication (Animation).....MDes 48FT
Visual Communication (Graphic Design).....MDes 48FT
Visual Communication (illustration).....MDes 48FT

University of Dundee
Animation and Visualisation.....MSc 12FT
Computing.....MSc 12FT
Computing Research.....MSc 12FT
Computing with International Business.....MSc 12FT
Computing with Vision and Imaging.....MSc 12FT
Design for Services.....MDes 12FT
Product Design.....MSc 12FT
User Experience Engineering.....MSc 12FT

Durham University
Design and Operations Engineering.....MSc 12FT

University of East Anglia
Computing Science.....MRes 12FT

University of East London
Architecture: Computing and Design MSc MSc 12FT 24PT/PGDip 8FT 16PT/PGCert 4FT 8PT
Architecture: Computing and Design PG Cert.....PGCert 8PT

Edinburgh Napier University
Computing.....MSc 12FT 24PT
Design (Digital Arts).....MA/MDes 12FT
Design (Product).....MA/MDes 12FT
Engineering Design.....MSc 12FT 36PT/PGDip 9FT 24PT/PGCert 6FT 12PT
Interaction Design.....MDes 12FT
Mechanical Engineering.....MSc 12FT 24PT

Glasgow Caledonian University
Design Practice & Management.....MA 12FT 24PT/PGDip 9FT

University of Glasgow
Computer Systems Engineering.....MSc 12FT
Medical Visualisation & Human Anatomy.....MSc 12FT
Product Design Engineering.....MSc 12FT 24PT

Glyndwr University
Computing.....MSc 12FT

Goldsmiths, University of London
Computer Games & Entertainment.....MSc 12FT 24PT
Computing.....MSc 12FT 24PT
Design Futures.....MA 12FT 24PT

University of Greenwich
Applied Mathematical Modelling and Scientific Computing..... MSc 12FT 24PT

University of Kent
Digital Visual Effects.....MSc 12FT/PGDip 12FT
Future Computing.....MSc 12FT

Computer sciences and IT

Kingston University
Advanced Industrial and Manufacturing Systems .... MSc 12FT 24-36PT
Professional Practice (Design) .... MA 12-36PT
Sustainable Design .... MA 12FT 24PT

University of Leeds
Computational Fluid Dynamics .... MSc 12FT

University of Limerick
Computer Aided Engineering Product Design...... PGDip 9FT/MSc 12FT

University of Liverpool
Product Design and Management .... MSc 12FT

London Metropolitan University
Product Design .... MA 12FT 24PT

Loughborough University
Design and Innovation for Sustainability .... MSc 12FT 24PT

Nottingham Trent University
Computer Aided Product Design .... MA 12FT/PGDip 7FT/PGCert 4FT

Oxford Brookes University
Advanced Engineering Design .... MSc 12FT 24PT

University of Oxford
Software Engineering .... MSc 48PT

University of Portsmouth
Advanced Manufacturing Technology .... MSc 12/16FT 36PT

Queen Mary, University of London
Computer Aided Engineering .... MSc 12FT

University of Salford
Advanced Computer Science ......MSc 12FT 36PT/PGDip 6FT 24PT
Aerospace Design and Manufacture ... MSc 12FT 24PT/PGDip 9FT
Aerospace Engineering .... MSc 12FT/PGDip 9FT/PGCert 9FT
Art and Design: Communication Design .... MA 12FT 24PT/PGDip 8FT 15PT
Art and Design: Product Design .. MA 12FT 24PT/PGDip 9FT 15PT
Software Engineering .... MSc 12FT 38PT/PGDip 8FT 24PT

Sheffield Hallam University
Advanced Engineering and Management .... MSc 12FT 36PT/PGDip 12FT 24PT/PGCert 6FT 12PT
Advanced Manufacturing Engineering .... MSc 12FT 36PT/PGDip 8FT 24PT/PGCert 4FT 12PT

University of Sheffield
Advanced Manufacturing Technologies with the AMRC .... MSc(Res) 12FT

University of South Wales
Computer Animation .... MA 12FT

University of Southampton
Maritime Engineering Science: Maritime Computational Fluid Dynamics .... MSc 12FT

University of St Andrews
Advanced Computer Science .... MSc 12FT 24PT
Software Engineering .... MSc 12FT 24PT

University of Stirling
Advanced Computing .... MSc 12FT/PGDip 9FT/PGCert 9FT

University of Strathclyde
Advanced Computer Science .... MSc 12FT/PGDip 9FT
Advanced Manufacturing: Technology and Systems..... MSc 12FT 24PT/PGDip 9FT 18PT/PGCert 9FT 18PT
Computer Aided Engineering Design.. MSc 12FT 24PT/PGDip 9FT 18PT/PGCert 6FT 12PT
Digital Creativity .... MSc 12FT 24PT/PGDip 9FT 18PT

Teesside University
Advanced Manufacturing Systems .... MSc 12-16FT 24PT/PGDip 8FT

UCL - University College London
Built Environment: Environmental Design and Engineering .... MSc 12FT 24-60PT/PGDip 9FT
Built Environment: Heritage Science MRes 12FT 24-60PT/PGCert 6FT

University of the West of Scotland
Computer-Aided Engineering .... MSc 12FT 36PT/Diploma 9FT 30PT

University of Westminster
Architecture and Digital Media .... MA 12FT 24PT

University of Wolverhampton
Computer Aided Design for Construction .... MSc 12FT 24PT

Computer aided design
Research Courses

University of Bath
Digital Architectonics .... MPhil 12FT 24PT

University for the Creative Arts
Design .... MPhil 24FT 36PT/PhD 36FT 60PT

University of Dundee
Architecture .... MPhil 24FT MSc by research 12FT PhD 36FT
Computing .... MPhil 24FT MSc by research 12FT PhD 36FT

University of Strathclyde
Design Manufacture and Engineering Management - Research.. PhD 36FT 72PT/MPhil 12FT 24PT

Swansea University
Computational Modelling in Engineering .... MRes 12FT 36PT

Teesside University
Design .... PhD 24-60FT 36-72PT/MPhil 18-36FT 30-48PT

University of Wolverhampton
School of Engineering and the Built Environment: Engineering Division .... MPhil/PhD

Computer engineering
Taught Courses

University of Aberdeen
Advanced Computer Science .... MSc 12FT/PGDip 9FT
Advanced Information Systems .... MSc 12FT/PGDip 9FT

Aberystwyth University
Remote Sensing with Computer Sciences .... MSc 12FT 24PT/PGDip 9FT 18PT/PGCert 5FT 10PT

Bangor University
Computer Science .... MSc 12FT
Computer Science with Artificial Intelligence .... MSc 12FT 24PT

University of Bedfordshire
Embedded Systems Engineering .... MSc 12FT 24-36PT

Birmingham City University
Computer Science ......PGCert 4FT 10PT/PGDip 4FT 10PT/MSc 4FT 10PT
Computing .... PGCert 4FT 10PT/PGDip 4FT 10PT/MSc 4FT 10PT

University of Birmingham
Electronic and Computer Engineering .... MSc 12FT 24PT
Electronic and Computer Engineering with Industrial Studies..... MSc 18FT

Bournemouth University
Design Engineering .... MSc 12FT/MSc 24-60PT

University of Bradford
Advanced Computer Science .... MSc 12FT 24PT

University of Bristol
Advanced Computing (Creative Technology) .... MSc 12FT 24PT
Advanced Computing - Character Animation .... MSc 12FT 24PT
Advanced Microelectronic Systems Engineering .. MSc 12FT 24PT

Brunel University
Advanced Computing .... MSc 12FT
Computer Communication Networks .... MSc 12FT
Distributed Computing Systems Engineering .... MSc 12FT

University of Cambridge
Advanced Computer Science .... MPhil 9FT

Cardiff Metropolitan University
Computing .... MSc 12FT 24PT/PGDip 24PT/PGCert 12PT

Cardiff University
Computer Science .... MSc 12FT 36PT

University College Cork
Computing Science .... MSc 12FT

De Montfort University
Computing .... MSc 12FT 24-72PT/PGDip 8FT 24PT/PGCert 4FT 12PT

University of Derby
Advanced Computer Networks .... MSc 12FT 36-72PT
Mobile Device Software Development .... MSc 12FT 36PT

Dublin Institute of Technology
Engineering Computation .... MSc 12FT 24PT

University of Dundee
Advanced Practice (Diagnostic Imaging) .... MSc 36DL
Architecture: Advanced Practice, Management and Law ...... MSc 18DL
Computing .... MSc 12FT
Computing Research .... MSc 12FT
Computing with International Business .... MSc 12FT
Computing with Vision and Imaging .... MSc 12FT
Data Science .... MSc 24PT MSc 12FT PGCert 6FT
Advanced Computing Science .... MSc 12FT 24PT

University of Glasgow
Computer Systems Engineering .... MSc 12FT
Embedded Electronic Systems .... MSc 12FT 24PT
Search Engine Technologies .... MRes 12FT 24PT/PGDip 9FT 21PT/PGCert 9FT 9PT MSc 12FT 24PT/

Glyndwr University
CCNA/CCNP Cisco Networking Academy .... CCNA 6FT 12+PT/CCNP 6FT 12+PT
Computer Science .... MSc 12FT 24-36PT/MRes 12FT 24-36PT
Computing .... MSc 12FT

Goldsmiths, University of London
Computing .... MSc 12FT 24PT

University of Greenwich
Embedded Systems .... MSc 12FT 24PT

Heriot-Watt University
Computational Mathematics......MSc 12FT 24PT/PGDip 9FT 20PT
Computer Vision and Robotics (VIBOT) .... MSc 48FT
Robotics, Autonomous and Interactive Systems (RAIS) MSc 12FT/PGDip 9FT

University of Hertfordshire
Advanced Digital Systems .... MSc 12FT 36PT/MSc 16FT
Biometrics and Cybersecurity .... MSc 12-16FT 36PT
Distributed Systems and Networks .... MSc 12-16FT
Embedded Intelligent Systems .... MSc 12-16FT 36-48PT
Mobile Computing .... MSc 12-16FT

University of Huddersfield
Electronic and Communication Engineering .... MSc 12FT

University of Hull
Embedded Systems .... MSc 12FT

Imperial College London
Advanced Computing .... MRes 12FT MSc 12FT
Computing (Specialism) .... MSc 12FT

University of Kent
Computer Animation .... MSc 12FT
Computer Science .... MSc 12FT 36PT
Computing .... GradDip 9FT
Future Computing .... MSc 12FT
Networks and Security .... MSc 12FT 36PT

King's College London
Advanced Computing .... MSc 12FT
Intelligent Systems .... MSc 12FT

Leeds Metropolitan University
Mobile & Distributed Computer Networks .... MSc 12FT 24PT/PGDip 12FT 24PT/PGCert 4FT 12PT
Software Engineering.. MSc 12FT 24PT/PGCert 12FT 24PT/PGDip 12FT 24PT
Sustainable Computing .... MSc 12FT 24PT

University of Leeds
Embedded Systems Engineering .... MSc(Eng) 12FT

University of Leicester
Advanced Distributed Systems .... MSc 12FT/PGDip 9FT
Embedded Systems and Control .... MSc 12FT/PGDip 9FT/PGCert 3FT

University of Lincoln
Computer Science .... MSc 12FT 24PT

Liverpool Hope University
Computer Science .... MSc 12FT 24PT/PGDip 12FT 24PT/PGCert 6FT 12PT
Networks & Security .... MSc 12FT

University of Liverpool
Advanced Science (Computer Sciences pathway) .... MSc 12FT/PGDip 12FT/PGCert 12FT

London Metropolitan University
Computer Science .... MSc 12-18FT 24PT
Embedded Systems .... MSc 12FT 24PT

London South Bank University
Embedded and Distributed Systems .... MSc 12FT 24PT

Loughborough University
Science of the Internet .... MSc 12FT 24PT
Systems Engineering .... MSc 12FT 36PT

University of Manchester
ACS: Multi-Core Computing .... MSc 12FT

Newcastle University
Advanced Computer Science .... MSc 12FT 24PT
Computer Science .... MSc 12FT 24PT

Northumbria University
Information and Records Management .... MSc 24DL
Pipeline Integrity Management .... PGCert 36DL
Professional Engineering .... MSc 36PT

Nottingham Trent University
Computer Science .... MRes 12FT
Computing Systems .... MSc 12/24FT 24PT
Electronic Systems .... MRes 12FT
Multimedia Engineering .... MSc 12FT 24PT

University of Nottingham
Computational Engineering: Electromagnetics .... MSc 12FT
Computational Engineering: Finite Element Analysis... MSc 12FT
Computational Fluid Dynamics .... MSc 12FT
Electronic Communications and Computer Engineering........ MSc 12FT/PGDip 9FT

Oxford Brookes University
Broadband Networks .... MSc 12FT 24PT
Computer Science .... MSc 12FT 24PT
Computing .... MSc 12FT 24PT

University of Reading
Cybernetics .... MSc 12FT 24PT
Intelligent Buildings: Design, Construction and Management .... MSc 24PT
Systems Engineering (MRes) .... MRes 12FT 24PT

Computer sciences and IT

Robert Gordon University
Computing: Information Engineering (with/without Network Management) .... MSc 12FT 36PT/PGDip 9FT 24PT/PGCert 4FT 12PT
Computing: Software Technology with Network Management...
MSc 12FT 36PT/PGDip 9FT 24PT/PGCert 4FT 12PT

University of Salford
Advanced Computer Science.......MSc 12FT 36PT/PGDip 6FT 24PT
BIM and Integrated Design............................. MSc 12FT 28PT 28DL/PGDip 8FT 20PT 20DL/PGCert 4FT 8PT 8DL

Sheffield Hallam University
Computer and Network Engineering......................MSc 12FT 36PT/PGDip 12FT 24PT/PGCert 6FT 12PT

University of Sheffield
Computer Vision Engineering ....MSc(Eng) 12FT

University of South Wales
Computer Systems Engineering .... MSc 12FT 36PT

University of Southampton
Information Technology and Commerce................. LLM 12FT 24PT
Information Technology and Telecommunications Law.................
LLM 24DL

University of St Andrews
Advanced Computer Science.....................................MSc 12FT 24PT
Networks & Distributed Systems................................MSc 12FT 24PT

Staffordshire University
Advanced Technology....................................MSc 12-24FT 24-60PT
Computing Soluttions for Business .... MSc 12-18FT
Mobile Computer Systems............MSc 12-24FT 24-84PT 24-84DL/PGCert 12FT/PGDip 12FT

University of Stirling
Advanced Computing...................MSc 12FT/PGDip 9FT/PGCert 9FT
Information Technology .... MSc 12FT/PGDip 9FT

University of Strathclyde
Advanced Computer Science........................... MSc 12FT/PGDip 9FT

University of Surrey
Information and Business Systems Engineering............. MSc 12FT

University of Sussex
Human-Computer Interaction....................................MSc 12FT 24PT
Scientific Computation .... MSc 12FT

Swansea University
Modelling, Uncertainty and Data .... MSc 12FT 24/36PT

Swansea Metropolitan University
Computing and Information Systems......................MSc 12FT 24PT

Teesside University
Advanced Computer Science.......................................MSc 12FT 36PT
Computing ....MSc 12FT 24-36PT/PGDip 8FT 24PT/PGCert 4FT 12PT
Electronics & Communications .....MSc 12- 18FT 24PT/PGDip 8FT

Trinity College Dublin - the University of Dublin
Computer Science (Mobile and Ubiquitous Computing)
.... MSc 12FT
Computer Science (Networks and Distributed Systems)
.... MSc 12FT
High Performance Computing...MSc 12FT

UCL - University College London
Computer Science .... MSc 12FT

University of West London
Computing ....MSc 12FT 24PT
Network and Mobile Computing ....MSc 15FT 24PT

University of Westminster
Computer Science .... MRes 12FT 24PT 12-24BM
Microelectronic System Design ....MSc 12FT 24PT 24BM

Computer engineering
Research Courses

Aberystwyth University
Computer Science ....MPhil 12FT 24PT
Computer Science ....PhD 36FT 60PT

Anglia Ruskin University
Digital Modelling...PhD 24 - 60FT 36 - 72PT

University of Birmingham
Electronic, Electrical and Computer Engineering ....PhD 36FT/MSc by research 12FT 24PT

Canterbury Christ Church University
Computing .... PhD 36FT 60PT/MPhil 24FT 48PT

Cardiff University
Visual Computing.... PhD 36FT possiblePT/MPhil 12FT possiblePT

Coventry University
Biomedical Computing ....MSc by research 12FT

University of Dundee
Computing .... MPhil 24FT
Computing ....MSc by research 12FT
Computing ....PhD 36FT
Electronic Engineering and Physics .... MPhil 24FT
Electronic Engineering and Physics ....MSc by research 12FT

Goldsmiths, University of London
Computer Science ....PhD 36-48FT 48-72PT/MPhil 24FT 36FT

University of Kent
Computer Science .....PhD 24FT 60PT/MSc by research 12FT 24PT

University of Manchester
Numerical Analysis .... PhD 36FT 72PT/MPhil 12FT 24PT

Newcastle University
Computer Science .... Integrated PhD 48FT 72PT
Electrical and Electronic Engineering......................PhD 36FT 72PT

Oxford Brookes University
Computing and Communication Technologies .... PhD 24-60FT 36-72PT/MPhil 24-36FT 36-48PT
Electronics and Communications .... PhD 24-60FT 36-72PT/MPhil 24-36FT 36-48PT

Queen's University Belfast
Theoretical Atomic, Molecular and Optical Physics ....PhD 36FT 72PT/MPhil 24FT 48PT

University of Sheffield
Computer Science: Integrated Studies ....Integrated PhD 48FT

Staffordshire University
Computing Science.. MRes 12FT 24-72PT

University of Westminster
Electronics and Computer Science............MPhil 18-36FT 30-60PT

Computer forensics
Taught Courses

University of Abertay Dundee
Digital Forensics...MSc 12FT/PGDip 9FT

Aston University
Forensic Linguistics .... MSc 24 -60DL/PGDE 24 - 60DL/PGCert 24 - 60DL/Diploma 24-60DL

University of Bedfordshire
Computer Security and Forensics..................MSc 12-15FT 24-36PT

MSc PROGRAMMES IN INFORMATION TECHNOLOGY AND COMPUTING

UNIVERSITY OF STIRLING

Our University is situated on a modern campus in the historic city of Stirling, centred around a large loch in the 300 acre estate of the 18th century Airthrey Castle – "some of the most beautiful campus scenery in the world". We extend a warm welcome to students from all countries – around 23 percent of our 12,000 students come from outside the UK, representing around 100 nationalities.

The University offers four taught MSc programmes to cover a range of interests in Computing and related subjects: The **MSc in Information Technology** and the **MSc in Computing for Financial Markets and the MSc in Computing for Business** are one year courses for graduates who have completed a non-IT degree, and who wish to enter the IT field.

The Information Technology course is concerned with the practical application of computers to Business generally, whereas the Computing for Financial Markets programme focuses on the application of computing technology in the financial sector, and the Computing for Business course covers computer technologies and management techniques for software and IT projects. Graduates are able to offer a valuable mixture of applicable practical skills to prospective employers.

The **MSc in Advanced Computing** is a one year course for graduates who have already completed a computing degree. It offers a flexible choice of modules to complement and extend a student's experience of computing, and students may specialise in one of the distinct streams, including eBusiness, Software Engineering, Computer Network Systems and Games Technologies.

To find out more visit www.cs.stir.ac.uk/entrants/msc/
Email us at pginfo-4@cs.stir.ac.uk
Call us on 01786 467 436

The University of Stirling is a recognised Scottish Charity, number SC 011159

Computer sciences and IT

University of Bradford
Forensic Computing ... MSc 12FT 24PT

Canterbury Christ Church University
Cybercrime Forensics ... MSc 24PT

Cardiff University
Computer Science with Placement ... MSc 12FT

University of Central Lancashire
Criminal Investigation ... MSc 12PT
Forensic Toxicology ... MSc 12FT
IT Security ... MSc 12FT 36PT/PGDip 9FT 18PT/PGCert 6FT 12PT

Cranfield University, Shrivenham
Forensic Computing ... MSc 12FT 36PT/PGDip 12FT 24PT/PGCert 12FT 12PT
Forensic Investigation ... MSc 12FT 60PT/PGDip 12FT 60PT/PGCert 12FT 60PT

De Montfort University
Forensic Computing ... MSc 12FT 24-36PT 24-36DL/PGDip 8FT 24PT/PGCert 4FT 12PT
Professional Practice in Digital Forensics and Security ... MSc 12FT 24PT 24-72DL/PGDip 12FT 24PT 24-72DL/PGCert 12FT 24PT 24-72DL

University of Derby
Computer Forensic Investigation ... MSc 12FT 36PT
Criminal Investigation ... MSc 12FT 24PT

University of Dundee
Anatomy and Advanced Forensic Anthropology ... MSc 12FT
Forensic Facial Identification ... MSc 12FT
Forensic Odontology ... MFOdont 12FT

Edinburgh Napier University
Advanced Security and Digital Forensics ... MSc 12FT 24PT

Glasgow Caledonian University
Network Security ... MSc 13FT 27PT/PGDip 9FT

University of Glasgow
Information Security ... MRes 12FT 24PT/PGDip 9FT 21PT/PGCert 9FT 9PT

University of Greenwich
Computer Forensics and Systems Security ... MSc 12FT 24PT
Computer Security Forensics and Risk Management ... MSc 12FT 24PT

King's College London
Computing & Security ... MSc 12FT

Kingston University
Cybercrime ... MA 12FT 24PT

University of Leicester
Terrorism, Security and Policing ... MSc 12FT 24PT/PGDip 12FT 24PT

University of Liverpool
Computer Security (Online Degree) ... MSc 24FT 24+PT

London Metropolitan University
Computer Forensics and IT Security ... MSc 12FT 24PT

London South Bank University
International Criminal Law & Procedure ... LLM 14FT 26PT

Middlesex University
Electronic Security and Digital Forensics ... MSc 12-15FT 24-27PT

Nottingham Trent University
Human Security and Environmental Change ... MA 12FT 24PT/PGDip 9FT 18PT/PGCert 9FT
MSc Internet and Security ... MSc 12FT 24PT

University of Portsmouth
Forensic Information Technology ... MSc 12FT 36PT

Sheffield Hallam University
Forensic Accounting ... MSc 12FT 24PT
Forensic Criminolgy ... MSc 12FT 24PT

University of South Wales
Computer Forensics ... MSc 12FT 36PT
Forensic Audit and Accounting ... MSc 12FT

Staffordshire University
Digital Forensics and Cybercrime Analysis ... MSc 12FT

University of Westminster
Computer Forensics ... MSc 12FT 24-60PT

Computer forensics
Research Courses

University of Central Lancashire
Forensic and Investigative Science ... PhD 48FT 84PT/MPhil 36FT 60PT/MD 48PT/MSc by research 24FT 36PT

Computer game design
Taught Courses

University of Aberdeen
Cloud Computing ... MSc 12FT 9PT/PGDip 9FT

University of Abertay Dundee
Computer Games Technology ... MSc 16FT 33PT/PGDip 9FT 21PT
Games Development ... MProf 12FT

Bangor University
Advanced Visualization, Virtual Environments and Computer Animation ... MRes 12FT

University of Bedfordshire
Computer Animation and Games Technology ... MSc 12FT 24-36PT

Birmingham City University
Video Game Enterprise and Production ... MSc 12FT
Video Games Development (Gamer Camp) ... MA 12FT/MSc 12FT

Arts University Bournemouth
Graphic Design ... MA 12FT 24PT
Animation Production ... MA 12FT

Bournemouth University
Computer Games Technology ... MSc 12FT/MSc 24PT
Design Engineering ... MSc 12FT/MSc 24-60PT

University of Bradford
Artificial Intelligence for Games ... MSc 12FT 24PT
Mobile Computing ... MSc 12FT 24PT
Networks and Performance Engineering ... MSc 12FT 24PT

University of Bristol
Advanced Computing (Creative Technology) ... MSc 12FT 24PT

British Institute of Technology & E-commerce
Innovative Technology ... PGCert 3FT/DipHE 6FT/MScD 12FT

Brunel University
Digital Games: Theory and Design ... MA 12FT 24PT

Cardiff University
Computer Science with Placement ... MSc 12FT
Computing with Placement ... MSc 12FT

University of Central Lancashire
Animation ... MA 12FT/PGDip 12FT/PGCert 12FT
Child Computer Interaction ... MRes 12FT 24PT
Games Design ... MA 12FT 24PT/PGDip 12FT/PGCert 12FT
Games Design by distance learning ... MA 12-36DL/PGCert 12-24DL/PGDip 12-24DL

City University London
Computer Games Technology ... MSc 12FT 28PT

Coventry University
Digital Games and Business Innovation ... MSc 12FT 36PT 12DL/PGDip 6FT 18PT 6DL/PGCert 3FT 9PT 3DL

Cranfield University
Computational Software Techniques in Engineering (Distributed Computing and e-Science) ... MSc 12FT 24PT

University for the Creative Arts
Design: Digital Design ... MA 12FT 24PT

University of Derby
Computer Graphics Production ... MSc 12FT 36PT
Mobile Device Software Development ... MSc 12FT 36PT

University of East Anglia
Advanced Computing Science ... MSc 12FT 24PT
Games Development ... MSc 12FT 24PT

Edinburgh Napier University
Computing ... MSc 12FT 24PT
Design (Digital Arts) ... MA/MDes 12FT
Design (Graphics) ... MA/MDes 12FT

Glyndwr University
Computing ... MSc 12FT

Goldsmiths, University of London
Computational Arts ... MA 24-36FT 36-48PT
Computer Games & Entertainment ... MSc 12FT 24PT
Computing ... MSc 12FT 24PT

University of Hertfordshire
Games Art ... MA 12FT 24PT/PGDip 12FT 24PT

University of Hull
Games Programming ... MSc 12FT

University of Kent
Computer Animation ... MSc 12FT

Kingston University
Computer Animation ... MA 12FT 24PT
Games Development ... MSc 12FT 24PT

Leeds Metropolitan University
Creative Technology ... MSc 12FT 24PT
Mobile Device Application Development ... MSc 12FT 24PT/PGCert 12FT 24PT/PGDip 12FT 24PT
Software Engineering ... MSc 12FT 24PT/PGCert 12FT 24PT/PGDip 12FT 24PT
Sound & Music for Interactive Games ... MSc 12FT 24PT

University of Liverpool
Advanced Computer Science with Internet Economics ... MSc 12FT

London Metropolitan University
Interactive Media and Games Technologies ... MSc 12FT 24-48PT

Newcastle University
Computer Game Engineering ... MSc 12FT

Nottingham Trent University
Computer Games Systems ... MSc 12FT 24PT
Games and Play (Technology and Culture) ... MSc 12FT 24PT
Multimedia Games Engineering ... MSc 12FT 24PT

University of Portsmouth
Computer Animation ... MSc 12FT 24PT
Computer Games Technology ... MSc 12FT 24PT

University of Salford
Art and Design: Creative Technology ... MA 12FT 24PT/PGDip 9FT 15PT

Sheffield Hallam University
Animation for Computer Games ... MA 12FT 36PT
Games Software Development ... MSc 13FT 36PT/PGDip 3FT 24PT/PGCert 4FT 12PT

Staffordshire University
3D Games Modelling ... MSc 12-18FT
Advanced Technology ... MSc 12-24FT 24-60PT
Computer Games Design ... MSc 12-18FT 24-32PT
Computer Games Programming ... MSc 12FT 24PT/PGCert 12FT 24PT/PGDip 12FT 24PT

University of Sunderland
Animation and Design ... MA 12FT 24PT

Teesside University
Computer Games Art (Character) ... MA 12FT 24-36PT/PGDip 8FT 24PT/PGCert 4FT 12PT
Computer Games Art (Environment) ... MA 12FT 24-36PT/PGDip 8FT 24PT/PGCert 4FT 12PT
Computer Games Art (Vehicle) ... MA 12FT 24-36PT/PGDip 8FT 24PT/PGCert 4FT 12PT
Concept Art for Games and Animation ... MA 12FT 36PT

Trinity College Dublin - the University of Dublin
Computer Science (Interactive Entertainment Technology) ... MSc 12FT

UCL - University College London
Computer Graphics, Vision and Imaging ... MSc 12FT

Computer game design
Research Courses

University of Bolton
Games Computing and Creative Technology Specialisms ... MPhil 18FT 30 - 36PT/PhD 36FT 60 - 72PT

University of Kent
Digital Arts ... MSc(Res) 12FT 24PT/MPhil 24FT 36PT/PhD 36FT 60PT

Computer graphics
Taught Courses

University of Aberdeen
Cloud Computing ... MSc 12FT 9PT/PGDip 9FT

University of Abertay Dundee
Games Development ... MProf 12FT

University of the Arts London - Central Saint Martins College of Art and Design
Character Animation ... MA 24FT

Bangor University
Advanced Visualization, Virtual Environments and Computer Animation ... MRes 12FT
Computer Science with Visualisation ... MSc 12FT 24PT

University of Bedfordshire
Computer Animation and Games Technology ... MSc 12FT 24-36PT

Birmingham City University
Video Game Enterprise and Production ... MSc 12FT

Arts University Bournemouth
Graphic Design ... MA 12FT 24PT
Animation Production ... MA 12FT

Bournemouth University
3D Computer Animation ... MA 12FT
Computer Animation and Visual Effects ... MSc 12FT

University of Bradford
Advanced Computer Animation and Visual Effects ... MA 12FT 24PT/MSc 12FT 24PT
Computer Animation and Visual Effects ... MSc 12FT 24PT/MA 12FT 24PT
Visual Computing ... MSc 12FT 24PT
Visual Effects for Post-Production ... MSc 12FT 24PT

Brunel University
Advanced Multimedia Design and 3D Technologies ... MSc 12FT 24PT

Cardiff University
Computer Science with Placement ... MSc 12FT

University of Central Lancashire
Animation ... MA 12FT/PGDip 12FT/PGCert 12FT
Children's Book Illustration ... MA 12FT/PGDip 12FT/PGCert 12FT
Interaction Design ... MRes 12FT 24-36PT
Toy Design ... MA 12FT 24PT/PGDip 12-18FT/PGCert 12-18FT

City University London
Human-Centred Systems ... MSc 12FT 28PT

Computer sciences and IT

University of Derby
Computer Graphics Production .... MSc 12FT 36PT
Visual Communication (Animation) .... MDes 48FT
Visual Communication (Graphic Design) .... MDes 48FT
Visual Communication (illustration) .... MDes 48FT

Dublin Institute of Technology
Professional Design Practice (Visual Communications) .. MA 12FT

University of Dundee
Computing .... MSc 12FT
Computing Research .... MSc 12FT
Computing with International Business .... MSc 12FT
Computing with Vision and Imaging .... MSc 12FT
Design Ethnography .... MSc 12FT

University of East Anglia
Advanced Computing Science .... MSc 12FT 24PT
Games Development .... MSc 12FT 24PT

Edinburgh Napier University
Design (Graphics) .... MA/MDes 12FT
Design (Interaction) .... MA/MDes 12FT
Interaction Design .... MDes 12FT

Glasgow School of Art
Sound for the Moving Image.. PGCert 4FT/PGDip 8FT/MDes 12FT

Glyndwr University
Computing .... MSc 12FT

Goldsmiths, University of London
Computational Studio Arts .... MFA 24FT
Computer Games & Entertainment .... MSc 12FT 24PT
Computing .... MSc 12FT 24PT
Design: Interaction Research .... MA 15FT 30PT
Photography: The Image and Electronic Arts .... MA 12FT

University of Hertfordshire
Human Computer Interaction (Online) .... MSc 12FT 24-36PT 12-36DL
Multimedia Technology .... MSc 12-16FT
Two Dimensional Digital Animation .. MA 12FT 24PT/PGDip 12FT 24PT

University of Hull
Computer Graphics Programming .... MSc 12FT

University of Kent
Computer Animation .... MSc 12FT
Digital Visual Effects .... MSc 12FT/PGDip 12FT

Kingston University
Computer Animation .... MA 12FT 24PT
Games Development .... MSc 12FT 24PT
Sustainable Design .... MA 12FT 24PT

University of Liverpool
Advanced Computer Science with Internet Economics .... MSc 12FT

London Metropolitan University
Interactive Media and Games Technologies ..... MSc 12FT 24-48PT

University of the Arts London - London College of Communication
Graphic Moving Image .... MA 12FT

Loughborough University
Interaction Design .... MA 12FT 24PT

Newcastle University
Computer Game Engineering .... MSc 12FT

Norwich University of the Arts
Communication Design .... MA 12FT 24PT
Moving Image and Sound .... MA 12FT 24PT

Nottingham Trent University
Computer Games Systems .... MSc 12FT 24PT
Motion Graphic Design .... MA 12FT/PGDip 7FT/PGCert 4FT
Puppetry and Digital Animation .... MA 12FT/PGDip 7FT/PGCert 4FT

University of Nottingham
Human Computer Interaction .... MSc 12FT 24-48PT

Ravensbourne
Animation Futures .... MA 12FT 24PT
Communication Design .... MA 12FT 24PT
Moving Image .... MA 12FT 24PT

University of Salford
Art and Design: Creative Technology ... MA 12FT 24PT/PGDip 9FT 15PT
Professional Sound and Video Technology .... MSc 12FT 36PT/PGDip 9FT 24PT

Sheffield Hallam University
Animation for Computer Games .... MA 12FT 36PT

University of South Wales
Graphic Communication .... MA 12FT 24PT
Visual Effects .... MA 12FT 24PT

Staffordshire University
3D Games Modelling .... MSc 12-18FT
Computer Games Design .... MSc 12-18FT 24-32PT
Computer Games Programming ...... MSc 12FT 24PT/PGCert 12FT 24PT/PGDip 12FT 24PT

University of Sunderland
Animation and Design .... MA 12FT 24PT

Swansea University
Advanced Computer Science with Specialism in Visual Computing .... MSc 12FT
Advanced Computer Science with a specialisation in Human Computer-Interaction .... MSc 12FT

Swansea Metropolitan University
3D Computer Animation .... MA 12FT 24PT

Teesside University
Computer Games Art (Character) ... MA 12FT 24-36PT/PGDip 8FT 24PT/PGCert 4FT 12PT
Computer Games Art (Environment) ..... MA 12FT 24-36PT/PGDip 8FT 24PT/PGCert 4FT 12PT
Computer Games Art (Vehicle) .... MA 12FT 24-36PT/PGDip 8FT 24PT/PGCert 4FT 12PT
Digital Character Animation MA 12FT 24-36PT/PGDip 8FT 24PT/PGCert 4FT 12PT

UCL - University College London
Computer Graphics, Vision and Imaging .... MSc 12FT
Human-Computer Interaction with Ergonomics .MSc 12FT 24PT/PGDip 9FT 24PT/PGCert 3FT 24PT

University of Westminster
Design for Communication .... MA 12FT/MA 12FT

Computer graphics
Research Courses

Bangor University
Medical Visualization and Simulation .... MPhil 24FT/PhD 36FT

University of Bradford
Electronic Imaging and Media Communications.PhD 36FT 48PT/MPhil 12FT 24PT

Cardiff University
Visual Computing.... PhD 36FT possiblePT/MPhil 12FT possiblePT

City University London
Centre for Human Computer Interaction Design .... PhD/MPhil

Coventry University
Visual and Information Design (VIDe) Research CentrePhD 36FT/MPhil 24FT/MA by research 12FT

University of Dundee
Computing .... MPhil 24FT MSc by research 12FT PhD 36FT

University of Gloucestershire
Computing and ITPhD 30-48FT 48-84PT/MPhil 18-36FT 30-60PT/MSc by research 12-24FT 18-36PT

Goldsmiths, University of London
Arts & Computational Technology .... MPhil 24FT 36PT/PhD 36-48FT 48-72PT

University of Kent
Digital Arts .... MSc(Res) 12FT 24PT/MPhil 24FT 36PT/PhD 36FT 60PT

The Open University
Design Processes and Products .... PhD 36FT 72PT variableDL/MPhil 15FT 24PT variableDL

Sheffield Hallam University
Communication and Computing Research Centre ... PhD 36-48FT 48-60PT/MPhil 24-36FT 48-60PT

UCL - University College London
Virtual Environments, Imaging and Visualisation .... EngD 48FT

Computer sciences and IT
Taught Courses

University of Aberdeen
Cloud Computing .... MSc 12FT 9PT/PGDip 9FT
Information Technology .... PGDip 9FT 18DL/MSc 12FT 24DL

University of Abertay Dundee
Information Technology .... MSc 16FT 33PT/PGDip 9FT 24PT

Aberystwyth University
3D Imaging, Analysis and Applications ... MRes 12FT 24PT/PGDip 9FT 21PT/PGCert 5FT 17PT
Intelligent Autonomous Systems .... MSc 12FT 24PT/PGDip 9FT 18PT/PGCert 5FT 10PT
Intelligent Systems .... MSc 12FT 24PT/PGDip 9FT 21PT/PGCert 5FT 17PT

Anglia Ruskin University
Computer Science .... MSc 12 - 15FT 24 - 30PT
Information Systems Management .... MBA 12FT 24PT
Information and Communication Technology (Conversion) .. MSc 12 - 15FT 24 - 30PT
Mobile Telecommunications .... MSc 12 - 15FT 24 - 30PT
Network Security .... MSc 12 - 15FT 24 - 30PT
Sound Engineering .... MSc 12FT 24PT

Bangor University
Advanced Visualization, Virtual Environments and Computer Animation .... MRes 12FT
Computer Science .... MSc 12FT
Computer Science with Artificial Intelligence/ ..... MSc 12FT 24PT
Computer Science with Security .... MSc 12FT 24PT
Computer Science with Visualisation .... MSc 12FT 24PT

University of Bath
Human Computer Interaction .... MSc 12FT

University of Bedfordshire
Applied Computing and Information Technology .... MSc 12-15FT 24-36PT
Computer Science .... MSc 12-15FT 24-36PT
Pre Masters Computing .... MSc 24FT
Research in Computing .... MSc 12FT 24-36PT/MPhil 12+FT/Phd 12+FT

Birkbeck, University of London
Advanced Computing Technologies .... MSc 12FT 24PT/PGDip 12FT 24PT/PGCert 12-24PT
Business Technologies .... MSc 12FT 24PT/PGDip 12FT 24PT
Cloud and Data Technology .... PGCert 12-24PT
Computer Science .... MRes 12FT 24PT
Computer Science .... MSc 12FT 24PT/PGDip 12FT 24PT
Computing for the Financial Services .... MSc 24PT
Creative Industries (Computing) .... MSc 12FT 24PT
Financial Engineering .... GradDip 12FT 24PT
Financial Engineering .... MSc 12FT 24PT
Information Systems and Management .... MSc 12FT 24PT/PGDip 12FT 24PT
Information Technology .... MSc 12FT 24PT
Learning Technologies .... MSc 12FT 24PT

University of Birmingham
Advanced Computer Science .... MSc 12FT
Computer Science .... MSc 12FT
Financial Engineering .... MSc 12FT
Human Computer Interaction .... MSc 12FT
Mathematics and Computing in Biology and Medicine .... MSc 12FT
Multidisciplinary Optimisation .... MSc 12FT

Bournemouth University
Enterprise Information Systems .... MSc 12FT 24PT

University of Bradford
Advanced Computer Science .... MSc 12FT 24PT
Computing .... MSc 12FT 24PT/PGDip 9FT
Multidisciplinary Computing .... MSc 12FT 24PT
Visual Computing .... MSc 12FT 24PT

University of Brighton
Applied Computer Science .... MSc 24FT 60PT/PGDip 24FT 60PT/PGCert 24FT 60PT
Computer Science .... MSc 13FT 24-60PT/PGDip 13FT 24-60PT/PGCert 5FT 24-60PT
Computing .... MSc 13FT 24-60PT/PGDip 10FT 24-60PT/PGCert 5FT 24PT
Information Management .... MSc 12FT 24PT/PGDip 12FT 24PT/PGCert 12FT 24PT

University of Bristol
Computer Science (conversion) .... MSc 12FT 24PT
Biomedical Engineering .... MSc 12FT

British Institute of Technology & E-commerce ....
Innovative Technology .... PGCert 3FT/DipHE 6FT/MScD 12FT

Brunel University
Advanced Electronic and Electrical Engineering .... MSc 12FT
Advanced Multimedia Design and 3D Technologies ...... MSc 12FT 24PT
Business Intelligence and Social Media .... MSc 12FT
Computer Communication Networks .... MSc 12FT
Distributed Computing Systems Engineering .... MSc 12FT
Embedded Systems (with Signal Processing and Multimedia Communications pathways) .... MSc 12FT
Wireless Communication Systems .... MSc 12FT

University of Buckingham
Applied Computing .... MSc 12FT 24PT/MSc 18FT
Innovative Computing .... MSc 12FT 24PT

University of Cambridge
Advanced Computer Science .... MPhil 9FT
Computational Biology .... MPhil 11FT
Computational Biology .... MPhil 11FT
Technology Policy .... MPhil 9FT

Canterbury Christ Church University
Computing .... MSc 12FT 36PT

Cardiff Metropolitan University
Computing .... MSc 12FT 24PT/PGDip 24PT/PGCert 12PT

Cardiff University
Computing .... MSc 12FT 36PT

University of Central Lancashire
Computing .... MSc 12FT 24PT/PGDip 12PT/PGCert 6PT
Construction Management (Project Management) ..... MSc 24DL/PGDip 12DL/PGCert 6DL
Database Systems .... MSc 12FT 36PT/PGDip 12FT 36PT
IT Security .... MSc 12FT 36PT/PGDip 9FT 18PT/PGCert 6FT 12PT
IT and Statistics for Health .... UniCert 3PT
Network Computing .... MSc 12FT 36PT/PGDip 12FT 24PT

Computer sciences and IT

University of Chester
Information Systems MSc 12FT 24 - 36PT/PGDip 12FT 24 - 36PT/
PGCert 12FT 12 - 24PT

University of Chichester
Secondary ICT .... PGCE(QTS) 9.5FT 5 maxPT

University College Cork
Applied Science (Software & Systems for Mobile Networks) ....
MSc 12FT
Computing Science .... MSc 12FT

Coventry University
Computer Science ... MSc 12FT 24PT/PGDip 9FT 18PT/PGCert 4FT
8PT
Computing .. MSc 12FT 24-36PT/PGDip 8FT 16PT/PGCert 4FT 8PT

University of Cumbria
Computing and IT.. PGDip 12PT/PGCert 12PT
Innovative Technology Solutions..... MBA 12FT 48PT/PGCert 12FT
48PT/PGDip 12FT 48PT

University of Derby
Advanced Computer Networks...........................MSc 12FT 36-72PT
Information Security ....MSc 12FT 36PT

Dublin Institute of Technology
Applied Computing for Technologists......................MSc 12FT 24PT
Computer Science ......PGDip 12FT 24PT/MPhil 24FT 36PT/PhD by
taught 40FT 60PT
Computing (Information Technology) ....MSc 12FT 24PT

University of Dundee
Applied Computing .... MSc 12FT
Computing .... MSc 12FT
Computing Research .... MSc 12FT
Computing with International Business .... MSc 12FT
Computing with Vision and Imaging .... MSc 12FT
Data Science .... MSc 24PT MSc 12FT PGCert 6FT
Information Technology and International Business .... MSc 12FT
User Experience Engineering .... MSc 12FT

Durham University
Internet Systems and E-Business .... MSc 12FT

University of East Anglia
Advanced Computing Science................................MSc 12FT 24PT
Computational Biology.........MSc 12FT/MSc 24PT/MSc 48PT
Computing Science.........................MSc 12FT 24PT MRes 12FT
Games Development...MSc 12FT 24PT

Information Systems.. MSc 12FT 24PT

University of East London
Information Technology .... MSc 12FT 24PT/PGDip 8FT 16PT/
PGCert 4FT 8PT

Edge Hill University
Computing ....MRes 12FT 24PTMSc 12FT 24PT
Master of Business Administration (Information Technology) .....
MBA 12-18FT

Edinburgh Napier University
Flexible Managed Programme (FECCI)... MA 12FT 24PT/MSc 12FT
24PT/PGCert 12FT 24PT

University of Edinburgh
Advanced Design Informatics .... MSc 21FT
Animation ....MA 12FT/MFA 24FT
Artificial Intelligence .... MSc 12FT 36FT
Bioinformatics..................................... MSc 12FT/PGDip 9FT
Biomechanics .... MSc 12FT
Biotechnology .... MSc 12FT/PGDip 9FT
Cognitive Science.................................... MSc 12FT 36PT
Composition for Screen .... MSc 12FT 24PT
Computer Science .... MSc 12FT 36PT
Copy of Cognitive Science .... MSc 12FT 36PT
Design Informatics.........................MSc 12FT MA 12FT/MFA 24FT
Design and Digital Media........................ MSc 12FT 24PT
Digital Animation...........................MSc(Res) 12FT 24PT
Digital Composition and Performance .... MSc 12FT 24PT
Digital Education (Online Distance Learning)..........MSc 12-72DL/
PGCert 12-24DL/PGDip 12-48DL
Digital Media and Culture........................MSc(Res) 12FT 24PT
Digital Studio Practice ....MSc(Res) 12FT 24PT
High Performance Computing............ MSc 12FT 36PT/PGDip 9FT
Scientific Computing .... MSc 12FT

University of Essex
Advanced Web Engineering............................ MSc 12FT 24PT
Big Data and Text Analytics .... MSc 12FT 24PT
Cloud Computing .... MSc 12FT 24PT
Computational Finance .... MSc 12FT 24PT
Computational Intelligence............................ MSc 12FT 24PT
Computer Engineering .... MSc 12FT 24PT
Computer Networks and Security..................... MSc 12FT 24PT
Computer Science .... MSc 12FT 24PT
Computer Science with English for Academic Purposes ....
Diploma 9FT

Electronic Engineering .... MSc 12FT 24PT
Embedded Systems................................... MSc 12FT 24PT
High Frequency Finance and Trading .... MSc 12FT 24PT
Intelligent Systems and Robotics .... MSc 12FT 24PT
Multimedia Networking................................. MSc 12FT 24PT
Operational Research and Computer Science.......MSc 12FT 24PT/
PGDip 9FT
Statistics and Computer Science.................... MSc 12FT/PGDip 9FT
Telecommunication and Information Systems...... MSc 12FT 24PT

National University of Ireland Galway
Information Technology .... MIT 12FT

Glasgow Caledonian University
Advanced Computer NetworkingMSc 13FT 36PT/PGDip 9FT 24PT
Computer Science.. MSc 12FT
Digital Forensics.. MSc 12FT

University of Glasgow
Computing Science .... MSc 12FT 24PT/PGDip 9FT 21PT/
PGCert 9FT 9PT
Computing Science ....MRes 12FT 24PT/PGDip 9FT 21PT/
PGCert 9FT 9PT
Information Technology ....MSc 12FT 24PT/PGDip 9FT 21PT
Search Engine Technologies ....MRes 12FT 24PT/PGDip 9FT 21PT/
PGCert 9FT 9PT
Search Engine Technologies ...... MSc 12FT 24PT/PGDip 9FT 21PT/
PGCert 9FT 9PT
Software Engineering ....MRes 12FT 24PT/PGCert 9FT 9PT/PGDip
9FT 21PT MSc 12FT 24PT/PGCert 9FT 9PT/PGDip 9FT 21PT

University of Gloucestershire
Computing (IT Management) ... MSc 12FT 24PT/PGDip 8FT 20PT/
PGCert 4FT 8PT
Information Technology Management (Top Up)................MSc 6FT

Glyndwr University
Computer Science .... MSc 12FT 24-36PT/MRes 12FT 24-36PT
Computing .... MSc 12FT

Goldsmiths, University of London
Computing .... MSc 12FT 24PT

University of Greenwich
Computing .... MSc 12FT 24PT
Computing and Information Systems...................... MSc 12FT 24PT
Distributed Computing Systems .... MSc 12FT 24PT
Information Technology Management.................... MBA 12FT 36PT
Internet Technology....................................... MSc 12FT 24PT

Griffith College Dublin
Computing (HETAC) .... MSc 12FT 24PT/PGDip 12FT 18PT

Heriot-Watt University
Advanced Internet Applications...........MSc 12FT 24PT/PGDip 9FT
Artificial Intelligence ....MSc 12FT 24PT/PGDip 9FT
Computer Services ManagementMSc 12FT 24PT/PGDip 9FT 21PT
Creative Software Systems ....MSc 12FT 24PT/PGDip 9FT 21PT
Information Technology (Business) .....MSc 12FT 24PT/PGDip 9FT
21PT
Information Technology (Software Systems) ....MSc 12FT 24PT/
PGDip 9FT 21PT
Robotics, Autonomous and Interactive Systems (RAIS)MSc 12FT/
PGDip 9FT
Software Engineering....................MSc 12FT 24PT/PGDip 9FT 21PT

University of Hertfordshire
Business Computing...MSc 12-16FT
Computer Science ....MSc 12-16FT
Computer Science (Online) ....MSc 12FT 24-36PT
E-Learning Technology..MSc 12-16FT
Multimedia Technology..MSc 12-16FT

University of Huddersfield
Advanced Computer Science...........................MSc 12FT 24 - 36PT

University of Hull
Computer Science .... MSc 12FT

Imperial College London
Communications and Signal Processing .... MSc 12FT
Computing (Specialism) .... MSc 12FT
Computing Science .... MSc 12FT
Computing for Industry.......................................MSc 12FT 48PT

Keele University
Information Technology and Management .... MSc 12FT

University of Kent
Advanced Computer Science.....................................MSc 12FT 36PT
Advanced Computer Science (Computational Intelligence)... MSc
12FT 36PT
Advanced Software Development ....MSc 12FT 36PT
Computer Animation .... MSc 12FT
Computer Science ....MSc 12FT 36PT
Computing and Entrepreneurship...........................MSc 12FT 36PT
Digital Visual Effects...........................MSc 12FT/PGDip 12FT
Future Computing .... MSc 12FT
IT Consultancy...MSc 12FT 36PT
Information Security and Biometrics ....MSc 12FT 24PT/
PGDip 12FT 24PT
Mobile Application Design...............................MSc 12FT 24PT
Networks and Security.......................................MSc 12FT 36PT
Social Anthropology and Computing........................ MA 12FT 24PT

Computer sciences and IT

King's College London
Computer Science (Research)....MSc 12FT
Computing & Internet Systems....MSc 12FT
Computing, IT Law & Management....MSc 12FT

Kingston University
Communication Design: Illustration....MA 12FT 24PT
Computer Animation....MA 12FT 24PT
Digital Image & Signal Processing....MSc 12FT 24-36PT
Digital Image & Signal Processing with Management Studies....MSc 12FT 24-36PT
IT and Strategic Innovation....MSc 12FT 24-36PT/PGDip 12FT 24-36PT
Information Systems (Health Information Management)....MSc 12FT 24PT
Software Engineering (Web)....MSc 12FT 24-36PT
Software Engineering (Web) with Management Studies....MSc 12FT 24-36PT

Lancaster University
Computer Science....MSc 12FT 24-48PT

Leeds Metropolitan University
Business Intelligence (SAS)....MSc 12FT 24PT
Digital Forensics & Security....MSc 12FT 24PT
Information & Technology....MSc 12FT 24PT/PGDip 12FT 24PT/PGCert 4FT 24PT

University of Leeds
Advanced Computer Science....MSc 12FT
Advanced Computer Science (Cloud Computing)....MSc 12FT
Advanced Computer Science (Data Analytics)....MSc 12FT
Advanced Computer Science (Intelligent Systems)....MSc 12FT

University of Leicester
Advanced Computer Science....MSc 12FT/PGDip 9FT
Advanced Scientific Computing....MSc 12FT/PGDip 9FT

University of Limerick
Computer Aided Engineering Product Design....PGDip 9FT/MSc 12FT
Computer Engineering....PGDip 9FT/MEng 24FT
Computer and Communications Systems....MEng 12FT 24PT
Computing....PGDip 9FT
Health Informatics....MSc(Eng) 12FT
Information and Network Security....MEng 12FT
Interactive Media....MA 12FT/MSc 12FT
Multilingual Computing and localisation....MSc 12FT

University of Lincoln
Computer Science....MSc 12FT 24PT

Liverpool Hope University
Computer Science....MSc 12FT 24PT/PGDip 12FT 24PT /PGCert 6FT 12PT
Education & Computer Science....MA 36PT
International MBA....International MBA 12FT 24PT
MBA (Information Technology)....MBA 12FT 24PT
Networks & Security....MSc 12FT

Liverpool John Moores University
Advanced Computer Studies....MSc 12FT 24PT
Computing Information Systems....MSc 12FT 24PT
Computing: Distance Learning in Computing, Network Security and Information Systems....MSc 12-48DL

University of Liverpool
Advanced Computer Science....MSc 12FT/PGCert 12FT/PGDip 12FT
Advanced Computer Science with Internet Economics....MSc 12FT
Advanced Science (Computer Sciences pathway)....MSc 12FT/PGDip 12FT/PGCert 12FT
Computer Science....MSc 12FT/PGDip 8FT/PGCert 4FT
Information Technology (Online Degree)....MSc 24FT 24+PT

London Metropolitan University
Computer Science....MSc 12-18FT 24PT
Computing....GradCert 6FT 12PT
Information Technology....MSc 12FT 24PT
Professional Information Technology....MSc 12FT 24-48PT

London School of Hygiene and Tropical Medicine
Clinical Trials (by Distance Learning)....MSc 24 - 60DL/PGDip 12 - 60DL/PGCert 12-60DL

Loughborough University
Advanced Chemical Engineering with Information Technology & Management....MSc 12FT 12-96PT/PGDip 12FT 24-96PT/PGCert 12FT 24-96PT
Information Technology....MSc 12FT 24PT/PGDip 7FT 24PT
International Computing for the Internet....MSc 12FT 24PT
Science of the Internet....MSc 12FT 24PT
Visual Systems and Technology....MSc 12FT 24-60PT

Manchester Metropolitan University
Advanced Computing....MSc 12FT 36PT/PGCert 12FT 36PT/PGDip 12FT 36PT
Computing....MSc 12FT 36PT

University of Manchester
ACS: Digital Biology....MSc 12FT
Advanced Computer Science....MSc 12FT/MRes 12FT
Advanced Computer Science and IT Management....MSc 12FT 24PT/Modular 24PT
Computer Science Foundation Route to MSc (E-Learning)....MSc 12FT 12PT

National University of Ireland, Maynooth
Computer Science....MCompSci 24FT
Information Technology....HDip 12FT

Middlesex University
Business Information Technology....MSc 12FT 36PT
Computer Science....MSc 12FT 36PT

Newcastle University
Advanced Computer Science....MSc 12FT 24PT
Bioinformatics....MSc 12FT
Cloud Computing....MSc 12FT 24PT
Computer Game Engineering....MSc 12FT
Computer Science....MSc 12FT 24PT
Wireless Embedded Systems....MSc 12FT

Newman University
PGCE Secondary Computer Science and ICT....PGCE(QTS) 12FT

University of Northampton
Computing....MSc 12FT 36PT/PGDip 12PT

Northumbria University
Business Information Systems Management....MSc 12/16FT
Computer Network Technology....MSc 12/16FT
Computer Science....MSc 12/16FT/PGDip 9FT/PGCert 4FT
Computing and Information Technology....MSc 12/16FT 36DL/PGDip 9FT 24DL/PGCert 4FT 12DL

Nottingham Trent University
Computer Games Systems....MSc 12FT 24PT
Computer Science....MRes 12FT
Computing Systems....MSc 12/24FT 24PT
Internet and Enterprise Computing....MSc 12FT 24PT
MSc Internet and Security....MSc 12FT 24PT

University of Nottingham
Advanced Computing Science....MSc 12FT 24-48PT
Computer Science and Entrepreneurship....MSc 12FT 24-48PT
Information Technology....MSc 12FT 24-48PT/PGDip 9FT 24PT
Learning, Technology and Education/Learning, Technology and Education (online)....MA 12FT 24-48PT/MA 24DL
Scientific Computation with Mathematical Medicine and Biology....MSc 12FT
Usability and Human Computer Interaction by Distance Learning PGCert....PGCert 12DL

The Open University
Computing....MSc variableDL/PGCert 12DL/PGDip variableDL
Computing....PGCert variableDL
Computing for Commerce and Industry....MSc variableDL/PGDip variableDL

Oxford Brookes University
Computer Science....MSc 12FT 24PT
Computing....MSc 12FT 24PT
Software Engineering....MSc 12FT 24PT
Two Year Master's Degree - Technology, Design and Environment MSc 21-24FT
Wireless Communication Systems....MSc 12FT 24PT

University of Oxford
Computer Science....MSc 12FT
Mathematical Modelling and Scientific Computing....MSc 12FT
Mathematics and the Foundations of Computer Science....MSc 12FT
Social Science of the Internet....MSc 10FT
Software and Systems Security....MSc 24-48PT

Plymouth University
Computer Science....MSc 12FT 24PT MRes 12FT
Digital Art and Technology....MRes 12FT

University of Portsmouth
Partnership Masters Programme....MA 12PT/MSc 12PT

Queen Mary, University of London
Computer Science....MSc 12FT 24PT
Computer Science by Research....MSc 12FT 24PT
Computer Vision....MSc 12FT 24PT
Computer and Communications Law....LLM 12FT 24PT
Computing and Information Systems (generalist)....MSc 12FT 24PT
Media and Arts Technology (MSc by Research)....MSc(Res) 12FT
Software Engineering....MSc 12FT

Queen's University Belfast
Software Development (Conversion)....MSc 12FT

University of Reading
Cybernetics....MSc 12FT 24PT
Data Assimilation and Inverse Modelling in Geoscience....MSc 12FT/PGDip 12FT
Financial Engineering....MSc 10FT
Systems Engineering....MRes 12FT 24PT

Robert Gordon University
Computing: Information Engineering (with/without Network Management)....MSc 12FT 36PT/PGDip 9FT 24PT/PGCert 4FT 12PT
Computing: Software Technology with Network Management....MSc 12FT 36PT/PGDip 9FT 24PT/PGCert 4FT 12PT
IT Management....MSc 12FT 36DL

Royal Holloway, University of London
Computer Science by Research....MSc 12FT 24PT

University of Salford
Advanced Computer Science....MSc 12FT 36PT/PGDip 6FT 24PT
Data Telecommunications Networks....MSc 12FT 24PT/PGDip 9FT 18PT
Databases and Web-based Systems....MSc 12FT 24PT/PGDip 9FT 18PT
Industrial and Commercial Combustion Engineering....MSc 36DL/PGDip 12DL/PGCert 12DL
Information Security....MSc 12FT 24PT/PGDip 9FT 18PT/PGCert 9FT 18PT
Information Security Management....MSc 12FT 24PT/PGDip 9FT 18PT/PGCert 9FT 18PT
Information Systems Management....MSc 12FT 36PT/PGDip 8FT 24PT/PGCert 4FT 9PT
Social Media....MA 9FT/PGDip 9FT

Sheffield Hallam University
Electronics and Information Technology....MSc 12FT 36PT/PGDip 8FT 24PT/PGCert 4FT 12PT
IT Professional....MSc 36DL
Information Technology and Management....MSc 30DL/PGDip 24DL/PGCert 12DL
Infromation Technology....MSc 12FT 36-72PT
Networking Technologies and Management....MSc 36-72DL
Online Communication....MA 36DL
Online Communication....MA 18-60DL/PGDip 24-36DL/PGCert 12-18DL
Software Engineering....MSc 12FT 36PT
Technical Consulting....MSc 18FT 36PT
Technology Enhanced Learning, Innovation and Change....MSc 36PT/PGDip 24PT/PGCert 12PT
Web and Cloud Computing....MSc 12FT

University of Sheffield
Advanced Computer Science....MSc 12FT
Computational Intelligence and Robotics....MSc 12FT
Information Management....MSc 12FT 24-36PT
Information Management (Professional Enhancement Programme)....MSc Up to 12FT 24-36PT/PGDip 9FT 18PT/PGCert 6FT 12PT
Information Systems....MSc 12FT 24-36PT
Information Systems (Professional Enhancement Programme)....MSc Up to 12FT 24-36PT/PGDip 9FT 18PT/PGCert 6FT 12PT
Information Systems Management....MSc 12FT
Wireless Communication Systems....MSc(Eng) 12FT

University of South Wales
Computer Science....MSc 12FT 36PT
Computing and Information Systems....MSc 12FT 36PT
Electronics and Information Technology....MSc 12FT 24PT

University of Southampton
Information Technology and Commerce....LLM 12FT 24PT
Information Technology and Telecommunications Law....LLM 24DL
Digital Marketing (1 yrs)....MSc 12FT
Operational Research....MSc 12FT 24PT/PGDip 9FT

University of St Andrews
Advanced Computer Science....MSc 12FT 24PT
Artificial Intelligence....MSc 12FT 24PT
Information Technology....MSc 12FT 24PT
Networks & Distributed Systems....MSc 12FT 24PT

Staffordshire University
Computer Games Design....MSc 12-18FT 24-32PT
Computer Games Programming....MSc 12FT 24PT/PGCert 12FT 24PT/PGDip 12FT 24PT
Computer Networks and Security....MSc 12FT 24PT/PGCert 12FT 24PT/PGDip 12FT 24PT
Computer Science via Distance Learning....MSc 24-60DL/PGCert 24-60DL/PGDip 24-60DL
Computing Solutions for Business via Distance Learning....MSc 24-60FT/PGCert 24-60FT/PGDip 24-60FT
Computing Soluttions for Business....MSc 12-18FT
Digital Forensics and Cybercrime Analysis....MSc 12FT
Film Production Technology....MSc 12-18FT
Film Production and Visual Cultures....MA 12FT
Film Production: Theory and Practice....MA 12FT
Mobile Computer Systems....MSc 12-24FT 24-84PT 24-84DL/PGCert 12FT/PGDip 12FT
Web Development....MSc 12FT 24-60PT

University of Stirling
Advanced Computing....MSc 12FT/PGDip 9FT/PGCert 9FT
Computing for Business....MSc 12FT
Information Technology....MSc 12FT/PGDip 9FT

University of Strathclyde
Advanced Computer Science....MSc 12FT/PGDip 9FT
Advanced Software Engineering....MSc 12FT/PGDip 9FT
Communications Technology and Policy....MSc 12FT 24PT/PGDip 9FT 18PT
Enterprise Information Systems....MSc 12FT/PGDip 9FT

Computer sciences and IT

Information Management.........MSc 12FT/PGDip 9FT/PGCert 4FT
Internet Law and Policy.....LLM 12FT 24PT 24DL/PGDip 9FT 21PT 21DL/PGCert 9FT
Management of Information Technology Systems.......MSc 12FT/PGDip 9FT
Mobile Systems.....MSc 12FT/PGDip 9FT

University of Sussex
Advanced Computer Science.....MSc 12FT 24PT
Computing with Digital Media.....MSc 12FT 24PT
Information Technology with Business and Management.... MSc 12FT 24PT
Intelligent Systems.....MSc 12FT 24PT

Swansea University
Advanced Computer Science.....MSc 12FT
Advanced Computer Science with Specialism in Visual Computing.....MSc 12FT
Advanced Computer Science with a specialisation in Human Computer-Interaction.....MSc 12FT
Advanced Computer Science with a specialisation in Safe and Secure Systems.....MSc 12FT
Advanced Computer Science with a specialisation in Software Technology.....MSc 12FT
Computer Modelling and Finite Elements in Engineering Mechanics.....MSc 12FT 36PT/PGDip 12FT
Computer Science.....MSc 12FT
Health Informatics....... MSc 12FT 36PT/PGDip 12FT 24PT/PGCert 12FT 12PT
Mathematics and Computing for Finance....... MSc 12FT 24/36PT
Visual Computing.....MRes 12FT 24PT

Swansea Metropolitan University
Computing and Information Systems.....MSc 12FT 24PT

Teesside University
Advanced Computer Science.....MSc 12FT 36PT
Applied Computing...MSc 12FT 24-36PT/PGDip 8FT 24PT/PGCert 4FT 12PT
Computer Games Art (Character)... MA 12FT 24-36PT/PGDip 8FT 24PT/PGCert 4FT 12PT
Computer Games Art (Environment).....MA 12FT 24-36PT/PGDip 8FT 24PT/PGCert 4FT 12PT
Computer Games Art (Vehicle)........MA 12FT 24-36PT/PGDip 8FT 24PT/PGCert 4FT 12PT
Computing.....MSc 12FT 24-36PT/PGDip 8FT 24PT/PGCert 4FT 12PT
Networks and Communications.....MSc 12FT 36PT
Network Systems.....MSc 12FT 24-36PT/PGDip 8FT 24PT/PGCert 4FT 12PT

Trinity College Dublin - the University of Dublin
Computer Science (Networks and Distributed Systems)..... MSc 12FT
High Performance Computing.....MSc 12FT
Technology and Learning.....MSc 24PT

UCL - University College London
Computer Graphics, Vision and Imaging.....MSc 12FT
Computer Science.....MSc 12FT
ICT Innovation.....MSc 24FT
Networked Computer Systems.....MSc 12FT
Software Systems Engineering.....MSc 12FT
Technology Entrepreneurship.....MSc 12FT 24PT/PGDip 9FT
Web Science.....MSc 12FT/MRes 12FT

University of Warwick
Complexity Science.....MSc 12FT/PGDip 12FT/PGCert 12FT
Finance & Information Technology.....MSc 12FT

University of West London
Computing.....MSc 12FT 24PT
Computing Interaction Design.....MSc 12FT 24PT
Intelligent Computing Systems.....MSc 12FT 24PT

University of the West of Scotland
Advanced Computer Systems Development.. MSc 12FT 24-36PT/Diploma 9FT 24PT
Information Technology.... MSc 12FT 24-36PT/Diploma 9FT 24PT

University of the West of England, Bristol
Information Technology.....MSc 12FT 24PT

University of Westminster
Computer Science.......MSc 12FT 24PT MRes 12FT 24PT 12-24BM
Embedded Systems.....MSc 12FT 24PT 24BM

University of Wolverhampton
Advanced Technology Management.....MSc 12FT 24PT
Computational Bioinformatics.....MSc 12FT 24PT
Computer Aided Design for Construction.....MSc 12FT 24PT
Computer Science.....MSc 12FT 24PT
Computer Science (Multimedia Technology).....MSc 12-18FT 24-36PT
Computer Systems Security.....MSc 12FT 24PT/PGCert 12FT 24PT
Information Technology.....MSc 12FT 24PT/PGCert 12FT 24PT
Information Technology Management.....MSc 12FT 24PT
Rapid Product Development and Advanced Manufacturing..... MSc 12FT 24PT
Strategic Information Technology Management.....MSc 12FT 12-16PT/PGCert 12FT 24PT

University of York
Advanced Computer Science.....MSc 12FT
Archaeological Information Systems.....MSc 12FT 24PT
Computational Biology.....MRes 12FT
Computing.....MSc 12FT
Information Technology.....MSc 12FT

Computer sciences and IT
Research Courses

University of Aberdeen
Computing Science.....PhD 36FT/MPhil 24FT/MSc by research 12FT

Aberystwyth University
Computer Science.....MPhil 12FT 24PT PhD 36FT 60PT

Anglia Ruskin University
Digital Modelling.....PhD 24 - 60FT 36 - 72PT
Sound and Audio Engineering...... MPhil 18 - 36FT 30 - 48PT/PhD 24 - 60FT 36 - 72PT
Telecommunications Engineering.....PhD 24 - 60FT 30-48PT

Aston University
Information Processing and Pattern Analysis Research Group..... PhD 36FT/MPhil 24FT

Bangor University
Communication Networks and Protocols...MPhil 24FT/PhD 36FT
Pattern Recognition / Classifiers.....MPhil 24FT/PhD 36FT

University of Bath
Computer Science.....PhD 24-48FT 36-72PT/MPhil 12-36FT 24-48PT

University of Bedfordshire
Research in Computing.....MSc by research 12FT 24PT

Birkbeck, University of London
Computer Science and Information Systems.....PhD 36FT 60-72PT/MPhil 24FT 48PT

Birmingham City University
Computing.....MPhil 36-72PT/PhD 36-72PT

University of Birmingham
Computer Science/Cognitive Science.....PhD 36FT/MSc by research 24FT

University of Bradford
Department of Computing PhD 36-48FT 48-60PT/MPhil 12-24FT 24-48PT

University of Brighton
Information Technology Research Institute: Research Division.... PhD 24-60FT 36PT/MPhil 18-36FT 30-48PT

University of Bristol
Complexity Sciences.....PhD 48FT/MRes 48FT
Computer Science.....PhD 36FT 72PT

Brunel University
Department of Information Systems and Computing. PhD 36FT/New Route PhD 48FT/MRes 18FT

University of Buckingham
Bioinformatics.....MSc by research 12FT
Computing.....DPhil 36FT 72PT/MPhil 24FT 48PT

University of Cambridge
Computer Science.....PhD 36FT

Canterbury Christ Church University
Computing.....PhD 36FT 60PT/MPhil 24FT 48PT

Cardiff University
Computer Science.....MRes 12FT
Distributed and Scientific Computing.........PhD 36FT/MPhil 12FT

University of Central Lancashire
Computing......PhD 48FT 84PT/MPhil 36FT 60PT/MSc by research 24FT 36PT

City University London
Department of Information Science.....PhD/MPhil

Coventry University
Biomedical Computing.....PhD 36FT/MPhil 24FT/MRes 12FT

Cranfield University, Shrivenham
Informatics and Simulation.....PhD/MSc by research 12FT

De Montfort University
Computer Science and Informatics......... PhD 24 - 36FT 48 - 72PT/MPhil 12 - 24FT 24 - 48PT

University of Dundee
Computing.....MPhil 24FT MSc by research 12FT PhD 36FT

Durham University
Engineering and Computing Sciences.....MSc by research 12FT/PhD 36FT

University of East Anglia
Computer Science.....PhD 36FT 72PT/MPhil 24FT 48PT

University of Edinburgh
Computer Science...PhD 36FT/MPhil 24FT/MSc by research 12FT
Digital Communications...PhD 36FT 72PT/MPhil 24FT 48PT/MSc by research 12FT 24PT
Informatics (with Beihang University).....PhD 36FT
Informatics: Centre for Intelligent Systems and their Applications....PhD 36FT 72PT/MPhil 24FT 48PT/MSc by research 12FT 24PT
Informatics: Doctoral Training Centre in Neuroinformatics and Computational Neuroscience.....MSc by research 12FT
Informatics: Institute for Adaptive & Neural Computation... MSc by research 12FT 24PT/PhD 36FT 72PT/MPhil 24FT 48PT
Informatics: Institute for Computing Systems Architecture ....MPhil 24FT 48PT/PhD 36FT 72PT/MSc by research 12FT 24PT
Informatics: Institute for Language, Cognition and Communication.....PhD 36FT 72PT/MPhil 24FT 48PT/MSc by research 12FT 24PT
Informatics: Institute of Perception, Action & Behaviour... MPhil 24FT 48PT/PhD 36FT 72PT/MSc by research 12FT 24PT
Informatics: Laboratory for Foundations of Computer Science.... MPhil 24FT 48PT/PhD 36FT 72PT/MSc by research 12FT 24PT
Informatics: Life Sciences Institute.....PhD 36FT 72PT
Integrated Micro and Nano Systems......... PhD 36FT 72PT/MSc by research 12FT 24PT/MPhil 24FT 48PT

University of Essex
Computational Finance.....PhD 36FT
Computer Science..........PhD 36FT 72PT/MPhil 24FT 48PT/MSc by research 12FT 24PT
Computing and Electronic Systems....PhD 36FT 72PT/MPhil 24FT 48PT/MSc by research 12FT 24PT
Electronic Systems EngineeringPhD 36FT 72PT/MPhil 24FT 48PT/MSc by research 12FT 24PT
Operational Research and Computer Science.......PhD 36FT 72PT/MPhil 24FT 48PT/MSc by research 12FT 24PT

University of Exeter
Computer Science..........PhD 36FT 72PT/MPhil 24FT 48PT/MSc by research 12-24FT 24-36PT

National University of Ireland Galway
Computer Science & Information Technology.....MSc by research 24FT 48PT

University of Glasgow
Computing Science.....PhD 36FT/MSc by research 12FT

University of Gloucestershire
Computing and ITPhD 30-48FT 48-84PT/MPhil 18-36FT 30-60PT/MSc by research 12-24FT 18-36PT

Goldsmiths, University of London
Computer Science...........PhD 36-48FT 48-72PT/MPhil 24FT 36PT

University of Greenwich
Computing and Mathematical Sciences.....PhD 36-48FT 60-84PT MSc by research 12FT 24PT

University of Hertfordshire
Algorithms.....PhD 36FT 72PT/MRes 12FT 24PT

University of Hull
Computer Science MSc by research 12FT 24PT/MPhil 24FT 36PT/PhD 36FT 60PT

Imperial College London
Department of Computing.....PhD 36FT/MPhil 24FT

Keele University
Computer Science/Software Engineering. PhD 24-48FT 48-84PT/MPhil 12-24FT 24-36PT

University of Kent
Computer Science.....PhD 24FT 60PT/MSc by research 12FT 24PT

King's College London
Computer Science Research........... PhD 36FT 48-72PT/MPhil 36FT 48-72PT
Digital Humanities Research......... PhD 36FT 48-72PT/MPhil 36FT 48-72PT

Kingston University
Research in Faculty of Computing, Information Systems and Mathematics.............PhD 36-48FT 48-72PT 36-72DL/MPhil 24FT 36-48PT 24-48DL/MSc by research 12FT 24PT 12-24DL

University of Leeds
Computational and Systems Science.........PhD 36+FT/MPhil 24FT

University of Leicester
Computer Science.....PhD 24-48FT 36-72PT/MPhil 12-24FT 24-48PT

University of Lincoln
Computer Science By Research..........MSc by research 12FT 24PT/MPhil 24FT 48PT/PhD 12-33FT 24-60PT

Liverpool Hope University
Postgraduate Research.....PhD 24FT 48PT/MPhil 12FT 24PT

University of Liverpool
Advanced Science (Computer Sciences pathway) (Algorithmics) .....MRes 12FT
Advanced Science MRes (Computer Sciences pathway)........ MRes 12FT
Computer Science.....MPhil 12-24FT/PhD 36-48FT

London Metropolitan University
Dept of Computing.....PhD Max 60FT Max 96PT/MPhil Max 36FT Max 54PT

Loughborough University
Computer Science.....MPhil 24FT 36PT/PhD 36FT 60PT

Computer sciences and IT

University of Manchester
Computer Science .... PhD 36FT 72PT/MPhil 12FT 24PT

Middlesex University
Computing Science.........PhD 36FT 48PT/MPhil 24FT 36PT/MA by research 12FT 24PT

Newcastle University
Computer Science .... Integrated PhD 48FT 72PT PhD 36FT 72PT/MPhil 12FT 24PT

University of Northampton
Technology and Design............... PhD 36FT 48PT/MPhil 24FT 36PT

Nottingham Trent University
Multidisciplinary Engineering... MPhil 18FT 30PT/PhD 33FT 66PT
School of Computing and Informatics.. MPhil .FT/PhD 48FT 96PT
School of Computing and Technology .....MPhil .FT/PhD .FT/MRes 12FT

University of Nottingham
Automated Scheduling, Optimisation and Planning Group...PhD 36FT/MPhil 24FT/MRes 12FT
Computer Science and Entrepreneurship.........MSc 12FT 24-48PT
School of Computer Science research areas....... MRes 12FT 24PT/MPhil 12-24FT 24-48PT/PhD 24-36FT 48-72PT

The Open University
Computing ....PhD 36FT 72PT variableDL/MPhil 15FT 24PT variableDL
Digital classics.......... PhD 36FT 72PT variableDL/MPhil 15FT 24PT variableDL
Human-Centred Computing...................PhD variableFT variablePT variableDL/MPhil variableFT variablePT variableDL
Inquiry-based science learning............. PhD 36FT 72PT variableDL

Oxford Brookes University
Computing and Communication Technologies .... PhD 24-60FT 36-72PT/MPhil 24-36FT 36-48PT

University of Oxford
Computer Science .... DPhil 48FT/MSc by research 24FT
Information, Communication and the Social Sciences.................... DPhil 48FT

University of Portsmouth
Computing .... MPhil 24FT 48PT/PhD 36FT 72PT

Queen Mary, University of London
Department of Computer Science ....PhD

Queen's University Belfast
Computer Science .... PhD 36FT 72PT/MPhil 24FT 48PT

Royal Holloway, University of London
Computer Science ....PhD 36FT/MPhil 24FT

University of Sheffield
Computer Science .... PhD 36FT 72PT/MPhil 24FT 48PT
Computer Science: Integrated Studies ....Integrated PhD 48FT

University of Southampton
Computer Science .... PhD 36FT 72PT/MPhil 36FT 72PT
School of Management: Health ....MPhil 24FT 48PT/PhD 26FT 72PT
School of Management: Management Sciences .... MPhil 24FT 48PT/PhD 36FT 72PT
School of Management: Organisation and Management... MPhil 24FT 48PT/PhD 36FT 72PT

University of St Andrews
Computer Science .... PhD 36-48FT 72-96PT/MPhil 24-36FT 36-48PT

Staffordshire University
Computing Science .... MRes 12FT 24-72PT

University of Strathclyde
Computer and Information Sciences - Research ..PhD 36FT 48PT/MPhil 12FT 24PT

University of Sussex
Science and Technology Policy Studies...... PhD 24-48FT 36-72PT/MPhil 12-36FT 24-48PT
Technology and Innovation Management PhD 24-48FT 36-72PT/MPhil 12-36FT 24-48PT

Swansea University
Computer Science .... MSc by research 12FT 12-24PT MPhil 12FT 24PT/PhD 36FT 60PT
Computing and Future Interaction TechnologiesMRes 12FT 24PT
Human Computer Interaction ....MSc by research 12FT 24PT

Teesside University
Computing ... PhD 24FT 36PT/MPhil 18FT 30PT/DProf 24FT 36PT/MProf by research 18FT 30PT

University of Ulster
Computer Science .... PhD 36FT 72PT/MPhil 24FT 48PT

UCL - University College London
Computer Science .... PhD 36FT 60PT
Science and Technology Studies................................ PhD 36FT 60PT

University of Warwick
Computer Science ... PhD 36FT/MPhil 24FT/MSc by research 12FT

University of West London
School of Computing................... PhD 36FT 72PT/MPhil 24FT 48PT

University of the West of Scotland
Department of Computing and Information Systems ....PhD/MPhil

University of the West of England, Bristol
Faculty of Environment and Technology .... PhD .FT

University of Westminster
Electronics and Computer Science.............MPhil 18-36FT 30-60PT

University of Wolverhampton
School of Computing and Information Technology......MPhil/PhD

University of Worcester
Business Management and I.T. ....PhD 48FT 70PT/MPhil 24FT 48PT
Computing .... PhD 48FT 70PT/MPhil 24FT 48PT

University of York
Computer Science ... PhD 36FT/MPhil 24FT/MSc by research 12FT
Engineering Doctorate in Large-Scale Complex IT Systems .... EngD 48FT

Computer security
Taught Courses

University of Aberdeen
Advanced Information Systems...................... MSc 12FT/PGDip 9FT

University of Abertay Dundee
Ethical Hacking and Computer Security....... MSc 16FT/PGDip 9FT
Intelligence and Security Informatics ....MSc 16FT 33PT/PGDip 9FT 24PT

Anglia Ruskin University
Network Security...MSc 12 - 15FT 24 - 30PT

University of Bath
Internet Systems and Security .... MSc 12FT

University of Bedfordshire
Computer Security and Forensics..................MSc 12-15FT 24-36PT
Information Management and Security .....MSc 12-15FT 24-36PT

Birmingham City University
Data Networks and Security... PGCert 4FT 10PT/PGDip 4FT 10PT/MSc 4FT 10PT

University of Birmingham
Computer Security .... MSc 12FT

University of Bradford
Analytical Sciences....... MSc 12FT 60PT/PGDip 12FT 60PT/PGCert 12FT 60PT
Internet, Computer and System Security................ MSc 12FT 24PT

Bucks New University
Business Continuity, Security and Emergency Management .... MSc 18PT

University of Cambridge
Advanced Computer Science..MPhil 9FT

Cardiff University
Computer Science .... MSc 12FT 36PT
Computer Science with Placement..................................... MSc 12FT
Computing and IT Management............................... MSc 12FT 36PT
Information Security and Privacy............................. MSc 12FT 36PT
Information Security and Privacy with Placement .... MSc 12FT

University of Central Lancashire
IT Security........MSc 12FT 36PT/PGDip 9FT 18PT/PGCert 6FT 12PT

City University London
Information Security and Risk.................................... MSc 12FT 28PT

Cranfield University
Information Capability Management...........MSc(Eng) 12FT 60PT/PGCert 3FT 36PT/PGDip 6FT 48PT

Cranfield University, Shrivenham
Cyber Defence and Information Assurance .... PGCert 18FT
International Defence and Security..........MSc 12FT/PGCert 12FT/PGDip 12FT
Security Sector Management .... MSc 12FT 30PT

De Montfort University
Computer Security ....MSc 12FT 24-36PT 24-36DL/PGDip 8FT 24PT/PGCert 4FT 12PT
Professional Practice in Digital Forensics and Security.................... MSc 12FT 24PT 24-72DL/PGDip 12FT 24PT 24-72DL/PGCert 12FT 24PT 24-72DL

University of Derby
Computer Forensic Investigation .... MSc 12FT 36PT
Information Security .... MSc 12FT 36PT

University of East Anglia
Computing Science .... MRes 12FT
Information Systems... MSc 12FT 24PT

University of East London
Cyber Crime .... MSc 12FT 24PT
Information Security .... DProf by taught 72PT
Information Security and Computer Forensics ....MSc 12FT 24PT/PGDip 8FT 16PT/PGCert 4FT 8PT

Edge Hill University
Information Security and IT Management .... MSc 12FT 24PT

Edinburgh Napier University
Advanced Security and Digital Forensics................. MSc 12FT 24PT

Glasgow Caledonian University
Network Security..................................... MSc 13FT 27PT/PGDip 9FT

University of Glasgow
Information Security .... MSc 12FT 24PT/PGCert 9FT 9PT/PGDip 9FT 21PT
Information Security (MRes).... MRes 12FT 24PT/PGDip 9FT 21PT/PGCert 9FT 9PT
International Law and Security.................................. LLM 12FT 24PT

University of Gloucestershire
Computing (Information Security)....... MSc 12FT 24PT/PGDip 8FT 20PT/PGCert 4FT 8PT

Glyndwr University
Computer Science .... MSc 12FT 24-36PT/MRes 12FT 24-36PT

University of Greenwich
Computer Forensics and Systems Security............. MSc 12FT 24PT
Computer Security Forensics and Risk Management .... MSc 12FT 24PT
Information Technology with e-Business / with Security....... MSc 12FT 24PT

Heriot-Watt University
Computer Services ManagementMSc 12FT 24PT/PGDip 9FT 21PT
Information Technology (Business) ..... MSc 12FT 24PT/PGDip 9FT 21PT
Information Technology (Software Systems) ....MSc 12FT 24PT/PGDip 9FT 21PT

University of Hertfordshire
Biometrics and Cybersecurity...............................MSc 12-16FT 36PT
Secure Computing Systems .... MSc 12-16FT

University of Kent
Computer Security .... MSc 12FT 36PT
Information Security and Biometrics ....MSc 12FT 24PT/PGDip 12FT 24PT
Networks and Security... MSc 12FT 36PT

King's College London
Computing & Security.. MSc 12FT
Non-Proliferation & International Security............. MA 12FT 24PT

Kingston University
Network and Information Security.....................MSc 12FT 24-36PT

Lancaster University
Cyber Security... MSc 12FT 24PT

University of Leeds
CyberLaw: Information Technology, Law & Society.........LLM 12FT 24PT

Liverpool Hope University
Networks & Security... MSc 12FT

Liverpool John Moores University
Advanced Computer Studies..................................... MSc 12FT 24PT
Computer Network Security...................................... MSc 12FT 24PT
Computing Information Systems............................. MSc 12FT 24PT

University of Liverpool
Computer Security (Online Degree).........................MSc 24FT 24+PT

London Metropolitan University
Computer Forensics and IT Security .... MSc 12FT 24PT
Network Management and Security......................... MSc 12FT 24PT

Loughborough University
Internet Computing and Network Security...........MSc 12FT 96PT/Diploma 7FT 60PT

Manchester Metropolitan University
Advanced Computing.. MSc 12FT 36PT/PGCert 12FT 36PT/PGDip 12FT 36PT
Computing .... MSc 12FT 36PT
Digital Media Computing... MSc 12FT 36PT
Geographical Information Systems..........................MSc 36PT 36DL
Information Systems .... MSc 12FT 36PT

University of Manchester
ACS: Computer Security... MSc 12FT

Middlesex University
Computer and Network Security................................ MSc 12FT 36PT
Electronic Security and Digital Forensics.....MSc 12-15FT 24-27PT

Newcastle University
Advanced Computer Science...................................... MSc 12FT 24PT
Computer Security and Resilience .... MSc 12FT 24PT

Northumbria University
Computer Network Technology.....................................MSc 12/16FT
Computer Science ....MSc 12/16FT/PGDip 9FT/PGCert 4FT
Information and Records Management ....MSc 24DL

Nottingham Trent University
Internet and Security.. MSc 12FT 24PT

The Open University
Advanced Networking...............PGDip variableDL/MSc variableDL

University of Oxford
Software and Systems Security .... MSc 24-48PT

Computer sciences and IT

Plymouth University
Computer and Information Security .... MSc 12FT MRes 12FT

University of Portsmouth
Computer and Information Security .... MSc 12FT 36PT

Royal Holloway, University of London
Information Security .... MSc 12FT 24PT PGCert 48PT
Mathematics of Cryptography and Communications ... MSc 12FT 24PT

University of Salford
Information Security .... MSc 12FT 24PT/PGDip 9FT 18PT/PGCert 9FT 18PT
Information Security Management..... MSc 12FT 24PT/PGDip 9FT 18PT/PGCert 9FT 18PT
Intelligence and Security Studies MA 12FT 36PT/PGDip 9FT 20PT

Sheffield Hallam University
IT Professional .... MSc 36DL
Information Systems Security .... MSc 12FT 24PT
Information Systems with SAP .... MBA 12FT 36PT

University of Sheffield
Contemporary Global Security.................................... MA 12FT 24PT

University of South Wales
Computer Forensics .... MSc 12FT 36PT
Computer Systems Security.. MSc 12FT 36PT

Staffordshire University
Digital Forensics and Cybercrime Analysis........................ MSc 12FT

University of Strathclyde
Internet Law and Policy ..... LLM 12FT 24PT 24DL/PGDip 9FT 21PT 21DL/PGCert 9FT

University of Surrey
Security Technologies and Applications .... MSc 12FT

Swansea University
Advanced Computer Science with a specialisation in Safe and Secure Systems .... MSc 12FT

Teesside University
Advanced Computer Science...................................... MSc 12FT 36PT

University of Wales Trinity Saint David
Information Security Management........................ MBA 12FT 24PT

UCL - University College London
Information Security .... MSc 12FT/PGDip 9FT

University of York
Cyber Security...... MSc 12FT 36PT/PGDip 12FT 24PT/PGCert 20PT

Computer security
Research Courses

Aberystwyth University
Computer Science (MPhil)........... MPhil 12FT 24PT PhD 36FT 60PT

Birmingham City University
Software Development and Security Research.... MSc by research 12FT 24PT

Royal Holloway, University of London
Information Security .... PhD 36FT 72PT/MPhil 24FT 48PT

Swansea University
Computer Science .... MSc by research 12FT 12-24PT

UCL - University College London
Security Science .... MRes 12FT/DPhil 36FT

Database systems
Taught Courses

Bangor University
Computer Science .... MSc 12FT
Information Management... MBA 12FT

Cardiff University
Computing with Placement .... MSc 12FT

University of Central Lancashire
Database Systems....................... MSc 12FT 36PT/PGDip 12FT 36PT

Cranfield University
Pharmacovigilance Data Management........... MSc 12FT 24-36PT/PGDip 12FT 24-36PT

Cranfield University, Shrivenham
Cyber Defence and Information Assurance .... PGCert 18FT
Defence Sensors and Data Fusion........ MSc 12FT 36PT/PGDip 6FT 24PT

De Montfort University
Business Intelligence Systems and Data Mining... MSc 12FT 36PT 24DL/PGDip 8FT 24PT/PGCert 4FT 12PT

University of Dundee
Business Intelligence .... MSc 12FT

University of East Anglia
Computational Biology.................. MSc 12FT/MSc 24PT/MSc 48PT
Computing Science .... MSc 12FT 24PT
Information Systems .... MSc 12FT 24PT
Knowledge Discovery and Data Mining .... MSc 12FT/MSc 24PT/MSc 36PT

Edinburgh Napier University
Computing .... MSc 12FT 24PT

National University of Ireland Galway
Software Engineering & Database Technologies .... MSc 24PT
Software and Information Systems [by distance learning].... MSc 24DL

University of Greenwich
Enterprise Systems and Data Warehousing .... MSc 12FT 24PT

University of Hertfordshire
Distributed Data Management .... MSc 12-16FT

Liverpool Hope University
Networks & Security.. MSc 12FT

London South Bank University
Internet and Database Systems .... MSc 15FT MSc 24PT

University of Manchester
ACS: Data and Knowledge Management.......................... MSc 12FT

Northumbria University
Computing and Information Technology....... MSc 12/16FT 36DL/PGDip 9FT 24DL/PGCert 4FT 12DL

University of Salford
Databases and Web-based Systems.... MSc 12FT 24PT/PGDip 9FT 18PT

Sheffield Hallam University
Database Professional (incorporating Oracle certification training) .... MSc 12FT 36PT

University of Sheffield
Software Systems and Internet Technology .... MSc 12FT

University of St Andrews
Applied Statistics and Datamining...... MSc 12FT 24PT/PGDip 9FT

University of Westminster
Business Intelligence and Analytics (evening study) ..... MSc 24PT
Database Systems .... MSc 12FT 24PT
Database Systems (Evening Study)..................................... MSc 24PT

Database systems
Research Courses

Aston University
Knowledge Engineering and Data Management Research Group... PhD 36FT/MRes 12FT/MPhil 12FT

Bangor University
Communication Networks and Protocols ... MPhil 24FT/PhD 36FT

Cranfield University, Shrivenham
Procurement and Systems Integration for Defence, Security and Civil Services .... PhD 24FT

University of Liverpool
Advanced Science (Computer Sciences pathway) (Data Mining).. MRes 12FT

University of Southampton
School of Social Sciences - Demography ..... PhD 36FT 72PT/MPhil 24FT 48PT
School of Social Sciences - Gerontology ...... PhD 36FT 72PT/MPhil 24FT 48PT

Digital media
Taught Courses

University of Abertay Dundee
Games Development... MProf 12FT

Aberystwyth University
3D Imaging, Analysis and Applications ... MRes 12FT 24PT/PGDip 9FT 21PT/PGCert 5FT 17PT
Digital Marketing .... MSc 12FT 24PT
Information Technology Law .... LLM 12FT
International Politics of the Internet.................................... MA 12FT
International Technology Law (Distance-Learning)...... LLM 36DL/PGDip 24DL
Management and Digital Business .... MSc 12FT 24PT

University of the Arts London - Camberwell College of Arts
Fine Art Digital .... MA 12FT 24PT 24DL

University of the Arts London - London College of Fashion
Digital Fashion .... MA 15FT 30PT

Bangor University
Creative Practice .... MRes 12FT 24PT
International Media Management............................ MSc 12FT 24PT

University of Bedfordshire
Art Design and Internet Technology........................... MA 12FT 24PT
Media, Culture and Technology .... MA 12FT 24PT

Birkbeck, University of London
Creative Industries (Arts and Media)........................ MA 12FT 24PT
Creative Industries (Computing) .... MSc 12FT 24PT
Creative Industries (Management).......................... MSc 12FT 24PT
Digital Media Management .... PGCert 12PT

Birmingham City University
Digital Arts in Performance .... MA 12FT 24PT
Interactive Media .... PGCert 5FT 9PT/PGDip 9FT 21PT/MSc 16/19FT 28PT
Social Media.. MA 12FT 24PT 12-36DL
Video Game Enterprise and Production .... MSc 12FT

Arts University Bournemouth
Interactive Media .... MA 12FT 24PT
Design Interaction.. MA 12FT 24PT

Bournemouth University
Creative and Media Education .... MA 18PT
Digital Effects .... MA 12FT

University of Bradford
Digital Arts and Media .... MA 12FT 24PT/PGDip 9FT

University of Brighton
Creative Media .... MA 12FT 24PT/PGDip 12FT variesPT/PGCert 12FT variesPT
Digital Media Arts .... PGDip 12FT 24PT/MA 12FT 24PT
Digital Media Production .... MSc 12FT 24-60PT/PGDip 12FT 24-60PT/PGCert 12FT 24-60PT

University of Central Lancashire
Broadcast Journalism .... PGDip 9FT/MA 12FT
Digital Marketing (CAM)... Diploma 7.5DL
Film Production............................... MA 12FT 24PT/PGDip 9FT 24PT/PGCert 9FT 24PT
Journalism .... MA 12FT 36PT
Journalism Practice .... MA 12FT 24-36PT/PGDip 9FT 18-24PT
Journalism Studies .... MA 12FT 24PT

City University London
Social Media.. MSc 12FT 24PT

University College Cork
Interactive Media .... MSc 12FT 24PT

University for the Creative Arts
Design: Digital Design.. MA 12FT 24PT

Dublin Institute of Technology
Digital Media Technologies........... MA 12FT 24PT/PGDip 9FT 21PT

University of Dundee
Film Studies .... MLitt 12FT

University of Edinburgh
Design and Digital Media.. MSc 12FT 24PT
Digital Animation... MSc(Res) 12FT 24PT
Digital Media and Culture.. MSc(Res) 12FT 24PT
Digital Studio Practice .... MSc(Res) 12FT 24PT

National University of Ireland Galway
Digital Media .... MA 12FT/PGDip 12FT

Glasgow Caledonian University
3D Design for Virtual Environments... MA 12FT 24PT/PGDip 12FT 24PT
Digital Forensics.. MSc 12FT

Glasgow School of Art
Digital Culture .... MDes 12FT 24PT/PGDip 9FT 21PT/PGCert 4FT 9PT
Medical Visualisation and Human Anatomy ... PGCert 4FT/PGDip 8FT/MSc 12FT

University of Gloucestershire
Media and Creative Enterprise.... MA 12FT/AdvPGDip 8FT/PGCert 4FT

Glyndwr University
Creative Media .... MA 12FT 24PT
Creative Media Technology.. MSc 12FT

Goldsmiths, University of London
Computational Studio Arts... MFA 24FT
Creating Social Media .... MA 12FT 24PT/MSc 12FT 24PT
Digital Entrepreneurship.. MSc 12FT
Digital Journalism .... MA 12FT/MSc 12FT
Digital Media: Technology and Cultural Form .... MA 12FT 24PT
Digital Sociology.. MA 12FT 24PT/MSc 12FT 24PT
Interactive Media: Critical Theory and Practice...... MA 12FT 24PT
Media and Communications .... GradDip 12FT

University of Hertfordshire
Animation ....MA 12FT 24PT/PGDip 12FT 24PT/PGCert 12FT 24PT
Digital and Lens Art .... MA 12FT 24PT/PGDip 12FT 24PT/PGCert 12FT 24PT
Two Dimensional Digital Animation .. MA 12FT 24PT/PGDip 12FT 24PT

University of Huddersfield
3D Digital Design .... MA 12/16FT
Digital Media .... MA 12/16FT

University of Hull
Business Technology Management .... MSc 12FT

Imperial College London
Science Media Production... MSc 12FT

University of Kent
Advanced Electronic Systems Engineering .... PGDip 12FT 24PT/MSc 12FT 24PT
Architectural Visualisation.. MA 12FT
Broadband and Mobile Communication Networks..... PGDip 12FT 24PT/MSc 12FT 24PT
Computer Animation .... MSc 12FT
Digital Visual Effects... MSc 12FT/PGDip 12FT

Computer sciences and IT

Embedded Systems and Instrumentation ....PGDip 12FT 24PT/MSc 12FT 24PT
Wireless Communications and Signal Processing ....PGDip 12FT 24PT/MSc 12FT 24PT

King's College London
Digital Asset & Media Management .... MA 12FT 24PT
Digital Culture and Society .... MA 12FT 24PT

Leeds Metropolitan University
Creative Technology .... MSc 12FT 24PT
Digital Visual Effects .... MSc 12FT 24PT
Information Management .... MSc 12FT 36PT

University of Leicester
New Media and Society .... MA 12FT

University of Limerick
Interactive Media .... MA 12FT/MSc 12FT

University of Lincoln
Digital Media .... MA 12FT 24PT

London Metropolitan University
Digital Media .... MA 12FT 24PT

London South Bank University
Creative Media Industries: Journalism .... MA 13FT
Digital Film .... MA 24PT
Digital Photography .... MA 24PT
Media Arts .... MA 12FT
New Media .... MA 24PT

University of the Arts London - London College of Communication
Digital Media Futures .... MA 12FT

Loughborough University
Digital Media and Society .... MA 12FT

Middlesex University
Creative Technology .... MA 12FT 24PT/MSc 12FT 24PT
Digital Media .... MA 12FT 24PT
Film, Television, Animation .... MA 12FT 24PT
Creative Technology .... MSc 12FT 36PT

Manchester Metropolitan University ....
Digital Media Computing .... MSc 12FT 36PT

Newcastle University
Creative Arts Practice .... MA 12FT 24PT
Digital Architecture .... MSc 12FT 24PT
Film: Theory and Practice .... MA 12FT 24PT

Nottingham Trent University
Film Practice .... MA 12FT/PGDip 7FT/PGCert 4FT
Interaction Design .... MA 12FT/PGCert 7FT/PGDip 4FT
Product Design .... MA 12FT/PGDip 7FT/PGCert 4FT
Product Design Innovation Management .... MA 12FT

Oxford Brookes University
Digital Media Production .... MSc 12FT 24PT
Digital Publishing .... MA 12FT 24PT/PGDip 9FT 18PT
Film Studies: Popular Cinema .... MA 12FT 24PT/PGDip 8FT 6-8PT/PGCert 4FT 6PT

Plymouth University
Contemporary Art Practice .... MA 12FT
Digital Art and Technology .... MRes 12FT

University of Portsmouth
Design for Digital Media .... MA 12FT 24PT
Digital Marketing .... MA 12FT
Digital Media .... MSc 12FT 36PT

Queen Mary, University of London
Computer Vision .... MSc 12FT 24PT
Media and Arts Technology (MSc by Research) ...... MSc(Res) 12FT

Ravensbourne
3D Stereoscopic Media .... MSc 12FT 24PT/MA 12FT 24PT
Animation Futures .... MA 12FT 24PT
Applied Technologies, Rapid Prototyping and Digital Technologies .... MSc 12FT 24PT
Interactive Digital Media .... MA 12FT 24PT
Professional Media Practice .... MA 12FT 24PT

Royal College of Art
Animation .... PhD by taught 72PT/MPhil 24FT 48PT/MA 24FT

University of Salford
Animation .... MA 12FT
Children's Digital Media Production .... MA 12FT/PGDip 9FT
International and Online Journalism .... MA 12FT 36PT
Social Media .... MA 9FT/PGDip 9FT

School of Oriental and African Studies - SOAS
Critical Media and Cultural Studies .... MA 12FT 24-36PT
Global Media and Postnational Communication .... MA 12FT 24-36PT

Sheffield Hallam University
Animation and Special Effects .... MA 12FT 36PT
Animation for Computer Games .... MA 12FT 36PT
Film Studies .... MA 12FT 36-72PT
MPhil 36FT 84PT/PhD by taught 36FT 84PT
Film Studies with Screenwriting .... MA 12FT 24PT
Research Degrees - Cultural, Communication and Computing Research Institute .... MPhil 24-36FT 48-60PT/PhD by taught 36-48FT 60-72PT

University of Sheffield
Sonic Arts .... MA 12FT 24PT
Web Journalism .... MA 12FT/PGDip 9FT

University of South Wales
Visual Effects .... MA 12FT 24PT

Southampton Solent University
Digital Marketing and Media .... MA 12FT

University of Southampton
Digital Marketing .... MSc 12FT
Sound and Vibration Studies .... MSc 12FT 36PT

Staffordshire University
Film Production Technology .... MSc 12-18FT
Film Production and Visual Cultures .... MA 12FT
Film Production: Theory and Practice .... MA 12FT

University of Strathclyde
Digital Creativity .... MSc 12FT 24PT/PGDip 9FT 18PT

University of Sunderland
Animation and Design .... MA 12FT 24PT

University of Sussex
Computing with Digital Media .... MSc 12FT 24PT
Creative Media Practice .... MA 12FT 24PT
Digital Media .... MA 12FT 24PT
Embedded Digital Systems .... MSc 12FT 24PT

Swansea University
Digital Media .... MA 12FT 36PT

Swansea Metropolitan University
3D Computer Animation .... MA 12FT 24PT

Teesside University
Concept Art for Games and Animation .... MA 12FT 36PT
Digital Arts and Design ... MA 12FT 24PT/PGDip 8FT 16PT/PGCert 4FT 8PT
Digital Effects for Film and Television .... MA 12FT 36PT
Future Design ..... MA 12FT 24PT/PGDip 8FT 16PT/PGCert 4FT 8PT
Mass Communications .... MA 12FT 24PT

Trinity College Dublin - the University of Dublin
Interactive Digital Media .... MSc 12FT

University of Ulster
Digital Media Communication .... PGCert 10PT

UCL - University College London
Film Studies .... MA 12FT 24PT

University of Winchester
Digital Media Practice ... MA 12FT 24PT/PGDip 12FT 24PT/PGCert 12FT 24PT

University of Wolverhampton
Digital and Visual Communications .... MA 12FT 24PT

University of Worcester
Creative Digital Media .... MA 36FT 72PT/MSc 36FT 72PT/PGDip 24FT 48PT/PGCert 12FT 24PT

University of York
Human-Centred Interactive Technologies .... MSc 12FT
Social Media and Interactive Technologies .... MSc 12FT

Digital media
Research Courses

Bangor University
Creative and Critical Writing, Film and Media, Professional Writing .... MPhil 24FT 48PT/PhD 36FT 72PT
Creative and Critical Writing, Film and Media, Professional Writing: Practice-Led Research .... MPhil 24FT 48PT/PhD 36FT 72PT

University of Bath
Digital Media EngD .... EngD 48FT

University of Bradford
Electronic Imaging and Media Communications. PhD 36FT 48PT/MPhil 12FT 24PT

Cardiff University
Distributed and Scientific Computing .... PhD 36FT/MPhil 12FT

University of Central Lancashire
Arts and Media.... PhD 30-48FT 66-84PT/MPhil 18-36FT 42-60PT/MA by research 12FT 24PT

University for the Creative Arts
Arts & Media .... PhD 36FT 60PT/MPhil 24FT 36PT

University of Edinburgh
Digital Communications ... PhD 36FT 72PT/MPhil 24FT 48PT/MSc by research 12FT 24PT

Goldsmiths, University of London
Arts & Computational Technology .... MPhil 24FT 36PT/PhD 36-48FT 48-72PT

Heriot-Watt University
Digital Tools and Technologies .... EngD 48FT

University of Hertfordshire
Centre for Research in Electronic Art and Communication (CREAC)........... PhD 36FT 72PT/MPhil 24FT 48PT/MRes 12FT 24PT

University of Kent
Digital Arts .... MSc(Res) 12FT 24PT/MPhil 24FT 36PT/PhD 36FT 60PT
Electronic Engineering .... MSc by research 12FT 24PT/MPhil 24FT 36PT/PhD 36FT 60PT
Film (Practice by Research) .... MA by research 12FT 24PT/MPhil 24FT 36PT/PhD 36FT 60PT

Newcastle University
Digital Media .... PhD 36FT 72PT
Film Studies .... MLitt by research 12FT 24PT
PhD 36FT 72PT/MPhil 12FT 24PT

Newman University
Creative Arts .... PhD 36FT 72PT/MPhil 24FT 48PT

University of Portsmouth
Creative Technologies .... MPhil 24FT 48PT/PhD 36FT 72PT

Queen's University Belfast
Film Studies .... PhD 36FT 72PT/MPhil 24FT 48PT

School of Oriental and African Studies - SOAS
Media and Film Studies .... PhD 36-48FT

University of Southampton
Digital Arts and Design .... MRes 12FT 24PT

UCL - University College London
Film Studies .... PhD 36FT 60PT

Digital signal processing
Taught Courses

Aberystwyth University
3D Imaging, Analysis and Applications ... MRes 12FT 24PT/PGDip 9FT 21PT/PGCert 5FT 17PT
Remote Sensing & Geographical Information Systems (GIS) .... MSc 12FT 24PT/PGDip 9FT 18PT/PGCert 5FT 10PT

Aston University
Sensors and Sensing Systems .... MSc(Eng) 12FT

Bangor University
Broadband and Optical Communications .... MSc 12FT 24PT

University of Bath
Digital Communications .... MSc 12FT

University of Bristol
Communications Networks and Signal Processing .... MSc 12FT
Image and Video Communications and Signal Processing..... MSc 12FT
Optical Communications and Signal Processing .... MSc 12FT
Wireless Communications and Signal Processing .... MSc 12FT

Cardiff University
Wireless and Microwave Communication Engineering .... MSc 12FT 24PT

University of Central Lancashire
Digital Marketing (CAM) .... Diploma 7.5DL
Digital Signal and Image Processing ... MSc 12FT 24PT/PGDip 9FT 20PT

City University London
Signals and Sensor Systems .... MSc 12FT 36PT

Cranfield University
Computational & Software Techniques in Engineering (Digital Signal and Image Processing) .... MSc 12FT 24PT
Computational and Software Techniques in Engineering ...... MSc 12FT 24-36PT

University of Cumbria
The Research Process .... PGCert 12 - 18PT

Dublin Institute of Technology
Electronics and Communications Engineering...... MSc 12FT 24PT
Signal Processing Engineering .... MEng 12FT 24PT

University of Dundee
Advanced Practice (Diagnostic Imaging) .... MSc 36DL
Computing with Vision and Imaging .... MSc 12FT

Edinburgh Napier University
Digital Systems .... MA/MDes 12FT 24PT

University of Edinburgh
Signal Processing and Communications .... MSc 12FT 24PT/PGDip 9FT 18PT

University of Greenwich
Geographical Information Systems with Remote Sensing..... MSc 12FT 24 - 36PT/PGDip 12FT 24-36PT
Wireless Mobile Communications Systems Engineering........ MSc 12FT 24PT

Heriot-Watt University
Computer Vision and Robotics (VIBOT) .... MSc 48FT
Mobile Communications .... MSc 12FT 24PT/PGDip 9FT 21PT/PGCert 6FT 12PT
Robotics, Autonomous and Interactive Systems (RAIS) MSc 12FT/PGDip 9FT
Software Engineering .... MSc 12FT 24PT/PGDip 9FT 21PT

Computer sciences and IT

University of Hertfordshire
Data Communications and Networks................MSc 12-16FT 36-48PT

University of Hull
Wireless Systems.. MSc 12FT
Wireless Systems and Logistics Technology .... MSc 12FT

Imperial College London
Communications and Signal Processing .... MSc 12FT

University of Kent
Engineering with Finance...MSc 12FT 24PT
Wireless Communications and Signal Processing ....PGDip 12FT 24PT/MSc 12FT 24PT

Kingston University
Digital Image & Signal Processing.......................MSc 12FT 24-36PT

University of Leeds
Communications Studies..MA 12FT
Communications and Signal Processing ....MSc(Eng) 12FT
Digital Communications Networks ....MSc(Eng) 12FT

University of Leicester
Control and Signal Processing......................... MSc 12FT/PGDip 9FT

Loughborough University
Digital Communication Systems......................MSc 12FT 36PT
Signal Processing in Communication Systems ...... MSc 12FT 36PT

University of Manchester
Digital Image and Signal Processing ....MSc 12FT 24PT

Newcastle University
Communications and Signal Processing .... MSc 12FT

Plymouth University
Electrical and Electronic Engineering............MSc 12FT/MRes 12FT

University of Portsmouth
Digital Systems Engineering.................................. MSc 12FT 36PT

Queen Mary, University of London
Digital Signal Processing...................................... MSc 12FT 24PT

University of Reading
Cybernetics .... MSc 12FT 24PT
Digital Signal Processing and Communications ...MSc 12FT 24PT

University of South Wales
Electronic Mobile Communications .... MSc 12FT 36PT

University of Southampton
Applied Digital Signal Processing...............MSc 40PT/PGCert 36PT
Sound and Vibration Studies.....................................MSc 12FT 36PT

University of Strathclyde
Communications, Control and Digital Signal Processing
(CCDSP) .... MSc 12FT

University of Sussex
Digital Communication Systems........................... MSc 12FT 24PT
Digital Communication Systems with Business Management.....
MSc 12FT 24PT

Teesside University
Electronics & Communications .....MSc 12- 18FT 24PT/PGDip 8FT

UCL - University College London
Remote Sensing .... MSc 12FT 24PT

University of Westminster
Microelectronic System Design ....MSc 12FT 24PT 24BM

University of York
Digital Signal Processing .... MSc 12FT
Digital Systems Engineering......................................MSc 12FT

Digital signal processing
Research Courses

Anglia Ruskin University
Digital Modelling.............................PhD 24 - 60FT 36 - 72PT

Aston University
Information Processing and Pattern Analysis Research Group .....
PhD 36FT/MPhil 24FT

Bangor University
Pattern Recognition / Classifiers ....MPhil 24FT/PhD 36FT

University of Brighton
Engineering Research Division.......... PhD 24-60FT 36-72PT/MPhil 18-36FT 30-48PT

University of Bristol
Communications ....PhD 48FT

De Montfort University
Earth and Planetary Remote Sensing Research......... PhD 24-36FT 48-72PT/MPhil 12-24FT 24-48PT

University of Kent
Electronic Engineering ....MSc by research 12FT 24PT/MPhil 24FT 36FT/PhD 36FT 60PT

Lancaster University
Communication Systems .... PhD 36FT 48PT/MPhil 24FT 36PT

University of Leeds
Institute of Integrated Information Systems .....PhD 36+FT/MPhil 24FT

University of Nottingham
Biophysics, Imaging and Optical Science ....PhD 36FT 48PT/MPhil 24FT 36PT
Cell Signalling.. PhD 36FT 72PT/MPhil 24FT 48PT/MRes 12FT/DM 36FT 72PT

Oxford Brookes University
Electronics and Communications .... PhD 24-60FT 36-72PT/MPhil 24-36FT 36-48PT

Swansea University
Intelligent Wireless Networks for Healthcare......MSc by research 12FT 24PT

E-learning studies
Taught Courses

Birkbeck, University of London
Learning Technologies...MSc 12FT 24PT

University of Bolton
E-Learning for Educationalists .... MA 12FT 24-60PT

Bucks New University
Technology Enhanced Learning .... MSc 12FT 24PT 12DL

University of Chester
Learning and Development (Work Based and Integrative Studies) ....MA 24-72PT/MSc 24-72PT/PGDip 24-60PT/PGCert 12-36PT

Dublin Institute of Technology
Applied E Learning .... MSc 24PT

Edinburgh Napier University
Advanced Practice and Applied Education (Distance Learning).... Msc/PGDip/PGCert 36PT
Blended and Online Education ....MSc 12-24PT/PGDip 9-18PT/PGCert 6-12PT

University of Glasgow
Learning and Teaching in Higher Education.......MEd 36DL/PGDip 24DL

Glyndwr University
Learning & Technology ....MSc 36FT/PGDip 24PT/PGCert 12FT

University of Hertfordshire
E-Learning Technology .... MSc 12-16FT

University of Huddersfield
Technology Enhanced Learning ....MSc 12FT 36PT

University of Hull
E-Learning (Education) (via the internet)...... MEd 30-108PT 36DL

King's College London
ICT Education... MA 12FT 24-48PT

Manchester Metropolitan University
Computing .... MSc 12FT 36PT
Information Systems .... MSc 12FT 36PT

Newcastle University
E-Business .... MSc 12FT
E-Business (E-Marketing) .... MSc 12FT

The Open University
Academic Practice ....PGCert 24DL
Online and Distance Education .... MA variableDL/PGDip variableDL/PGCert variableDL

University of Oxford
Educational Studies (E-learning) .... MSc 12FT

University of Reading
Informatics (MSc - Beijing)................... MSc 18FT 36PT/PGDip 9FT/PGCert 6FT

University of Southampton
Authoring and Researching eLearning and eTeaching .... PCES 12DL

University of Wales Trinity Saint David
Technology Enhanced Learning .... PGCert 24PT 24DL

University of York
Human-Centred Interactive Technologies .... MSc 12FT

E-learning studies
Research Courses

Bath Spa University
Educational Innovation and Technology
....PhD 24 - 60FT 36 - 72PT

University of Nottingham
Cognitive Development and Learning ....PhD 36FT 72PT/MPhil 24FT 48PT

The Open University
Education and Educational Technology.......EdD 36PT variableDL/PhD 36FT 72PT variableDL/MRes 12FT/MPhil 15FT 24PT variableDL
Educational DialoguePhD 36FT 72PT variableDL/EdD 36PT/MRes 12FT
Educational studies.............PhD 36FT 72PT/EdD 36PT/MRes 12FT
Language Learning and Teaching....... PhD 36FT 72PT variableDL/MRes 12FT/EdD 36PT

Multimodal meaning making......PhD 36FT 72PT variableDL/EdD 36PT/MRes 12FT
Technology Enhanced Learning ...PhD 36FT 72PT variableDL/EdD 36PT/MRes 12FT
Technology, communication and education .... PhD 36FT 72PT variableDL/MPhil 15FT 24PT variableDL

Informatics
Taught Courses

University of Abertay Dundee
Intelligence and Security Informatics ....MSc 16FT 33PT/PGDip 9FT 24PT

Bangor University
Computer Science .... MSc 12FT
Computer Science with Security .... MSc 12FT 24PT

British Institute of Technology & E-commerce
Innovative Technology ....PGCert 3FT/DipHE 6FT/MScD 12FT

University of Central Lancashire
Health Informatics ....MSc 33PT/PGDip 24PT

City University London
Health Informatics .... MSc 12FT 28PT/PGDip 12FT 24PT
Information Leadership .... MIL 28PT
Information Science..MSc 12FT 28PT
Information Systems and Technology................MSc 12FT 24-36PT

Cranfield University
Clinical Research Executive...........MSc 36PT/PGDip 9FT 24-36PT/PGCert 6FT 12-24PT
Clinical Research Management ....MSc 12FT 36PT/PGDip 12FT 36PT
Environmental Informatics......MSc 12FT 60PT/PGDip 12FT 60PT/PGCert 12FT 60PT

University of Dundee
Applied Health Statistics .... MSc 12FT

University of East London
Health Informatics .... MSc 12FT 24PT/PGDip 8FT 16PT/PGCert 4FT 8PT

University of Edinburgh
Cognitive Science...MSc 12FT 36PT
Informatics... MSc 12FT

University of Greenwich
Information Technology with e-Business / with Security....... MSc 12FT 24PT

Heriot-Watt University
Advanced Internet Applications...........MSc 12FT 24PT/PGDip 9FT
Artificial Intelligence ....MSc 12FT 24PT/PGDip 9FT
Computer Services ManagementMSc 12FT 24PT/PGDip 9FT 21PT
Creative Software Systems ....MSc 12FT 24PT/PGDip 9FT 21PT
Information Technology (Business) .....MSc 12FT 24PT/PGDip 9FT 21PT
Information Technology (Software Systems) ....MSc 12FT 24PT/PGDip 9FT 21PT
Mobile Communications............MSc 12FT 24PT/PGDip 9FT 21PT/PGCert 6FT 12PT
Software Engineering....................MSc 12FT 24PT/PGDip 9FT 21PT

Kingston University
Information Systems (Health Information Management) ..... MSc 12FT 24PT

University of Leeds
Advanced Computer Science (Intelligent Systems) .... MSc 12FT

University of Leicester
Advanced Computational Methods .... MSc 12FT/PGDip 9FT
Medical Statistics ....MSc 12FT 24PT

University of Limerick
Health Informatics ....MSc(Eng) 12FT

Liverpool Hope University
Mathematical Informatics Dual International Masters
.... MSc 24PT

London Metropolitan University
Information Technology ....MSc 12FT 24PT

London School of Hygiene and Tropical Medicine
Clinical Trials (by Distance Learning)..........MSc 24 - 60DL/PGDip 12 - 60DL/PGCert 12-60DL

Manchester Metropolitan University
Informatics.. MSc 36PT

Newcastle University
Computational Systems Biology .... MSc 12FT
Hydroinformatics and Water Management (Euro Aquae)...... MSc 24FT
Neuroinformatics .... MSc 12FT

University of Northampton
Environmental Informatics......................................MSc 12FT 24PT

Oxford Brookes University
Medical Statistics ....MSc 12FT 24PT

Queen Margaret University, Edinburgh
Health Systems ....MSc 12FT 24PT/PGDip 8FT 16PT/PGCert 4FT 8PT

Computer sciences and IT

University of Reading
Business Information Management .... MSc 12FT
Business Technology Consulting .... MSc 12FT
Informatics (MSc - Beijing)............ MSc 18FT 36PT/PGDip 9FT/PGCert 6FT
Information Management & Systems ....MSc 12FT 36PT/PGDip 9FT/PGCert 6FT
Intelligent Buildings: Design, Construction and Management .... MSc 24PT

University of Sheffield
Health Informatics .... MSc 36 PTDL

University of Southampton
Health Informatics............ MSc 24DL/PGDip 16DL

Staffordshire University
Public Health (Health Informatics) ....PGCert 8PT/PGDip 16PT/MPH 24PT

University of Sunderland
Health Information Management............MSc 36PT/PGDip 24PT/PGCert 12PT

University of Sussex
Advanced Computer Science............ MSc 12FT 24PT

Swansea University
Health Informatics....... MSc 12FT 36PT/PGDip 12FT 24PT/PGCert 12FT 12PT

Trinity College Dublin - the University of Dublin
Health Informatics............ MSc 24PT

University of Ulster
Health Informatics............PGCert 9PT/PGDip 18PT/MSc 27PT

UCL - University College London
Computational Statistics and Machine Learning............ MSc 12FT
Health Informatics.....MSc 24-60PT/PGDip 24-60PT/PGCert 24PT

University of Westminster
Business Information Systems............ MSc 12FT 24PT
Business Information Systems (evening study)............ MSc 24PT

University of York
Social Media and Management............ MSc 12FT

Informatics
Research Courses

Bangor University
Pattern Recognition / Classifiers............MPhil 24FT/PhD 36FT

Cardiff University
Informatics............ PhD 36FT possiblePT/MPhil 12FT possiblePT

City University London
Centre for Measurement and Information in Medicine.........PhD/MPhil

Cranfield University, Shrivenham
Informatics and Simulation............ PhD/MSc by research 12FT

University of Edinburgh
Informatics......PhD 36FT 72PT/MPhil 24FT 48PT/MSc by research 12FT 24 - 36PT
Informatics (Masters by Research)......MSc by research 12FT 24PT
Informatics: Institute for Adaptive & Neural Computation... MSc by research 12FT 24PT/PhD 36FT 72PT/MPhil 24FT 48PT
Informatics: Institute for Computing Systems Architecture.......... MPhil 24FT 48PT/PhD 36FT 72PT/MSc by research 12FT 24PT
Informatics: Institute of Perception, Action & Behaviour ... MPhil 24FT 48PT/PhD 36FT 72PT/MSc by research 12FT 24PT
Informatics: Laboratory for Foundations of Computer Science .... MPhil 24FT 48PT/PhD 36FT 72PT/MSc by research 12FT 24PT
Informatics: Life Sciences Institute............ PhD 36FT 72PT
Institute for Communicating & Collaborative Systems .... PhD 36FT 72PT/MPhil 24FT 48PT/MSc by research 12FT 24PT
Neuroinformatics............MSc by research 12FT
Neuroinformatics & Computational Neuroscience Doctoral Training Centre (DTC)............MSc by research 12FT

National University of Ireland Galway
College of Engineering & Informatics............PhD 48FT 72PT/MEngSci by research 24FT 48PT/MAppSci by research 24FT 48PT/MEng by research 24FT

University of Manchester
Computer Science (CDT)............PhD 48FT

Nottingham Trent University
School of Computing and Informatics.. MPhil .FT/PhD 48FT 96PT
School of Computing and Technology .....MPhil .FT/PhD .FT/MRes 12FT

The Open University
Bayesian Statistics... PhD 36FT 72PT variableDL/MPhil 15FT 24PT variableDL
Medical Statistics .... PhD 36FT 72PT variableDL/MPhil 15FT 24PT variableDL
Multivariate Statistics...... PhD 36FT 72PT variableDL/MPhil 15FT 24PT variableDL

University of Salford
Health Informatics............ PhD 36FT 60PT/MSc by research 24PT

University of Sussex
Informatics Research Programme.... PhD 24-48FT 36-72PT/MPhil 12-36FT 24-48PT

UCL - University College London
Health Informatics............ PhD 36FT 60PT

Information systems and networking
Taught Courses

University of Aberdeen
Advanced Information Systems............ MSc 12FT/PGDip 9FT
E - Commerce Technology .... MSc 12FT 24-36PT/PGDip 9FT/PGCert 9FT

Aberystwyth University
Information and Library Studies (distance-learning).... MA 36DL/PGDip 24DL
Intelligent Autonomous Systems.........MSc 12FT 24PT/PGDip 9FT 18PT/PGCert 5FT 10PT
Intelligent Systems .... MSc 12FT 24PT/PGDip 9FT 21PT/PGCert 5FT 17PT

Anglia Ruskin University
Information and Communication Technology (Conversion).. MSc 12 - 15FT 24 - 30PT
Network Security............MSc 12 - 15FT 24 - 30PT

Aston University
Data Communication Networks............ MSc 12FT 24-36DL

Bangor University
Broadband and Optical Communications............MSc 12FT 24PT
Computer Science .... MSc 12FT
Computer Science with Artificial Intelligence/ .....MSc 12FT 24PT
Computer Science with Security ....MSc 12FT 24PT
Electronic Engineering .... MSc 12FT
Information Management............ MBA 12FT

University of Bath
Digital Communications .... MSc 12FT
Internet Systems and Security .... MSc 12FT
Wireless Systems............ MSc 12FT

University of Bedfordshire
Business Information Systems............MSc 12-15FT 24-36PT
Computer Networking............MSc 12-15FT 24-36PT
Embedded Systems Engineering............MSc 12FT 24-36PT
Information Management and Security .....MSc 12-15FT 24-36PT
Information Systems and Business Management.......... MSc 12FT

Birkbeck, University of London
Advanced Computing Technologies............MSc 12FT 24PT/PGDip 12FT 24PT/PGCert 12-24PT
Information Systems and Management....MSc 12FT 24PT/PGDip 12FT 24PT
Learning Technologies............MSc 12FT 24PT

Birmingham City University
Business Computing............ PGCert 4FT 10PT/PGDip 4FT 10PT/MSc 4FT 10PT
Data Networks and Security... PGCert 4FT 10PT/PGDip 4FT 10PT/MSc 4FT 10PT
Enterprise Systems Management............ MSc 12/16FT 30PT

University of Birmingham
Digital Entrepreneurship............MSc 12FT 24PT
Electromagnetic Sensor Networks............MSc 12FT 24PT
Electromagnetic Sensor Networks with Industrial Studies.... MSc 18FT
Electronic and Computer Engineering............MSc 12FT 24PT
Embedded Systems............MSc 12FT 24PT
Embedded Systems with Industrial Studies............ MSc 18FT

Bournemouth University
Information Technology .... MSc 12FT

University of Bradford
Information Technology Management......... MSc 12FT/PGDip 9FT
Networks and Performance Engineering............MSc 12FT 24PT
Wireless Sensors and Embedded Systems... MSc 12FT/PGDip 9FT

University of Brighton
Information Systems............MSc 13 or 18FT 24-60PT/PGDip 10 or 13FT 24-60PT/PGCert 5FT 24-60PT
Internet and Distributed Systems............ MSc 13FT 24-60PT/PGDip 10FT 24-60PT/PGCert 5FT 24PT

University of Bristol
Advanced Computing - Internet Technologies with Security ....MSc 12FT 24PT
Systems............MRes 24PT
Wireless Communications and Signal Processing.......... MSc 12FT

Brunel University
Advanced Computing............ MSc 12FT
Business Intelligence and Social Media............ MSc 12FT
Computer Communication Networks............ MSc 12FT
Distributed Computing Systems Engineering .... MSc 12FT
Information Systems Management ....MSc 12FT 24PT
Wireless Communication Systems .... MSc 12FT

Bucks New University
Communications Management .... MCM 18PT 18DL

University of Cambridge
Advanced Computer Science............MPhil 9FT

Cardiff Metropolitan University
Finance and Information Management ....MSc 12FT 24PT
Information & Communication Technology Management.... MSc 12FT 24PT/PGDip 24PT/PGCert 12PT
Mobile Technologies.... MSc 12FT 24PT/PGDip 24PT/PGCert 12PT
Technology Project Management....MSc 12FT 24PT/PGDip 24PT/PGCert 12PT

Cardiff University
Computer Science ....MSc 12FT 36PT
Computing and IT Management............MSc 12FT 36PT
Computing and IT Management with Placement.......... MSc 12FT

University of Central Lancashire
Network Computing............ MSc 12FT 36PT/PGDip 12FT 24PT

University of Chester
Information Systems MSc 12FT 24 - 36PT/PGDip 12FT 24 - 36PT/PGCert 12FT 12 - 24PT

City University London
Information Management............MSc 12FT 28PT
Information Systems and Technology............MSc 12FT 24-36PT

University College Cork
Applied Science (Applied Computing Technology) .... HDip 9FT
Applied Science (Software & Systems for Mobile Networks) MSc 12FT
Computing Science .... MSc 12FT
Information Systems for Business Performance............MBS 12FT
Management Information and Managerial Accounting Systems MBS 15FT

Coventry University
Information Technology ....MSc 12FT 24-36PT 20DL/PGDip 8FT 16PT/PGCert 4FT 8PT
Information Technology for Management ..... MSc 12FT 24-36PT/PGDip 8FT 16PT/PGCert 4FT 8PT
Management Information Systems ...... MSc 12FT 24-36PT 20DL/PGDip 8FT 16PT/PGCert 4FT 8PT
Network Computing............MSc 12FT 24-36PT/PGDip 8FT 16PT/PGCert 4FT 8PT
Systems and Control............MSc 12FT 24-36PT

Cranfield University
Computational and Software Techniques in Engineering...... MSc 12FT 24-36PT
Management & Information Systems............ MSc 12FT 24-60PT/PGDip 6FT 24PT/PGCert 5FT 24PT

Cranfield University, Shrivenham
Information Capability Management......... MSc 12FT 48PT 48DL/PGCert 5FT 24PT 18DL/PGDip 8FT 12PT 36DL

De Montfort University
Business Intelligence Systems and Data Mining...MSc 12FT 36PT 24DL/PGDip 8FT 24PT/PGCert 4FT 12PT
Information Systems Management .... MSc 12FT 24-72PT/PGDip 8FT 24PT/PGCert 4FT 12PT

University of Derby
Advanced Computer Networks............MSc 12FT 36-72PT
Information Technology ....MSc 36PT 36DL

Dublin Institute of Technology
Engineering Computation............MSc 12FT 24PT

Durham University
Internet and Distributed Systems............ MSc 12FT
Management (Innovation Technology and Operations Management) .... MSc 12FT

University of East Anglia
Advanced Computing Science............MSc 12FT 24PT
Computing Science............MSc 12FT 24PT MRes 12FT
Information Systems ....MSc 12FT 24PT
Knowledge Discovery and Data Mining .... MSc 12FT/MSc 24PT/MSc 36PT
Strategic Information Systems .... MSc 12FT

University of East London
Business Information Systems ....MSc 12FT 24PT/PGDip 8FT 16PT/PGCert 4FT 8PT
Computer Networks MSc.......... MSc 12FT 24PT/PGDip 8FT 16PT/PGCert 4FT 8PT
Enterprise Architecture .... MSc 12FT 24PT/PGDip 8FT 16PT/PGCert 4FT 8PT
Information & Communication Technologies and Development .. .. MSc 12FT 24PT/PGDip 8FT 16PT/PGCert 4FT 8PT
Information Security and Computer Forensics ....MSc 12FT 24PT/PGDip 8FT 16PT/PGCert 4FT 8PT
Mobile Communications .... MSc 12FT 24PT/PGDip 8FT 16PT/PGCert 4FT 8PT
Technology Management ....MSc 12FT 24PT

Edinburgh Napier University
Advanced Networking..........MSc 12FT 24-36PT/PGDip 9FT 24PT/PGCert 6FT 12PT
Information Systems Development ....MSc 12FT 24PT/PGDip 9FT 18PT/PGCert 6FT 12PT

University of Exeter
Information Technology Management for Business...... MSc 12FT

Computer sciences and IT

GCU London
IT Security....MSc 12FT/MSc 12-15FT/PGDip 36PT
Information Technology ....MSc 12FT/PGDip 36PT
Web Systems Development (.net) .... MSc 13FT

National University of Ireland Galway
Enterprise Systems.... MAppSci 12FT 24PT
Finance and Information Systems .... MSc 12FT
Information Systems Management .... MSc 12FT 24PT
Software and Information Systems [by distance learning].... MSc 24DL

Glasgow Caledonian University
Advanced Computer Networking ....MSc 13FT 36PT/PGDip 9FT 24PT
Applied Instrumentation & Control .... MSc 12FT 24PT 36DL/PGDip 9FT 18PT
Network Security....MSc 13FT 27PT/PGDip 9FT
Voice Over IP and Unified Communications....MSc 12FT 27PT/PGDip 9FT
Wireless Communication Technologies....MSc 12FT 24PT/PGDip 9FT 18PT
Wireless Networking....MSc 13FT 36PT/PGDip 9FT 12PT

University of Glasgow
Computer Systems Engineering.... MSc 12FT
Mobile Design & Engineering..MRes 12FT 24PT/PGCert 9FT 9PT/PGDip 9FT 21PT

Glyndwr University
CCNA/CCNP Cisco Networking Academy....CCNA 6FT 12+PT/CCNP 6FT 12+PT
Computer Networking.... MSc 12FT
Computer Science .... MSc 12FT 24-36PT/MRes 12FT 24-36PT

University of Greenwich
Computer Networking....MSc 12FT 24PT
Computer Systems & Networking....MSc 12FT 24PT
Computer Systems and Software Engineering....MSc 12FT 24PT
Computing and Information Systems....MSc 12FT 24PT
Information Systems Management ....MSc 12FT 24PT
Information Technology with e-Business / with Security.... MSc 12FT 24PT
Information and Communications Technology....MSc 12FT 24PT
Information and Communications Technology (Operations Technology)....MSc 12FT 24PT
Information and Communications Technology (e-Technology).... MSc 12FT 24PT
Internet Engineering and Web Management....MSc 12FT 24PT
Web Technology....MSc 12FT 24PT

Heriot-Watt University
Advanced Internet Applications....MSc 12FT 24PT/PGDip 9FT
Artificial Intelligence....MSc 12FT 24PT/PGDip 9FT
Computer Services ManagementMSc 12FT 24PT/PGDip 9FT 21PT
Creative Software Systems....MSc 12FT 24PT/PGDip 9FT 21PT
Information Technology (Business)....MSc 12FT 24PT/PGDip 9FT 21PT
Information Technology (Software Systems)....MSc 12FT 24PT/PGDip 9FT 21PT
Mobile Communications.... MSc 12FT 24PT/PGDip 9FT 21PT/PGCert 6FT 12PT
Software Engineering....MSc 12FT 24PT/PGDip 9FT 21PT

University of Hertfordshire
Computer Networking Principles and Practice....MSc 12-16FT
Data Communications and Networks....MSc 12-16FT 36-48PT
Distributed Data Management....MSc 12-16FT
Distributed Systems and Networks....MSc 12-16FT
Internet Engineering....MSc 12-16FT 36PT

University of Huddersfield
Information Systems Management....MSc 15FT 24-36PT
Electronic and Communication Engineering .... MSc 12FT
Network Technology and Management....MSc 15FT 36PT

University of Hull
.NET Financial Systems Development.... MSc 12FT
Business Technology Management.... MSc 12FT
Distributed Systems Development (.NET) .... MSc 12FT
Financial Systems Development (.NET).... MSc 12FT

Keele University
Information Technology and Management .... MSc 12FT

University of Kent
Advanced Electronic Systems Engineering....PGDip 12FT 24PT/MSc 12FT 24PT
Broadband and Mobile Communication Networks....PGDip 12FT 24PT/MSc 12FT 24PT
Computer Science....MSc 12FT 36PT
Computer Security....MSc 12FT 36PT
Computing....GradDip 9FT
IT Consultancy....MSc 12FT 36PT
Information Security and Biometrics....MSc 12FT 24PT/PGDip 12FT 24PT
Networks and Security....MSc 12FT 36PT
Wireless Communications and Signal Processing....PGDip 12FT 24PT/MSc 12FT 24PT

Kingston University
Information Systems (E-commerce)....MSc 12FT 24-36PT
Network and Information Security....MSc 12FT 24-36PT
Network and Information Security with Management Studies.... MSc 12FT 24-36PT
Networking and Data Communications ....MSc 12FT 24-36PT
Networking and Data Communications with Management Studies....MSc 12FT 24-36PT

Lancaster University
Information Technology, Management and Organisational Change .... MSc 12FT/PGDip 12FT/MRes 12FT
Network and Internet Systems.... MSc 12FT

Leeds Metropolitan University
Advanced Engineering Management .... MSc 12FT 24PT/PGCert 12PT/PGDip 12FT 24PT
Information & Technology....MSc 12FT 24PT/PGDip 12FT 24PT/PGCert 4FT 24PT
Information Management....MSc 12FT 36PT
Mobile & Distributed Computer Networks....MSc 12FT 24PT/PGDip 12FT 24PT/PGCert 4FT 12PT

University of Leeds
Digital Communications Networks....MSc(Eng) 12FT

University of Leicester
Advanced Computational Methods .... MSc 12FT/PGDip 9FT

University of Limerick
Computer and Communications Systems .... MEng 12FT 24PT
Information and Network Security.... MEng 12FT
Quality Management.... PGDip 9FT/MSc 12FT

Liverpool Hope University
Networks & Security.... MSc 12FT

Liverpool John Moores University
Computer Network Security....MSc 12FT 24PT
Computing Information Systems....MSc 12FT 24PT
Wireless and Mobile Computing ....MSc 12FT 24PT

University of Liverpool
Advanced Science (Computer Sciences pathway)....MSc 12FT/PGDip 12FT/PGCert 12FT
Information Systems Management (Online Degree).... MSc 24FT 24+PT
Internet Systems (Online degree) ....MSc 24FT 24+PT

London Metropolitan University
Business Information Systems.... MSc 12FT
Computer Networking....MSc 12FT 24PT
Computer Science ....MSc 12-18FT 24PT
Information Technology....MSc 12FT 24PT
Network Management and Security....MSc 12FT 24PT
Professional Information Technology ....MSc 12FT 24-48PT

London South Bank University
Computer Systems and Networking....MSc 12FT 24PT
Electrical & Electronic Engineering....MRes 12FT 24PT
Information Systems Management .... MSc 15FT MSc 24PT
Internet and Database Systems - PT.... MSc 24PT
Telecommunications and Computer Networks Engineering - FT. MSc 12FT MSc 24PT
Web & Mobile Computing.... MSc 18FT

Loughborough University
Information Management and Business Technology.... MSc 12FT 24-60PT/PGDip 9FT 24-36PT/PGCert 6FT
International Computing for the Internet ....MSc 12FT 24PT
Internet Computing and Network Security....MSc 12FT 96PT/Diploma 7FT 60PT
Networked Comunications....MSc 12FT 36PT
Visual Systems and Technology....MSc 12FT 24-60PT

Manchester Metropolitan University
Information Systems....MSc 12FT 36PT

University of Manchester
Information Systems - Organisations and Management .... MSc 12FT
Management and Information Systems: Change and Development....MSc 12FT 24PT/PGDip 9FT 21PT

Middlesex University
Business Information Systems Management.... MA 12FT 24PT
Computer Network Management....MSc 12FT 24PT
Computer Networks....MSc 12FT 36PT

Newcastle University
Advanced Computer Science....MSc 12FT 24PT
Cloud Computing ....MSc 12FT 24PT
Communications and Signal Processing .... MSc 12FT
E-Business (Information Systems) .... MSc 12FT
Wireless Embedded Systems.... MSc 12FT

University of Northampton
IT Service Management..MSc 12FT 24PT 24DL/PGDip 12PT 12DL

Northumbria University
Business Information Systems Management....MSc 12/16FT
Computer Network Technology....MSc 12/16FT
Computing and Information Technology....MSc 12/16FT 36DL/PGDip 9FT 24DL/PGCert 4FT 12DL
Engineering Management....MSc 12/16FT
Information and Library Management..MA 12FT 24PT/MSc 12FT 24PT
Information and Records Management ....MSc 24DL

Nottingham Trent University
Electronic Systems ....MRes 12FT

University of Nottingham
Management of Information Technology....MSc 12FT 24-48PT

The Open University
Advanced Networking....PGDip variableDL/MSc variableDL

Oxford Brookes University
Broadband Networks ....MSc 12FT 24PT
Mobile and High Speed Telecommunication Networks ....MSc 12FT 24PT
Wireless Communication Systems ....MSc 12FT 24PT

Plymouth University
Computer Science ....MSc 12FT 24PT
Computer Science ....MRes 12FT
Computer and Information Security ....MSc 12FT MRes 12FT
Network Systems Engineering.. MSc 12FT/MRes 12FT/PGDip 6FT

University of Portsmouth
Communication Network Planning and Management.... MSc 12/16FT 36PT
Communication Systems Engineering.... MSc 12/16FT 36PT
Computer Network Administration and Management .... MSc 12/16FT 36PT
Information Systems....MSc 12FT 36PT

Queen Mary, University of London
Computing and Information Systems (generalist).... MSc 12FT 24PT
Mobile and Wireless Networks.... MSc 12FT 24PT 24DL

Queen's University Belfast
Advance Wireless Communications..MSc 12FT 24PT/PGDip 12FT 24PT/PGCert 12FT 24PT

University of Reading
Information Management & Systems ....MSc 12FT 36PT/PGDip 9FT/PGCert 6FT

Robert Gordon University
Communications and Computer Network Engineering.... MSc 12FT 24PT
Computing: Information Engineering (with/without Network Management) .... MSc 12FT 36PT/PGDip 9FT 24PT/PGCert 4FT 12PT
Computing: Software Technology with Network Management... MSc 12FT 36PT/PGDip 9FT 24PT/PGCert 4FT 12PT
IT Management ....MSc 12FT 36DL

University of Roehampton
International Management with Information Systems.... MSc 12FT 24PT

Royal Holloway, University of London
Information Security ....PGCert 48PT

University of Salford
Advanced Computer Science....MSc 12FT 36PT/PGDip 6FT 24PT
Aerospace Engineering....MSc 12FT/PGDip 9FT/PGCert 9FT
Data Telecommunications Networks.. MSc 12FT 24PT/PGDip 9FT 18PT
Databases and Web-based Systems.... MSc 12FT 24PT/PGDip 9FT 18PT
Information Security .... MSc 12FT 24PT/PGDip 9FT 18PT/PGCert 9FT 18PT
Information Security Management.... MSc 12FT 24PT/PGDip 9FT 18PT/PGCert 9FT 18PT

Sheffield Hallam University
Computer and Network Engineering....MSc 12FT 36PT/PGDip 12FT 24PT/PGCert 6FT 12PT
Database Professional (incorporating Oracle certification training)....MSc 12FT 36PT
IT Professional....MSc 36DL
Information Systems Security....MSc 12FT 24PT
Information Systems with SAP ....MBA 12FT 36PT
Infromation Technology ....MSc 12FT 36-72PT
Networking Professional (incorporating Cisco Certification Training).... MSc 12FT 36PT/PGDip 9FT/PGCert 5FT
Networking Technologies and Management....MSc 36-72DL
Technical Consulting....MSc 18FT 36PT
Web and Cloud Computing .... MSc 12FT

University of Sheffield
Computer Vision Engineering....MSc(Eng) 12FT
Data Communications....MSc(Eng) 12FT
Electronic and Electrical Engineering.... MSc(Res) 12FT
Information Management....MSc 12FT 24-36PT
Information Management (Professional Enhancement Programme).... MSc Up to 12FT 24-36PT/PGDip 9FT 18PT/PGCert 6FT 12PT
Information Systems....MSc 12FT 24-36PT
Information Systems (Professional Enhancement Programme)... MSc Up to 12FT 24-36PT/PGDip 9FT 18PT/PGCert 6FT 12PT
Information Systems Management .... MSc 12FT
Librarianship (Professional Enhancement Programme) MA Up to 12FT 24-36PT/PGDip 9FT/PGCert 6FT
Wireless Communication Systems ....MSc(Eng) 12FT

University of South Wales
Electronic Mobile Communications ....MSc 12FT 36PT

Computer sciences and IT

University of Southampton
Archaeological Computing ....MSc 12FT 24PT
Digital Marketing.. MSc 12FT
Information Systems ....MSc 12FT 27PT/PGDip 9FT 21PT
Information Technology and Commerce........... LLM 12FT 24PT
Information Technology and Telecommunications Law.................
LLM 24DL

University of St Andrews
Advanced Computer Science......................................MSc 12FT 24PT
Artificial Intelligence ....MSc 12FT 24PT
Management and Information Technology ....MSc 12FT/
PGDip 9FT

Staffordshire University
Advanced Technology...MSc 12-24FT 24-60PT
Digital Forensics and Cybercrime Analysis........................ MSc 12FT

University of Stirling
Advanced Computing..................MSc 12FT/PGDip 9FT/PGCert 9FT
Information Technology .... MSc 12FT/PGDip 9FT

University of Strathclyde
Advanced Computer Science..........................MSc 12FT/PGDip 9FT
Information Management.........MSc 12FT/PGDip 9FT/PGCert 4FT
Signal Processing..... MSc 12FT 24PT/PGDip 9FT 18PT/PGCert 6FT
12PT

University of Sunderland
Information Technology Management........MSc 14FT/PGDip 9FT/
PGCert 5FT
Network Systems ....MSc 14FT/PGDip 9FT/PGCert 5FT

University of Surrey
Communications Networks and Software........MSc 12FT 24-60PT
Information Systems .... MSc 12FT
Management Information Systems .... MSc 12FT
Security Technologies and Applications .... MSc 12FT

University of Sussex
Management of Information Technology...............MSc 12FT 24PT

Swansea University
Advanced Computer Science .... MSc 12FT

Swansea Metropolitan University
Computer Networks ....MSc 12FT 24PT
Computing and Information Systems.....................MSc 12FT 24PT

Teesside University
Advanced Computer Science ....MSc 12FT 36PT
Information Technology Project Management .... MSc 12FT
24-36PT/PGDip 8FT 24PT/PGCert 4FT 12PT
Networks and Comminucations...........................MSc 12FT 36PT
Network Systems ....MSc 12FT 24-36PT/PGDip 8FT 24PT/
PGCert 4FT 12PT

Trinity College Dublin - the University of Dublin
Computer Science (Mobile and Ubiquitous Computing)...............
MSc 12FT
Computer Science (Networks and Distributed Systems) ....
MSc 12FT
Management of Information Systems .... MSc 24PT

UCL - University College London
Information Science.........MSc 12FT 24-60PT/PGDip 9FT 24-60PT/
PGCert 3FT 12-48PT
Information Security .... MSc 12FT/PGDip 9FT
Internet Engineering .... MSc 12FT
Networked Computer Systems...MSc 12FT
Photonics Systems Development.......................................MRes 12FT
Web Science...MSc 12FT/MRes 12FT

University of Warwick
Information Systems Management & Innovation......... MSc 12FT
International Technology Management............................ MSc 12FT

University of West London
Digital Services Architecture ....MSc 12FT 24PT
Information Systems ....MSc 12FT 24PT
Network and Mobile Computing ....MSc 15FT 24PT

University of Westminster
Business Information Systems...................................MSc 12FT 24PT
Business Information Systems (evening study)...............MSc 24PT
Computer Networks ....MSc 12FT 24PT 24BM

University of Wolverhampton
Strategic Information Technology Management............ MSc 12FT
12-16PT/PGCert 12FT 24PT

University of York
Internet and Wireless Computing.. MSc 12FT

Information systems and networking
Research Courses

Aberystwyth University
Computer Science ....MPhil 12FT 24PT PhD 36FT 60PT

Anglia Ruskin University
Digital Modelling.............................PhD 24 - 60FT 36 - 72PT

Aston University
Adaptive Communications Networks Research Group PhD 36FT/
MPhil 24FT

Bangor University
Communication Networks and Protocols ...MPhil 24FT/PhD 36FT

Birkbeck, University of London
Computer Science and Information Systems. PhD 36FT 60-72PT/
MPhil 24FT 48PT

University of Bradford
Wireless Technologies .... PhD 36FT 48PT/MPhil 12FT 24PT

University of Bristol
Systems Engineering ....EngD 48FT 84PT

Cardiff University
Computer Science ....MRes 12FT
Information Systems ....MRes 12FT

City University London
Department of Electrical, Electronic and Information
Engineering..PhD/MPhil

Coventry University
Information Systems ....MSc by research 12FT 24PT

University of Hertfordshire
Adaptive Systems ....PhD 36FT 72PT/MRes 12FT 24PT

University of Hull
Internet Computing.......PhD 36FT 60PT/MPhil 24FT 36PT/MSc by
research 12FT 24PT

University of Kent
Computer Science ..... PhD 24FT 60PT/MSc by research 12FT 24PT
Electronic Engineering .... MSc by research 12FT 24PT/MPhil 24FT
36PT/PhD 36FT 60PT

University of Leeds
Institute of Integrated Information Systems .....PhD 36+FT/MPhil
24FT

London School of Economics and Political Science (LSE)
Management Science.......................... MPhil 36-48FT/PhD 36-48FT

University of Nottingham
Location-aware Ubiquitous Computing for the Digital Society....
PhD 36FT

Oxford Brookes University
Computing and Communication Technologies (MPhil/PhD)........
PhD 24-60FT 36-72PT/MPhil 24-36FT 36-48PT

Royal Holloway, University of London
Information Security ....PhD 36FT

University of Salford
Centre for Networking and Telecommunications Research....PhD
36FT 72PT/MPhil 12FT 24PT/MSc by research 12FT 24PT
Information Systems Research Centre...........................PhD/MPhil

University of Sheffield
Automatic Control and Systems Engineering: Integrated
Studies..Integrated PhD 48FT

University of Southampton
School of Management: Information Systems.....PhD 36FT 72PT/
MPhil 24FT 48PT

Swansea University
Computer Science ....MSc by research 12FT 12-24PT
Intelligent Wireless Networks for Healthcare......MSc by research
12FT 24PT

UCL - University College London
Communications .... EngD 48PT

Mechatronics
Taught Courses

University of Bolton
Systems Engineering & Engineering Management ....MSc Dual
Award 18FT/MSc 18FT 36PT

University of Bristol
Advanced Engineering Robotics .... MSc 12FT
Robotics .... MSc 12FT

University College Cork
Mechanical Engineering (Manufacturing Process & Automation
Systems)..MEngSci 12FT 24PT

Coventry University
Manufacturing Systems Engineering..MSc 12FT 36PT/PGDip 9FT
24PT

Cranfield University
Automotive Mechatronics .... MSc 12FT

De Montfort University
Mechatronics H73071..........MSc 12FT 24-72PT/PGDip 8FT 24PT/
PGCert 4FT 12PT

University of Derby
Mechanical and Manufacturing Engineering ..MSc 12FT 36-72PT

Edinburgh Napier University
Automation and control .... MSc 12FT
Mechanical Engineering..MSc 12FT 24PT

University of Exeter
Advanced Mechanical Engineering .... MSc 12FT

University of Glasgow
Mechatronics.. MSc 12FT

University of Greenwich
Mechanical and Manufacturing Engineering ....MSc 12FT 24PT

Harper Adams University
Applied Mechatronic Engineering ... PGCert 12FT 24PT/MSc 12FT
24PT/PGDip 12FT 24PT

Heriot-Watt University
Robotics, Autonomous and Interactive Systems (RAIS) MSc 12FT/
PGDip 9FT

Imperial College London
Medical Robotics and Image Guided Intervention ....MRes 12FT

Kingston University
Embedded Systems.............................MSc 12FT 24-36PT
Embedded Systems with Management Studies .... MSc 12FT
24-36PT
Mechatronic Systems ....MSc 12FT 24PT

London South Bank University
Mechatronics Engineering ....MSc 12FT 24PT

Manchester Metropolitan University
Mechanical Engineering..MSc 12FT 24PT

Newcastle University
Automation and Control .... MSc 12FT
Mechanical Engineering .... MSc 12FT
Mechatronics.. MSc 12FT

Queen's University Belfast
Mechanical Engineering (Advanced)..................MSc 12FT 24-36PT

University of Salford
Robotics and Automation .... MSc 12FT/PGDip 9FT

Sheffield Hallam University
Advanced Manufacturing Engineering..................MSc 12FT 36PT/
PGDip 8FT 24PT/PGCert 4FT 12PT

University of Sheffield
Advanced Manufacturing Technologies with the AMRC ....
MSc(Res) 12FT
Advanced Mechanical Engineering .... MSc(Res) 12FT

University of Southampton
Advanced Mechanical Engineering Science (Mechatronics).. MSc
12FT 24PT

University of Strathclyde
Advanced Manufacturing: Technology and Systems ..... MSc 12FT
24PT/PGDip 9FT 18PT/PGCert 9FT 18PT
Advanced Mechanical Engineering .....MSc 12FT 24PT/PGDip 9FT
18PT/PGCert 9FT 18PT
Mechatronics and Automation...MSc 12FT 24PT/PGDip 9FT 18PT

Teesside University
Mechanical Engineering...............MSc 12 - 16FT 24PT/PGDip 8FT

UCL - University College London
Mechanical Engineering..MSc 12FT 24-60PT

Mechatronics
Research Courses

De Montfort University
Mechanical, Aeronautical and Manufacturing Engineering...PhD
24-36FT 48-72PT/MPhil 12-24FT 24-48PT

University of Dundee
Mechanical Engineering ....MPhil 24FT MSc by research 12FT

King's College London
Robotics .... MPhil 24FT 48PT/PhD 36FT 48-72PT

University of Leeds
Institute of Engineering Systems and Design....PhD 36+FT/MPhil
24FT

University of Nottingham
Manufacturing Technology .... EngD 48FT

Oxford Brookes University
Mechanical Engineering ....PhD 24-60FT 36-72PT/MPhil 24-36FT
36-48PT

University of Salford
Centre for Robotics and Automation...................... PhD 36FT 60PT
48DL/MPhil 24FT 24PT 24DL/MSc by research 24FT 24PT 24DL/
MRes 24FT 24PT

University of Surrey
Mechatronics Systems and Robotics ..PhD 33FT 45PT/MPhil 21FT
33PT/EngD 48FT 60PT

Multimedia design
Taught Courses

Bangor University
Computer Science with Visualisation ....MSc 12FT 24PT

Birkbeck, University of London
Creative Industries (Management)..........................MSc 12FT 24PT

Birmingham City University
Interactive Media ....PGCert 5FT 9PT/PGDip 9FT 21PT/
MSc 16/19FT 28PT
Television Production ....MA 12FT
Video Game Enterprise and Production .... MSc 12FT

Computer sciences and IT

Arts University Bournemouth
Interactive Media .... MA 12FT 24PT
MA Animation Production ....MA 12FT
MA Design Interaction .... MA 12FT 24PT

University of Brighton
Media Assisted Language Teaching...MA 12FT 24PT/PGCert 12FT
24PT/PGDip 12FT 24PT
User Experience Design ....MSc 12FT 24-60PT/PGCert 12FT
24-60PT/PGDip 12FT 24-60PT

University of Bristol
Image and Video Communications and Signal Processing..... MSc
12FT

Brunel University
Advanced Multimedia Design and 3D Technologies...... MSc 12FT
24PT

University of Cambridge
Screen Media and Cultures.....................................MPhil 9FT

University of Central Lancashire
Child Computer Interaction.....................................MRes 12FT 24PT
Interaction Design.............................. MRes 12FT 24-36PT

City University London
Human-Centred Systems ....MSc 12FT 28PT

University College Cork
Interactive Media .... MSc 12FT 24PT

De Montfort University
Multimedia Design .... MA 12FT 24PT

University of Derby
Computer Graphics Production ....MSc 12FT 36PT
Mobile Device Software Development ....MSc 12FT 36PT
Visual Communication (Animation).............................MDes 48FT
Visual Communication (Graphic Design) ....MDes 48FT
Visual Communication (illustration)...........................MDes 48FT

Dublin Institute of Technology
Professional Design Practice (Visual Communications)..MA 12FT

University of Dundee
Animation and Visualisation .... MSc 12FT
Design for Services .... MDes 12FT
Product Design .... MSc 12FT
User Experience Engineering .... MSc 12FT

Edinburgh Napier University
Design (Interaction).................................MA/MDes 12FT

University of Edinburgh
Design and Digital Media..........................MSc 12FT 24PT

University of Gloucestershire
Visual Communication .... PGCert 4FT/PGDip 8FT/MA 12FT

Glyndwr University
Creative Media Technology......................................MSc 12FT

Goldsmiths, University of London
Design: Interaction Research................................. MA 15FT 30PT
Interactive Media: Critical Theory and Practice...... MA 12FT 24PT

University of Hertfordshire
Character Creation and Technical Effects.... MA 12FT 24PT/PGDip
12FT 24PT
E-Learning Technology ....MSc 12-16FT
Human Computer Interaction (Online) ....MSc 12FT 24-36PT
12-36DL
Interactive Media ....MA 12FT 24PT/PGDip 12FT 24PT
Multimedia Technology..MSc 12-16FT
Special Effects..........................MA 12FT 24PT/PGDip 12FT 24PT

Kingston University
User Experience Design ....MSc 12FT 24-36PT

University of Limerick
Interactive Media .... MA 12FT/MSc 12FT

London Metropolitan University
Interactive Media and Games Technologies.....MSc 12FT 24-48PT

Loughborough University
Interaction Design................................... MA 12FT 24PT
Performance and Multi-Media .... MA 12FT 24PT

Norwich University of the Arts
Communication Design.. MA 12FT 24PT

Nottingham Trent University
Interaction Design.................. MA 12FT/PGCert 7FT/PGDip 4FT
Games and Play (Technology and Culture)............. MSc 12FT 24PT
Multimedia Games Engineering .... MSc 12FT 24PT

Ravensbourne
3D Stereoscopic Media.................MSc 12FT 24PT/MA 12FT 24PT
Communication Design... MA 12FT 24PT
Interactive Product Futures ..... MA 12FT 24PT/MSc 12FT 24-36PT

University of Salford
Art and Design: Creative Technologies ... MA 12FT 24PT/PGDip 9FT
15PT
Digital Architectural Design ....MSc 12FT 28PT/PGDip 8FT 16PT
Professional Sound and Video Technology ....MSc 12FT 36PT/
PGDip 9FT 24PT

Sheffield Hallam University
Online Communication ......MA 18-60DL/PGDip 24-36DL/PGCert
12-18DL

Southampton Solent University
Interactive Production....................MA 12FT 18PT/PGDip 9FT 12PT

University of Strathclyde
Signal Processing..... MSc 12FT 24PT/PGDip 9FT 18PT/PGCert 6FT
12PT

University of Surrey
Monolingual Subtitling and Audio Description ....MA 12FT

Swansea Metropolitan University
Multimedia .... MSc 12FT 24PT

Trinity College Dublin - the University of Dublin
Computer Science (Interactive Entertainment Technology) .. MSc
12FT
Interactive Digital Media.. MSc 12FT

University of the West of Scotland
Multimedia and Web Authoring .... MSc 12FT 24-36PT/
Diploma 9FT 24PT

University of Westminster
Multimedia ....MSc 12FT 24-48PT 24BM

University of Wolverhampton
Computer Science (Multimedia Technology) ....MSc 12-18FT
24-36PT

Multimedia design
Research Courses

Arts University Bournemouth
MPhil / PhD..MPhil 24FT/PhD 36FT

Coventry University
Visual and Information Design (VIDe) Research CentrePhD 36FT/
MPhil 24FT/MA by research 12FT

University of Gloucestershire
Computing and ITPhD 30-48FT 48-84PT/MPhil 18-36FT 30-60PT/
MSc by research 12-24FT 18-36PT

The Open University
Design ... PhD 36FT 72PT variableDL/MPhil 15FT 24PT variableDL
Interdisciplinary themes in music research including film and
literature................... PhD 36FT 72PT variableDL/MPhil 15FT 24PT
variableDL
Multimodal meaning making......PhD 36FT 72PT variableDL/EdD
36FT/MRes 12FT
Next Generation Multimedia Technologies .... PhD variableFT
variablePT variableDL/MPhil variableFT variablePT variableDL

Natural language processing
Taught Courses

Bangor University
Bilingualism...............PhD by taught 36-48FT 60-84PT/MPhil 24FT
Cognitive Linguistics .... MA 12FT 24PT
Linguistics... MA 12FT 24PT
Linguistics and Applied Linguistics............PhD by taught 36-48FT
60-84PT/MPhil 24FT
Psychological Research ..MSc 12FT 24PT/PGDip 8FT 16PT/PGCert
4FT 8PT
Psychology..........MA 12FT 24PT/PGDip 9FT 18PT/PGCert 4FT 8PT

University of Central Lancashire
Rhetoric.. MA 12FT 24PT

University of Cumbria
The Research Process..........................PGCert 12 - 18PT

University of Edinburgh
Cognitive Science..MSc 12FT 36PT
Speech and Language Processing .... MSc 12FT/PGDip 9FT

Heriot-Watt University
Artificial Intelligence ....MSc 12FT 24PT/PGDip 9FT

University of Limerick
Interactive Media .... MA 12FT/MSc 12FT

University of Roehampton
Specialised Translation................MA 12FT 24PT/PGDip 9FT 24PT

School of Oriental and African Studies - SOAS
Linguistics.......................................MA 12FT 24-36PT

University of Sheffield
Computer Science with Speech and Language Processing..... MSc
12FT

Trinity College Dublin - the University of Dublin
Speech and Language Processing ....MPhil 12FT 24PT

Natural language processing
Research Courses

Bangor University
Bilingualism.......................MPhil 24FT/PhD 36-48FT 60-84PT
Doctorate by Research ....PhD 36FT/MPhil 24FT
Linguistics........................... PhD 36-48FT 60-84PT/MPhil 24FT

Cardiff University
Language and Translation Studies......PhD 36FT 60PT/MPhil 24FT
48PT

University of Central Lancashire
Translation, English as a Foreign Language, Learning & Teaching
Methodology, Language.....PhD 30-48FT 66-84PT/MPhil 18-36FT
42-60PT/MA by research 12FT 24PT

University of Edinburgh
Speech Technology Research (Centre for) ....PhD 36FT

Operating systems
Taught Courses

Northumbria University
Computing and Information Technology.......MSc 12/16FT 36DL/
PGDip 9FT 24DL/PGCert 4FT 12DL

Operating systems
Research Courses

University of Kent
Operational Research and Systems ....PhD 36FT 60PT/MPhil 24FT
36PT/MSc by research 12FT 24PT

Software engineering
Taught Courses

University of Aberdeen
Cloud Computing .... MSc 12FT 9PT/PGDip 9FT
Informatics Software Project Management.......MSc 30DL/PGDip
18DL/PGCert 9DL

Aberystwyth University
Computer Science (Software Engineering)............MSc 12FT 24PT/
PGDip 9FT 21PT/PGCert 5FT 17PT
Remote Sensing with Computer Sciences ....MSc 12FT 24PT/
PGDip 9FT 18PT/PGCert 5FT 10PT

Anglia Ruskin University
Information and Communication Technology (Conversion).. MSc
12 - 15FT 24 - 30PT

Aston University
Telecommunications Technology.......................MSc 12FT 24-36PT

Bangor University
Computer Science .... MSc 12FT
Computer Science with Artificial Intelligence/ ..... MSc 12FT 24PT
Computer Science with Security .... MSc 12FT 24PT

University of Bath
Software Systems .... MSc 12FT

University of Bradford
Mobile Applications...MSc 12FT 24PT
Mobile Computing ....MSc 12FT 24PT
Software Engineering...MSc 12FT 24PT

Brunel University
Computer Communication Networks............................ MSc 12FT

University of Cambridge
Advanced Computer Science..MPhil 9FT

Cardiff Metropolitan University
Mobile Technologies.... MSc 12FT 24PT/PGDip 24PT/PGCert 12PT
Technology Project Management ....MSc 12FT 24PT/PGDip 24PT/
PGCert 12PT

Cardiff University
Building Energy and Environmental Performance Modelling
....MSc 12FT 24PT
Computer Science ....MSc 12FT 36PT
Computer Science with Placement................................... MSc 12FT
Computing with Placement .... MSc 12FT

University of Central Lancashire
Agile Software Projects......... MSc 36PT/PGDip 24PT/PGCert 12PT
Maintenance Engineering................... MSc 12FT 24PT/PGDip 24PT

City University London
Software Engineering...MSc 12FT 28PT

University College Cork
Applied Science (Software & Systems for Mobile Networks)
.... MSc 12FT
Computing Science .... MSc 12FT

Coventry University
Software Development.........MSc 12FT 24-36PT/PGDip 8FT 16PT/
PGCert 4FT 8PT

Cranfield University
Computational Software Techniques for Engineering- Software
Engineering for Technical Comp.............................MSc 12FT 36PT
Computational Software Techniques in Engineering (Distributed
Computing and e-Science)..MSc 12FT 24PT
Computational and Software Techniques in Engineering ...... MSc
12FT 24-36PT

Cranfield University, Shrivenham
Scientific Computation ....MSc 24FT 60PT/PGCert 4FT 36PT/
PGDip 9FT 48PT

Computer sciences and IT

De Montfort University
Software Engineering .... MSc 12FT 24-72PT/PGDip 8FT/PGCert 4FT

University of Derby
Mobile Device Software Development .... MSc 12FT 36PT

Dublin Institute of Technology
Engineering Computation.. MSc 12FT 24PT

Durham University
Advanced Software Engineering .... MSc 12FT
Software Engineering Management................................. MSc 12FT
Technology Enhanced Learning................................ MSc 12FT 36PT

University of East Anglia
Computing Science .... MRes 12FT
Information Systems.. MSc 12FT 24PT

University of East London
Enterprise Architecture .... MSc 12FT 24PT/PGDip 8FT 16PT/PGCert 4FT 8PT
Software Engineering .... MSc 12FT 24PT/PGDip 8FT 16PT/PGCert 4FT 8PT

Edge Hill University
Advanced Software Application Development................ MSc 36PT

Edinburgh Napier University
Advanced Software EngineeringMSc 12FT 24PT/PGDip 9FT 18PT/PGCert 6FT 12PT
Computing .... MSc 12FT 24PT
Software Technology for the Web........ MSc 12FT 24PT/PGDip 9FT 18PT/PGCert 6FT 12PT

University of Edinburgh
High Performance Computing............. MSc 12FT 36PT/PGDip 9FT

University of Essex
Financial Software Engineering................................ MSc 12FT 24PT

National University of Ireland Galway
Applied Science (Software Design and Development) .. MSc 12FT
Applied Science (Software Design and Development) - Industry Stream .... HDip 12FT
Enterprise Systems... MAppSci 12FT 24PT
Software Design & Development .... MSc 24FT
Software Design and Development (Fidelity Stream)... MSc 12FT
Software Engineering & Database Technologies........... MSc 24PT
Software and Information Systems [by distance learning].... MSc 24DL

Glasgow Caledonian University
Web Systems Development (.NET) .... MSc 12FT

University of Glasgow
Computer Systems Engineering .... MSc 12FT
Computing Science .... MSc 12FT 24PT/PGDip 9FT 21PT/PGCert 9FT 9PT
Information Security .... MSc 12FT 24PT/PGCert 9FT 9PT/PGDip 9FT 21PT
Information Security .... MRes 12FT 24PT/PGDip 9FT 21PT/PGCert 9FT 9PT
Mobile Design & Engineering.. MRes 12FT 24PT/PGCert 9FT 9PT/PGDip 9FT 21PT
Mobile Design & Engineering... MSc 12FT 24PT/PGDip 9FT 21PT/PGCert 9FT 9PT
Software Development.. MSc 12FT 24PT/PGDip 9FT 21PT/PGCert 9FT 21PT
Software Engineering .... MRes 12FT 24PT/PGCert 9FT 9PT/PGDip 9FT 21PT MSc 12FT 24PT

University of Gloucestershire
Computing (Dependable Software)..... MSc 12FT 24PT/PGDip 8FT 20PT/PGCert 4FT 8PT

Glyndwr University
Computer Science .... MSc 12FT 24-36PT/MRes 12FT 24-36PT

University of Greenwich
Computer Systems and Software Engineering...... MSc 12FT 24PT
Enterprise Software Engineering .... MSc 12FT 24PT
Web Design and Content Planning............................ MA 12FT 24PT

Heriot-Watt University
Creative Software Systems .... MSc 12FT 24PT/PGDip 9FT 21PT
Embedded Systems....................... MSc 12FT 24PT/PGDip 9FT 21PT
Information Technology (Software Systems) .... MSc 12FT 24PT/PGDip 9FT 21PT
Mobile Communications .... MSc 12FT 24PT/PGDip 9FT 21PT/PGCert 6FT 12PT
Software Engineering.................... MSc 12FT 24PT/PGDip 9FT 21PT

University of Hertfordshire
Advanced Digital Systems........................ MSc 12FT 36PT/MSc 16FT
Embedded Intelligent Systems...................... MSc 12-16FT 36-48PT
Mobile Computing .... MSc 12-16FT
Software Engineering.. MSc 12-16FT

University of Hull
.NET Financial Systems Development................................ MSc 12FT
Financial Systems Development (.NET)............................. MSc 12FT

Imperial College London
Computing (Specialism) .... MSc 12FT

University of Kent
Advanced Electronic Systems Engineering........ PGDip 12FT 24PT/MSc 12FT 24PT
Advanced Software Development .... MSc 12FT 36PT
Broadband and Mobile Communication Networks..... PGDip 12FT 24PT/MSc 12FT 24PT
Computer Science .... MSc 12FT 36PT
Embedded Systems and Instrumentation . PGDip 12FT 24PT/MSc 12FT 24PT
Mobile Application Design.. MSc 12FT 24PT
Wireless Communications and Signal Processing .... PGDip 12FT 24PT/MSc 12FT 24PT

King's College London
Advanced Software Engineering .... MSc 12FT

Kingston University
Software Engineering.. MSc 12FT 24-36PT
Software Engineering with Management Studies .... MSc 12FT 24-36PT

Leeds Metropolitan University
Software Engineering.. MSc 12FT 24PT/PGCert 12FT 24PT/PGDip 12FT 24PT

University of Leicester
Advanced Distributed Systems....................... MSc 12FT/PGDip 9FT
Agile Software Engineering Techniques .... MSc 12FT/PGDip 9FT
Software Engineering for Financial Services .... MSc 12FT/PGDip 9FT

University of Limerick
Computer Engineering.................................. PGDip 9FT/MEng 24FT
Computer and Communications Systems .... MEng 12FT 24PT

Liverpool Hope University
Computer Science .... MSc 12FT 24PT/PGDip 12FT 24PT/PGCert 6FT 12PT

University of Liverpool
Advanced Science (Computer Sciences pathway).......... MSc 12FT/PGDip 12FT/PGCert 12FT
Software Engineering (Online Degree).................. MSc 24FT 24+PT

London Metropolitan University
Computer Science .... MSc 12-18FT 24PT
Information Technology .... MSc 12FT 24PT
Professional Information Technology .... MSc 12FT 24-48PT

London South Bank University
Telecommunications and Computer Networks Engineering - PT . MSc 24PT

Manchester Metropolitan University
Mechanical Engineering... MSc 12FT 24PT

University of Manchester
ACS: Computer Systems Engineering................................ MSc 12FT
ACS: Software Engineering .... MSc 12FT

Newcastle University
Advanced Computer Science...................................... MSc 12FT 24PT
Computer Game Engineering .... MSc 12FT
Computer Science .... MSc 12FT 24PT

Northumbria University
Professional Engineering.. MSc 36PT

Nottingham Trent University
Computer Games Systems.. MSc 12FT 24PT
Computer Science .... MRes 12FT MSc 12FT 24PT
Computing Systems... MSc 12/24FT 24PT

University of Nottingham
Human Computer Interaction .... MSc 12FT 24-48PT

Oxford Brookes University
Computer Science .... MSc 12FT 24PT
Computing .... MSc 12FT 24PT
Software Engineering .... MSc 12FT 24PT

University of Oxford
Computer Science .... MSc 12FT
Software Engineering... MSc 48PT
Software and Systems Security .... MSc 24-48PT

Plymouth University
Computer Science .... MSc 12FT 24PT MRes 12FT

University of Portsmouth
Software Engineering.. MSc 12FT 36PT

Queen Mary, University of London
Computer Vision .... MSc 12FT 24PT
Software Engineering... MSc 12FT

Queen's University Belfast
Software Development (Conversion) .... MSc 12FT

Robert Gordon University
Computing: Information Engineering (with/without Network Management) .... MSc 12FT 36PT/PGDip 9FT 24PT/PGCert 4FT 12PT
Computing: Software Technology....... MSc 12FT 24DL/PGDip 9FT 18DL/PGCert 6FT 12DL
Computing: Software Technology with Network Management... MSc 12FT 36PT/PGDip 9FT 24PT/PGCert 4FT 12PT

University of Salford
Advanced Computer Science....... MSc 12FT 36PT/PGDip 6FT 24PT
Aerospace Engineering .... MSc 12FT/PGDip 9FT/PGCert 9FT
Databases and Web-based Systems.... MSc 12FT 24PT/PGDip 9FT 18PT
Digital Architectural Design .... MSc 12FT 28PT/PGDip 8FT 16PT
Software Engineering.................... MSc 12FT 38PT/PGDip 8FT 24PT

Sheffield Hallam University
Software Engineering.. MSc 12FT 36PT

University of Sheffield
Advanced Software Engineering .... MSc(Eng) 12FT
Computer Science with Speech and Language Processing..... MSc 12FT
Computer Vision Engineering .... MSc(Eng) 12FT
Software Systems and Internet Technology .... MSc 12FT

University of South Wales
Mobile and Satellite Communications .... MSc 12/FT 36PT

Southampton Solent University
Software Engineering Management........................ MSc 12FT 36PT

University of St Andrews
Advanced Computer Science...................................... MSc 12FT 24PT
Networks & Distributed Systems.............................. MSc 12FT 24PT
Software Engineering.. MSc 12FT 24PT

Staffordshire University
Advanced Technology....................................... MSc 12-24FT 24-60PT
Computer Games Design .... MSc 12-18FT 24-32PT
Computer Games Programming ...... MSc 12FT 24PT/PGCert 12FT 24PT/PGDip 12FT 24PT
Computing Soluttions for Business.............................. MSc 12-18FT

University of Stirling
Advanced Computing.................. MSc 12FT/PGDip 9FT/PGCert 9FT

University of Strathclyde
Advanced Computer Science........................... MSc 12FT/PGDip 9FT

University of Sunderland
Computing .... MSc 14FT/PGDip 9FT/PGCert 5FT

University of Surrey
Communications Networks and Software........ MSc 12FT 24-60PT

Swansea University
Advanced Computer Science with a specialisation in Software Technology .... MSc 12FT

Swansea Metropolitan University
Computing and Information Systems...................... MSc 12FT 24PT

Teesside University
Advanced Computer Science...................................... MSc 12FT 36PT
Computer Games Art (Character) ... MA 12FT 24-36PT/PGDip 8FT 24PT/PGCert 4FT 12PT
Computer Games Art (Environment) ..... MA 12FT 24-36PT/PGDip 8FT 24PT/PGCert 4FT 12PT
Computer Games Art (Vehicle) .... MA 12FT 24-36PT/PGDip 8FT 24PT/PGCert 4FT 12PT
Computing .... MSc 12FT 24-36PT/PGDip 8FT 24PT/PGCert 4FT 12PT

Trinity College Dublin - the University of Dublin
Computer Science (Networks and Distributed Systems) .... MSc 12FT

University of Ulster
Professional Software Development................................. MSc 12FT

UCL - University College London
Computer Graphics, Vision and Imaging.......................... MSc 12FT
Computer Science .... MSc 12FT
Software Systems Engineering .... MSc 12FT

University of Warwick
Computer Science and Applications................................. MSc 12FT
Engineering Systems .... MSc 12FT

University of West London
Computing Interaction Design .... MSc 12FT 24PT
Software Engineering.. MSc 12FT 24PT

University of the West of England, Bristol
Software Engineering.. MSc 12FT 24PT

University of Westminster
Computer Science .... MRes 12FT 24PT 12-24BM
Software Engineering.. MSc 12FT 24PT

University of York
Software Engineering... MSc 12FT

Software engineering
Research Courses

Aberystwyth University
Computer Science .... MPhil 12FT 24PT PhD 36FT 60PT

Bangor University
Artificial Intelligence and Intelligent Agents .... MPhil 24FT/PhD 36FT

Birmingham City University
Computing... MPhil 36-72PT/PhD 36-72PT
Software Development and Security Research.... MSc by research 12FT 24PT

Computer sciences and IT

University of Birmingham
Engineered Materials for High Performance Applications in Aerospace and Related Technologies .... EngD 48FT

Cardiff University
Visual Computing.... PhD 36FT possiblePT/MPhil 12FT possiblePT

Coventry University
Software Engineering.......... MSc by research 12FT 24PT

University of Kent
Computer Science ..... PhD 24FT 60PT/MSc by research 12FT 24PT

University of Leicester
General Engineering.......... PhD 36FT 48PT/MPhil 24FT 36PT

University of Liverpool
Advanced Science (Computer Sciences pathway)......... MRes 12FT

Newcastle University
Computer Science .... Integrated PhD 48FT 72PT

The Open University
Computing .... PhD 36FT 72PT variableDL/MPhil 15FT 24PT variableDL
Software Engineering and Design .... PhD variableFT variablePT variableDL/MPhil variableFT variablePT variableDL

Oxford Brookes University
Computing and Communication Technologies .... PhD 24-60FT 36-72PT/MPhil 24-36FT 36-48PT

University of Oxford
Computer Science .... DPhil 48FT/MSc by research 24FT
Software Engineering.......... PGDipRes 24FT

Staffordshire University
Computing Science .... MRes 12FT 24-72PT

University of Strathclyde
Computer and Information Sciences - Research ..PhD 36FT 48PT/MPhil 12FT 24PT

Swansea University
Computational Modelling in Engineering .... MRes 12FT 36PT

Virtual reality
Taught Courses

University of Aberdeen
Cloud Computing .... MSc 12FT 9PT/PGDip 9FT

Aston University
IT Project Management .... MSc 12FT

Bangor University
Advanced Visualization, Virtual Environments and Computer Animation .... MRes 12FT

Birmingham City University
Video Game Enterprise and Production .... MSc 12FT

University of Bradford
Advanced Computer Animation and Visual Effects.......... MA 12FT 24PT/MSc 12FT 24PT
Computer Animation and Visual Effects .... MSc 12FT 24PT/MA 12FT 24PT

Brunel University
Advanced Multimedia Design and 3D Technologies...... MSc 12FT 24PT

Cardiff University
Computing with Placement .... MSc 12FT

Cranfield University, Shrivenham
Cyber Defence and Information Assurance .... PGCert 18FT
Defence Simulation and Modelling..... MSc 12FT 60PT/PGDip 9FT 48PT/PGCert 4FT 36PT

University of Derby
Computer Graphics Production .... MSc 12FT 36PT

University of Dundee
Animation and Visualisation .... MSc 12FT
Architecture: Advanced Practice, Management and Law ...... MSc 18DL
User Experience Engineering .... MSc 12FT

University of East Anglia
Games Development.......... MSc 12FT 24PT

Glasgow Caledonian University
3D Design for Virtual Environments... MA 12FT 24PT/PGDip 12FT 24PT

Glyndwr University
Computing.......... MSc 12FT

Goldsmiths, University of London
Computing.......... MSc 12FT 24PT

Heriot-Watt University
Advanced Internet Applications.......... MSc 12FT 24PT/PGDip 9FT
Artificial Intelligence .... MSc 12FT 24PT/PGDip 9FT
Computer Services ManagementMSc 12FT 24PT/PGDip 9FT 21PT
Creative Software Systems .... MSc 12FT 24PT/PGDip 9FT 21PT
Information Technology (Business) ..... MSc 12FT 24PT/PGDip 9FT 21PT
Information Technology (Software Systems)........ MSc 12FT 24PT/PGDip 9FT 21PT
Marine Biodiversity and Biotechnology ..... MSc 12FT 24PT/PGDip 9FT 21PT
Robotics, Autonomous and Interactive Systems (RAIS) MSc 12FT/PGDip 9FT
Software Engineering.......... MSc 12FT 24PT/PGDip 9FT 21PT

University of Kent
Architectural Visualisation.......... MA 12FT

Kingston University
Computer Animation .... MA 12FT 24PT

University of Liverpool
Advanced Computer Science with Internet Economics .... MSc 12FT

Newcastle University
Computer Game Engineering .... MSc 12FT

Nottingham Trent University
Computer Games Systems.......... MSc 12FT 24PT

Ravensbourne
Applied Technologies, Rapid Prototyping and Digital Technologies .... MSc 12FT 24PT
Web Applications .... MA 12FT 24PT

University of Reading
Business Technology Consulting .... MSc 12FT

University of Salford
Art and Design: Creative Technology... MA 12FT 24PT/PGDip 9FT 15PT

University of Sheffield
Sustainable Architectural Studies.......... MSc 12FT 24PT

Staffordshire University
3D Games Modelling.......... MSc 12-18FT
Computer Games Design .... MSc 12-18FT 24-32PT
Computer Games Programming ...... MSc 12FT 24PT/PGCert 12FT 24PT/PGDip 12FT 24PT

Swansea University
Advanced Computer Science with Specialism in Visual Computing .... MSc 12FT

Teesside University
Computer Games Art (Character) ... MA 12FT 24-36PT/PGDip 8FT 24PT/PGCert 4FT 12PT
Computer Games Art (Environment) ..... MA 12FT 24-36PT/PGDip 8FT 24PT/PGCert 4FT 12PT
Computer Games Art (Vehicle)........ MA 12FT 24-36PT/PGDip 8FT 24PT/PGCert 4FT 12PT

UCL - University College London
Adaptive Architecture and Computation........ MSc 12FT 24-60PT/PGDip 9FT/MRes 12FT 24-60PT
Computer Graphics, Vision and Imaging.......... MSc 12FT

University of the West of England, Bristol
Education in Virtual Worlds.......... MA 24PT

University of York
Human-Centred Interactive Technologies .... MSc 12FT

Virtual reality
Research Courses

Bangor University
Artificial Intelligence and Intelligent Agents .... MPhil 24FT/PhD 36FT

University of Dundee
Architecture .... MPhil 24FT MSc by research 12FT PhD 36FT

Queen's University Belfast
Atomistic Simulation.......... PhD 36FT 72PT/MPhil 24FT 48PT

UCL - University College London
Virtual Environments, Imaging and Visualisation .... EngD 48FT

Web development and e-commerce
Taught Courses

Aberystwyth University
Management and Digital Business .... MSc 12FT 24PT

University of Bedfordshire
Business Web Analytics and Management .... MSc 12-18FT
Art Design and Internet Technology.......... MA 12FT 24PT
Media, Culture and Technology.......... MA 12FT 24PT

Birkbeck, University of London
Web Design and Development.......... PGCert 12PT

University of Bradford
Mobile Applications.......... MSc 12FT 24PT
Mobile Computing.......... MSc 12FT 24PT
Web Technologies .... MSc 12FT 24PT

University of Brighton
Internet and Distributed Systems.......... MSc 13FT 24-60PT/PGDip 10FT 24-60PT/PGCert 5FT 24PT
User Experience Design .... MSc 12FT 24-60PT/PGCert 12FT 24-60PT/PGDip 12FT 24-60PT

Brunel University
Advanced Multimedia Design and 3D Technologies...... MSc 12FT 24PT
Computer Communication Networks.......... MSc 12FT

University of Cambridge
Bioscience Enterprise .... MPhil 10FT

University of Central Lancashire
Computing .... MSc 12FT 24PT/PGDip 12PT/PGCert 6PT
Network Computing.......... MSc 12FT 36PT/PGDip 12FT 24PT

City University London
E-Business Systems.......... MSc 12FT 28PT
Electronic Publishing .... MSc 12FT/MA 12FT/PGDip 9FT

University of Cumbria
Computing and IT.......... PGDip 12PT/PGCert 12PT

Durham University
Internet Systems and E-Business .... MSc 12FT

University of East London
Technology Management .... MSc 12FT 24PT

Edge Hill University
Computing (Web).......... MSc 12FT 24PT

Edinburgh Napier University
Software Technology for the Web........ MSc 12FT 24PT/PGDip 9FT 18PT/PGCert 6FT 12PT

University of Essex
Advanced Web Engineering.......... MSc 12FT 24PT
Big Data and Text Analytics .... MSc 12FT 24PT
Cloud Computing .... MSc 12FT 24PT
Computer Networks and Security.......... MSc 12FT 24PT
Computer Science .... MSc 12FT 24PT
Intelligent Systems and Robotics .... MSc 12FT 24PT

University of Exeter
Information Technology Management for Business...... MSc 12FT

GCU London
Digital Marketing .... MSc 12FT
Web Systems Development (.net) .... MSc 13FT

Glasgow Caledonian University
Microsoft .NET Web Systems Development..PGDip 9FT 12-24PT/PGCert 6FT
Web Systems Development (.NET) .... MSc 12FT

University of Gloucestershire
Computing (E-Business).......... MSc 12FT 24PT/PGDip 8FT 20PT/PGCert 4FT 8PT

University of Greenwich
Internet Engineering and Web Management........ MSc 12FT 24PT
Internet Technology with e-Business/ with Security..... MSc 12FT 24PT
Web Design and Content Planning.......... MA 12FT 24PT
Web Technology.......... MSc 12FT 24PT

Heriot-Watt University
Advanced Internet Applications .... MSc 12FT 24PT/PGDip 9FT

University of Hertfordshire
E-Commerce Law.......... LLM 12FT 24PT
E-Learning Technology .... MSc 12-16FT
Internet Engineering .... MSc 12-16FT 36PT

University of Hull
.NET Financial Systems Development.......... MSc 12FT

Keele University
Internet and Web Technologies.......... MSc 12FT

University of Kent
Mobile Application Design.......... MSc 12FT 24PT

King's College London
Computing & Internet Systems.......... MSc 12FT
Mobile Internet Research .... MSc 12FT
Web Intelligence.......... MSc 12FT

Kingston University
Electronic Commerce.......... MSc 12FT 24-36PT
Software Engineering (Web) .... MSc 12FT 24-36PT
Software Engineering (Web) with Management Studies....... MSc 12FT 24-36PT

Lancaster University
Network and Internet Systems.......... MSc 12FT

Leeds Metropolitan University
Mobile Device Application Development.......... MSc 12FT 24PT/PGCert 12FT 24PT/PGDip 12FT 24PT
Web Applications Development......... MSc 12FT 24PT/PGDip 12FT 24PT/PGCert 6FT 12PT

University of Leicester
Web Applications and Services.......... MSc 12FT/PGDip 9FT

University of Liverpool
E-Business Strategy and Systems.......... MSc 12FT 24PT
Internet Systems (Online degree) .... MSc 24FT 24+PT

London Metropolitan University
Professional Information Technology .... MSc 12FT 24-48PT

London South Bank University
Internet and Database Systems .... MSc 15FT

Loughborough University
International Computing for the Internet .... MSc 12FT 24PT
Science of the Internet.......... MSc 12FT 24PT

Computer sciences and IT

University of Manchester
ACS: Advanced Web Technologies .... MSc 12FT 24PT

Newcastle University
E-Business .... MSc 12FT
E-Business (E-Marketing) .... MSc 12FT
E-Business (Information Systems) .... MSc 12FT

Northumbria University
Computing and Information Technology .... MSc 12/16FT 36DL/
PGDip 9FT 24DL/PGCert 4FT 12DL

Nottingham Trent University
Internet and Enterprise Computing .... MSc 12FT 24PT

Oxford Brookes University
Broadband Networks .... MSc 12FT 24PT
E-Business .... MSc 12FT 24PT

Ravensbourne
Web Applications .... MA 12FT 24PT

Sheffield Hallam University
Enterprise Systems Professional (SAP) .... MSc 12FT 36PT/PGDip
24PT/PGCert 12PT

Online Communication ...... MA 18-60DL/PGDip 24-36DL/PGCert
12-18DL

University of Sheffield
Software Systems and Internet Technology .... MSc 12FT

Staffordshire University
Advanced Technology .... MSc 12-24FT 24-60PT
Computing Solutions for Business .... MSc 12-18FT

University of Strathclyde
Signal Processing ..... MSc 12FT 24PT/PGDip 9FT 18PT/PGCert 6FT
12PT

University of Surrey
Internet Computing .... MSc 12FT

University of Sussex
Information Technology with Business and Management .... MSc
12FT 24PT

Swansea Metropolitan University
E-Commerce .... MSc 12FT 24PT
Web Management .... MSc 12FT 24PT

Teesside University
Digital Animation, Sound and Visual Media .... MA 12FT 24-36PT/
PGDip 8FT 24PT/PGCert 4FT 12PT

University of West London
Network and Mobile Computing .... MSc 15FT 24PT

Web development and e-commerce
Research Courses

University of Essex
Computer Science ....PhD 36FT 72PT/MPhil 24FT 48PT/MSc by
research 12FT 24PT
Computing and Electronic Systems....PhD 36FT 72PT/MPhil 24FT
48PT/MSc by research 12FT 24PT

University of Hull
Internet Computing .... PhD 36FT 60PT/MPhil 24FT 36PT/MSc by
research 12FT 24PT

The Open University
Computing .... PhD 36FT 72PT variableDL/MPhil 15FT 24PT
variableDL

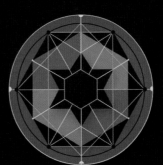

Your essential guide to funding postgraduate study

Postgraduate Funding Guide

Available from your university careers service,
graduate fair or visit us online

www.prospects.ac.uk/funding

Prospects

Engineering, aerospace

Engineering, aerospace
Taught Courses

Anglia Ruskin University
Engineering Management...........................MSc 12 - 15FT 24 - 30PT

University of Bath
Aerospace Engineering .... MSc 12FT

University of Bristol
Integrated Aerospace Systems Design.....................MSc 12FT 24PT

Brunel University
Aerospace Engineering .... MSc 12FT

City University London
Air Safety Management...................................... MSc 12FT 36PT
Aircraft Maintenance Management........................MSc 12FT 36PT

Cranfield University
Advanced Lightweight Structures and Impact .... MSc 12FT
Aerodynamics (Option of Aerospace Dynamics)............. MSc 12FT
Aerospace Dynamics .... MSc 12FT
Aerospace Propulsion (Option of Thermal Power).......... MSc 12FT
Aerospace Vehicle Design.. MSc 12FT
Aircraft Design (Option of Aerospace Vehicle Design MSc).... MSc 12FT
Aircraft Engineering............... MSc 36PT/PGDip 36PT/PGCert 36PT
Airworthiness......MSc 24 - 48PT/PGDip 24-48PT/PGCert 24-48PT
Astronautics and Space Engineering.......................MSc 12FT 24PT
Autonomous Vehicle Dynamics and Control.........MSc 12FT 24PT/
PGDip 12FT 24PT/PGCert 12FT 24PT
Avionic Systems Design (Option of Aerospace Vehicle Design) ....
MSc 12FT
Flight Dynamics (Option of Aerospace Dynamics) .... MSc 12FT
Gas Turbine Technology (Option of Thermal Power MSc)....... MSc 12FT
Human Factors and Safety Assessment in Aeronautics
.... MSc 12FT 24-48PT/PGCert 12FT 24-36PT/PGDip 12FT 24-36PT
Rotating Machinery, Engineering and Management (Option of
Thermal Power MSc)... MSc 12FT
Safety and Accident Investigation - Air Transport ....MSc 24-36PT
Structural Design (Option of Aerospace Vehicle Design MSc)
.... MSc 12FT
Thermal Power.. MSc 12FT

Cranfield University, Shrivenham
Defence Sensors and Data Fusion........MSc 12FT 36PT/PGDip 6FT 24PT
Guided Weapon Systems .... MSc 12FT

University of Glasgow
Aeronautical Engineering.. MSc 12FT
Aerospace Engineering & Management.......................... MSc 12FT
Aerospace Systems .... MSc 12FT

Glyndwr University
Aeronatical Engineering .... MSc 12FT 24-36PT/
MRes 12FT 24-36PT
Composites ....MSc 12FT 24PT/MRes 12FT 24PT

University of Hertfordshire
Aerospace Engineering ....MSc 12FT 36PT/MSc 16FT

Imperial College London
Advanced Computational Methods for Aeronautics, Flow Mgt
and Fluid Structure Interaction..................................MSc 12FT 24PT
Composites: The Science, Technology and Engineering
Application of Advanced Composites ....MSc 12FT 24PT

Kingston University
Aerospace Engineering .... MSc 12FT 24PT

University of Limerick
Aeronautical Engineering.. MEng 12FT

University of Lincoln
Sustainable Power and Energy Engineering .... MSc 24PT

University of Liverpool
Aerospace and Mechanical Systems Engineering MSc(Eng) 12FT/
PGDip 12FT/PGCert 12FT
Simulation in Aerospace Engineering............ MSc(Eng) 12FT 24PT

Manchester Metropolitan University
Sustainable Aviation.................................MSc 12FT 12-36PT

University of Manchester
Aerospace Engineering .... MSc 12FT

University of Nottingham
Aerospace Technologies .... MSc 12FT
Civil Engineering: Environmental Fluid Mechanics........ MSc 12FT

Queen Mary, University of London
Aerospace Engineering .... MSc 12FT

Queen's University Belfast
Advanced Aerospace Engineering........................MSc 12FT 24-36PT

University of Salford
Aerospace Design and Manufacture ...MSc 12FT 24PT/PGDip 9FT
Aerospace Engineering ....MSc 12FT/PGDip 9FT/PGCert 9FT

University of Sheffield
Aerodynamics and Aerostructures .... MSc(Res) 12FT
Aerospace Materials.. MSc(Eng) 12-24FT
Avionic Systems .... MSc 12FT

University of South Wales
Aeronautical Engineering............................MSc 12FT 24PT
Aircraft Maintenance Systems................................MSc 12FT 36PT
Professional Engineering...MSc 12-60PT

University of Southampton
Aerodynamics and Computation .... MSc 12FT 24PT
Space Systems Engineering .... MSc 12FT
Race Car Aerodynamics.. MSc 12FT 24PT

Staffordshire University
Aeronautical Engineering........................MSc 12-18FT 24-32PT
Professional Engineering..MSc 12-18FT

University of Surrey
Space Technology and Planetary Exploration .... MSc 12FT 48PT

University of Sussex
Satellite Communication Systems.............................MSc 12FT 24PT

Swansea University
Aerospace Engineering .... MSc 12FT 36PT

Swansea Metropolitan University
Non Destructive Testings and Evaluation .... MSc 12FT 24PT

UCL - University College London
Space Science ....MSc 12FT 24PT/PGDip 9FT 18PT
Spacecraft Technology and Satellite Communications
...................................MSc 12FT 24PT/PGDip 9FT 18PT

University of the West of England, Bristol
Aerospace (CPDA) - Bristol & West of England Consortium for
Prof Dev in Aerospace .... MSc 36PT

Engineering, aerospace
Research Courses

Anglia Ruskin University
Engineering Analysis, Simulation and Tribology ..... PhD 24 - 60FT
36 - 72PT

University of Birmingham
Engineered Materials for High Performance Applications in
Aerospace and Related Technologies .... EngD 48FT

University of Bolton
Engineering Specialisms............. PhD 36FT 72PT/MPhil 18FT 36PT

University of Bristol
Advanced Composites...PhD 48FT
Aerospace Engineering ...... PhD 36FT 72PT/MSc by research 12FT 24PT

University of Cambridge
Engineering..PhD 36FT 60PT/MPhil 12FT

Cardiff University
Astronomy Instrumentation ....MPhil 12-24FT possiblePT/
PhD 36FT possiblePT

City University London
Aeronautical Engineering...PhD/MPhil
Aeronautical, Automotive, Mechanical and Civil Engineering......
PhD/MPhil

Cranfield University
PhD Studentship - Transforming composite structural design by
use of structural health mon...PhD 36FT

Cranfield University, Shrivenham
Aerospace Research ....PhD/MPhil
Defence Systems and Analysis: Disaster Preparedness...................
PhD/MPhil

De Montfort University
Mechanical, Aeronautical and Manufacturing Engineering ...PhD
24-36FT 48-72PT/MPhil 12-24FT 24-48PT

University of Hertfordshire
Aeroelasticity and Non-linear Systems.........PhD 36FT 72PT/MRes
12FT 24PT

Imperial College London
Aeronautics...PhD 36FT
The Composites Centre, Aeronautics Department.........PhD 36FT

Lancaster University
Engineering................................. PhD 36FT 48PT/MPhil 24FT 36PT

University of Lincoln
Engineering.......... MPhil 18-36FT 30-48PT/PhD 18-36FT 30-48PT

University of Liverpool
Simulation in Aerospace Engineering...........................MRes 12FT

Loughborough University
Aeronautical and Automotive Engineering...........PhD 36FT 60PT/
MPhil 24FT 36PT

University of Manchester
Advanced Aerospace Materials Engineering........MSc by research
12FT 24PT
Aerospace Engineering ....PhD 36FT 72PT/MPhil 12FT 24PT/
MSc by research 12FT

The Open University
Planetary and Space Sciences ...PhD 36FT 72PT variableDL/MPhil
15FT 24PT variableDL
STEM Education and engagement....... PhD 36FT 72PT variableDL

Space Science and Space Technology PhD 36FT 72PT variableDL/
MPhil 15FT 24PT variableDL

Queen's University Belfast
Mechanical and Aerospace Engineering .....PhD 36FT 72PT/MPhil
24FT 48PT

Swansea University
Aerospace Engineering ...MSc by research 12FT 24PT/MPhil 24FT
48PT/PhD 36FT 72PT
Engineering Metals for High Performance Applications in
Aerospace and Related Technologies .... EngD 48FT
Erasmus Mundus Simulation in Engineering and
Entrepreneurship Development................................. PhD 36FT 72PT
Materials Engineering..MRes 12FT 24PT

University of Warwick
Engineering.... MSc by research 12FT 24PT/MPhil 24FT 36PT/PhD
36FT 60PT/EngD 60PT

Military engineering
Taught Courses

Bangor University
Electronic Engineering .... MSc 12FT

Cranfield University, Shrivenham
Cyber Defence and Information Assurance ....PGCert 18FT
Defence Acquisition Management..MSc 12FT 24PT/PGCert 12FT
24PT/PGDip 12FT 24PT
Defence Simulation and Modelling.....MSc 12FT 60PT/PGDip 9FT
48PT/PGCert 4FT 36PT
Explosives Ordnance Engineering......MSc 12FT 60PT/PGDip 12FT
60PT
Forensic Ballistics.....................MSc 12FT 60PT/PGDip 12FT 60PT/
PGCert 12FT 60PT
Forensic Explosives and Explosion Investigation .MSc 12FT 60PT/
PGDip 12FT 60PT/PGCert 12FT 60PT
Guided Weapon Systems .... MSc 12FT
Gun Systems Design .... MSc 12FT
Military Electronic Systems Engineering ..... MSc 12FT/PGDip 6FT
Military Operational Research ....MSc 12FT 60PT/
PGDip 9FT 48PT/PGCert 4FT 36PT
Military Vehicle Technology ....MSc 12FT 60PT/PGDip 7FT 60PT
Systems Engineering for Defence Capability ....MSc 12FT 60PT
60-96DL/PGCert 3FT 48PT 12-36DL/PGDip 9FT 24PT 24-48DL

University of Liverpool
Simulation in Aerospace Engineering............ MSc(Eng) 12FT 24PT

Queen's University Belfast
Advanced Concrete Technology......MSc 24PT/PGDip 24PT/PGCert
24PT

Military engineering
Research Courses

Cranfield University, Shrivenham
Defence Systems and Analysis: Disaster Preparedness..........PhD/
MPhil
High Explosives and High Velocity Attacks..... PhD 36FT 60-96PT/
MPhil 24FT 24-60PT
Informatics and Simulation................. PhD/MSc by research 12FT
Procurement and Systems Integration for Defence, Security and
Civil Services ....PhD 24FT

National University of Ireland Galway
College of Engineering & Informatics...................PhD 48FT 72PT/
MEngSci by research 24FT 48PT/MAppSci by research 24FT 48PT/
MEng by research 24FT

King's College London
Defence Studies Research .... MPhil 24FT 48PT/PhD 36FT 72PT

Satellite communications
Taught Courses

University of Bradford
Personal, Mobile and Satellite Communications...........MSc 12FT/
PGDip 9FT

Cranfield University, Shrivenham
Cyber Defence and Information Assurance ....PGCert 18FT

University of Glasgow
Mobile Design & Engineering ..MRes 12FT 24PT/PGCert 9FT 9PT/
PGDip 9FT 21PT MSc 12FT 24PT/

London Metropolitan University
Mobile and Satellite Communications ....MSc 12FT 24PT

Newcastle University
Communications and Signal Processing .... MSc 12FT

Robert Gordon University
Communications and Computer Network Engineering
....MSc 12FT 24PT

University of South Wales
Electronic Mobile Communications ....MSc 12FT 36PT
Mobile and Satellite Communications .... MSc 12/FT 36PT

University of Southampton
Space Systems Engineering .... MSc 12FT

Engineering, aerospace

University of Sussex
Satellite Communication Systems..........................MSc 12FT 24PT

UCL - University College London
Spacecraft Technology and Satellite Communications
....MSc 12FT 24PT/PGDip 9FT 18PT

University of Westminster
Mobile, Wireless and Broadband Communications....... MSc 12FT 24PT 24BM

Satellite communications
Research Courses

University of Bradford
Communication Systems Engineering....................PhD 36FT 48PT/ MPhil 12FT 24PT

Cranfield University, Shrivenham
Procurement and Systems Integration for Defence, Security and Civil Services ....PhD 24FT

Lancaster University
Communication Systems .... PhD 36FT 48PT/MPhil 24FT 36PT

University of Leeds
Institute of Integrated Information Systems .....PhD 36+FT/MPhil 24FT

University of Nottingham
Engineering and Surveying Space Geodesy...........PhD 36FT 72PT/ MPhil 24FT 48PT

University of Salford
Centre for Robotics and Automation....................... PhD 36FT 60PT 48DL/MPhil 24FT 24PT 24DL/MSc by research 24FT 24PT 24DL/ MRes 24FT 24PT

UCL - University College London
Communications... EngD 48PT

Engineering, electronic and electrical

Acoustic engineering
Taught Courses

Bangor University
Composition/Electroacoustic Composition/Sonic Art.................... MMus 12FT 24PT
Music .... MA 12FT 24PT/PGDip 9FT

Bath Spa University
Creative Sound and Media Technology .... MMus 12FT 24PT/PGDip 9FT 18PT/PGCert 4FT 9PT

University of Derby
Applied Acoustics ....MSc 24-36PT

Edinburgh Napier University
Sound Production... MA 12FT 24PT

University of Edinburgh
Acoustics and Music Technology.............................MSc 12FT 24PT

Leeds Metropolitan University
Acoustics and Noise Control... PGDip 12PT

London South Bank University
Environmental and Architectural Acoustics..........MSc 12FT 24PT

North East Surrey College of Technology
Acoustics and Noise Control..................................IOA Diploma 9PT
Applied Acoustics and Noise Control ....MSc 9PT

Queen Margaret University, Edinburgh
Audiology (Pre-Registration) ....PGDip 24FT/MSc 30FT

University of Salford
Audio Acoustics....... MSc 12FT 24-48PT 24-48DL/PGDip 9FT 18PT
Environmental Acoustics...MSc 12FT 28PT 28DL/PGDip 9FT 18PT 18DL

University of Southampton
Automotive Refinement .... MSc 36PT
Advanced Tribology... MSc 12FT
Sound and Vibration Studies...MSc 12FT 36PT

UCL - University College London
Audiological Science.. MSc 12FT/PGDip 9FT

University of York
Forensic Speech Science ....MSc 12FT 24PT

Acoustic engineering
Research Courses

Anglia Ruskin University
Sound and Audio Engineering ...... MPhil 18 - 36FT 30 - 48PT/PhD 24 - 60FT 36 - 72PT

Cardiff University
Musical Acoustics..PhD 36FT/MPhil 12-24FT

University of Edinburgh
Acoustics...................PhD 36FT/MPhil 24FT/MSc by research 12FT

National University of Ireland Galway
College of Engineering & Informatics.....................PhD 48FT 72PT/MEngSci by research 24FT 48PT/MAppSci by research 24FT 48PT/MEng by research 24FT

The Open University
Acoustics................... PhD 36FT 72PT variableDL/MPhil 15FT 24PT variableDL
Environmental acoustics .... PhD 36FT 72PT/MPhil 15FT 24PT
Music computing and acoustics......... PhD 36FT 72PT variableDL/MPhil 15FT 24PT variableDL
Musical acoustics .... PhD 36FT 72PT/MPhil 15FT 24PT
Non-invasive monitoring .... PhD 36FT 72PT/MPhil 15FT 24PT

University of Salford
Acoustics Research CentrePhD 36FT/MSc by research 12FT/MPhil 12FT

University of Southampton
Institute of Sound and Vibration Research............PhD 36FT 72PT/MPhil 24FT 48PT

Control engineering
Taught Courses

Birmingham City University
Automotive Calibration and Control....PGCert 10PT/PGDip 10PT/MSc 10PT

City University London
Systems and Control..MSc 12FT 24PT

Coventry University
Control Engineering...MSc 12FT 24-36PT
Systems and Control...MSc 12FT 24-36PT

Cranfield University
Energy Systems and Thermal Processes.................MSc 12FT 36PT

University of Derby
Control and Instrumentation.............................MSc 12FT 36-72PT

Edinburgh Napier University
Automation and control... MSc 12FT

Glasgow Caledonian University
Applied Instrumentation & Control .... MSc 12FT 24PT 36DL/PGDip 9FT 18PT

University of Glasgow
Embedded Electronic Systems ....MSc 12FT 24PT

Glyndwr University
CCNA/CCNP Cisco Networking Academy............CCNA 6FT 12+PT/CCNP 6FT 12+PT

Heriot-Watt University
Renewable Energy and Distributed Generation...MSc 12FT 24PT/PGDip 9FT 21PT
Robotics, Autonomous and Interactive Systems (RAIS) MSc 12FT/PGDip 9FT

University of Huddersfield
Embedded Systems Engineering.. MSc 12FT
Engineering Control Systems and Instrumentation....... MSc 12FT 24-36PT

University of Hull
Automatic Control.. MSc 12FT

Imperial College London
Control Systems.. MSc 12FT/DIC 12FT

University of Kent
Embedded Systems and Instrumentation ....PGDip 12FT 24PT/MSc 12FT 24PT
Engineering with Finance...MSc 12FT 24PT

University of Leicester
Advanced Control and Dynamics .... MSc 12FT/PGDip 9FT/PGCert 3FT
Embedded Systems and ControlMSc 12FT/PGDip 9FT/PGCert 3FT

University of Liverpool
Simulation in Aerospace Engineering........... MSc(Eng) 12FT 24PT

University of Manchester
Advanced Control and Systems Engineering.................... MSc 12FT

Newcastle University
Applied Process Control ....MSc 12FT/PGDip 9-12FT
Automation and Control .... MSc 12FT
Chemical and Process Engineering..........................GradDip 9-12FT
Communications and Signal Processing .... MSc 12FT

Robert Gordon University
Communications and Computer Network Engineering
....MSc 12FT 24PT

University of Salford
Advanced Control Systems ....MSc 12FT 24PT/PGDip 9FT

University of Sheffield
Computational Intelligence and Robotics........................ MSc 12FT
Control Systems... MSc 12FT

University of Southampton
Advanced Tribology.. MSc 12FT

Teesside University
Control and Electronics.....................MSc 12-18FT 24PT/PGDip 8FT

Control engineering
Research Courses

University of Bradford
Automotive, Modelling and Control Engineering PhD 36FT 48PT/MPhil 12FT 24PT

Coventry University
Control Theory and Applications.. MSc by research 12FT 24-36PT

University of Greenwich
Engineering (by Research).....................MSc by research 12FT 24PT

University of Manchester
Instrumentation .... PhD 36FT 72PT/MPhil 12FT 24PT

University of Sheffield
Automatic Control and Systems Engineering.......PhD 36FT 72PT/MPhil 24FT 48PT
Automatic Control and Systems Engineering: Integrated Studies Integrated PhD 48FT

Digital signal processing
Taught Courses

Aberystwyth University
3D Imaging, Analysis and Applications... MRes 12FT 24PT/PGDip 9FT 21PT/PGCert 5FT 17PT
Remote Sensing & Geographical Information Systems (GIS) .... MSc 12FT 24PT/PGDip 9FT 18PT/PGCert 5FT 10PT

Aston University
Sensors and Sensing Systems ....MSc(Eng) 12FT

Bangor University
Broadband and Optical Communications..............MSc 12FT 24PT

University of Bath
Digital Communications .... MSc 12FT

University of Bristol
Communications Networks and Signal Processing........ MSc 12FT
Image and Video Communications and Signal Processing..... MSc 12FT
Optical Communications and Signal Processing............ MSc 12FT
Wireless Communications and Signal Processing.......... MSc 12FT

Cardiff University
Wireless and Microwave Communication Engineering
....MSc 12FT 24PT

University of Central Lancashire
Digital Marketing (CAM)...Diploma 7.5DL
Digital Signal and Image Processing ... MSc 12FT 24PT/PGDip 9FT 20PT

City University London
Signals and Sensor Systems.......................................MSc 12FT 36PT

Cranfield University
Computational & Software Techniques in Engineering (Digital Signal and Image Processing) ....MSc 12FT 24PT
Computational and Software Techniques in Engineering ...... MSc 12FT 24-36PT

University of Cumbria
The Research Process...PGCert 12 - 18PT

Dublin Institute of Technology
Electronics and Communications Engineering...... MSc 12FT 24PT
Signal Processing Engineering ....MEng 12FT 24PT

University of Dundee
Advanced Practice (Diagnostic Imaging) ....MSc 36DL
Computing with Vision and Imaging .... MSc 12FT

Edinburgh Napier University
Digital Systems ....MA/MDes 12FT 24PT

University of Edinburgh
Signal Processing and Communications ....MSc 12FT 24PT/PGDip 9FT 18PT

University of Greenwich
Geographical Information Systems with Remote Sensing..... MSc 12FT 24 - 36PT/PGDip 12FT 24-36PT
Wireless Mobile Communications Systems Engineering........ MSc 12FT 24PT

Heriot-Watt University
Computer Vision and Robotics (VIBOT) .... MSc 48FT
Mobile Communications............ MSc 12FT 24PT/PGDip 9FT 21PT/PGCert 6FT 12PT
Robotics, Autonomous and Interactive Systems (RAIS) MSc 12FT/PGDip 9FT
Software Engineering...................MSc 12FT 24PT/PGDip 9FT 21PT

University of Hertfordshire
Data Communications and Networks..........MSc 12-16FT 36-48PT

University of Hull
Wireless Systems... MSc 12FT
Wireless Systems and Logistics Technology .... MSc 12FT

Imperial College London
Communications and Signal Processing .... MSc 12FT

University of Kent
Engineering with Finance...MSc 12FT 24PT
Wireless Communications and Signal Processing.......PGDip 12FT 24PT/MSc 12FT 24PT

Kingston University
Digital Image & Signal Processing......................MSc 12FT 24-36PT

University of Leeds
Communications Studies ....MA 12FT
Communications and Signal Processing ....MSc(Eng) 12FT
Digital Communications Networks ....MSc(Eng) 12FT

University of Leicester
Control and Signal Processing.......................... MSc 12FT/PGDip 9FT

Loughborough University
Digital Communication Systems...............................MSc 12FT 36PT
Signal Processing in Communication Systems...... MSc 12FT 36PT

University of Manchester
Digital Image and Signal Processing........................MSc 12FT 24PT

Newcastle University
Communications and Signal Processing .... MSc 12FT

Plymouth University
Electrical and Electronic Engineering............MSc 12FT/MRes 12FT

University of Portsmouth
Digital Systems Engineering......................................MSc 12FT 36PT

Queen Mary, University of London
Digital Signal Processing ....MSc 12FT 24PT

University of Reading
Cybernetics ....MSc 12FT 24PT
Digital Signal Processing and Communications ... MSc 12FT 24PT

University of South Wales
Electronic Mobile Communications ....MSc 12FT 36PT

University of Southampton
Applied Digital Signal Processing............... MSc 40PT/PGCert 36PT
Sound and Vibration Studies......................................MSc 12FT 36PT

University of Strathclyde
Communications, Control and Digital Signal Processing (CCDSP)..
.... MSc 12FT

University of Sussex
Digital Communication Systems...............................MSc 12FT 24PT

Engineering, electronic and electrical

Digital Communication Systems with Business Management..... MSc 12FT 24PT

Teesside University
Electronics & Communications .....MSc 12- 18FT 24PT/PGDip 8FT

UCL - University College London
Remote Sensing... MSc 12FT 24PT

University of Westminster
Microelectronic System Design .... MSc 12FT 24PT 24BM

University of York
Digital Signal Processing .... MSc 12FT
Digital Systems Engineering... MSc 12FT

Digital signal processing
Research Courses

Anglia Ruskin University
Digital Modelling...PhD 24 - 60FT 36 - 72PT

Aston University
Information Processing and Pattern Analysis Research Group .....
PhD 36FT/MPhil 24FT

Bangor University
Pattern Recognition / Classifiers ....MPhil 24FT/PhD 36FT

University of Brighton
Engineering Research Division.......... PhD 24-60FT 36-72PT/MPhil 18-36FT 30-48PT

University of Bristol
Communications ....PhD 48FT

De Montfort University
Earth and Planetary Remote Sensing Research......... PhD 24-36FT 48-72PT/MPhil 12-24FT 24-48PT

University of Kent
Electronic Engineering .... MSc by research 12FT 24PT/MPhil 24FT 36PT/PhD 36FT 60PT

Lancaster University
Communication Systems .... PhD 36FT 48PT/MPhil 24FT 36PT

University of Leeds
Institute of Integrated Information Systems .....PhD 36+FT/MPhil 24FT

University of Nottingham
Biophysics, Imaging and Optical Science ....PhD 36FT 48PT/MPhil 24FT 36PT
Cell Signalling.. PhD 36FT 72PT/MPhil 24FT 48PT/MRes 12FT/DM 36FT 72PT

Oxford Brookes University
Electronics and Communications .... PhD 24-60FT 36-72PT/MPhil 24-36FT 36-48PT

Swansea University
Intelligent Wireless Networks for Healthcare......MSc by research 12FT 24PT

Engineering, electronic and electrical
Taught Courses

Anglia Ruskin University
Electronic and Electrical Engineering................................ MSc 12FT
Engineering Management...........................MSc 12 - 15FT 24 - 30PT
Mobile Telecommunications ....MSc 12 - 15FT 24 - 30PT

Aston University
Professional Engineering.......................................MSc(Eng) 24-60DL

Bangor University
Broadband and Optical Communications............... MSc 12FT 24PT
Electronic Engineering ....MSc 12FT MRes 12FT
Electronic Engineering (Bio-Electronics)......................... MRes 12FT
Electronic Engineering (Micromachining) .... MRes 12FT
Electronic Engineering (Microwave Devices).................. MRes 12FT
Electronic Engineering (Nanotechnology)...................... MRes 12FT
Electronic Engineering (Optical Communications)....... MRes 12FT
Electronic Engineering (Optoelectronics)...................... MRes 12FT
Electronic Engineering (Organic Electronics) .... MRes 12FT
Electronic Engineering (Polymer Electronics)................ MRes 12FT
Electronic Engineering (VLSI Design)............................. MRes 12FT
Laser Micromachining and Laboratory-on-a-Chip. PhD by taught 36FT/MPhil 24FT
Nanotechnology and Microfabrication .... MSc 12FT
Optical Communications.............PhD by taught 36FT/MPhil 24FT

University of Bath
Mechatronics.. MSc 12FT

University of Birmingham
Communications Engineering and Networks .... MSc 12FT
Communications Engineering with Industrial Studies
.... MSc 18FT
Electromagnetic Sensor Networks...........................MSc 12FT 24PT
Electromagnetic Sensor Networks with Industrial Studies.... MSc 18FT
Electronic and Computer Engineering.....................MSc 12FT 24PT
Electronic and Computer Engineering with Industrial Studies.....
MSc 18FT
Embedded Systems...MSc 12FT 24PT
Embedded Systems with Industrial Studies.................... MSc 18FT

RF and Microwave Engineering .... MSc 12FT 24PT
RF and Microwave Engineering with Industrial Studies
.... MSc 18FT

University of Bolton
Systems Engineering & Engineering Management ....MSc Dual Award 18FT/MSc 18FT 36PT

University of Bradford
Electrical Engineering..MSc 12-18PT
Electrical Engineering with Power Electronics....MSc 12FT/PGDip 9FT
Electrical and Electronic Engineering............ MSc 12FT/PGDip 9FT

University of Brighton
Automotive Electronic Engineering...MSc 12FT 24PT/PGDip 12FT 24PT/PGCert 12FT 24PT
Learning Objectives ..... MSc 12FT 24PT/PGCert 12FT 24PT/PGDip 12FT 24PT

University of Bristol
Advanced Microelectronic Systems Engineering..MSc 12FT 24PT
Image and Video Communications and Signal Processing..... MSc 12FT
MSc in Robotics.. MSc 12FT
Optical Communications and Signal Processing............. MSc 12FT
Wireless Communications and Signal Processing .... MSc 12FT

Brunel University
Advanced Electronic and Electrical Engineering .... MSc 12FT
Advanced Manufacturing Systems.................... MSc 12FT 36-60DL
Advanced Multimedia Design and 3D Technologies...... MSc 12FT 24PT
Computer Communication Networks............................ MSc 12FT
Digital Design and Branding .... MSc 12FT
Distributed Computing Systems Engineering .... MSc 12FT
Embedded Systems (with Signal Processing and Multimedia Communications pathways).. MSc 12FT
Sustainable Electrical Power .... MSc 12FT 24PT
Wireless Communication Systems .... MSc 12FT

Cardiff University
Biophotonics..MSc 12FT 24PT
Electrical Energy Systems.. MSc 12FT
Professional Engineering... MSc 12FT

City University London
Engineering-Modular.. MSc 12FT 24PT/PGDip 24PT/PGCert 24PT

Cranfield University
Pre-Master's Course in Engineering Bridging course to MSc 10FT

Cranfield University, Shrivenham
Military Electronic Systems Engineering ..... MSc 12FT/PGDip 6FT

De Montfort University
Electronic Engineering ....MSc 12FT 24-72PT/PGDip 8FT 24PT/PGCert 4FT 12PT

University of Derby
Control and Instrumentation ....MSc 12FT 36-72PT

Dublin Institute of Technology
Electronics and Communications Engineering......MSc 12FT 24PT

Edinburgh Napier University
Electronic and Electrical Engineering.....................MSc 12FT 24PT
Flexible Managed Programme (FECCI)...MA 12FT 24PT/MSc 12FT 24PT/PGCert 12FT 24PT

University of Edinburgh
Advanced Design Informatics .... MSc 21FT
Bioelectronics and Biosensors....................................... MSc 12FT
Electronics .... MSc 12FT
Offshore Renewable Energy (Industrial Doctorate Centre).. EngD by taught 48FT
Signal Processing and Communications ....MSc 12FT 24PT/PGDip 9FT 18PT

University of Essex
Advanced Web Engineering.....................................MSc 12FT 24PT
Computer Engineering...MSc 12FT 24PT
Computer Networks and Security............................MSc 12FT 24PT
Electronic Engineering ....MSc 12FT 24PT
Electronic Engineering with English for Academic Purposes......... Diploma 9FT
Multimedia Networking...MSc 12FT 24PT
Telecommunication and Information Systems......MSc 12FT 24PT

University of Glasgow
Electronics & Electrical Engineering.........................MSc 12FT 60PT
Electronics & Electrical Engineering with Management ....
MSc 12FT
Electronics Design ....MSc 12FT 60PT
Embedded Electronic Systems ....MSc 12FT 24PT

Glyndwr University
Advanced Electronic Techniques ....MSc 12FT 24-36PT
Digital and Radio Frequency Communication Systems....................
MSc 12FT
Electrical and Electrical Systems ...MSc 12FT 24-36PT/MRes 12FT

University of Greenwich
Electrical Power Engineering....................................MSc 12FT 24PT
Electrical and Communications Engineering.........MSc 12FT 24PT
Electrical and Electronic Engineering.....................MSc 12FT 24PT

Embedded Systems...MSc 12FT 24PT
Internet Engineering and Web Management........MSc 12FT 24PT
Wireless Mobile Communications Systems Engineering........ MSc 12FT 24PT

Heriot-Watt University
Computer Vision and Robotics (VIBOT) .... MSc 48FT
Embedded Systems......................MSc 12FT 24PT/PGDip 9FT 21PT
Renewable Energy and Distributed Generation...MSc 12FT 24PT/PGDip 9FT 21PT
Robotics, Autonomous and Interactive Systems (RAIS) MSc 12FT/PGDip 9FT
Safety, Risk and Reliability Engineering (Distance Learning Only) .
....MSc 24-84DL/PGDip 24-84DL
Smart Grid and Demand Management......MSc 12FT 24PT/PGDip 9FT 18PT
Smart Systems Integration .... MSc 24FT

University of Hertfordshire
Data Communications and Networks..........MSc 12-16FT 36-48PT
Embedded Intelligent Systems ....MSc 12-16FT 36-48PT
Internet Engineering ....MSc 12-16FT 36PT
Radio and Mobile Communication Systems ....MSc 12-16FT 48PT

University of Huddersfield
Embedded Systems Engineering.. MSc 12FT
Electronic and Communication Engineering .... MSc 12FT

University of Hull
Electronic Engineering .... MSc 12FT
Embedded Systems.. MSc 12FT
Wireless Systems... MSc 12FT
Wireless Systems and Logistics Technology .... MSc 12FT

Imperial College London
Analogue and Digital Integrated Circuit Design .... MSc 12FT
Communications and Signal Processing .... MSc 12FT
Control Systems...MSc 12FT/DIC 12FT

University of Kent
Advanced Electronic Systems Engineering................................
PGDip 12FT 24PT/MSc 12FT 24PT
Broadband and Mobile Communication Networks.....PGDip 12FT 24PT/MSc 12FT 24PT
Embedded Systems and Instrumentation ....PGDip 12FT 24PT/MSc 12FT 24PT
Engineering with Finance................................MSc 12FT 24PT
Mobile Application Design..............................MSc 12FT 24PT
Wireless Communications and Signal Processing ....PGDip 12FT 24PT/MSc 12FT 24PT

King's College London
Electronic Engineering with Business Management ..... MSc 12FT

Kingston University
Digital Image & Signal Processing.......................MSc 12FT 24-36PT
Embedded Systems...MSc 12FT 24-36PT
Embedded Systems with Management Studies .... MSc 12FT 24-36PT

Leeds Metropolitan University
Audio Engineering...MSc 12FT 24PT
Building Services Engineering.................................MSc 12FT 24PT

University of Leeds
Electrical Engineering and Renewable Energy Systems ....
MSc(Eng) 12FT
Electronic and Electrical Engineering................................ MSc 12FT
Embedded Systems Engineering................................MSc(Eng) 12FT

University of Leicester
Advanced Electrical and Electronic Engineering ....MSc 12FT/PGDip 9FT/PGCert 3FT
Advanced Engineering ....MSc 12FT/PGDip 9FT/PGCert 3FT
Embedded Systems and ControlMSc 12FT/PGDip 9FT/PGCert 3FT

University of Limerick
VLSI..MEng 12FT 24PT

University of Lincoln
Sustainable Power and Energy Engineering .... MSc 24FT

Liverpool John Moores University
Power and Control Engineering ....MSc 12FT 24PT

University of Liverpool
Energy and Power Systems......................................MSc 12FT 24PT
Microelectronic Systems .... MSc(Eng) 12FT 24PT/PGDip 12FT/PGCert 12FT
Microelectronic Systems and Telecommunications ....MSc(Eng) 12FT 24PT/PGDip 12FT/PGCert 12FT

London South Bank University
Electrical & Electronic Engineering..........................MRes 12FT 24PT
Embedded and Distributed Systems........................MSc 12FT 24PT

Loughborough University
Mobile Communications..MSc 12FT 36PT
Systems Engineering ....MSc 12FT 36PT

Manchester Metropolitan University
Electronic Engineering ....MSc 12FT 24PT

University of Manchester
Digital Image and Signal Processing ....MSc 12FT 24PT

Newcastle University
Automation and Control .... MSc 12FT

Engineering, electronic and electrical

Communications and Signal Processing .... MSc 12FT
Electrical Power.. MSc 12FT
Marine Electrical Power Technology....................MSc 12 or 24FT
Microelectronics .... MSc 12FT
Process Automation...................... MSc 60PT/PGDip 48PT/CPD 3PT

University of Northampton
Engineering... MSc 12FT 24PT

Northumbria University
Business with Pipeline Integrity Management .... MSc 12FT
Electrical Power Engineering............................... MSc 12-16FT
Engineering Management...............................MSc 12/16FT
Professional Engineering.. MSc 36PT

Nottingham Trent University
Engineering (Cybernetics and Communications)..MSc 12FT 24PT
Engineering (Electronics)......................................MSc 12FT 24PT

University of Nottingham
Biophotonics... MSc(Res) 12FT
Computational Engineering: Electromagnetics .... MSc 12FT
Electrical Engineering .... MSc 12FT
Electrical and Electronic Engineering and Entrepreneurship........
MSc 12FT 24PT
Electromagnetics Design.. MSc(Res) 12FT
Power Electronics, Machines and Drives .... MSc 24-48PT

The Open University
Engineering................ MSc(Eng) 12-24DL/MEng variableDL/PGDip
variableDL

Oxford Brookes University
Racing Engine Design .... MSc 12FT 24PT

University of Portsmouth
Electronic Engineering .... MSc 12/16FT 36PT

Queen Mary, University of London
Digital Music Processing......................................MSc 12FT 24PT
Medical Electronics and Physics .... MSc 12FT 24PT
Mobile and Wireless Networks................... MSc 12FT 24PT 24DL

Queen's University Belfast
Electronics ....MSc 12FT 24-36PT/PGDip 12FT 24-36PT
Process Engineering......................................MSc 12FT/Diploma 9FT

University of Reading
Cybernetics .... MSc 12FT 24PT
Digital Signal Processing and Communications ... MSc 12FT 24PT
Systems Engineering .... MRes 12FT 24PT

Robert Gordon University
Communications and Computer Network Engineering MSc 12FT
24PT

Royal College of Art
Vehicle Design...MA 24FT

University of Salford
Quantity Surveying (Mechanical and Electrical) .MSc 12FT 28DL/
PGDip 8FT 16DL

Sheffield Hallam University
Advanced Engineering and Management ....MSc 12FT 36PT/
PGDip 12FT 24PT/PGCert 6FT 12PT
Electronics and Information Technology....MSc 12FT 36PT/PGDip
8FT 24PT/PGCert 4FT 12PT
Telecommunication and Electronic Engineering..MSc 12FT 24PT/
PGDip 8FT 16PT/PGCert 4FT 8PT

University of Sheffield
Avionic Systems .... MSc 12FT
Computer Vision Engineering ....MSc(Eng) 12FT
Electronic Engineering ....MSc(Eng) 12FT
Electronic and Electrical Engineering....................... MSc(Res) 12FT
Semiconductor Photonics and Electronics...............MSc(Eng) 12FT

University of South Wales
Electronic Mobile Communications .... MSc 12FT 36PT
Electronic Product Design .... MSc 12FT 36PT
Electronics and Information Technology................ MSc 12FT 24PT
Embedded Systems Design.. MSc 12FT 36PT

University of Southampton
Applied Digital Signal Processing.............MSc 40PT/PGCert 36PT

Staffordshire University
Electrical Engineering..............................MSc 12-18FT 24-32PT
Electronic Engineering ..... MSc 12-18FT 24-32PT/PGCert 12-18FT
24-32PT/PGDip 12-18FT 24-32PT
Professional Engineering....................................MSc 12-18FT
Telecommunication Engineering ...MSc 12-18FT 24-32PT/PGCert
12-18FT 24-32PT/PGDip 12-18FT 24-32PT

University of Strathclyde
Electrical Power Engineering with Business..........MSc 12FT 24PT/
PGCert 6FT 12PT
Electronic and Electrical Engineering......................MSc 12FT 24PT
High Power Radio Frequency Science and Engineering
.... MSc 12FT 24-36PT/PGDip 9FT/PGCert 9FT
Wind Energy Systems... MSc 12FT

University of Surrey
Microwave Engineering and Wireless Subsystems Design .... MSc
12FT 48PT

University of Sussex
Embedded Digital Systems ....MSc 12FT 24PT

Swansea University
Communication Systems ....MSc 12FT 24-36PT
Electrical and Electronic Engineering.......................MSc 12FT 36PT
Electronics Technology for Sustainable Energy ....
MSc 12FT 24-36PT

Swansea Metropolitan University
Non Destructive Testings and Evaluation ....MSc 12FT 24PT

Teesside University
Electronics & Communications .....MSc 12- 18FT 24PT/PGDip 8FT

UCL - University College London
Nanotechnology ....MSc 12FT 24PT
Telecommunications .... MSc 12FT 24-60PT/MRes 12FT
Wireless and Optical Communications ....MSc 12FT 24-60PT

University of Warwick
Engineering Systems .... MSc 12FT
International Technology Management.......................... MSc 12FT

University of the West of England, Bristol
Advanced Technologies in Electronics.....................MSc 12FT 24PT

University of Westminster
Electronics ....MRes 12FT 24PT 24BM
Electronics (Evening Study)..MRes 24PT
Embedded Systems..MSc 12FT 24PT 24BM

University of York
Digital Signal Processing .... MSc 12FT
Digital Systems Engineering.. MSc 12FT
Engineering Management .... MSc 12FT

Engineering, electronic and electrical
Research Courses

University of Aberdeen
Engineering... PhD 36FT/MPhil 24FT/MSc by research 12FT/EngD
36FT

Anglia Ruskin University
Digital Modelling..PhD 24 - 60FT 36 - 72PT
Engineering Analysis, Simulation and Tribology ..... PhD 24 - 60FT
36 - 72PT
Sound and Audio Engineering ...... MPhil 18 - 36FT 30 - 48PT/PhD
24 - 60FT 36 - 72PT
Telecommunications Engineering...............PhD 24 - 60FT 30-48PT

Bangor University
Electrical Materials Science ....MPhil 24FT/PhD 36FT
Laboratory-on-a-Chip........................MPhil 24FT/PhD 36FT
Molecular Sensors.............................MPhil 24FT/PhD 24-36FT
Optoelectronics.................................MPhil 24FT/PhD 36FT
Organic Electronics ....MPhil 24FT/PhD 36FT
Quantum Transport and Nanoelectronics ..MPhil 24FT/PhD 36FT

University of Bath
Electronic and Electrical EngineeringPhD 24-48FT 36-72PT/MPhil
12-36FT 24-48PT

University of Birmingham
Electronic, Electrical and Computer Engineering ....PhD 36FT/
MSc by research 12FT 24PT
Railway Systems with Integrated Study................MRes 12FT 24PT

University of Bolton
Engineering Specialisms............. PhD 36FT 72PT/MPhil 18FT 36PT

University of Bristol
Electrical and Electronic Engineering........ PhD 36FT 72PT/MSc by
research 12FT 24PT

Brunel University
Electrical Engineering and Electronics ....PhD/MPhil

University of Cambridge
Engineering......................................PhD 36FT 60PT/MPhil 12FT

Cardiff University
Institute of Green Electronic Systems; Communications, Sensors
and Materials .... EngD 48FT/PhD 36FT/MPhil 12FT

City University London
Department of Electrical, Electronic and Information
Engineering...PhD/MPhil

Coventry University
School of Engineering ....PhD/MPhil

De Montfort University
Electronic and Electrical Engineering Research ....PhD 36FT 48PT/
MPhil 12FT 24PT

University of Dundee
Electronic Engineering and Physics .MPhil 24FT MSc by research
12FT PhD 36FT

Durham University
Engineering and Computing Sciences .... MSc by research 12FT/
PhD 36FT

University of Edinburgh
Digital Communications ... PhD 36FT 72PT/MPhil 24FT 48PT/MSc
by research 12FT 24PT
Energy Systems ....PhD 36FT 72PT/MPhil 24FT 48PT/MSc by
research 12FT 24PT

Integrated Micro and Nano Systems......... PhD 36FT 72PT/MSc by
research 12FT 24PT/MPhil 24FT 48PT

University of Essex
Applied Physics ....PhD 36FT 72PT/MPhil 24FT 48PT/MSc by
research 12FT 24PT
Computing and Electronic Systems....PhD 36FT 72PT/MPhil 24FT
48PT/MSc by research 12FT 24PT
Electronic Systems EngineeringPhD 36FT 72PT/MPhil 24FT 48PT/
MSc by research 12FT 24PT

University of Exeter
Engineering................................... PhD 36FT 72PT/MPhil 24FT 48PT

National University of Ireland Galway
College of Engineering & Informatics....................PhD 48FT 72PT/
MEngSci by research 24FT 48PT/MAppSci by research 24FT 48PT/
MEng by research 24FT

University of Greenwich
Engineering (by Research)....................MSc by research 12FT 24PT

Heriot-Watt University
Electrical, Electronic and Computer Engineering.PhD 36FT 48PT/
MPhil 24FT/MSc by research 12FT

University of Hull
Engineering - Environment, Energy and Sensors .PhD 36FT 60PT/
MPhil 24FT 36PT/MSc by research 12FT 24PT

Imperial College London
Research in Electrical/Electronic Engineering........MPhil 12-36FT/
PhD 36-48FT

University of Kent
Electronic Engineering ....MSc by research 12FT 24PT/MPhil 24FT
36PT/PhD 36FT 60PT

Lancaster University
Engineering.................................. PhD 36FT 48PT/MPhil 24FT 36PT

University of Leeds
Institute of Integrated Information Systems .....PhD 36+FT/MPhil
24FT
Institute of Microwaves and Photonics ....PhD 36+FT/MPhil 24FT

University of Leicester
General Engineering.................... PhD 36FT 48PT/MPhil 24FT 36PT

University of Lincoln
Engineering........... MPhil 18-36FT 30-48PT/PhD 18-36FT 30-48PT

Liverpool John Moores University
Electrical and Electronic Engineering....................PhD 36FT 72PT/
MPhil 24FT 48PT/PGDip by research 9FT 18PT

University of Liverpool
Electrical Engineering and Electronics .... PhD 24-48FT 48-84PT/
MPhil 12-48FT 48-72PT
Engineering..PhD 36FT/MPhil 12FT 24PT

Loughborough University
Electronic, Electrical and Systems Engineering ....PhD 36FT 60PT/
MPhil 24FT 36PT
Engineering Doctorate... EngD 48FT

University of Manchester
Electrical and Electronic Engineering...................MPhil 12FT 24PT/
PhD 36FT 72PT

Newcastle University
Electrical and Electronic Engineering...................... PhD 36FT 72PT

University of Nottingham
Electrical and Electronic Engineering............PhD 36FT/MRes 12FT
Electromagnetics Design (by Research).......MSc by research 12FT
Power Electronics, Machines and Control.............PhD tbcFT tbcPT

The Open University
STEM Education and engagement....... PhD 36FT 72PT variableDL

Oxford Brookes University
Electronics and Communications .... PhD 24-60FT 36-72PT/MPhil
24-36FT 36-48PT

University of Portsmouth
Engineering.......................... MPhil 24FT 48PT/PhD 36FT 72PT

Queen Mary, University of London
Electronic Engineering ....PhD/MPhil
Engineering ....PhD 36FT/MPhil

Queen's University Belfast
Electrical and Electronic Engineering.....................PhD 36FT 72PT/
MPhil 24FT 48PT

University of Sheffield
Automatic Control and Systems Engineering: Integrated Studies.
....Integrated PhD 48FT

University of Southampton
Electronics/Electrical Engineering ......PhD 36FT 72PT/MPhil 12FT
24PT
School of Engineering Sciences ....PhD 36FT 72PT/
MPhil 12FT 24PT EngD 36FT

University of Strathclyde
Electronic and Electrical Engineering - Research..PhD 36FT 72PT/
MPhil 12FT 24PT/EngD 36FT

Swansea University
Communication Systems ....MRes 12FT 24PT

Imperial College
London

Electrical and Electronic Engineering
Imperial College London

The Department is one of the largest in the UK devoted to electrical and electronic engineering and has earned an international reputation based on the quality of its doctoral graduates. Currently over 200 research students work closely with academic supervisors of international standing in an environment that is both immersive and broadening.

Entry Requirements
For research degrees, a minimum of an integrated masters (MEng) honours degree passed at 2.1 or 1st, OR a bachelors (BEng) honours degree passed at 2.1 or 1st and a Masters degree. For MSc courses, a 1st class honours Degree is required.

Research
Research is carried out within a structure comprising five groups whose interests are indicated below. Our innovative and competitive research work is widely supported by EU funding, the UK government's research councils, and industrial contracts. Full details of the current programme in any group may be found at www.imperial.ac.uk/electricalengineering/research

- Circuits and Systems
- Communications and Signal Processing
- Control and Power
- Intelligent Systems and Networks
- Optical and Semiconductor Devices

In addition to the research areas listed, we also offer topics which involve collaboration between groups, other Imperial College departments and institutes, or external organisations.

MSc Courses
The Department offers three MSc degree courses leading to the Imperial College Master of Science degree. All are one year, full-time taught courses. Further details can be found at http://www3.imperial.ac.uk/electricalengineering/courses/msc.

- Analogue and Digital Integrated Circuit Design
- Communications and Signal Processing
- Control Systems

Contact
Ms Kay Hancox, UG and PG Admissions, Department of Electrical and Electronic Engineering, Imperial College London, London SW7 2AZ email: admit.eee@imperial.ac.uk
www.imperial.ac.uk/electricalengineering
Electrical and Electronic Engineering
Imperial College London

Engineering, electronic and electrical

Electrical and Electronic Engineering.................PhD 36FT 72PT/
MPhil 24FT 48PT/MSc by research 12FT 24FT
Erasmus Mundus Simulation in Engineering and
Entrepreneurship Development.............................. PhD 36FT 72PT

Teesside University
Electrical and ElectronicsPhD 24-60FT 36-72PT/MPhil 18FT 30PT/
DProf 36PT/MProf by research 30PT

UCL - University College London
Communications...EngD 48PT
Electronic and Electrical Engineering....................... PhD 36FT 60PT

University of Warwick
Engineering.......EngD 36-48FT MSc by research 12FT 24PT/MPhil
24FT 36PT/PhD 36FT 60PT/EngD 60PT

University of the West of Scotland
Department of Electronic Engineering and Physics .....PhD/MPhil

University of Westminster
Electronics and Computer Science.............MPhil 18-36FT 30-60PT

University of York
Electronic Engineering ....PhD 36FT 72PT/MPhil 24FT 48PT/
MSc by research 12FT 24PT
Safety Critical Systems Engineering..MSc 12FT/PGDip 12FT 24PT

Mechatronics
Taught Courses

Birmingham City University
Enterprise Systems Management......................MSc 12/16FT 30PT

University of Bolton
Systems Engineering & Engineering Management ....MSc Dual
Award 18FT/MSc 18FT 36PT

University of Bristol
Advanced Engineering Robotics ....MSc 12FT
Robotics ....MSc 12FT

University College Cork
Mechanical Engineering (Manufacturing Process & Automation
Systems)..MEngSci 12FT 24PT

Coventry University
Manufacturing Systems Engineering..MSc 12FT 36PT/PGDip 9FT
24PT

Cranfield University
Automotive Mechatronics .... MSc 12FT

De Montfort University
Mechatronics H73071...........MSc 12FT 24-72PT/PGDip 8FT 24PT/
PGCert 4FT 12PT

University of Derby
Mechanical and Manufacturing Engineering ..MSc 12FT 36-72PT

Edinburgh Napier University
Automation and control .... MSc 12FT
Mechanical Engineering..MSc 12FT 24PT

University of Exeter
Advanced Mechanical Engineering .... MSc 12FT

University of Glasgow
Mechatronics... MSc 12FT

University of Greenwich
Mechanical and Manufacturing Engineering ....MSc 12FT 24PT

Harper Adams University
Applied Mechatronic Engineering ... PGCert 12FT 24PT/MSc 12FT
24PT/PGDip 12FT 24PT

Heriot-Watt University
Renewable Energy and Distributed Generation...MSc 12FT 24PT/
PGDip 9FT 21PT
Robotics, Autonomous and Interactive Systems (RAIS) MSc 12FT/
PGDip 9FT
Safety, Risk and Reliability Engineering (Distance Learning Only) .
....MSc 24-84DL/PGDip 24-84DL

Imperial College London
Medical Robotics and Image Guided Intervention .... MRes 12FT

Kingston University
Embedded Systems...MSc 12FT 24-36PT
Embedded Systems with Management Studies .... MSc 12FT
24-36PT
Mechatronic Systems..MSc 12FT 24PT

London South Bank University
Mechatronics Engineering ....MSc 12FT 24PT

Manchester Metropolitan University
Mechanical Engineering..MSc 12FT 24PT

Newcastle University
Automation and Control ....MSc 12FT
Mechanical Engineering ....MSc 12FT
Mechatronics...MSc 12FT

Queen's University Belfast
Mechanical Engineering (Advanced).................MSc 12FT 24-36PT

University of Salford
Robotics and Automation .... MSc 12FT/PGDip 9FT

Sheffield Hallam University
Advanced Manufacturing Engineering...................MSc 12FT 36PT/
PGDip 8FT 24PT/PGCert 4FT 12PT

University of Sheffield
Advanced Manufacturing Technologies with the AMRC ....
MSc(Res) 12FT
Advanced Mechanical Engineering .... MSc(Res) 12FT

University of Southampton
Advanced Mechanical Engineering Science (Mechatronics) .. MSc
12FT 24PT

University of Strathclyde
Advanced Manufacturing: Technology and Systems ..... MSc 12FT
24PT/PGDip 9FT 18PT/PGCert 9FT 18PT
Advanced Mechanical Engineering .....MSc 12FT 24PT/PGDip 9FT
18PT/PGCert 9FT 18PT
Mechatronics and Automation...MSc 12FT 24PT/PGDip 9FT 18PT

Teesside University
Mechanical Engineering.................MSc 12 - 16FT 24PT/PGDip 8FT

UCL - University College London
Mechanical Engineering.......................................MSc 12FT 24-60PT

Mechatronics
Research Courses

De Montfort University
Mechanical, Aeronautical and Manufacturing Engineering...PhD
24-36FT 48-72PT/MPhil 12-24FT 24-48PT

University of Dundee
Mechanical Engineering ....MPhil 24FT MSc by research 12FT

King's College London
Robotics ....MPhil 24FT 48PT/PhD 36FT 48-72PT

University of Leeds
Institute of Engineering Systems and Design....PhD 36+FT/MPhil
24FT

University of Nottingham
Manufacturing Technology .... EngD 48FT

Engineering, electronic and electrical

Oxford Brookes University
Mechanical Engineering.....PhD 24-60FT 36-72PT/MPhil 24-36FT 36-48PT

University of Salford
Centre for Robotics and Automation........................ PhD 36FT 60PT 48DL/MPhil 24FT 24PT 24DL/MSc by research 24FT 24PT 24DL/ MRes 24FT 24PT

University of Surrey
Mechatronics Systems and Robotics..PhD 33FT 45PT/MPhil 21FT 33PT/EngD 48FT 60PT

Microelectronics
Taught Courses

Bangor University
Electronic Engineering ....MSc 12FT MRes 12FT
Electronic Engineering (Micromachining) ....MRes 12FT
Electronic Engineering (Microwave Devices)..................MRes 12FT
Electronic Engineering (Nanotechnology) ....MRes 12FT
Electronic Engineering (Polymer Electronics).................MRes 12FT
Electronic Engineering (VLSI Design)..........................MRes 12FT
Laser Micromachining and Laboratory-on-a-Chip..........................
PhD by taught 36FT/MPhil 24FT

University of Bristol
Advanced Microelectronic Systems Engineering ..MSc 12FT 24PT

University of Cambridge
Micro- and Nanotechnology Enterprise .... MPhil 10FT

University College Cork
Microelectronic Design ....PGDip 12FT 24PT MEngSci 12FT 24PT

Cranfield University
Microsystems and Nanotechnology..... MSc 12FT 24-60PT/PGDip 6FT 24PT/MTech 24FT

De Montfort University
Micro Electronics and Nano Technologies ..... MSc 12FT 24-72PT/ MSc(Res) 12FT 24-72PT/PGDip 8FT 24PT/PGCert 4FT 12PT

University of Glasgow
Electronics Design ....MSc 12FT 60PT

Heriot-Watt University
Smart Systems Integration ....MSc 24FT

Institute for System Level Integration - iSLI
System Level Integration MSc 12FT 24-72PT/PGDip 9FT 18-60PT/ PGCert 6FT 12-36PT

University of Limerick
VLSI.. MEng 12FT 24PT

Liverpool John Moores University
Microelectronic System Design ....MSc 12FT 24PT/PGDip 12FT 24PT/PGCert 6FT 12PT

University of Liverpool
Microelectronic Systems .... MSc(Eng) 12FT 24PT/PGDip 12FT/ PGCert 12FT
Microelectronic Systems and Telecommunications ....MSc(Eng) 12FT 24PT/PGDip 12FT/PGCert 12FT

Newcastle University
Microsystems Engineering.. MSc 12FT

Northumbria University
Microelectronic and Communications Engineering.......................
MSc 12-16FT

University of Southampton
Microelectronics Systems Design........................... MSc 12FT 24PT

Swansea University
Electronics Technology for Sustainable Energy ....
MSc 12FT 24-36PT

University of Warwick
Electronic Systems .... MSc 12FT

Microelectronics
Research Courses

Bangor University
Electrical Materials Science ....MPhil 24FT/PhD 36FT
Laboratory-on-a-Chip..............................MPhil 24FT/PhD 36FT
Molecular Sensors.............................MPhil 24FT/PhD 24-36FT
Quantum Transport and Nanoelectronics ..MPhil 24FT/PhD 36FT

University of Edinburgh
Integrated Micro and Nano Systems......... PhD 36FT 72PT/MSc by research 12FT 24PT/MPhil 24FT 48PT

University of Glasgow
Electronics and Nanoscale Engineering .... PhD 36-48FT 60-72PT/ MSc by research 12-24FT 24-36PT

Heriot-Watt University
Microsystems .... EngD 48FT

Institute for System Level Integration - iSLI
Engineering Doctorate in System Level Integration ..... EngD 48FT

University of Surrey
Micro- and NanoMaterials and Technologies (MiNMaT) ...... EngD 48FT

Molecular electronics
Taught Courses

Bangor University
Electronic Engineering ....MRes 12FT
Electronic Engineering (Bio-Electronics).....................MRes 12FT
Electronic Engineering (Nanotechnology) ....MRes 12FT
Electronic Engineering (Organic Electronics) ....MRes 12FT
Electronic Engineering (Polymer Electronics)................MRes 12FT

University of Westminster
Electronics ....MRes 12FT 24PT 24BM
Electronics (Evening Study)...................................MRes 24PT

Molecular electronics
Research Courses

Bangor University
Electrical Materials Science ....MPhil 24FT/PhD 36FT
Molecular Sensors.............................MPhil 24FT/PhD 24-36FT
Organic Electronics ....MPhil 24FT/PhD 36FT
Quantum Transport and Nanoelectronics ..MPhil 24FT/PhD 36FT

The Open University
Atomic, Molecular and Optical Physics.................MPhil 15FT 24PT variableDL
Fabrication ....PhD 36FT 72PT variableDL/MPhil 15FT 24PT variableDL

Nanoelectronics
Taught Courses

Bangor University
Electronic Engineering ....MRes 12FT
Electronic Engineering (Nanotechnology) ....MRes 12FT
Electronic Engineering (Polymer Electronics)................MRes 12FT
Laser Micromachining and Laboratory-on-a-Chip. PhD by taught 36FT/MPhil 24FT
Nanotechnology and Microfabrication .... MSc 12FT

University of Birmingham
Human and Environmental Health Impacts of Nanoscience and Nanotechnology ....MRes 12FT

British Institute of Technology & E-commerce
Nano Technology.....................PGCert 3FT/DipHE 6FT/MScD 12FT

University of Edinburgh
Bioelectronics and Biosensors.................................. MSc 12FT

University of Glasgow
Electronics Design ....MSc 12FT 60PT
Nanoscience and Nanotechnology .... MSc 12FT

University of Hull
Physics with Nanotechnology..................................... MSc 12FT

University of Leeds
Nanoelectronics and Nanomechanics .... MSc 12FT

University of Sheffield
Nanoelectronics and Nanomechanics .... MSc 12FT
Semiconductor Photonics and Electronics...............MSc(Eng) 12FT

University of Strathclyde
Photonics and Device Microfabrication........ MSc 12FT/PGDip 9FT

University of Surrey
Nanotechnology and Nanoelectronic Devices................. MSc 12FT

Swansea University
Nanoscience to Nanotechnology.........................MSc 12FT 24-36PT

UCL - University College London
Nanotechnology ....MSc 12FT 24PT

University of Westminster
Electronics ....MRes 12FT 24PT 24BM
Electronics (Evening Study)...................................MRes 24PT

Nanoelectronics
Research Courses

Bangor University
Electrical Materials Science ....MPhil 24FT/PhD 36FT
Laboratory-on-a-Chip..............................MPhil 24FT/PhD 36FT
Molecular Sensors.............................MPhil 24FT/PhD 24-36FT
Quantum Transport and Nanoelectronics ..MPhil 24FT/PhD 36FT

University of Cambridge
Nanotechnology ....PhD 36FT

University of Dundee
Electronic Engineering and Physics .... MPhil 24FT MSc by research 12FT

University of Edinburgh
Integrated Micro and Nano Systems......... PhD 36FT 72PT/MSc by research 12FT 24PT/MPhil 24FT 48PT

University of Glasgow
Electronics and Nanoscale Engineering .... PhD 36-48FT 60-72PT/ MSc by research 12-24FT 24-36PT

University of Surrey
Micro- and NanoMaterials and Technologies (MiNMaT) ...... EngD 48FT

Swansea University
Nanotechnology (Physics).....................MSc by research 12FT 24PT

Optoelectronics
Taught Courses

Bangor University
Broadband and Optical Communications.............. MSc 12FT 24PT
Electronic Engineering ....MSc 12FT MRes 12FT
Electronic Engineering (Microwave Devices)..................MRes 12FT
Electronic Engineering (Optical Communications)......MRes 12FT
Electronic Engineering (Optoelectronics)......................MRes 12FT
Optical Communications.............PhD by taught 36FT/MPhil 24FT

Cardiff University
Biophotonics...................................MSc 12FT 24PT

University College Cork
Photonics ....MSc 12FT 36PT

Edinburgh Napier University
Design (Lighting) ....MA/MDes 12FT

Heriot-Watt University
Photonics and Optoelectronic Devices .... MSc 12FT 24PT

King's College London
Analytical Science for Industry ....MSc 12FT 24PT

Nottingham Trent University
Medical and Materials Imaging...........................MRes 12FT

University of Nottingham
Photonic and Optical Engineering .... MSc 12FT/PGDip 9FT

University of Sheffield
Semiconductor Photonics and Electronics...............MSc(Eng) 12FT

University of St Andrews
Photonics and Optoelectronic Devices .... MSc 12FT

University of Strathclyde
Optical Technologies...............................MSc 12FT 24PT/PGDip 9FT

UCL - University College London
Light and Lighting...............................MSc 12FT 24-60PT
Photonics Systems Development........................MRes 12FT

University of Warwick
Electronic Systems .... MSc 12FT

Optoelectronics
Research Courses

Bangor University
Optoelectronics...............................MPhil 24FT/PhD 36FT

Cardiff University
Photons and Matter..............PhD 36FT possiblePT/MPhil 12-24FT possiblePT

University of Edinburgh
Molecular and Optical Physics...PhD 36FT

University of Nottingham
Applied Optics .... PhD 36FT 72PT/MPhil 24FT 48PT
Biophysics, Imaging and Optical Science ....PhD 36FT 48PT/MPhil 24FT 36FT

The Open University
Plasma Science and Engineering........ PhD 36FT 72PT variableDL/ MPhil 15FT 24PT variableDL

Swansea University
Cold Atoms and Quantum Optics ....MSc by research 12FT 12-24PT

Photonics
Taught Courses

Bangor University
Broadband and Optical Communications.............. MSc 12FT 24PT
Electronic Engineering ....MRes 12FT
Electronic Engineering (Microwave Devices)..................MRes 12FT
Electronic Engineering (Optical Communications).......MRes 12FT
Electronic Engineering (Optoelectronics)......................MRes 12FT
Optical Communications.............PhD by taught 36FT/MPhil 24FT

University of Birmingham
RF and Microwave Engineering .... MSc 12FT 24PT
RF and Microwave Engineering with Industrial Studies ....
MSc 18FT

Cardiff University
Biophotonics...................................MSc 12FT 24PT

University College Cork
Photonics...................................MSc 12FT 36PT

University of Derby
Still and Moving Image...................................MA 12FT

University of Greenwich
Science (Open).....................................MSc 12FT 24-36PT

Heriot-Watt University
Photonics and Optoelectronic Devices .... MSc 12FT 24PT

Imperial College London
Optics and Photonics...................................MSc 12FT 24PT
Plasmonics and Metamaterials ....MRes 12FT

Engineering, electronic and electrical

University of Liverpool
Engineering Applications of Lasers........... MSc(Eng) 12FT 24-36PT

University of Sheffield
Semiconductor Photonics and Electronics.............. MSc(Eng) 12FT

University of St Andrews
Erasmus Mundus Masters: Photonics.................. Erasmus Mundus Masters 24FT
Photonics and Optoelectronic Devices .... MSc 12FT

University of Strathclyde
Optical Technologies.............................. MSc 12FT 24PT/PGDip 9FT
Photonics and Device Microfabrication........ MSc 12FT/PGDip 9FT
Quantum Information and Coherence .... MSc 12FT 24PT/PGDip 9FT

Teesside University
Control and Electronics.................... MSc 12-18FT 24PT/PGDip 8FT

Photonics
Research Courses

Aston University
Photonics Research Group .... PhD 36FT/MPhil 24FT

Bangor University
Optoelectronics.................................... MPhil 24FT/PhD 36FT

University of Cambridge
Photonic Systems Development..................................... MRes 12FT

Cardiff University
Photons and Matter.............. PhD 36FT possiblePT/MPhil 12-24FT possiblePT

Heriot-Watt University
Photonics.. EngD 48FT

University of Leeds
Institute of Microwaves and Photonics..... PhD 36+FT/MPhil 24FT

University of Manchester
Photon Physics .... PhD 36FT 72PT/MSc by research 12FT 24PT

University of Nottingham
Electromagnetics Design (by Research)....... MSc by research 12FT
Photonic and Radio Frequency Engineering......... PhD 36FT tbcPT/MPhil 24FT tbcPT/MRes 12FT tbcPT

University of Salford
Photonics and Non-Linear Science...... PhD 36FT 60PT/MPhil 24FT 24PT/MRes 24FT 24PT/MSc by research 24FT 24PT

University of Southampton
Photonics.. PhD 42FT 72PT

Swansea University
Cold Atoms and Quantum Optics .... MSc by research 12FT 12-24PT
Lattice Gauge Theory........................... MSc by research 12FT 24PT

Power engineering
Taught Courses

Bangor University
Electronic Engineering .... MSc 12FT

University of Bath
Electrical Power Systems..................................... MSc 12FT 36-60DL

University of Bradford
Electrical Engineering with Power Electronics.... MSc 12FT/PGDip 9FT

Brunel University
Sustainable Electrical Power .... MSc 12FT 24PT

Cardiff University
Electrical Energy Systems..................................... MSc 12FT

University of Central Lancashire
Renewable Energy Engineering......... MSc 12FT 24PT/PGDip 24PT

City University London
Power Systems & Energy Management................... MSc 18FT 36PT

Cranfield University
Aerospace Propulsion (Option of Thermal Power).......... MSc 12FT
Gas Turbine Technology (Option of Thermal Power MSc)....... MSc 12FT
Power, Propulsion and the Environment (Option of Thermal Power) .... MSc 12FT/PGCert 12FT/PGDip 12FT
Rotating Machinery, Engineering and Management (Option of Thermal Power .... MSc 12FT

University of Greenwich
Electrical Power Engineering .... MSc 12FT 24PT

Heriot-Watt University
Renewable Energy and Distributed Generation...MSc 12FT 24PT/PGDip 9FT 21PT

University of Leeds
Electrical Engineering and Renewable Energy Systems .... MSc(Eng) 12FT
Electronic and Electrical Engineering................................. MSc 12FT

Liverpool John Moores University
Power and Control Engineering .... MSc 12FT 24PT

University of Liverpool
Energy Generation .... MSc 12FT 24PT
Energy and Power Systems..................................... MSc 12FT 24PT

London South Bank University
Electrical & Electronic Engineering........................ MRes 12FT 24PT

University of Manchester
Electrical Energy Conversion Systems..................... MSc 12FT 24PT
Electrical Power Systems Engineering .... MSc 12FT 24PT

Newcastle University
Electrical Power... MSc 12FT
Marine Electrical Power Technology.................... MSc 12 or 24FT
Marine and Offshore Power Systems..................... MSc 12 or 24FT
Power Distribution Engineering .... MSc 12FT 36PT/PGDip 24PT/PGCert 12PT

Northumbria University
Electrical Power Engineering.. MSc 12-16FT

University of Nottingham
Electromagnetics Design.. MSc(Res) 12FT
Power Electronics and Drives .... MSc 12FT/PGDip 12FT
Power Electronics, Machines and Drives.................... MSc 24-48PT

Queen's University Belfast
Sustainable Electrical Energy Systems............................... MSc 12FT

Robert Gordon University
Energy Management.... MSc 12FT 36DL/PGDip 8FT 24DL/PGCert 4FT 12DL
Energy and Sustainability ...MSc 42DL/PGDip 24DL/PGCert 12DL
Offshore Renewables ....MSc 42DL

University of Sheffield
Computer Vision Engineering .... MSc(Eng) 12FT
Electronic Engineering ....MSc(Eng) 12FT
Electronic and Electrical Engineering...................... MSc(Res) 12FT
Environmental and Energy Engineering..... MSc(Eng) 12FT/PGDip 9FT
Semiconductor Photonics and Electronics.............. MSc(Eng) 12FT

University of South Wales
Energy Systems Engineering .... MSc 12FT 36PT
Sustainable Power Technology .... MSc 12FT 36PT

Staffordshire University
Electrical Engineering......................... MSc 12-18FT 24-32PT

University of Strathclyde
Electrical Power Engineering with Business.......... MSc 12FT 24PT/PGCert 6FT 12PT
Power Plant Engineering .... MSc 36FT/PGDip 24FT/PGCert 12FT
Power Plant Technologies........... MSc 12FT/PGDip 9FT/PGCert 6FT

Swansea University
Electrical and Electronic Engineering...................... MSc 12FT 36PT

Teesside University
Energy and Environmental Management......... MSc 12-16FT 24PT

UCL - University College London
Energy Demand Studies .... MRes 12FT
Energy and Resources: Policy and Practice, Australia .... MSc 24FT 36-48PT
Engineering with Finance............................... MSc 12FT/PGDip 9FT
Engineering with Innovation and Entrepreneurship ....MSc 12FT/PGDip 9FT
Materials for Energy and Environment.......................... MSc 12FT
Power Systems Engineering .... MSc 12FT 24-60PT

Power engineering
Research Courses

Aston University
Bio-Energy Research Group .... PhD 36FT/MPhil 24FT

University of Bath
Electronic and Electrical EngineeringPhD 24-48FT 36-72PT/MPhil 12-36FT 24-48PT

University of Bristol
Electrical and Electronic Engineering........ PhD 36FT 72PT/MSc by research 12FT 24PT

University of Edinburgh
Energy Systems...............PhD 36FT 72PT/MPhil 24FT 48PT/MSc by research 12FT 24PT

University of Glasgow
Systems, Power and Energy ....PhD 36-48FT 60-72PT/MSc by research 12-24FT 24-36PT

Liverpool John Moores University
Electrical and Electronic Engineering.....................PhD 36FT 72PT/MPhil 24FT 48PT/PGDip by research 9FT 18PT

Loughborough University
Electronic, Electrical and Systems Engineering ....PhD 36FT 60PT/MPhil 24FT 36PT

Newcastle University
Energy............................... PhD 36FT 72PT/MPhil 12FT 24PT

University of Nottingham
Electrical and Electronic Engineering............PhD 36FT/MRes 12FT
Power Electronics, Machines and Control.............PhD tbcFT tbcPT

The Open University
Residual stress.......... PhD 36FT 72PT variableDL/MPhil 15FT 24PT variableDL

Satellite communications
Taught Courses

University of Bradford
Personal, Mobile and Satellite Communications .... MSc 12FT/PGDip 9FT

Cranfield University, Shrivenham
Cyber Defence and Information Assurance .... PGCert 18FT

University of Glasgow
Mobile Design & Engineering ..MRes 12FT 24PT/PGCert 9FT 9PT/PGDip 9FT 21PT
Mobile Design & Engineering ... MSc 12FT 24PT/PGDip 9FT 21PT/PGCert 9FT 9PT

London Metropolitan University
Mobile and Satellite Communications .... MSc 12FT 24PT

Newcastle University
Communications and Signal Processing .... MSc 12FT

University of Oxford
Social Science of the Internet... MSc 10FT

Robert Gordon University
Communications and Computer Network Engineering................. MSc 12FT 24PT

University of South Wales
Electronic Mobile Communications .... MSc 12FT 36PT
Mobile and Satellite Communications .... MSc 12/FT 36PT

University of Southampton
Space Systems Engineering .... MSc 12FT

University of Sussex
Satellite Communication Systems.....................MSc 12FT 24PT

UCL - University College London
Spacecraft Technology and Satellite Communications .... MSc 12FT 24PT/PGDip 9FT 18PT

University of Westminster
Mobile, Wireless and Broadband Communications....... MSc 12FT 24PT 24BM

Satellite communications
Research Courses

University of Bradford
Communication Systems Engineering................... PhD 36FT 48PT/MPhil 12FT 24PT

Cranfield University, Shrivenham
Procurement and Systems Integration for Defence, Security and Civil Services..PhD 24FT

Lancaster University
Communication Systems .... PhD 36FT 48PT/MPhil 24FT 36PT

University of Leeds
Institute of Integrated Information Systems .....PhD 36+FT/MPhil 24FT

University of Nottingham
Engineering and Surveying Space Geodesy..........PhD 36FT 72PT/MPhil 24FT 48PT

University of Salford
Centre for Robotics and Automation...................... PhD 36FT 60PT 48DL/MPhil 24FT 24PT 24DL/MSc by research 24FT 24PT 24DL/MRes 24FT 24PT

UCL - University College London
Communications.. EngD 48PT

Telecommunication studies
Taught Courses

Anglia Ruskin University
Mobile Telecommunications ....MSc 12 - 15FT 24 - 30PT

Aston University
Data Communication Networks........................ MSc 12FT 24-36DL
Telecommunications Technology ....MSc 12FT 24-36PT

Bangor University
Broadband and Optical Communications.............. MSc 12FT 24PT

University of Bath
Wireless Systems... MSc 12FT

University of Bedfordshire
Telecommunications Management............................MSc 12-15FT

Birmingham City University
Telecommunications by Distance Learning........PGCert 8FT 84PT/PGDip 8FT/MSc 8FT

University of Bradford
Electrical and Electronic Engineering............ MSc 12FT/PGDip 9FT
Personal, Mobile and Satellite Communications ....MSc 12FT/PGDip 9FT
Wireless Sensors and Embedded Systems... MSc 12FT/PGDip 9FT

Engineering, electronic and electrical

University of Bristol
Communications Networks and Signal Processing........ MSc 12FT
Image and Video Communications and Signal Processing..... MSc 12FT
Systems...MRes 24PT

Brunel University
Computer Communication Networks................................ MSc 12FT

Bucks New University
Communications Management .... MCM 18PT 18DL

University of Central Lancashire
Strategic Communication ....MA 24PT

City University London
Telecommunications and Networks..........................MSc 12FT 24PT

De Montfort University
Communications Engineering ....MSc 12FT 24-72PT

University of Derby
Advanced Computer Networks...........................MSc 12FT 36-72PT

Durham University
Communications Engineering .... MSc 12FT

University of East London
Information & Communication Technologies and Development...
.... MSc 12FT 24PT/PGDip 8FT 16PT/PGCert 4FT 8PT
Mobile Communications MSc... MSc 12FT 24PT/PGDip 8FT 16PT/
PGCert 4FT 8PT

Edinburgh Napier University
Digital Systems ....MA/MDes 12FT 24PT

Glasgow Caledonian University
Voice Over IP and Unified Communications..........MSc 12FT 27PT/
PGDip 9FT
Wireless Communication Technologies......MSc 12FT 24PT/PGDip
9FT 18PT

University of Glasgow
Telecommunication Electronics... MSc 12FT

University of Gloucestershire
Visual Communication .... PGCert 4FT/PGDip 8FT/MA 12FT

University of Greenwich
Wireless Mobile Communications Systems Engineering........ MSc 12FT 24PT

University of Hertfordshire
Broadband Telecommunication Networks .... MSc 12-16FT
Data Communications and Networks..........MSc 12-16FT 36-48PT
Radio and Mobile Communication Systems ....MSc 12-16FT 48PT
Telecommunications Law.. LLM 12FT 24PT

University of Hull
Wireless Systems.. MSc 12FT
Wireless Systems and Logistics Technology .... MSc 12FT

University of Kent
Advanced Electronic Systems Engineering........PGDip 12FT 24PT/
MSc 12FT 24PT
Broadband and Mobile Communication Networks.....PGDip 12FT
24PT/MSc 12FT 24PT
Embedded Systems and Instrumentation ....PGDip 12FT 24PT/
MSc 12FT 24PT
Mobile Application Design..MSc 12FT 24PT

King's College London
Mobile & Personal Communications .... MSc 12FT
Telecommunications & Internet Technology .... MSc 12FT
Telecommunications Research .... MSc 12FT

University of Leeds
Communications Studies..MA 12FT
Digital Communications Networks ....MSc(Eng) 12FT

University of Leicester
Information and Communications Engineering ....MSc 12FT/
PGDip 9FT/PGCert 3FT

Liverpool John Moores University
Telecommunications Engineering......MSc 12FT 24PT/PGDip 12FT
24PT/PGCert 6FT 12PT

London South Bank University
Telecommunications and Computer Networks Engineering
.... MSc 12FT

Loughborough University
Mobile Communications...MSc 12FT 36PT

University of Manchester
Communication Engineering .... MSc 12FT

Middlesex University
Mobile Telecommunication Engineering ....MSc 24PT 24DL
Telecommunication Engineering ....MSc 12FT 24PT

Newcastle University
Communications and Signal Processing ....MSc 12FT

University of Nottingham
Electronic Communications and Computer Engineering........ MSc 12FT/PGDip 9FT

Oxford Brookes University
Mobile and High Speed Telecommunication Networks.................
MSc 12FT 24PT

Engineering, electronic and electrical

Plymouth University
Electrical and Electronic Engineering............MSc 12FT/MRes 12FT

University of Portsmouth
Communication Systems Engineering.............. MSc 12/16FT 36PT
Digital Systems Engineering.......................................MSc 12FT 36PT

Queen Mary, University of London
Mobile and Wireless Networks.......................MSc 12FT 24PT 24DL
Telecomunications ....MSc 12FT 24PT

Queen's University Belfast
Telecommunications ....MSc 12FT 24-36PT/
Diploma 12FT 24-36PT

Robert Gordon University
Communications and Computer Network Engineering..................
MSc 12FT 24PT

University of Salford
Data Telecommunications Networks..MSc 12FT 24PT/PGDip 9FT 18PT
Databases and Web-based Systems....MSc 12FT 24PT/PGDip 9FT 18PT

Sheffield Hallam University
Telecommunication and Electronic Engineering..MSc 12FT 24PT/ PGDip 8FT 16PT/PGCert 4FT 8PT

University of South Wales
Electronic Mobile Communications ....MSc 12FT 36PT
Mobile Computing...MSc 12/FT 36PT
Mobile and Satellite Communications ....MSc 12/FT 36PT

University of Southampton
Applied Digital Signal Processing...............MSc 40PT/PGCert 36PT
Radio Frequency Communication Systems ....MSc 12FT 24PT

Staffordshire University
Telecommunication Engineering ...MSc 12-18FT 24-32PT/PGCert 12-18FT 24-32PT/PGDip 12-18FT 24-32PT

University of Strathclyde
Communications, Control and Digital Signal
Processing (CCDSP) .... MSc 12FT

High Power Radio Frequency Science and Engineering..................
MSc 12FT 24-36PT/PGDip 9FT/PGCert 9FT

University of Sunderland
Telecommunications Engineering... MSc 14FT/PGDip 9FT/PGCert 5FT

University of Surrey
Communications Networks and Software........MSc 12FT 24-60PT
Satellite Communications Engineering............MSc 12FT 24-48PT

Swansea University
Communication Systems ....MSc 12FT 24-36PT

Teesside University
Control and Electronics....................MSc 12-18FT 24PT/PGDip 8FT
Electronics & Communications .....MSc 12- 18FT 24PT/PGDip 8FT
Networks and Comminucations................................MSc 12FT 36PT

UCL - University College London
Telecommunications ....MSc 12FT 24-60PT/MRes 12FT
Telecommunications with Business ....MSc 12FT 36-60PT
Wireless and Optical Communications ....MSc 12FT 24-60PT

University of Warwick
Electronic Systems with Communications .... MSc 12FT

University of Westminster
Mobile, Wireless and Broadband Communications....... MSc 12FT 24PT 24BM

University of York
Communications Engineering .... MSc 12FT

Telecommunication studies
Research Courses

Anglia Ruskin University
Telecommunications Engineering...............PhD 24 - 60FT 30-48PT

Bangor University
Communication Networks and Protocols...MPhil 24FT/PhD 36FT

University of Bradford
Communication Systems Engineering....................PhD 36FT 48PT/ MPhil 12FT 24PT

Wireless Technologies................ PhD 36FT 48PT/MPhil 12FT 24PT

University of Bristol
Communications ....PhD 48FT

De Montfort University
Mechanical, Aeronautical and Manufacturing Engineering...PhD 24-36FT 48-72PT/MPhil 12-24FT 24-48PT

University of Edinburgh
Digital Communications ...PhD 36FT 72PT/MPhil 24FT 48PT/MSc by research 12FT 24PT

University of Kent
Electronic Engineering ....MSc by research 12FT 24PT/MPhil 24FT 36PT/PhD 36FT 60PT

King's College London
Telecommunications .... MPhil 24FT 48PT/PhD 36FT 48-72PT

Lancaster University
Communication Systems .... PhD 36FT 48PT/MPhil 24FT 36PT

University of Nottingham
Location-aware Ubiquitous Computing for the Digital Society.... PhD 36FT
Photonic and Radio Frequency Engineering.........PhD 36FT tbcPT/ MPhil 24FT tbcPT/MRes 12FT tbcPT

Oxford Brookes University
Electronics and Communications .... PhD 24-60FT 36-72PT/MPhil 24-36FT 36-48PT

University of Salford
Centre for Networking and Telecommunications Research....PhD 36FT 72PT/MPhil 12FT 24PT/MSc by research 12FT 24PT

Swansea University
Communication Systems ....MRes 12FT 24PT

UCL - University College London
Communications .... EngD 48PT

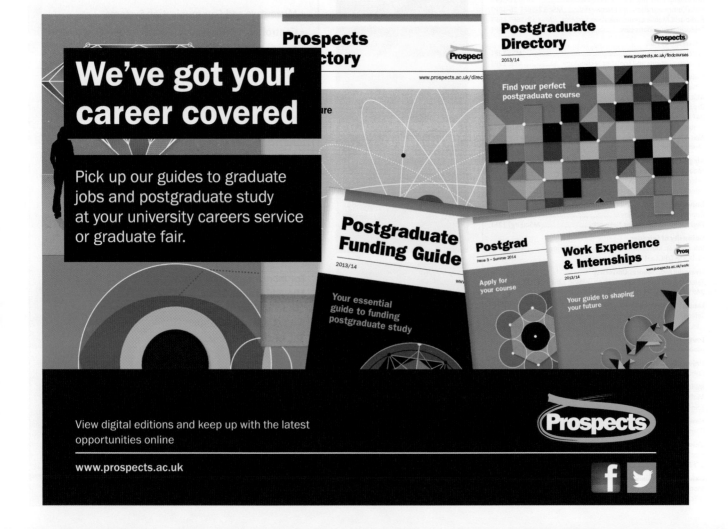

Engineering, mechanical

Acoustic engineering
Taught Courses

Bangor University
Composition/Electroacoustic Composition/Sonic Art.................... MMus 12FT 24PT
Music .... MA 12FT 24PT/PGDip 9FT

Bath Spa University
Creative Sound and Media Technology .... MMus 12FT 24PT/ PGDip 9FT 18PT/PGCert 4FT 9PT

University of Derby
Applied Acoustics ....MSc 24-36PT

Edinburgh Napier University
Sound Production .... MA 12FT 24PT

University of Edinburgh
Acoustics and Music Technology ....MSc 12FT 24PT

Leeds Metropolitan University
Acoustics and Noise Control .... PGDip 12PT

London South Bank University
Environmental and Architectural Acoustics .... MSc 12FT 24PT

North East Surrey College of Technology
Acoustics and Noise Control....................................IOA Diploma 9PT
Applied Acoustics and Noise Control ....MSc 9PT

Queen Margaret University, Edinburgh
Audiology (Pre-Registration) ....PGDip 24FT/MSc 30FT

University of Salford
Audio Acoustics........ MSc 12FT 24-48PT 24-48DL/PGDip 9FT 18PT
Environmental Acoustics...MSc 12FT 28PT 28DL/PGDip 9FT 18PT 18DL

University of Southampton
Automotive Refinement... MSc 36PT
Advanced Tribology.. MSc 12FT
Sound and Vibration Studies..............................MSc 12FT 36PT

UCL - University College London
Audiological Science....................................... MSc 12FT/PGDip 9FT

University of York
Forensic Speech Science .... MSc 12FT 24PT

Acoustic engineering
Research Courses

Anglia Ruskin University
Sound and Audio Engineering ...... MPhil 18 - 36FT 30 - 48PT/PhD 24 - 60FT 36 - 72PT

Cardiff University
Musical Acoustics.....................................PhD 36FT/MPhil 12-24FT

University of Edinburgh
Acoustics....................PhD 36FT/MPhil 24FT/MSc by research 12FT

National University of Ireland Galway
College of Engineering & Informatics....................PhD 48FT 72PT/ MEngSci by research 24FT 48PT/MAppSci by research 24FT 48PT/ MEng by research 24FT

The Open University
Acoustics...................PhD 36FT 72PT variableDL/MPhil 15FT 24PT variableDL
Environmental acoustics .... PhD 36FT 72PT/MPhil 15FT 24PT
Music computing and acoustics......... PhD 36FT 72PT variableDL/ MPhil 15FT 24PT variableDL
Musical acoustics .... PhD 36FT 72PT/MPhil 15FT 24PT
Non-invasive monitoring .... PhD 36FT 72PT/MPhil 15FT 24PT

University of Salford
Acoustics Research CentrePhD 36FT/MSc by research 12FT/MPhil 12FT

University of Southampton
Institute of Sound and Vibration Research ....PhD 36FT 72PT/ MPhil 24FT 48PT

Automotive engineering
Taught Courses

University of Bath
Automotive Engineering .... MSc 12FT

Birmingham City University
Automotive Calibration and Control ....PGCert 10PT/PGDip 10PT/ MSc 10PT
Automotive Engineering .... PGCert 4FT 10PT/PGDip 4FT 10PT/ MSc 4FT 10PT

University of Bradford
Automotive Engineering .... MSc 12FT/PGDip 9FT
Automotive Engineering Quality Improvement............MSc 12FT/ PGDip 9FT

University of Brighton
Automotive Electronic Engineering...MSc 12FT 24PT/PGDip 12FT 24PT/PGCert 12FT 24PT
Automotive Engineering .... MSc 12FT 24PT/PGCert 12FT 24PT/ PGDip 12FT 24PT

Brunel University
Automotive and Motorsport Engineering .... MSc 12FT

City University London
Automotive Engineering ....MSc 12FT 24PT

Coventry University
Automotive Design.. MA 15FT 30PT
Automotive Design Research .... MA 12FT 24PT
Automotive Engineering .... MSc 12FT 24-36PT/PGDip 9FT 24PT

Cranfield University
Advanced Lightweight Structures and Impact .... MSc 12FT
Advanced Motorsport Engineering .... MSc 12FT 24-60PT/ PGDip 6FT 24PT/PGCert 5FT 24PT/MTech 24FT
Automotive Engineering ....MSc 12FT 24-36PT
Automotive Mechatronics .... MSc 12FT
Integrated Vehicle Health Management........MSc 24-60PT/PGDip 24PT/PGCert 12PT

Edinburgh Napier University
Mechanical Engineering ....MSc 12FT 24PT

University of Exeter
Advanced Mechanical Engineering .... MSc 12FT

University of Glasgow
Aeronautical Engineering .... MSc 12FT

University of Hertfordshire
Automotive Engineering ....MSc 12FT 36PT/MSc 16FT

University of Huddersfield
Automotive Engineering .... MSc 12FT

Kingston University
Automotive Engineering .... MSc(Eng) 12FT 24PT

University of Leeds
Automotive Engineering ....MSc(Eng) 12FT

Loughborough University
Automotive Systems Engineering...........................MSc 12FT 30PT

Manchester Metropolitan University
Mechanical Engineering ....MSc 12FT 24PT

University of Nottingham
Sustainable Transportation and Electrical Power Systems (Erasmus Mundus) .... MSc 24FT

The Open University
Engineering............... MSc(Eng) 12-24DL/MEng variableDL/PGDip variableDL

Oxford Brookes University
Automotive Engineering ....MSc 12FT 24PT
Motorsport Engineering ....MSc 12FT 24PT
Racing Engine Design ....MSc 12FT 24PT

Royal College of Art
Vehicle Design..MA 24FT

Sheffield Hallam University
Advanced Design Engineering ....MSc 12FT 36PT/ PGDip 8FT 24PT/PGCert 4FT 12PT
Advanced Manufacturing Engineering.................MSc 12FT 36PT/ PGDip 8FT 24PT/PGCert 4FT 12PT

University of Sheffield
Advanced Manufacturing Technologies with the AMRC .... MSc(Res) 12FT
Advanced Mechanical Engineering .... MSc(Res) 12FT

University of South Wales
Aeronautical Engineering.....................................MSc 12FT 24PT

University of Southampton
Advanced Tribology.. MSc 12FT
Race Car Aerodynamics...................................MSc 12FT 24PT

Staffordshire University
Aeronautical Engineering...........................MSc 12-18FT 24-32PT
Automotive Engineering/Autosport Engineering..... MSc 12-18FT 24-60PT

University of Strathclyde
Advanced Manufacturing: Technology and Systems..... MSc 12FT 24PT/PGDip 9FT 18PT/PGCert 9FT 18PT
Advanced Mechanical Engineering ..... MSc 12FT 24PT/PGDip 9FT 18PT/PGCert 9FT 18PT

University of Sussex
Automotive Engineering ....MSc 12FT 24PT/PGDip 9FT 24PT

Swansea Metropolitan University
Automotive Engineering .... MSc 12FT 24PT

Automotive engineering
Research Courses

University of Aberdeen
Engineering... PhD 36FT/MPhil 24FT/MSc by research 12FT/EngD 36FT

Birmingham City University
Automotive Calibration & Control Research........MSc by research 12FT 24PT

University of Bradford
Automotive, Modelling and Control Engineering PhD 36FT 48PT/ MPhil 12FT 24PT

City University London
Aeronautical, Automotive, Mechanical and Civil Engineering...... PhD/MPhil

Cranfield University
PhD Studentship - Transforming composite structural design by use of structural health mon..PhD 36FT

University of Exeter
Engineering .... EngD 48FT

University of Hertfordshire
Engineering ....EngD 36-60PT

University of Liverpool
Engineering.................................PhD 36FT/MPhil 12FT 24PT

Loughborough University
Aeronautical and Automotive Engineering...........PhD 36FT 60PT/ MPhil 24FT 36PT

Queen Mary, University of London
Engineering .... PhD 36FT/MPhil

Royal College of Art
Vehicle Design............................PhD/MPhil/MA by research 24FT

Desalination technology
Taught Courses

Cardiff University
Hydro-environment Engineering .... MSc 12FT 24PT

Cranfield University
Water and Wastewater Engineering .... MSc 12FT 24-60PT/PGDip 6FT 24PT/PGCert 5FT 24PT

University of Cumbria
The Research Process...............................PGCert 12 - 18PT

Imperial College London
Environmental Engineering, also with Business Management or Sustainable Development....................................MSc 12FT 24-36PT

Leeds Metropolitan University
Advanced Engineering Management .... MSc 12FT 24PT/PGCert 12PT/PGDip 12FT 24PT

Desalination technology
Research Courses

Imperial College London
Chemical Engineering Research .... PhD 36FT 72PT

Engineering, mechanical
Taught Courses

Anglia Ruskin University
Engineering Management.........................MSc 12 - 15FT 24 - 30PT
Manufacturing Systems ....MSc 12FT 24PT

Aston University
Mechanical Engineering (Modelling) .... MSc 12FT
Professional Engineering.......................................MSc(Eng) 24-60DL

University of Bath
Engineering Design.. MSc 12FT
Innovation and Technology Management..MSc 12FT/PGDip 6FT/ PGCert 3FT
Mechatronics... MSc 12FT

Birmingham City University
Mechanical Engineering .. PGCert 4FT 10PT/PGDip 4FT 10PT/MSc 4FT 10PT

University of Bolton
Systems Engineering & Engineering Management ....MSc Dual Award 18FT/MSc 18FT 36PT

University of Bradford
Mechanical Engineering ....MSc 12FT MSc 12-18PT

University of Bristol
Advanced Mechanical Engineering ....MSc 12FT/Diploma 12FT/ Cert 12FT
Biomedical Engineering.. MSc 12FT

Brunel University
Advanced Manufacturing Systems.................... MSc 12FT 36-60DL
Advanced Mechanical Engineering .... MSc 12FT
Aerospace Engineering .... MSc 12FT
Automotive and Motorsport Engineering .... MSc 12FT
Biomedical Engineering... MSc 12FT
Building Services Engineering........................... MSc 12FT 36-60DL
Building Services Engineering Management.............MSc 36-60DL
Building Services Engineering with Sustainable Energy................ MSc 12FT 36-60DL
Embedded Systems (with Signal Processing and Multimedia Communications pathways).. MSc 12FT
Renewable Energy Engineering .... MSc 12FT
Sustainable Energy : Technologies and Management... MSc 12FT

Bucks New University
Mechanical Engineering Design................................MEng 12-15PT

Cardiff University
Advanced Mechanical Engineering .... MSc 12FT
Professional Engineering...MSc 12FT

Engineering, mechanical

University of Central Lancashire
Maintenance Engineering................... MSc 12FT 24PT/PGDip 24PT

City University London
Engineering-Modular.. MSc 12FT 24PT/PGDip 24PT/PGCert 24PT
Mechanical Engineering................................MSc 12FT 24PT

University College Cork
Mechanical Engineering (Manufacturing Process & Automation Systems)................................MEngSci 12FT 24PT

Coventry University
Mechanical Engineering................MSc 12FT 24-36PT

Cranfield University
Advanced Lightweight Structures and Impact................ MSc 12FT
Advanced Mechanical Engineering MSc 12FT/PGDip 9FT/PGCert 6FT
Design of Rotating Machines...........................MSc 12FT 24-36PT
Pre-Master's Course in Engineering Bridging course to MSc 10FT
Welding Engineering MSc 12FT 24-60PT/PGDip 6FT 24PT/PGCert 5FT 24PT

De Montfort University
Mechanical Engineering .... MSc 12FT 24-72PT 24+DL/PGDip 8FT 24PT/PGCert 4FT 12PT

University of Derby
Control and Instrumentation...............................MSc 12FT 36-72PT
Mechanical and Manufacturing Engineering ..MSc 12FT 36-72PT

Dublin Institute of Technology
ME Mechanical Engineering................................MEng 12FT 24PT

Durham University
Design and Operations Engineering.................................. MSc 12FT

Edinburgh Napier University
Engineering Design......................MSc 12FT 36PT/PGDip 9FT 24PT/PGCert 6FT 12PT
Flexible Managed Programme (FECCI)...MA 12FT 24PT/MSc 12FT 24PT/PGCert 12FT 24PT

University of Edinburgh
Biomechanics .... MSc 12FT

University of Exeter
Advanced Mechanical Engineering .... MSc 12FT

National University of Ireland Galway
Engineering... HDip 12FT 24PT

Glasgow Caledonian University
Maintenance Management.........MSc 12FT 24PT/PGDip 9FT 18PT
Mechanical Engineering..............MSc 12FT 24PT/PGDip 9FT 18PT

Glasgow School of Art
Product Design Engineering......PGCert 4FT 8PT/PGDip 8FT 20PT/MSc 12FT 24PT

University of Glasgow
Mechanical Engineering .... MSc 12FT 24PT
Mechanical Engineering & Management........................ MSc 12FT

Glyndwr University
Mechanical Engineering/Manufacturing ... MSc 12FT 24PT/MRes 12FT 24PT/MSc 12FT 24PT/MRes 12FT 24PT

University of Greenwich
Mechanical and Manufacturing Engineering ....MSc 12FT 24PT

Grimsby Institute of Further and Higher Education
Productivity and Innovation Development ....MSc 12FT 24PT

Heriot-Watt University
Energy.............MSc 12FT 24PT 24-84DL/PGDip 9FT 21PT 21-84DL
Renewable Energy Engineering ..MSc 12FT 24PT/PGDip 9FT 21PT
Robotics, Autonomous and Interactive Systems (RAIS) MSc 12FT/PGDip 9FT
Smart Grid and Demand Management......MSc 12FT 24PT/PGDip 9FT 18PT

University of Hertfordshire
Aerospace Engineering ....MSc 12FT 36PT/MSc 16FT
Mechanical Engineering..MSc 12-16FT 36PT

University of Huddersfield
Mechanical Engineering .... MSc 12FT 24PT
Mechanical Engineering Design............................. MSc 12FT 24PT

Imperial College London
Advanced Mechanical Engineering .... MSc 12FT 24-36PT/Diploma 12FT 24-36PT

Kingston University
Advanced Industrial and Manufacturing Systems .... MSc 12FT 24-36PT
Mechanical Engineering .... MSc 12FT 24PT
Professional Engineering..................................MSc 24-48PT

Lancaster University
Engineering (by research)...................................MSc 12FT 24PT
Mechanical Engineering............ MSc 12FT 24PT/PGDip 12FT 24PT

Leeds Metropolitan University
Building Services Engineering..................................MSc 12FT 24PT

University of Leeds
Advanced Mechanical Engineering ....MSc(Eng) 12FT

University of Leicester
Advanced Mechanical Engineering ....MSc 12FT/PGDip 9FT/PGCert 3FT

University of Limerick
Mechanical Engineering.. MEng 12FT

University of Lincoln
Sustainable Power and Energy Engineering .... MSc 24PT

Liverpool John Moores University
Manufacturing Engineering ....MSc 12FT 24PT
Mechanical Engineering ....MSc 12FT 24PT

University of Liverpool
Aerospace and Mechanical Systems Engineering MSc(Eng) 12FT/PGDip 12FT/PGCert 12FT
Simulation in Aerospace Engineering............ MSc(Eng) 12FT 24PT

Loughborough University
Advanced Engineering ....MSc 24 - 96PT
Mechanical Engineering ....MSc 12FT 24 - 72PT

Manchester Metropolitan University
Engineering with Management ....MSc 12FT 24PT
Environmental Management and Business ....MSc 12FT 24PT
Forensic and Analytical Science...............................MSc 12FT 24PT
Industrial Communication and Automation..........MSc 12FT 24PT
Mechanical Engineering ....MSc 12FT 24PT

University of Manchester
Advanced Manufacturing Technology & Systems Management.. MSc 12FT
Mechanical Engineering Design.. MSc 12FT

Middlesex University
Design Engineering and Manufacturing Management .... MSc 12-14FT 24-26PT

Newcastle University
Marine Engineering ....MSc 12 or 24FT
Mechanical Engineering .... MSc 12FT
Mechatronics.. MSc 12FT
Process Automation...................... MSc 60PT/PGDip 48PT/CPD 3PT

University of Northampton
Engineering...MSc 12FT 24PT
Lift Engineering..MSc 24-60DL

Northumbria University
Business with Pipeline Integrity Management .... MSc 12FT
Mechanical Engineering...................................MSc 12/16FT
Microelectronic and Communications Engineering........................ MSc 12-16FT
Professional Engineering................................... MSc 36PT

University of Nottingham
Civil Engineering: Environmental Fluid Mechanics........ MSc 12FT
Civil Engineering: Geotechnical Engineering.................... MSc 12FT
Manufacturing Engineering and Management .... MSc 12FT 24PT
Mechanical Engineering .... MSc 12FT
Research...MRes 12FT 24PT
Usability and Human Computer Interaction by Distance Learning PGCert..PGCert 12DL

The Open University
Engineering............... MSc(Eng) 12-24DL/MEng variableDL/PGDip variableDL

Oxford Brookes University
Advanced Engineering Design ....MSc 12FT 24PT
Racing Engine Design ....MSc 12FT 24PT

University of Portsmouth
Advanced Manufacturing Technology .... MSc 12/16FT 36PT
Mechanical Engineering ....MSc 12/16FT 36PT
Technology Management ....MSc 12/16FT 36PT

Queen Mary, University of London
Energy and Natural Resources Law...........................LLM 12FT 24PT

Queen's University Belfast
Mechanical Engineering (Advanced)................MSc 12FT 24-36PT
Process Engineering.............................MSc 12FT/Diploma 9FT

Royal College of Art
Vehicle Design...MA 24FT

University of Salford
Quantity Surveying (Mechanical and Electrical) .MSc 12FT 28DL/PGDip 8FT 16DL

Sheffield Hallam University
Advanced Design Engineering .. MSc 12FT 36PT/PGDip 8FT 24PT/PGCert 4FT 12PT
Advanced Mechanical Engineering .....MSc 12FT 36PT/PGDip 8FT 24PT/PGCert 4FT 12PT

University of Sheffield
Advanced Manufacturing Technologies with the AMRC .... MSc(Res) 12FT
Advanced Mechanical Engineering .... MSc(Res) 12FT
Mechanical Engineering and Industrial Management .. MSc 12FT

University of South Wales
Mechanical Engineering..MSc 12/FT 36PT
Professional Engineering..MSc 12-60PT

University of Southampton
Advanced Mechanical Engineering Science (Bioengineering)....... MSc 12FT 24PT
Advanced Mechanical Engineering Science (Mechatronics) .. MSc 12FT 24PT
MSc Advanced Tribology.. MSc 12FT

Staffordshire University
Advanced Technology..........................MSc 12-24FT 24-60PT
Aeronautical Engineering.......................MSc 12-18FT 24-32PT
Automotive Engineering/Autosport Engineering.....MSc 12-18FT 24-60PT
Professional Engineering..MSc 12-18FT

University of Strathclyde
Advanced Manufacturing: Technology and Systems ..... MSc 12FT 24PT/PGDip 9FT 18PT/PGCert 9FT 18PT
Advanced Mechanical Engineering .....MSc 12FT 24PT/PGDip 9FT 18PT/PGCert 9FT 18PT

University of Sussex
Advanced Mechanical Engineering ....MSc 12FT 24PT
Mechanical Engineering................................MSc 12FT/PGDip 24PT

Swansea University
Computational Mechanics (Erasmus Mundus) .... MSc 18FT
Mechanical Engineering ....MSc 12FT 24-36PT

Teesside University
Advanced Manufacturing Systems................... MSc 12-16FT 24PT/PGDip 8FT
Mechanical Engineering................MSc 12 - 16FT 24PT/PGDip 8FT

Trinity College Dublin - the University of Dublin
Engineering (M.A.I.) Recurrent Education ....MAI 12FT

University of Ulster
Professional Practice......................................PGDip 24FT/MSc 36FT

UCL - University College London
Marine Engineering ....MSc 12FT 24-60PT
Mechanical Engineering ....MSc 12FT 24-60PT

University of Warwick
Engineering Business Management MSc 12FT 36PT/PGDip 24PT/PGCert 18PT
Manufacturing Systems Engineering ....MSc 12FT 36PT
Mechanical Systems .... MSc 12FT

University of the West of England, Bristol
Mechanical Engineering...MSc 12FT 24PT

University of Wolverhampton
Polymer Engineering Design ...MSc 12FT 24PT/PGCert 12FT 24PT

Engineering, mechanical
Research Courses

Anglia Ruskin University
Built Environment......................................MPhil 24 - 60FT 36 - 72PT
Engineering Analysis, Simulation and Tribology..... PhD 24 - 60FT 36 - 72PT

University of Bath
Mechanical Engineering.....PhD 24-48FT 36-72PT/MPhil 12-36FT 24-48PT

University of Birmingham
Engineered Materials for High Performance Applications in Aerospace and Related Technologi .... EngD 48FT
Mechanical and Manufacturing Engineering .... PhD 36FT 72PT 72DL/MSc by research 12FT 24PT

University of Brighton
Engineering Research Division.......... PhD 24-60FT 36-72PT/MPhil 18-36FT 30-48PT

University of Bristol
Mechanical Engineering..... PhD 36FT 72PT/MSc by research 12FT 24PT

Brunel University
Mechanical Engineering ..PhD 36FT 48PT/MPhil 12FT 24PT/EngD 48FT
Systems Engineering ....PhD/MPhil/EngD

Cardiff University
Institute of Mechanical and Manufacturing Engineering ....PhD 36FT/MPhil 12FT/EngD 48FT

City University London
Aeronautical, Automotive, Mechanical and Civil Engineering...... PhD/MPhil

Coventry University
School of Engineering ....PhD/MPhil

Cranfield University
Integrated Studies in Manufacturing ..... Integrated PhD 36-48FT
Manufacturing Department Research Opportunities.............PhD 24-36FT/Integrated PhD 36-45FT/MRes 12-36FT
Transforming composite structural design by use of structural health mon...PhD 36FT
Improving overall yield during the manufacturing process....PhD 36FT

De Montfort University
Mechanical, Aeronautical and Manufacturing Engineering ...PhD 24-36FT 48-72PT/MPhil 12-24FT 24-48PT

Engineering, mechanical

University of Dundee
Mechanical Engineering .... MPhil 24FT
Mechanical Engineering .... MSc by research 12FT PhD 36FT

Durham University
Engineering and Computing Sciences ....
MSc by research 12FT/PhD 36FT

University of Exeter
Engineering.................................. PhD 36FT 72FT/MPhil 24FT 48PT

University of Greenwich
Engineering (by Research)....................MSc by research 12FT 24PT

Harper Adams University
Precision Farming (MRes is Subject to Validation)...... MRes 12FT/
MPhil 24FT/PhD 38FT

Heriot-Watt University
Mechanical Engineering.. PhD 36FT/MPhil 24FT/MSc by research
12FT

University of Hull
Engineering - Medical Engineering and Technology ....PhD 36FT
60PT/MPhil 24FT 36FT/MSc by research 12FT 24PT

Imperial College London
Department of Mechanical Engineering.........................MPhil/PhD

University of Leeds
Institute of Engineering Systems and Design....PhD 36+FT/MPhil
24FT

University of Lincoln
Engineering........... MPhil 18-36FT 30-48PT/PhD 18-36FT 30-48PT

University of Liverpool
Engineering.................................PhD 36FT/MPhil 12FT 24PT

Loughborough University
Engineering Doctorate.. EngD 48FT
Mechanical and Manufacturing Engineering .... PhD 36FT 60PT
60DL/MPhil 24FT 36PT 36DL/EngD 48FT
Sustainable Design .... PhD 36FT 60PT/MPhil 24FT 36PT
Transport Safety Research.......... PhD 36FT 60PT/MPhil 24FT 36PT
User Centred Design Research .. PhD 36FT 60PT/MPhil 24FT 36PT

University of Manchester
Advanced Manufacturing Technology .... MEnt 12FT
Mechanical Engineering............PhD 36FT 72PT/MPhil 12FT 24PT/
MSc by research 12FT
Mechanical Engineering Design .... MEnt 12FT

Newcastle University
Mechanical and Systems Engineering ....PhD 36FT 72PT/
MPhil 12FT 24PT

Nottingham Trent University
Mechanical and Manufacturing Engineering ....PhD/MPhil
Multidisciplinary Engineering... MPhil 18FT 30PT/PhD 33FT 66PT

University of Nottingham
Manufacturing Engineering .... PhD 36FT/MPhil 24FT
Manufacturing Technology EngD.. EngD 48FT
Mechanical Engineering .... PhD 36FT/MPhil 24FT

The Open University
Materials Engineering....... PhD 36FT 72PT variableDL/MPhil 15FT
24PT variableDL
STEM Education and engagement .... PhD 36FT 72PT variableDL

Oxford Brookes University
Mechanical Engineering MPhil/PhD PhD 24-60FT 36-72PT/MPhil
24-36FT 36-48PT

University of Portsmouth
Engineering.................................... MPhil 24FT 48PT/PhD 36FT 72PT

Queen's University Belfast
Mechanical and Aerospace Engineering .....PhD 36FT 72PT/MPhil
24FT 48PT

University of Sheffield
Engineering Materials: Integrated Studies...Integrated PhD 48FT
Mechanical Engineering............. PhD 36FT 72PT/MPhil 24FT 48PT

University of Southampton
School of Engineering Sciences ....PhD 36FT 72PT/
MPhil 12FT 24PT
School of Engineering Sciences .... EngD 36FT

University of Strathclyde
Mechanical and Aerospace Engineering - Research ....PhD 36FT
72PT/MPhil 12FT 24PT

University of Surrey
Mechanical Engineering............PhD 33FT 45PT/MPhil 21FT 33PT/
EngD 48FT 60PT

University of Sussex
Engineering Research Programme... PhD 24-48FT 36-72PT/MPhil
12-36FT 24-48PT

Swansea University
Mechanical Engineering............PhD 36FT 72PT/MPhil 24FT 48PT/
MSc by research 12FT 24PT

Swansea Metropolitan University
Research Degrees .... PhD 36FT 60PT/MPhil 12FT 24PT

UCL - University College London
Mechanical Engineering...PhD 36FT 60PT

University of Warwick
Engineering...EngD 36-48FT
Engineering.... MSc by research 12FT 24PT/MPhil 24FT 36PT/PhD
36FT 60PT/EngD 60PT

University of the West of Scotland
Department of Mechanical and Manufacturing Engineering and
Quality Centre ....PhD/MPhil

Ergonomics
Taught Courses

University of Aberdeen
Patient Safety: A Clinical Human Factors Approach.....MRes 12FT

University of Chester
Wellbeing in the Workplace (Work Based and Integrative
Studies) ....MA 24-72PT/PGDip 24-60PT/PGCert 12-36PT

University of Derby
Ergonomics ....MSc 42PT 42DL/PGDip 30PT 30DL/
PGCert 18PT 18DL

University of East London
Applied Ergonomics PG Cert....................................PGCert 6FT 12PT

National University of Ireland Galway
Occupational Health & Safety ....MSc 12FT 24PT/
HDipAppSc 12FT 24PT
Occupational Safety Engineering and Ergonomics MAppSci 12FT
24PT

Glyndwr University
Construction Health and Safety ....NEBOSH NGC 4PT

Heriot-Watt University
Applied Psychology...........MSc 12FT 24-48PT/PGDip 9FT 15-48PT/
PGCert 6FT 12-48PT
Engineering Psychology with Ergonomics............. MSc 12FT 24PT
24-84DL/PGDip 9FT 21PT 21-84DL/PGCert 6FT 18PT 18-84DL
Safety and Risk Management (Distance Learning Only)......... MSc
24-84DL/PGDip 21-84DL

University of Limerick
Safety and Ergonomics .... GradDip 9FT/MTech 12FT

Loughborough University
Ergonomics and Human Factors...MSc 12FT 24 - 36PT/PGDip 8FT
20PT
Ergonomics for Health and Community CareMSc 12FT 24 - 36PT/
PGDip 8FT 20PT
Human Factors for Inclusive Design....MSc 12FT 24 - 36PT/PGDip
8FT 20PT
Human Factors in Transport .... MSc 12FT 24 - 36PT/
PGDip 8FT 20PT

University of Nottingham
Applied Ergonomics (by distance learning) ....MSc 24-48DL/
PGCert 12DL
Human Factors and Ergonomics.............................MSc 12FT 24-36PT
Postgraduate Certificate in Applied Ergonomics (by distance
Learning)...PGCert 12FT 12-24DL
Workplace Health (Distance E-Learning) .... MSc 24PT

UCL - University College London
Human-Computer Interaction with Ergonomics .MSc 12FT 24PT/
PGDip 9FT 24PT/PGCert 3FT 24PT

Ergonomics
Research Courses

Loughborough University
Design Ergonomics .... PhD 36FT 60PT/MPhil 24FT 36PT
Environmental Ergonomics........ PhD 36FT 60PT/MPhil 24FT 36PT
Human Factors and Complex Systems ....PhD 36FT 60PT/MPhil
24FT 36PT
User Centred Design Research .. PhD 36FT 60PT/MPhil 24FT 36PT

University of Nottingham
Human Factors.. PhD 36FT/MPhil 24FT

HVAC
Taught Courses

Middlesex University
Business Information Modelling Management (BIM) .....MSc 12 /
24DL

HVAC
Research Courses

University of Brighton
Engineering Research Division.......... PhD 24-60FT 36-72PT/MPhil
18-36FT 30-48PT

University of Manchester
Process Integration .... MPhil 12FT 24PT/PhD 36FT 72PT

Industrial design
Taught Courses

**University of the Arts London - Central Saint Martins College of
Art and Design**
Industrial Design ....MA 24FT

Aston University
Product Design Enterprise .... MSc 12FT
Product Design Innovation .... MSc 12FT

University of Bath
Engineering Design... MSc 12FT

Birmingham City University
Design Management............................... MA 12FT 24FT

University of Bolton
Advanced Composites Design...........................MSc 12FT 36PT

Bournemouth University
Engineering Design Innovation .... MSc 24FT
Product Design................................ MSc 12FT/MSc 24-60PT
Product Design Management....................MA 12FT/MSc 24-60PT

University of Brighton
Learning Objectives ..... MSc 12FT 24PT/PGCert 12FT 24PT/PGDip
12FT 24PT
Product Innovation and Development ..... MSc 12FT/PGDip 12FT/
PGCert 12FT

Brunel University
Advanced Engineering Design .... MSc 12FT 24PT
Design Strategy and Innovation ....MA 12FT
Integrated Product Design....................................... MSc 12FT

Bucks New University
Engineering Management and Design...................MSc 12FT 24PT

University of Cambridge
Industrial Systems, Manufacturing and Management ....
MPhil 9FT

Cardiff Metropolitan University
Advanced Product Design .... MSc 12FT
Product Development Management .... MBA 12FT 24PT

University of Central Lancashire
Consumer Product Design ..... MA 12FT 24PT/PGDip 12FT/PGCert
12FT

Coventry University
Design and Transport ....MSc 12FT 24PT
Industrial Product Design.........................MSc 12FT 24PT
Vehicle Interiors ....MA 12FT 24PT

Cranfield University
Global Product Development and Management............ MSc 12FT
24-60PT/PGDip 6FT 24PT/PGCert 5FT 24PT
Innovation and Creativity in Industry .... MDes 12FT 24-60PT/
PGCert 12FT 24-26PT/PGDip 12FT 24-36PT/MTech 24FT

University for the Creative Arts
Design .... MA 12FT 24PT
Design: Product Design .... MA 12FT 24PT
Sustainable Product Design ....MA 24FT

De Montfort University
Design Management.....................MA 12FT 24PT/PGDip 9FT 18PT
Product Design .... MA 12FT 24PT

University of Dundee
Advanced Sustainable Urban Design .... MSc 12FT
Product Design .... MSc 12FT

Edinburgh Napier University
Advanced Materials Engineering .... MSc 12FT 24PT
Design (Interaction)....................................MA/MDes 12FT
Interaction Design ....MDes 12FT
Interdisciplinary Design................................MDes 12FT 24PT

University of Edinburgh
Product Design...MA 12FT/MFA 24FT

National University of Ireland Galway
Engineering... HDip 12FT 24PT
Engineering Design..................................MED 12 - 24FT 24PT

Glasgow School of Art
Product Design Engineering......PGCert 4FT 8PT/PGDip 8FT 20PT/
MSc 12FT 24PT

Goldsmiths, University of London
Design: Interaction Research..................................... MA 15FT 30PT

University of Hertfordshire
Product Design........................MA 12FT 24PT/PGDip 12FT 24PT

Imperial College London
Innovation Design Engineering ....MA 12FT/MSc 9FT

Kingston University
Advanced Industrial and Manufacturing Systems .... MSc 12FT
24-36PT
Advanced Product Design Engineering .... MSc 12FT 24PT
Design: Product and Space & the Creative Economy.......MA 12FT
24PT

Leeds Metropolitan University
Advanced Engineering Management .... MSc 12FT 24PT/PGCert
12PT/PGDip 12FT 24PT

Engineering, mechanical

Liverpool John Moores University
Sustainable Built Environment .... MSc 12FT

University of Liverpool
Product Design and Management.. MSc 12FT

London Metropolitan University
Product Design.. MA 12FT 24PT

University of the Arts London - London College of Communication
MDes Service Design Innovation....................................... MDes 12FT

Loughborough University
Design and Innovation for Sustainability ....MSc 12FT 24PT
Engineering Design.......................................MSc 12FT 24 - 96PT
Engineering Design and Manufacture........................MSc 36- 72DL
Industrial Design and Technology............................... MA 12FT 24PT
Interaction Design... MA 12FT 24PT

Manchester Metropolitan University
Three Dimensional Design..................................... MA 12FT 24PT

Newcastle University
Design and Manufacturing Engineering.......................... MSc 12FT

Northumbria University
Design Management...MA 12FT

Nottingham Trent University
Advanced Product Design Engineering .... MSc 12FT
Smart Design...MA 12FT/MSc 12FT

Plymouth University
Design .... MA 12FT 24PT

Ravensbourne
Interactive Product Futures ..... MA 12FT 24PT/MSc 12FT 24-36PT

Royal College of Art
Design Products..MA 24FT
Industrial Design Engineering................................MA 24FT
Vehicle Design...MA 24FT

University of Salford
BIM and Integrated Design........................... MSc 12FT 28PT 28DL/
PGDip 8FT 20PT 20DL/PGCert 4FT 8PT 8DL
Doctorate in the Built Environment (Professional Doctorate).......
DBEnv 60PT
Industrial and Commercial Combustion Engineering .MSc 36DL/
PGDip 12DL/PGCert 12DL

Sheffield Hallam University
Built Environment.....MPhil 24FT 36PT/PhD by taught 24FT 60PT
Design (Industrial Design)..... MA 12-16FT 36PT/PGDip 9FT 24PT/
PGCert 6FT 12PT

University of Strathclyde
Global Innovation Management... MSc 24FT
Product Engineering Design........MSc 12FT 24PT/PGDip 9FT 21PT

University of Sunderland
3D Design Innovation....MA 12FT 24PT/PGDip 15FT 10PT/PGCert
7FT 7PT

Swansea Metropolitan University
Industrial Design ....MSc 12FT 24PT
Product Design and Innovation .... MA 12FT 24PT

Trinity College Dublin - the University of Dublin
Engineering (M.A.I.) ....MAI 12FT
Engineering (M.A.I.) Recurrent Education ....MAI 12FT

UCL - University College London
Built Environment: Environmental Design and Engineering.........
MSc 12FT 24-60PT/PGDip 9FT
Built Environment: Heritage Science ....MRes 12FT 24-60PT/
GCert 6FT
Built Environment: Sustainable Heritage .... MSc 12FT 24-60PT/
PGDip 9FT

University of Wolverhampton
Advanced Technology Management......................MSc 12FT 24PT

Industrial design
Research Courses

University of the Arts London - Central Saint Martins College of Art and Design
Graphic and Industrial Design .... PhD 24-48FT 36-96PT/MPhil
15-36FT 24-72PT

University of Birmingham
Engineering, Sustainability and Resilience MRes ....MRes 12FT

University of Brighton
Technology and Innovation Management PhD 24-60FT 36-72PT/
MPhil 18-36FT 30-48PT

Brunel University
Industrial Design ....PhD/MPhil

University for the Creative Arts
Design .... MPhil 24FT 36PT/PhD 36FT 60PT

De Montfort University
Design and New Product Development .MPhil 12-24FT 24-48PT/
PhD 24-36FT 36-72PT

University of Leeds
Institute of Engineering Systems and Design....PhD 36+FT/MPhil
24FT

Loughborough University
Design Practice............................ PhD 36FT 60PT/MPhil 24FT 36PT

Middlesex University
Design and Engineering...PhD 36FT 60PT/EngD 36FT 60PT/MPhil
18FT 36PT

The Open University
Complexity Science and Design.......... PhD 36FT 72PT variableDL/
MPhil 15FT 24PT variableDL
Design ... PhD 36FT 72PT variableDL/MPhil 15FT 24PT variableDL
Design Processes and Products.PhD 36FT 72PT variableDL/MPhil
15FT 24PT variableDL
Sustainable Design .... PhD 36FT 72PT variableDL/
MPhil 15FT 24PT variableDL

Plymouth University
Design Thinking..MRes 12FT 24PT

Royal College of Art
Design Products.............................PhD/MPhil/MA by research
Industrial Design Engineering.............PhD/MPhil/MA by research
Interaction Design................................PhD/MPhil/MA by research
Vehicle Design.....PhD 36-48FT 48-72PT/MPhil 12-36FT 24-48PT/
MA by research 24FT

University of Salford
Institute for Materials ResearchPhD 36FT/MSc by research 12FT/
MPhil 12FT

University of Strathclyde
Advanced Manufacturing: Forging and Forming.........EngD 48FT/
PGCert by research 9FT

Swansea Metropolitan University
Research Degrees .... PhD 36FT 60PT/MPhil 12FT 24PT

University of Wolverhampton
School of Engineering and the Built Environment: Engineering
Division...MPhil/PhD

Mechanics
Taught Courses

Cranfield University
Design of Rotating Machines ....MSc 12FT 24-36PT

Edinburgh Napier University
Mechanical Engineering...MSc 12FT 24PT

Heriot-Watt University
Robotics, Autonomous and Interactive Systems (RAIS) MSc 12FT/
PGDip 9FT

Manchester Metropolitan University
Mechanical Engineering...MSc 12FT 24PT

Newcastle University
Mechanical Engineering .... MSc 12FT
Mechatronics.. MSc 12FT

Queen's University Belfast
Mechanical Engineering (Advanced)...................MSc 12FT 24-36PT

University of Sheffield
Advanced Manufacturing Technologies with the AMRC ....
MSc(Res) 12FT
Advanced Mechanical Engineering .... MSc(Res) 12FT

University of Strathclyde
Advanced Manufacturing: Technology and Systems ..... MSc 12FT
24PT/PGDip 9FT 18PT/PGCert 9FT 18PT
Advanced Mechanical Engineering .....MSc 12FT 24PT/PGDip 9FT
18PT/PGCert 9FT 18PT

Teesside University
Mechanical Engineering.................MSc 12 - 16FT 24PT/PGDip 8FT

UCL - University College London
Mechanical Engineering......................................MSc 12FT 24-60PT

Mechanics
Research Courses

Cardiff University
Gravitational Physics.............PhD 36FT possiblePT/MPhil 12-24FT
possiblePT
Institute of Mechanics and Advanced Materials...........PhD 36FT/
MPhil 12FT

University of Dundee
Mechanical Engineering .... MPhil 24FT
Mechanical Engineering ....MSc by research 12FT

Oxford Brookes University
Mechanical Engineering MPhil/PhD .... PhD 24-60FT 36-72PT/
MPhil 24-36FT 36-48PT

Queen's University Belfast
Mechanical and Aerospace Engineering .....PhD 36FT 72PT/MPhil
24FT 48PT

Mechatronics
Taught Courses

Birmingham City University
Enterprise Systems Management..................... MSc 12/16FT 30PT

University of Bolton
Systems Engineering & Engineering Management ....MSc Dual
Award 18FT/MSc 18FT 36PT

University of Bristol
Advanced Engineering Robotics .... MSc 12FT
MSc in Robotics... MSc 12FT

University College Cork
Mechanical Engineering (Manufacturing Process & Automation
Systems)...MEngSci 12FT 24PT

Coventry University
Manufacturing Systems Engineering.....................MSc 12FT 36PT/
PGDip 9FT 24PT

Cranfield University
Automotive Mechatronics .... MSc 12FT

De Montfort University
Mechatronics H73071...........MSc 12FT 24-72PT/PGDip 8FT 24PT/
PGCert 4FT 12PT

University of Derby
Mechanical and Manufacturing Engineering ..MSc 12FT 36-72PT

Edinburgh Napier University
Automation and control .... MSc 12FT
Mechanical Engineering..MSc 12FT 24PT

University of Exeter
Advanced Mechanical Engineering .... MSc 12FT

University of Glasgow
Mechatronics... MSc 12FT

University of Greenwich
Mechanical and Manufacturing Engineering ....MSc 12FT 24PT

Harper Adams University
Applied Mechatronic Engineering ... PGCert 12FT 24PT/MSc 12FT
24PT/PGDip 12FT 24PT

Heriot-Watt University
Renewable Energy and Distributed Generation...MSc 12FT 24PT/
PGDip 9FT 21PT
Robotics, Autonomous and Interactive Systems (RAIS)...................
MSc 12FT/PGDip 9FT
Safety, Risk and Reliability Engineering (Distance Learning
Only) ....MSc 24-84DL/PGDip 24-84DL

Imperial College London
Medical Robotics and Image Guided Intervention ....MRes 12FT

Kingston University
Embedded Systems..MSc 12FT 24-36PT
Embedded Systems with Management Studies .... MSc 12FT
24-36PT
Mechatronic Systems...MSc 12FT 24PT

London South Bank University
Mechatronics Engineering ....MSc 12FT 24PT

Manchester Metropolitan University
Mechanical Engineering...MSc 12FT 24PT

Newcastle University
Automation and Control .... MSc 12FT
Mechanical Engineering .... MSc 12FT
Mechatronics.. MSc 12FT

Queen's University Belfast
Mechanical Engineering (Advanced)...................MSc 12FT 24-36PT

University of Salford
Robotics and Automation ....MSc 12FT/PGDip 9FT

Sheffield Hallam University
Advanced Manufacturing Engineering...................MSc 12FT 36PT/
PGDip 8FT 24PT/PGCert 4FT 12PT

University of Sheffield
Advanced Manufacturing Technologies with the AMRC ....
MSc(Res) 12FT
Advanced Mechanical Engineering .... MSc(Res) 12FT

University of Southampton
Advanced Mechanical Engineering Science (Mechatronics) .. MSc
12FT 24PT

University of Strathclyde
Advanced Manufacturing: Technology and Systems ..... MSc 12FT
24PT/PGDip 9FT 18PT/PGCert 9FT 18PT
Advanced Mechanical Engineering .....MSc 12FT 24PT/PGDip 9FT
18PT/PGCert 9FT 18PT
Mechatronics and Automation...MSc 12FT 24PT/PGDip 9FT 18PT

Teesside University
Mechanical Engineering.................MSc 12 - 16FT 24PT/PGDip 8FT

UCL - University College London
Mechanical Engineering......................................MSc 12FT 24-60PT

Engineering, mechanical

Mechatronics
Research Courses

De Montfort University
Mechanical, Aeronautical and Manufacturing Engineering...PhD 24-36FT 48-72PT/MPhil 12-24FT 24-48PT

University of Dundee
Mechanical Engineering (MPhil) .... MPhil 24FT
Mechanical Engineering (MSc by research) MSc by research 12FT

King's College London
Robotics .... MPhil 24FT 48PT/PhD 36FT 48-72PT

University of Leeds
Institute of Engineering Systems and Design....PhD 36+FT/MPhil 24FT

University of Nottingham
Manufacturing Technology EngD........ EngD 48FT

Oxford Brookes University
Mechanical Engineering MPhil/PhD .... PhD 24-60FT 36-72PT/MPhil 24-36FT 36-48PT

University of Salford
Centre for Robotics and Automation........ PhD 36FT 60PT 48DL/MPhil 24FT 24PT 24DL/MSc by research 24FT 24PT 24DL/MRes 24FT 24PT

University of Surrey
Mechatronics Systems and Robotics..PhD 33FT 45PT/MPhil 21FT 33PT/EngD 48FT 60PT

Offshore engineering
Taught Courses

University of Aberdeen
Oil and Gas Engineering........ MSc 12FT 24PT
Renewable Energy........ MSc 12FT/PGDip 9FT

Bangor University
Renewable Materials........ PhD by taught 36FT 60PT/MPhil 24FT 36PT

University of Cambridge
Energy Technology .... MPhil 12FT

University of Central Lancashire
Renewable Energy Engineering........ MSc 12FT 24PT/PGDip 24PT
Wind Energy Engineering........ MSc 12FT 24PT/PGDip 9FT 24PT

Cranfield University
Offshore and Ocean Technology with Offshore Materials Engineering ....MSc 12FT 24-60PT/MTech 24FT/PGCert 5FT 24PT/PGDip 6FT 24PT
Offshore and Ocean Technology with Offshore Renewable Energy .... MSc 12FT 24-60PT/MTech 24FT/PGDip 6FT 24PT/PGCert 5FT 24PT
Offshore and Ocean Technology with Pipeline Engineering .... MSc 12FT 24-60PT/MTech 24FT/PGCert 5FT 24PT/PGDip 6FT 24PT
Offshore and Ocean Technology with Risk Management ...... MSc 12FT 24-60PT/MTech 24FT/PGDip 6FT 24PT/PGCert 5FT 24PT
Offshore and Ocean Technology with Subsea Engineering ... MSc 12FT 24-60PT/MTech 24FT/PGDip 6FT 24PT/PGCert 5FT 24PT

Edinburgh Napier University
Renewable Energy........ MSc 12FT 24PT

University of Exeter
Energy Policy........ MSc 12FT 24PT
Environment, Energy and Resilience .... MRes 12FT 24PT

Heriot-Watt University
Petroleum Geoscience (PetGeo) .... MSc 12FT
Renewable Energy Engineering..MSc 12FT 24PT/PGDip 9FT 21PT
Reservoir Evaluation and Management .... MSc 12FT 24PT

University of Hull
Petroleum, Oil and Gas: Chemical Engineering Management...... MSc 12FT
Petroleum, Oil and Gas: Chemical Engineering Technologies .... MSc 12FT

Kingston University
Renewable Energy Engineering........ MSc 12FT 24PT

University of Leeds
Oilfield Corrosion Engineering........ MSc(Eng) 12FT

Liverpool John Moores University
Marine and Offshore Engineering MSc........ MSc 12FT 24PT/PGDip 9FT 18PT/PGCert 6FT 12PT/CPD 3-4FT 3-4PT

Newcastle University
Marine Structures and Integrity........ MSc 12 or 24FT
Marine and Offshore Power Systems........ MSc 12 or 24FT
Offshore Engineering .... MSc 12 or 24FT
Offshore and Environmental Technology........ MSc 12 or 24FT
Pipeline Engineering.... MSc 12FT 24PT/PGDip 12FT 24PT/PGCert 12FT 24PT
Subsea Engineering and Management .... MSc 12FT 24-36PT

Northumbria University
Renewable and Sustainable Energy Technologies .... MSc 12 or 16FT

University of Nottingham
Electrical Engineering for Sustainable and Renewable Energy..... MSc 12FT/PGDip 9FT

Robert Gordon University
Energy Management.... MSc 12FT 36DL/PGDip 8FT 24DL/PGCert 4FT 12DL
Energy and Sustainability ...MSc 42DL/PGDip 24DL/PGCert 12DL
Offshore Renewables .... MSc 42DL
Subsea Engineering .... MSc 36DL

University of Salford
Petroleum and Gas Engineering........ MSc 12FT/PGDip 9FT

University of Strathclyde
Offshore Floating Systems........ MSc 12FT/PGDip 9FT
Ship and Offshore Structures........ MSc 12FT/PGDip 9FT
Ship and Offshore Technology .... MSc 24FT
Subsea Engineering .... MSc 12FT/PGDip 9FT
Sustainable Engineering: Marine Technology ....MSc 12FT/PGDip 9FT
Sustainable Engineering: Offshore Renewable Energy MSc 12FT/PGDip 9FT

Swansea University
Materials Engineering........ MSc 12FT 24-36PT

Teesside University
Energy and Environmental Management........ MSc 12-16FT 24PT

UCL - University College London
Energy Demand Studies .... MRes 12FT
Energy and Resources: Policy and Practice, Australia .... MSc 24FT 36-48PT

Offshore engineering
Research Courses

Cardiff University
Institute of Energy .... EngD 48FT/PhD 36FT/MPhil 12FT

University of Exeter
Environment, Energy and Resilience ..MPhil 36FT 60PT/PhD 36FT 84PT
Offshore Renewable Energy .... EngD 48FT
Renewable Energy MSc by research 12FT 24PT/MPhil 36FT 60PT/PhD 48FT 80PT

Heriot-Watt University
Petroleum Engineering........ PhD 36FT 48PT/MPhil 12-24FT 24PT

Newcastle University
Energy........ PhD 36FT 72PT/MPhil 12FT 24PT

UCL - University College London
Offshore Engineering........ PhD 36FT 60PT

Sustainable development
Taught Courses

University of Abertay Dundee
Energy Industry Economics........ MSc 12FT/PGDip 9FT

Anglia Ruskin University
Sustainability: Working for Positive Change....MSc 12FT 24-30PT

Aston University
MSc Social Responsibility & Sustainability........ MSc 12FT 24PT

Bangor University
Conservation and Land Management .... MSc 12FT/PGDip 9FT
Environmental Management........ MBA 12FT
Environmental Management........ MBA 12FT
Forestry (Distance Learning with International Commonwealth Scholarship) .... MSc 12DL
Rheolaeth Amgylcheddol Gynaliadwy (Sustainable Environmental Management)........ MSc 12FT 24PT/MA 12FT 24PT
Sustainable Tropical Forestry (SUTROFOR) (Erasmus Mundus course)........ MSc 24FT
Tropical Forestry........ MSc 36PT/PGDip 24PT/PGCert 12PT

Birmingham City University
Environmental Sustainability...... PGCert 4FT 8PT/PGDip 4FT 8PT/MSc 4FT 8PT
Environmental Sustainability (Design and Construction) .... PGCert 4FT 8PT/PGDip 4FT 8PT/MSc 4FT 8PT

University of Birmingham
Materials for Sustainable Energy Technologies...MRes 12FT 24PT
Resilience and Urban Living........ MSc 12FT 24PT/MRes 12FT 24PT

University of Bolton
Regeneration and Sustainable CommunitiesMA 15FT/MSc 15FT/PGDip 12FT/PGCert 6FT

Bournemouth University
Green Economy........ MSc 12DL

University of Bradford
Applied Management and Sustainability........ MSc 12FT
MSc Applied Management and Sustainability........ MSc 12FT

University of Brighton
Sustainability of the Built Environment.....MSc 12FT 24PT/PGDip 12FT 24PT/PGCert 12FT 24PT
Sustainable Design ....MA 12FT 24-60PT/PGDip 12FT 24-60PT/PGCert 12FT 24-60PT

Brunel University
Building Services Engineering with Sustainable EnergyMSc 12FT 36-60DL
Renewable Energy Engineering........ MSc 12FT
Sustainable Electrical Power .... MSc 12FT 24PT
Sustainable Energy : Technologies and Management... MSc 12FT

University of Cambridge
Engineering for Sustainable Development........ MPhil 11FT
Sustainability Leadership........ MSt 24PT

Cardiff University
Sustainability, Planning and Environmental Policy .... MSc 12FT 24PT
Sustainable Energy and Environment........ MSc 12FT 24-36PT
Theory and Practice of Sustainable Design .... MSc 12FT 24PT

University of Chester
Sustainability for Community and Business........ MSc 12FT 24PT/PGDip 12FT 24PT/PGCert 12FT 12-24PT

University College Cork
Planning & Sustainable Development .... MPlan 24FT
Sustainable Energy .... MEngSci 12FT

Cranfield University
Design and Innovation for Sustainability .... MDes 12FT 24-60PT/PGDip 6FT 12PT/PGCert 5FT 12PT
Environment and Public Policy........ MSc 12FT 60PT/PGCert 12FT 60PT/PGDip 12FT 60PT
Environmental Informatics......MSc 12FT 60PT/PGDip 12FT 60PT/PGCert 12FT 60PT
Through-life System Sustainment........ MSc 24-36PT

University for the Creative Arts
Sustainable Product Design .... MA 24PT

University of Cumbria
Greening Outdoor Practice .... PGCert 24-36PT

De Montfort University
Architecture and Sustainability........ MSc 12FT 24PT
Energy and Industrial Sustainability H22172........ MSc 12FT 24PT 36DL/PGDip 32DL/PGCert 16DL

University of Derby
Sustainable Architecture and Healthy Environments .....MA 12FT
Sustainable Design and Innovation........ MSc 12FT 36-72PT

Dublin Institute of Technology
Sustainable Development........ MSc 12FT
Sustainable Electrical Energy Systems........ MEng 12FT 24PT

University of Dundee
Advanced Sustainability of the Built Environment .... MSc 12FT
Advanced Sustainable Urban Design .... MSc 12FT
Renewable Energy and Sustainable Building in a Global Context .... MSc 12FT
Spatial Planning with Marine Spatial Planning .... MSc 12FT
Spatial Planning with Sustainable Urban Design........ MSc 12FT
Spatial Planning with Urban Conservation .... MSc 12FT

University of East Anglia
Environmental Assessment and Management..... MSc 12FT 24PT
Sustainable Business........ MSc 12FT

University of East London
Architecture: Advanced Environmental and Energy Studies .... MSc 12FT 24PT
Architecture: Sustainability And Design .... MA 12FT 24PT/PGDip 8FT 16PT/PGCert 4FT 8PT
Renewable Energy and the Built Environment ..... MSc 12FT 24PT
Sustainability and Energy Management .... MBA 12FT 24PT

Edinburgh Napier University
Design (Sustainability)........ MA/MDes 12FT
Energy and Environmental Engineering........ MSc 12FT 36PT
Environmental Sustainability.... MSc 12FT 36PT/PGDip 9FT 24PT/PGCert 6FT 12PT
Polymer Engineering .... MSc 12FT
Renewable Energy........ MSc 12FT 24PT
Safety and Environmental Management..... MSc 12FT 36PT 36DL

University of Edinburgh
Advanced Sustainable Design........ MSc 12FT 24PT
Environmental Sustainability........ MSc 12FT 24-36PT/PGDip 9FT
Global Development Challenges (Online Distance Learning)........ PGCert 12-24DL
Global Environment Challenges Certificate (Online distance learning) .... PGCert 9DL
Soils and Sustainability........ MSc 12FT
Sustainable Energy Systems........ MSc 12FT/PGDip 9FT

University of Exeter
Applied Ecology........ MSc 12FT
Food Security and Sustainable Agriculture........ MSc 12FT 24PT

Forum for the Future
Leadership for Sustainable Development........ MA 10.5FT

Glasgow Caledonian University
Sustainable Energy Technology........ MSc 12FT 24PT

University of Glasgow
Environment & Sustainable Development........ MSc 12FT
Sustainable Energy .... MSc 12FT

Engineering, mechanical

Glyndwr University
Renewable Energy Systems and Sustainability .... MSc 12FT 24-36PT/MRes 12FT

Goldsmiths, University of London
Design & Environment .... MA 12FT 24PT
Design Futures .... MA 12FT 24PT

University of Greenwich
Natural Resources .... MSc 12FT 24PT/PGDip 12FT 24PT
Sustainable Futures .... MSc 12FT

Harper Adams University
International Agri-business and Food Chain Management... MSc 12FT 48PT/PGDip 12FT 48PT/PGCert 6FT 48PT

Heriot-Watt University
Climate Change: Impacts and Mitigation..MSc 12FT 24PT/PGDip 9FT 21PT
Climate Change: Managing The Marine Environment.. MSc 12FT 24PT/PGDip 9FT 21PT
Energy.............MSc 12FT 24PT 24-84DL/PGDip 9FT 21PT 21-84DL
Int'nl Business Management with Finance / HRM / Logistics / Marketing /Sustainability Mgmt. ....MSc 12FT 24PT/PGDip 9FT 21PT
Marine Resource Development and Protection....MSc 12FT 24PT/PGDip 9FT 21PT
Materials for Sustainable and Renewable Energies....... MSc 12FT 24PT/PGDip 9FT 21PT/PGCert 6FT 12PT
Renewable Energy Engineering..MSc 12FT 24PT/PGDip 9FT 21PT
Smart Grid and Demand Management......MSc 12FT 24PT/PGDip 9FT 18PT
Sustainability Engineering......... MSc 12FT 24PT/PGDip 9FT 21PT/PGCert 6FT 12PT

University of Hertfordshire
Water and Environmental Management..........MSc 12FT 24-60PT 24DL/PGDip 12FT 18-48PT 18DL/PGCert 12FT 18-48PT 18DL

University of Huddersfield
Architecture/Architecture (International) (RIBA Part 2)......MArch 24FT
Sustainable Architecture..MSc 12FT 24PT

University of Hull
Environmental Technology ....MSc 12FT 24PT
Environmental Technology (renewable energy)....MSc 12FT 24PT

Imperial College London
Transport, also with Business Management or Sustainable Development...MSc 12FT 24-36PT

Keele University
Environmental Sustainability and Green Technology..... Cert 4FT/Diploma 8FT/MSc 12FT

University of Kent
Environmental Anthropology.........MA 12FT 24PT/MSc 12FT 24PT

King's College London
Sustainable Cities...MSc 12FT 24PT

Kingston University
Sustainability & Environmental Change.................MSc 12FT 24PT
Sustainability for Built Environment PracticeMA 12FT/MSc 12FT/PGCert 6FT 12PT/PGDip 12FT
Sustainable Environmental Development with Management Studies...MSc 12FT 24PT

Leeds Metropolitan University
Sustainable Computing...MSc 12FT 24PT

University of Leeds
Sustainability (Business, Environment and Corporate Responsibility)................................MA 12FT 48PT/PGDip 12FT 48PT
Sustainability (Climate Change).. MSc 12FT
Sustainability (Ecological Economics).....................MSc 12FT 48PT
Sustainability (Environment and Development)............ MSc 12FT 12-48PT
Sustainability (Environmental Consultancy)....MSc 12FT 12-48PT
Sustainability (Environmental Politics and Policy).......... MSc 12FT 12-48PT
Sustainability (Transport) MSc 12FT 24-36PT/PGDip 9FT 18-24PT
Sustainability Research....................................... MRes 12FT 12-48PT
Water, Sanitation and Health Engineering.............MSc(Eng) 12FT

University of Leicester
Environmental Informatics..........MSc 12FT 24PT/PGDip 9FT 18PT
Sustainable Management of Natural Resources..MSc 12FT 24PT/PGDip 9FT 18PT

London Metropolitan University
Planning and Sustainable Communities.................MSc 12FT 24PT
Sustainable Cities...MSc 12FT 24+PT

London School of Economics and Political Science (LSE)
Environment and Development...............................MSc 12FT 24PT

Loughborough University
Design and Innovation for Sustainability ....MSc 12FT 24PT
Low Carbon Building Design and Modelling.. MSc 12FT 24-60PT/PGDip 12FT 24-60PT/PGCert 12FT 24-60PT
Sustainable Engineering...MSc 12FT 96PT

Manchester Metropolitan University
Environment, Management and Sustainable Development. MSc 12FT 36PT
Sustainable Aviation..MSc 12FT 12-36PT

University of Manchester
Competition, Regulation and Development .... MSc 12FT 12PT
Environment and Sustainable Technology.MSc 12FT/PGDip 9FT/PGCert 6FT

Middlesex University
Sustainable Development......... MA 12FT 24PT/PGDip 12FT 24PT/PGCert 12FT 24PT
Sustainable Environmental Management...... MA 12FT 24PT/MSc 12FT 24PT

Newcastle University
Environmental Regulation and Sustainable Development.....LLM 12FT 24PT
Hydrology and Climate Change.................................MSc 12FT 48PT
Planning for Sustainability and Climate Change........... MSc 12FT
Sustainable Buildings and Environments......................... MSc 12FT

University of Northampton
Sustainable Urban Environments................................... PGCert 6PT

Northumbria University
Disaster Management and Sustainable Development .... PGCert 4FT 8DL/PGDip 8FT 12DL/MSc 12FT 36-60DL
Electrical Power Engineering..MSc 12-16FT
Renewable and Sustainable Energy TechnologiesMSc 12 or 16FT

Nottingham Trent University
Planning, Urban Design and Sustainable Development.... PGCert 12PT

University of Nottingham
Energy Conversion and Management (Nottingham/ Ningbo)...... MSc 12FT
Environmental Design...MArch 12FT 24PT
Renewable Energy and Architecture.MSc 12FT 24PT/PGDip 12FT 24PT
Sustainable Bioenergy ....MSc 12FT 36PT
Sustainable Bioenergy (MRes) ....MRes 12-36PT
Sustainable Building Technology (Nottingham/ Ningbo) ...... MSc 12FT 24PT
Sustainable Building Technology (collaborative)........... MSc 12FT
Sustainable Energy Engineering... MSc 12FT
Sustainable Energy and Entrepreneurship .... MSc 12FT
Sustainable Tall Buildings ....MArch 12FT
Sustainable Transportation and Electrical Power Systems (Erasmus Mundus) .... MSc 24FT

The Open University
Conflict and Development................................... PGCert variableDL
Development Management..MSc variableDL/PGDip variableDL/PGCert 12DL
Human Rights and Development Management........PGCert 12DL

Oxford Brookes University
Sustainable Building: Performance and Design ..MSc 12FT 27PT/PGDip 9FT 18PT

Plymouth University
Design .... MA 12FT 24PT
Marine Renewable Energy ....MSc 12FT/MRes 12FT

Queen's University Belfast
Environmental Law and Sustainable Development........LLM 12FT
Leadership for Sustainable Rural Development............. MSc 12FT
Sustainable Design .... MSc 12FT/PGDip 9FT
Sustainable Electrical Energy Systems............................. MSc 12FT

Ravensbourne
Environment Design... MA 12FT 24PT

University of Reading
Agricultural Economics ....MSc 12FT 24PT
Agriculture and Development ....MSc 12FT 24PT
Construction Management .... MSc 12FT
Project Management .... MSc 24PT
Renewable Energy..........................MSc 12FT 24PT/PGDip 9FT 21PT
Social Development and Sustainable Livelihoods ....MA 12FT

Robert Gordon University
Energy and Sustainability ...MSc 42DL/PGDip 24DL/PGCert 12DL

Royal Holloway, University of London
Practising Sustainable Development..... MSc 12FT 24PT/Diploma 6FT 12PT
Sustainability and Management..............................MSc 12FT 24PT

University Campus Suffolk
MA Sustainable Business .... MA 12FT 24PT

University of Salford
Real Estate Development ....MSc 12FT 28DL/PGDip 8FT 20DL
Sustainable Building Design...... MSc 12FT 28PT/PGDip 8FT 20PT/PGCert 4FT 8PT

School of Oriental and African Studies - SOAS
Development Studies...MSc 12FT 24PT
Development Studies with Special Reference to Central Asia...... MSc 12FT 24PT
Environmental Law and Sustainable Development......................... MA 12FT 24PT
Labour, Social Movements and Development .... MSc 12FT 24PT
Research for International Development...............MSc 12FT 24PT
State, Society and Development..............................MSc 12FT 24PT

Schumacher College
Economics for Transition ....MA 12FT
Holistic Science .... MSc 12FT

University of Sheffield
Planning and Development..MA 12FT

University of South Wales
Sustainable Power Technology ....MSc 12FT 36PT

University of Southampton
Sustainable Energy Technologies.............................MSc 12FT 24PT

University of St Andrews
Sustainable Aquaculture.MSc 12FT 24PT/PGDip 9FT 24PT 24DL/Cert 12DL
Sustainable Development............................... MSc 12FT/PGDip 9FT

Staffordshire University
Governance and Sustainable Development..........MA 36PT 36DL/PGCert 36PT 20DL/PGDip 36PT 9DL
MA Regeneration.. MA 24FT 60PT

University of Stirling
Energy and the Environment ... MSc 12FT 27PT/MRes 12FT 27PT/PGDip 9FT/PGCert 4FT

University of Strathclyde
International Law and Sustainable Development..........LLM 12FT 24PT/PGDip 9FT 21PT/PGCert 4FT 8PT
Sustainability and Environmental Studies ....MSc 12FT 24PT/PGDip 9FT 18PT
Sustainable Engineering............ MSc 12FT 24PT/PGDip 9FT 18PT/PGCert 9FT 18PT
Sustainable Engineering: Building Design and Management....... MSc 12FT 24PT/PGDip 9FT 18PT/PGCert 6FT 12PT
Sustainable Engineering: Sustainable Product Development....... MSc 12FT 24PT/PGDip 9FT 21PT/PGCert 6FT 12PT

University of Surrey
Sustainable Development.....................................MSc 12FT 12-48PT

University of Sussex
Climate Change and Development...........................MSc 12FT 24PT
Climate Change and Policy ....MSc 12FT 24PT
Energy Policy for Sustainability ....MSc 12FT 24PT
Innovation and Sustainability for International Development..... MSc 12FT 24PT

Trinity College Dublin - the University of Dublin
Environment and Development .... MSc 12FT

University of the Highlands and Islands
Developing Low Carbon Communities ....MSc 12FT 36PT/PGDip 12FT 24PT/PGCert 12FT 12PT
Managing Sustainable Mountain Development MSc 36PT 36DL/PGDip 24PT 24DL/PGCert 24PT 12DL
Managing Sustainable Rural DevelopmentMSc 24FT 36PT/PGDip 12FT 24PT/PGCert 12FT 24PT

UCL - University College London
Energy and Resources: Policy and Practice, Australia .... MSc 24FT 36-48PT
Environment and Sustainable Development. MSc 12FT 24-60PT/PGDip 9FT
Sustainable Urbanism.......................MSc 12FT 24-60PT/PGDip 9FT

University of West London
Development and Management of Sustainable Built Environment..MSc 12FT 24PT

University of the West of England, Bristol
Environmental Law and sustainable developmentLLM 12FT 36PT

University of Worcester
Sustainable Development Advocacy (Professional Practice) ...MA 12FT 36PT

University of York
Green Chemistry and Sustainable Industrial Technology....... MSc 12FT 24-36PT

Sustainable development
Research Courses

Anglia Ruskin University
Sustainability...PhD 24 - 60FT 36 - 72PT

Bangor University
Renewable Materials.................. MPhil 24FT 36PT/PhD 36FT 60PT

University of Birmingham
Engineering, Sustainability and Resilience MRes .... MRes 12FT

Cardiff University
Institute of Environment and Sustainability........ PhD 36FT/MPhil 60PT
Institute of Green Electronic Systems; Communications, Sensors and Materials .... EngD 48FT/PhD 36FT/MPhil 12FT
Sustainable Engineering...PhD 36FT

Cranfield University
Sustainable Systems Research Opportunities .... PhD 36FT/Integrated PhD 36-45FT/MTech 24FT

De Montfort University
Energy and Sustainable Development Research ENG503 ... MPhil 12-24FT 24-48PT/PhD 36-48FT 48-72PT

Engineering, mechanical

University of Gloucestershire
Sustainability...PhD 36FT

University of Greenwich
Development Studies - Research...... MPhil 18-36FT 30-48PT/PhD 33-60FT 45-72PT
Environmental and Earth Sciences Research .....MPhil 36FT 72PT/PhD 36FT 72PT
Natural Resources by Research ....MSc by research 12FT 24PT

University of Hertfordshire
Agriculture and the Environment .... PhD 36FT 72PT/MRes 12FT 24PT

University of Leeds
Environmental Sustainability....PhD 36FT 60PT 60DL/MPhil 24FT 48PT 48DL

University of Manchester
Environment and Sustainable Technology .PhD 36FT 72PT/MPhil 12FT 24PT
Sustainable Consumption...PhD 48FT

Newcastle University
Sustainability........................... MPhil variesFT/PhD variesFT

University of Nottingham
Sustainable Energy Technology.............................PhD 36FT

The Open University
Asian drivers and Africa... PhD 36FT 72PT variableDL/MPhil 15FT 24PT variableDL
Environment, governance and justicePhD 36FT 72PT variableDL/MPhil 15FT 24PT variableDL
Sustainable Design .... PhD 36FT 72PT variableDL/MPhil 15FT 24PT variableDL

Oxford Brookes University
Sustainable Development MPhil/PhD .... PhD 24-60FT 36-72PT/MPhil 24-36FT 36-48PT

School of Oriental and African Studies - SOAS
Development Studies..PhD 36FT 48-60PT
Economics...................... PhD 36FT 72PT/MPhil 24FT 36PT

Sheffield Hallam University
Environment and Development .... MPhil 36PT
Environment and Development - Facilities Management.......PhD 33FT 45PT/MPhil 18FT 30PT
School of Environment and Development.....................PhD/MPhil

University of Strathclyde
Building Design and Management for Sustainability .MRes 12FT 36PT

University of Surrey
Sustainability for Engineering and Energy Systems (SEES) .. EngD 48FT

University of the Highlands and Islands
Sustainability Studies... MPhil 24FT 48PT/PhD 36FT 72PT/MSc by research 12FT 24PT

Thermodynamics
Taught Courses

University of Aberdeen
Divinity and Religious Studies.....................................MTh 12FT 24PT

University of Central Lancashire
Wind Energy Engineering.............MSc 12FT 24PT/PGDip 9FT 24PT

Cranfield University
Aerospace Propulsion (Option of Thermal Power).......... MSc 12FT
Gas Turbine Technology (Option of Thermal Power MSc)....... MSc 12FT
Power, Propulsion and the Environment (Option of Thermal Power) ....MSc 12FT/PGCert 12FT/PGDip 12FT
Rotating Machinery, Engineering and Management (Option of Thermal Power MSc)... MSc 12FT
Thermal Power... MSc 12FT

University of Glasgow
Aeronautical Engineering... MSc 12FT

King's College London
Air Power in the Modern World .... MA 24 - 72DL

Kingston University
Renewable Energy Engineering................................. MSc 12FT 24PT

University of Manchester
Thermal Power and Fluid Engineering............................. MSc 12FT

Queen Mary, University of London
Aerospace Engineering .... MSc 12FT

University of Salford
Industrial and Commercial Combustion Engineering .MSc 36DL/PGDip 12DL/PGCert 12DL

University of Strathclyde
Lean Six Sigma for Process Excellence MSc 12FT 24PT/PGDip 9FT 18PT/PGCert 9FT 18PT

Thermodynamics
Research Courses

Anglia Ruskin University
Engineering Analysis, Simulation and Tribology..... PhD 24 - 60FT 36 - 72PT

University of Glasgow
Aerospace Sciences...........PhD 36-48FT 60-72PT/MSc by research 12-24FT 24-36PT
Systems, Power and Energy.............PhD 36-48FT 60-72PT/MSc by research 12-24FT 24-36PT

University of Leeds
Institute of Engineering Thermofluids, Surfaces and Interfaces .. PhD 36+FT/MPhil 24FT

University of Nottingham
Thermofluids .... MRes 12FT

Underwater technology
Taught Courses

University of Aberdeen
Oil and Gas Engineering...MSc 12FT 24PT
Subsea Engineering .... MSc 12FT 24PT 24DL

Bangor University
Renewable Materials............................... PhD by taught 36FT 60PT/MPhil 24FT 36PT

Cranfield University
Offshore and Ocean Technology with Offshore Materials Engineering MSc........MSc 12FT 24-60PT/MTech 24FT/PGCert 5FT 24PT/PGDip 6FT 24PT
Offshore and Ocean Technology with Offshore Renewable

Energy MSc....... MSc 12FT 24-60PT/MTech 24FT/PGDip 6FT 24PT/PGCert 5FT 24PT
Offshore and Ocean Technology with Risk Management MSc......MSc 12FT 24-60PT/MTech 24FT/PGDip 6FT 24PT/PGCert 5FT 24PT
Renewable Energy Technology ....MSc 12FT 24-60PT/PGDip 6FT 24PT/PGCert 5FT 24PT

University of Dundee
Water Law (PGDip part time) ...PGDip 18-60DL/PGCert 12-60DL/LLM 24-60DL

University of Exeter
Environment, Energy and Resilience ....MRes 12FT 24PT

Heriot-Watt University
Marine Biodiversity and Biotechnology .....MSc 12FT 24PT/PGDip 9FT 21PT
Marine Resource Development and Protection....MSc 12FT 24PT/PGDip 9FT 21PT
Robotics, Autonomous and Interactive Systems (RAIS) MSc 12FT/PGDip 9FT

Newcastle University
Marine Structures and Integrity...............................MSc 12 or 24FT
Marine Technology Education Consortium ...MSc 24-60PT/PGDip 24-60PT/PGCert 24-60PT/CPD 2PT
Offshore Engineering ....MSc 12 or 24FT

University of Nottingham
Electrical Engineering for Sustainable and Renewable Energy .....MSc 12FT/PGDip 9FT

Plymouth University
Marine Renewable Energy ....MSc 12FT/MRes 12FT

Robert Gordon University
Offshore Renewables ....MSc 42DL

University of Southampton
Freshwater Sciences ....MRes 12FT

University of St Andrews
Ecosystem-based Management of Marine Systems....MRes 12FT

University of Strathclyde
Offshore Floating Systems............................. MSc 12FT/PGDip 9FT
Ship and Offshore Structures......................... MSc 12FT/PGDip 9FT
Ship and Offshore Technology .... MSc 24FT
Sustainable Engineering: Marine Technology ....MSc 12FT/PGDip 9FT
Sustainable Engineering: Offshore Renewable Energy MSc 12FT/PGDip 9FT

Underwater technology
Research Courses

Cranfield University
Marine Technology PhD with Integrated Studies ....Integrated PhD 36-48FT

University of Exeter
Environment, Energy and Resilience ..MPhil 36FT 60PT/PhD 36FT 84PT

Newcastle University
Marine Technology...................... PhD 36FT 72PT/MPhil 12FT 24PT
Technology in the Marine Environment ....MRes 12FT

Engineering, transport

Automotive engineering
Taught Courses

University of Bath
Automotive Engineering .... MSc 12FT

Birmingham City University
Automotive Calibration and Control ....PGCert 10PT/PGDip 10PT/
MSc 10PT
Automotive Engineering .... PGCert 4FT 10PT/PGDip 4FT 10PT/
MSc 4FT 10PT

University of Bradford
Automotive Engineering .... MSc 12FT/PGDip 9FT
Automotive Engineering Quality Improvement. MSc 12FT/PGDip
9FT

University of Brighton
Automotive Electronic Engineering...MSc 12FT 24PT/PGDip 12FT
24PT/PGCert 12FT 24PT
Automotive Engineering .... MSc 12FT 24PT/PGCert 12FT 24PT/
PGDip 12FT 24PT

Brunel University
Automotive and Motorsport Engineering .... MSc 12FT

City University London
Automotive Engineering .... MSc 12FT 24PT

Coventry University
Automotive Design .... MA 15FT 30PT
Automotive Design Research .... MA 12FT 24PT
Automotive Engineering .... MSc 12FT 24-36PT/PGDip 9FT 24PT

Cranfield University
Advanced Lightweight Structures and Impact .... MSc 12FT
Advanced Motorsport EngineeringMSc 12FT 24-60PT/PGDip 6FT
24PT/PGCert 5FT 24PT/MTech 24FT
Automotive Engineering ....MSc 12FT 24-36PT
Automotive Mechatronics .... MSc 12FT
Integrated Vehicle Health Management........MSc 24-60PT/PGDip
24PT/PGCert 12PT

Edinburgh Napier University
Mechanical Engineering...............................MSc 12FT 24PT

University of Exeter
Advanced Mechanical Engineering .... MSc 12FT

University of Glasgow
Aeronautical Engineering.. MSc 12FT

University of Hertfordshire
Automotive Engineering ....MSc 12FT 36PT/MSc 16FT

University of Huddersfield
Automotive Engineering .... MSc 12FT

Kingston University
Automotive Engineering .... MSc(Eng) 12FT 24PT

University of Leeds
Automotive Engineering ....MSc(Eng) 12FT

Loughborough University
Automotive Systems Engineering....................MSc 12FT 30PT

Manchester Metropolitan University
Mechanical Engineering...............................MSc 12FT 24PT

University of Nottingham
Sustainable Transportation and Electrical Power Systems
(Erasmus Mundus) .... MSc 24FT

The Open University
Engineering.............. MSc(Eng) 12-24DL/MEng variableDL/PGDip
variableDL

Oxford Brookes University
Automotive Engineering .... MSc 12FT 24PT
Motorsport Engineering .... MSc 12FT 24PT
Racing Engine Design .... MSc 12FT 24PT

Royal College of Art
Vehicle Design...MA 24FT

Sheffield Hallam University
Advanced Design Engineering.....................MSc 12FT 36FT/
PGDip 8FT 24PT/PGCert 4FT 12PT
Advanced Manufacturing Engineering....................MSc 12FT 36FT/
PGDip 8FT 24PT/PGCert 4FT 12PT

University of Sheffield
Advanced Manufacturing Technologies with the AMRC MSc(Res)
12FT
Advanced Mechanical Engineering .... MSc(Res) 12FT

University of South Wales
Aeronautical Engineering......................................MSc 12FT 24PT

University of Southampton
MSc Advanced Tribology.......................................MSc 12FT
Race Car Aerodynamics..MSc 12FT 24PT

Staffordshire University
Aeronautical Engineering........................MSc 12-18FT 24-32PT
Automotive Engineering/Autosport Engineering..... MSc 12-18FT
24-60PT

University of Strathclyde
Advanced Manufacturing: Technology and Systems..... MSc 12FT
24PT/PGDip 9FT 18PT/PGCert 9FT 18PT

Advanced Mechanical Engineering ..... MSc 12FT 24PT/PGDip 9FT
18PT/PGCert 9FT 18PT

University of Sussex
Automotive Engineering ....MSc 12FT 24PT/PGDip 9FT 24PT

Swansea Metropolitan University
Automotive Engineering .... MSc 12FT 24PT

Teesside University
Civil Engineering...............................MSc 12 - 16FT 24PT/PGDip 8FT

Automotive engineering
Research Courses

University of Aberdeen
Engineering... PhD 36FT/MPhil 24FT/MSc by research 12FT/EngD
36FT

Birmingham City University
Automotive Calibration & Control Research ....MSc by research
12FT 24PT

University of Bradford
Automotive, Modelling and Control Engineering PhD 36FT 48PT/
MPhil 12FT 24PT

City University London
Aeronautical, Automotive, Mechanical and Civil Engineering......
PhD/MPhil

Cranfield University
Transforming composite structural design by use of structural
health mon..PhD 36FT

University of Exeter
Engineering.. EngD 48FT

University of Hertfordshire
Engineering (Professional Doctorate) ....EngD 36-60PT

University of Liverpool
Engineering..PhD 36FT/MPhil 12FT 24PT

Loughborough University
Aeronautical and Automotive Engineering...........PhD 36FT 60PT/
MPhil 24FT 36PT

Queen Mary, University of London
Engineering..PhD 36FT/MPhil

Royal College of Art
Vehicle Design...........................PhD/MPhil/MA by research 24FT

Boat building
Taught Courses

Manchester Metropolitan University
Design (with pathways in design and contemporary craft
practice) .... MA 12FT 24PT

Newcastle University
Small Craft Design ....MSc 12 or 24FT

University of Roehampton
Art, Craft and Design Education .... PGCert 6FT 24PT
PGDip 9FT 24PT

University of Southampton
Maritime Engineering Science: Ship Science .... MSc 12FT
Maritime Engineering Science: Yacht and Small Craft .. MSc 12FT

Engineering, transport
Taught Courses

Anglia Ruskin University
Engineering Management ....MSc 12 - 15FT 24 - 30PT

Brunel University
Automotive and Motorsport Engineering .... MSc 12FT

Cranfield University
Autonomous Vehicle Dynamics and Control.........MSc 12FT 24PT/
PGDip 12FT 24PT/PGCert 12FT 24PT
Safety and Accident Investigation - Rail...MSc 36FT/PGDip 36PT/
PGCert 36PT

University of Greenwich
Transport and Logistics ManagementMA 12FT 24PT/PGDip 12FT
24PT

University of Leeds
Transport Planning and Engineering...... MSc(Eng) 12FT 24-36PT/
PGDip 9FT 18-24PT/PGCert 3FT 6-9PT

University of Lincoln
Sustainable Power and Energy Engineering .... MSc 24PT

Loughborough University
Road and Vehicle Safety............................. MSc 1FT 24PT
Transport.....................................MSc 12FT 24-60PT

Newcastle University
Low Carbon Transport Engineering .... MSc 12FT
Rail Freight and Logistics....................................... MSc 12FT
Transport Planning and Engineering.............MSc 12FT 24-48PT
Transport Planning and Intelligent Transport Systems...................
MSc 12FT 24PT
Transport Planning and the Environment ....MSc 12FT 24-48PT

Northumbria University
Business with Pipeline Integrity Management .... MSc 12FT

University of Salford
Transport Engineering and Planning......................MSc 12FT 36PT

Sheffield Hallam University
Advanced Design Engineering .. MSc 12FT 36PT/PGDip 8FT 24PT/
PGCert 4FT 12PT
Logistics and Supply Chain Management..MSc 12FT 36PT/PGDip
8FT 24PT/PGCert 4FT 12PT
Transport Planning and Management.....................MSc 12FT 36PT

University of South Wales
Aeronautical Engineering...........................MSc 12FT 24PT
Aircraft Maintenance Systems................................MSc 12FT 36PT
Professional Engineering..MSc 12-60PT

University of Southampton
Transportation Planning and Engineering.....MSc 12FT 24PT/
PGDip 12FT

Staffordshire University
Automotive Engineering/Autosport Engineering..... MSc 12-18FT
24-60PT
Professional Engineering.................................MSc 12-18FT

Swansea Metropolitan University
Logistics .... MSc 24PT
Non Destructive Testings and Evaluation .... MSc 12FT 24PT

University of Wolverhampton
Polymer Engineering Design ...MSc 12FT 24PT/PGCert 12FT 24PT

Engineering, transport
Research Courses

Anglia Ruskin University
Built Environment ....MPhil 24 - 60FT 36 - 72PT
Engineering Analysis, Simulation and Tribology..... PhD 24 - 60FT
36 - 72PT

Harper Adams University
Precision Farming (MRes is Subject to Validation)...... MRes 12FT/
MPhil 24FT/PhD 38FT

Loughborough University
Transport Safety Research.......... PhD 36FT 60PT/MPhil 24FT 36PT

Oxford Brookes University
Intelligent Transport Systems MPhil/PhD. PhD 24-60FT 36-72PT/
MPhil 24-36FT 36-48PT

Naval engineering
Taught Courses

City University London
Maritime Operations and Management...........MSc 12FT 24-36PT

University of Greenwich
Marine Engineering Management ....MSc 12FT 24PT

Heriot-Watt University
Architectural Engineering .....MSc 12FT 24PT 24-84DL/PGDip 9FT
21PT 24-84DL/PGCert 6FT 12PT 24-84DL
Marine Biodiversity and Biotechnology .....MSc 12FT 24PT/PGDip
9FT 21PT
Marine Spatial Planning ....MSc 12FT 24PT/PGDip 9FT

Liverpool John Moores University
Maritime Operations MSc......... MSc 12FT 24PT/PGDip 12FT 24PT

University of Liverpool
Marine Planning and Management ....MSc 12FT 24PT

Newcastle University
Marine Electrical Power Technology....................MSc 12 or 24FT
Marine Engineering....................................MSc 12 or 24FT
Marine Structures and Integrity....................MSc 12 or 24FT
Marine Technology (International) - Dubai .. MSc 24 or 36FT/CPD
2PT
Marine Technology (International) - Singapore....... MSc 24-36PT/
PGDip 24-36PT/PGCert 18-30PT/CPD 2PT
Marine Technology Education Consortium ...MSc 24-60PT/PGDip
24-60PT/PGCert 24-60PT/CPD 2PT
Marine Transport with Management .... MSc 12FT
Marine and Offshore Power Systems.....................MSc 12 or 24FT
Naval Architecture.......................................MSc 12 or 24FT
Small Craft Design ....MSc 12 or 24FT

Southampton Solent University
Shipping Operations...MSc 12-24DL

University of Southampton
Marine Technology...MSc 24PT 36DL
Maritime Engineering Science: Advanced Materials ..... MSc 12FT
Maritime Engineering Science: Marine Engineering ..... MSc 12FT
Maritime Engineering Science: Maritime Computational Fluid
Dynamics... MSc 12FT
Maritime Engineering Science: Naval Architecture........ MSc 12FT
24PT
Maritime Engineering Science: Nuclear Safety Management
.... MSc 12FT
Maritime Engineering Science: Ocean Resource EngineeringMSc
12FT
Maritime Engineering Science: Ship Science .... MSc 12FT

Engineering, transport

Maritime Engineering Science: Yacht and Small Craft .... MSc 12FT

University of St Andrews
Ecosystem-based Management of Marine Systems .... MRes 12FT

University of Strathclyde
Marine Engineering .... MSc 12FT/PGDip 9FT
Offshore Floating Systems .... MSc 12FT/PGDip 9FT
Offshore Renewable Energy .... MSc 12FT
Ship and Offshore Technology .... MSc 24FT
Sustainable Engineering: Marine Technology .... MSc 12FT/PGDip 9FT

Sustainable Engineering: Offshore Renewable Energy MSc 12FT/ PGDip 9FT
Technical Ship Management .... MSc 12FT 24PT/PGDip 9FT 24PT

University of Ulster
Marine Spatial Planning .... PGDip 24DL/MSc 36DL

UCL - University College London
Marine Engineering .... MSc 12FT 24-60PT
Naval Architecture .... MSc 12FT 60PT

Naval engineering
Research Courses

Newcastle University
Marine Sciences .... PhD 36FT 72PT/MPhil 12FT 24PT

Southampton Solent University
Maritime Research Centre .... PhD/MPhil

University of Strathclyde
Naval Architechture and Marine Engineering - Research .... PhD 36FT 72PT/MPhil 12FT 24PT

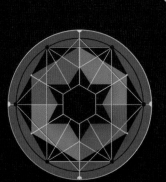

Environmental science and ecology

Atmospheric sciences
Taught Courses

University of Aberdeen
Climate Change Law and Sustainable Development......LLM 12FT 24--36PT

Birkbeck, University of London
Climate Change Management MSc 12FT 24PT/PGDip 12FT 24PT/PGCert 12PT
Environment and Sustainability.........MSc 12FT 24PT/PGDip 12FT 24PT/PGCert 12PT

University of Bristol
Climate Change Science and Policy ....MSc 12FT 24PT

Brunel University
Climate Change Impacts and Sustainability..........MSc 12FT 24PT

University of Cambridge
Polar Studies..MPhil 9FT

University of Chester
Sustainability for Community and Business.........MSc 12FT 24PT/PGDip 12FT 24PT/PGCert 12FT 12-24PT

De Montfort University
Climate Change and Sustainable Development .... MSc 12FT 24PT 36DL/PGDip 32DL/PGCert 16DL

University of Dundee
Climate Change and Energy Law and Policy ....LLM 12FT

University of East Anglia
Atmospheric Sciences .... MSc 11FT
Climate Change .... MSc 12FT
Climate Change and International Development............................. MSc 12FT 24PT
Environmental Sciences...MSc 12FT 24PT

University of Edinburgh
Carbon Capture & Storage..MSc 12FT 36PT
Carbon Finance .... MSc 12FT
Carbon Management.. MSc 12FT
GeoSciences (Individual Project) ....MSc(Res) 12FT 24PT

University of Exeter
Climate Change Impacts and Feedbacks..............MRes 12FT 24PT
Climate Change and Risk Management.................MSc 12FT 24PT

University of Glasgow
Environmental Science, Technology & Society (Dumfries Campus)...MSc 12FT 24PT

Heriot-Watt University
Applied Mathematical Sciences with Climate Change Impact Modelling...MSc 12FT 24PT/PGDip 9FT 21PT
Climate Change: Impacts and Mitigation.............MSc 12FT 24PT/PGDip 9FT 21PT
Climate Change: Managing The Marine Environment.. MSc 12FT 24PT/PGDip 9FT 21PT

Keele University
Climate Change Studies - Policy, Justice and Global Politics....MA 12FT 24PT

King's College London
Global Environmental Change...................................MSc 12FT 24PT

University of Leeds
Atmosphere-Ocean Dynamics .... MSc 12FT
Physics of the Earth and Atmosphere ....MRes 12FT

University of Liverpool
Environment and Climate Change...................................... MSc 12FT

London School of Economics and Political Science (LSE)
Environmental Economics and Climate Change ... MSc 12FT 24PT

The Open University
Earth Science ....MSc variablePT
Professional Science ....MSc variableDL

University of Portsmouth
Science with Physics ....PGCE (Postgraduate) 12FT/PGCE (Professional) 12FT

University of Reading
Applied Meteorology .... MSc 12FT 24PT/PGDip 12FT 24PT
Applied Meteorology and Climate with Management MSc 12FT 24PT
Atmosphere, Ocean & Climate ....MSc 12FT/PGDip 12FT
Chemical Research...PGDip 9FT 18PT
Chemical Research ....MSc 12FT 24PT
The Economics of Climate Change .... MSc 12FT

School of Oriental and African Studies - SOAS
Global Energy and Climate Policy ....MSc 12FT 24PT

University of Sheffield
Polar and Alpine Change ....MSc 12FT 24PT

Swansea University
Environmental Dynamics and Climate Change..... MSc 12FT 36PT
Geographic Information and Climate Change......MSc 12FT 36PT/PGCert 12FT 12PT

UCL - University College London
Climate Change ....MSc 12FT 24PT

University of the West of England, Bristol
Air Quality and Carbon Management................MSc 12FT 24-36PT

Atmospheric sciences
Research Courses

Aberystwyth University
Physics .... MPhil 12FT 24PT
PhD 36FT 60PT

University of Birmingham
Atmospheric Sciences and Air Pollution PhD with Integrated Study..PhD 48FT
Earth Sciences PhD/MPhil.......... PhD 36FT 72PT/MPhil 24FT 48PT

University of Cambridge
Polar Studies ....PhD 36FT

University of East Anglia
Copy of Environmental Sciences: Geosciences and Natural Hazards .... PhD 36FT 72PT/MPhil 24FT 48PT
Environmental Sciences: Climate, Ocean and Atmospheric Sciences.. PhD 36FT 72PT/MPhil 24FT 48PT
Environmental Sciences: Resources, Sustainability and Governance................................... PhD 36FT 72PT/MPhil 24FT 48PT

University of Hertfordshire
Atmospheric Dynamics and Air Quality (ADAQ) ..PhD 36FT 72PT/MPhil 24FT 48PT/MRes 12FT 24PT

Keele University
Earth Sciences .... PhD 36FT/MPhil 12FT

University of Leeds
Atmospheric and Climate Science .....PhD 36FT 60PT 60DL/MPhil 24FT 48PT 48DL

University of Liverpool
Earth and Ocean Sciences..PhD 24-48FT 48-84PT/MPhil 12-24FT

University of Manchester
Atmospheric Sciences ...PhD 36FT 72PT/MPhil 12FT 24PT/MSc by research 12FT
Earth, Atmospheric and Envrionmental Sciences ....PhD 36FT 72PT/MPhil 12FT 24PT/MSc by research 12FT 24PT/MSc by research 12FT 24PT

University of Nottingham
Carbon Capture and Storage..... PhD 24FT 48PT/MPhil 24FT 48PT

The Open University
Atomic, Molecular and Optical Physics................MPhil 15FT 24PT variableDL

University of Oxford
Atmospheric, Oceanic and Planetary Physics................ DPhil 48FT
Earth Sciences .... DPhil 48FT/MSc by research 24FT

Queen's University Belfast
Environmental Change .... PhD 36FT 72PT/MPhil 24FT 48PT

UCL - University College London
Earth Sciences .... PhD 36FT 60PT
Space and Climate Physics... PhD 36FT 60PT

Biodiversity
Taught Courses

Anglia Ruskin University
Applied Wildlife Conservation .... MSc 24PT

Bangor University
Biodiversity Conservation .... PhD by taught 36FT 60PT/MPhil 24FT 36PT
Conservation and Land Management .... MSc 12FT/PGDip 9FT
Ecology..MRes 12FT
Marine Biology..................................MSc 12FT 24-36PT/PGDip 9FT
Marine Environmental Protection ....MSc 12FT 24-36PT
Natural Sciences ....MRes 12FT
Physical Oceanography....................MSc 12FT 24-36PT/PGDip 9FT

Bournemouth University
Biodiversity Conservation ....MSc 12FT 24PT

Cranfield University
Applied Bioinformatics ....MSc 12FT 24PT

University of Derby
Conservation Biology..MSc 12FT 36PT

University of East Anglia
Environmental Sciences..MSc 12FT 24PT

Edinburgh Napier University
Wildlife Biology and Conservation...MSc 12FT 24-48PT 24-48DL/PGDip 9FT 18-36PT 18-36DL/PGCert 6FT 12-24PT 12-24DL

University of Edinburgh
Biodiversity and Taxonomy of Plants........... MSc 12FT/PGDip 9FT
Biodiversity, Wildlife & Ecosystem Health (online distance learning) ...MSc 36PT 36DL/PGDip 24PT 24DL/PGCert 12PT 12DL
Ecosystem Services ....MSc 12FT 24-36PT

University of Exeter
Conservation and Biodiversity.. MSc 12FT

University of Glasgow
Animal Welfare Science, Ethics & Law.......... MSc 12FT/PGDip 9FT
Quantitative Methods in Biodiversity, Conservation and Epidemiology... MSc 12FT/PGDip 9FT

University of Greenwich
Natural Resources .... MSc 12FT 24PT/PGDip 12FT 24PT

Heriot-Watt University
Climate Change: Managing The Marine Environment.................. MSc 12FT 24PT/PGDip 9FT 21PT
Marine Biodiversity and Biotechnology .....MSc 12FT 24PT/PGDip 9FT 21PT

University of Hertfordshire
Environmental Management.......................MSc 12-15FT 24-60PT/PGDip 12FT 18-48PT/PGCert 12FT 18-48PT

Imperial College London
Advanced Methods in Taxonomy and Biodiversity........MSc 12FT/DIC 12FT
Biodiversity, Informatics and Genomics.......................... MRes 12FT

University of Kent
Agri-Environmental Economics and Policy .... MSc 12FT 24PT
Conservation Biology..MSc 12FT 24PT
Conservation Project Management.........................MSc 12FT 24PT
Conservation and Business.......................................MSc 12FT 24PT
Environmental Anthropology.........MA 12FT 24PT/MSc 12FT 24PT
Ethnobotany...MSc 12FT 24PT

University of Leeds
Biodiversity and Conservation ....MSc 12FT 24PT
Biological Identification and Conservation............MSc 12FT 24PT

Nottingham Trent University
Biodiversity Conservation .... MSc 12FT 24PT/MRes 12FT 24PT/PGDip 12FT 24PT/PGCert 12FT 24PT
Endangered Species Recovery and Conservation .MSc 12FT 24PT/MRes 12FT 24PT
Human Security and Environmental Change.........MA 12FT 24PT/PGDip 9FT 18PT/PGCert 9FT

Oxford Brookes University
Conservation Ecology ....MSc 12FT 24PT/PGDip 8FT 20PT/PGCert 8FT 8PT

University of Oxford
Biodiversity, Conservation & Management .... MSc 12FT
Geography and the Environment..................................... MPhil 24FT

Plymouth University
Marine Biology..MRes 12FT 24PT

University of Reading
Plant Diversity ....MSc 12FT 24PT
Species Identification and Survey Skills .... MSc 12FT
Wildlife Management and Conservation .... MSc 12FT

University of Salford
Wildlife Documentary Production..MA 12FT

Schumacher College
Holistic Science .... MSc 12FT

University of Southampton
Biodiversity and Conservation ....MSc 12FT 27PT

Staffordshire University
Invertebrate Ecology and Conservation......MSc 15FT/PGDip 15FT

Swansea University
Aquatic Ecology and Conservation .... MRes 12FT 24-36PT

Trinity College Dublin - the University of Dublin
Biodiversity and Conservation .... MSc 12FT

UCL - University College London
Biodiversity, Evolution and Conservation MRes .... MRes 12FT

University of Warwick
MBA Global Energy .... MBA 36PT

Biodiversity
Research Courses

Aberystwyth University
IBERS - Environmental Science ....MPhil 12FT 24PT
PhD 36FT 60PT

Anglia Ruskin University
Animal and Environmental.............................PhD 24-60FT 36-72PT

Bangor University
Biodiversity Conservation .... MPhil 24FT 36PT/PhD 36FT 60PT
Ecology..MRes 12FT
Natural Sciences ....MRes 12FT
Ocean Sciences...MPhil 24FT/PhD 36FT
Tropical Ecosystems..................... MPhil 24FT 36PT/PhD 36FT 60PT

University of East Anglia
Copy of Environmental Sciences: Geosciences and Natural Hazards .... PhD 36FT 72PT/MPhil 24FT 48PT
Environmental Sciences: Climate, Ocean and Atmospheric Sciences.. PhD 36FT 72PT/MPhil 24FT 48PT
Environmental Sciences: Resources, Sustainability and Governance................................... PhD 36FT 72PT/MPhil 24FT 48PT

University of Greenwich
Natural Resources by Research...........MSc by research 12FT 24PT

University of Kent
Biodiversity Management. PhD 36FT 60PT/MSc by research 12FT 24PT

Environmental science and ecology

Nottingham Trent University
Environmental Biology....MRes 12FT 24PT

The Open University
Biodiversity and Conservation .... PhD 36FT 72PT variableDL/ MPhil 15FT 24PT variableDL

University of Oxford
Geography and the Environment.... DPhil 48FT/MSc by research 24FT

Queen's University Belfast
Environmental Change .... PhD 36FT 72PT/MPhil 24FT 48PT

Swansea University
Aquatic Biology....MSc by research 12FT 24PT

Contaminated land
Taught Courses

Brunel University
Toxicology and Risk Assessment .... MSc 12FT 24PT

Cardiff University
Applied Environmental Geology .... MSc 12FT

Heriot-Watt University
Environmental Analysis and Assessment .... MRes 12FT 24PT/ PGDip 9FT 18PT/PGCert 9FT 18PT

Lancaster University
Contamination, Risk Assessment and Remediation .... MSc 12FT 24PT
Environmental and Biochemical Toxicology.... MSc 12FT 24PT

University of Leeds
Hydrogeology....MSc 12FT 24-48PT/PGDip 12FT 24-48PT

University of Portsmouth
Environmental Geology and Contamination .... MSc 12FT 24PT

University of Reading
Environmental Management .... MSc 12FT 24PT

University of Sheffield
Contaminant HydrogeologyMSc 12FT 24PT/PGDip 9FT 18PT/Cert 6FT 12PT

University of Ulster
Environmental Toxicology & Pollution Monitoring by e-Learning....PGDip 24DL/MSc 36DL

Contaminated land
Research Courses

University of Nottingham
Contaminated Land Management ....MRes 24PT
Risk Analysis, Social Processes and Health .MPhil 36FT/PhD 24FT

Ecology
Taught Courses

University of Aberdeen
Ecology and Environmental Sustainability.MSc 12FT/PGDip 9FT/ MRes 12FT

Bangor University
Ecology....MRes 12FT
Forestry (Distance Learning with International Commonwealth Scholarship) ....MSc 12DL
Marine Biology....MSc 12FT 24-36PT/PGDip 9FT
Marine Environmental Protection ....MSc 12FT 24-36PT
Natural Sciences ....MRes 12FT
Physical Oceanography....MSc 12FT 24-36PT/PGDip 9FT
Sustainable Tropical Forestry (SUTROFOR) (Erasmus Mundus course).... MSc 24FT
Tropical Forestry.... MSc 36PT/PGDip 24PT/PGCert 12PT

University of Brighton
Ecology....MRes 12FT 24PT

Brunel University
Climate Change Impacts and Sustainability.... MSc 12FT 24PT

University of Cambridge
Polar Studies....MPhil 9FT

University of Central Lancashire
Urban Environmental Management... MSc 12FT 24PT/PGDip 9FT 18PT/PGCert 6FT 12PT
Values and Environment .... MA 12FT 24PT

University of Chester
Applied Wildlife Conservation ....PGCert 12FT 12 - 36PT
Applied Wildlife Forensics ....PGCert 12FT 12 - 36PT
Conservation in Practice ....PGCert 12FT 12 - 36PT
Wildlife Conservation.. MSc 12FT 24PT/PGDip 12FT 24PT/PGCert 12FT 12-24PT

Cranfield University
Integrated Landscape Ecology MSc 12FT 60PT/PGDip 12FT 60PT/ PGCert 12FT 60PT

University of Cumbria
Conservation Biology.... MSc 12FT min 24PT/GradDip 6FT min 12PT/GradCert 3FT min 6PT
Forest Ecosystem Management .... MSc 12FT 24PT/GradDip 6FT 12PT/GradCert 3FT 6PT

University of East Anglia
Applied Ecology and Conservation .... MSc 12FT 24PT
Climate Change .... MSc 12FT
Climate Change and International Development.... MSc 12FT 24PT
Ecology .... GradDip 12FT 24PT
Environment and International Development .... MSc 12FT 24PT
Environmental Assessment and Management.... MSc 12FT 24PT
Environmental Sciences.... MSc 12FT 24PT

University of Edinburgh
Biodiversity, Wildlife & Ecosystem Health (online distance learning) ...MSc 36PT 36DL/PGDip 24PT 24DL/PGCert 12PT 12DL
Conservation Medicine .... MVetSci 36DL/PGDip 24DL/ PGCert 12DL
Ecological Economics....MSc 12FT 24-36PT/PGDip 9FT
Ecosystem Services ....MSc 12FT 24-36PT
One Health....MSc 36DL/PGDip 24DL/PGCert 12DL

University of Essex
Environmental Governance: the Natural World, Science and Society....MSc 12FT 24PT/MA 12FT 24PT
Environmental Resource Management.... MSc 12FT 24PT
Marine Biology.... MSc 12FT
Natural Environment and Society.... MSc 12FT

University of Exeter
Applied Ecology.... MSc 12FT
Biosciences....MSc(Res) 12FT 36PT
Evolutionary and Behavioural Ecology.... MSc 12FT

University of Glasgow
Animal Welfare Science, Ethics & Law.... MSc 12FT/PGDip 9FT
Ecology & Environmental Biology.... MRes 12FT/PGDip 9FT
Marine & Freshwater Ecology & Environmental Management.... MRes 12FT/PGDip 9FT
Quantitative Methods in Biodiversity, Conservation and Epidemiology.... MSc 12FT/PGDip 9FT

Harper Adams University
Ecological Applications .... MSc 12FT 24PT/PGDip 12FT 24PT

Heriot-Watt University
Applied Mathematical Sciences with Biological and Ecological Modelling .... MSc 12FT 24-84PT/PGDip 9FT 15-48PT
Climate Change: Impacts and Mitigation..MSc 12FT 24PT/PGDip 9FT 21PT
Climate Change: Managing The Marine Environment.. MSc 12FT 24PT/PGDip 9FT 21PT
Food and Beverage Science....MSc 12FT 24PT/PGDip 9FT 21PT
Marine Biodiversity and Biotechnology .....MSc 12FT 24PT/PGDip 9FT 21PT

Imperial College London
Ecology, Evolution and Conservation .... MSc 12FT
Ecology, Evolution and Conservation ....MRes 12FT 24PT

University of Kent
Conservation Biology.... MSc 12FT 24PT
Conservation Project Management.... MSc 12FT 24PT
Conservation and Business.... MSc 12FT 24PT
Conservation and International Wildlife Trade.... MSc 12FT 24PT
Conservation and Plant Science .... MSc 12FT 24PT
Conservation and Primate Behaviour .... MSc 12FT 24PT
Conservation and Rural Development.... MSc 12FT 24PT
Conservation and Tourism .... MSc 12FT 24PT
Environmental Anthropology.... MA 12FT 24PT/MSc 12FT 24PT
Ethnobotany .... MSc 12FT 24PT

Lancaster University
Ecology (by research)....MSc(Res) 12FT 24PT
Ecology and Conservation.... MSc 12FT 24PT

University of Leeds
Biological Identification and Conservation.... MSc 12FT 24PT
Sustainability (Ecological Economics) .... MSc 12FT 48PT

Manchester Metropolitan University
Countryside Management....MSc 36PT 36DL

Newcastle University
Ecological Consultancy .... MSc 12FT

Nottingham Trent University
Human Security and Environmental Change.... MA 12FT 24PT/ PGDip 9FT 18PT/PGCert 9FT
Research Ecology ....MSc(Res) 12FT 24PT

Oxford Brookes University
Environmental Impact Assessment (MRes)....MRes 12FT 24PT

Queen Mary, University of London
Aquatic Ecology by Research .... MSc 12FT 24PT

Queen's University Belfast
Ecological Management and Conservation Biology.... MSc 12FT 24PT/PGDip 9FT

University of Reading
Biometry .... MSc 12FT 24PT

Royal Veterinary College
Wild Animal Biology - MSc (F/T).... MSc 12FT
Wild Animal Biology - PGCert (F/T).... PGDip 8FT
Wild Animal Health - PGCert (F/T).... PGDip 8FT

Schumacher College
Ecological Design....New course - see website
Holistic Science ....MSc/PGCert

University of Sheffield
Polar and Alpine Change .... MSc 12FT 24PT

University of Southampton
Water Resources Management .... MSc 12FT 27PT

University of St Andrews
Evolutionary and Comparative Psychology: The Origins of Mind. MSc 12FT 24PT

Staffordshire University
Ecology and Conservation.... MSc 15FT

Swansea University
Environmental Dynamics and Climate Change.... MSc 12FT 36PT

UCL - University College London
Biodiversity, Evolution and Conservation MRes .... MRes 12FT

Ecology
Research Courses

Aberystwyth University
IBERS - Biological Sciences (MPhil).... MPhil 12FT 24PT
IBERS - Biological Sciences (PhD).... PhD 36FT 60PT

Bangor University
Biodiversity Conservation .... MPhil 24FT 36PT/PhD 36FT 60PT
Biological Sciences ....MPhil 12FT/PhD 24-36FT
Ecology.... MRes 12FT
Environmental and Soil Science MPhil 24FT 36PT/PhD 36FT 60PT
Natural Sciences .... MRes 12FT
Ocean Sciences....MPhil 24FT/PhD 36FT
Tropical Ecosystems .... MPhil 24FT 36PT/PhD 36FT 60PT

Bath Spa University
Ecology....PhD 24 - 60FT 36 - 72PT/MPhil 18 - 36FT 30 - 48PT

University of Cambridge
Polar Studies....PhD 36FT

University of East Anglia
Copy of Environmental Sciences: Geosciences and Natural Hazards .... PhD 36FT 72PT/MPhil 24FT 48PT
Environmental Sciences: Climate, Ocean and Atmospheric Sciences.... PhD 36FT 72PT/MPhil 24FT 48PT
Environmental Sciences: Resources, Sustainability and Governance.... PhD 36FT 72PT/MPhil 24FT 48PT

University of Essex
Environmental Governance.... PhD 36FT 72PT/MPhil 24FT 48PT/ MSc by research 12FT 24PT
Environmental Sciences....PhD 36FT 72PT/MPhil 24FT 48PT/ MSc by research 12FT 24PT
Marine BiologyPhD 36FT 72PT/MPhil 24FT 48PT/MSc by research 12FT 24PT

University of Exeter
Biosciences......PhD 36FT 72PT/MPhil 24FT 48PT/MSc by research 12FT 36PT

University of Hull
Marine or Terrestrial Ecology.... MSc by research 12FT 24PT/PhD 36FT 72PT

University of Liverpool
Biological Sciences (Evolution, Ecology and Behaviour).... MPhil 12-24FT 24-72PT/PhD 24-48FT 48-84PT
Biological Sciences (Functional and Comparative Genomics) .... MPhil 12-48FT 24-72PT/PhD 24-48FT 48-84PT
Ecology .... MPhil 12FT/PhD 24-48FT 48-84PT

Nottingham Trent University
Environmental Biology....MRes 12FT 24PT

University of Nottingham
Animal Behaviour & Ecology Research Group ....PhD 36FT 72PT/ MPhil 24FT 48PT
Ecology.... MRes 12FT
Evolutionary Biology....MRes 12FT 24PT

Oxford Brookes University
Biological Sciences - Environmental Ecology MPhil/PhD....PhD 24-60FT 36-72PT/MPhil 24-36FT 36-48PT
Biological Sciences - Spatial Ecology and Land Use MPhil/PhD .... PhD 24-60FT 36-72PT/MPhil 24-36FT 36-48PT

University of Oxford
Plant Sciences.... DPhil 48FT/MSc by research 24FT

Plymouth University
Speciation and Environmental Analysis Research Group (SEA).... PhD 36FT/MPhil 24FT

Queen's University Belfast
Ecology, Evolution, Behaviour and Environmental Economics .... PhD 36FT 72PT/MPhil 24FT 48PT

University of Roehampton
Ecology.... PhD 24-48FT 36-60PT/MPhil 21-36FT 33-48PT

Swansea University
Aquatic Biology....MSc by research 12FT 24PT
Mathematical Ecology ....MSc by research 12FT 24PT

Environmental science and ecology

Ecotourism
Taught Courses

Bangor University
Biodiversity Conservation .... PhD by taught 36FT 60PT/MPhil 24FT 36PT

University of Bedfordshire
Tourism and Environmental Management .... MSc 12-15FT 24PT/PGDip 12FT/PGCert 12FT

Bournemouth University
Tourism Management.......................................MSc 12-15FT 24PT
Tourism Management and Marketing............. MSc 12/15FT 24PT

Edinburgh Napier University
Ecotourism ....MSc 12FT 24-48PT/PGDip 9FT 18-36PT/PGCert 6FT 12-24PT

University of Exeter
Tourism, Development and Policy........MSc 12FT 24PT/PGDip 9FT

University of Kent
Conservation and Tourism ....MSc 12FT 24PT

London Metropolitan University
International Sustainable Tourism Management.............MA 12FT

Oxford Brookes University
Tourism: Environment and Development .MSc 12FT 24PT/PGDip 9FT 21PT/PGCert 9PT

School of Oriental and African Studies - SOAS
Anthropology of Travel, Tourism and Pilgrimage ... MA 12FT 24PT
Environmental Law and Sustainable Development........................ MA 12FT 24PT

University of Wales Trinity Saint David
Heritage Tourism ....MA 12-24FT 18-48PT/PGDip 9FT 18-36PT/PGCert 9FT 18PT

UCL - University College London
Built Environment: Sustainable Heritage .... MSc 12FT 24-60PT/PGDip 9FT

Ecotourism
Research Courses

University of Southampton
MRes Science and Heritage...MRes 12FT

Environmental conservation
Taught Courses

Anglia Ruskin University
Applied Wildlife Conservation .... MSc 24PT

Bangor University
Conservation and Land Management .... MSc 12FT/PGDip 9FT
Environmental Forestry .... MSc 12FT
Environmental Management... MBA 12FT
Environmental Management... MBA 12FT
Forestry (Distance Learning with International Commonwealth Scholarship) ....MSc 12DL
Marine Biology....................................MSc 12FT 24-36PT/PGDip 9FT
Marine Environmental Protection ....MSc 12FT 24-36PT
Physical Oceanography.....................MSc 12FT 24-36PT/PGDip 9FT
Rheolaeth Amgylcheddol Gynaliadwy (Sustainable Environmental Management)........MSc 12FT 24PT/MA 12FT 24PT
Sustainable Tropical Forestry (SUTROFOR) (Erasmus Mundus course).. MSc 24FT
Tropical Forestry.................... MSc 36PT/PGDip 24PT/PGCert 12PT

Birkbeck, University of London
Environmental Management (Protected Area/ Countryside Management) ....MSc 24PT/PGDip 24PT

University of Bristol
Environmental Policy and Management.. MSc 12FT 24PT/PGCert 12FT 24PT/PGDip 12FT 24PT

College of Estate Management
Conservation of Historic Environment ......PGDip 24DL/MSc 36DL

Cardiff University
Care of Collections ....MSc 12FT 24PT
Conservation Practice... MSc 24FT

University of Central Lancashire
Values and Environment .... MA 12FT 24PT

University of Chester
Archaeology and Heritage Practice .....MSc 12FT 24 - 36PT/PGDip 12FT 24 - 36PT/PGCert 12FT 12 - 24PT
Regeneration for Practitioners.....MA 12FT 24 - 72PT/PGDip 12FT 24 - 60PT/PGCert 12FT 12 - 36PT
Sustainability for Community and Business.........MSc 12FT 24PT/PGDip 12FT 24PT/PGCert 12FT 12-24PT

University of Cumbria
Conservation Biology.......... MSc 12FT min 24PT/GradDip 6FT min 12PT/GradCert 3FT min 6PT
Greening Outdoor Practice ....PGCert 24-36PT
Sustainable Uplands................ MSc 12FT 24PT/GradDip 6FT 12PT/GradCert 3FT 6PT

De Montfort University
Environmental Protection Diploma PGDip 18-24DL/PGCert 8DL/Professional Diploma 16DL

University of Derby
Environmental Health....................................... MSc 24FT 48PT 48DL

University of Dundee
Design and Construction of Zero Carbon and Ultra-Low Energy Buildings .... MSc 12FT
Spatial Planning with Environmental Assessment .... MSc 12FT
Spatial Planning with Marine Spatial Planning .... MSc 12FT
Spatial Planning with Sustainable Urban Design .... MSc 12FT
Spatial Planning with Urban Conservation .... MSc 12FT

Durham University
Risk and Environmental Hazards...MA 12FT

University of East Anglia
Applied Ecology and Conservation .... MSc 12FT 24PT
Environmental Sciences.. MSc 12FT 24PT

Edge Hill University
Conservation Management.. MSc 12FT 48PT

Edinburgh Napier University
Conservation and Management of Protected Areas...... MSc 12FT 24-36PT/PGDip 9FT 18-27PT/PGCert 6FT 12-18PT
Environmental Sustainability.... MSc 12FT 36PT/PGDip 9FT 24PT/PGCert 6FT 12PT
Wildlife Biology and Conservation... MSc 12FT 24-48PT 24-48DL/PGDip 9FT 18-36PT 18-36DL/PGCert 6FT 12-24PT 12-24DL

University of Edinburgh
Environmental Protection and Management.......MSc 12FT 24PT/PGDip 9FT
Environmental Sustainability..........MSc 12FT 24-36PT/PGDip 9FT

University of Exeter
Biosciences..MSc(Res) 12FT 36PT
Conservation and Biodiversity .... MSc 12FT

Falmouth University
Art and Environment... MA 12FT 24PT

Goldsmiths, University of London
Design & Environment .... MA 12FT 24PT

University of Greenwich
Environmental Conservation...................................... MSc 12FT 24PT
Natural Resources .... MSc 12FT 24PT/PGDip 12FT 24PT

Heriot-Watt University
Climate Change: Impacts and Mitigation..MSc 12FT 24PT/PGDip 9FT 21PT
Climate Change: Managing The Marine Environment.. MSc 12FT 24PT/PGDip 9FT 21PT
Renewable Energy and Distributed Generation...MSc 12FT 24PT/PGDip 9FT 21PT

University of Hertfordshire
Environmental Management.......................MSc 12-15FT 24-60PT/PGDip 12FT 18-48PT/PGCert 12FT 18-48PT

University of Hull
Environmental Technology (renewable energy).... MSc 12FT 24PT

Imperial College London
Conservation Science .... MSc 12FT

University of Kent
Anthropology and Conservation .... MA 12FT 24PT
Conservation Biology.. MSc 12FT 24PT
Conservation Project Management.......................... MSc 12FT 24PT
Conservation and Business.. MSc 12FT 24PT
Conservation and International Wildlife Trade...... MSc 12FT 24PT
Conservation and Plant Science .... MSc 12FT 24PT
Conservation and Primate Behaviour .... MSc 12FT 24PT
Conservation and Rural Development..................... MSc 12FT 24PT
Conservation and Tourism .... MSc 12FT 24PT
Endangered Species Recovery ....PGDip 5FT

Kingston University
Environmental Law and Sustainability.................... LLM 12FT 24PT

Lancaster University
Ecology and Conservation.. MSc 12FT 24PT
Environment and Development................................ MSc 12FT 24PT
Environment and Development................................. MA 12FT 24PT
Environment, Culture & Society................................ MSc 12FT 24PT
Resource and Environmental Management........... MSc 12FT 24PT

University of Leeds
Biodiversity and Conservation .... MSc 12FT 24PT

University of Liverpool
Conservation and Resource Management...MSc 12FT/MRes 12FT

London School of Economics and Political Science (LSE)
Environment and Development .... MSc 12FT 24PT

Manchester Metropolitan University
Countryside Management...MSc 36PT 36DL
Environment, Management and Sustainable Development .... MSc 12FT 36PT

Middlesex University
Sustainable Environmental Management...... MA 12FT 24PT/MSc 12FT 24PT

Newcastle University
Ecological Consultancy .... MSc 12FT
Environmental Consultancy .... MSc 12FT 48PT
Environmental Regulation and Sustainable Development..... LLM 12FT 24PT
Sustainable Buildings and Environments .... MSc 12FT

Nottingham Trent University
Endangered Species Recovery and Conservation .MSc 12FT 24PT/MRes 12FT 24PT

The Open University
Environmental Management.........MSc variableDL/PGCert 12DL/PGDip variableDL

Oxford Brookes University
Conservation Ecology ....MSc 12FT 24PT/PGDip 8FT 20PT/PGCert 8FT 8PT
Historic Conservation ....MSc 12FT 24PT/PGDip 12FT 24PT/PGCert 12PT
Primate Conservation ...... MSc 12FT 24PT/PGDip 8FT 16PT 16DL/PGCert 8PT

University of Oxford
Biodiversity, Conservation & Management .... MSc 12FT

Plymouth University
Sustainable Environmental Management............MRes 12FT 24PT
Sustainable Environmental Management.MSc 12FT 24PT/PGDip 9FT
Zoo Conservation Biology.............MSc 12FT 24PT/PGDip 9FT 18PT

Queen's University Belfast
Archaeology and EnvironmentMSc 12FT 24PT/PGDip 12FT 24PT/PGCert 12FT 24PT
Ecological Management and Conservation Biology....... MSc 12FT 24PT/PGDip 9FT
Sustainable Design .... MSc 12FT/PGDip 9FT

University of Reading
Environmental Management .... MSc 12FT 24PT
Plant Diversity .... MSc 12FT 24PT
Species Identification and Survey Skills .... MSc 12FT
Wildlife Management and Conservation .... MSc 12FT

Reseau Universitaire Transmanche
Transmanche Environment Programme .... MSc 24FT

University of Salford
Safety, Health and Environment MSc 12FT 36PT/PGDip 8FT 24PT

School of Oriental and African Studies - SOAS
Environmental Law and Sustainable Development......................... MA 12FT 24PT
Environmental Management...............................MSc 12FT 24-36PT
Global Energy and Climate Policy ....MSc 12FT 24PT

Schumacher College
Holistic Science .... MSc 12FT

Sheffield Hallam University
Environmental Management.........................MSc 12-24FT 24-36PT
Environmental Management (International Resource and Climate Management).....................................MSc 12-18FT 24-36PT
Environmental Management (Wildlife and Landscape Conservation) ....MSc 12-18FT 24-36PT
Sustainable Communities and Environments .... MSc 12-18FT 24-36PT

University of Sheffield
Environmental Archaeology and Palaeoeconomy MSc 12FT 24PT

University of South Wales
Environmental Conservation Management........... MSc 12FT 36PT

University of Southampton
Biodiversity and Conservation ....MSc 12FT 27PT
Wildlife Conservation...MRes 12FT

St Mary's University College, Twickenham
Managing for Sustainability....................................... MA 12FT 24PT

Staffordshire University
Ecology and Conservation.. MSc 15FT
Habitat Management and Conservation ... MSc 15FT/PGDip 12FT
Invertebrate Ecology and Conservation...... MSc 15FT/PGDip 15FT

University of Stirling
Aquaculture: Sustainable Aquaculture .... MSc 12FT
Aquatic Pathobiology .... PGCert 4FT/PGDip 11FT/MSc 12FT
Energy Management.. MSc 12FT
Energy and the Environment ... MSc 12FT 27PT/MRes 12FT 27PT/PGDip 9FT/PGCert 4FT

University of Strathclyde
Offshore Floating Systems............................... MSc 12FT/PGDip 9FT
Power Plant Engineering ....MSc 36FT/PGDip 24FT/PGCert 12FT
Power Plant Technologies...........MSc 12FT/PGDip 9FT/PGCert 6FT

University of Surrey
Radiation and Environmental Protection................ MSc 12FT 24PT

Swansea University
Aquatic Ecology and Conservation .... MRes 12FT 24-36PT
Environmental Biology: Conservation and Resource Management... MSc 12FT 36PT

Swansea Metropolitan University
Environmental Conservation and Management... MSc 12FT 24PT

Environmental science and ecology

Trinity College Dublin - the University of Dublin
Biodiversity and Conservation .... MSc 12FT
Environmental Sciences .... MSc 12FT

University of Wales Trinity Saint David
Landscape Management and Environmental Archaeology ..... MA 12FT 24PT/PGCert 12FT 24PT/PGDip 12FT 24PT

UCL - University College London
Biodiversity, Evolution and Conservation MRes .... MRes 12FT
Built Environment: Sustainable Heritage .... MSc 12FT 24-60PT/PGDip 9FT
Climate Change .... MSc 12FT 24PT
Conservation Studies .... MSc 24FT
Conservation for Archaeology and Museums .... MSc 24FT
Environmental Archaeology .... MSc 12FT 24PT
Managing Archaeological Sites .... MA 12FT 24PT
Principles of Conservation .... MSc 12FT 24PT

Writtle College
Conservation Management under Global Change......... MSc 12FT 24-36PT/PGDip 8FT 20-36PT/PGCert 4FT 16-36PT
Environmental Resource Management (Joint degree) .. MSc 12FT
Natural Environment and Society (Joint degree) .... MSc 12FT

Environmental conservation
Research Courses

Bangor University
Biodiversity Conservation .... MPhil 24FT 36PT/PhD 36FT 60PT
Ocean Sciences .... MPhil 24FT/PhD 36FT
Renewable Materials .... MPhil 24FT 36PT/PhD 36FT 60PT

Coventry University
Environmental & Climate Change......MSc by research 12FT 24PT

University of East Anglia
Copy of Environmental Sciences: Geosciences and Natural Hazards .... PhD 36FT 72PT/MPhil 24FT 48PT
Environmental Sciences: Climate, Ocean and Atmospheric Sciences .... PhD 36FT 72PT/MPhil 24FT 48PT
Environmental Sciences: Resources, Sustainability and Governance .... PhD 36FT 72PT/MPhil 24FT 48PT

University of Exeter
Biosciences......PhD 36FT 72PT/MPhil 24FT 48PT/MSc by research 12FT 36PT

University of Hertfordshire
Agriculture and the Environment .... PhD 36FT 72PT/MRes 12FT 24PT

University of Kent
Biodiversity Management. PhD 36FT 60PT/MSc by research 12FT 24PT

University of Liverpool
Conservation and Resource Management .... MRes 12FT

Newcastle University
Environmental Science .... MPhil 12FT 24PT/PhD 36FT 72PT
Environmental Science .... Integrated PhD 48FT

University of Nottingham
Conservation Biology .... MRes 12FT

The Open University
Biodiversity and Conservation ..PhD 36FT 72PT variableDL/MPhil 15FT 24PT variableDL

Oxford Brookes University
Environmental Design and Conservation MPhil/PhD .... MPhil/PhD 36-60FT 48-72PT/PhD 24-60FT 36-72PT/MPhil 24-36FT 36-48PT

Queen's University Belfast
Ecology, Evolution, Behaviour and Environmental Economics .... PhD 36FT 72PT/MPhil 24FT 48PT

Sheffield Hallam University
Countryside Research Unit .... PhD/MPhil

Swansea University
Environmental Conservation .... MSc by research 12FT 24PT
Environmental Sustainability .... MSc by research 12FT 24PT
Sustainable Resources .... MSc by research 12FT

University of York
Conservation Studies......PhD 36FT 72PT/MPhil 24FT 48PT/MA by research 12FT 24PT

Environmental engineering
Taught Courses

University of Abertay Dundee
Urban Water and Environmental Management ... MSc 12FT 24PT

Anglia Ruskin University
Business Management of Waste and Resources.......MSc 12-24DL

Bangor University
Environmental Management .... MBA 12FT
Rheolaeth Amgylcheddol Gynaliadwy (Sustainable Environmental Management)........MSc 12FT 24PT/MA 12FT 24PT

University of Brighton
Environmental Geology............MSc 12FT 24PT/PGDip 12FT 24PT/PGCert 12FT 24PT
Water and Environmental Management ...MSc 12FT 24PT/PGDip 12FT 24PT

University of Bristol
Water and Environmental Management .... MSc 12FT 24PT

University of Cambridge
Engineering for Sustainable Development .... MPhil 11FT
Fluid Flow in Industry and the Environment .... MPhil 11FT
Geographical Research .... MPhil 12FT

Cardiff University
Geoenvironmental Engineering .... MSc 12FT 24-36PT
Hydro-environment Engineering .... MSc 12FT 24PT

University of Central Lancashire
Carbon and Resource Management.... MSc 12FT 24PT/PGDip 9FT 18PT/PGCert 6FT 12PT
Sustainable Waste Management.......MSc 12FT 24PT/PGDip 12FT 24PT/PGCHE 4FT

Cranfield University
Agricultural and Environmental Engineering .... MSc(Res) 12FT 24-36PT
Environmental Engineering .... MSc 12FT 24-60PT/PGDip 6FT 24PT/PGCert 5FT 24PT/MTech 24FT
Environmental Risk Management .... MSc 12FT 24-60PT/PGDip 6FT 24PT/PGCert 5FT 24PT
Waste and Resource Management....... MSc 12FT 24-60PT/PGDip 12FT 24PT/PGCert 12FT 24PT/MTech 24FT

De Montfort University
Environmental Technology and Management F85172 . MSc 12FT

University of Derby
Sustainable Architecture and Healthy Environments ..... MA 12FT

University of Dundee
Civil Engineering .... MSc 12FT
Concrete Engineering and Environmental Management ...... MSc 12FT
Spatial Planning with Environmental Assessment .... MSc 12FT

University of East Anglia
Energy Engineering with Environmental ManagementMSc 12FT/MSc 24PT/MSc 36PT/MSc 48PT

Edinburgh Napier University
Energy and Environmental Engineering .... MSc 12FT 36PT

University of Exeter
Advanced Civil Engineering .... MSc 12FT
Engineering and Management .... MSc 12FT
Surveying and Land/ Environmental Management .... MSc 12FT 24-36PT/PGDip 12FT 24-36PT

GCU London
International Project Management (Oil and Gas)........... MSc 15FT

Glasgow Caledonian University
Energy and Environmental Management............MSc 12FT 24PT/PGDip 8FT 20PT/PGCert 4FT 8PT
Sustainable Energy Technology .... MSc 12FT 24PT
Waste Management .... MSc 12FT 24PT/PGDip 8FT 20PT/PGCert 4FT 8PT

Heriot-Watt University
Sustainability Engineering......... MSc 12FT 24PT/PGDip 9FT 21PT/PGCert 6FT 12PT
Urban Strategies and Design.......MSc 12FT 24PT/PGDip 9FT 21PT

University of Hertfordshire
Water and Environmental Management ....MSc 12FT 24-60PT 24DL/PGDip 12FT 18-48PT 18DL/PGCert 12FT 18-48PT 18DL

Imperial College London
Environmental Engineering, also with Business Management or Sustainable Development .... MSc 12FT 24-36PT
General Structural Engineering .... MSc 12FT 24-36PT
Systems Engineering and Innovation .... MSc 24PT

University of Leeds
Environmental Engineering & Project Management .....MSc(Eng) 12FT
Water, Sanitation and Health Engineering .... MSc(Eng) 12FT

University of Leicester
Environmental Informatics..........MSc 12FT 24PT/PGDip 9FT 18PT

Loughborough University
Sustainable Engineering .... MSc 12FT 96PT
Water and Environmental Management by Distance Learning.... MSc 96DL/PGDip 60DL/PGCert 36DL
Water and Waste Engineering ..MSc 12FT/PGDip 6FT/PGCert 3FT
Water and Waste Engineering by Distance Learning...MSc 96DL/PGDip 60DL/PGCert 36DL

Manchester Metropolitan University
Sustainable Aviation .... MSc 12FT 12-36PT

University of Manchester
Renewable Energy and Clean Technology .... MSc 12FT

Middlesex University
Environmental Pollution Control .... MSc 12FT 24PT

Newcastle University
Agricultural and Environmental Science .... MSc 12FT
Clean Technology .... MSc 12FT/PGDip 7FT
Environmental Engineering .... MSc 12FT 48PT
Environmental and Petroleum Geochemistry .... MSc 12FT 48PT
Offshore and Environmental Technology .... MSc 12 or 24FT
Skills, Technology, Research and Management for the UK Water Sector (STREAM) .... EngD by taught 48FT
Structural Engineering .... MSc 12FT 48PT
Transport Planning and the Environment .... MSc 12FT 24-48PT

University of Northampton
International Wastes Management .... MSc 24DL
Wastes Management .... MSc 12FT 24PT 36DL/PGDip 12PT

Nottingham Trent University
Structural Engineering with Management .... MSc 12FT 24PT
Structural Engineering with Materials .... MSc 12FT 24PT

University of Nottingham
Civil Engineering: Geotechnical Engineering .... MSc 12FT
Engineering Surveying with Geographical Information Science .. MSc 12FT
Environmental Engineering .... MSc 12FT
Environmental and Resource Engineering .... MSc 12FT

Plymouth University
Civil Engineering .... MSc 12FT/PGDip 12FT/PGCert 6FT

University of Portsmouth
Civil Engineering with Environmental Engineering .... MSc 12FT 24PT

Queen's University Belfast
Advanced Concrete Technology.....MSc 24PT/PGDip 24PT/PGCert 24PT
Durability of Structures ....MSc 12FT 24PT/PGDip 12FT 24PT/PGCert 12FT 24PT
Environmental Engineering .... MSc 12FT 24-36PT/PGDip 12FT 24PT
Environmental Planning .... MSc 12FT

University of Reading
Renewable Energy (MSc/PGDip) MSc 12FT 24PT/PGDip 9FT 21PT

Robert Gordon University
Energy Management.... MSc 12FT 36DL/PGDip 8FT 24DL/PGCert 4FT 12DL
Energy and Sustainability ...MSc 42DL/PGDip 24DL/PGCert 12DL

University of Salford
Environmental Acoustics...MSc 12FT 28PT 28DL/PGDip 9FT 18PT 18DL

School of Oriental and African Studies - SOAS
Environmental Management .... MSc 12FT 24-36PT

Sheffield Hallam University
Built Environment..... MPhil 24FT 36PT/PhD by taught 24FT 60PT
Environmental Management .... MSc 12-24FT 24-36PT
Environmental Management (International Resource and Climate Management) .... MSc 12-18FT 24-36PT
Environmental Management (Wildlife and Landscape Conservation) .... MSc 12-18FT 24-36PT

University of Sheffield
Environmental Management of Urban Land and Water .... MSc 12FT 24PT/PGDip 9FT 18PT/PGCert 6FT 12PT
Structural and Concrete Engineering............MSc(Eng) 12FT 24PT/Diploma 9FT 18PT/Cert 6FT 12PT

University of Southampton
Civil and Environmental Engineering .... MSc 12FT 24PT
Environmental Coastal Engineering .... MSc 12FT 24PT
Environmental Monitoring and Assessment .... MSc 12FT 27PT
Freshwater Sciences .... MRes 12FT

University of Strathclyde
Environmental Engineering....... MSc 12FT 24PT/PGDip 9FT 18PT/PGCert 6FT 12PT
Environmental Entrepreneurship......... MSc 12FT 24PT/PGDip 9FT 18PT/PGCert 6FT 12PT
Environmental Health.... MSc 12FT 24PT/PGDip 9FT 18PT/PGCert 6FT 12PT
Sustainability and Environmental Studies .... MSc 12FT 24PT/PGDip 9FT 18PT

University of Surrey
Process and Environmental Systems Engineering .... MSc 12FT
Water and Environmental Engineering .... MSc 12FT 72PT

Teesside University
Civil Engineering .... MSc 12 - 16FT 24PT/PGDip 8FT
Energy and Environmental Management......... MSc 12-16FT 24PT

Trinity College Dublin - the University of Dublin
Engineering (Environmental/Structural & Geotechnics/Transport) .... MSc 12FT 24PT
Environmental Engineering .... PGDip 12PT
Environmental Sciences .... MSc 12FT

UCL - University College London
Built Environment: Environmental Design and Engineering......... MSc 12FT 24-60PT/PGDip 9FT
Built Environment: Heritage Science .... MRes 12FT 24-60PT/PGCert 6FT
Energy Demand Studies .... MRes 12FT
Energy and Resources: Policy and Practice, Australia .... MSc 24FT 36-48PT

Environmental science and ecology

Environmental Systems Engineering....................... MSc 12FT 24PT

University of the West of Scotland
Waste Management with Environmental Management .... MSc 12FT 30PT/Diploma 9FT 20PT

University of Wolverhampton
Environmental Technology .... MSc 12FT 24PT

Environmental engineering
Research Courses

Bangor University
Agricultural Systems.................... MPhil 24FT 36PT/PhD 36FT 60PT
Renewable Materials.................. MPhil 24FT 36PT/PhD 36FT 60PT

University of Brighton
School of the Environment Research Division .... PhD 24-60FT 36-72PT/MPhil 18-36FT 30-48PT

Cranfield University
Agricultural and Environmental Engineering ....MPhil 24FT 96PT/PhD 36FT 96PT/MSc by research 12FT 24-60PT

University of Dundee
Civil Engineering .... MPhil 24FT MSc by research 12FT

Durham University
Earth Sciences ....PhD 36FT 72PT/MPhil 24FT 48PT/MSc by research 12FT 24PT

University of Glasgow
Infrastructure and Environment (Civil, Structural & Environmental Engineering)...........PhD 36-48FT 60-72PT/MSc by research 12-24FT 24-36PT

University of Greenwich
Engineering (by Research).....................MSc by research 12FT 24PT

Harper Adams University
Engineering..MPhil 24FT/PhD 38FT

University of Leeds
Energy and Resources Research Institute .PhD 36+FT/MPhil 24FT
Low Carbon Technologies..................................Integrated PhD 48FT
Pathogen Control Engineering Institute....PhD 36+FT/MPhil 24FT

University of Liverpool
Engineering...PhD 36FT/MPhil 12FT 24PT

University of Manchester
Environmental Engineering....... PhD 36FT 72PT/MPhil 12FT 24PT

Newcastle University
Civil Engineering (Environmental) ......PhD 36FT 72PT/MPhil 12FT 24PT
Energy... PhD 36FT 72PT/MPhil 12FT 24PT
Environmental Science.............. MPhil 12FT 24PT/PhD 36FT 72PT
Environmental Science......................................Integrated PhD 48FT

Nottingham Trent University
Applied Energy and Environmental Engineering .... MPhil 18FT 30PT/PhD 33FT 66PT

The Open University
Integrated Waste Systems .... PhD 36FT 72PT variableDL/MPhil 15FT 24PT variableDL

University of Sheffield
Civil and Structural Engineering: Integrated Studies....Integrated PhD 48FT
Environmental and Energy Engineering: Integrated Studies......... Integrated PhD 48FT

University of Southampton
Coastal Engineering for Climate Change ....MRes 12FT 24PT
Doctorate by research ....PhD 36FT/MPhil 24FT

University of Strathclyde
Building Design and Management for Sustainability .... MRes 12FT 36PT

University of Surrey
Sustainability for Engineering and Energy Systems (SEES) .. EngD 48FT

Swansea University
Environmental Management..................................MRes 12FT 24PT
Erasmus Mundus Simulation in Engineering and Entrepreneurship Development............................... PhD 36FT 72PT

UCL - University College London
Civil, Environmental and Geomatic Engineering .. PhD 36FT 60PT
Environmental Engineering Science................................ EngD 48FT

University of the West of Scotland
Department of Civil, Structural and Environmental Engineering PhD/MPhil

Environmental health
Taught Courses

University of Birmingham
Environmental Health..MSc 12FT 72PT
Public and Environmental Health Science .... MSc 12FT

Cranfield University
Health and the Environment........ MSc 12FT 24-36PT/PGDip 12FT 24-36PT

University of Cumbria
International Health............... MSc 12FT 24PT/GradDip 6FT 12PT/GradCert 3FT 6PT
Public Health and Social Change....MSc 36FT 60PT/GradDip 24FT 36PT/GradCert 12FT 18PT

University of Derby
Environmental Health....................................... MSc 24FT 48PT 48DL
Sustainable Architecture and Healthy Environments .....MA 12FT

Dublin Institute of Technology
Environmental Health and Safety Management.. MSc 12FT 24PT

University of Dundee
Epidemiology and Global Health International Prevention Research Institute Summer School.......................................Cert 1FT
Spatial Planning with Environmental Assessment .... MSc 12FT

Durham University
Risk, Health and Public Policy..MA 12FT

University of East Anglia
Applied Ecology and Conservation .... MSc 12FT 24PT
Climate Change .... MSc 12FT
Climate Change and International Development. MSc 12FT 24PT
Ecology.. GradDip 12FT 24PT
Environmental Sciences... MSc 12FT 24PT
Environmental Sciences and Humanities .... MA 12FT 24PT/MSc 12FT 24PT
Environmental Sciences and Humanities .... MA 12FT 24PT/MSc 12FT 24PT

University of East London
Public Health .... MSc 12FT 48PT/PGCert 4FT 8PT/PGDip 8FT 16PT

University of Edinburgh
Global Health Challenges (Online Distance Learning) .... PGCert 12-24DL
Global Health Policy (Online Distance Learning) ...PGCert 9-21DL
Global Health Studies (online distance learning)......PGCert 36DL
Global Health and Infectious Diseases (Online Distance Learning).................................MSc 36DL/PGDip 24DL/PGCert 12DL
Global Health and Public Policy..........................MSc 12FT 24-36PT
Global Health: Non Communicable Diseases (online distance learning) ....MSc 36DL/PGDip 24DL/PGCert 12DL
One Health.............................MSc 36DL/PGDip 24DL/PGCert 12DL

University of Exeter
Environment and Human Health.......PGCert 6FT/PGDip 9FT/MSc 12FT 24PT

Heriot-Watt University
Food Science, Safety and Health MSc 12FT 24PT 24-84DL/PGDip 9FT 21PT 24-84DL
Food and Beverage Science..........MSc 12FT 24PT/PGDip 9FT 21PT

Leeds Metropolitan University
Acoustics and Noise Control.. PGDip 12PT
Environmental Health..MSc 12FT 36PT
Public Health (Health Promotion and Environmental Health) Zambia .... MSc 36PT

London School of Hygiene and Tropical Medicine
Public Health (Environment & Health)...................MSc 12FT 24PT
Public Health (Health Economics)............................MSc 12FT 24PT

Middlesex University
Environmental Health...MSc 12FT 24PT

Royal Veterinary College
One Health (Infectious Diseases) - PGDip (F/T) .... PGDip 8FT

University of Salford
Environmental Acoustics...MSc 12FT 28PT 28DL/PGDip 9FT 18PT 18DL
Environmental and Public Health ..MSc 12FT 24-36PT/PGDip 8FT 24PT
Safety, Health and Environment MSc 12FT 36PT/PGDip 8FT 24PT

Sheffield Hallam University
Built Environment.....MPhil 24FT 36PT/PhD by taught 24FT 60PT
Housing for Environmental Health...............................CertHE 18PT

University of Strathclyde
Environmental Health....MSc 12FT 24PT/PGDip 9FT 18PT/PGCert 6FT 12PT

UCL - University College London
Built Environment: Environmental Design and Engineering......... MSc 12FT 24-60PT/PGDip 9FT
Built Environment: Heritage Science ....MRes 12FT 24-60PT/PGCert 6FT
Built Environment: Sustainable Heritage .... MSc 12FT 24-60PT/PGDip 9FT

University of West London
Health and Social Care Leadership.................................... MSc 24PT

University of the West of England, Bristol
Environmental Health... MSc 15FT 27PT

Environmental health
Research Courses

University of East Anglia
Copy of Environmental Sciences: Geosciences and Natural Hazards .... PhD 36FT 72PT/MPhil 24FT 48PT
Environmental Sciences: Climate, Ocean and Atmospheric Sciences.. PhD 36FT 72PT/MPhil 24FT 48PT
Environmental Sciences: Resources, Sustainability and Governance.................................. PhD 36FT 72PT/MPhil 24FT 48PT

University of Edinburgh
Global Health .... MPhil 24FT 48PT/PhD 36FT 72PT

Middlesex University
Health or Environment DProf 24FT 60PT/MProf by research 24FT 60PT

Environmental policy
Taught Courses

University of Aberdeen
Climate Change Law and Sustainable Development......LLM 12FT 24--36PT

University of Abertay Dundee
Energy & Environmental Management .... MSc 12FT

Aberystwyth University
Remote Sensing & Geographical Information Systems (GIS) .... MSc 12FT 24PT/PGDip 9FT 18PT/PGCert 5FT 10PT
Remote Sensing and GeographyMSc 12FT 24PT/PGDip 9FT 18PT/PGCert 5FT 10PT

School of Advanced Study, University of London
Advanced Legislative Studies ....LLM 12FT 24PT 24DL

Bangor University
Conservation and Land Management .... MSc 12FT/PGDip 9FT
Environmental Forestry .... MSc 12FT
Environmental Management... MBA 12FT
Environmental Management... MBA 12FT
Forestry and Environmental Management degrees (TRANSFOR-M)... MSc 24FT
Marine Biology...................................MSc 12FT 24-36PT/PGDip 9FT
Marine Environmental Protection .... MSc 12FT 24-36PT
Physical Oceanography.....................MSc 12FT 24-36PT/PGDip 9FT
Rheolaeth Amgylcheddol Gynaliadwy (Sustainable Environmental Management)........MSc 12FT 24PT/MA 12FT 24PT

University of Bath
Environment, Energy & Resilience (MRes) ..... MRes 12FT 24-36PT

University of Bedfordshire
Environmental Management..............................MSc 12-18FT 36PT

Birmingham City University
Environmental Sustainability...... PGCert 4FT 8PT/PGDip 4FT 8PT/MSc 4FT 8PT
Environmental Sustainability (Design and Construction) . PGCert 4FT 8PT/PGDip 4FT 8PT/MSc 4FT 8PT

University of Birmingham
Environmental and Natural Resource Economics . MSc 12FT 24PT

University of Brighton
Environmental Assessment and Management ....MSc 12FT 24PT/PGCert 12FT 24PT/PGDip 12FT 24PT

University of Bristol
Climate Change Science and Policy ....MSc 12FT 24PT
Environmental Policy and Management.. MSc 12FT 24PT/PGCert 12FT 24PT/PGDip 12FT 24PT

Brunel University
Climate Change Impacts and Sustainability..........MSc 12FT 24PT
Environmental Science: Legislation and Management. MSc 12FT 24PT

University of Cambridge
Environmental Policy.. MPhil 10FT
Land Economy Research .... MPhil 10FT

Cardiff University
Sustainability, Planning and Environmental Policy .... MSc 12FT 24PT

University of Central Lancashire
Energy and Environmental Management.MSc 12FT 24PT/PGDip 9FT 18PT/PGCert 6FT 12PT

University of Chester
Regeneration for Practitioners.....MA 12FT 24 - 72PT/PGDip 12FT 24 - 60PT/PGCert 12FT 12 - 36PT
Sustainability for Community and Business.........MSc 12FT 24PT/PGDip 12FT 24PT/PGCert 12FT 12-24PT

Cranfield University
Economics for Natural Resource & Environmental Management MSc 12FT 24-60PT/PGCert 5FT 24PT/PGDip 6FT 24PT
Environment and Public Policy.......... MSc 12FT 60PT/PGCert 12FT 60PT/PGDip 12FT 60PT
Environmental Informatics......MSc 12FT 60PT/PGDip 12FT 60PT/PGCert 12FT 60PT
Environmental Risk Management .MSc 12FT 24-60PT/PGDip 6FT 24PT/PGCert 5FT 24PT

University of Cumbria
Leadership and Management in Policing MBA 36PT/PGDip 36PT/PGCert 36PT

University of Dundee
Climate Change Economics and Policy .... MSc 12FT
Climate Change and Energy Law and Policy ....LLM 12FT

Environmental science and ecology

Energy Studies with Specialisation in Energy Policy ..... MSc 12FT
Environmental Law ....LLM 12FT
Environmental Law and Policy ....LLM 12FT
Mineral Law and Policy ....LLM 12FT
Mineral Law and Policy ....LLM 60DL
Natural Resources Law and Policy....LLM 60DL
Non-Graduating Taught Postgrad Grad School of Natural Resources Law, Policy & Management .... PG module variableFT
Petroleum Law and Policy ....LLM 12FT/PGDip 9FT
Petroleum Law and Policy ....LLM 24-60DL
Spatial Planning with Environmental Assessment .... MSc 12FT
Spatial Planning with Marine Spatial Planning .... MSc 12FT
Supplementary Studies in Graduate School of Natural Resources, Law, Policy and Management ....Masters Level Modules 6-9FT

University of East Anglia
Climate Change .... MSc 12FT
Climate Change and International Development.... MSc 12FT 24PT
Energy Engineering with Environmental ManagementMSc 12FT/MSc 24PT/MSc 36PT/MSc 48PT
Environment and International Development ...... MSc 12FT 24PT
Environmental Sciences....MSc 12FT 24PT
Environmental Sciences and Humanities .... MA 12FT 24PT/MSc 12FT 24PT
Environmental Sciences and Humanities .... MA 12FT 24PT/MSc 12FT 24PT
Impact Evaluation for International Development .... MSc 12FT 24PT
Public Policy and Public Management ....MRes 12FT 24PT

University of Edinburgh
Carbon Capture & Storage....MSc 12FT 36PT
Carbon Finance .... MSc 12FT
Carbon Management .... MSc 12FT
Environmental Protection and Management.......MSc 12FT 24PT/PGDip 9FT
Environmental Sustainability..........MSc 12FT 24-36PT/PGDip 9FT
Global Environment Challenges Certificate (Online distance learning) ....PGCert 9DL
Global Environment and Climate Change Law...... LLM 12FT 24PT
Integrated Resource Management.... MSc 12FT

University of Exeter
Climate Change Impacts and Feedbacks..............MRes 12FT 24PT
Climate Change and Risk Management....MSc 12FT 24PT
Conservation Science and Policy ....MSc 11FT
Critical Human Geographies ....MRes 12FT
Energy Policy....MSc 12FT 24PT
Environment, Energy and Resilience ....MRes 12FT 24PT
Sustainable Development....MSc 12FT 24PT

National University of Ireland Galway
Economic and Environmental Modelling... MEconSci 10approxFT

University of Glasgow
Applied Carbon Management (Dumfries Campus)........ MSc 12FT 24PT
Environmental Science, Technology & Society (Dumfries Campus)....MSc 12FT 24PT
Environmental Statistics .... MSc 12FT

Goldsmiths, University of London
Design & Environment .... MA 12FT 24PT

Heriot-Watt University
Climate Change: Impacts and Mitigation..MSc 12FT 24PT/PGDip 9FT 21PT
Climate Change: Managing The Marine Environment.. MSc 12FT 24PT/PGDip 9FT 21PT
Environmental Analysis and Assessment .... MRes 12FT 24PT/PGDip 9FT 18PT/PGCert 9FT 18PT
Marine Resource Development and Protection....MSc 12FT 24PT/PGDip 9FT 21PT

Institute of Education
Educational Planning, Economics and International Development.... MA 12FT 24-48PT

Keele University
Climate Change Studies - Policy, Justice and Global Politics.... MA 12FT 24PT

University of Kent
Agri-Environmental Economics and Policy ....MSc 12FT 24PT
Anthropology and Conservation .... MA 12FT 24PT
Conservation and Business....MSc 12FT 24PT
Environmental Law and Policy....LLM 12FT 24PT/PGDip 12FT 24PT

Kingston University
Sustainability & Environmental Change................MSc 12FT 24PT

University of Leeds
Sustainability (Climate Change).... MSc 12FT
Sustainability (Environment and Development)............ MSc 12FT 12-48PT
Sustainability (Environmental Politics and Policy).......... MSc 12FT 12-48PT

London School of Economics and Political Science (LSE)
Environmental Economics and Climate Change ... MSc 12FT 24PT
Environmental Policy and Regulation ....MSc 12FT 24PT

London South Bank University
Management in Civil Society - Blended.... MSc 24PT

Loughborough University
Sustainable Engineering....MSc 12FT 96PT

Middlesex University
Global Governance and Public Policy .... MA 12FT 24PT
Sustainable Environmental Management...... MA 12FT 24PT/MSc 12FT 24PT

Newcastle University
Environmental Law and Policy (Research).............. LLM 12FT 24PT
Environmental Regulation and Sustainable Development.....LLM 12FT 24PT
Sustainable Buildings and Environments .... MSc 12FT

Nottingham Trent University
Human Security and Environmental Change.........MA 12FT 24PT/PGDip 9FT 18PT/PGCert 9FT

University of Nottingham
Economic Development and Policy Analysis .... MSc 12FT

The Open University
Science and Society....MSc variableDL/PGDip variableDL

Oxford Brookes University
Environmental Assessment and Management ...MSc 12FT 24PT/PGDip 9FT 21PT

University of Oxford
Environmental Change & Management.... MSc 12FT
Nature, Society and Environmental Policy.... MSc 12FT
Water Science, Policy and Management .... MSc 12FT

Queen Mary, University of London
Environmental Science: Integrated Management of Freshwater Environments ....MSc 12FT 24-36PT

Queen's University Belfast
Environmental Planning.... MSc 12FT
Sustainable Design .... MSc 12FT/PGDip 9FT

Ravensbourne
Environment Design.... MA 12FT 24PT

University of Reading
Applied Development Studies ....MSc 12FT 24PT
Climate Change & Development ....MSc 12FT 24PT
Economics of Climate Change ....MSc 12FT 24PT
Environment and Development .... MSc 12FT
The Economics of Climate Change .... MSc 12FT

Robert Gordon University
Energy Management.... MSc 12FT 36DL/PGDip 8FT 24DL/PGCert 4FT 12DL
Energy and Sustainability ...MSc 42DL/PGDip 24DL/PGCert 12DL

Royal Holloway, University of London
Global Health: Pathogens and Policy .. MSc 12FT 24PT/PGDip 9FT

University of Salford
Environmental Assessment and Management....MSc 12FT 36PT/PGDip 8FT 24PT
Environmental and Public Health ..MSc 12FT 24-36PT/PGDip 8FT 24PT

School of Oriental and African Studies - SOAS
Environmental Law and Sustainable DevelopmentMA 12FT 24PT
Environmental Management....MSc 12FT 24-36PT
Global Energy and Climate Policy ....MSc 12FT 24PT
MA Globalisation and Multinational CorporationsMA 12FT 24PT

Schumacher College
Holistic Science .... MSc 12FT

Sheffield Hallam University
Environmental Management....MSc 12-24FT 24-36PT
Environmental Management (International Resource and Climate Management)....MSc 12-18FT 24-36PT
Environmental Management (Wildlife and Landscape Conservation) ....MSc 12-18FT 24-36PT
Sustainable Communities and Environments .... MSc 12-18FT 24-36PT

University of South Wales
Environmental Conservation Management........... MSc 12FT 36PT

University of Southampton
Environmental Monitoring and Assessment .... MSc 12FT 27PT
Environmental Pollution Control....MSc 12FT 27PT

University of St Andrews
Sustainable Aquaculture. MSc 12FT 24PT/PGDip 9FT 24PT 24DL/Cert 12DL

Staffordshire University
Habitat Management and Conservation ... MSc 15FT/PGDip 12FT

University of Stirling
Environmental Policy and Governance........... LLM 12FT/MSc 12FT

University of Strathclyde
Applied Economics ... MSc 12FT 24PT 24DL/PGDip 9FT 18PT 18DL
Sustainability and Environmental Studies ....MSc 12FT 24PT/PGDip 9FT 18PT

University of Surrey
Environmental Strategy....MSc 12FT 12-60PT

University of Sussex
Environment, Development and Policy .... MA 12FT 24PT

Swansea University
Environmental Dynamics and Climate Change..... MSc 12FT 36PT
Geographic Information and Climate Change......MSc 12FT 36PT/PGCert 12FT 12PT

Teesside University
Energy and Environmental Management.........MSc 12-16FT 24PT

Trinity College Dublin - the University of Dublin
Environment and Development .... MSc 12FT
Environmental Sciences.... MSc 12FT

UCL - University College London
Anthropology, Environment and Development .... MSc 12FT 24PT
Biodiversity, Evolution and Conservation MRes .... MRes 12FT
Climate Change ....MSc 12FT 24PT
Energy Demand Studies ....MRes 12FT
Energy and Resources: Policy and Practice, Australia .... MSc 24FT 36-48PT
Global Health and Development: tropEd programme .. MSc 12FT 24-60PT

University of the West of England, Bristol
Environmental Consultancy ....MSc 36-60DL

Environmental policy
Research Courses

Aberystwyth University
Earth Sciences ....MPhil 12FT 24PT
Earth Sciences .... PhD 36FT 60PT
Human Geography .... PhD 36FT 60PT

Bangor University
Biodiversity Conservation .... MPhil 24FT 36PT/PhD 36FT 60PT
Ocean Sciences....MPhil 24FT/PhD 36FT

University of Bedfordshire
Environmental Studies.... PhD 36FT 72PT

Brunel University
Environmental Issues and Environmental Change.....MPhil 12FT/PhD 36FT

University of Cambridge
Land Economy (by thesis).... MPhil 11FT

Cardiff University
Environment.... PhD 36FT 60PT/MPhil 36FT 60PT
Institute of Environment and Sustainability........ PhD 36FT/MPhil 60PT

Coventry University
Environmental & Climate Change......MSc by research 12FT 24PT

University of Dundee
Non-Graduating Research in Natural Resources Law, Policy and Management (6 months or more) ....Non-Grad 6-24FT
Non-Graduating Research in Natural Resources Law, Policy and Management (less than 6 mths).... Non-Grad 1-5FT
Town and Regional Planning (MPhil) .... MPhil 24FT

University of East Anglia
Copy of Environmental Sciences: Geosciences and Natural Hazards .... PhD 36FT 72PT/MPhil 24FT 48PT
Environmental Sciences: Climate, Ocean and Atmospheric Sciences.... PhD 36FT 72PT/MPhil 24FT 48PT
Environmental Sciences: Resources, Sustainability and Governance.... PhD 36FT 72PT/MPhil 24FT 48PT

University of Exeter
Environment, Energy and Resilience ..MPhil 36FT 60PT/PhD 36FT 84PT
Human Geography.........PhD 48FT 84PT/MPhil 36FT 60PT/MSc by research 12FT 24PT

University of Gloucestershire
Sustainability....PhD 36FT

University of Kent
Biodiversity Management....PhD 36FT 60PT/MSc by research 12FT 24PT

London School of Economics and Political Science (LSE)
Environmental Policy and Development ....MPhil 36-48FT/PhD 36-48FT

Manchester Metropolitan University
Environmental and Geographical Sciences .... MSc by research/MPhil/PhD

Newcastle University
Energy.... PhD 36FT 72PT/MPhil 12FT 24PT
Environmental Science................ MPhil 12FT 24PT/PhD 36FT 72PT
Environmental Science....Integrated PhD 48FT

University of Nottingham
Environmental and Geomorphological Sciences .PhD 36FT 72PT/MPhil 24FT 48PT

The Open University
Environment, governance and justicePhD 36FT 72PT variableDL/MPhil 15FT 24PT variableDL
Geography................ PhD 36FT 72PT variableDL/MPhil 15FT 24PT variableDL

Environmental science and ecology

Political ideas, policies and actions.... PhD 36FT 72PT variableDL/ MPhil 15FT 24PT variableDL

Oxford Brookes University
Impact Assessment MPhil/PhD...... MPhil/PhD 36-60FT 48-72PT/ PhD 24-60FT 36-72PT/MPhil 24-36FT 36-48PT

Queen's University Belfast
Environmental Change............... PhD 36FT 72PT/MPhil 24FT 48PT

Sheffield Hallam University
Centre for Regional Economic and Social Research Applied Social Research.......... PhD 36FT 60PT
Environment and Development.......... MPhil 36PT
Environment and Development - Facilities Management.......PhD 33FT 45PT/MPhil 18FT 30PT

Swansea University
Environmental Sustainability..............MSc by research 12FT 24PT
Sustainable Resources..........MSc by research 12FT

Environmental science and ecology
Taught Courses

University of Aberdeen
Environmental Science.......... MSc 12FT/PGDip 9FT

University of Abertay Dundee
Energy & Environmental Management .... MSc 12FT
Industrial Environmental Management.....MSc 12FT 24PT/PGDip 9FT 18PT

Aberystwyth University
Environmental Monitoring and Analysis ....MSc 12FT/PGDip 9FT/ PGCert 9FT
Food & Water Security ....MSc 12FT 24PT/PGDip 9FT 18PT
Managing the Environment........MSc 12FT 24PT/PGDip 9FT 18PT
Remote Sensing and The Living Environment ......MSc 12FT 24PT/ PGDip 9FT 18PT/PGCert 5FT 10PT

Anglia Ruskin University
Applied Wildlife Conservation .... MSc 24PT
Sustainability: Working for Positive Change....MSc 12FT 24-30PT

Bangor University
Agroforestry...... MSc 12FT 24PT/PhD by taught 36FT 60PT/MPhil 24FT 36PT
Ecology.......... MRes 12FT
Environmental Forestry .... MSc 12FT
Environmental Management.......... MBA 12FT
Forestry (Distance Learning).......... MSc 36DL/PGDip 24DL/ PGCert 12DL
Forestry and Environmental Management degrees (TRANSFOR-M).......... MSc 24FT
Marine Biology..........MSc 12FT 24-36PT/PGDip 9FT
Marine Environmental Protection ....MSc 12FT 24-36PT
Natural Sciences .... MRes 12FT
Physical Oceanography..........MSc 12FT 24-36PT/PGDip 9FT
Rheolaeth Amgylcheddol Gynaliadwy (Sustainable Environmental Management)........MSc 12FT 24PT/MA 12FT 24PT
Rheolaeth Amgylcheddol Gynaliadwy / Sustainable Environmental Managem (Welsh-medium) .. MA 12FT 24PT/MSc 12FT 24PT
Sustainable Forest and Nature Management (SUFONAMA) (Erasmus Mundus course).......... MSc 24FT
Tropical Ecosystems.. PhD by taught 36FT 60PT/MPhil 24FT 36PT
Wetland Science and Conservation .... MSc 12FT

Bath Spa University
Environmental management..........MA 12FT

University of Bath
Integrated Environmental Management by Distance Learning.... MSc 24-60DL/PGDip 24-60DL

University of Bedfordshire
Environmental Management..........MSc 12-18FT 36PT

Birkbeck, University of London
Children, Youth and International Development.. MSc 12FT 24PT
Environment and Sustainability.........MSc 12FT 24PT/PGDip 12FT 24PT/PGCert 12PT

University of Birmingham
Human and Environmental Health Impacts of Nanoscience and Nanotechnology.......... MRes 12FT
River Environments and their Management.......... MSc 12FT 24PT

University of Brighton
Environmental Assessment and Management ....MSc 12FT 24PT/ PGCert 12FT 24PT/PGDip 12FT 24PT
Geographical Information Systems and Environmental Management.......... MSc 12FT 24PT/PGDip 12FT 24PT

University of Bristol
Ecology and Management of the Natural Environment.......... MSc 24PT

Brunel University
Sustainability, Entrepreneurship and Design (with Professional Development).......... MSc 18FT
Water Engineering .... MSc 12FT

University of Cambridge
Fluid Flow in Industry and the Environment.......... MPhil 11FT
Geographical Research.......... MPhil 12FT

University of Central Lancashire
Carbon and Resource Management....MSc 12FT 24PT/PGDip 9FT 18PT/PGCert 6FT 12PT
Energy and Environmental Management.MSc 12FT 24PT/PGDip 9FT 18PT/PGCert 6FT 12PT
Urban Environmental Management...MSc 12FT 24PT/PGDip 9FT 18PT/PGCert 6FT 12PT
Values and Environment .... MA 12FT 24PT

City University London
Energy and Environmental Technology and Economics.......... MSc 12FT 24PT

University College Cork
Applied Science (Ecological Assessment).......... MSc 12FT
Applied Science (Ecological Assessment)..........PGDip 9FT
Applied Science (Geographical Information Systems & Remote Sensing.......... MSc 12FT
Applied Science (Marine Biology).......... MSc 12FT
Geography (Coastal Management Systems)..........MA 12FT

Coventry University
Environmental Management..........MSc 12FT 24-30PT

Cranfield University
Economics for Natural Resource & Environmental Management MSc 12FT 24-60PT/PGCert 5FT 24PT/PGDip 6FT 24PT
Environmental Diagnostics and Management.......... MSc 12FT 24-60PT/PGDip 6FT 24PT/PGCert 5FT 24PT
Environmental Management for Business..... MSc 12FT 24-60PT/ PGDip 6FT 24PT/PGCert 5FT 24PT

University of Cumbria
Conservation Biology.......... MSc 12FT min 24PT/GradDip 6FT min 12PT/GradCert 3FT min 6PT
Forest Ecosystem Management .... MSc 12FT 24PT/GradDip 6FT 12PT/GradCert 3FT 6PT
Greening Outdoor Practice ....PGCert 24-36PT

De Montfort University
Environmental Quality Management F85171.........MSc 12-18DL/ PGDip 3-4DL/PGCert 3-4DL

University of Derby
Environmental Health.......... MSc 24FT 48PT 48DL
Environmental Management..........MSc 12FT 24-36PT
Sustainable Architecture and Healthy Environments .....MA 12FT

University of Dundee
Civil Engineering .... MSc 12FT
Energy Studies with Specialisation in Energy and the Environment .... MSc 12FT
Environmental Law ....LLM 12FT
Non-Graduating Taught Postgraduate in School of the Environment.......... PG module variableFT
Renewable Energy and Environmental Modelling .... MSc 12FT
Spatial Planning with Marine Spatial Planning .... MSc 12FT

University of East Anglia
Applied Ecology - European Programme.......... MSc 24FT
Applied Ecology and Conservation .... MSc 12FT 24PT
Atmospheric Sciences .... MSc 11FT
Ecology.......... GradDip 12FT 24PT
Environmental Assessment and Management..... MSc 12FT 24PT
Environmental Economics.......... MSc 12FT 24PT
Environmental Sciences.......... MSc 12FT 24PT
Environmental Sciences and Humanities .... MA 12FT 24PT/MSc 12FT 24PT
Public Policy and the Environment .... MA 12FT 24PT

University of East London
Architecture: Advanced Environmental and Energy Studies .... MSc 24DL

University of Edinburgh
Biodiversity and Taxonomy of Plants .... MSc 12FT/PGDip 9FT
Biodiversity, Wildlife & Ecosystem Health (online distance learning) ...MSc 36PT 36DL/PGDip 24PT 24DL/PGCert 12PT 12DL
Carbon Capture & Storage.......... MSc 12FT 36PT
Carbon Finance .... MSc 12FT
Carbon Management .... MSc 12FT
Ecological Economics..........MSc 12FT 24-36PT/PGDip 9FT
Ecosystem Services ....MSc 12FT 24-36PT
Environment and Development .... MSc 12FT 24PT/PGDip 9FT
Environment, Culture and Society .... MSc 12FT 24PT
Environmental Protection and Management.......MSc 12FT 24PT/ PGDip 9FT
Environmental Sustainability..........MSc 12FT 24-36PT/PGDip 9FT
GeoSciences (Individual Project) .... MSc(Res) 12FT 24PT
Global Environment Challenges Certificate (Online distance learning) ....PGCert 9DL
Global Environment and Climate Change Law...... LLM 12FT 24PT
Global Health Studies (online distance learning) ......PGCert 36DL
Global Health and Infectious Diseases (Online Distance Learning)..........MSc 36DL/PGDip 24DL/PGCert 12DL
Integrated Resource Management.......... MSc 12FT
Management of Bioeconomy, Innovation and Governance... MSc 12FT 24PT
Petroleum Geoscience.......... MSc 12FT

University of Essex
Environmental Resource Management.......... MSc 12FT 24PT
Marine Biology.......... MSc 12FT

Natural Environment and Society.......... MSc 12FT

University of Exeter
Biosciences.......... MSc(Res) 12FT 36PT
Climate Change Impacts and Feedbacks..........MRes 12FT 24PT
Climate Change and Risk Management.......... MSc 12FT 24PT
Conservation Science and Policy .... MSc 11FT
Evolutionary and Behavioural Ecology.......... MSc 12FT
Surveying and Land/ Environmental Management....... MSc 12FT 24-36PT/PGDip 12FT 24-36PT
Sustainable Development.......... MSc 12FT 24PT
Water Management .... MSc 12FT 24PT

National University of Ireland Galway
Economic and Environmental Modelling ... MEconSci 10approxFT

Glasgow Caledonian University
Energy and Environmental Management..MSc 12FT 24PT/PGDip 8FT 20PT/PGCert 4FT 8PT

University of Glasgow
Environmental Science, Technology & Society (Dumfries Campus).......... MSc 12FT 24PT
Marine System Science ....MSc 12FT 24PT/PGDip 8FT 16PT
Physics: Energy and the Environment.......... MSc 12FT
Quantitative Methods in Biodiversity, Conservation and Epidemiology.......... MSc 12FT/PGDip 9FT

University of Greenwich
Natural Resources .... MSc 12FT 24PT/PGDip 12FT 24PT

Heriot-Watt University
Carbon Management .. MSc 12FT 24PT 24-84DL/PGDip 9FT 21PT 24-84DL
Climate Change: Impacts and Mitigation..MSc 12FT 24PT/PGDip 9FT 21PT

University of Hertfordshire
Environmental Management for BusinessMSc 12-15FT 24-60PT/ PGDip 12FT 18-48PT/PGCert 12FT 18-48PT

University of Hull
Environmental Technology .... MSc 12FT 24PT
Environmental Technology (renewable energy).... MSc 12FT 24PT

Imperial College London
Environmental Technology .... MSc 12FT 24PT

University of Kent
Environmental Social Science .... MSc 12FT 24PT

King's College London
Environment & Development........MA 12FT 24PT/MSc 12FT 24PT
Environment, Politics & Globalisation ... MA 12FT 24PT/MSc 12FT 24PT
Environmental Monitoring, Modelling & ManagementMSc 12FT 24PT
Global Environmental Change.......... MSc 12FT 24PT

Kingston University
Sustainability & Environmental Change.......... MSc 12FT 24PT

Lancaster University
(Research) International Masters in Environmental Science and Technology.......... MSc(Res) 21FT
Environment and Development (Overseas Placement)MRes 12FT 24PT
Environmental Science (by research) .... MSc(Res) 12FT 24PT
Environmental Science and Technology.......... MSc 12FT 24PT
Science of the Environment..........MRes 12FT 14PT

University of Leeds
Catchment Dynamics and Management...MSc 12FT 24PT/PGDip 12FT 24PT/MRes 12FT 24PT
Earth, Energy and Environment..........MSc 12FT/PGDip 12FT
Energy and Environment.......... MSc 12FT
Sustainability (Environmental Consultancy).... MSc 12FT 12-48PT

University of Leicester
Environmental Informatics..........MSc 12FT 24PT/PGDip 9FT 18PT
Global Environmental Change....MSc 12FT 24PT/PGDip 9FT 12PT

Liverpool Hope University
Environmental Management.... MSc 12FT 24PT/PGDip 9FT 18PT/ PGCert 6FT 12PT

University of Liverpool
Environmental Management and Planning.......... MA 12FT 24PT
Environmental Sciences.......... MSc 12FT

London Metropolitan University
Architecture, Energy and Sustainability.......... MSc 12FT 24PT

London School of Hygiene and Tropical Medicine
Public Health (Environment & Health).......... MSc 12FT 24PT

Loughborough University
Analytical Chemistry and Environmental Science.......... MSc 12FT 24 - 60PT
Environmental Monitoring for Management........ MSc 12FT 24PT
Environmental Studies. MSc 12FT 24-96PT/PGDip 12FT 24-60PT/ PGCert 12-36PT

Manchester Metropolitan University
Bird Conservation.......... MSc 12FT 24PT
Conservation Genetics .... MSc 12FT 24PT
Countryside Management..........MSc 36PT 36DL

Environmental science and ecology

Environment, Management and Sustainable Development .... MSc 12FT 36PT

University of Manchester
Advanced Process Design for Energy.. MSc 12FT 60DL/PGDip 9FT 24DL/PGCert 6FT 12DL
Applications in Environmental Science .... MSc 12FT
Environment and Sustainable Technology .... MSc 12FT/PGDip 9FT/PGCert 6FT
Environmental Governance .... MSc 12FT 24PT
Environmental Impact Assessment & Management .... MSc 12FT 24PT
Environmental Impact Assessment and Management.................. MSc 12FT 24PT
Environmental Monitoring, Modelling and Reconstruction .... MSc 12FT 24PT
Environmental Sciences, Policy & Management (MESPOM).......... MSc 24FT
International Development: Environment and DevelopmentMSc 12FT 24PT

Newcastle University
Agricultural and Environmental Science .... MSc 12FT
Ecological Consultancy .... MSc 12FT
Environmental Resource Assessment .... MSc 12FT
International Marine Environmental Consultancy (IMEC) ..... MSc 12FT/PGDip 9FT
Tropical Coastal Management .... MSc 12FT/PGDip 9FT

University of Northampton
Environmental Management .... MSc 12FT 24PT

Northumbria University
Business with Pipeline Integrity Management .... MSc 12FT

University of Nottingham
Environmental History .... MSc 12FT 24PT
Environmental Management....... MA 12FT 24PT/MSc 12FT 24PT/PGDip 9FT 18PT
Environmental Management and Earth Observation ... MSc 12FT 24-36PT/PGDip 9FT 24-36PT
Law and Environmental Science .... MSc 12FT 24PT

The Open University
Earth Science .... MSc variablePT
Environmental Management.........MSc variableDL/PGCert 12DL/PGDip variableDL
Professional Science .... MSc variableDL
Science .... MSc variableDL

Oxford Brookes University
Environmental Impact Assessment (MRes).......... MRes 12FT 24PT
Two Year Master's Degree - Technology, Design and Environment MSc 21-24FT

University of Oxford
Environmental Change & Management .... MSc 12FT
Geography and the Environment .... MPhil 24FT
Nature, Society and Environmental Policy .... MSc 12FT

Plymouth University
Environmental Consultancy .... MSc 12FT 24PT
Marine Biology .... MRes 12FT 24PT
Sustainable Environmental Management............ MRes 12FT 24PT
Sustainable Environmental Management............ MSc 12FT 24PT/PGDip 9FT

Queen Mary, University of London
Energy and Natural Resources Law........................... LLM 12FT 24PT
Environmental Law .... LLM 12FT 24PT

Queen's University Belfast
Ecological Management and Conservation Biology .... MSc 12FT 24PT/PGDip 9FT

University of Reading
Environmental Management .... MSc 12FT 24PT
Plant Diversity .... MSc 12FT 24PT
Species Identification and Survey Skills .... MSc 12FT
The Economics of Climate Change .... MSc 12FT

Robert Gordon University
Energy Management.... MSc 12FT 36DL/PGDip 8FT 24DL/PGCert 4FT 12DL
Instrumental Analytical Sciences: Oilfield Chemicals ... MSc 12FT 36PT/PGDip 9FT 24PT/PGCert 4FT 12PT

Royal Agricultural University
Climate Change and Development.......................... MSc 12FT 24PT
Fisheries and Aquaculture Management................ MSc 12FT 24PT
Natural Resource Management .... MSc 12FT 24PT
Organic Agricultural Systems .... MSc 12FT 24PT
Sustainable Agricultural Systems .... MSc 12FT 24PT
Sustainable Agriculture and Food Security............. MSc 15FT 24PT
Sustainable Business .... MSc 12FT 24PT
Sustainable Rural Tourism .... MSc 12FT 24PT
Sustainable Soil Management .... MSc 12FT 24PT

Royal Holloway, University of London
Environmental Diagnosis and Management .... MSc 12FT 24PT

School of Oriental and African Studies - SOAS
Environmental Law and Sustainable Development .... MA 12FT 24PT
Environmental Management .... MSc 12FT 24-36PT

Schumacher College
Holistic Science .... MSc 12FT

Scotland's Rural College
Countryside Management ..MSc 36DL/PGDip 24DL/PGCert 12DL

Sheffield Hallam University
Environmental Management......................... MSc 12-24FT 24-36PT
Environmental Management (International Resource and Climate Management) .... MSc 12-18FT 24-36PT
Environmental Management (Wildlife and Landscape Conservation) .... MSc 12-18FT 24-36PT
Environmental management (Business)...... MSc 12FT 36PT 36DL
Public Rights of Way and Countryside Access Management .... MSc 36DL

University of Sheffield
Earthquake and Civil Engineering Dynamics .... MSc(Eng) 12FT 24PT
Environmental Change and International Development .... MSc 12FT 24PT
Environmental Management of Urban Land and Water .... MSc 12FT 24PT/PGDip 9FT 18PT/PGCert 6FT 12PT

University of South Wales
Civil Engineering and Environmental Management...... MSc 12FT 36PT
Conservation and Geographical Information Systems.. MSc 12FT 24PT
Environmental Conservation Management........... MSc 12FT 36PT
Environmental Management .... MSc 12FT 36PT
Renewable Energy and Resource Management.... MSc 12FT 36PT
Safety, Health and Environmental Management .... MSc 12/FT 36PT

University of Southampton
Biodiversity and Conservation .... MSc 12FT 27PT
Ecological and Environmental Sciences.......................... MRes 12FT
Environmental Monitoring and Assessment .... MSc 12FT 27PT
Environmental Pollution Control............................. MSc 12FT 27PT
Freshwater Sciences .... MRes 12FT
Integrated Environmental Studies.......................... MSc 12FT 27PT
MSc Marine Resource Management .... MSc 12FT

University of St Andrews
Ecosystem-based Management of Marine Systems .... MRes 12FT
Environmental Biology (collab)... MRes 12FT
Environmental Biology Conversion for Mathematical, Physical & Molecular Sciences (collab) .... MRes 12FT

Staffordshire University
Ecology and Conservation .... MSc 15FT
Habitat Management and Conservation ... MSc 15FT/PGDip 12FT
Urban Ecology and Conservation .... MSc 15FT

University of Stirling
Aquaculture: Sustainable Aquaculture (Named Degree Outcomes) .... MSc 12FT/PGDip 9FT/PGCert 6FT
Conservation and Sustainability MSc 12FT 27PT/PGDip 9FT 21PT
Energy Management .... MSc 12FT
Energy and the Environment ... MSc 12FT 27PT/MRes 12FT 27PT/PGDip 9FT/PGCert 4FT
Environment, Heritage and Policy............................ MSc 12FT 24PT
Environmental Economics.. MSc 12FT
Environmental Management.... MSc 12FT 27PT/PGDip 9FT 18PT/PGCert 6FT 12PT

University of Strathclyde
Environmental Engineering....... MSc 12FT 24PT/PGDip 9FT 18PT/PGCert 6FT 12PT
Environmental Health.... MSc 12FT 24PT/PGDip 9FT 18PT/PGCert 6FT 12PT
Hydrogeology .... MSc 12FT 24PT/PGDip 9FT 18PT
Integrated Pollution Prevention and Control ..... MRes 12FT 36PT/PGCert 10FT 24PT
Offshore Floating Systems .... MSc 12FT/PGDip 9FT
Sustainable Engineering: Renewable Energy Systems and the Environment ... MSc 12FT 24PT/PGDip 9FT 18PT/PGCert 6FT 12PT

University of Sunderland
Environmental Management and Assessment - Health and Safety.. MSc 12DL/MSc 24DL

University of Surrey
Corporate Environmental Management .... MSc 12FT 12-60PT

Trinity College Dublin - the University of Dublin
Environmental Sciences... MSc 12FT

University of Ulster
Coastal Zone Management .... MSc 24DL/PGDip 33DL
Environmental Management by e-Learning ...... PGDip 24DL/MSc 36DL
Environmental Management with/and Geographic Information Systems .... PGDip 24DL/MSc 36DL

UCL - University College London
Anthropology, Environment and Development .... MSc 12FT 24PT
Biodiversity, Evolution and Conservation .... MRes 12FT
Climate Change .... MSc 12FT 24PT
Energy Demand Studies .... MRes 12FT
Environment, Science and Society .... MSc 12FT 24PT
Environmental Modelling .... MSc 12FT 24PT
Geophysical Hazards .... MSc 12FT 24PT

Materials for Energy and Environment............................. MSc 12FT

University of Warwick
Environmental Bioscience in a Changing ClimateMSc 12FT 24PT/PGDip 12FT 24PT

University of the West of England, Bristol
Air Quality and Carbon Management................ MSc 12FT 24-36PT
Environmental Consultancy .... MSc 36-60DL

University of Winchester
Managing Contemporary Global Issues with Environment and Development.. MSc 12FT 24PT/PGDip 9FT 18PT/PGCert 9FT 18PT

University of Wolverhampton
Climate Change Management .... MSc 12FT 24PT
Environmental Management .... MSc 12FT 24PT
Environmental Pollution Control .... MSc 12FT 24PT
Oil and Gas Management .... MSc 12FT 24PT
Waste and Resource Management .... MSc 12FT 24PT

University of York
Corporate Social Responsibility with Environmental Management.. MSc 12FT
Ecology and Environmental Management .... MRes 12FT
Environmental Economics... MSc 12FT
Environmental Economics and Environmental ManagementMSc 12FT/PGDip 9FT
Environmental Science and Management... MSc 12FT/PGDip 9FT
Marine Environmental Management .... MSc 12FT/PGDip 9FT

Environmental science and ecology
Research Courses

Aberystwyth University
Earth Sciences .... MPhil 12FT 24PT
Earth Sciences .... PhD 36FT 60PT
IBERS - Environmental Science .... MPhil 12FT 24PT PhD 36FT 60PT

Anglia Ruskin University
Animal and Environmental............................. PhD 24-60FT 36-72PT
Sustainability.. PhD 24 - 60FT 36 - 72PT

Aston University
Environmental Systems and Safety Management Research Group... PhD 36FT/MPhil 24FT

Bangor University
Agroforestry .... MPhil 24FT 36PT/PhD 36FT 60PT
Biodiversity Conservation .... MPhil 24FT 36PT/PhD 36FT 60PT
Ecology .... MRes 12FT
Environmental and Soil Science .... MPhil 24FT 36PT/PhD 36FT 60PT
Forest Ecology and Management........ MPhil 24FT 36PT/PhD 36FT 60PT
Natural Sciences .... MRes 12FT
Ocean Sciences.. MPhil 24FT/PhD 36FT
Tropical Ecosystems .... MPhil 24FT 36PT/PhD 36FT 60PT

University of Bedfordshire
Environmental Studies.. PhD 36FT 72PT

Birkbeck, University of London
Geography and Environmental Management.................. PhD 36FT 60 - 72PT/MPhil 24FT 36PT

University of Birmingham
Environmental Science and Risk Management PhD/MSc (Research) .... PhD 36FT/MSc by research 12FT

University of Bradford
Environmental and Infrastructure Engineering ... PhD 36FT 48PT/MPhil 12FT 24PT
Geography and Environmental Science..... PhD 36-48FT 48-60PT/MPhil 12-24FT 24-48PT

University of Brighton
School of the Environment Research Division .... PhD 24-60FT 36-72PT/MPhil 18-36FT 30-48PT

Brunel University
Environmental Issues and Environmental Change..... MPhil 12FT/PhD 36FT
Environmental Research............. PhD 36FT 72PT/MPhil 12FT 24PT
Physical Geography and Earth Science .... MPhil/PhD

University of Central Lancashire
Environmental Management ... PhD 48FT 84PT/MPhil 36FT 60PT/MSc by research 24FT 36PT/MA by research 24FT 36PT

Coventry University
Environmental Science.................... MSc by research 12FT 24-36PT

Cranfield University
Natural Resources Research Opportunities .... PhD 36FT/Integrated PhD 36-45FT

University of Dundee
Civil Engineering .... MPhil 24FT MSc by research 12FT
Geography .... MPhil 24FT

University of East Anglia
Copy of Environmental Sciences: Geosciences and Natural Hazards .... PhD 36FT 72PT/MPhil 24FT 48PT
Environmental Sciences: Climate, Ocean and Atmospheric Sciences... PhD 36FT 72PT/MPhil 24FT 48PT

Environmental science and ecology

Environmental Sciences: Resources, Sustainability and Governance .... PhD 36FT 72PT/MPhil 24FT 48PT

University of Edinburgh
Atmospheric and Environmental Sciences .PhD 36FT 72PT/MPhil 24FT 48PT
Atmospheric and Environmental Sciences (Environmental Sustainability) .... PhD 36FT 72PT/MPhil 24FT 48PT
Energy Systems ....PhD 36FT 72PT/MPhil 24FT 48PT/MSc by research 12FT 24PT
Global Health .... MPhil 24FT 48PT/PhD 36FT 72PT

University of Essex
Environmental Governance ......PhD 36FT 72PT/MPhil 24FT 48PT/MSc by research 12FT 24PT
Environmental SciencesPhD 36FT 72PT/MPhil 24FT 48PT/MSc by research 12FT 24PT
Marine BiologyPhD 36FT 72PT/MPhil 24FT 48PT/MSc by research 12FT 24PT

University of Exeter
Biosciences ......PhD 36FT 72PT/MPhil 24FT 48PT/MSc by research 12FT 36FT

University of Glasgow
Environmental and Evolutionary Biology............PhD 36FT/MSc by research 12FT

University of Gloucestershire
Biological Sciences .... PhD 30-48FT

University of Greenwich
Environmental Sciences Research.......MSc by research 12FT 24PT
Environmental and Earth Sciences Research .....MPhil 36FT 72PT/PhD 36FT 72PT
Natural Resources by Research ....MSc by research 12FT 24PT

University of Hull
Environmental Studies................MSc(Res) 12FT 24PT
Environmental Technology ....MSc by research 12FT 24PT

Imperial College London
Biological Sciences ....PhD/MPhil
Department of Civil and Environmental Engineering ....PhD
Environment................................... PhD 36FT/MPhil 24FT
Environment................................... PhD 36FT/MPhil 24FT

Keele University
Environmental Social Sciences.......... PhD 24-48FT 48-84PT/MPhil 12-24FT 24-36PT

University of Kent
Environmental Social Science ..PhD 36FT 60PT/MPhil 24FT 36PT/MSc by research 12FT 24PT

Lancaster University
Environmental Science................................... PhD 36FT 72PT

University of Leeds
Environmental Sustainability....PhD 36FT 60PT 60DL/MPhil 24FT 48PT 48DL

Manchester Metropolitan University
Conservation Biology (by Research)..............MSc by research 12FT 24-60PT
Environmental and Geographical Sciences .... MSc by research/MPhil/PhD

University of Manchester
Environment and Sustainable Technology .PhD 36FT 72PT/MPhil 12FT 24PT
Environmental Biology....PhD 36-48FT 72-96PT/MPhil 12FT 24PT
Planning and Environmental Management.....................PhD 36FT

Middlesex University
Environmental Studies........PhD 33-60FT 45-72PT/MPhil 18-36FT 30-48PT

Newcastle University
Environmental Science...............................Integrated PhD 48FT
Environmental Science.............. MPhil 12FT 24PT/PhD 36FT 72PT
Technology in the Marine Environment ....MRes 12FT

University of Northampton
School of Environmental Science ....PhD 24FT 36PT/MPhil 36FT 48PT

Nottingham Trent University
Environmental Biology...............................MRes 12FT 24PT

University of Nottingham
Agricultural and Environmental Sciences ....PhD 36FT
Carbon Capture and Storage ..... PhD 24FT 48PT/MPhil 24FT 48PT
Environmental Engineering .... PhD 36FT/MPhil 24FT
Environmental and Geomorphological Sciences .PhD 36FT 72PT/MPhil 24FT 48PT

The Open University
Biogeochemistry and ecosystem ecology ....MPhil 15FT 24PT variableDL/PhD 36FT 72PT variableDL
Climate change and ecosystem services..............MPhil 15FT 24PT variableDL/PhD 36FT 72PT variableDL
Earth Sciences .... PhD 36FT 72PT variableDL/MPhil 15FT 24PT
Ecosystems and Biodiversity .....PhD 36FT 72PT variableDL/MPhil 15FT 24PT
Environment, governance and justicePhD 36FT 72PT variableDL/MPhil 15FT 24PT variableDL

Geography.................. PhD 36FT 72PT variableDL/MPhil 15FT 24PT variableDL
Isotope Geochemistry and Earth Systems .... PhD 36FT 72PT variableDL

University of Oxford
Earth Sciences .... DPhil 48FT/MSc by research 24FT
Geography and the Environment...... DPhil 48FT/MSc by research 24FT
Plant Sciences .... DPhil 48FT/MSc by research 24FT

Plymouth University
Biogeochemistry Research Centre PhD 36FT 36-72PT/MPhil 24FT 24-36PT
Biogeochemistry and Environmental Analytical Chemistry Research Group (BEAch) ....MPhil 24FT/PhD 36FT
Integrated PhD in Marine and Environmental SciencesPhD 48FT/PGCert by research 12FT
Marine Biology & Ecology .... PhD 36FT 36-72PT/MPhil 24FT 24-36PT
Petroleum and Environmental Geochemistry Research Group..... MPhil 24FT/PhD 36FT
Speciation and Environmental Analysis Research Group (SEA)..... PhD 36FT/MPhil 24FT

University of Portsmouth
Earth and Environmental Sciences .....MPhil 24FT 48PT/PhD 36FT 72PT

Queen's University Belfast
Ecology, Evolution, Behaviour and Environmental EconomicsPhD 36FT 72PT/MPhil 24FT 48PT
Environmental Change .... PhD 36FT 72PT/MPhil 24FT 48PT

Sheffield Hallam University
Environment and Development .... MPhil 36PT

University of Southampton
Centre of Environmental Studies ....PhD 36FT 72PT/MPhil 24FT 48PT
School of Biological Sciences: Ecology and the Environment .... PhD 36FT 72PT

Staffordshire University
Biology Division ....PhD 72PT/MPhil 72PT

University of Sussex
Environmental Science Research Programme .... PhD 24-48FT 36-72PT/MPhil 12-36FT 24-48PT

Swansea University
Environmental Dynamics......................MSc by research 12FT 24PT
Glaciology......................................MSc by research 12FT 24PT
Global Environmental Modelling ....MSc by research 12FT 24PT

Teesside University
The Environment .... PhD 24- 60FT 36-72PT/MPhil 18FT 30PT/DProf 36PT/MProf by research 30PT

University of the Highlands and Islands
Environmental Sciences..... PhD 36FT 72PT/MSc by research 12FT 48PT

University of Ulster
Environmental Sciences and Earth System............PhD 36FT 72PT/MPhil 24FT 48PT

University of Warwick
Plant and Environmental Sciences............. PhD 36FT/MPhil 24FT/MSc by research 12FT

University of the West of England, Bristol
Faculty of Environment and Technology .... PhD .FT
School of the Built and Natural Environment.....................PhD -FT

University of Worcester
Ecology .... MPhil 24FT 48PT/PhD 48FT 70PT

University of York
Environmental Economics and Environmental Management (EEEM) .... PhD 36FT 72PT/MPhil 24FT 48PT
Environmental Science................................. PhD 36FT/MPhil 24FT

Human ecology
Taught Courses

University of Cambridge
Social Anthropology .... PhD by taught 11FT

Durham University
Evolutionary Anthropology....................................... MSc 12FT
Evolutionary Medicine .... MSc 12FT
Sustainability, Culture and Development .... MSc 12FT

University of East Anglia
Applied Ecology and Conservation .... MSc 12FT 24PT
Climate Change .... MSc 12FT
Climate Change and International Development.MSc 12FT 24PT
Ecology .... GradDip 12FT 24PT
Environment and International Development ...... MSc 12FT 24PT
Environmental Assessment and Management .....MSc 12FT 24PT

University of Edinburgh
Conservation Medicine MVetSci 36DL/PGDip 24DL/PGCert 12DL
Evolutionary Genetics ....MSc 12FT 24PT/PGDip 9FT
Human Complex Trait Genetics............MSc 12FT 24PT/PGDip 9FT

University of Exeter
Applied Ecology .... MSc 12FT
Biosciences.................................MSc(Res) 12FT 36FT

Heriot-Watt University
Applied Psychology..........MSc 12FT 24-48PT/PGDip 9FT 15-48PT/PGCert 6FT 12-48PT
Engineering Psychology with Ergonomics............. MSc 12FT 24PT 24-84DL/PGDip 9FT 21PT 21-84DL/PGCert 6FT 18PT 18-84DL

University of Kent
Evolution and Human Behaviour (taught jointly with the School of Psychology)....................................MSc 12FT 24PT

Leeds Metropolitan University
Housing, Regeneration and Urban Management MA 12FT 24PT/PGCert 12FT 12PT/PGDip 12FT 24PT

London School of Economics and Political Science (LSE)
Anthropology and Development Management....MSc 12FT 24PT

Nottingham Trent University
Ecology ....MSc(Res) 12FT 24PT

Schumacher College
Holistic Science .... MSc 12FT

University of St Andrews
Behavioural and Neural Sciences ....MPhil 12FT 24PT

University of Stirling
Behavioural Science for Management.......... MSc 12FT/PGDip 9FT

UCL - University College London
Genetics of Human Disease .... MSc 12FT
Human Evolution and Behaviour ....MSc 12FT 24PT

University of York
Human Evolution ....MSc 12FT 24PT

Human ecology
Research Courses

University of Edinburgh
Evolutionary Biology...............................PhD 36FT 72PT

University of Exeter
Biosciences ......PhD 36FT 72PT/MPhil 24FT 48PT/MSc by research 12FT 36FT

University of Leeds
Genetics, Ecology and Evolution...PhD 36+FT/MPhil 24FT/MSc by research 12FT

London Consortium
Humanities and Cultural Studies.......................PhD 36FT

University of Roehampton
Ecology .... PhD 24-48FT 36-60PT/MPhil 21-36FT 33-48PT

UCL - University College London
Genetics, Evolution and Environment....................... PhD 36FT 60FT

Pollution
Taught Courses

Bangor University
Marine Environmental Protection ....MSc 12FT 24-36PT
Physical Oceanography.....................MSc 12FT 24-36PT/PGDip 9FT

University of Birmingham
Air Pollution Management and Control .....MSc 12FT 24PT/PGDip 12FT 24PT

Brunel University
Environmental Science: Pollution and Monitoring
....MSc 12FT 24PT

University of Central Lancashire
Carbon and Resource Management....MSc 12FT 24PT/PGDip 9FT 18PT/PGCert 6FT 12PT

University of Derby
Environmental Health....................... MSc 24FT 48PT 48DL

University of Dundee
Water Hazards, Risks & Resilience .... MSc 12FT

University of East Anglia
Applied Ecology and Conservation ....MSc 12FT 24PT
Climate Change .... MSc 12FT
Climate Change and International Development.MSc 12FT 24PT
Ecology .... GradDip 12FT 24PT
Environmental Assessment and Management .....MSc 12FT 24PT

Kingston University
Environmental Politics ....MSc 12FT 24PT

Lancaster University
(Research) International Masters in Environmental Science and Technology .... MSc(Res) 21FT
Environmental and Biochemical Toxicology....MSc 12FT 24PT

Leeds Metropolitan University
Acoustics and Noise Control... PGDip 12PT

University of Manchester
Pollution and Environmental Control .... MSc 12FT

Middlesex University
Environmental Pollution Control...............................MSc 12FT 24PT

Environmental science and ecology

North East Surrey College of Technology
Acoustics and Noise Control......................................IOA Diploma 9PT
Applied Acoustics and Noise Control ....MSc 9PT

Newcastle University
Clean Technology.. MSc 12FT/PGDip 7FT

University of Salford
Environmental Acoustics...MSc 12FT 28PT 28DL/PGDip 9FT 18PT 18DL

Schumacher College
Holistic Science .... MSc 12FT

University of Southampton
Environmental Pollution Control................................ MSc 12FT 27PT

University of Stirling
Energy and the Environment ... MSc 12FT 27PT/MRes 12FT 27PT/
PGDip 9FT/PGCert 4FT

University of Strathclyde
Hydrogeology..............................MSc 12FT 24PT/PGDip 9FT 18PT
Integrated Pollution Prevention and Control ..... MRes 12FT 36PT/
PGCert 10FT 24PT

Teesside University
Control and Electronics....................MSc 12-18FT 24PT/PGDip 8FT

University of Ulster
Environmental Toxicology & Pollution Monitoring by
e-Learning ....PGDip 24DL/MSc 36DL

Pollution
Research Courses

Bangor University
Environmental and Soil Science ....MPhil 24FT 36PT/
PhD 36FT 60PT
Ocean Sciences... MPhil 24FT/PhD 36FT

University of Dundee
Water Law, Policy and Science .... LLM by research 12FT

University of the Highlands and Islands
Environmental Sciences..... PhD 36FT 72PT/MSc by research 12FT 48PT

Sustainable development
Taught Courses

University of Abertay Dundee
Energy Industry Economics.............................. MSc 12FT/PGDip 9FT

Anglia Ruskin University
Sustainability: Working for Positive Change....MSc 12FT 24-30PT

Aston University
Social Responsibility & Sustainability.....................MSc 12FT 24PT

Bangor University
Conservation and Land Management .... MSc 12FT/PGDip 9FT
Environmental Management.. MBA 12FT
Environmental Management.. MBA 12FT
Forestry (Distance Learning with International Commonwealth
Scholarship) ....MSc 12DL
Rheolaeth Amgylcheddol Gynaliadwy (Sustainable
Environmental Management).........MSc 12FT 24PT/MA 12FT 24PT
Sustainable Tropical Forestry (SUTROFOR) (Erasmus Mundus
course)... MSc 24FT
Tropical Frorestry.................... MSc 36PT/PGDip 24PT/PGCert 12PT

Birmingham City University
Environmental Sustainability......PGCert 4FT 8PT/PGDip 4FT 8PT/
MSc 4FT 8PT
Environmental Sustainability (Design and Construction) . PGCert
4FT 8PT/PGDip 4FT 8PT/MSc 4FT 8PT

University of Birmingham
Materials for Sustainable Energy Technologies...MRes 12FT 24PT
Resilience and Urban Living........ MSc 12FT 24PT/MRes 12FT 24PT

University of Bolton
Regeneration and Sustainable CommunitiesMA 15FT/MSc 15FT/
PGDip 12FT/PGCert 6FT

Bournemouth University
Green Economy...MSc 12DL

University of Bradford
Applied Management and Sustainability......................... MSc 12FT

University of Brighton
Sustainability of the Built Environment.....MSc 12FT 24PT/PGDip
12FT 24PT/PGCert 12FT 24PT
Sustainable Design ....MA 12FT 24-60PT/PGDip 12FT 24-60PT/
PGCert 12FT 24-60PT

Brunel University
Building Services Engineering with Sustainable EnergyMSc 12FT
36-60DL
Renewable Energy Engineering.. MSc 12FT
Sustainable Electrical Power .... MSc 12FT 24PT
Sustainable Energy : Technologies and Management... MSc 12FT

University of Cambridge
Engineering for Sustainable Development................... MPhil 11FT
Sustainability Leadership .... MSt 24PT

Cardiff University
Sustainability, Planning and Environmental Policy.........................
MSc 12FT 24PT
Sustainable Energy and Environment...............MSc 12FT 24-36PT
Theory and Practice of Sustainable Design ....MSc 12FT 24PT

University of Chester
Sustainability for Community and Business.........MSc 12FT 24PT/
PGDip 12FT 24PT/PGCert 12FT 12-24PT

University College Cork
Planning & Sustainable Development .... MPlan 24FT
Sustainable Energy .... MEngSci 12FT

Cranfield University
Design and Innovation for Sustainability .... MDes 12FT 24-60PT/
PGDip 6FT 12PT/PGCert 5FT 12PT
Environment and Public Policy...........MSc 12FT 60PT/PGCert 12FT
60PT/PGDip 12FT 60PT
Environmental Informatics......MSc 12FT 60PT/PGDip 12FT 60PT/
PGCert 12FT 60PT
Through-life System Sustainment..............................MSc 24-36PT

University for the Creative Arts
Sustainable Product Design ....MA 24PT

University of Cumbria
Greening Outdoor Practice ....PGCert 24-36PT

De Montfort University
Architecture and Sustainability................................MSc 12FT 24PT
Energy and Industrial Sustainability H22172........MSc 12FT 24PT
36DL/PGDip 32DL/PGCert 16DL

University of Derby
Sustainable Architecture and Healthy Environments .....MA 12FT
Sustainable Design and Innovation....................MSc 12FT 36-72PT

Dublin Institute of Technology
Sustainable Development.. MSc 12FT
Sustainable Electrical Energy Systems.................. MEng 12FT 24PT

University of Dundee
Advanced Sustainability of the Built Environment .... MSc 12FT
Advanced Sustainable Urban Design .... MSc 12FT
Renewable Energy and Sustainable Building in a Global Context
.... MSc 12FT
Spatial Planning with Marine Spatial Planning .... MSc 12FT
Spatial Planning with Sustainable Urban Design .... MSc 12FT
Spatial Planning with Urban Conservation .... MSc 12FT

University of East Anglia
Environmental Assessment and Management ..... MSc 12FT 24PT
Sustainable Business.. MSc 12FT

University of East London
Architecture: Advanced Environmental and Energy Studies
.... MSc 12FT 24PT
Architecture: Sustainability And Design .... MA 12FT 24PT/PGDip
8FT 16PT/PGCert 4FT 8PT
Renewable Energy and the Built Environment......MSc 12FT 24PT
Sustainability and Energy Management ....MBA 12FT 24PT

Edinburgh Napier University
Design (Sustainability)..MA/MDes 12FT
Energy and Environmental Engineering................MSc 12FT 36PT
Environmental Sustainability.... MSc 12FT 36PT/PGDip 9FT 24PT/
PGCert 6FT 12PT
Polymer Engineering .... MSc 12FT
Renewable Energy .... MSc 12FT 24PT
Safety and Environmental Management..... MSc 12FT 36PT 36DL

University of Edinburgh
Advanced Sustainable Design..................................MSc 12FT 24PT
Environmental Sustainability.........MSc 12FT 24-36PT/PGDip 9FT
Global Development Challenges (Online Distance Learning).......
PGCert 12-24DL
Global Environment Challenges Certificate (Online distance
learning).. PGCert 9DL
Soils and Sustainability.. MSc 12FT
Sustainable Energy Systems........................... MSc 12FT/PGDip 9FT

University of Exeter
Applied Ecology.. MSc 12FT
Food Security and Sustainable Agriculture..............MSc 12FT 24PT

Forum for the Future
Leadership for Sustainable Development...................... MA 10.5FT

Glasgow Caledonian University
Sustainable Energy Technology................................MSc 12FT 24PT

University of Glasgow
Environment & Sustainable Development .... MSc 12FT
Sustainable Energy .... MSc 12FT

Glyndwr University
Renewable Energy Systems and Sustainability.............. MSc 12FT
24-36PT/MRes 12FT

Goldsmiths, University of London
Design & Environment .... MA 12FT 24PT
Design Futures .... MA 12FT 24PT

University of Greenwich
Natural Resources .... MSc 12FT 24PT/PGDip 12FT 24PT
Sustainable Futures .... MSc 12FT

Harper Adams University
International Agri-business and Food Chain Management... MSc
12FT 48PT/PGDip 12FT 48PT/PGCert 6FT 48PT

Heriot-Watt University
Climate Change: Impacts and Mitigation..............MSc 12FT 24PT/
PGDip 9FT 21PT
Climate Change: Managing The Marine Environment.. MSc 12FT
24PT/PGDip 9FT 21PT
Energy.............MSc 12FT 24PT 24-84DL/PGDip 9FT 21PT 21-84DL
Int'nl Business Management with Finance / HRM / Logistics /
Marketing /Sustainability Mgmt. ....MSc 12FT 24PT/PGDip 9FT
21PT
Marine Resource Development and Protection....MSc 12FT 24PT/
PGDip 9FT 21PT
Materials for Sustainable and Renewable Energies....... MSc 12FT
24PT/PGDip 9FT 21PT/PGCert 6FT 12PT
Renewable Energy Engineering..MSc 12FT 24PT/PGDip 9FT 21PT
Smart Grid and Demand Management......MSc 12FT 24PT/PGDip
9FT 18PT
Sustainability Engineering......... MSc 12FT 24PT/PGDip 9FT 21PT/
PGCert 6FT 12PT

University of Hertfordshire
Water and Environmental Management..........MSc 12FT 24-60PT
24DL/PGDip 12FT 18-48PT 18DL/PGCert 12FT 18-48PT 18DL

University of Huddersfield
Architecture/Architecture (International) (RIBA Part 2)......MArch
24FT
Sustainable Architecture..MSc 12FT 24PT

University of Hull
Environmental Technology ....MSc 12FT 24PT
Environmental Technology (renewable energy)....MSc 12FT 24PT

Imperial College London
Transport, also with Business Management or Sustainable
Development...MSc 12FT 24-36PT

Keele University
Environmental Sustainability and Green Technology..... Cert 4FT/
Diploma 8FT/MSc 12FT

University of Kent
Environmental Anthropology.........MA 12FT 24PT/MSc 12FT 24PT

King's College London
Sustainable Cities...MSc 12FT 24PT

Kingston University
Sustainability & Environmental Change.................MSc 12FT 24PT
Sustainability for Built Environment PracticeMA 12FT/MSc 12FT/
PGCert 6FT 12PT/PGDip 12FT
Sustainable Environmental Development with Management
Studies...MSc 12FT 24PT

Leeds Metropolitan University
Sustainable Computing..MSc 12FT 24PT

University of Leeds
Sustainability (Business, Environment and Corporate
Responsibility)...................................MA 12FT 48PT/PGDip 12FT 48PT
Sustainability (Climate Change)... MSc 12FT
Sustainability (Ecological Economics) ....MSc 12FT 48PT
Sustainability (Environment and Development)............ MSc 12FT
12-48PT
Sustainability (Environmental Consultancy)....MSc 12FT 12-48PT
Sustainability (Environmental Politics and Policy).......... MSc 12FT
12-48PT
Sustainability (Transport).................................MSc 12FT 24-36PT/
PGDip 9FT 18-24PT
Sustainability Research............................... MRes 12FT 12-48PT
Water, Sanitation and Health Engineering.............MSc(Eng) 12FT

University of Leicester
Environmental Informatics..........MSc 12FT 24PT/PGDip 9FT 18PT
Sustainable Management of Natural Resources..MSc 12FT 24PT/
PGDip 9FT 18PT

London Metropolitan University
Planning and Sustainable Communities.................MSc 12FT 24PT
Sustainable Cities..MSc 12FT 24+PT

London School of Economics and Political Science (LSE)
Environment and Development ....MSc 12FT 24PT

Loughborough University
Design and Innovation for Sustainability ....MSc 12FT 24PT
Low Carbon Building Design and Modelling.. MSc 12FT 24-60PT/
PGDip 12FT 24-60PT/PGCert 12FT 24-60PT
Sustainable Engineering...MSc 12FT 96PT

Manchester Metropolitan University
Environment, Management and Sustainable Development . MSc
12FT 36PT
Sustainable Aviation.................................MSc 12FT 12-36PT

University of Manchester
Competition, Regulation and Development ....MSc 12FT 12PT
Environment and Sustainable Technology .MSc 12FT/PGDip 9FT/
PGCert 6FT

Middlesex University
Sustainable Development.........MA 12FT 24PT/PGDip 12FT 24PT/
PGCert 12FT 24PT

Environmental science and ecology

Sustainable Environmental Management......MA 12FT 24PT/MSc 12FT 24PT

Newcastle University
Environmental Regulation and Sustainable Development.....LLM 12FT 24PT
Hydrology and Climate Change....MSc 12FT 48PT
Planning for Sustainability and Climate Change....MSc 12FT
Sustainable Buildings and Environments....MSc 12FT

University of Northampton
Sustainable Urban Environments....PGCert 6PT

Northumbria University
Disaster Management and Sustainable Development ....PGCert 4FT 8DL/PGDip 8FT 12DL/MSc 12FT 36-60DL
Electrical Power Engineering....MSc 12-16FT
Renewable and Sustainable Energy Technologies.... MSc 12 or 16FT

Nottingham Trent University
PG Cert Planning, Urban Design and Sustainable Development....PGCert 12PT

University of Nottingham
Energy Conversion and Management (Nottingham/ Ningbo)MSc 12FT
Environmental Design....MArch 12FT 24PT
Renewable Energy and Architecture.MSc 12FT 24PT/PGDip 12FT 24PT
Sustainable Bioenergy....MSc 12FT 36PT
Sustainable Bioenergy....MRes 12-36PT
Sustainable Building Technology (Nottingham/ Ningbo)...... MSc 12FT 24PT
Sustainable Building Technology (collaborative)....MSc 12FT
Sustainable Energy Engineering....MSc 12FT
Sustainable Energy and Entrepreneurship....MSc 12FT
Sustainable Tall Buildings....MArch 12FT
Sustainable Transportation and Electrical Power Systems (Erasmus Mundus)....MSc 24FT

The Open University
Conflict and Development....PGCert variableDL
Development Management..MSc variableDL/PGDip variableDL/PGCert 12DL
Human Rights and Development Management........PGCert 12DL

Oxford Brookes University
Sustainable Building: Performance and Design ..MSc 12FT 27PT/PGDip 9FT 18PT

Plymouth University
Design....MA 12FT 24PT
Marine Renewable Energy....MSc 12FT/MRes 12FT

Queen's University Belfast
Environmental Law and Sustainable Development........LLM 12FT
Leadership for Sustainable Rural Development....MSc 12FT
Sustainable Design....MSc 12FT/PGDip 9FT
Sustainable Electrical Energy Systems....MSc 12FT

Ravensbourne
Environment Design....MA 12FT 24PT

University of Reading
Agricultural Economics....MSc 12FT 24PT
Agriculture and Development....MSc 12FT 24PT
Construction Management....MSc 12FT
Project Management....MSc 24PT
Renewable Energy....MSc 12FT 24PT/PGDip 9FT 21PT
Social Development and Sustainable Livelihoods....MA 12FT

Reseau Universitaire Transmanche
Transmanche Environment Programme....MSc 24FT

Robert Gordon University
Energy and Sustainability...MSc 42DL/PGDip 24DL/PGCert 12DL

Royal Holloway, University of London
Practising Sustainable Development..... MSc 12FT 24PT/Diploma 6FT 12PT
Sustainability and Management....MSc 12FT 24PT

University Campus Suffolk
MA Sustainable Business....MA 12FT 24PT

University of Salford
Real Estate Development....MSc 12FT 28DL/PGDip 8FT 20DL
Sustainable Building Design...... MSc 12FT 28PT/PGDip 8FT 20PT/PGCert 4FT 8PT

School of Oriental and African Studies - SOAS
Development Studies....MSc 12FT 24PT
Development Studies with Special Reference to Central Asia....... MSc 12FT 24PT
Environmental Law and Sustainable DevelopmentMA 12FT 24PT
Labour, Social Movements and Development....MSc 12FT 24PT
Research for International Development....MSc 12FT 24PT
State, Society and Development....MSc 12FT 24PT

Schumacher College
Economics for Transition....MA 12FT
Holistic Science....MSc 12FT

University of Sheffield
Planning and Development....MA 12FT

University of South Wales
Sustainable Power Technology....MSc 12FT 36PT

University of Southampton
Sustainable Energy Technologies....MSc 12FT 24PT

University of St Andrews
Sustainable Aquaculture.MSc 12FT 24PT/PGDip 9FT 24PT 24DL/Cert 12DL
Sustainable Development....MSc 12FT/PGDip 9FT

Staffordshire University
Governance and Sustainable Development....MA 36PT 36DL/PGCert 36PT 20DL/PGDip 36PT 9DL
Regeneration....MA 24FT 60PT

University of Stirling
Energy and the Environment ... MSc 12FT 27PT/MRes 12FT 27PT/PGDip 9FT/PGCert 4FT

University of Strathclyde
International Law and Sustainable Development ....LLM 12FT 24PT/PGDip 9FT 21PT/PGCert 4FT 8PT
Sustainability and Environmental Studies....MSc 12FT 24PT/PGDip 9FT 18PT
Sustainable EngineeringMSc 12FT 24PT/PGDip 9FT 18PT/PGCert 9FT 18PT
Sustainable Engineering: Building Design and Management....... MSc 12FT 24PT/PGDip 9FT 18PT/PGCert 6FT 12PT
Sustainable Engineering: Sustainable Product Development....... MSc 12FT 24PT/PGDip 9FT 21PT/PGCert 6FT 12PT

University of Surrey
Sustainable Development....MSc 12FT 12-48PT

University of Sussex
Climate Change and Development....MSc 12FT 24PT
Climate Change and Policy....MSc 12FT 24PT
Energy Policy for Sustainability....MSc 12FT 24PT
Innovation and Sustainability for International Development..... MSc 12FT 24PT

Trinity College Dublin - the University of Dublin
Environment and Development....MSc 12FT

University of the Highlands and Islands
Developing Low Carbon Communities.......MSc 12FT 36PT/PGDip 12FT 24PT/PGCert 12FT 12PT
Managing Sustainable Mountain Development MSc 36PT 36DL/PGDip 24PT 24DL/PGCert 24PT 12DL
Managing Sustainable Rural DevelopmentMSc 24FT 36PT/PGDip 12FT 24PT/PGCert 12FT 24PT

UCL - University College London
Energy and Resources: Policy and Practice, Australia .... MSc 24FT 36-48PT
Environment and Sustainable Development. MSc 12FT 24-60PT/PGDip 9FT
Sustainable Urbanism....MSc 12FT 24-60PT/PGDip 9FT

University of West London
Development and Management of Sustainable Built Environment....MSc 12FT 24PT

University of the West of England, Bristol
Environmental Law and sustainable development ....LLM 12FT 36PT

University of Worcester
Sustainable Development Advocacy (Professional Practice) ...MA 12FT 36PT

University of York
Green Chemistry and Sustainable Industrial Technology....... MSc 12FT 24-36PT

Sustainable development
Research Courses

Anglia Ruskin University
Sustainability....PhD 24 - 60FT 36 - 72PT

Bangor University
Renewable Materials....MPhil 24FT 36PT/PhD 36FT 60PT

University of Birmingham
Engineering, Sustainability and Resilience....MRes 12FT

Cardiff University
Institute of Environment and Sustainability........ PhD 36FT/MPhil 60PT
Institute of Green Electronic Systems; Communications, Sensors and Materials....EngD 48FT/PhD 36FT/MPhil 12FT
Sustainable Engineering....PhD 36FT

Cranfield University
Sustainable Systems Research Opportunities....PhD 36FT/Integrated PhD 36-45FT/MTech 24FT

De Montfort University
Energy and Sustainable Development Research ENG503 ... MPhil 12-24FT 24-48PT/PhD 36-48FT 48-72PT

University of Gloucestershire
Sustainability....PhD 36FT

University of Greenwich
Development Studies - Research...... MPhil 18-36FT 30-48PT/PhD 33-60FT 45-72PT

Environmental and Earth Sciences Research .....MPhil 36FT 72PT/PhD 36FT 72PT
Natural Resources by Research....MSc by research 12FT 24PT

University of Hertfordshire
Agriculture and the Environment....... PhD 36FT 72PT/MRes 12FT 24PT

University of Leeds
Environmental Sustainability....PhD 36FT 60PT 60DL/MPhil 24FT 48PT 48DL

University of Manchester
Environment and Sustainable Technology....PhD 36FT 72PT/MPhil 12FT 24PT
Sustainable Consumption....PhD 48FT

Newcastle University
Sustainability....MPhil variesFT/PhD variesFT

University of Nottingham
Sustainable Energy Technology....PhD 36FT

The Open University
Asian drivers and Africa... PhD 36FT 72PT variableDL/MPhil 15FT 24PT variableDL
Environment, governance and justicePhD 36FT 72PT variableDL/MPhil 15FT 24PT variableDL
Sustainable Design....PhD 36FT 72PT variableDL/MPhil 15FT 24PT variableDL

Oxford Brookes University
Sustainable Development....PhD 24-60FT 36-72PT/MPhil 24-36FT 36-48PT

School of Oriental and African Studies - SOAS
Development Studies....PhD 36FT 48-60PT
Economics....PhD 36FT 72PT/MPhil 24FT 36PT

Sheffield Hallam University
Environment and Development....MPhil 36PT
Environment and Development - Facilities Management.......PhD 33FT 45PT/MPhil 18FT 30PT

University of Strathclyde
Building Design and Management for Sustainability .MRes 12FT 36PT

University of Surrey
Sustainability for Engineering and Energy Systems (SEES).. EngD 48FT

University of the Highlands and Islands
Sustainability Studies... MPhil 24FT 48PT/PhD 36FT 72PT/MSc by research 12FT 24PT

Water resources engineering
Taught Courses

University of Abertay Dundee
Urban Water and Environmental Management ... MSc 12FT 24PT

Anglia Ruskin University
Business Management of Waste and Resources.......MSc 12-24DL

University of Birmingham
Hydrogeology....MSc 12FT
River Environments and their Management....MSc 12FT 24PT
Water Resources Technology and Management..MSc 12FT 24PT/PGDip 9FT 24PT

University of Brighton
Water and Environmental Management...MSc 12FT 24PT/PGDip 12FT 24PT

University of Bristol
Water and Environmental Management....MSc 12FT 24PT

Brunel University
Water Engineering....MSc 12FT

Cardiff University
Hydro-environment Engineering....MSc 12FT 24PT

University of Central Lancashire
Carbon and Resource Management.... MSc 12FT 24PT/PGDip 9FT 18PT/PGCert 6FT 12PT

University of Chester
Leadership and Management (Work Based and Integrative Studies)....MA 24-72PT/MSc 24-72PT/PGDip 24-60PT/PGCert 12-36PT

Cranfield University
Community Water and Sanitation....MSc 12FT 24-60PT/PGDip 6FT 24PT/PGCert 5FT 24PT/MTech 24FT
Environmental Water Management .... MSc 12FT 24-60PT/PGDip 6FT 24PT/PGCert 5FT 24PT/MTech 24FT
Waste and Resource Management....... MSc 12FT 24-60PT/PGDip 12FT 24PT/PGCert 12FT 24PT/MTech 24FT
Water and Wastewater Engineering.... MSc 12FT 24-60PT/PGDip 6FT 24PT/PGCert 5FT 24PT

University of Dundee
Catchment Hydrology & Management....MSc 12FT
International Mineral Resources Management....MBA 18DL
International Mineral Resources Management (MBA). MBA 12FT
Non-Graduating Taught Postgrad Grad School of Natural Resources Law, Policy & Management....... PG module variableFT

Environmental science and ecology

Supplementary Studies in Graduate School of Natural Resources, Law, Policy and Management ....Masters Level Modules 6-9FT
Water Hazards, Risks & Resilience .... MSc 12FT
Water Law .... PGDip 18-60DL/PGCert 12-60DL/LLM 24-60DL

University of East Anglia
Environmental Assessment and Management ..... MSc 12FT 24PT
Water Security and International Development ... MSc 12FT 24PT

University of Exeter
Water Management .... MSc 12FT 24PT

Glasgow Caledonian University
Waste ManagementMSc 12FT 24PT/PGDip 8FT 20PT/PGCert 4FT 8PT

Heriot-Watt University
Environmental Analysis and Assessment .... MRes 12FT 24PT/ PGDip 9FT 18PT/PGCert 9FT 18PT
Marine Spatial Planning........................MSc 12FT 24PT/PGDip 9FT
Sustainable Urban ManagementMSc 12FT 24PT 24-84DL/PGDip 9FT 21PT 24-84DL
Water Resources .... MSc 12FT 24PT 24-84DL/PGDip 9FT 21PT 24-84DL/PGCert 6FT 12PT 24-84DL

University of Hertfordshire
Water and Environmental Management ....MSc 12FT 24-60PT 24DL/PGDip 12FT 18-48PT 18DL/PGCert 12FT 18-48PT 18DL

Imperial College London
Environmental Engineering, also with Business Management or Sustainable Development.....................................MSc 12FT 24-36PT
Hydrology for Water Resource Management, also with Business Management and Sustainable Dev ....MSc 12FT 24-36PT

Keele University
Urban Futures and Sustainable Communities.......MA 12FT 24PT/ PGDip 12FT 24PT/PGCert 12FT 24PT

King's College London
Water: Science and Governance...............................MSc 12FT 24PT

Lancaster University
Sustainable Water Management .... MSc 12FT 24PT

University of Leeds
Hydrogeology ....MSc 12FT 24-48PT/PGDip 12FT 24-48PT
Water, Sanitation and Health Engineering..............MSc(Eng) 12FT

Liverpool John Moores University
Water, Energy & the Environment ....MSc 12FT 24PT/ PGDip 24PT/PGCert 12PT

University of Liverpool
Marine Planning and Management .... MSc 12FT 24PT

Loughborough University
Water and Environmental Management ....MSc 12FT/PGDip 6FT/ PGCert 3FT
Water and Environmental Management by Distance Learning.... MSc 96DL/PGDip 60DL/PGCert 36DL
Water and Waste Engineering ..MSc 12FT/PGDip 6FT/PGCert 3FT
Water and Waste Engineering by Distance Learning...MSc 96DL/ PGDip 60DL/PGCert 36DL

Manchester Metropolitan University
Science, Technology, Engineering and Maths (STEM) .... MSc 24-72PT

Newcastle University
Environmental Engineering..MSc 12FT 48PT
Flood Risk Management...................MSc 36-60PT/PGDip 36-60PT
Hydrogeology and Water ManagementMSc 12FT 48PT 36-60DL/ PGDip 36-60DL
Hydroinformatics and Water Management (Euro Aquae)...... MSc 24FT
Hydrology and Climate Change.................................MSc 12FT 48PT
Skills, Technology, Research and Management for the UK Water Sector (STREAM)...EngD by taught 48FT

University of Northampton
International Wastes Management ....MSc 24DL

University of Oxford
Water Science, Policy and Management .... MSc 12FT

Queen Mary, University of London
Environmental Science: Integrated Management of Freshwater Environments ....MSc 12FT 24-36PT

University of Sheffield
Contaminant Hydrogeology...... MSc 12FT 24PT/PGDip 9FT 18PT/ Cert 6FT 12PT
Environmental Management of Urban Land and WaterMSc 12FT 24PT/PGDip 9FT 18PT/PGCert 6FT 12PT
Urban Water Engineering and Management........MSc 12FT 24PT/ PGDip 9FT 18PT/Cert 6FT 12PT

University of Southampton
Engineering for Development - Infrastructure, Water Supply and Sanitation.....................................MSc 12FT 24PT/PGDip 9FT
Freshwater Sciences .... MRes 12FT
Marine Resource Management .... MSc 12FT
Water Resources Management .... MSc 12FT 27PT

University of Strathclyde
Hydrogeology ....MSc 12FT 24PT/PGDip 9FT 18PT
Offshore Floating Systems .... MSc 12FT/PGDip 9FT
Ship and Offshore Structures .... MSc 12FT/PGDip 9FT
Ship and Offshore Technology .... MSc 24FT
Sustainable Engineering: Marine Technology ....MSc 12FT/PGDip 9FT
Sustainable Engineering: Offshore Renewable Energy MSc 12FT/ PGDip 9FT

University of Surrey
Water Regulation and Management........................MSc 12FT 72PT
Water and Environmental Engineering...................MSc 12FT 72PT

Trinity College Dublin - the University of Dublin
Environmental Engineering .... PGDip 12FT

UCL - University College London
Hydrographic Surveying .... MSc 12FT

University of the West of England, Bristol
River and Coastal Engineering .... GradDip 36PT

Water resources engineering
Research Courses

Coventry University
Water Science....................................... MSc by research 12FT 24-36PT

Cranfield University
EngD Studentship: Disinfection Modelling for Water Distribution Systems.. EngD 48FT
EngD Studentship: Process robustness tools in drinking water treatment .... EngD 48FT
Land and Water Management PhD with Integrated Studies......... Integrated PhD 48FT
Land and Water Management PhD with Integrated Studies......... Integrated PhD 48FT
Land and Water Management PhD with Intergrated Studies PhD 42FT
Changing practice in water and sanitation technology introduction.. MSc(Res) 12FT
Flow cytometry for rapid analysis of microbiological water quality ....MSc by research 12FT
Pesticides in Groundwater............................MSc by research 12FT
Drinking water distribution: elucidating the chemistry ....MSc by research 12FT

University of Dundee
Non-Graduating Research in Natural Resources Law, Policy and Management (6 months or more) ....Non-Grad 6-24FT
Non-Graduating Research in Natural Resources Law, Policy and Management (less than 6 mths)............................ Non-Grad 1-5FT
Water Law, Policy and Science (LLM by research) LLM by research 12FT

University of Exeter
Engineering.. EngD 48FT

Newcastle University
Civil Engineering (Water Resources)...MPhil 12FT 24PT/PhD 36FT 72PT

The Open University
Integrated Waste Systems .... PhD 36FT 72PT variableDL/ MPhil 15FT 24PT variableDL

Swansea University
Desalination and Water Re-Use..........MSc by research 12FT 24PT
Sustainable Resources..............................MSc by research 12FT

UCL - University College London
Environmental Engineering Science............................... EngD 48FT

Food sciences

Animal nutrition
Taught Courses

Aberystwyth University
Animal Science...MSc 12FT 24PT
Livestock Science...MSc 12FT 24PT

University of Edinburgh
Applied Animal Behaviour and Animal Welfare.... MSc 12FT 24PT

University of Glasgow
Animal Welfare Science, Ethics & Law.......... MSc 12FT/PGDip 9FT

Harper Adams University
Ruminant Nutrition......PGCert 12FT 24PT/MSc 12FT 24PT/PGDip
12FT 24PT

Newcastle University
Aquaculture Enterprise and Technology................. MSc 12FT 24PT

University of Roehampton
Clinical Nutrition.................................PGCert 6FT 24PT 24DL

Royal Veterinary College
Veterinary Education .... MSc 24-60PT PGCert 6-24DL
PGCert 6-24PT PGDip 24-60PT
Veterinary Epidemiology and Public Health by Distance Learning
MSc 24-60DL/PGDip 24-60DL/PGCert 12-60DL
Veterinary Epidemiology- MSc (P/T)...................................MSc 24PT
Wild Animal Biology - MSc (F/T).....................MSc 12FT PGDip 8FT
Wild Animal Health ....PGDip 8FT

University of Salford
Wildlife Documentary Production ....MA 12FT

Scotland's Rural College
Applied Poultry Science .... MSc 27DL/PGDip 18DL

University of Southampton
Wildlife Conservation..MRes 12FT

University of Stirling
Aquaculture: Sustainable Aquaculture .... MSc 12FT
Aquatic Pathobiology............... PGCert 4FT/PGDip 11FT/MSc 12FT

University of Ulster
Food Regulatory Affairs (Veterinary Public Health)..PGDip 15DL/
MSc 24DL

Animal nutrition
Research Courses

Aberystwyth University
IBERS - Biological Sciences ....MPhil 12FT 24PT PhD 36FT 60PT
IBERS - Rural Sciences ....MPhil 12FT 24PT PhD 36FT 60PT

University of Edinburgh
Animal Health & Welfare...PhD 36FT

Harper Adams University
Animal Nutrition ....MPhil 24FT/PhD 38FT

University of Nottingham
Animal Population Heath and Welfare........PhD 36FT 72PT/MPhil
24FT 48PT

Brewing science
Taught Courses

Heriot-Watt University
Brewing and Distilling...................MSc 12FT 24PT/PGDip 9FT 21PT

University of Nottingham
Brewing Science...................MSc 24-48PT/PGDip 24-48PT
Brewing and Packaging...............................PGCert 12-24PT 12-24DL
Brewing: Optimisation Using Technical Approaches (E-Learning)
PGCert 12-24PT
Brewing: Principles and Practice (E-learning) ....PGCert 12-24PT

University of Sheffield
Microbrewing.............................MSc 12FT/PGDip 9FT/PGCert 6FT

Brewing science
Research Courses

Heriot-Watt University
International Centre for Brewing and Distilling (ICBD)..PhD 36FT
48PT/MPhil 24FT

Dietetics
Taught Courses

Cardiff Metropolitan University
Advanced Dietetic Practice ....MSc 36FT
Dietetics .... MSc 30FT 42PT/PGDip 24FT 36FT

University of Chester
Human Nutrition........... MSc 12FT 24-48PT/PGDip 12FT 24-48PT/
PGCert 12FT 12-24PT
Nutrition and Dietetics ....MSc 24FT/PGDip 24FT
Weight ManagementMSc 12FT 24 - 48PT/PGDip 12FT 24 - 48PT/
PGCert 12FT 12 - 24PT
Weight Management (Taught in Dublin, Ireland) .. MSc 24-48PT/
PGDip 24-48PT/PGCert 12-24PT

Coventry University
Sport and Exercise Nutrition .... PGCert 12 MinPT

Glasgow Caledonian University
Clinical Nutrition and Health .... MSc 12FT
Diabetes Care and Management .... MSc 12FT 36FT
Dietetics...PGDip 20FT

University of Greenwich
Nutritional Sciences .... MSc 12FT 24PT/PGDip 12FT 24PT

Heriot-Watt University
Food Science and Nutrition..........MSc 12FT 24PT/PGDip 9FT 21PT

University of Hertfordshire
Dietetics (Advanced Practice)MSc 72PT/PGDip 72PT/PGCert 72PT

University of Huddersfield
Nutrition and Food Sciences.. MSc 12FT

King's College London
Dietetics ....MSc 24FT/PGDip 17FT
Nutrition .... MSc 12FT/PGDip 8FT

Leeds Metropolitan University
Dietetics ....PGDip 24FT

Leeds Trinity University
Health and Wellbeing .... MSc 24PT 24DL/PGCert 12PT 12DL/
PGDip 24PT 24DL

University of Leeds
Nutrition .... MSc 12FT

London Metropolitan University
Dietetics and Nutrition ....MSc 30FT/PGDip 36FT
International Public Health Nutrition................MSc 12FT 36-48PT
Obesity and Weight Management .... MSc 12FT
Sports Nutrition (Top-Up)...........................MSc 12FT 24+PT

University of Nottingham
Advanced Dietetic Practice .... MSc 24-72PT/PGDip 24-48PT/
PGCert 12-36PT
Clinical Nutrition ....MSc 24-72PT/PGDip 24-72PT
Dietetics ....MRes 12FT

Oxford Brookes University
Applied Sport & Exercise Nutrition ....MSc 12FT 24PT/
PGDip 8FT 20PT

Plymouth University
Advanced Professional Practice ....PGCert 6FT 12PT/PGDip 10FT
12PT/MSc 12FT 24PT

Queen Margaret University, Edinburgh
Dietetics..MSc 18FT/PGDip 15FT
Public Health Nutrition.... MSc 12FT 24-60PT/PGDip 9FT 24-60PT

University of Roehampton
Clinical Nutrition ......MSc 12FT 24PT 24DL PGCert 6FT 24PT 24DL
PGDip 9FT 24PT 24DL

Sheffield Hallam University
Nutrition with Public Health Management .... MSc 12FT

University of Sheffield
Human Nutrition.................MMedSci 12FT 24PT/PGDip 9FT 18PT

St Mary's University College, Twickenham
Applied Sports Nutrition .... PGDip 12PT
Nutrition and Physical Activity for Public Health........... MSc 12FT

Swansea University
Education for the Health Professions......... MA 36PT/PGDip 24PT/
PGCert 12PT

Trinity College Dublin - the University of Dublin
Cardiovascular Rehabilitation and Prevention ......MSc 12FT 24PT

University of Ulster
Dietetics..PGDip 24FT/MSc 24FT

UCL - University College London
Cardiovascular Science .... MSc 12FT
Clinical and Public Health Nutrition.............MSc 12FT/PGDip 9FT/
PGCert 3FT
Clinical and Public Health Nutrition: Eating Disorders...................
MSc 12FT/PGDip 9FT/PGCert 3FT

University of West London
Advanced Professional Practice .... PGCert 24DL/PGDip 24DL

University of Westminster
International Public Health Nutrition....................MSc 12FT 24PT

Dietetics
Research Courses

Barts and the London School of Medicine and Dentistry
Department of Human Nutrition ....PhD/MPhil/MD/FRCP

University of Cambridge
Human Nutrition...PhD 36FT

Newcastle University
Food and Human Nutrition .... MPhil 12FT 24PT/PhD 36FT 72PT

Plymouth University
Dietetics and Health...MPhil tbcFT

University of Surrey
Cardiovascular Dietary Research ....MPhil 24FT 36PT/
PhD 36FT 48PT

Food marketing management
Taught Courses

BPP Business School
Professional Marketing................................MSc 12FT 24+PT

Bangor University
Marketing... MBA 12FT/PGDip 9FT

University of Brighton
Food Services and Wellbeing Management... MSc 12FT 24-72PT/
PGDip 12FT 24-72PT/PGCert 12FT 24-72PT

Cardiff Metropolitan University
Food Technology for Industry......................................MSc 24-60DL

University of Central Lancashire
Marketing Management... MSc 12FT
Marketing and PR..MA 12FT

University College Cork
Co-operative Organisation Food Marketing & Rural
Development ....PGDip 12FT
Food Business .... MSc 24FT

Cranfield University
Food Chain Systems.........MSc 12FT 24-36PT/PGDip 6FT 24-36PT/
PGCert 4FT 24-36PT

University of Derby
Marketing Management .... MSc 12FT

University of East Anglia
Marketing and Management .... MSc 12FT
Supply Chain Management .... MSc 12FT
Sustainable Agriculture and Food Security..................... MSc 12FT

University of Exeter
Food Security and Sustainable Agriculture............. MSc 12FT 24PT
International Supply Chain Management .... MSc 12FT
Management ....MRes 12FT
Marketing ....MSc 12FT

Glasgow Caledonian University
Marketing .... MSc 12FT/PGDip 9FT

Harper Adams University
European Masters in Regional Food Production & Global
Marketing ....MSc 24FT
Food Industry Management............................... PGCert 12FT 24PT/
MSc 12FT 24PT/PGDip 12FT 24PT
Meat Business Management (PgD & MSc are /subject to
validation) .. PGCert 12FT 24PT/PGDip 12FT 24PT/MSc 12FT 24PT

Manchester Metropolitan University
International Food Management....................MSc 12FT 24-60PT
Logistics and Supply Chain Management...................... MSc 12FT

Newcastle University
Advanced Food Marketing .... MSc 12FT

University of Nottingham
Food Production Management.......MSc 12FT 24PT/PGDip 9-12FT
18-24PT

University of Reading
Food Economics and Marketing .... MSc 12FT

University of Roehampton
Marketing... MSc 12FT 24PT

University of Salford
Marketing.......... MSc 12FT 36PT/PGDip 8FT 24PT/PGCert 4FT 9PT

University of Sheffield
Marketing Management Practice .... MSc 12FT

University of Southampton
Marketing Management .... MSc 12FT/PGDip 9FT

University of St Andrews
Marketing...MLitt 12FT

University of Stirling
Marketing.. MSc 12FT/PGDip 9FT

University of Strathclyde
Marketing...............................MSc 12FT 24PT/PGDip 9FT 18PT

University of Surrey
Food Management.. MSc 12FT
Marketing Management... MSc 12FT

University of West London
Gastronomy and Food Management.......................GradDip 12FT
Gastronomy and Food Management .... MA 12FT 24PT

Food marketing management
Research Courses

University of Exeter
Management................................ PhD 48FT 84PT/MPhil 36FT 60PT

The Open University
Marketing.................. PhD 36FT 72PT variableDL/MPhil 15FT 24PT
variableDL

Sheffield Hallam University
School of Leisure and Food Management......................PhD/MPhil

Food sciences

Food product development
Taught Courses

Bangor University
Agricultural Systems................................ PhD by taught 36FT 60PT/MPhil 24FT 36PT

University College Birmingham
Culinary Arts Management.. MA 15FT 24PT

Cardiff Metropolitan University
Food Technology for Industry..MSc 24-60DL
Product Development Management ....MBA 12FT 24PT

University College Cork
Applied Science (Food Science).. MSc 12FT
Co-operative Organisation Food Marketing & Rural Development...PGDip 12FT
Food Business... MSc 24FT

Dublin Institute of Technology
Culinary Innovation and Food Product Development.... MSc 12FT 24PT

University of East Anglia
Sustainable Agriculture and Food Security....................... MSc 12FT

University of Exeter
Food Security and Sustainable Agriculture............. MSc 12FT 24PT

Goldsmiths, University of London
Management of Innovation .... MSc 12FT

Harper Adams University
European Masters in Regional Food Production & Global Marketing... MSc 24FT

Heriot-Watt University
Biotechnology ....MSc 12FT 24PT/PGDip 9FT 20PT

London School of Economics and Political Science (LSE)
Development Studies.. MSc 12FT 24PT

University of the Arts London - London College of Communication
Service Design Innovation.. MDes 12FT

Manchester Metropolitan University
Food and Nutrition..MSc 12FT 24-60PT
International Food Management........................MSc 12FT 24-60PT

Newcastle University
Advanced Food Marketing .... MSc 12FT
Organic Farming and Food Production Systems............. MSc 12FT

University of Nottingham
Food Production Management.......MSc 12FT 24PT/PGDip 9-12FT 18-24PT
Global Food Security (MRes)....................................MRes 12FT 36PT

University of Reading
Food Science ....MSc 12FT 24PT
Food Technology - Quality Assurance .... MSc 12FT

Royal Veterinary College
Intensive Livestock Health and Production ....MSc 24-60DL PGCert 12-36DL

University of Surrey
Food Management... MSc 12FT

University of West London
Gastronomy and Food Management..........................GradDip 12FT

Food product development
Research Courses

London School of Economics and Political Science (LSE)
Development Studies.......................... PhD 36-48FT/MPhil 36-48FT

Manchester Metropolitan University
Research in Food and Nutrition ....PhD VariableFT VariablePT/MPhil VariableFT VariablePT/MSc by research 12FT 24PT

Food safety
Taught Courses

University of Birmingham
Food Safety, Hygiene and Management ....MSc 12FT 24PT/PGDip 12PT/PGCert 6PT
University Certificate in Food Safety and Food Legislation .... Cert 12PT
University Diploma in Food Safety and Food Legislation............... Diploma 24PT

Cardiff Metropolitan University
Food Safety Management......... MSc 12FT 24PT/PGDip 12FT 24PT
Food Science & Technology............................MSc 12FT/PGDip 12FT

University of Central Lancashire
Food Safety Management (e-learning).....MSc 24PT/PGDip 12PT/PGCert 6PT
Hazard Analysis Critical Control Point Management by elearning PGDip 24-48PT/PGCert 24PT

De Montfort University
Food Law.. PGDip 15DL/LLM 15-27DL

Dublin Institute of Technology
Food Safety Management.. MSc 24PT

University of Edinburgh
Food Security ....MSc 12FT 24PT

Glasgow Caledonian University
Food Bioscience.. MSc 12FT

University of Greenwich
Food Safety and Quality Management........... MSc 12FT 24-36PT/PGDip 12FT 24-36PT

Harper Adams University
European Masters in Regional Food Production & Global Marketing... MSc 24FT

Heriot-Watt University
Food Science, Safety and Health MSc 12FT 24PT 24-84DL/PGDip 9FT 21PT 24-84DL
Food and Beverage Science..........MSc 12FT 24PT/PGDip 9FT 21PT

Leeds Metropolitan University
Environmental Health...MSc 12FT 36PT

London South Bank University
Food Safety and Control ....MSc 12FT 24PT

Manchester Metropolitan University
Food Safety..MSc 12FT 24-60PT

University of Nottingham
Food Production Management.......MSc 12FT 24PT/PGDip 9-12FT 18-24PT

University of Reading
Food Technology - Quality Assurance .... MSc 12FT

Royal Veterinary College
Intensive Livestock Health and Production ....MSc 24-60DL PGCert 12-36DL
Risk Analysis in Health and Food Safety - PGCert........ PGCert 6FT

University of Warwick
Food Security ....MSc 12FT 36PT

Food safety
Research Courses

University of Greenwich
Food Safety and Quality Management by Research ....MSc by research 12FT 24PT/PGDip by research 12FT 24PT

Harper Adams University
Food Quality and Safety ....MPhil 24FT/PhD 38FT

University of Liverpool
Food Security ....MPhil 12FT/PhD 36FT

Manchester Metropolitan University
Research in Consumer Marketing, Consumer Protection and Trading Standards ... PhD VariableFT VariablePT/MPhil VariableFT VariablePT/MSc by research 12FT 24PT
Research in Trading Standards, Consumer Advice & Environmental Health.................PhD VariableFT VariablePT/MPhil VariableFT VariablePT/MSc by research 12FT 24PT

University of Surrey
Food Safety; Nutrition................ MPhil 24FT 36PT/PhD 36FT 48PT

Food sciences
Taught Courses

University of Abertay Dundee
Food Biotechnology.. MSc 12FT/PGDip 9FT
Food and Drink Innovation (Sustainability and Packaging) .... MProf 12FT 24PT

Bangor University
Agricultural Systems................................ PhD by taught 36FT 60PT/MPhil 24FT 36PT

University of Birmingham
Food Safety, Hygiene and Management ....MSc 12FT 24PT/PGDip 12PT/PGCert 6PT
University Certificate in Food Safety and Food Legislation .... Cert 12PT
University Diploma in Food Safety and Food Legislation............... Diploma 24PT

University College Birmingham
Culinary Arts Management.. MA 15FT 24PT

University of Bristol
Meat Science and Technology.... MSc 12FT 24 - 36PT/PGDip 12FT 24 - 36PT/PGCert 12FT 24 - 36PT

University of Cambridge
Bioscience Enterprise .... MPhil 10FT

University of Central Lancashire
Food Microbiology.....................MSc 24PT/PGDip 12PT/PGCert 6PT

City University London
Food Policy...MSc 12FT 24PT

University College Cork
Applied Science (Food Science).. MSc 12FT
Co-operative Organisation Food Marketing & Rural Development...PGDip 12FT
Food Business... MSc 24FT
Food Microbiology.. MSc 24FT
Food Science & Technology...HDip 9FT 18PT

Nutritional Sciences.. MSc 24FT

Cranfield University
Food Chain Systems.........MSc 12FT 24-36PT/PGDip 6FT 24-36PT/PGCert 4FT 24-36PT

Dublin Institute of Technology
European MSc in Food Science, Technology and Nutrition..... MSc 12FT 24PT

University of Edinburgh
Food Security ....MSc 12FT 24PT

Glasgow Caledonian University
Food Bioscience.. MSc 12FT

University of Greenwich
Nutritional Sciences.................... MSc 12FT 24PT/PGDip 12FT 24PT

Heriot-Watt University
Food Science and Nutrition..........MSc 12FT 24PT/PGDip 9FT 21PT
Food Science, Safety and Health .... MSc 12FT 24PT 24-84DL/PGDip 9FT 21PT 24-84DL
Food and Beverage Science..........MSc 12FT 24PT/PGDip 9FT 21PT

University of Huddersfield
Nutrition and Food Sciences.. MSc 12FT

University of Leeds
Food Quality and Innovation .... MSc 12FT
Food Science ....MSc 12FT/PGCert 12FT/PGDip 12FT
Food Science (Food Biotechnology) .... MSc 12FT
Food Science and Nutrition.. MSc 12FT
Nutrition .... MSc 12FT

London Metropolitan University
Food Science ....MSc 12FT 24PT

London School of Hygiene and Tropical Medicine
Nutrition for Global Health ....MSc 12FT 24PT

Manchester Metropolitan University
Food and Nutrition..MSc 12FT 24-60PT
International Food Management........................MSc 12FT 24-60PT

Newcastle University
Advanced Food Marketing .... MSc 12FT
Medicinal Plants and Functional Foods............................ MSc 12FT

Northumbria University
Food Science ....MSc 12FT 30PT
Nutritional Science ....MSc 12FT 24PT

University of Nottingham
Agrifood .... MSc 24PT/PGCert 21PT/PGDip 21PT
Brewing Science..MRes 12FT 24PT

The Open University
Professional Science ....MSc variableDL
Science ....MSc variableDL

Queen's University Belfast
Advanced Food Safety .... MSc 12FT

University of Reading
Food Science ....MSc 12FT 24PT
Food Technology - Quality Assurance .... MSc 12FT
Nutrition and Food Science .... MSc 12FT/PGDip 9FT

Royal Agricultural University
Business Management in the Food Industries ..... MBA 15FT 24PT
International Food and Agribusiness .... MBA 15FT
Sustainable Agriculture and Food Security............ MSc 15FT 24PT

Schumacher College ....
Sustainable Horticulture and Food Production..........MSc/PGDip/PGCert

Staffordshire University
Computer Science via Distance Learning.... MSc 24-60DL/PGCert 24-60DL/PGDip 24-60DL

Swansea Metropolitan University
Food Logistics .... MSc 24PT

University of Ulster
Agri-food Business Development..............................MSc 12FT 26PT/PGDip 9FT 21PT
Food Regulatory Affairs by e-Learning.....PGCert 8PT/PGDip 10PT 8DL/MSc 18-20PT 10DL
Nutraceuticals, Functional Foods and Supplements... PGCert 8PT 4DL/PGDip 16PT 8DL/MSc 20PT 12DL

University of Warwick
Food Security ....MSc 12FT 36PT

Food sciences
Research Courses

City University London
Health Management and Food Policy..MSc by research/MHM by research

Coventry University
Wine...MSc by research 12FT 24PT

University of Greenwich
Agricultural and Food Sciences..... MPhil 18 - 36FT 30 - 48PT/PhD 33 - 60FT 45 - 72PT

Harper Adams University
Crop Protection ....MPhil 24FT/PhD 36FT

Food sciences

Food and Consumers Studies.........................MPhil 24FT/PhD 38FT

University of Leeds
Food Science ....PhD 36+FT/MPhil 24FT/MSc by research 12FT

University of Lincoln
Food Manufacturing and Technology ....MPhil 18FT 36PT

University of Nottingham
Food Sciences PhD 36FT 72PT/MPhil 24FT 48PT/MRes 12FT 24PT

Oxford Brookes University
Health and Biomedical Sciences - The Functional Food Centre
MPhil/PhD............ PhD 24-60FT 36-72PT/MPhil 24-36FT 36-48PT

Plymouth University
Food, Nutrition and Health...........................PhD 36FT/MPhil 24FT

University of Surrey
Food Management........................ PhD 36FT 48PT/MPhil 24FT 36PT

Teesside University
Food Science and Technology. PhD 24-60FT 36-72PT 30DL/MPhil
18FT 30PT 30DL/DProf 36PT 36DL/MProf by research 30PT 30DL

Nutrition
Taught Courses

University of Aberdeen
Human Nutrition and Metabolism................ MSc 12FT/PGDip 8FT
Public Health Nutrition.................MSc 12FT 24PT/PGDip 9FT 18PT

University of Bedfordshire
Physical Activity, Nutrition and Health Promotion........MSc 12FT/
PGDip 12FT/PGCert 12FT

University College Birmingham
Culinary Arts Management .... MA 15FT 24PT

University of Brighton
Food Services and Wellbeing Management ... MSc 12FT 24-72PT/
PGDip 12FT 24-72PT/PGCert 12FT 24-72PT

University of Bristol
Nutrition, Physical Activity and Public Health .... MSc 12FT 24PT

Bucks New University
Health, Exercise & Wellbeing................................ MSc 12FT 24PT

Cardiff Metropolitan University
Food Science & Technology...........................MSc 12FT/PGDip 12FT
Food Technology for Industry.............................MSc 24-60DL

University of Chester
Exercise and Nutrition Science .. MSc 12FT 24 - 48PT/PGDip 12FT
24 - 48PT/PGCert 12FT 12 - 24PT
Exercise and Nutrition Science (Taught in Dublin, Ireland).... MSc
24 - 48PT/PGDip 24 - 48PT/PGCert 12 - 24PT
Human Nutrition........... MSc 12FT 24-48PT/PGDip 12FT 24-48PT/
PGCert 12FT 12-24PT
Nutrition and Dietetics.............................MSc 24FT/PGDip 24FT
Public Health Nutrition............... MSc 12FT 24 - 72PT/PGDip 12FT
24 - 60PT/PGCert 12FT 12 - 36PT
Sports Sciences (with named pathways)..... MA 12FT 24PT/PGDip
12FT 24PT/PGCert 12FT 12-24PT
Weight ManagementMSc 12FT 24 - 48PT/PGDip 12FT 24 - 48PT/
PGCert 12FT 12 - 24PT
Weight Management (Taught in Dublin, Ireland) .. MSc 24-48PT/
PGDip 24-48PT/PGCert 12-24PT

City University London
Food and Nutrition Policy..................................MSc 12FT 24PT

University College Cork
Applied Science (Food Science)................................. MSc 12FT
Food Science & Technology...........................HDip 9FT 18PT
Nutritional Sciences.. MSc 24FT

Coventry University
Sport and Exercise Nutrition .... PGCert 12 MinPT
Weight Management..PGCert 12PT

Dublin Institute of Technology
European MSc in Food Science, Technology and Nutrition..... MSc
12FT 24PT

University of Dundee
Sports and Biomechanical Medicine (MSc Full time in-house) .....
MSc 12FT
Sports and Biomechanical Medicine (MSc Part time with
externally arranged project)..................................... MSc 24PT
Sports and Biomechanical Medicine (MSc Part time with in-
house project) .... MSc 24PT

University of East Anglia
Midwifery ....PGDip 18FT

University of Exeter
Paediatric Exercise and Health...........................MSc 12FT 24PT
Sport and Health Sciences ....MSc 12FT 24PT

Glasgow Caledonian University
Clinical Nutrition and Health .... MSc 12FT

University of Glasgow
Clinical Nutrition.............................MSc(MedSci) 12FT 24PT
Human Nutrition........... MSc(MedSci) 12FT 24PT/PGDip 9FT 18PT
Sports Nutrition .... PGCert 4FT

University of Greenwich
Nutritional Sciences................... MSc 12FT 24PT/PGDip 12FT 24PT

Heriot-Watt University
Food Science and Nutrition..........MSc 12FT 24PT/PGDip 9FT 21PT
Food and Beverage Science..........MSc 12FT 24PT/PGDip 9FT 21PT

University of Huddersfield
Nutrition and Food Sciences.................................... MSc 12FT

Leeds Metropolitan University
Community Specialist Practitioner - Practice Nursing..MSc 24PT/
PGDip 24PT
Dietetics ....PGDip 24FT

Leeds Trinity University
Health and Wellbeing MSc 24PT 24DL/PGCert 12PT 12DL/PGDip
24PT 24DL

University of Leeds
Food Science and Nutrition .... MSc 12FT
Nutrition... MSc 12FT

Liverpool Hope University
Health, Exercise and Nutrition....................MSc 12-15FT 24-36PT/
PGDip 12FT 24PT/PGDip 6FT 12PT

Liverpool John Moores University
Health Sciences..MRes 12FT 24PT

London Metropolitan University
Dietetics and Nutrition ....MSc 30FT/PGDip 36FT
Human Nutrition (Public Health/Sports)................ MSc 12FT 24PT

Manchester Metropolitan University
Biomedical Science featuring Exercise and Health options ... MSc
12FT 24-36PT
Food and Nutrition...................................MSc 12FT 24-60PT
Nutrition and Health...............................MSc 12FT 24-60PT

Northumbria University
Food Science ....MSc 12FT 30PT
Nutritional Science ....MSc 12FT 24PT

University of Nottingham
Clinical Nutrition ....MSc 24-72PT/PGDip 24-72PT
Global Food Security (MRes)............................MRes 12FT 36PT
Nutritional Sciences...MSc 12FT 24PT

Oxford Brookes University
Applied Human Nutrition ....MSc 12FT 24PT/PGDip 8FT 20PT/
PGCert 8FT 8PT
Applied Sport & Exercise Nutrition .....MSc 12FT 24PT/PGDip 8FT
20PT

University of Portsmouth
Clinical Exercise Science .... MSc 12FT 24PT

Queen Margaret University, Edinburgh
Dietetics..MSc 18FT/PGDip 15FT
Public Health Nutrition.... MSc 12FT 24-60PT/PGDip 9FT 24-60PT

Queen's University Belfast
Nursing Practice..................................... DMP (Doctorate) 36FT 60PT

University of Reading
Food Science ....MSc 12FT 24PT
Medieval Archaeology ....MA 12FT
Nutrition and Food Science ....MSc 12FT/PGDip 9FT

University of Roehampton
Clinical Nutrition ....MSc 12FT 24PT 24DL
Health Sciences...MSc 12FT 24PT
Clinical Nutrition .... PGCert 6FT 24PT 24DL PGDip 9FT 24PT 24DL

Sheffield Hallam University
Nutrition with Public Health Management .... MSc 12FT

University of Sheffield
Human Nutrition ....MMedSci 12FT 24PT/PGDip 9FT 18PT

University of Southampton
Public Health Nutrition.............MSc 12FT 36PT/PGDip 12FT 24PT/
PGCert 12FT 12PT

St Mary's University College, Twickenham
Applied Sports Nutrition .... PGDip 12PT
Nutrition and Physical Activity for Public Health........... MSc 12FT
Strength and Conditioning .... MSc 12FT

University of Stirling
Sport Nutrition (International Olympic Committee Upgrade)......
MSc 6FT 12PT

University of Surrey
Nutritional Medicine..MSc 24-72PT

Teesside University
Strength & Conditioning..MSc 12FT 24PT

Trinity College Dublin - the University of Dublin
Cardiovascular Rehabilitation and Prevention ......MSc 12FT 24PT

University of Ulster
Human Nutrition............................MSc 12FT 36PT/PGDip 9FT 24PT
Sport and Exercise Nutrition ..... PGDip 18PT 9DL/MSc 22PT 12DL

UCL - University College London
Cardiovascular Science... MSc 12FT
Clinical and Public Health Nutrition.............MSc 12FT/PGDip 9FT/
PGCert 3FT
Clinical and Public Health Nutrition: Eating Disorders.MSc 12FT/
PGDip 9FT/PGCert 3FT

University of Warwick
Nutritional Management in Diabetes Care.... PGA 12PT/CPDMod
1PT

University of West London
Nursing and Healthcare Intergrated .... MSc 12FT

University of Westminster
International Public Health Nutrition.....................MSc 12FT 24PT
Nutritional Therapy ....MSc 12FT 24PT
Public Health Nutrition... MSc 12FT

University of Worcester
Nutritional Therapy ...MSc 18-24FT 36-48PT/PGDip 18PT/PGCert
9PT

Nutrition
Research Courses

University of Aberdeen
Nutrition and Health........PhD 36FT/MPhil 24FT/MSc by research
12FT

Barts and the London School of Medicine and Dentistry
Department of Human Nutrition ....PhD/MPhil/MD/FRCP

University of Bristol
Policy Studies .... PhD 36FT 72PT/MPhil 36FT 72PT

University of Cambridge
Human Nutrition..PhD 36FT

Cardiff University
Nursing, Medicine, Health and Social Care (PhD)........ MPhil 12FT
36PT/PhD 36FT 60PT

University of Exeter
Health and Wellbeing .... MPhil 36FT 60FT/PhD 48FT 84PT
Sport and Health Sciences .... PhD 48FT 84PT/MPhil 36FT 60PT

King's College London
Diabetes & Nutritional Sciences .. MPhil 24FT/PhD 36-48FT 72PT

University of Leeds
Exercise and Health ....PhD 36+FT/MPhil 24FT/MSc by research
12FT

Liverpool John Moores University
Health Sciences...MRes 12FT 24PT

Manchester Metropolitan University
Research in Food and Nutrition ....PhD VariableFT VariablePT/
MPhil VariableFT VariablePT/MSc by research 12FT 24PT

Newcastle University
Food and Human Nutrition .... MPhil 12FT 24PT/PhD 36FT 72PT

Nottingham Trent University
Performance Nutrition...MRes 12FT 24PT

University of Nottingham
Early life nutrition and disease ....PhD 36FT 72PT/DM 24FT 48PT/
MPhil 24FT 48PT
Health Science: Doctor of Health Science.........................PhD 36FT
Nutritional Sciences....... DPhil 36FT 72PT/MPhil 24FT 48PT/MRes
12FT 24PT

Plymouth University
Dietetics and Health..MPhil tbcFT
Food, Nutrition and Health...........................PhD 36FT/MPhil 24FT

University of Roehampton
Health Sciences.... PhD 24-48FT 36-60PT/MPhil 21-36FT 36-60PT

University of Stirling
Sports Studies .... PhD 36FT 72PT/MPhil 12FT 24PT

University of Surrey
Food Safety; Nutrition................. MPhil 24FT 36PT/PhD 36FT 48PT
Medicine and Health .....PhD 36FT 48PT/MPhil 24FT 36PT/MSc by
research 12FT
Nutrition and Health: Cardiovascular Disease .....PhD 36FT 48PT/
MPhil 24FT 36PT

Geology and geographical science

Astrobiology
Research Courses

University of Nottingham
Magnetic Resonance ....PhD 36FT 72PT/MPhil 24FT 48PT/MRes 12FT

The Open University
Astrobiology and Habits for Life......... PhD 36FT 72PT variableDL/MPhil 15FT 24PT variableDL

Cartography
Taught Courses

Aberystwyth University
Remote Sensing and GeographyMSc 12FT 24PT/PGDip 9FT 18PT/PGCert 5FT 10PT

University of Glasgow
Geoinformation Technology & Cartography.. MSc 12FT 24-48PT/PGDip 9FT 21-44PT/PGCert 3.5FT 9-32PT
Geomatics & Management.................................. MSc 12FT
Landscape Monitoring & Mapping................... MSc 12FT 24-36PT/PGDip 9FT 18-21PT

University of Nottingham
Environmental Management and Earth Observation ... MSc 12FT 24-36PT/PGDip 9FT 24-36PT

Trinity College Dublin - the University of Dublin
Digital Humanities and Culture ....MPhil 12FT 24PT

UCL - University College London
Digital Humanities.... MA 12FT 24PT/MSc 12FT 24PT/PGDip 12FT 24PT/PGCert 3FT 24PT
Environmental Mapping.. MSc 12FT 24PT

Cultural geography
Taught Courses

University of Aberdeen
Transitional Justice and Reconciliation...................MSc 12FT 24PT/PGDip 9FT 18PT

University of Bath
Global Political Economy: transformations and policy analysis ... MRes 12FT 24-36PT

University of Birmingham
International Development ....MSc 24-48DL/PGDip 18-48DL

University of Brighton
Cultural and Critical Theory (Aesthetics and Cultural Theory) ...... MA 12FT 24PT/PGDip 12FT 24PT/PGCert 12FT 24PT
Cultural and Critical Theory (Globalisation, Politics and Culture) .. ..MA 12FT 24PT/PGDip 12FT 24PT/PGCert 12FT 24PT

Brunel University
Globalisation and Governance .... MA 12FT 30PT

University of Cambridge
Geographical Research.. MPhil 12FT

Cardiff University
Geography, Policy and Practice .... MSc 12FT

University College Cork
Arts (Geography) ....HDip 9FT 18PT
European Development Studies.................................MA 12FT
Sociology of Development and Globalisation ....MA 12FT

Coventry University
Global Development and International Law....MSc 12FT 24-30PT

University of East Anglia
Cultural Heritage and International Development .... MA 12FT 24PT
Globalisation, Business and Sustainable Development..MA 12FT 24PT

University of East London
NGO and Development Management...................MSc 12FT 24PT/PGDip 8FT 16PT/PGCert 4FT 8PT

University of Edinburgh
Cultural Studies.. MSc 12FT 24PT
Global Social Change... MSc 12FT 24PT

University of Exeter
Critical Human Geographies ....MRes 12FT
Energy Policy ....MSc 12FT 24PT
Environment, Energy and Resilience ....MRes 12FT 24PT
Sustainable Development..MSc 12FT 24PT

University of Glasgow
Equality & Human Rights......................................MSc 12FT 24PT
Global Economy...MSc 12FT 24PT

Goldsmiths, University of London
World Cities and Urban Life.............................. MA 12FT 24PT

University of Kent
Anthropology and Conservation .... MA 12FT 24PT
Anthropology of Ethnicity, Nationalism and Identity......MA 12FT 24PT
Architecture and Cities .... MA 12FT 24PT
Architecture and Cities (Paris option) ....MA 12FT

King's College London
Cities..MA 12FT 24PT/MSc 12FT 24PT
Environment, Politics & Globalisation...MA 12FT 24PT/MSc 12FT 24PT

Leeds Metropolitan University
Urban DesignMA 12FT 24PT/PGDip 12FT 24PT/PGCert 12FT 24PT

University of Leeds
Social and Cultural Geography ....MA 12FT 24PT/PGDip 12FT 24PT

University of Leicester
European Urbanisation ....MA 12FT

University of Liverpool
Cities, Culture and Regeneration............................... MA 12FT 24PT
Geographies of Globalisation and Development... MA 12FT 24PT
Population Studies (Research Methodology).....................MA 12FT
Research Methodology (Civic Design)...................... MA 12FT 24PT
Research Methodology (Lifecourse, Population and Mobility) MA 12FT 24PT

London Metropolitan University
Sustainable Cities..MSc 12FT 24+PT

London School of Economics and Political Science (LSE)
Global Politics...MSc 12FT 24PT
Health, Population and Society ....MSc 12FT 24PT

London School of Hygiene and Tropical Medicine
Global Health Policy (by Distance Learning) ....MSc 24-60DL/PGDip 12-60DL/PGCert 12-60DL

Loughborough University
Globalization and Sport.. MSc 12FT

Manchester Metropolitan University
European Urban Cultures...MA 12FT

Newcastle University
Human Geography Research....................................... MA 12FT 24PT
World Politics and Popular Culture........................... MA 12FT 24PT

University of Northampton
Integrated Urbanism..MSc 12FT 24PT

University of Nottingham
Economy, Space and Society ....MSc 12FT 24PT

Oxford Brookes University
Food, Wine and Culture ....MA 12FT 36PT 24DL

University of Oxford
Nature, Society and Environmental Policy......................MSc 12FT

Queen Mary, University of London
Cities and Cultures... MA 12FT 24PT
Cities and Cultures..MRes 12FT 24PT
Community Organising ....MA 12FT 24PT
Globalisation and Development .... MA 12FT 24PT
Globalisation and Development ....MRes 12FT 24PT

Reseau Universitaire Transmanche
Intercultural Relations..MA 15FT

Royal Holloway, University of London
Cultural Geography (Research).............................. MA 12FT 24PT
Masters by Research (Comparative Literature and Culture).....MA 12FT 24PT

University of Salford
International Relations and Globalisation...MA 12FT 36PT 36DL/PGDip 8FT 24PT 36DL

School of Oriental and African Studies - SOAS
Global Media and Postnational Communication.............MA 12FT 24-36PT
Law, Development and Globalisation .... MA 12FT 24PT
Globalisation and Multinational Corporations ...... MA 12FT 24PT
Political Economy of Development....................MSc 12FT 24-36PT
Research for International Development................MSc 12FT 24PT

Sheffield Hallam University
Cultural Studies ....MRes variousFT variousPT

University of Sheffield
Comparative Governance and Public Policy .... MA 12FT 24PT
Globalisation and Development .... MA 12FT 24PT
Social Research... MA 12FT 24PT
Social and Spatial Inequalities.................................MSc 12FT 24PT

University of St Andrews
Health Geography Research ... MRes 12FT 24PT/PGDip 10FT 20PT

University of Strathclyde
Social Research...MRes 12FT 24PT

University of Sussex
Climate Change and Policy ....MSc 12FT 24PT
Global Health .... MSc 12FT
Globalisation and Development .... MA 12FT 24PT

Swansea University
Human Geography... MA 12FT 24-36PT

Teesside University
Cultural History.. MA 12FT 24-36PT
Global Development & Social Research .....MSc 12FT 24PT/PGDip 12FT 24PT

Trinity College Dublin - the University of Dublin
Digital Humanities and Culture ....MPhil 12FT 24PT
Public History and Cultural Heritage.......................MPhil 12FT 24PT

University of Wales Trinity Saint David
Health, Ethics and Society............... MA 12-24DL/PGDip 12-24DL

UCL - University College London
Cultural Heritage Studies... MA 12FT 24PT
East European Studies...MRes 24FT
European Culture and Thought: Culture.....MA 12FT 24PT/PGDip 9FT 18PT/PGCert 3FT 6PT
European Culture and Thought: Thought... MA 12FT 24PT/PGDip 9FT 18PT/PGCert 3FT 6PT
Globalisation ....MSc 12FT 24PT/PGDip 9FT
Globalisation and Latin American Development.. MSc 12FT 24PT
Identity, Culture and Power .... MA 12FT 24PT
Institutions, Development and Globalisation......... MA 12FT 24PT
Language, Culture and History .... MA 12FT 24PT
Modernity, Space and Place...................................MSc 12FT
Social and Cultural Anthropology ....MSc 12FT 24PT
Urban Studies...MSc 12FT 24-60PT

University of Winchester
Managing Contemporary Global Issues ...... MA 12FT 24PT/PGDip 12FT 24PT/PGCert 12FT 24PT
Managing Contemporary Global Issues with Environment and Development..MSc 12FT 24PT/PGDip 9FT 18PT/PGCert 9FT 18PT

Cultural geography
Research Courses

University of Bath
Global Political Economy: transformations and policy analysis ... MRes 12FT 24-36PT

Coventry University
Cultural Geography.......................... MSc by research 12FT 24-36PT

University of Edinburgh
Cultural Studies .... PhD 36FT 72PT

University of Exeter
Environment, Energy and Resilience ..MPhil 36FT 60PT/PhD 36FT 84PT
Human Geography.........PhD 48FT 84PT/MPhil 36FT 60PT/MSc by research 12FT 24PT

University of Kent
Anthropology ....PhD 36FT 60PT/MPhil 12FT 36PT/MA by research 12FT 24PT/MSc by research 12FT 24PT

University of Leeds
Geography...................................PhD 36FT 60PT/MPhil 24FT

London School of Economics and Political Science (LSE)
Cities.. PhD 36-48FT/MPhil 36-48FT
Economic Geography.........................MPhil 36-48FT/PhD 36-48FT

University of Nottingham
Cultural and Historical Geography ....PhD 36FT
New Economic Geographies....................................PhD 36FT

The Open University
Globalisation, Transnationalism and Social Welfare.......PhD 36FT 72PT variableDL/MPhil 15FT 24PT variableDL
Politics of urban culture and space.... PhD 36FT 72PT variableDL/MPhil 15FT 24PT variableDL

Queen's University Belfast
Geography: Society, Space and Culture ....PhD 36FT 72PT/MPhil 24FT 48PT
Past Cultural Change.................. PhD 36FT 72PT/MPhil 24FT 48PT

Swansea University
Human Geography...................... PhD 36FT 60PT/MPhil 24FT 48PT
Urban Studies..MSc by research 12FT 24PT

UCL - University College London
East European Society and National Identity......... PhD 36FT 60PT

Geochemistry
Taught Courses

University of Aberdeen
Analytical Chemistry for Environmental Life Sciences .MSc 12FT/PGDip 9FT/PGCert 4FT

Bangor University
Analytical Chemistry ....MSc 12FT/Diploma 9FT
Chemistry...MRes 12FT
Environmental Chemistry .... MSc 12FT/PGDip 9FT
Physical Oceanography...................MSc 12FT 24-36PT/PGDip 9FT

University College Cork
Applied Science (Environmental Analytical Chemistry)..................
MSc 12FT 24PT

Imperial College London
Green Chemistry: Engineering, Energy and the Environment.......
MRes 12FT

University of Leeds
Environmental Geochemistry ....MSc 12FT 12-48PT
Geochemistry ....MSc 12FT 24-48PT

Newcastle University
Petroleum Geochemistry .... MSc 12FT

Geology and geographical science

Geochemistry
Research Courses

Bangor University
Chemistry ....PhD 36FT
Chemistry ....MRes 12FT
Chemistry ....MPhil 24FT
Ocean Sciences........................MPhil 24FT/PhD 36FT

University of Bath
Sustainable Chemical Technologies ....Integrated PhD 48FT

University of Birmingham
Earth Sciences .... PhD 36FT 72PT/MPhil 24FT 48PT

University of Leeds
Atmospheric and Climate Science .....PhD 36FT 60PT 60DL/MPhil 24FT 48PT 48DL

University of Manchester
Environmental Geochemistry and Geomicrobiology.... PhD 36FT/MPhil 12FT 24PT/MSc by research 12FT
Isotope Geochemistry and Cosmochemistry PhD 36FT 72PT/MSc by research 12FT/MPhil 12FT 24PT
Structural and Petrological Geoscience.... PhD 36FT 72PT/MSc by research 12FT/MPhil 12FT 24PT

Newcastle University
Geochemistry .... PhD 36FT 72PT/MPhil 12FT 24PT

The Open University
Cosmochemistry...... PhD 36FT 72PT variableDL/MPhil 15FT 24PT variableDL
Isotope Geochemistry and Earth Systems .... PhD 36FT 72PT variableDL

Plymouth University
Biogeochemistry and Environmental Analytical Chemistry Research Group (BEAch) .... MPhil 24FT/PhD 36FT
Palaeontology and Palaeonenvironments Research Group ....PhD 36FT/MPhil 24FT
Petroleum and Environmental Geochemistry Research Group..... MPhil 24FT/PhD 36FT

Geographical information systems
Taught Courses

University of Aberdeen
Applied Geospatial Information Science....MSc 12FT 24PT/PGDip 9FT 20PT/PGCert 4FT 8PT

Aberystwyth University
Remote Sensing & Geographical Information Systems (GIS) MSc 12FT 24PT/PGDip 9FT 18PT/PGCert 5FT 10PT
Remote Sensing and GeographyMSc 12FT 24PT/PGDip 9FT 18PT/PGCert 5FT 10PT
Remote Sensing and Planetary Science....MSc 12FT 24PT/PGDip 9FT 18PT/PGCert 5FT 10PT
Remote Sensing and The Living Environment ......MSc 12FT 24PT/PGDip 9FT 18PT/PGCert 5FT 10PT
Remote Sensing with Computer Sciences .MSc 12FT 24PT/PGDip 9FT 18PT/PGCert 5FT 10PT

Birkbeck, University of London
Geographic Information Science (GISc) ....MSc 24PT/PGDip 24PT/PGCert 12PT

University of Brighton
Geographical Information Systems and Environmental Management................... MSc 12FT 24PT/PGDip 12FT 24PT

University of Central Lancashire
Osteoarchaeology: Techniques and Data Analysis .... MSc 12FT

University College Cork
Applied Science (Geographical Information Systems & Remote Sensing... MSc 12FT
Geography (Coastal Management Systems).....................MA 12FT

Cranfield University
Geographical Information Management........ MSc 12FT 24-60PT/PGDip 6FT 24PT/PGCert 5FT 24PT

Dublin Institute of Technology
Spatial Information Management..............MSc 30PT/PGDip 24PT

Edinburgh Napier University
Digital Systems ....MA/MDes 12FT 24PT

University of Edinburgh
Geographical Information Science ....MSc 12FT 24-36PT
Geographical Information Science and Archaeology..... MSc 12FT

University of Glasgow
Aquatic System Science ....MSc 12FT 24PT/PGDip 8FT 16PT
Coastal System Management .....MSc 12FT 24PT/PGDip 8FT 16PT
Freshwater System Science..........MSc 12FT 24PT/PGDip 8FT 16PT
Geoinformation Technology & Cartography.. MSc 12FT 24-48PT/PGDip 9FT 21-44PT/PGCert 3.5FT 9-32PT
Geomatics & Management .... MSc 12FT
Geospatial & Mapping Sciences.....MSc 12FT 24-48PT/PGDip 9FT 21-44PT/PGCert 3.5FT 9-32PT
Landscape Monitoring & MappingMSc 12FT 24-36PT/PGDip 9FT 18-21PT
Marine System Science ....MSc 12FT 24PT/PGDip 8FT 16PT

University of Greenwich
Geographical Information Systems with Remote Sensing..... MSc 12FT 24 - 36PT/PGDip 12FT 24-36PT
Remote Sensing with Geographical Information Systems..... MSc 12FT 24PT/PGDip 12FT 24PT

Heriot-Watt University
Marine Spatial Planning ....MSc 12FT 24PT/PGDip 9FT

Kingston University
Geographical Information Systems and Science... MSc 12FT 24PT

University of Leeds
Geographical Information Systems (GIS) ...MSc 12FT 24PT/PGDip 9FT 18PT
River Basin Dynamics and Management with GIS .... MSc 12FT 24PT/PGDip 9FT 21PT
GIS via Online Distance Learning .... MSc 36DL/PGDip 24DL

University of Leicester
Environmental Informatics ....MSc 12FT 24PT/PGDip 9FT 18PT
GIS and Human Geography ....MSc 12FT 24PT/PGDip 9FT 18PT
Geographical Information Systems .....MSc 12FT 24PT/PGDip 9FT 18PT

London South Bank University
Information Systems Management ....MSc 24PT

Manchester Metropolitan University
Geographical Information Systems..........................MSc 36PT 36DL

University of Manchester
Geographical Information Science ....MSc 12FT 24PT

University of Nottingham
Engineering Surveying with Geographical Information Science .. MSc 12FT
Geographical Information Science ....MSc 12FT 24PT
Geospatial Intelligence (by Research) ....MSc(Res) 12FT 24PT

University of Portsmouth
Geographical Information Systems..........................MSc 12FT 24PT

University of Salford
Geographical Information Systems........... MSc 36DL/PGDip 24DL

School of Oriental and African Studies - SOAS
MA Globalisation and Multinational CorporationsMA 12FT 24PT

Sheffield Hallam University
Geographical Information SystemsMSc 12FT 24PT/PGCert 12PT/PGDip 6PT

University of South Wales
Conservation and Geographical Information Systems.. MSc 12FT 24PT
Geographical Information Systems..........................MSc 12FT 36PT

University of Southampton
Archaeological Computing ....MSc 12FT 24PT
Crime Analysis..MSc 12FT 24PT

University of Sussex
Applied Geomorphology ....MSc 12FT 24PT

Swansea University
Geographic Information and Climate Change......MSc 12FT 36PT/PGCert 12FT 12PT
Modelling, Uncertainty and Data .... MSc 12FT 24/36PT

Trinity College Dublin - the University of Dublin
Digital Humanities and Culture ....MPhil 12FT 24PT

University of Ulster
Environmental Management with/and Geographic Information Systems...PGDip 24DL/MSc 36DL
Geographic Information Systems (GIS).. PGCert 3-4FT 8PT/PGDip 8FT 24PT/MSc 12FT 36PT

UCL - University College London
Advanced Spatial Analysis and Visualisation.................MRes 12FT
Digital Humanities.... MA 12FT 24PT/MSc 12FT 24PT/PGDip 12FT 24PT/PGCert 3FT 24PT
Environmental Mapping.......................................MSc 12FT 24PT
GIS and Spatial Analysis in Archaeology ....MSc 12FT 24PT
Geographic Information Science.....................MSc 12FT 24-36PT
Geospatial Analysis ....MSc 12FT 24PT
Remote Sensing ....MSc 12FT 24PT

Geographical information systems
Research Courses

Aberystwyth University
Earth Sciences ....MPhil 12FT 24PT PhD 36FT 60PT
Human Geography ....PhD 36FT 60PT

Birkbeck, University of London
Geographic Information Science.. PhD 36FT 60-72PT/MPhil 24FT 36PT

Cardiff University
Spatial Analysis ....PhD 36FT 60PT

City University London
Engineering Surveying Research Centre.........................PhD/MPhil
Geographic Information.................................... PhD 24-84PT

Coventry University
Geographical Information Systems ....MSc by research 12FT 24PT

De Montfort University
Earth and Planetary Remote Sensing Research......... PhD 24-36FT 48-72PT/MPhil 12-24FT 24-48PT

University of Edinburgh
Geographical Information Science .....MSc by research 12FT 24PT

Newcastle University
Geomatics .... PhD 36FT 72PT/MPhil 12FT 24PT

University of Nottingham
Efficient Fossil Energy Technologies .... EngD 48FT
Engineering and Surveying Space GeodesyPhD 36FT 72PT/MPhil 24FT 48PT
Geosciences (formerly GIS) PhD ....PhD 36-48FT
Geospatial Science ....PhD 12-48FT
Location-aware Ubiquitous Computing for the Digital Society.... PhD 36FT

The Open University
Materialities, Space and Power........... PhD 36FT 72PT variableDL/MPhil 15FT 24PT variableDL

Plymouth University
Geomatics Research Group...........................MPhil 24FT/PhD 36FT

Geology and geographical science
Taught Courses

University of Aberdeen
Integrated Petroleum Geoscience............................... MSc 12FT

Aberystwyth University
Environmental Monitoring and Analysis ....MSc 12FT/PGDip 9FT/PGCert 9FT
Glaciology..MSc 12FT 24PT/PGDip 9FT 18PT

Bangor University
Applied Marine Geoscience ....MSc 12FT 24-36PT/PGDip 9FT
Rheolaeth Amgylcheddol Gynaliadwy / Sustainable Environmental Managem (Welsh-medium) .. MA 12FT 24PT/MSc 12FT 24PT
Wetland Science and Conservation ....MSc 12FT

Birkbeck, University of London
Children, Youth and International Development.. MSc 12FT 24PT
Climate Change ManagementMSc 12FT 24PT/PGDip 12FT 24PT/PGCert 12PT
Environment and Sustainability.........MSc 12FT 24PT/PGDip 12FT 24PT/PGCert 12PT
Environmental Geology.................... GradCert 12PT 12DL
Geographic Information Science (GISc) ....MSc 24PT/PGDip 24PT/PGCert 12PT
Geology.................... GradCert 12PT 12DL

University of Birmingham
Nuclear Decommissioning and Waste Management.... MSc 12FT 24PT

University of Brighton
Environmental Geology............MSc 12FT 24PT/PGDip 12FT 24PT/PGCert 12FT 24PT

University of Bristol
Palaeobiology ....MSc 12FT 24 - 36PT
Science of Natural Hazards...................................MRes 12FT 24PT

University of Cambridge
Geographical Research...................................... MPhil 12FT

Cardiff University
Geoenvironmental Engineering ....MSc 12FT 24-36PT

University of Dundee
Catchment Hydrology & Management .... MSc 12FT
Non-Graduating Taught Postgraduate in School of the Environment .... PG module variableFT

University of Edinburgh
Ecological Economics.........................MSc 12FT 24-36PT/PGDip 9FT
GeoSciences (Individual Project) ....MSc(Res) 12FT 24PT
Geographical Information Science ....MSc 12FT 24-36PT
Geographical Information Science and Archaeology..... MSc 12FT
Human Geography...............................MSc(Res) 12FT 24PT
Petroleum Geoscience....................................... MSc 12FT

University of Exeter
Climate Change Impacts and Feedbacks..............MRes 12FT 24PT
Mining Geology .... MSc 12FT

Heriot-Watt University
Petroleum Geoscience (PetGeo) .... MSc 12FT
Reservoir Evaluation and Management ....MSc 12FT 24PT

Imperial College London
Petroleum Geoscience...................................... MSc 12FT

Institute of Education
Geography in Education .... MA 12FT 24-48PT 12-24DL

Kingston University
Environmental and Earth Resources Management.. MSc 12-20FT 24PT
Geographical Information Systems and Science... MSc 12FT 24PT
Hazards and Disaster Management......................MSc 12FT 24PT

Lancaster University
Volcanology and Geological Hazards......................MSc 12FT 24PT

Geology and geographical science

University of Leeds
Structural Geology with Geophysics ....MSc 12FT 48PT

Liverpool Hope University
Education & Geography ....MA 36PT

London School of Hygiene and Tropical Medicine
Demography & Health...MSc 12FT 24PT
Global Health Policy (by Distance Learning) MSc 24-60DL/PGDip 12-60DL/PGCert 12-60DL
Public Health in Developing Countries ....MSc 12FT 24PT

University of Manchester
Petroleum Exploration Geoscience...................................MSc 12FT
Petroleum Geoscience for Reservoir Development and
Production...MSc 12FT

National University of Ireland, Maynooth
Geographical Analysis...MA 12FT 24PT

Newcastle University
Hydroinformatics ....MSc 12FT 48PT

University of Nottingham
Geography (by Research).....MA 12FT 24PT/MSc 24PT/MRes 12FT

The Open University
Earth Science ....MSc variablePT
Professional Science ....MSc variableDL
Science ....MSc variableDL

University of Oxford
Geography and the Environment...................................MPhil 24FT

University of Portsmouth
Geological and Environmental Hazards ....MSc 12FT 24PT

Royal Holloway, University of London
Petroleum Geoscience (Basin Evolution)...........MSc 12FT 24-36PT
Petroleum Geoscience (Tectonics) ....MSc 12FT 24-36PT
Quaternary Science...MSc 12FT 24PT

University of Salford
Geographical Information Systems........... MSc 36DL/PGDip 24DL

University of Sheffield
Environmental Change and International Development .... MSc 12FT 24PT
Geoarchaeology...MSc 12FT 24PT
International Development.. MA 12FT 24PT

University of Southampton
Marine Geology and Geophysics......................................MRes 12FT

Marine Resource Management .... MSc 12FT

Swansea University
Environmental Dynamics and Climate Change..... MSc 12FT 36PT
Geographic Information and Climate Change......MSc 12FT 36PT/PGCert 12FT 12PT
Human Geography.. MA 12FT 24-36PT

UCL - University College London
Environmental Mapping...MSc 12FT 24PT
Environmental Modelling ....MSc 12FT 24PT
Geoscience .... MSc 12FT
Natural Hazards for Insurers .... PGCert 4PT

Geology and geographical science
Research Courses

University of Aberdeen
Geography and Environment .... PhD 36FT/MPhil 24FT/MSc by research 12FT/MRes 12FT
Geology and Petroleum Geology ... PhD 36FT/MPhil 24FT/MSc by research 12FT

Aberystwyth University
Earth Sciences ....MPhil 12FT 24PT PhD 36FT 60PT
Human Geography ....MPhil 12FT 24PT PhD 36FT 60PT

Birkbeck, University of London
Geographic Information Science.. PhD 36FT 60-72PT/MPhil 24FT 36PT
Geography and Environmental Management...................PhD 36FT 60 - 72PT/MPhil 24FT 36PT
Geology.. PhD 24FT 36PT/MPhil 24FT 36PT

University of Birmingham
Geography and Environmental SciencesPhD 36FT/MSc(Res) 12FT

University of Bradford
Geography and Environmental Science..... PhD 36-48FT 48-60PT/MPhil 12-24FT 24-48PT

University of Bristol
Earth Sciences ....PhD 36FT 72PT/MSc by research 12FT 24PT

Brunel University
Environmental Hazards .... PhD 36FT 72PT/MPhil 24FT 48PT

University of Buckingham
Anthropology .... MA by research 12FT

University of Cambridge
Earth Sciences .... PhD 36FT 60PT
Geography.. PhD 36FT 60PT

Canterbury Christ Church University
Geography........................... PhD 48FT 60PT/MPhil 24FT 48PT

Coventry University
Development Geography .... MSc by research 12FT 24-36PT
Geomorphology................................. MSc by research 12FT 24-36PT
Natural Hazards................................ MSc by research 12FT 24-36PT
Quaternary Science.......................... MSc by research 12FT 24-36PT

University of Dundee
Geography .... MPhil 24FT PhD 36FT
Non-Graduating Research in School of the Environment (6 months or more)...Non-Grad 6-24FT
Non-Graduating Research in School of the Environment (less than 6 months) .... Non-Grad 1-5FT

Durham University
Geography...PhD 36FT/MPhil 24FT

University of Edinburgh
Atmospheric and Environmental Sciences ....PhD 36FT 72PT/MPhil 24FT 48PT
Atmospheric and Environmental Sciences (Environmental Sustainability) .... PhD 36FT 72PT/MPhil 24FT 48PT
Geographical Information Science .....MSc by research 12FT 24PT
Geography (Human Geography)PhD 36FT 72PT/MPhil 24FT 48PT
Geology and Geophysics .... PhD 36FT 72PT/MPhil 24FT 48PT

University of Exeter
Earth Resources.............. MPhil 36FT 60PT/PhD 48FT 89PT/MSc by research 12FT 24PT
Geology....MSc (Res) 12FT 24PT/MPhil 36FT 60PT/PhD 48FT 84PT
Offshore Renewable Energy .... EngD 48FT
Physical Geography....... MPhil 36FT 60PT/PhD 48FT 84PT/MSc by research 12FT 24PT

University of Glasgow
Earth Sciences ....PhD 36FT/MSc by research 12FT
Geography and Earth Science Qualification.......PhD 36FT/MSc by research 12FT

Heriot-Watt University
Petroleum Engineering .... PhD 36FT 48PT/MPhil 12-24FT 24PT

Keele University
Earth Sciences ....PhD 36FT/MPhil 12FT

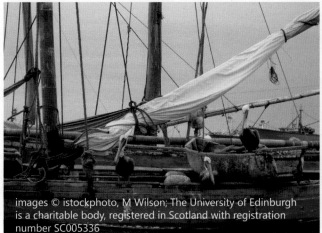

The School of GeoSciences at the University of Edinburgh is ranked top in our field for research, within the UK*.

We collaborate with leading industry partners and other research institutes and we are home to the largest group of Geoscientists in the UK with over 370 academics, researchers and research students.

The University is consistently ranked one of the top 50 universities in the world* and 97%** of our disciplines have research that is world leading.

*Research Assessment Exercise
**Times Higher-Reuter Ranking

15 Unique Masters Programmes

Exciting Research Opportunities

www.ed.ac.uk/geosciences

images © istockphoto, M Wilson; The University of Edinburgh is a charitable body, registered in Scotland with registration number SC005336

THE UNIVERSITY *of* EDINBURGH

Geology and geographical science

Geography............. PhD 24-48FT 48-84PT/MPhil 12-24FT 24-36PT

King's College London
Geography.................................. PhD 36FT 60PT/MPhil 24FT 36-48PT

Lancaster University
Geography.........................PhD 36FT 72PT/MPhil 24FT 36PT 36DL

University of Leeds
Earth Sciences .... PhD 36+FT/MPhil 24FT/MRes 12+FT/MSc by research 12FT
School of Geography ......PhD 36+FT/MPhil 24FT/MSc by research 12FT/MA by research 12FT

University of Leicester
Department of Geography............... PhD 36FT/MPhil 24FT/MSc by research 12FT
Department of Geology............. PhD 36FT 72PT/MPhil 12FT 24PT

University of Liverpool
Geography.................................... MPhil 12FT 24PT/PhD 36FT 60PT

London School of Economics and Political Science (LSE)
Human Geography and Urban Studies............ PhD 36-48FT 72PT/MPhil 36-48FT 72PT

Manchester Metropolitan University
Environmental and Geographical Sciences .... MSc by research/MPhil/PhD

University of Manchester
Basin Studies and Petroleum Geoscience ...PhD 36FT 72PT/MPhil 12FT 24PT/MSc by research 12FT

National University of Ireland, Maynooth
Geography.....................PhD 36 - 60FT/MLitt by research 12 - 36FT

Newcastle University
Geography....................... PhD 36FT 72PT/MPhil 12FT 24PT

Nottingham Trent University
Geography....................... PhD 48FT 96PT/MPhil 36FT 72PT

University of Nottingham
Environmental and Geomorphological Sciences .... PhD 36FT 72PT/MPhil 24FT 48PT
Geography.................. MA by research 12FT 24PT MRes 12FT 48PT MSc by research 12FT 24PT
Geography research areas.......... PhD 36FT 60PT/MPhil 24FT 48PT

The Open University
Biogeochemistry and ecosystem ecology .... MPhil 15FT 24PT variableDL/PhD 36FT 72PT variableDL
Climate change and ecosystem services.............. MPhil 15FT 24PT variableDL/PhD 36FT 72PT variableDL
Cosmology and extragalactic astronomy .... PhD 15FT 24PT variableDL/MPhil 36FT 72PT variableDL
Earth Sciences .... PhD 36FT 72PT variableDL/MPhil 15FT 24PT
Exoplanets and planetary physics... MPhil 15FT 24PT variableDL/PhD 36FT 72PT variableDL
Geography.................. PhD 36FT 72PT variableDL/MPhil 15FT 24PT variableDL
Isotope Geochemistry and Earth Systems .... PhD 36FT 72PT variableDL
Oceanography and paleaoceanography.................. PhD 36FT 72PT variableDL/MPhil 15FT 24PT variableDL
Planetary and Space Sciences ...PhD 36FT 72PT variableDL/MPhil 15FT 24PT variableDL
Sedimentology and stratigraphy..... MPhil 15FT 24PT variableDL/PhD 36FT 72PT variableDL
Star formation.......... MPhil 15FT 24PT variableDL/PhD 36FT 72PT variableDL
Tectonics and mountain building .... PhD 36FT 72PT variableDL
Volcano dynamics ... PhD 36FT 72PT variableDL/MPhil 15FT 24PT variableDL

University of Oxford
Geography and the Environment...... DPhil 48FT/MSc by research 24FT

Plymouth University
Biogeochemistry Research Centre .... PhD 36FT 36-72PT/MPhil 24FT 24-36PT
Geodynamics and Palaeonmagnetism Research GroupPhD 36FT/MPhil 24FT
Physical Geography and Geology..... PhD 24-48FT 36-72PT/MPhil 12-36FT 24-48PT

University of Portsmouth
Earth and Environmental Sciences .....MPhil 24FT 48PT/PhD 36FT 72PT
Geography....................... MPhil 24FT 48PT/PhD 36FT 72PT

Queen's University Belfast
Environmental Engineering....... PhD 36FT 72PT/MPhil 24FT 48PT
Geography: Society, Space and Culture.......PhD 36FT 72PT/MPhil 24FT 48PT

Royal Holloway, University of London
Department of Geography......... PhD 36FT 72PT/MPhil 24FT 48PT
Geology..............................PhD 36FT/MPhil 24FT
Geology by Research.............................MSc by research 12FT 24PT

University of Sheffield
Geography....................... PhD 36FT 72PT/MPhil 24FT 48PT

University of Southampton
Earth and Ocean Science at the NOCS.................... PhD 36FT 72PT

Earth and Ocean Science at the SOC...................... PhD 36FT 72PT
School of Geography: Research Awards ......PhD 36FT 72PT/MPhil 24FT 48PT

University of St Andrews
Geography and Geology..........................PhD 36FT/MPhil 12-24FT

Staffordshire University
Biology Division ....PhD 72PT/MPhil 72PT

University of Sussex
Geography Research Programme..... PhD 24-48FT 36-72PT/MPhil 12-36FT 24-48PT

Swansea University
Earth Observation ....MSc by research 12FT 24PT
Environmental Dynamics.....................MSc by research 12FT 24PT
Environmental Sustainability..............MSc by research 12FT 24PT
Glaciology...MSc by research 12FT 24PT
Global Environmental Modelling........MSc by research 12FT 24PT
Global Migration ....MSc by research 12FT 24PT
Human Geography...................... PhD 36FT 60PT/MPhil 24FT 48PT
Media Geographies.............................MSc by research 12FT 24PT
Urban Studies.......................................MSc by research 12FT 24PT

UCL - University College London
Advanced Spatial Analysis .... PhD 36FT 60PT
Geography.. PhD 36FT 60PT

University of Worcester
Geography .... PhD 48FT 70PT/MPhil 24FT 48PT

Geophysics
Taught Courses

University of Bradford
Archaeological Prospection .... MSc 12FT/PGDip 9FT

University of Central Lancashire
Osteoarchaeology: Techniques and Data Analysis......... MSc 12FT

University of Edinburgh
GeoSciences (Individual Project) ....MSc(Res) 12FT 24PT

University of Leeds
Exploration Geophysics ....MSc 12FT 12-48PT
Structural Geology with Geophysics......................... MSc 12FT 48PT

The Open University
Earth Science ....MSc variablePT

University of Sheffield
Geoarchaeology... MSc 12FT 24PT

University of Southampton
Marine Geology and Geophysics...................................MRes 12FT

UCL - University College London
Geophysical Hazards .... MSc 12FT 24PT

Geophysics
Research Courses

University of Aberdeen
Archaeology..............MSc by research 12FT/MPhil 24FT/PhD 36FT

Plymouth University
Geodynamics and Palaeonmagnetism Research GroupPhD 36FT/MPhil 24FT

Geotechnical engineering
Taught Courses

University of Birmingham
Geotechnical Engineering.................................... MSc 12FT 24-36PT/PGDip 8FT 16-24PT
Geotechnical Engineering and Management MSc 12FT 24-36PT/PGDip 8FT 16-24PT/PGCert 4FT 8PT

Cardiff University
Applied Environmental Geology .... MSc 12FT

University of Dundee
Geotechnical Engineering .... MSc 12FT

University of Edinburgh
GeoSciences (Individual Project) ....MSc(Res) 12FT 24PT
Petroleum Geoscience.. MSc 12FT

University of Exeter
Advanced Civil Engineering .... MSc 12FT
Applied Geotechnics.................. MSc 12FT 36PT/PGDip 12FT 36PT

Heriot-Watt University
Environmental Analysis and Assessment ....MRes 12FT 24PT/PGDip 9FT 18PT/PGCert 9FT 18PT

Imperial College London
Engineering Geology for Ground Models, also with Business Management or Sustainable Dev .... MSc 12FT 24PT
General Structural Engineering...........................MSc 12FT 24-36PT
Soil Mechanics and Environmental Geotechnics...MSc 12FT 24PT
Systems Engineering and Innovation................................. MSc 24PT

University of Leeds
Engineering Geology....................................MSc 12FT 12-48PT

Newcastle University
Engineering Geology ....MSc 12FT 48PT
Environmental Engineering..MSc 12FT 48PT

Geotechnical Engineering....................................... MSc 12FT 48PT

University of Nottingham
Engineering Surveying with Geographical Information Science .... MSc 12FT

University of Portsmouth
Engineering Geology ....MSc 12FT 24PT

University of Sheffield
Osteoarchaeology ....MSc 12FT 24PT

University of Southampton
Environmental Monitoring and Assessment .... MSc 12FT 27PT

University of Sussex
Applied Geomorphology ....MSc 12FT 24PT

Teesside University
Civil Engineering................MSc 12 - 16FT 24PT/PGDip 8FT

Trinity College Dublin - the University of Dublin
Engineering (Environmental/Structural & Geotechnics/Transport)..MSc 12FT 24PT
Environmental Engineering .... PGDip 12PT
Highway and Geotechnical Engineering .... PGDip 12PT

Geotechnical engineering
Research Courses

City University London
Geotechnical Engineering Research Centre...................PhD/MPhil

Durham University
Earth Sciences ....PhD 36FT 72PT/MPhil 24FT 48PT/MSc by research 12FT 24PT

Newcastle University
Civil Engineering (Geotechnical and Engineering Geology)..........MPhil 12FT 24PT/PhD 36FT 72PT

Swansea University
Biomathematics ....MSc by research 12FT 24PT
Environmental Sustainability..............MSc by research 12FT 24PT

UCL - University College London
Environmental Engineering Science................................EngD 48FT

Human geography
Taught Courses

University of Aberdeen
Human Geography..MRes 12FT

Aberystwyth University
Food & Water Security ....MSc 12FT 24PT/PGDip 9FT 18PT
Landscape and Territory............... MA 12FT 24PT/PGDip 9FT 18PT
Practising Human Geography.... MA 12FT/PGDip 9FT/PGCert 9FT
Regional and Environmental Policy ...... MA 12FT 24PT/PGDip 9FT 18PT
Remote Sensing & Geographical Information Systems (GIS) .... MSc 12FT 24PT/PGDip 9FT 18PT/PGCert 5FT 10PT

University of Bristol
Human Geography: Society and Space.....................MSc 12FT 24PT

Brunel University
Children, Youth and International Development... MA 12FT 24PT

University of Cambridge
Environment, Society and Development.........................MPhil 9FT
Polar Studies...MPhil 9FT

University College Cork
Arts (Geography) ....HDip 9FT 18PT
European Development Studies...............................MA 12FT

Durham University
Geography (Research Methods) ....MA 12FT

University of Edinburgh
Human Geography..............................MSc(Res) 12FT 24PT

University of Exeter
Critical Human Geographies ....MRes 12FT

National University of Ireland Galway
Environment, Society and Development...........................MA 12FT

University of Glasgow
Human Geography: Space, Politics & Power........MRes 12FT 24PT

King's College London
Environment & Development........MA 12FT 24PT/MSc 12FT 24PT
Geography......................................MSc 12FT 24PT/MA 12FT 24PT
Tourism, Environment & Development...................MA 12FT 24PT/MSc 12FT 24PT

Kingston University
Language and Society .... MA 12FT 24PT

University of Leeds
Social and Cultural Geography ..MA 12FT 24PT/PGDip 12FT 24PT

University of Leicester
GIS and Human Geography ....MSc 12FT 24PT/PGDip 9FT 18PT
Research in Human Geography ..MSc 12FT 24PT/PGDip 9FT 18PT

University of Liverpool
Population Studies... MA 12FT 24PT

London School of Economics and Political Science (LSE)
Human Geography and Urban Studies (Research)MSc 12FT 24PT

Geology and geographical science

Loughborough University
Human Geography Research........MSc 12FT 24PT

Newcastle University
Human Geography Research........MA 12FT 24PT
International Politics (Critical Geopolitics)........MA 12FT 24PT

University of Nottingham
Human Geography and Chinese Studies (2 years)........MSc 24FT

University of Oxford
Nature, Society and Environmental Policy........MSc 12FT

Queen Mary, University of London
Cities and Cultures........MA 12FT 24PT
Cities and Cultures........MRes 12FT 24PT
Community Organising........MA 12FT 24PT
Geography........MSc 12FT 24PT/MRes 12FT/MA 12FT
Globalisation and Development........MA 12FT 24PT
London Studies........MA 12FT 24PT

University of Reading
Human Geography........MSc(Res) 12FT 24PT

University of Sheffield
Environmental Change and International Development........MSc 12FT 24PT

University of St Andrews
Health Geography Research...MRes 12FT 24PT/PGDip 10FT 20PT

Swansea University
Human Geography........MA 12FT 24-36PT

UCL - University College London
Modernity, Space and Place........MSc 12FT

University of York
Human-Centred Interactive Technologies........MSc 12FT

Human geography
Research Courses

Aberystwyth University
Human Geography........MPhil 12FT 24PT
Human Geography........PhD 36FT 60PT

University of Bristol
Geographical Sciences (Human Geography)........PhD 36FT 72PT/MPhil 12FT 24PT

Brunel University
Physical and Human Geography Research........PhD/MPhil

Coventry University
Geographies of Gender........MSc by research 12FT 24-36PT
Historical Geography........MSc by research 12FT 24-36PT

University of Dundee
Geography........MPhil 24FT PhD 36FT
Non-Graduating Research in School of Humanities (6 months or more)........Non-Grad 6-24FT
Non-Graduating Research in School of Humanities (less than 6 months)........Non-Grad 1-5FT
Non-Graduating Research in School of the Environment (6 months or more)........Non-Grad 6-24FT
Non-Graduating Research in School of the Environment (less than 6 months)........Non-Grad 1-5FT

University of Edinburgh
Geography (Human Geography)PhD 36FT 72PT/MPhil 24FT 48PT

University of Exeter
Human Geography........PhD 48FT 84PT/MPhil 36FT 60PT/MSc by research 12FT 24PT

University of Hull
Human Geography........PhD 36FT 60PT/MPhil 24FT 36PT/MA by research 12FT 24PT/MS by research 12FT 24PT
Human Geography........MRes 12FT 24PT

Keele University
Geography........PhD 24-48FT 48-84PT/MPhil 12-24FT 24-36PT

University of Leeds
Geography........PhD 36FT 60PT/MPhil 24FT
School of Geography......PhD 36+FT/MPhil 24FT/MSc by research 12FT/MA by research 12FT

London School of Economics and Political Science (LSE)
Economic Geography........MPhil 36-48FT/PhD 36-48FT
Environmental Economics........MPhil 36-48FT/PhD 36-48FT
Environmental Policy and Development........MPhil 36-48FT/PhD 36-48FT

University of Manchester
Human Geography........PhD 36FT/MPhil 12FT

University of Nottingham
Cultural and Historical Geography........PhD 36FT
Environment and Society........PhD 36-48FT

The Open University
Materialities, Space and Power PhD 36FT 72PT variableDL/MPhil 15FT 24PT variableDL

Oxford Brookes University
Anthropology and Geography - MPhil/PhD........PhD 24-60FT 36-72PT/MPhil 24-36FT 36-48PT

Plymouth University
Human Geography........PhD 24-48FT 36-72PT/MPhil 12-36FT 24-48PT

Queen Mary, University of London
Human Geography........PhD 36FT 50PT/MPhil 24FT 36PT

Queen's University Belfast
Geography: Society, Space and Culture........PhD 36FT 72PT/MPhil 24FT 48PT

University of Sheffield
Geography........PhD 36FT 72PT/MPhil 24FT 48PT

Swansea University
Human Geography........PhD 36FT 60PT/MPhil 24FT 48PT
Physical Geography........MPhil 24FT 48PT/PhD 36FT 72PT
Urban Studies........MSc by research 12FT 24PT

Meteorology
Taught Courses

University of Aberdeen
Climate Change Law and Sustainable Development......LLM 12FT 24--36PT

University of Birmingham
Applied Meteorology and Climatology..... MSc 12FT/PGDip 12FT/PGCert 12FT

De Montfort University
Climate Change and Sustainable Development F85071MSc 12FT 24PT 36DL/PGDip 32DL/PGCert 16DL

Durham University
Risk and Environmental Hazards........MA 12FT

University of Glasgow
Environmental Science, Technology & Society (Dumfries Campus)........MSc 12FT 24PT

University of Leeds
Atmosphere-Ocean Dynamics........MSc 12FT

London School of Economics and Political Science (LSE)
Environmental Economics and Climate Change...MSc 12FT 24PT

The Open University
Earth Science........MSc variablePT

University of Reading
Applied Meteorology........MSc 12FT 24PT/PGDip 12FT 24PT
Applied Meteorology and Climate with Management........MSc 12FT 24PT
Atmosphere, Ocean & Climate........MSc 12FT/PGDip 12FT
The Economics of Climate Change........MSc 12FT

School of Oriental and African Studies - SOAS
Global Energy and Climate Policy........MSc 12FT 24PT

University of Sussex
Climate Change and Development........MSc 12FT 24PT
Climate Change and Policy........MSc 12FT 24PT

Swansea University
Environmental Dynamics and Climate Change.....MSc 12FT 36PT
Geographic Information and Climate Change......MSc 12FT 36PT/PGCert 12FT 12PT

UCL - University College London
Natural Hazards for Insurers........PGCert 4PT

Meteorology
Research Courses

Coventry University
Natural Hazards........MSc by research 12FT 24-36PT

University of Hertfordshire
Atmospheric Dynamics and Air Quality (ADAQ)..PhD 36FT 72PT/MPhil 24FT 48PT/MRes 12FT 24PT

University of Leeds
Atmospheric and Climate Science.....PhD 36FT 60PT 60DL/MPhil 24FT 48PT 48DL

The Open University
Atomic, Molecular and Optical Physics........MPhil 15FT 24PT variableDL

Plymouth University
Geomatics Research Group........MPhil 24FT/PhD 36FT

Mining engineering
Taught Courses

University of Exeter
Applied Geotechnics........MSc 12FT 36PT/PGDip 12FT 36PT
Minerals Engineering........MSc 12FT
Mining Engineering........MSc 12FT 24-36PT/PGDip 12FT 24-36PT
Mining Geology........MSc 12FT
Surveying and Land/ Environmental Management........MSc 12FT 24-36PT/PGDip 12FT 24-36PT

Newcastle University
Geotechnical Engineering........MSc 12FT 48PT

Northumbria University
Surveying (Minerals)........MSc 24DL

The Open University
Engineering........MSc(Eng) 12-24DL/MEng variableDL/PGDip variableDL

Robert Gordon University
Drilling and Well Engineering....MSc 12FT 36DL/PGDip 9FT 24DL

Mining engineering
Research Courses

University of Exeter
Earth Resources........MPhil 36FT 60PT/PhD 48FT 89PT/MSc by research 12FT 24PT
Engineering........EngD 48FT
Geology........MSc by research 12FT 24PT/MPhil 36FT 60PT/PhD 48FT 84PT
Mining and Minerals Engineering.....MSc by research 12FT 24PT/MPhil 36FT 60PT/PhD 48FT 80PT

University of Greenwich
Engineering (by Research)........MSc by research 12FT 24PT

University of Liverpool
Engineering........PhD 36FT/MPhil 12FT 24PT

Oceanography
Taught Courses

Bangor University
Applied Marine Geoscience........MSc 12FT 24-36PT/PGDip 9FT
Marine Biology........MSc 12FT 24-36PT/PGDip 9FT
Marine Environmental Protection........MSc 12FT 24-36PT
Physical Oceanography........MSc 12FT 24-36PT/PGDip 9FT

University College Cork
Geography (Coastal Management Systems)........MA 12FT

University of Dundee
Spatial Planning with Marine Spatial Planning........MSc 12FT

University of Edinburgh
GeoSciences (Individual Project)........MSc(Res) 12FT 24PT

University of Glasgow
Aquatic System Science........MSc 12FT 24PT/PGDip 8FT 16PT
Coastal System Management.....MSc 12FT 24PT/PGDip 8FT 16PT
Freshwater System Science........MSc 12FT 24PT/PGDip 8FT 16PT
Marine & Freshwater Ecology & Environmental Management.... MRes 12FT/PGDip 9FT
Marine System Science........MSc 12FT 24PT/PGDip 8FT 16PT

Heriot-Watt University
Climate Change: Managing The Marine Environment.. MSc 12FT 24PT/PGDip 9FT 21PT
Marine Resource Development and Protection....MSc 12FT 24PT/PGDip 9FT 21PT
Marine Resource Management (MRM)........MSc 12FT 24PT
Marine Spatial Planning........MSc 12FT 24PT/PGDip 9FT

Newcastle University
International Marine Environmental Consultancy (IMEC)..... MSc 12FT/PGDip 9FT
Tropical Coastal Management........MSc 12FT/PGDip 9FT

The Open University
Earth Science........MSc variablePT

Plymouth University
Applied Marine Science........MRes 12FT 24PT
Applied Marine Science........MSc 12FT 24PT/PGDip 9FT
Coastal Engineering........MSc 12FT/PGDip 12FT/PGCert 6FT
Hydrography........MSc 12FT/PGDip 9FT

University of Portsmouth
Coastal and Marine Resource Management........MSc 12FT 24PT

University of Reading
Atmosphere, Ocean & Climate........MSc 12FT/PGDip 12FT

University of Southampton
Biodiversity and Conservation........MSc 12FT 27PT
Environmental Coastal Engineering........MSc 12FT 24PT
Marine Geology and Geophysics........MRes 12FT
Ocean Science........MRes 12FT
Marine Environment and Resources........MSc 12FT
Marine Resource Management........MSc 12FT
Marine Science, Policy and Law........MSc 12FT
Oceanography........MSc 12FT
Maritime Engineering Science: Marine Engineering........MSc 12FT
Maritime Engineering Science: Naval Architecture........MSc 12FT 24PT
Maritime Engineering Science: Ocean Resource EngineeringMSc 12FT
Maritime Engineering Science: Ship Science........MSc 12FT
Maritime Engineering Science: Yacht and Small Craft..MSc 12FT

University of St Andrews
Ecosystem-based Management of Marine Systems....MRes 12FT
Marine Mammal Science........MRes 12FT

University of Stirling
Marine Biotechnology........MSc 12FT 24PT/PGDip 9FT

University of Strathclyde
Marine Engineering........MSc 12FT/PGDip 9FT
Offshore Floating Systems........MSc 12FT/PGDip 9FT

Geology and geographical science

University of Ulster
Coastal Zone Management .... MSc 24DL/PGDip 33DL
Marine Spatial Planning ....PGDip 24DL/MSc 36DL

UCL - University College London
Aquatic Science .... MSc 12FT
Hydrographic Surveying .... MSc 12FT

University of the West of England, Bristol
River and Coastal Engineering .... GradDip 36PT

University of York
Marine Environmental Management .... MSc 12FT/PGDip 9FT

Oceanography
Research Courses

University of Aberdeen
Environmental Science..... PhD 36FT/MPhil 24FT/MSc by research
12FT

Bangor University
Ocean Sciences...MPhil 24FT/PhD 36FT

Cardiff University
Gravitational Physics.............PhD 36FT possiblePT/MPhil 12-24FT
possiblePT

University of Hull
Marine or Terrestrial Ecology...... MSc by research 12FT 24PT/PhD
36FT 72PT

Keele University
Earth Sciences ....PhD 36FT/MPhil 12FT

University of Liverpool
Earth and Ocean Sciences ..PhD 24-48FT 48-84PT/MPhil 12-24FT

Newcastle University
Marine Sciences............................ PhD 36FT 72PT/MPhil 12FT 24PT

Nottingham Trent University
Environmental Biology..MRes 12FT 24PT

University of Nottingham
Coastal Dynamics and Engineering Group............PhD 24FT 48PT/
MPhil 24FT 48PT

University of Oxford
Atmospheric, Oceanic and Planetary Physics................. DPhil 48FT
Engineering Science....................DPhil 48FT/MSc by research 24FT

Plymouth University
Centre for Marine and Coastal Policy Research Group (MarCoPol)
PhD 36FT/MPhil 24FT
Coastal Processes/Marine Sports Science... PhD 36FT/MPhil 24FT
Integrated PhD in Marine and Environmental SciencesPhD 48FT/
PGCert by research 12FT
Marine Physics Research Group....................PhD 36FT/MPhil 24FT
Marine Studies..PhD/MPhil
Speciation and Environmental Analysis Research Group (SEA).....
PhD 36FT/MPhil 24FT

University of Southampton
Coastal Engineering for Climate Change ....MRes 12FT 24PT
Earth and Ocean Science at the NOCS................... PhD 36FT 72PT
Earth and Ocean Science at the SOC.....................PhD 36FT 72PT

University of the Highlands and Islands
Marine SciencePhD 36FT 72PT/MPhil 24FT 48PT/MSc by research
12FT 24PT

Petroleum engineering
Taught Courses

University of Aberdeen
Hydrocarbon Exploration .... PGDip 9FT/MSc 12FT
Integrated Petroleum Geoscience..MSc 12FT
Oil & Gas Chemistry ....MSc 12FT/PGDip 9FT/PGCert 4FT
Oil & Gas Structural Engineering ....MSc 36DL
Oil and Gas Enterprise Management......................MSc 12FT 24PT
Oil and Gas Law ....LLM 12FT 24PT
Pertroleum, Energy Economics and Finance..........MSc(Econ) 12FT

University of Birmingham
Applied and Petroleum Micropalaeontology...................MSc 12FT

University of Central Lancashire
Oil and Gas Operations Management ....MSc 12FT

Cranfield University
Flow Assurance for Oil and Gas Production .....MSc 12FT 24-60PT

University of Derby
Applied Petroleum Geoscience........... MSc 4FT/PGDip 12FT 24PT/
PGCert 3FT

University of Dundee
Energy Studies with Specialisation in Oil and Gas Economics .....
MSc 12FT
International Oil and Gas Management ....MBA 24DL
International Oil and Gas Management ....MBA 12FT
International Oil and Gas Management .... MSc 12FT
Managing in the Energy Industries .... MSc 12FT
Petroleum Law and Policy ....LLM 12FT PGDip 9FT LLM 24-60DL

University of Edinburgh
GeoSciences (Individual Project) ....MSc(Res) 12FT 24PT
Petroleum Geoscience..MSc 12FT

Glasgow Caledonian University
Master of Accounting (Oil and Gas Accounting) ....MAcc 12FT
FlexiblePT

Heriot-Watt University
Petroleum Engineering.................................... MSc 12FT 21-84DL
Petroleum Geoscience (PetGeo) ....MSc 12FT
Reservoir Evaluation and Management ....MSc 12FT 24PT

University of Hull
Petroleum, Oil and Gas: Chemical Engineering ManagementMSc
12FT

Imperial College London
Petroleum Engineering .... MSc 12FT
Petroleum Geophysics.. MSc 12FT
Petroleum Geoscience... MSc 12FT

University of Leeds
Oilfield Corrosion Engineering.................................MSc(Eng) 12FT

London South Bank University
Petroleum Engineering...MSc 12FT 24PT

University of Manchester
Petroleum Exploration Geoscience....................................MSc 12FT
Petroleum Geoscience for Reservoir Development and
Production...MSc 12FT

Middlesex University
Oil and Gas ....MBA 24PT

Newcastle University
Environmental and Petroleum Geochemistry ....MSc 12FT 48PT
Petroleum Geochemistry ....MSc 12FT
Pipeline Engineering.... MSc 12FT 24PT/PGDip 12FT 24PT/PGCert
12FT 24PT

Robert Gordon University
Oil and Gas Engineering ....MSc 12FT 36DL/PGDip 9FT 24DL
Petroleum Production Engineering .... MSc 12FT 36DL/PGDip 9FT
24DL

Royal Holloway, University of London
Petroleum Geoscience (Tectonics) ....MSc 12FT 24-36PT

University of Salford
Gas Engineering and Management.............. MSc 12FT/PGDip 9FT
Petroleum and Gas Engineering..................... MSc 12FT/PGDip 9FT

University of Surrey
MSc Petroleum Downstream Technology.... MSc 36FT up to 72PT
Petroleum Refining Systems Engineering........................ MSc 12FT

Teesside University
Petroleum Engineering ....MSc 12 - 18FT 24PT/PGDip 8FT

Petroleum engineering
Research Courses

University of Aberdeen
Geology and Petroleum Geology ...PhD 36FT/MPhil 24FT/MSc by
research 12FT

University of Dundee
Energy, Petroleum and Mineral Law and Policy ....
LLM by research 12FT
Energy, Petroleum and Mineral Law and Policy .... MPhil 24FT
Energy, Petroleum and Mineral Law and Policy ....MSc by
research 12FT
Energy, Petroleum and Mineral Law and Policy ....PhD 36FT

Heriot-Watt University
Petroleum Engineering .... PhD 36FT 48PT/MPhil 12-24FT 24PT

University of Nottingham
Efficient Fossil Energy Technologies .... EngD 48FT
Fuel, energy and CO2 mitigation.........PhD 36FT 72PT/MPhil 24FT
48PT

Plymouth University
Petroleum and Environmental Geochemistry Research Group.....
MPhil 24FT/PhD 36FT

Physical geography
Taught Courses

Aberystwyth University
Remote Sensing & Geographical Information Systems (GIS) ....
MSc 12FT 24PT/PGDip 9FT 18PT/PGCert 5FT 10PT
Remote Sensing and GeographyMSc 12FT 24PT/PGDip 9FT 18PT/
PGCert 5FT 10PT

University of Chester
Regeneration for Practitioners.....MA 12FT 24 - 72PT/PGDip 12FT
24 - 60PT/PGCert 12FT 12 - 36PT
Sustainability for Community and Business ....MSc 12FT 24PT/
PGDip 12FT 24PT/PGCert 12FT 12-24PT

University College Cork
Geography (Coastal Management Systems).....................MA 12FT

University of Dundee
Water Law ....PGDip 18-60DL/PGCert 12-60DL/LLM 24-60DL

King's College London
Geography...............................MSc 12FT 24PT/MA 12FT 24PT
Water: Science and Governance................................... MSc 12FT 24PT

University of Leicester
Physical Geography by Individually Supervised Research ...... MSc
12FT 24PT

University of Nottingham
Landscape and Culture .... MA 12FT 24PT

Queen Mary, University of London
Environmental Science: Integrated Management of Freshwater
Environments ....MSc 12FT 24-36PT
Geography.............................MSc 12FT 24PT/MRes 12FT/MA 12FT

University of Reading
Species Identification and Survey Skills .... MSc 12FT

Swansea University
Environmental Dynamics and Climate Change..... MSc 12FT 36PT
Geographic Information and Climate Change......MSc 12FT 36PT/
PGCert 12FT 12PT

Physical geography
Research Courses

University of Aberdeen
Physics.............PhD 36FT/MPhil 24FT/MSc by research 12FT 24PT

Aberystwyth University
Earth Sciences ....MPhil 12FT 24PT PhD 36FT 60PT

University of Bristol
Geographical Sciences (Physical Geography)......... PhD 36FT 72PT

Brunel University
Physical Geography and Earth Science ....MPhil/PhD
Physical and Human Geography Research ....PhD/MPhil

Coventry University
Water Science.................................... MSc by research 12FT 24-36PT

University of Exeter
Physical Geography....... MPhil 36FT 60PT/PhD 48FT 84PT/MSc by
research 12FT 24PT

University of Glasgow
Geography and Earth Science Qualification.......PhD 36FT/MSc by
research 12FT
Geography and Geomatics ....PhD 36FT/MSc by research 12FT/
PGDip by research 12FT/MRes 12FT

University of Hull
Physical Geography.........PhD 36FT 60PT/MPhil 24FT 36PT/MA by
research 12FT 24PT/MSc(Res) 12FT 24PT

London School of Economics and Political Science (LSE)
Economic Geography.......................... MPhil 36-48FT/PhD 36-48FT

University of Manchester
Physical Geography...............................PhD 36FT/MPhil 12FT 24PT

Oxford Brookes University
Anthropology and Geography .... PhD 24-60FT 36-72PT/MPhil
24-36FT 36-48PT

Queen Mary, University of London
Physical Geography.....................PhD 36FT 50PT/MPhil 24FT 36PT

Swansea University
Earth Observation ....MSc by research 12FT 24PT
Glaciology...MSc by research 12FT 24PT
Physical Geography.....................MPhil 24FT 48PT/PhD 36FT 72PT

Quarry management
Taught Courses

University of Exeter
Mining Geology .... MSc 12FT

Seismology
Taught Courses

University of Bristol
Science of Natural Hazards.....................................MRes 12FT 24PT

Durham University
Risk and Environmental Hazards...MA 12FT

Imperial College London
Engineering Geology for Ground Models, also with Business
Management or Sustainable Dev ....MSc 12FT 24PT
Soil Mechanics and Engineering Seismology......... MSc 12FT 24PT

Lancaster University
Volcanology and Geological Hazards ....MSc 12FT 24PT

UCL - University College London
Earthquake Engineering with Disaster Management ... MSc 12FT
24PT

Seismology
Research Courses

Coventry University
Natural Hazards................................ MSc by research 12FT 24-36PT

The Open University
Volcano dynamics ... PhD 36FT 72PT variableDL/MPhil 15FT 24PT
variableDL

Health sciences

Animal nutrition
Taught Courses

Aberystwyth University
Animal Science....MSc 12FT 24PT
Livestock Science....MSc 12FT 24PT

University of Edinburgh
Applied Animal Behaviour and Animal Welfare....MSc 12FT 24PT

University of Glasgow
Animal Welfare Science, Ethics & Law....MSc 12FT/PGDip 9FT

Harper Adams University
Ruminant Nutrition....PGCert 12FT 24PT/MSc 12FT 24PT/PGDip 12FT 24PT

Newcastle University
Aquaculture Enterprise and Technology....MSc 12FT 24PT

University of Roehampton
Clinical Nutrition....PGCert 6FT 24PT 24DL

Royal Veterinary College
Veterinary Education....MSc 24-60PT PGCert 6-24DL PGCert 6-24PT PGDip 24-60PT
Veterinary Epidemiology and Public Health by Distance Learning MSc 24-60DL/PGDip 24-60DL/PGCert 12-60DL
Veterinary Epidemiology....MSc 24PT
Wild Animal Biology....MSc 12FT PGDip 8FT
Wild Animal Health....PGDip 8FT

University of Salford
Wildlife Documentary Production....MA 12FT

Scotland's Rural College
Applied Poultry Science....MSc 27DL/PGDip 18DL

University of Southampton
Wildlife Conservation....MRes 12FT

University of Stirling
Aquaculture: Sustainable Aquaculture....MSc 12FT
Aquatic Pathobiology....PGCert 4FT/PGDip 11FT/MSc 12FT

University of Ulster
Food Regulatory Affairs (Veterinary Public Health)..PGDip 15DL/MSc 24DL

Animal nutrition
Research Courses

Aberystwyth University
IBERS - Biological Sciences....MPhil 12FT 24PT PhD 36FT 60PT
IBERS - Rural Sciences....MPhil 12FT 24PT PhD 36FT 60PT

University of Edinburgh
Animal Health & Welfare....PhD 36FT

Harper Adams University
Animal Nutrition....MPhil 24FT/PhD 38FT

University of Nottingham
Animal Population Heath and Welfare....PhD 36FT 72PT/MPhil 24FT 48PT

Art therapy
Taught Courses

Birmingham City University
Art Health and Well-being....MA 12FT 24PT

University of Central Lancashire
Arts Health....MA 12FT 24-68PT/PGDip 12FT 24-68PT/PGCert 12FT 24-68PT/UniCert 3PT
Arts-Health Analysis....PGCert 6PT

University of Chester
Health and Social Care - Art Therapy....MA 24 - 72PT/PGDip 24 - 60PT/PGCert 12 - 36PT

University of Derby
Art Therapy....MA 24FT

University of East London
Art Psychotherapy....MSc 36PT/PGDip 24PT/PGCert 12PT

University of Glasgow
Primary Expressive Arts....PGCert 12PT

Goldsmiths, University of London
Art Psychotherapy....PGDip 24FT 36PT/MA 32FT 48PT
Participatory and Community Arts..PGCert 12FT 24-60PT/PGDip 12FT 24-60PT/MA 12FT 24-60PT

University of Hertfordshire
Art Therapy....MA 24FT 36PT

Leeds Metropolitan University
Art Psychotherapy (Post - Registration)....MA 12PT
Art Psychotherapy Practice....MA 24FT 36PT
Associated Art Psychotherapy Research....MA 24PT
Psychotherapy....MA 48PT

National University of Ireland, Maynooth
Arts (Adult Guidance & Counselling)....HDip 12FT

Queen Margaret University, Edinburgh
Art Psychotherapy (International)MSc 24FT 36-72PT/PGDip 24FT 36-60PT

University of Roehampton
Art Psychotherapy....MA 24FT 36PT

University of South Wales
Art Psychotherapy....MA 36PT
Buddhist Studies....PGCert 12DL/PGDip 24DL/MA 36DL
Evaluation Studies....PGCert 9-12DL
Music Therapy....MA 36PT

Staffordshire University
Community & Participatory Arts....MA 12FT 24PT

Art therapy
Research Courses

University of Dundee
Duncan of Jordanstone College of Art & Design....MPhil 24FT PhD 36FT

Goldsmiths, University of London
Art....MPhil 24FT 36PT/PhD 36-48FT 48-72PT
Art Psychotherapy....PhD 36-48FT 48-72PT/MPhil 24FT 36PT MRes 12FT 24PT

University of Roehampton
Arts and Play Therapies....PhD 24-48FT 36-60PT/MPhil 21-36FT 33-48PT

Audiology
Taught Courses

University of Manchester
Advanced Audiology Studies....MSc 12FT 24PT/PGDip 9FT 24PT/PGCert 9PT
Audiology....MSc 12FT

Norwich University of the Arts
Moving Image and Sound....MA 12FT 24PT

Queen Margaret University, Edinburgh
Audiology (Pre-Registration)....PGDip 24FT/MSc 30FT

University of Southampton
Audiology....MSc 12FT 24PT/PGDip 9FT 18PT/PGCert 9FT 18PT
Clinical Practice....DClinP 48FT 84PT/MSc 12FT 24PT/PGDip 12FT 24PT/PGCert 8FT 16PT

UCL - University College London
Advanced Audiology....MSc 12FT/PGDip 9FT
Audiological Science....MSc 12FT/PGDip 9FT
Audiovestibular Medicine....MSc 12FT/PGDip 9FT/PGCert 3FT
ENT Practice (Voice Pathology)....MSc 12FT 24PT/PGDip 9FT 18PT

Audiology
Research Courses

University of Bristol
Deaf Studies....PhD 36FT 72PT/MPhil 36FT 72PT

University of Manchester
Audiology....PhD 48FT/PhD 36FT 72PT/MPhil 12FT 24PT

University of Nottingham
Institute of Hearing Research....PhD 36FT 72PT/MRes 12FT 24PT

University of Southampton
Hearing Sciences....PhD 36FT/MPhil 24FT

UCL - University College London
Audiological Science....PhD 36FT 60PT/MD(Res) 24FT 24PT

Bioengineering
Taught Courses

University of Aberdeen
Medical Imaging....MSc 12FT 24PT/PGDip 9FT 21PT

University of Dundee
Design for Medical Technologies....MSc 12FT

University of Edinburgh
Bioelectronics and Biosensors....MSc 12FT

University of Exeter
Advanced Materials Engineering....MSc 12FT
Advanced Mechanical Engineering....MSc 12FT

Heriot-Watt University
Smart Systems Integration....MSc 24FT

Imperial College London
Systems and Synthetic Biology....MRes 12FT

University of Kent
Biotechnology and Bioengineering....MSc 12FT 24PT
Drug Design....MSc 12FT

King's College London
Medical Engineering & Physics....MSc 12FT 24PT

Liverpool Hope University
Mathematical Informatics Dual International Masters.... MSc 24FT

Newcastle University
Bioinformatics....MSc 12FT
Biomedical Engineering....MSc 12FT

Nottingham Trent University
Biomedical Science....MSc 12FT 24PT
Biotechnology....MSc 12FT 24PT
Applied Biosciences....MSc(Res) 12FT 24PT
Biotechnology....MSc(Res) 12FT 24PT

University of Nottingham
Bioengineering....MSc 12FT
Bioengineering: Biomaterials and Biomechanics....MSc 12FT
Bioengineering: Imaging and Sensing....MSc 12FT
Bioengineering: The Digital Body....MSc 12FT

Robert Gordon University
Clinical Biomechanics....MSc 12FT

Sheffield Hallam University
Biomedical Sciences....MSc 12FT 24PT/PGDip 8FT 16PT/PGCert 4FT 8PT
Biotechnology..MSc 12FT 24PT/PGDip 8FT 16PT/PGCert 4FT 8PT

University of Sheffield
Translational Oncology....MSc(Res) 12FT
Materials Science and Engineering....MSc 12-24FT
Prosthodontics....DClinDent 36FT

University of Southampton
Advanced Mechanical Engineering Science (Bioengineering).... MSc 12FT 24PT

St George's, University of London
Biomedical Science....MRes 12FT

Staffordshire University
Clinical Biomechanics and Diabetes....PGCert 12PT
Clinical Biomechanics and Pain Management in the Lower limb....PGCert 12PT

University of Strathclyde
Biomedical Engineering....MSc 12FT 21-24PT/PGDip 9FT 21PT/PGCert 6FT 12PT
Nanoscience....MSc 12FT 24PT/PGDip 9FT

Swansea University
Materials Engineering....MSc 12FT 24-36PT

Trinity College Dublin - the University of Dublin
Bioengineering....MSc 12FT

UCL - University College London
Biomedical Sciences....MSc 12FT 24PT
Biosciences....MRes 12FT
Cell and Gene Therapy....MSc 12FT 24-60PT/PGDip 9FT 24-60PT/PGDip 3FT 6-24PT
Engineering with Innovation and Entrepreneurship....MSc 12FT/PGDip 9FT
Physics and Engineering in Medicine by Distance Learning.. MSc 24-60PT/PGDip 24-60PT/PGCert 24-60PT
Physics and Engineering in Medicine: Biomedical Engineering and Medical Imaging....MSc 12FT 24PT

Bioengineering
Research Courses

University of Aberdeen
Biomedical Physics and Bioengineering....PhD 36FT/MSc by research 12FT/MPhil 24FT

University of Edinburgh
Medical Physics & Medical Engineering....PhD 36FT 48PT/MPhil 24FT 36PT/MSc by research 12FT 24PT

University of Exeter
Engineering....PhD 36FT 72PT/MPhil 24FT 48PT

National University of Ireland Galway
College of Engineering & Informatics....PhD 48FT 72PT/MEngSci by research 24FT 48PT/MAppSci by research 24FT 48PT/MEng by research 24FT

Heriot-Watt University
International Centre for Brewing and Distilling (ICBD)..PhD 36FT 48PT/MPhil 24FT

Imperial College London
Biological and Medical Systems....PhD/MPhil
EPSRC Doctoral Training Studentships....PhD 36FT

University of Kent
Genetics....MSc by research 12FT 24PT/MPhil 24FT 36PT/PhD 36FT 60PT

University of Leeds
Centre for Doctoral Training in Molecular-Scale Engineering.... Integrated PhD 48FT
Institute of Medical and Biological Engineering....PhD 36+FT/MPhil 24FT

Loughborough University
Biological Engineering....PhD 36FT 60PT/MPhil 24FT 36PT

Newcastle University
Biological Sciences....PhD 36FT 72PT/MPhil 12FT 24PT
Biomedicine....MPhil 12FT 24PT/PhD 36FT 72PT/MD 24FT 48PT
Biotechnology....MPhil 12FT 24PT/PhD 36FT 72PT
Biotechnology and Business Enterprise....MRes 12FT
Stem Cells and Regenerative Medicine....MRes 12FT

Nottingham Trent University
Biomechanics and Kinesiology....MRes 12FT 24PT
Cell Biology....MRes 12FT 24PT

Health sciences

University of Nottingham
Bioengineering ... MRes 12FT

Oxford Brookes University
Biological Sciences - Biofilm Development ... PhD 24-60FT 36-72PT/MPhil 24-36FT 36-48PT
Biological Sciences - Bioprocess Research ... PhD 24-60FT 36-72PT/MPhil 24-36FT 36-48PT
Biological Sciences - Cell Systems Modelling ... PhD 24-60FT 36-72PT/MPhil 24-36FT 36-48PT
Biological Sciences - Environmental Ecology ... PhD 24-60FT 36-72PT/MPhil 24-36FT 36-48PT
Biological Sciences - Evolutionary Developmental Biology ... PhD 24-60FT 36-72PT/MPhil 24-36FT 36-48PT
Biological Sciences - Invertebrate Ecology and Biogeography ... PhD 24-60FT 36-72PT/MPhil 24-36FT 36-48PT
Biological Sciences - Plant Cell Biology ... PhD 24-60FT 36-72PT/MPhil 24-36FT 36-48PT
Biological Sciences - Spatial Ecology and Land Use ... PhD 24-60FT 36-72PT/MPhil 24-36FT 36-48PT
Biological and Biomedical Science ... PhD 36FT 48PT/MPhil 24FT 36PT
Health and Biomedical Sciences - Peptide Transport ... MPhil/PhD 36-60FT 48-72PT/PhD 24-60FT 36-72PT/MPhil 24-36FT 36-48PT

University of Salford
Institute for Materials ResearchPhD 36FT/MSc by research 12FT/MPhil 12FT

University of Southampton
School of Health Professions and Rehabilitation Sciences .. MPhil 36FT 60PT/PhD 36FT 60PT

St George's, University of London
Cellular and Molecular Medicine ... PhD 36FT 72PT/MPhil 24FT 48PT/MD(Res) 24 minFT 48 minPT

University of Strathclyde
Biomedical Engineering ... MRes 12FT

UCL - University College London
Biomedical Research ... PhD 36FT 60PT

Biomedical engineering
Taught Courses

University of Aberdeen
Biomedical Engineering ... MSc 12FT 24PT/PGDip 9FT 21PT
Medical Education ... PGCert 12PT
Medical Research Skills ... PGCert 24PT

Anglia Ruskin University
Biomedical Science ... MSc 36 - 60DL

Bangor University
Medical Molecular Biology with Genetics ... MSc 12-24FT
Medical Sciences ... MRes 12FT 24PT/PGCert 3FT 15PT
Molecular Biology with Biotechnology ... MSc 12FT

Barts and the London School of Medicine and Dentistry
Medical Electronics and Physics ... MSc 12FT 24PT

University of Bath
Orthopaedic Engineering - Joint Replacement ... PGCert 12PT

University of Bedfordshire
Biomedical Engineering ... MSc 12FT 36PT

University of Birmingham
Biomedical Research in vivo ... MRes 12FT
Chemical Biology and Biomedical Imaging ... MSc 12FT
Physical Sciences of Imaging in the Biomedical Sciences ... MSc 48FT
Translational Medicine: Interdisciplinary Biomedical Technologies ... MSc 12FT

University of Bolton
Medical & Health Care Devices ... MSc 12FT 36PT

University of Bradford
Biomedical Sciences ... MSc 12FT
Medical Engineering ... MSc 12FT
MSc 12-18PT

University of Brighton
Biomedical Sciences ... MSc 12FT 24PT/PGDip 12FT/PGCert 12FT
Pharmaceutical and Biomedical Sciences ... MRes 12FT 24PT/PGCert 12FT 24PT/PGDip 12FT 24PT

University of Bristol
Biomedical Sciences Research ... MSc 12FT/PGDip 12FT/PGCert 12FT
Stem Cells and Regeneration ... MSc 12-24DL/PGDip 12-24DL/PGCert 12-24DL

Brunel University
Biomedical Engineering ... MSc 12FT

University of Cambridge
Computational Biology ... MPhil 11FT

Cardiff Metropolitan University
Biomedical Science ... MSc 12FT 24PT/PGDip 12FT 24PT/PGCert 12FT 12PT

Cardiff University
Clinical Engineering ... MSc 12FT 24-36PT
Orthopaedic Engineering ... MSc 12-24DL

University of Central Lancashire
Biomedical Science ... MSc 12FT

University of Chichester
Sport and Exercise Biomechanics ... MSc 12FT 24PT/PGDip 9FT 18PT/PGCert 9FT 12PT

City University London
Clinical Engineering with Healthcare Technology Management ... MSc 12-18FT 24-30PT

University College Cork
Biomedical Sciences ... MSc 24PT

De Montfort University
Advanced Biomedical Science ... MSc 12FT 36PT/PGDip 24PT/PGCert 12PT

University of Dundee
Biomedical Engineering ... MSc 12FT
Design for Medical Technologies ... MSc 12FT
Non-Graduating Taught Postgraduate in School of Engineering, Physics and Mathematics ... PG module variableFT
Orthopaedic and Rehabilitation Technology ... MSc 24-60DL
Sports and Biomechanical Medicine (MSc full-time in house) ... MSc 12FT
Sports and Biomechanical Medicine (MSc Part time with externally arranged project) ... MSc 24PT
Sports and Biomechanical Medicine (MSc Part time with in-house project) ... MSc 24PT

University of East London
Biomedical Immunology ... MSc 12FT 24PT/PGDip 8FT 16PT/PGCert 4FT 8PT
Biomedical Science ... MSc 12FT 24PT/PGDip 8FT 16PT/PGCert 4FT 8PT
Biomedical Science DBMS ... DProf by taught VariousFT

University of Edinburgh
Biomechanics ... MSc 12FT
Regenerative Medicine: Industrial and Clinical DeliveryMSc 12FT

University of Essex
Biomedical Science ... MSc 12FT 24PT

National University of Ireland Galway
Biomedical Science ... MSc 12FT 24DL/PGCert 12DL
Sustainable Resource Management: Policy and Practice ... MSc 12FT

Glasgow Caledonian University
Biomolecular and Biomedical Sciences ... MSc 12FT
Life Sciences - Biological and Biomedical Sciences/Psychology/Vision Sciences ... MRes 12FT

University of Glasgow
Applied Medical Science ... MSc 12FT
Biomedical Sciences ... MRes 12FT/PGDip 8FT

University of Greenwich
Biomedical Sciences ... MSc 12FT 24PT/PGDip 12FT 24PT MSc 12-24DL/PGDip 12-24DL

Heriot-Watt University
Computer Vision and Robotics (VIBOT) ... MSc 48FT

University of Huddersfield
Analytical Bioscience ... MSc 12FT 24-48PT

University of Hull
Biomedical Science ... MSc 12FT
Medical Engineering ... MSc 12FT
Molecular Medicine ... MSc 12FT

Imperial College London
Biomedical Engineering ... MSc 12FT
Biomedical Research ... MRes 12FT
Biomedical Research: Microbial Pathogensis ... MRes 12FT
Biomedical Research: Personalised Healthcare ... MRes 12FT

Keele University
Biomedical Engineering ... MSc 12FT 24PT

University of Kent
Biotechnology and Bioengineering ... MSc 12FT 24PT

King's College London
Biomedical Sciences & Scientific English ... GradDip 12FT
Complex Systems Modelling - From Biomedical and Natural to Economic and Social Sciences ... MSc 12FT 24PT
Radiopharmaceutics & PET Radiochemistry ... MSc 12FT 24PT

Kingston University
Biomedical Science (Haematology/Medical Microbiology) ... MSc 12FT 24PT
Biomedical Science with Management Studies ... MSc 12FT 24PT

Lancaster University
Biomedical Science (by research) ... MSc 12FT 24PT
Biomedicine ... MSc 12FT 24PT/PGDip 12FT 24PT

Leeds Metropolitan University
Applied Biomedical Sciences Research ... MSc 12FT
Biomedical Sciences ... MSc 12FT unknownPT
Integrated Masters Biomedical Sciences ... MBIOMS 48FT

University of Leeds
Medical Engineering ... MSc(Eng) 12FT

University of Leicester
Molecular Genetics ... MSc 12FT/PGDip 9FT/PGCert 4FT
Molecular Pathology and Toxicology ... MSc 12FT 24-36PT/PGDip 12FT

London Metropolitan University
Biomedical Science ... MSc 12FT 24+PT

London South Bank University
Biomedical Engineering & Instrumentation ... MSc 12FT 24PT

Manchester Metropolitan University
Biomedical Science ... MSc 12FT 30PT
Biomedical Science featuring Exercise and Health options ... MSc 12FT 24-36PT

University of Manchester
Medical Physics and Clinical Engineering ... MSc 12FT 24-36PT/PGDip 9FT 24PT
Tissue Engineering for Regenerative Medicine ... MRes 12FT

Middlesex University
Biomedical Science (Cellular Pathology) ... MSc 12FT 24PT
Biomedical Science (Haematology and Transfusion Science) MSc 12FT 24PT
Biomedical Science (Medical Microbiology) ... MSc 12FT 24PT
Biomedical Science (Clinical Biochemistry) ... MSc 12FT 36PT

Nottingham Trent University
Biomedical Science ... MSc 12FT 24PT MSc 24DL

University of Nottingham
Bioengineering: Biomaterials and Biomechanics ... MSc 12FT
Bioengineering: Imaging and Sensing ... MSc 12FT
Bioengineering: The Digital Body ... MSc 12FT
Statistics with Biomedical Applications ... MSc 12FT

University of Oxford
Biomedical Engineering ... MSc 12FT

University of Portsmouth
Biomedicine ... MSc 12FT

Queen Mary, University of London
Biomaterials ... MSc 12FT
Biomedical Engineering ... MSc 12FT 24PT
Medical Electronics and Physics ... MSc 12FT 24PT

Robert Gordon University
Clinical Biomechanics ... MSc 12FT

University of Roehampton
Biomechanics ... MSc 12FT 24-48PT

Sheffield Hallam University
Biomedical Sciences ... MSc 12FT 24PT/PGDip 8FT 16PT/PGCert 4FT 8PT

University of Sheffield
Biological and Bioprocess Engineering ... MSc(Eng) 12FT
Biomaterials and Regenerative Medicine ... MSc 12FT
Bionanotechnology ... MSc(Eng) 12FT
Molecular Medicine ... MSc 12FT
Stem Cell and Regenerative Medicine ... MSc 12FT

St George's, University of London
Biomedical Science ... MRes 12FT

Staffordshire University
Clinical Biomechanics ... PGCert 9PT/PGDip 15PT/MSc 36PT
Clinical Biomechanics and Diabetes ... PGCert 12PT
Clinical Biomechanics and Pain Management in the Lower limb PGCert 12PT
Clinical Podiatric Biomechanics ... PGCert 9PT/PGDip 15PT/MSc 36PT

University of Strathclyde
Biomedical Sciences ... MSc 12FT/PGDip 9FT
Biotechnology ... MSc 12FT
Medical Devices ... MSc 12FT/PGDip 9FT
Medical Technology ... MRes 12FT 24PT
Prosthetics and / or Orthotics Rehabilitation Studies .. MSc 36PT/PGDip 24PT/PGCert 12PT

University of Surrey
Biomedical Engineering ... MSc 12FT 24PT

Teesside University
Health & Social Care Sciences (Generic Pathway) MSc 18FT 36PT
Health & Social Care Sciences (Public Health) ... MSc 18FT 36PT

Trinity College Dublin - the University of Dublin
Biomedical Sciences (Intercalated) ... MSc 12FT

University of Ulster
Biomedical Engineering ... MSc 12FT 36PT/PGDip 9FT 24PT
Biomedical Science .. MSc 12FT 18PT 18DL/PGDip 9FT 16PT 16DL

UCL - University College London
Biomaterials and Tissue Engineering ... MSc 12FT 24 - 60PT
Biomedical Sciences ... MSc 12FT 24PT
Physics and Engineering in Medicine by Distance Learning .. MSc 24-60PT/PGDip 24-60PT/PGCert 24-60PT
Physics and Engineering in Medicine: Biomedical Engineering and Medical Imaging ... MSc 12FT 24PT

University of Warwick
Biomedical Engineering ... MSc 12FT

Health sciences

University of the West of Scotland
Medical Technology ......Cert 6FT 12-24PT/Diploma 12FT 24-48PT

University of the West of England, Bristol
Biomedical Science (5 specialist subject options).............................
MSc 12FT 36PT
Biomedical Science (Professional Doctorate)....... DProf by taught
60PT

University of Westminster
Biomedical Sciences... MSc 12FT

University of Wolverhampton
Biomedical Science ....MSc 12FT 24PT/DPhil by taught 12FT 24PT

Biomedical engineering
Research Courses

University of Aberdeen
Biological Science ....MSc by research 12FT/MPhil 24FT/PhD 36FT
Biomedical Physics and Bioengineering..............PhD 36FT/MSc by
research 12FT/MPhil 24FT
Biomedical Sciences .... PhD 36FT/MPhil 24FT/
MSc by research 12FT

Anglia Ruskin University ....
Medical Engineering............MPhil 18-36FT 30-48PT/PhD 24-60FT
36-72PT

Aston University
Biomaterials and Bio-molecular Science Research Group ....PhD
36FT/MPhil 24FT
Biomedical Engineering Research Group .... PhD 36FT/MPhil 24FT
Biomedical Sciences...............................PhD 36FT/MPhil 12-24FT

Barts and the London School of Medicine and Dentistry
Medical Electronics..PhD/MPhil
Medical Electronics and Physics ....PhD/MPhil/MSc by research
12FT

University of Birmingham
Biomaterials...MRes 12FT 24PT
Biomedical Ethics PhD by research .... PhD 36FT 72PT/MSc by
research 12FT 24PT
Natural Computation...MRes 12FT

University of Bradford
Medical Biosciences.............PhD 36-48FT 48-60PT/MPhil 12-24FT
24-48PT

Cardiff University
Biomedical Research...MRes 12FT
Clinical Kinaesiology.................... MPhil 24FT 48PT/PhD 36FT 60PT
Institute of Medical Engineering and Medical Physics......... MPhil
12-24FT/PhD 36FT/EngD 48FT

University of Central Lancashire
Biological and Biomedical.........PhD 48FT 84PT/MPhil 36FT 60PT/
MSc by research 24FT 36PT/MD 48PT

Coventry University
Biomedical Computing ....MSc by research 12FT
PhD 36FT/MPhil 24FT/MRes 12FT

Cranfield University, Shrivenham
Materials and Medical Sciences ....PhD/MPhil
Smart Materials - (Medical Sciences) ....PhD/MPhil

Durham University
Biological and Biomedical Sciences........... PhD 36FT 72PT/MSc by
research 12FT 24PT

University of Edinburgh
Regenerative Medicine .... MPhil 24FT 48PT/PhD 36FT 72PT

Glasgow Caledonian University
Biological and Biomedical Sciences/Psychology/Vision Sciences
MRes 12FT

University of Glasgow
Biomedical Engineering...PhD 36-48FT 60-72PT/MSc by research
12-24FT 24-36PT
Neuroscience and Biomedical Systems ....PhD 36FT/MSc by
research 12FT

University of Greenwich
Biomedical Sciences - Research ....MPhil 36FT 72PT/
PhD 36FT 72PT

Imperial College London
Biological and Medical Systems ....PhD/MPhil
Biomedical Research...MRes 12FT
Biomedical Research (Microbial Pathogenesis) ....MRes 12FT
Biomedical Sciences...PhD/MPhil
EPSRC Doctoral Training Studentships..............................PhD 36FT

University of Leeds
Biomedical Sciences........PhD 36+FT/MPhil 24FT/MSc by research
12FT
Institute of Medical and Biological Engineering..........PhD 36+FT/
MPhil 24FT
Tissue Engineering and Regenerative Medicine...............PhD 48FT

University of Lincoln
Biomedical and Medical Science ....MPhil 18FT 30PT/
PhD 33FT 60PT

University of Liverpool
Biomedical Sciences and Translational Medicine..........MRes 12FT

Manchester Metropolitan University
Biomedical Science by Research .... PhD 24-48FT 42-84PT/MPhil
18-36FT 36-72PT/MSc by research 9-18FT 18-36PT

University of Manchester
Biomaterials Science and Dental Technology ....MPhil 12FT 24PT/
PhD 36FT 72PT
Biomedical Materials.....PhD 36FT 72PT/MPhil 12FT 24PT/MSc by
research 12FT 24PT

Newcastle University
Biomedicine ....MPhil 12FT 24PT/PhD 36FT 72PT/MD 24FT 48PT
MRes 12FT
Medical Sciences...MRes 12FT

University of Nottingham
Biomedical Sciences Research Areas .... PhD 36FT 72PT
Cell Signalling.. PhD 36FT 72PT/MPhil 24FT 48PT/MRes 12FT/DM
36FT 72PT
Medical Physics (Division of Radiological and Imaging Sciences) ..
.......................PhD 36FT 72PT/MPhil 24FT 48PT/DM 36FT 72PT
Wolfson Centre for Stem Cells, Tissue Engineering and Modelling
(STEM)................... PhD 24-36FT 48-72PT/MPhil 12-24FT 24-48PT

Oxford Brookes University
Health & Biomedical Sciences - Glycobiology and Cancer .....PhD
24-60FT 36-72PT/MPhil 24-36FT 36-48PT
Health & Biomedical Sciences - Human Health & Performance
Research Group .... PhD 24-60FT 36-72PT/
MPhil 24-36FT 36-48PT
Health & Biomedical Sciences - Molecular Neuroscience ......PhD
24-60FT 36-72PT/MPhil 24-36FT 36-48PT
Health and Biomedical Sciences - Peptide Transport ..MPhil/PhD
36-60FT 48-72PT/PhD 24-60FT 36-72PT/MPhil 24-36FT 36-48PT

University of Portsmouth
Pharmacy and Biomedical Science .....MPhil 24FT 48PT/PhD 36FT
72PT/MD 24FT 48PT
Professional Doctorate in Biomedical Science..............DBMS 48PT

University of Salford
Biosciences.....................................PhD 36FT/MSc by research 12FT

University of Sheffield
Biomedical Science .... PhD 36FT 72PT/MPhil 24FT 48PT
Medical Physics and Clinical Engineering ...PhD 36FT 72PT/MPhil
24FT 48PT

University of Strathclyde
Biomedical Engineering - Research... MPhil 12FT/PhD 36FT/MRes
12FT/EngD 36FT
Biomedical Sciences.................................MRes 12FT 24PT
Medical Devices ....EngD 48FT
Pharmacy and Biomedical Sciences - Research ...PhD 36FT 48PT/
MPhil 12FT 24PT/MRes 12FT/DPharm 36FT
Prosthetics and / or Orthotics Rehabilitation Studies ....PhD 36FT
72PT/MPhil 12FT 24PT

University of Surrey
Engineering and Physical Sciences ....PhD 36FT 48PT/PhD 48FT
96PT

UCL - University College London
Biomedical Research..PhD 36FT 60PT
Medical Physics and Bioengineering........................ PhD 36FT 60PT

Chinese medicine
Taught Courses

University of Central Lancashire
Herbal Medicine by elearning...............MSc 36-48PT/PGDip 24PT/
PGCert 12PT

University of Hertfordshire
Western Medical Acupuncture .... MSc up to 60PT

School of Oriental and African Studies - SOAS
Chinese Studies.. MA 12FT 24-36PT
Medical Anthropology .... MA 12FT 24-36PT

UCL - University College London
Chinese Health and Humanity ....MA 12FT
Chinese Studies (Health and Humanity)............................MA 24FT

University of West London
Women's Health and Fertility in Traditional Chinese
Acupuncture .... CPPD 4DL

University of Westminster
Chinese Herbal Medicine .... MSc 12FT 24PT
Chinese Medicine: Acupuncture .... MSc 12FT 24PT
Herbal Medicine .... MSc 12FT 24PT

Chiropractic
Taught Courses

Anglo-European College of Chiropractic
Chiropractic............................MSc 30DL/PGDip 24DL/PGCert 12DL

Queen Mary, University of London
Musculoskeletal Clinical Sciences............................MSc 12FT 24PT
Musculoskeletal Sciences...MSc 12FT 24PT

Chiropractic
Research Courses

University of Portsmouth
Chiropractic...DChiro 48PT

Complementary and alternative medicine
Taught Courses

University of Central Lancashire
Herbal Medicine by elearning...............MSc 36-48PT/PGDip 24PT/
PGCert 12PT
Integrated Healthcare by elearning.....MSc 36-48PT/PGDip 24PT/
PGCert 12PT
Non-Surgical Facial Aesthetics for Registered Healthcare
Professionals..MSc 36PT/PGDip 24PT

University of Derby
International Spa Management ....MA 36FT

University of Dundee
Medical Education .... MMedEd 12FT
Motion Analysis (.................................... MSc 12FT 24PT 24DL

University of Glasgow
Translational Medicine...MRes 12FT

King's College London
Translational Medicine........ MSc 24-48PT/PGDip 24-48PT/PGCert
24-48PT

School of Oriental and African Studies - SOAS
Medical Anthropology ....MA 12FT 24-36PT

University of Southampton
Research Methods in Health ..MSc 24PT/PGDip 12PT/PGCert 6PT

University of St Andrews
Medicine...MRes 12FT 24PT

University of Westminster
Complementary Medicine .... MSc 12FT 24PT
Herbal Medicine .... MSc 12FT 24PT

Complementary and alternative medicine
Research Courses

University of Cambridge
Medical Sciences... MPhil 12FT

University of Dundee
Social Dimensions of Health Institute .... MPhil 24FT
PhD 36FT

Middlesex University
Complementary Therapies.......... PhD 36FT 60PT/MPhil 36FT 60PT

University of Southampton
Research Methods in Health ....MSc by research 24PT/PGDip by
research 12PT/PGCert by research 6PT

Dance movement therapy
Taught Courses

Canterbury Christ Church University
Dance Movement Therapy..MA 24PT

Central School of Speech and Drama, University of London
Drama and Movement Therapy (Sesame) ....MA 18FT
Movement Studies.. MA 12FT 24PT

University of Derby
Dance Movement Therapy/Psychotherapy ....MA 36FT

University of Dundee
Eye Movements & Cognition ....MSc 12FT

Edge Hill University
Dance Movement Psychotherapy .... MA 24FT 48PT

University of Glasgow
Primary Expressive Arts ....PGCert 12PT

Goldsmiths, University of London
Dance Movement Psychotherapy .... PGDip 24FT 36PT/MA 32FT
48PT

Leeds Metropolitan University
Art Psychotherapy Practice .... MA 24FT 36PT
Psychotherapy..MA 48PT

Manchester Metropolitan University
Movement Practice for Theatre ....MA 12FT

University of Roehampton
Dance Movement Psychotherapy .... MA 24FT 36PT
Dance Studies...PGDip 9FT 24PT

UCL - University College London
Performing Arts Medicine............MSc 12FT 24PT/PGDip 9FT 24PT

Dance movement therapy
Research Courses

Goldsmiths, University of London
Dance Movement Psychotherapy .... PhD 36-48FT 48-72PT/MPhil
24FT 36PT

Health sciences

Deaf teaching
Taught Courses

University of Birmingham
Multisensory Impairment (Deafblindness) ...PGCert 12DL/PGDip 24DL/MEd 36-72DL
Teachers of Children with Hearing Impairment.......... MEd 36DL/PGDip 24DL

University of Bristol
Deafhood Studies...MPhil 12FT 60PT

University of Central Lancashire
Child Care Practice, PQ Specialist Award with Children, Young People, Families & Carers ....PGCert 18PT

University of Edinburgh
Additional Support for Learning (Deaf Education).......MEd 72PT/PGDip 48PT/PGCert 24PT

University of Hertfordshire
Education of Deaf Children..PGDip 12FT 24PT/PGCert 12FT 24PT

University of Leeds
Deaf Education (Teacher of the Deaf Qualification)......................... MA 12FT 24PT

University of Manchester
Deaf Education....................................... MSc 36PT/PGDip 12FT 24PT MSc 36PT/PGDip 12FT 24PT 24DL

Newcastle University
Evidence Based Practice in Communication Disorders.. MSc 12FT 24PT/PGDip 24PT/PGCert 12PT

University of Reading
Speech and Language Therapy .... MSc 24FT

University of Sheffield
Professional Practice with Children and Families ....MA 36PT

University of South Wales
SEN Hearing Impairment .... PGDip leading to MA SEN 24PT

Deaf teaching
Research Courses

University of Bristol
Deaf Studies.................................. PhD 36FT 72PT/MPhil 36FT 72PT

UCL - University College London
Speech, Hearing and Phonetic Sciences .... PhD 36FT 60PT

Dramatherapy
Taught Courses

Anglia Ruskin University
Dramatherapy..MA 24FT

Central School of Speech and Drama, University of London
Applied Theatre (Drama in the Community and Drama Education) .... MA 12FT 24PT
Drama and Movement Therapy (Sesame) ....MA 18FT

University of Derby
Drama Therapy..MA 24FT

University of Dundee
Eye Movements & Cognition .... MSc 12FT

University of Exeter
Theatre Practice: Applied Theatre............................ MA 12FT 24PT
Theatre Practice: Directing and Actor Training...... MA 12FT 24PT
Theatre Practice: General Programme..................... MA 12FT 24PT
Theatre Practice: Physical Performance & Actor Training.............. MA 12FT 24PT
Theatre Practice: Staging Shakespeare...................MA 12FT 24PT/MFA 24FT

University of Glasgow
Primary Expressive Arts ....PGCert 12PT

Manchester Metropolitan University
Movement Practice for Theatre ....MA 12FT

University of Roehampton
Dramatherapy.. MA 24FT 36PT

UCL - University College London
Performing Arts Medicine...........MSc 12FT 24PT/PGDip 9FT 24PT

University of Worcester
Dramatherapy...MA 36PT
Psychodrama Psychotherapy.......................MSc 60PT/PGDip 48PT/PGCert 24PT

Dramatherapy
Research Courses

University of Exeter
Drama... PhD 48FT 89PT/MPhil 36FT 60PT

Health sciences
Taught Courses

Aberystwyth University
Childhood Health and Well-being ....MA 12FT 24PT/PGDip 9FT 21PT
Exercise and Health Research......MSc 12FT 24PT/PGDip 9FT 21PT

Anglia Ruskin University
Biomedical Science ....MSc 36 - 60DL
Biotechnology ....MSc 12FT 24PT

Anglo-European College of Chiropractic
Chiropractic............................MSc 30DL/PGDip 24DL/PGCert 12DL
Medical Ultrasound .... MSc 36PT

Bangor University
Advanced Clinical Practice ....MSc 12FT 24 - 60PT/PGDip 9FT
Clinical and Functional Brain Imaging.........................PGCert 12PT
Health Science..................................MSc 12FT 24 - 60PT/PGDip 9FT
Health Studies/Health Science, Nursing, Midwifery, Radiography and Allied Health Professions .... PhD by taught 36FT 48-60PT/MPhil 24FT 36PT
Implementing Evidence in Health & Social CareMRes 12FT 24PT/PGCert 3FT 15PT
Medical Molecular Biology with Genetics ....MSc 12-24FT
Neuroimaging...MSc 12FT 24PT
Occupational Therapy ....MSc 24FT/PGDip 24FT
Risk Management in Health and Social Care......MSc 36PT/PGDip 24PT/PGCert 12PT

University of Bath
Research in Health Practice .... MSc 24-60PT/PGDip 24-60PT/PGCert 12-60PT
Wellbeing and Human Development ....MSc 12FT 30PT/PGDip 9FT 21PT/PGCert 4FT

University of Bedfordshire
Health Related Studies...................................DProf by taught 48PT
Research and Evaluation......................................MSc 12FT 24-36PT

Birmingham City University
Dimensions in Healthcare......................PGCert 12PT/PGCert 36PT

University of Birmingham
Health Studies........MSc 13FT 72PT/PGDip 10FT 48PT/PGCert 6FT 24PT
Philosophy of Health and Happiness........................ MA 12FT 24PT
Philosophy of Health and Happiness MA (Distance learning)....... MA 12FT 36PT

University of Bolton
Advanced Practice (Health and Social Care).................... MSc 24PT
Health and Social Care.... MSc 36-60PT/PGDip 24PT/PGCert 12PT

Bournemouth University
Professional Practice................Dr Professional Practice up to 48PT

University of Brighton
Clinical Research..........MRes 18FT 24-72PT/PGDip 18FT 24-72PT/PGCert 18FT 24-72PT
Health........MSc 12FT 24-72PT/PGDip 12FT 24-72PT/PGCert 12FT 24-72PT
Health and Education.. MSc 12FT 24 - 72PT/PGDip 12FT 24 - 72PT
Health and Management........... MSc 12FT 24 - 72PT/PGDip 12FT 24 - 72PT
Healthcare Ethics....... MA 12FT 24 - 72PT/PGCert 12FT 24 - 72PT/PGDip 12FT 24 - 72PT
Women's Health and Education.MSc 12 - 36FT 24 - 72PT/PGCert 12 - 36FT 24 - 72PT/PGDip 12 - 36FT 24 - 72PT
Women's Health and Management....... MSc 12 - 36FT 24 - 72PT/PGCert 12 - 36FT 24 - 72PT/PGDip 12FT 24 - 72PT

University of Buckingham
General Internal Medicine ....MD 24/36FT

Bucks New University
Health Care Practice ....MSc 36-72PT
Advanced Practice (Gastrointestinal Care) ....MSc 36-72PT

University of Cambridge
Public Health ....MPhil 12FT

Canterbury Christ Church University
Interprofessional Health and Social Care..........MSc 12FT 24-72PT

Cardiff University
Ageing, Health and Disease........................ MSc 24PT/PGDip 12FT/PGCert 12PT
Healthcare Sciences................................MSc 12FT 24PT/PGDip 9FT

University of Central Lancashire
Advanced Practice (Health and Social Care)..................... MSc 24PT
Advanced Stroke Practice......MSc 36FT 60PT/PGDip 24PT/PGCert 12PT
Allied Health Practice .... MSc up to 60PT
Allied Health Practice; MSc Allied Health Practice (Occupational Therapy)................................... MSc 36PT/PGDip 24PT/PGCert 12PT
Arts-Health Analysis .... PGCert 6PT
Health & Social Care Education.....................................PGCert 12PT
Health Improvement: Settings Approaches...............PGCert 12PT
Health Informatics...MSc 33PT/PGDip 24PT
Health Research Methods..................... PGCert 12PT/Cert 3PT 3DL
Health and Social Care Education ....PGCert 12PT
Integrated Healthcare by elearning.....MSc 36-48PT/PGDip 24PT/PGCert 12PT
Nursing ....MSc 12FT 24-60PT
Primary Care Mental Health Practice...........................PGCert 12PT
Professional Practice: Research and Development...MSc 36-60PT
Research Methods in Health and Social Care.............PGCert 36PT
Research for Professional Practice ... Professional Doctorate 24PT

University of Chester
Public Health Nutrition................ MSc 12FT 24 - 72PT/PGDip 12FT 24 - 60PT/PGCert 12FT 12 - 36PT
Weight ManagementMSc 12FT 24 - 48PT/PGDip 12FT 24 - 48PT/PGCert 12FT 12 - 24PT
Weight Management (Taught in Dublin, Ireland) .. MSc 24-48PT/PGDip 24-48PT/PGCert 12-24PT

University of Chichester
Management (Health and Social Care Services) .... MA 27PT/PGDip 18PT/PGCert 12PT

Coventry University
Assistive Technology......... MSc 36- 60PT/PGDip 24 - 48PT/PGCert 12 - 36PT
Health Journalism .... MA 12FT 24PT
Research................ MSc 15FT 32PT MSc 15FT 36PT MSc 15FT 32PT

University of Cumbria
Advanced Practice in Health and Social Care...........MSc 24 - 60PT
International Health...MSc 12FT 24PT

De Montfort University
Advanced Health and Professional Practice .... MSc 12FT 36-72PT/PGDip 24PT/PGCert 12PT
Applied Health Studies (Research/Management) .... MA 12FT 24 - 72PT/PGDip 12FT 12-24PT/PGCert 12FT 24-48PT/PGDIP in Management 24-48PT
Doctorate in Health Science ....DHSci 48-72PT
Health and Community Studies ...MA 36DL/PGDip 18DL/PGCert 12DL/MA 12FT
Masters By Research... MRes 12-15FT 24PT
Masters in Research (Applied Health Studies, Criminology and Criminal Justice, or Social Work............................ MRes 12FT 24PT/PGDip 24-48PT/PGCert 12-24PT

University of Derby
Community Specialist Practice ....MSc 12FT 24PT
Education.. MA 24-36PT
Health Psychology...MSc 12FT 24PT
Management of Long Term Conditions........................PGCert 12PT
Nursing (Specialist Community Public Health)..... MSc 12FT 24PT

University of Dundee
Advanced Practice (Cancer Care) ....MSc 36DL
Advanced Practice (Clinical Assessment) ....MSc 36DL
Advanced Practice (Health & Social Care) ....MSc 36DL
Advanced Practice (Individual Modules) .... PG module 6DL
Advanced Practice (Medical Imaging) ....MSc 36DL
Advanced Practice (Mental Health) ....MSc 36DL
Advanced Practice (Midwifery)...MSc 36DL
Advanced Practice (Nursing) ....MSc 36DL
Advanced Practice (Palliative Care)......................................MSc 36DL
Advanced Practice (Practice Education) ....PGCert 12DL PGDip 24DL
Applied Health Statistics .... MSc 12FT
Diabetes Care and Education ....MSc 36-40PT PGCert 12-15PT PGDip 24-27PT
Epidemiology and Global Health International Prevention Research Institute Summer School..Cert 1FT
Eye Movements & Cognition .... MSc 12FT
Global Health and Wellbeing ....MSc 36DL
Health Studies (Post Registration by distance learning, January entry) ....BSc variableDL
Health and Social Care ....MRes 24DL
Healthcare Law and Ethics (LLM by distance learning) . LLM 36DL
Oral Cancer.. MRes 12FT
Orthopaedic Science (MSc by distance learning)............................ MSc up to 60DL
Orthopaedic Science.. MSc 12FT
Orthopaedic Surgery (MChOrth)..................................MChOrth 9FT
Orthopaedic and Rehabilitation Technology ....MSc 24-60DL
Public Health (MPH)...MPH 12-24FT
Quality Improvement ....MSc 36DL PGCert 12DL PGDip 24DL

Durham University
Health Research Methods...PGCert 10PT

University of East Anglia
Clinical Education..............MClinEd 12FT 36PT/PGDip 12FT 24PT/PGCert 12PT
Clinical Research.......................... MSc 12FT 36PT/PGDip 12FT 24PT
Clinical Research – NIHR Route.................................. MSc 12FT 24PT
Clinical Science... MRes 12FT
Cognitive Behavioural Therapy...PGDip 12FT
Coloproctology...PGDip 2PT MS 3PT
Health EconomicsMSc 12FT 36PT/PGDip 12FT 24PT/PGCert 12PT
Leadership in Dementia Care ....MSc 36PT PGDip 24PT
Leading Innovation for Clinical Practitioners .... PGDip 24PT MA 36PT
Occupational Therapy .... MSc 24FT
Physiotherapy.. MSc 24FT
Regional Anaesthesia .... MSc 36PT

University of East London
Applied Health Sciences ....PGCert 5FT 12-36PT
Health Science ....MRes 12FT 24PT
Working with Groups ....MA 36PT/PGDip 24PT/PGCert 12PT

Health sciences

Edge Hill University
Advanced Practice ... MSc 36-72PT
Professional Clinical Practice ... MSc 24FT 72PT
Public Health and Wellbeing ... MSc 24FT 72PT
Simulation and Clinical Learning ... PGCert 12-36DL

University of Edinburgh
Advanced Social Work Studies (Mental Health) ... PGCert 12PT
Advancing Nursing Practice ... MSc 12FT/MSc 24PT/PGCert 9PT/PGDip 21PT
Applied Psychology (Healthcare) for Children and Young People ... MSc 12FT
Clinical Trials ... MSc 36DL/PGDip 24DL/PGCert 12DL
Cognitive Behaviour Therapy for Children and Young People ... PGCert 24PT
Conservation Medicine MVetSci 36DL/PGDip 24DL/PGCert 12DL
Dementia: International Experience, Policy and Practice (Online Distance Learning) ... MSc 24DL/PGDip 21DL/PGCert 9DL
Health & Social Care - Children & Young People's Mental Health: Ecological Approaches ODL ... PGCert 9DL
Health Inequalities and Public Policy ... MSc 12FT 24-36PT
Health Systems and Public Policy ... MSc 12FT 24-36PT
Imaging ... MSc 36DL/PGDip 24DL/PGCert 12DL
Integrated Service Improvement: Health and Social Care ... MSc 24-36PT/PGDip 20PT/PGCert 12PT
Nursing in Clinical Research ... MN 12FT
Public Health ... MPH 12FT 24-36PT
Public Health Policy ... MSc(Res) 12FT 24-36PT

University of Essex
Adult Nursing ... MSc 24FT
Advanced Musculoskeletal Assessment ... MSc 24-60PT/Diploma 18-60PT/Cert 12-60PT
Clinical Psychology ... Prof Doc 24PT
Counselling Psychology ... Prof Doc 24PT
Health Care Management ... Diploma 18-60PT/MSc 24-60PT
Health Care Practice ... MSc 24-60PT/PGCert 18-60PT/PGDip 18-60PT
Health Research ... MA 12FT 24PT/MSc 12FT 24PT
Health Services Management ... Prof Doc 48-84PT
Health and Organisational Research ... MSc 12FT 24PT
Infection Control ... MSc 24-60PT/Diploma 18-60PT/Cert 12-60PT
Medical and Clinical Education ... MSc 24-60PT/Diploma 18-60PT/Cert 12-60PT
Mental Health Nursing ... MSc 24FT
Nursing (Professional Doctorate) ... Prof Doc 48-84PT
Occupational Therapy ... MSc 24FT Prof Doc 48-84PT
Physiotherapy ... MSc 24FT Prof Doc 48-84PT
Psychological Wellbeing Practitioner (Low-Intensity Therapy) ... PGCert 18-60PT
Public Health ... MA 12FT 24-60PT Prof Doc 48-84PT
Public Health Management ... MSc 24-60PT/Diploma 18-60PT/Cert 12-60PT
Social Care Education ... Prof Doc 48-84PT
Social Care Practice Management ... Prof Doc 48-84PT
Social Services Management ... Prof Doc 48-84PT
Speech and Language Therapy ... MSc 24FT

University of Exeter
Environment and Human Health ... PGCert 6FT/PGDip 9FT/MSc 12FT 24PT
Paediatric Exercise and Health ... MSc 12FT 24PT
Sport and Exercise Medicine ... MSc 12FT 24PT
Sport and Health Sciences ... MSc 12FT 24PT

National University of Ireland Galway
Health Promotion ... MA 12FT 24PT/PGDip 12FT 24PT
Health Sciences (Clinical Education) ... MHSc 12FT/PGDip 12FT/PGCert 12FT
Health Sciences (Clinical Primary Care) ... PGDip 12PT/PGCert 12PT
Health Sciences (Primary Care) ... PGDip 12PT
Medical Science (Health Informatics) ... PGDip 12PT/MMedSci 12PT

Glasgow Caledonian University
Advanced Practice with Older People ... MSc 12FT
Advancing Practice in Primary Care ... MSc 24FT
Clinical Nutrition and Health ... MSc 12FT
Counselling Skills in Health and Social Care ... PGCert 12-24FT
Diagnostic Imaging ... MSc 12-24FT
Health and Social Care (Social Work) ... MSc 12-24FT 12-72PT
Health and Social Care Education ... MSc 12FT
Musculoskeletal Management ... MSc 36-72PT
Optimal Heart Failure Care ... MSc 12FT
Perinatal Mental Health ... MSc 12FT
Professional Doctorate for Health, Social Care Sector and Nursing Professionals ... DProf by taught 48FT
Public Health with Social Action ... MSc 12FT
Radiotherapy and Oncology ... MSc 12-24FT
Sexual Health ... MSc 24-60FT On-lineDL
Telehealthcare ... MSc 12FT

University of Glasgow
Global Health ... MSc 12FT 24PT
Health Care ... MSc(MedSci) 12FT 24PT/PGDip 9FT 18PT/PGCert 5FT 10PT
Managing Health and Wellbeing (Dumfries Campus) ... MLitt 12FT 24PT/PGDip 12FT 24PT/PGCert 12FT 24PT

University of Gloucestershire
Non-Medical Prescribing ... PGCert 8PT

Heriot-Watt University
Food Science, Safety and Health MSc 12FT 24PT 24-84DL/PGDip 9FT 21PT 24-84DL

University of Huddersfield
Health & Social Care (Approved Mental Health Practice) ... MSc 36PT
Health Studies ... MSc 12FT 36PT
Health Studies (Advanced Diabetes Care) ... MSc 12FT 36PT
Health Studies (Advanced Practice in Acute and Critical Care) ... MSc 12FT 36PT
Health Studies (Advancing Midwifery Practice) ... MSc 12FT 36PT
Health Studies (Health Professional Education: Teaching) ... MSc 12FT 36PT
Health Studies (Healthy Lifestyles) ... MSc 12FT 36PT
Health Studies (Long-term Conditions) ... MSc 12FT 36PT
Health and Social Care ... MSc 12FT 36PT
Multi Disciplinary Care of High Risk Patients ... PGCert 24PT
Musculoskeletal Management of the Lower Limb ... PGDip 24BM

Keele University
Neuromusculoskeletal Health Care ... MSc 16FT 24-60PT/PGDip 12FT 24-60PT/PGCert 12FT 24PT

University of Kent
Advanced and Specialist Healthcare (Minimally Invasive Surgery) ... MSc 24-36PT
Advanced and Specialist Healthcare (Supportive and Palliative Care) ... MSc 24-36PT
Advanced and Specialist Healthcare (Surgical Practice) ... MSc 24-36PT
Health Services Research ... MSc 12FT 24PT
Independent/Supplementary Prescribing ... PGCert 8PT
Independent/Supplementary Prescribing for Nurses (Level H) (Short Course Programme) ... PGCert 8PT/PGDip 8PT/MSc 8PT

King's College London
Global Health & Social Justice ... MSc 12FT 24PT
Health Studies ... PGCert 12FT 24PT
Primary Health Care ... MSc 12FT 24PT

Kingston University
Advanced Practice (Healthcare) ... MSc 24PT/PGDip 24PT/PGCert 24PT
Biomedical Science (Haematology/Medical Microbiology) ... MSc 12FT 24PT
Rehabilitation ... MSc 12FT 24PT

Lancaster University
Health Research ... MPhil 24FT/PhD by taught 24FT

Leeds Metropolitan University
Nutrition In Practice ... MSc(Eng) 12-15FT up to 60PT

University of Leeds
Health Research ... PGCert 12FT/PGDip 12PT/MSc 24PT
International Health ... PGCert 3FT/PGDip 9FT/MSc 12FT

University of Leicester
Applied Health Research ... MRes 12FT 24PT

University of Limerick
Advanced Clinical Practice ... PGCert 12FT 24PT
Advanced Healthcare practice ... MSc 12FT 69PT
Developmental Speech and Language Disorder ... PGCE 12PT
Musculoskeletal Therapy ... PGCert 12PT
Neurological Rehabilitation ... PGCert 12PT
Occupation and Wellbeing ... PGCert 12PT
Occupational Therapy ... MSc 24FT
Pain ... PGCert 12PT

Liverpool Hope University
Exercise Testing & Prescription ... PGCert 12FT

Liverpool John Moores University
Advanced Healthcare Practice ... MSc 36PT
Health Sciences ... MRes 12FT 24PT

University of Liverpool
Advanced Practice in Healthcare ... MSc 36FT 72PT
Clinical Research (Online Degree) ... MSc 24FT 24+PT
Clinical Science (Medical Physics) ... MSc 36PT

London School of Economics and Political Science (LSE)
Health, Population and Society ... MSc 12FT 24PT

London School of Hygiene and Tropical Medicine
Clinical Trials (by Distance Learning) ... MSc 24 - 60DL/PGDip 12 - 60DL/PGCert 12-60DL
Control of Infectious Diseases ... MSc 12FT 24PT
Demography & Health ... MSc 12FT 24PT
Epidemiology ... MSc 12FT 24PT
Epidemiology (by Distance Learning) ... MSc 24 - 60DL/PGDip 12 - 60DL/PGCert 12-60DL
Global Health Policy (by Distance Learning) MSc 24-60DL/PGDip 12-60DL/PGCert 12-60DL
Global Mental Health ... MSc 12FT 24PT
Health Policy, Planning and Financing ... MSc 12FT 24PT
Immunology of Infectious Diseases ... MSc 12FT 24PT
Infectious Diseases (by Distance Learning) MSc 24 - 60DL/PGDip 12 - 60DL/PGCert 12-60DL
Medical Entomology for Disease Control ... MSc 12FT 24PT
Medical Microbiology ... MSc 12FT 24PT
Medical Parasitology ... MSc 12FT 24PT
Medical Statistics ... MSc 12FT 24PT
Molecular Biology of Infectious Diseases ... MSc 12FT 24PT
Nutrition for Global Health ... MSc 12FT 24PT
One Health ... MSc 12FT 24PT
Public Health ... MSc 12FT 24PT
Public Health (Environment & Health) ... MSc 12FT 24PT
Public Health (Health Economics) ... MSc 12FT 24PT
Public Health (Health Promotion) ... MSc 12FT 24PT
Public Health (Health Services Management) ... MSc 12FT 24PT
Public Health (Health Services Research) ... MSc 12FT 24PT
Public Health (Public Health) ... MSc 12FT 24PT
Public Health (by Distance Learning) ... MSc 24 - 60DL/PGDip 12 - 60DL/PGCert 12-60DL
Public Health for Eye Care ... MSc 12FT 24PT
Public Health in Developing Countries ... MSc 12FT 24PT
Reproductive & Sexual Health Research ... MSc 12FT 24PT
Tropical Medicine & International Health ... MSc 12FT 24PT
Veterinary Epidemiology ... MSc 12FT 24PT

London South Bank University
Professional Development for Allied Health Professions ... MSc 12-36PT

Manchester Metropolitan University
Dental Technology ... MSc 12FT 36PT

University of Manchester
Health and Social Care ... MRes HSC 12-24DL/PGCert Res 24DL/PGDip Res 12-24DL

Middlesex University
Dual Diagnosis ... MSc 36PT 36DL/AdvDip 12PT 12DL/PGCert 12PT 12DL
Professional Practice (Health, Social Care, Public and Community Sectors) ... MSc tbcDL/MA tbcDL

North East Surrey College of Technology
Perfusion Science ... MSc 27PT/PGDip 18PT/PGCert 9PT

Newcastle University
Clinical Dentisty in Restorative Dentistry, Master of ... MSc 24FT
Clinical Education ... MClinEd 12FT 12-24PT/PGDip 12-24PT/PGCert 12PT
Clinical Implant Dentistry ... PGCert 18PT
Medical Genetics ... MRes 12FT
Medical Sciences ... MSc 12FT
Public Health and Health Services Research ... MSc 12FT 24-36PT/PGDip 9FT 21PT/PGCert 9PT
Social Science and Health Research ... MSc 12FT 24PT/PGDip 9FT 18PT

University of Northampton
Autonomous Healthcare Practice ... MSc 12FT 24-48PT/PGDip 12PT
Health Studies ... MSc 12FT 24-60PT/PGDip 12PT
Human Bioscience ... MSc 12FT 24-48PT/PGDip 12PT

Northumbria University
Exercise Science ... MRes 12FT 24PT
Health Sciences (Management) ... MSc 12FT
Occupational Therapy ... Professional Doctorate 48-72PT

Nottingham Trent University
Biomedical Science ... MSc 12FT 24PT
Public Health ... MA 12FT 24PT

University of Nottingham
Health Communication by Web Based Distance Learning ... MA 24-48DL
Health and Social Care ... MSc 12FT 24-48PT/PGCert 24-48PT/PGDip 12FT 24-48PT
Research ... MRes 12FT 24PT
Research Methods (Health) ... MA 12FT 24PT

The Open University
Advancing Healthcare Practice ... PGCert 12DL/PGDip variableDL/MSc variableDL
Advancing Professional Practice ... MSc variableDL
Medicinal Chemistry ... MSc variableDL/PGDip variableDL
Professional Science ... MSc variableDL
Science ... MSc variableDL

Oxford Brookes University
Advanced Practice (Clinical) ... MSc 36-60PT/PGDip 24-48PT/PGCert 18-24PT
Applied Human Nutrition ... MSc 12FT 24PT/PGDip 8FT 20PT/PGCert 8FT 8PT
Cancer Studies ... MSc 12FT 36PT/PGDip 12FT/PGCert 6FT
Community Children's Nursing ... PGDip 12FT 24PT
Community Nursing in the Home / District Nursing ... PGDip 12FT 24PT
Health and Social Care, Student Designed Award MA 12FT 60PT/MSc 12FT 60PT/PGDip 12FT 48PT/PGCert 36PT
Higher Professional Education ... MSc 12FT 12-36PT/PGDip 12FT 24PT/PGCert 12FT 18PT
Infection Prevention and Control ... MSc 12FT Up to 36PT/PGDip 9FT Up to 36PT/PGCert 4FT Up to 36PT
Rehabilitation ... MSc 12FT Up to 36PT

University of Oxford
Biomedical Engineering ... MSc 12FT

Health sciences

Cognitive & Evolutionary Anthropology .... MSc 12FT
Global Health Science .... MSc 12FT

Peninsula College of Medicine and Dentistry
Clinical Education Research/Clinical Education Practice.... PGCert 12PT/PGDip 24PT/MClinEd 36PT
Infection Prevention & Control .... PGCert 12PT
Remote and Isolated Health Care Environment....... PGCert 12PT/PGDip 24PT/MSc 36PT

Plymouth University
Advanced Professional Practice ....PGCert 6FT 12PT/PGDip 10FT 12PT/MSc 12FT 24PT

Queen Margaret University, Edinburgh
Diabetes..........MSc 12FT 24-60PT/PGDip 12FT 12-24PT
Diagnostic Radiography (Pre-Registration).....PGCert 12FT/PGDip 24FT/MSc 26FT
Health Systems .... MSc 12FT 24PT/PGDip 8FT 16PT/PGCert 4FT 8PT
International Health .... MSc 12FT 60PT
Public Health Nutrition.... MSc 12FT 24-60PT/PGDip 9FT 24-60PT
Public Health Practice.......... MSc 12FT 48PT

Queen Mary, University of London
Healthcare Research Methods .... PGCert 1FT/MSc 24FT

Queen's University Belfast
Clinical Anatomy ......MSc 12FT TBCPT/PGDip 12FT TBCPT/PGCert 12FT TBCPT
Interprofessional Health and Social Care Management......... MSc 24-36PT
Public Health .... MPH 12FT
Translational Medicine.......... MRes 12FT 24PT

Royal College of Nursing
Advancing Healthcare Pratice .... MSc 23-50DL

University of Reading
Neuroscience of Language .... MSc 12FT 24PT

Robert Gordon University
Advanced Clinical Practice ... MSc 36PT/PGDip 24PT/PGCert 12PT
Clinical Biomechanics.......... MSc 12FT
Clinical Pharmacy Practice ....MSc 24DL/PGDip 18DL/PGCert 9DL
Diagnostic Radiography (pre-registration) .... MSc 24FT
Health Improvement and Health Promotion.......... MSc 24DL

University of Roehampton
Health Sciences.......... MSc 12FT 24PT PGDip 9FT 24PT
Stress and Health .... PGDip 9FT 24PT

University Campus Suffolk
Health and Social Care Practice ...... MA 60PT/PGCert 36PT/PGDip 48PT

University of Salford
Advanced Occupational Therapy............MSc 36DL/PGCert 12DL/PGDip 24DL
Advanced Practice (Health and Social Care) ....MSc 24PT/PGDip 18PT/PGCert 12PT
Advancing Physiotherapy........... MSc 12FT 36PT/PGDip 9FT 24PT/PGCert 6FT 12PT
Child and Adolescent Mental Health ....MSc 24PT/PGDip 18PT/PGCert 9PT
Cognitive Behaviour Therapy .... PGCert 12PT
Cognitive Behavioural Psychotherapy....... MSc 36PT/PGDip 24PT/PGCert 12PT
Geriatric Medicine.......... MSc 48-60PT/PGDip 24-60PT/PGCert 12-60PT
Health Care Law..LLM 27DL/MA 27DL/PGDip 20DL/PGCert 12DL
International Hospital and Health Service Leadership and Management.......... MSc 12FT/PGDip 8FT/PGCert 4FT
Lower Limb Health, Disease and Rehabilitation.........PGCert 12PT
Strength and Conditioning.. MSc 36PT/PGDip 24PT/PGCert 12PT

Sheffield Hallam University
Advanced Practice (Radiotherapy and Oncology) MSc 3DL/PGDip 2DL/PGCert 1DL
Advanced Professional Development ....MSc VAFT/PGDip VAFT/PGCert VAFT
Advancing Paediatric Practice .... MSc 18FT/PGDip 12FT/PGCert 6FT
Biomedical Sciences.......... MSc 12FT 24PT/PGDip 8FT 16PT/PGCert 4FT 8PT
Breast Imaging and Diagnosis ....MSc 36PT/PGDip 24PT/PGCert 12PT
Clinical Education .... MSc 24PT/PGDip 24PT/PGCert 12PT
Health and Society.......... MRes 12FT 36PT
Public Health .... MA 18FT 36PT

University of Sheffield
Advanced Emergency Care.......... MSc 12FT 24 - 60PT
Advanced Nursing Studies ... MMedSci 36DL/Diploma 36DL/Cert 36DL
Advancing Practice......... MMedSci 12FT 24PT/Diploma 9FT 18PT/Cert 6FT 12PT
Biomaterials and Regenerative Medicine .... MSc 12FT
Cognitive Neuroscience and Human Neuroimaging...... MSc(Res) 12FT
Cognitive Studies.......... MA 12FT 24PT
European Health Law and Policy.......... LLM 12FT 24PT
Health Economics and Decision Modelling ......MSc 12FT 24-36PT
Human Nutrition.......... MMedSci 12FT 24PT/PGDip 9FT 18PT
Long-Term Health Conditions .... PGCert FlexiblePT

University of South Wales
Disaster Healthcare (Online Delivery).......... MSc 36DL
Professional Practice.......... MSc 12FT 24 -84PT

University of Southampton
Advanced Clinical Practice ....MSc 12FT 24PT/PGDip 12FT/PGCert 12FT
Audiology ....MSc 12FT 24PT/PGDip 9FT 18PT/PGCert 9FT 18PT
Cognitive Behavioural Therapy .... PGCert 3FT
Cognitive Therapy for Severe Mental Health Problems........PGDip 12PT
Doctorate in Clinical Practice . DClinP 48FT 84PT/MSc 12FT 24PT/PGDip 12FT 24PT/PGCert 8FT 16PT
Gerontology .... MSc 12FT 24PT/PGDip 9FT 21PT
Gerontology (Distance Learning) .... MSc 12DL/PGDip 9DL
Health Informatics .... MSc 24DL/PGDip 16DL
Health Psychology.......... MSc 12FT/PGDip 12FT
Clinical research.......... MRes 12FT 48PT
Health Science (General Pathway).......... MSc 12FT 24PT
Health and Rehabilitation........MSc 12FT 24PT/PGDip 12FT 24PT/PGCert 8FT 16PT
Physiotherapy.......... MSc 24FT
Public Health Practice...MSc 12FT 24PT/PGDip 12FT/PGCert 12FT
Management of Diabetes ....MSc 15FT 24PT/PGDip 12FT 18PT/PGCert 6FT 6PT
Professional Studies..........MSc 30PT/PGCert 12PT/PG Cert in Management and Leadership 12-24 PTDL
Research Methods in Health ..MSc 24PT/PGDip 12PT/PGCert 6PT

University of St Andrews
Health Geography Research ... MRes 12FT 24PT/PGDip 10FT 20PT
Health Psychology.......... MSc 12FT

St George's, University of London
Advanced Practice .... MSc 24PT
Biomedical Science .... MRes 12FT
Clinical Practice.......... MRes 12FT 24PT
Health Sciences.......... MSc 24PT
Maternal and Child Health .... MSc 12FT 24PT
Physician Assistant Studies .... PGDip 24FT
Rehabilitation.......... MSc 12FT 24PT

St Loye's School of Occupational Therapy
Advanced Programme in Occupational Therapy. BPhil 24DL/MSc 24DL
Health Studies.......... BPhil 24PT/MSc 24PT

Staffordshire University
Advanced Clinical Practice ....PGCert 12PT/PGDip 24PT/MSc 36PT
Clinical Biomechanics.............. PGCert 9PT/PGDip 15PT/MSc 36PT
Clinical Biomechanics and Diabetes.......... PGCert 12PT
Clinical Biomechanics and Pain Management in the Lower limb PGCert 12PT
Clinical Biomechanics in Orthotic Therapy.......... PGCert 12PT
Clinical Podiatric Biomechanics .... PGCert 9PT/PGDip 15PT/MSc 36PT
Community Practice .... MA 12FT 48PT
Health Management and Policy (Distance Learning) .... PGCert 12PT/PGDip 24PT/MA 36PT
Health Psychology.......... MSc 12FT 24PT
PsychD by taught 24FT 48PT
Health by Negotiated Learning .... MSc 36PT
Healthcare Practice .... MSc 36FT 60PT
Master of Public Health (MPH) .... MPH 24-60DL
Medical Education.......... MSc 36PT/PGCert 24PT/PGDip 12PT
Musculoskeletal Diagnosis .... PGCert 9PT
Practitioner with a Special Interest in Mental Health ... MSc 36PT
Public Health (Distance Learning)..........PGCert 7DL/PGDip 14DL/MPH 24DL
Public Health (Health Informatics) .... PGCert 8PT/PGDip 16PT/MPH 24PT
Public Health (Health Informatics) MPH .... MPH 24-60DL/PGCert 24-60DL/PGDip 24-60DL

University of Stirling
Advanced Practice .... MSc 18PT/MSc 18PT
Health Psychology.......... MSc 12FT 24PT/PGDip 6FT 12PT
Health Research.......... MRes 12FT 24/36PT 24/36DL
Health and Wellbeing of the Older Person .... MSc 24FT
Psychology Applied to Health .....MSc 12FT 24PT/PGDip 9FT 18PT

University of Strathclyde
Analysis of Medicines..........MSc 36DL/PGDip 24DL/PGCert 12DL
Health History.... MSc 12FT 24PT/PGDip 9FT 18PT/PGDip 9FT 9PT

University of Sunderland
Health and Social Care Research .... MSc 12FT 24PT
Cognitive Behavioural Therapy & Recovery in Psychosis and Complex Mental Health .... MSc 12-36PT

University of Surrey
Professional Practice..........MSc 60 maxPT/PGCert 60 maxPT/PGDip 60 maxPT

Swansea University
Abnormal and Clinical Psychology.......... MSc 12FT 24PT
Advanced Practice in Health Care .... MSc 36PT/PGDip 24PT
Advanced Practice in Health Care - Infection Control ...MSc 36PT/PGDip 24PT
Ageing Studies .... MSc 12FT 36PT/PGDip 12FT 24PT/PGCert 12FT 12PT
Approved Mental Health Professional .... PGCert 12FT
Autism and Related Conditions ....MSc 12FT 36PT/PGDip 12FT 24PT/PGCert 12FT 12PT
Childhood Studies .... MA 12FT 24PT
Chronic Conditions Management........ MSc 12FT 36PT/PGDip 9FT 24PT/PGCert 6FT 12PT
Clinical Science (Medical Physics) .... MSc 36PT
Community and Primary Healthcare Practice .... MSc 36PT/PGDip 24PT/PGCert 12PT
Developmental and Therapeutic Play .... MA 12FT 36PT/PGDip 12FT 24PT/PGCert 12FT 12PT
Education for the Health Professions......... MA 36PT/PGDip 24PT/PGCert 12PT
Enhanced Professional Practice (EPP)........ MSc 36PT/PGDip 24PT/PGCert 12PT
Health Informatics....... MSc 12FT 36PT/PGDip 12FT 24PT/PGCert 12FT 12PT
Healthcare Management .... MSc 12FT 36PT
Infection Prevention and Control .... PGCert 12PT

Teesside University
Advanced Clinical Practice (Cardiac Care) .... MSc 36PT
Advanced Clinical Practice (Management of Long-term Health Conditions) .... MSc 36PT
Advanced Clinical Practice (Manipulative Therapy) .... MSc 36PT
Advanced Clinical Practice (Neurolgical Rehabilitation) .... MSc 36PT
Advancing Practice.......... MA 36PT
Clinical Research.......... MRes 18FT 36PT
Doctor of Health and Social Care .... DProf by taught 72PT
Health & Social Care Sciences (End of Life Care)... MSc 18FT 36PT
Health & Social Care Sciences (Generic Pathway) MSc 18FT 36PT
Health & Social Care Sciences (Public Health)....... MSc 18FT 36PT
Public Health .... MSc 18FT 36PT 36DL
Rehabilitation (Occupational Therapy) .... MSc 36PT
The Management of Long-term Health Conditions.. PGCert 12PT

Trinity College Dublin - the University of Dublin
Advanced Radiotherapy Practice .... MSc 12FT
Cardiology .... MSc 12FT
Cardiovascular Rehabilitation and Prevention ...... MSc 12FT 24PT
Clinical Dental Technology .... PGDip 18PT
Clinical Dentistry .... PGDip 24PT
Community Pharmacy .... PGDip 24PT/MSc 36PT
Health Informatics .... MSc 24PT
Healthcare Infection Management .... MSc 24PT
Hospital Pharmacy .... MSc 24PT
Master in Obstetrics .... MAO 12FT 60PT
Masters in Medicine .... MSc 24PT
Mental Health .... MSc 12FT 24PT

University of the Highlands and Islands
Professional Development..... MA 36PT/PGCert 12PT/PGDip 24PT

University of Ulster
Advancing Practice in an AHP Specialism ....PGCert 9PT/PGDip 18PT/MSc 27PT
Health Studies.......... MSc 12-36DL/PGDip 12-36DL
Health and Wellbeing .... PGDip 12-36PT/MSc 12-36PT
Prescribing for Allied Health Professionals........... PGCert 9PT 9DL

UCL - University College London
Biology of Vision .... MSc 12FT
Biomedical Sciences.......... MSc 12FT 24PT
Brain Sciences MRes .... MRes 12FT
Burns, Plastic and Reconstructive SurgeryMSc 12FT 24PT/PGCert 36PT
Cancer.......... MSc 12FT 24-36PT/PGDip 9FT 18PT/PGCert 3FT
Cardiovascular Science.......... MSc 12FT
Chinese Health and Humanity .... MA 12FT
Chinese Studies (Health and Humanity).......... MA 24FT
Clinical Neurology (by Distance Learning)..............PGDip 12-36DL
Clinical Ophthalmology.......... MSc 24FT 36PT/PGCert 24FT 36PT/PGDip 24FT 36PT
Clinical and Experimental Medicine.. MSc 12FT/MRes 12FT 24PT/PGDip 9FT
Clinical and Public Health Nutrition.............MSc 12FT/PGDip 9FT/PGCert 3FT
Clinical and Public Health Nutrition: Eating Disorders. MSc 12FT/PGDip 9FT/PGCert 3FT
Global Health and Development.... MSc 12FT 24-60PT/PGDip 9FT 24-60PT/PGCert 12-24PT
Health Informatics ..... MSc 24-60PT/PGDip 24-60PT/PGCert 24PT
Health and Medical Sciences.......... MSc 24-60PT
Health and Society: Social Epidemiology... MSc 12FT 24PT/PGDip 9FT 18PT
Healthcare Associated Infection Control........MSc 24-60PT/PGDip 24-60PT
Infection and Immunity.. MSc 12FT 24-60PT/PGDip 9FT 24-60PT/PGCert 3FT 6-24PT
International Health Euro .... MSc 12FT
Medical Bacteriology (by Distance Learning)... MSc 24FT 24-60PT
Musculoskeletal Science.......... MSc 24FT 24-60PT/PGDip 9FT 18-45PT/PGCert 3FT
Musculoskeletal Science (by Distance Learning)........... MSc 12FT/PGDip 9FT 24-60PT/PGCert 3FT

Health sciences

Ophthalmology: Cataract and Refractive Surgery.......................... MSc 12FT 24PT
Ophthalmology: Retina .... MSc 12FT 24PT
Reproductive Science and Women's Health ... MSc 12FT 24-36PT/PGDip 9FT 24PT

University of Warwick
Access and Equality in Health Care........... PGA 12PT/CPDMod 1PT
Counselling Skills for Health Care Professionals............. PGA 12PT
Diabetes.. MSc 12FT 24-96PT/PGA 12PT
Health Sciences....MSc 36PT/PGDip 24PT/PGCert 12PT/PGA 12PT
Health Sciences: Palliative Care....MSc 36PT/PGDip 24PT/PGCert 12PT/PGA 12PT
Health Sciences: Public Health ......MSc 36PT/PGDip 24PT/PGCert 12PT/PGA 12PT
Sexual and Reproductive Health Care.. MSc 12FT 36-96PT/PGDip 24FT 36-60PT/PGCert 12FT 24-60PT

University of West London
Advancing Practice.. MSc 24PT
Health Psychology.. MSc 12FT 24PT
Nursing and Healthcare Intergrated .... MSc 12FT
Research MSc 15FT 15-84PT/PGDip 15FT 15PT/MA 15FT 15-84PT

University of the West of Scotland
Nursing Studies.. BSc variablePT

University of the West of England, Bristol
Advanced Practice.. MSc 36PT
Health and Social Care .... DProf by taught 60PT
Specialist Practice.. PGCert 36PT

University of Westminster
Biomedical Sciences.. MSc 12FT
Leading and Managing Health and Social Care (Advanced Professional Practice) .... MSc 24PT PGDip 12PT PGCert 12PT
Work-based Tutoring ....PGCert 6-12DL

University of Wolverhampton
Commissioning for Health and Social Care .... MSc 24PT/PGDip 24PT/PGCert 12PT
Emergency Planning Resilience and Response .... MSc 24PT/PGCert 12PT
Health and Social Care .... MSc 12FT 24PT/MA 12FT 24PT
Health and Wellbeing (top-up)......MSc 12FT 12PT/MA 12FT 12PT
Health, Social Care and Allied Professionals .... PGCE 12PT
Management of Passenger Transport Emergency Incidents.......... PGCert 6FT 12PT
Mental Health .... MSc 24PT/MA 24PT/PGCert 12PT/PGDip 12PT
Mental Health Practice (for Approved Mental Health Professionals) ....PGCert 12PT
Palliative and End of Life Care .... MSc 24PT
Primary Health Care (top-up)............................... MSc 12PT
Public Health (MPH)...................................MPH 12FT 24PT
Social Work..MA 24FT
Specialist Community Nursing (District Nursing) ....PGDip 12FT
Specialist Community Nursing (General Practice Nursing)........... PGDip 12FT
Specialist Community Public Health Nursing (Health Visiting) .... PGDip 12FT 24PT
Specialist Community Public Health Nursing (School Nursing).... PGDip 12FT

University of Worcester
Advancing Practice..................... MA 36FT 72PT/PGDip 24FT 48PT/PGCert 12FT 24PT

University of York
Applied Health Research .... MSc 12FT 24PT
Health Sciences.. MSc 12FT 24PT

York St John University
Professional Health and Social Care Studies.............. MSc 12-48PT

Health sciences
Research Courses

Aberystwyth University
Sport & Exercise Science .... MPhil 12FT 24PT PhD 36FT 60PT MPhil 12FT 24PT PhD 36FT 60PT

Anglia Ruskin University
Anglia Vision Research .... PhD 48 - 60FT 30-48PT
Cellular Pathology and Molecular Genetics .... PhD 24 - 60FT 36 - 72PT
Health Social Care and Education ...... MPhil 24FT 24DL/PhD 36FT
Medical Engineering...... MPhil 18 - 36FT 30 - 48PT/PhD 24 - 60FT 36 - 72PT
Professional Doctorate in Health and Social Care.........DProf 36FT 36 - 72PT

Bangor University
Health Studies/Health Science, Nursing, Midwifery, Radiography & Allied Health Professions......................................MPhil 24FT 36PT/PhD 36FT 48-60PT

University of Bath
Health.................................. MPhil 12FT 24PT/PhD 36FT 72PT
Health and Wellbeing .... MRes 12FT 24-36PT
Professional Doctorate in Health ....DHealth 24-60FT 36-96PT

University of Bolton
Health and Wellbeing Specialisms ....MPhil 18FT 24 - 42PT/PhD 36FT 60 - 72PT

University of Bradford
School of Health Studies ....PhD 36-48FT 48-60PT/MPhil 12-24FT 24-48PT

University of Brighton
Healthcare Professions Research Division PhD 24-60FT 36-72PT/MPhil 18-36FT 30-48PT

University of Bristol
Social and Community Medicine ....PhD 36FT 72PT/MSc by research 12FT 24PT/MD 24-60PT

Brunel University
Health Studies.............................. PhD 36FT 72PT/MPhil 36FT 72PT

Bucks New University
Health Studies .... PhD 36FT 48PT

University of Cambridge
Biostatistics...PhD 36FT
Epidemiology..PhD 36FT

Cardiff Metropolitan University
Health Sciences.......................................PhD 12-60FT 12-60PT

Cardiff University
Health Studies ....DHS 60-84PT
Health, Wellbeing and Social Care..... PhD 36FT possiblePT/MPhil 12FT possiblePT

University of Chester
Higher Degrees by Research .... MPhil 12 - 48FT 24 - 72PT/PhD 24 - 48FT 48 - 84PT

City University London
Institute of Health Sciences...PhD/MPhil

Coventry University
Health Studies......MSc by research 15FT 32PT/PGDip by research 12FT 18PT/PGCert by research 7FT 7PT
School of Health and Social Sciences ....PhD/MPhil

De Montfort University
Health Studies............... MPhil 12 - 24FT 24 - 48PT/PhD 24 - 36FT 48 - 72PT
Health and Applied Social Sciences .... PhD 24 - 36FT 48 -72PT/MPhil 12 - 24FT 24 - 48PT

University of Dundee
Life Sciences ....PhD 48FT
MPhil 24FT MSc by research 12FT
Life Sciences - A/Star Dundee Programme (4 year PhD) PhD 48FT
Life Sciences - EMBL Joint Programme (PhD) ....PhD 36FT
Life Sciences - Wellcome Programme (PhD) ....PhD 48FT
Social Dimensions of Health Institute .... MPhil 24FT PhD 36FT

University of East Anglia
Medicine......................................PhD 36FT 72PT/MPhil 24FT 48PT/MSc by research 12FT 24PT/MD 24PT
Occupational Therapy ...PhD 36FT 72PT/MPhil 24FT 48PT/MSc by research 12FT 24PT
Physiotherapy..............................PhD 36FT 72PT/MPhil 24FT 48PT/MSc by research 12FT 24PT

University of East London
Research Programmes..PhD/MPhil

University of Edinburgh
Clinical & Health Psychology ..... PhD 36FT 72PT/MSc by research 12FT 24PT
Dermatology.. MSc by research 12FT 24PT/PhD 36FT 72PT/MPhil 24FT 48PT
Interdisciplinary Social Sciences in Health .... PhD 36FT 72PT
Nursing Studies.................PhD 36FT 72PT/MPhil 24FT 48PT/MSc by research 12FT 24-36PT
Nursing Studies .... MSc by research 12FT 24-36PT
Public Health Policy .... MSc by research 12FT 24-36PT
Public Health Sciences .... MPhil 24FT 48PT/PhD 36FT 72PT/MSc by research 12FT 24PT
Sociology and Anthropology of Health and Illness ....MSc by research 12FT 24PT

University of Essex
Clinical Psychology...PhD 72PT/MPhil 48PT
Health Research.......................... PhD 36FT 72PT/MPhil 24FT 48PT
Health Studies........ PhD 72PT/MPhil 48PT/MSc by research 24PT
Nursing Studies....... PhD 72PT/MPhil 48PT/MSc by research 24PT
Occupational Therapy ......PhD 72PT/MPhil 48PT/MSc by research 24PT
Physiotherapy.......... PhD 72PT/MPhil 48PT/MSc by research 24PT
Public Health .... PhD 72PT/MPhil 48PT/MSc by research 24PT
Social Policy.............. PhD 72PT/MPhil 48PT/MSc by research 24PT
Speech and Language Therapy ....PhD 72PT/MPhil 48PT/MSc by research 24PT

University of Exeter
Health and Wellbeing .... MPhil 36FT 60PT/PhD 48FT 84PT
Sport and Health Sciences .... PhD 48FT 84PT/MPhil 36FT 60PT

National University of Ireland Galway
College of Medicine, Nursing and Health Sciences ....
PhD 48FT 72PT/MSc by research 24FT 48PT/MD 24FT 48PT/MAO by research 24FT 48PT

University of Glasgow
Community Based Sciences.......... PhD 36FT 60PT/MD 24FT 48PT/MSc(MedSci) by research 12FT 24PT

University of Gloucestershire
Health... PhD 30-48FT

Imperial College London
Primary Care and Population Health Science.................PhD/MPhil

University of Kent
Sport, Exercise and Health Science .. Professional Doctorate 72PT

King's College London
Health & Social Care (Research Division)........ PhD 36FT 48-72PT/MPhil 36FT 48-72PT/DHC 36FT 48-72PT
Health Service & Population Research Department ....PhD 36FT 72PT/MPhil 36FT 72PT/MDes by research 36FT 72PT

University of Leeds
Exercise and Health ....PhD 36+FT/MPhil 24FT/MSc by research 12FT
Nuffield Institute for Health........... PhD 36+FT/MPhil 24FT/MA by research 12+FT

University of Leicester
Department of Health SciencesPhD 36FT 60PT/MPhil 12FT 36PT/MD 36PT

Liverpool John Moores University
Health Sciences...MRes 12FT 24PT
Professional Doctorate, Health and Applied Social Sciences .... PDNurs 36FT 48PT/PDMidw 36FT 48PT/PDHSci 36FT 48PT

Liverpool School of Tropical Medicine
International Health.................................. PhD/MPhil/MIHR

University of Liverpool
Health Services Research.............. MPhil 12FT/PhD 36FT/MD 60FT
Obstetrics and Gynaecology........ MPhil 12FT/PhD 36FT/MD 60FT
One Health (Medical) ....MPhil 12-48FT 24-72PT/PhD 24-48FT 48-84PT/MD 24-72FT

London School of Hygiene and Tropical Medicine
Epidemiology & Population Health (Research) ..DrPH 42FT 42PT/PhD 42FT 42PT/MPhil 12FT 12PT
Infectious & Tropical Diseases (Research)....DrPH 42FT 42PT/PhD 42FT 42PT/MPhil 12FT 12PT
Public Health & Policy (Research).........DrPH 42FT 42PT/PhD 42FT 42PT/MPhil 12FT 12PT

London South Bank University
Faculty of Health & Social Care ....PhD 36FT 60PT/MPhil 24FT 36PT
Professional Doctorate for Allied Health Professions ....Doctorate 60PT

Loughborough University
Design Ergonomics .... PhD 36FT 60PT/MPhil 24FT 36PT
Environmental Ergonomics........ PhD 36FT 60PT/MPhil 24FT 36PT
Human Factors and Complex Systems ....PhD 36FT 60PT/MPhil 24FT 36PT
Transport Safety Research.......... PhD 36FT 60PT/MPhil 24FT 36PT
User Centred Design Research .. PhD 36FT 60PT/MPhil 24FT 36PT

Manchester Metropolitan University
Faculty of Health, Psychology & Social Care ....
PhD 24FT 60PT/MPhil 12FT 24PT/MA by research 12FT 24PT/MSc by research 12FT 24PT
Clinical Researc 60PT 48PT/MRes 36PT

Middlesex University
Health Studies.................PhD 36FT 60PT 33-60DL/MPhil 18-36DL
Health, including Nursing and Midwifery PhD 33-60FT 45-72DL/MPhil 18-36DL/MA by research 12-24FT 18-30DL
Health or Environment DProf 24FT 60PT/MProf by research 24FT 60PT

Newcastle University
Biological Sciences .... PhD 36FT 72PT/MPhil 12FT 24PT
Biomedicine.......MPhil 12FT 24PT/PhD 36FT 72PT/MD 24FT 48PT
Cancer..MRes 12FT
Clinical Linguistics and Evidence Based Practice (Research) .. MSc by research 12FT 24PT/PGDip by research 8FT 16PT
Diabetes...MRes 12FT
Epidemiology...MRes 12FT
Public Health, Epidemiology and Health Services Research ....
MPhil 12FT 24PT/PhD 36FT 72PT/MD 24FT 48PT
Translational Medicine and Therapeutics......................MRes 12FT

University of Northampton
Centre for Healthcare Education ....PhD 36FT 48PT/MPhil 24FT 36PT

Nottingham Trent University
Cancer Biology.. MRes 12FT 24PT

University of Nottingham
GEM research areas ...PhD 36FT 72PT/MPhil 24FT 48PT/DM 36FT 72PT
Health Science: Doctor of Health Science.........................PhD 36FT

Health sciences

Maternal and Fetal Health........PhD 36FT 72PT/MPhil 24FT 48PT/DM 36FT 72PT
Risk Analysis, Social Processes and Health ....MPhil 36FT/PhD 24FT
Social Research in Medicines and Health..............PhD 36FT 72PT/MPhil 36FT

The Open University
Biomedical Sciences.............................. PhD 36FT 72PT variableDL/MPhil 15FT 24PT
Health, Social Work and Social Care.. PhD 36FT 72PT variableDL/MPhil 15FT 24PT variableDL
Reproductive and Sexual Health........ PhD 36FT 72PT variableDL/MPhil 15FT 24PT variableDL

Oxford Brookes University
Biological Sciences - Biofilm Development .... PhD 24-60FT 36-72PT/MPhil 24-36FT 36-48PT
Biological Sciences - Bioprocess Research .... PhD 24-60FT 36-72PT/MPhil 24-36FT 36-48PT
Biological Sciences - Cell Systems Modelling .... PhD 24-60FT 36-72PT/MPhil 24-36FT 36-48PT
Biological Sciences - Environmental Ecology .... PhD 24-60FT 36-72PT/MPhil 24-36FT 36-48PT
Biological Sciences - Evolutionary Developmental Biology ....PhD 24-60FT 36-72PT/MPhil 24-36FT 36-48PT
Biological Sciences - Invertebrate Ecology and Biogeography .... PhD 24-60FT 36-72PT/MPhil 24-36FT 36-48PT
Biological Sciences - Plant Cell Biology ..... PhD 24-60FT 36-72PT/MPhil 24-36FT 36-48PT
Biological Sciences - Spatial Ecology and Land Use .... PhD 24-60FT 36-72PT/MPhil 24-36FT 36-48PT
Biological and Biomedical Science .....PhD 36FT 48PT/MPhil 24FT 36PT
Health & Biomedical Sciences - Glycobiology and Cancer .....PhD 24-60FT 36-72PT/MPhil 24-36FT 36-48PT
Health & Biomedical Sciences - Human Health & Performance Research Group ... PhD 24-60FT 36-72PT/MPhil 24-36FT 36-48PT
Health & Biomedical Sciences - Molecular Neuroscience ......PhD 24-60FT 36-72PT/MPhil 24-36FT 36-48PT
Health Care Studies MPhil/PhD........ PhD 24-60FT 36-72PT/MPhil 24-36FT 36-48PT
Health and Biomedical Sciences - Cell Biology of Trypanosomes .... PhD 24-60FT 36-72PT/MPhil 24-36FT 36-48PT
Health and Biomedical Sciences - Cell Systems Modelling ....PhD 24-60FT 36-72PT/MPhil 24-36FT 36-48PT
Health and Biomedical Sciences - Chromatin and Non-coding ... PhD 24-60FT 36-72PT/MPhil 24-36FT 36-48PT
Health and Biomedical Sciences - Genomic Instability ....PhD 24-60FT 36-72PT/MPhil 24-36FT 36-48PT
Health and Biomedical Sciences - Insect Virology & Protein Expression .... PhD 24-60FT 36-72PT/MPhil 24-36FT 36-48PT
Health and Biomedical Sciences - Movement Science ....PhD 24-60FT 36-72PT/MPhil 24-36FT 36-48PT
Health and Biomedical Sciences - Peptide Transport ..MPhil/PhD 36-60FT 48-72PT/PhD 24-60FT 36-72PT/MPhil 24-36FT 36-48PT
Health and Biomedical Sciences - The Functional Food Centre .... PhD 24-60FT 36-72PT/MPhil 24-36FT 36-48PT

Plymouth University
Developmental Disability Research & Education Group...... MPhil tbcFT
Dietetics and Health.. MPhil tbcFT
Rehabilitation Research Group .... MPhil tbcFT

University of Portsmouth
Health Sciences and Social Work.........MPhil 24FT 48PT/PhD 36FT 72PT/MD 24FT 48PT
Health Science... DHealthSci 48PT

Queen's University Belfast
Public Health ... PhD 36FT 72PT/MD 24FT 48PT/MPhil 24FT 48PT/MCh by research 12FT 24PT

University of Roehampton
Health Sciences.... PhD 24-48FT 36-60PT/MPhil 21-36FT 36-60PT

University of Salford
Health Informatics............. PhD 36FT 60PT/MSc by research 24PT

Sheffield Hallam University
Division of Nursing and Social Work ....PhD/MPhil
Professions Allied to Medicine..PhD/MPhil

University of Sheffield
Health and Related Research..... PhD 36FT 72PT/MPhil 24FT 48PT

University of Southampton
Doctorate in Clinical Practice .... PhD 36FT 72PT
Research Methods in Health ....MSc by research 24PT/PGDip by research 12PT/PGCert by research 6PT
Research Methods in Health ....MSc by research 24PT/PGDip by research 12PT/PGCert by research 6PT
School of Health Professions and Rehabilitation Sciences......PhD 36FT 72PT/MPhil 36FT 60PT

St George's, University of London
Cardiovascular Medicine ....PhD 36FT 84PT/MPhil 24FT 48PT/MDRes 24PT
Community Health Sciences .... PhD 36FT 72PT/MPhil 24FT 48PT/MD(Res) 24 minFT 48 minPT
Mental health......... PhD 36FT 72PT/MPhil 24FT 48PT/MD(Res) 24 minFT 48 minPT

St Loye's School of Occupational Therapy
Health Studies.. PhD 72FT/MPhil

Staffordshire University
Health Studies.............................. MPhil 24FT 36PT/PhD 36FT 60PT

University of Surrey
Health and Medical Sciences..... PhD 36FT 60PT/MPhil 24FT 48PT

Swansea University
Ageing Studies .... MPhil 24FT 48PT/PhD 36FT 72PT
Childhood Studies ....MPhil 12FT/PhD 36FT
Health Science.............................. PhD 36FT 60PT/MPhil 24FT 48PT
Intelligent Wireless Networks for Healthcare......MSc by research 12FT 24PT

Teesside University
Community-Based Clinical Subjects...PhD 36FT 72PT/MPhil 24FT 48PT/DProf 36FT 60PT
School of Health and Social Care.........PhD 36FT 72PT/MPhil 24FT 48PT/DProf 36FT 60PT/MProf by research 30PT

University of Ulster
Master of Research ....MRes 12FT

UCL - University College London
Cancer.. PhD 36FT 60PT
Health Informatics... PhD 36FT 60PT
Infection and Immunity... PhD 36FT 60PT
Infection and Population Health.... PhD 36FT 60PT/MD(Res) 24FT 24PT
Mental Health Sciences ....PhD 36FT 60PT/MD(Res) 24FT 24PT
Primary Health Care and Population Sciences......PhD 36FT 60PT/MD(Res) 24FT 24PT

University of Warwick
Health and Social Studies .. PhD 36FT 60PT/MPhil 24FT 36PT/MA by research 12FT 24PT

University of West London
Health Science.. (PD) 33FT 45PT

University of the West of Scotland
Department of Nursing, Midwifery and Health Care ..PhD/MPhil

University of the West of England, Bristol
Faculty of Health and Life Sciences....................................... PhD .FT
School of Health and Social Care..................................... PhD TBCFT
School of Life Sciences...PhD -FT

University of Westminster
Health Sciences... DProf 48-96PT

University of Wolverhampton
Health and Wellbeing .... DProf 72PT

University of Worcester
Doctor of Health Science (DHSc) ....DHSci 36PT
Health Science.............................. PhD 48FT 70PT/MPhil 24FT 48PT

University of York
Health Sciences............................ PhD 36FT 72PT/MPhil 24FT 48PT

York St John University
Health & Life Science.............PhD 12-36FT/MPhil 12-36FT/MA by research 12-36FT

Health services management
Taught Courses

University of Aberdeen
Health Services and Public Health Research ....MSc 12FT 24PT/PGDip 9FT 21PT
International Healthcare Management .....MBA 12FT/PGDip 9FT/PGCert 6FT
Public Health Nutrition.................MSc 12FT 24PT/PGDip 9FT 18PT

Anglia Ruskin University
Advanced Practice .... MSc 12FT 24PT
Healthcare Management...MSc 24DL
Hospital Management.. MBA 12FT 24PT

Bangor University
Health Science..................................MSc 12FT 24 - 60PT/PGDip 9FT
Health Studies/Health Science, Nursing, Midwifery, Radiography and Allied Health Professio.............PhD by taught 36FT 48-60PT/MPhil 24FT 36PT
Health and Social Care Leadership.................. MSc 12FT 24 - 60PT/PGDip 9FT
Policy Research and Evaluation........ MA 12FT 21-30PT/PGDip 9FT 17-21PT/PGCert 5FT 12-21PT
Public Health and Health Promotion .... MSc 12FT 24 - 60PT/PGDip 9FT
Risk Management in Health and Social Care......MSc 36PT/PGDip 24PT/PGCert 12PT
Social Policy, Sociology. PhD by taught 36FT 60PT/MPhil 12-24FT 24-36PT

University of Bedfordshire
Enhancing Quality Through Patient Safety ....MSc 12FT 24PT/PGCert 12FT 24PT/PGDip 12FT 24PT
Leadership in Healthcare Practice..................................... MSc 24PT
Medical Education Leadership ....PGCert 12-36PT
Medical Stimulation ....PGCert 12-36PT

Birmingham City University
Dimensions in Healthcare.......................PGCert 12PT/PGCert 36PT
Health and Social Care (Leadership)........PGDip 12PT/PGDip 36PT

University of Birmingham
Health Care Policy and Management .....MSc 12FT 24PT/GradDip 9FT 21PT
Leadership and Management for Social Care ...... MA 36PT/PGDip 24PT
Leadership and Management for Social Work..... PGDip 18PT/MA 36PT
Leadership for Health Services Improvement.................. MSc 24PT
Managing Integration for Health and Well-beingMSc 12FT 24PT/PGDip 12FT 24PT

University of Bolton
Leadership in Health and Social Care..MSc 36-60PT/PGDip 24PT/PGCert 12PT

Bournemouth University
Leading and Developing Services...MA 36PT

University of Bradford
Diversity Management .... MSc 24PT
Health and Social Care Management ....MSc 24-36PT/PGDip 12-24PT/PGCert 9-12PT
Leadership, Management and Change............MSc 12FT 24 - 60PT

University of Brighton
Clinical Studies and Management..... MSc 12FT 24 - 72PT/PGCert 12FT 24 - 72PT/PGDip 12FT 24 - 72PT
Food Services and Wellbeing Management ... MSc 12FT 24-72PT/PGDip 12FT 24-72PT/PGCert 12FT 24-72PT
Health Promotion and Management...MA 12FT 24 - 72PT/PGDip 12FT 24 - 72PT
Physiotherapy and Management............ MSc 12 - 24FT 24 - 72PT/PGCert 12 - 24FT 24 - 72PT/PGDip 12 - 24FT 24 - 72PT
Public Service Management ...MBA 18FT 36PT/PGDip 18FT 24PT/PGCert 18FT 24PT

Brunel University
Ageing Studies ....PGCert 12PT/PGDip 24PT/MSc 36PT

Bucks New University
Leadership & Management in the Public Sector...............MA 24PT

University of Central Lancashire
Advanced Practice (Health and Social Care)..................... MSc 24PT
Advanced Stroke Practice ......MSc 36FT 60PT/PGDip 24PT/PGCert 12PT
Clinical Leadership for Practice Innovation...................Module 4PT
Integrated Healthcare by elearning.....MSc 36-48PT/PGDip 24PT/PGCert 12PT

University of Chester
Health Care Leadership (Work Based and Integrative Studies) ....MA 24-72PT/MSc 24-72PT/PGDip 24-60PT/PGCert 12-36PT
Health and Social Care - Commissioning.............PGCert 12 - 36PT
Public Services Management (Work Based and Integrative Studies) ....MA 24-72PT/PGDip 24-60PT/PGCert 12-36PT

University of Chichester
Management (Health and Social Care Services) .... MA 27PT/PGDip 18PT/PGCert 12PT

City University London
Clinical Leadership for Allied Health Professionals ....MSc 24PT/PGCert 12PT/PGDip 24PT
Health Management in Strategic Management and Leadership.. MSc 12FT 24PT
Health Services Research............. MSc 12FT 24PT/MRes 12FT 24PT

Cranfield University
Clinical Research ...... MSc 12FT 36PT/PGCert 9FT 24PT/PGDip 6FT 24PT
Clinical Research Executive .... MSc 36PT/PGDip 9FT 24-36PT/PGCert 6FT 12-24PT
Clinical Research Management ....MSc 12FT 36PT/PGDip 12FT 36PT
Health Administration ...MSc 12FT 24-36PT/PGDip 12FT 24-36PT

University of Cumbria
Advanced Practice in Health and Social Care ....MSc 24 - 60PT
Leadership in Health and Social Care.................... MBA 12FT 36PT/PGDip 12FT 36PT/PGCert 12FT 36PT

De Montfort University
Clinically-Led Commissioning ....PGCert 12PT
Foundation In Professional Practice .....PGCert 12PT/PGCert 12PT

University of Derby
Clinical Supervision.. PGCert 12PT 12DL
Community Specialist Practice ....MSc 12FT 24PT
Management of Long Term Conditions........................PGCert 12PT

University of Dundee
Clinical Audit and Research for Allied Healthcare Professionals .... PGCert 6DL
Quality Improvement ....MSc 36DL PGCert 12DL PGDip 24DL

University of East London
Leadership and Team Development ....PGCert 5FT 12 - 36PT
Planning and Developing Health Care ....PGCert 5FT 12-36PT

Edge Hill University
Leadership Development (Clinical Leadership / Leadership and

Health sciences

Management) .... MSc 36-72PT

University of Edinburgh
Health Systems and Public Policy .... MSc 12FT 24-36PT
Integrated Service Improvement: Health and Social Care...... MSc 24-36PT/PGDip 20PT/PGCert 12PT

University of Essex
Health Care Management .... Diploma 18-60PT/MSc 24-60PT
Health Services Management .... Prof Doc 48-84PT
Public Health Management .... MSc 24-60PT/Diploma 18-60PT/Cert 12-60PT
Social Care Practice Management .... Prof Doc 48-84PT
Social Services Management .... Prof Doc 48-84PT

National University of Ireland Galway
Health Services Research .... MHSc 24PT/PGDip 24PT

Glasgow Caledonian University
Advanced Practice with Older People .... MSc 12FT
Advancing Practice in Primary Care .... MSc 24FT
Counselling Skills in Health and Social Care .... PGCert 12-24FT
Diagnostic Imaging .... MSc 12-24FT
Musculoskeletal Management .... MSc 36-72PT
Optimal Heart Failure Care .... MSc 12FT
Perinatal Mental Health .... MSc 12FT
Professional Doctorate for Health, Social Care Sector and Nursing Professionals .... DProf by taught 48FT
Public Health with Social Action .... MSc 12FT
Radiatiotherapy and Oncology .... MSc 12-24FT
Telehealthcare .... MSc 12FT

University of Glasgow
Mental Health, Global....MSc 12FT 24PT/PGDip 9FT 18PT/PGCert 9FT 18PT
Public Policy & Management ... MSc 12FT 24PT 60BM/PGDip 9FT 21PT

University of Greenwich
Professional Practice in Health & Social Care .... MA 12FT 24PT 27DL/PGDip 12FT 24PT 27DL

Imperial College London
International Health Management .... MSc 12FT

Keele University
Health Executive .... MBA 30PT
Health Services Management .... PGDip 24PT

King's College London
Advanced Practice (Leadership)..... MSc 36-72PT/PGDip 24-72PT/PGCert 12-72PT
Public Services Policy & Management .... MSc 12FT 24PT

Kingston University
Biomedical Science with Management Studies.... MSc 12FT 24PT
Clinical Leadership .... MSc 24PT
Leadership and Management in Health....... MSc 12FT 24-48PT/PGDip 12FT 24-48PT/PGCert 12FT 24-48PT

Lancaster University
Medical Leadership .... PGCert 12PT
Organisational Change (Health Care) .... PGCert 12PT

Leeds Metropolitan University
Environmental Health .... MSc 12FT 36PT
Public Health (Health Promotion and Environmental Health) Zambia .... MSc 36PT

University of Leeds
Health Management, Planning and PolicyPGCert 3FT/PGDip 9FT/MA 12FT
Hospital Management .... PGCert 3FT/PGDip 9FT/MA 12FT
Patient Safety and Clinical Risk Management .... PGCert 4FT

Liverpool John Moores University
Advanced Healthcare Practice .... MSc 36PT
International Public Health .... MSc 12FT 24PT

London College UCK
Leadership and Management in the Health and Social Care Sector .... PGDip 12FT 24PT

London School of Economics and Political Science (LSE)
Health Policy, Planning and Financing .... MSc 12FT 24PT
International Health Policy .... MSc 12FT 24PT
Public Management and Governance .... MSc 12FT

London School of Hygiene and Tropical Medicine
Health Policy, Planning and Financing .... MSc 12FT 24PT
Public Health (Environment & Health) .... MSc 12FT 24PT
Public Health (Health Economics) .... MSc 12FT 24PT
Public Health (Health Services Management) .... MSc 12FT 24PT
Public Health (Health Services Research) .... MSc 12FT 24PT

London South Bank University
Construction Project Management (Health Care) .... MSc 24PT
International Health Services and Hospital Management..... MSc 15FT

University of Manchester
Healthcare Management .... MSc 12FT

Middlesex University
Development with Work Experience .... MA 12-15FT 24PT
Development with Work-based Learning .... MA 12-15FT 24PT
Leading and Developing Public and Community Services, ... PGCert 12PT/AdvDip 12PT

Managing Major Projects .... PGCert 9DL
Managing Major Projects and Programmes .... MSc 24PT

University of Northampton
Healthcare Management .... MBA 24PT
Leadership for Health and Social Care .... PGCert 12PT

Northumbria University
Master of Clinical Practice (Advanced Critical Care Practice)...MA 36FT
Systemic Teaching, Training and Supervision .... MA 24PT

Nottingham Trent University
Public Services Management .... MSc 12PT/PGDip 12PT/PGCert 12PT

University of Nottingham
Clinical Leadership for Innovative Practice Certificate....... PGCert 12-24PT

The Open University
Advancing Healthcare Practice..PGCert 12DL/PGDip variableDL/MSc variableDL
Advancing Professional Practice .... MSc variableDL
Clinical Leadership .... PGCert 12DL

Oxford Brookes University
Management in Health and Social Care .... MSc 12FT 30-36PT/PGCert 12FT 12PT/PGDip 12FT 12-18PT

Plymouth University
Healthcare Strategy & Performance .... MSc 24PT

University of Portsmouth
Leadership in Health and Wellbeing .... MSc 36PT

Queen Margaret University, Edinburgh
Human Resources for Health .... MSc 12FT 24PT/PGDip 8FT 16PT/PGCert 4FT 8PT
Public Services Governance .... PGCert 12FT 24-84PT

Queen Mary, University of London
Health Systems and Global Policy .... MSc 12FT 24-48PT

Royal College of Nursing
Advancing Healthcare Pratice .... MSc 23-50DL

Royal Holloway, University of London
Leadership & Management in Health .... MSc 12FT 24PT

University of Salford
Advanced Practice (Health and Social Care) .... MSc 24PT/PGDip 18PT/PGCert 12PT
International Hospital and Health Service Leadership and Management .... MSc 12FT/PGDip 8FT/PGCert 4FT
Leadership and Management for Healthcare Practice.. MSc 12FT 36PT/PGDip 8FT 24PT/PGCert 4FT 9PT
Public Health .... MSc 12FT 36PT/PGDip 8FT 24PT/PGCert 9PT

Sheffield Hallam University
Health and Social Care Leadership .... MSc 36PT/PGDip 24PT/PGCert 12PT
Nutrition with Public Health Management .... MSc 12FT

University of Sheffield
International Development .... MPH 12FT 24PT
International Health Technology Assessment..... MSc 24-60 PTDL
Public Health .... MPH 12FT 24-36PT
Public Health (Health Services Research) .... MPH 12FT 24-36PT
Public Health (Management and Leadership) .... MPH 12FT 24-36PT

University of South Wales
Health & Public Service Management .... MSc 12FT 36PT/PGCert 4FT 12PT/PGDip 8FT 24PT
Leadership and Management (Health Promotion & Education).. MA 36-60PT

University of Southampton
Clinical Leadership in Cancer, Palliative and End of Life Care MSc 24FT 48PT
Leadership and Management Health and Social Care... MSc 12FT 48PT

Staffordshire University
Health Management and Policy (Distance Learning) .... PGCert 12PT/PGDip 24PT/MA 36PT

University of Stirling
Applied Studies (Management and Leadership in Social Services) MSc 30PT/PGDip 24PT/PGCert 12PT

University of Surrey
Advanced Practice .... MSc 12FT 24PT
Health Care Management .... MSc 12FT 24PT 24DL

University of Sussex
Leadership and Management in Integrated Children's Services... MA 60PT/PGDip 60PT/PGCert 60PT

Swansea University
Healthcare Management .... MSc 12FT 36PT
Public Health and Partnerships in Care .... MSc 12FT 36PT

Teesside University
Leadership in Health and Social Care .... PGCert 12PT
Transformational Leadership in Health and Social Care .... MSc 36PT

Trinity College Dublin - the University of Dublin
Health Services Management .... MSc 24PT

University of the Highlands and Islands
Chartered Management Institute - Diploma Public Service Leadership .... Chartered Management Institute 12PT

University of Ulster
Health Communication .... PGDip 9FT 18PT/MSc 12FT 24PT

UCL - University College London
CYP IAPT Management .... PGCert 12FT
International Health Euro .... MSc 12FT

University of Warwick
Accounting and Finance in Health Service Organisations .... PGA 12PT/CPDMod 1PT
Child Health Services: Management, Organisations and Data Systems .... PGA 12PT/CPDMod 1PT
Clinical Quality Improvement and Risk Management..PGA 12PT/CPDMod 1PT
Health Sciences: Health Services Management .... MSc 36PT/PGDip 24PT/PGCert 12PT/PGA 12PT
Health Services Management .... MSc 36PT/PGDip 24PT/PGCert 12PT
International Health Policy .... PGA 12PT/cpdmod 1PT
Introduction to Management in Health Service Organisations.... PGA 12PT/CPDMod 1PT
Managing People in Health Service Organisations .... PGA 12PT/CPDMod 1PT
Models of Emergency Care .... PGA 12PT/CPDMod 1PT
Organisational Behaviour and Health Service Policy....PGA 12PT/CPDMod 1PT

University of West London
Health and Social Care Leadership .... MSc 24PT
Management Studies (Health and Social Care) .... PGDip 24PT
Top up .... MA 12PT

University of the West of England, Bristol
Leadership and Management in Health and Social Care .... MSc 33PT

University of Westminster
Integrated Governance in Health in Healthcare Communities..... MSc 24-60PT

University of Worcester
MBA in Executive Leadership & Management (Health & Social Care) .... MBA 12FT 36PT

Health services management
Research Courses

Anglia Ruskin University
Health Social Care and Education .... MPhil 24FT 24DL/PhD 36FT

Bangor University
Health Studies/Health Science, Nursing, Midwifery, Radiography & Allied Health Professions .... MPhil 24FT 36PT/PhD 36FT 48-60PT
Social Policy .... PhD 36FT 60PT/MPhil 12-24FT 24-36PT

University of Birmingham
Health Services Management..PhD 36FT 72PT/MPhil 24FT 48PT/MSc by research 12FT

University of Brighton
Applied Social Sciences Division....... PhD 24-60FT 36-72PT/MPhil 18-36FT 30-48PT
School of Service Management Research Student Division....PhD 48FT 60PT/MPhil 24FT 36PT

University of Bristol
Social Science (Policy Studies Doctorate) .... DSocSci 36FT 96PT

City University London
Health Management and Food Policy..MSc by research/MHM by research

University of Dundee
Social Dimensions of Health Institute .... MPhil 24FT PhD 36FT

Keele University
Health Management Professional Doctorate .... DBA 48-84PT
Health Policy and Governance/Public Policy .... PhD 24-48FT 48-96PT/MPhil 12-24FT 24-36PT

University of Leeds
Nuffield Institute for Health....... PhD 36+FT/MPhil 24FT/MA by research 12+FT
Public Management .... PhD 36FT 60PT

London School of Hygiene and Tropical Medicine
Public Health & Policy (Research) .... DrPH 42FT 42PT/PhD 42FT 42PT/MPhil 12FT 12PT

University of Nottingham
Public Policy - Professional Doctorate in Public Policy .... PDPP 48-96PT

The Open University
Public Leadership and Social Enterprise .... PhD 36FT 72PT variableDL/MPhil 15FT 24PT variableDL

University of Oxford
Public Health .... DPhil 48FT/MSc by research 24FT

Health sciences

Plymouth University
Professional and Organisational Issues........................MPhil tbcFT

University of Sheffield
Public Health: Integrated Studies.................New Route PhD 48FT

University of Surrey
Health Care.................................. PhD 36FT 48PT/MPhil 24FT 36PT
Health Care Management......... PhD 36FT 48PT/MPhil 24FT 36PT

University of West London
Service Management (Health and Social Care).......... Professional Doctorate (PD) 33FT 45PT

University of Westminster
Health Sciences.. DProf 48-96PT

Herbalism
Taught Courses

University of Central Lancashire
Herbal Medicine by elearning..............MSc 36-48PT/PGDip 24PT/PGCert 12PT

School of Oriental and African Studies - SOAS
Medical Anthropology .... MA 12FT 24-36PT

University of Westminster
Chinese Herbal Medicine ....MSc 12FT 24PT
Herbal Medicine ....MSc 12FT 24PT

Homeopathy
Taught Courses

University of Central Lancashire
Homeopathy by e-learning....MSc 36PT 36DL/PGDip 24PT 24DL/PGCert 12PT 12DL

Medical teaching
Taught Courses

Anglia Ruskin University
Medical & Healthcare Education ....MSc 12FT 36PT

Bangor University
Medical Education Practice...PGCert 12FT

University of Bedfordshire
Academic and Clinical Education (BSO).......................PGCert 12PT
Medical Education............................ MA 24-60PT/PGCert 24-60PT/PGDip 24-60PT
Medical Education Leadership...................................PGCert 12-36PT
Medical Stimulation ....PGCert 12-36PT

Birmingham City University
Practice Teacher Preparations ....PGCert 12DL

University of Birmingham
Education for Health Professionals.......PGCert 12PT/PGDip 24PT/MEd 36PT

University of Bolton
Teaching and Learning for Professional Practice........PGCert 12PT

University of Brighton
Clinical Education..PGCert 24PT
MA 36 - 72PT/PGDip 36 - 72PT
Health and Social Care Education ....PGCert 12 - 18PT
Medical Education...PGCert 12PT
Teaching in Clinical Settings...................................PGCert 12 - 24PT

University of Bristol
Teaching and Learning for Health Professionals....MSc 12 - 24FT/Diploma 12 - 36FT/Cert 12 - 36FT

Cardiff University
Medical Education...MSc 12FT 24PT
Medical Education (e-Learning).... PGCert 12FT/PGDip 12FT/MSc 12FT

University of Central Lancashire
Enhancing Learning, Teaching and Assessing in Multi-professional Practice ....Uni Cert 3PT
Nursing ....MSc 12FT 24-60PT
Research for Professional Practice ... Professional Doctorate 24PT

University of Chester
Health and Social Care - Education for Postgraduate Medical Practice.. MA 24 - 72PT

University of Dundee
Advanced Practice (Clinical Governance) ....MSc 36DL
Medical Education ....MMedEd 12FT

Durham University
Medical Education...MSc 12FT 24PT

University of East Anglia
Clinical Education..............MClinEd 12FT 36PT/PGDip 12FT 24PT/PGCert 12PT

Edge Hill University
Clinical Education... MA 24-60PT
Teaching and Learning in Clinical Practice........................PGCert 12PT
Workplace-based Postgraduate Medical Education........... PGCert 12-36DL

Edinburgh Napier University
Advanced Practice and Applied Education (Distance Learning).... Msc/PGDip/PGCert 36PT

University of Edinburgh
Clinical Education (Online Distance learning) ... MSc 36DL/PGDip 24PT 24DL/PGCert 12PT 12DL
Medical Sciences...MMedSci 12FT

National University of Ireland Galway
Nursing (Education)...PGDip 12FT

Glasgow Caledonian University
Medical Ultrasound ....MSc 12-24FT
Professional Doctorate for Health, Social Care Sector and Nursing Professionals...................................... DProf by taught 48FT

University of Glasgow
Leadership Drugs & Alcohol Setting .... PGCert 9FT 18PT

Glyndwr University
Professional Education.......... MSc 12FT 24-60PT/DipMedEd 24FT 24-36PT/CertMedEd 6FT 12PT

Goldsmiths, University of London
Practice Education..............................MA 36-60PT/PGDip 36-60PT/PGCert 36-60PT

University of Hertfordshire
Health and Medical Education. MA 15FT 60PT/PGDip 15FT 60PT/PGCert 15FT 60PT
Supervision of Midwives .... PGCert 1BM

Institute of Education
Clinical Education... MA 12FT 24PT

Keele University
Medical Education........................ MA 60PT/PGDip 60PT/Cert 60PT

University of Kent
Strategic Leadership and Medical Education ......PGCert 12 - 24PT

King's College London
Clinical Nursing for International Students....... MSc 12FT/PGCert 12FT
Clinical Pedagogy ....MA 24PT/PGDip 18PT/PGCert 12PT
Education for Healthcare Professionals......MSc 12FT 36PT/PGDip 12FT 36PT

Leeds Metropolitan University
Professional Development..PGCert 12PT

University of Leeds
Clinical Education...MEd 36PT/PGCert 12PT

LUniversity of Manchester
Medical Education...........................MSc 12-36PT/PGCert 12-36PT/PGDip 12-36PT

Newcastle University
Clinical Education........... MClinEd 12FT 12-24PT/PGDip 12-24PT/PGCert 12PT
Medical Sciences.. MSc 12FT

Northumbria University
Education in Professional Practice............MSc 36PT/PGDip 24PT/PGCert 12PT
Nursing ....Professional Doctorate 48-72PT
Systemic Teaching, Training and Supervision ....MA 24PT

University of Nottingham
Medical Education... MMedSci 12FT 24PT

Oxford Brookes University
Medical & Dental Education (a collaborative programme with Oxford PGMDE).. PGCert 9PT

Peninsula College of Medicine and Dentistry
Clinical Education Research/Clinical Education Practice.... PGCert 12PT/PGDip 24PT/MClinEd 36PT

Plymouth University
Clinical Education...........MClinEd 36PT/PGDip 24PT/PGCert 12PT
Simulation and Patient Safety .... MSc 36FT

Queen Mary, University of London
Health Systems and Global Policy......................MSc 12FT 24-48PT

Queen's University Belfast
Clinical Education..........MMedSci 36PT/PGDip 24PT/PGCert 12PT

Robert Gordon University
Advanced Clinical Practice ... MSc 36PT/PGDip 24PT/PGCert 12PT

University Campus Suffolk
Clinical Effectiveness.. MA Max 60FT
Healthcare Education................MA 18PT/PGCert 18PT/PGDip 18PT

University of Salford
Nursing (Education, International, Practice, Research) .... MSc 12FT 36PT/PGDip 9FT 24PT/PGCert 6FT 12PT
Professional Doctorate (Health and Social Care) ... PhD by taught 60PT

Sheffield Hallam University
Clinical Education.................. MSc 24PT/PGDip 24PT/PGCert 12PT
Health Care Education (including teacher status for health professionals) ....MSc variablePT
Healthcare Education...........MSc VAPT/PGDip VAPT/PGCert VAPT

University of Sheffield
Europubhealth: European Masters Programme in Public Health. MPH 24FT
Medical Education..PGCert 12-24PT

University of South Wales
Education for Health and Social Care Professionals......MSc 12PT/PGCert 12PT

University of Southampton
Education for Health Professionals...... MSc 12FT 24PT/PGDip 9FT 18PT/PGCert 5PT

St George's, University of London
Clinical Practice..MRes 12FT 24PT

Staffordshire University
Advanced Clinical Practice ....PGCert 12PT/PGDip 24PT/MSc 36PT
Postgraduate Certificate in Medical Education ....MSc 36PT/PGCert 24PT/PGDip 12PT

University of Stirling
Psychological Therapy in Primary Care .... MSc 12FT

University of Surrey
Learning and Teaching for Professional Practice...... PGCert 12PT/PGDip 24PT/MSc 36PT/Practice Teacher 4PT

Teesside University
Advanced Clinical Practice (Cardiac Care) .... MSc 36PT
Advanced Clinical Practice (Management of Long-term Health Conditions).. MSc 36PT
Advanced Clinical Practice (Manipulative Therapy) .... MSc 36PT
Advanced Clinical Practice (Neurolgical Rehabilitation)MSc 36PT
Clinical Research ....MRes 18FT 36PT
Doctor of Health and Social Care ....DProf by taught 72PT

University of Ulster
Education (Primary) ....PGCE 9FT
Education for Nurses and Midwives.............................PGCert 12PT

UCL - University College London
Medical Education.................. MSc 36PT/PGDip 24PT/PGCert 12PT

University of Warwick
Learning in Practice...................................... PGA 12PT/CPDMod 1PT
Medical Education.................PGA 12PT/MA 36-96PT/MSc 36-96PT

University of Winchester
Education: Early Years, School, College and Workplace Educators' Pathway .... MA(Ed) up to 60PT
Medical Education...MA 36PT

Medical teaching
Research Courses

University of Dundee
Dental School (Clinical 4 year PhD).......................................PhD 48FT
Dental School (Clinical 5 year PhD).......................................PhD 60FT
Dental School (Clinical MDSc by research) .... MDSc by research 12FT
Dental School (Non-clinical MDSc by research)................................ MDSc by research 12FT

University of Edinburgh
Medical Sciences............PhD 36FT 72PT/MPhil 24FT 36PT/MSc by research 12FT 24PT
Medical Sciences (MMedSci) ......MMedSci by research 12FT 24PT

King's College London
Medical Education (Research Division)......... MPhil 36FT 48-72PT/PhD 36FT 48-72PT

University of Liverpool
Medical Education................MPhil 12-48FT 48-72PT/PhD 24-48FT 48-84PT/MD 24-72FT

Newcastle University
Clinical Linguistics and Evidence Based Practice (Research) .. MSc by research 12FT 24PT/PGDip by research 8FT 16PT

University of Nottingham
Education and Technology for Health.................................PhD 36FT

UCL - University College London
Medical Education.. PhD 36FT 60PT

Mental health care
Taught Courses

University of Aberdeen
Patient Safety: A Clinical Human Factors Approach..... MRes 12FT

Anglia Ruskin University
Mental Health Services..PGCert 36PT

Bangor University
Applied Behaviour Analysis ....PGCert 4FT 9PT/PGDip 9FT 18PT/MSc 12FT 24PT
Psychology.. MRes 12FT/PGCert 3FT

Barts and the London School of Medicine and Dentistry
Transcultural Mental health..... MSc 12FT 24PT/PGDip 12FT 24PT

University of Bedfordshire
Psychosocial Interventions...PGCert 12FT

Birmingham City University
Mental Health .... MSc 24PT/PGDip 18PT/PGCert 12PT

Health sciences

Bournemouth University
Advanced Mental Health Practice..MA 36PT/PGDip 36PT/PGCert 36PT

University of Bradford
Mental Health Practice .... MA 12FT/PGDip 12FT
Mental Health Studies.......MA 12FT 24PT/PGCert 9PT/PGDip 9FT 21PT

University of Brighton
Mental Health .... MSc 24 - 72PT/PGCert 24 - 72PT/PGDip 24 - 72PT

University of Central Lancashire
Advanced Legal Practice ....LLM 12FT 24PT/PGDip 12FT
Advanced Practice (Health and Social Care)..................... MSc 24PT
Advanced Stroke Practice......MSc 36FT 60PT/PGDip 24PT/PGCert 12PT
Health & Social Care Education......................................PGCert 12PT
Health Informatics..MSc 33PT/PGDip 24PT
Health and Social Care Education.................................PGCert 12PT
Mental Health Practice (Including approved mental health professional training).........................MA 12-60PT/PGDip 12-60PT/PGCert 12PT
Personality Disorder ....PGCert 12PT
Personality Disorder (Practice Development) .... MSc 36-60PT/PGDip 24PT
Personality Disorder (Research).......MSc 36-60PT/PGDip 12-24PT
Philosophy & Mental Health.......................MA 36DL/PGDip 24DL/PGCert 12DL
Primary Care Mental Health Practice...........................PGCert 12PT
Psychology.......MSc 12FT 24PT/PGDip 9FT 24PT/PGCert 9FT 24PT
Psychology of Child Development.......MSc 12FT 24PT/PGDip 9FT 24PT/PGCert 9FT 24PT
Social Psychology...MSc 12FT 24PT

University of Chester
Health and Social Care - Advanced Practice .... MSc 24 - 72PT/PGDip 24 - 60PT/PGCert 12 - 36PT
Health and Social Care - Art Therapy ....MA 24 - 72PT/PGDip 24 - 60PT/PGCert 12 - 36PT
Health and Social Care - Intercultural Psychotherapy: Theory and Research....................... MSc 12FT 24 - 72PT/PGDip 12FT 24 - 60PT/PGCert 12FT 12 - 36PT
Health and Social Care - Multi-Method Therapy.....MA 24 - 72PT/PGDip 24 - 60PT/PGCert 12 - 36PT

City University London
Adult Nursing (Graduate Entry).......................................PGDip 36FT
Mental Health Nursing (Graduate Entry)......................PGDip 24FT

University of Cumbria
Advanced Practice in Health and Social Care...........MSc 24 - 60PT
Community Specailist Practice Nursing..................PGDE 9FT 18PT
Mental Health Practice: Approved Medical Health Practitioner... MA min 24FT max 60PT/PGCert 12FT/PGDip 12FT

University of Dundee
Advanced Practice (Mental Health) ....MSc 36DL

University of East Anglia
Clinical Science..MRes 12FT
Mental Health..... MSc 12FT 36PT/PGDip 12FT 24PT/PGCert 12PT
Occupational Therapy .... MSc 24FT

University of East London
Approved Mental Health Practice (AMHP) ....PGDip 8FT
Child and Adolescent Primary Mental Health Care Work ....MA 36PT/PGDip 24PT/PGCert 12PT
Infant Mental Health (Early Years Development) M9 ...MA 36PT/PGDip 24PT/PGCert 12PT

Edinburgh Napier University
Advanced Practice in Intellectual Disabilities.......MSc 12FT 36PT/PGDip 9FT 24PT/PGCert 6FT 12PT
Advanced Practice in Intellectual Disabilities and Applied Education.........MSc 12FT 36PT/PGDip 9FT 24PT/PGCert 6FT 12PT

University of Edinburgh
Advanced Social Work Studies (Mental Health).........PGCert 12PT
Dementia: International Experience, Policy and Practice (Online Distance Learning) ....MSc 24DL/PGDip 21DL/PGCert 9DL
Health & Social Care - Children & Young People's Mental Health: Ecological Approaches ODL..PGCert 9DL

University of Essex
Mental Health Nursing .... MSc 24FT

University of Exeter
Clinical Practice...DClinPrac 42DL
Clinical Psychology...................................... DClinPsy by taught 36FT
Mindfulness-based Cognitive Therapies and Approaches............. PGCert 12PT/PGDip 24PT/MSc 24-36PT

National University of Ireland Galway
Nursing (Mental Health, Community & Inpatient Acute Care)..... PGDip 12FT 24PT

Glasgow Caledonian University
Mental Health Social Work (Mental Health Officer) .... PGCert 12PT

University of Glasgow
Healthcare Chaplaincy...PGCert 12PT

Mental Health, Global....MSc 12FT 24PT/PGDip 9FT 18PT/PGCert 9FT 18PT

University of Greenwich
Child and Adolescent Mental Health .... GradDip 24-36PT

University of Hertfordshire
Mental Health (Primary Care) ....PGCert 12PT
Mental Health Practice MSc 15FT 24-60PT/PGDip 15FT 24-60PT/PGCert 15FT 24-60PT

University of Huddersfield
Health & Social Care (Approved Mental Health Practice)....... MSc 36PT

King's College London
Advanced Care in Dementia ....MSc 12FT 24PT
Advanced Practice (Cardiac Care).. MSc 36-72PT/PGDip 24-72PT/PGCert 12-72PT
Early Intervention in Psychosis .... MSc 12FT 24,36,48PT N/ADL
Global Mental Health...MSc 12FT 24PT
Mental Health Service & Population Research......MSc 12FT 24PT
Mental Health Studies ....MSc 12FT 24PT
Mental Health in Learning Disabilities ....MSc 12FT 24PT

Leeds Metropolitan University
Mental Health Practice ....MSc 24PT
Mental Health Studies............................. PGCert 24PT/PGDip 24PT

University of Leicester
Child and Adolescent Mental Health.... PGCert 12FT 12PT/PGDip 12FT 24PT/MSc 12FT 36PT

University of Liverpool
Advanced Science..........MSc 12FT 24PT/PGDip 12FT/PGCert 12FT

London Metropolitan University
Mental Health and Well-being ....MSc 12FT 24PT

London School of Hygiene and Tropical Medicine
Global Mental Health...MSc 12FT 24PT

London South Bank University
Acute and Psychiatric Intensive Care Settings....MSc 36PT/PGDip 24PT
Forensic Mental Health Care ....MSc 36PT
Mental Health Practice ....MSc 36PT
Mental Health Practice (Older People).............................MSc 36PT
Primary Care and Mental Health..................................PGCert 12PT

University of Manchester
Applied Mental Health..PGCert 12FT 24PT
Dementia Care - Advanced Practice Interventions for Mental Health..MSc N/AFT 36PT/PGDip 36PT
Forensic Mental Health..................................MSc 36PT/PGDip 12PT
Primary Mental Health Care pathway - APIMH..MSc 36PT/PGDip 24PT
Psychosocial Interventions for Psychosis (COPE) pathway ..... MSc 36PT/PGDip 24PT

Middlesex University
Child and Family Mental Health Work.......................AdvDip 12PT/PGCert 12PT
Child, Adolescent and Family Mental Health Work... AdvDip 7PT/PGCert 7PT
Mental Health Studies, MSc ....MSc 36PT

University of Northampton
Child and Adolescent Mental Health ....MSc 12FT 24PT/PGDip 12PT
Mental Health...MSc 24PT/PGDip 12PT

Northumbria University
Mental Health Law Policy and Practice....LLM 24DL/PGDip 18DL/PGCert 9DL
Nursing (MNurs) Registered Nurse (Mental Health)....................... MA 24-48FT

University of Nottingham
Graduate Entry Nursing - Mental Health.........................MSc 36FT
Mental Health Research ....MSc 12FT 24PT
Psychological Therapies...PGCert 12PT

Oxford Brookes University
Nursing, Mental Health (Pre-registration).. MA 24FT 48PT/PGDip 24FT 48PT/PGCert 24FT 48PT

Queen Mary, University of London
Mental Health: Psychological Therapies D/L option...... MSc 12FT 24PT
Mental Health: Transcultural Mental Healthcare. MSc 12FT 24PT 24DL

Queen's University Belfast
Mental Health ....Diploma 4FT

University of Reading
Clinical Aspects of Psychology ....MSc 12FT 24PT
Evidence-Based Psychological Treatments .....PGDip 12FT/PGCert 12FT

University of Salford
Child and Adolescent Mental Health........MSc 24PT/PGDip 18PT/PGCert 9PT

School of Oriental and African Studies - SOAS
Medical Anthropology .... MA 12FT 24-36PT

Sheffield Hallam University
Nursing Studies - Adult or Mental Health Nursing.....PGDip 24FT
Nursing Studies (Adult / Mental Health).......................PGDip 24FT
Specialist Mental Health Practice .. MA 36PT/PGDip 24PT/PGCert 12PT

University of South Wales
Child and Adolescent Mental Health .... MA 12FT 36PT

University of Southampton
Cognitive Therapy for Severe Mental Health Problems........PGDip 12PT
Health Psychology...MSc 12FT/PGDip 12FT
Leadership and Management Health and Social Care... MSc 12FT 48PT
Mental Health Studies. MSc 15FT 24-60PT/PGDip 12FT 18-60PT/PGCert 6FT 6PT
Nursing (Pre-registration) .... MSc 36FT

University of St Andrews
Adults Support, Protection and Safeguarding............PGCert 12DL
Adults with Learning Disabilities who have Significant and Complex Needs......................MSc 12DL/PGDip 12DL/PGCert 12DL
Health Psychology.. MSc 12FT

Staffordshire University
Ageing, Mental Health and Dementia...............................MSc 36DL
Practitioner with a Special Interest in Mental Health ... MSc 36PT

University of Stirling
Health Psychology...........................MSc 12FT 24PT/PGDip 6FT 12PT
Health and Wellbeing of the Older Person .... MSc 24FT

University of Sussex
Foundations of Clinical Psychology and Mental Health................. MSc 12FT 24PT

Swansea University
Approved Mental Health Professional..........................PGCert 12FT

Trinity College Dublin - the University of Dublin
Dementia...MSc 12FT 24PT
Mental Health ....MSc 12FT 24PT

UCL - University College London
CYP IAPT Therapy ....PGDip 12FT
Child and Adolescent Mental Health ... MSc 12FT 24-60PT/PGDip 24-60PT/PGCert 12PT

University of West London
Advanced Psychosocial Interventions for Psychosis PGCert 24PT/PGDip 24PT/MSc 36PT
Women, Mental Health and Childbearing: Developing the Service .... CPPD 4PT 4DL

University of the West of Scotland
Mental Health Care...PGCert 12PT

University of the West of England, Bristol
Mental Health .... MSc 36PT

University of Wolverhampton
Mental Health .... MSc 24PT/MA 24PT/PGCert 12PT/PGDip 12PT

Mental health care
Research Courses

University of Aberdeen
Mental Health ....PhD 36FT/MSc by research 12FT/MPhil 24FT

Bangor University
Ageing and Cognitive Health .... PhD 36FT 60PT
Ageing and Dementia Studies ....MSc by research 12FT 24PT PhD 36FT 60PT/MPhil 24FT 48PT

University of Exeter
Clinical Practice...DClinPrac 42DL
Clinical Psychology..DClinPsy 36FT

University of Hertfordshire
Arts Psychotherapies and Counselling in Health .PhD 36FT 72PT/MRes 12FT 24PT/MPhil 24FT 48PT
Centre for Community Research ....PhD 36FT 72PT/MPhil 24FT 48PT/MRes 12FT 24PT

University of Kent
Mental Health (Social and Community Care) ....MPhil 24FT 36PT/PhD 36FT 60PT

University of Nottingham
Mental Health .... PhD 36FT/DHSci 36FT/New Route PhD 48FT

Plymouth University
Mental Health .... MPhil tbcFT

University of Southampton
School of Social Sciences - Gerontology......PhD 36FT 72PT/MPhil 24FT 48PT

St George's, University of London
Mental health......... PhD 36FT 72PT/MPhil 24FT 48PT/MD(Res) 24 minFT 48 minPT

UCL - University College London
Mental Health Sciences ....PhD 36FT 60PT/MD(Res) 24FT 24PT

Health sciences

Music therapy
Taught Courses

University of Aberdeen
Studies in Mindfulness .... MSc 36PT/PGDip 24PT/PGCert 12PT

Anglia Ruskin University
Music Therapy .... MA 24FT

City University London
Music Therapy .... MMT 24FT

Goldsmiths, University of London
Music, Mind and Brain .... MSc 12FT 24PT

Leeds Metropolitan University
Psychological Therapies .... MA 48PT

University of Limerick
Music Therapy .... MA 24FT

University of Roehampton
Applied Music Psychology .... MA 12FT 24PT
Music Therapy .... MA 24FT 36PT
Applied Music Psychology .... PGCert 6FT 24PT
PGDip 9FT 24PT

University of Sheffield
Music Psychology in Education .... MA 24 PTDL
Psychology of Music .... MA 12FT 24PT

University of South Wales
Art Psychotherapy .... MA 36PT
Buddhist Studies .... PGCert 12DL/PGDip 24DL/MA 36DL
Evaluation Studies .... PGCert 9-12DL
Music Therapy .... MA 36PT

University of the West of England, Bristol
Music Therapy .... MA 36PT

Nutrition
Taught Courses

University of Aberdeen
Human Nutrition and Metabolism .... MSc 12FT/PGDip 8FT
Public Health Nutrition .... MSc 12FT 24PT/PGDip 9FT 18PT

University of Bedfordshire
Physical Activity, Nutrition and Health Promotion .... MSc 12FT/PGDip 12FT/PGCert 12FT

University College Birmingham
Culinary Arts Management .... MA 15FT 24PT

University of Brighton
Food Services and Wellbeing Management ... MSc 12FT 24-72PT/PGDip 12FT 24-72PT/PGCert 12FT 24-72PT

University of Bristol
Nutrition, Physical Activity and Public Health .... MSc 12FT 24PT

Bucks New University
Health, Exercise & Wellbeing .... MSc 12FT 24PT

Cardiff Metropolitan University
Food Science & Technology .... MSc 12FT/PGDip 12FT
Food Technology for Industry .... MSc 24-60DL

University of Chester
Exercise and Nutrition Science .. MSc 12FT 24 - 48PT/PGDip 12FT 24 - 48PT/PGCert 12FT 12 - 24PT
Exercise and Nutrition Science (Taught in Dublin, Ireland) .... MSc 24 - 48PT/PGDip 24 - 48PT/PGCert 12 - 24PT
Human Nutrition .... MSc 12FT 24-48PT/PGDip 12FT 24-48PT/PGCert 12FT 12-24PT
Nutrition and Dietetics .... MSc 24FT/PGDip 24FT
Public Health Nutrition .... MSc 12FT 24 - 72PT/PGDip 12FT 24 - 60PT/PGCert 12FT 12 - 36PT
Sports Sciences (with named pathways) ..... MA 12FT 24PT/PGDip 12FT 24PT/PGCert 12FT 12-24PT
Weight ManagementMSc 12FT 24 - 48PT/PGDip 12FT 24 - 48PT/PGCert 12FT 12 - 24PT
Weight Management (Taught in Dublin, Ireland) .. MSc 24-48PT/PGDip 24-48PT/PGCert 12-24PT

City University London
Food and Nutrition Policy .... MSc 12FT 24PT

University College Cork
Applied Science (Food Science) .... MSc 12FT
Food Science & Technology .... HDip 9FT 18PT
Nutritional Sciences .... MSc 24FT

Coventry University
Sport and Exercise Nutrition .... PGCert 12 MinPT
Weight Management .... PGCert 12PT

Dublin Institute of Technology
European MSc in Food Science, Technology and Nutrition ..... MSc 12FT 24PT

University of Dundee
Sports and Biomechanical Medicine (MSc Full time in-house) ..... MSc 12FT
Sports and Biomechanical Medicine (MSc Part time with externally arranged project) .... MSc 24PT
Sports and Biomechanical Medicine (MSc Part time with in-house project) .... MSc 24PT

University of Exeter
Paediatric Exercise and Health .... MSc 12FT 24PT
Sport and Health Sciences .... MSc 12FT 24PT

Glasgow Caledonian University
Clinical Nutrition and Health .... MSc 12FT

University of Glasgow
Clinical Nutrition .... MSc(MedSci) 12FT 24PT
Human Nutrition .... MSc(MedSci) 12FT 24PT/PGDip 9FT 18PT
Sports Nutrition .... PGCert 4FT

University of Greenwich
Nutritional Sciences .... MSc 12FT 24PT/PGDip 12FT 24PT

Heriot-Watt University
Food Science and Nutrition .... MSc 12FT 24PT/PGDip 9FT 21PT
Food and Beverage Science .... MSc 12FT 24PT/PGDip 9FT 21PT

University of Huddersfield
Nutrition and Food Sciences .... MSc 12FT

Leeds Metropolitan University
Community Specialist Practitioner - Practice Nursing..MSc 24PT/PGDip 24PT
Dietetics .... PGDip 24FT

Leeds Trinity University
Health and Wellbeing .... MSc 24PT 24DL/PGCert 12PT 12DL/PGDip 24PT 24DL

University of Leeds
Food Science and Nutrition .... MSc 12FT
Nutrition .... MSc 12FT

Liverpool Hope University
Health, Exercise and Nutrition .... MSc 12-15FT 24-36PT/PGDip 12FT 24PT/PGCert 6FT 12PT

Liverpool John Moores University
Health Sciences .... MRes 12FT 24PT

London Metropolitan University
Dietetics and Nutrition .... MSc 30FT/PGDip 36FT
Human Nutrition (Public Health/Sports) .... MSc 12FT 24PT

Manchester Metropolitan University
Biomedical Science featuring Exercise and Health options ... MSc 12FT 24-36PT
Food and Nutrition .... MSc 12FT 24-60PT
Nutrition and Health .... MSc 12FT 24-60PT

Northumbria University
Food Science .... MSc 12FT 30PT
Nutritional Science .... MSc 12FT 24PT

University of Nottingham
Clinical Nutrition .... MSc 24-72PT/PGDip 24-72PT
Global Food Security .... MRes 12FT 36PT
Nutritional Sciences .... MSc 12FT 24PT

Oxford Brookes University
Applied Human Nutrition .... MSc 12FT 24PT/PGDip 8FT 20PT/PGCert 8FT 8PT
Applied Sport & Exercise Nutrition .... MSc 12FT 24PT/PGDip 8FT 20PT

University of Portsmouth
Clinical Exercise Science .... MSc 12FT 24PT

Queen Margaret University, Edinburgh
Dietetics .... MSc 18FT/PGDip 15FT
Public Health Nutrition .... MSc 12FT 24-60PT/PGDip 9FT 24-60PT

Queen's University Belfast
Nursing Practice .... DMP (Doctorate) 36FT 60PT

University of Reading
Food Science .... MSc 12FT 24PT
Nutrition and Food Science .... MSc 12FT/PGDip 9FT

University of Roehampton
Clinical Nutrition .... MSc 12FT 24PT 24DL
Health Sciences .... MSc 12FT 24PT
Clinical Nutrition .... PGCert 6FT 24PT 24DL
PGDip 9FT 24PT 24DL

Sheffield Hallam University
Nutrition with Public Health Management .... MSc 12FT

University of Sheffield
Human Nutrition .... MMedSci 12FT 24PT/PGDip 9FT 18PT

University of Southampton
Public Health Nutrition .... MSc 12FT 36PT/PGDip 12FT 24PT/PGCert 12FT 12PT

St Mary's University College, Twickenham
Applied Sports Nutrition .... PGDip 12PT
MSc in Nutrition and Physical Activity for Public Health .... MSc 12FT
Strength and Conditioning .... MSc 12FT

University of Stirling
Sport Nutrition (International Olympic Committee Upgrade)MSc 6FT 12PT

University of Surrey
Nutritional Medicine .... MSc 24-72PT

Teesside University
Strength & Conditioning .... MSc 12FT 24PT

Trinity College Dublin - the University of Dublin
Cardiovascular Rehabilitation and Prevention ...... MSc 12FT 24PT

University of Ulster
Human Nutrition .... MSc 12FT 36PT/PGDip 9FT 24PT
Sport and Exercise Nutrition ..... PGDip 18PT 9DL/MSc 22PT 12DL

UCL - University College London
Cardiovascular Science .... MSc 12FT
Clinical and Public Health Nutrition .... MSc 12FT/PGDip 9FT/PGCert 3FT
Clinical and Public Health Nutrition: Eating Disorders .... MSc 12FT/PGDip 9FT/PGCert 3FT

University of Warwick
Nutritional Management in Diabetes Care .... PGA 12PT/CPDMod 1PT

University of West London
Nursing and Healthcare Intergrated .... MSc 12FT

University of Westminster
International Public Health Nutrition .... MSc 12FT 24PT
Nutritional Therapy .... MSc 12FT 24PT
Public Health Nutrition .... MSc 12FT

University of Worcester
Nutritional Therapy ... MSc 18-24FT 36-48PT/PGDip 18PT/PGCert 9PT

Nutrition
Research Courses

University of Aberdeen
Nutrition and Health .... PhD 36FT/MPhil 24FT/MSc by research 12FT

Barts and the London School of Medicine and Dentistry
Department of Human Nutrition .... PhD/MPhil/MD/FRCP

University of Cambridge
Human Nutrition .... PhD 36FT

Cardiff University
Nursing, Medicine, Health and Social Care (PhD) .... MPhil 12FT 36PT/PhD 36FT 60PT

University of Exeter
Health and Wellbeing .... MPhil 36FT 60PT/PhD 48FT 84PT
Sport and Health Sciences .... PhD 48FT 84PT/MPhil 36FT 60PT

King's College London
Diabetes & Nutritional Sciences .. MPhil 24FT/PhD 36-48FT 72PT

University of Leeds
Exercise and Health .... PhD 36+FT/MPhil 24FT/MSc by research 12FT

Liverpool John Moores University
Health Sciences .... MRes 12FT 24PT

Manchester Metropolitan University
Research in Food and Nutrition .... PhD VariableFT VariablePT/MPhil VariableFT VariablePT/MSc by research 12FT 24PT

Newcastle University
Food and Human Nutrition .... MPhil 12FT 24PT/PhD 36FT 72PT

Nottingham Trent University
Performance Nutrition .... MRes 12FT 24PT

University of Nottingham
Early life nutrition and disease .... PhD 36FT 72PT/DM 24FT 48PT/MPhil 24FT 48PT
Health Science: Doctor of Health Science .... PhD 36FT
Nutritional Sciences .... DPhil 36FT 72PT/MPhil 24FT 48PT/MRes 12FT 24PT

Plymouth University
Dietetics and Health .... MPhil tbcFT
Food, Nutrition and Health .... PhD 36FT/MPhil 24FT

University of Roehampton
Health Sciences.... PhD 24-48FT 36-60PT/MPhil 21-36FT 36-60PT

University of Stirling
Sports Studies .... PhD 36FT 72PT/MPhil 12FT 24PT

University of Surrey
Food Safety; Nutrition .... MPhil 24FT 36PT/PhD 36FT 48PT
Medicine and Health ..... PhD 36FT 48PT/MPhil 24FT 36PT/MSc by research 12FT
Nutrition and Health: Cardiovascular Disease ..... PhD 36FT 48PT/MPhil 24FT 36PT

Occupational hygiene
Taught Courses

University of Birmingham
Food Safety, Hygiene and Management .... MSc 12FT 24PT/PGDip 12PT/PGCert 6PT

Cardiff Metropolitan University
Occupational Health, Safety and Wellbeing .... MSc 12FT 24PT/PGDip 12FT 24PT

Cardiff University
Occupational Health (Policy & Practice) .... MSc VariesDL/PGDip VariesDL

Health sciences

University of Chester
Wellbeing in the Workplace (Work Based and Integrative
Studies) .... MA 24-72PT/PGDip 24-60PT/PGCert 12-36PT

National University of Ireland Galway
Occupational Health & Safety .. MSc 12FT 24PT/HDipAppSc 12FT
24PT

Glyndwr University
Construction Health and Safety .... NEBOSH NGC 4PT

University of Greenwich
Occupational Hygiene .... PGCert 24 - 36DL/PGDip 24 - 36DL/MSc
24 - 36DL

Leeds Metropolitan University
Occupational Therapy (Pre Registration) .... MSc 24FT
Public Health (Health Promotion and Environmental Health)
Zambia .... MSc 36PT

Loughborough University
Occupational Health and Safety Management .... MSc 24-36PT/
PGDip 12-24PT/PGCert 12PT

University of Manchester
Occupational Hygiene .... MSc 36DL/PGDip 24DL/PGCert 12DL
Occupational Medicine .... MSc 36DL/AdvDip 24DL/PGCert 12DL/
CPD 6DL

Middlesex University
Occupational Safety & Health Management .... MSc 12-18FT
24minPT/PGDip 12-18FT 24minPT/PGCert 12-18FT 24PT

Nottingham Trent University
Occupational Health and Safety Management .. MSc 24PT/PGDip
12PT

University of Nottingham
Workplace Health (Distance E-Learning) .... MSc 24PT

University of Salford
Environmental Acoustics ... MSc 12FT 28PT 28DL/PGDip 9FT 18PT
18DL

St Loye's School of Occupational Therapy
Advanced Programme in Occupational Therapy. BPhil 24DL/MSc
24DL

University of Warwick
Occupational Health .... Diploma 12PT/Cert 12PT

University of the West of Scotland
Occupational Safety & Health .... DipHE 24PT/BSc 36PT

Occupational hygiene
Research Courses

University of Aberdeen
Environmental and Occupational Medicine .... PhD 36FT/MSc by
research 12FT/MPhil 24FT
Patient Safety .... PhD 36FT/MPhil 24FT/MSc by research 12FT

Cardiff University
Occupation and Health .... MPhil 24FT possiblePT/PhD 36FT
possiblePT

Occupational therapy
Taught Courses

Bangor University
Health Science .... MSc 12FT 24 - 60PT/PGDip 9FT
Health Studies/Health Science, Nursing, Midwifery, Radiography
and Allied Health Profession PhD by taught 36FT 48-60PT/MPhil
24FT 36PT
Occupational Therapy .... MSc 24FT/PGDip 24FT

University of Brighton
Health through Occupation .... MSc 24FT/PGDip 24FT
Occupational Therapy ...... MSc 12-24FT 24 - 72PT/PGDip 24-48PT
Occupational Therapy and Education .... MSc 24 - 72PT/PGCert
24 - 72PT/PGDip 24 - 72PT
Occupational Therapy and Management .. MSc 24 - 72PT/PGCert
24 - 72PT/PGDip 24 - 72PT
Rehabilitation Science .... MSc 24FT/PGCert 24FT/PGDip 24FT

Brunel University
Hand Therapy .... MSc 12FT 36PT
Occupational Therapy .... MSc 12FT 24-48PT
Occupational Therapy (Pre-Registration) .... MSc 12FT 24PT

Bucks New University
Advancing Spinal Cord Rehabilitation and Management ...... MSc
36PT

Canterbury Christ Church University
Advanced Occupational Therapy Practice ..... MSc 24PT/MSc 60PT

Cardiff Metropolitan University
Occupational Health, Safety and Wellbeing .... MSc 12FT 24PT/
PGDip 12FT 24PT

Cardiff University
Neuorehabilitation .... MSc 18FT 36-48PT/PGDip 12FT 24PT
Occupational Therapy .... MSc 18FT 36-48PT/PGDip 12FT 24PT

University of Central Lancashire
Allied Health Practice; MSc Allied Health Practice (Occupational
Therapy) .... MSc 36PT/PGDip 24PT/PGCert 12PT

Coventry University
Neurological Occupational Therapy .... MSc 12 MinFT 26 MinPT
Occupational Therapy .... MSc 12 MinFT 30 MinPT

University of Cumbria
Occupational Therapy - Accelerated Route .... MSc 24FT

University of Derby
Occupational Therapy (Pre-Registration) .... MSc 24FT
Occupational Therapy Incorporating Occupational Therapy
(Community) Pathway .... MSc 24-72PT

University of East Anglia
Advanced Practitioner (Profession) .... MSc 12FT 36PT
Occupational Therapy .... MSc 24FT

University of Essex
Occupational Therapy .... MSc 24FT Prof Doc 48-84PT

Glasgow Caledonian University
Health and Social Care (Occupational Therapy) .... MSc 12-24FT
12-72PT
Occupational Therapy (pre-registration) (with eligibility for
registration) .... MSc 15FT/PGDip 9FT/PGCert 6FT

University of Glasgow
Health Professions Education .... MSc(MedSci) 12FT 36PT 36DL/
DHPE 48FT 72PT

King's College London
Family Therapy .... GradCert 9FT 24PT

Leeds Metropolitan University
Occupational Therapy (Pre Registration) .... MSc 24FT

University of Limerick
Occupational Therapy .... MSc 24FT

London South Bank University
Occupational Therapy .... MSc 24FT
Professional Development for Allied Health Professions
(Occupational Therapy) .... MSc 12-36PT

University of Northampton
Advanced Occupational Therapy .... MSc 12FT 24-48PT/
PGDip 12PT

Northumbria University
Occupational Therapy .... Professional Doctorate 48-72PT
Occupational Therapy (Pre Registration) .... MSc 24FT

University of Nottingham
Workplace Health (Distance E-Learning) .... MSc 24PT

Oxford Brookes University
Contemporary Occupational Therapy (post-registration) ...... MSc
12FT 36-60PT
Occupational Therapy (Pre-registration) .... MSc 24FT

Plymouth University
Advanced Professional Practice .... PGCert 6FT 12PT/PGDip 10FT
12PT/MSc 12FT 24PT
Occupational Therapy (Pre-registration) .... MSc 24FT 48PT

Queen Margaret University, Edinburgh
Occupational Therapy (Post-Registration) ..... MSc 24-84PT/PGDip
8FT 24PT
Occupational Therapy (Pre-registration) .... MSc 30FT 48PT/PGDip
24FT 42PT

University of Salford
Advanced Occupational Therapy. MSc 36DL/PGCert 12DL/PGDip
24DL

Sheffield Hallam University
Applying Occupational Therapy .... MSc 18FT/PGDip 12FT/PGCert
6FT
Occupational Therapy (pre-registration) .... MSc 28FT
Vocational Rehabilitation .... MSc 36PT

University of Sheffield
Work Psychology .... MSc 12FT

University of Southampton
Health and Rehabilitation .... MSc 12FT 24PT/PGDip 12FT 24PT/
PGCert 8FT 16PT
Physiotherapy .... MSc 24FT

St Loye's School of Occupational Therapy
Advanced Programme in Occupational Therapy. BPhil 24DL/MSc
24DL

Teesside University
Control and Electronics .... MSc 12-18FT 24PT/PGDip 8FT
Occupational Therapy (Pre-registration) .... MSc 26FT/PGDip 23FT
Rehabilitation (Occupational Therapy) .... MSc 36PT

Trinity College Dublin - the University of Dublin
Occupational Therapy .... MSc 24PT

UCL - University College London
CYP IAPT Therapy .... PGDip 12FT

University of Warwick
Occupational Health .... Diploma 12PT/Cert 12PT

Occupational therapy
Research Courses

University of Aberdeen
Environmental and Occupational Medicine .... PhD 36FT/MSc by
research 12FT/MPhil 24FT

Bangor University
Health Studies/Health Science, Nursing, Midwifery, Radiography
& Allied Health Professions .... MPhil 24FT 36PT/
PhD 36FT 48-60PT

Cardiff University
Occupation and Health .... MPhil 24FT possiblePT/PhD 36FT
possiblePT

University of East Anglia
Occupational Therapy ... PhD 36FT 72PT/MPhil 24FT 48PT/MSc by
research 12FT 24PT

University of Essex
Occupational Therapy ...... PhD 72FT/MPhil 48FT/MSc by research
24PT

University of Liverpool
Occupational Therapy .... PhD 36FT/MPhil 12FT/MD 12FT

University of Nottingham
Rehabilitation and Ageing .... PhD 36FT 72PT

Ophthalmics
Taught Courses

Cardiff University
Continuing Education and Continuing Professional Development
for Optometrists/Physicians .... Varies VariesFT VariesPT VariesDL

University of Dundee
Eye Movements & Cognition .... MSc 12FT

Glasgow Caledonian University
Clinical Opthamology and Vision Research .... MSc 12FT

University of Glasgow
Brain Sciences: From Molecules to Mind .... MSc 12FT

London School of Hygiene and Tropical Medicine
Public Health for Eye Care .... MSc 12FT 24PT

University of Manchester
Investigative Ophthalmology and Vision Science .... MSc 12FT
24-48PT

University of Sheffield
Vision and Strabismus .... MMedSci 24-36 PTDL/Diploma 18-24
PTDL/PGCert 12-18 PTDL

University of Ulster
Cataract and Refractive Surgery (Theory) .... MSc 19DL/
PGDip 10DL
Clinical Visual Science .... MSc 20DL/PGDip 10DL/PGCert 8DL

UCL - University College London
Biology of Vision .... MSc 12FT
Clinical Ophthalmology .... MSc 24FT 36PT/PGCert 24FT 36PT/
PGDip 24FT 36PT
Ophthalmology: Cataract and Refractive Surgery ....
MSc 12FT 24PT
Ophthalmology: Retina .... MSc 12FT 24PT

University of Warwick
Diabetic Retinopathy .... PGA 12PT

Ophthalmics
Research Courses

University of Aberdeen
Ophthalmology .... PhD 36FT/MSc by research 12FT/MPhil 24FT

Anglia Ruskin University
Vision and Eye Research Unit .... PhD 24 - 60FT 36 - 72PT

Glasgow Caledonian University
Biological and Biomedical Sciences/Psychology/
Vision Sciences .... MRes 12FT

University of Liverpool
Eye and Vision Sciences .... MPhil 12FT/PhD 36FT/MD 60FT

University of Manchester
Ophthalmology .... PhD 36FT/MPhil 12FT 24PT

University of Nottingham
Ophthalmology and Visual Sciences ... PhD 24-36FT 48-72PT/DM
24-36FT 48-72PT

University of Oxford
Ophthalmology .... DPhil 48FT/MSc by research 24FT

UCL - University College London
Ophthalmology .... PhD 36FT 60PT/MD(Res) 24FT 24PT

Optometry
Taught Courses

University of Bristol
Optical Communications and Signal Processing .... MSc 12FT

Cardiff University
Clinical Optometry .... MSc 24PT possibleDL/PGDip 24PT
possibleDL/PGCert 24PT possibleDL

Health sciences

Continuing Education and Continuing Professional Development for Optometrists/Physicians .... Varies VariesFT VariesPT VariesDL

City University London
Clinical Optometry................ MSc 36PT/PGDip 36PT/PGCert 36PT

Glasgow Caledonian University
Clinical Opthamology and Vision Research...................... MSc 12FT
Life Sciences - Biological and Biomedical Sciences/Psychology/Vision Sciences.. MRes 12FT

UCL - University College London
Biology of Vision.. MSc 12FT

Optometry
Research Courses

Anglia Ruskin University
Anglia Vision Research.................................. PhD 48 - 60FT 30-48PT
Vision and Eye Research Unit..................... PhD 24 - 60FT 36 - 72PT

Aston University
Optometry and Vision Science.. PhD 36FT 60PT/MPhil 24FT 48PT
Vision Sciences... PhD 36FT/MPhil 12FT

University of Bradford
Vision Science....... PhD 36-48FT 48-60PT/MPhil 12-24FT 24-48PT

Cardiff University
Clinical Investigation and Vision Sciences .... MPhil 24FT/PhD 36-48FT
Structural Biophysics................................. PhD 36-48FT/MPhil 24FT
Visual Neuroscience and Molecular BiologyPhD 36FT/MPhil 24FT

City University London
Optometry and Visual Science.......... PhD 24-36FT 36-60PT/MPhil 12-24FT 24-36PT

University of Liverpool
Eye and Vision Sciences................ MPhil 12FT/PhD 36FT/MD 60FT

University of Manchester
Optometry.......................... PhD 36-48FT 72-96PT/MPhil 12FT 24PT

University of Nottingham
Biophysics and Surface Analysis.........PhD 36FT 72PT/MPhil 24FT 36PT/MRes 12FT

Osteopathy
Taught Courses

University of Central Lancashire
Advanced Stroke Practice......MSc 36FT 60PT/PGDip 24PT/PGCert 12PT

University of Derby
Osteoporosis and Falls Management........................... PGCert 24PT

University of Glasgow
Healthcare Chaplaincy... PGCert 12PT

Queen Mary, University of London
Critical Care.. MSc 12FT 24PT
Musculoskeletal Clinical Sciences............................ MSc 12FT 24PT
Musculoskeletal Sciences.. MSc 12FT 24PT

Staffordshire University
Musculoskeletal Diagnosis .... PGCert 9PT

University of Warwick
Evidence Based Muscucloskeletal Care: External Fixation ...... PGA 12PT
Evidence Based Musculoskeletal Care: Intra-medullary Nailing... PGA 12PT

Physiotherapy
Taught Courses

Anglia Ruskin University
Physiotherapy... MSc 12FT 24PT

Bangor University
Applied Sport Science... MA 12FT 36PT
Applied Sport Science (Outdoor Activities)............. MA 12FT 36PT MSc 12FT 36PT
Applied Sport and Exercise Physiology..................... MA 12FT 36PT MSc 12FT 36PT/PGDip 8FT
Applied Sport and Exercise Psychology .... MA 12FT 36PT MSc 12FT 36PT
Exercise Rehabilitation..................... MA 12FT 36PT MSc 12FT 36PT
Occupational Therapy .... MSc 24FT/PGDip 24FT
Sport and Exercise Physiology.................................. MRes 12FT 36PT MRes 12FT 36PT
Sport and Exercise Psychology (BPS Accredited)... MSc 12FT 36PT
Sport and Exercise Sciences..................................... MRes 12FT 36PT

University of Bath
Sports Physiotherapy..... MSc 36FT Up to 60DL/PGDip 24FT Up to 60DL/PGCert 12FT Up to 60DL

University of Bedfordshire
Sport and Exercise Rehabilitation .... MSc 12FT 24-72PT

University of Birmingham
Advanced Manipulative Physiotherapy........... MSc 13-36FT 72PT/PGDip 10-24FT 48PT
Physiotherapy (pre-registration) .... MSc 24FT

University of Bradford
Rehabilitation Studies........... MSc 12FT 24-36PT/PGDip 12-24PT/PGCert 9-12PT
Sports Physiotherapy... PGCert 6FT 18PT

University of Brighton
Independent Practice (Physiotherapy)............ MSc 12FT 24-72PT/PGDip 12FT 24-72PT/PGCert 12FT 24-72PT
Neuromusculoskeletal Physiotherapy........MSc 15FT 72PT/PGDip 12FT 48PT/PGCert 12FT 36PT
Physiotherapy................ MSc 12 - 24FT 24 - 72PT/PGDip 12 - 24FT 24 - 48PT/PGCert 12FT 24PT
Physiotherapy and Education....... MSc 12 - 24FT 24 - 72PT/PGDip 12 - 24FT 24 - 72PT/PGCert 12 - 24FT 24 - 72PT
Physiotherapy and Management........... MSc 12 - 24FT 24 - 72PT/PGCert 12 - 24FT 24 - 72PT/PGDip 12 - 24FT 24 - 72PT
Rehabilitation Science........... MSc 24FT/PGCert 24FT/PGDip 24FT

Brunel University
Physiotherapy (pre-registration programme)................. MSc 12FT 12 - 36DL

Bucks New University
Health Rehabilitation and Exercise..................................... MSc 18DL
Health, Exercise & Wellbeing.................................... MSc 12FT 24PT

Cardiff Metropolitan University
Sport & Exercise Medicine .... MSc 12FT 12-36PT/PGDip 12FT 12-36PT
Strength and Conditioning .... MSc 12FT 24-60PT

Cardiff University
Neuorehabilitation .... MSc 18FT 36-48PT/PGDip 12FT 24PT
Neuromusculoskeletal Physiotherapy .... MSc 36-48PT/PGDip 24PT
Physiotherapy........................ MSc 18FT 36-48PT/PGDip 12FT 24PT
Sports and Exercise Physiotherapy...... MSc 12FT 24PT/PGDip 9FT 18PT

University of Central Lancashire
Physiotherapy Professional Practice............ MSc 12FT up to 60PT
Sport and Exercise Biomechanics.......MSc 12FT 24PT/PGDip 12FT 24PT
Sport and Exercise Physiology.................................. MSc 12FT 24PT/PGDip 12FT 24PT
Sport and Exercise Psychology................................. MSc 12FT 24PT/PGDip 9FT 24PT/PGCert 9FT 24PT
Sport and Exercise Science........ MSc 12FT 24PT/PGDip 12FT 24PT
Sports Therapy .... MSc 18FT 36PT/PGDip 18FT 24PT
Sports Therapy Professional Practice .... MSc up to 24FT

University of Chester
Cardiovascular Health and Rehabilitation.... MSc 12FT 24 - 48PT/PGDip 12FT 24 - 48PT/PGCert 12FT 12 - 24PT

University of Chichester
Sport and Exercise Physiology.................................. MSc 11FT 22+PT

Coventry University
Advancing Physiotherapy Practice........................... MSc 12FT 24PT
Manual Therapy.. MSc 15 MinFT 26 MinPT
Neurological Physiotherapy.......... MSc 15FT 24-60PT/PGDip 12FT 18-36PT
Physiotherapy.. MSc 15 MinFT 26 MinPT

University of Cumbria
Advanced Practice in Physiotherapy........ MSc 18FT 36PT/GradDip 12FT 24PT/GradCert 6FT 12PT

University of Derby
Hand Therapy .... MSc 24-72PT

University of East Anglia
Advanced Practitioner (Profession)........................... MSc 12FT 36PT
Physiotherapy.. MSc 24FT

University of East London
Applied Ergonomics.. PGCert 6FT 12PT
Physiotherapy.. MSc 12FT 24-48PT
Strength and Conditioning........ MSc 12FT 24PT/PGDip 8FT 16PT/PGCert 4FT 8PT

University of Essex
Physiotherapy.. MSc 24FT
Prof Doc 48-84PT

University of Exeter
Paediatric Exercise and Health.................................. MSc 12FT 24PT
Sport and Health Sciences .... MSc 12FT 24PT

National University of Ireland Galway
Sports & Exercise Physiotherapy.. MSc 24PT

Glasgow Caledonian University
Health and Social Care (Musculoskeletal Management)........ MSc 12-24FT 12-72PT
Musculoskeletal Management..................................... MSc 36-72PT
Physiotherapy.......................... MSc 24FT/PGDip 24PT/PGCert 12PT
Physiotherapy (pre-registration) .... MSc 24FT

University of Glasgow
Health Professions Education .... MSc(MedSci) 12FT 36PT 36DL/DHPE 48FT 72PT

University of Hertfordshire
Advanced Physiotherapy .... MSc 16FT 72PT/PGDip 16FT 72PT/PGCert 16FT 72PT
Advanced Physiotherapy (Neuromusculoskeletal)......... MSc 16FT 72PT/PGDip 16FT 72PT

Keele University
Neuromusculoskeletal Health Care...... MSc 16FT 24-60PT/PGDip 12FT 24-60PT/PGCert 12FT 24PT

University of Kent
Sports Therapy and Rehabilitation ....MSc 12FT 24PT/PGDip 12FT 24PT

King's College London
Advanced (Neuromusculo-skeletal) Physiotherapy........ MSc 12FT 24PT
Physiotherapy (pre-registration) .... MSc 24FT

Leeds Metropolitan University
Physiotherapy (Pre - Registration)...................................... MSc 24FT

Liverpool John Moores University
Clinical Exercise Physiology .... MSc 12FT

London Metropolitan University
Sports Rehabilitation and Therapy .... MSc 12FT 24+PT

Manchester Metropolitan University
Cardiorespiratory Physiotherapy and by Research ...... MDSc 15FT flexiblePT
Musculoskeletal Physiotherapy and by Research .... MSc 15FT flexiblePT
Physiotherapy (Pre-registration) .... MSc 24FT
Physiotherapy and Physiotherapy by Research .... MSc 15FT flexiblePT

Middlesex University
Sports Massage Therapy and Rehabilitation.......... MSc 12FT 24PT
Strength & Conditioning.. MSc 12FT 24PT

Northumbria University
Occupational Therapy .... Professional Doctorate 48-72PT
Occupational Therapy (Pre Registration).......................... MSc 24FT
Physiotherapy (Pre Registration) .... MSc 24FT
Physiotherapy Studies.. MSc 12FT 24/36PT

University of Nottingham
Physiotherapy......... MSc 12FT 24-48PT/PGCert 12-36FT 24-48PT/PGDip 12-36FT 24-48PT
Physiotherapy (Manual Therapy) .... MSc 12FT 24-48PT/PGCert 12-36FT 24-48PT/PGDip 12-36FT 24-48PT
Physiotherapy (Neurorehabilitation) .. MSc 12FT 24-48PT/PGCert 12-36FT 24-48PT/PGDip 12-36FT 24-48PT

Oxford Brookes University
Physiotherapy (Pre-registration) .... MSc 24FT

Plymouth University
Advanced Professional Practice....... PGCert 6FT 12PT/PGDip 10FT 12PT/MSc 12FT 24PT

University of Portsmouth
Clinical Exercise Science .... MSc 12FT 24PT

Queen Margaret University, Edinburgh
Physiotherapy (Post-Registration).. MSc 12FT 12-36PT/PGDip 8FT 24PT
Physiotherapy (Pre-registration) .... MSc 24FT

Queen Mary, University of London
Musculoskeletal Clinical Sciences............................ MSc 12FT 24PT
Musculoskeletal Sciences.. MSc 12FT 24PT

Robert Gordon University
Physiotherapy (Pre-registration) .... MSc 24FT

University of Roehampton
Health Sciences... MSc 12FT 24PT

University of Salford
Advancing Physiotherapy........... MSc 12FT 36PT/PGDip 9FT 24PT/PGCert 6FT 12PT
Lower Limb Health, Disease and Rehabilitation......... PGCert 12PT

Sheffield Hallam University
Advancing Physiotherapy......... MSc 18FT 36PT/PGDip 12FT 24PT/PGCert 6FT 12PT
Applying Physiotherapy............ MSc 18FT 36PT/PGDip 12FT 24PT/PGCert 6FT 12PT
Sport Injury Management and Therapy..... MSc 12FT 24PT/PGDip 8FT 16PT/PGCert 4FT 8PT
Vocational Rehabilitation... MSc 36PT

University of Southampton
Health and Rehabilitation........ MSc 12FT 24PT/PGDip 12FT 24PT/PGCert 8FT 16PT
Physiotherapy.. MSc 24FT

St Mary's University College, Twickenham
Sport Rehabilitation .... GradDip 24PT

Swansea University
Chronic Conditions Management........ MSc 12FT 36PT/PGDip 9FT 24PT/PGCert 6FT 12PT
Education for the Health Professions......... MA 36PT/PGDip 24PT/PGCert 12PT

Teesside University
Advanced Clinical Practice (Manipulative Therapy) .... MSc 36PT
Advanced Clinical Practice (Neurolgical Rehabilitation) .... MSc 36PT

Health sciences

Advanced Sports Therapy and Rehabilitation Science... MSc 12FT 24PT
Manipulative Therapy ... PGCert 24PT
Movement Science and Rehabilitation ... MSc 12FT 24PT
Physiotherapy (Pre-registration) ... MSc 24FT
Rehabilitation (Physiotherapy) ... MSc 36PT

Trinity College Dublin - the University of Dublin
Cardiovascular Rehabilitation and Prevention ... MSc 12FT 24PT
Respiratory Physiotherapy ... MSc 12FT 24PT

UCL - University College London
Advanced Physiotherapy: Cardiorespiratory .. MSc 12FT 24-60PT/PGDip 9FT 36-60PT/PGCert 9PT
Advanced Physiotherapy: Paediatrics .. MSc 12FT 24-60PT/PGDip 9FT 36-60PT/PGCert 9PT

York St John University
Physiotherapy (pre-registration) ... MSc 24FT

Physiotherapy
Research Courses

Bangor University
Sport, Health and Exercise Sciences ... MPhil 12FT/PhD 36FT

University of Cambridge
Orthopaedic Research ... PhD 36FT/MPhil 12FT

Cardiff University
Clinical Kinaesiology ... MPhil 24FT 48PT/PhD 36FT 60PT

University of Chichester
Centre for Sports Science, Physical Education and Recreation Studies ... PhD 36-48FT 84PT/MPhil 24-36FT 84PT

University of Cumbria
Rehabilitation and Public Health ... PhD 48FT 72PT 72DL/MPhil 36FT 60PT 60DL

University of East Anglia
Physiotherapy ... PhD 36FT 72PT/MPhil 24FT 48PT/MSc by research 12FT 24PT

University of Edinburgh
Rehabilitation Studies ... PhD 36FT

University of Essex
Physiotherapy ... PhD 72PT/MPhil 48PT/MSc by research 24PT

Keele University
Physiotherapy ... PhD 24-48FT 48-84PT/MPhil 12-24FT 24-36PT

University of Liverpool
Physiotherapy ... MPhil 12FT 24PT/PhD 36FT/MD 12FT 24PT

University of Nottingham
Maternal and Fetal Health ... PhD 36FT 72PT/MPhil 24FT 48PT/DM 36FT 72PT
Physiotherapy ... PhD 36-48FT/MPhil 24FT
Rehabilitation and Ageing ... PhD 36FT 72PT

Plymouth University
Rehabilitation Research Group ... MPhil tbcFT

University of Roehampton
Health Sciences.... PhD 24-48FT 36-60PT/MPhil 21-36FT 36-60PT

University of Sheffield
Health and Related Research..... PhD 36FT 72PT/MPhil 24FT 48PT

University of Southampton
Doctorate in Clinical Practice ... PhD 36FT 72PT
School of Health Professions and Rehabilitation Sciences ... PhD 36FT 72PT/MPhil 24FT 48FT 36FT 60PT

Podiatry
Taught Courses

University of Brighton
Podiatry ... MSc 12 - 24FT 24 - 72PT/PGDip 12 - 24FT 24 - 48PT/PGCert 12FT 24PT
Podiatry and Education ... MSc 12 - 24FT 24 - 72PT/PGCert 12FT 24PT/PGDip 12 - 24FT 24 - 48PT
Podiatry and Management ... MSc 12 - 24FT 24 - 72PT/PGCert 12FT 24PT/PGDip 12 - 24FT 24 - 48PT
Podiatry with Clinical Biomechanics ... MSc 12-24FT 12-72PT/PGDip 12-24FT 12-48PT/PGCert 12FT 24PT
Podiatry with Diabetes ... MSc 12-24FT 24-72PT/PGDip 12-24FT 24-48PT/PGCert 12FT 24PT
Podiatry with Rheumatology ... MSc 12-24FT 24-72PT/PGDip 12-24FT 24-48PT/PGCert 12FT 24PT
Principles of Podiatric Surgery ... MSc 12-24FT 24-72PT/PGDip 12-24FT 24-48PT/PGCert 12FT 24PT

Cardiff Metropolitan University
Musculoskeletal Studies (Lower Limb) ..... MSc 36PT/PGDip 36PT/PGCert 36PT

University of Dundee
Advanced Practice (Clinical Governance) ... MSc 36DL

University of East London
Podiatric Medicine ... MSc 12FT 24-72PT

Glasgow Caledonian University
Podiatric Medicine ... MSc 12FT
Podiatry ... MSc 12FT
Theory of Podiatric Medicine ... MSc 12-24FT 12-72PT
Theory of Podiatric Surgery ... MSc 12-24FT 12-72PT

University of Huddersfield
Forensic Podiatry ... PGCert 18-24BM
Musculoskeletal Management of the Lower Limb ... PGDip 24BM
Podiatry ... MSc 36PT
Theory of Podiatric Surgery ... MSc 36BM

University of Northampton
Advanced Podiatry ... MSc 12FT 36PT/PGDip 24PT

Queen Margaret University, Edinburgh
Podiatric Medicine ... PGCert 36-60PT/PGDip 36-60PT/MSc 36-60PT
Podiatry ... MSc 36PT
Theory of Podiatric Surgery ... MSc 36PT

Staffordshire University
Clinical Podiatric Biomechanics ... PGCert 9PT/PGDip 15PT/MSc 36PT

University of Warwick
Diabetes and the Foot ... PGA 12PT/CPDMod 1PT

Podiatry
Research Courses

University of Southampton
School of Health Professions and Rehabilitation Sciences .. MPhil 36FT 60PT/PhD 36FT 60PT

Radiography and radiology
Taught Courses

University of Aberdeen
Medical Imaging ... MSc 12FT 24PT/PGDip 9FT 21PT
Medical Physics ... MSc 12FT 24PT/PGDip 9FT 21PT
Medical Physics (Computing) ... MSc 12FT/PGDip 9FT

Anglia Ruskin University
Magnetic Resonance Imaging (MRI) (Distance Learning) ... MSc 24DL

Bangor University
Health Science ... MSc 12FT 24 - 60PT/PGDip 9FT
Health Studies/Health Science, Nursing, Midwifery, Radiography and Allied Health Profession ... PhD by taught 36FT 48-60PT/MPhil 24FT 36PT
Clinical and Functional Brain Imaging ... PGCert 8PT

Birmingham City University
Medical Ultrasound ... PGCert 12-18PT/PGDip 18-24PT/MSc 12FT 24PT
Radiography ... PGCert 12PT/PGDip 18PT/MSc 12FT 24PT

University of Bradford
Medical Imaging ..... MSc 24-36PT/PGDip 12-24PT/PGCert 9-12PT

University of Buckingham
General Internal Medicine ... MD 24/36FT

Canterbury Christ Church University
Medical Imaging ... PGCert 12PT
Nuclear Medicine ... MSc 60PT/PGDip 24PT/PGCert 12PT
Radiopharmacy Practice ... PGCert 12PT

Cardiff University
Clinical Engineering ... MSc 12FT 24-36PT
Image Appreciation ... PGDip 24PT/PGCert 12PT
Radiographic Reporting ... PGDip 24PT/PGCert 12PT
Radiography ... MSc 12FT 24PT/PGDip 9FT

City University London
Medical Ultrasound ... MSc 24PT/PGDip 18PT/PGCert 12PT
Nuclear Medicine Technology ... MSc 24PT/PGDip 12PT/PGCert 9PT
Radiography - Computed Tomography ... MSc 24 (min) PT/PGDip 18 (min)PT/PGCert 12 (min)PT
Radiography - Diagnostic Imaging ... MSc 30PT/PGDip 18PT/PGCert 12PT
Radiography - Medical Magnetic Resonance ... MSc 30PT/PGDip 18PT/PGCert 12PT
Radiography - Medical Ultrasound ... MSc 30PT/PGDip 18PT/PGCert 12PT
Radiography - Radiotherapy ... MSc 30PT/PGDip 18PT/PGCert 12PT

University of Cumbria
Medical Imaging ... MSc 36 - 60PT

University of Dundee
Advanced Practice (Diagnostic Imaging) ... MSc 36DL
Medical Imaging ... MSc 12FT

Glasgow Caledonian University
Diagnostic Imaging ... MSc 12-24FT
Health and Social Care (Medical Ultrasound) ... MSc 12-24FT 12-72PT/PGDip 24FT/PGCert 12FT
Health and Social Care (Radiation Oncology) ... MSc 12-24FT 12-72PT
Medical Ultrasound ... MSc 12-24FT
Radiatiotherapy and Oncology ... MSc 12-24FT

University of Glasgow
Clinical Radiation Physics ... MSc(MedSci) 12FT

University of Hertfordshire
Diagnostic Imaging ... MSc variousPT/PGDip variousPT/PGCert variousPT
Diagnostic Ultrasound ... MSc variousPT/PGDip variousPT/PGCert variousPT
Image Interpretation ... MSc 24PT/PGDip 24PT/PGCert 24PT
Oncological Sciences ... MSc 24PT/PGDip 24PT/PGCert 24PT

Imperial College London
Medical Robotics and Image Guided Intervention ... MRes 12FT
Medical Ultrasound ... MSc 12FT 24PT
Medical Ultrasound/Medical Ultrasound (Echocardiography) ... MSc 12FT

University of Kent
Biotechnology and Bioengineering ... MSc 12FT 24PT

King's College London
Medical Imaging Sciences ... MRes 12FT
Medical Ultrasound ... MSc 27PT/PGDip 18PT/PGCert 9PT
Radiopharmaceutics & PET Radiochemistry ... MSc 12FT 24PT
Vascular Ultrasound ... PGCert 9PT/PGDip 18PT/MSc 27PT

Kingston University
Radiography: Breast Evaluation... MSc 24FT 24-60PT/PGDip 24FT 24-60PT/PGCert 24FT 24-60PT
Radiography: Medical Imaging.... MSc 24FT 24-60PT/PGDip 24FT 24-60PT/PGCert 24FT 24-60PT
Radiography: Medical Imaging (Mammography) ... MSc 24FT 24-60PT/PGCert 24FT 24-60PT/PGDip 24FT 24-60PT
Radiography: Oncology Practice ... MSc 24FT 24-60PT/PGCert 24FT 24-60PT/PGDip 24FT 24-60PT

University of Leeds
Advanced Gastrointestinal Practice ... PGCert p/t onlyPT
Medical Imaging ... MSc 12FT 33-60PT/PGDip 9FT 21-48PT/PGCert 4-9FT 9-24PT

University of Liverpool
Medical Diagnostic Ultrasound ... MSc 36-72PT

London South Bank University
Clinical Ultrasound ... MSc 18PT
Mammographic Studies ... MSc 12PT
Professional Development for Allied Health Professions (Therapeutic Radiography) ... MSc 12-36PT
Radiographic Reporting of the Skeletal System ... MSc 18PT
Therapeutic Radiography ... PGDip 24FT/MSc 24FT

Manchester Metropolitan University
Science, Technology, Engineering and Maths (STEM) ... MSc 24-72PT

University of Manchester
Cognitive Brain Imaging ... MSc 12FT
Medical Imaging ... MSc 12FT 24PT/PGDip 12FT 24PT
Medical Physics and Clinical Engineering ... MSc 12FT 24-36PT/PGDip 9FT 24PT

Newcastle University
Clinical Sciences (Medical Physics) with specialisms in: Radiotherapy Physics; Radiation Safety; Imaging with Ionising Radiation; Imaging with Non-Ionising Radiation ... MSc 36PT

University of Nottingham
Bioengineering: The Digital Body ... MSc 12FT

University of Oxford
Diagnostic Imaging ... MSc 12FT 24PT

Queen Margaret University, Edinburgh
Diagnostic Radiography (Pre-Registration)..... PGCert 12FT/PGDip 24FT/MSc 26FT
Mammography ... PGCert 12PT/PGDip 24PT/MSc 48PT
Radiotherapy (Post-Registration) .. MSc 36PT/PGDip 24PT/PGCert 12PT
Radiotherapy and Oncology (Pre-Registration) ... MSc 30FT/PGDip 24FT

Robert Gordon University
Diagnostic Radiography (pre-registration) ... MSc 24FT

University of Salford
Advanced Medical Imaging ... MSc 24-60PT/PGDip 18-36PT/PGCert 12-24PT
Nuclear Medicine Imaging ... MSc 24PT/PGDip 18PT

Sheffield Hallam University
Advanced Practice (Radiotherapy and Oncology) ... MSc 3DL/PGDip 2DL/PGCert 1DL
Applying Radiographics ... MSc 18FT/PGDip 12FT/PGCert 6FT
Breast Imaging and Diagnosis ... MSc 36PT/PGDip 24PT/PGCert 12PT
Medical Imaging Programme ... MSc VAPT/PGDip VAPT/PGCert VAPT
Radiotherapy Planning ... MSc 36PT/PGDip 24PT/PGCert 12PT
Radiotherapy and Oncology ... MSc 72DL/PGDip 24PT/PGCert 12PT
Radiotherapy and Oncology in Practice ... PGDip 24FT

University of South Wales
Diagnostic Clinical Ultrasound . PGCert 12-60PT/PGDip 12-60PT/MSc 12-60PT

University of Surrey
Medical Imaging ... MSc 12FT 48PT

Health sciences

Medical Physics .... MSc 12FT

Swansea University
Clinical Science (Medical Physics) .... MSc 36PT
Medical Radiation Physics .... MSc 12FT 24-36PT

Teesside University
Diagnostic Radiography (Pre-registration) .... MSc 26FT/PGDip 22FT
Forensic Radiography .... PGCert 12PT 12DL MSc 36PT 36DL
Medical Ultrasound .... PGDip 24PT/PGCert 12PT/MSc 36PT

Trinity College Dublin - the University of Dublin
Advanced Radiotherapy Practice .... MSc 12FT
Medical Imaging .... MSc 12PT

UCL - University College London
European Medical Physics .... MSc 12FT
Physics and Engineering in Medicine: Radiation Physics ..... PGDip 9FT 18PT

University of the West of England, Bristol
Medical Ultrasound .... MSc 36FT
Nuclear Medicine .... MSc 24-36PT
Radiotherapy and Oncology .... MSc 36FT

Radiography and radiology
Research Courses

University of Aberdeen
Biomedical Physics and Bioengineering .... PhD 36FT/MSc by research 12FT/MPhil 24FT
Imaging .... PhD 36FT/MPhil 24FT/MSc by research 12FT
Radiology .... PhD 36FT/MD 36FT/MSc by research 12FT

Bangor University
Health Studies/Health Science, Nursing, Midwifery, Radiography & Allied Health Professions .... MPhil 24FT 36PT/PhD 36FT 48-60PT

University of Cambridge
Radiology .... PhD 36FT 60PT/MPhil 12FT

Cardiff University
Radiography/Radiotherapy .... PhD 36FT 60PT/MPhil 12FT 24PT

City University London
Department of Radiography .... PhD 24-84FT 36-84PT/MPhil 12-60FT 24-60PT

University of Cumbria
Medical Imaging Sciences .... PhD 48FT 72PT 72DL/MPhil 36FT 60PT 60DL

University of Glasgow
Clinical Physics .... PhD 36FT 48PT/MSc by research 24FT

Imperial College London
Imaging .... PhD
Molecular Imaging Using Ultrasound and Targeted Microbubbles .... PhD 36FT

King's College London
Imaging Sciences & Biomedical Engineering (Research Division) .... PhD 36FT 48-72PT/MPhil 36FT 48-72PT

University of Liverpool
Magnetic Resonance and Image Analysis Research Centre (MARIARC) .... MPhil 12FT/PhD 36FT
Medical Imaging. PhD 24-48FT 48-84PT/MPhil 12-48FT 24-72PT/MD 24-72FT
Radiotherapy .... MPhil 12-48FT/PhD 24-84FT/MD 60FT

University of Nottingham
Biophysics, Imaging and Optical Science .... PhD 36FT 48PT/MPhil 24FT 36PT
Magnetic Resonance .... PhD 36FT 72PT/MPhil 24FT 48PT/MRes 12FT
Medical Physics (Division of Radiological and Imaging Sciences) .... PhD 36FT 72PT/MPhil 24FT 48PT/DM 36FT 72PT
Radiological and Imaging Sciences.. MRes 12FT 24PT/MPhil 12FT 24PT/PhD 36FT 48PT/DM 24FT 48PT
Radiology - Academic Radiology .... PhD 36FT 72PT

University of Oxford
Life Sciences Interface Doctoral Training Centre .... DPhil 48FT
Radiobiology .... DPhil 48FT/MSc by research 24FT

University of Portsmouth
Medical Imaging .... DMedimaging 48PT

Queen Mary, University of London
Radiation Physics .... PhD 36FT/MPhil

University of Sheffield
Medical Physics and Clinical Engineering ... PhD 36FT 72PT/MPhil 24FT 48PT

UCL - University College London
Medical Physics and Bioengineering .... PhD 36FT 60PT

Reflexology
Taught Courses

University of Central Lancashire
Dance and Somatic Well-being .... MA 24PT/PGDip 24PT/PGCert 24PT

University of Dundee
Advanced Practice (Physiotherapeutic Practice) .... MSc 36DL

Speech therapy
Taught Courses

Canterbury Christ Church University
Speech and Language Therapy .... PGDip 24FT

Cardiff University
Language and Communication Research.... MA 12FT 24PT/PGDip 9FT 18PT

City University London
Human Communication .... MSc 24-48PT/PGDip 24PT
Speech and Language Therapy .... MSc 23FT/PGDip 23FT

University of Dundee
Language & Communication .... MSc 12FT

University of Essex
Speech and Language Therapy .... MSc 24FT

University of Greenwich
Speech and Language Therapy .... PGDip 24FT

University of Limerick
Developmental Speech and Language Disorder .... PGCE 12PT
Speech and Language Therapy .... MSc 24FT

Manchester Metropolitan University
Clinical Communication .... MSc 12FT 24-60PT

University of St Mark and St John
Advanced Speech and Language Therapy: Peninsula Postgraduate Health Institute .... MSc 36PT
Speech and Language Therapy .... MSc 36PT

Newcastle University
Evidence Based Practice in Communication Disorders.. MSc 12FT 24PT/PGDip 24PT/PGCert 12PT
Language Pathology .... MSc 24FT

Northumbria University
Occupational Therapy .... Professional Doctorate 48-72PT
Occupational Therapy (Pre Registration) .... MSc 24FT

Queen Margaret University, Edinburgh
Speech And Language Therapy .... PGDip 24FT/MSc 28FT

University of Reading
Neuroscience of Language .... MSc 12FT 24PT
Speech and Language Therapy .... MSc 24FT

University of Sheffield
Cleft Palate Studies .... PGCert 12PT
Clinical Communication Studies .... MMedSci 24FT
Computer Science with Speech and Language Processing..... MSc 12FT
Language and Communication Impairment in Children .... PGDip 24 PTDL/PGCert 12 PTDL
Science Communication .... MSc 12FT
Speech Difficulties .... PGDip 12FT 24PT/PGCert 12FT 24PT
Speech and Cleft Palate .... PGDip 12FT 24PT

Trinity College Dublin - the University of Dublin
Clinical Speech and Language Studies .... MSc 12FT 24PT
Clinical Speech and Language Studies (Dysphagia) .... PGDip 12PT

UCL - University College London
ENT Practice (Voice Pathology) ... MSc 12FT 24PT/PGDip 9FT 18PT
Language Sciences .... MSc 12FT 24PT
Neuroscience, Language and Communication ...... MSc 12FT 24PT
Speech and Language Sciences .... MSc 24FT
Speech, Language and Cognition .... MRes 12FT 24PT

Speech therapy
Research Courses

City University London
Human Communication .... PhD/MPhil

University of East Anglia
Speech and Language Therapy PhD 36FT 72PT/MPhil 24FT 48PT/MSc by research 12FT 24PT

University of Essex
Speech and Language Therapy .... PhD 72PT/MPhil 48PT/MSc by research 24PT

University of Manchester
Speech and Language Therapy .... MPhil 12FT 24PT/PhD 36FT 72PT

Newcastle University
Linguistics, Speech and Language Sciences .... PhD 36FT 72PT/MPhil 12FT 24PT

UCL - University College London
Cognitive, Perceptual and Brain Sciences .... PhD 36FT 60PT
Developmental Science .... PhD 36FT 60PT
Human Communication Science .... PhD 36FT 60PT
Speech and Language Therapy .... Doctorate in Speech and Language Therapy 48PT
Speech, Hearing and Phonetic Sciences .... PhD 36FT 60PT

Sports therapy
Taught Courses

Bangor University
Applied Sport Science .... MA 12FT 36PT MSc 12FT 36PT
Applied Sport Science (Outdoor Activities)...... MA 12FT 36PT MSc 12FT 36PT
Applied Sport and Exercise Physiology .... MSc 12FT 36PT/PGDip 8FT
Applied Sport and Exercise Physiology .... MA 12FT 36PT
Applied Sport and Exercise Psychology .... MSc 12FT 36PT
Applied Sport and Exercise Psychology .... MA 12FT 36PT
Exercise Rehabilitation .... MSc 12FT 36PT
Exercise Rehabilitation .... MA 12FT 36PT
Occupational Therapy .... MSc 24FT/PGDip 24FT
Sport and Exercise Physiology .... MRes 12FT 36PT
Sport and Exercise Psychology .... MRes 12FT 36PT
Sport and Exercise Psychology (BPS Accredited) ... MSc 12FT 36PT
Sport and Exercise Sciences .... MRes 12FT 36PT

Barts and the London School of Medicine and Dentistry
Sports Medicine .... MSc 12FT 24PT/PGDip 8FT

University of Bath
Sport and Exercise Medicine .... MSc 36-60PT/PGDip 24-48PT

University of Bedfordshire
Sport and Exercise Rehabilitation .... MSc 12FT 24-72PT

University of Birmingham
Exercise and Sports Medicine (Football)..... MSc 13FT 72PT/PGDip 10FT 48PT

University of Bradford
Sports Physiotherapy .... PGCert 6FT 18PT

University of Brighton
Sports Injury Management .... MSc 12FT 24-36PT/PGDip 12FT 24-36PT/PGCert 12FT 24PT

Bucks New University
Advancing Spinal Cord Rehabilitation and Management ...... MSc 36PT
Health, Exercise & Wellbeing .... MSc 12FT 24PT

Cardiff Metropolitan University
Sport & Exercise Medicine .... MSc 12FT 12-36PT/PGDip 12FT 12-36PT

University of Central Lancashire
Psychology of Sport and Exercise .... MSc 12FT 24PT/PGDip 9FT 24PT/PGCert 9FT 24PT
Sports Therapy .... MSc 18FT 36PT/PGDip 18FT 24PT
Sports Therapy Professional Practice .... MSc up to 24FT

University of Chichester
Psychology of Sport and Exercise .... MSc 12-15FT 24-36PT/PGDip 9-12FT 18-24PT/PGCert 6-9FT 12-18PT

Coventry University
Sport and Exercise Nutrition .... PGCert 12 MinPT

University of Dundee
Sports and Biomechanical Medicine (MSc Full time in-house) ..... MSc 12FT
Sports and Biomechanical Medicine (MSc Part time with externally arranged project) .... MSc 24PT
Sports and Biomechanical Medicine (MSc Part time with in-house project) .... MSc 24PT

University of East Anglia
Physiotherapy .... MSc 24FT

University of East London
Sports Rehabilitation .... PGCert 5FT 12 - 36PT
Strength and Conditioning .... MSc 12FT 24PT/PGDip 8FT 16PT/PGCert 4FT 8PT

Edge Hill University
Football Rehabilitation .... MSc 24PT
Sports Therapy .... MRes 12FT 24PT

University of Exeter
Sport and Exercise Medicine .... MSc 12FT 24PT

National University of Ireland Galway
Sports and Exercise Medicine .... MSc 24PT

University of Glasgow
Evidence Based Medicine & Education .... MSc (ClinSci) 12FT
Sport & Exercise Medicine .... MSc(MedSci) 12FT 24PT
Sports Nutrition .... PGCert 4FT

University of Gloucestershire
Sports Therapy .... MSc 12FT 24PT

University of Kent
Sports Therapy and Rehabilitation .... MSc 12FT 24PT/PGDip 12FT 24PT

Leeds Metropolitan University
Sport Coaching .... MSc 12FT 24PT
Sport and Exercise Biomechanics .... MSc 12FT 24PT/PGCert 4FT 12PT/PGDip 12FT 24PT
Sport, Law & Society .... MA 12FT 24PT
Sports Therapy .... MSc 12FT 24PT

University of Lincoln
Sport Science .... MSc 12FT 24PT

Health sciences

Liverpool John Moores University
Clinical Exercise Physiology .... MSc 12FT
Sports Physiology ....MSc 12FT 24PT/PGDip 12FT 18PT/
PGCert 6FT 12PT

London Metropolitan University
Sports Rehabilitation and Therapy ....MSc 12FT 24+PT
Sports Therapy ....MSc 12FT 24+PT

Loughborough University
Sports Biomechanics .... MSc 12FT

Manchester Metropolitan University
Biomedical Science featuring Exercise and Health options ... MSc 12FT 24-36PT
Exercise and Sport- Sport Development............. MA 12FT 24-36PT

Middlesex University
Sports Massage Therapy and Rehabilitation.......... MSc 12FT 24PT

University of Northampton
Sports Therapy ....MSc 12FT 24PT

Northumbria University
Clinical Exercise Physiology ....MSc 12FT 36FT
Sport Marketing...MSc 12FT 24PT

University of Nottingham
Rehabilitation Psychology..................................MSc 12FT 24PT
Sports and Exercise Medicine... MSc 12FT 24PT/PGDip 12FT 24PT

University of Portsmouth
Clinical Exercise Science ....MSc 12FT 24PT

Queen Mary, University of London
Sport and Exercise Medicine ....MSc 12FT/PGDip 12FT 24PT

University of Roehampton
Biomechanics .... PGDip 9FT 24-48PT

University of Salford
Sports Injury Rehabilitation........................MSc 36PT/PGDip 24PT/
PGCert 12PT
Trauma and Orthopaedics .... MSc 12FT 36PT/PGDip 8FT 24PT/
PGCert 4FT 9PT

Sheffield Hallam University
Sport Injury Management and Therapy .....MSc 12FT 24PT/PGDip
8FT 16PT/PGCert 4FT 8PT
Sport and Exercise Psychology..................MSc 12FT 24PT

University of Southampton
Health and Rehabilitation........MSc 12FT 24PT/PGDip 12FT 24PT/
PGCert 8FT 16PT
Physiotherapy... MSc 24FT

St Mary's University College, Twickenham
Applied Sport Psychology.......MA 12FT 24PT/PGDip 24PT/PGCert 12PT
Applied Sport and Exercise Physiology........ MA 12FT 24PT/PGDip 12PT/PGCert 12PT
MSc in Nutrition and Physical Activity for Public HealthMSc 12FT
Sport Rehabilitation .... GradDip 24PT

Staffordshire University
Applied Sport and Exercise Science .... PGCert 12FT 7DL/PGDip 14DL/MSc 24DL
Sport and Exercise Psychology (Distance Learning) ..PGCert 7DL/PGDip 14DL/MSc 24DL

University of Stirling
Psychology of Sport ...MSc 9FT 24PT/PGDip 9FT 24PT/PGCert 6FT 12PT
Sport Nutrition (International Olympic Committee Upgrade)MSc 6FT 12PT

Teesside University
Advanced Clinical Practice (Manipulative Therapy) .... MSc 36PT

Advanced Clinical Practice (Neurolgical Rehabilitation)MSc 36PT
Advanced Sports Therapy and Rehabilitation Science... MSc 12FT 24PT
Movement Science and Rehabilitation...................MSc 12FT 24PT
Sports Therapy ....MSc 18FT 36PT

Trinity College Dublin - the University of Dublin
Sports and Exercise Medicine............................. MSc 12FT

UCL - University College London
Sports Medicine, Exercise and Health.. MSc 12FT 24-60PT/PGDip 9FT

University of Worcester
Sports Therapy .... MSc 12FT

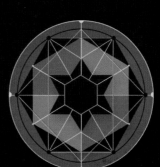

Manufacturing management

Manufacturing management
Taught Courses

Anglia Ruskin University
Engineering Management ... MSc 12 - 15FT 24 - 30PT
Manufacturing Systems ... MSc 12FT 24PT

Aston University
Industrial Enterprise Management ... MSc 12FT

University of Bedfordshire
Engineering Business Management ... MSc 12FT

Birmingham City University
Enterprise Systems Management ... MSc 12/16FT 30PT
Quality Management ... MSc 30PT

University of Bradford
Manufacturing Management ... MSc 12FT

University of Bristol
Biomedical Engineering ... MSc 12FT
Systems ... MRes 24PT

Brunel University
Advanced Engineering Design ... MSc 12FT 24PT
Engineering Management ... MSc 12FT 36-60DL
Packaging Technology Management ... MSc 12FT 36-60DL

University of Buckingham
Lean Enterprise ... MSc 24PT

Bucks New University
Engineering Management and Design ... MSc 12FT 24PT

University of Cambridge
Industrial Systems, Manufacturing and Management ... MPhil 9FT

Coventry University
Engineering Business Management ... MSc 12FT 24-36PT
Engineering and Management ... MSc 12FT 24-36PT
Manufacturing Systems Engineering.. MSc 12FT 36PT/PGDip 9FT 24PT

Cranfield University
Cost Engineering ... PGCert 12-36PT
Engineering & Management of Manufacturing Systems ... MSc 12FT 24-60PT/PGDip 6FT 24PT/PGCert 5FT 24PT
Global Product Development and Management ... MSc 12FT 24-60PT/PGDip 6FT 24PT/PGCert 5FT 24PT
Manufacturing Consultancy ... MSc 12FT 24-60PT/PGDip 6FT 24PT/PGCert 5FT 24PT
Manufacturing Technology and Management MSc/PgDip/PgCert ... MSc 12FT 24-60PT/PGCert 5FT 24-36PT/PGDip 6FT 24-36PT
Operations Excellence ... MSc 24-36PT
Process Systems Engineering ... MSc 12FT 36PT
Sustainable Manufacturing. MSc 12FT 24-60PT/PGDip 6FT 24PT/PGCert 5FT 24PT

University of Derby
Mechanical and Manufacturing Engineering .. MSc 12FT 36-72PT

University of Exeter
Engineering and Management ... MSc 12FT

National University of Ireland Galway
Technology Management ... MSc 24PT 24DL

Glasgow Caledonian University
Maintenance Management ... MSc 12FT 24PT/PGDip 9FT 18PT

University of Glasgow
Civil Engineering & Management ... MSc 12FT
Mechanical Engineering & Management ... MSc 12FT

University of Greenwich
Engineering Management ... MSc 12FT 24PT
Engineering Management (Enterprise Engineering) ... MSc 12FT 24PT
Global Manufacturing ... MSc 12FT 24PT
Innovative Product Development ... MSc 12FT 24PT
Manufacturing Systems ... MSc 12FT 24PT

Heriot-Watt University
Logistics and Supply Chain Management.. MSc 12FT 24PT/PGDip 9FT 24PT
Maritime Logistics and Supply Chain Management ... MSc 12FT 24PT/PGDip 9FT 21PT

University of Hertfordshire
Manufacturing Management ... MSc 12-16FT 36PT
Professional Engineering Doctorate (EngD) ... EngD by taught 36-60PT

University of Huddersfield
Engineering Management ... MSc 12FT

King's College London
Engineering with Management ... MSc 12FT

Kingston University
Advanced Industrial and Manufacturing Systems ... MSc 12FT 24-36PT
Engineering Projects & Systems Management ... MSc 12FT 24PT

Liverpool John Moores University
Manufacturing Engineering ... MSc 12FT 24PT

University of Liverpool
Product Design and Management ... MSc 12FT

London College UCK
International Engineering and Manufacturing Management ... PGDip 12FT 24PT

London South Bank University
Design and Manufacturing Management ... MSc 12FT 24PT
Quality Engineering Management ... MSc 12FT 24PT

Loughborough University
Advanced Engineering ... MSc 24 - 96PT
Advanced Manufacturing Engineering and Management ... MSc 12FT 24 - 96PT
Engineering Design and Manufacture ... MSc 36- 72DL
Management for Engineers (ECITB) ... PGCert 12-24PT

University of Manchester
Maintenance Engineering & Asset Management ... MSc 12FT 36PT 36DL/PGDip 9FT 24PT 24DL/PGCert 6FT 12PT 12DL

Middlesex University
Design Engineering and Manufacturing Management ... MSc 12-14FT 24-26PT

Newcastle University
Design and Manufacturing Engineering ... MSc 12FT

Nottingham Trent University
Engineering Management ... MSc 12FT 24PT

University of Nottingham
Manufacturing Engineering and Management ... MSc 12FT 24PT

The Open University
Engineering ... MSc(Eng) 12-24DL/MEng variableDL/PGDip variableDL

Oxford Brookes University
Advanced Engineering Design ... MSc 12FT 24PT

University of Portsmouth
Advanced Manufacturing Technology ... MSc 12/16FT 36PT

Ravensbourne
Design Management ... MDes 12FT 24PT

Robert Gordon University
Design Management ... MSc 36DL

University of Salford
Aerospace Design and Manufacture ... MSc 12FT 24PT/PGDip 9FT
Manufacturing Systems and Management ... MSc 12FT/PGDip 9FT
Project Management ... MSc 12FT 36PT/PGDip 8FT 24PT/PGCert 4FT 9PT

Sheffield Hallam University
Advanced Design Engineering ... MSc 12FT 36PT/PGDip 8FT 24PT/PGCert 4FT 12PT
Advanced Engineering ... MSc 12FT 36PT/PGDip 12FT 24PT/PGCert 6FT 12PT
Advanced Engineering and Management ... MSc 12FT 36PT/PGDip 12FT 24PT/PGCert 6FT 12PT
Advanced Manufacturing Engineering ... MSc 12FT 36PT/PGDip 8FT 24PT/PGCert 4FT 12PT
Materials and Manufacturing Management ... MSc 36PT

University of South Wales
Engineering Management ... MSc 12FT 36PT

University of Strathclyde
Continuous Manufacturing and Crystallisation ... MSc 12FT
Global Innovation Management ... MSc 24FT
Lean Six Sigma for Process Excellence ... MSc 12FT 24PT/PGDip 9FT 18PT/PGCert 9FT 18PT
Sustainable Engineering: Sustainable Product DevelopmentMSc 12FT 24PT/PGDip 9FT 21PT/PGCert 6FT 12PT

University of Sunderland
Engineering Management ... MSc 14FT/PGDip 9FT/PGCert 5FT

Swansea Metropolitan University
Lean and Agile Manufacturing ... MSc 12FT 24PT

Teesside University
Engineering Management ... MSc 12-18FT 24PT/PGDip 8FT

University of Ulster
Manufacturing Management ... MSc 12FT 24-36PT/PGDip 9FT 18PT

UCL - University College London
Systems Engineering Management ... MSc 12FT 24PT

University of Warwick
Engineering Systems ... MSc 12FT
Process Business Management ... MSc 12FT

University of the West of England, Bristol
Engineering Management ... MSc 12FT

University of Wolverhampton
Advanced Technology Management ... MSc 12FT 24PT
Rapid Product Development and Advanced Manufacturing ... MSc 12FT 24PT
Strategic Information Technology Management ... MSc 12FT 12-16PT/PGCert 12FT 24PT

University of York
Engineering Management ... MSc 12FT

Manufacturing management
Research Courses

Anglia Ruskin University
Engineering Analysis, Simulation and Tribology ... PhD 24 - 60FT 36 - 72PT

Aston University
Industrial Management and Design Research Group ... PhD 36FT/MPhil 24FT

University of Bristol
Systems Engineering ... EngD 48FT 84PT

University of Cambridge
Engineering ... PhD 36FT 60PT/MPhil 12FT

Cardiff University
Institute of Mechanical and Manufacturing Engineering ... PhD 36FT/MPhil 12FT/EngD 48FT

Cranfield University
Manufacturing Department Research Opportunities ... PhD 24-36FT/Integrated PhD 36-45FT/MRes 12-36FT
Manufacturing PhD with Intergrated Studies ... PhD 42 - 48FT
PhD Studentship - Complex Supply Network Dynamics ... PhD 36FT
PhD Studentship - Transforming composite structural design by use of structural health mon ... PhD 36FT
PhD studentship - Improving overall yield during the manufacturing process ... PhD 36FT

University of Greenwich
Engineering (by Research) ... MSc by research 12FT 24PT

University of Hertfordshire
Condition Monitoring and Asset Management ... PhD 36FT 72PT/MPhil 24FT 48PT/MRes 12FT 24PT

Lancaster University
Engineering ... PhD 36FT 48PT/MPhil 24FT 36PT

University of Liverpool
Engineering ... PhD 36FT/MPhil 12FT 24PT

University of Nottingham
Manufacturing Engineering ... PhD 36FT/MPhil 24FT

University of Strathclyde
Design Manufacture and Engineering Management - Research.. PhD 36FT 72PT/MPhil 12FT 24PT

University of Warwick
Engineering ... EngD 36-48FT
Engineering.... MSc by research 12FT 24PT/MPhil 24FT 36PT/PhD 36FT 60PT/EngD 60PT

University of the West of Scotland
Department of Mechanical and Manufacturing Engineering and Quality Centre ... PhD/MPhil

Operations management
Taught Courses

Aston University
Operational Research & Management Studies ... MSc 12FT

University of Bath
Management with Operations Management ... MSc 12FT

University of Bedfordshire
Engineering Business Management ... MSc 12FT
Information Systems and Business Management ... MSc 12FT
Telecommunications Management ... MSc 12-15FT

University of Birmingham
Industrial Project Management ... MSc 36PT/Diploma 12-24PT/Cert 12-24PT
Operations Management ... MSc 12FT 24-36PT
Project Management ... MSc 12FT 24PT

University of Bolton
Systems Engineering & Engineering Management ... MSc Dual Award 18FT/MSc 18FT 36PT

University of Bradford
Sustainable Operations and Management ... MSc 12FT

University of Cambridge
Management Science & Operations ... MPhil 9FT

Cardiff Metropolitan University
Finance and Information Management ... MSc 12FT 24PT

Cardiff University
Lean Operations ... MSc 12FT 24PT
Logistics and Operations Management ... MSc 12FT

University of Central Lancashire
Management Studies ... DMS 18PT
Oil and Gas Operations Management ... MSc 12FT
Operations Management ... MSc 12FT

University of Chester
Change Management (Work Based and Integrative Studies) ... MSc 24-72PT/MA 24-72PT/PGDip 24-60PT/PGCert 12-36PT

Manufacturing management

Cranfield University
Management & Information Systems............. MSc 12FT 24-60PT/
PGDip 6FT 24PT/PGCert 5FT 24PT
Managing Organisational Performance........................... MSc 24PT
Operations Leadership - Fellowship in Operations Leadership .....
PGCert 9FT

Cranfield University, Shrivenham
Information Operations..PGCert 18FT 36PT

University of Cumbria
Management Studies...................... GradDip 24PT/GradCert 12PT

De Montfort University
Lean Operations Management ....MSc 12FT 24-72PT

University of Exeter
International Supply Chain Management .... MSc 12FT

GCU London
International Operations and Supply Chain Management .... MSc
12FT

Glasgow Caledonian University
Financial Services, Risk and Operations......MSc 12FT 24PT/PGDip
9FT 24PT
Operations and Business Management .... MSc 12FT

University of Glasgow
Management.. MSc 12FT

University of Gloucestershire
Information Technology Management (Top Up)................MSc 6FT

University of Greenwich
Information Technology Management...................MBA 12FT 36PT

Heriot-Watt University
Logistics and Supply Chain Management..MSc 12FT 24PT/PGDip
9FT 24PT
Maritime Logistics and Supply Chain Management ...... MSc 12FT
24PT/PGDip 9FT 21PT

University of Hertfordshire
Operations and Supply Chain Management....MSc 12-16FT 36PT

University of Hull
Sustained Professional Development.........................AdvCert 12PT

University of Kent
Logistics .... MSc 12FT 24PT

Lancaster University
Operational Research and Management Science .... MSc 12FT

London School of Economics and Political Science (LSE)
Management Science...MSc 12FT 24PT

University of Manchester
Management and Information Systems: Change and
Development...................................MSc 12FT 24PT/PGDip 9FT 21PT

Middlesex University
Business Practice, ...MA 24PT

Newcastle University
Dual Award in Operations Management (Newcastle and
Groningen)...............................MSc/MSc (Dual Award) 17FT
Operations Management, Logistics and Accounting ..... MSc 12FT
Operations and Supply Chain Management.................... MSc 12FT

Nottingham Trent University
Engineering Management .... MSc 12FT 24PT

University of Nottingham
Industrial Engineering and Operations Management... MSc 12FT
Operations Management... MSc 12FT
Operations Management and Manufacturing Systems ....
MSc 12FT
Supply Chain and Operations Management.................... MSc 12FT

University of Reading
Applied Management ....MA 36PT/PGDip 24PT

Robert Gordon University
MBA Oil and Gas Management .... MBA 14FT 36/40DL

University of Salford
Management.... MSc 12FT 36PT/PGDip 8FT 24PT/PGCert 4FT 9PT
Transport Engineering and Planning........................ MSc 12FT 36PT

University of Sheffield
Logistics and Supply Chain Management........................ MSc 12FT
Management.. MSc 12FT
Management (Creative and Cultural Industries) .... MSc 12FT
Management (International Business)............................ MSc 12FT
Mechanical Engineering and Industrial Management.. MSc 12FT

University of Southampton
Transportation Planning and Engineering.............MSc 12FT 24PT/
PGDip 12FT

University of St Andrews
Management..MLitt 12FT 24PT
Management (Human Resource Management) .... MLitt 12FT

Management and Information Technology ....MSc 12FT/
PGDip 9FT

University of Stirling
Management....................................MSc 12FT 27PT/PGDip 9FT 21PT

University of Strathclyde
Lean Six Sigma for Process Excellence ....MSc 12FT 24PT/
PGDip 9FT 18PT/PGCert 9FT 18PT
Master in Business Administration (MBA).............MBA 12FT 36PT
30-60DL/PGDip 9FT 24PT 36DL
Operations Management in Engineering ....MSc 12FT 24PT/
PGDip 9FT 21PT
Supply Chain Management........MSc 12FT 24PT/PGDip 9FT 18PT

University of Surrey
Information and Business Systems Engineering............. MSc 12FT
Information and Process Systems Engineering .... MSc 12FT
Operations and Logistics Management .... MSc 12FT

Teesside University
Engineering Management...............MSc 12-18FT 24PT/PGDip 8FT

UCL - University College London
Systems Engineering Management ....MSc 12FT 24PT

University of Warwick
Business Analytics & Consulting....................................... MSc 12FT
International Technology Management............................. MSc 12FT

Operations management
Research Courses

Aston University
Industrial Management and Design Research Group... PhD 36FT/
MPhil 24FT

University of Bath
Engineering Doctorate in Systems.................................... EngD 48FT
Systems Engineering .... EngD 48FT

University of Bolton
Supply Chain, Business IT, Music and Creative Industries
Management Specialisms........... MPhil 18FT 24 - 42PT/PhD 36FT
48 - 72PT

University of Cambridge
Management Studies...PhD 36FT

Cardiff University
Logistics and Operations Management .... PhD 36-48FT
possiblePT

Cranfield University
PhD Studentship - Complex Supply Network Dynamics.................
PhD 36FT

University of Kent
Operational Research and Systems ....PhD 36FT 60PT/MPhil 24FT
36PT/MSc by research 12FT 24PT

London School of Economics and Political Science (LSE)
Management Science.......................... MPhil 36-48FT/PhD 36-48FT

Newcastle University
Mechanical and Systems Engineering ....PhD 36FT 72PT/
MPhil 12FT 24PT

University of Sheffield
Management................................. PhD 36FT 72PT/MPhil 24FT 48PT

University of Southampton
EngD Transport Knowledge and Systems Engineering....................
EngD 48FT
School of Engineering Sciences (EngD)........................... EngD 36FT

Packaging engineering
Taught Courses

Brunel University
Packaging Technology Management .... MSc 12FT 36-60DL

Glasgow Caledonian University
Design Practice & Management .... MA 12FT 24PT/PGDip 9FT

Loughborough University
Packaging Technology (MST) ... MSc 12FT 36PT 36DL/PGDip 24PT
24DL/PGCert 12PT 12DL

Sheffield Hallam University
Advanced Manufacturing Engineering...................MSc 12FT 36PT/
PGDip 8FT 24PT/PGCert 4FT 12PT
Design (Packaging Design).... MA 12-15FT 36PT/PGDip 9FT 24PT/
PGCert 4FT 8PT

University of Sheffield
Advanced Manufacturing Technologies with the AMRC ....
MSc(Res) 12FT

University of Strathclyde
Advanced Manufacturing: Technology and Systems..... MSc 12FT
24PT/PGDip 9FT 18PT/PGCert 9FT 18PT

Quality assurance
Taught Courses

Aberystwyth University
Information Governance and Assurance (distance-learning)........
MSc 60DL/PGDip 48DL

Cranfield University
Pre-Master's Course in Engineering Bridging course to MSc 10FT
Quality Management in Scientific Research and Development ...
MSc 36PT/PGDip 36PT/PGCert 36PT

Cranfield University, Shrivenham
Information Assurance for the Public Sector.......MSc 36FT/PGDip
24FT/PGCert 12FT

De Montfort University
Environmental Quality Management ....MSc 12-18DL/PGDip
3-4DL/PGCert 3-4DL

King's College London
Pharmaceutical Analysis & Quality Control ....MSc 12FT 24PT

University of Limerick
Quality Management....................................... PGDip 9FT/MSc 12FT

University of Portsmouth
Strategic Quality Management ....MSc 12FT 36PT
MSc 24DL

University of Reading
Food Technology - Quality Assurance .... MSc 12FT

Robert Gordon University
Quality Management...........MSc 36DL/PGDip 24DL/PGCert 12DL

Sheffield Hallam University
Total Quality Management and Organisational Excellence... MSc
24DL/PGDip 12DL

University of South Wales
Total Quality ....MSc 12FT 36PT

University of the West of Scotland
Quality Management...MBA 36DL
MSc 12FT 33PT/Diploma 9FT 24PT

Quality assurance
Research Courses

Manchester Metropolitan University
Research in Consumer Marketing, Consumer Protection and
Trading Standards ... PhD VariableFT VariablePT/MPhil VariableFT
VariablePT/MSc by research 12FT 24PT

University of the West of Scotland
Quality Centre...PhD/MPhil

Reliability engineering
Taught Courses

University of Aberdeen
Safety and Reliability Engineering......................MSc 12FT 24-36PT

Heriot-Watt University
Applied Psychology ....MSc 12FT 24-48PT/PGDip 9FT 15-48PT/
PGCert 6FT 12-48PT
Engineering Psychology with Ergonomics.............MSc 12FT 24PT
24-84DL/PGDip 9FT 21PT 21-84DL/PGCert 6FT 18PT 18-84DL
Safety and Risk Management (Distance Learning Only)......... MSc
24-84DL/PGDip 21-84DL

Lancaster University
Safety Engineering (Industry-Based)................................MSc 24PT

Loughborough University
Industrial Mathematical Modelling .... MSc 12FT

University of Nottingham
Risk and Reliability Methods by Distance Learning.. MSc 24-48FT
30DL

Reliability engineering
Research Courses

University of Liverpool
Advanced Science (Computer Sciences pathway) (Safety Critical
Systems)...MRes 12FT

The Open University
Residual stress.......... PhD 36FT 72PT variableDL/MPhil 15FT 24PT
variableDL

Materials science

Ceramics
Taught Courses

Bath Spa University
Design: Ceramics......MA 12FT 24PT 24DL/PGDip 9FT 18PT 18DL/
PGCert 4FT 9PT 9DL

Cardiff Metropolitan University
Ceramics .... MA 12FT 24PT

University of Central Lancashire
Ceramics .... MA 12FT 30PT/PGDip 12FT/PGCert 12FT

University for the Creative Arts
Contemporary Crafts (Ceramics, Glass, Jewellery)..........................
MA 12FT 24PT

University of Edinburgh
Glass ....MA 12FT/MFA 24FT

Glasgow School of Art
Architecture .... Diploma 24FT

Goldsmiths, University of London
Innovation in Practice...MA 12FT

London Metropolitan University
Metal MA by Project .... MA 12FT 24PT

Loughborough University
Studio Ceramics: Methodologies and Practice .... MA 12FT 24PT

Manchester Metropolitan University
Design (with pathways in design and contemporary craft
practice) .... MA 12FT 24PT
MA by Research.. MA by Research 12FT 24PT

University of Roehampton
Art, Craft and Design Education .... PGCert 6FT 24PT
Art, Craft and Design Education ....PGDip 9FT 24PT

Royal College of Art
Ceramics and Glass...MA 24FT

School of Oriental and African Studies - SOAS
History of Art and/or Archaeology...................... MA 12FT 24-36PT

University of Sheffield
Ceramic Science and Engineering .... MSc(Eng) 12-24FT

University of Southampton
Ceramic and Lithic Analysis for Archaeologists...... MA 12FT 24PT

Staffordshire University
Ceramic Design .... MA 18FT 32PT

University of Sunderland
Glass .... MA 12FT 24PT/PGDip 10FT 15PT/PGCert 7FT 7PT

Swansea Metropolitan University
Glass ....MA 12FT

West Herts College
Ceramics ....PGDip 12-24PT

University of York
Stained Glass Conservation and Heritage Management...............
MA 24FT

Ceramics
Research Courses

Bath Spa University
Ceramics ....PhD 24 - 60FT 36 - 72PT/MPhil 18 - 36FT 30 - 48PT

Glasgow School of Art
Architecture ....MPhil 24FT/PhD 36FT 60FT

Royal College of Art
Ceramics and Glass................................PhD/MPhil/MA by research

School of Oriental and African Studies - SOAS
Art and Archaeology..............................PhD 36FT/MPhil 24FT
Department of Art and Archaeology ....PhD 36FT 72PT/
MPhil 24FT 36PT

University of Sheffield
Engineering Materials: Integrated Studies...Integrated PhD 48FT

Crystals
Taught Courses

Birkbeck, University of London
Protein Crystallography ....PGCert 12DL

Glasgow Caledonian University
Particulate Solids Handling .... MSc 30DL/PGDip 30DL

Crystals
Research Courses

University of Manchester
Colloids, Crystals, Interfaces and Materials........MPhil 12FT 24PT/
PhD 36FT 72PT

The Open University
Atomic, Molecular and Optical Physics.................MPhil 15FT 24PT
variableDL

Swansea University
Cold Atoms and Quantum Optics ....MSc by research
12FT 12-24PT

Materials science
Taught Courses

University of Birmingham
Materials for Sustainable Energy Technologies...MRes 12FT 24PT
Science and Engineering of Materials...................MRes 12FT 24PT

University of Bolton
Advanced Composites Design...................................MSc 12FT 36FT
Advanced Materials...MSc 12FT 24 - 36PT

University of Bradford
Advanced Materials Engineering .... MSc 12FT/PGDip 9FT

University of Cambridge
Materials Science...MASt 9FT

University of Central Lancashire
Surface Pattern ....MA 12-18FT 24PT/PGDip 12-18FT/PGCert
12-18FT

Cranfield University
Advanced Materials .... MSc 12FT 24-60PT/PGCert 5FT 24PT/
PGDip 6FT 24PT/MTech 24FT
Materials for Energy Systems..........MSc 12FT 24-60PT/PGDip 6FT
24PT/PGCert 5FT 24PT

Edinburgh Napier University
Advanced Materials Engineering ...MSc 12FT 24-36PT/PGDip 9FT
24-36PT

University of Exeter
Advanced Materials Engineering .... MSc 12FT

Glasgow Caledonian University
Particulate Solids Handling .... MSc 30DL/PGDip 30DL

University of Glasgow
Physics: Advanced Materials .... MSc 12FT

Glyndwr University
Composites ....MSc 12FT 24PT/MRes 12FT 24PT

Heriot-Watt University
Materials for Sustainable and Renewable Energies....... MSc 12FT
24PT/PGDip 9FT 21PT/PGCert 6FT 12PT

Imperial College London
Advanced Materials Science and Engineering .... MSc 12FT
Theory and Simulation of Materials................. MSc 12FT

University of Limerick
Advanced Materials .... PGDip 9FT/MSc 12FT

University of Liverpool
Advanced Engineering Materials ......MSc(Eng) 12FT/PGDip 12FT/
PGCert 12FT
Advanced Manufacturing Systems and Technology ....MSc(Eng)
12FT

Loughborough University
Materials Physics and Applications .... MSc 12FT 24PT
Materials Science and Technology...MSc 12FT 36PT/PGDip 24PT/
PGCert 12PT

University of Manchester
Advanced Composites............. MSc 12FT 24PT/PGCert 12FT 24PT/
PGDip 12FT 24PT
Advanced Engineering Materials .... MSc 12FT
up to 60PT up to 60DL/PGDip 9FT up to 60PT up to 60DL/PGCert
6FT up to 60PT up to 60DL
Biomaterials..................................MSc 12FT/PGDip 9FT/PGCert 6FT
Corrosion Control Engineering.......................MSc 12FT Up to 60PT
Up to 60DL/PGDip 9FT Up to 60PT Up to 60DL/PGCert 6FT Up to
60PT Up to 60DL/Modular up to 60PT up to 60DL
Materials and Surface Design ....MRes 12FT 24PT

Newcastle University
Materials Design and Engineering..........................MSc 12 or 24FT

University of Northampton
Leather Technology... MSc 12FT

Nottingham Trent University
Advanced Materials Engineering ....MRes 12FT 24PT
Structural Engineering with Materials ....MSc 12FT 24PT

University of Nottingham
Advanced Materials .... MSc 12FT
Advanced Materials Manufacture ....MSc 12FT 24PT

University of Oxford
Material Anthropology & Museum Ethnography (Research
Methods).. MSc 12FT

Queen Mary, University of London
Biomaterials.. MSc 12FT
Dental Materials.. MSc 12FT
Materials Research.......................................MSc 12FT/MRes 12FT

Royal College of Art
Ceramics and Glass ....MA 24FT

University of Salford
Aerospace Engineering ....MSc 12FT/PGDip 9FT/PGCert 9FT

Sheffield Hallam University
Advanced Engineering Metals ....MSc 36PT/PGDip 24PT/PGCert
12PT
Advanced Materials Engineering ....MSc 12FT 36PT/PGDip 8FT
24PT/PGCert 4FT 12PT

Materials and Manufacturing Management.................MSc 36PT

University of Sheffield
Ceramic Science and Engineering .... MSc(Eng) 12-24FT
Materials Science and Engineering..............................MSc 12-24FT
Nuclear Environmental Science and Technology ....MSc(Eng)
12-24FT
Prosthodontics...DClinDent 36FT
Solid State Chemistry and its Applications....... MSc(Eng) 12-24FT
Structural and Concrete Engineering............MSc(Eng) 12FT 24PT/
Diploma 9FT 18PT/Cert 6FT 12PT

University of Southampton
Maritime Engineering Science: Advanced Materials ..... MSc 12FT

Staffordshire University
Ceramic Design .... MA 18FT 32PT

University of Sunderland
Glass .... MA 12FT 24PT/PGDip 10FT 15PT/PGCert 7FT 7PT

University of Surrey
Advanced Materials.......................................MSc 12FT 72PT

Swansea University
Materials Engineering......................................MSc 12FT 24-36PT

UCL - University College London
Materials for Energy and Environment.................... MSc 12FT

Materials science
Research Courses

Aberystwyth University
Physics ....MPhil 12FT 24PT PhD 36FT 60PT

Anglia Ruskin University
Built Environment ....MPhil 24 - 60FT 36 - 72PT

Aston University
Engineering Materials Research Group .... PhD 36FT/MPhil 24FT
Surface Science Research Group.................... PhD 36FT/MPhil 24FT

University of Bath
Materials ResearchPhD 24-48FT 36-72PT/MPhil 12-36FT 24-48PT

University of Birmingham
Engineered Materials for High Performance Applications in
Aerospace and Related Technologies .... EngD 48FT
Formulation Engineering ....DEng 48FT

University of Bolton
Materials Research and Innovation Specialisms .... MPhil 18FT
24 - 42PT/PhD 36FT 60 - 72PT
PhD by Practice ....PhD 36-48FT 60-72PT
PhD by publication...PhD 36FT

University of Bradford
Advanced Materials Engineering ....PhD 36FT 48PT/MPhil 12FT
24PT
Polymer Engineering .... PhD 36FT 48PT/MPhil 12FT 24PT

University of Brighton
Engineering Research Division.......... PhD 24-60FT 36-72PT/MPhil
18-60FT 30-72PT

University of Bristol
Advanced Composites...PhD 48FT

Brunel University
Materials Engineering...PhD/MPhil
Wolfson Centre for Materials Processing ....PhD

University of Cambridge
Materials Science and Metallurgy .... PhD 36FT 60PT/PhD 48FT/
MPhil 12FT/MSc(Res) 24FT

Cardiff University
Heterogeneous Catalysis and surface science..... PhD 36FT/MPhil
12FT/MSc by research 12FT
Institute of Mechanics and Advanced Materials...........PhD 36FT/
MPhil 12FT

University of Central Lancashire
Materials Science............PhD 36FT 84PT/MPhil 36FT 60PT/MSc by
research 24FT 36PT

Cranfield University
Materials Department Research Opportunities.............PhD 36FT

Cranfield University, Shrivenham
Smart Materials - (Medical Sciences) ....PhD/MPhil

University of Edinburgh
Materials and Processes ....PhD 36FT 72PT/MPhil 24FT 48PT/
MSc by research 12FT 24PT

University of Greenwich
Chemical and Pharmaceutical Sciences - Research ..... MPhil 36FT
72PT/PhD 36FT 72PT

University of Hull
Engineering - Design, Materials and Process Performance.....PhD
36FT 48PT/MPhil 24FT 36PT/MSc by research 12FT 24PT

Imperial College London
Centre for Composite Materials ....PhD/MPhil
Materials Science and Engineering...............................PhD 36FT
The Composites Centre, Aeronautics Department..........PhD 36FT
Theory and Simulation of Materials...............PhD 36FT/MSc 12FT

Materials science

University of Leeds
Institute for Materials Research ....PhD 36+FT/MPhil 24FT
Institute of Engineering Systems and Design....PhD 36+FT/MPhil 24FT
Institute of Engineering Thermofluids, Surfaces and Interfaces ..
PhD 36+FT/MPhil 24FT
Low Carbon Technologies....................................Integrated PhD 48FT

University of Liverpool
Physical Analysis of Biological Interactions at Surfaces........ MRes 12FT 24PT

Loughborough University
Micro/Nano-Materials Engineering ...PhD 36FT 60PT/MPhil 24FT 36PT
Polymer Technology and Materials Engineering..PhD 36FT 60PT/MPhil 24FT 36PT

Manchester Metropolitan University
Advanced Materials: Synthesis, Properties and ApplicationsPhD/MPhil/MSc by research 12FT
Surface Coatings and Characterisation ....PhD/MPhil/MSc by research 12FT

University of Manchester
Advanced Aerospace Materials Engineering........ MSc by research 12FT 24PT
Biomaterials Science and Dental Technology ....MPhil 12FT 24PT/PhD 36FT 72PT
Ceramics and Glasses....PhD 36FT 72PT/MPhil 12FT 24PT/MSc by research 12FT 24PT
Composite Materials ....PhD 36FT 72PT/MSc by research 12FT 24PT
Corrosion and Protection...PhD 36FT 72PT/MPhil 12FT 24PT/MSc by research 12FT 24PT
Materials............................. PhD 36FT 72PT/MPhil 12FT 24PT
Nanostructured Materials.............................PhD 36FT 72PT/MPhil 12FT 24PT/MSc by research 12FT 24PT

Newcastle University
Chemical Engineering................. PhD 36FT 72PT/MPhil 12FT 24PT
Materials Engineering................. MPhil 12FT 24PT/PhD 36FT 72PT

Nottingham Trent University
Materials Science and Engineering.....MPhil 18FT 30PT/PhD 33FT 66PT

University of Nottingham
Advanced Materials ....MRes 12FT
Materials Engineering and Materials Design....... PhD 36FT/MPhil 24FT

The Open University
Fabrication .... PhD 36FT 72PT variableDL/MPhil 15FT 24PT variableDL
High Temperature ... PhD 36FT 72PT variableDL/MPhil 15FT 24PT variableDL
Materials Engineering...... PhD 36FT 72PT variableDL/MPhil 15FT 24PT variableDL
Residual stress.......... PhD 36FT 72PT variableDL/MPhil 15FT 24PT variableDL

University of Oxford
Materials............ DPhil 48FT/MSc by research 24-36FT/EngD 48FT

Plymouth University
Environmental and Fluids Modelling .....PhD 36FT 36-72PT/MPhil 24FT 24-36PT
Structural Integrity ....PhD/MPhil

Queen Mary, University of London
IRC in Biomedical Materials.................................PhD/MPhil
Materials...................... PhD/MPhil/MSc by research 12FT

Queen's University Belfast
Nanostructured Media .... PhD 36FT 72PT/MPhil 24FT 48PT

University of Salford
Atomic Collisions in Solids and Ion Beam PhysicsPhD 36FT 60PT/MPhil 24FT 24PT/MRes 24FT 24PT/MSc by research 24FT 24PT
Chemical Physics and Biomaterials ....PhD 36FT 60PT/MPhil 24FT 24PT/MRes 24FT 24PT/MSc by research 24FT 24PT
Magnetic Materials and Nanostructures....PhD 36FT 60PT/MPhil 24FT 24PT/MRes 24FT 24PT/MSc by research 24FT 24PT
Materials Characterisation and Modelling............PhD 36FT 60PT/MPhil 24FT 24PT/MRes 24FT 24PT/MSc by research 24FT 24PT
Spray Research ....PhD 36FT 24PT/MPhil 24FT 24PT/MRes 24FT 24PT/MSc by research 24FT 24PT
Stress Analysis.........PhD 36FT 60PT/MPhil 24FT 24PT/MRes 24FT 24PT/MSc by research 24FT 24PT

University of Sheffield
Engineering Materials................. PhD 36FT 72PT/MPhil 24FT 48PT
Engineering Materials: Integrated Studies...Integrated PhD 48FT

University of Southampton
Engineering Materials................ PhD 36FT 72PT/MPhil 24FT 48PT

University of Surrey
Engineering and Physical Sciences ....PhD 36FT 48PT/PhD 48FT 96PT
Materials, Surfaces and Structural SystemsMPhil 21FT 33PT/PhD 33FT 45PT/EngD 48FT

Swansea University
Materials Engineering...MRes 12FT 24PT

Steel Process and Product Development.......................MRes 36PT
Steel Technology .... EngD 48FT

University of Ulster
Nanotechnology, Advanced Materials and Bioengineering....PhD 36FT 72PT/MPhil 24FT 48PT

Metallurgy
Taught Courses

University of Cambridge
Materials Science... MASt 9FT

Cranfield University
Welding Engineering MSc 12FT 24-60PT/PGDip 6FT 24PT/PGCert 5FT 24PT

University of Cumbria
The Research Process...PGCert 12 - 18PT

Imperial College London
Metals and Energy Finance.................................. MSc 12FT
Structural Steel Design, also with Business Management or Sustainable Development....................................MSc 12FT 24-36PT

London Metropolitan University
Metal MA by Project .... MA 12FT 24PT

Royal College of Art
Goldsmithing, Silversmithing, Metalwork and Jewellery.. PhD by taught/MPhil/MA 24FT

University of Sheffield
Advanced Metallurgy .... MMet 12-24FT
Materials Science and Engineering........................MSc 12-24FT

University of Strathclyde
Lean Six Sigma for Process Excellence MSc 12FT 24PT/PGDip 9FT 18PT/PGCert 9FT 18PT

Swansea University
Materials Engineering...MSc 12FT 24-36PT

Metallurgy
Research Courses

University of Birmingham
Biomaterials...MRes 12FT 24PT
Engineered Materials for High Performance Applications in Aerospace and Related Technologies .... EngD 48FT
Metallurgy and Materials................................PhD 36FT/MPhil 12FT

University of Cambridge
Materials Science and Metallurgy .... PhD 36FT 60PT/PhD 48FT/MPhil 12FT/MSc(Res) 24FT

University of Manchester
Advanced Metallic Systems DTC...........................PhD 48FT
Metallic Materials ....PhD 36FT 72PT/MPhil 12FT 24PT/MSc by research 12FT 24PT

The Open University
Fabrication .... PhD 36FT 72PT variableDL/MPhil 15FT 24PT variableDL
High Temperature ... PhD 36FT 72PT variableDL/MPhil 15FT 24PT variableDL

University of Oxford
Engineered Metals .... EngD 48FT
Materials .... DPhil 48FT/MSc by research 24-36FT/EngD 48FT

University of Salford
Magnetic Materials and Nanostructures....PhD 36FT 60PT/MPhil 24FT 24PT/MRes 24FT 24PT/MSc by research 24FT 24PT

Swansea University
Steel Process and Product Development.......................MRes 36PT
Steel Technology .... EngD 48FT

University of Ulster
Nanotechnology, Advanced Materials and Bioengineering....PhD 36FT 72PT/MPhil 24FT 48PT

Mineralogy
Taught Courses

University of Dundee
Energy Studies (MSc by distance learning).................MSc 24-60DL
International Mineral Resources Management (MBA by distance learning) ....MBA 18DL
International Mineral Resources Management (MBA). MBA 12FT
Mineral Law and Policy (LLM Full/Part Time) ....LLM 12FT
Mineral Law and Policy (LLM by distance learning)........ LLM 60DL
Natural Resources Law and Policy (LLM by distance learning) ...... LLM 60DL
Petroleum Law and Policy (LLM Full/Part Time) .... LLM 12FT/PGDip 9FT
Petroleum Law and Policy (LLM by distance learning)..............LLM 24-60DL

Mineralogy
Research Courses

University of Exeter
Earth Resources............. MPhil 36FT 60PT/PhD 48FT 89PT/MSc by research 12FT 24PT

University of Leeds
Institute of Particle Science & Engineering........PhD 36+FT/MPhil 24FT

University of Manchester
Physics and Chemistry of Minerals and Fluids......PhD 36FT 72PT/MPhil 12FT 24PT/MSc by research 12FT

The Open University
Atomic, Molecular and Optical Physics................ MPhil 15FT 24PT variableDL

Plymouth University
Environmental and Fluids Modelling.....PhD 36FT 36-72PT/MPhil 24FT 24-36PT

Molecular modelling
Taught Courses

Bangor University
Analytical Chemistry ....MSc 12FT/Diploma 9FT
Chemistry...MRes 12FT
Environmental Chemistry .... MSc 12FT/PGDip 9FT

University of Hull
Molecular Medicine.. MSc 12FT

University of Leeds
Chemical Biology.. MSc 12FT

University of Nottingham
Applied Biomolecular Technology for the Pharmaceutical, Biotechnology and Food Industries ....MSc 12FT 24PT

UCL - University College London
Modelling Biological Complexity ....MRes 12FT

Molecular modelling
Research Courses

Bangor University
Chemistry.......................... MPhil 24FT PhD 36FT MRes 12FT

Cardiff University
Molecular and Experimental Medicine......PhD 36-48FT 84PT/MD 24FT 48PT

University of Leeds
Centre for Doctoral Training in Molecular-Scale Engineering........ Integrated PhD 48FT
Pathogen-host Interactions and Cell Biology.....PhD 36+FT/MPhil 24FT/MSc by research 12FT

University of Manchester
Multi-scale Modelling .... PhD 36FT 72PT/MPhil 12FT 24PT

Nottingham Trent University
Cell Biology...MRes 12FT 24PT

Oxford Brookes University
Biological Sciences - Biofilm Development .... PhD 24-60FT 36-72PT/MPhil 24-36FT 36-48PT
Biological Sciences - Cell Systems Modelling .... PhD 24-60FT 36-72PT/MPhil 24-36FT 36-48PT

Plymouth University
Environmental and Fluids Modelling .....PhD 36FT 36-72PT/MPhil 24FT 24-36PT

Queen's University Belfast
Atomistic Simulation................... PhD 36FT 72PT/MPhil 24FT 48PT

St George's, University of London
Cellular and Molecular Medicine ....PhD 36FT 72PT/MPhil 24FT 48PT/MD(Res) 24 minFT 48 minPT

UCL - University College London
Molecular Modelling and Materials Simulation .... EngD 48FT

Nanoscience
Taught Courses

Bangor University
Electronic Engineering ....MRes 12FT
Electronic Engineering (Nanotechnology)....................MRes 12FT
Electronic Engineering (Polymer Electronics).................MRes 12FT
Laser Micromachining and Laboratory-on-a-Chip...................PhD by taught 36FT/MPhil 24FT
Nanotechnology and Microfabrication .... MSc 12FT

University of Birmingham
Human and Environmental Health Impacts of Nanoscience and Nanotechnology ....MRes 12FT
Human and Environmental Impacts of Nanoscience and Nanotechnology ....MRes 12FT

University of Bristol
Nanoscience and Functional Nanomaterials................... MSc 12FT

University of Cambridge
Micro- and Nanotechnology Enterprise ....MPhil 10FT

Cranfield University
Microsystems and Nanotechnology..... MSc 12FT 24-60PT/PGDip 6FT 24PT/MTech 24FT
Nanomedicine............... MSc 12FT 24-36PT/PGDip 6-9FT 24-36PT

University of Glasgow
Nanoscience and Nanotechnology...................................MSc 12FT

Materials science

University of Hull
Chemistry with Nanotechnology ... MSc 12FT

Imperial College London
Nanomaterials ... MRes 12FT

University of Leeds
Bionanotechnology ... MSc 12FT 24PT/Diploma 12FT 24PT/PGCert 12FT 24PT
Nanomaterials for Nanoengineering ... MSc 12FT
Nanoscale Science & Technology ... MSc 12FT

University of Liverpool
Advanced Chemical Sciences (Nanoscale With Interfacial Science) ... MSc 12FT
Advanced Chemical Sciences (Nanoscale With Materials Chemistry) ... MSc 12FT

Loughborough University
Nanoscience ... MSc 12FT 24PT

The Open University
Professional Science ... MSc variableDL
Science ... MSc variableDL

University of Reading
Chemical Research ... PGDip 9FT 18PT MSc 12FT 24PT

Royal Holloway, University of London
Nanotechnology and Low Temperature Physics ... MSc 12FT 24PT

University of Sheffield
Bionanotechnology ... MSc(Eng) 12FT
Translational Oncology ... MSc(Res) 12FT
Nanoelectronics and Nanomechanics ... MSc 12FT
Nanomaterials for Nanoengineering ... MSc 12FT
Nanoscale Science and Technology ... MSc 12FT

University of Strathclyde
Nanoscience ... MSc 12FT 24PT/PGDip 9FT
Optical Technologies ... MSc 12FT 24PT/PGDip 9FT

Swansea University
Nanoscience to Nanotechnology ... MSc 12FT 24-36PT

University of Ulster
Nanotechnology ... PGDip 9FT 18PT/MSc 12FT 27PT

UCL - University College London
Nanotechnology ... MSc 12FT 24PT
Nanotechnology and Regenerative Medicine ... MSc 12FT 24PT

Nanoscience
Research Courses

Bangor University
Electrical Materials Science ... MPhil 24FT/PhD 36FT
Laboratory-on-a-Chip ... MPhil 24FT/PhD 36FT
Molecular Sensors ... MPhil 24FT/PhD 24-36FT
Quantum Transport and Nanoelectronics ... MPhil 24FT/PhD 36FT

University of Bristol
Nanoscience ... PhD 48FT

University of Cambridge
Nanotechnology ... PhD 36FT

Cardiff University
Drug Delivery and Microbiology ... PhD 36FT/MPhil 24FT
Nanophysics ... MPhil 12-24FT possiblePT/PhD 36FT possiblePT

Cranfield University
Characterisation of physicochemical properties of engineering thermoplas ... MSc by research 12FT

University of Leeds
Centre for Doctoral Training in Molecular-Scale Engineering ... Integrated PhD 48FT

Loughborough University
Micro/Nano-Materials Engineering ... PhD 36FT 60PT/MPhil 24FT 36PT

University of Manchester
Nanoscience DTC ... PhD 48FT

Newcastle University
Materials Engineering ... MPhil 12FT 24PT/PhD 36FT 72PT
Nanomedicine ... MRes 12FT
Nanoscale Science and Technology ... PhD 36FT 72PT/MPhil 12FT 24PT

University of Nottingham
Experimental Condensed Matter and Nanoscience PhD 36-48FT/MRes 12FT/MPhil 36FT

The Open University
Atomic, Molecular and Optical Physics ... MPhil 15FT 24PT variableDL
Fabrication ... PhD 36FT 72PT variableDL/MPhil 15FT 24PT variableDL
High Temperature ... PhD 36FT 72PT variableDL/MPhil 15FT 24PT variableDL

Queen's University Belfast
Nanostructured Media ... PhD 36FT 72PT/MPhil 24FT 48PT

University of Salford
Chemistry and Nanotechnology ... PhD 36FT 60PT/MPhil 24FT 24PT/MRes 24FT 24PT/MSc by research 24FT 24PT
Magnetic Materials and Nanostructures ... PhD 36FT 60PT/MPhil 24FT 24PT/MRes 24FT 24PT/MSc by research 24FT 24PT

University of Sheffield
Engineering Materials: Integrated Studies ... Integrated PhD 48FT

University of Strathclyde
Medical Devices ... EngD 48FT

University of Surrey
Micro- and NanoMaterials and Technologies (MiNMaT) ... EngD 48FT

Swansea University
Antimatter Physics ... MSc by research 12FT 24PT
Nanotechnology (Physics) ... MSc by research 12FT 24PT

Paper engineering
Research Courses

University of Manchester
Paper Science ... PhD 36FT 72PT/MPhil 12FT 24PT/MSc by research 12FT 24PT

Plymouth University
Environmental and Fluids Modelling ... PhD 36FT 36-72PT/MPhil 24FT 24-36PT

Polymer science
Taught Courses

University of Bristol
Advanced Composites ... MSc 12FT

University of Cambridge
Materials Science ... MASt 9FT

Cranfield University
Advanced Materials ... MSc 12FT 24-60PT/PGCert 5FT 24PT/PGDip 6FT 24PT/MTech 24FT

University of Exeter
Advanced Materials Engineering ... MSc 12FT

Imperial College London
Advanced Materials Science and Engineering ... MSc 12FT
Plastic Electronic Materials ... MRes 12FT

University of Leeds
Polymers and Surface Coatings Science and Technology ... MSc 12FT

Loughborough University
Materials Science and Technology ... MSc 12FT 36PT/PGDip 24PT/PGCert 12PT
Polymer Technology ... MSc 12FT 36PT/PGDip 24PT/PGCert 18PT

Manchester Metropolitan University
Science, Technology, Engineering and Maths (STEM) ... MSc 24-72PT

University of Manchester
Polymer Materials Science and Engineering ... MSc 12FT Up to 60PT Up to 60DL/PGDip 9FT Up to 60PT Up to 60DL/PGCert 6FT Up to 60PT Up to 60DL

Nottingham Trent University
Advanced Materials Engineering ... MRes 12FT 24PT

Queen Mary, University of London
Aerospace Engineering ... MSc 12FT
Biomedical Engineering ... MSc 12FT 24PT
Dental Materials ... MSc 12FT
Materials Research ... MRes 12FT

University of Reading
Chemical Research ... PGDip 9FT 18PT MSc 12FT 24PT

Sheffield Hallam University
Advanced Engineering Metals ... MSc 36PT/PGDip 24PT/PGCert 12PT
Advanced Manufacturing Engineering ... MSc 12FT 36PT/PGDip 8FT 24PT/PGCert 4FT 12PT
Advanced Materials Engineering ... MSc 12FT 36PT/PGDip 8FT 24PT/PGCert 4FT 12PT

University of Sheffield
Advanced Manufacturing Technologies with the AMRC ... MSc(Res) 12FT
Ceramic Science and Engineering ... MSc(Eng) 12-24FT
Materials Science and Engineering ... MSc 12-24FT
Polymers and Polymer Composite Science and Engineering ... MSc(Eng) 12-24FT
Polymers for Advanced Technologies ... MSc 12FT

University of Strathclyde
Advanced Manufacturing: Technology and Systems ... MSc 12FT 24PT/PGDip 9FT 18PT/PGCert 9FT 18PT

Swansea University
Materials Engineering ... MSc 12FT 24-36PT

University of Ulster
Advanced Composites and Polymers ... MSc 12FT 36PT/PGDip 9FT 24PT

Polymer science
Research Courses

Aston University
Polymer Research Group ... PhD 36FT/MPhil 24FT

University of Bradford
Polymer Engineering ... PhD 36FT 48PT/MPhil 12FT 24PT

University of Bristol
Advanced Composites ... PhD 48FT
Synthetic Chemistry ... PhD 48FT

Imperial College London
Materials Science and Engineering ... PhD 36FT

University of Leeds
Department of Colour and Polymer Chemistry ... PhD 36+FT/MPhil 12+FT/MSc by research 12FT
IRC in Polymer Science and Technology ... PhD 36+FT/MPhil 24FT/MSc by research 12FT
Institute of Particle Science & Engineering ... PhD 36+FT/MPhil 24FT

Loughborough University
Polymer Technology and Materials Engineering ... PhD 36FT 60PT/MPhil 24FT 36PT

Manchester Metropolitan University
Organic Polymer Materials and their Properties ... PhD/MPhil/MSc by research 12FT

University of Manchester
Polymer Science and Engineering ... PhD 36FT 72PT/MPhil 12FT 24PT/MSc by research 12FT 24PT

Nottingham Trent University
Materials Science and Engineering ... MPhil 18FT 30PT/PhD 33FT 66PT

Queen Mary, University of London
IRC in Biomedical Materials ... PhD/MPhil

University of Sheffield
Engineering Materials: Integrated Studies ... Integrated PhD 48FT

Textile technology
Taught Courses

University of the Arts London - London College of Fashion
Fashion Design & Technology ... MA 15FT 30PT
Fashion Footwear ... MA 15FT 30PT

Birmingham City University
Fashion Design ... MA 12FT 24PT

De Montfort University
Textile Design ... MA 12FT 24PT

University of Edinburgh
Textiles ... MA 12FT/MFA 24FT

Glasgow School of Art
Fashion and Textiles ... PGCert 4FT 8PT/PGDip 8FT 16PT/MDes 12FT 24PT

University of Glasgow
Art History: Dress & Textile Histories ... MLitt 12FT 24PT
Textile Conservation ... MPhil 24FT 48PT

Goldsmiths, University of London
Fashion ... MA 12FT

Heriot-Watt University
Fashion and Textile Innovation and New Applications ... MA 12FT/MSc 12FT/PGDip 9FT
Fashion and Textile Management ... MSc 12FT/PGDip 9FT
Fashion and Textiles Design ... MA 12FT/PGDip 9FT
Strategic Innovation Management Fashion and Textiles ... MSc 12FT/PGDip 9FT

University of Huddersfield
Textiles ... MA 12/16FT
Textiles with Professional Engagement ... MA 16FT

University of Leeds
Advanced Textiles and Performance Clothing ... MSc 12FT 24PT

Manchester Metropolitan University
Clothing Product Development ... MSc 12FT 36-60PT

University of Manchester
Textile Technology ... MSc 12FT Up to 60PT Up to 60DL/PGDip 9FT Up to 60PT Up to 60DL/PGCert 6FT Up to 60PT Up to 60DL
Textile Technology (Technical Textiles) ... MSc 12FT

University of Northampton
Leather Technology (International Environmental Management) MSc 12FT
Leather Technology (International Marketing) ... MSc 12FT
Leather Technology (Professional) ... MSc 12PT

Norwich University of the Arts
Fashion ... MA 12FT 24PT

Nottingham Trent University
Technology Integrated Knit Design ... MA 12FT/MSc 12FT

Royal College of Art
Constructed Textiles ... MA 24FT

Materials science

University of Southampton
Textile Conservation ....MA 24FT 48PT/MPhil 36FT 72PT/PhD by taught 36FT 72PT

Textile technology
Research Courses

University of Bolton
Textile Specialisms .... PhD 36FT 72PT/MPhil 24FT 36PT

University for the Creative Arts
Fashion and Textiles.................... PhD 36FT 60PT/MPhil 24FT 36PT

De Montfort University
Textile Engineering and Materials (TEAM)............... MPhil 12-24FT 24-48PT/PhD 24-36FT 36-72PT

Heriot-Watt University
Textiles .... PhD 36FT 48PT/MPhil 12FT 24PT

Manchester Metropolitan University
Clothing Design and Technology......... PhD variableFT variablePT/ MPhil variableFT variablePT/MSc by research 12FT 24PT
Research in Clothing Design and Technology .... PhD VariableFT VariablePT/MPhil VariableFT VariablePT

University of Manchester
Technical Textiles......................................MSc by research 12FT 24PT
Textile Design, Fashion and Management..PhD 36FT 72PT/MPhil 12FT 24PT/MS by research 12FT 24PT
Textile Science and TechnologyPhD 36FT 72PT/MPhil 12FT 24PT/ MSc by research 12FT 24PT
Textiles .... PhD 36-48FT/MPhil 12-24FT

Textiles and Fashion...MEnt 12FT

University of Northampton
British School of Leather Technology ....PhD 36FT 48PT/ MPhil 24FT 36PT

Royal College of Art
Fashion and Textiles..............................PhD/MPhil/MA by research

University of Southampton
MA Textile Conservation.. MA by research 36FT 72PT/MPhil 24FT 48PT
Science and Heritage...MRes 12FT

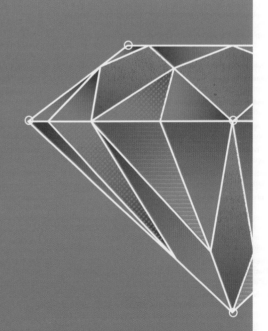

Mathematics

Applied mathematics
Taught Courses

University of Aberdeen
Mathematics .... MSc 12FT

University of Bath
Modern Applications of Mathematics .... MSc 12FT 24PT

University of Birmingham
Applied Mathematics .... MRes 12FT 24PT

University of Bristol
Mathematical Sciences .... MSc 12FT

University of Chester
Mathematics (and Statistics)...... MSc 12FT 24 - 36PT/PGDip 12FT 24 - 36PT/PGCert 12FT 12 - 24PT

University College Cork
Applied Science (Applied Physics) .... MSc 12FT 24PT PGDip 9FT
Applied Science (Mathematical Modelling & Scientific Computing) .... MSc 12FT
Applied Science (Modelling & Numerical Computing)... HDip 9FT

Dublin Institute of Technology
Applied Mathematics and Theoretical Physics ...... MSc 12FT 24PT

University of Dundee
Mathematical Biology .... MSc 12FT

Durham University
Biomathematics .... MSc 12FT
Mathematical Sciences .... MSc 12FT
Particles, Strings and Cosmology .... MSc 12FT

University of Edinburgh
Financial Modelling and Optimization .... MSc 12FT 24PT/PGDip 9FT

University of Exeter
Advanced Mathematics .... MSc 12FT

National University of Ireland Galway
Applied Mathematics .... HDipAppSc 12FT

University of Glasgow
Mathematics/Applied Mathematics .... MSc 12FT 24PT

University of Greenwich
Applied Mathematical Modelling and Scientific Computing .... MSc 12FT 24PT

Heriot-Watt University
Applied Mathematical Sciences MSc 12FT 24PT/PGDip 9FT 21PT/PGCert 6FT 12PT
Applied Mathematical Sciences with Biological and Ecological Modelling .... MSc 12FT 24-84PT/PGDip 9FT 15-48PT
Applied Mathematical Sciences with Climate Change Impact Modelling .... MSc 12FT 24PT/PGDip 9FT 21PT
Computational Mathematics...... MSc 12FT 24PT/PGDip 9FT 20PT
Financial Mathematics .... MSc 12FT

Imperial College London
Applied Mathematics .... MSc 12FT 24PT

London Metropolitan University
Mathematics .... MSc 12FT 24-48PT

Loughborough University
Industrial Mathematical Modelling .... MSc 12FT

University of Manchester
Applied Mathematics .... MSc 12FT 24PT

National University of Ireland, Maynooth
Mathematical Science .... HDip 12FT

University of Nottingham
Gravity, Particles and Fields .... MSc 12FT
Scientific Computation .... MSc 12FT
Scientific Computation with Industrial Mathematics ... MSc 12FT
Scientific Computation with Mathematical Medicine and Biology .... MSc 12FT

The Open University
Mathematics .... MSc variableDL/PGDip variableDL/PGCert variableDL

University of Oxford
Mathematical & Computational Finance .... MSc 10FT
Mathematical Modelling and Scientific Computing...... MSc 12FT
Mathematics and the Foundations of Computer Science ...... MSc 12FT

Queen Mary, University of London
Mathematical Finance .... MSc 12FT 24PT

University of Reading
Data Assimilation and Inverse Modelling in Geoscience .... MSc 12FT/PGDip 12FT

University of Sheffield
Mathematics .... MSc 12FT
Statistics .... MSc 12FT 24-36 PTDL
Statistics with Financial Mathematics........ MSc 12FT 24-36 PTDL
Statistics with Medical Applications........ MSc 12FT 24-36 PTDL

University of St Andrews
Mathematics .... MSc 12FT 24PT/PGDip 9FT
Statistics .... MSc 12FT 24PT/PGDip 9FT

University of Strathclyde
Quantitative Finance .... MSc 12FT/PGDip 9FT

University of Sussex
Scientific Computation .... MSc 12FT

Applied mathematics
Research Courses

Aberystwyth University
Applied Mathematics .... MPhil 12FT 24PT PhD 36FT 60PT

University of Birmingham
Applied Mathematics......... PhD 36FT/MSc by research 12FT 24PT

University of Bristol
Complexity Sciences .... PhD 48FT/MRes 48FT
Engineering Mathematics .... PhD 43FT
Mathematics .... PhD 36FT 72PT/MSc by research 12FT 24PT

University of Cambridge
Applied Mathematics and Theoretical Physics .... PhD 36FT
Mathematics .... PhD 36FT

Cardiff University
Applied Mathematics .... PhD 36FT/MPhil 12FT
Probability and Statistics .... PhD 36FT/MPhil 12FT

Coventry University
Applied Mathematics....PhD 36FT 60PT/MPhil 24FT 36PT/MSc by research 12FT 24PT

Cranfield University, Shrivenham
Applied Mathematics and Operational Research .... PhD 36FT/MPhil 24FT
Applied Mathematics and Operational Research PhD 24FT 36PT/MPhil

University of Dundee
Mathematics .... MPhil 24FT MSc by research 12FT

University of East Anglia
Applied Mathematics .... PhD 36FT 72PT/MPhil 24FT 48PT
Pure Mathematics .... PhD 36FT 72PT/MPhil 24FT 48PT

University of Edinburgh
Applied and Computational Mathematics .... PhD 36FT 72PT

University of Essex
Applied Mathematics....PhD 36FT 72PT/MPhil 24FT 48PT/MSc by research 12FT 24PT

University of Exeter
Engineering .... EngD 48FT
Mathematics .... PhD 48FT 84PT/MPhil 36FT 60PT

University of Greenwich
Computing and Mathematical Sciences .....PhD 36-48FT 60-84PT

Keele University
Applied Mathematics Group .... PhD 36FT

University of Leeds
Applied Mathematics............ PhD 36-42FT/MSc by research 12FT

University of Liverpool
Mathematical Sciences.......PhD 36-48FT 72-84PT/MPhil 12-24FT 36-48PT

Loughborough University
Applied Mathematics .... PhD 36FT 60PT/MPhil 24FT 36PT

University of Manchester
Applied Mathematics .... PhD 36FT 72PT

Newcastle University
Mathematics .... PhD 36FT 72PT/MPhil 12FT 24PT

University of Nottingham
Algebra and Analysis .... PhD 36FT
Mathematical Physics .... PhD 36-48FT 72PT

The Open University
Applied Mathematics....... PhD 36FT 72PT variableDL/MPhil 15FT 24PT variableDL
Bayesian Statistics... PhD 36FT 72PT variableDL/MPhil 15FT 24PT variableDL
Distributionology.... PhD 36FT 72PT variableDL/MPhil 15FT 24PT variableDL
History of Mathematics... PhD 36FT 72PT variableDL/MPhil 15FT 24PT variableDL
Mathematics .... PhD 36FT 72PT variableDL/MPhil 15FT 24PT variableDL
Medical Statistics .... PhD 36FT 72PT variableDL/MPhil 15FT 24PT variableDL
Multivariate Statistics...... PhD 36FT 72PT variableDL/MPhil 15FT 24PT variableDL

University of Oxford
Mathematics .... DPhil 48FT/MSc by research 24FT
Numerical Analysis .... DPhil 36-48FT/MSc by research 24FT
Statistics .... DPhil 48FT/MSc by research 24-36FT

University of Salford
Applied Mathematics....... PhD 36FT 60PT 48DL/MPhil 24FT 24PT 24DL/MSc by research 24FT 24PT 24DL

University of Sheffield
Applied Mathematics........ PhD 36FT 72PT/MPhil 24FT 48PT

University of St Andrews
Applied Mathematics .... PhD 36FT 72PT/MPhil 12-24FT

Staffordshire University
Applied Mathematics Group......... PhD 36FT 36-60PT/MPhil 18FT 18-36PT

Swansea University
Mathematics .... MSc by research 12FT 24PT

UCL - University College London
Mathematics .... PhD 36FT 60PT

Discrete mathematics
Taught Courses

University of Bristol
Logic and Philosophy of Mathematics .... MA 12FT 24PT

University of Dundee
Mathematical Biology .... MSc 12FT

Durham University
Mathematical Sciences .... MSc 12FT

University of Essex
Discrete Mathematics and its Applications .... MSc 12FT/PGDip 9FT

Heriot-Watt University
Applied Mathematical Sciences MSc 12FT 24PT/PGDip 9FT 21PT/PGCert 6FT 12PT
Applied Mathematical Sciences with Biological and Ecological Modelling .... MSc 12FT 24-84PT/PGDip 9FT 15-48PT
Applied Mathematical Sciences with Climate Change Impact Modelling .... MSc 12FT 24PT/PGDip 9FT 21PT
Computational Mathematics......MSc 12FT 24PT/PGDip 9FT 20PT
Graduate Certificate in Mathematical Sciences........GradCert 9FT
Quantitative Finance and Mathematics MSc 12FT 24PT/Diploma 9FT 21PT

Leeds Metropolitan University
Community Specialist Practitioner - Practice Nursing..MSc 24PT/PGDip 24PT

London Metropolitan University
Mathematics .... MSc 12FT 24-48PT

Manchester Metropolitan University
Advanced Computing.. MSc 12FT 36PT/PGCert 12FT 36PT/PGDip 12FT 36PT
Computing .... MSc 12FT 36PT
Digital Media Computing .... MSc 12FT 36PT
Geographical Information Systems .... MSc 36PT 36DL
Information Systems .... MSc 12FT 36PT

University of Oxford
Mathematics and the Foundations of Computer Science ...... MSc 12FT

Royal Holloway, University of London
Mathematics for Applications .... MSc 12FT 24PT
Mathematics of Cryptography and Communications ... MSc 12FT 24PT

University of Sheffield
Mathematics .... MSc 12FT

University of St Andrews
Mathematics .... MSc 12FT 24PT/PGDip 9FT

UCL - University College London
Mathematical Modelling .... MSc 12FT

Discrete mathematics
Research Courses

University of Birmingham
Management Mathematics .... PhD 36FT/MPhil 24FT

University of Cambridge
Applied Mathematics and Theoretical Physics .... PhD 36FT
Mathematics .... PhD 36FT

University of Dundee
Mathematics .... MPhil 24FT MSc by research 12FT

University of Edinburgh
Analysis .... PhD 36FT 72PT

University of Essex
Discrete Mathematics...PhD 36FT 72PT/MPhil 24FT 48PT/MSc by research 12FT 24PT

University of Exeter
Mathematics .... PhD 48FT 84PT/MPhil 36FT 60PT

University of Hertfordshire
Algorithms .... PhD 36FT 72PT/MRes 12FT 24PT

London School of Economics and Political Science (LSE)
Mathematics .... PhD 36-48FT/MPhil 36-48FT

University of Manchester
Mathematical Logic .... PhD 36FT 72PT

University of Oxford
Mathematics .... DPhil 48FT/MSc by research 24FT

Mathematics

Swansea University
Mathematical Ecology ..... MSc by research 12FT 24PT
Mathematics ..... MSc by research 12FT 24PT

Econometrics
Taught Courses

Bangor University
Banking and Finance - London Centre ..... MBA 12FT

Birkbeck, University of London
Econometrics ..... PGCert 12PT
Financial Economics ..... MSc 12FT 24PT
Financial Engineering ..... MSc 12FT 24PT
Financial Engineering ..... GradDip 12FT 24PT

University of Bristol
Economics and Econometrics ..... MSc 12FT

University of Dundee
Financial Economics ..... PGDip 9FT

University of East Anglia
Development Economics ..... MSc 12FT 24PT
Economics ..... MSc 12FT PGDip 10FT
Economics and International Relations ..... MA 12FT
Experimental Economics ..... MSc 12FT
Finance and Economics ..... MSc 12FT
Health Economics ..... MSc 12FT 36PT/PGDip 12FT 24PT/PGCert 12PT
Impact Evaluation for International Development MSc 12FT 24PT
Industrial Economics ..... MSc 12FT
Media Economics ..... MA 12FT
Statistics ..... MSc 12FT 24PT

University of Essex
Accounting and Financial Economics ..... MSc 12FT 24PT
Applied Economics and Data Analysis ..... MA 12FT 24PT
Computational Economics, Financial Markets and Policy ..... MSc 12FT 24PT
Economics ..... MSc 12FT/PGDip 9FT
Economics and Econometrics ..... MSc 12FT 24PT
Financial Econometrics ..... MSc 12FT
Financial Economics ..... MSc 12FT
Financial Economics and Econometrics ..... MSc 12FT
International Economics ..... MSc 12FT 24PT

European Business School London
Global Banking & Finance ..... MSc 12-16FT

University of Exeter
Economics ..... MSc 12FT
Economics and Econometrics ..... MSc 12FT
Economics and Experimental Economics ..... MSc 12FT

National University of Ireland Galway
Economic and Environmental Modelling ... MEconSci 10approxFT

Heriot-Watt University
Quantitative Financial Engineering ..... MSc 12FT 24PT/Diploma 9FT 21PT
Quantitative Financial Risk Management ... MSc 12FT/PGDip 9FT

University of Kent
Economics Conversion ..... MSc 24FT
Economics and Econometrics ..... MSc 12FT 24PT
Economics and Finance ..... MSc 12FT 24PT
Finance and Econometrics ..... MSc 12FT 24PT
International Finance and Economic Development ..... MSc 12FT 24PT

Kingston University
Applied Econometrics ..... MSc 12FT 24PT

University of Leeds
Economics ..... MA 12FT

University of Leicester
Banking and Finance ..... MSc 12FT 24PT
Financial Economics ..... MSc 12FT 24PT

London School of Economics and Political Science (LSE)
Econometrics and Mathematical Economics ..... MSc 10 or 22FT

Loughborough University
Banking and Finance ..... MSc 12FT
Economics and Finance ..... MSc 12FT

University of Manchester
Econometrics ..... MSc 12FT 24PT

University of Nottingham
Economics and Econometrics ..... MSc 12FT

University of Oxford
Financial Economics ..... MSc 9FT

Queen Mary, University of London
Banking and Finance ..... MSc 12FT 24PT
Finance ..... MSc 12FT
Finance and Econometrics ..... MSc 12FT 24PT

University of Reading
Agricultural Development Economics ..... MSc 12FT 24PT
Agricultural Economics ..... MSc 12FT 24PT
Banking and Finance in Emerging Economies ..... MSc 12FT 24PT
Business Economics ..... MSc 12FT 24PT
Food Economics and Marketing ..... MSc 12FT
Real Estate Finance ..... MSc 12FT
Real Estate Investment and Finance ..... MSc 24-72PT
The Economics of International Business and Finance ..... MSc 12FT

Royal Holloway, University of London
Financial and Industrial Economics ..... MSc 12FT

School of Oriental and African Studies - SOAS
Development Economics ..... MSc 12FT 24-36PT
International Management (Japan) ..... MSc 12FT 24-36PT

University of Sheffield
Financial Economics ..... MSc 12FT 24PT

University of Southampton
Economics and Econometrics ..... MSc 12FT 24PT/PGDip 9FT 21PT
Finance and Economics ..... MSc 12FT 24PT/PGDip 9FT 21PT

Swansea University
Economics ..... MSc 12FT
Economics with International Banking ..... MSc 12FT
International Banking, Finance and Economics ..... MSc 12FT

Swansea Metropolitan University
Chartered Institute of Management Accountants (CIMA) ... CIMA 12FT

University of York
Finance and Econometrics ..... MSc 12FT
Financial Engineering ..... MSc 12FT

Econometrics
Research Courses

University of Dundee
Economics ..... MPhil 24FT MSc by research 12FT

University of East Anglia
Applied and Financial Economics ..... PhD 36FT 72PT/MPhil 24FT 48PT
Experimental Economics ..... PhD 36FT 72PT/MPhil 24FT 48PT
Industrial Economics ..... PhD 36FT 72PT/MPhil 24FT 48PT

University of Essex
Economics ..... PhD 36FT 72PT/MPhil 24FT 48PT

University of Exeter
Economics ..... PhD 48FT 89PT/MPhil 36FT 60PT

Heriot-Watt University
Economics, including CERT (Centre for Economic Reform & Transformation) ..... PhD 36FT/MPhil 12FT

Loughborough University
Economics ..... PhD 36FT 60PT/MPhil 24FT 36PT

The Open University
Economics of Innovation and Development ..... PhD 36FT 72PT variableDL/MPhil 15FT 24PT variableDL

Swansea University
Economics ..... PhD 36FT 60PT/MPhil 12FT 24PT

Geometry
Research Courses

University of Exeter
Mathematics ..... PhD 48FT 84PT/MPhil 36FT 60PT

Mathematical finance
Taught Courses

Birkbeck, University of London
Applied Statistics ..... MSc 24PT/PGCert 12PT
Applied Statistics and Operational Research ..... MSc 24PT
Applied Statistics and Stochastic Modelling ..... MSc 24PT
Applied Statistics with Medical Applications ..... MSc 24PT
Financial Engineering ..... MSc 12FT 24PT
Financial Risk Management ..... MSc 12FT 24PT

University of Birmingham
Financial Engineering ..... MSc 12FT
Mathematical Finance ..... MSc 12FT

University of Bristol
Mathematical Sciences ..... MSc 12FT

Brunel University
Financial Mathematics ..... MSc 12FT 24PT

University of Central Lancashire
Finance and Development ..... MSc 12FT

City University London
Financial Mathematics ..... MSc 12FT
Mathematical Trading and Finance ..... MSc 9FT 24PT
Project Management, Finance and Risk ..... MSc 12-18FT 24-30PT
Quantitative Finance ..... MSc 9-12FT

University of Edinburgh
Financial Mathematics ..... MSc 12FT
Financial Modelling and Optimization ..... MSc 12FT 24PT/PGDip 9FT
Financial Operational Research ..... MSc 12FT/PGDip 9FT

University of Essex
Mathematics and Finance ..... MSc 12FT 24PT/PGDip 9FT

University of Exeter
Financial Mathematics ..... MSc 9FT/MSc 12FT

Glasgow Caledonian University
Financial Services, Risk and Operations ..... MSc 12FT 24PT/PGDip 9FT 24PT

University of Glasgow
Financial Modelling ..... MSc 12FT

Heriot-Watt University
Applied Mathematical Sciences MSc 12FT 24PT/PGDip 9FT 21PT/PGCert 6FT 12PT
Applied Mathematical Sciences with Biological and Ecological Modelling ..... MSc 12FT 24-84PT/PGDip 9FT 15-48PT
Applied Mathematical Sciences with Climate Change Impact Modelling ..... MSc 12FT 24PT/PGDip 9FT 21PT
Computational Mathematics ..... MSc 12FT 24PT/PGDip 9FT 20PT
Financial Mathematics ..... MSc 12FT
Quantitative Finance and Mathematics ..... MSc 12FT 24PT/Diploma 9FT 21PT

University of Hertfordshire
Financial Market Analysis ..... MSc 12FT

University of Hull
Financial Mathematics ..... MSc 12FT

University of Kent
Finance, Investment and Risk ..... MSc 12FT/PGDip 12FT
International Master's in Statistics with Finance ..... MSc 24FT/GradDip 24FT
International Masters in Statistics ..... MSc 24FT
Statistics with Finance ..... MSc 12FT

King's College London
Financial Mathematics ..... MSc 12FT 24PT

University of Leeds
Financial Mathematics ..... MSc 12FT

University of Leicester
Financial Mathematics and Computation ..... MSc 12FT 24PT/PGDip 9FT

University of Liverpool
Financial Mathematics ..... MSc 12FT

London Metropolitan University
Finance ..... MSc 12FT 24PT
Mathematics ..... MSc 12FT 24-48PT

London School of Economics and Political Science (LSE)
Financial Mathematics ..... MSc 10FT

Loughborough University
Mathematical Finance ..... MSc 12FT

University of Manchester
Mathematical Finance ..... MSc 12FT
Quantitative Finance: Financial Engineering ..... MSc 12FT
Quantitative Finance: Risk Management ..... MSc 12FT

Newcastle University
Finance ..... MSc 12FT
Finance and Economics (Research) ..... MA 12FT 24PT
Finance and Financial Regulation ..... MSc 12FT
Finance and Law with Islamic Finance ..... MSc 12FT
Finance, Accounting and Business ..... GradDip 9FT
Quantitative Finance and Risk Management ..... MSc 12FT

University of Nottingham
Numerical Techniques for Finance ..... MSc 12FT

Oxford Brookes University
Finance ..... MSc 12FT 24PT

University of Oxford
Mathematical & Computational Finance ..... MSc 10FT

Plymouth University
Finance ..... MSc 12FT 24PT

University of Portsmouth
Mathematics ..... PGCE (Postgraduate) 12FT/PGCE (Professional) 12FT

University of Reading
Financial Engineering ..... MSc 10FT

Royal Holloway, University of London
Financial and Industrial Economics ..... MSc 12FT

University of Sheffield
Statistics with Financial Mathematics ..... MSc 12FT 24-36 PTDL

University of Southampton
Advanced Tribology ..... MSc 12FT

University of Stirling
Computing for Financial Markets ... MSc 12FT/PGDip 9FT/PGCert 9FT

University of Strathclyde
Quantitative Finance ..... MSc 12FT/PGDip 9FT

University of Sussex
Financial Mathematics ..... MSc 12FT

Swansea University
Mathematics and Computing for Finance ..... MSc 12FT 24/36PT

Mathematics

Trinity College Dublin - the University of Dublin
Finance .... MSc 12FT 24PT

UCL - University College London
Engineering with Finance .... MSc 12FT/PGDip 9FT
Financial Computing .... MSc 12FT
Financial Mathematics .... MSc 12FT
Financial Risk Management .... MSc 12FT
Financial Systems Engineering .... MSc 12FT

University of Warwick
Financial Mathematics .... MSc 12FT

University of York
Financial Engineering .... MSc 12FT
Mathematical Finance .... MSc 12FT
Mathematical Finance Conversion Year for the MSc... Conversion Year 9FT
Mathematical Finance by Online Distance Learning .... MSc 18-36DL/PGDip 12-24DL/PGCert 6-12DL

Mathematical finance
Research Courses

University of Cambridge
Applied Mathematics and Theoretical Physics .... PhD 36FT
Mathematics .... PhD 36FT

University of Exeter
Mathematics .... PhD 48FT 84PT/MPhil 36FT 60PT

University of Manchester
Financial Mathematics .... PhD 36FT 72PT

Newcastle University
Finance and Accounting .... PhD 36FT 72PT/MPhil 12FT 24PT

Queen's University Belfast
Finance .... PhD 36FT 72PT/MPhil 24FT 48PT

Mathematics
Taught Courses

University of Bath
Mathematical Sciences .... MSc 12FT 24PT

Birkbeck, University of London
Applied Statistics and Operational Research .... MSc 24PT
Financial Risk Management .... MSc 12FT 24PT
Mathematics .... MSc 24PT

University of Birmingham
Mathematics and Computing in Biology and Medicine .... MSc 12FT
Mathematics, Operational Research, Statistics and Econometrics (MORSE) .... MSc 12FT/PGCert 12FT/PGDip 12FT
Mathematics, Operational Research, Statistics and Econometrics (MORSE) .... MSc 12FT
Multidisciplinary Optimisation .... MSc 12FT

University of Bristol
Logic and Philosophy of Mathematics .... MA 12FT 24PT

University of Cambridge
Advanced Study in Mathematics .... PGCert 9FT

Cardiff University
Operational Research, Applied Statistics and Risk .... MSc 12FT 24-36PT

Cranfield University, Shrivenham
Scientific Computation .... MSc 24FT 60PT/PGCert 4FT 36PT/PGDip 9FT 48PT

University of Dundee
Mathematical Biology .... MSc 12FT
Mathematics .... Diploma 9FT

University of Edinburgh
Financial Mathematics .... MSc 12FT
Financial Modelling and Optimization .... MSc 12FT 24PT/PGDip 9FT
Financial Operational Research .... MSc 12FT/PGDip 9FT
Mathematics .... MSc 12FT 24PT/PGDip 9FT
Operational Research with Computational Optimization .... MSc 12FT 24PT/PGDip 9FT
Operational Research with Risk .... MSc 12FT 24PT/PGDip 9FT

University of Essex
Discrete Mathematics and its Applications .... MSc 12FT/PGDip 9FT
Financial Decision Making with Applications .... MSc 12FT 24PT/PGDip 9-12FT
Mathematics and Finance .... MSc 12FT 24PT/PGDip 9FT
Operational Research and Computer Science .... MSc 12FT 24PT/PGDip 9FT
Statistics and Computer Science .... MSc 12FT/PGDip 9FT
Statistics and Data Analysis .... MSc 12FT
Statistics and Econometrics .... MSc 12FT/PGDip 9FT
Statistics and Operational Research .... MSc 12FT/PGDip 9FT

University of Exeter
Advanced Mathematics .... MSc 12FT
Financial Mathematics .... MSc 9FT/MSc 12FT

National University of Ireland Galway
Mathematics .... MSc 12FT/HDipAppSc 12FT PGDip 12FT/MA 12 or 24FT

University of Glasgow
Mathematics/Applied Mathematics .... MSc 12FT 24PT

Heriot-Watt University
Applied Mathematical Sciences MSc 12FT 24PT/PGDip 9FT 21PT/PGCert 6FT 12PT
Applied Mathematical Sciences with Climate Change Impact Modelling .... MSc 12FT 24PT/PGDip 9FT 21PT

Imperial College London
Mathematics and Finance .... MSc 12FT

University of Kent
International Master's in Mathematics and its Applications .... MSc 24FT
Mathematics and its Applications .... MSc 12FT 24PT

King's College London
Complex Systems Modelling - From Biomedical and Natural to Economic and Social Sciences .... MSc 12FT 24PT
Mathematics .... MSc 12FT 24PT

University of Leeds
Mathematics .... MSc 12FT

University of Limerick
Education Mathematics Teaching .... Professional Diploma 12FT
Mathematical Modelling .... MSc 12FT

Liverpool Hope University
Education & Mathematics .... MA 36PT
Mathematical Informatics Dual International Masters .... MSc 24FT

University of Liverpool
Mathematical Sciences .... MSc 12FT 24PT/PGDip 12FT 16PT/PGCert 12FT 8PT

London Metropolitan University
Mathematics .... MSc 12FT 24-48PT

London School of Hygiene and Tropical Medicine
Medical Statistics .... MSc 12FT 24PT

Loughborough University
Industrial Mathematical Modelling .... MSc 12FT

National University of Ireland, Maynooth
Mathematical Science .... HDip 12FT
Mathematics .... MSc 12-24FT/MA 12-24FT HDip 12FT

Nottingham Trent University
Subject Knowledge Enhancement (SKE) Courses (Chemistry, Physics, Mathematics) .... SKE 9FT

University of Nottingham
Mathematical Medicine and Biology .... MSc 12FT

The Open University
Mathematics .... MSc variableDL/PGDip variableDL/PGCert variableDL

University of Oxford
Mathematical & Computational Finance .... MSc 10FT
Mathematical Modelling and Scientific Computing .... MSc 12FT
Mathematics and the Foundations of Computer Science .... MSc 12FT

University of Portsmouth
Mathematics .... PGCE (Postgraduate) 12FT/PGCE (Professional) 12FT

Queen Mary, University of London
Mathematics .... MSc 12FT 24PT

University of Reading
Biometry .... MSc 12FT 24PT
Data Assimilation and Inverse Modelling in Geoscience .... MSc 12FT/PGDip 12FT
Mathematics (Secondary Teaching) .... PGCE 10FT

Royal Holloway, University of London
Mathematics for Applications .... MSc 12FT 24PT

University of Sheffield
Mathematics .... MSc 12FT
Statistics .... MSc 12FT 24-36 PTDL
Statistics with Financial Mathematics .... MSc 12FT 24-36 PTDL
Statistics with Medical Applications .... MSc 12FT 24-36 PTDL

University of St Andrews
Mathematics .... MSc 12FT 24PT/PGDip 9FT
Statistics .... MSc 12FT 24PT/PGDip 9FT

Staffordshire University
Mathematics .... PGCE 9FT

University of Strathclyde
Quantitative Finance .... MSc 12FT/PGDip 9FT

University of Sunderland
Mathematics Enhancement Course (Followed by the 1 year PGCE) .... PGCE(QTS) 18FT

University of Sussex
Mathematics .... MSc 12FT

Swansea University
Mathematics and Computing for Finance .... MSc 12FT 24/36PT
Modelling, Uncertainty and Data .... MSc 12FT 24/36PT

UCL - University College London
Mathematical Modelling .... MSc 12FT

University of Warwick
Complexity Science .... MSc 12FT/PGDip 12FT/PGCert 12FT
Interdisciplinary Mathematics .... MSc 12FT
Mathematical Biology and Biophysical Chemistry .... MSc 12FT 24PT
Mathematics .... MSc 12FT 24PT

University of Wolverhampton
Mathematics .... MSc 12FT 24PT/PGCert 12FT 24PT

Mathematics
Research Courses

University of Bath
Mathematical Sciences PhD (integrated).. PhD 24-48FT 36-72PT/MPhil 12-36FT 24-48PT
Mathematics .... PhD 24-48FT 36-72PT/MPhil 12-36FT 24-48PT

Birkbeck, University of London
Mathematics and Statistics .... PhD 24FT 36PT/MPhil 24FT 36PT

Brunel University
Department of Mathematical Sciences .... PhD 48FT 96PT/MPhil 24FT 48PT
Department of Mathematical Sciences .... PhD 48FT/MPhil 36FT

University of Cambridge
Applied Mathematics and Theoretical Physics .... PhD 36FT
Mathematics .... PhD 36FT

University of Chester
Higher Degrees by Research .... MPhil 12 - 48FT 24 - 72PT/PhD 24 - 48FT 48 - 84PT

City University London
Mathematical Sciences .... PhD/MPhil
Mathematics .... PhD/MPhil

Coventry University
Control Theory and Applications.. MSc by research 12FT 24-36PT

University of Dundee
Mathematics .... MPhil 24FT MSc by research 12FT PhD 36FT

Durham University
Mathematical Sciences .... PhD 36FT 72PT/MSc by research 12FT 24PT

University of East Anglia
Mathematics Education .... PhD 36FT 72PT/MPhil 24FT 48PT/MA by research 12FT 24PT

University of Edinburgh
Algebra and Number Theory .... PhD 36FT 72PT
Analysis .... PhD 36FT 72PT
Applied and Computational Mathematics .... PhD 36FT 72PT
Geometry and Topology .... PhD 36FT 72PT
Operational Research and Optimization .... PhD 36FT 72PT
Probability & Stochastic Analysis .... PhD 36FT 72PT
Pure Mathematics... PhD 36FT/MPhil 24FT/MSc by research 12FT

University of Essex
Applied Mathematics.... PhD 36FT 72PT/MPhil 24FT 48PT/MSc by research 12FT 24PT
Bioinformatics .... PhD 36FT 72PT/MPhil 24FT 48PT/MSc by research 12FT 24PT
Biostatistics..... PhD 36FT 72PT/MPhil 24FT 48PT/MSc by research 12FT 24PT
Discrete Mathematics... PhD 36FT 72PT/MPhil 24FT 48PT/MSc by research 12FT 24PT
Mathematical Biology... PhD 36FT 72PT/MPhil 24FT 48PT/MSc by research 12FT 24PT
Mathematics .... PhD 36FT 72PT/MPhil 24FT 48PT/MSc by research 12FT 24PT
Operational Research.... PhD 36FT 72PT/MPhil 24FT 48PT/MSc by research 12FT 24PT
Operational Research and Computer Science .... PhD 36FT 72PT/MPhil 24FT 48PT/MSc by research 12FT 24PT
Pure Mathematics .... PhD 36FT 72PT/MPhil 24FT 48PT/MSc by research 12FT 24PT
Statistics .... PhD 36FT 72PT/MPhil 24FT 48PT/MSc by research 12FT 24PT
Statistics and Data Analysis ..... PhD 36FT 72PT/MPhil 24FT 48PT/MSc by research 12FT 24PT
Statistics and Operational Research... PhD 36FT 72PT/MPhil 24FT 48PT/MSc by research 12FT 24PT

University of Exeter
Mathematics .... PhD 48FT 84PT/MPhil 36FT 60PT

University of Glasgow
Mathematics .... PhD 36FT/MSc by research 12FT

University of Greenwich
Computing and Mathematical Sciences MSc by Research MSc by research 12FT 24PT

Heriot-Watt University
Mathematics .... PhD 36FT 72PT

Mathematics

University of Kent
Mathematics .... MSc by research 12FT 24PT/MPhil 24FT 36PT/
PhD 36FT 60PT

King's College London
Mathematics Research....PhD 36FT 48-72PT/MPhil 36FT 48-72PT

Lancaster University
Applied Social Statistics............. MPhil 24FT 36PT/PhD 36FT 48PT
Mathematics .... PhD 36FT 48PT/MPhil 24FT 36PT

University of Leicester
Department of Mathematics ....PhD 36FT/MPhil 24FT

University of Liverpool
Advanced Science (Computer Sciences pathway)
(Algorithms)..MRes 12FT

University of Manchester
Mathematical Sciences...............................MPhil 12FT 24PT

University of Nottingham
Mathematical Sciences............... PhD 36FT 72PT/MPhil 24FT 48PT

The Open University
Distributionology .... PhD 36FT 72PT variableDL/MPhil 15FT 24PT
variableDL
History of Mathematics... PhD 36FT 72PT variableDL/MPhil 15FT
24PT variableDL
Mathematics .... PhD 36FT 72PT variableDL/MPhil 15FT 24PT
variableDL
STEM Education and engagement....... PhD 36FT 72PT variableDL

University of Oxford
Mathematics .... DPhil 48FT/MSc by research 24FT
Statistics ....DPhil 48FT/MSc by research 24-36FT

Plymouth University
Mathematics and Statistics ....PhD 36FT/MPhil 24FT
School of Mathematics and Statistics/CTM ....PhD 48FT 72PT/
MPhil 36FT 48PT

University of Portsmouth
Mathematics .... MPhil 24FT 48PT/PhD 36FT 72PT

Queen Mary, University of London
Mathematical Sciences..PhD/MPhil

Royal Holloway, University of London
Mathematics .... PhD 36FT 72PT/MPhil 24FT 48PT

University of Southampton
Graduate School in Mathematical Studies............PhD 36FT 72PT/
MPhil 24FT 48PT

Staffordshire University
Applied Mathematics Group .... PhD 36FT 36-60PT/MPhil 18FT
18-36PT

University of Strathclyde
Mathematics and Statistics - Research PhD 36-42FT/MPhil 12FT/
MRes 12FT

University of Surrey
Mathematics and Statistics ....MPhil 24FT/PhD 36FT

University of Sussex
Mathematics Research Programme .... PhD 24-48FT 36-72PT/
MPhil 12-36FT 24-48PT

Swansea University
Logic and Computation................................MRes 12FT 24PT
Mathematical Ecology ....MSc by research 12FT 24PT
Mathematics .... PhD 36FT 72PT/MPhil 24FT 48PT
MSc by research 12FT 24PT
Stochastic Processes: Theory and Application .....MRes 12FT 24PT

UCL - University College London
Mathematics and Physics in the Life Sciences and Experimental
Biology ....MRes +PhD 48FT

University of Warwick
Mathematical Interdisciplinary Research at Warwick ....PhD 36FT
60PT
Mathematics .... PhD 42FT 60PT

University of the West of Scotland
Department of Mathematics and Statistics...................PhD/MPhil

University of York
Mathematics ....PhD 36FT 72PT/MPhil 24FT 48PT/
MSc by research 12FT 24PT

Operational research
Taught Courses

University of Aberdeen
Mathematics .... MSc 12FT

Aston University
Operational Research & Management Studies............... MSc 12FT
Operational Research & Performance Management..... MSc 12FT

Birkbeck, University of London
Applied Statistics.................................MSc 24PT/PGCert 12PT
Applied Statistics and Operational Research .... MSc 24PT
Applied Statistics and Stochastic Modelling................... MSc 24PT
Applied Statistics with Medical Applications.................. MSc 24PT
Mathematics .... GradCert 12PT/GradDip 24PT

University of Birmingham
Mathematics, Operational Research, Statistics and Econometrics
(MORSE) ....MSc 12FT/PGCert 12FT/PGDip 12FT
Statistics ....MRes 12FT 24PT

Bournemouth University
Applied Data Analytics..MSc 12FT/MSc 24PT

University of Bristol
Mathematical Sciences.. MSc 12FT
Statistics ....MRes 12FT

Brunel University
Modelling and Management of Risk................................ MSc 12FT

Cardiff University
Operational Research and Applied Statistics .... MSc 12FT 24PT

University of Central Lancashire
Operations Management... MSc 12FT

University of Chester
Mathematics (and Statistics)...... MSc 12FT 24 - 36PT/PGDip 12FT
24 - 36PT/PGCert 12FT 12 - 24PT

University College Cork
Applied Science (Mathematical Modelling & Scientific
Computing)...MSc 12FT
Applied Science (Modelling & Numerical Computing)...HDip 9FT

Cranfield University, Shrivenham
Military Operational Research ....MSc 12FT 60PT/PGDip 9FT
48PT/PGCert 4FT 36PT
Scientific Computation ....MSc 24FT 60PT/PGCert 4FT 36PT/
PGDip 9FT 48PT

University of Dundee
Psychological Research Methods .... MSc 12FT

Durham University
Mathematical Sciences.. MSc 12FT

University of East London
Organisational Analysis .....MA 24 - 36PT/PGDip 18-24PT/PGCert
12-18PT

University of Edinburgh
Financial Operational Research .... MSc 12FT/PGDip 9FT
Operational Research ....MSc 12FT 24PT
Operational Research with Computational Optimization...... MSc
12FT 24PT/PGDip 9FT
Operational Research with Risk...........MSc 12FT 24PT/PGDip 9FT
Statistics and Operational Research.................MSc 12FT 24PT

University of Glasgow
Statistics .... MSc 12FT

University of Hertfordshire
Manufacturing Management ....MSc 12-16FT 36PT

University of Kent
Management Science .... MSc 12FT

University of Liverpool
Clinical Research (Online Degree) ....MSc 24FT 24+PT

London School of Economics and Political Science (LSE)
Statistics (Financial Statistics)................. MSc 9 or 12FT 21 or 24PT

University of Manchester
Analytics: Operational Research and Risk Analysis .... MSc 12FT

Middlesex University
Professional Studies..MProf 12-24DL
Work Based Studies ....MA 12-24DL
Public Works (DProf PW)........................ DProf by taught 24-36DL

Newcastle University
Research Training ....PGCert 9FT 21PT

University of Salford
Transport Engineering and Planning........................MSc 12FT 36PT

Southampton Solent University
Research..PGCert 12PT

University of Southampton
Operational Research ....MSc 12FT 24PT/PGDip 9FT
Transportation Planning and Engineering............MSc 12FT 24PT/
PGDip 12FT

University of Strathclyde
Operational Research ....MSc 12FT 24PT/PGDip 9FT 21PT

University of Surrey
Social Research Methods................................. MA 12FT 24PT

University of Sussex
Social Research Methods.......MSc 12FT/PGDip 12FT/PGCert 12FT

University of Warwick
Applied Social Research with Specialism in Health Studies.....MA
12FT/MA 24PT
Applied Social Research with Specialism in Social Work...............
MA 12FT 24PT
Management Science & Operational Research ..... MSc 12FT 24PT

Operational research
Research Courses

University of Aberdeen
Mathematical Sciences....PhD 36FT/MPhil 24FT/MSc by research
12FT

University of Birmingham
Management Mathematics...........................PhD 36FT/MPhil 24FT

Cardiff University
Applied Mathematics ....PhD 36FT/MPhil 12FT
Operational Research ....PhD 36FT/MPhil 12FT

Cranfield University, Shrivenham
Applied Mathematics and Operational Research ....PhD 36FT/
MPhil 24FT

University of East Anglia
Applied Mathematics................... PhD 36FT 72PT/MPhil 24FT 48PT
Pure Mathematics........................ PhD 36FT 72PT/MPhil 24FT 48PT

University of Edinburgh
Analysis ....PhD 36FT 72PT
Operational Research and Optimization................. PhD 36FT 72PT

University of Exeter
Mathematics .... PhD 48FT 84PT/MPhil 36FT 60PT

University of Hertfordshire
Algorithms ....PhD 36FT 72PT/MRes 12FT 24PT

University of Hull
Centre for Systems Studies........ PhD 36FT 60PT/MPhil 24FT 36PT

University of Kent
Operational Research and Systems ....PhD 36FT 60PT/MPhil 24FT
36PT/MSc by research 12FT 24PT

London School of Economics and Political Science (LSE)
Management Science .... MPhil 36-48FT/PhD 36-48FT

Loughborough University
Statistics and Operational Research...PhD 36FT 60PT/MPhil 24FT
36PT

The Open University
Applied Mathematics....... PhD 36FT 72PT variableDL/MPhil 15FT
24PT variableDL

Queen's University Belfast
Statisical Science and Operational Research........PhD 36FT 72PT/
MPhil 24FT 48PT

University of Salford
Centre for Operational Research and Applied StatisticsPhD 36FT/
MSc by research 24FT

University of Southampton
Graduate School in Mathematical Studies: Operational Research
PhD 36FT 72PT/MPhil 24FT 48PT

Swansea University
Mathematics ....MSc by research 12FT 24PT

Probability theory
Taught Courses

Birkbeck, University of London
Mathematics .... GradCert 12PT/GradDip 24PT
Statistics ....GradDip 24PT/GradCert 12-24PT

University of Glasgow
Financial Forecasting and Investment .... MSc 12FT
Financial Modelling .... MSc 12FT
Financial Risk Management .... MSc 12FT

Heriot-Watt University
Actuarial Management.................MSc 12FT 48PT/PGDip 9FT 48PT
Actuarial Science ....MSc 12FT 24PT/PGDip 9FT 18PT
Financial Mathematics... MSc 12FT
Quantitative Financial Engineering........................MSc 12FT 24PT/
Diploma 9FT 21PT
Quantitative Financial Risk Management ... MSc 12FT/PGDip 9FT

London School of Economics and Political Science (LSE)
Risk and Stochastics ....MSc 10FT 22PT
Statistics .... MSc 9 or 12FT 21 or 24PT
Statistics (Financial Statistics)................. MSc 9 or 12FT 21 or 24PT

University of Nottingham
Statistics and Applied Probability .... MSc 12FT

University of Sheffield
Statistics ....MSc 12FT 24-36 PTDL
Cert 9 PTDL
Statistics with Financial Mathematics.........MSc 12FT 24-36 PTDL
Statistics with Medical Applications .... MSc 12FT 24-36 PTDL

University of St Andrews
Statistics ....MSc 12FT 24PT/PGDip 9FT

University of Warwick
Statistics ....MSc 12FT 24PT/PGDip 9FT 18PT

Probability theory
Research Courses

Cardiff University
Applied Mathematics....................................PhD 36FT/MPhil 12FT

Mathematics

University of Edinburgh
Probability & Stochastic Analysis.............................PhD 36FT 72PT

University of Exeter
Mathematics .... PhD 48FT 84PT/MPhil 36FT 60PT

University of Leeds
Statistics ....PhD 36+FT/MSc by research 12FT

University of Manchester
Probability...PhD 36FT 72PT

University of Nottingham
Risk Analysis, Social Processes and Health ....MPhil 36FT/PhD 24FT
Statistics and Probability.......................................PhD 36-48FT 72PT

The Open University
Applied Mathematics....... PhD 36FT 72PT variableDL/MPhil 15FT 24PT variableDL
Distributionology.... PhD 36FT 72PT variableDL/MPhil 15FT 24PT variableDL

University of Oxford
Statistics ....DPhil 48FT/MSc by research 24-36FT

University of Sheffield
Probability and Statistics.. PhD 36FT 72PT/MPhil 24FT 48PT/New Route PhD 48FT

Swansea University
Stochastic Processes: Theory and Application.....MRes 12FT 24PT

Pure mathematics
Taught Courses

Birkbeck, University of London
Mathematics ....MSc 24PT

University of Dundee
Mathematical Biology ....MSc 12FT

University of East Anglia
Mathematics ....MSc 12FT

University of Essex
Mathematics and Finance.....................MSc 12FT 24PT/PGDip 9FT

University of Exeter
Advanced Mathematics..MSc 12FT

University of Glasgow
Mathematics/Applied Mathematics ....MSc 12FT 24PT

Heriot-Watt University
Applied Mathematical Sciences MSc 12FT 24PT/PGDip 9FT 21PT/PGCert 6FT 12PT
Applied Mathematical Sciences with Biological and Ecological Modelling .... MSc 12FT 24-84PT/PGDip 9FT 15-48PT
Applied Mathematical Sciences with Climate Change Impact Modelling ....MSc 12FT 24PT/PGDip 9FT 21PT
Computational Mathematics......MSc 12FT 24PT/PGDip 9FT 20PT
Quantitative Finance and Mathematics MSc 12FT 24PT/Diploma 9FT 21PT

Imperial College London
Pure Mathematics...MSc 12FT 24PT

University of Kent
Economic Analysis...MSc 24FT

London School of Economics and Political Science (LSE)
Applicable Mathematics...MSc 12FT

University of Manchester
Pure Mathematics & Mathematical Logic ....MSc 12FT 24PT

University of Nottingham
Pure Mathematics..MSc 12FT

The Open University
Mathematics ....MSc variableDL/PGDip variableDL/PGCert variableDL

University of Oxford
Mathematics and the Foundations of Computer Science ...... MSc 12FT

University of Portsmouth
Mathematics .... PGCE (Postgraduate) 12FT/PGCE (Professional) 12FT

Royal Holloway, University of London
Mathematics for Applications...................................MSc 12FT 24PT

University of Sheffield
Mathematics ....MSc 12FT
Statistics ....MSc 12FT 24-36 PTDL
Statistics with Financial Mathematics.........MSc 12FT 24-36 PTDL
Statistics with Medical Applications...........MSc 12FT 24-36 PTDL

University of St Andrews
Mathematics ....MSc 12FT 24PT/PGDip 9FT
Statistics ....MSc 12FT 24PT/PGDip 9FT

UCL - University College London
Mathematical Modelling...MSc 12FT

Pure mathematics
Research Courses

Aberystwyth University
Pure Mathematics ....MPhil 12FT 24PT PhD 36FT 60PT

University of Birmingham
Management Mathematics...........................PhD 36FT/MPhil 24FT
Pure Mathematics...PhD 36FT/MPhil 24FT

University of Cambridge
Applied Mathematics and Theoretical Physics ....PhD 36FT
Mathematics ....PhD 36FT

Cardiff University
Applied Mathematics......................................PhD 36FT/MPhil 12FT
Pure Mathematics...PhD 36FT/MPhil 12FT

University of Dundee
Mathematics ....MPhil 24FT MSc by research 12FT

University of Edinburgh
Algebra and Number Theory ....PhD 36FT 72PT
Geometry and Topology ....PhD 36FT 72PT
Pure Mathematics... PhD 36FT/MPhil 24FT/MSc by research 12FT

University of Essex
Applied Mathematics....PhD 36FT 72PT/MPhil 24FT 48PT/MSc by research 12FT 24PT
Mathematics ....PhD 36FT 72PT/MPhil 24FT 48PT/MSc by research 12FT 24PT
Pure Mathematics.........PhD 36FT 72PT/MPhil 24FT 48PT/MSc by research 12FT 24PT

University of Exeter
Mathematics .... PhD 48FT 84PT/MPhil 36FT 60PT

University of Hertfordshire
Algorithms ....PhD 36FT 72PT/MRes 12FT 24PT

Keele University
Pure Mathematics Group ....PhD 36FT

University of Leeds
Pure Mathematics.................. PhD 36-42FT/MSc by research 12FT

Loughborough University
Pure Mathematics....................... PhD 36FT 60PT/MPhil 24FT 36PT

University of Manchester
Pure Mathematics..PhD 36FT 72PT

Newcastle University
Mathematics .... PhD 36FT 72PT/MPhil 12FT 24PT

Nottingham Trent University
Pure Mathematics..................................... MPhil .FT/PhD 48FT 96PT

The Open University
History of Mathematics... PhD 36FT 72PT variableDL/MPhil 15FT 24PT variableDL
Mathematics .... PhD 36FT 72PT variableDL/MPhil 15FT 24PT variableDL
Pure Mathematics... PhD 36FT 72PT variableDL/MPhil 15FT 24PT variableDL

University of Oxford
Mathematics ....DPhil 48FT/MSc by research 24FT
Statistics ....DPhil 48FT/MSc by research 24-36FT

Queen's University Belfast
Pure Mathematics....................... PhD 36FT 72PT/MPhil 24FT 48PT

University of Sheffield
Pure Mathematics....................... PhD 36FT 72PT/MPhil 24FT 48PT

University of St Andrews
Pure Mathematics........................... PhD 36FT 72PT/MPhil 12-24FT

Swansea University
Mathematical Ecology ....MSc by research 12FT 24PT
Mathematics ....MSc by research 12FT 24PT

Statistics
Taught Courses

Bangor University
Consumer Psychology with Business........... MSc 12FT/PGDip 9FT MA 12FT

Birkbeck, University of London
Applied Statistics...MSc 24PT/PGCert 12PT
Applied Statistics and Operational Research .... MSc 24PT
Applied Statistics and Stochastic Modelling.................... MSc 24PT
Applied Statistics with Medical Applications................... MSc 24PT
Financial Engineering.. GradDip 12FT 24PT
Financial Engineering...MSc 12FT 24PT
Financial Risk Management ....MSc 12FT 24PT
Mathematics ....MSc 24PT
Statistics .... GradDip 24PT/GradCert 12-24PT

University of Birmingham
Mathematics, Operational Research, Statistics and Econometrics (MORSE) ....MSc 12FT/PGCert 12FT/PGDip 12FT
Statistics ....MRes 12FT 24PT

Bournemouth University
Applied Data Analytics......................................MSc 12FT/MSc 24PT

University of Bristol
Mathematical Sciences.. MSc 12FT
Statistics ....MRes 12FT

University of Cambridge
Statistical Science... MPhil 10FT

Cardiff University
Operational Research and Applied Statistics ....MSc 12FT 24PT

University of Central Lancashire
IT and Statistics for Health..UniCert 3PT
Statistics For Clinical Trials..PGCert 12-36PT

University of Chester
Mathematics (and Statistics)...... MSc 12FT 24 - 36PT/PGDip 12FT 24 - 36PT/PGCert 12FT 12 - 24PT

University College Cork
Statistics ....HDip 9FT 18PT

University of Dundee
Applied Health Statistics .... MSc 12FT

University of East Anglia
Computing Science ....MSc 12FT 24PT
Information Systems ....MSc 12FT 24PT
Knowledge Discovery and Data Mining ....MSc 12FT/MSc 24PT/MSc 36PT
Statistics ....MSc 12FT 24PT

University of Edinburgh
Financial Modelling and Optimization ....MSc 12FT 24PT/PGDip 9FT
Financial Operational Research .... MSc 12FT/PGDip 9FT
Statistics and Operational Research........................MSc 12FT 24PT

University of Essex
Cognitive Neuropsychology.. MSc 12FT
Cognitive Neuroscience .... MSc 12FT
Discrete Mathematics and its Applications....................MSc 12FT/PGDip 9FT
Financial Decision Making with Applications.......MSc 12FT 24PT/PGDip 9-12FT
Mathematics and Finance.....................MSc 12FT 24PT/PGDip 9FT
Operational Research and Computer Science.......MSc 12FT 24PT/PGDip 9FT
Psychology...MSc 12FT/GradDip 12FT
Research Methods in Psychology .... MSc 12FT
Statistics and Computer Science.................... MSc 12FT/PGDip 9FT
Statistics and Data Analysis .... MSc 12FT
Statistics and Econometrics................................. MSc 12FT/PGDip 9FT
Statistics and Operational Research............. MSc 12FT/PGDip 9FT

Glasgow Caledonian University
Social Research..MSc 12FT 24PT

University of Glasgow
Advanced Statistics ....MRes 12FT
Biostatistics... MSc 12FT
Environmental Statistics .... MSc 12FT
Financial Modelling .... MSc 12FT
Geomatics & Management .... MSc 12FT
Health Technology Assessment..MSc 12FT 24PT/PGDip 9FT 18PT
Social Statistics .... MSc 12FT
Statistics .... MSc 12FT

Heriot-Watt University
Actuarial Management................MSc 12FT 48PT/PGDip 9FT 48PT
Actuarial Science ....MSc 12FT 24PT/PGDip 9FT 18PT
Applied Mathematical Sciences with Biological and Ecological Modelling .... MSc 12FT 24-84PT/PGDip 9FT 15-48PT
Applied Mathematical Sciences with Climate Change Impact Modelling ....MSc 12FT 24PT/PGDip 9FT 21PT
Financial Mathematics.. MSc 12FT
Quantitative Finance and Mathematics................MSc 12FT 24PT/Diploma 9FT 21PT
Quantitative Financial Engineering........................MSc 12FT 24PT/Diploma 9FT 21PT
Quantitative Financial Risk Management ... MSc 12FT/PGDip 9FT

University of Hull
Economics and Business.. MSc 12FT

Imperial College London
Statistics .... MSc 12FT

University of Kent
Actuarial Science ....PGDip 9FT
International Masters in Applied Actuarial Science......MSc 24FT/PGDip 24FT
International Masters in Statistics with Finance ....MSc 24
International Masters in Statistics........... GradDip 24FT/MSc 24FT
Research Methods in Psychology ....MSc 12FT 24PT
Statistics .... MSc 12FT
Statistics with Finance .... MSc 12FT

Kingston University
Applied Social Research Methods .... MA 12FT 24PT
Business and Economic Forecasting........................MSc 12FT 24PT

Lancaster University
Statistics ....MSc 12FT/PGDipRes 9FT

University of Leeds
Statistics .... MSc 12FT

Mathematics

Statistics with Applications to Finance............................ MSc 12FT

University of Leicester
Medical Statistics ....MSc 12FT 24PT

London School of Economics and Political Science (LSE)
Risk and Stochastics ....MSc 10FT 22PT
Statistics ....MSc 9 or 12FT 21 or 24PT
Statistics (Financial Statistics).....MSc 9 or 12FT 21 or 24PT

London School of Hygiene and Tropical Medicine
Medical Statistics ....MSc 12FT 24PT

University of Manchester
Social Research Methods and Statistics .....MSc 12FT 24PT/PGDip 9FT 24PT
Statistics ....MSc 12FT 24PT/PGDip 12FT

National University of Ireland, Maynooth
Statistics ....HDip 12FT

Middlesex University
Statistics Practice, MProf...MA 24PT

University of Nottingham
Statistics .... MSc 12FT
Statistics and Applied Probability............................ MSc 12FT
Statistics with Biomedical Applications .... MSc 12FT

Oxford Brookes University
Medical Statistics ....MSc 12FT 24PT

University of Oxford
Applied Statistics................................ MSc 12FT/PGDip 9FT
Mathematics and the Foundations of Computer Science ...... MSc 12FT

Queen's University Belfast
Dating and Chronology... MSc 12FT

University of Reading
Data Assimilation and Inverse Modelling in Geoscience .... MSc 12FT/PGDip 12FT
Financial Engineering .... MSc 10FT
Research Methods in Psychology ....MSc 12FT 24PT/PGDip 8FT 20PT

University of Sheffield
Mathematics .... MSc 12FT
Statistics ....MSc 12FT 24-36 PTDL
Statistics with Financial Mathematics.........MSc 12FT 24-36 PTDL
Statistics with Medical Applications ....MSc 12FT 24-36 PTDL

University of Southampton
Official Statistics...MSc 30-60PT/PGDip 24-54PT/PGCert 12-24PT
Operational Research ....MSc 12FT 24PT/PGDip 9FT
Social Statistics .... MSc 12-24FT 24PT/PGDip 9FT 21PT
Statistics with Applications in Medicine....MSc 12FT 24PT/PGDip 9FT

University of St Andrews
Applied Statistics and Datamining......MSc 12FT 24PT/PGDip 9FT
Mathematics ....MSc 12FT 24PT/PGDip 9FT
Statistics ....MSc 12FT 24PT/PGDip 9FT

University of Stirling
Applied Social Research ....MSc 12FT 30PT/PGDip 9FT 18PT
Applied Social Research (Criminology) ....MSc 12FT 30PT/PGDip 9FT 18PT
Applied Social Research ....MRes 12FT 30PT

Trinity College Dublin - the University of Dublin
Statistics ....PGDip 12/24PT

UCL - University College London
Statistics .... MSc 12FT 24PT
Statistics: Medical Statistics............................MSc 12FT 24PT

University of Warwick
Statistics ....MSc 12FT 24PT/PGDip 9FT 18PT

University of York
Statistics and Computational Finance............................ MSc 11FT

Statistics
Research Courses

University of Aberdeen
Mathematical Sciences....PhD 36FT/MPhil 24FT/MSc by research 12FT

University of Bath
Statistics .... PhD 24-48FT 36-72PT/MPhil 12-36FT 24-48PT

Birkbeck, University of London
Mathematics and Statistics....... PhD 24FT 36PT/MPhil 24FT 36PT

University of Birmingham
Statistics ....PhD 36FT/MSc by research 12FT

University of Bristol
Complexity Sciences......................................PhD 48FT/MRes 48FT

Cardiff University
Applied Mathematics......................................PhD 36FT/MPhil 12FT
Operational Research ....PhD 36FT/MPhil 12FT
Probability and Statistics................................PhD 36FT/MPhil 12FT

City University London
Actuarial Science and Statistics...............MPhil 12FT/PhD 24-36FT

Cranfield University, Shrivenham
Applied Mathematics and Operational Research ....PhD 36FT/MPhil 24FT

University of East Anglia
Applied Mathematics.................. PhD 36FT 72PT/MPhil 24FT 48FT
Pure Mathematics...................... PhD 36FT 72PT/MPhil 24FT 48FT

University of Edinburgh
Analysis ....PhD 36FT 72PT
Probability & Stochastic Analysis...........................PhD 36FT 72PT
Statistics ....PhD 36FT 72PT

University of Essex
Applied Mathematics....PhD 36FT 72PT/MPhil 24FT 48PT/MSc by research 12FT 24PT
Applied Social and Economic Research........PhD 36FT 72PT/MPhil 24FT 48PT
Bioinformatics............................PhD 36FT 72PT/MPhil 24FT 48PT/MSc by research 12FT 24PT
Biostatistics.....PhD 36FT 72PT/MPhil 24FT 48PT/MSc by research 12FT 24PT
Discrete Mathematics...PhD 36FT 72PT/MPhil 24FT 48PT/MSc by research 12FT 24PT
Mathematical Biology...PhD 36FT 72PT/MPhil 24FT 48PT/MSc by research 12FT 24PT
Mathematics ....PhD 36FT 72PT/MPhil 24FT 48PT/MSc by research 12FT 24PT
Operational Research ....PhD 36FT 72PT/MPhil 24FT 48PT/MSc by research 12FT 24PT
Operational Research and Computer Science.......PhD 36FT 72PT/MPhil 24FT 48PT/MSc by research 12FT 24PT
Pure Mathematics..........PhD 36FT 72PT/MPhil 24FT 48PT/MSc by research 12FT 24PT
Statistics ....PhD 36FT 72PT/MPhil 24FT 48PT/MSc by research 12FT 24PT
Statistics and Data Analysis .....PhD 36FT 72PT/MPhil 24FT 48PT/MSc by research 12FT 24PT
Statistics and Operational Research...PhD 36FT 72PT/MPhil 24FT 48PT/MSc by research 12FT 24PT
Survey Methodology .... PhD 36FT 72PT/MPhil 24FT 48PT

University of Exeter
Mathematics .... PhD 48FT 84PT/MPhil 36FT 60PT

University of Glasgow
Statistics .... PhD 36-42FT/MSc by research 12FT

Imperial College London
Medical Statistics ....PhD

Keele University
Statistics Group..PhD 36FT

University of Kent
Statistics ....PhD 36FT 60PT/MPhil 24FT 36PT/MSc by research 12FT 24PT

Lancaster University
Applied Social Statistics.............. MPhil 24FT 36PT/PhD 36FT 48PT
Statistics .... PhD 36FT 48PT/MPhil 24FT 36PT
Statistics and Epidemiology ....PhD 36PT

University of Leeds
Statistics ....PhD 36+FT/MSc by research 12FT

London School of Economics and Political Science (LSE)
Management Science......................... MPhil 36-48FT/PhD 36-48FT

Statistics .... PhD 36-48FT/MPhil 36-48FT

Loughborough University
Statistics and Operational Research...PhD 36FT 60PT/MPhil 24FT 36PT

University of Manchester
Social Statistics ....PhD 36FT 48-72PT
Statistics .... PhD 36FT 72PT

Newcastle University
Statistics .... PhD 36FT 72PT/MPhil 12FT 24PT

University of Nottingham
Statistics and Probability......................................PhD 36-48FT 72PT

The Open University
Applied Mathematics........ PhD 36FT 72PT variableDL/MPhil 15FT 24PT variableDL
Bayesian Statistics... PhD 36FT 72PT variableDL/MPhil 15FT 24PT variableDL
Distributionology .... PhD 36FT 72PT variableDL/MPhil 15FT 24PT variableDL
Medical Statistics .... PhD 36FT 72PT variableDL/MPhil 15FT 24PT variableDL
Multivariate Statistics...... PhD 36FT 72PT variableDL/MPhil 15FT 24PT variableDL
Statistics PhD 36FT 72PT variableDL/MPhil 15FT 24PT variableDL

University of Oxford
Mathematics .... DPhil 48FT/MSc by research 24FT
Numerical Analysis ....DPhil 36-48FT/MSc by research 24FT
Statistics ....DPhil 48FT/MSc by research 24-36FT

Plymouth University
Mathematics and Statistics............................PhD 36FT/MPhil 24FT
School of Mathematics and Statistics/CTM ....PhD 48FT 72PT/MPhil 36FT 48PT

Queen's University Belfast
Statisical Science and Operational Research.........PhD 36FT 72PT/MPhil 24FT 48PT

University of Salford
Centre for Operational Research and Applied StatisticsPhD 36FT/MSc by research 24FT

University of Sheffield
Probability and Statistics.. PhD 36FT 72PT/MPhil 24FT 48PT/New Route PhD 48FT

University of Southampton
Graduate School in Mathematical Studies: Statistics.....PhD 36FT 72PT/MPhil 24FT 48PT
School of Social Sciences - Demography .....PhD 36FT 72PT/MPhil 24FT 48PT
School of Social Sciences - Gerontology ......PhD 36FT 72PT/MPhil 24FT 48PT
School of Social Sciences - Social Statistics............PhD 36FT 72PT/MPhil 24FT 48PT

University of St Andrews
Applied Mathematics...................... PhD 36FT 72PT/MPhil 12-24FT
Statistics .... PhD 36FT 72PT/MPhil 12-24FT

University of Strathclyde
Drug Delivery Systems ....MRes 12FT 24PT
Drug Delivery Systems with International Placement ....MRes 12FT 24PT

University of Surrey
Mathematics and Statistics ....MPhil 24FT/PhD 36FT

Swansea University
Stochastic Processes: Theory and Application.....MRes 12FT 24PT

UCL - University College London
Statistical Science... PhD 36FT 60PT

University of Warwick
Statistics ....PhD 36FT/MPhil 24FT

University of the West of Scotland
Department of Mathematics and Statistics...................PhD/MPhil

Medicine and surgery

Anaesthetics
Taught Courses

Bangor University
Medical Sciences.....................MRes 12FT 24PT/PGCert 3FT 15PT

University of Dundee
Minimal Access Surgery (MMAS) ....MMAS 12FT

University of Edinburgh
Clinical Management of Pain........MSc 36-72DL/PGDip 24-48DL/
PGCert 12-24DL
General Surgery (Online Distance Learning)..................ChM 24DL
Surgery ....ChM 24DL
Surgical Sciences .... MSc 36DL/Diploma 24DL/Cert 12DL

University of Salford
Surgical Practice..........................MSc 36PT/PGDip 24PT/PGCert 9PT

Teesside University
Evidence-based Medicine (Anaesthesia)......MSc 24 or 36PT 24 or
36DL
Surgical Care Practitioner (Cardiothoracic Surgery) ... PGDip 24PT
Surgical Care Practitioner (General Surgery)................ PGDip 24PT
Surgical Care Practitioner (Orthopaedic Surgery) .... PGDip 24PT

Anaesthetics
Research Courses

Barts and the London School of Medicine and Dentistry
Anaesthetics Unit..PhD/MPhil

University of Birmingham
Anaesthetics and Intensive Care.............................PhD 36FT 72PT/
MSc by research 12FT 24PT

University of Cambridge
Anaesthesia ....PhD 36FT

University of Edinburgh
Anaesthesia and Pain MedicineMPhil 24FT 48PT/PhD 36FT 72PT/
MSc by research 12FT 24PT
Anaesthesia, Critical Care and Pain Medicine...................PhD 36FT
Surgery .. PhD 36FT 72PT/MPhil 24FT 48PT/MSc by research 12FT
24PT

Imperial College London
Anaesthesia ....PhD

University of Nottingham
Anaesthesia and Intensive CarePhD 36FT 72PT/MPhil 24FT 48PT/
DM 24FT 48PT

University of Oxford
Surgery ....DPhil 48FT/MSc by research 24-36FT

Art therapy
Taught Courses

Birmingham City University
Art Health and Well-being.. MA 12FT 24PT

University of Central Lancashire
Arts Health.........................MA 12FT 24-68PT/PGDip 12FT 24-68PT/
PGCert 12FT 24-68PT/UniCert 3PT
Arts-Health Analysis .... PGCert 6PT

University of Chester
Health and Social Care - Art Therapy ....MA 24 - 72PT/PGDip
24 - 60PT/PGCert 12 - 36PT

University of Derby
Art Therapy ....MA 24FT

University of East London
Art Psychotherapy .... MSc 36PT/PGDip 24PT/PGCert 12PT

University of Glasgow
Primary Expressive Arts ....PGCert 12PT

Goldsmiths, University of London
Art Psychotherapy........................PGDip 24FT 36PT/MA 32FT 48PT
Participatory and Community Arts..PGCert 12FT 24-60PT/PGDip
12FT 24-60PT/MA 12FT 24-60PT

University of Hertfordshire
Art Therapy .... MA 24FT 36PT

Leeds Metropolitan University
Art Psychotherapy (Post - Registration).............................MA 12PT
Art Psychotherapy Practice .... MA 24FT 36PT
Associated Art Psychotherapy Research...........................MA 24PT
Psychotherapy..MA 48PT

National University of Ireland, Maynooth
Arts (Adult Guidance & Counselling)..............................HDip 12FT

Queen Margaret University, Edinburgh
Art Psychotherapy (International) .... MSc 24FT 36-72PT/
PGDip 24FT 36-60PT

University of Roehampton
Art Psychotherapy .... MA 24FT 36PT

University of South Wales
Art Psychotherapy..MA 36PT
Buddhist Studies .... PGCert 12DL/PGDip 24DL/MA 36DL
Evaluation Studies..PGCert 9-12DL
Music Therapy...MA 36PT

Staffordshire University
Community & Participatory Arts............................... MA 12FT 24PT

Art therapy
Research Courses

University of Dundee
Duncan of Jordanstone College of Art & Design .... MPhil 24FT
PhD 36FT

Goldsmiths, University of London
Art...MPhil 24FT 36PT/PhD 36-48FT 48-72PT
Art Psychotherapy.........PhD 36-48FT 48-72PT/MPhil 24FT 36PT
MRes 12FT 24PT

University of Roehampton
Arts and Play Therapies.......PhD 24-48FT 36-60PT/MPhil 21-36FT
33-48PT

Biomedical engineering
Taught Courses

University of Aberdeen
Biomedical Engineering................MSc 12FT 24PT/PGDip 9FT 21PT

Anglia Ruskin University
Biomedical Science ....MSc 36 - 60DL

Bangor University
Medical Molecular Biology with Genetics .... MSc 12-24FT
Medical Sciences........................MRes 12FT 24PT/PGCert 3FT 15PT
Molecular Biology with Biotechnology .... MSc 12FT

Barts and the London School of Medicine and Dentistry
Medical Electronics and Physics .... MSc 12FT 24PT

University of Bath
Orthopaedic Engineering - Joint Replacement...........PGCert 12PT

University of Bedfordshire
Biomedical Engineering .... MSc 12FT 36PT

University of Birmingham
Biomedical Research - in vivo...MRes 12FT
Chemical Biology and Biomedical Imaging .... MSc 12FT
Physical Sciences of Imaging in the Biomedical Sciences....... MSc
48FT
Translational Medicine: Interdisciplinary Biomedical
Technologies .... MSc 12FT

University of Bolton
Medical & Health Care Devices .... MSc 12FT 36PT

University of Bradford
Biomedical Sciences.. MSc 12FT
Medical Engineering - full-time.. MSc 12FT
Medical Engineering - part-time ....MSc 12-18PT

University of Brighton
Biomedical Sciences......MSc 12FT 24PT/PGDip 12FT/PGCert 12FT
Pharmaceutical and Biomedical Sciences........... MRes 12FT 24PT/
PGCert 12FT 24PT/PGDip 12FT 24PT

University of Bristol
Biomedical Sciences Research........MSc 12FT/PGDip 12FT/PGCert
12FT
Stem Cells and Regeneration ....MSc 12-24DL/PGDip 12-24DL/
PGCert 12-24DL

Brunel University
Biomedical Engineering.. MSc 12FT

University of Cambridge
Computational Biology.. MPhil 11FT

Cardiff Metropolitan University
Biomedical Science ...... MSc 12FT 24PT/PGDip 12FT 24PT/PGCert
12FT 12PT

Cardiff University
Clinical Engineering.....................................MSc 12FT 24-36PT
Orthopaedic Engineering ....MSc 12-24DL

University of Central Lancashire
Biomedical Science .... MSc 12FT

University of Chichester
Sport and Exercise Biomechanics.........MSc 12FT 24PT/PGDip 9FT
18PT/PGCert 9FT 12PT

City University London
Clinical Engineering with Healthcare Technology Management .
MSc 12-18FT 24-30PT

University College Cork
Biomedical Sciences... MSc 24PT

De Montfort University
Advanced Biomedical Science ....MSc 12FT 36PT/PGDip 24PT/
PGCert 12PT

University of Dundee
Biomedical Engineering .... MSc 12FT
Design for Medical Technologies .... MSc 12FT
Orthopaedic and Rehabilitation Technology.............MSc 24-60DL
Sports and Biomechanical Medicine (MSc Full time in-house).....
MSc 12FT
Sports and Biomechanical Medicine (MSc Part time with
externally arranged project)....................................... MSc 24PT

Sports and Biomechanical Medicine (MSc Part time with in-
house project) .... MSc 24PT

University of East London
Biomedical Immunology ....
MSc 12FT 24PT/PGDip 8FT 16PT/PGCert 4FT 8PT
Biomedical Science MSc .... MSc 12FT 24PT/PGDip 8FT 16PT/
PGCert 4FT 8PT
Biomedical Science DBMS ....DProf by taught VariousFT

University of Edinburgh
Biomechanics .... MSc 12FT
Regenerative Medicine: Industrial and Clinical Delivery...............
MSc 12FT

University of Essex
Biomedical Science .... MSc 12FT 24PT

National University of Ireland Galway
Biomedical Science ....MSc 12FT 24DL/PGCert 12DL
Sustainable Resource Management: Policy and Practice .... MSc
12FT

Glasgow Caledonian University
Biomolecular and Biomedical Sciences .... MSc 12FT
Life Sciences - Biological and Biomedical Sciences/Psychology/
Vision Sciences .... MRes 12FT

University of Glasgow
Applied Medical Science .... MSc 12FT
Biomedical Sciences....................................MRes 12FT/PGDip 8FT

University of Greenwich
Biomedical Sciences................... MSc 12FT 24PT/PGDip 12FT 24PT
Biomedical Sciences (online)...........MSc 12-24DL/PGDip 12-24DL

Heriot-Watt University
Computer Vision and Robotics (VIBOT) .... MSc 48FT

University of Huddersfield
Analytical Bioscience ....MSc 12FT 24-48PT

University of Hull
Biomedical Science .... MSc 12FT
Medical Engineering .... MSc 12FT
Molecular Medicine .... MSc 12FT

Imperial College London
Biomedical Engineering.. MSc 12FT
Biomedical Research ....MRes 12FT
Biomedical Research: Microbial Pathogensis............MRes 12FT
Biomedical Research: Personalised Healthcare............MRes 12FT

Keele University
Biomedical Engineering.......................................MSc 12FT 24PT

University of Kent
Biotechnology and Bioengineering ....MSc 12FT 24PT

King's College London
Complex Systems Modelling - From Biomedical and Natural to
Economic and Social Sciences ....MSc 12FT 24PT
Radiopharmaceutics & PET Radiochemistry ....MSc 12FT 24PT

Kingston University
Biomedical Science (Haematology/Medical Microbiology) ... MSc
12FT 24PT
Biomedical Science with Management Studies....MSc 12FT 24PT

Lancaster University
Biomedical Science (by research) ....MSc 12FT 24PT
Biomedicine .... MSc 12FT 24PT/PGDip 12FT 24PT

Leeds Metropolitan University
Applied Biomedical Sciences Research ....MSc 12FT
Biomedical Sciences..................................MSc 12FT unknownPT
Integrated Masters Biomedical Sciences ....MBIOMS 48FT

University of Leeds
Medical Engineering..MSc(Eng) 12FT

University of Leicester
Molecular Genetics ....MSc 12FT/PGDip 9FT/PGCert 4FT
Molecular Pathology and Toxicology.... MSc 12FT 24-36PT/PGDip
12FT

London Metropolitan University
Biomedical Science ....MSc 12FT 24+PT

London South Bank University
Biomedical Engineering & Instrumentation ....MSc 12FT 24PT

Manchester Metropolitan University
Biomedical Science .... MSc 12FT 30PT
Biomedical Science featuring Exercise and Health options ... MSc
12FT 24-36PT

University of Manchester
Medical Physics and Clinical Engineering .... MSc 12FT 24-36PT/
PGDip 9FT 24PT
Tissue Engineering for Regenerative Medicine.............MRes 12FT

Middlesex University
Biomedical Science (Cellular Pathology) ....MSc 12FT 24PT
Biomedical Science (Haematology and Transfusion Science) MSc
12FT 24PT
Biomedical Science (Medical Microbiology)..........MSc 12FT 24PT
Biomedical Science (Clinical Biochemistry) ....MSc 12FT 36PT

Nottingham Trent University
Biomedical Science ....MSc 12FT 24PT

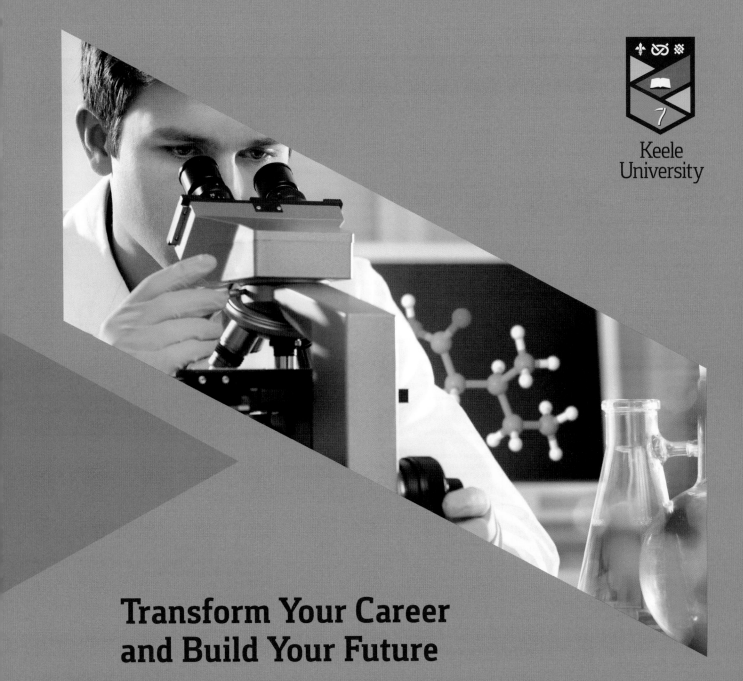

Transform Your Career and Build Your Future

MSc in Biomedical Engineering
MSc in Cell & Tissue Engineering

- Taught within a hospital based and international recognised research department
- Experience laboratory and hospital-based research projects
- Competitive bursaries available for international applicants
- Attendance of international research conference

Today's health challenges require cross-disciplinary knowledge. Our Master programmes meet this demand and provide in-depth coverage over a wide range of topics. These include Physiological measurement, Medical equipment & technology management, Biomedical signal process; Medical device design principles; Introduction to medical imaging; Biomaterials; Biomechanics; Cell biomechanics; Bioreactor design; Stem cell and Tissue engineering.

www.keele.ac.uk/biomed
www.keele.ac.uk/pgtcourses/cellandtissueengineering

Apply now
for September 2013 intake
and January 2014 intake

Keele University

Medicine and surgery

Biomedical Science by Flexible Learning........MSc 24DL

University of Nottingham
Bioengineering: Biomaterials and Biomechanics........MSc 12FT
Bioengineering: Imaging and Sensing........MSc 12FT
Bioengineering: The Digital Body........MSc 12FT
Statistics with Biomedical Applications........MSc 12FT

University of Oxford
Biomedical Engineering........MSc 12FT

University of Portsmouth
Biomedicine........MSc 12FT

Queen Mary, University of London
Biomaterials........MSc 12FT
Biomedical Engineering........MSc 12FT 24PT
Medical Electronics and Physics........MSc 12FT 24PT

Robert Gordon University
Clinical Biomechanics........MSc 12FT

University of Roehampton
Biomechanics........MSc 12FT 24-48PT

Sheffield Hallam University
Biomedical Sciences........MSc 12FT 24PT/PGDip 8FT 16PT/PGCert 4FT 8PT

University of Sheffield
Biological and Bioprocess Engineering........MSc(Eng) 12FT
Biomaterials and Regenerative Medicine........MSc 12FT
Bionanotechnology........MSc(Eng) 12FT
Molecular Medicine........MSc 12FT
Stem Cell and Regenerative Medicine........MSc 12FT

St George's, University of London
Biomedical Science........MRes 12FT

Staffordshire University
Clinical Biomechanics........PGCert 9PT/PGDip 15PT/MSc 36PT
Clinical Biomechanics and Diabetes........PGCert 12PT
Clinical Biomechanics and Pain Management in the Lower limb........PGCert 12PT
Clinical Podiatric Biomechanics........PGCert 9PT/PGDip 15PT/MSc 36PT

University of Strathclyde
Biomedical Sciences........MSc 12FT/PGDip 9FT
Biotechnology........MSc 12FT
Medical Devices........MSc 12FT/PGDip 9FT
Medical Technology........MRes 12FT 24PT
Prosthetics and / or Orthotics Rehabilitation Studies..MSc 36PT/PGDip 24PT/PGCert 12PT

University of Surrey
Biomedical Engineering........MSc 12FT 24PT

Trinity College Dublin - the University of Dublin
Biomedical Sciences (Intercalated)........MSc 12FT

University of Ulster
Biomedical Engineering........MSc 12FT 36PT/PGDip 9FT 24PT
Biomedical Science..MSc 12FT 18PT 18DL/PGDip 9FT 16PT 16DL

UCL - University College London
Biomaterials and Tissue Engineering........MSc 12FT 24 - 60PT
Biomedical Sciences........MSc 12FT 24PT
Physics and Engineering in Medicine by Distance Learning..MSc 24-60PT/PGDip 24-60PT/PGCert 24-60PT
Physics and Engineering in Medicine: Biomedical Engineering and Medical Imaging........MSc 12FT 24PT

University of Warwick
Biomedical Engineering........MSc 12FT

University of the West of Scotland
Medical Technology......Cert 6FT 12-24PT/Diploma 12FT 24-48PT

University of the West of England, Bristol
Biomedical Science (5 specialist subject options)........MSc 12FT 36PT
Biomedical Science (Professional Doctorate)........DProf by taught 60PT

University of Westminster
Biomedical Sciences........MSc 12FT

University of Wolverhampton
Biomedical Science....MSc 12FT 24PT/DPhil by taught 12FT 24PT

Biomedical engineering
Research Courses

University of Aberdeen
Biological Science....MSc by research 12FT/MPhil 24FT/PhD 36FT
Biomedical Physics and Bioengineering........PhD 36FT/MSc by research 12FT/MPhil 24FT
Biomedical Sciences........PhD 36FT/MPhil 24FT/MSc by research 12FT

Aston University
Biomaterials and Bio-molecular Science Research Group.......PhD 36FT/MPhil 24FT
Biomedical Engineering Research Group....PhD 36FT/MPhil 24FT
Biomedical Sciences........PhD 36FT/MPhil 12-24FT

Barts and the London School of Medicine and Dentistry
Medical Electronics........PhD/MPhil
Medical Electronics and Physics........PhD/MPhil/MSc by research 12FT

University of Birmingham
Biomaterials........MRes 12FT 24PT
Biomedical Ethics PhD by research........PhD 36FT 72PT/MSc by research 12FT 24PT
Natural Computation........MRes 12FT

University of Bradford
Medical Biosciences........PhD 36-48FT 48-60PT/MPhil 12-24FT 24-48PT

Cardiff University
Biomedical Research........MRes 12FT
Clinical Kinaesiology........MPhil 24FT 48PT/PhD 36FT 60PT
Institute of Medical Engineering and Medical Physics........MPhil 12-24FT/PhD 36FT/EngD 48FT

University of Central Lancashire
Biological and Biomedical........PhD 48FT 84PT/MPhil 36FT 60PT/MSc by research 24FT 36PT/MD 48PT

Coventry University
Biomedical Computing........MSc by research 12FT PhD 36FT/MPhil 24FT/MRes 12FT

Cranfield University, Shrivenham
Materials and Medical Sciences........PhD/MPhil
Smart Materials - (Medical Sciences)........PhD/MPhil

University of Dundee
Mechanical Engineering........PhD 36FT

Durham University
Biological and Biomedical Sciences........PhD 36FT 72PT/MSc by research 12FT 24PT

University of Edinburgh
Regenerative Medicine........MPhil 24FT 48PT/PhD 36FT 72PT

Glasgow Caledonian University
Biological and Biomedical Sciences/Psychology/Vision Sciences MRes 12FT

University of Glasgow
Biomedical Engineering...PhD 36-48FT 60-72PT/MSc by research 12-24FT 24-36PT
Neuroscience and Biomedical Systems........PhD 36FT/MSc by research 12FT

University of Greenwich
Biomedical Sciences - Research........MPhil 36FT 72PT/PhD 36FT 72PT

Imperial College London
Biological and Medical Systems........PhD/MPhil
Biological and Medical Systems........PhD/MPhil
Biomedical Research........MRes 12FT
Biomedical Research (Microbial Pathogenesis)........MRes 12FT
Biomedical Sciences........PhD/MPhil
EPSRC Doctoral Training Studentships........PhD 36FT

University of Leeds
Biomedical Sciences........PhD 36+FT/MPhil 24FT/MSc by research 12FT
Institute of Medical and Biological Engineering........PhD 36+FT/MPhil 24FT
Tissue Engineering and Regenerative Medicine........PhD 48FT

University of Lincoln
Biomedical and Medical Science........MPhil 18FT 30PT/PhD 33FT 60PT

University of Liverpool
Biomedical Sciences and Translational Medicine........MRes 12FT

Manchester Metropolitan University
Biomedical Science by Research........PhD 24-48FT 42-84PT/MPhil 18-36FT 36-72PT/MSc by research 9-18FT 18-36PT

University of Manchester
Biomaterials Science and Dental Technology....MPhil 12FT 24PT/PhD 36FT 72PT
Biomedical Materials.....PhD 36FT 72PT/MPhil 12FT 24PT/MSc by research 12FT 24PT

Newcastle University
Biomedicine.......MPhil 12FT 24PT/PhD 36FT 72PT/MD 24FT 48PT
Biosciences........MRes 12FT
Medical Sciences........MRes 12FT

University of Nottingham
Biomedical Sciences Research Areas........PhD 36FT 72PT
Cell Signalling..PhD 36FT 72PT/MPhil 24FT 48PT/MRes 12FT/DM 36FT 72PT
Medical Physics (Division of Radiological and Imaging Sciences) PhD 36FT 72PT/MPhil 24FT 48PT/DM 36FT 72PT
Wolfson Centre for Stem Cells, Tissue Engineering and Modelling (STEM)........PhD 24-36FT 48-72PT/MPhil 12-24FT 24-48PT

Oxford Brookes University
Health & Biomedical Sciences - Glycobiology and Cancer MPhil/PhD........PhD 24-60FT 36-72PT/MPhil 24-36FT 36-48PT
Health & Biomedical Sciences - Human Health & Performance Research Group MPhil/PhD........PhD 24-60FT 36-72PT/MPhil 24-36FT 36-48PT
Health & Biomedical Sciences - Molecular Neuroscience MPhil/PhD........PhD 24-60FT 36-72PT/MPhil 24-36FT 36-48PT
Health and Biomedical Sciences - Peptide Transport ....MPhil/PhD 36-60FT 48-72PT/PhD 24-60FT 36-72PT/MPhil 24-36FT 36-48PT

University of Portsmouth
Pharmacy and Biomedical Science.....MPhil 24FT 48PT/PhD 36FT 72PT/MD 24FT 48PT
Biomedical Science........DBMS 48PT

University of Salford
Biosciences........PhD 36FT/MSc by research 12FT

University of Sheffield
Biomedical Science........PhD 36FT 72PT/MPhil 24FT 48PT
Medical Physics and Clinical Engineering...PhD 36FT 72PT/MPhil 24FT 48PT

University of Strathclyde
Biomedical Engineering - Research...MPhil 12FT/PhD 36FT/MRes 12FT/EngD 36FT
Biomedical Sciences........MRes 12FT 24PT
Medical Devices........EngD 48FT
Pharmacy and Biomedical Sciences - Research....PhD 36FT 48PT/MPhil 12FT 24PT/MRes 12FT/DPharm 36FT
Prosthetics and / or Orthotics Rehabilitation Studies....PhD 36FT 72PT/MPhil 12FT 24PT

University of Surrey
Engineering and Physical Sciences........PhD 36FT 48PT/PhD 48FT 96PT

Swansea University
Sports Science........MPhil 24FT 48PT/PhD 36FT 72PT/MSc by research 12FT 24PT

University of Ulster
Master of Research........MRes 12FT

UCL - University College London
Biomedical Research........PhD 36FT 60PT
Medical Physics and Bioengineering........PhD 36FT 60PT

Cardiology
Taught Courses

Barts and the London School of Medicine and Dentistry
Mechanisms of Vascular Disease........MRes 12FT

University of Buckingham
General Internal Medicine........MD 24/36FT

Canterbury Christ Church University
Cardiology........MSc 12FT/MSc 36PT

University of Central Lancashire
Advanced Stroke Practice......MSc 36FT 60PT/PGDip 24PT/PGCert 12PT

University of Chester
Cardiovascular Health and Rehabilitation....MSc 12FT 24 - 48PT/PGDip 12FT 24 - 48PT/PGCert 12FT 12 - 24PT

University of East Anglia
Stroke Recovery...MSc 12FT 36PT/PGDip 12FT 24PT/PGCert 12PT

University of Edinburgh
Cardiovascular Biology........MSc(Res) 12FT

University of Essex
Cardiac Rehabilitation........MSc 12FT 24PT

University of Glasgow
Cardiovascular Sciences........MSc(MedSci) 12FT
Sport & Exercise Medicine........MSc(MedSci) 12FT 24PT

Imperial College London
Cardiology........PGDip 9FT
Preventive Cardiology: Cardiovascular Health and Disease Prevention........MSc 12FT 24PT

King's College London
Advanced Practice (Cardiac Care)..MSc 36-72PT/PGDip 24-72PT/PGCert 12-72PT
Cardiovascular Research........MSc 12FT

University of Manchester
Cardiovascular Health and Disease........MRes 12FT

North East Surrey College of Technology
Perfusion Science........MSc 27PT/PGDip 18PT/PGCert 9PT

Newcastle University
Clinical Sciences (Physiological Sciences) with specialisms in: Cardiac Science; Vascular Science; Respiratory and Sleep Science; Gastrointestinal Physiology; Urodynamic Science........MSc 36PT

Queen Mary, University of London
Inflammation: Cellular and Vascular Aspects........MRes 12FT

Sheffield Hallam University
Cardiovascular Medicine for Primary Care Physicians........PGDip 24PT/PGCert 12PT

Trinity College Dublin - the University of Dublin
Cardiology........MSc 12FT
Cardiovascular Rehabilitation and Prevention......MSc 12FT 24PT

UCL - University College London
Cardiovascular Science........MSc 12FT

Medicine and surgery

Cardiology
Research Courses

Barts and the London School of Medicine and Dentistry
Department of Cardiac, Vascular and Inflammation Research comprising Cardiology .... PhD
Experimental Pathology .... PhD

University of Birmingham
Cardiovascular Medicine ... PhD 36FT 72PT/MSc by research 12FT 24PT/MD 24PT

University of Edinburgh
Cardiovascular .... MSc by research 12FT 24PT
Cardiovascular Research .... PhD 36FT 48PT/MPhil 24FT 36PT
Wellcome Trust Cardiovascular Research Initiative .... PhD 36FT 72PT/MPhil 24FT 36PT/MSc by research 12FT 24PT

University of Glasgow
Cardiovascular and Medical Sciences..... PhD 36FT 60PT/MD 24FT 48PT/MSc(MedSci) by research 12FT 24PT

King's College London
Cardiovascular (Research Division) .... PhD 36FT 48-72PT/MPhil 36FT 48-72PT

University of Leeds
Cardiac Function in Health and Disease.. PhD 36+FT/MPhil 24FT/MSc by research 12FT
Computational Biology of the Heart .... PhD 36+FT/MPhil 24FT/MSc by research 12FT

University of Leicester
Cardiovascular Sciences .... PhD 36FT/MD 24FT

University of Nottingham
Cardiovascular Medicine .... PhD 36FT 72PT/MPhil 24FT 48PT/MRes 12FT/DM 36FT 72PT
Integrative Cardiovascular and Metabolic Physiology and Pharmacology . PhD 36FT 72PT/MPhil 24FT 48PT/DM 36FT 72PT/MRes 12FT 24PT
Molecular and Cellular Science PhD 36FT 72PT/MPhil 24FT 48PT/MRes 12FT
Rehabilitation and Ageing .... PhD 36FT 72PT
Stroke Medicine PhD 36FT 72PT/MPhil 24FT 48PT/DM 36FT 72PT

University of Oxford
Cardiovascular Medicine .... DPhil 48FT/MSc by research 24FT

Queen Mary, University of London
Mechanisms of Vascular Disease .... MRes 12FT

University of Sheffield
Cardiovascular Science .... PhD 36FT 72PT/MPhil 24FT 48PT
Infection, Inflammation and Immunity .... PhD 36FT 72PT/MPhil 24FT 48PT

St George's, University of London
Cardiovascular Medicine .... PhD 36FT 84PT/MPhil 24FT 48PT/MDRes 24PT

University of Surrey
Cardiovascular Dietary Research .... MPhil 24FT 36PT/PhD 36FT 48PT
Nutrition and Health: Cardiovascular Disease ..... PhD 36FT 48PT/MPhil 24FT 36PT

Child development
Taught Courses

Aberystwyth University
Childhood and Creative Development .... MA 12FT 24PT/PGDip 9FT 21PT

Anglia Ruskin University
Clinical Child Psychology .... MSc 12 - 15FT 24 - 30PT

Bangor University
Applied Behaviour Analysis .... PGCert 4FT 9PT/PGDip 9FT 18PT/MSc 12FT 24PT
Language Development .... MSc 12FT 36PT
Psychological Research .. MSc 12FT 24PT/PGDip 8FT 16PT/PGCert 4FT 8PT
Psychology........ MRes 12FT/PGCert 3FT MA 12FT 24PT/PGDip 9FT 18PT/PGCert 4FT 8PT

University of Bolton
Children's Literature and Culture .... MA 24PT
Safeguarding and Promoting Children's Welfare.... MSc 36-60PT/PGDip 24PT/PGCert 12PT

University of Brighton
Child Health and Education .... MSc 12 - 36FT 24 - 72PT/PGCert 12 - 36FT 24 - 72PT/PGDip 12 - 36FT 24 - 72PT
Child Health and Management ... MSc 12 - 36FT 24 - 72PT/PGDip 12 - 36FT 24 - 72PT/PGCert 12 - 36FT 24 - 72PT

Bucks New University
Child & Adolescent Studies .... MSc 12FT 24PT

University of Central Lancashire
Child Care Practice, PQ Specialist Award with Children, Young People, Families & Carers .... PGCert 18PT
Child Care and Welfare .... MA 12FT 24-60PT
Child Computer Interaction .... MRes 12FT 24PT
Child Health .... MSc 36PT
Neonatal Studies .... MA 60PT/PGDip 24PT/PGCert 12PT
Psychology of Child Development .... MSc 12FT 24PT/PGDip 9FT 24PT/PGCert 9FT 24PT

University of Chester
Family and Child Psychology ... MSc 12FT 24PT/PGDip 12FT 24PT/PGCert 12FT 12-24PT

University of Cumbria
Leading Intergrated Children's Services ... MSc 24 - 60PT/GradDip 12 - 36PT

University of Derby
Cognitive Behavioural Psychotherapy (Children and Adolescents) (BABCP accredited) .... MSc 24-36PT

University of Dundee
Developmental Psychology .... MSc 12FT

University of East Anglia
Child and Family Psychology .... MSc 12FT 24PT

University of East London
Child Psychoanalytic Psychotherapy Prof Doc (D. Ch. Psych. Psych.) .... DProf by taught 48FT 60PT
Child and Adolescent Primary Mental Health Care Work .... MA 36PT/PGDip 24PT/PGCert 12PT
Infant Mental Health (Early Years Development) .... MA 36PT/PGDip 24PT/PGCert 12PT
Professional Doctorate in Educational and Child Psychology D.Ed. Ch.Psy .... DProf by taught 36FT
Psychological Therapy with Children, Young People and Families MA 36PT
Therapeutic Communication with Children PG Cert PGCert 12PT

Edge Hill University
Integrated Children and Young People's Practice...... MSc 36-72PT

University of Edinburgh
Applied Psychology (Healthcare) for Children and Young People .... MSc 12FT
Childhood Studies .... MSc 12FT 24PT
Children & Young People's Mental Health and Psychological Practice.. MSc 12FT 24-72PT/PGCert 12-24PT/PGDip 9FT 24-48PT
Health & Social Care - Children & Young People's Mental Health: Ecological Approaches ODL .... PGCert 9DL

University of Glasgow
Child Health .... PGDip 12-24PT PGCert 12-24FT

University of Gloucestershire
Play and Playwork .... PGCert 12-24DL/PGDip 12-24DL/MA 24-48DL
Teacher Training PGCE (Primary) .... PGCE 12FT

Goldsmiths, University of London
Education: School-Based Explorations .... MA 24-60PT
The Science of Psychology, Genetics & Education .... MSc 12FT 24PT

Institute of Education
Child Development .... MA 12FT 24-48PT/MSc 12FT 24-48PT

Keele University
Child Social Development .... MSc 12FT 24PT

University of Kent
Analysis and Intervention in Intellectual and Development Disabilities .... MSc 12FT 24PT/PGDip 12FT 24PT
Applied Behaviour Analysis (Intellectual and Developmental Disabilities) .... MSc 12FT 24PT/PGCert 12FT 24PT/PGCert 12FT 24PT

King's College London
Advanced Practice (Child Health).. MSc 36-72PT/PGDip 24-72PT/PGCert 12-72PT
Child & Adolescent Mental Health .... MSc 12FT 24PT

Kingston University
Child Psychology .... MSc 12FT
Maternal and Child Health: Socio-Cultural Perspectives .... MSc 12FT 24PT

Leeds Metropolitan University
Childhood Studies and Early Years .... MA 12FT 24PT

University of Leeds
Child Health .... MMedSci 36PT/PGDip 24PT

University of Leicester
Child and Adolescent Mental Health .... PGCert 12FT 12PT/PGDip 12FT 24PT/MSc 12FT 36PT

Liverpool John Moores University
Early Years (3 -7 years) .... PGCE 12FT

London Metropolitan University
Child, Adolescent and Family Mental Health .... MSc 12FT 24PT

London School of Economics and Political Science (LSE)
Anthropology and Development .... MSc 12FT 24PT
Anthropology and Development Management .... MSc 12FT 24PT

Manchester Metropolitan University
Autistic Spectrum Conditions .... MA 12-60PT

Middlesex University
Child and Family Mental Health Work .... AdvDip 12PT/PGCert 12PT
Child, Adolescent and Family Mental Health Work... AdvDip 7PT/PGCert 7PT

Newman University
Children, Young People and Families .... MA 24FT 36-48PT
Early Years Teacher Status .... Early Years Teacher Status 6FT/Early Years Teacher Status 12FT

University of Northampton
Child and Adolescent Mental Health .... MSc 12FT 24PT/PGDip 12PT
Counselling Children and Young People .... MSc 18FT 36PT

Northumbria University
Leadership and Management in Integrated Childrens Services ... MA 36PT/PGDip 24PT/PGCert 12PT
Nursing (MNurs) Registered Nurse (Child) .... MA 24-48FT
Psychoanalytical Observational Studies .... MA 36/24PT

Nottingham Trent University
Applied Child Psychology .... MSc 12FT 24PT

University of Nottingham
Counselling Children and Young People .... MA 12FT

Oxford Brookes University
Childhood Studies .... MA 12FT 24PT/PGDip 12FT 24PT/PGCert 12FT 12PT
Children, Young People and Family Well-Being .... MSc 12-36DL/PGDip 8-36DL/PGCert 4-36DL

University of Oxford
Education (Child Development and Education) .... MSc 12FT

University of Portsmouth
Child Forensic Studies: Psychology and Law .... MSc 12/24DL

Queen Margaret University, Edinburgh
Collaborative Working: Education and Therapy ... PGCert 12-48PT

Queen Mary, University of London
Mental Health: Psychological Therapies D/L option ...... MSc 12FT 24PT

Queen's University Belfast
Atypical Child Development .... MSc 12FT

University of Roehampton
Attachment Studies .... PGCert 6FT 12PT PGDip 6-12FT 12PT

University Campus Suffolk
Childhood and Youth Studies .... MA 12FT 24 - 36PT

University of Salford
Child and Adolescent Mental Health .... MSc 24PT/PGDip 18PT/PGCert 9PT

Sheffield Hallam University
Early Childhood Studies MA 12FT 36PT/PGDip 12FT 24PT/PGCert 12FT 12PT
Early Years Education .... PGCE 12FT
Early Years Professional Status .... EYPS 12FT 6-15PT

University of Sheffield
Educational and Child Psychology .... Doctor 36FT

University of South Wales
Child Health and Welfare Studies (Online Delivery) MSc 12-48FT 36-60DL
Child and Adolescent Mental Health .... MA 12FT 36PT
Consultative Supervision .... MA 24PT/PGDip 12PT
Counselling Children and Young People .... MA 24PT
Developmental Disorders .... MSc 24-60PT

St George's, University of London
Maternal and Child Health .... MSc 12FT 24PT

University of Strathclyde
Early Childhood Studies........ MSc 24PT/PGDip 24PT/PGCert 24PT
Educational Support...... MSc max 60PT/PGDip max 48PT/PGCert max 24PT

University of Surrey
Health Psychology .... MA 12FT 24PT

University of Sussex
Foundations of Clinical Psychology and Mental Health .... MSc 12FT 24PT

Swansea University
Childhood Studies .... MA 12FT 24PT

University of Wales Trinity Saint David
Adolescent Psychology .... GradCert 12PT
Plentyndod Cynnar .... MA 48PT/PGCert 12PT/PGDip 18PT

UCL - University College London
Child and Adolescent Mental Health ... MSc 12FT 24-60PT/PGDip 24-60PT/PGCert 12PT
International Child Health .... MSc 12FT 24-60PT/PGDip 9FT 24-60PT/PGCert 12FT 24PT
Paediatrics and Child Health: Advanced PaediatricsMSc 36-60PT/PGCert 12-24PT/PGDip 36-60PT
Paediatrics and Child Health: Community Child Health .... MSc 12FT 36-60PT/PGCert 12-24PT/PGDip 9FT 18-45PT

University of Warwick
Child Health .... PGA 12PT
MSc 12FT 24-96PT/PGDip 12FT 24PT/PGCert 12FT 24PT

Medicine and surgery

Child Health Services: Management, Organisations and Data Systems.......PGA 12PT/CPDMod 1PT
Health Sciences: Child Health........MSc 36PT/PGDip 24PT/PGCert 12PT/PGA 12PT

University of Winchester
Child Development...... MSc 12FT 24PT/PGDip 12FT 24PT/PGCert 12FT 24PT

York St John University
Psychology of Child & Adolescent Development .... MSc 12FT 36PT

Child development
Research Courses

Aberystwyth University
Psychology (PhD) .... PhD 36FT 60PT

Bangor University
Doctorate by Research .... PhD 36FT/MPhil 24FT

University of Birmingham
Applied Educational and Child Psychology..... AppEd / Child PsyD 36FT

University College Cork
Doctor of Social Science....... DSocSci 48FT

Heriot-Watt University
Applied Psychology....... PhD 36FT 48PT/MPhil 24FT 36PT

King's College London
Child & Adolescent Psychiatry. PhD 36FT 72PT/MPhil 36FT 72PT/MD 36FT 72PT

Liverpool School of Tropical Medicine
Child & Reproductive Health....... PhD/MPhil/MIHR

University of Liverpool
Child Health....... PhD 24-84FT/MPhil 12-48FT/MD 24-84FT

University of Nottingham
Early life nutrition and disease.... PhD 36FT 72PT/DM 24FT 48PT/MPhil 24FT 48PT

The Open University
Doctorate in Education .... EdD 36PT

Plymouth University
Behaviour .... PhD 36FT/MPhil 24FT
Developmental Disability Research & Education Group...... MPhil tbcFT
Parenting and Child Welfare....... MPhil tbcFT

Swansea University
Childhood Studies....... MPhil 12FT/PhD 36FT

UCL - University College London
Child Health....... PhD 36FT 60PT/MD(Res) 24FT
Developmental Science .... PhD 36FT 60PT

Chinese medicine
Taught Courses

University of Aberdeen
Practical Theology....... MTh 12FT 24PT

University of Central Lancashire
Herbal Medicine by elearning....... MSc 36-48PT/PGDip 24PT/PGCert 12PT

University of Hertfordshire
Western Medical Acupuncture....... MSc up to 60PT

School of Oriental and African Studies - SOAS
Chinese Studies....... MA 12FT 24-36PT
Medical Anthropology....... MA 12FT 24-36PT

UCL - University College London
Chinese Health and Humanity....... MA 12FT
Chinese Studies (Health and Humanity)....... MA 24FT

University of West London
Women's Health and Fertility in Traditional Chinese Acupuncture....... CPPD 4DL

University of Westminster
Chinese Herbal Medicine .... MSc 12FT 24PT
Chinese Medicine: Acupuncture .... MSc 12FT 24PT
Herbal Medicine .... MSc 12FT 24PT

Chiropractic
Taught Courses

Anglo-European College of Chiropractic
Chiropractic....... MSc 30DL/PGDip 24DL/PGCert 12DL

Queen Mary, University of London
Musculoskeletal Clinical Sciences....... MSc 12FT 24PT
Musculoskeletal Sciences....... MSc 12FT 24PT

Chiropractic
Research Courses

University of Portsmouth
Professional Doctorate in Chiropractic....... DChiro 48PT

Complementary and alternative medicine
Taught Courses

University of Central Lancashire
Herbal Medicine by elearning....... MSc 36-48PT/PGDip 24PT/PGCert 12PT
Integrated Healthcare by elearning..... MSc 36-48PT/PGDip 24PT/PGCert 12PT
Non-Surgical Facial Aesthetics for Registered Healthcare Professionals....... MSc 36PT/PGDip 24PT

University of Derby
International Spa Management....... MA 36FT

University of Dundee
Medical Education .... MMedEd 12FT
Motion Analysis .... MSc 12FT 24PT 24DL

Glasgow Caledonian University
Health and Social Care Education .... MSc 12FT

University of Glasgow
Translational Medicine....... MRes 12FT

King's College London
Translational Medicine........ MSc 24-48PT/PGDip 24-48PT/PGCert 24-48PT

School of Oriental and African Studies - SOAS
Medical Anthropology .... MA 12FT 24-36PT

University of Southampton
Research Methods in Health .. MSc 24PT/PGDip 12PT/PGCert 6PT

University of St Andrews
Medicine....... MRes 12FT 24PT

University of Westminster
Complementary Medicine .... MSc 12FT 24PT
Herbal Medicine .... MSc 12FT 24PT

Complementary and alternative medicine
Research Courses

University of Cambridge
Medical Sciences....... MPhil 12FT

University of Dundee
Social Dimensions of Health Institute .... MPhil 24FT PhD 36FT

Middlesex University
Complementary Therapies......... PhD 36FT 60PT/MPhil 36FT 60PT

University of Southampton
Research Methods in Health .... MSc by research 24PT/PGDip by research 12PT/PGCert by research 6PT

Dance movement therapy
Taught Courses

Canterbury Christ Church University
Dance Movement Therapy....... MA 24PT

Central School of Speech and Drama, University of London
Drama and Movement Therapy (Sesame) .... MA 18FT
Movement Studies....... MA 12FT 24PT

University of Derby
Dance Movement Therapy/Psychotherapy .... MA 36FT

University of Dundee
Eye Movements & Cognition .... MSc 12FT

Edge Hill University
Dance Movement Psychotherapy .... MA 24FT 48PT

University of Glasgow
Primary Expressive Arts .... PGCert 12PT

Goldsmiths, University of London
Dance Movement Psychotherapy .... PGDip 24FT 36PT/MA 32FT 48PT

Leeds Metropolitan University
Art Psychotherapy Practice .... MA 24FT 36PT
Psychotherapy....... MA 48PT

Manchester Metropolitan University
Movement Practice for Theatre .... MA 12FT

University of Roehampton
Dance Movement Psychotherapy .... MA 24FT 36PT
Post Graduate Diploma- Dance Studies .... PGDip 9FT 24PT

UCL - University College London
Performing Arts Medicine....... MSc 12FT 24PT/PGDip 9FT 24PT

Dance movement therapy
Research Courses

Goldsmiths, University of London
Dance Movement Psychotherapy.... PhD 36-48FT 48-72PT/MPhil 24FT 36PT

Dental science
Taught Courses

Barts and the London School of Medicine and Dentistry
Clinical Dentistry: Paediatric Dentistry....... MClinDent 24FT 36PT
Dental Materials Science....... MSc 12FT 24PT
Dental Public Health....... MSc 12FT 24PT
Experimental Oral Pathology .... MSc 12FT
Orthodontics .... MSc 36FT
Peridontology....... MClinDent 24FT

University of Bedfordshire
Dental Education .... PGCert 12-36PT
Dental Law and Ethics....... MSc 12-24PT

University of Birmingham
Advanced General Dental Practice....... MSc 36-60PT/PGDip 36-60PT
Advanced General Dental Practice (Distance Learning)....... MSc 36-60PT

University of Bristol
Dental Implantology .... Diploma 24PT/MSc 48PT
Dental Postgraduate Studies........ MSc 12 - 24DL/DPDS 36 - 60DL
Orthodontics .... DDS 36FT

Cardiff Metropolitan University
Dental Technology....... MSc 36PT/PGDip 24PT/PGCert 12PT

Cardiff University
Clinical Dentistry....... DClinDent 3FT
Conscious Sedation in Dentistry....... MSc 36PT/PGDip 24PT
Implantology....... MSc 12FT/PGDip 12FT
Orthodontics .... MScD 36FT
Tissue Engineering....... MSc 12FT

University of Central Lancashire
Aesthetic Dental Implantology....... MSc 36PT/PGDip 24PT
Clinical Periodontology......... MSc 36PT/PGDip 24PT/PGCert 12PT
Cosmetic Dentistry....... MSc 36PT/PGDip 24PT
Endodontology....... MSc 36PT/PGDip 24PT
Non-Surgical Facial Aesthetics for Registered Healthcare Professionals....... MSc 36PT/PGDip 24PT
Oral Surgery....... MSc 36PT/PGDip 24PT/PGCert 12PT

University of Chester
Health and Social Care - Endodontology........ MSc 24-72PT/PGDip 24-60PT/PGCert 12-36PT

University College Cork
Dental Public Health....... MA 24PT

Cranfield University
Clinical Research...... MSc 12FT 36PT/PGCert 9FT 24PT/PGDip 6FT 24PT

University of Dundee
Forensic Odontology .... MFOdont 12FT
Non-Graduating Taught Postgraduate in Dental School .... PG module variableFT
Orthodontics .... MSc 36PT
Prosthodontics .... MDentSci 24FT

University of Edinburgh
Oral Surgery....... MClinDent 24FT
Orthodontics .... MClinDent 24FT
Paediatric Dentistry....... MClinDent 24FT
Primary Dental Care....... MSc 36DL/PGDip 24DL/PGCert 12DL
Prosthodontics....... MClinDent 24FT

University of Glasgow
Fixed & Removable Prosthodontics....... MSc (Dent Sci) 24FT
Oral and Maxillofacial Surgery .... MSc(DentSci) 24FT
Orthodontics .... DClinDent 36FT
Primary Dental Care....... MSc (DentSci) 36PT

University of Kent
Advanced and Specialist Healthcare (Minimally Invasive Surgery)....... MSc 24-36PT
Advanced and Specialist Healthcare (Supportive and Palliative Care)....... MSc 24-36PT
Primary Dental Care....... MSc 36PT
Primary Dental Care for Foundation Dentists....... PGCert 12FT

King's College London
Advanced General Dental Practice....... MSc 24-36DL
Aesthetic Dentistry .... MSc 36DL
Conscious Sedation for Dentistry....... PGDip 9FT
Dental Public Health....... MSc 12-24FT
Endodontology....... MClinDent 36-48FT
Fixed & Removable Prosthodontics....... MClinDent 48DL
Maxillofacial & Craniofacial Technology....... MSc 24FT
Maxillofacial Prosthetic Rehabilitation .... MSc 36DL
Orthodontics .... MSc 36FT
Paediatric Dentistry .... MSc 24FT
Periodontology....... MClinDent 36-48FT
Prosthodontics....... MClinDent 36-48FT
Regenerative Dentistry .... MSc 12FT
Special Care Dentistry....... MSc 24FT

University of Manchester
Dental Implantology (Dental Specialties)....... MSc 24PT/PGDip 18PT/PGCert 12PT
Dental Public Health...... MDPH 12-60DL/PGDip 12-60DL/PGCert 12-60DL
Dental Public Health........ MRes 12-60DL/PGCert 12-60DL/PGDip 12-60DL
Endodontics (Clin) .... MSc (Clin) 36FT
Endodontics: Dental Specialties....... MSc 12FT/PGDip 18PT
Fixed & Removable Prosthodontics (Dental Specialties) .... MSc 12FT 24PT

Medicine and surgery

Fixed and Removable Prosthodontics .... MSc (Clin) 36FT
Oral & Maxillofacial Surgery (Dental Specialties) MSc 12FT 24PT/PGDip 9FT 18PT
Oral and Maxillofacial Surgery .... Msc (Clin) 36FT
Orthodontics .... MSc (Clin) 36FT
Periodontology .... MSc 36FT
Restorative and Aesthetic Dentistry..................................MSc 24DL

Newcastle University
Clinical Dentisty in Restorative Dentistry .... MSc 24FT
Clinical Implant Dentistry ....PGCert 18PT
Conscious Sedation in Dentistry....................................PGDip 12PT
Orthodontics .... MSc 36FT

Plymouth University
Restorative Dentistry.. MSc 36PT

Queen Mary, University of London
Dental Clinical Sciences .... Diploma 12FT
Dental Materials .... MSc 12FT
Dental Public Health.. Diploma 12FT
Dental Technology... MSc 12FT/PGDip 9FT
Endodontic Practice .... MSc 36PT
Experimental Oral Sciences .... MSc 12FT
Periodontology.. MClinDent 24FT
Oral Medicine .... MClinDent 12FT 24PT
Oral Surgery.. MClinDent 24FT 36PT
Orthodontics (incorporated in MOrth Training)............. MSc 36FT
Paediatric Dentistry .... MClinDent 24FT 36PT
Prosthodontics .... MSc 24FT

Queen's University Belfast
Clinical Education..........MMedSci 36PT/PGDip 24PT/PGCert 12PT
Translational Medicine... MRes 12FT 24PT

University of Salford
Dental Implantology .... MSc 18FT 36PT/PGDip 12FT 24PT

University of Sheffield
Dental Implantology .... MMedSci 24PT
Dental Materials Science... MSc 12FT
Dental Public Health.......................... MDPH 12FT MClinDent 24FT
Dental Technology.. MSc 12FT
Diagnostic Oral Pathology .... MMedSci 12FT
Endodontics .... DClinDent 36FT
Orthodontics .... MClinDent 24FT
Paediatric Dentistry .... MClinDent 24FT
Prosthodontics .... DClinDent 36FT
Social Science and Oral Health .... MSc 12FT 24PT

University of South Wales
Clinical Endodontics (Online Delivery)................. PGDip 24PT 24DL

Staffordshire University
Clinical Photography .... GradCert 12DL

Trinity College Dublin - the University of Dublin
Clinical Dental Technology .... PGDip 18PT
Clinical Dentistry .... PGDip 24PT
Conscious Sedation in Dentistry..................................... PGDip 18PT
Dental Surgery - Oral Surgery......................... D.Ch.Dent. 36FT 60PT
Dental Surgery - Orthodontics...................... D.Ch.Dent. 36FT 60PT
Dental Surgery - Paediatric Dentistry........... D.Ch.Dent. 36FT 60PT
Dental Surgery - Periodontics......................... D.Ch.Dent. 36FT 60PT
Dental Surgery - Prosthodontics.................. D.Ch.Dent. 36FT 60PT
Dental Surgery - Special Care Dentistry...... D.Ch.Dent. 36FT 60PT
Special Care Dentistry .... PGDip 18PT

UCL - University College London
Advanced Aesthetic Dentistry.. PGCert 12PT
Conservative Dentistry.. MSc 12FT 24PT
Dental Public Health.. MSc 12FT 24PT
Dental Sedation and Pain Management...................... PGCert 12PT
Endodontic Practice .... PGDip 24-60PT/PGCert 12PT
Endodontics .... MSc 12FT 24PT/PGCert 12PT
Endodontology.. MClinDent 24FT 36-48PT
Endodontology (Advanced Training) .... MClinDent 36FT
Implant Dentistry .... PGDip 48PT
Oral Medicine .... MSc 12FT
Oral Surgery .... MClinDent 24FT
Oral Surgery (Advanced Training)........................... MClinDent 36FT
Orthodontics (Advanced Training).......................... MClinDent 36FT
Paediatric Dentistry .... MClinDent 24FT/PGCert 12PT
Periodontology... MClinDent 36FT
Prosthodontics.. MClinDent 24FT 36-48PT
Prosthodontics (Advanced Training)....................... MClinDent 36FT
Restorative Dental Practice........................ MSc 60PT/PGCert 12PT/PGDip -60PT
Special Care Dentistry .... MSc 12FT PGDip 12-60PT/PGCert 12-24PT

University of Warwick
Implant Dentistry.................. MSc 36PT/PGDip 24PT/PGCert 12PT

Dental science
Research Courses

University of Aberdeen
Epidemology............PhD 36FT/MPhil 24FT/MSc by research 12FT
Translational Medicine...PhD 36FT/MPhil 24FT/MD 24FT/ChM by research 24FT

Barts and the London School of Medicine and Dentistry
Biomaterials in relation to Dentistry................................ PhD/MPhil
Cell and Molecular Oral Biology .... PhD/MPhil
Centre for Oral Biometrics... PhD/MPhil
Clinical and Oral Health Services Research.................... PhD/MPhil
Development, Function and Ageing............................... PhD/MPhil
Mineralised Tissue Research... PhD/MPhil

University of Birmingham
Dentistry .... PhD 12-36FT/MSc by research 12FT
Primary Dental Care.. PhD 36FT/MPhil 12FT

University of Bristol
Oral and Dental Sciences... PhD 36FT 72PT/MSc by research 12FT 24PT

Cardiff University
Medical and Dental Education.. PhD 36FT
Tissue Engineering and Reparative Dentistry............................ PhD 36FT possiblePT/MPhil 12FT possiblePT/MScD by research 12FT possiblePT

University of Dundee
Dental School (Clinical)... PhD 48FT 60FT
Dental School .... MDSc by research 12FT
Dental School (Non-clinical)...PhD 36FT
MDSc by research 12FT
Forensic Medicine (MSc by research) .... MSc by research 12FT

University of Edinburgh
Dentistry.. PhD 36FT 72PT/MPhil 24FT 48PT
Postgraduate Dental Institute .... PhD 36FT 72PT

University of Glasgow
Dental School .... PhD 36FT/MSc by research 12FT
Dental School ....PhD 36FT 60PT/DDS 24FT 48PT/MSc(MedSci) by research 12FT 24PT

King's College London
Dentistry & Oral Science (Research Division)............ PhD 36-48FT 48-72PT/MPhil 36-48FT 48-72PT

University of Leeds
School of Dentistry....................................... PhD 36+FT/DDSc 36+FT

University of Liverpool
Dental Microbiology...................... MPhil 12FT/PhD 36FT/MD 60FT
Orthodontics .... DDSc 36FT

University of Manchester
Basic Dental Science (Cancer Studies).................... PhD 36FT 72PT/MPhil 12FT 24PT
Basic Dental Science (Molecular Genetics)........... PhD 36FT 72PT/MPhil 12FT 24PT
Biomaterials Science and Dental Technology .... MPhil 12FT 24PT/PhD 36FT 72PT
Dental Public Health/Community Dentistry......... PhD 36FT 72PT/MPhil 12FT 24PT
Dental Science Clinical.. PhD (Clin) 48FT
Endodontology............................ MPhil 12FT 24PT/PhD 36FT 72PT
Fixed and Removable Prosthodontics PhD 36FT 72PT/MPhil 12FT 24PT
Operative Dentistry .... PhD 36FT 72PT/MPhil 12FT 24PT
Oral Radiology............................... PhD 36FT 72PT/MPhil 12FT 24PT
Oral and Maxillo-Facial Surgery........................... MPhil 12FT 24PT/PhD 36FT 72PT
Orthodontics .... MPhil 12FT 24PT/PhD 36FT 72PT
Restorative Dentistry................... PhD 36FT 72PT/MPhil 12FT 24PT
Stem Cell Biology (Basic Dental Sciences)............. PhD 36FT 72PT/MPhil 12FT 24PT

Newcastle University
Dentistry and Dental Sciences .. PhD 36FT 72PT/MPhil 12FT 24PT
Translational Medicine and Therapeutics .... MRes 12FT

UCL - University College London
Dentistry and Oral Health Care Sciences............... PhD 36FT 60PT/MD(Res) 24FT 24PT

Dermatology
Taught Courses

University of Buckingham
General Internal Medicine .... MD 24/36FT

Cardiff University
Clinical Dermatology....................................... MSc 12FT/PGDip 9FT
Practical Dermatology............................ MSc 12-18DL/PGDip 12DL
Wound Healing and Tissue Repair .... MSc 36-60PT 36-60DL/PGDip 36-60PT 36-60DL

University of Edinburgh
General Surgery (Online Distance Learning) .... ChM 24DL

University of Hertfordshire
Dermatology Skills and Treatment .... MSc 12FT 60PT/PGDip 12FT 60PT/PGCert 12FT 60PT

King's College London
Advanced Practice (Dermatology). MSc 36-72PT/PGDip 24-72PT/PGCert 12-72PT
Clinical Dermatology... MSc 12FT

Queen Mary, University of London
Aesthetic Plastic Surgery.. PGDip 24PT 24DL
Burn Care (Distance Learning) .... PGAdvDip 24FT
Clinical Dermatology... Diploma 12FT 12DL

University of Warwick
Principles of Dermatology........................... PGA 12PT/CPDMod 1PT

Dermatology
Research Courses

Anglia Ruskin University
Medical Engineering...... MPhil 18 - 36FT 30 - 48PT/PhD 24 - 60FT 36 - 72PT

Barts and the London School of Medicine and Dentistry
Department of Dermatology .... PhD/MPhil/MD

University of Cambridge
Brain Repair.. PhD 36FT

University of Edinburgh
Dermatology............ MSc by research 12FT 24PT/PhD 36FT 72PT/MPhil 24FT 48PT

University of Greenwich
Pharmacy - Research........................... MPhil 36-72FT/PhD 36-72FT

University of Nottingham
Drug Delivery and Tissue Engineering .... PhD 36FT 72PT

Dramatherapy
Taught Courses

Anglia Ruskin University
Dramatherapy .... MA 24FT

Central School of Speech and Drama, University of London
Applied Theatre (Drama in the Community and Drama Education) .... MA 12FT 24PT
Drama and Movement Therapy (Sesame) .... MA 18FT

University of Derby
Drama Therapy... MA 24FT

University of Dundee
Eye Movements & Cognition .... MSc 12FT

University of Exeter
Theatre Practice: Applied Theatre............................. MA 12FT 24PT
Theatre Practice: Directing and Actor Training....... MA 12FT 24PT
Theatre Practice: General Programme..................... MA 12FT 24PT
Theatre Practice: Physical Performance & Actor Training .... MA 12FT 24PT
Theatre Practice: Staging Shakespeare.................... MA 12FT 24PT/MFA 24FT

University of Glasgow
Primary Expressive Arts .... PGCert 12PT

Manchester Metropolitan University
Movement Practice for Theatre .... MA 12FT

University of Roehampton
Dramatherapy .... MA 24FT 36PT

UCL - University College London
Performing Arts Medicine........... MSc 12FT 24PT/PGDip 9FT 24PT

University of Worcester
Dramatherapy .... MA 36PT
Psychodrama Psychotherapy...................... MSc 60PT/PGDip 48PT/PGCert 24PT

Dramatherapy
Research Courses

University of Exeter
Drama... PhD 48FT 89PT/MPhil 36FT 60PT

Endocrinology
Taught Courses

University of Brighton
Podiatry with Diabetes ...... MSc 12-24FT 24-72PT/PGDip 12-24FT 24-48PT/PGCert 12FT 24PT

Cardiff University
Diabetes.. PGDip 24DL

University of Dundee
Diabetes Care and Education .... MSc 36-40PT PGCert 12-15PT PGDip 24-27PT

King's College London
Advanced Practice (Diabetes Care) MSc 36-72PT/PGDip 24-72PT/PGCert 12-72PT

Queen Margaret University, Edinburgh
Diabetes............................ MSc 12FT 24-60PT/PGDip 12FT 12-24PT

Queen Mary, University of London
Endocrinology and Diabetes .... MSc 12FT/PGDip 9FT

University of South Wales
Diabetes (Online Delivery) .... MSc 12DL/PGDip 12DL
Endocrinology (Online Delivery)................... PGDip 12PT/MSc 12PT

University of Southampton
Management of Diabetes .... MSc 15FT 24PT/PGDip 12FT 18PT/PGCert 6FT 6PT

Staffordshire University
Clinical Biomechanics and Diabetes............................ PGCert 12PT

Medicine and surgery

University of Warwick
Applied Pharmacology and Therapeutics in Diabetes Care.....PGA 12PT/CPDMod 1PT
Diabetes.....MSc 12FT 24-96PT/PGA 12PT
Diabetes and the Foot.....PGA 12PT/CPDMod 1PT
Diabetes in Pregnancy.....PGA 12PT
Diabetic Retinopathy.....PGA 12PT
Health Sciences: Diabetes...MSc 36PT/PGDip 24PT/PGCert 12PT/PGA 12PT
Hypertension and Nephropathy.....PGA 12PT
Menopause and Beyond.....PGA 12PT
Mind / Hormone Interface in Community Gynaecology.....PGA 12PT
Nutritional Management in Diabetes Care.... PGA 12PT/CPDMod 1PT
Organisation and Delivery of Diabetes Care.....PGA 12PT/CPDMod 1PT
Principles of Diabetes Care.....PGA 12PT/CPDMod 1PT
The Theory and Practice of Insulin Initiation.....PGA 12PT

Endocrinology
Research Courses

Barts and the London School of Medicine and Dentistry
Department of Chemical Endocrinology.......PhD/MA by research
Department of Diabetes and Metabolism.....MD/FRCP
Endocrinology.....PhD/MPhil/MD
Medical Professorial Unit (West Smithfield).....PhD/MD
Paediatric Endocrinology.....PhD/MPhil/MA by research
Paediatric Endocrinology.....MD/FRCP

Imperial College London
Neuroendocrinology.....PhD 36FT 36-60PT/MPhil 24FT 24PT

University of Liverpool
Endocrinology.....PhD 36FT/MPhil 12FT 24PT/MD 12FT 24PT
Obesity and Endocrinology (Medicine)...... PhD 36FT/MPhil 12FT/MD 60FT

Newcastle University
Diabetes.....MRes 12FT

University of Sheffield
Endocrinology and Reproduction........PhD 36FT 72PT/MPhil 24FT 48PT

Gastroenterology
Taught Courses

Barts and the London School of Medicine and Dentistry
Gastroenterology.....MSc 12FT 24PT

University of Central Lancashire
Advanced Stroke Practice......MSc 36FT 60PT/PGDip 24PT/PGCert 12PT

University of Leeds
Advanced Gastrointestinal Practice.....PGCert p/t onlyPT

Newcastle University
Clinical Sciences (Physiological Sciences) with specialisms in: Cardiac Science; Vascular Science; Respiratory and Sleep Science; Gastrointestinal Physiology; Urodynamic Science.....MSc 36PT

Queen Mary, University of London
Gastroenterology.....MSc 12FT/PGDip 8FT

Sheffield Hallam University
Advancing Paediatric Practice.....MSc 18FT/PGDip 12FT/PGCert 6FT

Trinity College Dublin - the University of Dublin
Clinical Speech and Language Studies (Dysphagia).....PGDip 12PT

Gastroenterology
Research Courses

Barts and the London School of Medicine and Dentistry
Department of Diabetes and Metabolism.....MD/FRCP
Department of Gastrointestinal Science.....PhD/MPhil/MD
Paediatric Gastroenterology.....PhD/MPhil/MD

University of Liverpool
GastroenterologyPhD 24-48FT 48-84PT/MPhil 12-48FT 24-72PT/MD 24-72FT
Gastrointestinal Diseases.....PhD 36FT/MPhil 12FT

University of Nottingham
Gastrointestinal Surgery.... PhD 36FT 72PT/MPhil 24FT 48PT/DM 36FT 72PT
Medical GastroenterologyPhD 36FT 72PT/MPhil 24FT 48PT/MRes 12FT/DM 36FT 72PT

Herbalism
Taught Courses

University of Central Lancashire
Herbal Medicine by elearning.....MSc 36-48PT/PGDip 24PT/PGCert 12PT

School of Oriental and African Studies - SOAS
Medical Anthropology.....MA 12FT 24-36PT

University of Westminster
Chinese Herbal Medicine.....MSc 12FT 24PT
Herbal Medicine.....MSc 12FT 24PT

Homeopathy
Taught Courses

University of Central Lancashire
Homeopathy by e-learning....MSc 36PT 36DL/PGDip 24PT 24DL/PGCert 12PT 12DL

Infectious diseases
Taught Courses

University of Bedfordshire
Sexual Health.....PGCert 12-36PT

University of Cambridge
Public Health.....MPhil 12FT

University of Dundee
Advanced Practice (Infection: Diseases, Prevention & Control) ... MSc 36DL
Global Health and Wellbeing.....MSc 36DL

University of Edinburgh
Global Health and Infectious Diseases (Online Distance Learning).....MSc 36DL/PGDip 24DL/PGCert 12DL

University of Exeter
Biosciences.....MSc(Res) 12FT 36PT

Glasgow Caledonian University
Sexual Health.....MSc 24-60FT On-lineDL

Heriot-Watt University
Biotechnology.....MSc 12FT 24PT/PGDip 9FT 20PT

Imperial College London
Allergy.......... MSc(MedSci) -FT 24-36PT 24-36DL/AdvCert -FT 9PT 9DL
Infection.....MSc 24PT/PGDip 16PT/PGCert 8PT
Infection Management for Pharmacists.....MSc 24PT/PGDip 16PT/PGCert 8PT
Epidemiology.....MSc 12FT
Molecular Biology and Pathology of Viruses.....MSc 12FT

King's College London
Advanced Practice (Infection Control).....MSc 36FT 72PT/PGDip 24FT 48PT/PGCert 12FT 24PT

Leeds Metropolitan University
Integrated Masters Biomedical Sciences.....MBIOMS 48FT

University of Leeds
Human Disease and Therapy.....MSc 12FT
Infection and Immunity.....MSc 12FT

University of Leicester
Infection and Immunity.....MSc 12FT/Diploma 12FT

Liverpool School of Tropical Medicine
Molecular Biology of Parasites & Disease Vectors.........MSc 12FT/PGDip 8FT
Tropical Medicine.....MTropMed 12FT
Tropical Paediatrics.....MTropPaed 12FT

University of Liverpool
Biology and Control of Parasites and Disease Vectors..MSc 12FT/PGDip 6FT/PGCert 3FT
Molecular Biology of Parasites and Disease Vectors...... MSc 12FT
Tropical Medicine and Hygiene (DTM&H).....Diploma 3FT
Tropical Paediatrics.....MSc 12FT/PGDip 6FT/PGCert 3FT
Tropical and Infectious Diseases.....MSc 12FT

London School of Hygiene and Tropical Medicine
Control of Infectious Diseases.....MSc 12FT 24PT
Immunology of Infectious Diseases.....MSc 12FT 24PT
Infectious Diseases (by Distance Learning).....MSc 24 - 60DL/PGDip 12 - 60DL/PGCert 12-60DL
Medical Entomology for Disease Control.....MSc 12FT 24PT
Molecular Biology of Infectious Diseases.....MSc 12FT 24PT
Public Health for Eye Care.....MSc 12FT 24PT
Tropical Medicine & International Health.....MSc 12FT 24PT

University of Manchester
Medical Mycology... MSc 12FT 60PT/PGDip 9FT 48PT/PGCert 5FT 36PT
Medical Virology.....MSc 12FT 24PT/PGDip 9FT 24PT

Oxford Brookes University
Infection Prevention and Control..... MSc 12FT Up to 36PT/PGDip 9FT Up to 36PT/PGCert 4FT Up to 36PT

Peninsula College of Medicine and Dentistry
Infection Prevention & Control.....PGCert 12PT

Royal Veterinary College
One Health (Infectious Diseases).....MSc 12FT

University of Salford
Lower Limb Health, Disease and Rehabilitation.........PGCert 12PT

Sheffield Hallam University
Biomedical Basis of Disease....... MSc 12FT 36PT/PGDip 8FT 24PT/PGCert 4FT 12PT

University of Sheffield
Molecular and Cellular Basis of Disease.....MSc 12FT

University of Strathclyde
Health History....MSc 12FT 24PT/PGDip 9FT 18PT/PGDip 9FT 9PT

Swansea University
Infection Prevention and Control.....PGCert 12PT

Trinity College Dublin - the University of Dublin
Healthcare Infection Management.....MSc 24PT

UCL - University College London
Healthcare Associated Infection Control........MSc 24-60PT/PGDip 24-60PT
Infection and Immunity..MSc 12FT 24-60PT/PGDip 9FT 24-60PT/PGCert 3FT 6-24PT
Medical Bacteriology (by Distance Learning)...MSc 24FT 24-60PT

University of Warwick
Infections and Women's Health.....PGA 12PT

University of West London
Communicable Diseases.......... MPhil 36FT 45PT/PhD 36FT 45PT

University of Worcester
Airborne Infectious Agents and Allergens.............MSc 12FT 24PT

Infectious diseases
Research Courses

Barts and the London School of Medicine and Dentistry
Infectious Diseases.....PhD/MPhil

University of Birmingham
Immunity and Infection..... PhD 36FT 72PT/MSc by research 12FT 24PT/MD 24PT

University of Cambridge
Epidemiology.....PhD 36FT

Cardiff University
Infection and Immunity.....PhD 36-48FT/MPhil 12FT

University of Edinburgh
Animal Genomics & Disease Resistance (Veterinary Science)....... PhD 36FT
Centre for Infectious Diseases.....PhD 36FT 72PT
Epidemiology of Infectious Disease (Veterinary Science)........PhD 36FT
Host Pathogen Interactions in Infectious Disease (Veterinary Medicine).....PhD 36FT
Immunology & Infection Research.....PhD 36FT 72PT
Infection and Immunity... PhD 36FT/MPhil 24FT/MSc by research 12FT
Infectious Diseases.....MSc by research 12FT

University of Exeter
Biosciences......PhD 36FT 72PT/MPhil 24FT 48PT/MSc by research 12FT 36PT

Imperial College London
Biomedical Research (Microbial Pathogenesis).............MRes 12FT
Virology.....PhD 36PT

King's College London
Immunology, Infection and Inflammatory Disease (DIID) (Research Division)...........PhD 36FT 48-72PT/MPhil 36FT 48-72PT

University of Leicester
Infection, Immunity and InflammationPhD 36 - 48FT 72PT/MPhil 24FT 36PT/MSc by research 12FT/MD 24FT

Liverpool School of Tropical Medicine
Molecular & Biochemical Parasitology.....PhD/MPhil/MIHR
Vector Research.....PhD/MPhil/MIHR

University of Liverpool
Infection and Immunity.....MPhil 12FT/PhD 36FT/MD 24FT
Medical Parasitology...........MPhil 12-48FT 48-72PT/PhD 24-48FT 48-84PT/MD 24-72FT
Tropical MedicineMPhil 12-24FT 24-48PT/PhD 24-36FT 48-72PT/MIHR 24FT
Virology..........MPhil 12-48FT 24-48PT/PhD 24-72FT 48-84PT/MD 24-72FT

London School of Hygiene and Tropical Medicine
Infectious & Tropical Diseases (Research)....DrPH 42FT 42PT/PhD 42FT 42PT/MPhil 12FT 12PT

University of Nottingham
Parasite Biology and Immunogenetics........PhD 36FT/MPhil 24FT

Oxford Brookes University
Health and Biomedical Sciences - Insect Virology & Protein Expression............ PhD 24-60FT 36-72PT/MPhil 24-36FT 36-48PT

University of Oxford
Infection, Immunology and Translational Medicine.... DPhil 48FT
Primary Health Care.............DPhil 48FT/MSc by research 24-36FT

Royal Veterinary College
PhD Opportunities at the Royal Veterinary College.....PhD 36-48FT 48-72PT

University of Sheffield
Cardiovascular Science................ PhD 36FT 72PT/MPhil 24FT 48PT
Infection, Inflammation and Immunity.......PhD 36FT 72PT/MPhil 24FT 48PT

UCL - University College London
Infection and Immunity.....PhD 36FT 60PT

Medicine and surgery

Infection and Population Health....PhD 36FT 60PT/MD(Res) 24FT 24PT
Medical Microbiology.. PhD 36FT 60PT
Sexually Transmitted Diseases........PhD 36FT 60PT/MD(Res) 24FT 24PT

Medical diagnostics
Taught Courses

Anglia Ruskin University
Magnetic Resonance Imaging (MRI) (Distance Learning)....... MSc 24DL

Bangor University
Advanced Clinical Practice ....MSc 12FT 24 - 60PT/PGDip 9FT
Clinical and Functional Brain Imaging.........................PGCert 12PT
Health Science..................................MSc 12FT 24 - 60PT/PGDip 9FT
Health Studies/Health Science, Nursing, Midwifery, Radiography and Allied Health Profession ....PhD by taught 36FT 48-60PT/MPhil 24FT 36PT
Neuroimaging...MSc 12FT 24PT
Clinical and Functional Brain Imaging...........................PGCert 8PT

Canterbury Christ Church University
Magnetic Resonance Imaging...........MSc 12FT 60PT/PGDip 24PT/PGCert 12PT
Medical Imaging..PGCert 12PT
Medical Ultrasound .... MSc 60PT/PGDip 24PT/PGCert 12PT

Cardiff University
Medical Ultrasound ......PGDip 12FT 24PT/PGCert 12PT/MSc 18FT 36PT
Therapeutics...MSc 12PT/PGDip 12PT

City University London
Medical Ultrasound .... MSc 24PT/PGDip 18PT/PGCert 12PT

Cranfield University
Medical Diagnostics .... MSc 12FT 36PT/PGDip 12FT 36PT

University of Cumbria
Medical Imaging...MSc 36 - 60PT

University of Derby
Medical Ultrasound ....MSc 36-72PT

University of Dundee
Advanced Practice (Diagnostic Imaging)..........................MSc 36DL
Advanced Practice (Medical Imaging)...............................MSc 36DL
Medical Imaging ....MSc 12FT
Minimal Access Surgery ....MMAS 12FT
Oral Cancer ....MRes 12FT
Orthodontics ....MSc 36PT
Prosthodontics ....MDentSci 24FT

University of East Anglia
Clinical Education...............MClinEd 12FT 36PT/PGDip 12FT 24PT/PGCert 12PT
Clinical Science...MRes 12FT

National University of Ireland Galway
Medical Physics..MSc 12FT

Glasgow Caledonian University
Health and Social Care (Diagnostic Imaging).............MSc 12-24FT 24-72PT

University of Hertfordshire
Diagnostic Imaging.........MSc variousPT/PGDip variousPT/PGCert variousPT
Diagnostic Ultrasound...MSc variousPT/PGDip variousPT/PGCert variousPT
Image Interpretation............. MSc 24PT/PGDip 24PT/PGCert 24PT

Imperial College London
Medical Robotics and Image Guided Intervention ....MRes 12FT
Medical Ultrasound ....MSc 12FT 24PT
Medical Ultrasound/Medical Ultrasound (Echocardiography)...... MSc 12FT

King's College London
Specialist Ultrasound Practice ....PGCert 9PT
Ultrasound in Emergency and Critical Care...................PGCert 9PT
Vascular Ultrasound ....PGCert 9PT/PGDip 18PT/MSc 27PT

Kingston University
Radiography: Medical Imaging.... MSc 24FT 24-60PT/PGDip 24FT 24-60PT/PGCert 24FT 24-60PT
Radiography: Medical Imaging (Mammography)........... MSc 24FT 24-60PT/PGCert 24FT 24-60PT/PGDip 24FT 24-60PT

University of Leeds
Medical Imaging...............MSc 12FT 33-60PT/PGDip 9FT 21-48PT/PGCert 4-9FT 9-24PT

University of Liverpool
Medical Diagnostic Ultrasound ....MSc 36-72PT

London School of Hygiene and Tropical Medicine
Clinical Trials (by Distance Learning)...........MSc 24 - 60DL/PGDip 12 - 60DL/PGCert 12-60DL

University of Manchester
Medical Imaging......................... MSc 12FT 24PT/PGDip 12FT 24PT

University of Nottingham
Molecular Genetics and Diagnostics.................................. MSc 12FT

University of Oxford
Clinical Embryology... MSc 12FT
Diagnostic Imaging..MSc 12FT 24PT

Queen Margaret University, Edinburgh
Diagnostic Radiography (Pre-Registration).....PGCert 12FT/PGDip 24FT/MSc 26FT

Robert Gordon University
Diagnostic Radiography (pre-registration) .... MSc 24FT

University of Salford
Advanced Medical Imaging .... MSc 24-60PT/PGDip 18-36PT/PGCert 12-24PT
Dental Implantology .... MSc 18FT 36PT/PGDip 12FT 24PT
Nuclear Medicine Imaging............................MSc 24PT/PGDip 18PT

Sheffield Hallam University
Medical Imaging Programme........ MSc VAPT/PGDip VAPT/PGCert VAPT
Medical Ultrasound .... MSc 36PT/PGDip 24PT/PGCert 24PT

University of Sheffield
Clinical Neurology... MSc 12FT
Clinical Research............................MSc 12FT 24PT/PGDip 9FT 18PT
Dental Implantology ....MMedSci 24PT
Dental Materials Science... MSc 12FT
Dental Public Health.......................... MClinDent 24FT MDPH 12FT
Dental Technology.. MSc 12FT
Diagnostic Oral Pathology ....MMedSci 12FT
Statistics with Medical Applications .... MSc 12FT 24-36 PTDL

University of South Wales
Advanced Clinical Practitioner....................................MSc 12 -60PT
Diagnostic Clinical Ultrasound . PGCert 12-60PT/PGDip 12-60PT/MSc 12-60PT

University of Southampton
Clinical Psychology..................................... DClinPsy by taught 36FT

University of Strathclyde
Biomedical Sciences... MSc 12FT/PGDip 9FT
Biotechnology .... MSc 12FT
Clinical Pharmacy...........................MSc 12FT 24PT/PGDip 9FT 18PT

Teesside University
Diagnostic Radiography (Pre-registration) ....MSc 26FT/PGDip 22FT

Trinity College Dublin - the University of Dublin
Medical Imaging... MSc 12PT

UCL - University College London
Genetics of Human Disease .... MSc 12FT

University of the West of England, Bristol
Medical Ultrasound .... MSc 36FT

University of York
Haematopathology................ MSc 24PT/PGCert 24PT/PGDip 24PT

Medical diagnostics
Research Courses

Bangor University
Health Studies/Health Science, Nursing, Midwifery, Radiography & Allied Health Professions ....MPhil 24FT 36PT/PhD 36FT 48-60PT
Medical Visualization and Simulation ....MPhil 24FT/PhD 36FT

University of Cambridge
Medical Sciences.. MPhil 12FT

Imperial College London
Molecular Imaging Using Ultrasound and Targeted Microbubbles...PhD 36FT

University of Oxford
Clinical Neurosciences ....DPhil 48FT/MSc by research 24-36FT
Radiobiology................................ DPhil 48FT/MSc by research 24FT

University of Strathclyde
Biomedical Sciences..MRes 12FT 24PT

University of Surrey
HPRU Medical Research Centre ....PhD/MPhil

UCL - University College London
Genetics, Evolution and Environment...................... PhD 36FT 60PT

Medical illustration
Taught Courses

Cardiff University
Medical Illustration...PGCert 14DL

University of Central Lancashire
Photography .... MA 12FT 24PT/PGDip 12FT 24PT/PGCert 12FT 24PT

University of Cumbria
Medical Imaging...MSc 36 - 60PT
Photography .... MA 12FT 24PT

University of Derby
Medical Ultrasound ....MSc 36-72PT

University of Dundee
Advanced Practice (Medical Imaging) ....MSc 36DL
Anatomy and Advanced Forensic Anthropology .... MSc 12FT
Forensic Art .... MSc 12FT
Forensic Facial Identification .... MSc 12FT
Medical Art .... MSc 12FT MSc 48PT
Medical Imaging .... MSc 12FT
Minimal Access Surgery ....MMAS 12FT
Primary Care ....MSc 36-60PT
Prosthodontics ....MDentSci 24FT

Glasgow School of Art
Medical Visualisation and Human Anatomy ... PGCert 4FT/PGDip 8FT/MSc 12FT

University of Glasgow
Medical Visualisation & Human Anatomy .... MSc 12FT

University of Nottingham
Biological Photography and Imaging................................ MSc 12FT

University of Oxford
Diagnostic Imaging..MSc 12FT 24PT

Queen Mary, University of London
Media and Arts Technology ....MSc(Res) 12FT

Queen's University Belfast
Clinical Anatomy ......MSc 12FT TBCPT/PGDip 12FT TBCPT/PGCert 12FT TBCPT

University of Salford
Advanced Medical ImagingMSc 24-60PT/PGDip 18-36PT/PGCert 12-24PT

University of Sheffield
Cognitive Neuroscience and Human Neuroimaging ...... MSc(Res) 12FT

Staffordshire University
Clinical Photography ....GradCert 12DL

Medical illustration
Research Courses

University for the Creative Arts
Photography .... MPhil 24FT 36PT/PhD 36FT 60PT

University of Oxford
Clinical Neurosciences ....DPhil 48FT/MSc by research 24-36FT

Medicine and surgery
Taught Courses

Anglia Ruskin University
Advanced Pre-Hospital Trauma Care................................. MSc 24FT
Biomedical Science ....MSc 36 - 60DL
Biotechnology ....MSc 12FT 24PT
Minimally Invasive & Robotic Surgery....................MCh 12FT 24PT
Otorhinolaryngology...PGCert 24 PT
Plastic and Aesthetic Surgery Practice.............................MCh 24DL

Anglo-European College of Chiropractic
Chiropractic.............................MSc 30DL/PGDip 24DL/PGCert 12DL
Medical Ultrasound .... MSc 36PT

Bangor University
Medical Molecular Biology with Genetics .... MSc 12-24FT
Medical Sciences.........................MRes 12FT 24PT/PGCert 3FT 15PT

University of Bath
Regenerative Medicine ....MRes 12FT
Sport and Exercise Medicine .... MSc 36-60PT/PGDip 24-48PT

University of Bedfordshire
Academic and Clinical Education (BSO)........................PGCert 12PT
Diabetes...MSc 12-36FT 72PT
Sexual Health ....PGCert 12-36PT

University of Birmingham
Advancing Practice....................MSc 13FT 72PT/PGDip 10FT 48PT/PGCert 3FT
Exercise and Sports Medicine (Football).....MSc 13FT 72PT/PGDip 10FT 48PT
Health Research - Academic Clinical Fellows (ACF) Framework.... MRes 24PT

University of Bolton
Medical & Health Care Devices .... MSc 12FT 36PT

University of Brighton
Clinical Research.........MRes 18FT 24-72PT/PGDip 18FT 24-72PT/PGCert 18FT 24-72PT
Women's Health and Management....... MSc 12 - 36FT 24 - 72PT/PGCert 12 - 36FT 24 - 72PT/PGDip 12FT 24 - 72PT

Brunel University
Medicine, Bioscience and Society.............................. MSc 12FT 30PT

University of Buckingham
General Internal Medicine ....MD 24/36FT

Bucks New University
Psychotherapeutic Approaches in Mental Health .... MSc 24PT

Canterbury Christ Church University
Clinical Reporting (Appendicular and Axial Skeleton)........ PGCert 18PT/PGDip 36PT/MSc 54PT
Nuclear Medicine .... MSc 60PT/PGDip 24PT/PGCert 12PT

Cardiff University
Advanced Clinical Practice .... MSc 36PT/PGCert 24PT

UNIVERSITY OF
Southampton

Leading healthcare.
Postgraduate courses at Southampton

In establishing Health Sciences we have developed a world class learning environment that focuses on the improvement of health outcomes and the transformation of healthcare delivery.

Our programmes benefit from solid partnerships with practice settings, clinical and strategic leaders, and close involvement with service users.

Furthermore, leading professors contribute to the educational and research experience, whilst undertaking research of international renown themselves.

As Dean, I am passionate about striving to improve the experience of healthcare for service users in order to address their needs more personally, and also to give them more power and control over their health and wellbeing.

If you choose to study with us, you too will have the opportunity to make your own personal contribution to healthcare in the challenging but exciting times that lie ahead.

Professor Jessica Corner,
Dean of Health Sciences.

www.southampton.ac.uk/healthsciences

UNIVERSITY OF Southampton

www.southampton.ac.uk/healthsciences
healthsciences@southampton.ac.uk
twitter.com/unisouthampton
facebook.com/healthsciences

The University of Southampton is one of the UK's top research universities, providing access to a world-class academic environment and offering a growing range of flexible postgraduate-level programmes

RESEARCH AT SOUTHAMPTON

Choosing to study with us at health sciences will give you access to a learning environment which focuses on the improvement of health outcomes and the transformation of healthcare delivery as well as enhancing your professional career.

Our faculty is one of the largest in the UK educating a wide range of health professionals. We work collaboratively with other disciplines within the university and in partnership with practice settings, clinical and strategic leaders, and are closely involved with service users.

On all measures of academic excellence, we have received rankings that place us among the leading centres in Britain in terms of research output and expertise. We have continued to receive high scores in the research assessment exercises, delivered high-quality publications and also have a successful record of raising research funding and grants from funding organisations. We are committed to promoting a dynamic interface between our research and education portfolios.

Our research groups have expertise in: cancer, palliative and end of life care; chronic health needs, rehabilitation and health technologies; and the organisation of service and education delivery in healthcare.

We emphasise the value of drawing on evidence-based research to underpin decisions for practice. Many of our researchers play key roles in the development of major healthcare programmes.

WHY CHOOSE HEALTH SCIENCES AT SOUTHAMPTON

When you study with us at Southampton, you will work with internationally respected academics and experience world-leading research as it happens, with access to state-of-the-art resources.

You will become part of the close-knit postgraduate society within your area of study as well as the wider, 5,000-strong postgraduate student community.

You will be supervised by our team of academic staff who are committed to high-quality research and teaching. You may also have co-supervision from colleagues from other related disciplines such as psychology, medicine and education.

THE CITY

Southampton is a thriving modern city, steeped in history with a rich mix of recreation, culture, entertainment, internationally acclaimed arts venues and one of the UK's top shopping centres. The city has something for everyone. It is located within easy reach of the New Forest National Park, the coast and with easy access to London.

Our Uni-link buses provide an excellent service within the city, to the airport, coach and train stations. In addition, there are cross channel ferries to Europe from Portsmouth and Poole, and frequent flights to continental destinations from Southampton and Bournemouth International Airports.

ESSENTIAL INFORMATION

OUR PROGRAMMES
- BSc (Hons) Clinical Practice
- MSc Advanced Clinical Practice (Eight pathways: Standard pathway, Neonatal, Midwifery, District Nursing/Children's Community Nursing, Critical Care, Children and Young People, Advanced [Nurse] Practitioner)
- MRes Clinical and Health Research
- MSc Clinical Leadership in Cancer, Palliative and End of Life Care
- MSc Health and Rehabilitation
- MSc Health Sciences (Standard and Mental Health pathways)
- Postgraduate Diploma in Nursing – Adult (pre-registration)
- Postgraduate Diploma in Nursing – Child (pre-registration)
- Postgraduate Diploma in Nursing – Mental Health (pre-registration)
- MSc Leadership and Management in Health and Social Care
- MSc Mental Health Studies
- MSc Physiotherapy (pre-registration)
- Postgraduate Diploma in Public Health Practice: Specialist Community Public Health Nursing
- Doctorate in Clinical Practice
- MPhil/PhD Health Sciences

FINANCIAL SUPPORT AND FEES
For information visit
www.southampton.ac.uk/postgraduate/ feesandfunding or email
healthsciences@southampton.ac.uk

HOW TO APPLY
To apply online, please visit
www.southampton.ac.uk/pgapply

CONTACT DETAILS
University of Southampton
University Road
Southampton, Hampshire
SO17 1BJ
+44 (0)23 8059 7979
healthsciences@southampton.ac.uk
www.southampton.ac.uk/healthsciences

Medicine and surgery

Advanced Surgical Practice .... MSc 24DL/PGDip 18DL/PGCert 18DL
Surgical Care Practice .... MSc 12FT 24PT/PGDip 9FT
Wound Healing and Tissue Repair . MSc 36-60PT 36-60DL/PGDip 36-60PT 36-60DL

University of Central Lancashire
Clinical Leadership for Practice Innovation................... Module 4PT
Statistics For Clinical Trials .... PGCert 12-36PT
The Management of Long-Term Conditions.......... MSc 12FT 24PT/PGDip 12FT/PGCert 9FT

University of Chester
Health and Social Care - Clinical Bariatric Practice .... MSc 12FT 24 - 72PT/PGDip 12FT 24 - 60PT/PGCert 12FT 12 - 36PT
Regeneration for Practitioners.......MA 12FT 24-72PT/PGDip 12FT 24-60PT/PGCert 12FT 12-36PT

Cranfield University
Clinical Research...... MSc 12FT 36PT/PGCert 9FT 24PT/PGDip 6FT 24PT
Clinical Research Executive........... MSc 36PT/PGDip 9FT 24-36PT/PGCert 6FT 12-24PT
Clinical Research Management .... MSc 12FT 36PT/PGDip 12FT 36PT
Translational Medicine............... MSc 12FT 36PT/PGDip 12FT 24PT

University of Derby
Clinical Supervision........................... PGCert 12PT 12DL

University of Dundee
Forensic Medicine .... MFM 12FT
Medical Education .... MMedEd 12FT
Minimal Access Surgery .... MMAS 12FT
Motion Analysis .... MSc 12FT 24PT 24DL
Orthopaedic Science .... MSc up to 60DL MSc 12FT
Orthopaedic Surgery .... MChOrth 9FT
Quality Improvement ....MSc 36DL PGCert 12DL PGDip 24DL
Sports and Biomechanical Medicine .... MSc 12FT
Sports and Biomechanical Medicine (MSc Part time with externally arranged project)........................ MSc 24PT
Sports and Biomechanical Medicine (MSc Part time with in-house project) .... MSc 24PT

University of East Anglia
Clinical Science .... MRes 12FT
Oncoplastic Breast Surgery........................ MS 36PT/PGDip 24PT
Regional Anaesthesia .... MSc 36PT
Stroke Recovery ... MSc 12FT 36PT/PGDip 12FT 24PT/PGCert 12PT

Edge Hill University
Advanced Clinical Practice .... PGCert 12-36PT
Evidence Based Medicine and Practice .... MSc 36PT
Master of Surgery .... MCh 24-36PT
Master of Surgery Studies........................... MCh 18FT

University of Edinburgh
Clinical Trials ....MSc 36DL/PGDip 24DL/PGCert 12DL
General Surgery (Online Distance Learning) .... ChM 24DL
Global Health and Infectious Diseases (Online Distance Learning)................MSc 36DL/PGDip 24DL/PGCert 12DL
Internal Medicine (online distance learning)....MSc 36DL/PGCert 12DL/Diploma 24DL
Medical Sciences..........................MMedSci 12FT
Paediatric Emergency Medicine ..MSc 36DL/PGDip 24DL/PGCert 12DL
Regenerative Medicine: Industrial and Clinical Delivery................ MSc 12FT
Surgery .... ChM 24DL
Surgical Sciences................. MSc 36DL/Diploma 24DL/Cert 12DL
Transfusion, Transplanting and Tissue Banking .... MSc 36PT
Trauma and Orthopaedics .... ChM 24DL
Urology.. ChM 24DL
Vascular and Endovascular Surgery................ ChM 24DL

National University of Ireland Galway
Medical Science (Endovascular Surgery) .... PGDip 12PT/MMedSci 24PT
Medical Science (Health Informatics) ....PGDip 12PT/MMedSci 12PT
Regenerative Medicine .... MSc 12FT
Surgery .... MCh 36PT

University of Glasgow
Applied Medical Science............................... MSc 12FT
Cardiovascular Sciences.........................MSc(MedSci) 12FT
Sport & Exercise Medicine ....MSc(MedSci) 12FT 24PT
Surgical Oncology .... MSc (ClinSci) 12FT
Translational Medicine............................ MRes 12FT

University of Hertfordshire
Clinical Research .... MSc 12FT
Medical and Healthcare Simulation....................MSc 12FT 60PT/PGDip 12FT 60PT/PGCert 12FT 60PT
Medicine (Doctorate/MD)..........Professional Doctorate/MD 24PT

Imperial College London
Biomedical Research: Personalised Healthcare............. MRes 12FT
MEd in Surgical Education............................MEd 12FT 24PT
Medical Robotics and Image Guided Intervention .... MRes 12FT
Respiratory Medicine.......................... MSc 12FT 24PT
Surgical Science .... MSc 12FT
Surgical Technology .... MSc 12FT 24PT

Keele University
Medical Education..................MA 24PT/PGDip 12FT/PGCert 9FT
Medical Science .... MMedSci 24PT
Medical Science ....MMedSci 60PT/PGDip 48PT/PGCert 36PT

University of Kent
Advanced and Specialist Healthcare (Minimally Invasive Surgery)................................MSc 24-36PT
Advanced and Specialist Healthcare (Supportive and Palliative Care)....................................MSc 24-36PT
Advanced and Specialist Healthcare (Surgical Practice).......... MSc 24-36PT

King's College London
Aviation Medicine............................MSc 12FT 24-36PT
Drug Development Science ....MSc 24-48PT
Medical Humanities .... MSc 12FT 24PT
Nuclear Medicine: Science & Practice............MSc 12FT 24PT/PGDip 12FT 24PT/PGCert 6FT 18PT
Translational Medicine........ MSc 24-48PT/PGDip 24-48PT/PGCert 24-48PT

Lancaster University
Medicine .... MD 24FT

University of Leeds
Patient Safety and Clinical Risk Management .... PGCert 4FT

University of Leicester
Clinical Science......MSc 36-60PT/PGDip 24-48PT/PGCert 12-24PT

Liverpool School of Tropical Medicine
Tropical Medicine ....MTropMed 12FT

University of Liverpool
Clinical Research (Online Degree) ....MSc 24FT 24+PT
Clinical Science (Medical Physics) .... MSc 36PT
Medical Science .... MSc 12-15FT 72PT/PGDip 10FT 72PT/PGCert 5FT 36PT

London School of Hygiene and Tropical Medicine
Clinical Trials (by Distance Learning)...........MSc 24 - 60DL/PGDip 12 - 60DL/PGCert 12-60DL
Control of Infectious Diseases .... MSc 12FT 24PT
Epidemiology............................... MSc 12FT 24PT
Epidemiology (by Distance Learning)...........MSc 24 - 60DL/PGDip 12 - 60DL/PGCert 12-60DL
Global Health Policy (by Distance Learning) ....MSc 24-60DL/PGDip 12-60DL/PGCert 12-60DL
Global Mental Health............................ MSc 12FT 24PT
Health Policy, Planning and Financing.............. MSc 12FT 24PT
Immunology of Infectious Diseases .... MSc 12FT 24PT
Infectious Diseases (by Distance Learning) ....MSc 24 - 60DL/PGDip 12 - 60DL/PGCert 12-60DL
Medical Entomology for Disease Control............... MSc 12FT 24PT
Medical Microbiology........................... MSc 12FT 24PT
Medical Parasitology .... MSc 12FT 24PT
Medical Statistics .... MSc 12FT 24PT
Molecular Biology of Infectious Diseases .... MSc 12FT 24PT
Nutrition for Global Health .... MSc 12FT 24PT
One Health .... MSc 12FT 24PT
Public Health .... MSc 12FT 24PT
Public Health (Environment & Health)................ MSc 12FT 24PT
Public Health (Health Economics)................ MSc 12FT 24PT
Public Health (Health Promotion)................ MSc 12FT 24PT
Public Health (Health Services Management)........ MSc 12FT 24PT
Public Health (Health Services Research)................ MSc 12FT 24PT
Public Health (Public Health)................... MSc 12FT 24PT
Public Health (by Distance Learning) ....MSc 24 - 60DL/PGDip 12 - 60DL/PGCert 12-60DL
Public Health for Eye Care .... MSc 12FT 24PT
Public Health in Developing Countries .... MSc 12FT 24PT
Reproductive & Sexual Health Research .... MSc 12FT 24PT
Tropical Medicine & International Health .... MSc 12FT 24PT
Veterinary Epidemiology....................... MSc 12FT 24PT

Manchester Metropolitan University
Emergency Medicine .... MSc 72PT

University of Manchester
Clinical Research...MClin Res 12 - 24DL/PG Dip Clin Res 24DL/PG Cert Clin Res 24DL
Medical Sciences.............................. MRes 12FT
Translational Medicine.......................... MRes 12FT

Newcastle University
Clinical Research/ Clinical Research (Ageing)/ Clinical Research (Leadership) .... PGCert 12PT/PGDip 24PT/MClinRes 36PT
Clinical Sciences (Medical Physics) with specialisms in: Radiotherapy Physics; Radiation Safety; Imaging with Ionising Radiation; Imaging with Non-Ionising Radiation .... MSc 36PT
Clinical Sciences (Physiological Sciences) with specialisms in: Cardiac Science; Vascular Science; Respiratory and Sleep Science; Gastrointestinal Physiology; Urodynamic Science .... MSc 36PT
Clinical Transplantation .... PGCert 12-36 monthsPT

Nottingham Trent University
Pharmaceutical and Medicinal Science ....MRes 12FT 24PT

University of Nottingham
Drug Discovery and Pharmaceutical Sciences .... MSc 12FT
Graduate Entry Medicine .... BM BS 48FT
Mathematical Medicine and Biology.................. MSc 12FT

Molecular Medical Microbiology................................ MSc 12FT
Psychologically-Minded Environments in Intellectual Disability.. PGCert 21PT
Research................................MRes 12FT 24PT

Oxford Brookes University
Cancer Studies .... MSc 12FT 36PT/PGDip 12FT/PGCert 6FT

University of Oxford
Clinical Embryology .... MSc 12FT
History of Science, Medicine & Technology................MPhil 24FT/MSc 12FT
Medical Anthropology .... MPhil 24FT/MSc 12FT

Peninsula College of Medicine and Dentistry
Remote and Isolated Health Care Environment .... PGCert 12PT/PGDip 24PT/MSc 36PT

Plymouth University
Clinical Education...........MClinEd 36PT/PGDip 24PT/PGCert 12PT
Remote Healthcare .... MSc 36PT
Simulation and Patient Safety .... MSc 36FT

New School of Psychotherapy and Counselling
Psychotherapy & Counselling .... Cert 12PT
Counselling Psychology and Psychotherapy by Professional Studies DCPsych Counselling Psychology & Psychotherapy 48FT 96PT/PGCert 12FT 24PT/PGDip 24FT 48PT/MSc 24FT 48PT
Existential Psychotherapy & Counselling by Professional Studies ...... DProf by taught 48FT 96PT/MA 24FT 48PT/PGDip 24FT 48PT/PGCert 12FT 24PT
Psychotherapy Studies ....MSc 24FT 48PT
Existential Supervision & Group Leadership............. Professional Certificate 12PT

Queen Margaret University, Edinburgh
Podiatric Medicine ....PGCert 36-60PT/PGDip 36-60PT/MSc 36-60PT
Theory of Podiatric Surgery........................ MSc 36PT

Queen Mary, University of London
Aesthetic Plastic Surgery ....PGDip 24PT 24DL
Burn Care (Distance Learning) .... PGAdvDip 24FT
Clinical Research.................. MRes 24PT/PGDip 24PT/PGCert 12PT
Forensic Medical Sciences ....MSc 12FT 24-60PT
Mental Health and Law ....MSc 12FT 24PT 24DL/PGCert 3FT/PGDip 12FT 24PT
Surgical Skills and Sciences................. MSc 12FT 24PT

Queen's University Belfast
Translational Medicine.......................MRes 12FT 24PT

University of Salford
Geriatric Medicine .... MSc 48-60PT/PGDip 24-60PT/PGCert 12-60PT
Surgical Practice........................MSc 36PT/PGDip 24PT/PGCert 9PT
Trauma and Orthopaedics .... MSc 12FT 36PT/PGDip 8FT 24PT/PGCert 4FT 9PT
Upper Limb Orthopaedics....................... PGCert 12PT

Sheffield Hallam University
Breast Imaging and Diagnosis ....MSc 36PT/PGDip 24PT/PGCert 12PT

University of Sheffield
Clinical Neurology.............................. MSc 12FT
Clinical Research..................MSc 12FT 24PT/PGDip 9FT 18PT
Molecular Medicine .... MSc 12FT
Reproductive and Developmental Medicine .... MSc 12FT
Stem Cell and Regenerative Medicine .... MSc 12FT
Translational Oncology .... MSc(Res) 12FT

University of South Wales
Disaster Healthcare (Online Delivery)...........................MSc 36DL

University of Southampton
Advanced Clinical Practice ....MSc 12FT 24PT/PGDip 12FT/PGCert 12FT
Clinical Psychology................................ DClinPsy by taught 36FT
Gerontology.......................MSc 12FT 24PT/PGDip 9FT 21PT
Gerontology (Distance Learning) ....MSc 12DL/PGDip 9DL

University of St Andrews
Medicine................................MRes 12FT 24PT

Staffordshire University
Clinical Biomechanics in Orthotic Therapy.................PGCert 12PT

University of Strathclyde
Analysis of Medicines...........MSc 36DL/PGDip 24DL/PGCert 12DL
Clinical Pharmacy............................MSc 12FT 24PT/PGDip 9FT 18PT

University of Surrey
Professional Practice.................MSc 60 maxPT/PGCert 60 maxPT/PGDip 60 maxPT

Swansea University
Autism and Related Conditions ....MSc 12FT 36PT/PGDip 12FT 24PT/PGCert 12FT 12PT
Trauma Surgery ....MSc 36PT/PGDip 18PT
Trauma Surgery (Military) ....MSc 36PT/PGDip 18PT

Teesside University
Advanced Clinical Practice .... MSc 36PT/PGCert 12PT
Advanced Clinical Practice (Management of Long-term Health Conditions)...............................MSc 36PT
Evidence-based Medicine.................... MSc 24 or 36PT 24 or 36DL

Medicine and surgery

Evidence-based Medicine (Anaesthesia)......MSc 24 or 36PT 24 or 36DL
Evidence-based Practice .... MSc 24 or 36PT 24 or 36DL
Surgical Care Practitioner (Cardiothoracic Surgery) ... PGDip 24PT
Surgical Care Practitioner (General Surgery) .... PGDip 24PT
Surgical Care Practitioner (Orthopaedic Surgery) .... PGDip 24PT

Trinity College Dublin - the University of Dublin
Cardiology .... MSc 12FT
Cardiovascular Rehabilitation and Prevention ...... MSc 12FT 24PT
Dental Surgery - Oral Surgery......................... D.Ch.Dent. 36FT 60PT
Dental Surgery - Paediatric Dentistry.......... D.Ch.Dent. 36FT 60PT
Doctor in Medicine .... MD 12FT 60PT
Surgery .... MCh 12FT
Medicine .... MSc 24PT
Physical Sciences in Medicine .... MSc 12FT 24PT

University of the Highlands and Islands
Medical Device Decontamination...MSc 12PT 12DL/PGDip 12PT/PGCert 12PT

University of Ulster
Cataract and Refractive Surgery (Theory) .... MSc 19DL/PGDip 10DL

UCL - University College London
Biomedicine .... MRes 12FT
Brain Sciences .... MRes 12FT
Burns, Plastic and Reconstructive SurgeryMSc 12FT 24PT/PGCert 36PT
Cancer.................. MSc 12FT 24-36PT/PGDip 9FT 18PT/PGCert 3FT
Clinical and Experimental Medicine................................ MSc 12FT/MRes 12FT 24PT/PGDip 9FT
Evidence-Based Healthcare .. MSc 12FT 24-48PT/PGDip 24-48PT/PGCert 24-48PT
Health and Medical Sciences.. MSc 24-60PT
Sexually Transmitted Infections and HIV........ MSc 12FT 24-60PT/PGDip 9FT 18-45PT
Surgical Science .... MSc 12FT 24PT

University of Warwick
Evidence Based Muscucloskeletal Care: External Fixation ......PGA 12PT
Evidence Based Musculoskeletal Care: Intra-medullary Nailing... PGA 12PT

University of the West of England, Bristol
Nuclear Medicine .... MSc 24-36PT

Medicine and surgery
Research Courses

University of Aberdeen
Surgery & Orthopaedics..... PhD 36FT/MD 24FT/MCh by research 12FT/MSc by research 12FT
Translational Medicine...PhD 36FT/MPhil 24FT/MD 24FT/ChM by research 24FT

Anglia Ruskin University
Medicine .... MPhil 24 - 72PT/PhD 24 - 72PT
Medical Engineering...... MPhil 18 - 36FT 30 - 48PT/PhD 24 - 60FT 36 - 72PT

Barts and the London School of Medicine and Dentistry
Academic Department of Surgery .... MS by research/FRCS
Academic Medical Unit (Whitechapel).................. PhD/MPhil/MD
Medical Professorial Unit (West Smithfield)...................... PhD/MD

University of Bath
Doctor of Medicine Master of Surgery .... MD 24-48FT 36-72PT/MS by research 12-36FT 24-48PT

University of Bedfordshire
Medicine: Related Studies....... MA by research 12FT 24PT/MSc by research 12FT 24PT/MPhil 24FT/PhD 36FT

University of Birmingham
Anaesthetics and Intensive Care .... PhD 36FT 72PT/MSc by research 12FT 24PT
Medicine .... PhD 36FT 72PT
Tissue Injury and Repair.................................. PhD 36FT/MPhil 12FT

University of Bristol
Clinical Sciences....... PhD 36FT 72PT/MSc by research 12FT 24PT/MD 24FT

University of Buckingham
Clinical Science.. MSc by research 36FT
Diabetes, Obesity and Metabolic Disease........... DPhil 36FT 72PT/MPhil 24FT 48PT

University of Cambridge
Clinical Medicine .... PhD 36FT
Medical Sciences.. MPhil 12FT
Medicine .... PhD 36FT
Surgery .... PhD 36FT

City University London
Measurement and Information in Medicine................. PhD/MPhil

University of Dundee
Dental School .... PhD 48FT 60FT
Dental School (Clinical MDSc by research) .... MDSc by research 12FT
Dental School (Non-clinical MDSc by research)................................ MDSc by research 12FT

Durham University
Medicine ... PhD 36FT 72PT/MD 24FT 48PT/MPhil 24FT 48PT/MSc by research 12FT 24PT

University of East Anglia
Medicine .... PhD 36FT 72PT/MPhil 24FT 48PT/MSc by research 12FT 24PT/MD 24PT

University of Edinburgh
Genito-Urinary Medicine... PhD 36FT 72PT/MPhil 24FT 36PT/MSc by research 12FT 24PT
Geriatric Medicine.........PhD 36FT 72PT/MPhil 24FT 48PT/MSc by research 12FT 24PT
Inflammation .PhD 36FT 72PT/MPhil 24FT 48PT/MSc by research 12FT 24PT
Integrative Physiology............ PhD 36FT 72PT/MPhil 24FT/MSc by research 12FT 24PT
Internal Medicine .... PhD 36FT
Medical Microbiology....PhD 36FT 72PT/MPhil 24FT 36PT/MSc by research 12FT 24PT
Medical Sciences............PhD 36FT 72PT/MPhil 24FT 36PT/MSc by research 12FT 24PT
Medical Sciences .... MMedSci by research 12FT 24PT
Orthopaedic Surgery .....PhD 36FT 72PT/MPhil 24FT 36PT/MSc by research 12FT 24PT
Orthopaedic and Trauma Medicine .... PhD 36FT 72PT/MPhil 24FT 48PT/MSc by research 12FT 24PT
Pathway Medicine...PhD 36FT 72PT/MPhil 24FT/MSc by research 12FT 24PT
Regenerative Medicine .... MPhil 24FT 48PT/PhD 36FT 72PT
Respiratory Medicine (Royal Infirmary of Edinburgh).....PhD 36FT 72PT/MPhil 24FT 36PT/MSc by research 12FT 24PT
Surgery .... PhD 36FT 72PT/MPhil 24FT 48PT/MSc by research 12FT 24PT

National University of Ireland Galway
College of Medicine, Nursing and Health Sciences .... PhD 48FT 72PT/MSc by research 24FT 48PT/MD 24FT 48PT/MAO by research 24FT 48PT

University of Glasgow
Community Based Sciences.......... PhD 36FT 60PT/MD 24FT 48PT/MSc(MedSci) by research 12FT 24PT
Developmental Medicine.............. PhD 36FT 60PT/MD 24FT 48PT/MSc(Eng) by research 12FT 24PT

University of Hull
Medicine ... PhD 36FT 60PT/MD 12FT 24PT/MPhil 24FT 36PT/MSc by research 12FT 24PT

Imperial College London
Medicine .... PhD 36FT 48PT
Musculoskeletal......MSc by research 12FT 36PT/MBBS 12FT 36PT

Keele University
Department of Medicine.. PhD/MPhil

University of Kent
Doctor of Medicine .... MD 24FT 60PT

Lancaster University
Medicine .... MD 24FT 48PT
Statistics and Epidemiology .... PhD 36PT

University of Leeds
School of Medicine... PhD 36-48FT 60-84PT/MPhil 24-36FT 48-72PT/MSc by research 12FT 24PT MD 24-36FT 24-60PT/ChM by research 24-36FT 24-60PT

University of Lincoln
Biomedical and Medical Science .... MPhil 18FT 30PT/PhD 33FT 60PT

Liverpool School of Tropical Medicine
Clinical research.. PhD/MPhil/MIHR
Disease control... PhD/MPhil/MIHR

University of Liverpool
Clinical Sciences... MRes 12FT 24/36PT
Critical Care........................... MPhil 12FT 24PT/PhD 36FT/MD 60FT
Surgery and Oncology......... PhD 12-48FT 24-84PT/MPhil 12-48FT 24-84PT/MD 12-48FT 24-84PT

London School of Hygiene and Tropical Medicine
Epidemiology & Population Health (Research) ..DrPH 42FT 42PT/PhD 42FT 42PT/MPhil 12FT 12PT
Infectious & Tropical Diseases (Research).... DrPH 42FT 42PT/PhD 42FT 42PT/MPhil 12FT 12PT
Public Health & Policy (Research).........DrPH 42FT 42PT/PhD 42FT 42PT/MPhil 12FT 12PT

Manchester Metropolitan University
Professional Doctorate... Professional Doctorate 60PT/Masters in Clinical Research 48PT/MRes 36PT

University of Manchester
Medicine .... PhD 36FT 72PT/MPhil 12FT 24PT MD/ChM 24FT 48PT
Operative Dentistry .... PhD 36FT 72PT/MPhil 12FT 24PT

Newcastle University
Cancer.. MRes 12FT
Medical Sciences.. MRes 12FT
Medicine and Surgery .... MPhil 12FT 24PT/PhD 36FT 72PT/MD 24FT 48PT
Mitochondrial Biology and Medicine................................ MRes 12FT
Translational Medicine and Therapeutics....................... MRes 12FT
Transplantation... MRes 12FT

Nottingham Trent University
Cancer Biology... MRes 12FT 24PT

University of Nottingham
Breast Surgery .... PhD 36FT
Clinical Sciences..... MRes 12FT/MPhil 24FT 48PT/PhD 36FT 72PT/DM 36FT 72PT
GEM research areas ... PhD 36FT 72PT/MPhil 24FT 48PT/DM 36FT 72PT
Orthopaedic and Accident Surgery...... DM 24-36FT 48-72PT/PhD 24-36FT 48-72PT
Otorhinolaryngology and Head and Neck Surgery..PhD 36-48FT/DM 24FT
Stroke Medicine .... PhD 36FT 72PT/MPhil 24FT 48PT/DM 36FT 72PT
Therapeutics and Molecular Medicine ...... PhD 24-36FT 48-72PT/MPhil 12-24FT 24-48PT

The Open University
Biomedical Sciences............................... PhD 36FT 72PT variableDL/MPhil 15FT 24PT
Cell and molecular biomedicineMPhil 15FT 24PT variableDL/PhD 36FT 72PT variableDL
Medicinal chemistry and diagnostics .... MPhil 15FT 24PT variableDL/PhD 36FT 72PT variableDL

University of Oxford
Biomedical and Clinical Sciences....................................... DPhil 36FT
Cardiovascular Medicine .... DPhil 48FT/MSc by research 24FT
Cardiovascular Science... DPhil 48FT
Clinical Laboratory Sciences .... DPhil 48FT/MSc by research 24-36FT
Clinical Medicine .... DPhil 48FT/MSc by research 24FT
Clinical Neurosciences .... DPhil 48FT/MSc by research 24-36FT
Oncology... DPhil 48FT/MSc by research 24FT
Surgery .... DPhil 48FT/MSc by research 24-36FT

Plymouth University
Medicine .... PhD/MPhil/MD
Surgery .... PhD/MPhil/MD

Queen's University Belfast
Cancer Research and Cell Biology........PhD 36FT 72PT/MPhil 24FT 48PT/MD 24FT 48PT/MCh by research 12FT 24PT
Vision and Vascular Science.......... PhD 36FT 72PT/MD 24FT 48PT/MPhil 24FT 48PT

University of Sheffield
Cardiovascular Science................ PhD 36FT 72PT/MPhil 24FT 48PT
Oncology.. PhD 36FT 72PT/MPhil 24FT 48PT

University of Southampton
Clinical Research.. MRes 12FT 48PT
School of Medicine....................... MPhil 48FT 72PT/PhD 48FT 72PT

University of St Andrews
Medicine .... MPhil 12-24FT/PhD 36FT/MD 24FT

St George's, University of London
Basic Medical Sciences.............. PhD 36FT 84PT/MPhil 24FT 48PT/MDRes 24PT
Cardiovascular Medicine .... PhD 36FT 84PT/MPhil 24FT 48PT/MDRes 24PT
Cellular and Molecular Medicine ....PhD 36FT 72PT/MPhil 24FT 48PT/MD(Res) 24 minFT 48 minPT

University of Surrey
Clinical Practice................................ DClinPrac 48PT/DClinPrac 60PT
Health and Medical Sciences..... PhD 36FT 60PT/MPhil 24FT 48PT
Medical School.............................. PhD 36FT 48PT/MPhil 24FT 36PT
Medical School .... MD 24FT 48PT

University of Ulster
Doctor of Medicine .... MD 36FT 60PT

UCL - University College London
Cancer... PhD 36FT 60PT
Medicine........PhD 36FT 60PT/MPhil 36-48FT 60PT/MD(Res) 24FT 24PT/PhD 48FT
Surgery and Interventional Science......................... PhD 36FT 60PT/MD(Res) 24FT 24PT

University of Warwick
Medicine and allied disciplines.... PhD 36FT 60PT/MD 24FT 36PT/MPhil 24FT 36PT/MSc by research 12FT 24PT

Music therapy
Taught Courses

University of Aberdeen
Studies in Mindfulness .... MSc 36PT/PGDip 24PT/PGCert 12PT

Anglia Ruskin University
Music Therapy .... MA 24FT

City University London
Music Therapy .... MMT 24FT

Goldsmiths, University of London
Music, Mind and Brain .... MSc 12FT 24PT

Medicine and surgery

Leeds Metropolitan University
Psychological Therapies....MA 48PT

University of Limerick
Music Therapy....MA 24FT

University of Roehampton
Applied Music Psychology....MA 12FT 24PT
Music Therapy....MA 24FT 36PT
Applied Music Psychology.........PGCert 6FT 24PT PGDip 9FT 24PT

University of Sheffield
Music Psychology in Education....MA 24 PTDL
Psychology of Music....MA 12FT 24PT

University of South Wales
Art Psychotherapy....MA 36PT
Buddhist Studies....PGCert 12DL/PGDip 24DL/MA 36DL
Evaluation Studies....PGCert 9-12DL
Music Therapy....MA 36PT

University of the West of England, Bristol
Music Therapy....MA 36PT

Nephrology
Taught Courses

University of Brighton
Nephrology and Education........MSc 36 - 72PT/PGCert 36 - 72PT/PGDip 36 - 72PT
Nephrology and Management. MSc 36 - 72PT/PGCert 36 - 72PT/PGDip 36 - 72PT

University of Buckingham
General Internal Medicine....MD 24/36FT

University of Warwick
Hypertension and Nephropathy....PGA 12PT

Nephrology
Research Courses

Barts and the London School of Medicine and Dentistry
Experimental Medicine and Nephrology....PhD

Neurology
Taught Courses

Bangor University
Clinical and Functional Brain Imaging....PGCert 12PT
Neuroimaging....MSc 12FT 24PT
Clinical and Functional Brain Imaging....PGCert 8PT

University of Birmingham
Physiotherapy (pre-registration)....MSc 24FT

Bucks New University
Advancing Spinal Cord Rehabilitation and Management......MSc 36PT

Cardiff University
Neuorehabilitation....MSc 18FT 36-48PT/PGDip 12FT 24PT
Neuroimaging Methods & Applications....MSc 12FT

Coventry University
Neurological Occupational Therapy........MSc 12 MinFT 26 MinPT
Neurological Physiotherapy..........MSc 15FT 24-60PT/PGDip 12FT 18-36PT

University of East London
Neurological Rehabilitation....PGCert 5FT 12 - 36PT

University of Glasgow
Brain Imaging....MSc 12FT
Brain Sciences: From Molecules to Mind....MSc 12FT

University of Greenwich
Science (Open)....MSc 12FT 24-36PT

King's College London
Analytical Science for Industry....MSc 12FT 24PT
Neuroimaging....MSc 12FT

Newcastle University
Neuroinformatics....MSc 12FT

University of Oxford
Endovascular Neurosurgery (Interventional Neuroradiology).......MSc 12FT
Neuroscience....MSc 12FT

University of Salford
Surgical Practice....MSc 36PT/PGDip 24PT/PGCert 9PT

University of Sheffield
Clinical Neurology....MSc 12FT
Translational Neuroscience....MSc 12FT

Teesside University
Neurological Rehabilitation....PGCert 12PT

UCL - University College London
Advanced Neuroimaging....MSc 12FT 24PT
Brain and Mind Sciences....MSc 24FT
Clinical Neurology....MSc 12FT/PGDip 6FT
Clinical Neurology (by Distance Learning)....PGDip 12-36DL
Neurology for Clinical Trainees....MSc 24-48PT

Neurology
Research Courses

Barts and the London School of Medicine and Dentistry
Department of Neurosurgery....PhD/MPhil/MD

University of Cambridge
Neurology....PhD 36FT
Neurosurgery....PhD 36FT

University of Liverpool
Neurological Science...........PhD 12-48FT 48-84PT/MPhil 12-48FT 24-72PT/MD 24-72FT

University of Nottingham
Neurology - Clinical Neurology....PhD 36-48FT

University of Oxford
Clinical Neurosciences.........DPhil 48FT/MSc by research 24-36FT
Neuroscience....DPhil 48FT
Surgery....DPhil 48FT/MSc by research 24-36FT

University of Sheffield
Motor Neurone Disease....PhD 36FT
Neuroscience....PhD 36FT 72PT/MPhil 24FT 48PT

University of Strathclyde
Neuroscience....MRes 12FT

UCL - University College London
Neurology....PhD 36FT 60PT/MD(Res) 24FT 24PT

Oncology
Taught Courses

University of Birmingham
Clinical Oncology ... MSc 12FT/PGDip 9FT MSc 24PT/PGDip 24PT
Clinical Oncology MSc/Postgraduate Diploma - Full-time..... MSc 12FT/GradDip 12FT

University of Bradford
Cancer Pharmacology....MSc 12FT
Drug Discovery....MSc 12FT 24PT/PGDip 12FT 24PT

Brunel University
Molecular Medicine and Cancer Research....MSc 12FT 24PT

Bucks New University
Advanced Practice (Critical Care)....MSc 36PT

University of Central Lancashire
Cancer Biology and Therapy....MSc 12FT

University of Dundee
Advanced Practice....MSc 18DL
Cancer Biology....MRes 12FT

University of East Anglia....
Oncoplastic Breast Surgery....MSc 36PT/PGDip 24PT

National University of Ireland Galway
Nursing (Oncology)....PGDip 12FT 24PT

Glasgow Caledonian University
Health and Social Care (Radiation Oncology)............MSc 12-24FT 12-72PT
Radiatiotherapy and Oncology....MSc 12-24FT

University of Glasgow
Surgical Oncology....MSc (ClinSci) 12FT

University of Hertfordshire
Oncological Sciences............MSc 24PT/PGDip 24PT/PGCert 24PT

University of Hull
Translational Oncology....MSc 12FT

Imperial College London
Cancer Biology....MRes 12FT

Keele University
Ethics of Cancer and Palliative Care... MA 12FT 24PT 24DL/PGDip 12PT 12DL

University of Kent
Cancer Biology....PGDip 12FT 24PT/MSc 12FT 24PT

King's College London
Advanced Practice (Cancer Nursing)....MSc 36-72PT/PGDip 24-72PT/PGCert 12-72PT
Nuclear Medicine: Science & Practice....MSc 12FT 24PT/PGDip 12FT 24PT/PGCert 6FT 18PT
Translational Cancer Medicine....MRes 12FT 24PT

Kingston University
Cancer Biology....MSc 12FT 24PT
Radiography: Oncology Practice....MSc 24FT 24-60PT/PGCert 24FT 24-60PT/PGDip 24FT 24-60PT

University of Leicester
Cancer Chemistry....MSc 12FT

University of Manchester
Cancer Research and Molecular Biomedicine....MSc 12FT
Oncology....MRes 12FT

Newcastle University
Oncology/ Palliative Care/ Oncology for the Pharmaceutical Industry....MSc 36DL/PGDip 24DL/PGCert 12DL

University of Northampton
Applied Cancer Studies....MSc 36PT/PGDip 24PT

Nottingham Trent University
Biomedical Science....MSc 12FT 24PT
Cancer Biology....MSc(Res) 12FT 24PT

University of Nottingham
Cancer Immunology and Biotechnology....MSc 12FT
Oncology....MSc 12FT 24PT/PGCert 12PT

Oxford Brookes University
Cancer Studies....MSc 12FT 36PT/PGDip 12FT/PGCert 6FT

University of Oxford
Medicinal Chemistry for Cancer....MSc 12FT

Queen Margaret University, Edinburgh
Radiotherapy and Oncology (Pre-Registration)..............MSc 30FT/PGDip 24FT

Queen Mary, University of London
Cancer Therapeutics....MSc 12FT 24PT

University of Salford
Psycho-Oncology....MSc 36PT/PGDip 24PT/PGCert 12PT

Sheffield Hallam University
Advanced Practice (Radiotherapy and Oncology) MSc 3DL/PGDip 2DL/PGCert 1DL
Breast Imaging and Diagnosis.......MSc 36PT/PGDip 24PT/PGCert 12PT
Radiotherapy and Oncology in Practice....PGDip 24FT

University of Sheffield
Translational Oncology....MSc(Res) 12FT

University of South Wales
Cancer Care (Approved by the European Oncology Nursing Society)....BSc 24-72PT

University of Southampton
Clinical Leadership in Cancer, Palliative and End of Life Care MSc 24FT 48PT
Health and Rehabilitation........MSc 12FT 24PT/PGDip 12FT 24PT/PGCert 8FT 16PT

Trinity College Dublin - the University of Dublin
Advanced Radiotherapy Practice....MSc 12FT
Cancer Care....MSc 24PT
Oncological Nursing....PGDip 12FT

UCL - University College London
Cancer....MSc 12FT 24-36PT/PGDip 9FT 18PT/PGCert 3FT

University of the West of England, Bristol
Radiotherapy and Oncology....MSc 36FT

University of York
Haematopathology....MSc 24PT/PGCert 24PT/PGDip 24PT

Oncology
Research Courses

University of Aberdeen
Cancer Medicine......MSc by research 12FT/MPhil 24FT/PhD 36FT

Barts and the London School of Medicine and Dentistry
Department of Medical Oncology....PhD/MPhil/MD
Gynaecological Oncology....PhD/MPhil
Paediatric Oncology....PhD/FRCPCH

University of Birmingham
Cancer Studies....PhD 36FT 72PT/MSc by research 12FT 24PT/MD 24PT

University of Bradford
Cancer Therapeutics...........PhD 36-48FT 48-60PT/MPhil 12-24FT 24-48PT

University of Cambridge
Clinical Oncology....PhD 36FT
Oncology....PhD 36FT 60PT

Cardiff University
Cancer and Genetics....PhD 36-48FT/MPhil 12FT/MD 12FT

University of Dundee....
Oral Cancer....MRes 12FT

University of Edinburgh
Cancer....PhD 36FT
Edinburgh Cancer Research Centre... PhD 36FT 72PT/MPhil 24FT/MSc by research 12FT 24PT
Oncology....PhD 36FT 72PT

National University of Ireland Galway
College of Science....MSc by research 24FT

University of Glasgow
Cancer Sciences and Molecular Pathology (including Surgery).....PhD 36FT 69PT/MD 24FT 48PT/MSc(MedSci) by research 12FT 24PT

Institute of Cancer Research
CRC Cancer Therapeutics....PhD
Institute of Cancer Research....PhD

King's College London
Cancer Studies (Research Division)....PhD 36FT 48-72PT/MPhil 36FT 48-72PT

University of Liverpool
Cancer Biology............MPhil 12FT 48PT/PhD 36FT 72PT/MD 60FT

Medicine and surgery

Cancer Medicine.......MPhil 12FT 24-72PT/PhD 36FT 48-84PT/MD 12-72FT

Ocular Oncology...........MPhil 12-48FT 24-72PT/MD 24-72FT/PhD 24-48FT 48-84PT

Orthopaedic Biology............MPhil 12-48FT 24-72PT/PhD 24-48FT 48-84PT/MD 24-72FT

Pancreatology......MPhil 12-48FT 24-72PT/PhD 24-48FT 48-84PT/MD 24-72FT

Newcastle University
Cancer...MRes 12FT
PhD 36FT 72PT/MD 24FT 48PT/MPhil 12FT 24PT

Nottingham Trent University
Cancer Biology..MRes 12FT 24PT

University of Nottingham
Brain Tumour Research - The Children's Brain Tumour Research Centre (CBTRC) .... PhD 36FT 72PT
Breast Surgery..PhD 36FT
Pre-Clinical Oncology .... PhD 36FT 72PT

Oxford Brookes University
Health & Biomedical Sciences - Glycobiology and Cancer .....PhD 24-60FT 36-72PT/MPhil 24-36FT 36-48PT

University of Oxford
Medical Oncology..................DPhil 48FT/MSc by research 24-36FT
Medicinal Chemistry for Cancer.....................................DPhil 48FT
Primary Health Care ....DPhil 48FT/MSc by research 24-36FT

University of Sheffield
Oncology.. PhD 36FT 72PT/MPhil 24FT 48PT

UCL - University College London
Cancer.. PhD 36FT 60PT
Oncology.. PhD 36FT 60PT

Ophthalmics
Taught Courses

University of Dundee
Eye Movements & Cognition .... MSc 12FT

Glasgow Caledonian University
Clinical Opthamology and Vision Research.....................MSc 12FT

University of Glasgow
Brain Sciences: From Molecules to Mind........................ MSc 12FT

London School of Hygiene and Tropical Medicine
Public Health for Eye Care......................................MSc 12FT 24PT

University of Manchester
Investigative Ophthalmology and Vision Science........... MSc 12FT 24-48PT

University of Sheffield
Vision and Strabismus .... MMedSci 24-36 PTDL/Diploma 18-24 PTDL/PGCert 12-18 PTDL

University of Ulster
Cataract and Refractive Surgery (Theory) ....MSc 19DL/PGDip 10DL
Clinical Visual Science ....MSc 20DL/PGDip 10DL/PGCert 8DL

UCL - University College London
Biology of Vision.. MSc 12FT
Clinical Ophthalmology.......... MSc 24FT 36PT/PGCert 24FT 36PT/PGDip 24FT 36PT
Ophthalmology: Cataract and Refractive Surgery MSc 12FT 24PT
Ophthalmology: Retina ....MSc 12FT 24PT

University of Warwick
Diabetic Retinopathy.. PGA 12PT

Ophthalmics
Research Courses

University of Aberdeen
Ophthalmology........PhD 36FT/MSc by research 12FT/MPhil 24FT

Anglia Ruskin University
Vision and Eye Research Unit ....PhD 24 - 60FT 36 - 72PT

Glasgow Caledonian University
Biological and Biomedical Sciences/Psychology/
Vision Sciences...MRes 12FT

University of Liverpool
Eye and Vision Sciences................. MPhil 12FT/PhD 36FT/MD 60FT

University of Manchester
Ophthalmology......................................PhD 36FT/MPhil 12FT 24PT

University of Nottingham
Ophthalmology and Visual Sciences ... PhD 24-36FT 48-72PT/DM 24-36FT 48-72PT

University of Oxford
Ophthalmology........................... DPhil 48FT/MSc by research 24FT

UCL - University College London
Ophthalmology.......................PhD 36FT 60PT/MD(Res) 24FT 24PT

Orthopaedics
Taught Courses

University of Bath
Orthopaedic Engineering - Joint Replacement...........PGCert 12PT

University of Brighton
Trauma and Orthopaedics ....MSc 36 - 72PT/PGDip 36 - 72PT/PGCert 36 - 72PT

Cardiff Metropolitan University
Musculoskeletal Studies (Lower Limb) .....MSc 36PT/PGDip 36PT/PGCert 36PT

Cardiff University
Orthopaedic Engineering ....MSc 12-24DL

University of Central Lancashire
Osteoarchaeology: Techniques and Data Analysis......... MSc 12FT
Physiotherapy Professional Practice..............MSc 12FT up to 60PT

University of Dundee
Orthopaedic Science ....MSc up to 60DL MSc 12FT MChOrth 9FT
Orthopaedic and Rehabilitation Technology ....MSc 24-60DL

University of Edinburgh
General Surgery (Online Distance Learning) ....ChM 24DL
Trauma and Orthopaedics ....ChM 24DL

National University of Ireland Galway
Nursing (Orthopaedics) ....PGDip 12FT 24PT

Manchester Metropolitan University
Cardiorespiratory Physiotherapy and by Research ...... MDSc 15FT flexiblePT

Queen Mary, University of London
Musculoskeletal Clinical Sciences...........................MSc 12FT 24PT
Musculoskeletal Sciences...MSc 12FT 24PT
Trauma Sciences..MSc 12FT 24PT

University of Salford
Trauma and Orthopaedics .... MSc 12FT 36PT/PGDip 8FT 24PT/PGCert 4FT 9PT
Upper Limb Orthopaedics...PGCert 12PT

Swansea University
Trauma Surgery (Military) ....MSc 36PT/PGDip 18PT

Teesside University
Orthopaedics .... MCh 24PT
Surgical Care Practitioner (Orthopaedic Surgery) .... PGDip 24PT

UCL - University College London
Musculoskeletal Science....................................MSc 24FT 24-60PT/PGDip 9FT 18-45PT/PGCert 3FT
Musculoskeletal Science (by Distance Learning)............MSc 12FT/PGDip 9FT 24-60PT/PGCert 3FT
Trauma and Orthopaedics .... MSc 12FT 24-48PT/PGDip 24-48PT/PGCert 24-48PT

University of Warwick
Health Sciences: Trauma and Orthopaedic Surgery........................MSc 24-96PT

Orthopaedics
Research Courses

University of Cambridge
Orthopaedic Research.....................................PhD 36FT/MPhil 12FT

University of Edinburgh
Orthopaedic Surgery .....PhD 36FT 72PT/MPhil 24FT 36PT/MSc by research 12FT 24PT
Orthopaedic and Trauma Medicine ....PhD 36FT 72PT/MPhil 24FT 48PT/MSc by research 12FT 24PT

University of Liverpool
Orthopaedic Biology............MPhil 12-48FT 24-72PT/PhD 24-48FT 48-84PT/MD 24-72FT

University of Nottingham
Orthopaedic and Accident Surgery...... DM 24-36FT 48-72PT/PhD 24-36FT 48-72PT

University of Oxford
Engineering Science...................DPhil 48FT/MSc by research 24FT
Musculoskeletal Sciences..........DPhil 48FT/MSc by research 24FT

University of Sheffield
Musculoskeletal Science............. PhD 36FT 72PT/MPhil 24FT 48PT

University of Strathclyde
Prosthetics and / or Orthotics Rehabilitation Studies ....PhD 36FT 72PT/MPhil 12FT 24PT

UCL - University College London
Orthopaedics and Musculo-Skeletal Science ....PhD 36FT 60PT/MD(Res) 24FT 24PT

Osteopathy
Taught Courses

University of Central Lancashire
Advanced Stroke Practice ......MSc 36FT 60PT/PGDip 24PT/PGCert 12PT

University of Derby
Osteoporosis and Falls Management...........................PGCert 24PT

Queen Mary, University of London
Critical Care..MSc 12FT 24PT
Musculoskeletal Clinical Sciences...........................MSc 12FT 24PT
Musculoskeletal Sciences...MSc 12FT 24PT

University of Roehampton
Attachment Studies...PGCert 6FT 12PT

Staffordshire University
Musculoskeletal Diagnosis ....PGCert 9PT

University of Warwick
Evidence Based Musculoskeletal Care: External Fixation ......PGA 12PT
Evidence Based Musculoskeletal Care: Intra-medullary Nailing...PGA 12PT

Osteopathy
Research Courses

Anglia Ruskin University
Medical Engineering...... MPhil 18 - 36FT 30 - 48PT/PhD 24 - 60FT 36 - 72PT

Paediatrics
Taught Courses

University of Bolton
Safeguarding and Promoting Children's Welfare.... MSc 36-60PT/PGDip 24PT/PGCert 12PT

University of Brighton
Child Health and Education.........MSc 12 - 36FT 24 - 72PT/PGCert 12 - 36FT 24 - 72PT/PGDip 12 - 36FT 24 - 72PT
Child Health and Management... MSc 12 - 36FT 24 - 72PT/PGDip 12 - 36FT 24 - 72PT/PGCert 12 - 36FT 24 - 72PT

University of Central Lancashire
Child Care and Welfare ....MA 12FT 24-60PT
Child Health .... MSc 36FT

University of Chester
Family and Child Psychology ...MSc 12FT 24PT/PGDip 12FT 24PT/PGCert 12FT 12-24PT

University of East London
Paediatric Studies ....PGCert 5FT 12 - 36PT

Edge Hill University
Integrated Children and Young People's Practice......MSc 36-72PT

University of Edinburgh
Paediatric Dentistry ....MClinDent 24FT
Paediatric Emergency Medicine .. MSc 36DL/PGDip 24DL/PGCert 12DL

University of Glasgow
Child Health.................................... PGCert 12-24FT PGDip 12-24PT
Paediatric Science... MSc (Clin Sci) 12FT

Imperial College London
Paediatrics and Child Health ... MSc 24-36PT/PGDip 24PT/PGCert 12PT

King's College London
Advanced Paediatrics ....MSc 12FT 24PT
Advanced Practice (Child Health).. MSc 36-72PT/PGDip 24-72PT/PGCert 12-72PT
Child & Adolescent Mental Health................MSc 12FT 24PT

Kingston University
Maternal and Child Health: Socio-Cultural PerspectivesMSc 12FT 24PT

University of Leeds
Child Health...MMedSci 36PT/PGDip 24PT

Liverpool John Moores University
Advanced Neonatal Practitioner in Neonatal Critical Care .... MSc 36PT
Advanced Paediatric Nurse Practitioner (APNP) in Ambulatory Care..MSc 12FT 24PT
Advanced Paediatric Nurse Practitioner (APNP) in Critical Care ... MSc 12FT

Liverpool School of Tropical Medicine
Tropical Paediatrics ....MTropPaed 12FT

University of Liverpool
Tropical Paediatrics ....MSc 12FT/PGDip 6FT/PGCert 3FT

Newman University
Children, Young People and Families................... MA 24FT 36-48PT

Oxford Brookes University
Children, Young People and Family Well-Being ....MSc 12-36DL/PGDip 8-36DL/PGCert 4-36DL

University of Salford
Surgical Practice.......................MSc 36PT/PGDip 24PT/PGCert 9PT

Sheffield Hallam University
Advanced Practice (Radiotherapy and Oncology) ....MSc 3DL/PGDip 2DL/PGCert 1DL
Advancing Paediatric Practice .... MSc 18FT/PGDip 12FT/PGCert 6FT

University of Sheffield
Paediatric Dentistry ....MClinDent 24FT

Swansea University
Childhood Studies.. MA 12FT 24PT

Trinity College Dublin - the University of Dublin
Child Protection and Welfare ....MSc 24PT PGDip 12PT

Medicine and surgery

Children's Nursing (H.Dip.)...HDip 12FT
Dental Surgery Paediatric Dentistry.............D.Ch.Dent. 36FT 60PT
Paediatrics ....MSc 12FT

UCL - University College London
Advanced Physiotherapy: Paediatrics .. MSc 12FT 24-60PT/PGDip 9FT 36-60PT/PGCert 9PT
Applied Paediatric Neuropsychology .... MSc 12FT
Child and Adolescent Mental Health ... MSc 12FT 24-60PT/PGDip 24-60PT/PGCert 12PT
Clinical Paediatric Neuropsychology ...MSc 12FT 24PT/PGDip 9FT 18PT
Paediatrics and Child Health: Advanced Paediatrics.........................
MSc 36-60PT/PGCert 12-24PT/PGDip 36-60PT
Paediatrics and Child Health: Community Child Health................
MSc 12FT 36-60PT/PGCert 12-24PT/PGDip 9FT 18-45PT

University of Warwick
Child Health....... PGA 12PT MSc 12FT 24-96PT/PGDip 12FT 24PT/
PGCert 12FT 24PT
Child Health Services: Management, Organisations and Data
Systems... PGA 12PT/CPDMod 1PT
Health Sciences: Child Health........MSc 36PT/PGDip 24PT/PGCert 12PT/PGA 12PT

Paediatrics
Research Courses

University of Aberdeen
Child Health..............PhD 36FT/MPhil 24FT/MSc by research 12FT

Barts and the London School of Medicine and Dentistry
Paediatric Endocrinology.....................PhD/MPhil/MA by research MD/FRCP
Paediatric Gastroenterology.....................................PhD/MPhil/MD
Paediatric Oncology..PhD/FRCPCH

University of Birmingham
Paediatrics and Child Health ....PhD 3FT 6PT/MPhil 1FT 2PT

University of Cambridge
Paediatrics ....PhD 36FT

Imperial College London
Paediatrics ....PhD

King's College London
Child & Adolescent Psychiatry .PhD 36FT 72PT/MPhil 36FT 72PT/
MD 36FT 72PT

University of Liverpool
Obstetrics and Gynaecology........ MPhil 12FT/PhD 36FT/MD 60FT
Pancreatology......MPhil 12-48FT 24-72PT/PhD 24-48FT 48-84PT/
MD 24-72FT

University of Oxford
Paediatrics .... DPhil 48FT/MSc by research 24FT
Primary Health Care ....DPhil 48FT/MSc by research 24-36FT
Surgery ....DPhil 48FT/MSc by research 24-36FT

Plymouth University
Preventive and Supportive Care ....MPhil TBCFT

Swansea University
Childhood Studies..MPhil 12FT/PhD 36FT

UCL - University College London
Child Health..PhD 36FT 60PT/MD(Res) 24FT
Paediatrics..............................PhD 36FT 60PT/MD(Res) 24FT 24PT

Pain management
Taught Courses

Birmingham City University
Pain Management....................PGCert 12PT/PGDip 18PT/MSc 24PT

Cardiff University
Pain Management.................MSc 24DL/PGDip 18DL/PGCert 18DL

University of Edinburgh
Clinical Management of Headache Disorders ... MSc 36DL/PGDip 24DL/PGCert 12DL
Clinical Management of Pain........MSc 36-72DL/PGDip 24-48DL/
PGCert 12-24DL

Keele University
Pain Science and Management MSc 24-60PT/PGCert 12FT 24PT/
PGDip 12FT 24-60PT

King's College London
Conscious Sedation for Dentistry.......................................PGDip 9FT
Pain: Science & Society .... MSc 12FT 24PT

Leeds Metropolitan University
Community Specialist Practitioner - Practice Nursing..MSc 24PT/
PGDip 24PT
Integrated Masters Biomedical Sciences ....MBIOMS 48FT

University of Leicester
Pain Management....................... MSc 12FT 24PT/PGDip 12FT 24PT

Newcastle University
Conscious Sedation in Dentistry................................. PGDip 12PT

Queen Mary, University of London
Burn Care (Distance Learning) .... PGAdvDip 24FT

Staffordshire University
Clinical Biomechanics and Pain Management in the Lower limb...
....PGCert 12PT

Swansea University
Chronic Conditions Management........MSc 12FT 36PT/PGDip 9FT 24PT/PGCert 6FT 12PT

Trinity College Dublin - the University of Dublin
Conscious Sedation in Dentistry...................................PGDip 18PT

UCL - University College London
Dental Sedation and Pain Management ....PGCert 12PT

University of Warwick
Evidence Based Musculoskeletal Care: Managing Lower Limb
Pain .... PGA 12PT
Evidence Based Musculoskeletal Care: Managing Neck and Back
Pain .... PGA 12PT
Evidence Based Musculoskeletal Care: Managing Upper Limb
Pain .... PGA 12PT

Pain management
Research Courses

University of Aberdeen
Translational Medicine...PhD 36FT/MPhil 24FT/MD 24FT/ChM by research 24FT

University of Birmingham
Biomaterials..MRes 12FT 24PT

University of Edinburgh
Anaesthesia and Pain MedicineMPhil 24FT 48PT/PhD 36FT 72PT/
MSc by research 12FT 24PT
Anaesthesia, Critical Care and Pain Medicine...................PhD 36FT

Palliative care
Taught Courses

University of Bedfordshire
Palliative Care .... MSc 24-36PT

University of Bradford
Practitioners with a Special Interest ....MSc 24PT/PGDip 12PT

University of Bristol
Palliative Medicine.........................MSc 24-36PT/Diploma 24-36FT

Bucks New University
Advanced Practice (Cancer and Palliative Care)............... MSc 36PT
Advanced Practice (Critical Care)................................. MSc 36PT

Canterbury Christ Church University
Palliative Care...MSc 36-72PT

Cardiff University
Palliative Medicine/Palliative Care ...... MSc 36-48DL/PGDip 24DL

University of Chester
Health and Social Care - Advanced Practice .... MSc 24 - 72PT/
PGDip 24 - 60PT/PGCert 12 - 36PT
Health and Social Care - Oncology for Health and Social Care
Practitioners ....PGCert 12 - 36PT

De Montfort University
Palliative Care ....MSc 39-72PT

University of Derby
Management of Long Term Conditions.......................PGCert 12PT

University of Dundee
Advanced Practice ....MSc 18DL
Advanced Practice (Palliative Care) ....MSc 36DL
Palliative Care.......................................MSc 36DL
Palliative Care Research ....MPH 12-24FT
Quality Improvement ....MSc 36DL PGCert 12DL
PGDip 24DL

Edinburgh Napier University
Advanced Practice in Palliative Care..........MSc 36PT/PGDip 24PT/
PGCert 12PT
Advanced Practice in Palliative Care and Applied Education ....
MSc 12FT 36PT/PGDip 9FT 24PT/PGCert 6FT 12PT

National University of Ireland Galway
Nursing (Palliative Care) ....PGDip 12FT 24PT

University of Glasgow
Evidence Based Medicine & Education............. MSc (ClinSci) 12FT

Keele University
Ethics of Cancer and Palliative Care... MA 12FT 24PT 24DL/PGDip 12PT 12DL
End of Life Care ....PGCert 12FT

University of Kent
Advanced and Specialist Healthcare (Minimally Invasive
Surgery)..MSc 24-36PT
Advanced and Specialist Healthcare (Supportive and Palliative
Care)..MSc 24-36PT

King's College London
Advanced Practice (Palliative Care Nursing)............. MSc 36-72PT/
PGDip 24-72PT/PGCert 12-72PT
Palliative Care ...... MSc 12FT 24PT/PGDip 12FT 24PT/PGCert 12FT
Translational Cancer Medicine..............................MRes 12FT 24PT

LOROS
MCS Palliative Care .... MSc 36PT

Newcastle University
Oncology/ Palliative Care/ Oncology for the Pharmaceutical
Industry..................................MSc 36DL/PGDip 24DL/PGCert 12DL

University of Northampton
Applied Cancer Studies ....MSc 36PT/PGDip 24PT

University of Nottingham
Cancer Immunology and Biotechnology.......................... MSc 12FT

Oxford Brookes University
Palliative Care: Global Perspectives ....MSc 12-36DL

Reseau Universitaire Transmanche
Palliative and Chronic Illness Care .... MSc 24PT

Sheffield Hallam University
Supportive and Palliative Care.......... MSc 36PT 36DL/PGDip 24PT 24DL/PGCert 12PT 12DL

University of Sheffield
Biomaterials and Regenerative Medicine .... MSc 12FT

University of South Wales
Palliative Care (Online Delivery) ....PGCert 24-60DL

University of Southampton
Clinical Leadership in Cancer, Palliative and End of Life Care MSc 24FT 48PT

Swansea University
Chronic Conditions Management........MSc 12FT 36PT/PGDip 9FT 24PT/PGCert 6FT 12PT

Trinity College Dublin - the University of Dublin
Cancer Care .... MSc 24PT
Palliative Care .... MSc 24PT

University of Ulster
Palliative Care ....PGDip 24PT/MSc 36PT

University of Warwick
Health Sciences: Palliative Care.....MSc 36PT/PGDip 24PT/PGCert 12PT/PGA 12PT
Palliative Care: Care of the Dying............. PGA 12PT/CPDMod 1PT
Palliative Care: Important Principles and Developments ....PGA 12PT/CPDMod 1PT
Palliative Care: Non-cancer diagnosis...... PGA 12PT/CPDMod 1PT

University of the West of Scotland
Cancer and Palliative Care..PGCert 12PT

Palliative care
Research Courses

King's College London
Cicely Saunders Institute of Palliative Care & Rehabilitation
Research................PhD 36-48FT 48-72PT/MPhil 36-48FT 48-72PT/
MDes by research 24FT

University of Liverpool
Cancer Biology..............MPhil 12FT 48PT/PhD 36FT 72PT/MD 60FT
Cancer Medicine.......MPhil 12FT 24-72PT/PhD 36FT 48-84PT/MD 12-72FT

University of Nottingham
Supportive and Palliative Care.............................MRes 12FT 24PT/
PhD 36FT 72PT/DHSci 24FT 48PT

The Open University
Ageing and Later LifePhD 36FT 72PT variableDL/MPhil 15FT 24PT variableDL
Death, Dying and Bereavement.......... PhD 36FT 72PT variableDL/
MPhil 15FT 24PT variableDL

Paramedic studies
Taught Courses

University of Dundee
Medical Education ....MMedEd 12FT

University of East Anglia
Advanced Practitioner (Profession)...........................MSc 12FT 36PT

Queen Mary, University of London
Critical Care...MSc 12FT 24PT
Trauma Sciences ....MSc 12FT 24PT
Trauma Sciences (Military and Austere)...................MSc 12FT 24PT

University of Sheffield
Advanced Emergency Care................................MSc 12FT 24 - 60PT

University of Warwick
Models of Emergency Care .... PGA 12PT/CPDMod 1PT

University of York
Development Economics and Emerging Markets........... MSc 12FT

Paramedic studies
Research Courses

University of Cambridge
Medical Sciences.. MPhil 12FT

Play therapy
Taught Courses

University of Central Lancashire
Playwriting.. MA 12FT 24PT

Medicine and surgery

University of Glasgow
Primary Expressive Arts ....PGCert 12PT

University of Gloucestershire
Play and Playwork ....PGCert 12-24DL/PGDip 12-24DL/
MA 24-48DL

University of Roehampton
Art Psychotherapy... MA 24FT 36PT

University of Sheffield
Music Psychology in Education...MA 24 PTDL

University of South Wales
Play and Therapeutic Play ....MSc 12FT 36PT 18BM

Swansea University
Developmental and Therapeutic Play ....MA 12FT 36PT/
PGDip 12FT 24PT/PGCert 12FT 12PT

Play therapy
Research Courses

University of Roehampton
Arts and Play Therapies.......PhD 24-48FT 36-60PT/MPhil 21-36FT
33-48PT

Podiatry
Taught Courses

University of Brighton
Podiatry........MSc 12 - 24FT 24 - 72PT/PGDip 12 - 24FT 24 - 48PT/
PGCert 12FT 24PT
Podiatry and Education.......MSc 12 - 24FT 24 - 72PT/PGCert 12FT
24PT/PGDip 12 - 24FT 24 - 48PT
Podiatry and Management.......................MSc 12 - 24FT 24 - 72PT/
PGCert 12FT 24PT/PGDip 12 - 24FT 24 - 48PT
Podiatry with Clinical Biomechanics ....MSc 12-24FT 12-72PT/
PGDip 12-24FT 12-48PT/PGCert 12FT 24PT
Podiatry with Diabetes ......MSc 12-24FT 24-72PT/PGDip 12-24FT
24-48PT/PGCert 12FT 24PT
Podiatry with Rheumatology ....MSc 12-24FT 24-72PT/PGDip
12-24FT 24-48PT/PGCert 12FT 24PT
Principles of Podiatric Surgery ....MSc 12-24FT 24-72PT/PGDip
12-24FT 24-48PT/PGCert 12FT 24PT

Cardiff Metropolitan University
Musculoskeletal Studies (Lower Limb) .....MSc 36PT/PGDip 36PT/
PGCert 36PT

University of Dundee
Advanced Practice (Clinical Governance) ....MSc 36DL

University of East London
Podiatric Medicine ....MSc 12FT 24-72PT

Glasgow Caledonian University
Podiatric Medicine .... MSc 12FT
Podiatry.. MSc 12FT
Theory of Podiatric Medicine.......................MSc 12-24FT 12-72PT
Theory of Podiatric Surgery............................MSc 12-24FT 12-72PT

University of Huddersfield
Forensic Podiatry ....PGCert 18-24BM
Multi Disciplinary Care of High Risk Patients...............PGCert 24PT
Musculoskeletal Management of the Lower Limb... PGDip 24BM
Podiatry.. MSc 36PT
Theory of Podiatric Surgery.................................... MSc 36BM

University of Northampton
Advanced Podiatry .... MSc 12FT 36PT/PGDip 24PT

Queen Margaret University, Edinburgh
Podiatric Medicine ....PGCert 36-60PT/PGDip 36-60PT/
MSc 36-60PT
Podiatry.. MSc 36PT
Theory of Podiatric Surgery................................... MSc 36PT

Staffordshire University
Clinical Podiatric Biomechanics....... PGCert 9PT/PGDip 15PT/MSc
36PT

University of Warwick
Diabetes and the Foot................................ PGA 12PT/CPDMod 1PT

Podiatry
Research Courses

University of Southampton
School of Health Professions and Rehabilitation Sciences.. MPhil
36FT 60PT/PhD 36FT 60PT

Primary care
Taught Courses

University of Aberdeen
Primary Care..MSc 48-60PT

Barts and the London School of Medicine and Dentistry
Primary Care .... MSc 12FT 24PT/PGDip 12FT 24PT

University of Bath
Primary Care .... MSc 96PT/PGDip 72PT/PGCert 48PT

Birmingham City University
Advanced Healthcare (Nursing, Midwifery or Primary Care).........
PGDip 12PT/MSc 24PT

University of Birmingham
Advancing Practice.....................MSc 13FT 72PT/PGDip 10FT 48PT/
PGCert 3FT
Clinical Primary and Community Care........MSc 12FT 60PT/PGDip
12FT 60PT/PGCert 12FT 60PT
Primary and Community Care, Clinical.......MSc 12FT 24PT/PGDip
12FT 24PT/PGCert 12FT 24PT

University of Central Lancashire
Evidence Based Practice...PGCert 12PT
Excellence in Leadership for Inclusion and Community..... PGCert
12-24PT
General Practice..........MSc 36-60PT/PGDip 24-60PT/PGCert 12PT
Health & Social Care Education..................................PGCert 12PT
Health Informatics.....................................MSc 33PT/PGDip 24PT
Health and Social Care Education ....PGCert 12PT
Research for Professional Practice ... Professional Doctorate 24PT

University of Chester
Health and Social Care - Advanced Practice .... MSc 24 - 72PT/
PGDip 24 - 60PT/PGCert 12 - 36PT

City University London
Primary Care ....MSc 12FT 24PT
Primary Care (Advanced Nurse Practitioner)..........MSc 12FT 24PT
Primary Care (District Nursing)..............................MSc 12FT 24PT
Primary Care (Long Term Conditions)......................MSc 12FT 24PT

University of Derby
Community Specialist Practice ....MSc 12FT 24PT

University of Dundee
Primary Care (MSc part time)..MSc 36-60PT
Psychological Therapy in Primary Care .... MSc 12FT

National University of Ireland Galway
Health Sciences (Clinical Primary Care) PGDip 12PT/PGCert 12PT
Health Sciences (Primary Care).............................. PGDip 12PT

Glasgow Caledonian University
Diagnostic Imaging...MSc 12-24FT
Musculoskeletal Management..................................MSc 36-72PT
Radiatiotherapy and Oncology ....MSc 12-24FT

University of Glasgow
Primary Care ..... MPC 12FT 24-60PT/PGDip 12FT 24-36PT/PGCert
24PT

University of Greenwich
Independent and Supplementary Prescribing / Supplementary
Prescribing...PGCert 8DL

University of Kent
Primary Dental Care...MSc 36PT
Primary Dental Care for Foundation Dentists.............PGCert 12FT

King's College London
Primary Health Care ....MSc 12FT 24PT

Leeds Metropolitan University
Environmental Health ....MSc 12FT 36PT
Health Care Studies ....MA 24PT

University of Leeds
Primary Care Education ....PGCert 12-24PT
Primary Health Care .....MMedSci 30PT/PGDip 24PT/PGCert 12PT

University of Liverpool
Diploma in International Community Health Care ...Diploma 3FT

London South Bank University
Primary Care .... MSc 12FT up to 72PT
Primary Care and Mental Health..............................PGCert 12PT

Manchester Metropolitan University
Community Health ....MSc 12FT 24-36PT

University of Manchester
Primary Care .... MRes 12 - 60DL

University of Northampton
Community Practice .... MSc 24-60PT/PGDip 12PT

The Open University
Advancing Professional Practice...............................MSc variableDL

Queen Mary, University of London
International Primary Health Care......................MSc 12FT 24-48PT

University of Roehampton
Health Sciences ....MSc 12FT 24PT

University of Salford
Public Health ....MSc 12FT 36PT/PGDip 8FT 24PT/PGCert 9PT

Sheffield Hallam University
Cardiovascular Medicine for Primary Care Physicians..........PGDip
24PT/PGCert 12PT

University of Sheffield
Public Health ....MPH 12FT 24-36PT
Public Health (Health Services Research).........MPH 12FT 24-36PT
Public Health (Management and Leadership) ....
MPH 12FT 24-36PT

University of South Wales
Community Health Studies ....BSc 24-36PT/MSc 36PT

St George's, University of London
Physician Assistant Studies ....PGDip 24FT

University of Stirling
Psychological Therapy in Primary Care .... MSc 12FT

Swansea University
Advanced Practice in Health Care ....MSc 36PT/PGDip 24PT
Advanced Practice in Health Care - Infection Control...MSc 36PT/
PGDip 24PT

University of Ulster
Primary Care and General Practice ....MSc 36DL

University of Warwick
Diabetes in Pregnancy ....PGA 12PT
Patient and Public Involvement in Healthcare ....
PGA 12PT/CPDMod 1PT
Sexual Health in Primary Care ....PGA 12PT

University of the West of England, Bristol
Community Practice ....MSc 12FT 60PT

University of Winchester
Delivery of Primary Health Care ....PGCert 24PT

University of Wolverhampton
Primary Health Care Practice....................................... MSc 12PT

Primary care
Research Courses

University of Aberdeen
General Practice and Primary Care .... PhD 36FT/MD 24FT/MSc by
research 12FT

Barts and the London School of Medicine and Dentistry
Department of General Practice and Primary Care .... PhD/MPhil/
MSc by research/MD

University of Birmingham
Primary Care Clinical Sciences.... PhD 36FT 72PT/MSc by research
12FT 24PT

University of Cambridge
Public Health and Primary Care .... PhD 36FT 60PT

Cardiff University
Primary Care and Public Health ....PhD 36FT/MPhil 36FT

University of Central Lancashire
Healthcare/Public Health....................MSc by research 12FT 24PT/
MPhil 24FT 36-48PT/PhD 36FT 60PT/MD 36FT 60PT

University of Cumbria
Public Health and Primary Care ....PhD 48FT 72PT 72DL/
MPhil 36FT 36PT 36DL

University of East Anglia
Nursing ....PhD 36FT 72PT/MPhil 24FT 48PT/
MSc by research 12FT 24PT

University of Edinburgh
General Practice..............PhD 36FT 72PT/MPhil 24FT 36PT/MSc by
research 12FT 24PT

University of Hertfordshire
Centre for Research in Primary and Community Care ....PhD 36FT
72PT/MPhil 24FT 48PT/MRes 12FT 24PT/DHRes 36FT 72PT

Imperial College London
Primary Care and Population Health Science................PhD/MPhil

King's College London
Health & Social Care (Research Division) .... PhD 36FT 48-72PT/
MPhil 36FT 48-72PT/DHC 36FT 48-72PT

University of Liverpool
Primary Care ....MPhil 12-48FT 24-72PT/PhD 24-48FT 48-84PT/
MD 24-72PT

University of Nottingham
Epidemiology and Public Health ....PhD 36FT 72PT/
MPhil 24FT 48PT
Primary Care...PhD 36FT

University of Oxford
Primary Health Care ....DPhil 48FT/MSc by research 24-36FT
Public Health .... DPhil 48FT/MSc by research 24FT

University of Roehampton
Health Sciences.... PhD 24-48FT 36-60PT/MPhil 21-36FT 36-60PT

University of Sheffield
Primary Medical Care and Ageing.......PhD 36FT 72PT/MPhil 24FT
48PT

St George's, University of London
Community Health Sciences ....PhD 36FT 72PT/MPhil 24FT 48PT/
MD(Res) 24 minFT 48 minPT

UCL - University College London
Primary Health Care and Population Sciences......PhD 36FT 60PT/
MD(Res) 24FT 24PT

Psychiatry
Taught Courses

Aston University
Psychiatric Pharmacy..PGDip 12DL

Bangor University
Foundations of Clinical Psychology .....MSc 12FT 24PT/PGDip 8FT
16PT/PGCert 4FT 8PT

Medicine and surgery

Barts and the London School of Medicine and Dentistry
Transcultural Mental health..... MSc 12FT 24PT/PGDip 12FT 24PT

Cardiff University
Psychiatry . MSc 12FT 36PT 36DL/PGDip 12FT 24PT 24DL/PGCert 12FT 24PT 24DL

University of Central Lancashire
Child Health ... MSc 36PT
Mental Health Practice (Including approved mental health professional training) ... MA 12-60PT/PGDip 12-60PT/PGCert 12PT
Personality Disorder (Practice Development) ... MSc 36-60PT/PGDip 24PT
Personality Disorder (Research) ... MSc 36-60PT/PGDip 12-24PT
Philosophy & Mental Health ... MA 36DL/PGDip 24DL/PGCert 12DL
Primary Care Mental Health Practice ... PGCert 12PT
Professional Integrative Psychotherapy ... MA 36PT/PGDip 24PT
Psychology ... MSc 12FT 24PT/PGDip 9FT 24PT/PGCert 9FT 24PT
Psychology of Child Development ... MSc 12FT 24PT/PGDip 9FT 24PT/PGCert 9FT 24PT
Psychology of Sport and Exercise ... MSc 12FT 24PT/PGDip 9FT 24PT/PGCert 9FT 24PT

University of Chester
Family and Child Psychology ... MSc 12FT 24PT/PGDip 12FT 24PT/PGCert 12FT 12-24PT

University of Chichester
Psychology of Sport and Exercise ... MSc 12-15FT 24-36PT/PGDip 9-12FT 18-24PT/PGCert 6-9FT 12-18PT

De Montfort University
Psychological Wellbeing ... MSc 12FT 24PT

University of Edinburgh
Children & Young People's Mental Health and Psychological Practice..MSc 12FT 24-72PT/PGCert 12-24PT/PGDip 9FT 24-48PT
Cognitive Behaviour Therapy for Children and Young People ... PGCert 24PT

University of Glasgow
Mental Health, Global ... MSc 12FT 24PT/PGDip 9FT 18PT/PGCert 9FT 18PT

Goldsmiths, University of London
The Science of Psychology, Genetics & Education ... MSc 12FT 24PT

University of Hertfordshire
Mental Health (Primary Care) ... PGCert 12PT
Mental Health Practice ... MSc 15FT 24-60PT/PGDip 15FT 24-60PT/PGCert 15FT 24-60PT

King's College London
Child & Adolescent Mental Health ... MSc 12FT 24PT
Clinical Forensic Psychiatry ... MSc 12FT 24-36PT
Epilepsy ... MSc 12FT 24PT
Forensic Mental Health Research ... MSc 12FT 24PT
Global Mental Health ... MSc 12FT 24PT
Health Psychology ... MSc 12FT
Mental Health Service & Population Research ... MSc 12FT 24PT
Mental Health Studies ... MSc 12FT 24PT
Mental Health in Learning Disabilities ... MSc 12FT 24PT
Organisational Psychiatry & Psychology ... MSc 12FT 24PT
Philosophy of Mental Disorder ... MSc 12FT 24PT
Psychiatric Research ... MSc 12FT 24PT
Social, Genetic & Developmental Psychiatry ... MSc 12+36FT
War & Psychiatry ... MSc 12FT 24PT/PGDip 12FT 24PT

University of Leeds
Psychiatry ... MSc 48PT

University of Leicester
Child and Adolescent Mental Health ... PGCert 12FT 12PT/PGDip 12FT 24PT/MSc 12FT 36PT

University of Liverpool
MRCPsych ... MRCPsych 12PT

London Metropolitan University
Mental Health and Wellbeing ... MA 12FT 24PT

London South Bank University
Acute and Psychiatric Intensive Care Settings ... MSc 36PT/PGDip 24PT

University of Manchester
Psychiatry ... MSc 36PT/Diploma 24PT
Psychiatry (blended learning) ... MSc 36PT/PGDip 24PT

Middlesex University
Dual Diagnosis ... MSc 36PT 36DL/AdvDip 12PT 12DL/PGCert 12PT 12DL

Newcastle University
Cognitive Behavioural Therapy ... PGDip 12FT 24PT
High Intensity Psychological Therapies ... Diploma 12FT

University of Nottingham
Rehabilitation Psychology ... MSc 12FT 24PT

Queen Margaret University, Edinburgh
Cognitive Behavioural Therapy ... PGDip 24PT/PGCert 12PT

Queen Mary, University of London
Mental Health: Psychological Therapies D/L option ... MSc 12FT 24PT
Mental Health: Transcultural Mental Healthcare ... MSc 12FT 24PT 24DL

Queen's University Belfast
Cognitive Behavioural Practice ... PGCert 12PT
Cognitive Behavioural Therapy ... PGDip 12PT

Sheffield Hallam University
Cognitive Analytic Therapy Practitioner ... MSc VAPT/PGDip VAPT

University of Southampton
Health Psychology ... MSc 12FT/PGDip 12FT

University of St Andrews
Health Psychology ... MSc 12FT

Staffordshire University
Practitioner with a Special Interest in Mental Health ... MSc 36PT

University of Stirling
Health Psychology ... MSc 12FT 24PT/PGDip 6FT 12PT
Psychological Research Methods ... MSc 12FT 24PT/PGDip 9FT 18PT

University of Sussex
Foundations of Clinical Psychology and Mental Health ... MSc 12FT 24PT

Trinity College Dublin - the University of Dublin
Child and Adolescent Psychoanalytic Psychotherapy ... MSc 24PT
Cognitive Psychotherapy ... MSc 24PT
Cognitive Psychotherapy (PG. Dip) ... PGDip 12PT
Psychoanalytic Psychotherapy ... MSc 36PT

UCL - University College London
CYP IAPT Therapy ... PGDip 12FT
Cognitive Behavioural Therapy for Children and Young People ... MSc 24-36PT/PGDip 24PT/PGCert 12PT
Cognitive Neuroscience ... MSc 12FT 24PT/PGDip 9FT MRes 12FT
Developmental Psychology and Clinical Practice ... MSc 24FT/PGDip 12FT
Psychiatric Research ... MSc 24-60PT

University of Warwick
Philosophy and Ethics of Mental Health ... MSc 12FT 24PT 36DL/MA 12FT 24PT 36DL/PGA 6FT

University of Winchester
Psychological Disorders ... MSc 12FT 24PT/PGDip 12FT 24PT/PGCert 12FT 24PT

Psychiatry
Research Courses

Aberystwyth University
Psychology ... PhD 36FT 60PT

Bangor University
Clinical Psychology ... DClinPsy 36FT

Barts and the London School of Medicine and Dentistry
Department of Psychiatry ... PhD/MPhil

University of Birmingham
Psychiatry ... PhD 36FT 72PT/MPhil 12FT 24PT

University of Cambridge
Brain Repair ... PhD 36FT
Psychiatry ... PhD 36FT 60PT

University of Edinburgh
Psychiatry ... PhD 36FT 72PT/MPhil 24FT/MSc by research 12FT 24PT

King's College London
Biostatistics ... PhD 36FT 72PT/MPhil 36FT 72PT
Child & Adolescent Psychiatry ... PhD 36FT 72PT/MPhil 36FT 72PT/MD 36FT 72PT
Forensic and Neurodevelopmental Science PhD 36FT 72PT/MPhil 36FT 72PT
Psychological Medicine ... PhD 36FT 72PT/MPhil 36FT 72PT/MD (Res) 36FT 72PT
Psychosis Studies ... MPhil 36FT 72PT/PhD 36FT 72PT
Social Genetic & Developmental Psychiatry .. PhD 36FT 60-72PT/MPhil 36FT 60-72PT

University of Liverpool
Psychiatry ... PhD 24-48FT 48-84PT/MPhil 12-48FT 24-72PT/MD 24-72PT

London School of Economics and Political Science (LSE)
Social Psychology ... PhD 36-48FT/MPhil 36-48FT

University of Nottingham
Psychiatry ... PhD 36FT
Social Research in Medicines and Health ... PhD 36FT 72PT/MPhil 36FT

University of Oxford
Psychiatry ... DPhil 48FT/MSc by research 24-36FT

UCL - University College London
Cognitive Neuroscience ... PhD 36FT 60PT
Cognitive, Perceptual and Brain Sciences ... PhD 36FT 60PT

Pulmonology
Taught Courses

Bucks New University
Advanced Practice (Respiratory Care) ... MSc 36PT

University of Edinburgh
General Surgery (Online Distance Learning) ... ChM 24DL

University of Glasgow
Cardiovascular Sciences ... MSc(MedSci) 12FT
Sport & Exercise Medicine ... MSc(MedSci) 12FT 24PT
Translational Medicine ... MRes 12FT

University of Salford
Psycho-Oncology ... MSc 36PT/PGDip 24PT/PGCert 12PT

University of Ulster
Respiratory Health ... PGCert 24PT

Pulmonology
Research Courses

University of Edinburgh
Respiratory Medicine (Royal Infirmary of Edinburgh) ... PhD 36FT 72PT/MPhil 24FT 36PT/MSc by research 12FT 24PT

Imperial College London
National Heart and Lung Institute ... PhD 36FT 48PT 48DL/MD 12FT 24PT/MSc by research 12FT 24PT/PGDip by research 9FT

King's College London
Asthma, Allergy and Lung Biology (AALB) (Research Division) ... PhD 36FT 48-72PT/MPhil 36FT 48-72PT/MDes by research 36FT 48-72PT

University of Liverpool
Inflammation Research ... PhD 36FT/MPhil 12FT/MD 12FT
Respiratory Diseases ... MPhil 12-48FT 24-72PT/PhD 24-48FT 48-84PT/MD 24-72FT

University of Nottingham
Respiratory Medicine ... DM 36FT 72PT/MPhil 24FT 48PT/PhD 36FT 72PT
Therapeutics and Molecular Medicine ... PhD 24-36FT 48-72PT/MPhil 12-24FT 24-48PT

Queen Mary, University of London
Mechanisms of Vascular Disease ... MRes 12FT

Radiography and radiology
Taught Courses

University of Aberdeen
Medical Imaging ... MSc 12FT 24PT/PGDip 9FT 21PT
Medical Physics ... MSc 12FT 24PT/PGDip 9FT 21PT
Medical Physics (Computing) ... MSc 12FT/PGDip 9FT

Anglia Ruskin University
Magnetic Resonance Imaging (MRI) (Distance Learning) ... MSc 24DL

Bangor University
Health Science ... MSc 12FT 24 - 60PT/PGDip 9FT
Health Studies/Health Science, Nursing, Midwifery, Radiography and Allied Health Profession ... PhD by taught 36FT 48-60PT/MPhil 24FT 36PT
Clinical and Functional Brain Imaging ... PGCert 8PT

Birmingham City University
Medical Ultrasound ... PGCert 12-18PT/PGDip 18-24PT/MSc 12FT 24PT
Radiography ... PGCert 12PT/PGDip 18PT/MSc 12FT 24PT

University of Bradford
Medical Imaging ... MSc 24-36PT/PGDip 12-24PT/PGCert 9-12PT

University of Buckingham
General Internal Medicine ... MD 24/36FT

Canterbury Christ Church University
Medical Imaging ... PGCert 12PT
Nuclear Medicine ... MSc 60PT/PGDip 24PT/PGCert 12PT
Radiopharmacy Practice ... PGCert 12PT

Cardiff University
Clinical Engineering ... MSc 12FT 24-36PT
Image Appreciation ... PGDip 24PT/PGCert 12PT
Radiographic Reporting ... PGDip 24PT/PGCert 12PT
Radiography ... MSc 12FT 24PT/PGDip 9FT

City University London
Medical Ultrasound ... MSc 24PT/PGDip 18PT/PGCert 12PT
Nuclear Medicine Technology ... MSc 24PT/PGDip 12PT/PGCert 9PT
Radiography - Computed Tomography ... MSc 24 (min)PT/PGDip 18 (min)PT/PGCert 12 (min)PT
Radiography - Diagnostic Imaging ... MSc 30PT/PGDip 18PT/PGCert 12PT
Radiography - Medical Magnetic Resonance ... MSc 30PT/PGDip 18PT/PGCert 12PT
Radiography - Medical Ultrasound ... MSc 30PT/PGDip 18PT/PGCert 12PT
Radiography - Radiotherapy ... MSc 30PT/PGDip 18PT/PGCert 12PT

Medicine and surgery

University of Cumbria
Medical Imaging .... MSc 36 - 60PT

University of Dundee
Advanced Practice (Diagnostic Imaging) .... MSc 36DL
Medical Imaging .... MSc 12FT

Glasgow Caledonian University
Diagnostic Imaging .... MSc 12-24FT
Health and Social Care (Medical Ultrasound) .... MSc 12-24FT 12-72PT/PGDip 24FT/PGCert 12FT
Health and Social Care (Radiation Oncology) .... MSc 12-24FT 12-72PT
Medical Ultrasound .... MSc 12-24FT
Radiatiotherapy and Oncology .... MSc 12-24FT

University of Glasgow
Clinical Radiation Physics .... MSc(MedSci) 12FT

University of Hertfordshire
Diagnostic Imaging .... MSc variousPT/PGDip variousPT/PGCert variousPT
Diagnostic Ultrasound ... MSc variousPT/PGDip variousPT/PGCert variousPT
Image Interpretation .... MSc 24PT/PGDip 24PT/PGCert 24PT
Oncological Sciences .... MSc 24PT/PGDip 24PT/PGCert 24PT

Imperial College London
Medical Robotics and Image Guided Intervention .... MRes 12FT
Medical Ultrasound .... MSc 12FT 24PT
Medical Ultrasound/Medical Ultrasound (Echocardiography)MSc 12FT

University of Kent
Biotechnology and Bioengineering .... MSc 12FT 24PT

King's College London
Medical Imaging Sciences .... MRes 12FT
Medical Ultrasound .... MSc 27PT/PGDip 18PT/PGCert 9PT
Radiopharmaceutics & PET Radiochemistry .... MSc 12FT 24PT
Vascular Ultrasound .... PGCert 9PT/PGDip 18PT/MSc 27PT

Kingston University
Radiography: Breast Evaluation... MSc 24FT 24-60PT/PGDip 24FT 24-60PT/PGCert 24FT 24-60PT
Radiography: Medical Imaging.... MSc 24FT 24-60PT/PGDip 24FT 24-60PT/PGCert 24FT 24-60PT
Radiography: Medical Imaging (Mammography) .... MSc 24FT 24-60PT/PGCert 24FT 24-60PT/PGDip 24FT 24-60PT
Radiography: Oncology Practice .... MSc 24FT 24-60PT/PGCert 24FT 24-60PT/PGDip 24FT 24-60PT

University of Leeds
Advanced Gastrointestinal Practice .... PGCert p/t onlyPT
Medical Imaging .... MSc 12FT 33-60PT/PGDip 9FT 21-48PT/PGCert 4-9FT 9-24PT

University of Liverpool
Medical Diagnostic Ultrasound .... MSc 36-72PT

London South Bank University
Clinical Ultrasound .... MSc 18PT
Mammographic Studies .... MSc 12PT
Professional Development for Allied Health Professions (Therapeutic Radiography) .... MSc 12-36PT
Radiographic Reporting of the Skeletal System .... MSc 18PT
Therapeutic Radiography .... PGDip 24FT/MSc 24FT

Manchester Metropolitan University
Science, Technology, Engineering and Maths (STEM) .... MSc 24-72PT

University of Manchester
Cognitive Brain Imaging .... MSc 12FT
Medical Imaging .... MSc 12FT 24PT/PGDip 12FT 24PT
Medical Physics and Clinical Engineering .... MSc 12FT 24-36PT/PGDip 9FT 24PT

Newcastle University
Clinical Sciences (Medical Physics) with specialisms in: Radiotherapy Physics; Radiation Safety; Imaging with Ionising Radiation; Imaging with Non-Ionising Radiation .... MSc 36PT

University of Nottingham
Bioengineering: The Digital Body .... MSc 12FT

University of Oxford
Diagnostic Imaging .... MSc 12FT 24PT

Queen Margaret University, Edinburgh
Diagnostic Radiography (Pre-Registration).....PGCert 12FT/PGDip 24FT/MSc 26FT
Mammography .... PGCert 12PT/PGDip 24PT/MSc 48PT
Radiotherapy (Post-Registration) .... MSc 36PT/PGDip 24PT/PGCert 12PT
Radiotherapy and Oncology (Pre-Registration) .... MSc 30FT/PGDip 24FT

Queen's University Belfast
Dating and Chronology .... MSc 12FT

Robert Gordon University
Diagnostic Radiography (pre-registration) .... MSc 24FT

University of Salford
Advanced Medical Imaging .... MSc 24-60PT/PGDip 18-36PT/PGCert 12-24PT
Nuclear Medicine Imaging .... MSc 24PT/PGDip 18PT

Sheffield Hallam University
Advanced Practice (Radiotherapy and Oncology) .... MSc 3DL/PGDip 2DL/PGCert 1DL
Applying Radiographics .... MSc 18FT/PGDip 12FT/PGCert 6FT
Breast Imaging and Diagnosis .... MSc 36PT/PGDip 24PT/PGCert 12PT
Medical Imaging Programme .... MSc VAPT/PGDip VAPT/PGCert VAPT
Radiotherapy Planning .... MSc 36PT/PGDip 24PT/PGCert 12PT
Radiotherapy and Oncology .... MSc 72DL/PGDip 24PT/PGCert 12PT
Radiotherapy and Oncology in Practice .... PGDip 24FT

University of South Wales
Diagnostic Clinical Ultrasound . PGCert 12-60PT/PGDip 12-60PT/MSc 12-60PT

University of Surrey
Medical Imaging .... MSc 12FT 48PT
Medical Physics .... MSc 12FT

Swansea University
Clinical Science (Medical Physics) .... MSc 36PT
Medical Radiation Physics .... MSc 12FT 24-36PT

Teesside University
Diagnostic Radiography (Pre-registration) MSc 26FT/PGDip 22FT
Forensic Radiography .... PGCert 12PT 12DL MSc 36PT 36DL
Medical Ultrasound .... PGDip 24PT/PGCert 12PT/MSc 36PT

Trinity College Dublin - the University of Dublin
Advanced Radiotherapy Practice .... MSc 12FT
Medical Imaging .... MSc 12PT

UCL - University College London
European Medical Physics .... MSc 12FT
Physics and Engineering in Medicine: Radiation Physics.....PGDip 9FT 18PT

University of the West of England, Bristol
Medical Ultrasound .... MSc 36FT
Nuclear Medicine .... MSc 24-36PT
Radiotherapy and Oncology .... MSc 36FT

Radiography and radiology
Research Courses

University of Aberdeen
Biomedical Physics and Bioengineering .... PhD 36FT/MSc by research 12FT/MPhil 24FT
Imaging .... PhD 36FT/MPhil 24FT/MSc by research 12FT
Radiology .... PhD 36FT/MD 36FT/MSc by research 12FT

Bangor University
Health Studies/Health Science, Nursing, Midwifery, Radiography & Allied Health Professions .... MPhil 24FT 36PT/PhD 36FT 48-60PT

University of Cambridge
Radiology .... PhD 36FT 60PT/MPhil 12FT

Cardiff University
Radiography/Radiotherapy .... PhD 36FT 60PT/MPhil 12FT 24PT

City University London
Department of Radiography .... PhD 24-84FT 36-84PT/MPhil 12-60FT 24-60PT

University of Cumbria
Medical Imaging Sciences .... PhD 48FT 72PT 72DL/MPhil 36FT 60PT 60DL

University of Glasgow
Clinical Physics .... PhD 36FT 48PT/MSc by research 24FT

Imperial College London
Imaging .... PhD
Molecular Imaging Using Ultrasound and Targeted Microbubbles .... PhD 36FT

King's College London
Imaging Sciences & Biomedical Engineering (Research Division) .... PhD 36FT 48-72PT/MPhil 36FT 48-72PT

University of Liverpool
Magnetic Resonance and Image Analysis Research Centre (MARIARC) .... MPhil 12FT/PhD 36FT
Medical Imaging. PhD 24-48FT 48-84PT/MPhil 12-48FT 24-72PT/MD 24-72FT
Radiotherapy .... MPhil 12-48FT/PhD 24-84FT/MD 60FT

University of Nottingham
Biophysics, Imaging and Optical Science .... PhD 36FT 48PT/MPhil 24FT 36PT
Magnetic Resonance .... PhD 36FT 72PT/MPhil 24FT 48PT/MRes 12FT
Medical Physics (Division of Radiological and Imaging Sciences) PhD 36FT 72PT/MPhil 24FT 48PT/DM 36FT 72PT
Radiological and Imaging Sciences .... MRes 12FT 24PT/MPhil 12FT 24PT/PhD 36FT 48PT/DM 24FT 48PT
Radiology - Academic Radiology .... PhD 36FT 72PT

University of Oxford
Life Sciences Interface Doctoral Training Centre .... DPhil 48FT
Radiobiology .... DPhil 48FT/MSc by research 24FT

University of Portsmouth
Medical Imaging .... DMedimaging 48PT

Queen Mary, University of London
Radiation Physics .... PhD 36FT/MPhil

University of Sheffield
Medical Physics and Clinical Engineering ... PhD 36FT 72PT/MPhil 24FT 48PT

UCL - University College London
Medical Physics and Bioengineering .... PhD 36FT 60PT

Reflexology
Taught Courses

University of Central Lancashire
Dance and Somatic Well-being .... MA 24PT/PGDip 24PT/PGCert 24PT

University of Dundee
Advanced Practice (Physiotherapeutic Practice) .... MSc 36DL

Reflexology
Research Courses

University of Birmingham
Biomaterials .... MRes 12FT 24PT

University of Greenwich
Pharmacy - Research .... MPhil 36-72FT/PhD 36-72FT

Reproductive medicine
Taught Courses

Barts and the London School of Medicine and Dentistry
Obstetrics & Gynaecology ... MSc 12FT 24PT MMedSci 12FT 24PT

University of Bedfordshire
Sexual Health .... PGCert 12-36PT

University of Bristol
Reproduction and Development ... MSc 12FT 24PT/Diploma 12FT 24PT/Cert 12FT 24PT

Cardiff University
Obstetric and/or Gynaecological Ultrasound .... MSc 18FT 36PT/PGDip 12FT 24PT/PGCert 12PT

Edge Hill University
Advanced Fertility Practice .... MSc 24-60PT

University of Edinburgh
Reproductive Sciences .... MSc(Res) 12FT

Glasgow Caledonian University
Sexual Health .... MSc 24-60FT On-lineDL

University of Glasgow
Reproductive & Maternal Sciences .... MSc (ClinSci) 12FT

Imperial College London
Reproductive and Developmental Biology .... MSc 12FT

University of Kent
Reproductive Medicine: Science and Ethics .... MSc 12FT 24PT

King's College London
Advanced Practice (Women's Healthcare) ..... MSc 36-72PT/PGDip 24-72PT/PGCert 12-72PT

University of Leeds
Clinical Embryology .... MSc 24PT 24DL/PGDip 16PT 16DL

London School of Hygiene and Tropical Medicine
Reproductive & Sexual Health Research .... MSc 12FT 24PT

University of Manchester
Maternal and Fetal Health .... MRes 12FT

University of Nottingham
Assisted Reproduction Technology .... MMedSci 12FT

University of Oxford
Clinical Embryology .... MSc 12FT

University of Sheffield
Reproductive and Developmental Medicine .... MSc 12FT

University of Surrey
Advanced Gynaecological Endoscopy .... MSc 24FT 24-72PT

Trinity College Dublin - the University of Dublin
Obstetrics (M.A.O.) .... MAO 12FT 60PT

UCL - University College London
Prenatal Genetics and Fetal Medicine .... MSc 12FT 24PT
Reproductive Science and Women's Health ... MSc 12FT 24-36PT/PGDip 9FT 24PT

University of Warwick
Introduction to Mastery in Sexual and Reproductive Health Care PGA 12PT
Menopause and Beyond .... PGA 12PT
Mind / Hormone Interface in Community GynaecologyPGA 12PT
Reproductive Health in the Community .... PGA 12PT
Sexual Health in Primary Care .... PGA 12PT
Sexual and Reproductive Health Care .... MSc 12FT 36-96PT/PGDip 24FT 36-60PT/PGCert 12FT 24-60PT

Medicine and surgery

University of West London
Women, Mental Health and Childbearing: Developing the Service .... CPPD 4PT 4DL

Reproductive medicine
Research Courses

University of Aberdeen
Obstetrics and Gynaecology.....PhD 36FT 60PT/MPhil 24FT 42PT/ MSc by research 12FT 24PT

Barts and the London School of Medicine and Dentistry
Department of Obstetrics and Gynaecology ....PhD/MPhil
Obstetrics and Gynaecology (Reproductive Physiology)........PhD/ MPhil/MD

University of Birmingham
Obstetrics and Gynaecology...... PhD 36FT 72PT/MPhil 12FT 24PT

University of Cambridge
Obstetrics and Gynaecology.................PhD 36FT 60PT/MPhil 12FT

University of Edinburgh
Genito-Urinary Medicine... PhD 36FT 72PT/MPhil 24FT 36PT/MSc by research 12FT 24PT
Obstetrics & Gynaecology ....PhD 36FT
Reproductive & Developmental Science ....PhD 36FT
Reproductive Biology.................. PhD 36FT 72PT/MPhil 24FT 36PT
MSc by research 12FT

Imperial College London
Obstetrics and Gynaecology...PhD

Liverpool School of Tropical Medicine
Child & Reproductive Health................................ PhD/MPhil/MIHR

University of Liverpool
Medical Microbiology..........PhD 12-48FT 48-84PT/MPhil 12-48FT 48-72PT/MD 12-72FT
Obstetrics and Gynaecology........ MPhil 12FT/PhD 36FT/MD 60FT
Perinatal and Reproductive Health.......PhD 36FT/MPhil 12FT/MD 60FT

University of Nottingham
Reproductive Biology.................. PhD 36FT 72PT/MPhil 24FT 48PT
Reproductive Medicine .... MPhil 24FT 48PT/PhD 36FT 72PT/DM 36FT 72PT

The Open University
Reproductive and Sexual Health .... PhD 36FT 72PT variableDL/ MPhil 15FT 24PT variableDL

University of Oxford
Obstetrics and Gynaecology..... DPhil 48FT/MSc by research 24FT

University of Sheffield
Endocrinology and Reproduction........PhD 36FT 72PT/MPhil 24FT 48PT

UCL - University College London
Obstetrics and Gynaecology.....................................PhD 36FT 60PT/ MD(Res) 24FT 24PT
Sexually Transmitted Diseases........PhD 36FT 60PT/MD(Res) 24FT 24PT

Rheumatology
Taught Courses

University of Brighton
Podiatry with Rheumatology .... MSc 12-24FT 24-72PT/PGDip 12-24FT 24-48PT/PGCert 12FT 24PT

University of Buckingham
General Internal Medicine ....MD 24/36FT

University of Dundee
Primary Care ....MSc 36-60PT

Keele University
Rheumatology Nursing...............................PGDip 24PT/MSc 12PT

King's College London
Rheumatology...MSc 24PT/PGDip 24PT

University of Manchester
Clinical Rheumatology... MSc 24PT

Queen Mary, University of London
Musculoskeletal Clinical Sciences........................... MSc 12FT 24PT
Musculoskeletal Sciences...MSc 12FT 24PT

University of Warwick
Osteoporosis - A Practical Approach to Diagnosis and Clinincal Management...PGA 12PT

Rheumatology
Research Courses

University of Liverpool
Inflammation Research.................PhD 36FT/MPhil 12FT/MD 12FT

University of Nottingham
Rheumatology.......................................PhD 24-36FT 48-72PT

Sports therapy
Taught Courses

Bangor University
Applied Sport Science........................MA 12FT 36PT MSc 12FT 36PT

Applied Sport Science (Outdoor Activities).............. MA 12FT 36PT MSc 12FT 36PT
Applied Sport and Exercise Physiology ....MSc 12FT 36PT/ PGDip 8FT MA 12FT 36PT
Applied Sport and Exercise Psychology .... MSc 12FT 36PT MA 12FT 36PT
Exercise Rehabilitation..................... MSc 12FT 36PT MA 12FT 36PT
Occupational Therapy ....MSc 24FT/PGDip 24FT
Sport and Exercise Physiology............................MRes 12FT 36PT
Sport and Exercise Psychology (BPS Accredited) ... MSc 12FT 36PT
Sport and Exercise Sciences..............................MRes 12FT 36PT

Barts and the London School of Medicine and Dentistry
Sports Medicine...........................MSc 12FT 24PT/PGDip 8FT

University of Bath
Sport and Exercise Medicine .... MSc 36-60PT/PGDip 24-48PT

University of Bedfordshire
Sport and Exercise Rehabilitation ....MSc 12FT 24-72PT

University of Birmingham
Exercise and Sports Medicine (Football).....MSc 13FT 72PT/PGDip 10FT 48PT

University of Bradford
Sports Physiotherapy..................................... PGCert 6FT 18PT

University of Brighton
Sports Injury Management........... MSc 12FT 24-36PT/PGDip 12FT 24-36PT/PGCert 12FT 24PT

Bucks New University
Advancing Spinal Cord Rehabilitation and Management ...... MSc 36PT
Health, Exercise & Wellbeing ....MSc 12FT 24PT

Cardiff Metropolitan University
Sport & Exercise Medicine .... MSc 12FT 12-36PT/PGDip 12FT 12-36PT

University of Central Lancashire
Psychology of Sport and Exercise......... MSc 12FT 24PT/PGDip 9FT 24PT/PGCert 9FT 24PT
Sports Therapy .... MSc 18FT 36PT/PGDip 18FT 24PT
Sports Therapy Professional Practice .... MSc up to 24FT

University of Chichester
Psychology of Sport and Exercise.... MSc 12-15FT 24-36PT/PGDip 9-12FT 18-24PT/PGCert 6-9FT 12-18PT

Coventry University
Sport and Exercise Nutrition .... PGCert 12 MinPT

University of Dundee
Sports and Biomechanical Medicine .... MSc 12FT
Sports and Biomechanical Medicine (MSc Part time with externally arranged project)...MSc 24PT
Sports and Biomechanical Medicine (MSc Part time with in-house project) ....MSc 24PT

University of East Anglia
Physiotherapy.. MSc 24FT

University of East London
Sports Rehabilitation ....PGCert 5FT 12 - 36PT
Strength and Conditioning .... MSc 12FT 24PT/PGDip 8FT 16PT/ PGCert 4FT 8PT

Edge Hill University
Football Rehabilitation .... MSc 24PT
Sports Therapy ....MRes 12FT 24PT

University of Exeter
Sport and Exercise Medicine .... MSc 12FT 24PT

National University of Ireland Galway
Sports and Exercise Medicine....................................... MSc 24PT

University of Glasgow
Evidence Based Medicine & Education.............. MSc (ClinSci) 12FT
Sport & Exercise Medicine ....MSc(MedSci) 12FT 24PT
Sports Nutrition.. PGCert 4FT

University of Gloucestershire
Sports Therapy .... MSc 12FT 24PT

University of Kent
Sports Therapy and Rehabilitation ....MSc 12FT 24PT/PGDip 12FT 24PT

Leeds Metropolitan University
Sport Coaching.. MSc 12FT 24PT
Sport and Exercise Biomechanics........MSc 12FT 24PT/PGCert 4FT 12PT/PGDip 12FT 24PT
Sport, Law & Society.. MA 12FT 24PT
Sports Therapy ....MSc 12FT 24PT

University of Lincoln
Sport Science .... MSc 12FT 24PT

Liverpool John Moores University
Clinical Exercise Physiology .... MSc 12FT
Sports Physiology ....MSc 12FT 24PT/PGDip 12FT 18PT/ PGCert 6FT 12PT

London Metropolitan University
Sports Rehabilitation and Therapy ....MSc 12FT 24+PT
Sports Therapy ....MSc 12FT 24+PT

Loughborough University
Sports Biomechanics .... MSc 12FT

Manchester Metropolitan University
Biomedical Science featuring Exercise and Health options ... MSc 12FT 24-36PT
MA Exercise and Sport- Sport Development ..... MA 12FT 24-36PT

Middlesex University
Sports Massage Therapy and Rehabilitation.......... MSc 12FT 24PT

University of Northampton
Sports Therapy .... MSc 12FT 24PT

Northumbria University
Clinical Exercise Physiology .... MSc 12FT 36PT
Sport Marketing..MSc 12FT 24PT

University of Nottingham
Rehabilitation Psychology.................................. MSc 12FT 24PT
Sports and Exercise Medicine... MSc 12FT 24PT/PGDip 12FT 24PT

University of Portsmouth
Clinical Exercise Science .... MSc 12FT 24PT

Queen Mary, University of London
Sport and Exercise Medicine ....MSc 12FT/PGDip 12FT 24PT

University of Roehampton
Biomechanics .... PGDip 9FT 24-48PT

University of Salford
Sports Injury Rehabilitation. MSc 36PT/PGDip 24PT/PGCert 12PT
Trauma and Orthopaedics .... MSc 12FT 36PT/PGDip 8FT 24PT/ PGCert 4FT 9PT

Sheffield Hallam University
Sport Injury Management and Therapy .....MSc 12FT 24PT/PGDip 8FT 16PT/PGCert 4FT 8PT
Sport and Exercise Psychology...............................MSc 12FT 24PT

University of Southampton
Health and Rehabilitation..MSc 12FT 24PT/ PGDip 12FT 24PT/PGCert 8FT 16PT
MSc Physiotherapy.. MSc 24FT

St Mary's University College, Twickenham
Applied Sport Psychology.......MA 12FT 24PT/PGDip 24PT/PGCert 12PT
Applied Sport and Exercise Physiology........ MA 12FT 24PT/PGDip 12PT/PGCert 12PT
Nutrition and Physical Activity for Public Health............ MSc 12FT
Sport Rehabilitation .... GradDip 24PT

Staffordshire University
Applied Sport and Exercise Science .... PGCert 12FT 7DL/PGDip 14DL/MSc 24DL
Sport and Exercise Psychology (Distance Learning) ..PGCert 7DL/ PGDip 14DL/MSc 24DL

University of Stirling
Psychology of Sport ...MSc 9FT 24PT/PGDip 9FT 24PT/PGCert 6FT 12PT
Sport Nutrition (International Olympic Committee Upgrade)...... MSc 6FT 12PT

Teesside University
Advanced Clinical Practice (Manipulative Therapy) .... MSc 36PT
Advanced Clinical Practice (Neurolgical Rehabilitation) .... MSc 36PT
Advanced Sports Therapy and Rehabilitation Science... MSc 12FT 24PT
Movement Science and Rehabilitation.................... MSc 12FT 24PT
Sports Therapy ....MSc 18FT 36PT

Trinity College Dublin - the University of Dublin
Sports and Exercise Medicine.. MSc 12FT

UCL - University College London
Sports Medicine, Exercise and Health.. MSc 12FT 24-60PT/PGDip 9FT

University of Worcester
Sports Therapy .... MSc 12FT

Sports therapy
Research Courses

Bangor University
Sport, Health and Exercise Sciences ....MPhil 12FT/PhD 36FT

Barts and the London School of Medicine and Dentistry
Department of Sports Medicine..........................PhD/MPhil/FRCS

University of East Anglia
Physiotherapy..............................PhD 36FT 72PT/MPhil 24FT 48PT/ MSc by research 12FT 24PT

University of Kent
Sport, Exercise Science and Sports Therapy........MPhil 24FT 36PT/ PhD 36FT 60PT

University of Nottingham
Sports and Exercise Medicine.......DM 36FT 72PT/PhD 36FT 72PT/ MPhil 24FT 48PT

University of Stirling
Sports Studies .... PhD 36FT 72PT/MPhil 12FT 24PT

Medicine and surgery

Urology
Taught Courses

University of Birmingham
Urology...MSc 12FT/PGDip 12FT

University of Edinburgh
Urology..ChM 24DL

Newcastle University
Clinical Sciences (Physiological Sciences) with specialisms in:
Cardiac Science; Vascular Science; Respiratory and Sleep Science;
Gastrointestinal Physiology; Urodynamic Science.........MSc 36PT

University of Salford
Surgical Practice........................MSc 36PT/PGDip 24PT/PGCert 9PT

Swansea University
Infection Prevention and Control...................................PGCert 12PT

UCL - University College London
Reproductive Science and Women's Health... MSc 12FT 24-36PT/
PGDip 9FT 24PT
Urology..MSc 24PT/PGDip 12FT 12-60PT

University of Warwick
Infections and Women's Health..PGA 12PT

Urology
Research Courses

Barts and the London School of Medicine and Dentistry
Department of Medical Oncology...........................PhD/MPhil/MD
Urological Unit..PhD

Imperial College London
Biomedical Research (Microbial Pathogenesis)............MRes 12FT

University of Oxford
Surgery.....................................DPhil 48FT/MSc by research 24-36FT

Nursing and midwifery

Clinical nursing
Taught Courses

Bangor University
Advanced Clinical Practice ....MSc 12FT 24 - 60PT/PGDip 9FT

University of Bedfordshire
Advanced Nursing Studies (and Advanced Nursing Studies with Overseas Nursing Placements) ...... MSc 12FT/PGDip 12FT/PGCert 12FT
Advanced Practice .... MSc 24PT/PGCert 24PT/PGDip 24PT

University of Bradford
Practitioners with a Special Interest ....MSc 24PT/PGDip 12PT

University of Brighton
Clinical Research..........MRes 18FT 24-72PT/PGDip 18FT 24-72PT/PGCert 18FT 24-72PT
Clinical Studies..........MSc 12FT 24 - 72PT/PGCert 12FT 24 - 72PT/PGDip 12FT 24 - 72PT

Bucks New University
Advanced Practice (Nursing) .... MSc 36PT

Cardiff University
Advanced Practice .... MSc 12FT 24PT

University of Central Lancashire
Allied Health Practice .... MSc up to 60PT
Allied Health Practice; Allied Health Practice (Occupational Therapy) .... MSc 36PT/PGDip 24PT/PGCert 12PT
Enhanced Clinical Practice .... PGCert 15PT
Nursing .... MSc 12FT 24-60PT
Person-Centred Spiritual Care & Accompaniment .... PGCert 12PT
Professional Practice: Research and Development ... MSc 36-60PT
Sexual Health Studies .... MSc 60PT/PGDip 60PT/PGCert 24PT
Specialist Community Public Health Nurse - Health Visiting or School Nursing .... PGDip 12FT 24PT

Cranfield University
Clinical Research...... MSc 12FT 36PT/PGCert 9FT 24PT/PGDip 6FT 24PT

University of Cumbria
Specialist Community Public Health Nursing Practice .... MSc 12 - 48PT

University of Dundee
Advanced Practice (Cancer Care) .... MSc 36DL
Advanced Practice (Clinical Assessment) .... MSc 36DL
Advanced Practice (Clinical Governance) .... MSc 36DL
Advanced Practice (Diagnostic Imaging) .... MSc 36DL
Advanced Practice (Health & Social Care)......................... MSc 36DL
Advanced Practice .... MSc 18DL
Advanced Practice (Medical Imaging) .... MSc 36DL
Advanced Practice (Mental Health) .... MSc 36DL
Advanced Practice (Midwifery) .... MSc 36DL
Advanced Practice (Nursing) .... MSc 36DL
Advanced Practice (Palliative Care) .... MSc 36DL
Advanced Practice (Physiotherapeutic Practice) .... MSc 36DL
Advanced Practice (Practice Education) .... PGCert 12DL PGDip 24DL
Forensic Custody Nursing (GradCert)........................ GradCert 12FT
Nursing (Masters by distance learning) .... MN 36DL
Orthodontics .... MSc 36PT

Edinburgh Napier University
Advanced Practice in Cancer Care........ MSc 12FT 36PT/PGDip 9FT 24PT/PGCert 6FT 12PT
Clinical Research .... PGCert 12PT

University of Essex
Adult Nursing .... MSc 24FT
Mental Health Nursing .... MSc 24FT
Nursing (Professional Doctorate) .... Prof Doc 48-84PT

Glyndwr University
Advanced Clinical Nursing Practice .... MSc 12FT 24-36PT

University of Hertfordshire
Clinical Research .... MSc 12FT

Imperial College London
Cardio-respiratory Nursing .... MSc 27PT

University of Kent
Advanced and Specialist Healthcare (Minimally Invasive Surgery).. MSc 24-36PT
Advanced and Specialist Healthcare (Supportive and Palliative Care).. MSc 24-36PT

King's College London
Advanced Practice .... MSc 36-72PT/PGDip 24-72PT/PGCert 12-72PT
Advanced Practice (Cancer Nursing)................ MSc 36-72PT/PGDip 24-72PT/PGCert 12-72PT
Advanced Practice (Cardiac Care).. MSc 36-72PT/PGDip 24-72PT/PGCert 12-72PT
Advanced Practice (District Nursing)............ MSc 12FT up to 72PT
Clinical Nursing for International Students....... MSc 12FT/PGCert 12FT

Kingston University
Clinical Practice .... MRes 12FT 24PT

Leeds Metropolitan University
Advanced Practice .... MSc 36PT/PGDip 24PT/PGCert 12PT

University of Leeds
Advanced Gastrointestinal Practice .... PGCert p/t onlyPT

Liverpool John Moores University
Adult Nursing .... MSc 24FT 24PT

University of Liverpool
Clinical Research (Online Degree) .... MSc 24FT 24+PT
Clinical Science (Medical Physics) .... MSc 36PT

Manchester Metropolitan University
Practice Development .... MSc 24-72PT

University of Nottingham
Advanced Clinical Practice .... MSc 24PT
Advanced Clinical Skills.. PGCert 12-24PT

Oxford Brookes University
Advanced Practice (Clinical) .... MSc 36-60PT/PGDip 24-48PT/PGCert 18-24PT
Nursing, Adult (Pre-registration) .... MSc 24FT 48PT/PGDip 24FT 48PT/PGCert 24FT 48PT
Nursing, Adult (Pre-registration) (Swindon) .... MSc 24FT 48PT/PGDip 24FT 48PT/PGCert 24FT 48PT
Nursing, Children's (Pre-registration) .... MSc 24FT 48PT/PGDip 24FT 48PT/PGCert 24FT 48PT
Nursing, Mental Health (Pre-registration) .... MA 24FT 48PT/PGDip 24FT 48PT/PGCert 24FT 48PT

Queen Margaret University, Edinburgh
Nursing .... MSc 12FT 36PT/PGDip 8FT 24-36PT/PGCert 24-84PT

Queen's University Belfast
Nursing/Midwifery: Advanced Professional Practice..... MSc 24FT 60PT

Robert Gordon University
Nursing .... MSc 12FT 12/36DL

University of Salford
Advanced Practice (Neonatal) ... MSc 12FT 24PT/PGDip 9FT 18PT/PGCert 4FT 12PT
Advancing Physiotherapy........... MSc 12FT 36PT/PGDip 9FT 24PT/PGCert 6FT 12PT
Geriatric Medicine............................ MSc 48-60PT/PGDip 24-60PT/PGCert 12-60PT
Midwifery .... MSc 12FT 36PT/PGCert 4FT 12PT/PGDip 8FT 18PT
Nursing .... MA 36FT/PGDip 24FT/PGCert 12FT
Nursing (Education, International, Practice, Research) . MSc 12FT 36PT/PGDip 9FT 24PT/PGCert 6FT 12PT

Sheffield Hallam University
Advanced Practice (Radiotherapy and Oncology) .... MSc 3DL/PGDip 2DL/PGCert 1DL
Nursing Studies - Adult or Mental Health Nursing ..... PGDip 24FT

University of Sheffield
Advanced Emergency Care................................. MSc 12FT 24 - 60PT
Advanced Nursing Studies... MMedSci 36DL/Diploma 36DL/Cert 36DL
Advancing Practice. MMedSci 12FT 24PT/Diploma 9FT 18PT/Cert 6FT 12PT
Endodontics .... DClinDent 36FT
Midwifery .... MMid 36 PTDL/Diploma 27 PTDL/Cert 18 PTDL
Nursing Studies leading to professional registration as an Adult Nurse .... PGDip 24FT

University of South Wales
Advanced Clinical Practitioner.................................... MSc 12 -60PT
Cancer Care (Approved by the European Oncology Nursing Society)... BSc 24-72PT

University of Southampton
Advanced Clinical Practice .... MSc 12FT 24PT/PGDip 12FT/PGCert 12FT
Doctorate in Clinical Practice . DClinP 48FT 84PT/MSc 12FT 24PT/PGDip 12FT 24PT/PGCert 8FT 16PT
Gerontology .... MSc 12FT 24PT/PGDip 9FT 21PT
Gerontology (Distance Learning) .... MSc 12DL/PGDip 9DL
Clinical Leadership in Cancer, Palliative and End of Life Care MSc 24FT 48PT
Nursing (Pre-registration) .... MSc 36FT

St George's, University of London
Advanced Practice .... MSc 24PT

University of Stirling
Advanced Practice .... MSc 18PT/MSc 18PT
Health Research .... MRes 12FT 24/36PT 24/36DL

Swansea University
Advanced Practice in Health Care .... MSc 36PT/PGDip 24PT

Teesside University
Advanced Clinical Practice .... MSc 36PT/PGCert 12PT
Nursing .... MSc 12FT
Nursing (Advanced Cardiac Care)... MSc 36PT
Nursing (Advanced Nurse Practitioner)............................. MSc 36PT
Nursing (Advanced Surgical Care Practitioner)................ MSc 36PT
Nursing (Specialist Field).. MSc 36PT

Trinity College Dublin - the University of Dublin
Cancer Care .... MSc 24PT
Nursing (Child Health and Well-being Strand) ..... MSc 12FT 24PT
Nursing .... MSc 12FT 24PT
Nursing (Specialist) .... PGDip 24PT

University of West London
Midwives and High Dependency Practice......................... CPPD 8PT

Clinical nursing
Research Courses

Bucks New University
Nursing .... DNursing 48-84PT

University of Dundee
Nursing & Midwifery .... PhD 36FT PhD 48FT MPhil 24FT

University of East Anglia
Nursing .... PhD 36FT 72PT/MPhil 24FT 48PT/MSc by research 12FT 24PT

University of Essex
Nursing Studies....... PhD 72PT/MPhil 48PT/MSc by research 24PT

Liverpool School of Tropical Medicine
Clinical research... PhD/MPhil/MIHR

University of Southampton
Doctorate in Clinical Practice .... PhD 36FT 72PT

University of Stirling
Nursing and Midwifery - Research...... PhD 36FT 72PT/MPhil 24FT 48PT

Community nursing
Taught Courses

Anglia Ruskin University
Specialist Community Public Health Nursing (Health Visiting or School Nursing)... PGDip 12FT

University of Bedfordshire
Specialist Community Public Health Nursing / Specialist Community (District) Nursing.. MSc 12FT 24PT/PGDip 12FT 24PT

University of Birmingham
Primary and Community Care, Clinical....... MSc 12FT 24PT/PGDip 12FT 24PT/PGCert 12FT 24PT

University of Bolton
Community Specialist Practice (District Nursing)....... PGDip 12PT
Specialist Community Public Health Nursing (Health Visiting).... PGDip 12FT 24PT

Bournemouth University
Public Health Nursing .... MSc 12FT 24-36PT

University of Brighton
Health Promotion............ MA 12FT 24-72PT/PGDip 12FT 24-72PT/PGCert 12FT 24-72PT
International Health Promotion................................ MA 12FT 36PT/PGDip 12FT 36PT
Specialist Community Public Health Nursing MSc 12FT 24-72PT/PGDip 12FT 24-72PT/PGCert 12FT 24-72PT

Brunel University
Specialist Community Public Health Nursing......... MSc 0FT 12PT/PGDip 12FT 24PT

Bucks New University
Advanced Practice (Nursing) .... MSc 36PT
Community Health Care Nursing.............................. MSc 12FT 24PT
Specialist Community Public Health Nursing........ MSc 12FT 24PT

Canterbury Christ Church University
Community Specialist Practice .... PGDip 12FT 24PT
Specialist Community Public Health Nursing.... PGDip 12FT 24PT

Cardiff University
Specialist Community Public Health Nursing........... MSc 24-48FT 36-60PT/PGDip 12FT 24PT

University of Central Lancashire
Community Specialist Practitioner................. PGDip 12FT 24-48PT
Nursing .... MSc 12FT 24-60PT
Person-Centred Spiritual Care & Accompaniment .... PGCert 12PT

University of Chester
Nursing Studies (Work Based and Integrative Studies)............. MA 24-72PT/MSc 24-72PT/PGDip 24-60PT/PGCert 12-36PT

City University London
Mental Health Nursing (Graduate Entry)....................... PGDip 24FT
Primary Care (District Nursing)................................ MSc 12FT 24PT
Specialist Community Public Health Nurse (Health Visiting)........ MSc 12FT 24PT
Specialist Community Public Health Nurse (School Nursing)........ MSc 12FT 24PT

Coventry University
Nursing Studies... MSc 15 MinFT 60 MaxPT

University of Cumbria
Community Specalist Practice Nursing .... PGDE 9FT 18PT
Specialist Community Public Health Nursing Practice .... MSc 12 - 48PT

De Montfort University
Advanced Health and Professional Practice B70076....... MSc 12FT 36-72PT/PGDip 24PT/PGCert 12PT
Health and Community Studies L53072 .. MA 36DL/PGDip 18DL/PGCert 12DL/MA 12FT
Specialist Community Public Health Nursing..... MSc 36PT/PGDip 24PT

Nursing and midwifery

University of Derby
Community Specialist Practice .... MSc 12FT 24PT
Management of Long Term Conditions .... PGCert 12PT
Nursing (Specialist Community Public Health) ..... MSc 12FT 24PT

University of Dundee
Advanced Practice (Physiotherapeutic Practice) .... MSc 36DL
Diabetes Care and Education .... MSc 36-40PT PGCert 12-15PT PGDip 24-27PT
Global Health and Wellbeing .... MSc 36DL
Health and Social Care .... MRes 24DL
Nursing (Masters by distance learning) .... MN 36DL
Palliative Care .... MSc 36DL
Palliative Care Research .... MPH 12-24FT

University of East Anglia
Advanced Practitioner (Profession) .... MSc 12FT 36PT
Mental Health ..... MSc 12FT 36PT/PGDip 12FT 24PT/PGCert 12PT
Midwifery .... PGDip 18FT

Edinburgh Napier University
Advanced Practice in Diabetes Nursing ...... MSc 12FT 36PT/PGDip 9FT 24PT/PGCert 6FT 12PT
Health Administration .... MSc 12FT 24-36PT/PGDip 9FT 18-27PT/PGCert 6FT 12-18PT

National University of Ireland Galway
Nursing (Mental Health, Community & Inpatient Acute Care)..... PGDip 12FT 24PT
Nursing (Practice Nursing/ Community Nursing) .... PGDip 12FT 24PT

Glasgow Caledonian University
Advanced Practice with Older People .... MSc 12FT
Advancing Practice in Primary Care .... MSc 24FT
Diabetes Care and Management .... MSc 12FT 36PT
Optimal Heart Failure Care .... MSc 12FT
Perinatal Mental Health .... MSc 12FT
Specialist Community Public Health Nursing .... PGDip 12FT 24PT
Telehealthcare .... MSc 12FT

Glyndwr University
Community Specialist Practice Nursing .... MSc 12FT 24-36PT
Specialist Community Public Health Nursing .... MSc 12FT 24PT

University of Hertfordshire
Contemporary Nursing .... MSc 12FT
Specialist Community Nursing .... MSc 12FT 24PT/PGDip 12FT 24PT
Specialist Community Public Health Nursing .... MSc 12FT 24PT/PGDip 12FT 24PT/BSc Hons 12FT 24PT

University of Huddersfield
Community Nursing Practice (District Nursing) .... MSc 18FT 30-42PT
Public Health Nursing Practice: Health Visiting/School Nursing.. MSc 16FT 36PT

King's College London
Advanced Practice (Diabetes Care) MSc 36-72PT/PGDip 24-72PT/PGCert 12-72PT
Advanced Practice (Nurse Practitioner/Community Matron/Case Manager) .... MSc 36-72PT/PGDip 24-72PT/PGCert 12-72PT
Advanced Practice (Palliative Care Nursing) .... MSc 36-72PT/PGDip 24-72PT/PGCert 12-72PT
Advanced Practice (Specialist Community Public Health Nursing/ Public Health/ School Nurs) .... MSc 36-72PT/PGDip 24-72PT/PGCert 12-72PT

Leeds Metropolitan University
Community Specialist Practitioner - Community Children's Nursing .... PGDip 24PT
Community Specialist Practitioner - District Nursing... MSc 24PT/PGDip 12FT 24PT
Community Specialist Practitioner - Practice Nursing.. MSc 24PT/PGDip 24PT
Health Care Studies .... MA 24PT
Specialist Community Public Health Nursing - Health Visiting .... MSc 24PT/PGDip 12FT 24PT
Specialist Community Public Health Nursing - Occupational Health Nursing .... MSc 24PT/PGDip 12FT 24PT
Specialist Community Public Health Nursing - School Nursing.... MSc 24PT/PGDip 12FT 24PT

Liverpool John Moores University
Adult Nursing .... MSc 24FT 24PT
Advanced Paediatric Nurse Practitioner (APNP) in Ambulatory Care .... MSc 12FT 24PT

London School of Hygiene and Tropical Medicine
Public Health for Eye Care .... MSc 12FT 24PT

Manchester Metropolitan University
Advanced Practitioner Abuse Studies .... MA 24PT
Community Health .... MSc 12FT 24-36PT
Practice Development .... MSc 24-72PT
Specialist Community Public Health Nursing (Health Visiting or School Nursing).. MSc 12-24FT 24-36PT/PGDip 12-24FT 24-36PT/PGCert 12-24FT 24-36PT

Northumbria University
Midwifery .... Professional Doctorate 48-72PT
Midwifery Studies .... PGDip 18FT
Nursing .... Professional Doctorate 48-72PT
Systemic Teaching, Training and Supervision .... MA 24PT

University of Nottingham
Health and Social Care .... MSc 12FT 24-48PT/PGCert 24-48PT/PGDip 12FT 24-48PT

Oxford Brookes University
Community Children's Nursing .... PGDip 12FT 24PT
Community Nursing in the Home / District Nursing .... PGDip 12FT 24PT
Nursing, Adult (Pre-registration) .... MSc 24FT 48PT/PGDip 24FT 48PT/PGCert 24FT 48PT
Nursing, Adult (Pre-registration) (Swindon) .... MSc 24FT 48PT/PGDip 24FT 48PT/PGCert 24FT 48PT
Nursing, Children's (Pre-registration) .... MSc 24FT 48PT/PGDip 24FT 48PT/PGCert 24FT 48PT
Nursing, Mental Health (Pre-registration) .... MA 24FT 48PT/PGDip 24FT 48PT/PGCert 24FT 48PT
Specialist Community Public Health Nursing (Health Visiting) .... PGDip 12FT 24-26PT
Specialist Community Public Health Nursing (School Nursing).... PGDip 12FT 24-36PT

Queen Margaret University, Edinburgh
Nursing .... MSc 12FT 36PT/PGDip 8FT 24-36PT/PGCert 24-84PT

Queen's University Belfast
Nursing Practice .... DMP (Doctorate) 36FT 60PT
Nursing/Midwifery: Advanced Professional Practice..... MSc 24FT 60PT

Robert Gordon University
Nursing .... MSc 12FT 12/36DL

University of Salford
Child and Adolescent Mental Health .... MSc 24PT/PGDip 18PT/PGCert 9PT
Lower Limb Health, Disease and Rehabilitation .... PGCert 12PT
Nursing .... MA 36FT/PGDip 24FT/PGCert 12FT
Nursing (Education, International, Practice, Research) .... MSc 12FT 36PT/PGDip 9FT 24PT/PGCert 6FT 12PT
Health and Social Care .... PhD by taught 60PT

Sheffield Hallam University
Nursing Studies - Adult or Mental Health Nursing ..... PGDip 24FT
Specialist Mental Health Practice .. MA 36PT/PGDip 24PT/PGCert 12PT

University of Sheffield
Advanced Nursing Studies ... MMedSci 36DL/Diploma 36DL/Cert 36DL
Advancing Practice .... MMedSci 12FT 24PT/Diploma 9FT 18PT/Cert 6FT 12PT
Long-Term Health Conditions .... PGCert FlexiblePT
Nursing Studies leading to professional registration as an Adult Nurse .... PGDip 24FT

University of South Wales
Specialist Community Public Health Nursing (Health Visiting or School Health Nursing) .... MSc 12FT 36PT/PGDip 12FT 24PT

University of Southampton
Doctorate in Clinical Practice . DClinP 48FT 84PT/MSc 12FT 24PT/PGDip 12FT 24PT/PGCert 8FT 16PT
MSc Nursing (Pre-registration) .... MSc 36FT
Nursing, Midwifery & Health Visiting .... MSc 12FT

Staffordshire University
Community Practice .... MA 12FT 48PT

University of Stirling
Advanced Practice .... MSc 18PT/MSc 18PT
Health Research .... MRes 12FT 24/36PT 24/36DL

Teesside University
Nursing .... MSc 12FT
Nursing (Advanced Cardiac Care) .... MSc 36PT
Nursing (Advanced Nurse Practitioner) .... MSc 36PT
Nursing (Advanced Surgical Care Practitioner) .... MSc 36PT
Nursing (Specialist Field) .... MSc 36PT

Trinity College Dublin - the University of Dublin
Nursing (Child Health and Well-being Strand) (H. Dip.) .... MSc 12FT 24PT
Nursing .... MSc 12FT 24PT
Nursing (Specialist) .... PGDip 24PT

University of Ulster
Specialist Community Public Health Nursing (SCPHN) .... PGDip 12FT 24PT

University of Warwick
Diabetes in Pregnancy .... PGA 12PT
Organisation and Delivery of Diabetes Care .. PGA 12PT/CPDMod 1PT

University of West London
Advancing Practice (Community Matron) .... PGCert 12PT
Nursing and Healthcare .... MSc 12FT
The Management of Complex and Changing Health and Social Care Needs in Clients .... CPPD 4PT

University of Winchester
Delivery of Primary Health Care .... PGCert 24PT

Community nursing
Research Courses

Bucks New University
Nursing .... DNursing 48-84PT

Canterbury Christ Church University
Health & Social Care (inclduing Allied Health Profs Nursing & Midwifery, & Public Health .... PhD 48FT 60PT/MPhil 24FT 48PT

Cardiff University
Nursing, Medicine, Health and Social Care MPhil 12FT 36PT/PhD 36FT 60PT
Primary Care and Public Health .... PhD 36FT/MPhil 36FT

University of Dundee
Nursing & Midwifery .... PhD 36FT 48FT MPhil 24FT

University of Kent
Community Care .... MPhil 24FT 36PT/PhD 36FT 60PT

University of Sheffield
Primary Medical Care and Ageing .... PhD 36FT 72PT/MPhil 24FT 48PT

University of Stirling
Nursing and Midwifery - Research ...... PhD 36FT 72PT/MPhil 24FT 48PT

University of West London
Nursing .... Professional Doctorate (PD) 33FT 45PT

Critical care nursing
Taught Courses

Anglia Ruskin University
Adult Critical Care Nursing .... MSc 36DL

Bournemouth University
Advanced Nurse Practitioner .... PGDip 24PT

University of Bradford
Practitioners with a Special Interest .... MSc 24PT/PGDip 12PT

Bucks New University
Advanced Practice (Nursing) .... MSc 36PT

Cardiff University
Advanced Practice .... MSc 12FT 24PT
Critical Care .... MSc 24DL/PGDip 18DL/PGCert 18DL

University of Central Lancashire
Nursing .... MSc 12FT 24-60PT
Person-Centred Spiritual Care & Accompaniment .... PGCert 12PT
Sexual Health Studies .... MSc 60PT/PGDip 60PT/PGCert 24PT
Specialist Community Public Health Nurse - Health Visiting or School Nursing .... PGDip 12FT 24PT

University College Cork
Nursing (Cardiac & Intensive Care) .... PGDip 12FT
Nursing (Emergency Nursing) .... PGDip 12FT

University of Dundee
Advanced Practice (Cancer Care) .... MSc 36DL
Advanced Practice (Clinical Assessment) .... MSc 36DL
Advanced Practice (Physiotherapeutic Practice) .... MSc 36DL

University of East Anglia
Advanced Practitioner (Profession) .... MSc 12FT 36PT
Mental Health ..... MSc 12FT 36PT/PGDip 12FT 24PT/PGCert 12PT

National University of Ireland Galway
Nursing .... MHSc 24PT/MHSc 36PT
Nursing (Advanced Practice) .... PGDip 12FT
Nursing (Intensive Care) .... PGDip 12FT 24PT
Nursing (Mental Health, Community & Inpatient Acute Care)..... PGDip 12FT 24PT

Glasgow Caledonian University
Advanced Nursing .... MSc 12FT 36-60PT
Optimal Heart Failure Care .... MSc 12FT

King's College London
Advanced Practice (Critical Care)... MSc 36-72PT/PGDip 24-72PT/PGCert 12-72PT

Leeds Metropolitan University
Advanced Practice .... MSc 36PT/PGDip 24PT/PGCert 12PT

University of Leicester
Medical Statistics .... MSc 12FT 24PT

Liverpool John Moores University
Advanced Paediatric Nurse Practitioner (APNP) in Ambulatory Care .... MSc 12FT 24PT
Advanced Paediatric Nurse Practitioner (APNP) in Critical Care ... MSc 12FT

Northumbria University
Master of Clinical Practice (Advanced Critical Care Practice)... MA 36FT

Queen Mary, University of London
Critical Care .... MSc 12FT 24PT

University of Salford
Advanced Practice (Neonatal) ... MSc 12FT 24PT/PGDip 9FT 18PT/PGCert 4FT 12PT
Nursing .... MA 36FT/PGDip 24FT/PGCert 12FT

Nursing and midwifery

University of Sheffield
Advanced Emergency Care....MSc 12FT 24 - 60PT
Advanced Nursing Studies... MMedSci 36DL/Diploma 36DL/Cert 36DL
Advancing Practice....MMedSci 12FT 24PT/Diploma 9FT 18PT/Cert 6FT 12PT

University of South Wales
Acute and Critical Care....PGCert 12FT 36PT
Cancer Care (Approved by the European Oncology Nursing Society)....BSc 24-72PT

University of Southampton
Clinical Leadership in Cancer, Palliative and End of Life Care MSc 24FT 48PT

University of Stirling
Advanced Practice....MSc 18PT/MSc 18PT

Swansea University
Advanced Practice in Health Care....MSc 36PT/PGDip 24PT

Teesside University
Advanced Clinical Practice (Cardiac Care)....MSc 36PT

Critical care nursing
Research Courses

University of East Anglia
Nursing....PhD 36FT 72PT/MPhil 24FT 48PT/MSc by research 12FT 24PT

University of Stirling
Nursing and Midwifery - Research....PhD 36FT 72PT/MPhil 24FT 48PT

Gerontology
Taught Courses

University of Bradford
Dementia Studies. MSc 24-36DL/PGDip 12-24DL/PGCert 9-12DL

Brunel University
Ageing Studies....PGCert 12PT/PGDip 24PT/MSc 36PT

Cardiff University
Ageing, Health and Disease..MSc 24PT/PGDip 12FT/PGCert 12PT

University of East London
Long Term Conditions in Adults....PGCert 5FT 12 - 36PT

University of Edinburgh
Cognitive Ageing Research Methods for Medical Scientists (online distance learning)....PGCert 12PT 12DL
Dementia: International Experience, Policy and Practice (Online Distance Learning)....MSc 24DL/PGDip 21DL/PGCert 9DL

National University of Ireland Galway
Nursing (Gerontology)....PGDip 12FT 24PT

Glasgow Caledonian University
Life Sciences - Biological and Biomedical Sciences/Psychology/Vision Sciences....MRes 12FT

Keele University
Geriatric Medicine....MSc 24PT/PGDip 16PT
Gerontology....MA 12FT 24PT/PGDip 12PT

King's College London
Advanced Care in Dementia....MSc 12FT 24PT
Ageing & Society...MA 12FT/MSc 12FT/PGDip 12FT/PGCert 12FT
Gerontology....MSc 12FT 24PT/PGDip 12FT 24PT/PGCert 12FT 24PT
Public Policy & Ageing...MA 12FT 24PT/PGCert 12FT 24PT/PGDip 12FT 24PT
Research Methods for Social Science & Health.. PGCert 3FT 24PT

University Campus Suffolk
Science of Healthy Ageing....MSc 12FT

University of Salford
Geriatric Medicine....MSc 48-60PT/PGDip 24-60PT/PGCert 12-60PT

University of South Wales
Care of the Older Person (Distance Learning)....MSc 24 - 72DL

University of Southampton
Gerontology....MSc 12FT 24PT/PGDip 9FT 21PT
Gerontology (Distance Learning)....MSc 12DL/PGDip 9DL

Staffordshire University
Ageing, Mental Health and Dementia....MSc 36DL

University of Stirling
Dementia Studies....MSc 36PT/PGDip 24PT/PGCert 12PT
Health and Wellbeing of the Older Person....MSc 24FT

Swansea University
Ageing Studies.... MSc 12FT 36PT/PGDip 12FT 24PT/PGCert 12FT 12PT

Trinity College Dublin - the University of Dublin
Dementia....MSc 12FT 24PT
Gerontological Nursing....MSc 24PT

University of Ulster
Interdisciplinary Dementia Studies....PGDip 24DL/MSc 36DL

University of West London
Anti-ageing and Lifespan Medicine....PGDip 24DL

University of Worcester
Applied Psychology....MSc 12FT 24-72PT

Gerontology
Research Courses

Bangor University
Ageing and Cognitive Health....PhD 36FT 60PT
Ageing and Dementia Studies....MSc by research 12FT 24PT
Ageing and Dementia Studies.. PhD 36FT 60PT/MPhil 24FT 48PT

University of Edinburgh
Geriatric Medicine....PhD 36FT 72PT/MPhil 24FT 48PT/MSc by research 12FT 24PT
Pathology....PhD 36FT 72PT/MPhil 24FT/MSc by research 12FT 24PT

Keele University
Social Policy, Sociology, and Social Gerontology.... PhD 24-48FT 48-84PT/MPhil 12-24FT 24-36PT

King's College London
Age-Related Diseases (Wolfson Centre for)PhD 36-48FT 48-72PT/MPhil 36-48FT 36-48PT/MDS by research 36-48FT 36-48PT
Gerontology Research....PhD 36FT 72PT/MPhil 36FT 72PT
Old Age Psychiatry & Dementia....MPhil 36FT 72PT/PhD 36FT 72PT
Wolfson Centre for Age Related Diseases....PhD 36-48FT 48-72PT/MPhil 36-48FT 48-72PT/MD (Res) 36-48FT 48-72PT

Lancaster University
Biomedical and Life Sciences.... PhD 36FT 48PT/MPhil 24FT 36PT

Newcastle University
Ageing....MPhil 12FT 24PT/PhD 36FT 72PT/MD 24FT 48PT
Ageing and Health....MRes 12FT

The Open University
Ageing and Later Life....PhD 36FT 72PT variableDL/MPhil 15FT 24PT variableDL

Plymouth University
Preventive and Supportive Care....MPhil TBCFT

University of Sheffield
Primary Medical Care and Ageing....PhD 36FT 72PT/MPhil 24FT 48PT

University of Southampton
School of Social Sciences - Gerontology....PhD 36FT 72PT/MPhil 24FT 48PT

St George's, University of London
Clinical Developmental Sciences....PhD 36FT 84PT/MPhil 24FT 48PT/MDRes 24PT

University of the West of Scotland
Centre for Gerontology and Health Studies....PhD/MPhil/MSc by research 12FT

Mental health care
Taught Courses

University of Aberdeen
Patient Safety: A Clinical Human Factors Approach....MRes 12FT

Anglia Ruskin University
Mental Health Services....PGCert 36PT

Bangor University
Applied Behaviour Analysis....PGCert 4FT 9PT/PGDip 9FT 18PT/MSc 12FT 24PT
Psychology....MRes 12FT/PGCert 3FT

Barts and the London School of Medicine and Dentistry
Transcultural Mental health.... MSc 12FT 24PT/PGDip 12FT 24PT

University of Bedfordshire
Psychosocial Interventions....PGCert 12FT

Birmingham City University
Mental Health....MSc 24PT/PGDip 18PT/PGCert 12PT

Bournemouth University
Advanced Mental Health Practice.. MA 36PT/PGDip 36PT/PGCert 36PT

University of Bradford
Mental Health Practice....MA 12FT/PGDip 12FT
Mental Health Studies....MA 12FT 24PT/PGCert 9PT/PGDip 9FT 21PT

University of Brighton
Mental Health....MSc 24 - 72PT/PGCert 24 - 72PT/PGDip 24 - 72PT

University of Central Lancashire
Advanced Legal Practice....LLM 12FT 24PT/PGDip 12FT
Advanced Practice (Health and Social Care)....MSc 24PT
Advanced Stroke Practice....MSc 36FT 60PT/PGDip 24PT/PGCert 12PT
Health & Social Care Education....PGCert 12PT
Health Informatics....MSc 33PT/PGDip 24PT
Health and Social Care Education....PGCert 12PT
Mental Health Practice (Including approved mental health professional training). MA 12-60PT/PGDip 12-60PT/PGCert 12PT
Personality Disorder....PGCert 12PT
Personality Disorder (Practice Development)....MSc 36-60PT/PGDip 24PT
Personality Disorder (Research)....MSc 36-60PT/PGDip 12-24PT
Philosophy & Mental Health....MA 36DL/PGDip 24DL/PGCert 12DL
Primary Care Mental Health Practice....PGCert 12PT
Psychology....MSc 12FT 24PT/PGDip 9FT 24PT/PGCert 9FT 24PT
Psychology of Child Development....MSc 12FT 24PT/PGDip 9FT 24PT/PGCert 9FT 24PT
Social Psychology....MSc 12FT 24PT

University of Chester
Health and Social Care - Advanced Practice....MSc 24 - 72PT/PGDip 24 - 60PT/PGCert 12 - 36PT
Health and Social Care - Art Therapy....MA 24 - 72PT/PGDip 24 - 60PT/PGCert 12 - 36PT
Health and Social Care - Intercultural Psychotherapy: Theory and Research....MSc 12FT 24 - 72PT/PGDip 12FT 24 - 60PT/PGCert 12FT 12 - 36PT
Health and Social Care - Multi-Method Therapy....MA 24 - 72PT/PGDip 24 - 60PT/PGCert 12 - 36PT

City University London
Adult Nursing (Graduate Entry)....PGDip 36FT
Mental Health Nursing (Graduate Entry)....PGDip 24FT

University of Cumbria
Advanced Practice in Health and Social Care....MSc 24 - 60PT
Community Specalist Practice Nursing....PGDE 9FT 18PT
Mental Health Practice: Approved Medical Health Practitioner... MA min 24FT max 60PT/PGCert 12FT/PGDip 12FT

University of Dundee
Advanced Practice (Mental Health)....MSc 36DL

University of East Anglia
Clinical Science....MRes 12FT
Mental Health.... MSc 12FT 36PT/PGDip 12FT 24PT/PGCert 12PT
Occupational Therapy....MSc 24FT

University of East London
Approved Mental Health Practice (AMHP)....PGDip 8FT
Child and Adolescent Primary Mental Health Care Work (M42)... MA 36PT/PGDip 24PT/PGCert 12PT
Infant Mental Health (Early Years Development) M9 ... MA 36PT/PGDip 24PT/PGCert 12PT

Edinburgh Napier University
Advanced Practice in Intellectual Disabilities....MSc 12FT 36PT/PGDip 9FT 24PT/PGCert 6FT 12PT
Advanced Practice in Intellectual Disabilities and Applied Education....MSc 12FT 36PT/PGDip 9FT 24PT/PGCert 6FT 12PT

University of Edinburgh
Advanced Social Work Studies (Mental Health)....PGCert 12PT
Dementia: International Experience, Policy and Practice (Online Distance Learning)....MSc 24DL/PGDip 21DL/PGCert 9DL
Health & Social Care - Children & Young People's Mental Health: Ecological Approaches ODL....PGCert 9DL

University of Essex
Mental Health Nursing....MSc 24FT

University of Exeter
Clinical Practice....DClinPrac 42DL
Clinical Psychology....DClinPsy by taught 36FT
Mindfulness-based Cognitive Therapies and Approaches.... PGCert 12PT/PGDip 24PT/MSc 24-36PT

National University of Ireland Galway
Nursing (Mental Health, Community & Inpatient Acute Care).... PGDip 12FT 24PT

Glasgow Caledonian University
Mental Health Social Work (Mental Health Officer).... PGCert 12PT

University of Glasgow
Healthcare Chaplaincy....PGCert 12PT
Mental Health, Global....MSc 12FT 24PT/PGDip 9FT 18PT/PGCert 9FT 18PT

University of Hertfordshire
Mental Health (Primary Care)....PGCert 12PT
Mental Health Practice MSc 15FT 24-60PT/PGDip 15FT 24-60PT/PGCert 15FT 24-60PT

University of Huddersfield
Health & Social Care (Approved Mental Health Practice)....MSc 36PT

King's College London
Advanced Care in Dementia....MSc 12FT 24PT
Advanced Practice (Cardiac Care).. MSc 36-72PT/PGDip 24-72PT/PGCert 12-72PT
Early Intervention in Psychosis....MSc 12FT 24,36,48PT N/ADL
Global Mental Health....MSc 12FT 24PT
Mental Health Service & Population Research....MSc 12FT 24PT
Mental Health Studies....MSc 12FT 24PT
Mental Health in Learning Disabilities....MSc 12FT 24PT

Leeds Metropolitan University
Mental Health Practice....MSc 24PT
Mental Health Studies....PGCert 24PT/PGDip 24PT

Nursing and midwifery

University of Leicester
Child and Adolescent Mental Health.... PGCert 12FT 12PT/PGDip 12FT 24PT/MSc 12FT 36PT

University of Liverpool
Advanced Science..........MSc 12FT 24PT/PGDip 12FT/PGCert 12FT

London Metropolitan University
Mental Health and Well-being .... MSc 12FT 24PT

London School of Hygiene and Tropical Medicine
Global Mental Health.. MSc 12FT 24PT

London South Bank University
Acute and Psychiatric Intensive Care Settings....MSc 36PT/PGDip 24PT
Forensic Mental Health Care .... MSc 36PT
Mental Health Practice .... MSc 36PT
Mental Health Practice (Older People)............................. MSc 36PT
Primary Care and Mental Health..................................PGCert 12PT

University of Manchester
Applied Mental Health..PGCert 12FT 24PT
Dementia Care - Advanced Practice Interventions for Mental Health...MSc N/AFT 36PT/PGDip 36PT
Forensic Mental Health..................................MSc 36PT/PGDip 12PT
Primary Mental Health Care pathway - APIMH..MSc 36PT/PGDip 24PT
Psychosocial Interventions for Psychosis (COPE) pathway..... MSc 36PT/PGDip 24PT

Middlesex University
Child and Family Mental Health Work.......................AdvDip 12PT/PGCert 12PT
Child, Adolescent and Family Mental Health Work... AdvDip 7PT/PGCert 7PT
Mental Health Studies, ... MSc 36PT

University of Northampton
Child and Adolescent Mental Health........ 12FT 24PT/PGDip 12PT
Mental Health ....MSc 24PT/PGDip 12PT

Northumbria University
Mental Health Law Policy and Practice....LLM 24DL/PGDip 18DL/PGCert 9DL
Nursing (MNurs) Registered Nurse (Mental Health)........................ MA 24-48FT

University of Nottingham
Graduate Entry Nursing - Mental Health......................... MSc 36FT
Mental Health Research .... MSc 12FT 24PT
Psychological Therapies...PGCert 12PT

Oxford Brookes University
Nursing, Mental Health (Pre-registration).............MA 24FT 48PT/PGDip 24FT 48PT/PGCert 24FT 48PT

Queen Mary, University of London
Mental Health: Psychological Therapies D/L option...... MSc 12FT 24PT
Mental Health: Transcultural Mental Healthcare............................ MSc 12FT 24PT 24DL

Queen's University Belfast
Mental Health ....Diploma 4FT

University of Reading
Clinical Aspects of Psychology ....MSc 12FT 24PT
Evidence-Based Psychological Treatments .....PGDip 12FT/PGCert 12FT

University of Salford
Child and Adolescent Mental Health........MSc 24PT/PGDip 18PT/PGCert 9PT

School of Oriental and African Studies - SOAS
Medical Anthropology .... MA 12FT 24-36PT

Sheffield Hallam University
Nursing Studies - Adult or Mental Health Nursing.....PGDip 24FT
Postgraduate Diploma Nursing Studies (Adult / Mental Health) ....PGDip 24FT
Specialist Mental Health Practice.. MA 36PT/PGDip 24PT/PGCert 12PT

University of South Wales
Child and Adolescent Mental Health .... MA 12FT 36PT

University of Southampton
Cognitive Therapy for Severe Mental Health Problems........PGDip 12PT
Health Psychology...MSc 12FT/PGDip 12FT
MSc Leadership and Management Health and Social Care.... MSc 12FT 48PT
MSc Mental Health Studies.......... MSc 15FT 24-60PT/PGDip 12FT 18-60PT/PGCert 6FT 6PT
MSc Nursing (Pre-registration) .... MSc 36FT

University of St Andrews
Adults Support, Protection and Safeguarding...........PGCert 12DL
Adults with Learning Disabilities who have Significant and Complex Needs.....................MSc 12DL/PGDip 12DL/PGCert 12DL
Health Psychology... MSc 12FT

Staffordshire University
Ageing, Mental Health and Dementia..............................MSc 36DL
Practitioner with a Special Interest in Mental Health... MSc 36PT

University of Stirling
Health Psychology.........................MSc 12FT 24PT/PGDip 6FT 12PT
Health and Wellbeing of the Older Person .... MSc 24FT

University of Sussex
Foundations of Clinical Psychology and Mental Health................. MSc 12FT 24PT

Swansea University
Approved Mental Health Professional.......................... PGCert 12FT

Trinity College Dublin - the University of Dublin
Dementia...MSc 12FT 24PT
Mental Health ....MSc 12FT 24PT

UCL - University College London
CYP IAPT Therapy ....PGDip 12FT
Child and Adolescent Mental Health... MSc 12FT 24-60PT/PGDip 24-60PT/PGCert 12PT

University of West London
Advanced Psychosocial Interventions for Psychosis PGCert 24PT/PGDip 24PT/MSc 36PT
Women, Mental Health and Childbearing: Developing the Service .... CPPD 4PT 4DL

University of the West of Scotland
Mental Health Care...PGCert 12PT

University of the West of England, Bristol
Mental Health .... MSc 36PT

University of Wolverhampton
Mental Health....... MSc 24PT/MA 24PT/PGCert 12PT/PGDip 12PT

Mental health care
Research Courses

University of Aberdeen
Mental Health ....PhD 36FT/MSc by research 12FT/MPhil 24FT

Bangor University
Ageing and Cognitive Health .... PhD 36FT 60PT
Ageing and Dementia Studies ....MSc by research 12FT 24PT PhD 36FT 60PT/MPhil 24FT 48PT

University of East Anglia
Occupational Therapy...PhD 36FT 72PT/MPhil 24FT 48PT/MSc by research 12FT 24PT

University of Exeter
Clinical Practice..DClinPrac 42DL
Doctorate in Clinical Psychology ....DClinPsy 36FT

University of Hertfordshire
Arts Psychotherapies and Counselling in Health.PhD 36FT 72PT/MRes 12FT 24PT/MPhil 24FT 48PT
Centre for Community Research ....PhD 36FT 72PT/MPhil 24FT 48PT/MRes 12FT 24PT

University of Kent
Mental Health (Social and Community Care)....MPhil 24FT 36PT/PhD 36FT 60PT

University of Nottingham
Mental Health......... PhD 36FT/DHSci 36FT/New Route PhD 48FT

Plymouth University
Mental Health .... MPhil tbcFT

University of Southampton
School of Social Sciences - Gerontology......PhD 36FT 72PT/MPhil 24FT 48PT

St George's, University of London
Mental health......... PhD 36FT 72PT/MPhil 24FT 48PT/MD(Res) 24 minFT 48 minPT

UCL - University College London
Mental Health Sciences..........PhD 36FT 60PT/MD(Res) 24FT 24PT

Midwifery
Taught Courses

Anglia Ruskin University
Advanced Midwifery Practice.................................... MSc 12FT 36PT

Bangor University
Health Science.................................MSc 12FT 24 - 60PT/PGDip 9FT
Health Studies/Health Science, Nursing, Midwifery, Radiography and Allied Health Profession ....PhD by taught 36FT 48-60PT/MPhil 24FT 36PT

Birmingham City University
Midwifery; Shortened Programme......................... BSc(Hons) 18FT

University of Bradford
Midwifery .... MSc 36PT/PGDip 24PT/PGCert 12PT

University of Brighton
Clinical Studies and Education..MSc 12FT 24 - 72PT/PGCert 12FT 24 - 72PT/PGDip 12FT 24 - 72PT

Cardiff University
Advanced Practice .... MSc 12FT 24PT

University of Central Lancashire
Midwifery & Women's Health.......MSc 60PT/PGDip 24PT/PGCert 12PT

City University London
Child Nursing (Graduate Entry) ....PGDip 24FT
Midwifery .... MSc 12FT 24-60PT/PGDip 12FT

De Montfort University
Midwifery Practice B72075.. MSc 36PT/PGDip 24PT/PGCert 12PT

University of Dundee
Advanced Practice ....MSc 18DL
Advanced Practice (Midwifery) ....MSc 36DL
Advanced Practice (Organisational Leadership) ....MSc 36DL
Advanced Practice (Practice Education) ....MSc 36DL

University of East Anglia
Advanced Practitioner (Profession)..........................MSc 12FT 36PT
Midwifery ....PGDip 18FT

Edge Hill University
International Midwifery Studies .... MSc 24FT 36-72PT/MSc 36-72FT

Edinburgh Napier University
Advanced Practice in MidwiferyMSc 12FT 36PT/PGDip 9FT 24PT/PGCert 6FT 12PT

National University of Ireland Galway
Midwifery.................................MHSc 24PT/MHSc 36PT/HDip 18FT

Glasgow Caledonian University
European Midwifery.......................................MSc 12-24FT 24-60PT
Midwifery...MSc 12FT 24-60PT On-lineDL

University of Hertfordshire
Supervision of Midwives .... PGCert 1BM

University of Huddersfield
Health Studies (Advancing Midwifery Practice).... MSc 12FT 36PT

King's College London
Advanced Practice .... MSc 36-72PT/PGDip 24-72PT/PGCert 12-72PT
Advanced Practice (Cardiac Care).. MSc 36-72PT/PGDip 24-72PT/PGCert 12-72PT
Advanced Practice (Midwifery)...... MSc 36-72PT/PGDip 24-72PT/PGCert 12-72PT
Midwifery with registration (graduate entry)..............PGDip 18FT
Specialist Ultrasound Practice .... PGCert 9PT

Kingston University
Maternal and Child Health: Socio-Cultural Perspectives............... MSc 12FT 24PT

Leeds Metropolitan University
Advanced Practice .... MSc 36PT/PGDip 24PT/PGCert 12PT

University of Manchester
Maternal and Fetal Health..MRes 12FT

Middlesex University
Midwifery MSc ....MSc 12FT 24PT
Midwifery Studies, MSc ....MSc 24PT

Northumbria University
Midwifery ....Professional Doctorate 48-72PT
Midwifery Studies ....PGDip 18FT

University of Nottingham
Midwifery.....................MSc 12FT 24-48PT/PGDip 9-12FT 18-48PT

Oxford Brookes University
Midwifery (Pre-registration) .... MSc 24FT
Midwifery (Pre-registration-Post Experience Route) ..... MSc 21FT

Queen's University Belfast
Nursing Practice.................................... DMP (Doctorate) 36FT 60PT

University of Salford
Midwifery........MSc 12FT 36PT/PGCert 4FT 12PT/PGDip 8FT 18PT

University of Sheffield
Advancing Practice.........MMedSci 12FT 24PT/Diploma 9FT 18PT/Cert 6FT 12PT
Maternity Care.......MMedSci 36 PTDL/PGDip 27 PTDL/PGCert 18 PTDL
Midwifery............MMid 36 PTDL/Diploma 27 PTDL/Cert 18 PTDL
Neonatal Intensive Care ....PGCert FlexiblePT

University of Southampton
Nursing (Pre-registration) .... MSc 36FT

St George's, University of London
Maternal and Child Health ....MSc 12FT 24PT

University of Stirling
Advanced Practice .... MSc 18PT/MSc 18PT

Teesside University
Midwifery Studies (Pre-registration)..........MSc 24FT/PGDip 18FT

Trinity College Dublin - the University of Dublin
Midwifery ....MSc 12FT 24PT
Professional Midwifery Studies .... PGDip 12PT

University of Ulster
Specialised Midwifery Practice ....PGDip 12FT 24PT/MSc 15FT 36PT

University of West London
Midwifery and Women's Health..........PhD 33FT 45PT/MPhil 45PT
Midwives and High Dependency Practice........................ CPPD 8PT

Nursing and midwifery

University of the West of Scotland
Advanced Studies in Midwifery........MSc 12FT 36PT/Diploma 9FT 30PT
Midwifery....................MSc variableFT variablePT variableDL/Cert variableFT variablePT variableDL/Diploma variableFT variablePT variableDL

Midwifery
Research Courses

Bangor University
Health Studies/Health Science, Nursing, Midwifery, Radiography & Allied Health Professions.....................................MPhil 24FT 36PT/PhD 36FT 48-60PT

University of Central Lancashire
Midwifery.........MSc by research 12FT 24PT/MPhil 24FT 36-48PT/PhD 36FT 60PT/MD 36FT 60PT

City University London
Midwifery..PhD 36FT 60-74PT/MPhil

University of Dundee
Nursing & Midwifery .... PhD 36FT 48FT MPhil 24FT

University of Liverpool
Perinatal and Reproductive Health.......PhD 36FT/MPhil 12FT/MD 60FT

University of Manchester
Midwifery...................................... PhD 36FT 72PT/MPhil 12FT 24PT

University of Nottingham
Maternal and Fetal Health.......PhD 36FT 72PT/MPhil 24FT 48PT/DM 36FT 72PT

Queen's University Belfast
Nursing and Midwifery............... PhD 36FT 72PT/MPhil 24FT 48PT

University of Salford
Midwifery............MSc by research 36PT/PGDip by research 24PT/PGCert by research 12PT

University of Stirling
Nursing and Midwifery - Research......PhD 36FT 72PT/MPhil 24FT 48PT

University of West London
Midwifery........................... Professional Doctorate (PD) 33FT 45PT

Neonatal nursing
Taught Courses

Bucks New University
Advanced Practice (Nursing) .... MSc 36PT

University of Central Lancashire
Child Health.. MSc 36PT
Neonatal Studies....................MA 60PT/PGDip 24PT/PGCert 12PT

City University London
Child Nursing (Graduate Entry) ....PGDip 24FT

University of Dundee
Nursing (Masters by distance learning) ....MN 36DL

University of East Anglia
Advanced Practitioner (Profession)...........................MSc 12FT 36PT
Midwifery...PGDip 18FT

Glasgow Caledonian University
Advanced Nursing...MSc 12FT 36-60PT

Leeds Metropolitan University
Advanced Practice .... MSc 36PT/PGDip 24PT/PGCert 12PT

University of Leeds
Child Health...................................MMedSci 36PT/PGDip 24PT

Liverpool John Moores University
Adult Nursing... MSc 24FT 24PT
Advanced Neonatal Practitioner in Neonatal Critical Care .... MSc 36PT
Advanced Paediatric Nurse Practitioner (APNP) in Ambulatory Care.. MSc 12FT 24PT

University of Salford
Advanced Practice (Health and Social Care)........MSc 24PT/PGDip 18PT/PGCert 12PT
Advanced Practice (Neonatal)... MSc 12FT 24PT/PGDip 9FT 18PT/PGCert 4FT 12PT

University of Sheffield
Advancing Practice.........MMedSci 12FT 24PT/Diploma 9FT 18PT/Cert 6FT 12PT
Neonatal Intensive Care .... PGCert FlexiblePT
Nursing Studies leading to professional registration as an Adult Nurse..PGDip 24FT

St George's, University of London
Clinical Practice......................................MRes 12FT 24PT
Maternal and Child Health ....MSc 12FT 24PT

University of Stirling
Advanced Practice.. MSc 18PT/MSc 18PT

University of Warwick
Child Health....... PGA 12FT MSc 12FT 24-96PT/PGDip 12FT 24PT/PGCert 12FT 24PT

University of West London
Nursing ....MPhil 45PT/PhD 45PT

Neonatal nursing
Research Courses

Bucks New University
Nursing ....DNursing 48-84PT

University of Dundee
Nursing & Midwifery ....PhD 36FT PhD 48FT MPhil 24FT

University of East Anglia
Nursing ....PhD 36FT 72PT/MPhil 24FT 48PT/MSc by research 12FT 24PT

University of Liverpool
Perinatal and Reproductive Health.......PhD 36FT/MPhil 12FT/MD 60FT

University of Nottingham
Maternal and Fetal Health........PhD 36FT 72PT/MPhil 24FT 48PT/DM 36FT 72PT

University of Stirling
Nursing and Midwifery - Research......PhD 36FT 72PT/MPhil 24FT 48PT

University of West London
Nursing .... Professional Doctorate (PD) 33FT 45PT

Nurse practitioner training
Taught Courses

Bangor University
Advanced Clinical Practice ....MSc 12FT 24 - 60PT/PGDip 9FT

Bournemouth University
Advanced Nurse Practitioner... PGDip 24PT

University of Bradford
Practitioners with a Special Interest ....MSc 24PT/PGDip 12PT

University of Brighton
Advanced Nurse Practitioner.............................MSc 12FT 24 - 72PT

Bucks New University
Advanced Practice (Advanced Nurse Practitioner)..........MSc 36PT
Advanced Practice (Nursing) .... MSc 36PT

Cardiff University
Advanced Practice .... MSc 12FT 24PT

University of Central Lancashire
Advanced Practice (Health and Social Care)...................... MSc 24PT
Advanced Stroke Practice ......MSc 36FT 60PT/PGDip 24PT/PGCert 12PT
Allied Health Practice.............................. MSc up to 60PT
Allied Health Practice (Occupational Therapy) ...MSc 36PT/PGDip 24PT/PGCert 12PT
Community Specialist Practitioner.................PGDip 12FT 24-48PT
Enhanced Clinical Practice ....PGCert 15PT
General Practice..........MSc 36-60PT/PGDip 24-60PT/PGCert 12PT
Integrated Healthcare by elearning.....MSc 36-48PT/PGDip 24PT/PGCert 12PT
Nursing ....MSc 12FT 24-60PT
Professional Practice: Research and Development...MSc 36-60PT
Sexual Health Studies ....MSc 60PT/PGDip 60PT/PGCert 24PT

University of Chester
Health and Social Care - Advanced Practice .... MSc 24 - 72PT/PGDip 24 - 60PT/PGCert 12 - 36PT
Health and Social Care - Specialist Practice Community Public Health Nursing............MSc 12FT 24 - 72PT/PGDip 12FT 24 - 60PT
Health and Social Care - Specialist Practitioner Community.........MSc 12FT 24 - 72PT/PGDip 12FT 24 - 60PT

City University London
Child Nursing (Graduate Entry) ....PGDip 24FT
Nursing (Advanced Practice) ....MSc 24-60FT 24-60PT/PGDip 12-24FT 12-60PT
Primary Care (Advanced Nurse Practitioner)..........MSc 12FT 24PT

University College Cork
Nursing (Cardiac & Intensive Care).................................PGDip 12FT
Nursing (Emergency Nursing)...PGDip 12FT

Coventry University
Advancing Practice............. MSc 18FT 36-60PT/PGDip 12FT 24PT/PGCert 6FT 12PT
Nursing Studies... MSc 15 MinFT 60 MaxPT

University of Cumbria
Advanced Practice in Health and Social Care..........MSc 24 - 60PT
Community Specialist Practice Nursing ....PGDE 9FT 18PT

De Montfort University
Advanced Health and Professional Practice B70076...... MSc 12FT 36-72PT/PGDip 24PT/PGCert 12PT
Non Medical Prescribing PG Cert .... PGCert 6PT

University of Derby
Advanced Practice ....MSc 24-72PT

University of Dundee
Advanced Practice (Physiotherapeutic Practice) ....MSc 36DL
Practice Education...PGCert 12DL

University of East Anglia
Advanced Practitioner (Profession)...........................MSc 12FT 36PT

University of East London
Advanced Practice for Health Professions ....MSc 12FT 24+PT/PgCert - in Applied Health Sciences 4FT 8PT/PGDip 8FT 16PT

University of Edinburgh
Advancing Nursing Practice...... MSc 12FT/MSc 24PT/PGCert 9PT/PGDip 21PT

Glasgow Caledonian University
Health and Social Care Education ....MSc 12FT

University of Glasgow
Healthcare Chaplaincy...PGCert 12PT

University of Gloucestershire
Non-Medical Prescribing..................................... PGCert 8PT

Glyndwr University
Advanced Clinical Nursing Practice ....MSc 12FT 24-36PT

University of Kent
Advanced and Specialist Healthcare (Surgical Practice).......... MSc 24-36PT

King's College London
Advanced Practice .... MSc 36-72PT/PGDip 24-72PT/PGCert 12-72PT
Advanced Practice (Cardiac Care).. MSc 36-72PT/PGDip 24-72PT/PGCert 12-72PT
Advanced Practice (Nurse Practitioner/Community Matron/Case Manager)..............MSc 36-72PT/PGDip 24-72PT/PGCert 12-72PT
Clinical Nursing for International Students....... MSc 12FT/PGCert 12FT

Lancaster University
Developing Professional Practice (Health Care) ....MA 24PT
Developing Professional Practice in Management........MA 24PT/PGCert 12PT

Leeds Metropolitan University
Advanced Practice .... MSc 36PT/PGDip 24PT/PGCert 12PT
Community Specialist Practitioner - District Nursing...MSc 24PT/PGDip 12FT 24PT

University of Liverpool
Advanced Science.........MSc 12FT 24PT/PGDip 12FT/PGCert 12FT

London South Bank University
Children's Advanced Nurse Practitioner (Strategic Leadership and Expert Practice).....................................MSc 36PT
Nurse Practitioner (Strategic Leadership & Expert Practice).. MSc 36PT

Manchester Metropolitan University
Emergency Medicine ....MSc 72PT
LLM (Master of Laws)................................... LLM 12FT 24PT
Practice Development ....MSc 24-72PT

Northumbria University
Nursing (MNurs) Registered Nurse (Adult)................. MA 24-48FT
Nursing (MNurs) Registered Nurse (Child)................. MA 24-48FT
Nursing (MNurs) Registered Nurse (Mental Health). MA 24-48FT

University of Nottingham
Advanced Clinical Practice .... MSc 24PT
Advanced Nursing.......MSc 12FT 24-48PT/PGDip 9-12FT 18-48PT

The Open University
Advancing Professional Practice..............................MSc variableDL

Oxford Brookes University
Community Children's Nursing ....PGDip 12FT 24PT
Community Nursing in the Home / District Nursing..PGDip 12FT 24PT

Robert Gordon University
Advanced Clinical Practice ... MSc 36PT/PGDip 24PT/PGCert 12PT

University of Roehampton
Post Graduate Diploma- Stress and Health...........PGDip 9FT 24PT

University of Salford
Geriatric MedicineMSc 48-60PT/PGDip 24-60PT/PGCert 12-60PT
Lower Limb Health, Disease and Rehabilitation.........PGCert 12PT

University of Sheffield
Advanced Emergency Care..................................MSc 12FT 24 - 60PT
Advanced Nursing Studies ... MMedSci 36DL/Diploma 36DL/Cert 36DL
Long-Term Health Conditions .... PGCert FlexiblePT

University of South Wales
Advanced Clinical Practice.....................................MSc 12 -60PT

University of Southampton
Gerontology.....................MSc 12FT 24PT/PGDip 9FT 21PT
Gerontology (Distance Learning) ....MSc 12DL/PGDip 9DL
Research Methods in Health ....MSc 24PT/PGDip 12PT/PGCert 6PT

St George's, University of London
Maternal and Child Health ....MSc 12FT 24PT

Staffordshire University
Advanced Clinical Practice ....PGCert 12PT/PGDip 24PT/MSc 36PT
Community Practice .... MA 12FT 48PT

Nursing and midwifery

University of Stirling
Health Research....MRes 12FT 24/36PT 24/36DL

Swansea University
Advanced Practice in Health Care....MSc 36PT/PGDip 24PT
Education for the Health Professions.... MA 36PT/PGDip 24PT/PGCert 12PT

Teesside University
Advancing Practice....MA 36PT
Nursing (Advanced Nurse Practitioner).... MSc 36PT
The Management of Long-term Health Conditions..PGCert 12PT

Trinity College Dublin - the University of Dublin
Professional Nursing Studies .... PGDip 12PT

University of West London
Advanced Professional Practice....PGCert 24DL/PGDip 24DL
Advancing Practice....MSc 24PT
Advancing Practice (Community Matron)....PGCert 12PT
Nursing and Healthcare....MSc 12FT
The Management of Complex and Changing Health and Social Care Needs in Clients.... CPPD 4PT

University of the West of Scotland
Advanced Clinical Practice ....PGCert 12PT

University of York
Development Economics and Emerging Markets.... MSc 12FT

Nurse practitioner training
Research Courses

Bucks New University
Nursing ....DNursing 48-84PT

University of East Anglia
Nursing ....PhD 36FT 72PT/MPhil 24FT 48PT/MSc by research 12FT 24PT

University of Edinburgh
Nursing Studies....PhD 36FT 72PT/MPhil 24FT 48PT/MSc by research 12FT 24-36PT
Nursing Studies .... MSc by research 12FT 24-36PT

London South Bank University
Professional Doctorate ....DNursing 60PT

University of Southampton
Doctorate in Clinical Practice .... PhD 36FT 72PT

Nursing and midwifery
Taught Courses

University of Aberdeen
Nursing/Midwifery/Health Care/Transitions in Care/Palliative CareMSc 12FT 24-36PT/PGDip 9FT 21-33PT/PGCert 5FT 12 - 17PT

Anglia Ruskin University
Advancd Pre-Hospital Trauma Care .... MSc 24FT
International Nursing Studies (with option of Overseas Nursing Programme).... MSc 12FT

Anglo-European College of Chiropractic
Chiropractic....MSc 30DL/PGDip 24DL/PGCert 12DL
Medical Ultrasound .... MSc 36PT

Bangor University
Advanced Clinical Practice ....MSc 12FT 24 - 60PT/PGDip 9FT
Health Science....MSc 12FT 24 - 60PT/PGDip 9FT
Health Studies/Health Science, Nursing, Midwifery, Radiography and Allied Health Profession ....PhD by taught 36FT 48-60PT/MPhil 24FT 36PT

University of Bedfordshire
Advanced Nursing Studies (and Advanced Nursing Studies with Overseas Nursing Placements)....MSc 12FT/PGDip 12FT/PGCert 12FT
Health Studies.... MSc 24PT/PGCert 24PT/PGDip 24PT
Nursing: Registered Nurse (Adult, Mental Health).... MSc 24FT

Birmingham City University
Advanced Healthcare (Nursing, Midwifery or Primary Care).... PGDip 12PT/MSc 24PT
Advanced Practice (Nursing or Midwifery).. PGDip 9FT 18PT/MSc 12FT 24PT

University of Birmingham
Advancing Practice....MSc 13FT 72PT/PGDip 10FT 48PT/PGCert 3FT
Health Research - Academic Clinical Fellows (ACF) Framework.... MRes 24PT

University of Bolton
Specialist Community Public Health Nursing (Health Visiting).... PGDip 12FT 24PT

Bournemouth University
Return to Practice (Nursing) ....Professional Development FlexiblePT

University of Bradford
Nursing .... MSc 36PT/PGDip 24PT/PGCert 12PT

University of Brighton
Advanced Nurse Practitioner....MSc 12FT 24 - 72PT
Clinical Studies....MSc 12FT 24 - 72PT/PGCert 12FT 24 - 72PT/PGDip 12FT 24 - 72PT
Clinical Studies and Education..MSc 12FT 24 - 72PT/PGCert 12FT 24 - 72PT/PGDip 12FT 24 - 72PT
Clinical Studies and Management.... MSc 12FT 24 - 72PT/PGCert 12FT 24 - 72PT/PGDip 12FT 24 - 72PT
Health Promotion....MA 12FT 24-72PT/PGDip 12FT 24-72PT/PGCert 12FT 24-72PT
International Health Promotion....MA 12FT 36PT/PGDip 12FT 36PT

Bucks New University
Leadership in Multi-Agency Settings .... PGCert 9PT
Advanced Practice (Gastrointestinal Care) ....MSc 36-72PT
Nursing (Adult) ....PGDip 24FT
Nursing (Mental Health) ....PGDip 24FT
Psychotherapeutic Approaches in Mental Health .... MSc 24PT
Social Innovation .... PGDip 14PT

University of Central Lancashire
Clinical Leadership for Practice Innovation....Module 4PT
Neonatal Studies ....MA 60PT/PGDip 24PT/PGCert 12PT

University of Chester
Action Research and Appreciative Inquiry (Work Based and Integrative Studies)...MSc 24-72PT/MA 24-72PT/PGDip 24-60PT/PGCert 12-36PT
Health and Social Care - Clinical Bariatric Practice.... MSc 12FT 24 - 72PT/PGDip 12FT 24 - 60PT/PGCert 12FT 12 - 36PT
Health and Social Care - Professional Nursing.... MSc 12FT 24 - 72PT/PGDip 12FT 24 - 60PT/PGCert 12FT 12 - 36PT
Health and Social Care - Professional Studies.... MSc 24 - 72PT/PGDip 24 - 60PT/PGCert 12 - 36PT
Health and Social Care - Specialist Practice Community Public Health Nursing....MSc 12FT 24 - 72PT/PGDip 12FT 24 - 60PT
Health and Social Care - Specialist Practitioner Community.... MSc 12FT 24 - 72PT/PGDip 12FT 24 - 60PT
Nursing Studies (Work Based and Integrative Studies)....MA 24-72PT/MSc 24-72PT/PGDip 24-60PT/PGCert 12-36PT

City University London
Nursing .... MSc 24FT 24-60PT/PGDip 12-24FT 12-60PT
Nursing (Advanced Practice) .... MSc 24-60FT 24-60PT/PGDip 12-24FT 12-60PT

University College Cork
Nursing (Emergency Nursing)....PGDip 12FT
Nursing Studies (Clinical Practice) .... MSc 24FT

Coventry University
Nursing Studies....MSc 15 MinFT 60 MaxPT

University of Cumbria
Specialist Community Public Health Nursing Practice.... MSc 12 - 48PT

De Montfort University
Nursing Practice (with NMC Specialist qualification).... MSc 36-72PT/PGDip 24-48PT/PGCert 12-24PT/PG University Certificate in CPD 12-24PT

University of Derby
Advanced Practice ....MSc 24-72PT
Interprofessional Practice Education....PGCert 12-18PT

University of Dundee
Advanced Practice (Cancer Care) ....MSc 36DL
Advanced Practice (Clinical Assessment) ....MSc 36DL
Advanced Practice (Health & Social Care)....MSc 36DL
Advanced Practice (Individual Modules) .... PG module 6DL
Advanced Practice ....MSc 18DL
Advanced Practice (Medical Imaging) ....MSc 36DL
Advanced Practice (Mental Health) ....MSc 36DL
Advanced Practice (Midwifery) ....MSc 36DL
Advanced Practice (Nursing) ....MSc 36DL
Advanced Practice (Palliative Care) ....MSc 36DL
Advanced Practice (Practice Education) ....PGCert 12DL PGDip 24DL
Health and Social Care (MRes) ....MRes 24DL
Nursing (Masters by distance learning) ....MN 36DL
Palliative Care ....MSc 36DL
Palliative Care Research ....MPH 12-24FT
Primary Care ....MSc 36-60PT

University of East Anglia
Leadership in Dementia Care ....MSc 36PT
Leadership in Dementia Care .... PGDip 24PT
Leading Innovation for Clinical Practitioners .... PGDip 24PT
Leading Innovation for Clinical Practitioners ....MA 36PT
Mental Health.... MSc 12FT 36PT/PGDip 12FT 24PT/PGCert 12PT
Midwifery ....PGDip 18FT

Edge Hill University
Advanced Practice ....MSc 36-72PT
International Nursing Studies....MSc 24FT 36-72PT

Edinburgh Napier University
Advanced Practice .... MSc 36PT/PGDip 24PT/PGCert 12PT
Advanced Practice and Applied Education (Distance Learning).... Msc/PGDip/PGCert 36PT
Advanced Practice in Nursing....MSc 12FT 24-60PT/PGDip 9FT 24-60PT
Health Administration....MSc 12FT 24-36PT/PGDip 9FT 18-27PT/PGCert 6FT 12-18PT

University of Edinburgh
Advancing Nursing Practice.... MSc 12FT/MSc 24PT/PGCert 9PT/PGDip 21PT
Nursing in Clinical Research .... MN 12FT

University of Essex
Adult Nursing.... MSc 24FT
Mental Health Nursing .... MSc 24FT
Nursing (Professional Doctorate)....Prof Doc 48-84PT

National University of Ireland Galway
Midwifery....MHSc 24PT/MHSc 36PT/HDip 18FT
Nursing .... MHSc 24PT/MHSc 36PT
Nursing (Advanced Practice) ....PGDip 12FT
Nursing (Education)....PGDip 12FT
Nursing (Emergency Care) .... PGDip 12FT 24PT
Nursing (Gerontology) .... PGDip 12FT 24PT
Nursing (Intensive Care) .... PGDip 12FT 24PT
Nursing (Management of Chronic Health Conditions) ....PGDip 12FT
Nursing (Oncology).... PGDip 12FT 24PT
Nursing (Orthopaedics) .... PGDip 12FT 24PT
Nursing (Palliative Care) .... PGDip 12FT 24PT
Nursing (Perioperative).... PGDip 12FT 24PT
Nursing (Practice Nursing/ Community Nursing) ....PGDip 12FT 24PT
Nursing (Public Health Nursing)....PGDip 12FT
Nursing (Specialist Practice)....PGCert 12FT
Nursing/ Midwifery Education .... MHSc 24PT/MHSc 36PT
Nursing/Midwifery: Advanced Practice Nursing/ Midwifery.... MHSc 24PT/MHSc 36PT
Nursing: Specialist Nursing.... MHSc 12FT

Glasgow Caledonian University
Advanced Nursing....MSc 12FT 36-60PT
Advanced Practice with Older People .... MSc 12FT
Advancing Practice in Primary Care.... MSc 24FT
European Midwifery....MSc 12-24FT 24-60PT
Midwifery....MSc 12FT 24-60PT On-lineDL
Optimal Heart Failure Care.... MSc 12FT
Perinatal Mental Health .... MSc 12FT
Telehealthcare.... MSc 12FT

University of Hertfordshire
Clinical Research.... MSc 12FT
Contemporary Nursing.... MSc 12FT
Specialist Community Nursing.... MSc 12FT 24PT/PGDip 12FT 24PT
Specialist Community Public Health Nursing....MSc 12FT 24PT/PGDip 12FT 24PT

University of Huddersfield
Advanced Safeguarding....MSc 12FT 36PT

Keele University
Rheumatology Nursing....PGDip 24PT/MSc 12PT

King's College London
Advanced Practice (Child Health).. MSc 36-72PT/PGDip 24-72PT/PGCert 12-72PT
Advanced Practice (Leadership).... MSc 36-72PT/PGDip 24-72PT/PGCert 12-72PT
Advanced Practice (Neuroscience Care)....MSc 36-72PT/PGDip 24-72PT/PGCert 12-72PT
Advanced Practice (Nurse Practitioner/Community Matron/Case Manager)....MSc 36-72PT/PGDip 24-72PT/PGCert 12-72PT
Advanced Practice (Specialist Community Public Health Nursing/ Public Health/ School Nurs)....MSc 36-72PT/PGDip 24-72PT/PGCert 12-72PT
Clinical Nursing for International Students.... MSc 12FT/PGCert 12FT
Nursing .... MSc 12PT
Nursing with registration (graduate entry)....PGDip 24FT

Kingston University
Nursing/Registered Nurse ....PGDip 24FT

University of Limerick
Nursing Studies.... MSc 18FT
Nursing/Midwifery.... MSc 12FT

Liverpool John Moores University
Adult Nursing.... MSc 24FT
Child Nursing.... MSc 24FT

London School of Hygiene and Tropical Medicine
Control of Infectious Diseases ....MSc 12FT 24PT
Molecular Biology of Infectious Diseases ....MSc 12FT 24PT
Nutrition for Global Health ....MSc 12FT 24PT
One Health....MSc 12FT 24PT
Public Health for Eye Care ....MSc 12FT 24PT

Middlesex University
Midwifery Studies, MSc .... MSc 24PT
Nursing ....MSc 12FT 24PT
Nursing (Specialist Practice).... MSc 24PT
Nursing Studies....MSc 12FT 24PT

Northumbria University
Midwifery....Professional Doctorate 48-72PT
Midwifery Studies ....PGDip 18FT
Nursing ....Professional Doctorate 48-72PT
Nursing (MNurs) Registered Nurse (Adult).... MA 24-48FT

Nursing and midwifery

Nursing (MNurs) Registered Nurse (Child)................... MA 24-48FT
Nursing (MNurs) Registered Nurse (Mental Health)........................ MA 24-48FT
Physiotherapy...DProf by taught 48-84PT

University of Nottingham
Advanced Nursing.......MSc 12FT 24-48PT/PGDip 9-12FT 18-48PT
Graduate Entry Nursing - Child Branch .... MSc 36FT
Graduate Entry Nursing - Mental Health......................... MSc 36FT
Graduate Entry Nursing- Adult.. MSc 36FT
Research Methods (Health) .... MA 12FT 24PT

Oxford Brookes University
Midwifery (Pre-registration) .... MSc 24FT
Midwifery (Pre-registration-Post Experience Route) ..... MSc 21FT
Nursing Studies (Leadership in Clinical Practice)..MSc 12FT 24PT 12-36DL/PGDip 8FT 36PT 8-36DL/PGCert 4FT 36PT 4-36DL
Nursing, Adult (Pre-registration) ....MSc 24FT 48PT/PGDip 24FT 48PT/PGCert 24FT 48PT
Nursing, Adult (Pre-registration) (Swindon) ....MSc 24FT 48PT/PGDip 24FT 48PT/PGCert 24FT 48PT
Nursing, Children's (Pre-registration) ....MSc 24FT 48PT/PGDip 24FT 48PT/PGCert 24FT 48PT
Nursing, Mental Health (Pre-registration).............MA 24FT 48PT/PGDip 24FT 48PT/PGCert 24FT 48PT

Queen Margaret University, Edinburgh
Nursing.......MSc 12FT 36PT/PGDip 8FT 24-36PT/PGCert 24-84PT

Queen's University Belfast
Midwifery Practice .... DMP (Doctorate) 36FT 60PT
Nursing Practice.................................... DMP (Doctorate) 36FT 60PT
Nursing/Midwifery: Advanced Professional Practice..... MSc 24FT 60PT

Robert Gordon University
Nursing ....MSc 12FT 12/36DL

University Campus Suffolk
Advanced Healthcare Practice .... MSc 12FT

University of Salford
Advanced Practice (Health and Social Care)........MSc 24PT/PGDip 18PT/PGCert 12PT
Advanced Practice (Neonatal)... MSc 12FT 24PT/PGDip 9FT 18PT/PGCert 4FT 12PT
Child and Adolescent Mental Health........MSc 24PT/PGDip 18PT/PGCert 9PT
Midwifery........MSc 12FT 36PT/PGCert 4FT 12PT/PGDip 8FT 18PT
Nursing .... MA 36FT/PGDip 24FT/PGCert 12FT
Nursing (Education, International, Practice, Research) .... MSc 12FT 36PT/PGDip 9FT 24PT/PGCert 6FT 12PT
Professional Doctorate (Health and Social Care) ... PhD by taught 60PT

Sheffield Hallam University
Nursing Studies - Adult or Mental Health Nursing .....PGDip 24FT
Postgraduate Diploma Nursing Studies (Adult / Mental Health)..PGDip 24FT

University of Sheffield
Advanced Emergency Care.................................MSc 12FT 24 - 60PT
Advanced Nursing Studies... MMedSci 36DL/Diploma 36DL/Cert 36DL
Advancing Practice. MMedSci 12FT 24PT/Diploma 9FT 18PT/Cert 6FT 12PT
Midwifery.............MMid 36 PTDL/Diploma 27 PTDL/Cert 18 PTDL
Neonatal Intensive Care .... PGCert FlexiblePT
Nursing Studies leading to professional registration as an Adult Nurse ....PGDip 24FT

University of South Wales
Clinical Practice for Nurses and Midwives .... MSc 24PT

University of Southampton
Advanced Clinical Practice ....MSc 12FT 24PT/PGDip 12FT/PGCert 12FT
Doctorate in Clinical Practice . DClinP 48FT 84PT/MSc 12FT 24PT/PGDip 12FT 24PT/PGCert 8FT 16PT
Nursing (Pre-registration) .... MSc 36FT
Public Health Practice...MSc 12FT 24PT/PGDip 12FT/PGCert 12FT
Nursing, Midwifery & Health Visiting .... MSc 12FT

St George's, University of London
Clinical Practice..MRes 12FT 24PT
Maternal and Child Health .... MSc 12FT 24PT

Staffordshire University
Midwifery (Shortened)......................Registered Nurse (NMC) 20PT
Osteopathy ....M.Ost 60-66PT

University of Stirling
Advanced Practice .... MSc 18PT/MSc 18PT
Clinical Doctorates ....PGDip 18PT/MSc 24PT/PhD by taught 48-72PT
Health Research...................................MRes 12FT 24/36PT 24/36DL

University of Sunderland
Nursing .... MSc 12FT

Swansea University
Advanced Practice in Health Care ....MSc 36PT/PGDip 24PT
Advanced Practice in Health Care - Infection Control...MSc 36PT/PGDip 24PT
Community and Primary Healthcare Practice ....MSc 36PT/PGDip 24PT/PGCert 12PT
Enhanced Professional Practice (EPP)........MSc 36PT/PGDip 24PT/PGCert 12PT
Infection Prevention and Control ....PGCert 12PT
Nursing .... MA 12FT

Teesside University
Midwifery Studies (Pre-registration)...........MSc 24FT/PGDip 18FT
Nursing .... MSc 12FT
Nursing (Advanced Cardiac Care)....................................... MSc 36PT
Nursing (Advanced Surgical Care Practitioner)............... MSc 36PT
Nursing (Specialist Field)... MSc 36PT

Trinity College Dublin - the University of Dublin
Gerontological Nursing.. MSc 24PT
Midwifery .... MSc 12FT 24PT
Nursing (Child Health and Well-being Strand) (H. Dip.) MSc 12FT 24PT
Nursing .... MSc 12FT 24PT
Nursing (Specialist) .... PGDip 24PT
Oncological Nursing..PGDip 12FT
Professional Nursing Studies .... PGDip 12PT

University of the Highlands and Islands
Infection Control.................... MSc 36PT/PGDip 24PT/PGCert 12PT

University of Ulster
Education for Nurses and Midwives.............................PGCert 12PT
Nursing ....PGDip 9FT 24PT/MSc 12FT 36PT
Specialist Nursing Practice...........PGDip 9FT 18PT/MSc 12FT 24PT

University of West London
Advancing Practice (Community Matron)...................PGCert 12PT
Nursing ....MPhil 45PT/PhD 45PT

University of the West of Scotland
Nursing ....MSc 36-48PT/PGDip 24-36PT/PGCert 12-24PT

University of Wolverhampton
Specialist Community Nursing (District Nursing) ....PGDip 12FT
Specialist Community Nursing (General Practice Nursing).PGDip 12FT
Specialist Community Public Health Nursing (Health Visiting).... PGDip 12FT 24PT
Specialist Community Public Health Nursing (School Nursing).... PGDip 12FT

Nursing and midwifery
Research Courses

University of Aberdeen
Nursing ....PhD 36FT 60PT/MPhil 24FT 36PT/MSc by research 12FT 24PT

Bangor University
Health Studies/Health Science, Nursing, Midwifery, Radiography & Allied Health Professions...................................MPhil 24FT 36PT/PhD 36FT 48-60PT

University of Birmingham
Nursing ....PhD 36FT 72PT/MSc by research 12FT 24PT

University of Brighton
Nursing and Midwifery Research Division PhD 24-60FT 36-72PT/MPhil 18-36FT 30-48PT

Bucks New University
Nursing ....DNursing 48-84PT

Cardiff University
Advanced Healthcare Practice (Professional Doctorate)..... DNurs 48-72PT
Nursing, Medicine, Health and Social Care (PhD)........ MPhil 12FT 36PT/PhD 36FT 60PT

University of Central Lancashire
Nursing ..... MSc by research 12FT 24PT/MPhil 24FT 36-48PT/PhD 36FT 60PT/MD 36FT 60PT

City University London
Nursing ....PhD 36FT 60-84PT/MPhil

Coventry University
Nursing ....PhD/MPhil

De Montfort University
Nursing and Midwifery: Mary Seacole Research Centre ....PhD 36-48FT 48 - 72PT/MPhil 12FT 24PT

University of Dundee
Nursing & Midwifery .... PhD 36FT 48FT MPhil 24FT

University of East Anglia
Nursing ....PhD 36FT 72PT/MPhil 24FT 48PT/MSc by research 12FT 24PT

University of Edinburgh
Nursing Studies..............PhD 36FT 72PT/MPhil 24FT 48PT/MSc by research 12FT 24-36PT
Nursing Studies .... MSc by research 12FT 24-36PT

University of Essex
Nursing Studies....... PhD 72PT/MPhil 48PT/MSc by research 24PT

National University of Ireland Galway
College of Medicine, Nursing and Health Sciences .... PhD 48FT 72PT/MSc by research 24FT 48PT/MD 24FT 48PT/MAO by research 24FT 48PT

School of Nursing and Midwifery ....PhD 48FT 72PT/MPhil 24FT 48PT

University of Glasgow
Nursing & Midwifery....PhD 36FT 60PT/MSc(MedSci) by research 12FT 24PT

Keele University
Nursing .... PhD 24-48FT 48-84PT/MPhil 12-24FT 24-36PT

King's College London
Nursing Research / Midwifery Research / Health Studies Research... MPhil 36FT 72PT/PhD 36FT 72PT

University of Liverpool
Nursing ....PhD 36FT/MPhil 12FT/MD 12FT

London South Bank University
Professional Doctorate (D. Nursing) .... DNursing 60PT

University of Manchester
Nursing .... PhD 36FT 72PT 36-72DL/MPhil 12FT 24PT 12-24DL

Middlesex University
Health, including Nursing and Midwifery PhD 33-60FT 45-72DL/MPhil 18-36DL/MA by research 12-24FT 18-30DL
Nursing and Midwifery...... PhD 33-60FT 45-72PT 45-72DL/MPhil 18-36FT 30-48PT 30-48DL

Northumbria University
Clinical Research.............................. MSc by research 12FT 24-36PT

University of Nottingham
MPhil/PhD degree programme......................PhD 24-36FT 36-60PT

University of Portsmouth
Professional Doctorate in Nursing........................... DNursing 48PT

Sheffield Hallam University
Division of Nursing and Social Work ....PhD/MPhil

University of Sheffield
Nursing and Midwifery............... PhD 36FT 72PT/MPhil 24FT 48PT

University of Southampton
Doctorate in Clinical Practice .... PhD 36FT 72PT
Nursing and Midwifery.............. MPhil 24FT 48PT/PhD 36FT 72PT

University of Stirling
Nursing and Midwifery - Research......PhD 36FT 72PT/MPhil 24FT 48PT

Teesside University
Community-Based Clinical Subjects...PhD 36FT 72PT/MPhil 24FT 48PT/DProf 36FT 60PT
Nursing ....PhD 36FT 72PT/MPhil 24FT 48PT/DProf 36FT 60PT
School of Health and Social Care.........PhD 36FT 72PT/MPhil 24FT 48PT/DProf 36FT 60PT/MProf by research 30PT

University of Ulster
Nursing .... PhD 36FT 72PT/MPhil 24FT 48PT

University of West London
Midwifery .... Professional Doctorate (PD) 33FT 45PT

University of the West of Scotland
Department of Nursing, Midwifery and Health Care ..PhD/MPhil

Pain management
Taught Courses

Birmingham City University
Pain Management...................PGCert 12PT/PGDip 18PT/MSc 24PT

Cardiff University
Pain Management.................MSc 24DL/PGDip 18DL/PGCert 18DL

University of Edinburgh
Clinical Management of Headache Disorders ...MSc 36DL/PGDip 24DL/PGCert 12DL
Clinical Management of Pain........MSc 36-72DL/PGDip 24-48DL/PGCert 12-24DL

Keele University
Pain Science and Management MSc 24-60PT/PGCert 12FT 24PT/PGDip 12FT 24-60PT

King's College London
Conscious Sedation for Dentistry.......................................PGDip 9FT
Pain: Science & Society .... MSc 12FT 24PT

Leeds Metropolitan University
Community Specialist Practitioner - Practice Nursing..MSc 24PT/PGDip 24PT
Integrated Masters Biomedical Sciences ....MBIOMS 48FT

University of Leicester
Pain Management....................... MSc 12FT 24PT/PGDip 12FT 24PT

Newcastle University
Conscious Sedation in Dentistry...................................... PGDip 12PT

Queen Mary, University of London
Burn Care (Distance Learning) .... PGAdvDip 24FT

Staffordshire University
Clinical Biomechanics and Pain Management in the Lower limb...PGCert 12PT

Swansea University
Chronic Conditions Management........MSc 12FT 36PT/PGDip 9FT 24PT/PGCert 6FT 12PT

Nursing and midwifery

Trinity College Dublin - the University of Dublin
Conscious Sedation in Dentistry...... PGDip 18PT

UCL - University College London
Dental Sedation and Pain Management...... PGCert 12PT

University of Warwick
Evidence Based Musculoskeletal Care: Managing Lower Limb Pain...... PGA 12PT
Evidence Based Musculoskeletal Care: Managing Neck and Back Pain...... PGA 12PT
Evidence Based Musculoskeletal Care: Managing Upper Limb Pain...... PGA 12PT

Pain management
Research Courses

University of Aberdeen
Translational Medicine...PhD 36FT/MPhil 24FT/MD 24FT/ChM by research 24FT

University of Birmingham
Biomaterials...... MRes 12FT 24PT

University of Edinburgh
Anaesthesia and Pain MedicineMPhil 24FT 48PT/PhD 36FT 72PT/MSc by research 12FT 24PT
Anaesthesia, Critical Care and Pain Medicine...... PhD 36FT

Palliative care
Taught Courses

University of Bedfordshire
Palliative Care...... MSc 24-36PT

University of Bradford
Practitioners with a Special Interest ...... MSc 24PT/PGDip 12PT

University of Bristol
Palliative Medicine...... MSc 24-36PT/Diploma 24-36PT

Bucks New University
Advanced Practice (Cancer and Palliative Care)...... MSc 36PT
Advanced Practice (Critical Care)...... MSc 36PT

Canterbury Christ Church University
Palliative Care...... MSc 36-72PT

Cardiff University
Palliative Medicine/Palliative Care ...... MSc 36-48DL/PGDip 24DL

University of Chester
Health and Social Care - Advanced Practice ...... MSc 24 - 72PT/PGDip 24 - 60PT/PGCert 12 - 36PT
Health and Social Care - Oncology for Health and Social Care Practitioners...... PGCert 12 - 36PT

De Montfort University
Palliative Care ...... MSc 39-72PT

University of Derby
Management of Long Term Conditions...... PGCert 12PT

University of Dundee
Advanced Practice ...... MSc 18DL
Advanced Practice (Palliative Care) ...... MSc 36DL
Non-Graduating Taught Postgraduate in School of Nursing.... PG module variableFT
Palliative Care ...... MSc 36DL
Palliative Care Research ...... MPH 12-24FT
Quality Improvement ...... MSc 36DL PGCert 12DL PGDip 24DL

Edinburgh Napier University
Advanced Practice in Palliative Care...... MSc 36PT/PGDip 24PT/PGCert 12PT
Advanced Practice in Palliative Care and Applied Education ...... MSc 12FT 36PT/PGDip 9FT 24PT/PGCert 6FT 12PT

National University of Ireland Galway
Nursing (Palliative Care) ...... PGDip 12FT 24PT

University of Glasgow
Evidence Based Medicine & Education...... MSc (ClinSci) 12FT

Keele University
Ethics of Cancer and Palliative Care... MA 12FT 24PT 24DL/PGDip 12PT 12DL
End of Life Care ...... PGCert 12FT

University of Kent
Advanced and Specialist Healthcare (Minimally Invasive Surgery)...... MSc 24-36PT
Advanced and Specialist Healthcare (Supportive and Palliative Care)...... MSc 24-36PT

King's College London
Advanced Practice (Palliative Care Nursing)..MSc 36-72PT/PGDip 24-72PT/PGCert 12-72PT
Palliative Care...... MSc 12FT 24PT/PGDip 12FT 24PT/PGCert 12FT
Translational Cancer Medicine...... MRes 12FT 24PT

LOROS
MCS Palliative Care ...... MSc 36PT

Newcastle University
Oncology/ Palliative Care/ Oncology for the Pharmaceutical Industry...... MSc 36DL/PGDip 24DL/PGCert 12DL

University of Northampton
Applied Cancer Studies ...... MSc 36PT/PGDip 24PT

University of Nottingham
Cancer Immunology and Biotechnology...... MSc 12FT

Oxford Brookes University
Palliative Care: Global Perspectives ...... MSc 12-36DL

Reseau Universitaire Transmanche
Palliative and Chronic Illness Care ...... MSc 24PT

Sheffield Hallam University
Supportive and Palliative Care...... MSc 36PT 36DL/PGDip 24PT 24DL/PGCert 12PT 12DL

University of Sheffield
Biomaterials and Regenerative Medicine ...... MSc 12FT

University of South Wales
Palliative Care (Online Delivery) ...... PGCert 24-60DL

University of Southampton
MSc Clinical Leadership in Cancer, Palliative and End of Life Care...... MSc 24FT 48PT

Swansea University
Chronic Conditions Management...... MSc 12FT 36PT/PGDip 9FT 24PT/PGCert 6FT 12PT

Trinity College Dublin - the University of Dublin
Cancer Care ...... MSc 24PT
Palliative Care...... MSc 24PT

University of Ulster
Palliative Care...... PGDip 24PT/MSc 36PT

University of Warwick
Health Sciences: Palliative Care.....MSc 36PT/PGDip 24PT/PGCert 12PT/PGA 12PT
Palliative Care: Care of the Dying...... PGA 12PT/CPDMod 1PT
Palliative Care: Important Principles and Developments ......PGA 12PT/CPDMod 1PT
Palliative Care: Non-cancer diagnosis...... PGA 12PT/CPDMod 1PT

University of the West of Scotland
Cancer and Palliative Care...... PGCert 12PT

Palliative care
Research Courses

King's College London
Cicely Saunders Institute of Palliative Care & Rehabilitation Research...... PhD 36-48FT 48-72PT/MPhil 36-48FT 48-72PT/MDes by research 24FT

University of Liverpool
Cancer Biology...... MPhil 12FT 48PT/PhD 36FT 72PT/MD 60FT
Cancer Medicine ...... MPhil 12FT 24-72PT/PhD 36FT 48-84PT/MD 12-72FT

University of Nottingham
Supportive and Palliative Care. MRes 12FT 24PT/PhD 36FT 72PT/DHSci 24FT 48PT

The Open University
Ageing and Later Life...... PhD 36FT 72PT variableDL/MPhil 15FT 24PT variableDL
Death, Dying and Bereavement...... PhD 36FT 72PT variableDL/MPhil 15FT 24PT variableDL

Paramedic studies
Taught Courses

University of Dundee
Medical Education ...... MMedEd 12FT

University of East Anglia
Advanced Practitioner (Profession)...... MSc 12FT 36PT

Queen Mary, University of London
Critical Care...... MSc 12FT 24PT
Trauma Sciences ...... MSc 12FT 24PT
Trauma Sciences (Military and Austere)...... MSc 12FT 24PT

University of Sheffield
Advanced Emergency Care...... MSc 12FT 24 - 60PT

University of Warwick
Models of Emergency Care ...... PGA 12PT/CPDMod 1PT

Paramedic studies
Research Courses

University of Cambridge
Medical Sciences...... MPhil 12FT

Perioperative practice
Taught Courses

Bangor University
Advanced Clinical Practice ...... MSc 12FT 24 - 60PT/PGDip 9FT

University of Bradford
Practitioners with a Special Interest ...... MSc 24PT/PGDip 12PT

Cardiff University
Advanced Practice ...... MSc 12FT 24PT
Managing Care in Perioperative Practice ...MSc 12FT 24PT/PGDip 9FT 18PT

University of Chester
Dental Practice Management (Work Based and Integrative Studies) ...... MA 24-72PT/PGDip 24-60PT/PGCert 12-36PT
Developing RPL Policy and Practice (Work Based and Integrative Studies) ...... MA 24-72PT/PGDip 24-60PT/PGCert 12-36PT
Learning and Development (Work Based and Integrative Studies) ...... MA 24-72PT/MSc 24-72PT/PGDip 24-60PT/PGCert 12-36PT

University of Dundee
Advanced Practice (Practice Education) ...... MSc 36DL

National University of Ireland Galway
Nursing (Perioperative)...... PGDip 12FT 24PT

Leeds Metropolitan University
Advanced Practice ...... MSc 36PT/PGDip 24PT/PGCert 12PT
Specialist Community Public Health Nursing - Health Visiting .... MSc 24PT/PGDip 12FT 24PT

University of Roehampton
Attachment Studies...... MSc 18-24FT 24-36PT PGCert 6FT 12PT

University of Salford
Surgical Practice...... MSc 36PT/PGDip 24PT/PGCert 9PT

Perioperative practice
Research Courses

Cardiff University
Perioperative Practice...... PhD 36FT 60PT/MPhil 12FT 24PT

University of Oxford
Surgery...... DPhil 48FT/MSc by research 24-36FT

Primary care
Taught Courses

University of Aberdeen
Primary Care ...... MSc 48-60PT

Barts and the London School of Medicine and Dentistry
Primary Care ...... MSc 12FT 24PT/PGDip 12FT 24PT

University of Bath
Primary Care ...... MSc 96PT/PGDip 72PT/PGCert 48PT

Birmingham City University
Advanced Healthcare (Nursing, Midwifery or Primary Care)...... PGDip 12PT/MSc 24PT

University of Birmingham
Advancing Practice...... MSc 13FT 72PT/PGDip 10FT 48PT/PGCert 3FT
Clinical Primary and Community Care...... MSc 12FT 60PT/PGDip 12FT 60PT/PGCert 12FT 60PT
Primary and Community Care, Clinical...... MSc 12FT 24PT/PGDip 12FT 24PT/PGCert 12FT 24PT

University of Central Lancashire
Evidence Based Practice...... PGCert 12PT
Excellence in Leadership for Inclusion and Community..... PGCert 12-24PT
General Practice...... MSc 36-60PT/PGDip 24-60PT/PGCert 12PT
Health & Social Care Education...... PGCert 12PT
Health Informatics...... MSc 33PT/PGDip 24PT
Health and Social Care Education ...... PGCert 12PT
Research for Professional Practice ... Professional Doctorate 24PT

University of Chester
Health and Social Care - Advanced Practice ...... MSc 24 - 72PT/PGDip 24 - 60PT/PGCert 12 - 36PT

City University London
Primary Care ...... MSc 12FT 24PT
Primary Care (Advanced Nurse Practitioner)...... MSc 12FT 24PT
Primary Care (District Nursing)...... MSc 12FT 24PT
Primary Care (Long Term Conditions)...... MSc 12FT 24PT

University of Derby
Community Specialist Practice ...... MSc 12FT 24PT

University of Dundee
Primary Care ...... MSc 36-60PT
Psychological Therapy in Primary Care ...... MSc 12FT

National University of Ireland Galway
Health Sciences (Clinical Primary Care)...... PGDip 12PT/PGCert 12PT
Health Sciences (Primary Care)...... PGDip 12PT

Glasgow Caledonian University
Diagnostic Imaging...... MSc 12-24FT
Musculoskeletal Management...... MSc 36-72PT
Radiotherapy and Oncology ...... MSc 12-24FT

University of Glasgow
Primary Care ..... MPC 12FT 24-60PT/PGDip 12FT 24-36PT/PGCert 24PT

University of Greenwich
Independent and Supplementary Prescribing / Supplementary Prescribing...... PGCert 8DL

University of Kent
Primary Dental Care...... MSc 36PT
Primary Dental Care for Foundation Dentists...... PGCert 12FT

Nursing and midwifery

King's College London
Primary Health Care .... MSc 12FT 24PT

Leeds Metropolitan University
Environmental Health.. MSc 12FT 36PT
Health Care Studies ....MA 24PT

University of Leeds
Primary Care Education .... PGCert 12-24PT
Primary Health Care .....MMedSci 30PT/PGDip 24PT/PGCert 12PT

University of Liverpool
Diploma in International Community Health Care ...Diploma 3FT

London South Bank University
Primary Care .... MSc 12FT up to 72PT
Primary Care and Mental Health...................................PGCert 12PT

Manchester Metropolitan University
Community Health ....MSc 12FT 24-36PT

University of Manchester
Primary Care .... MRes 12 - 60DL

University of Northampton
Community Practice .... MSc 24-60PT/PGDip 12PT

The Open University
Advancing Professional Practice................................MSc variableDL

Queen Mary, University of London
International Primary Health Care.......................MSc 12FT 24-48PT

University of Roehampton
Health Sciences..MSc 12FT 24PT

University of Salford
Public Health ....MSc 12FT 36PT/PGDip 8FT 24PT/PGCert 9PT

Sheffield Hallam University
Cardiovascular Medicine for Primary Care Physicians ....PGDip
24PT/PGCert 12PT

University of Sheffield
Public Health ....MPH 12FT 24-36PT
Public Health (Health Services Research)........MPH 12FT 24-36PT
Public Health (Management and Leadership) .... MPH 12FT
24-36PT

University of South Wales
Community Health Studies ....BSc 24-36PT/MSc 36PT

St George's, University of London
Physician Assistant Studies ....PGDip 24FT

University of Stirling
Psychological Therapy in Primary Care .... MSc 12FT

Swansea University
Advanced Practice in Health Care ....MSc 36PT/PGDip 24PT
Advanced Practice in Health Care - Infection Control ...MSc 36PT/
PGDip 24PT

University of Ulster
Primary Care and General Practice ....MSc 36DL

University of Warwick
Diabetes in Pregnancy .... PGA 12PT
Patient and Public Involvement in Healthcare ....PGA 12PT/
CPDMod 1PT
Sexual Health in Primary Care .... PGA 12PT

University of the West of England, Bristol
Community Practice ....MSc 12FT 60PT

University of Winchester
Delivery of Primary Health Care ....PGCert 24PT

University of Wolverhampton
Primary Health Care Practice...MSc 12PT

Primary care
Research Courses

University of Aberdeen
General Practice and Primary Care .... PhD 36FT/MD 24FT/MSc by
research 12FT

Barts and the London School of Medicine and Dentistry
Department of General Practice and Primary Care .... PhD/MPhil/
MSc by research/MD

University of Birmingham
Primary Care Clinical Sciences.... PhD 36FT 72PT/MSc by research
12FT 24PT

University of Cambridge
Public Health and Primary Care .... PhD 36FT 60PT

Cardiff University
Primary Care and Public Health ....PhD 36FT/MPhil 36FT

University of Central Lancashire
Healthcare/Public Health.................... MSc by research 12FT 24PT/
MPhil 24FT 36-48PT/PhD 36FT 60PT/MD 36FT 60PT

University of Cumbria
Public Health and Primary Care....................PhD 48FT 72PT 72DL/
MPhil 36FT 36PT 36DL

University of East Anglia
Nursing ....PhD 36FT 72PT/MPhil 24FT 48PT/
MSc by research 12FT 24PT

University of Edinburgh
General Practice..............PhD 36FT 72PT/MPhil 24FT 36PT/MSc by
research 12FT 24PT

University of Hertfordshire
Centre for Research in Primary and Community Care ....PhD 36FT
72PT/MPhil 24FT 48PT/MRes 12FT 24PT/DHRes 36FT 72PT

Imperial College London
Primary Care and Population Health Science.................PhD/MPhil

King's College London
Health & Social Care (Research Division)........ PhD 36FT 48-72PT/
MPhil 36FT 48-72PT/DHC 36FT 48-72PT

University of Liverpool
Primary Care ....MPhil 12-48FT 24-72PT/PhD 24-48FT 48-84PT/
MD 24-72PT

University of Nottingham
Epidemiology and Public HealthPhD 36FT 72PT/MPhil 24FT 48PT
Primary Care ....PhD 36FT

University of Oxford
Primary Health Care ....DPhil 48FT/MSc by research 24-36FT
Public Health .... DPhil 48FT/MSc by research 24FT

University of Roehampton
Health Sciences.... PhD 24-48FT 36-60PT/MPhil 21-36FT 36-60PT

University of Sheffield
Primary Medical Care and Ageing.......PhD 36FT 72PT/MPhil 24FT
48PT

St George's, University of London
Community Health Sciences ....PhD 36FT 72PT/MPhil 24FT 48PT/
MD(Res) 24 minFT 48 minPT

UCL - University College London
Primary Health Care and Population Sciences......PhD 36FT 60PT/
MD(Res) 24FT 24PT

Pharmacy and pharmacology

Pharmacology
Taught Courses

University of Aberdeen
Clinical Pharmacology.................MSc 12FT/PGDip 9FT/PGCert 6FT
Drug Development.............................MSc 12FT/PGDip 9FT
Drug Development and Drug Safety............MSc 12FT/PGDip 9FT
Drug Development with Bio-Business.....................MSc 12FT 24PT/
PGDip 9FT 18PT/MRes 12FT 24PT

Barts and the London School of Medicine and Dentistry
Clinical Drug Development Health-care Research Methods.. MSc
12PT/PGDip 8PT

University of Bedfordshire
Pharmacology ....MSc 12FT 36PT

University of Bradford
Cancer Pharmacology.....................MSc 12FT
Drug Toxicology and Safety Pharmacology......MSc 12FT
Pharmaceutical Technology.....................MSc 12FT

University of Brighton
Pharmacology ....MSc 12FT/PGDip 12FT/PGCert 12FT

Cardiff University
Clinical Research.....................MSc 36PT/PGDip 24PT
International Pharmacoeconomics and Health Economics ... MSc
36DL/Diploma 24DL
Therapeutics..............................MSc 12PT/PGDip 12PT

University of Central Lancashire
Cancer Biology and Therapy ....MSc 12FT
Clinical Pharmacy Practice ....PGDip 24PT
Industrial Pharmaceutics ....MSc 12FT
Medicinal Chemistry ....MSc 12FT
Pharmaceutical Biotechnology.....................MSc 12FT

University College Cork
Applied Science (Analysis Of Pharmaceutical Compounds)... MSc
12FT 24PT

Cranfield University
Pharmacovigilance Data Management..........MSc 12FT 24-36PT/
PGDip 12FT 24-36PT

De Montfort University
Pharmaceutical Quality by Design.....................MSc 12FT

Dublin Institute of Technology
Pharmaceutical Quality Assurance and Biotechnology MSc 12FT/
PGDip 9FT

University of East Anglia
PG Diploma Pharmacy Practice ....PGDip 36PT

University of East London
Pharmacology ....MSc 12FT 24PT/PGDip 8FT 16PT/
PGCert 4FT 8PT

Edinburgh Napier University
Drug Design and Biomedical Science... MSc 12FT 24-48PT/PGDip
9FT 18-36PT/PGCert 6FT 12-24PT
Pharmaceutical Science..MSc 12FT 24-36PT/PGDip 9FT 18-27PT/
PGCert 6FT 12-18PT

University of Edinburgh
Drug Discovery & Translational Biology .... MSc 12FT/PGDip 9FT

National University of Ireland Galway
Neuropharmacology..............................MSc 12FT

Glasgow Caledonian University
Pharmacology ....MSc 12FT

University of Glasgow
Applied Medical Science ....MSc 12FT
Cardiovascular Sciences ....MSc(MedSci) 12FT
Clinical Pharmacology..............MSc(MedSci) 12FT 24PT

University of Gloucestershire
Non-Medical Prescribing.....................PGCert 8PT

University of Greenwich
Industrial Pharmaceutical Studies (MIPS)..................MSc 24-36PT
Pharmacotherapy and Service Development....... PGCert 12-24DL

University of Hertfordshire
Medicinal Chemistry ... MSc 12FT 24PT/PGDip 12FT 24PT/PGCert
12FT 24PT
Pharmacology .... MSc 12-16FT/PGDip 12-16FT/PGCert 12-16FT
Pharmacovigilance...............MSc 24DL/PGDip 24DL/PGCert 24DL

University of Kent
Applied Drug Discovery (Medway)...........................MSc 12FT 24DL
Independent/Supplementary Prescribing ....PGCert 8PT
Independent/Supplementary Prescribing for Nurses (Level H)
(Short Course Programme) ....PGCert 8PT/PGDip 8PT/MSc 8PT

King's College London
Biopharmaceuticals.....................MSc 12FT 24PT
Clinical Pharmacology.....................MSc 24-48PT
Drug Discovery Skills ....MSc 12FT
Pharmaceutical Analysis & Quality Control ....MSc 12FT 24PT
Pharmaceutical Technology.....................MSc 12FT 24PT
Pharmacology.....................MSc 12FT

University of Leeds
Pharmaceutical Science and Engineering.....................MSc 12FT

University of Leicester
Cancer Chemistry ....MSc 12FT

London Metropolitan University
Pharmaceutical Sciences ....MSc 12FT 24+PT

Manchester Metropolitan University
Clinical Physiology ....MSc 24-36PT

University of Manchester
Modelling and Simulation in Pharmacokinetics and
Pharmacodynamics ....MSc 24-36DL
Pharmaceutical Engineering (eLearning)..................PGCert 24PT
Pharmaceutical Manufacture and Engineering by Distance
Learning ....PGCert 24PT

Newcastle University
Drug Chemistry.....................MSc 12FT 24PT

Northumbria University
Drug Design with Pharmaceutical Analysis ....MSc 12FT

Nottingham Trent University
Biomedical Science ....MSc 12FT 24PT
Research Pharmacology.....................MSc(Res) 12FT 24PT
Pharmaceutical Analysis ....MRes 12FT 24PT
Pharmaceutical and Medicinal Science ....MRes 12FT 24PT
Pharmacology ....MSc 12FT 24PT

University of Oxford
Experimental Therapeutics ....MSc 24PT
Pharmacology.....................MSc 12FT

University of Portsmouth
Science with Physics ....PGCE (Postgraduate) 12FT/PGCE
(Professional) 12FT

Queen Mary, University of London
Clinical Drug Development..................MSc 12FT 24-60PT 12-60DL

Queen's University Belfast
Chemical Biology ....MSc 12FT
Translational Medicine.....................MRes 12FT 24PT

Robert Gordon University
Clinical Pharmacy Practice ....MSc 24DL/PGDip 18DL/PGCert 9DL
Instrumental Analytical Sciences: Drug Analysis and
Toxicology.....................MSc 12FT 36PT

University Campus Suffolk
Regenerative Medicine ....MSc 12FT

University of Salford
Analytical Biosciences and Drug Design ....MSc 12FT 36PT/PGDip
8FT 24PT

School of Pharmacy, University of London
Drug Delivery.....................MSc 12FT
Drug Discovery ....MSc 12FT

Sheffield Hallam University
Pharmaceutical Analysis ....MSc 12FT 24PT/PGDip 8FT/
PGCert 4FT
Pharmacology ....MSc 12FT 24PT/PGDip 8FT 16PT/
PGCert 4FT 8PT
Pharmacology and Biotechnology.....................MSc 12FT 24PT

University of Sheffield
Integrative Physiology and Pharmacology ....MSc 12FT

University of Strathclyde
Analysis of Medicines...........MSc 36DL/PGDip 24DL/PGCert 12DL
Pharmaceutical Analysis ....MSc 12-24FT/PGDip 12-24FT
Pharmaceutical Quality and Good Manufacturing Practice .. MSc
27PT/PGDip 21PT

University of Sunderland
Drug Discovery and Development ....MSc 12FT
Proteomics and Metabolomics ....MSc 12FT

University of Surrey
Clinical Pharmacology.....................MSc 24-72PT 24-72DL
Drug Discovery.....................MSc 12FT
Pharmaceutical Medicine..................MSc 24-72PT 24-72DL

Trinity College Dublin - the University of Dublin
Pharmaceutical Analysis ....MSc 12FT 24PT
Pharmaceutical Manufacturing Technology..................MSc 24PT
Pharmaceutical Medicine.....................MSc 24PT
Pharmaceutical Technology.....................MSc 12FT

University of Ulster
Pharmaceutical Sciences ....PGDip 9FT 18PT/MSc 12FT 18PT

UCL - University College London
Cell and Gene Therapy ....MSc 12FT 24-60PT/PGDip 9FT 24-60PT/
PGDip 3FT 6-24PT
Drug Design ....MSc 12FT/PGDip 9FT
Nanotechnology and Regenerative Medicine........MSc 12FT 24PT
Organic Chemistry: Drug Discovery.....................MRes 12FT
Pharmacogenetics and Stratified Medicine ....MSc 12FT

University of Warwick
Applied Pharmacology and Therapeutics in Diabetes Care.....PGA
12PT/CPDMod 1PT

University of the West of Scotland
Alcohol and Drug Studies..................MSc 48PT/Diploma 9FT 36PT/
Cert 21PT

University of Westminster
Pharmacology ....MSc 12FT 24PT

Pharmacology
Research Courses

University of Aberdeen
Pharmacology ....PhD 36FT/MPhil 24FT/MSc by research 12FT

Barts and the London School of Medicine and Dentistry
Clinical Pharmacology.....................PhD
Department of Cardiac, Vascular and Inflammation Research
comprising Cardiology ....PhD
Experimental Pathology ....PhD
Experimental Therapeutics.....................PhD
Rheumatology/Bone and Joint Research Unit.....................PhD

University of Birmingham
Pharmacology ....PhD 36FT 72PT/MPhil 12FT 24PT

University of Brighton
Pharmacy & Biomolecular Sciences ....PhD 24-60FT
36-72PT/MPhil 18-36FT 30-48PT/DProf 48-72FT 48-72PT/PhD by
publication 12FT
Pharmacy and Biomolecular Sciences Research........ PhD 24-60FT
30-72PT/MPhil 18-36FT 30-48PT

University of Cambridge
Clinical Pharmacology.....................PhD 36FT
Pharmacology ....PhD 36FT 60PT

Cardiff University
Drug Delivery and Microbiology..................PhD 36FT/MPhil 24FT
Medicinal Chemistry ....PhD 36FT/MPhil 24FT
Pharmacology and Physiology.....................PhD 36FT/MPhil 24FT

University of Central Lancashire
Pharmacy and Pharmaceutical Sciences.....PhD 48FT 84PT/MPhil
36FT 60PT/MD 48PT/MSc by research 24FT 36PT

Coventry University
Molecular Pharmacology ....MSc by research 12FT 24-36PT
Pharmaceutical Analysis ....MSc by research 12FT 24-36PT
Pharmaceutical Synthesis ....MSc by research 12FT 24-36PT

University of Dundee
Non-Graduating Research in Medical School (6 months or more)
Non-Grad 6-24FT
Non-Graduating Research in Medical School (less than 6
months)..............................Non-Grad 1-5FT

Imperial College London
Clinical Pharmacology.....................PhD

University of Kent
Biochemistry...PhD 36FT 60PT/MPhil 24FT 36PT/MSc by research
12FT 24PT

King's College London
Pharmaceutical Science Division.............PhD 36-48FT 72PT/MPhil
36-48FT 72PT

University of Leeds
Pharmacology ....PhD 36+FT/MPhil 24FT/MSc by research 12FT

University of Leicester
Department of Cell Physiology and Pharmacology.......PhD 36FT/
MRes 12FT

University of Liverpool
Pharmacology .....PhD 24-72FT 48-84PT/MPhil 12-48FT 24-72PT/
MD 48-72FT

University of Manchester
Pharmacology ....PhD 36-48FT 72-96PT/MPhil 12FT 24PT

Newcastle University
Biopharmaceutical Process Development ....EngD 48FT
Nanomedicine.....................MRes 12FT
Toxicology.....................MRes 12FT
Translational Medicine and Therapeutics ....MRes 12FT

University of Nottingham
Biophysics and Surface Analysis..........PhD 36FT 72PT/MPhil 24FT
36PT/MRes 12FT
CDT in Targeted Therapeutics and Formulation Sciences........PhD
48FT
Drug Delivery and Tissue Engineering ....PhD 36FT 72PT
EPSRC AstraZeneca Doctoral Training Centre in Targeted
Therapeutics ....PhD 48FT 72PT
Integrative Cardiovascular and Metabolic Physiology and
Pharmacology . PhD 36FT 72PT/MPhil 24FT 48PT/DM 36FT 72PT/
MRes 12FT 24PT
Medicinal Chemistry and Structural Biology ....PhD 36FT 72PT/
MPhil 24FT 48PT/MRes 12FT

The Open University
Cell and molecular biomedicine ...... MPhil 15FT 24PT variableDL/
PhD 36FT 72PT variableDL

University of Oxford
Medicinal Chemistry for Cancer ....DPhil 48FT
Oncology.....................DPhil 48FT/MSc by research 24FT
Pharmacology ....DPhil 48FT/MSc by research 24FT

School of Pharmacy, University of London
Pharmaceutical and Biological Chemistry..............PhD 36FT 60PT
Pharmaceutics.....................PhD 36FT 60PT

Pharmacy and pharmacology

Pharmacognosy and Phytotherapy .... PhD 36FT 60PT
Pharmacology .... PhD 36FT 60PT

University of Sheffield
Cardiovascular Science................ PhD 36FT 72PT/MPhil 24FT 48PT

University of Strathclyde
Drug Delivery Systems ....MRes 12FT 24PT
Drug Delivery Systems with International Placement ....
MRes 12FT 24PT
Drug Discovery ....MRes 12FT

University of Surrey
Biochemistry, Toxicology, Neuropharmacology, Chronobiology,
Apoptosis..................................... PhD 36FT 48PT/MPhil 24FT 36PT
HPRU Medical Research Centre ....PhD/MPhil
Pharmacology, Neuropharmacology, Chronobiology ....
MPhil 24FT 36PT/PhD 36FT 48PT

UCL - University College London
Pharmacology ....PhD 36FT 60PT/PhD 48FT

Pharmacy
Taught Courses

Aston University
Clinical Pharmacy......................................PGDip 24PT MSc 24PT
Pharmacy Practice... MSc 24PT
Psychiatric Pharmacy...PGDip 12DL

University of Bath
Advanced Programmes in Pharmaceutical Practice and
Therapeutics........................... MSc 36PT/PGDip 24PT/PGCert 12PT

University of Birmingham
Pharmaceutical Enterprise...................................MSc 12FT 24PT
Professional Doctorate in Pharmacy ...... DPharm by taught 48PT

University of Bradford
Clinical Pharmacy (Hospital or Community) ....MSc 24PT/PGDip
21PT
Drug Discovery .... MSc 12FT 24PT/PGDip 12FT 24PT
Pharmaceutical Services and Medicines Control .... MSc 12FT
Pharmaceutical Technology....................................... MSc 12FT

University of Brighton
Clinical Pharmacy Practice .... MSc 12PT PGDip 12FT 24PT/PGCert
12FT 24PT
Pharmacy (OSPAP)... PGDip 12FT 24PT

Cardiff University
Clinical Pharmacy................................MSc 36PT/PGDip 24PT
Pharmacist Independent Prescribing...........................PGCert 7FT
Pharmacy Clinical Practice (Community and Primary Care)... MSc
36PT/PGDip 24PT/PGCert 12PT

University of Central Lancashire
Cancer Biology and Therapy .... MSc 12FT
Clinical Pharmacy Practice .... PGDip 24PT
Industrial Pharmaceutics .... MSc 12FT
Medicinal Chemistry .... MSc 12FT
Pharmaceutical Biotechnology................................... MSc 12FT

University College Cork
Pharmaceutical Engineering ....MEngSci 24PT

De Montfort University
Clinical Pharmacy B23075 .... MSc 36DL/PGDip 24DL/
PGCert 12DL
Pharmaceutical Biotechnology ....MSc 12FT 24PT
Practice certificate in Independent Prescribing for Pharmacists ..
PGDip 8PT

University of East Anglia
Advanced Practitioner (Profession)..........................MSc 12FT 36PT
PG Diploma Pharmacy Practice .... PGDip 36PT

Edinburgh Napier University
Pharmaceutical Science..MSc 12FT 24-36PT/PGDip 9FT 18-27PT/
PGCert 6FT 12-18PT

University of Edinburgh
Regenerative Medicine: Industrial and Clinical Delivery................
MSc 12FT

University of Glasgow
Chemistry with Medicinal Chemistry .... MSc 12FT
Translational Medicine....................................... MRes 12FT

University of Gloucestershire
Non-Medical Prescribing.. PGCert 8PT

University of Greenwich
General Pharmacy Practice ....PGCert 24-48PT/PGDip 24-48PT
Independent and Supplementary Prescribing / Supplementary
Prescribing...PGCert 8DL
Medicines Management ....MSc 12 -48PT/PGDip 12 -48PT/
PGCert 12 -48PT
Pharmaceutical Sciences (MPS) .... MSc 12FT 24 - 36PT/
PGDip 12FT 24-36PT
Pharmacotherapy and Service Development........ PGCert 12-24DL

Harper Adams University
Veterinary Pharmacy ... MSc 12FT 48PT/PGDip 12FT 48PT/PGCert
12FT 24PT

University of Hertfordshire
Advancing Pharmacy Practice .... MSc 12FT/PGCert 12FT/PGDip
12FT
Medicinal Chemistry ... MSc 12FT 24PT/PGDip 12FT 24PT/PGCert
12FT 24PT
Pharmacology .... MSc 12-16FT/PGDip 12-16FT/PGCert 12-16FT

University of Huddersfield
MSc Pharmaceutical and Analytical Science.................... MSc 12FT

Imperial College London
Infection Management for Pharmacists ....MSc 24PT/
PGDip 16PT/PGCert 8PT

Keele University
Clinical Pharmacy .... PGCert 9DL/PGDip 21DL/MSc 33DL
Clinical/Community Pharmacy/Prescribing Studies........ MSc 9DL
Community Pharmacy .... PGCert 9DL/PGDip 21DL/MSc 33DL
Prescribing Studies.................. PGDip 18DL/PGCert 9DL/MSc 27DL
Prescribing Studies (Independent Prescribing).............PGCert 6DL

University of Kent
Applied Drug Discovery (Medway)......................MSc 12FT 24DL
General Pharmacy Practice ....PGCert 24-48PT/PGDip 24-48PT
Independent/Supplementary Prescribing .... PGCert 8PT
Independent/Supplementary Prescribing for Nurses (Level H)
(Short Course Programme) ....PGCert 8PT/PGDip 8PT/MSc 8PT
Medicines Management .... PGCert 12-72PT/PGDip 12-72PT/MSc
12-72PT
Pharmacotherapy and Service Development (Medway).... PGCert
FlexibleFT

King's College London
Pharmaceutical Technology..............................MSc 12FT 24PT
Pharmacology Practice...........PGCert 12PT/PGDip 24PT/MSc 36PT

Kingston University
Pharmaceutical Science..................................MSc 12 - 20FT 24PT
Pharmaceutical Science with Management Studies ..... MSc 12FT
Pharmacy Practice (Overseas Pharmacists Assessment
Programme)...PGDip 12FT

University of Leeds
Pharmaceutical Science and Engineering........................ MSc 12FT

Liverpool John Moores University
Clinical Pharmacy .... MSc 12FT

London South Bank University
Non-Medical Prescribing .... GradCert 6PT

Manchester Metropolitan University
Science, Technology, Engineering and Maths (STEM) .... MSc
24-72PT

University of Manchester
Clinical and Health Services Pharmacy......................AdvDip 24PT/
PGDip 24PT
Community Pharmacy Public Health Services .....MSc 36PT 36DL/
PGDip 24PT 24DL/PGCert 12PT 12DL
Pharmaceutical Industrial Advanced Training (PIAT) .... MSc
36-60DL/PGDip 36-60DL

Northumbria University
Drug Design with Pharmaceutical Analysis .... MSc 12FT

Nottingham Trent University
Biomedical Science ....MSc 12FT 24PT
Pharmaceutical and Medicinal Science.................MRes 12FT 24PT

University of Nottingham
Drug Discovery and Pharmaceutical Sciences .... MSc 12FT

The Open University
Medicinal Chemistry ....MSc variableDL/PGDip variableDL

Oxford Brookes University
Non-Medical Prescribing ....PGCert 18-24PT

University of Oxford
Pharmacology .... MSc 12FT

University of Portsmouth
Pharmacy Practice .... MSc 36PT

Queen's University Belfast
Advanced Pharmacy Practice ....MSc 30PT/PGDip 15PT
Clinical Pharmacy ....MSc 36DL/PGDip 24DL/PGCert 12DL
Community Pharmacy ....MSc 36DL/PGDip 24DL/PGCert 12DL
Prescribing for Pharmacists .... PGCert 9-12PT

Robert Gordon University
Advanced Pharmacy Practice ....MSc 23PT 23DL/
PGDip 14PT 14DL
Clinical Pharmacy Practice ....MSc 24DL/PGDip 18DL/PGCert 9DL
Overseas Pharmacists Assessment Programme (OSPAP)........ MSc
12FT/PGDip 9FT

School of Pharmacy, University of London
Clinical Pharmacy, International Practice and Policy...... MSc 12FT
Pharmacy Practice....................MSc 12PT/PGDip 12PT/PGCert 1PT

University of Sheffield
Health Economics and Decision Modelling ......MSc 12FT 24-36PT
Integrative Physiology and Pharmacology .... MSc 12FT

University of St Andrews
Medicine ....MRes 12FT 24PT

University of Strathclyde
Clinical Pharmacy..........................MSc 12FT 24PT/PGDip 9FT 18PT
Pharmaceutical Analysis .... MSc 12-24FT/PGDip 12-24FT
Pharmaceutical Quality and Good Manufacturing Practice .. MSc
27PT/PGDip 21PT

University of Sunderland
MSc OSPAP .... MSc 12FT
Medicines Management .... MSc 12FT 24-36PT/
PGDip 12FT 24-36PT

Swansea University
Applied Analytical Science (LCMS) .....MSc 12FT 36PT/PGDip 12FT
36PT

Trinity College Dublin - the University of Dublin
Community Pharmacy ....PGDip 24PT/MSc 36PT
Pharmaceutical Medicine................................... MSc 24PT
Pharmaceutical Technology................................... MSc 12FT

University of Ulster
Non-Medical Prescribing .... PGCert 9PT
Pharmacy Management ....PGDip 18DL
Prescribing for Allied Health Professionals...........PGCert 9PT 9DL

UCL - University College London
Drug Design .... MSc 12FT/PGDip 9FT
Pharmacogenetics and Stratified Medicine .... MSc 12FT

Pharmacy
Research Courses

University of Brighton
MPhil/PhD in Pharmacy & Biomolecular Sciences ... PhD 24-60FT
36-72PT/MPhil 18-36FT 30-48PT/DProf 48-72FT 48-72PT/PhD by
publication 12FT

University of Cambridge
Clinical Pharmacology..PhD 36FT

Cardiff University
Drug Delivery and Microbiology.................... PhD 36FT/MPhil 24FT
Pharmacy Practice and Clinical Pharmacy ....PhD 36FT

University of Central Lancashire
Pharmacy and Pharmaceutical Sciences .....PhD 48FT 84PT/MPhil
36FT 60PT/MD 48PT/MSc by research 24FT 36PT

University of East Anglia
Chemical Sciences .... PhD 36FT 72PT/MPhil 24FT 48PT
PharmacyPhD 36FT 72PT/MPhil 24FT 48PT/MSc by research 12FT
24PT

University of Edinburgh
Regenerative Medicine .... MPhil 24FT 48PT/PhD 36FT 72PT

Keele University
Department of Medicines Management ....PhD 48FT 84PT/MPhil
24FT 36PT

University of Kent
Pharmacy................................. PhD 36FT 60PT/MPhil 24FT 36PT

Liverpool John Moores University
Pharmacy and Chemistry .... PhD 36FT 72PT/MPhil 24FT 48PT

University of Manchester
Pharmacy and Pharmaceutical Sciences .... PhD 36-48FT 72PT/
MPhil 12FT 24PT

Newcastle University
Biopharmaceutical Process Development .... EngD 48FT

University of Nottingham
Biophysics and Surface Analysis..........PhD 36FT 72PT/MPhil 24FT
36PT/MRes 12FT
Drug Delivery and Tissue Engineering .... PhD 36FT 72PT
EPSRC AstraZeneca Doctoral Training Centre in Targeted
Therapeutics.. PhD 48FT 72PT
Pharmacy-split site PhD programme ....PhD 36FT
Social Research in Medicines and Health....PhD 36FT 72PT/MPhil
36FT

University of Oxford
Pharmacology ....DPhil 48FT/MSc by research 24FT

University of Portsmouth
Pharmacy and Biomedical Science ......MPhil 24FT 48PT/PhD 36FT
72PT/MD 24FT 48PT
Professional Doctorate in Pharmacy ....DPharm 48PT

Queen's University Belfast
Pharmacy................................. PhD 36FT 72PT/MPhil 24FT 48PT

School of Pharmacy, University of London
Pharmaceutics... PhD 36FT 60PT

University of Strathclyde
Drug Delivery Systems ....MRes 12FT 24PT
Drug Delivery Systems with International Placement ....
MRes 12FT 24PT
Drug Discovery ....MRes 12FT

Pharmacy and pharmacology
Taught Courses

Anglia Ruskin University
Forensic Science..MSc 12 - 15FT 24 - 30PT

Pharmacy and pharmacology

Anglo-European College of Chiropractic
Medical Ultrasound .... MSc 36PT

Aston University
Evidence-based Pharmacotherapy .... MSc 24-36PT

University of Bath
Chemistry for Drug Discovery .... MSc 12FT

University of Birmingham
Advanced Chemical Engineering....................... MSc 12FT 24-36PT/
PGDip 12FT 24-30PT
Drug Discovery and Medicinal Chemistry..MSc 18FT 32PT/PGDip
12FT 24PT
Pharmaceutical Enterprise... MSc 12FT 24PT

University of Brighton
Industrial Pharmaceutical Studies............. MSc 12FT/PGDip 12FT/
PGCert 12FT
Pharmaceutical and Biomedical Sciences........... MRes 12FT 24PT/
PGCert 12FT 24PT/PGDip 12FT 24PT

University of Central Lancashire
Cancer Biology and Therapy .... MSc 12FT
Clinical Pharmacy Practice.. PGDip 24PT
Industrial Pharmaceutics .... MSc 12FT
Medicinal Chemistry .... MSc 12FT
Pharmaceutical Biotechnology... MSc 12FT

University of Chester
Health and Social Care - Non Medical Prescribing............................
Credit-bearing 72PT

University College Cork
Applied Science (Analysis Of Pharmaceutical Compounds)... MSc
12FT 24PT

Cranfield University
Translational Medicine............... MSc 12FT 36PT/PGDip 12FT 24PT

Dublin Institute of Technology
Pharmaceutical Process Control and Automation....... MEng 12FT
24PT
Pharmaceutical Validation Technology............................. MSc 24PT
Pharmaceutical and Chemical Process Technology....... PGDip 9FT
21PT/MSc 12FT 24PT

University of East Anglia
Pharmacy Practice .... PGDip 36PT

University of East London
Pharmaceutical Science MSc..... MSc 12FT 24PT/PGDip 8FT 16PT/
PGCert 4FT 8PT

Edinburgh Napier University
Pharmaceutical Science..MSc 12FT 24-36PT/PGDip 9FT 18-27PT/
PGCert 6FT 12-18PT

University of Exeter
Biotechnology and Enterprise... MSc 12FT

University of Greenwich
Formulation Science ....MSc 12-24FT
Pharmaceutical Sciences .... MSc 12FT 24 - 36PT/PGDip 12FT
24-36PT
Pharmacotherapy and Service Development....... PGCert 12-24DL

University of Hertfordshire
Pharmacology .... MSc 12-16FT/PGDip 12-16FT/PGCert 12-16FT

University of Huddersfield
MSc Pharmaceutical and Analytical Science.................. MSc 12FT
Pharmaceutical and Analytical Science............MSc 12FT 24-48PT

University of Kent
Drug Design .... MSc 12FT
Medicines Management .... PGCert 12-72PT/PGDip 12-72PT/MSc
12-72PT
Pharmacotherapy and Service Development (Medway).... PGCert
FlexibleFT

King's College London
Analytical Science for Industry ....MSc 12FT 24PT
Biopharmaceuticals..MSc 12FT 24PT
Pharmacology Practice...........PGCert 12PT/PGDip 24PT/MSc 36PT

Kingston University
Pharmaceutical Analysis ....MSc 12FT 24PT
Pharmaceutical Analysis with Management Studies.... MSc 12FT
24PT
Pharmacy Practice (Overseas Pharmacists Assessment
Programme)..PGDip 12FT

University of Leeds
Pharmaceutical Science and Engineering........................ MSc 12FT

Loughborough University
Analytical and Pharmaceutical Science...........MSc 12FT 24 - 60PT
Pharmaceutical Science and Medicinal Chemistry........ MSc 12FT
24 - 60PT

University of Northampton
Autonomous Healthcare Practice .... MSc 12FT 24-48PT/
PGDip 12PT

Nottingham Trent University
Biomedical Science ....MSc 12FT 24PT

Oxford Brookes University
Non-Medical Prescribing...PGCert 18-24PT

University of Oxford
Medicinal Chemistry for Cancer .... MSc 12FT
Pharmacology .... MSc 12FT

Queen's University Belfast
Advanced Pharmacy Practice ....MSc 30PT/PGDip 15PT

Robert Gordon University
Advanced Pharmacy Practice ..MSc 23PT 23DL/PGDip 14PT 14DL
Clinical Pharmacy Practice .... MSc 24DL/PGDip 18DL/PGCert 9DL

Sheffield Hallam University
Pharmacology .. MSc 12FT 24PT/PGDip 8FT 16PT/PGCert 4FT 8PT
Pharmacology and Biotechnology.............................MSc 12FT 24PT

University of Sheffield
Integrative Physiology and Pharmacology .... MSc 12FT

University of Strathclyde
Medical Devices .... MSc 12FT/PGDip 9FT
Pharmaceutical Analysis .... MSc 12-24FT/PGDip 12-24FT
Pharmaceutical Quality and Good Manufacturing Practice ....
MSc 27PT/PGDip 21PT

University of Sunderland
Clinical Pharmacy...MSc 24PT/PGDip 24PT
Pharmaceutical and BioPharmaceutical Formulations...................
MSc 12FT

Trinity College Dublin - the University of Dublin
Hospital Pharmacy.. MSc 24PT
Pharmaceutical Medicine... MSc 24PT
Pharmaceutical Technology.. MSc 12FT

UCL - University College London
Drug Design .... MSc 12FT/PGDip 9FT
Pharmacogenetics and Stratified Medicine .... MSc 12FT

University of Wolverhampton
Pharmaceutical Science (Drug Discovery and Design)... MSc 12FT
Pharmaceutical Science (Pharmaceutical Analysis) .... MSc 12FT
Pharmaceutical Science (Pharmaceutical Manufacturing) .... MSc
12FT
Pharmaceutical Science (Pharmaceutical Quality Assurance)MSc
12FT
Pharmaceutical Science (Pharmacological Sciences) ..... MSc 12FT

Pharmacy and pharmacology
Research Courses

University of Bath
Pharmacy and Pharmacology .... PhD 24-48FT 36-72PT/MPhil
12-36FT 24-48PT

University of Cambridge
Clinical Pharmacology...PhD 36FT

University of Central Lancashire
Pharmacy and Pharmaceutical Sciences .....PhD 48FT 84PT/MPhil
36FT 60PT/MD 48PT/MSc by research 24FT 36PT

University of Greenwich
Chemical and Pharmaceutical Sciences - Research ..... MPhil 36FT
72PT/PhD 36FT 72PT
Pharmacy - Research........................... MPhil 36-72PT/PhD 36-72FT

University of Kent
Pharmacy..................................... PhD 36FT 60PT/MPhil 24FT 36PT

Loughborough University
Pharmaceutical Engineering ..... PhD 36FT 60PT/MPhil 24FT 36PT

Newcastle University
Biopharmaceutical Process Development .... EngD 48FT

University of Nottingham
Social Research in Medicines and Health....PhD 36FT 72PT/MPhil
36FT

The Open University
Biomedical Sciences............................. PhD 36FT 72PT variableDL/
MPhil 15FT 24PT

University of Oxford
Oncology......................................DPhil 48FT/MSc by research 24FT
Pharmacology ....DPhil 48FT/MSc by research 24FT

Queen's University Belfast
Pharmacy..................................... PhD 36FT 72PT/MPhil 24FT 48PT

School of Pharmacy, University of London
Pharmaceutics... PhD 36FT 60PT

University of Strathclyde
Doctor of Pharmacy...DPharm 36FT 48PT

Physics

Astrobiology
Research Courses

University of Nottingham
Magnetic Resonance ....PhD 36FT 72PT/MPhil 24FT 48PT/MRes 12FT

The Open University
Astrobiology and Habits for LifePhD 36FT 72PT variableDL/MPhil 15FT 24PT variableDL

Astronomy
Taught Courses

University of Glasgow
Astrophysics .... MSc 12FT

King's College London
Space Physiology & Health...................... MSc 12FT

University of Leeds
Quantum Technologies...........MSc 12FT/PGDip 12FT/PGCert 12FT

Loughborough University
Astrophysics and Cosmology .... MSc 12FT 24PT

University of Nottingham
Gravity, Particles and Fields .... MSc 12FT

Queen Mary, University of London
Astronomy and Astrophysics................................... PGCert 9PT
Astrophysics...MSc 12FT 24PT

University of Sussex
Astronomy...MSc 12FT 24PT

University of Wales Trinity Saint David
Cultural Astronomy and Astrology ...PGCert 12FT 24PT 12-60DL/ PGDip 12FT 24PT 12-60DL/MA 12FT 24PT 12-60DL

UCL - University College London
Astrophysics.....................MSc 12FT 24PT/PGDip 9FT 18PT
Planetary Science .... MSc 12FT 24PT

Astronomy
Research Courses

University of Birmingham
Physics and Astronomy...PhD 36-48FT 72PT/MPhil 12FT 24-48PT

University of Cambridge
Astronomy...PhD 36/42FT

Cardiff University
Astronomy Instrumentation ....MPhil 12-24FT possiblePT/ PhD 36FT possiblePT
Astronomy and Astrophysics....................PhD 36FT/MPhil 12-24FT

University of Central Lancashire
Astrophysics....PhD 48FT 84PT/MPhil 36FT 60PT/MSc by research 24FT 36PT

University of Edinburgh
Astrophysics...PhD 36FT

University of Exeter
Physics......................PhD 48FT 84PT 84DL/MPhil 36FT 60PT 60DL

University of Hertfordshire
Astrophysics........................... PhD 36FT 72PT/MPhil 24FT 48PT

Keele University
Astrophysics...PhD 36FT/MPhil 12FT

University of Leeds
Department of Physics and Astronomy... PhD 36+FT/MPhil 24FT/ MSc by research 12FT

University of Leicester
Physics and Astronomy............. PhD 36-48FT 36-72PT/MPhil 12FT 24-48PT

Liverpool John Moores University
Astrophysics.......................................PhD 36FT/MPhil 12FT

University of Liverpool
Advanced Science (Physical Science Pathway - Astrophysics)........ MRes 12FT

University of Manchester
Astronomy and Astrophysics...........PhD 36-48FT 72-96PT/MSc by research 12FT 24PT

University of Nottingham
Astronomy.................PhD 36FT 72PT/MPhil 24FT 48PT/MRes 12FT
Condensed Matter Theory ....PhD 36FT
Magnetic Resonance ....PhD 36FT 72PT/MPhil 24FT 48PT/MRes 12FT
Particle Theory...PhD 36-48FT

The Open University
Astrobiology and Habits for Life......... PhD 36FT 72PT variableDL/ MPhil 15FT 24PT variableDL
Astronomy.................PhD 36FT 72PT variableDL/MPhil 15FT 24PT variableDL
Atomic, Molecular and Optical Physics.................MPhil 15FT 24PT variableDL
Cosmochemistry...... PhD 36FT 72PT variableDL/MPhil 15FT 24PT variableDL
Planetary Science and Comparative Planetology.............PhD 36FT 72PT variableDL/MPhil 15FT 24PT variableDL

Planetary and Space Sciences ...PhD 36FT 72PT variableDL/MPhil 15FT 24PT variableDL
Space Science and Space Technology....................... PhD 36FT 72PT variableDL/MPhil 15FT 24PT variableDL

University of Oxford
Astrophysics... DPhil 48FT

Queen Mary, University of London
Astronomy, Astrophysics, Cosmology and Relativity ....PhD 36FT/ MPhil 12FT

Queen's University Belfast
Astrophysics............................ PhD 36FT 72PT/MPhil 24FT 48PT

University of Southampton
PhD Opportunities in Physics and Astronomy....... PhD 36FT 72PT

University of St Andrews
Physics and Astronomy.. PhD 42-48FT

University of Sussex
Astronomy Research Programme..... PhD 24-48FT 36-72PT/MPhil 12-36FT 24-48PT

Swansea University
Laser Physics ....MSc by research 12FT 24PT

UCL - University College London
Physics and Astronomy................................. PhD 36FT 60PT

Colour science
Taught Courses

University of Glasgow
Chemistry... MSc 12FT
Chemistry with Medicinal Chemistry .... MSc 12FT

University of Leeds
Colour and Imaging Science ....MSc 12FT/PGCert 12FT/ PGDip 12FT

University of Strathclyde
Analysis of Medicines...........MSc 36DL/PGDip 24DL/PGCert 12DL

Colour science
Research Courses

University of Leeds
Colour Chemistry .... PhD 36+FT
Department of Colour and Polymer Chemistry.PhD 36+FT/MPhil 12+FT/MSc by research 12FT

Desalination technology
Taught Courses

Cardiff University
Hydro-environment Engineering ....MSc 12FT 24PT

Cranfield University
Water and Wastewater Engineering .... MSc 12FT 24-60PT/PGDip 6FT 24PT/PGCert 5FT 24PT

University of Cumbria
The Research Process...................................PGCert 12 - 18PT

Imperial College London
Environmental Engineering, also with Business Management or Sustainable Development......................................MSc 12FT 24-36PT

Leeds Metropolitan University
Advanced Engineering Management .... MSc 12FT 24PT/PGCert 12PT/PGDip 12FT 24PT

Desalination technology
Research Courses

Imperial College London
Chemical Engineering Research .... PhD 36FT 72PT

Energy studies
Taught Courses

University of Aberdeen
Oil and Gas Engineering ....MSc 12FT 24PT
Oil and Gas Enterprise Management.......................MSc 12FT 24PT

University of Abertay Dundee
Energy & Environmental Management .... MSc 12FT
Energy Industry Economics.............................MSc 12FT/PGDip 9FT
Oil and Gas Accounting .... MSc 12FT/PGDip 9FT
Oil and Gas Finance .... MSc 12FT
Oil and Gas Management .... MSc 12FT/PGDip 9FT
Renewable Bio-Energy .... MSc 12FT

University of Bath
Environment, Energy & Resilience .... MRes 12FT 24-36PT

University of Birmingham
Materials for Sustainable Energy Technologies...MRes 12FT 24PT

University of Bolton
Renewable Energy and Environmental Technologies .... MSc 12FT 24PT

Brunel University
Building Services Engineering with Sustainable Energy............... MSc 12FT 36-60DL
Renewable Energy Engineering .... MSc 12FT

Sustainable Energy : Technologies and Management... MSc 12FT

University of Cambridge
Energy Technology .... MPhil 12FT

Cardiff University
Electrical Energy Systems..................................... MSc 12FT
Sustainable Energy and Environment...............MSc 12FT 24-36PT

University of Central Lancashire
Energy and Environmental Management............MSc 12FT 24PT/ PGDip 9FT 18PT/PGCert 6FT 12PT
Renewable Energy Engineering......... MSc 12FT 24PT/PGDip 24PT
Wind Energy Engineering..............MSc 12FT 24PT/PGDip 9FT 24PT

Centre for Alternative Technology
Renewable Energy and the Built Environment.....MSc 18FT 30PT/ PGCert 6FT 12PT/AdvPGDip 12FT 24PT

City University London
Energy Trade and Finance...................................MSc 12FT 24PT
Energy and Environmental Technology and Economics................ MSc 12FT 24PT
Power Systems & Energy Management...................MSc 18FT 36PT

University College Cork
Sustainable Energy ....MEngSci 12FT

Cranfield University
Biofuels Process Engineering ....MSc 12FT 24-36PT/PGDip 9FT 12-24PT/PGCert 6FT 12-24PT
Carbon Capture and Transport.....................MSc 12FT 60PT/ PGDip 12FT 60PT/PGCert 12FT 60PT
Energy Supply for Low Carbon Futures............ MSc 12FT 24-60PT/ PGDip 6FT 24PT/PGCert 5FT 24PT
Energy Systems and Thermal Processes.................MSc 12FT 36PT
Materials for Energy Systems..........MSc 12FT 24-60PT/PGDip 6FT 24PT/PGCert 5FT 24PT
Renewable Energy Engineering ....MSc 12FT 24-36PT
Renewable Energy Technology ....MSc 12FT 24-60PT/PGDip 6FT 24PT/PGCert 5FT 24PT

De Montfort University
Energy and Industrial Sustainability .... MSc 12FT 24PT 36DL/ PGDip 32DL/PGCert 16DL
Energy and Sustainable Building Design ....MSc 12FT 24PT 3 6DL/PGDip 32DL/PGCert 16DL

Dublin Institute of Technology
Energy Management.. MSc 24PT
Sustainable Electrical Energy Systems.................MEng 12FT 24PT

University of Dundee
Climate Change Economics and Policy .... MSc 12FT
Climate Change and Energy Law and Policy ....LLM 12FT
Design and Construction of Zero Carbon and Ultra-Low Energy Buildings .... MSc 12FT
Energy Law and Policy (by distance learning)............LLM 24-60DL
Energy Law and Policy ....LLM 12FT
Energy Studies (by distance learning)......................MSc 24-60DL
Energy Studies .... MSc 12FT
Energy Studies with Specialisation in Energy Economics ...... MSc 12FT/PGDip 9FT
Energy Studies with Specialisation in Energy Finance .... MSc 12FT/PGDip 9FT
Energy Studies with Specialisation in Energy Policy .... MSc 12FT
Energy Studies with Specialisation in Energy and the Environment .... MSc 12FT
Energy Studies with Specialisation in Oil and Gas Economics ..... MSc 12FT
Managing in the Energy Industries .... MSc 12FT
Non-Graduating Taught Postgrad Grad School of Natural Resources Law, Policy & Management .... PG module variableFT
Non-Graduating Taught Postgraduate in School of Engineering, Physics and Mathematics............................. PG module variableFT
Renewable Energy and Environmental Modelling ... MSc 12FT
Renewable Energy and Sustainable Building in a Global Context .... MSc 12FT
Sports and Biomechanical Medicine (Full time in-house) ...... MSc 12FT
Sports and Biomechanical Medicine (Part time with externally arranged project).. MSc 24PT
Sports and Biomechanical Medicine (Part time with in-house project)... MSc 24PT
Supplementary Studies in Graduate School of Natural Resources, Law, Policy and Management ....Masters Level Modules 6-9FT
Water Hazards, Risks & Resilience .... MSc 12FT

Durham University
Energy and Society.. MSc 12FT
New and Renewable Energy...MSc 12FT

University of East Anglia
Energy Engineering with Environmental ManagementMSc 12FT/ MSc 24PT/MSc 36PT/MSc 48PT

University of East London
Architecture: Advanced Environmental and Energy Studies MSc MSc 12FT 24PT
Architecture: Advanced Environmental and Energy Studies MSc by distance learning ....MSc 24DL
Architecture: Advanced Environmental and Energy Studies Prof Diploma ....Prof Dip 18PT

Physics

Architecture: Sustainability And Design MA..........MA 12FT 24PT/PGDip 8FT 16PT/PGCert 4FT 8PT
Renewable Energy and the Built Environment MSc....... MSc 12FT 24PT
Sustainability and Energy Management MBA......MBA 12FT 24PT

Edinburgh Napier University
Energy and Environmental Engineering..................MSc 12FT 36PT
Renewable Energy..MSc 12FT 24PT

University of Edinburgh
Sustainable Energy Systems............................ MSc 12FT/PGDip 9FT

University of Exeter
Energy Policy..MSc 12FT 24PT
Environment, Energy and Resilience......................MRes 12FT 24PT

Glasgow Caledonian University
Energy and Environmental Management..............MSc 12FT 24PT/PGDip 8FT 20PT/PGCert 4FT 8PT
Sustainable Energy Technology.................................MSc 12FT 24PT

University of Glasgow
Physics: Energy and the Environment............................... MSc 12FT
Sustainable Energy .... MSc 12FT

Glyndwr University
Renewable Energy Systems and Sustainability............... MSc 12FT 24-36PT/MRes 12FT

Heriot-Watt University
Energy..............MSc 12FT 24PT 24-84DL/PGDip 9FT 21PT 21-84DL
Materials for Sustainable and Renewable Energies....... MSc 12FT 24PT/PGDip 9FT 21PT/PGCert 6FT 12PT
Renewable Energy Development (RED) MSc 12FT 24PT 24-84DL/PGDip 9FT 21PT 24-84DL
Renewable Energy Engineering................................MSc 12FT 24PT/PGDip 9FT 21PT
Renewable Energy and Distributed Generation...MSc 12FT 24PT/PGDip 9FT 21PT
Smart Grid and Demand Management......MSc 12FT 24PT/PGDip 9FT 18PT
Sustainability Engineering......... MSc 12FT 24PT/PGDip 9FT 21PT/PGCert 6FT 12PT

University of Hull
Energy Markets... MSc 12FT
Environmental Technology (renewable energy).... MSc 12FT 24PT

Imperial College London
Metals and Energy Finance.. MSc 12FT

Lancaster University
Energy and the Environment ....MSc 12FT 24PT

University of Leeds
Earth, Energy and Environment....................MSc 12FT/PGDip 12FT
Energy and Environment.. MSc 12FT

Liverpool John Moores University
Water, Energy & the Environment ....MSc 12FT 24PT/PGDip 24PT/PGCert 12PT

University of Liverpool
Energy Generation ....MSc 12FT 24PT

London Metropolitan University
Architecture, Energy and Sustainability.................MSc 12FT 24PT

London South Bank University
Sustainable Energy System ....MSc 12FT 24PT

Loughborough University
Built Environment: Energy Demand Studies..................MRes 12FT
Low Carbon Building Design and Modelling.. MSc 12FT 24-60PT/PGDip 12FT 24-60PT/PGCert 12FT 24-60PT
Renewable Energy Systems Technology....... MSc 12FT 36PT 36DL

University of Manchester
Advanced Process Design for Energy.. MSc 12FT 60DL/PGDip 9FT 24DL/PGCert 6FT 12DL

Newcastle University
Power Distribution Engineering.......MSc 12FT 36PT/PGDip 24PT/PGCert 12PT
Renewable Energy Enterprise and Management (REEM)....... MSc 12FT 60PT/PGDip 9FT 60PT/PGCert 6FT 36PT
Renewable Energy Flexible Training Programme (REFLEX)..... MSc 12FT 60PT/PGDip 12FT 60PT/PGCert 6FT

Northumbria University
Renewable and Sustainable Energy Technologies..........MSc 12 or 16FT

University of Nottingham
Electrical Engineering for Sustainable and Renewable Energy..... MSc 12FT/PGDip 9FT
Energy Conservation and Management.....MSc 12FT 24PT/PGDip 9FT 24PT
Energy Conversion and Management (Nottingham/ Ningbo)...... MSc 12FT
Renewable Energy and Architecture (Nottingham/Ningbo) . MSc 12FT
Sustainable Bioenergy ....MSc 12FT 36PT
Sustainable Energy Engineering... MSc 12FT

Queen Mary, University of London
Sustainable Energy Systems......................................MSc 12FT 24PT

Queen's University Belfast
Sustainable Electrical Energy Systems.............................. MSc 12FT

University of Reading
Climate Change & Development ....MSc 12FT 24PT
Construction Management .... MSc 12FT
Economics of Climate Change ....MSc 12FT 24PT
Renewable Energy ....MSc 12FT 24PT/PGDip 9FT 21PT

Robert Gordon University
Commercial Practice for the Energy Sector ....MSc 24DL
Corporate Social Responsibility and Energy ....MSc 12FT 36DL/PGDip 8FT 24DL/PGCert 4FT 12DL
Energy Management.... MSc 12FT 36DL/PGDip 8FT 24DL/PGCert 4FT 12DL
Energy and Sustainability ...MSc 42DL/PGDip 24DL/PGCert 12DL
Offshore Renewables ....MSc 42DL

University of Salford
Industrial and Commercial Combustion Engineering .MSc 36DL/PGDip 12DL/PGCert 12DL
Sustainable Building Design...... MSc 12FT 28PT/PGDip 8FT 20PT/PGCert 4FT 8PT

School of Oriental and African Studies - SOAS
Development Studies...MSc 12FT 24PT
Global Energy and Climate Policy ....MSc 12FT 24PT

University of Sheffield
Environmental and Energy Engineering..... MSc(Eng) 12FT/PGDip 9FT

University of South Wales
Energy Systems Engineering ....MSc 12FT 36PT
Renewable Energy and Resource Management.... MSc 12FT 36PT

University of Southampton
Sustainable Energy Technologies.............................MSc 12FT 24PT

University of Stirling
Energy Management.. MSc 12FT
Energy and the Environment ... MSc 12FT 27PT/MRes 12FT 27PT/PGDip 9FT/PGCert 4FT

University of Strathclyde
Global Energy Management ....MSc 12FT 24PT
Sustainable Engineering: Renewable Energy Systems and the Environment...MSc 12FT 24PT/PGDip 9FT 18PT/PGCert 6FT 12PT

University of Surrey
Renewable Energy Systems Engineering .... MSc 12FT

University of Sussex
Energy Policy for Sustainability ....MSc 12FT 24PT
Sustainable Energy Technology................................MSc 12FT 24PT

Swansea University
Electronics Technology for Sustainable Energy .... MSc 12FT 24-36PT

Teesside University
Energy and Environmental Management.........MSc 12-16FT 24PT

University of the Highlands and Islands
Sustainable energy solutions ....MSc 12FT 24PT/PGDip 12FT 24PT/PGCert 12FT 12PT

University of Ulster
Renewable Energy & Energy Management by e-Learning..PGDip 18DL/MSc 27DL

UCL - University College London
Energy Demand Studies ....MRes 12FT
Energy and Resources: Policy and Practice, Australia .... MSc 24FT 36-48PT
Engineering with Finance................................ MSc 12FT/PGDip 9FT
Materials for Energy and Environment............................. MSc 12FT
Power Systems Engineering ....MSc 12FT 24-60PT

University of Warwick
MBA Global Energy .... MBA 36PT

University of York
Fusion Energy ....MSc 12FT 24PT/Diploma 9FT 18PT/Cert 9FT 18PT

Energy studies
Research Courses

Aston University
Bio-Energy Research Group ....PhD 36FT/MPhil 24FT

Bangor University
Renewable Materials.................. MPhil 24FT 36PT/PhD 36FT 60PT

Cardiff University
Institute of Energy .... EngD 48FT/PhD 36FT/MPhil 12FT

Cranfield University
PhD Studentship - Molecular dynamics simulations of polylactic acid (PLA) biodegradable po ....PhD 36FT

De Montfort University
Energy and Sustainable Development Research ENG503 ... MPhil 12-24FT 24-48PT/PhD 36-48FT 48-72PT

University of Dundee
Electronic Engineering and Physics .... MPhil 24FT
Electronic Engineering and Physics ....MSc by research 12FT
Energy, Petroleum and Mineral Law and Policy .... LLM by research 12FT
Energy, Petroleum and Mineral Law and Policy .... MPhil 24FT
Energy, Petroleum and Mineral Law and Policy ....MSc by research 12FT
Energy, Petroleum and Mineral Law and Policy ....PhD 36FT
Water Law, Policy and Science .... LLM by research 12FT

University of Edinburgh
Energy Systems...............PhD 36FT 72PT/MPhil 24FT 48PT/MSc by research 12FT 24PT

University of Exeter
Environment, Energy and Resilience ....MPhil 36FT 60PT/PhD 36FT 84PT

University of Glasgow
Systems, Power and Energy.............PhD 36-48FT 60-72PT/MSc by research 12-24FT 24-36PT

University of Leeds
Energy and Resources Research Institute ....PhD 36+FT/MPhil 24FT
Low Carbon Technologies..................................Integrated PhD 48FT

Newcastle University
Energy.. PhD 36FT 72PT/MPhil 12FT 24PT

Nottingham Trent University
Applied Energy and Environmental Engineering......... MPhil 18FT 30PT/PhD 33FT 66PT

University of Nottingham
Efficient Fossil Energy Technologies .... EngD 48FT
Fuel, energy and CO2 mitigation.........PhD 36FT 72PT/MPhil 24FT 48PT
Hydrogen, Fuel Cells and their Applications......................PhD 48FT

University of Sheffield
Environmental and Energy Engineering: Integrated Studies......... Integrated PhD 48FT

University of the Highlands and Islands
Energy: Energy Engineering; Energy Technology; Energy and the Environment.................................MPhil 24FT 48PT/PhD 36FT 60PT/MSc by research 12FT 24PT

Fluid mechanics
Taught Courses

University of Cambridge
Fluid Flow in Industry and the Environment................. MPhil 11FT

Cranfield University
Computational Fluid Dynamics......................... MSc 12FT 24-36PT/PGCert 12FT 24-36PT/PGDip 12FT 24-36PT
Process Systems Engineering.....................................MSc 12FT 36PT

De Montfort University
Mechanical Engineering H30071.........MSc 12FT 24-72PT 24+DL/PGDip 8FT 24PT/PGCert 4FT 12PT

Edinburgh Napier University
Mechanical Engineering...MSc 12FT 24PT

University of Exeter
Advanced Civil Engineering .... MSc 12FT
Advanced Mechanical Engineering .... MSc 12FT

Imperial College London
Advanced Computational Methods for Aeronautics, Flow Mgt and Fluid Structure Interaction.................................MSc 12FT 24PT

Manchester Metropolitan University
Mechanical Engineering...MSc 12FT 24PT

University of Manchester
Thermal Power and Fluid Engineering............................... MSc 12FT

University of Nottingham
Civil Engineering: Environmental Fluid Mechanics........ MSc 12FT
Computational Fluid Dynamics.. MSc 12FT

University of Southampton
MSc Advanced Tribology.. MSc 12FT

Staffordshire University
Aeronautical Engineering.................................MSc 12-18FT 24-32PT

University of Strathclyde
Power Plant Engineering.......MSc 36FT/PGDip 24FT/PGCert 12FT
Power Plant Technologies...........MSc 12FT/PGDip 9FT/PGCert 6FT
Quantum Information and Coherence ....MSc 12FT 24PT/PGDip 9FT

Fluid mechanics
Research Courses

Anglia Ruskin University
Engineering Analysis, Simulation and Tribology..... PhD 24 - 60FT 36 - 72PT

University of Leeds
Computational Fluid Dynamics..................PhD 36+FT/MPhil 24FT

University of Manchester
Physics and Chemistry of Minerals and Fluids......PhD 36FT 72PT/MPhil 12FT 24PT/MSc by research 12FT

Physics

University of Oxford
Engineering Science................... DPhil 48FT/MSc by research 24FT

Queen Mary, University of London
Physics and Astrophysics.......... PhD/MPhil/MSc by research 12FT

Mechanics
Taught Courses

Cranfield University
Design of Rotating Machines.............................MSc 12FT 24-36PT

Edinburgh Napier University
Mechanical Engineering..MSc 12FT 24PT

Heriot-Watt University
Robotics, Autonomous and Interactive Systems (RAIS) MSc 12FT/
PGDip 9FT

Manchester Metropolitan University
Mechanical Engineering..MSc 12FT 24PT

Newcastle University
Mechanical Engineering... MSc 12FT
Mechatronics.. MSc 12FT

Queen's University Belfast
Mechanical Engineering (Advanced)..................MSc 12FT 24-36PT

University of Sheffield
Advanced Manufacturing Technologies with the AMRC ....
MSc(Res) 12FT
Advanced Mechanical Engineering .... MSc(Res) 12FT

University of Strathclyde
Advanced Manufacturing: Technology and Systems..... MSc 12FT
24PT/PGDip 9FT 18PT/PGCert 9FT 18PT
Advanced Mechanical Engineering ..... MSc 12FT 24PT/PGDip 9FT
18PT/PGCert 9FT 18PT

Teesside University
Mechanical Engineering..................MSc 12 - 16FT 24PT/PGDip 8FT

UCL - University College London
Mechanical Engineering.............................MSc 12FT 24-60PT

Mechanics
Research Courses

Cardiff University
Gravitational Physics.............PhD 36FT possiblePT/MPhil 12-24FT
possiblePT
Institute of Mechanics and Advanced Materials............ PhD 36FT/
MPhil 12FT

University of Dundee
Mechanical Engineering .... MPhil 24FT
Mechanical Engineering ....MSc by research 12FT

Oxford Brookes University
Mechanical Engineering .... PhD 24-60FT 36-72PT/
MPhil 24-36FT 36-48PT

Queen's University Belfast
Mechanical and Aerospace Engineering .....PhD 36FT 72PT/MPhil
24FT 48PT

Molecular electronics
Taught Courses

Bangor University
Electronic Engineering ....MRes 12FT
Electronic Engineering (Bio-Electronics)..........................MRes 12FT
Electronic Engineering (Nanotechnology).....................MRes 12FT
Electronic Engineering (Organic Electronics) ....MRes 12FT
Electronic Engineering (Polymer Electronics)................MRes 12FT

University of Westminster
Electronics ....MRes 12FT 24PT 24BM
Electronics (Evening Study)..MRes 24PT

Molecular electronics
Research Courses

Bangor University
Electrical Materials Science ....MPhil 24FT/PhD 36FT
Molecular Sensors.....................................MPhil 24FT/PhD 24-36FT
Organic Electronics ....MPhil 24FT/PhD 36FT
Quantum Transport and Nanoelectronics ..MPhil 24FT/PhD 36FT

The Open University
Atomic, Molecular and Optical Physics................ MPhil 15FT 24PT
variableDL
Fabrication .... PhD 36FT 72PT variableDL/MPhil 15FT 24PT
variableDL

Nuclear engineering
Taught Courses

University of Aberdeen
Medical Physics (Computing) .... MSc 12FT/PGDip 9FT

University of Birmingham
Nuclear Decommissioning and Waste Management.... MSc 12FT
24PT
Physics and Technology of Nuclear Reactors.......... MSc 12FT 24PT

University of Central Lancashire
Nuclear Safety, Security and Safeguards....MSc 12FT 24PT/PGDip
9FT 18PT/PGCert 6FT 12PT

Cranfield University, Shrivenham
Guided Weapon Systems .... MSc 12FT

University of Liverpool
Nuclear Science and Technology .... MSc 12FT 72PT
Radioactive Waste Monitoring and Decommissioning...... PGCert
12-60PT

University of Manchester
Nuclear Science and Technology .... MSc 12FT 36PT 36DL/
PGDip 9FT 18PT 18DL/PGCert 9FT 18PT 18DL

University of Salford
Nuclear Medicine Imaging.............................MSc 24PT/PGDip 18PT

University of Sheffield
Nuclear Environmental Science and Technology ....MSc(Eng)
12-24FT
Nuclear Science and Technology .... MSc 12-24FT
Structural and Concrete Engineering.............MSc(Eng) 12FT 24PT/
Diploma 9FT 18PT/Cert 6FT 12PT

University of Southampton
Maritime Engineering Science: Nuclear Safety Management ......
MSc 12FT

University of Strathclyde
Power Plant Engineering.......MSc 36FT/PGDip 24FT/PGCert 12FT
Power Plant Technologies...........MSc 12FT/PGDip 9FT/PGCert 6FT

University of Surrey
Radiation Detection and Instrumentation .... MSc 12FT 24PT

Swansea University
Materials Engineering..MSc 12FT 24-36PT

University of York
Fusion Energy ....MSc 12FT 24PT/Diploma 9FT 18PT/
Cert 9FT 18PT

Nuclear engineering
Research Courses

University of Brighton
Engineering Research Division.......... PhD 24-60FT 36-72PT/MPhil
18-60FT 30-72PT

University of Edinburgh
Nuclear Physics ....PhD 36FT

University of Leeds
Nuclear Engineering ....Integrated PhD 48FT
Radiation research ....PhD 36+FT/MPhil 12+FT

University of Liverpool
Advanced Science (Physical Science Pathway - Nuclear Physics)..
MRes 12FT

University of Manchester
Nuclear Engineering.................... PhD 36FT 72PT/MPhil 12FT 24PT
EngD 48FT
Nuclear Fission DTC...PhD 48FT
Nuclear Physics ....PhD 36FT 72PT/MSc by research 12FT 24PT

The Open University
High Temperature ...PhD 36FT 72PT variableDL/MPhil 15FT 24PT
variableDL
Integrated Waste Systems ....PhD 36FT 72PT variableDL/
MPhil 15FT 24PT variableDL

University of Oxford
Particle and Nuclear Physics...DPhil 48FT/
MSc by research 24-36FT

Offshore engineering
Taught Courses

University of Aberdeen
Oil and Gas Engineering ....MSc 12FT 24PT
Renewable Energy..MSc 12FT/PGDip 9FT

Bangor University
Renewable Materials.............................. PhD by taught 36FT 60PT/
MPhil 24FT 36PT

University of Cambridge
Energy Technology .... MPhil 12FT

University of Central Lancashire
Renewable Energy Engineering .... MSc 12FT 24PT/PGDip 24PT
Wind Energy Engineering............MSc 12FT 24PT/PGDip 9FT 24PT

Cranfield University
Offshore and Ocean Technology with Offshore Materials
Engineering ....MSc 12FT 24-60PT/MTech 24FT/PGCert 5FT 24PT/
PGDip 6FT 24PT
Offshore and Ocean Technology with Offshore Renewable
Energy ....MSc 12FT 24-60PT/MTech 24FT/PGDip 6FT 24PT/
PGCert 5FT 24PT
Offshore and Ocean Technology with Pipeline Engineering
........MSc 12FT 24-60PT/MTech 24FT/PGCert 5FT 24PT/PGDip 6FT
24PT
Offshore and Ocean Technology with Risk Management ...... MSc
12FT 24-60PT/MTech 24FT/PGDip 6FT 24PT/PGCert 5FT 24PT

Offshore and Ocean Technology with Subsea Engineering ... MSc
12FT 24-60PT/MTech 24FT/PGDip 6FT 24PT/PGCert 5FT 24PT

Edinburgh Napier University
Renewable Energy...MSc 12FT 24PT

University of Exeter
Energy Policy..MSc 12FT 24PT
Environment, Energy and Resilience ....MRes 12FT 24PT

Heriot-Watt University
Petroleum Geoscience (PetGeo) .... MSc 12FT
Renewable Energy Engineering.......................MSc 12FT 24PT/
PGDip 9FT 21PT
Reservoir Evaluation and Management ....MSc 12FT 24PT

University of Hull
Petroleum, Oil and Gas: Chemical Engineering Management......
MSc 12FT
Petroleum, Oil and Gas: Chemical Engineering Technologies ....
MSc 12FT

Kingston University
Renewable Energy Engineering ....MSc 12FT 24PT

University of Leeds
Oilfield Corrosion Engineering................................MSc(Eng) 12FT

Liverpool John Moores University
Marine and Offshore Engineering ....MSc 12FT 24PT/PGDip 9FT
18PT/PGCert 6FT 12PT/CPD 3-4FT 3-4PT

Newcastle University
Marine Structures and Integrity...............................MSc 12 or 24FT
Marine and Offshore Power Systems...............MSc 12 or 24FT
Offshore Engineering ....MSc 12 or 24FT
Offshore and Environmental Technology................MSc 12 or 24FT
Pipeline Engineering.... MSc 12FT 24PT/PGDip 12FT 24PT/PGCert
12FT 24PT
Subsea Engineering and Management ....MSc 12FT 24-36PT

Northumbria University
Renewable and Sustainable Energy Technologies..........MSc 12 or
16FT

University of Nottingham
Electrical Engineering for Sustainable and Renewable Energy .....
MSc 12FT/PGDip 9FT

Robert Gordon University
Energy Management.... MSc 12FT 36DL/PGDip 8FT 24DL/PGCert
4FT 12DL
Energy and Sustainability ...MSc 42DL/PGDip 24DL/PGCert 12DL
Offshore Renewables ....MSc 42DL
Subsea Engineering ....MSc 36DL

University of Salford
Petroleum and Gas Engineering...................... MSc 12FT/PGDip 9FT

University of Strathclyde
Offshore Floating Systems ....MSc 12FT/PGDip 9FT
Ship and Offshore Structures.......................MSc 12FT/PGDip 9FT
Ship and Offshore Technology .... MSc 24FT
Subsea Engineering .... MSc 12FT/PGDip 9FT
Sustainable Engineering: Marine Technology .... MSc 12FT/PGDip
9FT
Sustainable Engineering: Offshore Renewable Energy MSc 12FT/
PGDip 9FT

Swansea University
Materials Engineering............................MSc 12FT 24-36PT

Teesside University
Energy and Environmental Management.........MSc 12-16FT 24PT

UCL - University College London
Energy Demand Studies ....MRes 12FT
Energy and Resources: Policy and Practice, Australia .... MSc 24FT
36-48PT

Offshore engineering
Research Courses

Cardiff University
Institute of Energy .... EngD 48FT/PhD 36FT/MPhil 12FT

University of Exeter
Environment, Energy and Resilience ....MPhil 36FT 60PT/
PhD 36FT 84PT
Offshore Renewable Energy .... EngD 48FT
Renewable Energy MSc by research 12FT 24PT/MPhil 36FT 60PT/
PhD 48FT 80PT

Heriot-Watt University
Petroleum Engineering.......... PhD 36FT 48PT/MPhil 12-24FT 24PT

Newcastle University
Energy...................................... PhD 36FT 72PT/MPhil 12FT 24PT

UCL - University College London
Offshore Engineering .... PhD 36FT 60PT

Optoelectronics
Taught Courses

Bangor University
Broadband and Optical Communications.............MSc 12FT 24PT
Electronic Engineering ....MSc 12FT MRes 12FT

Physics

Electronic Engineering (Microwave Devices)................MRes 12FT
Electronic Engineering (Optical Communications).......MRes 12FT
Electronic Engineering (Optoelectronics)......................MRes 12FT
Optical Communications..............PhD by taught 36FT/MPhil 24FT

Cardiff University
Biophotonics...MSc 12FT 24PT

University College Cork
Photonics..MSc 12FT 36FT

Edinburgh Napier University
Design (Lighting) ....MA/MDes 12FT

Heriot-Watt University
Photonics and Optoelectronic Devices ....MSc 12FT 24PT

King's College London
Analytical Science for Industry ....MSc 12FT 24PT

Nottingham Trent University
Medical and Materials Imaging...MRes 12FT

University of Nottingham
Photonic and Optical Engineering .... MSc 12FT/PGDip 9FT

University of Sheffield
Semiconductor Photonics and Electronics..............MSc(Eng) 12FT

University of St Andrews
Photonics and Optoelectronic Devices .... MSc 12FT

University of Strathclyde
Optical Technologies..............................MSc 12FT 24PT/PGDip 9FT

UCL - University College London
Light and Lighting ....MSc 12FT 24-60PT
Photonics Systems Development......................................MRes 12FT

University of Warwick
Electronic Systems .... MSc 12FT

Optoelectronics
Research Courses

Bangor University
Optoelectronics..MPhil 24FT/PhD 36FT

Cardiff University
Photons and Matter...............PhD 36FT possiblePT/MPhil 12-24FT
possiblePT

University of Edinburgh
Molecular and Optical Physics...PhD 36FT

University of Nottingham
Applied Optics............................... PhD 36FT 72PT/MPhil 24FT 48PT
Biophysics, Imaging and Optical Science ....PhD 36FT 48PT/MPhil
24FT 36PT

The Open University
Plasma Science and Engineering........ PhD 36FT 72PT variableDL/
MPhil 15FT 24PT variableDL

Swansea University
Cold Atoms and Quantum Optics MSc by research 12FT 12-24PT

Photonics
Taught Courses

Bangor University
Broadband and Optical Communications...............MSc 12FT 24PT
Electronic Engineering ....MRes 12FT
Electronic Engineering (Microwave Devices)...................MRes 12FT
Electronic Engineering (Optical Communications).......MRes 12FT
Electronic Engineering (Optoelectronics)......................MRes 12FT
Optical Communications..............PhD by taught 36FT/MPhil 24FT

University of Birmingham
RF and Microwave Engineering ....MSc 12FT 24PT
RF and Microwave Engineering with Industrial Studies MSc 18FT

Cardiff University
Biophotonics...MSc 12FT 24PT

University College Cork
Photonics..MSc 12FT 36PT

University of Derby
Still and Moving Image..MA 12FT

University of Greenwich
Science (Open)...MSc 12FT 24-36PT

Heriot-Watt University
Photonics and Optoelectronic Devices ....MSc 12FT 24PT

Imperial College London
Optics and Photonics...MSc 12FT 24PT
Plasmonics and Metamaterials ....MRes 12FT

University of Liverpool
Engineering Applications of Lasers........... MSc(Eng) 12FT 24-36PT

University of Sheffield
Semiconductor Photonics and Electronics..............MSc(Eng) 12FT

University of St Andrews
Erasmus Mundus Masters: Photonics. Erasmus Mundus Masters
24FT
Photonics and Optoelectronic Devices .... MSc 12FT

University of Strathclyde
Optical Technologies..............................MSc 12FT 24PT/PGDip 9FT
Photonics and Device Microfabrication........ MSc 12FT/PGDip 9FT
Quantum Information and Coherence ....MSc 12FT 24PT/
PGDip 9FT

Teesside University
Control and Electronics....................MSc 12-18FT 24PT/PGDip 8FT

Photonics
Research Courses

Aston University
Photonics Research Group ....PhD 36FT/MPhil 24FT

Bangor University
Optoelectronics..MPhil 24FT/PhD 36FT

University of Cambridge
Photonic Systems Development.......................................MRes 12FT

Cardiff University
Photons and Matter...............PhD 36FT possiblePT/MPhil 12-24FT
possiblePT

Heriot-Watt University
Photonics.. EngD 48FT

University of Leeds
Institute of Microwaves and Photonics.....PhD 36+FT/MPhil 24FT

University of Manchester
Photon Physics ....PhD 36FT 72PT/MSc by research 12FT 24PT

University of Nottingham
Electromagnetics Design (by Research).......MSc by research 12FT
Photonic and Radio Frequency Engineering.........PhD 36FT tbcPT/
MPhil 24FT tbcPT/MRes 12FT tbcPT

University of Salford
Photonics and Non-Linear Science......PhD 36FT 60PT/MPhil 24FT
24PT/MRes 24FT 24PT/MSc by research 24FT 24PT

University of Southampton
Photonics... PhD 42FT 72PT

Swansea University
Cold Atoms and Quantum Optics ....MSc by research 12FT

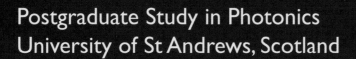

Physics

12-24PT
Lattice Gauge Theory....MSc by research 12FT 24PT

Physics
Taught Courses

Anglia Ruskin University
Forensic Science....MSc 12 - 15FT 24 - 30PT

Barts and the London School of Medicine and Dentistry
Medical Electronics and Physics....MSc 12FT 24PT

Bournemouth University
Applied Sciences by Research....MSc 12FT 24PT

University of Bristol
Physics....MSc 12FT

Brunel University
Renewable Energy Engineering....MSc 12FT

Cardiff University
Biophotonics....MSc 12FT 24PT

University College Cork
Applied Science (Applied Physics)....MSc 12FT 24PT PGDip 9FT

University of Cumbria
Subject Knowledge Enhancement - Physics 36 weeks...Graduate Certificate 8FT

University of Dundee
Non-Graduating Taught Postgraduate in School of Engineering, Physics and Mathematics....PG module variableFT

Durham University
Particles, Strings and Cosmology....MSc 12FT

University of East London
Radio Frequency and Microwave Engineering ....MSc 12FT 24PT/PGDip 8FT 16PT/PGCert 4FT 8PT

University of Edinburgh
Acoustics and Music Technology....MSc 12FT 24PT
Carbon Capture & Storage....MSc 12FT 36PT
Mathematical Physics....MSc 12FT
Structural Engineering and Mechanics....MSc 12FT 21-72PT/PGDip 9FT 18-60PT

National University of Ireland Galway
Medical Physics....MSc 12FT

University of Glasgow
Astrophysics....MSc 12FT
Physics: Advanced Materials....MSc 12FT
Physics: Energy and the Environment....MSc 12FT
Physics: Global Security....MSc 12FT
Physics: Life Sciences....MSc 12FT
Physics: Nuclear Technology....MSc 12FT
Theoretical Physics....MSc 12FT

Heriot-Watt University
Renewable Energy and Distributed Generation...MSc 12FT 24PT/PGDip 9FT 21PT

University of Huddersfield
Accelerator Science....MSc 12FT
MSc Accelerator Science....MSc 12FT
Pharmaceutical and Analytical Science....MSc 12FT 24-48PT

University of Hull
Physics....MSc 12FT
Physics with Nanotechnology....MSc 12FT

Imperial College London
Controlled Quantum Dynamics....MRes 12FT
Physics....MSc 12FT
Quantum Fields and Fundamental Forces....MSc 12FT 24PT
Shock Physics....MSc 12FT 24PT

University of Kent
Physics (Euromaster)....MSc 24FT

King's College London
Molecular Biophysics....MRes 12FT
Physics....MSc 12FT 24PT GradDip 12FT
Theoretical Physics....MSc 12FT 24PT

University of Leeds
Physics of the Earth and Atmosphere....MRes 12FT
Quantum Technologies....MSc 12FT/PGDip 12FT/PGCert 12FT

University of Limerick
Applied Physics....MSc 12FT

University of Liverpool
Advanced Science (Physical Sciences pathway) MSc 12FT/PGCert 12FT/PGDip 12FT
Medical Physics and Clinical Engineering....MSc 12FT 24PT
Radioactive Waste Monitoring and Decommissioning....PGCert 12-60PT
Radiometrics: Instrumentation and Modelling....MSc 12FT 72PT

Loughborough University
Experimental Condensed Matter Physics....MSc 12FT 24PT
Materials Physics and Applications....MSc 12FT 24PT
Psychophysics....MSc 12FT 24PT
Quantum Information and Computing....MSc 12FT 24PT
Quantum Structures and Phase Transitions....MSc 12FT 24PT
Research Studies in Physics....MSc 12FT 24PT

Surface Physics....MSc 12FT 24PT

National University of Ireland, Maynooth
Applied Physics....HDip 12FT
Mathematical Science....HDip 12FT

Nottingham Trent University
Subject Knowledge Enhancement (SKE) Courses (Chemistry, Physics, Mathematics)....SKE 9FT

University of Nottingham
Physics (by research)....MSc(Res) 12FT

The Open University
Professional Science....MSc variableDL
Science....MSc variableDL

University of Oxford
Philosophy of Physics....MSt 12FT

University of Portsmouth
Science....MRes 12FT 24PT

Queen Mary, University of London
Astronomy and Astrophysics....PGCert 9PT
Astrophysics....MSc 12FT 24PT
Medical Electronics and Physics....MSc 12FT 24PT

Queen's University Belfast
Plasma Physics....MSc 12FT
Plasma and Vacuum Technology....MSc Up to 96PT

University of Reading
Applied Meteorology....MSc 12FT 24PT/PGDip 12FT 24PT
Applied Meteorology and Climate with Management....MSc 12FT 24PT
Atmosphere, Ocean & Climate....MSc 12FT/PGDip 12FT

Royal Holloway, University of London
Euromasters in Physics....MSc 24FT
Nanotechnology and Low Temperature Physics....MSc 12FT 24PT
Physics by Research....MSc 12FT 24PT

University of Strathclyde
High Power Radio Frequency Science and Engineering.... MSc 12FT 24-36PT/PGDip 9FT/PGCert 9FT
Optical Technologies....MSc 12FT 24PT/PGDip 9FT
Quantum Information and Coherence....MSc 12FT 24PT/PGDip 9FT

University of Surrey
Physics (EuroMasters)....MSc 24FT/PGDip 12FT
Radiation and Environmental Protection....MSc 12FT 24PT

University of Sussex
Cosmology....MSc 12FT 24PT
Frontiers of Quantum Technology....MSc 12FT 24PT
Particle Physics....MSc 12FT 24PT
Physics....MSc 12FT 24PT
Physics (Euromasters)....MSc 24FT

Swansea University
Clinical Science (Medical Physics)....MSc 36PT
Modelling, Uncertainty and Data....MSc 12FT 24/36PT

UCL - University College London
Advanced High Energy Physics....MSc 21FT
Astrophysics....MSc 12FT 24PT/PGDip 9FT 18PT
Physics....MSc 12FT 24PT/PGDip 9FT 18PT
Physics and Engineering in Medicine by Distance Learning .. MSc 24-60PT/PGDip 24-60PT/PGCert 24-60PT
Physics and Engineering in Medicine: Biomedical Engineering and Medical Imaging....MSc 12FT 24PT
Physics and Engineering in Medicine: Radiation Physics....PGDip 9FT 18PT
Space Science....MSc 12FT 24PT/PGDip 9FT 18PT

University of Warwick
Complexity Science....MSc 12FT/PGDip 12FT/PGCert 12FT

Physics
Research Courses

University of Aberdeen
Physics....PhD 36FT/MPhil 24FT/MSc by research 12FT 24PT

Aberystwyth University
Physics....MPhil 12FT 24PT PhD 36FT 60PT

Anglia Ruskin University
Engineering Analysis, Simulation and Tribology.... PhD 24 - 60FT 36 - 72PT

Barts and the London School of Medicine and Dentistry
Medical Electronics and Physics....PhD/MPhil/MSc by research 12FT

University of Bath
Physics PhD....PhD 24-48FT 36-72PT/MPhil 12-36FT 24-48PT

University of Bristol
Physics....PhD 36FT/MSc by research 12FT

University of Cambridge
Applied Mathematics and Theoretical Physics....PhD 36FT
Physics....PhD 36FT 60PT/MPhil 12FT

Cardiff University
Institute of Medical Engineering and Medical Physics.... MPhil 12-24FT/PhD 36FT/EngD 48FT

University of Dundee
Electronic Engineering and Physics....MPhil 24FT MSc by research 12FT
Electronic Engineering and Physics....PhD 36FT
Non-Graduating Research in Engineering, Physics and Mathematics (6 months or more)....Non-Grad 6-24FT
Non-Graduating Research in Engineering, Physics and Mathematics (less than 6 months)....Non-Grad 1-5FT

Durham University
Physics....PhD 36FT 60PT/MSc by research 12FT 24PT

University of Edinburgh
Astrophysics....PhD 36FT
Condensed Matter....PhD 36FT
Geometry and Topology....PhD 36FT 72PT
Mathematical Physics....PhD 36FT 72PT
Medical Physics & Medical Engineering....PhD 36FT 48PT/MPhil 24FT 36PT/MSc by research 12FT 24PT
Molecular and Optical Physics....PhD 36FT
Nuclear Physics....PhD 36FT
Particle Physics....PhD 36FT

University of Essex
Applied Physics....PhD 36FT 72PT/MPhil 24FT 48PT/MSc by research 12FT 24PT

University of Exeter
Physics....PhD 48FT 84PT 84DL/MPhil 36FT 60PT 60DL

National University of Ireland Galway
College of Science.... PhD 48FT 72PT/MSc by research 24FT 48PT/Structured PhD 48FT

University of Glasgow
Physics and Astronomy....PhD 36FT/MSc by research 12FT

Heriot-Watt University
Physics....PhD 36FT 48PT/MPhil 24FT/MSc by research 12FT

University of Hertfordshire
Light Scattering & Analytical Systems....MPhil 24FT 48PT/PhD 36FT 72PT

University of Hull
Physics....PhD 36FT/MSc by research 12FT
Physics (NewRoutePhD)....PhD 48FT

Imperial College London
Department of Physics....PhD 36FT 68PT/MPhil 24FT

Institute of Cancer Research
Physics....PhD

University of Kent
Physics... PhD 36FT 60PT/MPhil 24FT 36PT/MSc by research 12FT 24PT

King's College London
Physics Research....PhD 36FT 48-72PT/MPhil 36FT 48-72PT

Lancaster University
Physics.... PhD 36-48FT 48-60PT/MPhil 24-36FT 36-60PT

University of Leeds
Department of Physics and Astronomy...PhD 36+FT/MPhil 24FT/MSc by research 12FT

University of Leicester
Physics and Astronomy.... PhD 36-48FT 36-72PT/MPhil 12FT 24-48PT

University of Liverpool
Advanced Science (Physical Science Pathway - Astrophysics).... MRes 12FT
Advanced Science (Physical Science Pathway - Nanoscale and Condensed Matter Physics)....MRes 12FT
Advanced Science (Physical Science Pathway - Nuclear Physics).. MRes 12FT
Advanced Science (Physical Science Pathway - Particle Physics)... MRes 12FT
Advanced Science (Physical Sciences pathway)....MRes 12FT
Physics.... PhD 24-48FT 48-84PT/MPhil 12-48FT 24-72PT

Loughborough University
Physics.... PhD 36FT 60PT/MPhil 24FT 36PT

University of Manchester
Condensed Matter Physics.... PhD 36FT 72PT/MSc by research 12FT 24PT
Particle Physics....PhD 36FT 72PT/MSc by research 12FT 24PT
Physics....PhD 36-48FT 72-96PT/MSc by research 12PT
Theoretical Physics....PhD 36FT 72PT/MSc by research 12FT 24PT

Newcastle University
Physics.... PhD 36FT 72PT/MPhil 12FT 24PT

University of Nottingham
Condensed Matter Theory....PhD 36FT
Experimental Condensed Matter and Nanoscience PhD 36-48FT/MRes 12FT/MPhil 36FT
Particle Theory....PhD 36-48FT
Ultracold Atoms....PhD 36FT 72PT/MPhil 24FT 48PT

The Open University
Astrochemistry....MPhil 15FT 24PT variableDL/PhD 36FT 72PT variableDL
Atomic, Molecular and Optical Physics....MPhil 15FT 24PT variableDL

Physics

Cosmology and extragalactic astronomy .... PhD 15FT 24PT variableDL/MPhil 36FT 72PT variableDL
Exoplanets and planetary physics... MPhil 15FT 24PT variableDL/PhD 36FT 72PT variableDL
High Temperature ... PhD 36FT 72PT variableDL/MPhil 15FT 24PT variableDL
Physics....................... PhD 36FT 72PT variableDL/MPhil 15FT 24PT variableDL
Physics education.... MPhil 15FT 24PT variableDL/PhD 36FT 72PT variableDL
Plasma Science and Engineering........ PhD 36FT 72PT variableDL/MPhil 15FT 24PT variableDL
STEM Education and engagement .... PhD 36FT 72PT variableDL
Star formation.......... MPhil 15FT 24PT variableDL/PhD 36FT 72PT variableDL
Stellar astrophysics .... MPhil 15FT 24PT variableDL/PhD 36FT 72PT variableDL
Theoretical and computational physics .... PhD 36FT 72PT variableDL/MPhil 15FT 24PT variableDL

University of Oxford
Atmospheric, Oceanic and Planetary Physics................. DPhil 48FT
Atomic and Laser Physics .... DPhil 48FT
Condensed Matter Physics........ DPhil 48FT/MSc by research 36FT
Particle and Nuclear PhysicsDPhil 48FT/MSc by research 24-36FT
Theoretical Physics............... DPhil 48FT/MSc by research 24-36FT

University of Portsmouth
Cosmology and Gravitation....... MPhil 24FT 48PT/PhD 36FT 72PT

Queen Mary, University of London
Physics and Astrophysics.......... PhD/MPhil/MSc by research 12FT

Queen's University Belfast
Atomistic Simulation.................. PhD 36FT 72PT/MPhil 24FT 48PT
Plasma Physics .... PhD 36FT 72PT/MPhil 24FT 48PT
Theoretical Atomic, Molecular and Optical Physics ....PhD 36FT 72PT/MPhil 24FT 48PT

Royal Holloway, University of London
Physics... MPhil 24FT

University of Salford
Atomic Collisions in Solids and Ion Beam PhysicsPhD 36FT 60PT/MPhil 24FT 24PT/MRes 24FT 24PT/MSc by research 24FT 24PT
Chemical Physics and Biomaterials ....PhD 36FT 60PT/MPhil 24FT 24PT/MRes 24FT 24PT/MSc by research 24FT 24PT
Institute for Materials ResearchPhD 36FT/MSc by research 12FT/MPhil 12FT

University of Sheffield
Physics and Astronomy............... PhD 36FT 72PT/MPhil 24FT 48PT

University of Southampton
PhD Opportunities in Physics and Astronomy....... PhD 36FT 72PT

University of St Andrews
Physics and Astronomy... PhD 42-48FT

University of Strathclyde
Physics - Research........................ MPhil 12FT/PhD 36FT/EngD 36FT

University of Surrey
Physics... MPhil 21FT 33PT/PhD 36FT 45PT

University of Sussex
Physics Research Programme............ PhD 24-48FT 36-72PT/MPhil 12-36FT 24-48PT

Swansea University
Antimatter Physics....................................MSc by research 12FT 24PT
Cold Atoms and Quantum Optics MSc by research 12FT 12-24PT
Laser Physics ....MSc by research 12FT 24PT
Lattice Gauge Theory............................MSc by research 12FT 24PT
Nanotechnology (Physics)....................MSc by research 12FT 24PT
Physics .... PhD 36FT 72PT/MPhil 24FT 48PT
Quantum Fields and Strings.................MSc by research 12FT
Theoretical Particle Physics...........................MSc by research 12FT

UCL - University College London
Mathematics and Physics in the Life Sciences and Experimental Biology...MRes +PhD 48FT
Space and Climate Physics.. PhD 36FT 60PT

University of Warwick
Physics.......................... PhD 36FT 60PT/MSc by research 12FT 24PT

University of the West of Scotland
Department of Electronic Engineering and Physics.....PhD/MPhil

University of York
Physics... PhD 36FT 72PT/MPhil 24FT 48PT/MSc by research 12FT 24PT

Underwater technology
Taught Courses

University of Aberdeen
Oil and Gas Engineering ....MSc 12FT 24PT
Subsea Engineering .... MSc 12FT 24PT 24DL

Bangor University
Renewable Materials............................... PhD by taught 36FT 60PT/MPhil 24FT 36PT

Cranfield University
Offshore and Ocean Technology with Offshore Materials Engineering ....MSc 12FT 24-60PT/MTech 24FT/PGCert 5FT 24PT/PGDip 6FT 24PT
Offshore and Ocean Technology with Offshore Renewable Energy ..MSc 12FT 24-60PT/MTech 24FT/PGDip 6FT 24PT/PGCert 5FT 24PT
Offshore and Ocean Technology with Risk Management ...... MSc 12FT 24-60PT/MTech 24FT/PGDip 6FT 24PT/PGCert 5FT 24PT
Renewable Energy Technology ....MSc 12FT 24-60PT/PGDip 6FT 24PT/PGCert 5FT 24PT

University of Dundee
Water Law (PGDip part time) ...PGDip 18-60DL/PGCert 12-60DL/LLM 24-60DL

University of Exeter
Environment, Energy and Resilience ....MRes 12FT 24PT

Heriot-Watt University
Marine Biodiversity and Biotechnology .....MSc 12FT 24PT/PGDip 9FT 21PT
Marine Resource Development and Protection....MSc 12FT 24PT/PGDip 9FT 21PT
Robotics, Autonomous and Interactive Systems (RAIS) MSc 12FT/PGDip 9FT

Newcastle University
Marine Structures and Integrity...............................MSc 12 or 24FT
Marine Technology Education Consortium ...MSc 24-60PT/PGDip 24-60PT/PGCert 24-60PT/CPD 2PT
Offshore Engineering ....MSc 12 or 24FT

University of Nottingham
Electrical Engineering for Sustainable and Renewable Energy ..... MSc 12FT/PGDip 9FT

Plymouth University
Marine Renewable Energy ....MSc 12FT/MRes 12FT

Robert Gordon University
Offshore Renewables ....MSc 42DL

University of Southampton
Freshwater Sciences ....MRes 12FT

University of St Andrews
Ecosystem-based Management of Marine Systems....MRes 12FT

University of Strathclyde
Offshore Floating Systems .... MSc 12FT/PGDip 9FT
Ship and Offshore Structures .... MSc 12FT/PGDip 9FT
Ship and Offshore Technology .... MSc 24FT
Sustainable Engineering: Marine Technology ....MSc 12FT/PGDip 9FT
Sustainable Engineering: Offshore Renewable Energy MSc 12FT/PGDip 9FT

Underwater technology
Research Courses

Cranfield University
Marine Technology..................................... Integrated PhD 36-48FT

University of Exeter
Environment, Energy and Resilience ....MPhil 36FT 60PT/PhD 36FT 84PT

Newcastle University
Marine Technology...................... PhD 36FT 72PT/MPhil 12FT 24PT
Technology in the Marine Environment ....MRes 12FT

We've got your career covered

Pick up our guides to graduate jobs and postgraduate study at your university careers service or graduate fair.

A comprehe
of graduat

Postgrad

Issue 2 – Spring 2014

Choose your course

Work Experience & Internships

2013/14

Your guide to shaping your future

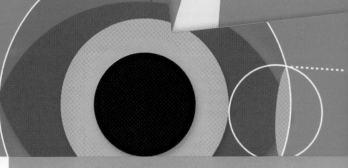

Postg
– Autumn 2

lore

options

Postgraduate Directory

2013/14

Find your perfect postgraduate course

Law

2013/14

www.prospects.ac.uk/la

Helping your legal career take shape

View digital editions and keep up with the latest

Prospects

Arts and humanities

This section includes articles and profiles specifically relating to the arts and humanities subject areas. There are student and graduate case studies, advice from an expert in the field and features on new and popular courses. Browse the following pages to gain a greater understanding of your chosen subject field and hear from other people who have been in a similar position

GOING TO APPLY? MENTION PROSPECTS' ADVICE ON YOUR APPLICATION

From passion to profession

Postgraduate courses in the arts and humanities let students pursue their passions while helping them gain the skills required to succeed in the world of work

Subjects that fall under the vast umbrella of arts and humanities are considered by some to amount to little more than hobbies and pastimes. The concern is that studying these subjects doesn't lead to employment as readily as a more vocational course in law or engineering, for example.

However, as the Arts and Humanities Research Council (AHRC) states, these disciplines cover 'the things in life that make life worth living'. In addition, they help to develop an understanding of the creative industries and they are vital to help boost the UK economy.

Tailored courses

With a postgraduate qualification in say, history, classics or cinema, a traditional role in a 9am to 5pm setting might not be your calling after you graduate. But that doesn't mean you're going to be stuck for employment – arts and humanities subjects can often appeal to the most entrepreneurial and adventurous, meaning freelance work and further study tends to be a popular option.

What's more, course providers realise that the job market remains extremely competitive and are tailoring their programmes accordingly. There are plenty of opportunities to increase your employability while at university, and students are encouraged by their departments

to seek out work experience, internships and placements during further study. This can be productive in the long run if you are to break into your preferred industry and begin flexing your creative muscle.

On completion of postgraduate study, arts and humanities graduates are equipped with the vocational knowledge and skills required to compete and succeed in the world of work.

That said, not all students in this area choose courses with their career in mind – a thirst for knowledge and a desire to explore their interests and become experts in a particular field often attracts postgraduates.

Whether you're after a course that will guarantee career progression or one that simply appeals because of your love of the subject, there is a plethora of programmes on offer, from drama therapy and photography, to linguistics and ancient history.

Ensuring you choose the right course is fundamental and it's important that you can relate the skills gained through your study to the requirements of employers.

....

'It's important that you can relate the skills gained through your study to the requirements of employers'

Make the headlines

Postgraduate journalism students at the University of Sheffield are required to work in a particular area of the city and write news stories in the first three months of their course. Students taking the MA Magazine Journalism will undertake a special project, designing, writing and producing their own weekly magazine, mirroring the skills they need once in employment.

The MA Journalism at Brunel University London is accredited by the National Council for the Training of Journalists (NCTJ), meaning that students on the course receive a Masters degree, as well as an NCTJ diploma. The diploma examines students in reporting, public affairs, media law, video and writing shorthand. Not all courses will be accredited by the NCTJ, though, so it's important to check with the university to which you are applying.

Colm Griffith is a journalism lecturer at the University of Central Lancashire (UCLan). He says that an MA in journalism should provide students with all the skills they need to enter a career in the industry.

'Such courses should also expose the student to experts in the field and put them in a position where they can pursue hands-on experience in the form of a placement, work experience or internship.

'If postgraduate students have studied a completely different subject at undergraduate level, such as politics or a foreign language, the MA should enable the student to convert that knowledge into something that will lead to a career in journalism.'

Stay tuned

Another popular discipline for arts and humanities postgraduate students is music.

Upon graduating from a course, they may find themselves teaching, doing session work,

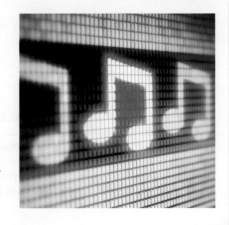

being commissioned to create their own musical pieces or working on music for film and television.

Many students who go on to study music at postgraduate level will have the option to study a research degree. The Royal Northern College of Music (RNCM) offers such programmes. Composers and performers, musicologists and music educators spend three or six years (full time or part time respectively) exploring a specific area in detail, leading to original contributions to the knowledge of music.

Professor Jane Ginsborg, programme leader for research degrees at the RNCM, has advice for those considering a research degree in music.

'First, you need to identify the broad topic you want to explore. Second, so as to formulate the questions you are going to ask, you need to read everything you can find that is relevant to that topic, and figure out where the gaps are. What questions remain unanswered? How could they be answered? By the time you have formulated your questions, you will have a good idea of who is working in the field and in which institutions they are based.'

She goes on to suggest that you must contact the people in your field, tell them a little about yourself and your questions and ask them if they are prepared to supervise your research. If they agree, you will then have to submit a research proposal, which will be assessed by several people. If it fits with your chosen supervisor's research interest and can feasibly be completed within three years (full time) at your chosen institution, you may then be called for interview.

'The bottom line is that you have to do your homework. Know your topic, questions, supervisor and proposal thoroughly if you are to be successful, not only in your application but also as a postgraduate research student,' Professor Ginsborg adds.

Environmentally friendly

There are other postgraduate arts and humanities courses that offer a route into a successful career, based on a different kind of creative vision. Landscape architecture provides students with a chance to secure a job in a thriving industry, as well as help make the world a greener place. It focuses on the planning of spaces in which we live, work and engage with our surroundings, and how we use land and resources.

The course has grown in popularity in recent years, among those who have already studied the subject at university and want to gain a professional qualification, as well as among students from other disciplines – related or otherwise – who want a change of scenery.

According to Professor Kathryn Moore, professor of landscape architecture at the Birmingham Institute of Art and Design (BIAD), a faculty of Birmingham

City University, an increasing desire to make the world greener and more eco friendly has created jobs in the UK and abroad. This has led to a rise in demand for courses of this kind.

'Demand is beginning to grow in the UK in response to an increasing awareness of the significance of the landscape as the cultural, physical and social context of our lives. People also now recognise that the aesthetics of a place is a vital component of sustainable economic growth and that the landscape is the context within which the processes of development take place,' she explains.

Professor Moore adds that because the environment is firmly on the political and societal agenda, landscape architects have a vital role to play in master-planning, detailed design and implementation, and creating sustainable policy.

Students leave the course with a professional qualification, as well as established international connections, experience working on high-profile infrastructure projects and the opportunity to apply to become a member of the Landscape Institute (LI).

Getting the most out of postgraduate study in the arts and humanities ultimately comes down to choosing the right course. While further study in this vast area isn't all about employability and careers, it's clear that there are now many programmes that combine theoretical an practical learning, with the chance to interact with, and learn from, industry professionals and experts. All of which will improve your chances of swimming, rather than sinking, when you graduate.

KEY QUESTIONS

If you're considering postgraduate study in an arts and humanities subject, but are concerned the course might not set you up for the world of work, ask yourself these questions:

Does the course give students employability skills?

Does the programme have links to industry professionals?

Does the university invite guest lecturers to speak?

What are the job prospects currently like in the industry?

What jobs have alumni secured since graduating?

Does a mandatory work placement make up part of the course?

Does the course cover basic business or entrepreneurial skills?

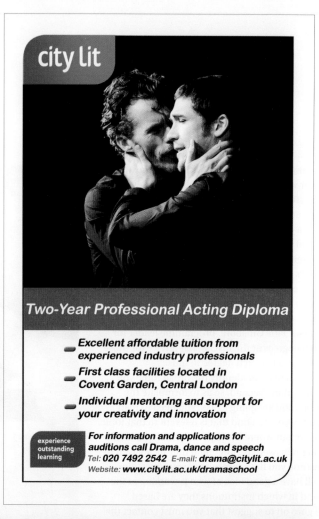

A design for life

Prepare for a career in graphic design by furthering your knowledge and expanding your professional portfolio...

Graphic design is also known as visual communication and is utilised for a range of reasons, from catching the attention of consumers to arranging the layout of magazines or instructing people how to use a product.

To apply to a graphic design postgraduate course you will usually be required to have studied an equivalent or relevant subject at undergraduate level or have significant experience in the industry.

Courses at this level can be competitive and for most programmes you will have to write a solid letter of intent and display examples of your work as part of the admission process.

If you want to work as a professional artist or designer in any capacity, a graphic design course can be a great stepping stone. Creative directors, art workers and web designers are just some of the roles that graphic designers can go into following postgraduate study.

Why do further study?

Students do Masters courses for a variety of reasons but the main purpose is to enhance their professional profile. In most cases, an MA portfolio shows a broader understanding of all the contexts that feed into a professional design brief, which appeals to employers.

While any portfolio work gathered on a Bachelors design programme might show you are ready for a career in the discipline, an MA shows that you can also contribute new thought and practice in the subject area.

Postgraduate graphic design courses allow you to explore and research comprehensively

into visual language, audiences, markets and technologies. You will learn how to link theory and practice more effectively, as well as how to manage large-scale projects. At the same time, you can set personal goals for learning new skills and processes at a level that will distinguish you from other candidates.

Top facilities

Peter Lester, a senior lecturer in graphic design at Nottingham Trent University (NTU), says one of the other benefits of further study in the discipline is access to top-of-the-range facilities and equipment.

'Postgraduate courses at NTU have use of a dedicated studio, meeting rooms and computer facilities. A range of other workshop facilities are shared with the rest of the school making it one of the largest and best-equipped art schools in the UK.'

He adds that students can also tap into the expertise of knowledgeable lecturers and tutors.

'The experienced team shares a range of professional and educational experiences, industry awards and research successes. Design students also benefit from a regular series of lectures and workshops conducted by professionals from some of the top design agencies in the UK.'

Different strands of design

Depending on the university and the different modules that are available, the content covered by a course can vary.

For example, the Masters course at Anglia Ruskin University is titled MA Graphic Design and Typography, while the University

....

'You will learn how to link theory and practice more effectively, as well as how to manage large-scale projects'

of Reading offers the MPhil in Typography and Graphic Communication. Both courses are concerned with the core aspects of the subject but offer slightly different routes.

Modules on offer range from 3D design, business and cultural theory, typography, digital-based media and branding. All while exploring innovative ways to solve problems that concern the visual and design industries in commercial, business and social contexts.

You may even study with students of different disciplines. On the MA International Graphic Design Practice at the University of Huddersfield 'cross fertilisation' within creative subjects is promoted, which sees students working with the likes of fashion promotion and photography students to develop their skills in other areas.

Peter explains that postgraduates at NTU have the chance to delve deeper into a range of subjects at the institution's School of Art and Design.

'The school has a large and diverse postgraduate area, covering all the major creative practices. In the area of visual communication, we offer Masters courses in graphic design, design for publication, illustration, branding and identity and motion graphics. While each award has its own title, students on all the visual communication courses share seminars, workshops and collaborative projects, as well as engaging in their own specialist areas.'

As for career prospects upon completing a postgraduate degree many go on to work for reputable companies of all sizes, open their own studios or continue with research careers.

If you're serious about developing your skills to a professional level, there is plenty to attract prospective graphic design students to postgraduate programmes.

Professor Paul Ward, course leader of MA Animation Production at Arts University Bournemouth (AUB), tells Prospects about its links with industry...

How do your animation courses prepare students for a career in the industry?

Simply put, we prepare students by taking them the 'extra mile' and getting them to think about the ways in which their practical work – whether animation, concept work or layouts – fits into the business side of animation.

The AUB approach to animation is studio-based, industry-modelled and collaborative – all things that our industry partners tell us are vital in making students stand out from the crowd. On the MA Animation Production course, students look at animation from practical, theoretical and professional perspectives and are asked to think about a 'synthesis' between these three approaches.

Does the university have good links with industry?

AUB has excellent industry links both in the UK and overseas. All subject areas have strong 'industry liaison groups', and expert practitioners act as advisers on all courses as they are written and go through validation, and then often come back as visiting tutors.

These strong links are further proved by our alumni presence: many of them come back and advise, teach and mentor students. AUB is also building a profile for industry-focused research and knowledge transfer, where we work with partners on specific projects; being a postgraduate animation student at AUB means you are working in this context. You will be at the cutting edge.

How can students make the most of these industry links?

Be prepared. Research your 'target' studios or companies. Know what they do, and what you can do to improve it. The animation industry is looking for good, strong-minded, creative thinkers, so be clear on what skills you have and what you offer, and look for ways to connect with the right people. This is where the research at MA level can be vital

– it allows you the space to build not only a stronger portfolio but also to develop your thinking skills in relation to industry liaison.

What facilities does the institution offer students?

We have studio spaces with light boxes, line-testers and related software, plus various production spaces and suites. The institution is an excellent, specialist university, with plenty of scope for cross-course collaboration with students from film, acting, costume and photography.

What do you look for in prospective students?

Ideally students need a good undergraduate degree in animation or a related subject such as illustration, graphics, fine art or digital media. But there is scope for people to join the course with equivalent professional experience. We also encourage applications from professional animators (or other artists) who want to return to education and explore their practice.

Research your 'target' studios or companies. Know what they do, and what you can do to improve it

The key things are for students to have a passion for animation and to be committed, organised and willing to challenge and develop their ideas. Students should have an interesting visual style or a desire to find out more about the animation industry – and to change it for the better.

What is the background of the teaching staff?

My background is in film and media studies, but I became interested in animation 20 years ago and subsequently did my PhD on animation studies. I am currently the president of the Society for Animation Studies, the only international scholarly society devoted to the study of animation, which includes academics, historians, producers and animators.

My main research is into animation 'communities of practice' and how we can understand animation from a 'production studies' perspective, so I have a range of interests in animation production: how it is made; how it is taught; where it is going next.

These research interests underpin my approach to teaching on the MA Animation Production course and the work I am doing with PhD students in animation. I also have research interests in how the animation industry is changing due to the challenges of multi-platform delivery; animation and documentary; and animation and memory.

My colleagues are all experienced teachers with a range of expertise – some have worked in the industry for companies such as Disney, Jim Henson's Creature Shop, Framestore and Aardman, or have their own animation company making TV commercials. Other staff have specific interests in fine art and more experimental work. You will benefit from this rich mix of experience and expertise, through mentoring and our ability to connect you with the right people in the business of animation.

CREATIVITY BY THE SEA, A CAREER ANYWHERE YOU WANT

Our approach means that 97.7% of our graduates are employed within six months of leaving*

Foundation, BA and MA courses in

Art, Design, Media and Performance

*2011 Destination of Leavers from Higher Education (DLHE) Survey - HESA. Percentage includes post-graduate studies.

ARTS
UNIVERSITY
BOURNEMOUTH

aucb.ac.uk

Dr Nicole Devarenne, convenor of the MLitt in Theatre Studies at the English department of the School of Humanities, University of Dundee, talks to Prospects

What Masters programmes does your department offer?

Appealing to students with both academic and creative/practical interests, our postgraduate programmes include; theatre studies; comics studies; film studies; gender, culture and society; Master of Fine Art (MFA) in Art and Humanities; philosophy and literature; and writing practice and study (creative writing).

Theatre studies is about to go into its second year and represents an exciting and productive partnership between the School of Humanities, Duncan of Jordanstone College of Art and Design (DJCAD) and Dundee Rep Theatre.

DJCAD is well established across a range of disciplines, from interior design to sculpture, performance and animation. The Rep is the only repertory theatre in Scotland and we are very fortunate to have the benefit of the skills and expertise of its staff. We also plan to introduce a Masters in Science Fiction Studies in the near future.

What are the benefits of studying in the English department?

Our degrees are innovative and distinctive: our MLitt Comics Studies, for example, is the only one of its kind in the UK. Our creative cultures degrees (creative writing, theatre studies, comics studies, film studies and the MFA) combine academic studies with some practical and creative work.

In our MLitt English Studies programme, students can take modules from old English to contemporary poetry, and even a unique special author option to examine the full range of their chosen writer's works.

The partnerships we enjoy with DJCAD and the Rep support our students in developing their understanding of theory and practice. Our theatre studies students benefit from the chance to explore the theatre from many perspectives, including literary history, creative writing, performance, directing and theatre design.

Our students are given a lot of autonomy in tailoring their studies. Some degrees, such as the MLitt in Theatre Studies, Gender,

Our students are given a lot of autonomy in tailoring their studies

Culture and Society, and the MFA in Art and Humanities, are highly interdisciplinary.

Some of our degrees offer 'module-only' study options, which give students flexibility in terms of pacing and financing their studies. The creative writing degree has been very popular and many of our students have performed their work at festivals and salons and organised literary events and initiatives. Some have already gone on to be published writers.

We have a lively postgraduate culture, including a regular forum, visiting speakers, an annual conference and the Dundee Literary Festival. Our staff are experts in a wide range of specialist areas.

What do you look for in a student?

Generally we look for a 2:1 degree in the same or a related subject. But we also look at practical experience, particularly for our more creative degrees. Theatre studies, creative writing, and gender, culture and society students come from a mixture of academic backgrounds; this year in theatre studies we have students who did their first degree at DJCAD, as well as students with degrees in literature or film or writing. In some cases we consider applicants who don't have a 2:1 but do have relevant experience or publications that could be considered equivalent to a degree.

If you're from a non-English speaking background, we require an International English Language Testing System (IELTS) score of seven or higher.

Tell us about any recent initiatives undertaken by the department...

English staff are involved in a wealth of academic and creative activities and communities, including: the Dundee Literary Festival; Dundee University Review of the Arts (DURA); comics festivals and exhibitions; the Scottish Centre for Comics Studies; and activities involving the DCA cinema.

What careers do your graduates go on to pursue?

A Masters is the entry route to Doctoral (PhD) study in UK universities and is also important for a 'conversion' career change from a first degree subject, or a 'top-up' in knowledge and skills for career enhancement.

Professions entered with a Masters degree are very varied but include teaching in secondary, further or higher education; media and publishing; or work related to museums, archives and galleries.

What advice can you give students considering their postgraduate funding options?

Apply early and consider all your options. We offer partial fee waivers and scholarships. Our alumni get a discount on postgraduate fees. There are Carnegie-Cameron bursaries, and beyond the MLitt there may also be Arts and Humanities Research Council (AHRC) funding available.

Top Marx

One of the most complex subjects in the arts and humanities, philosophy lets you navigate the thoughts of Plato, Marx, Socrates and more to learn about human existence...

Philosophy at postgraduate level gives students the chance to study in greater depth a topic that is concerned with asking, and attempting to answer, questions about society, the human mind, knowledge and beliefs.

If you would like to help improve our knowledge of all matters philosophical, and contribute to the current research around the world's biggest issues, a postgraduate degree could be an ideal choice.

The philosophy experience
Students who choose to pursue a course in philosophy are arguably more concerned with the potential to further their knowledge than improve their employability.

And there is a lot you could learn. For example, the taught MA Philosophy at Durham University gives students a broad range of topics to explore and study. From Buddhist philosophy to philosophy of language and metaphysics to phenomenology, all modules are taught by internationally recognised experts.

James Ladyman, professor of philosophy and head of the department of philosophy at the University of Bristol, believes that studying at postgraduate level offers the chance to investigate the subject in greater depth with more flexibility and opportunities for independent research.

'Students often have closer interaction with academics in smaller groups and there is increasingly more choice available for different courses. For example, at the University of Bristol, we offer a general MA in Philosophy alongside several more specialised programmes, such as: logic and philosophy of mathematics; philosophy

of biological and cognitive sciences; philosophy and history of science; and philosophy and law,' says James.

Options with philosophy
While philosophy may not appear to be the most vocational subject, it will allow you to develop a range of skills that are applicable to many roles.

Analytical researching, critical evaluation, meeting deadlines and planning are among some of the qualities that appeal to employers and could help you stand out from other job-hunting candidates.

As a result, and because of the broad nature of philosophy, studying the subject can leave you with multiple career options for you to consider.

There is no typical employment route for philosophy postgraduates. Many of them choose to go on to further research within academia, usually in philosophy. Others go on to train for additional qualifications, for example in law, teaching, international relations, management and journalism.

Philosophy students go on to work in a variety of sectors, doing a plethora of different jobs. From accountancy to publishing, business management and human resources to journalism and charity work. The skills gained from studying philosophy mean that they can be transferred to many sectors.

....

'A postgraduate degree in philosophy involves honing skills and creativity'

Dr Benedict Smith, teaching fellow in the department of philosophy and acting director of the MA Philosophy at Durham University, says, 'Postgraduate philosophers of all levels are sought after in a variety of jobs outside academia, including: the civil service; management consultancy; advertising; law; teaching, and many others. Jobs that demand intelligence, creativity, rigorous and independent thought are ideal for students with a postgraduate degree in philosophy.'

Dr Smith explains how certain topics on philosophy courses have important connections to the world of work.

'Some MA programmes offer modules in areas that have an intrinsic connection to professional settings – business ethics or philosophy of psychology, for example. The knowledge and understanding achieved in such modules, as well as in the degree overall, are attractive to a variety of employers.

'A postgraduate degree in philosophy involves honing skills and creativity, and can significantly enhance the range of contributions that can be made inside and outside the workplace.'

Match your interests
Whether you opt for a taught or research Masters in philosophy, it will require greater engagement and discipline than at undergraduate level.

As a postgraduate you will get more of an opportunity to follow individual interests within philosophy, and study them in more depth than would have previously been expected. Groups are often much smaller, which encourages more philosophical interaction with peers and academics.

James suggests that as the subject matter of a philosophy degree becomes more complex with the possibility to specialise, 'the need for effective self-management becomes greater, and more emphasis is placed on independent research'.

As a result, you need to make sure you do your own research into individual programmes and departments to best match your interests with a course and ensure you get the most from your philosophy programme.

Zanne Andrea is studying for an MA in Fine Art at Bath Spa University

Why did you choose this degree and institution?

In the year between my BA Fine Art degree and applying for the MA in Fine Art, I had some very encouraging opportunities and successes but felt there were some important things I hadn't resolved in my practice. The course has a great reputation for developing professional practice to a high standard. The professors and lecturers are well respected in their own right and have an incredible breadth of knowledge of contemporary art and research.

The course also offers study trips plus visiting lectures by artists and curators with national and international profiles. Being able to study and connect with practitioners who have such strong professional experience was important to me for developing my own artistic practice and lifting my work to a higher level.

Tell us a bit about the course...

The course is very self-directed and consists of six modules. Two are research modules allowing you to develop or strengthen your own line of enquiry and focus your interests, then expand and deepen your knowledge of contemporary art and the context surrounding your own practice. The other four are studio-based.

There is flexibility in the way the modules are organised so a student can switch between part time and full time if needed, depending on other commitments and responsibilities.

Did you manage to secure funding for your studies?

I was fortunate to be awarded an Arts and Humanities Research Council (AHRC) studentship that has paid for my tuition fees and living expenses, allowing me to pursue postgraduate study full time and focus intensely on the development of my practice without having the distractions of paid work. This was incredibly important and helpful, particularly as I have a family to consider.

What facilities are available at the institution?

The facilities include digital suites, a painting workshop with a dedicated technician, wood and metal workshops, ceramics, digital textile printing and heat-presses, photography and printmaking facilities and a plastics workshop. All are easily accessible to MA Fine Art students and staffed by knowledgeable, helpful technicians.

What are the main differences between undergraduate and postgraduate life?

During undergraduate study I felt I only started to explore the potential of my interests and ways of working just before graduating. The focus and level of inquiry becomes much stronger in postgraduate study, and the expectations are higher. The level of critical questioning, reflecting

The course has allowed me to establish a framework I can use to sustain and develop my practice throughout my artistic career, not just while studying

and positioning yourself in relation to your peers and your professional context, is much more intense. Pursuing postgraduate study, you're respected and taken seriously as a practitioner in your field.

How has the course helped you prepare for employment?

I've significantly developed my research and analytical skills as well as my ability to organise and disseminate information, which I believe will help me considerably in the job market. I've become increasingly confident in my work as well as my ability to present and discuss it with others. However, the most valuable thing is that the course has allowed me to establish a framework I can use to sustain and develop my practice throughout my artistic career, not just while studying.

What advice would you give other students considering taking this course?

I'd suggest spending time thinking about why you want to do the course and what you intend to get out of it. Be open to possibilities, but consider how you might want to develop as an artist so you're able to make the most of your time and opportunities while studying.

What are your plans after you graduate?

In terms of regular paid employment, I've previously worked in retail. It's a tough job market out there, but I really enjoy research so I'm hoping to use some of my transferable skills gained while studying to land a different type of job, possibly in the arts or cultural sector. I also plan to find a new studio in Bristol and continue working as a professional artist, building networks and opportunities.

At the moment I have an exhibition planned that is due to take place abroad a few months after completing my MA. This will be a great experience to have soon after finishing the course, and I'm really looking forward to seeing where else my skills and work might take me.

Falmouth University

www.falmouth.ac.uk
admissions@falmouth.ac.uk
twitter.com/falmouthuni
facebook.com/falmouthuni

In 2012 Falmouth was voted the third-most creative university in the UK in a *Which?* magazine poll and ranked 7th in *The Sunday Times'* UK subject league table for art and design. Find out what makes the institution so popular...

Falmouth University provides the best international student arrival and support services in the world, according to the International Student Barometer 2012, which carried out independent market research into 193 higher educational institutions in 14 countries.

Originally founded as Falmouth School of Art in 1902, Falmouth University has steadily grown its reputation for creative learning and innovation. It merged with Dartington College of Arts in 2008 adding performance to its portfolio of courses to become a leading specialist multi-arts institution.

Approximately 4,000 students study a range of undergraduate and postgraduate awards across the disciplines of art, design, performance, media, writing and business. Situated in a beautiful coastal area in the South West of England, students enjoy a creative community based at the Falmouth and Penryn campuses.

From its unique location, the university has established 61 international partnerships across 28 countries. Relationships with partner institutions include: Cal Arts, California; Nagoya University of the Arts, Japan; LASALLE College of Arts, Singapore; and Renmin University, China.

Falmouth University awards taught Master of Arts (MA) degrees, while research degrees are awarded through its partnership with University of the Arts London.

WHY CHOOSE FALMOUTH?

The opening of the Academy for Innovation and Research (AIR) in 2012 and the development of the new graduate school within it has created a unique space that encourages and fosters collaboration and innovative interdisciplinary outputs. It allows students to work alongside research staff at Falmouth as well as visiting researchers and businesses.

Research, advanced scholarship and professional creative practice constitute an increasingly important part of academic life and our postgraduate portfolio – taught MAs and Master of Fine Arts (MFA), Master of Business Administration (MBA), MPhil and PhD research – is at the very heart of that activity.

INDUSTRY STANDARD FACILITIES

Over £100million has been invested in the university in the last decade, ensuring our facilities are pitched at industry standard. Bespoke centres have been constructed and are at our postgraduate community's disposal. These include:

The Design Centre has rapid prototyping equipment, laser cutters, computer numerical control (CNC) milling and routing machines, digital printing capabilities and sustainable auditing and lifecycle design (LCD) and CAD/CAM equipment;

The Media Centre houses a large TV studio, gallery, newsroom, radio studio, digital animation suite and a specialist equipment store;

The Photography Centre offers large professional studios, darkrooms and process areas, printing services and a comprehensive range of quality still photography and filming equipment;

The Performance Centre provides specially designed studios for dance, acoustic music, amplified music, theatre and recording;

Art spaces with dedicated studios and seminar spaces for each art course. Shared facilities include a printmaking studio and a sculpture workshop.

CASE STUDY

Susanna Hill is working towards an MA in Art Gallery and Museum Studies at The University of Manchester and is a member of the Arts, Languages and Cultures Graduate School

Why did you choose this course and institution?

I want a career working in an art gallery, and when applying for jobs and looking at the criteria for applicants I found that it is necessary to have a Masters qualification in a relevant subject.

My decision to come to Manchester for my Masters was based on the strength of the university and the wide and varied culture on offer in the city. I had done my undergraduate course at St Andrews in Scotland and really wanted to go to a big city with many museums and galleries, as well as live music and theatres.

The fantastic thing about taking this programme at The University of Manchester is that the university owns and operates the Manchester Museum and the Whitworth Art Gallery, which means many lectures are delivered by practising professionals. Also, staff at these organisations are always keen and willing to support you in your studies. The museology department also has strong links with other cultural institutions in the city, all of which offer fantastic opportunities to get involved.

I would highly recommend this programme. I thought I knew everything there was to know about going to art galleries, but this Masters has made me rethink everything and recognise the wide and varied potential of gallery and museum spaces. It is very strongly directed towards preparation for employment and every part of the course is related to how a particular issue might be handled in practice.

Tell us a bit about the content of the course…

The programme is a clever balance of the practical and academic. The mandatory modules look at the history and motivations behind galleries and museums and tackle everything you need to know about the treatment of objects in museums – from theories of interpretation to how you should physically handle items. In addition to this every student undertakes a work placement, which provides

industry experience and the chance to network.

Beyond that students have the option of specialising in a specific area of curation (either art, ethnography or digital), taking a course in creative learning, or taking a course from a different Masters programme within the School of Arts, Languages and Culture.

I come from an art history background and am certain that I want to work in an art gallery rather than a museum, but because this course offers both options I have developed a versatile skill-set.

While studying for this Masters I have been introduced to the Musgrave Kinley Collection of Outsider Art at the Whitworth Art Gallery, and from September I will be working on a PhD looking at the history and continued relevance of this collection. My hope is that my PhD research will facilitate a large exhibition of the collection at the Whitworth Art Gallery in a few years time.

What are the main differences between undergraduate and postgraduate life?

I have found the postgraduate experience completely different

I thought I knew everything there was to know about going to art galleries, but this Masters has made me rethink everything

to being an undergraduate. This is partly because you're interacting with such a wide range of people of different ages and experience, and partly because the work ethic on my particular course is so strongly directed towards a professional outcome.

Being a postgraduate in the School of Arts, Languages and Culture at Manchester means a packed schedule of guest lectures and volunteer opportunities. It is a vibrant corner of the university, and very much feels like it's at the cutting edge of contemporary theory and practice.

THE ARTS, LANGUAGES AND CULTURE GRADUATE SCHOOL
Home to all postgraduate students studying in these areas, the graduate school offers support, advice, welfare, and training in all areas of intellectual and professional development. It has recently moved into a new dedicated building with computer clusters, teaching and meeting rooms, coffee lounges and social spaces – ensuring students get a world-class experience as a postgraduate in Manchester. With these excellent facilities and a strong community focus, the school aims to help students fulfil their potential and leave them well placed to face the future whatever they decide to do next. To find out more, visit www.alc.manchester.ac.uk/graduateschool

Lucas Yeung is studying for the MA Communication Design at Norwich University of the Arts. He lets us know more about life as a postgraduate at the university...

Why did you choose this specific course and institution?

I was looking for a professionally focused course to help me advance my studies and develop my skills for industry.

Initially I looked at US universities, but I found the fees to be very high so I decided to look at universities in the UK. I only considered specialist creative universities because I knew the workshops, facilities, library and teaching would all be geared towards creative subjects. Location wasn't my biggest concern. The university itself was the most important thing to me.

Tell us a bit about the content of your course...

It has really broadened my horizons. I've got involved in so many creative workshops in which we study subjects such as type, image making, web design and more. The seminars are also good because the class sizes are small. Our tutors are really

interested in our progress and we meet regularly, getting a lot of feedback from our peers along the way.

In addition, we take part in group projects where we work alongside students on other courses. This is good as it's important to work

It's important to work with people with different skills and different perspectives, plus it helps us prepare for the world of work

with people with different skills and different perspectives, plus it helps us prepare for the world of work.

What is the difference between undergraduate and postgraduate life?

The course can be challenging, but this helps to drive us to work as hard as possible. There is an atmosphere in the university that encourages students to work to the best of their abilities, which will help us in our future careers.

What advice would you give to others considering further study at Norwich University of the Arts?

Do it! I hadn't even heard of Norwich before but it looked like a lovely city. I went to London during the Christmas holidays and really missed Norwich – the people here are so nice. Now, having lived here for nearly nine months, it feels like home.

The blueprint for postgraduate success

Everything you need to make the right postgraduate choice

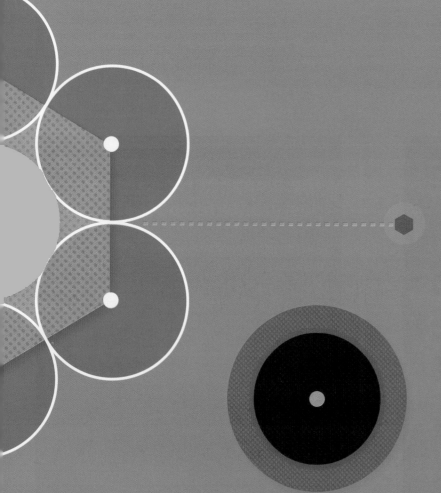

Arts and humanities
Course and research opportunities

This section sets out every UK and Ireland postgraduate opportunity in the area of arts and humanities. Use the following pages to browse the taught courses and research opportunities at each institution. The listings are divided into subject chapters which are subsequently divided into related subject areas. Taught courses and research opportunities are listed separately, each entry containing university name, course name, mode of study and type of study information. Please see the full A-Z index of all subjects in this publication on page 557. Further details of each course can be found at *www.prospects.ac.uk/findcourses*

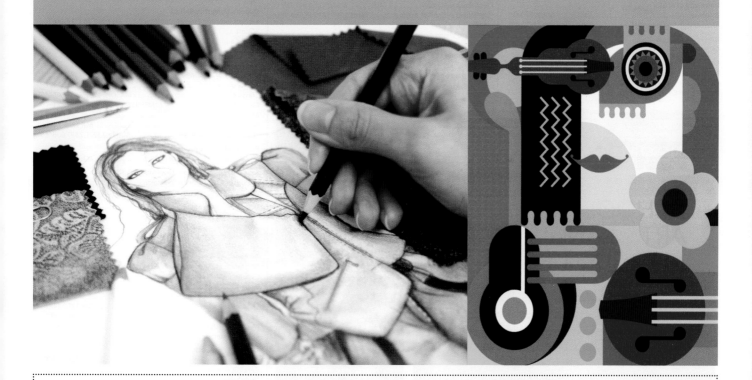

ARTS AND HUMANITIES SUBJECT CHAPTERS LIST

Archaeology

Archaeology
Taught Courses

University of Aberdeen
Archaeology of the North.............MSc 12FT 24PT/PGDip 9FT 18PT

Bangor University
Archaeology..............PhD by taught 36FT 48-72PT/MPhil 12-24FT 24-48PT
Heritage.... PhD by taught 36FT 48-72PT/MPhil 12-24FT 24-48PT
History............ PhD by taught 24-36FT 48-72PT/MPhil 12FT 24PT

Birkbeck, University of London
Archaeological Practice...................................MA 24PT

University of Birmingham
Environmental Archaeology and Palaeoenvironments...................
MSc 12FT 24PT
Greek Archaeology..................................MRes 12FT 24PT
Landscape Archaeology, GIS and Virtual Landscapes ......MA 12FT 24PT/PGDip 9FT 18PT
Professional Archaeology............MA 12FT 24PT/PGDip 12FT 24PT

Bishop Grosseteste University College Lincoln
Community Archaeology.................................. MA 12FT 24PT

Bournemouth University
Archaeological Practice....................................MSc 12FT 24PT
Forensic Archaeology ....MSc 12FT 24PT
Maritime Archaeology ....MSc 12FT 24PT
Osteoarchaeology ....MSc 12FT 24PT

University of Bradford
Archaeological Prospection ....MSc 12FT/PGDip 9FT
Archaeological Sciences...............................MSc 12FT 24PT
Archaeology..MA 12FT/PGDip 9FT
Forensic Archaeology and Crime Scene Investigation ..MSc 12FT/PGDip 9FT
Human Osteology and Palaeopathology ..... MSc 12FT/PGDip 9FT

University of Bristol
Archaeology.. MA 12FT 24PT
Archaeology for Screen Media .... MA 12FT 24PT

University of Cambridge
Archaeology..MPhil 11-15FT

Cardiff University
Archaeology.. MA 12FT 24PT
Care of Collections ....MSc 12FT 24PT
Professional Conservation..............................MSc 12FT 24PT

University of Central Lancashire
Archaeology of Death.................................MA 12FT
Osteoarchaeology: Techniques and Data Analysis......... MSc 12FT

University College Cork
Arts (Archaeology)......................................HDip 9FT
Human Osteoarchaeology.................................MA 12FT

Cranfield University
Forensic Archaeology and Anthropology ....MSc 12FT 60PT

Cranfield University, Shrivenham
Forensic Archaeology and Anthropology ....MSc 12FT 60PT

Durham University
Archaeological Science .... MSc 12FT
Archaeology... MA 12FT 24PT
Museum and Artefact Studies .... MA 12FT 24PT
Palaeopathology...MSc 12FT 24PT

University of East Anglia
World Art Studies ....PGDip 12FT 24PT

University of Edinburgh
Archaeology...MSc 12FT 24PT
European Archaeology..................................MSc 12FT 24PT
Geographical Information Science and Archaeology.....MSc 12FT
Human Osteoarchaeology...............................MSc 12FT 24PT
Mediterranean Archaeology............................MSc 12FT 24PT
Osteoarchaeology ....MSc 12FT 24PT

University of Exeter
Archaeology..MA 12FT 24PT 36DL
Bioarchaeology ....MSc 12FT 24PT
Experimental Archaeology............................. MA 12FT 24PT

National University of Ireland Galway
Archaeology..HDip 12FT 24PT
Landscape Archaeology ....MA 12FT

University of Glasgow
Archaeological Studies.............. MLitt 12FT 24PT/PGDip 9FT 18PT
Battlefield & Conflict Archaeology ....MLitt 12FT 24PT/PGDip 9FT 18PT
Celtic and Viking Archaeology .... MLitt 12FT 24PT/PGDip 9FT 18PT
Material Culture & Artefact Studies .... MLitt 12FT 24PT/PGDip 9FT 18PT
Mediterranean Archaeology..... MLitt 12FT 24PT/PGDip 9FT 18PT

University of Kent
Archaeology .... MA 12FT 24PT
Archaeology of the Transmanche Region................ MA 12FT 24PT
Heritage Management (Athens) ....MA 12FT
Roman History and Archaeology........................ MA 12FT 24PT
Roman History and Archaeology with a Term in Rome ...MA 12FT 24PT

King's College London
Classical Art & Archaeology .... MA 12FT 24PT

University of Leicester
Archaeology.......................................PGCert 12DL
Archaeology and Heritage .... MA 24DL
Archaeology: The Classical Mediterranean .MA 12FT 24PT 24DL/PGDip 9FT 18PT

University of Liverpool
Archaeology...................... MSc 12FT 24PT MA 12FT 24PT

University of Manchester
Archaeology: General....................................... MA 12FT 24PT

Newcastle University
Archaeology .... MA 12FT 24PT
Early Medieval and Byzantine Archaeology .... MA 12FT 24PT
Greek and Byzantine Archaeology............................ MA 12FT 24PT
Greek and Roman Archaeology .... MA 12FT 24PT
Heritage Practice..................................MHPrac 24FT 48PT
Roman and Byzantine Archaeology................... MA 12FT 24PT

University of Nottingham
Archaeological Science ....MSc(Res) 12FT 24PT
Archaeology (by Research)..............................MA 12FT 24PT

University of Oxford
Archaeological Science................................ MSt 9FT/MSc 12FT
Archaeology.. MSt 9FT/MPhil 24FT
Classical Archaeology..................................... MPhil 21FT/MSt 9FT
Islamic Art and Archaeology (Research Methods)............MSt 9FT

Queen's University Belfast
Archaeology and EnvironmentMSc 12FT 24PT/PGDip 12FT 24PT/PGCert 12FT 24PT
Dating and Chronology... MSc 12FT
Professional Archaeology.........MSc 12FT 24PT/PGDip 12FT 24PT/PGCert 12FT 24PT

University of Reading
Archaeology .... MA 12FT 24PT
Classics .... MA (Res) 12FT 24PT 60BM
Geoarchaeology .... MSc 12FT 24PT/PGDip 12FT 24PT
Medieval Archaeology ....MA 12FT
Research in Archaeology.................................. MA 12FT 24PT
The Classical Tradition .... MA(Res) 12FT 24PT 60BM

Royal Holloway, University of London
Classical Art and Archaeology.................................. MA 12FT 24PT

School of Oriental and African Studies - SOAS
History of Art and/or Archaeology.......................MA 12FT 24-36PT

University of Sheffield
Aegean Archaeology .... MA 12FT 24PT
Archaeological Materials................................... MSc 12FT
Archaeology .... MA 12FT 24PT
Archaeology of the Classical Mediterranean ....MA 12FT 24PT/PGDip 9FT/PGCert 6FT
Archaeology, Bible and Ancient Cultures.................. MA 12FT 24PT
Environmental Archaeology and Palaeoeconomy MSc 12FT 24PT
Experimental Archaeology...................................MSc 12FT 24PT
Geoarchaeology...MSc 12FT 24PT
Human Osteology and Funerary Archeology.................. MSc 12FT
Landscape Archaeology .... MA 12FT 24PT
Material Culture Studies .... MA 12FT 24PT
Medieval Archaeology .... MA 12FT 24PT
Osteoarchaeology ....MSc 12FT 24PT

University of Southampton
Archaeological Computing .... MSc 12FT 24PT
Ceramic and Lithic Analysis for Archaeologists...... MA 12FT 24PT
Vertebrate Palaeontology ....MRes 12FT 18PT
Maritime Archaeology ....MA 12FT 24PT/MSc 12FT 24PT
Osteoarchaeology .... MA 12FT 24PT
Social Archaeology...................................... MA 12FT 24PT

University of St Andrews
Ancient History ....PGDip 9FT/MLitt 12FT 24PT

University of Stirling
Environment, Heritage and Policy...........................MSc 12FT 24PT

University of Wales Trinity Saint David
Landscape Management and Environmental Archaeology .....MA 12FT 24PT/PGCert 12FT 24PT/PGDip 12FT 24PT

University of the Highlands and Islands
Archaeological Practice .... MA 12FT 24PT/PGDip 9FT 18PT

UCL - University College London
Archaeology..................................GradDip 9FT 18PT MA 12FT 24PT
Archaeology and Heritage of Asia .... MA 12FT 24PT
Archaeology of the Arab and Islamic World.....................MA 24FT
Archaeology of the Middle East................................ MA 12FT 24PT
Artefact Studies... MA 12FT 24PT
Conservation for Archaeology and Museums................. MSc 24FT

Archaeology

Environmental Archaeology .... MSc 12FT 24PT
Forensic Archaeological Science .... MSc 12FT 24PT
GIS and Spatial Analysis in Archaeology .... MSc 12FT 24PT
Mediterranean Archaeology .... MA 12FT 24PT
Public Archaeology .... MA 12FT 24PT
Research Methods for Archaeology .... MA 12FT 24PT
Skeletal and Dental Bioarchaeology .... MSc 12FT 24PT
Technology and Analysis of Archaeological Materials... MSc 12FT 24PT
Urban Archaeology .... MA 12FT 24PT

University of Winchester
Archaeology .... MRes 12FT 24PT/PGDip 12FT 24PT/PGCert 12FT 24PT
Regional and Local Archaeology.MA 12FT 24PT/PGDip 9FT 18PT/PGCert 9FT 18PT
Regional and Local History and Archaeology .... MA 12FT 24PT/PGDip 12FT 24PT/PGCert 12FT 24PT

University of Worcester
Archaeological Landscapes .... MA 24PT

University of York
Archaeological Information Systems .... MSc 12FT 24PT
Archaeology of Buildings .... MA 12FT 36PT
Bioarchaeology .... MSc 12FT 24PT
Coastal and Marine Archaeology .... MSc 12FT 24PT
Conservation Studies (Historic Buildings) .... MA 12FT 24-36PT
Cultural Heritage Management .... MA 12FT 36PT
Digital Heritage .... MSc 12FT 24PT/PGDip 9FT
Early Prehistory .... MSc 12FT 24PT
Field Archaeology .... MA 12FT 36PT
Historical Archaeology .... MA 12FT 24-36PT
Landscape Archaeology .... MA 12FT 24PT
Medieval Archaeology .... MA 12FT
Zooarchaeology .... MSc 12FT 24-36PT

Archaeology
Research Courses

University of Aberdeen
Archaeology .... MSc by research 12FT/MPhil 24FT/PhD 36FT

Bangor University
Archaeology .... PhD 36FT 48-72PT/MPhil 12-24FT 24-48PT
Heritage .... MPhil 12-24FT 24-48PT/PhD 36FT 48-72PT

Birkbeck, University of London
Archaeology .... MPhil 24FT 36PT/PhD 36FT 48PT

University of Birmingham
Archaeological Practice .... MRes 12FT 24PT
Archaeology, Heritage and Environment...PhD 36FT 72PT/MA by research 12FT 24PT
Cuneiform and Ancient Near Eastern Studies .... MRes 12FT 24PT
Greek Archaeology .... MRes 12FT 24PT
Ottoman Studies .... MPhil(B) 12FT 24PT

University of Bradford
Archaeological Sciences...... PhD 36-48FT 48-60PT/MPhil 12-24FT 24-48PT

University of Bristol
Archaeology and Anthropology .... PhD 36FT 72PT/MLitt by research 24FT 48PT/MPhil 12FT 24PT

University of Buckingham
Anthropology .... MA by research 12FT

University of Cambridge
Archaeological Research .... MPhil 12FT
Archaeology .... PhD 36FT 60PT

Cardiff University
Archaeology .... PhD 36FT possiblePT/MPhil 12FT possiblePT

Durham University
Archaeology .... MPhil 24FT/PhD 36FT
Archaeology .... MA by research 12FT/MSc by research 12FT

University of Edinburgh
Archaeology....PhD 36FT 72PT/MPhil 24FT 48PT/MSc by research 12FT 24PT
Classical Art & Archaeology .... MSc 12FT 24PT

University of Exeter
Archaeology..... PhD 36FT 72PT/MPhil 24FT 48PT/MA by research 12FT 24PT

University of Glasgow
Archaeology .... PhD 36FT/MPhil 12FT/MLitt by research 12FT

University of Kent
Classical and Archaeological Studies .... PhD 36FT 60PT/MPhil 24FT 36PT/MA by research 12FT 24PT

University of Leicester
Archaeology .... PhD 36FT 72PT 72DL/MPhil 24FT 48PT 48DL

University of Liverpool
Archaeology .... PhD 36FT 48PT/MPhil 12FT 24PT

University of Manchester
Archaeology .... PhD 36FT 72PT

Newcastle University
Archaeology .... MLitt by research 12FT 24PT
Archaeology .... MPhil 12FT 24PT/PhD 36FT 72PT

University of Nottingham
Archaeology..... PhD 36FT 72PT/MPhil 24FT 48PT/MA by research 12FT 24PT

University of Oxford
Archaeological Science .... DPhil 48FT
Archaeology .... DPhil 36-48FT
Archaeology (OUDCE) .... DPhil 48-72PT

Queen's University Belfast
Past Cultural Change .... PhD 36FT 72PT/MPhil 24FT 48PT

School of Oriental and African Studies - SOAS
Art and Archaeology .... PhD 36FT/MPhil 24FT
Department of Art and Archaeology .... PhD 36FT 72PT/MPhil 24FT 36PT

University of Southampton
Archaeology .... PhD 48FT 84PT/MPhil 48FT 84PT

University of St Andrews
Ancient History .... MPhil 24FT/PhD 36FT 72PT

University of Wales Trinity Saint David
Applied Archaeology .... PhD 60-108PT

University of the Highlands and Islands
Archaeology .... PhD 36FT 72PT/MPhil 24FT 48PT

UCL - University College London
Archaeology .... PhD 36FT 60PT

University of Worcester
Archaeology... PhD 48FT 70PT/MPhil 24FT 48PT/MRes 24FT 48PT

University of York
Archaeology..... PhD 36FT 72PT/MPhil 24FT 48PT/MA by research 12FT 24PT
Conservation Studies...... PhD 36FT 72PT/MPhil 24FT 48PT/MA by research 12FT 24PT

Classical archaeology
Taught Courses

University of Aberdeen
Archaeology of the North .... MSc 12FT 24PT/PGDip 9FT 18PT

Bangor University
Archaeology .... PhD by taught 36FT 48-72PT/MPhil 12-24FT 24-48PT

Birkbeck, University of London
Classical Archaeology .... MA 24PT

University of Birmingham
Antiquity .... MA 12FT 24PT

University of Bristol
Classical Reception .... MA 12FT 24PT

University of Cambridge
Archaeology .... MPhil 11-15FT

Cardiff University
History and Archaeology of the Greek & Roman World .... MA 12FT 24PT

University of Central Lancashire
Archaeology of Death .... MA 12FT
Osteoarchaeology: Techniques and Data Analysis .... MSc 12FT

University of Chester
Archaeology and Heritage Practice .....MSc 12FT 24 - 36PT/PGDip 12FT 24 - 36PT/PGCert 12FT 12 - 24PT
Archaeology of Death and Memory ..... MA 12FT 24 - 36PT/PGDip 12FT 24 - 36PT/PGCert 12FT 12 - 24PT

Durham University
Greece. Rome and the Near East .... MA 12FT 24PT

University of Edinburgh
Mediterranean Archaeology .... MSc 12FT 24PT

University of Exeter
Archaeology .... MA 12FT 24PT 36DL
Bioarchaeology .... MSc 12FT 24PT
Experimental Archaeology .... MA 12FT 24PT

National University of Ireland Galway
Classical Civilisation .... MA 12FT

University of Kent
Ancient History .... MA 12FT
Ancient History with a term in Rome .... MA 12FT 24PT
Graduate Diploma in Humanities (Classical & Archaeological Studies) .... GradDip 12FT
Hellenic and Hellenic Near East .... MA 12FT 24PT

University of Leicester
Archaeology and Heritage .... MA 24DL
Archaeology of the Roman World .... MA 12FT 24PT/PGDip 9FT 18PT
Archaeology: Historical Archaeology MA 12FT 24PT 24DL/PGDip 9FT 18PT 18DL
Archaeology: The Classical Mediterranean .... MA 12FT 24PT 24DL/PGDip 9FT 18PT

Newcastle University
Archaeology .... MA 12FT 24PT
Early Medieval and Byzantine Archaeology .... MA 12FT 24PT
Roman Frontier Studies .... MA 12FT 24PT

The Open University
Classical Studies .... MA variableDL

University of Oxford
Archaeological Science .... MSt 9FT/MSc 12FT
Archaeology .... MSt 9FT/MPhil 24FT
Social Anthropology (Research Methods) .... MSc 12FT

Queen's University Belfast
Archaeology and EnvironmentMSc 12FT 24PT/PGDip 12FT 24PT/PGCert 12FT 24PT

University of Sheffield
Archaeological Materials .... MSc 12FT
Archaeology .... MA 12FT 24PT
Archaeology, Bible and Ancient Cultures .... MA 12FT 24PT
Experimental Archaeology .... MSc 12FT 24PT
Geoarchaeology .... MSc 12FT 24PT
Osteoarchaeology .... MSc 12FT 24PT

University of Southampton
Archaeological Computing .... MSc 12FT 24PT
Social Archaeology .... MA 12FT 24PT

University of St Andrews
Social Anthropology with African Studies .... MRes 12FT

University of Strathclyde
Historical Studies .... MSc 12FT 24PT/PGDip 9FT 18PT

University of Wales Trinity Saint David
Ancient History .... MA 12FT 24PT 12-24DL

UCL - University College London
Archaeology .... GradDip 9FT 18PT MA 12FT 24PT
Archaeology and Heritage of Asia .... MA 12FT 24PT
Archaeology of the Arab and Islamic World .... MA 24FT
Archaeology of the Middle East .... MA 12FT 24PT
Culture, Materials and Design .... MA 12FT 24PT

Classical archaeology
Research Courses

University of Aberdeen
Archaeology .... MSc by research 12FT/MPhil 24FT/PhD 36FT

Birkbeck, University of London
Archaeology .... MPhil 24FT 36PT/PhD 36FT 48PT
Classical Archaeology and Ancient History .... MPhil 24FT 36PT/PhD 24FT 36PT

University of Birmingham
Late Antiquity .... MPhil(B) 12FT 24PT

University of Cambridge
Archaeological Research .... MPhil 12FT

University of Edinburgh
Classical Art & Archaeology .... MSc 12FT 24PT

University of Exeter
Archaeology..... PhD 36FT 72PT/MPhil 24FT 48PT/MA by research 12FT 24PT

Newcastle University
Archaeology .... MPhil 12FT 24PT/PhD 36FT 72PT

The Open University
Greek and Roman Material Culture... PhD 36FT 72PT variableDL/MPhil 15FT 24PT variableDL

School of Oriental and African Studies - SOAS
Art and Archaeology .... PhD 36FT/MPhil 24FT
Department of Art and Archaeology .... PhD 36FT 72PT/MPhil 24FT 36PT

Egyptology
Taught Courses

University of Aberdeen
Archaeology of the North .... MSc 12FT 24PT/PGDip 9FT 18PT

University of Birmingham
Antiquity .... MA 12FT 24PT
Egyptology .... MRes 12FT 24PT

University of Central Lancashire
Archaeology of Death .... MA 12FT

University of Exeter
Archaeology .... MA 12FT 24PT 36DL
Experimental Archaeology .... MA 12FT 24PT

University of Liverpool
Egyptology .... MA 12FT 24PT

University of Manchester
Biomedical and Forensic Studies in Egyptology.... MSc 12FT 24PT

University of Oxford
Egyptology .... MPhil 21FT

University of Sheffield
Experimental Archaeology .... MSc 12FT 24PT

Swansea University
Ancient Egyptian Culture .... MA 12FT 24-36PT

UCL - University College London
Archaeology .... GradDip 9FT 18PT
Egyptian Archaeology .... MA 12FT 24PT

Archaeology

Egyptology
Research Courses

University of Aberdeen
Archaeology..............MSc by research 12FT/MPhil 24FT/PhD 36FT

University of Birmingham
Egyptology...MSc by research 12FT 24PT

University of Exeter
Archaeology.....PhD 36FT 72PT/MPhil 24FT 48PT/MA by research 12FT 24PT

University of Liverpool
Egyptology...MPhil 12FT/PhD 36FT

University of Manchester
Egyptology.........................PhD 36-48FT 72-96PT/MPhil 12FT 24PT

Swansea University
Ancient History..MA by research 12FT 24PT
Egyptology.......MPhil 12FT 24PT/PhD 36FT 60PT/MA by research 12FT 24PT

Prehistoric archaeology
Taught Courses

University of Aberdeen
Archaeology of the North.............MSc 12FT 24PT/PGDip 9FT 18PT

University of Cambridge
Archaeology...MPhil 11-15FT

Cardiff University
European Neolithic.......................................MA 12FT 24PT

University of Central Lancashire
Archaeology of Death...MA 12FT
Osteoarchaeology: Techniques and Data Analysis.........MSc 12FT

University of Chester
Archaeology and Heritage Practice.....MSc 12FT 24 - 36PT/PGDip 12FT 24 - 36PT/PGCert 12FT 12 - 24PT
Archaeology of Death and Memory.....MA 12FT 24 - 36PT/PGDip 12FT 24 - 36PT/PGCert 12FT 12 - 24PT

University of Exeter
Archaeology...MA 12FT 24PT 36DL
Experimental Archaeology...MA 12FT 24PT

University of Liverpool
Palaeoanthropology...MSc 12FT 24PT

Newcastle University
Early Medieval and Byzantine Archaeology...........MA 12FT 24PT
Later European Prehistory...MA 12FT 24PT

University of Reading
Geoarchaeology.........................MSc 12FT 24PT/PGDip 12FT 24PT

University of Sheffield
Archaeological Materials.......................................MSc 12FT
Archaeology...MA 12FT 24PT
European Prehistory...MA 12FT 24PT
Experimental Archaeology.....................................MSc 12FT 24PT
Geoarchaeology...MSc 12FT 24PT
Osteoarchaeology...MSc 12FT 24PT

University of Southampton
Vertebrate Palaeontology...MRes 12FT 18PT
Palaeolithic Archaeology and Human Origins........MA 12FT 24PT

UCL - University College London
Archaeology..GradDip 9FT 18PT
Palaeoanthropology and Palaeolithic Archaeology........MSc 12FT 24PT

University of York
Coastal and Marine Archaeology..............................MSc 12FT 24PT
Early Prehistory..MSc 12FT 24PT
Mesolithic Studies...MA 12FT 24PT

Prehistoric archaeology
Research Courses

University of Aberdeen
Archaeology..............MSc by research 12FT/MPhil 24FT/PhD 36FT

University of Cambridge
Archaeological Research..MPhil 12FT

University of Exeter
Archaeology.....PhD 36FT 72PT/MPhil 24FT 48PT/MA by research 12FT 24PT

University of Manchester
Palaeontology.....................PhD 36FT 72PT/MSc by research 12FT/MPhil 12FT 24PT

Plymouth University
Palaeontology and Palaeoenvironments Research Group....PhD 36FT/MPhil 24FT

School of Oriental and African Studies - SOAS
Department of Art and Archaeology.....................PhD 36FT 72PT/MPhil 24FT 36PT

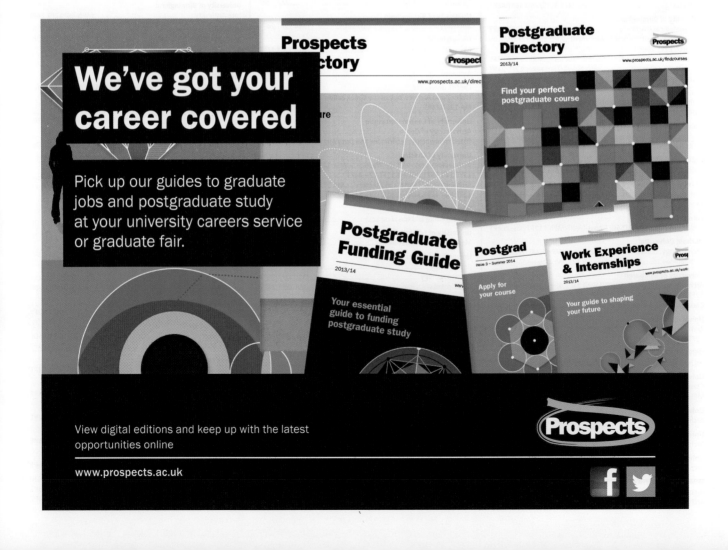

Architectural studies

Architectural studies
Taught Courses

University of Aberdeen
Art and Business ... MLitt 12FT 24PT

University of Bath
Conservation of Historic Buildings ... MSc 12FT 28PT/PGDip 9FT 20PT
Professional Practice (Part Three) ... PGCert 12PT

Birkbeck, University of London
History of Art and Architecture ... GradCert 12PT

Birmingham City University
Architectural Practice ... PGDip 24FT 36PT
Architectural Practice PgDip ... MA 12PT
Architecture ... MA 12FT 24PT MArch 24FT 36PT

Arts University Bournemouth
Architecture ... MA 12FT 24PT
MArch Master of Architecture ... MArch 24FT

University of Brighton
Architectural and Urban Studies ... MA 18FT 24-42PT/PGDip 18FT 24-42PT/PGCert 18FT 24-42PT
Architecture RIBA Part 2 ... PGDip 24-72FT
Architecture Research ... MPhil 12FT
Management, Practice and Law in Architecture ... PGDip 24FT
Sustainable Design ... MA 12FT 24-60PT/PGDip 12FT 24-60PT/PGCert 12FT 24-60PT

University of Cambridge
Environmental Design in Architecture Option B ... PGDip 21FT
History of Art and Architecture ... MPhil 9FT

Cardiff University
Architectural Studies ... MArch 24FT
Architecture: Professional Studies ... MA 24FT 36PT/PGDip 12FT
Theory and Practice of Sustainable Design ... MSc 12FT 24PT

University of Central Lancashire
Architecture ... MArch 24FT
Building Conservation and Regeneration ... MSc 12FT 24-30PT/PGDip 6FT 12PT/PGCert 3FT 6PT
Building Services ... MSc 12FT 30PT/PGDip 6FT 12PT/PGCert 3FT 6PT
Ceramics ... MA 12FT 30PT/PGDip 12FT/PGCert 12FT

Centre for Alternative Technology
Professional Diploma in Architecture: Advanced Environmental & Energy Studies ... PGDip 18FT

University for the Creative Arts
Architecture (ARB/RIBA Part 2) ... GradDip 24FT 48PT/BArch 12FT
Design ... MA 12FT 24PT
Design: Architectural and Interior Design ... MA 12FT 24PT

De Montfort University
Architectural Design ... MA 12FT 24PT
Architectural Practice ... PGDip 12PT
Architecture ... MArch 24FT 36PT
PEDR Architecture ... An Advisory, inspection and endorsement service up to 72FT up to 72PT

University of Derby
Sustainable Architecture and Healthy Environments ... MA 12FT

University of Dundee
Architecture: Advanced Practice, Management and Law ... MSc 18DL
Design and Construction of Zero Carbon and Ultra-Low Energy Buildings ... MSc 12FT
Non-Graduating Taught Postgraduate in School of the Environment ... PG module variableFT

University of East Anglia
Landscape History ... MA 12FT 24PT

University of East London
Architectural Design PG Diploma ... PGDip 24FT
Architecture ... MArch 12FT 24PT/PGDip 8FT 16PT/PGCert 4FT 8PT
Architecture: Advanced Environmental and Energy Studies ... MSc 12FT 24PT
Architecture: Advanced Environmental and Energy Studies Prof Diploma ... Prof Dip 18PT
Architecture: Computing and Design PG Cert ... PGCert 8PT
Architecture: Interpretation and Theories MA ... MA 12FT 24PT/PGDip 8FT 16PT/PGCert 4FT 8PT
Architecture: Professional Diploma (Prof Dip) ... Prof. Dip 24FT
Architecture: Sustainability And Design MA ... MA 12FT 24PT/PGDip 8FT 16PT/PGCert 4FT 8PT
Architecture: Urban Design MA . MA 12FT 24PT/PGDip 8FT 16PT/PGCert 4FT 8PT

University of Edinburgh
Advanced Sustainable Design ... MSc 12FT 24PT
Architectural Conservation ... MSc 12FT 24PT
Architectural Project Management (Distance Learning) ... MSc 84DL
Architectural and Urban Design ... MSc 12FT
Architecture ... MSc(Res) 12FT 24PT
Architecture ... MArch 24FT
Interior Architectural Design ... MA 12FT/MFA 24FT
Landscape Architecture ... MLA 21FT
Reflective Design Practices (MSc by Research) ... MSc(Res) 12FT 24PT

Glasgow School of Art
Architectural Studies ... PGCert 4FT 8PT/PGDip 8FT 16PT/MArch 12FT 24PT
Architecture ... Diploma 24FT
Creative Practices ... PGCert 4FT 8PT/PGDip 8FT 16PT/MRes 12FT 24PT

Goldsmiths, University of London
Research Architecture ... MA 12FT 24PT

University of Greenwich
Architectural Practice (ARB/ RIBA Part 3 Exemption) ... PGDip 12FT
Architecture ... MA 12FT 24PT/MSc 12FT 24PT
Architecture (ARB/ RIBA Part 2 Exemption) ... PGDip 24FT 36PT

University of Huddersfield
3D Digital Design ... MA 12/16FT
Architecture/Architecture (International) (RIBA Part 2) ... MArch 24FT
Professional Practice and Management in Architecture (RIBA Part 3) ... PGCert 12PT

University of Kent
Architectural Visualisation ... MA 12FT
Architecture and Cities ... MA 12FT 24PT
Architecture and Cities (Paris option) ... MA 12FT
Architecture and Sustainable Environments ... MSc 12FT 24PT
Master of Architecture (MArch with ARB/RIBA Part 2 exemption) ... MArch 24FT

Kingston University
Architecture (Part 2 RIBA/ARB exemption) ... GradDip 24FT 36PT
Architecture Professional Practice ... MA 12FT 24PT
Art & Space ... MA 12FT 24PT
Planning and Sustainability ... MA 12FT 24PT
Professional Practice Architecture (Part 3 ARB/RIBA exemption) ... PGDip 11PT

Leeds Metropolitan University
Architectural Professional Practice ... PGDip 24PT
Architecture ... MA 12FT 24PT
Art & Design ... MA 12FT 24PT
Landscape Architecture and Design ... MA 24FT 48PT
Professional Studies in Architecture ... GradCert 12PT

University of Lincoln
Architecture (Master of) ... MArch 12-18FT 24-36PT
Construction Project Management ... Diploma 12FT 36PT
Design for Museum and Exhibition ... MA 12FT 24PT 24DL
Development and Regeneration ... MA 12FT 24PT
Interior Architecture & Design ... MA 12FT 24PT
Planning and Urban Design ... MA 12FT
Practice and Management in Architecture RIBA/ARB III exemption ... PGDip 4PT
Sustainable Architectural Design ... MSc 12-15FT 24PT
Urban Design ... MA 12-18FT 24-36PT

Liverpool John Moores University
Architecture ... MArch 6FT 12PT/MA 36FT 48PT
Architecture MArch ... MArch 24FT 48PT
Architecture and Urban Design MA ... MA 6FT 38PT

University of Liverpool
Architecture ... MA 12FT 24PT
Architecture - London Based ... MSc 12FT 24PT
Architecture and Entrepreneurship - London Based ... MSc 12FT 24PT
Building Information Modelling - London Based .. MSc 12FT 24PT
Modern Architectural Heritage - London Based ... MSc 12FT 24PT
Sustainable Environmental Design in Architecture (SEDA) ... MSc 12FT

London Metropolitan University
Architectural History Theory and Interpretation ... MA 12FT 24PT
Architecture Professional Diploma RIBA 2 ... PGDip 24FT 36PT
Architecture: Examination in Professional Diploma RIBA 3 ... PGDip 6PT

London South Bank University
Architecture ... PGDip 24FT 36PT

Manchester Metropolitan University
Architecture ... MArch 24FT 48PT
Architecture and Urbanism ... MA 12FT 24PT
GDip Landscape Design ... GDip 12FT
Landscape Architecture ... MA 12FT 24PT
Secondary Education with QTS ... PGCE(QTS) 12FT

Newcastle University
Architectural Design Research ... MA 12FT
Architectural Practice and Management ... PGDip 12PT
Architectural Theory and Criticism ... MA 12FT 24PT
Architecture, Planning and Landscape ... MA 12FT 24PT
Architecture, Planning and Landscape (Design) ... MA 12FT
Digital Architecture ... MSc 12FT 24PT

Nottingham Trent University
Architectural Technology and Design ... MSc 12FT 24PT
Architecture ... MArch 24FT
Interior Architecture and Design ... MA 12FT 24PT
Professional Certificate in Architecture ... PGCert 15FT

University of Nottingham
Technology ... MArch 12FT
Theory and Design ... MArch 12FT
Visual Culture ... MA 12FT 24PT

Oxford Brookes University
Applied Design in Architecture ... MArchD 24FT
Architecture ... MArch 12FT/PGDip 6FT
International Architectural Regeneration and Development ... MA 12FT 24PT/PGDip 6FT 18PT

University of Oxford
Architectural History ... PGCert 12PT

Plymouth University
Architectural Conservation ... MA 12FT 24PT/PGDip 10FT 12-60PT
Architecture ... MA 12FT
Master of Architecture ... MArch 12FT 24PT

University of Portsmouth
Architecture ... MArch 24FT 48PT
Professional Practice: Architecture ... MA 24PT

Queen's University Belfast
Architecture: MArch ... MArch 24FT
Architecture: Professional Practice Architecture ... PGCert 12PT
Durability of Structures ... MSc 12FT 24PT/PGDip 12FT 24PT/PGCert 12FT 24PT

Ravensbourne
Architecture ... MA 12FT 24PT

University of Reading
History of Art and Architecture ... MA 12FT 24PT

Robert Gordon University
Architectural Studies ... MSc 12FT/PGDip 9FT/PGCert 5FT
Architecture MArch Part 2 ... MArch 24FT

Royal College of Art
Architecture and Interiors ... PhD by taught/MPhil/MA 23FT

University of Salford
Digital Architectural Design ... MSc 12FT 28PT/PGDip 8FT 16PT

Sheffield Hallam University
Architecture ... PGDip 36FT 72PT
Technical Architecture ... MSc 12FT 24PT

University of Sheffield
Architectural Design ... MA 12FT
Architectural Engineering Design ... MSc 12FT
Architecture ... MArch 24FT 36PT
Architecture and Town and Regional Planning ... MArch 24FT
Landscape Architecture ... MA 24FT/PGDip 18FT
Sustainable Architectural Studies ... MSc 12FT 24PT

University of St Andrews
Art History ... MLitt 12FT 24PT/PGDip 9FT 18PT

University of Strathclyde
Advanced Architectural Design ... MArch 12FT 24PT/PGDip 9FT 21PT
Advanced Architectural Studies ... MSc 12FT 24PT/PGDip 9FT 18PT
Architectural Design (International) ... MArch 24FT/PGDip 21FT
Sustainable Engineering: Building Design and ManagementMSc 12FT 24PT/PGDip 9FT 18PT/PGCert 6FT 12PT
Urban Design ... MSc 12FT 24PT/PGDip 9FT 18PT/PGCert 5FT 9PT

Swansea Metropolitan University
Glass ... MA 12FT

Trinity College Dublin - the University of Dublin
Irish Art History ... MPhil 12FT

University of Ulster
Architecture ... MArch 24FT

UCL - University College London
Advanced Architectural Studies ... MSc 12FT 24-60PT
Architectural History ... MA 12FT 24-60PT/PGDip 9FT
Architecture ... MArch 24FT
Graduate Architectural Design ... MArch 12FT
Professional Practice and Management in Architecture (Part 3).. Cert 6-12PT

University of the West of England, Bristol
MArch Architecture ... MArch 24FT 36PT
Professional Practice and Management in Architecture Pt 3 ... PGCert 12PT

University of Westminster
Architecture ... MA 12FT 24PT
Architecture (RIBA Pt II) ... MArch 24FT
Architecture and Digital Media ... MA 12FT 24PT
Architecture, Cultural Identity and Globalisation.. MA 12FT 24PT
Professional Practice in Architecture (RIBA Pt III) ... PGDip 12PT

Architectural studies
Research Courses

Anglia Ruskin University
Built Environment ... MPhil 24 - 60FT 36 - 72PT

Architectural studies

University of Bath
Architectural History and Theory ....MPhil 12-36FT 24-48PT
Architecture .... PhD 24-48FT 36-72PT/MPhil 12-36FT 24-48PT
Digital Architectonics...MPhil 12FT 24PT

Birmingham City University
Birmingham School of Architecture and Landscape....PhD/MPhil

University of Brighton
Arts and Architecture Research .... PhD 24-60FT 36-72PT/MPhil
18-36FT 30-48PT
Arts and Architecture Research Division ... PhD 24-60FT 36-72PT/
MPhil 18-36FT 30-48PT
Arts and Architecture Research Division ... PhD 24-60FT 36-72PT/
MPhil 18-36FT 30-48PT
Arts and Architecture Research Division ... PhD 24-60FT 36-72PT/
MPhil 18-36FT 30-48PT
Arts and Architecture Research Division ... PhD 24-60FT 36-72PT/
MPhil 18-36FT 30-48PT

University of Buckingham
Garden History.............................MA by research 12FT 24PT

University of Cambridge
Architecture .... PhD 36FT 60PT

Cardiff University
Architectural History and Theory .... PhD 36FT possiblePT/MPhil
12-24FT possiblePT
Architectural Practice ....PhD 36FT possiblePT/MPhil 12FT
possiblePT
Architectural Science...............PhD 36FT posiblePT/MPhil 12-24FT
possiblePT

University for the Creative Arts
Architecture .... MPhil 24FT 36PT/PhD 36FT 60PT
Architecture .... MPhil 24FT 36PT/PhD 36FT 60PT
Design .... MPhil 24FT 36PT/PhD 36FT 60PT

University of Dundee
Architecture (MPhil) .... MPhil 24FT
Architecture (MSc by research) ....MSc by research 12FT
Architecture (PhD)..PhD 36FT
Non-Graduating Research in School of the Environment (6
months or more)...Non-Grad 6-24FT
Non-Graduating Research in School of the Environment (less
than 6 months) .... Non-Grad 1-5FT

University of Edinburgh
Architecture .... PhD 36FT 72PT/MPhil 24FT 48PT
Landscape Architecture .... MPhil 24FT 48PT/PhD 36FT 72PT
Reflective Design Practices (Masters by Research) ....MSc by
research 12FT 24PT

Glasgow School of Art
Architecture ....MPhil 24FT/PhD 36FT 60PT
Art and Design .... PhD 36FT 60PT/MPhil 12FT 24PT

University of Glasgow
Architecture ....PhD 36FT/MLitt by research 12FT/MArch by
research 12FT

Goldsmiths, University of London
Research Architecture .....PhD 36-48FT 48-72PT/MPhil 24FT 36PT

University of Greenwich
Architecture and Construction- Research ...PhD 36FT 72PT/MPhil
12 - 18FT 24 - 36PT

University of Kent
Architecture .... MPhil 24FT 36PT/PhD 36FT 60PT

Kingston University
School of Architecture and Landscape: Landscape
Architecture .... MPhil 24FT 48PT/PhD 36FT 72PT

University of Lincoln
Architecture .... MPhil 12FT 24PT/PhD 36FT 60PT

University of Liverpool
Architecture .... PhD 24-48FT 48-84PT/MPhil 12-24FT 24-48PT

Loughborough University
History of Art, Architecture and Design ......PhD 36FT 60PT/MPhil
24FT 36PT

Manchester Metropolitan University
Department of Architecture, Landscape and 3D Design ....PhD/
MPhil/MA by research

University of Manchester
Architecture .... PhD 36FT 72PT

Newcastle University
Architecture, Planning and LandscapePhD 36FT 72PT/MPhil 12FT
24PT

University of Nottingham
Architectural Design (Social Science) ....PhD 36FT
Architecture (science)...PhD 36FT
Architecture (social science).......................................PhD 36FT
Art History ....MRes 12FT

Oxford Brookes University
Architecture MPhil/PhD ..... PhD 24-60FT 36-72PT/MPhil 24-36FT
36-48PT

Plymouth University
Architecture ....MRes 12FT

University of Portsmouth
Architecture .... MPhil 24FT 48PT/PhD 36FT 72PT

Queen's University Belfast
Built Environment .... PhD 36FT 72PT/MPhil 24FT 48PT

University of Roehampton
History................... PhD 24-48FT 36-60PT/MPhil 21-36FT 33-48PT

Royal College of Art
Architecture and Interiors ....PhD/MPhil/MA by research 24FT

University of Salford
SURFACE Inclusive Design Research Centre..........MSc by research
24DL/PhD 36FT 84PT

School of Oriental and African Studies - SOAS
Art and Archaeology...PhD 36FT/MPhil 24FT

University of Sheffield
Advanced Architectural Studies: Integrated Studies ....Integrated
PhD 48FT
Architecture .... PhD 36FT 72PT/MPhil 24FT 48PT

University of Strathclyde
Architecture - Research....PhD 36FT 72PT/MPhil 12FT 24PT/MRes
12FT 24PT
Building Design and Management for Sustainability ....
MRes 12FT 36PT

UCL - University College London
Advanced Spatial Analysis .... PhD 36FT 60PT
Architectural Design.. PhD 36FT 60PT

University of York
Conservation Studies......PhD 36FT 72PT/MPhil 24FT 48PT/MA by
research 12FT 24PT

Building architecture
Taught Courses

University of Aberdeen
Bayt al-Maqdis and Jerusalem Studies.... MLitt 12FT 24PT/PGDip
9FT 18PT

University of Bath
Architectural Engineering: Environmental Design......... MSc 12FT
24PT/PGDip 9FT 18PT
Environment, Energy & Resilience .... MRes 12FT 24-36PT
Facade Engineering.......................MSc 12FT 24PT/PGDip 9FT 18PT

Birmingham City University
Zero Carbon Architecture and Retrofit Design........ MA 12FT 24PT

Arts University Bournemouth
Architecture .... MA 12FT 24PT

University of Brighton
Architectural and Urban Studies...MA 18FT 24-42PT/PGDip 18FT
24-42PT/PGCert 18FT 24-42PT

University of Cambridge
Building History .... MSt 21PT
Environmental Design in Architecture - Option A .... MPhil 10FT
Environmental Design in Architecture Option B..........PGDip 21FT
Interdisciplinary Design for the Built Environment........ MSt 24PT

Cardiff University
Architecture: Professional Studies......MA 24FT 36PT/PGDip 12FT
Building Energy and Environmental Performance Modelling ....
MSc 12FT 24PT
Environmental Design of Buildings............... MSc 12FT 24PT 42DL

University of Central Lancashire
Building Conservation and Regeneration .... MSc 12FT 24-30PT/
PGDip 6FT 12PT/PGCert 3FT 6PT
Building Services...... MSc 12FT 30PT/PGDip 6FT 12PT/PGCert 3FT
6PT

Centre for Alternative Technology
Architecture: Advanced Environmental and Energy Studies ....
MSc 12FT 24PT
Architecture: Advanced Environmental and Energy Studies
(Distance Learning)...................MSc 16FT 28PT/PGDip 12FT 24PT/
PGCert 4FT 8PT
MSc Renewable Energy and the Built Environment....... MSc 18FT
30PT/PGCert 6FT 12PT/AdvPGDip 12FT 24PT

University College Cork
Information Technology in Architecture, Engineering and
Construction ....MEngSci 12FT 24PT

De Montfort University
Architecture and Sustainability...............................MSc 12FT 24PT
Energy and Sustainable Building Design ... MSc 12FT 24PT 36DL/
PGDip 32DL/PGCert 16DL

University of Derby
Sustainable Architecture and Healthy Environments .....MA 12FT

University of Dundee
Advanced Sustainability of the Built Environment .... MSc 12FT
Advanced Sustainable Urban Design .... MSc 12FT
Design and Construction of Zero Carbon and Ultra-Low Energy
Buildings .... MSc 12FT
Renewable Energy and Sustainable Building in a Global Context
MSc 12FT

University of East London
Architecture: Computing and Design ....MSc 12FT 24PT/
PGDip 8FT 16PT/PGCert 4FT 8PT

Edinburgh Napier University
Architectural Technology & Building PerformanceMSc 12FT 24PT
36DL
Design (Interaction)..MA/MDes 12FT
Design (Interdisciplinary) ....MA/MDes 12FT
Design (Interior Architecture) ....MA/MDes 12FT
Design (Sustainability).....................................MA/MDes 12FT
Design (Urbanism)...MA/MDes 12FT

Glasgow Caledonian University
Sustainable Energy Technology ....MSc 12FT 24PT

Glasgow School of Art
Architecture .... Diploma 24FT

University of Glasgow
Landscape: Integrated Research and Practice.......MSc 12FT 24PT/
PGDip 9FT 18PT

Goldsmiths, University of London
Design: Interaction Research...................................... MA 15FT 30PT
Research Architecture .... MA 12FT 24PT

University of Greenwich
Built Environment (Open) ....MSc 12FT 24PT

Heriot-Watt University
Carbon Management .... MSc 12FT 24PT 24-84DL/
PGDip 9FT 21PT 24-84DL
Sustainable Community Design. MSc 12FT 24PT 24-84DL/PGDip
9FT 21PT 24-84DL

University of Huddersfield
Sustainable Architecture...MSc 12FT 24PT

University of Kent
Architecture and Sustainable Environments .... MSc 12FT 24PT

Kingston University
Building Surveying...MSc 12FT 24PT
Landscape and Urbanism .... MA 12FT 24PT
Sustainability for Built Environment PracticeMA 12FT/MSc 12FT/
PGCert 6FT 12PT/PGDip 12FT
Sustainable Place Making and Urban Design .... MA 12FT 24PT

Leeds Metropolitan University
Architectural Professional Practice .... PGDip 24PT
Architecture .... MA 12FT 24PT
Landscape Architecture and Design .... MA 24FT 48PT
Professional Studies in Architecture ....GradCert 12PT
Urban DesignMA 12FT 24PT/PGDip 12FT 24PT/PGCert 12FT 24PT

Liverpool John Moores University
Sustainable Built Environment .... MSc 12FT

London Metropolitan University
Architecture, Energy and Sustainability..................MSc 12FT 24PT

London South Bank University
Built Environment Studies..MSc 12FT 30PT

Manchester Metropolitan University
Architecture ....MArch 24FT 48PT
Architecture and Urbanism .... MA 12FT 24PT

Middlesex University
Business Information Modelling Management (BIM).....MSc 12 /
24DL

Newcastle University
Architectural Design Research ....MA 12FT
Architecture, Master of..MArch 24FT
Architecture, Planning and Landscape .... MA 12FT 24PT
Architecture, Planning and Landscape (Design)...............MA 12FT
Urban Design..................................... MA 12FT 24PT/PGDip 9FT 21PT

Northumbria University
Architecture ....MArch 24FT 36PT
Building Design Management and Building Information
Modelling (BIM) ....MSc 18FT 36PT/PGCert 6FT 12PT
Surveying/Construction programme - Building Surveying
Pathway ....MSc 24DL

Nottingham Trent University
Architecture ....MArch 24FT

University of Nottingham
Design ....MArch 12FT
Renewable Energy and Architecture ....MSc 12FT 24PT/
PGDip 12FT 24PT
Renewable Energy and Architecture (Nottingham/Ningbo) ....
MSc 12FT
Sustainable Bioenergy ....MSc 12FT 36PT
Sustainable Building Design (with BCA Academy)......PGDip 12FT
Sustainable Building Technology ....MSc 12FT 24PT/PGDip 12FT
24PT
Sustainable Building Technology (Nottingham/ Ningbo) ...... MSc
12FT 24PT
Sustainable Building Technology (collaborative) .... MSc 12FT
Sustainable Energy and Entrepreneurship .... MSc 12FT
Sustainable Tall Buildings ....MArch 12FT

Oxford Brookes University
Applied Design in Architecture (MArchD)..................MArchD 24FT

Architectural studies

Architecture (MArch) ....MArch 12FT/PGDip 6FT
Sustainable Building: Performance and Design ..MSc 12FT 27PT/PGDip 9FT 18PT
Urban Design ....MA 12FT 24PT/PGDip 8FT 20PT/PGCert 8PT

Plymouth University
Architectural Conservation ....MA 12FT 24PT/PGDip 10FT 12-60PT

University of Portsmouth
Sustainable Architecture ....MA 12FT 24PT

Queen's University Belfast
Durability of Structures ....MSc 12FT 24PT/PGDip 12FT 24PT/PGCert 12FT 24PT
Urban and Rural Design ....MSc 12FT/PGDip 12FT

Ravensbourne
Architecture ....MA 12FT 24PT

University of Reading
Intelligent Buildings: Design, Construction and Management ....MSc 24PT

Robert Gordon University
Architecture MArch Part 2 ....MArch 24FT

Royal College of Art
Architecture and Interiors ....PhD by taught/MPhil/MA 23FT

University of Salford
Accessibility and Inclusive Design ....MSc 32DL/PGDip 20DL/PGCert 8DL
BIM and Integrated Design ....MSc 12FT 28PT 28DL/PGDip 8FT 20PT 20DL/PGCert 4FT 8PT 8DL
Doctorate in the Built Environment (Professional Doctorate) ....DBEnv 60PT
Sustainable Building Design ....MSc 12FT 28PT/PGDip 8FT 20PT/PGCert 4FT 8PT
Urban Design and Regeneration ....MSc 12FT 28PT/PGDip 8FT 20PT

Sheffield Hallam University
Architecture ....PGDip 36FT 72PT
Built Environment ....MPhil 24FT 36PT/PhD by taught 24FT 60PT
Technical Architecture ....MSc 12FT 24PT

University of Sheffield
Architectural Design ....MA 12FT
Architectural Engineering Design ....MSc 12FT
Designing Learning Environments ....MA 12FT 24PT
Sustainable Architectural Studies ....MSc 12FT 24PT
Urban Design ....MA 12FT 24PT
Urban Design and Planning ....MA 12FT

University of St Andrews
Sustainable Development ....MSc 12FT/PGDip 9FT

University of Strathclyde
Sustainable Engineering: Building Design and Management ....MSc 12FT 24PT/PGDip 9FT 18PT/PGCert 6FT 12PT
Urban Design.... MSc 12FT 24PT/PGDip 9FT 18PT/PGCert 5FT 9PT

UCL - University College London
Architecture ....MArch 24FT
Building and Urban Design in Development ....MSc 12FT 24-60PT/PGDip 9FT
Built Environment: Environmental Design and Engineering ....MSc 12FT 24-60PT/PGDip 9FT
Built Environment: Heritage Science ....MRes 12FT 24-60PT/PGCert 6FT
Built Environment: Sustainable Heritage ....MSc 12FT 24-60PT/PGDip 9FT
Urban Design ....MArch 12FT 24-60PT/PGDip 9FT

University of Westminster
Architecture ....MA 12FT 24PT
Continuing Professional Development in Architecture and the Built Environment ....Single postgraduate modules 4PT
Continuing Professional Development in Architecture and the Built Environment (Evening) ...Single postgraduate modules 4PT
International Planning and Sustainable Development ...MA 12FT 24PT
Urban Design ....MA 12FT 24PT
Urban Design Postgraduate Certificate ....PGCert 12PT
Urban Design Postgraduate Diploma ....PGDip 12FT 24PT

Building architecture
Research Courses

Birmingham City University
Birmingham School of Architecture and Landscape ....PhD/MPhil

University of Birmingham
Engineering, Sustainability and Resilience ....MRes 12FT

Cardiff University
Architectural Science ....PhD 36FT posiblePT/MPhil 12-24FT possiblePT

University for the Creative Arts
Architecture ....MPhil 24FT 36PT/PhD 36FT 60PT

University of Dundee
Architecture (MPhil) ....MPhil 24FT
Architecture (MSc by research) ....MSc by research 12FT
Architecture (PhD) ....PhD 36FT

Glasgow School of Art
Architecture ....MPhil 24FT/PhD 36FT 60PT

Goldsmiths, University of London
Research Architecture ....PhD 36-48FT 48-72PT/MPhil 24FT 36PT

Newcastle University
Architecture, Planning and Landscape PhD 36FT 72PT/MPhil 12FT 24PT

University of Nottingham
Building Services ....PhD 12FT
Building Technology ....PhD 36FT

Oxford Brookes University
Architecture MPhil/PhD ....PhD 24-60FT 36-72PT/MPhil 24-36FT 36-48PT
Urban Design MPhil/PhD ...PhD 24-60FT 36-72PT/MPhil 24-36FT 36-48PT

University of Portsmouth
Architecture ....MPhil 24FT 48PT/PhD 36FT 72PT

Royal College of Art
Interaction Design ....PhD/MPhil/MA by research

University of Salford
Doctorate in the Built Environment (Professional Doctorate) ....DBEnv 60PT/DRealEst 60PT/DConsMgt 60PT

University of Strathclyde
Building Design and Management for Sustainability ....MRes 12FT 36PT

University of Westminster
Architecture and the Built Environment ....MPhil 18-36FT 30-60PT

Landscape architecture
Taught Courses

University of Bath
Conservation of Historic Gardens and Cultural Landscapes .. MSc 12FT 28PT/PGDip 9FT 20PT

Birmingham City University
Landscape Architecture ....MA 12FT 24PT
Landscape Architecture ....PGDip 12FT
Landscape Architecture ....PGDip 9FT 18PT/MA 12FT 24PT
Landscape Architecture Graduate Diploma Conversion Course ....GradDip 12PT
Landscape Studies ....MA 36PT
Urban Design ....MA 12FT 24PT

Arts University Bournemouth
Architecture ....MA 12FT 24PT

University of Cambridge
Environmental Design in Architecture Option B ....PGDip 21FT
Interdisciplinary Design for the Built Environment ....MSt 24PT

University of Derby
Art and Design: Applied Practice and Theories (ADAPT) ....MA 17FT 34PT

University of Dundee
Architecture: Advanced Practice, Management and Law ....MSc 18DL
Spatial Planning with Urban Conservation ....MSc 12FT

University of East Anglia
Landscape History ....MA 12FT 24PT

University of East London
Architecture: Computing and Design MSc 12FT 24PT/PGDip 8FT 16PT/PGCert 4FT 8PT
Lanscape Architecture Graduate Diploma ....GradDip 12FT 24PT/GradCert 6FT 12PT
Lanscape Architecture ....MA 12FT 24PT/PGDip 8FT 16PT/PGCert 4FT 8PT
Professional Landscape Architecture ....MA 12FT 24PT/PGCert 4FT 8PT/PGDip 8FT 16PT

Edinburgh Napier University
Design (Urbanism) ....MA/MDes 12FT

University of Edinburgh
Landscape Architecture ....MLA 21FT

Glasgow School of Art
Architecture ....Diploma 24FT

University of Glasgow
Landscape Monitoring & Mapping ....MSc 12FT 24-36PT/PGDip 9FT 18-21PT
Landscape: Integrated Research and Practice ....MSc 12FT 24PT/PGDip 9FT 18PT

University of Gloucestershire
Landscape Architecture ....MA 12FT 24PT/PGDip 8FT 20PT
Landscape Architecture (Conversion) ....PGDip 20FT 48PT/MA 24FT 48PT

Goldsmiths, University of London
Research Architecture ....MA 12FT 24PT

University of Greenwich
European Landscape Architecture ....MA 24FT 36-42PT
Landscape Architecture ....MA 18FT 24PT
Landscape Architecture ....Diploma 12FT 24PT
Landscape Design ....Cert 12FT 18PT
Landscape Planning and Assessment ....MSc 12FT 18PT

Heriot-Watt University
Architectural Engineering ....MSc 12FT 24PT 24-84DL/PGDip 9FT 21PT 24-84DL/PGCert 6FT 12PT 24-84DL
Architectural Project Management (Distance Learning Only) ....MSc 24-84DL/PGDip 24-84DL/PGCert 24-84DL

University of Kent
Master of Architecture ....MArch 24FT

Kingston University
Architecture (Part 2 RIBA/ARB exemption) ....GradDip 24FT 36PT
Art & Space ....MA 12FT 24PT
Landscape Architecture (LI accredited) ....PGDip 12FT 24PT
Landscape and Urbanism ....MA 12FT 24PT
Planning and Sustainability ....MA 12FT 24PT
Sustainable Place Making and Urban Design ....MA 12FT 24PT

Leeds Metropolitan University
Architecture ....MA 12FT 24PT
Landscape Architecture ....MA 12FT 24PT/PGDip 12FT 24PT
Landscape Architecture and Design ....MA 24FT 48PT
Master of Architecture ....MArch 24FT 48PT
Urban Design MA 12FT 24PT/PGDip 12FT 24PT/PGCert 12FT 24PT

Manchester Metropolitan University
Architecture ....MArch 24FT 48PT
Architecture and Urbanism ....MA 12FT 24PT
GDip Landscape Design ....GDip 12FT
Landscape Architecture ....MA 12FT 24PT
Landscape Architecture ....BArch 12FT 24PT
Landscape Design ....GradDip 12FT
MA by Research ....MA by Research 12FT 24PT

Newcastle University
Architectural Design Research ....MA 12FT
Architecture, Master of ....MArch 24FT
Architecture, Planning and Landscape ....MA 12FT 24PT
Architecture, Planning and Landscape (Design) ....MA 12FT
Future Landscape Imaginaries ....MA 12FT 24PT
Urban Design ....MA 12FT 24PT/PGDip 9FT 21PT

Nottingham Trent University
Architecture ....MArch 24FT
Planning, Urban Design and Sustainable Development ....PGCert 12PT

University of Nottingham
Environmental Design ....MArch 12FT 24PT
Landscape and Culture ....MA 12FT 24PT
Part 3 Professional Practice Certificate / MArch conversion ....MArch 12FT

Oxford Brookes University
Applied Design in Architecture (MArchD) ....MArchD 24FT
Architecture (MArch) ....MArch 12FT/PGDip 6FT
Urban Design ....MA 12FT 24PT/PGDip 8FT 20PT/PGCert 8PT
Urban Design (MRes) ....MRes 12FT 24PT

Queen's University Belfast
Sustainable Design ....MSc 12FT/PGDip 9FT
Urban and Rural Design ....MSc 12FT/PGDip 12FT

Ravensbourne
Architecture ....MA 12FT 24PT

Robert Gordon University
Architecture MArch Part 2 ....MArch 24FT

Royal College of Art
Architecture and Interiors ....PhD by taught/MPhil/MA 23FT

University of Salford
Urban Design and Regeneration ....MSc 12FT 28PT/PGDip 8FT 20PT

Sheffield Hallam University
Architecture ....PGDip 36FT 72PT

University of Sheffield
Landscape Architecture ....MA 24FT/PGDip 18FT
Landscape Management ....MA 12FT 24-36PT/PGDip 9FT 18PT
Landscape Research ....MA 12FT
Landscape Studies ....MA 12FT/PGDip 9FT
Sustainable Architectural Studies ....MSc 12FT 24PT
Urban Design ....MA 12FT 24PT
Urban Design and Planning ....MA 12FT

Staffordshire University
Community & Participatory Arts ....MA 12FT 24PT

University of Strathclyde
Advanced Architectural Design ....MArch 12FT 24PT/PGDip 9FT 21PT
Advanced Architectural Studies ....MSc 12FT 24PT/PGDip 9FT 18PT
Urban Design.... MSc 12FT 24PT/PGDip 9FT 18PT/PGCert 5FT 9PT

University of Sussex
International Trade Law ....LLM 12FT 24PT

University of Wales Trinity Saint David
Landscape Management and Environmental Archaeology ....MA 12FT 24PT/PGCert 12FT 24PT/PGDip 12FT 24PT

Architectural studies

UCL - University College London
Adaptive Architecture and Computation........ MSc 12FT 24-60PT/
PGDip 9FT/MRes 12FT 24-60PT
Architecture ....MArch 24FT
Urban Design.................... MArch 12FT 24-60PT/PGDip 9FT

University of the West of England, Bristol
Urban Design... MA 18FT 27PT

University of Westminster
Architecture .... MA 12FT 24PT
Continuing Professional Development in Architecture and the
Built Environment (Evening) ... Single postgraduate modules 4PT
International Planning and Sustainable Development...MA 12FT
24PT
Urban Design.. MA 12FT 24PT
Urban Design Postgraduate Certificate......................PGCert 12PT
Urban Design Postgraduate Diploma .... PGDip 12FT 24PT

University of Worcester
Archaeological Landscapes.......................................MA 24FT

Writtle College
Landscape Architecture .....MA 12FT 24-36FT/PGDip 8FT 20-36PT

Landscape architecture
Research Courses

Birmingham City University
Birmingham School of Architecture and Landscape ....PhD/MPhil

University of Brighton
Arts and Architecture Research Division ... PhD 24-60FT 36-72PT/
MPhil 18-36FT 30-48PT

University for the Creative Arts
Architecture .... MPhil 24FT 36PT/PhD 36FT 60PT

University of Dundee
Architecture ....MPhil 24FT MSc by research 12FT
PhD 36FT

University of Edinburgh
Landscape Architecture .... MPhil 24FT 48PT/PhD 36FT 72PT

Glasgow School of Art
Architecture ....MPhil 24FT/PhD 36FT 60PT

Goldsmiths, University of London
Research Architecture .....PhD 36-48FT 48-72PT/MPhil 24FT 36PT

Kingston University
School of Architecture and Landscape: Landscape Architecture ..
MPhil 24FT 48PT/PhD 36FT 72PT

Manchester Metropolitan University
Department of Architecture, Landscape and 3D Design ....PhD/
MPhil/MA by research

University of Manchester
Planning and Landscape.......................................PhD 36FT

Newcastle University
Architecture, Planning and LandscapePhD 36FT 72PT/MPhil 12FT
24PT

Oxford Brookes University
Architecture MPhil/PhD ..... PhD 24-60FT 36-72PT/MPhil 24-36FT
36-48PT
Urban Design MPhil/PhD ...PhD 24-60FT 36-72PT/MPhil 24-36FT
36-48PT

University of Sheffield
Advanced Architectural Studies ....Integrated PhD 48FT
Landscape........................... PhD 36FT 72PT/MPhil 24FT 48PT

Landscape gardening
Taught Courses

Birmingham City University
Landscape Studies...MA 36PT

University of Glasgow
Landscape: Integrated Research and Practice.......MSc 12FT 24PT/
PGDip 9FT 18PT

University of Greenwich
Garden Design.. MA 18FT 30PT
Garden History..........................MA 18FT 30PT/PGCert 12DL

Inchbald School of Design
Garden Design.. MA 12FT 12PT

Manchester Metropolitan University
Landscape Design...GradDip 12FT

Writtle College
Garden Design.. MA 12FT 24-36FT
Historic Designed Landscapes ....MA 12FT 24PT/PGDip 6FT 12PT/
PGCert 3FT 6PT
Landscape Management MSc 12FT 24-36PT/PGDip 8FT 20-36PT/
PGCert 4FT 16-36PT

Landscape gardening
Research Courses

University of Buckingham
Garden History..................................MA by research 12FT 24PT

Restoration
Taught Courses

Anglia Ruskin University
Conservation of Buildings ....MSc 12FT 24 - 30PT

University of Bath
Conservation of Historic Buildings ......MSc 12FT 28PT/PGDip 9FT
20PT
Conservation of Historic Gardens and Cultural Landscapes .. MSc
12FT 28PT/PGDip 9FT 20PT

University of Bolton
Regeneration and Sustainable CommunitiesMA 15FT/MSc 15FT/
PGDip 12FT/PGCert 6FT

Bucks New University
Conservation of Furniture and Decorative Arts...... MA 12FT 24PT

College of Estate Management
Conservation of Historic Environment ......PGDip 24DL/MSc 36DL

Cardiff University
Conservation Practice... MSc 24FT
Professional Conservation................................... MSc 12FT 24PT

Cranfield University
Land Reclamation and Restoration ....MSc 12FT 60PT/
PGCert 12FT 60PT/PGDip 12FT 60PT

University of Dundee
Renewable Energy and Sustainable Building in a Global Context
MSc 12FT

Durham University
Conservation of Archaeological and Museum Objects
(Dissertation).. MA 24FT 36PT
Conservation of Archaeological and Museum Objects
(Professional Practice).................................... MA 24FT 36PT

Edinburgh Napier University
Architectural Technology & Building Performance ....
MSc 12FT 24PT 36DL
Timber Engineering ....MSc 12FT 36DL
Timber Industry Management...................... MSc 12FT 36PT 36DL

University of Edinburgh
Architectural Conservation .... MSc 12FT 24PT

University of Greenwich
Building Rehabilitation .... MSc 12FT 24PT

Heriot-Watt University
Building Conservation (Technology and Management)........... MSc
24-84DL/PGDip 24-84DL

Kingston University
Historic Building Conservation ....MSc 12FT 24PT

University of Leicester
Country House MA/Postgraduate Diploma/Postgraduate
Certificate.. MA 24-48DL
Urban Conservation..........................MA 12FT 24PT/MSc 12FT 24PT

University of Lincoln
Conservation Studies............................... GradDip 12FT 24PT
Conservation of Historic Objects............................ MA 12FT 24PT

London Metropolitan University
Restoration and Conservation MA by Project .... MA 12FT 24PT

Oxford Brookes University
Historic Conservation . MSc 12FT 24PT/PGDip 12FT 24PT/PGCert
12PT

Plymouth University
Architectural Conservation .. MA 12FT 24PT/PGDip 10FT 12-60PT

University of Portsmouth
Historic Building Conservation ....MSc 12FT 24PT

University of Reading
Geoarchaeology .... MSc 12FT 24PT/PGDip 12FT 24PT

Royal College of Art
Conservation.........................PhD by taught/MPhil/MA 24FT

School of Oriental and African Studies - SOAS
History of Art and/or Archaeology...................... MA 12FT 24-36FT

University of Sheffield
Conservation and Regeneration .... MA 12FT 24PT
Sustainable Architectural Studies................... MSc 12FT 24PT

University of Sussex
International Trade Law.. LLM 12FT 24PT

Trinity College Dublin - the University of Dublin
Applied Building Repair and Conservation .... PGDip 12PT

UCL - University College London
Built Environment: Sustainable Heritage .... MSc 12FT 24-60PT/
PGDip 9FT
Conservation................................MSc 12FT/PGDip 9FT/PGCert 3FT

University of York
Conservation Studies (Historic Buildings).......... MA 12FT 24-36FT
Stained Glass Conservation and Heritage Management MA 24FT

Restoration
Research Courses

Birmingham City University
Birmingham School of Architecture and Landscape ....PhD/MPhil

University of Cambridge
Brain Repair..PhD 36FT

School of Oriental and African Studies - SOAS
Department of Art and Archaeology ....PhD 36FT 72PT/
MPhil 24FT 36PT

Urban planning
Taught Courses

University of Aberdeen
Bayt al-Maqdis and Jerusalem Studies.... MLitt 12FT 24PT/PGDip
9FT 18PT

**University of the Arts London - Central Saint Martins College of
Art and Design**
Architecture: Cities and Innovation....................................MA 24FT

Birmingham City University
Environmental and Spatial Planning...PGCert 4FT 8PT/PGDip 4FT
8PT/MA 4FT 8PT
Urban Design .... MA 12FT 24PT

University of Birmingham
International Development (Urban Development).......MSc 12FT/
PGDip 9FT
Local and Regional Economic Development...........MSc 12FT 24PT/
PGDip 9FT 21PT/GradDip 9FT 21PT/GradCert 9FT 21PT
Resilience and Urban Living........MSc 12FT 24PT/MRes 12FT 24PT
Urban Regeneration and Renewal ... MSc 12FT 24PT/GradDip 9FT
21PT/GradCert 9FT 21PT/PGDip 9FT 21PT
Urban and Regional Planning (with RTPI accreditation) ....
MSc 12FT 24PT/PGCert 6FT 12PT/PGDip 12FT 24PT
Urban and Regional Studies ...... MSc 12FT 24PT/PGDip 9FT 21PT/
GradDip 9FT 21PT/GradCert 9FT 21PT

University of Cambridge
Environmental Design in Architecture Option B..........PGDip 21FT

Cardiff University
European Spatial Planning, Environmental Policies and Regional
Development .... MSc 24FT
International Planning and Development .... MSc 12FT
Regeneration Studies .... MSc 12FT 24PT
Urban Design...MA 12FT

University of Central Lancashire
Building Conservation and Regeneration .... MSc 12FT 24-30PT/
PGDip 6FT 12PT/PGCert 3FT 6PT
Building Services...... MSc 12FT 30PT/PGDip 6FT 12PT/PGCert 3FT
6PT
Urban Environmental Management... MSc 12FT 24PT/PGDip 9FT
18PT/PGCert 6FT 12PT

Dublin Institute of Technology
Spatial Planning.. MSc 30PT

University of Dundee
Advanced Sustainable Urban Design .... MSc 12FT
Spatial Planning with Marine Spatial Planning .... MSc 12FT
Spatial Planning with Sustainable Urban Design .... MSc 12FT
Spatial Planning with Urban Conservation .... MSc 12FT

University of East London
Architecture: Urban Design ....MA 12FT 24PT/PGDip 8FT 16PT/
PGCert 4FT 8PT

Edinburgh Napier University
Design (Urbanism) ....MA/MDes 12FT

University of Edinburgh
Architectural and Urban Design .... MSc 12FT

University of Glasgow
City & Regional Planning..............................MSc 12FT 24PT 60BM
City Planning & Real Estate Development.............MSc 12FT 24PT
60BM
City Planning & Regeneration.......................MSc 12FT 24PT 60BM
Spatial Planning..PGCert 48BM
Urban & Housing Practice......... MSc 12FT 24PT 60BM/PGDip 9FT
Urban Policy & Practice....MSc 12FT 24PT 60BM/PGDip 9FT 18PT
48BM
Urban Regeneration .... MSc 12FT 24PT 60BM/PGDip 9FT 18PT

Goldsmiths, University of London
Photography and Urban Cultures .... MA 12FT 24PT
World Cities and Urban Life...................................... MA 12FT 24PT

University of Greenwich
Built Environment (Open)..MSc 12FT 24PT
Urban Design.. MA 12FT 24PT

Heriot-Watt University
MRes Courses in Urban Studies/Housing/Planning Studies/Real
Estate Research... MSc(Res) 12FT
Sustainable Community Design............ MSc 12FT 24PT 24-84DL/
PGDip 9FT 21PT 24-84DL
Urban Strategies and Design.......MSc 12FT 24PT/PGDip 9FT 21PT
Urban and Regional Planning .... MSc 12FT 24PT 24-84DL/
PGDip 9FT 21PT 24-84DL

Architectural studies

Institute of Education
Educational Planning, Economics and International
Development.. MA 12FT 24-48PT

Keele University
Urban Futures and Sustainable Communities.......MA 12FT 24PT/
PGDip 12FT 24PT/PGCert 12FT 24PT

University of Kent
Architecture and Cities .... MA 12FT 24PT
Architecture and Cities (Paris option) ....MA 12FT
Architecture and Sustainable Environments ....MSc 12FT 24PT
Master of Architecture (MArch with ARB/RIBA Part 2 exemption)
MArch 24FT
Social and Public Policy: Urban Regeneration (Distance Learning,
Medway)..MA 24DL/PGDip 24DL

King's College London
Sustainable Cities...MSc 12FT 24PT

Kingston University
Landscape and Urbanism.. MA 12FT 24PT
Sustainable Place Making and Urban Design......... MA 12FT 24PT

Leeds Metropolitan University
Architectural Professional Practice.................................. PGDip 24PT
Housing, Regeneration and Urban Management MA 12FT 24PT/
PGCert 12FT 12PT/PGDip 12FT 24PT
Professional Studies in Architecture ....GradCert 12PT
Town and Regional Planning.. MA 12FT 24PT
Urban DesignMA 12FT 24PT/PGDip 12FT 24PT/PGCert 12FT 24PT

University of Leeds
Culture, Creativity and Entrepreneurship... MA 12FT 24PT/PGDip
9FT 21PT/PGCert 6FT 12PT

University of Leicester
Urban Conservation..........................MA 12FT 24PT/MSc 12FT 24PT

University of Lincoln
Development and Regeneration .... MA 12FT 24PT
Planning and Urban Design...MA 12FT

Liverpool John Moores University
Architecture and Urban Design MA.............................MA 6FT 38PT

University of Liverpool
Urban Regeneration and Management.....................MSc 12FT 24PT

London Metropolitan University
Planning and Sustainable Communities.................MSc 12FT 24PT
Spatial Planning and Urban Design........................... MA 12FT 27PT
Sustainable Cities..MSc 12FT 24+PT

London School of Economics and Political Science (LSE)
City Design and Social Science...................................MSc 12FT 24PT
Regional and Urban Planning Studies ....MSc 12FT 24-48PT
Urban Policy (Double Degree).. MSc 23FT
Urbanisation and Development..................................MSc 12FT 24PT

London South Bank University
Cities and Local Development.. MSc 24PT
Development and Urbanisation...............................MSc 13FT 24PT
Urban Planning Design.. MA 12FT 24PT
Urban Regeneration .... MA 13FT 30PT

University of Manchester
Global Urban Development and Planning.............MSc 12FT 24PT

Newcastle University
Architectural Design Research ....MA 12FT
Local and Regional Development (Research) ....MA 12FT 24PT
Planning and Environment Research .... MA 12FT 24PT
Planning for Developing Countries..................................... MSc 12FT
Planning for Sustainability and Climate Change ....MSc 12FT
Spatial Planning...PGDip 9FT 21PT
Urban Design..................................... MA 12FT 24PT/PGDip 9FT 21PT

University of Northampton
Sustainable Urban Environments...................................PGCert 6PT
Urbanism: Design and Environment......................MSc 12FT 24PT

Nottingham Trent University
PG Cert Planning, Urban Design and Sustainable
Development..PGCert 12PT

University of Nottingham
Urban Design..MArch 12FT

Oxford Brookes University
Applied Design in Architecture ....MArchD 24FT
Planning .... PGDip 12FT 24PT
Spatial Planning ....MSc 12FT 24PT/PGDip 9FT 21PT
Spatial Planning Studies (Certificate)................................Cert 12PT
Urban Design .... MA 12FT 24PT/PGDip 8FT 20PT/PGCert 8PT
MRes 12FT 24PT
Urban Planning ....MRes 12FT 24PT
Urban Planning: Developing and Transitional Regions
MSc 12FT 24PT
Urban and Regional Regeneration .... PGCert 9FT

Plymouth University
Master of Architecture...MArch 12FT 24PT
Planning .... MSc 12FT

University of Portsmouth
Urban Design .... MA 12FT 24PT

Queen's University Belfast
Planning and Regeneration ....MSc 12FT/PGDip 12FT
Urban and Rural Design................................MSc 12FT/PGDip 12FT

Ravensbourne
Environment Design... MA 12FT 24PT

University of Reading
Development Planning .... MSc 12FT 24PT/PGDip 12FT 24PT
Development Planning Research ......MSc 12FT 24PT/PGDip 12FT
24PT
International Planning and Sustainable Urban Management .....
MSc 12FT/PGCert 6FT/PGDip 9FT

University of Salford
Urban Design and Regeneration MSc 12FT 28PT/PGDip 8FT 20PT

Sheffield Hallam University
Built Environment.....MPhil 24FT 36PT/PhD by taught 24FT 60PT
Urban and Regional Planning ....MSc 12FT 24PT
Urban and Regional Planning (Transport)...............MSc 12FT 24PT

University of Sheffield
Architectural Design...MA 12FT
Conservation and Regeneration .... MA 12FT 24PT
Environmental Management of Urban Land and Water ....
MSc 12FT 24PT/PGDip 9FT 18PT/PGCert 6FT 12PT
Planning and Development...MA 12FT
Town and Regional Planning...MA 12FT
Urban Design.. MA 12FT 24PT
Urban Design and Planning..MA 12FT

University of Strathclyde
Advanced Architectural Design .... MArch 12FT 24PT/PGDip 9FT
21PT
Advanced Architectural Studies ....MSc 12FT 24PT/
PGDip 9FT 18PT
Urban Design.... MSc 12FT 24PT/PGDip 9FT 18PT/PGCert 5FT 9PT

Trinity College Dublin - the University of Dublin
Environment and Development .... MSc 12FT

UCL - University College London
Building and Urban Design in Development .... MSc 12FT
24-60PT/PGDip 9FT

Built Environment: Environmental Design and Engineering.........
MSc 12FT 24-60PT/PGDip 9FT
Built Environment: Heritage Science ....MRes 12FT 24-60PT/
PGCert 6FT
Built Environment: Sustainable Heritage .... MSc 12FT 24-60PT/
PGDip 9FT
Mega Infrastructure Planning, Appraisal and Delivery ....
MSc 12FT 24-60PT
Planning, Design and Development..... MSc 12FT 24-60PT/PGDip
9FT
Spatial Planning.................................MSc 12FT 24-60PT/PGDip 9FT
Sustainable Urbanism.......................MSc 12FT 24-60PT/PGDip 9FT
Urban Design................................... MArch 12FT 24-60PT/PGDip 9FT
Urban Development Planning ....MSc 12FT 24-60PT/PGDip 9FT
Urban Economic Development.......MSc 12FT 24-60PT/PGDip 9FT
Urban Regeneration ....MSc 12FT 24-60PT/PGDip 9FT

University of West London
Development and Management of Sustainable Built
Environment..MSc 12FT 24PT

University of the West of England, Bristol
Spatial Planning...MA TBCDL
Urban Design... MA 18FT 27PT

University of Westminster
Urban Design Postgraduate Diploma .... PGDip 12FT 24PT
Urban and Regional Planning .... MA 12FT 24PT

Urban planning
Research Courses

University of Birmingham
Urban and Regional Studies ...... PhD 36FT 72PT/MPhil 24FT 48PT

Cardiff University
Environment.................................... PhD 36FT 60PT/MPhil 36FT 60PT
Spatial Analysis .... PhD 36FT 60PT
Spatial Planning and City Environments................ PhD 36FT 60PT

University of Glasgow
Urban Studies............................... PhD 36FT/MLitt by research 12FT

London School of Economics and Political Science (LSE)
Cities.. PhD 36-48FT/MPhil 36-48FT
Regional and Urban Planning .... PhD 36-48FT/MPhil 36-48FT

The Open University
Materialities, Space and Power........... PhD 36FT 72PT variableDL/
MPhil 15FT 24PT variableDL

Oxford Brookes University
Planning .... PhD 24-60FT 36-72PT/MPhil 24-36FT 36-48PT
Urban Design .... PhD 24-60FT 36-72PT/MPhil 24-36FT 36-48PT

Plymouth University
Architecture ....MRes 12FT

University of Salford
Centre for Policy Studies...PhD/MPhil

Sheffield Hallam University
Centre for Regional Economic and Social Research Applied Social
Research... PhD 36FT 60PT
Centre for Regional Economic and Social Research Applied Social
Research... PhD 36FT 60PT
Environment and Development .... MPhil 36PT
Environment and Development - Facilities Management.......PhD
33FT 45PT/MPhil 18FT 30PT

University of Sheffield
City, Society and Planning: Integrated Studies.....New Route PhD
48FT

Art and design

Animation
Taught Courses

University of the Arts London - Central Saint Martins College of Art and Design
Character Animation .... MA 24FT

Bangor University
Advanced Visualization, Virtual Environments and Computer Animation .... MRes 12FT
Film and Visual Culture .... MRes 12FT 24PT

University of Bedfordshire
Computer Animation and Games Technology .... MSc 12FT 24-36PT

Arts University Bournemouth
Animation .... MA 12FT 24PT

University of Bradford
Advanced Computer Animation and Visual Effects .... MA 12FT 24PT/MSc 12FT 24PT
Computer Animation and Visual Effects MSc 12FT 24PT/MA 12FT 24PT
Visual Effects for Post-Production .... MSc 12FT 24PT

University of Bristol
Advanced Computing - Character Animation .... MSc 12FT 24PT

University of Central Lancashire
Animation .... MA 12FT/PGDip 12FT/PGCert 12FT

University for the Creative Arts
Animation .... MA 12FT 24PT
Graphic Storytelling and Comic Art .... MA 12FT 24PT

University of Derby
Visual Communication (Animation) .... MDes 48FT

University of Dundee
Animation and Visualisation .... MSc 12FT

University of East Anglia
Games Development .... MSc 12FT 24PT

University of Edinburgh
Animation .... MA 12FT/MFA 24FT
Digital Animation .... MSc(Res) 12FT 24PT

Glasgow School of Art
Animation .... PGCert 4FT/PGDip 8FT/MDes 12FT
Sound for the Moving Image .... PGCert 4FT/PGDip 8FT/MDes 12FT

University of Glasgow
Medical Visualisation & Human Anatomy .... MSc 12FT

Glyndwr University
Design Practice .... MA 12FT 24PT

University of Hertfordshire
Animation ....MA 12FT 24PT/PGDip 12FT 24PT/PGCert 12FT 24PT
Character Creation and Technical Effects.... MA 12FT 24PT/PGDip 12FT 24PT
Model Design and Model Effects........ MA 12FT 24PT/PGDip 12FT 24PT/PGCert 12FT 24PT
Two Dimensional Digital Animation .. MA 12FT 24PT/PGDip 12FT 24PT

University of Kent
Computer Animation .... MSc 12FT
Digital Visual Effects .... MSc 12FT/PGDip 12FT

Kingston University
Communication Design: Illustration .... MA 12FT 24PT

London Metropolitan University
Film and Animation .... MA 12FT

Nottingham Trent University
Puppetry and Digital Animation .... MA 12FT/PGDip 7FT/PGCert 4FT

Ravensbourne
Animation Futures .... MA 12FT 24PT
Applied Technologies, Rapid Prototyping and Digital Technologies .... MSc 12FT 24PT

Royal College of Art
Animation .... PhD by taught 72PT/MPhil 24FT 48PT/MA 24FT

University of Salford
Animation .... MA 12FT
Audio Production .... MSc 12FT 36PT
Professional Sound and Video Technology MSc 12FT 36PT/PGDip 9FT 24PT

Sheffield Hallam University
Animation and Special Effects .... MA 12FT 36PT
Animation for Computer Games .... MA 12FT 36PT

University of South Wales
Animation .... MA 12FT 24PT/MFA 24FT 36PT
Animation .... MA 12FT 24PT
Visual Effects .... MA 12FT 24PT

University of Sunderland
Animation and Design .... MA 12FT 24PT

Teesside University
Digital Character Animation MA 12FT 24-36PT/PGDip 8FT 24PT/PGCert 4FT 12PT

University of the West of England, Bristol
Animation .... MA 18FT 36PT/PGDip 12FT 24PT

University of Westminster
Design for Communication .... MA 12FT/MA 12FT

Animation
Research Courses

University of Kent
Cartoons and Caricature........ PhD 36FT 60PT/MPhil 24FT 36PT/MA by research 12FT 24PT

Royal College of Art
Animation .... PhD/MPhil/MA by research

Art and design
Taught Courses

Anglia Ruskin University
Fine Art .... MA 12FT 24PT
Illustration and Book Arts .... MA 12FT 24PT/PGCert 12FT 24PT/PGDip 12FT 24PT
Printmaking .... MA 12FT 24-36PT
Publishing .... MA 12FT

University of the Arts London - Camberwell College of Arts
Fine Art Digital .... MA 12FT 24PT 24DL
Illustration .... MA 12FT 24PT

University of the Arts London - Central Saint Martins College of Art and Design
Applied Imagination in the Creative Industries ..... MA 12FT 24PT
Art and Science .... MA 24FT
Art: Theory and Philosophy .... MRes 24FT
Communication Design .... MA 24FT
Fine Art .... MA 24FT

University of the Arts London - Chelsea College of Art and Design
Arts Practice .... MRes 12FT
Fine Art .... MA 12FT 24PT

University of the Arts London - Wimbledon College of Art
Fine Art: Drawing .... MA 15FT 15PT
Fine Art: Sculpture .... MA 15FT 15PT

Bangor University
Fine Art .... MA 36PT

Bath Spa University
Arts Management .....MA 12FT 24PT/PGDip 8FT 16PT/PGCert 4FT
Design: Brand Development ....MA 12FT 24PT/PGDip 9FT 18PT/PGCert 4FT 9PT
Fashion Portfolio .... MA 12FT
Visual Communication .... MA 12FT 24PT

University of Bedfordshire
Art Design and Internet Technology .... MA 12FT 24PT
Art and Design .... MA 12FT 24PT

Birmingham City University
Arts Practice and Education .... MA 12FT 24PT
Arts and Education .... MA 12FT 24PT
Contemporary Curatorial Practice .... MA 12FT 24PT
Art and Design .... MA 12FT 24PT
Surface Design .... MA 12FT 24PT

University of Bolton
Fine Art .... MA 12FT

Arts University Bournemouth
Illustration .... MA 12FT 24PT
Design Interaction .... MA 12FT 24PT

Bournemouth University
Computer Animation and Visual Effects .... MSc 12FT

University of Brighton
Arts and Design by Independent Project .... MA 12FT 24PT
Fine Art.........MA 12FT 24PT/PGDip 12FT 24PT/PGCert 12FT 24PT
Inclusive Arts Practice .... MA 24-72PT/PGCert 24-72PT

Brunel University
Design Strategy and Innovation .... MA 12FT
Design and Branding Strategy .... MA 12FT
Sustainability, Entrepreneurship and Design (with Professional Development) .... MSc 18FT

University of Buckingham
Decorative Arts and Historic Interiors .... MA 12FT

Bucks New University
Art and Design Practice .... MA 12FT 24PT

Cardiff Metropolitan University
Art and Design (with pathways) .... MA 12FT 24PT
Design (Master of) .... MDes 12FT 24PT

University of Central Lancashire
Arts Project Management .... PGCert 3PT
Design .... MA 12-18FT 24-30PT/PGCert 12FT/PGDip 12FT
Fashion Design .... MA 12FT/PGDip 12FT/PGCert 12FT
Interior Design .... MA 12FT 24PT/PGDip 12FT/PGCert 12FT
Surface Pattern .... MA 12-18FT 24PT/PGDip 12-18FT/PGCert 12-18FT
Toy Design .... MA 12FT 24PT/PGDip 12-18FT/PGCert 12-18FT
Transdisciplinary Design .... MA 12FT 24PT

University of Chester
Design .... MA 24PT/PGDip 24PT/PGCert 12 - 24PT

University of Chichester
Fine Art .... MA 12FT 24PT
Transpersonal Arts and Practice .... MA 12-15FT 24-36PT/PGDip 9-12FT 18-24PT/PGCert 6-9FT 12-18PT

University College Cork
Arts .... HDip 9FT MA 12FT

University for the Creative Arts
Artists' Film, Video and Photography .... MA 12FT
Design .... MA 12FT 24PT
Design for Performance and Events .... MA 12FT 24PT
Design: Digital Design .... MA 12FT 24PT

University of Cumbria
Contemporary Fine Art .... MA 12FT

De Montfort University
Design Entrepreneurship .... MA 12FT 24PT/PGDip 9FT 18PT
Design Innovation .... MA 12FT 24PT/MSc 12FT 24PT/PGDip 9FT 18PT
Independent Study in Art and Design ... MA 12FT 24PT/MSc 12FT 24PT

University of Derby
Art Therapy .... MA 24FT
Art and Design: Advanced Practice and Theories (ADAPT) .... MA 17FT 34PT
Art and Design: Applied Practice and Theories (ADAPT) . MA 17FT 34PT

University of Dundee
Art and Humanities .... MFA 12FT
Fine Art .... MFA 12FT
Forensic Art .... MSc 48PT
Product Design .... MSc 12FT

Edinburgh Napier University
Design (Interdisciplinary) .... MA/MDes 12FT
Interdisciplinary Design .... MDes 12FT 24PT

University of Edinburgh
Advanced Sustainable Design .... MSc 12FT 24PT
Animation .... MA 12FT/MFA 24FT
Art in the Global Middle Ages .... MSc 12FT 24PT
Art, Space and Nature .... MA 12FT/MFA 24FT
Contemporary Art Painting .... MA 12FT 24PT/MFA 24FT
Contemporary Art Photography .... MA 12FT 24PT/MFA 24FT
Contemporary Art Practice .... MA 12FT 24PT/MFA 24FT
Contemporary Art Sculpture .... MA 12FT 24PT/MFA 24FT
Contemporary Art Theory .... MA 12FT 24PT/MFA 24FT
Design Informatics .... MSc 12FT MA 12FT/MFA 24FT
Design and Digital Media .... MSc 12FT 24PT
Digital Animation .... MSc(Res) 12FT 24PT
Digital Studio Practice .... MSc(Res) 12FT 24PT
Fashion .... MA 12FT/MFA 24FT
Graphic Design .... MA 12FT/MFA 24FT
History of Art, Theory and Display .... MSc 12FT 24PT
Illustration .... MA 12FT/MFA 24FT
Interdisciplinary Creative Practices .... MSc 12FT 24PT
Interior Architectural Design .... MA 12FT/MFA 24FT
Interior Design .... MA 12FT
Jewellery .... MA 12FT/MFA 24FT
Modern and Contemporary Art: History, Curating, Criticism .... MSc 12FT 24PT
Performance Costume .... MA 12FT/MFA 24FT
Product Design .... MA 12FT/MFA 24FT
Scottish Art and Visual Culture 1750-2000 .... MSc 12FT 24PT/PGDip 9FT 18PT

Falmouth University
Art and Environment .... MA 12FT 24PT
MA Creative Education .... PGCHE 12PT/PGDip 12PT/MA 12PT
World First MBA .... MBA 12FT 24PT

National University of Ireland Galway
Arts Policy and Practice .... MA 12FT/PGDip 12FT

Glasgow School of Art
Creative Practices .... PGCert 4FT 8PT/PGDip 8FT 16PT/MRes 12FT 24PT
Design Innovation ... PGCert 4FT 8PT/PGDip 8FT 16PT/MDes 12FT 24PT
Design and Citizenship .... MDes 12FT 24PT/PGDip 9FT 21PT/PGCert 4FT 9PT

University of Glasgow
Technical Art History: Making & Meaning .... MLitt 12FT 24PT

University of Gloucestershire
Fine Art .... MA 12FT 24PT/PGDip 8FT 20PT/PGCert 4FT 8PT

Glyndwr University
Art Practice .... MA 12FT 24PT
Design Practice .... MA 12FT 24PT

Goldsmiths, University of London
Art & Politics .... MA 12FT 24PT
Art Psychotherapy .... PGDip 24FT 36PT/MA 32FT 48PT
Artist Teachers & Contemporary Practices ...... MA 36PT/MA 12FT
Aural and Visual Cultures .... MA 12FT 24PT
Computational Studio Arts .... MFA 24FT

Art and design

Curating .... MFA 24FT 36ft&ptPT
Design Futures .... MA 12FT 24PT
Innovation in Practice .... MA 12FT
Participatory and Community Arts .... PGCert 12FT 24-60PT/PGDip 12FT 24-60PT/MA 12FT 24-60PT
Visual Anthropology .... MA 12FT 24PT

University of Greenwich
Media, Arts, Philosophy and Practice .... MA 12FT 24PT

University of Hertfordshire
Applied Arts .... MA 12FT 24PT/PGDip 12FT 24PT
Fine Art .... MA 12FT 24PT/PGDip 12FT 24PT
Product Design .... MA 12FT 24PT/PGDip 12FT 24PT

University of Huddersfield
3D Digital Design .... MA 12/16FT

University of Kent
Curating .... MA 12FT 24PT
Fine Art .... MA 12FT 24PT

Kingston University
Art & Space .... MA 12FT 24PT
Communication Design: Graphic Design .... MA 12FT
Communication Design: Illustration .... MA 12FT 24PT
European Art Practice .... MA 12FT 24PT
Intensive Pre-masters Preparation: Art & Design .... Pre-masters preparation 3FT
Managing in the Creative Economy .... MA 12FT 24PT

Lancaster University
Contemporary Arts (With pathways) .... MA 12FT 24PT/PGCert 6FT 12PT
Design Management .... MA 12FT 24PT

Leeds Metropolitan University
Art & Design .... MA 12FT 24PT
Artist Teachers in Art & Design .... MA 24PT

University of Leeds
Culture, Creativity, and Enterpreneurship .... MA 12FT 24PT/PGDip 12FT 24PT/PGCert 9FT 18PT
Design .... MA 12FT 24PT/MSc 12FT 24PT/PGDip 12FT 24PT
Fine Art .... MFA 12FT 24PT

University of Limerick
History of Art and Architecture .... MA 12FT

University of Lincoln
Conservation of Historic Objects .... MA 12FT 24PT
Contemporary Curatorial Practice .... MA 12FT 24PT
Design .... MA 12FT 24PT
Fine Art .... MFA 24FT 48PT
Graphic Design .... MA 12FT
Interior Architecture & Design .... MA 12FT 24PT

Liverpool Hope University
Creative Practice .... MA 12FT 24PT/PGDip 12FT 24PT

Liverpool John Moores University
Art and Design .... MRes 12FT

London Metropolitan University
Applied Art (MA by Project) .... MA 12FT 24PT
Art, Design and Visual Culture (MA by project) .... MA 12FT 24PT
Design (MA by project) .... MA 12FT 24PT
Furniture .... MA 12FT 24PT
Jewellery .... MA 12FT 24PT
MA by Project (Visual Culture) .... MA 12FT 24PT

University of the Arts London - London College of Communication
Contemporary Typographic Media .... MA 12FT
Design for Visual Communication .... PGDip 30 weeksFT PGCert 30 weeksFT 30 weeksPT

Loughborough University
Art & the Public Sphere .... MA 12FT 24PT
Art and Design (Studio Practice) .... MA 12FT 24PT

Manchester Metropolitan University
Animation .... MA/MFA 12/24FT 24/48PT
Collaborative Practice .... MA/MFA 12/24FT 24/48PT
Contemporary Curating .... MA/MFA 12/24FT 24/48PT
Contemporary Visual Culture .... MA/MFA 12/24FT 24/48PT
Design (with pathways in design and contemporary craft practice) .... MA 12FT 24PT
Design Culture .... MA/MFA 12/24FT 24/48PT
Design for Performance .... MA/MFA 12/24FT 24/48PT
Design: Ceramics .... MA/MFA 12/24FT 24/48PT
Design: Furniture .... MA/MFA 12/24FT 24/48PT
Design: Glass .... MA/MFA 12/24FT 24/48PT
Design: Jewellery .... MA/MFA 12/24FT 24/48PT
Design: Lab .... MA/MFA 12/24FT 24/48PT
Drawing .... MA/MFA 12/24FT 24/48PT
Embroidery .... MA/MFA 12/24FT 24/48PT
Fashion: Fashion Graphics .... MA/MFA 12/24FT 24/48PT
Fashion: Knitwear .... MA/MFA 12/24FT 24/48PT
Fashion: Menswear .... MA/MFA 12/24FT 24/48PT
Fashion: Womenswear .... MA/MFA 12/24FT 24/48PT
Film and Media Studies .... MA/MFA 12/24FT 24/48PT
Filmmaking .... MA/MFA 12/24FT 24/48PT
Fine Art .... MA/MFA 12/24FT 24/48PT
Graphic Design and Art Direction .... MA/MFA 12/24FT 24/48PT
Illustration .... MA/MFA 12/24FT 24/48PT
Interior Design .... MA/MFA 12/24FT 24/48PT
International Creative Advertising .... MSc 12FT 24PT
MA by Research .... MA by Research 12FT 24PT
Media Arts .... MA/MFA 12/24FT 24/48PT
Photography .... MA/MFA 12/24FT 24/48PT
Product Design .... MA/MSc 12FT 24PT
Textile Practice .... MA/MFA 12/24FT 24/48PT
Textiles for Fashion .... MA/MFA 12/24FT 24/48PT
Three Dimensional Design .... MA 12FT 24PT

Middlesex University
Creative Technology .... MA 12FT 24PT/MSc 12FT 24PT

Newcastle University
Art Museum and Gallery Studies (with specialist pathways in: Curatorship, and Education) .... MA 12FT 24PT/PGDip 9FT 18PT
Creative Arts Practice .... MA 12FT 24PT
Fine Art .... MFA 24FT
Heritage Practice .... MHPrac 24FT 48PT

University of Northampton
Design .... MA 12FT 24PT/PGDip 8FT 16PT/PGCert 4FT 8PT

Northumbria University
Design .... MA 12FT
Fine Art and Education .... MA 24FT
Interior Design Futures .... MA 12FT 24PT
Fine Art .... MFA 24FT 48PT
Performance Product Design .... MA 12FT 24PT 12DL

Norwich University of the Arts
Fine Art .... MA 12FT 24PT
Photography .... MA 12FT 24PT

Nottingham Trent University
Contemporary Craft Practice .... MA 12FT
Design for Publication .... MA 12FT
Fine Art .... MA 12FT/PGDip 7FT/PGCert 4FT
Language & Culture Bridging Programme, School of Art & Design .... Language and Culture Bridging Programme 3FT
Product Design .... MA 12FT/PGDip 7FT/PGCert 4FT
Registered Project or Thesis (various Art & Design subject areas) MA 12FT 24PT
Technology Integrated Knit Design .... MA 12FT/MSc 12FT

University of Nottingham
Research .... MRes 12FT 24PT
Visual Culture .... MA 12FT 24PT

Oxford Brookes University
Composition and Sonic Art .... MA 12FT 24PT/PGDip 9FT 18PT
Contemporary Arts and Music .... MA 12FT 24PT/PGDip 9FT 18PT
Fine Art: Drawing for Fine Art Practice (at Swindon College) (MA) .... MA 18FT 36PT

Plymouth University
Design .... MA 12FT 24PT
Design Studies .... MRes 12FT
Design Thinking .... MRes 12FT 24PT
Photography .... MA 12FT

University of Portsmouth
Creative Professional Practice .... MSc 12PT/MA 12PT

Prince's School of Traditional Arts
Visual Islamic and Traditional Arts .... MA 24FT/PED 12FT 12PT

Queen's University Belfast
Arts Management .... MA 12FT 24PT

Ravensbourne
Animation Futures .... MA 12FT 24PT
Design Management .... MDes 12FT 24PT

University of Reading
Fine Art (MFA) .... MFA 21FT

Richmond, The American International University in London
Art History and Visual Culture .... MA 12FT 24PT

Robert Gordon University
Design Management .... MSc 36DL

Royal College of Art
Animation .... PhD by taught 72PT/MPhil 24FT 48PT/MA 24FT
Ceramics and Glass .... MA 24FT
Communication Art and Design .... MA 24FT
Design Products .... MA 24FT
Printed Textiles .... MA 24FT
Printmaking .... MA 24FT

Royal Welsh College of Music and Drama
Theatre Design .... MA 12FT 12PT

University of Salford
Art and Design: Communication Design .... MA 12FT 24PT/PGDip 8FT 15PT
Art and Design: Contemporary Fine Art .... MA 12FT 36PT/PGDip 8FT 24PT
Art and Design: Creative Education .... MA 12FT 24PT/PGDip 8FT 15PT
Art and Design: Museum and Heritage Interpretation .... MA 12FT 24PT/PGDip 8FT 15PT
Art and Design: Product Design .... MA 12FT 24PT/PGDip 9FT 15PT

Sheffield Hallam University
Animation and Special Effects .... MA 12FT 36PT
Animation for Computer Games .... MA 12FT 36PT
Fine Art .... MA 18FT 36PT
Research Degrees - Cultural, Communication and Computing Research Institute .... MPhil 24-36FT 48-60PT/PhD by taught 36-48FT 60-72PT

Sotheby's Institute of Art
Contemporary Art .... MA 14FT/PGDip 9FT
Contemporary Design .... MA 14FT/PGDip 9FT
East Asian Art .... MA 14FT/PGDip 9FT
Fine and Decorative Art .... MA 14FT/PGDip 9FT

University of South Wales
Arts Practice (Fine Art), (Arts, Health and Wellbeing) .... MA 12FT 24PT
Computer Animation .... MA 12FT
Contemporary Photography Practice .... MFA 18FT

University of Southampton
Arts (General) .... MA 12FT 24PT
Design .... MA 12FT

University of St Andrews
Art History .... MLitt 12FT 24PT/PGDip 9FT 18PT

Staffordshire University
Ceramic Design .... MA 18FT 32PT
Community & Participatory Arts .... MA 12FT 24PT
Creative Futures .... MA 12FT
Film Production Technology .... MSc 12-18FT
Film Production: Theory and Practice .... MA 12FT
Negotiated Study - Arts, Media and Design .... MA 12FT 36PT

University of Strathclyde
Advanced Architectural Design .... MArch 12FT 24PT/PGDip 9FT 21PT

University of Sunderland
3D Design Innovation .... MA 12FT 24PT/PGDip 15FT 10PT/PGCert 7FT 7PT
Curating .... MA 11FT 27PT
Design Studies .... MA 12FT 24PT
Illustration & Design .... MA 12FT 24PT/PGDip 15FT 10PT/PGCert 7FT 7PT
Ceramics .... MA 24PT

Swansea Metropolitan University
Fine Art .... MA 24FT 36PT
Visual Arts Enterprise .... MA 24FT 36PT/PGCert 9FT

Teesside University
Fine Art .... MA 12FT 24PT/PGDip 8FT 16PT/PGCert 4FT 8PT
Digital Arts and Design .... MA 12FT 24PT/PGDip 8FT 16PT/PGCert 4FT 8PT
Future Design .... MA 12FT 24PT/PGDip 8FT 16PT/PGCert 4FT 8PT

Trinity College Dublin - the University of Dublin
Irish Art History .... MPhil 12FT
Fine Art .... MFA 12FT 24PT

Trinity Laban Conservatoire of Music and Dance
Artist Diploma (PGD/AD) .... PGDip 12FT 24PT

University of Wales Trinity Saint David
Applied Arts .... MA 12FT 24PT/PGCert 12FT 24PT/PGDip 12FT 24PT
Design .... MA 12FT 24PT/PGCert 12FT 24PT/PGDip 12FT 24PT
Fine Art .... MA 12FT 24PT/PGCert 12FT 24PT/PGDip 12FT 24PT

University of Ulster
Design for Creative Practice .... MDes 12FT 28PT/PGDip 10FT 20PT
Multidisciplinary Design .... MFA 18FT 36-48PT

UCL - University College London
Fine Art .... MA 24FT

University of the West of England, Bristol
Art, Media and Design by Project (Fine Art/Media/Design) .... MA 12-18FT 24PT
Lifelong Learning .... MA 12FT
Media Practice and Culture .... MA 12FT

University of Westminster
Visual Culture .... MA 12FT 24PT

University of Winchester
Modern Liberal Arts .... MA 12FT 24PT/PGDip 12FT 24PT/PGCert 12FT 24PT

University of Wolverhampton
Design and Applied Arts .... MA 12FT 24PT

Art and design
Research Courses

Anglia Ruskin University
Fine Art .... MPhil 24FT/PhD 36FT
Art .... MPhil 24FT/PhD 36FT
Children's Book Illustration .... MPhil 24FT/PhD 36FT
Film and Television Production .... MPhil 24FT/PhD 36FT
Graphic Design and Typography .... MPhil 24FT/PhD 36FT
Publishing .... MPhil 24FT/PhD 36FT

University of the Arts London - Central Saint Martins College of Art and Design
Interdisciplinary Projects .... PhD 24-48FT 36-96PT/MPhil 16-36FT 24-72PT

Art and design

The History and Theory of Art & Design ... PhD 24-48FT 36-96PT/ MPhil 15-36FT 24-72PT
Three Dimensional Design ... PhD 24-48FT 36-96PT/ MPhil 15-36FT 24-72PT

University of the Arts London - Chelsea College of Art and Design
Art and Design ... MPhil 21-36FT 36-72PT/PhD 35-48FT 60-96PT

University of the Arts London - Wimbledon College of Art
MPhil or PhD ... PhD 33-48FT 45-60PT/MPhil 21-36FT 33-48PT

Bath Spa University
Art and Design ... PhD 24 - 60FT 36 - 72PT/MPhil 18 - 36FT 30 - 48PT

Birmingham City University
Art and Design ... MA by research 18FT 24PT

Arts University Bournemouth
MPhil / PhD ... MPhil 24FT/PhD 36FT

University of Brighton
Arts and Architecture Research ... PhD 24-60FT 36-72PT/MPhil 18-36FT 30-48PT

University of Buckingham
History of Art: Renaissance to Modernism.. MA by research 12FT

Cardiff Metropolitan University
Art & Design ... PhD 12-60FT

University of Central Lancashire
Arts and Media ... PhD 30-48FT 66-84PT/MPhil 18-36FT 42-60PT/ MA by research 12FT 24PT
Design ... PhD 18-36FT 42-60PT/MPhil 18-36FT 42-60PT/MA by research 12FT 24PT

University of Chester
Higher Degrees by Research ... MPhil 12 - 48FT 24 - 72PT/PhD 24 - 48FT 48 - 84PT

University for the Creative Arts
Arts & Media ... PhD 36FT 60PT/MPhil 24FT 36PT
Design ... MPhil 24FT 36PT/PhD 36FT 60PT

University of Cumbria
A programme of research may be proposed in any relevant field of study ... PhD xFT/MA by research xFT/MPhil xFT/MRes xFT

De Montfort University
Design and New Product Development . MPhil 12-24FT 24-48PT/ PhD 24-36FT 36-72PT

University of East Anglia
Art History and World Art Studies ... PhD 36FT 72PT/MPhil 24FT 48PT

University of Edinburgh
Art ... MPhil 24FT 48PT/PhD 36FT 72PT
Classical Art & Archaeology ... MSc 12FT 24PT
Design ... PhD 36FT 72PT/MPhil 24FT 48PT
Film Studies ... PhD 36FT 72PT/MSc by research 12FT 24PT
History of Art ... PhD 36FT 72PT/MPhil 24FT 48PT/ MSc by research 12FT 24PT
History of Art ... MSc by research 12FT 24PT

Falmouth University
Research Art, Design, Media or Performance ... PhD 24 -60FT 36-72PT

National University of Ireland Galway
College of Arts, Social Sciences & Celtic Studies .. PhD 48FT 72PT/ MLitt by research 24FT 48PT/Structured PhD 48FT 72PT

Glasgow School of Art
Art and Design ... PhD 36FT 60PT/MPhil 12FT 24PT

University of Gloucestershire
Art and Design ... PhD 30-48FT
Media, Film and Communication Studies. PhD 30-48FT 48-84PT/ MPhil 18-36FT 30-60PT/MA by research 12-24FT 18-36PT

Goldsmiths, University of London
Arts & Computational Technology ... MPhil 24FT 36PT/ PhD 36-48FT 48-72PT
Curating ... PhD 36-48FT 48-72PT/MPhil 24FT 36PT
Design ... MRes 12FT 24PT
PhD 36-48FT 48-72PT/MPhil 24FT 36PT
Visual Anthropology ... MPhil 24FT 36PT/PhD 36-48FT 48-72PT MRes 12FT 24PT

University of Hertfordshire
Centre for Research into Practice ... PhD 36FT 72PT/MPhil 24FT 48PT/MRes 12FT 24PT

University of Kent
Digital Arts ... MSc(Res) 12FT 24PT/MPhil 24FT 36PT/ PhD 36FT 60PT
Fine Art ... PhD 36FT 60PT

King's College London
Culture, Media & Creative Industries Research ... PhD 36FT/MPhil 36FT

Lancaster University
Art ... PhD 36FT 48-60PT/MPhil 24FT 36PT
Design ... PhD 36FT 48PT/MPhil 24FT 36PT
Visual Arts ... PhD 36PT

University of Leeds
School of Design ... MSc by research 12FT/MSc(Eng) by research 12FT/MPhil 12FT/PhD 36-42FT
School of Fine Art, History of Art and Cultural Studies/ CentreCATH ... PhD 36+FT/MPhil 24FT

University of Lincoln
Art & Design ... MPhil 24FT 48PT/PhD 12-33FT 24-60PT

London Metropolitan University
Sir John Cass Department of Art Media and Design ... PhD Max 60FT Max 96PT/MPhil Max 36FT Max 54PT

Loughborough University
Art and Design ... PhD 36FT 60PT/MPhil 24FT 36PT
Sustainable Design ... PhD 36FT 60PT/MPhil 24FT 36PT
Transport Safety Research ... PhD 36FT 60PT/MPhil 24FT 36PT
User Centred Design Research .. PhD 36FT 60PT/MPhil 24FT 36PT

Manchester Metropolitan University
Department of Arts, Design and Performance ... PhD/MPhil/ MA by research

Newcastle University
Fine Art ... PhD 36FT 72PT/MPhil 12FT 24PT

Newman University
Creative Arts ... PhD 36FT 72PT/MPhil 24FT 48PT

University of Northampton
Technology and Design ... PhD 36FT 48PT/MPhil 24FT 36PT

Norwich University of the Arts
Art, Design and Media ... PhD 36FT 72PT/MPhil 24FT 48PT

Nottingham Trent University
Art and Design Research ... MPhil 36FT 60PT/PhD 36FT 60PT
Higher Doctorate in Art and Design ... DArts .FT .PT/DDes .FT .PT

University of Nottingham
Visual Culture ... PhD 36FT 72PT/MPhil 24FT 48PT/MRes 12FT

The Open University
Design ... PhD 36FT 72PT variableDL/MPhil 15FT 24PT variableDL

Oxford Brookes University
Arts ... MPhil/PhD 36-60FT 48-72PT/PhD 24-60FT 36-72PT/MPhil 24-36FT 36-48PT

University of Oxford
Fine Art ... DPhil 48FT 96PT

Plymouth University
Art History ... MRes 12FT
Design Thinking ... MRes 12FT 24PT

University of Portsmouth
Art, Design and Media ... MPhil 24FT 48PT/PhD 36FT 72PT

Royal College of Art
Communication Art and Design ... PhD/MPhil/MA by research

University of Salford
Research Centre for Art and Design ... PhD/MPhil

School of Oriental and African Studies - SOAS
Department of Art and Archaeology ... PhD 36FT 72PT/ MPhil 24FT 36PT

Sotheby's Institute of Art
Applied and Decorative Arts ... PhD 36FT 60PT

Southampton Solent University
Art and Design ... PhD/MPhil
Fine Art ... PhD 36FT 60PT/MPhil 24FT 48PT
Media Arts Research Centre ... PhD/MPhil

University of Southampton
Design ... PhD 48FT 84PT

University of Strathclyde
Building Design and Management for Sustainability . MRes 12FT 36PT

Swansea Metropolitan University
Art and Design ... PhD 36FT 60PT/MPhil 12FT 24PT

Teesside University
Design ... PhD 24-60FT 36-72PT/MPhil 18-36FT 30-48PT

University of Ulster
Art and Design ... PhD 36FT 72PT/MPhil 24FT 48PT
Master of Research, Arts (MRes) ... MRes 12FT 24PT

University of the West of England, Bristol
Faculty of Creative Arts, Humanities and Education ... PhD .FT

University of Westminster
Media, Art and Design ... MPhil 18-36FT 30-60PT

University of Wolverhampton
Art and Design ... MPhil 24FT 36PT/PhD 36FT 48-72PT

University of Worcester
Art and Design and Creative Digital Media ... MPhil 24FT 48PT/ PhD 48FT 70PT

Art conservation
Taught Courses

University of the Arts London - Camberwell College of Arts
Conservation ... MA 24FT

Bangor University
Fine Art ... MA 36PT

University of Buckingham
Decorative Arts and Historic Interiors ... MA 12FT

Bucks New University
Conservation of Furniture and Decorative Arts ... MA 12FT 24PT

Cardiff University
Professional Conservation ... MSc 12FT 24PT

University of Central Lancashire
Antiques ... MA 30-36DL

Christie's Education London
The Arts of China: Cultural Crossroads in Asia ... MLitt 12FT/ PGDip 9FT

Courtauld Institute of Art
Conservation of Wall Painting ... MA 33FT
Conservation of Easel Paintings ... PGDip 33FT

Durham University
Conservation of Archaeological and Museum Objects (Dissertation) ... MA 24FT 36PT
Conservation of Archaeological and Museum Objects (Professional Practice) ... MA 24FT 36PT

University of East Anglia
Museum Studies ... MA 12FT

University of Glasgow
Art History: Dress & Textile Histories ... MLitt 12FT 24PT
Museum Studies ... MSc 12FT 24PT
Textile Conservation ... MPhil 24FT 48PT

University of Kent
Curating ... MA 12FT 24PT

Kingston University
Art Market Appraisal (Professional Practice) ... MA 12FT 24PT

University of Leicester
Country House ... MA 24-48DL

University of Lincoln
Conservation Studies ... GradDip 12FT 24PT
Conservation of Historic Objects ... MA 12FT 24PT

London Metropolitan University
Furniture MA by Project ... MA 12FT 24PT
Restoration and Conservation MA by Project ... MA 12FT 24PT

Northumbria University
Conservation of Fine Art ... MA 18FT
Fine Art and Education ... MA 24PT
Performance Product Design ... MA 12FT 24PT 12DL
Preventive Conservation ... MA 12FT 12DL/MA 24DL

Oxford Brookes University
Historic Conservation ... MSc 12FT 24PT/PGDip 12FT 24PT/ PGCert 12PT

Royal College of Art
Conservation ... PhD by taught/MPhil/MA 24FT

Sotheby's Institute of Art
East Asian Art ... MA 14FT/PGDip 9FT
Fine and Decorative Art ... MA 14FT/PGDip 9FT

University of Southampton
Textile Conservation ... MA 24FT 48PT/MPhil 36FT 72PT/PhD by taught 36FT 72PT

University of Wales Trinity Saint David
Fine Art ... MA 12FT 24PT/PGCert 12FT 24PT/PGDip 12FT 24PT

UCL - University College London
Conservation ... MSc 12FT/PGDip 9FT/PGCert 3FT
Conservation for Archaeology and Museums ... MSc 24FT

University of York
Stained Glass Conservation and Heritage Management ... MA 24FT

Art conservation
Research Courses

Royal College of Art
Conservation ... PhD/MPhil/MA by research

School of Oriental and African Studies - SOAS
Department of Art and Archaeology ... PhD 36FT 72PT/ MPhil 24FT 36PT

University of Southampton
Textile Conservation ... MA by research 36FT 72PT/ MPhil 24FT 48PT

Art therapy
Taught Courses

Birmingham City University
Art Health and Well-being ... MA 12FT 24PT

University of Central Lancashire
Arts Health ... MA 12FT 24-68PT/PGDip 12FT 24-68PT/ PGCert 12FT 24-68PT/UniCert 3PT
Arts-Health Analysis ... PGCert 6PT

Art and design

University of Chester
Health and Social Care - Art Therapy ....MA 24 - 72PT/PGDip 24 - 60PT/PGCert 12 - 36PT

University of Derby
Art Therapy ....MA 24FT

University of East London
Art Psychotherapy .... MSc 36PT/PGDip 24PT/PGCert 12PT

University of Glasgow
Primary Expressive Arts ....PGCert 12PT

Goldsmiths, University of London
Art Psychotherapy.........................PGDip 24FT 36PT/MA 32FT 48PT
Participatory and Community Arts.. PGCert 12FT 24-60PT/PGDip 12FT 24-60PT/MA 12FT 24-60PT

University of Hertfordshire
Art Therapy .... MA 24FT 36PT

Leeds Metropolitan University
Art Psychotherapy (Post - Registration).......................MA 12PT
Art Psychotherapy Practice .... MA 24FT 36PT
Associated Art Psychotherapy Research...........................MA 24PT
Psychotherapy...MA 48PT

National University of Ireland, Maynooth
Arts (Adult Guidance & Counselling)............................HDip 12FT

Queen Margaret University, Edinburgh
Art Psychotherapy (International) .... MSc 24FT 36-72PT/ PGDip 24FT 36-60PT

University of Roehampton
Art Psychotherapy... MA 24FT 36PT

University of South Wales
Art Psychotherapy...MA 36PT
Buddhist Studies .... PGCert 12DL/PGDip 24DL/MA 36DL
Evaluation Studies...PGCert 9-12DL
Music Therapy...MA 36PT

Staffordshire University
Community & Participatory Arts............................. MA 12FT 24PT

Art therapy
Research Courses

University of Dundee
Duncan of Jordanstone College of Art & Design .... MPhil 24FT PhD 36FT

Goldsmiths, University of London
Art.....................................MPhil 24FT 36PT/PhD 36-48FT 48-72PT
Art Psychotherapy...........PhD 36-48FT 48-72PT/MPhil 24FT 36PT MRes 12FT 24PT

University of Roehampton
Arts and Play Therapies.......PhD 24-48FT 36-60PT/MPhil 21-36FT 33-48PT

Arts management
Taught Courses

Anglia Ruskin University
Arts Management .... MA 18FT 24PT

University of the Arts London - Central Saint Martins College of Art and Design
Art: Exhibition Studies ....MRes 24FT

Birkbeck, University of London
Arts Management...PGDip 12FT 24PT
Arts Policy and Management........... MA 12FT 24PT/PGCert 12PT
Creative Industries (Arts and Media)........................ MA 12FT 24PT

Birmingham City University
Arts and Project Management....................................MA 12FT 24PT

University of Brighton
Arts and Cultural Research..MRes 12FT 24PT

University of Central Lancashire
Arts Project Management.......................................PGCert 3PT
Transdisciplinary Design....................................... MA 12FT 24PT

City University London
Culture, Policy and Management Pathways Programme ....MA 12FT 24PT

University for the Creative Arts
Creative Industries Management .... MBA 12FT

De Montfort University
Cultural Events Management........MA 12FT 24PT/MSc 12FT 24PT

University of Derby
Art and Design: Applied Practice and Theories (ADAPT)................ MA 17FT 34PT
Arts Practice...PGCert 12PT

University of East Anglia
Museum Studies..MA 12FT

Falmouth University
MFA...MFA 12FT 24PT

National University of Ireland Galway
Arts Policy and Practice.....................................MA 12FT/PGDip 12FT

Glasgow Caledonian University
Creative and Cultural Business...............................MA 12FT
Design Practice & Management .... MA 12FT 24PT/PGDip 9FT

University of Glasgow
Arts of China..MLitt 12FT
Arts of Europe....................................MLitt 12FT/PGDip 9FT
Composition ....PGDip 12FT 24PT/PGCert 12FT 24PT
Sonic Arts...PGDip 12FT 24PT

Glyndwr University
Creative Media .... MA 12FT 24PT

Goldsmiths, University of London
Arts Administration and Cultural Policy................. MA 12FT 24PT
Creative and Cultural Industries................................GradDip 12FT

University of Kent
Curating .... MA 12FT 24PT

Kingston University
Managing in the Creative Economy.......................... MA 12FT 24PT

Lancaster University
Design Management.. MA 12FT 24PT

London South Bank University
Critical Arts Management..MA 24PT
Cultural and Media Studies ....MA 24PT

University of Manchester
Arts Management, Policy & Practice...................... MA 12FT 24PT

Middlesex University
Media Management..MSc 12FT 24PT

Newcastle University
Art Museum and Gallery Practice.......................MPrac 24FT 48PT
Art Museum and Gallery Studies (with specialist pathways in: Curatorship, and Education).......... MA 12FT 24PT/PGDip 9FT 18PT
Arts, Business and Creativity....................................... MA 12FT 24PT

Northumbria University
Arts and Media Management.......MA 12/16FT 24/28PT 24/28DL
Business with Arts Management.....................................MSc 12FT
Conservation of Fine Art...MA 18FT
Fine Art and Education...MA 24FT

Nottingham Trent University
Design for Publication...MA 12FT

Plymouth University
Creativity and Enterprise.. MA 12FT 24PT

University of Roehampton
Performance and Creative Research...............................MRes 12FT

University of Salford
Art and Design: Design Management ....MSc 12FT 24PT/ PGDip 8FT 15PT
Creative Writing: Innovation and Experiment.......MA 12FT 36PT/ PGDip 8FT 24PT/PGCert 4FT 12PT

Sotheby's Institute of Art
Art Business ....MA 14FT/PGDip 9FT

University of St Andrews
Managing in the Creative Industries (collab)................MLitt 12FT

Staffordshire University
Community & Participatory Arts............................ MA 12FT 24PT

University of Sunderland
Applied Management ....MSc 24PT

Swansea Metropolitan University
Visual Arts Enterprise...............................MA 24FT 36PT/PGCert 9FT

University of Wales Trinity Saint David
Professional Arts Management................................MBA 12FT 24PT

University of Ulster
Cultural Management....MSc 12FT 30PT/PGDip 9FT 18PT/PGCert 4FT 8PT
Management in Creative Industries....................MSc 24FT 12PT

University of Warwick
Creative and Media Enterprises................................. MA 12FT 24PT

University of Winchester
Cultural and Arts ManagementMA 12FT 24PT/PGDip 12FT 24PT/ PGCert 12FT 24PT

York St John University
MBA Design Management..............................MBA 12FT 24 - 60PT

Arts management
Research Courses

Birkbeck, University of London
Arts Management........................ PhD 36FT 60PT/MPhil 24FT 36PT

City University London
Arts Policy and Management..PhD/MPhil
Department of Arts Policy and Management................PhD/MPhil

Goldsmiths, University of London

Art and design

Art....MPhil 24FT 36PT/PhD 36-48FT 48-72PT

University of Manchester
Arts Management & Cultural Policy....PhD 36FT 72PT
Arts and Cultural Management Professional Doctorate....Professional Doctorate 36FT 72PT

Oxford Brookes University
Arts (MPhil/PhD)....MPhil/PhD 36-60FT 48-72PT/PhD 24-60FT 36-72PT/MPhil 24-36FT 36-48PT

University of Roehampton
Media & Cultural Studies...PhD 24-48FT 36-60PT/MPhil 21-36FT 33-48PT

Royal Welsh College of Music and Drama
Arts Management....MA by research 12FT 24PT

University of Salford
Media, Music and Performing Arts Research Centre....PhD/MPhil

Branding
Taught Courses

Bangor University
Consumer Psychology with Business....MSc 12FT/PGDip 9FT MA 12FT
Marketing....MBA 12FT/PGDip 9FT

Bath Spa University
Design: Brand Development....MA 12FT 24PT/PGDip 9FT 18PT/PGCert 4FT 9PT

University of Brighton
Marketing....MSc see siteFT/PGDip see siteFT/PGCert see siteFT

Brunel University
Applied Corporate Brand Management....MSc 12FT
Design Strategy and Innovation....MA 12FT
Design and Branding Strategy....MA 12FT
Management....MSc 12FT
Marketing....MSc 12FT

Cardiff Metropolitan University
Marketing....MSc 12FT 24PT

University of Central Lancashire
Chartered Institute of Marketing (CIM) Chartered PG Diploma in Marketing (Stage 1)....CIM Diploma 12PT
Chartered Institute of Marketing (CIM) Chartered PG Diploma in Marketing (Stage 2)....CIM Diploma 12PT
Chartered Institute of Marketing (CIM) Professional Certificate in Marketing....CIM AdvCert 12PT
Chartered Institute of Marketing (CIM) Professional Diploma in Marketing....CIM Diploma 12PT
Fashion Brand Management..MBA 12FT 30PT/PGDip 12FT 30PT/PGCert 12FT 30PT
Marketing Management....MSc 12FT
Marketing and PR....MA 12FT
Strategic Marketing Leadership (Advanced Entry)....MA 12PT

Coventry University
Marketing....MBA 12FT 24-30PT
Strategic Marketing....MSc 12FT 24-30PT

University for the Creative Arts
Fashion: Promotion, Marketing and Branding....MA 12FT
Graphic Design and Communication....MA 12FT 24PT
Innovation & Brand Management....MA 12FT

University of Cumbria
International Marketing Management...MSc 12FT/PGCert 12FT/PGDip 12FT

University of Derby
Marketing Management....MSc 12FT

University of Dundee
Design for Services....MDes 12FT
Product Design....MSc 12FT

ESCP Europe Business School
Master in Marketing and Creativity....Master in Marketing and Creativity 15FT

University of East Anglia
Brand Leadership....MSc 12FT
Marketing....MSc 12FT
Marketing and Management....MSc 12FT

University of East London
Luxury Brand Management MSc....MSc 12FT 24PT/PGDip 8FT 16PT/PGCert 4FT 8PT

European Business School London
Luxury Brand Management....MA 12 - 16FT

GCU London
Brand Management....MSc 12FT
Digital Marketing....MSc 12FT
International Marketing....MSc 12FT
Luxury Brand Marketing (London)....MBA 12FT/MBA 12-15FT
Luxury Retail Management....MSc 12FT

Glasgow Caledonian University
Digital Marketing....MSc 12FT
Marketing....MSc 12FT/PGDip 9FT

University of Glasgow
International Management & Design Innovation....MSc 12FT
International Strategic Marketing....MSc 12FT

Goldsmiths, University of London
Brands, Communication and Culture....MA 12FT 24PT
Innovation in Practice....MA 12FT
Management of Innovation....MSc 12FT

Heriot-Watt University
International Marketing....PGDip 9FT 21PT/MSc 12FT 24PT

University of Huddersfield
International Design Marketing & Communication.MA 12/16FT
International Fashion Management....MA 12/16FT
International Fashion Promotion....MA 12/16FT

Kingston University
Marketing & Brand Management....MA 12FT

Leeds Metropolitan University
Chartered Institute of Marketing (CIM)....Diploma 12PT
Chartered Institute of Marketing (CIM)....Professional Certificate 12PT
Marketing....MSc 12FT

Liverpool Hope University
Marketing Management....MSc 12FT 24PT

London Metropolitan University
Marketing....MA 12FT 24PT

Manchester Metropolitan University
Marketing Communications....MSc 12FT 30PT/PGDip 24FT/PGCert 12PT

Northumbria University
Multidisciplinary Design Innovation....MA 12FT/MSc 12FT

Nottingham Trent University
Branding and Identity Design....MA 12FT/PGDip 7FT/PGCert 4FT
Fashion Marketing & Communication....MA 12FT
Marketing....MSc 12FT

Oxford Brookes University
Marketing....MSc 12FT 24PT

Plymouth University
Design....MA 12FT 24PT
Marketing Management and Strategy....MSc 12FT

Ravensbourne
Luxury Brand Management....MDes 12FT 24PT

University of Roehampton
Marketing....MSc 12FT 24PT
International Management with Marketing....PGDip 9FT 24PT

Royal Holloway, University of London
Marketing....MA 12FT

University of Salford
Marketing....MSc 12FT 36PT/PGDip 8FT 24PT/PGCert 4FT 9PT

Sheffield Hallam University
Global Strategic Marketing....MSc 12FT

University of Sheffield
Marketing Management Practice....MSc 12FT

Southampton Solent University
Marketing Management....MA 12FT 32PT

University of Southampton
Marketing Management....MSc 12FT/PGDip 9FT

University of St Andrews
Marketing....MLitt 12FT

University of Stirling
Marketing....MSc 12FT/PGDip 9FT

University of Strathclyde
Marketing....MSc 12FT 24PT/PGDip 9FT 18PT

Swansea University
Marketing....MSc 12FT

Teesside University
Marketing Management....MSc 12FT 24PT

University of Westminster
Marketing Management....MA 12FT

Branding
Research Courses

Birmingham City University
Marketing....MPhil 24FT 36PT/PhD 24FT 36PT

Cardiff University
Marketing and Strategy....PhD 36-48FT possiblePT

University of Kent
Marketing....MA by research 12FT 24PT/MPhil 24FT 36PT/PhD 36FT 60PT/New Route PhD 48FT

Newcastle University
Marketing....MPhil 12FT 24PT/PhD 36FT 72PT

Ceramics
Taught Courses

Bath Spa University
Design: Ceramics....MA 12FT 24PT 24DL/PGDip 9FT 18PT 18DL/PGCert 4FT 9PT 9DL

Cardiff Metropolitan University
Ceramics....MA 12FT 24PT

University of Central Lancashire
Ceramics....MA 12FT 30PT/PGDip 12FT/PGCert 12FT

University for the Creative Arts
Contemporary Crafts (Ceramics, Glass, Jewellery)....MA 12FT 24PT

University of Edinburgh
Glass....MA 12FT/MFA 24FT

Glasgow School of Art
Architecture....Diploma 24FT

Goldsmiths, University of London
Innovation in Practice....MA 12FT

London Metropolitan University
Metal MA by Project....MA 12FT 24PT

Loughborough University
Studio Ceramics: Methodologies and Practice....MA 12FT 24PT

Manchester Metropolitan University
Design (with pathways in design and contemporary craft practice)....MA 12FT 24PT
MA by Research....MA by Research 12FT 24PT

University of Roehampton
Art, Craft and Design Education....PGCert 6FT 24PT PGDip 9FT 24PT

Royal College of Art
Ceramics and Glass....MA 24FT

University of Sheffield
Ceramic Science and Engineering....MSc(Eng) 12-24FT

University of Southampton
Ceramic and Lithic Analysis for Archaeologists....MA 12FT 24PT

Staffordshire University
Ceramic Design....MA 18FT 32PT

University of Sunderland
Glass....MA 12FT 24PT/PGDip 10FT 15PT/PGCert 7FT 7PT

Swansea Metropolitan University
Glass....MA 12FT

West Herts College
Ceramics....PGDip 12-24PT

University of York
Stained Glass Conservation and Heritage Management....MA 24FT

Ceramics
Research Courses

Bath Spa University
Ceramics....PhD 24 - 60FT 36 - 72PT/MPhil 18 - 36FT 30 - 48PT

Glasgow School of Art
Architecture....MPhil 24FT/PhD 36FT 60PT

Royal College of Art
Ceramics and Glass....PhD/MPhil/MA by research

School of Oriental and African Studies - SOAS
Department of Art and Archaeology....PhD 36FT 72PT/MPhil 24FT 36PT

University of Sheffield
Engineering Materials: Integrated Studies...Integrated PhD 48FT

Cinema
Taught Courses

Aberystwyth University
Film Studies....MA 12FT 24PT

University of the Arts London - London College of Fashion
Fashion and Film....MA 15FT 30PT

Bangor University
Creative Practice....MRes 12FT 24PT
Film and Visual Culture....MRes 12FT 24PT
Filmmaking: Concept to Screen....MA 12FT 24PT

University of Bedfordshire
International Cinema....MA 12FT 24PT

Birkbeck, University of London
World Cinema....MA 12FT 24PT

University of Birmingham
Literature and Film....MRes 12FT 24PT

University of Bradford
Film Studies....MSc 12FT 24PT

University of Central Lancashire
Film Production....MA 12FT 24PT/PGDip 9FT 24PT/PGCert 9FT 24PT

Subject section sponsored by
NORWICH UNIVERSITY OF THE ARTS
Arts and humanities
www.prospects.ac.uk/findcourses POSTGRADUATE DIRECTORY 271

Art and design

University College Cork
English (American Literature & Film) .... MA 12FT
Film Studies .... MA 9FT
French Creativity/Literature & Film .... MA 12FT

University of Dundee
Film Studies .... MLitt 12FT

University of East Anglia
Film Studies .... MA 12FT 24PT
Film Studies with Archiving .... MA 12FT 24PT
Film, Television and Creative Practice .... MA 12FT 24PT

University of East London
Independent Film, Video and New Screen Media .... MA 12FT 24PT/PGDip 8FT 16PT/PGCert 4FT 8PT

Edge Hill University
Film Studies .... MRes 12FT 24PT

Edinburgh Napier University
Film .... MA 12FT 24PT
International Journalism for Media Professionals (Distance Learning) .... MA 12FT 24PT

University of Edinburgh
Film Studies .... MSc 12FT 24PT
Film, Exhibition and Curation .... MSc 12FT 24PT

University of Exeter
Independent Film Business .... MA 12FT 24PT

National University of Ireland Galway
Film Studies (Film, Culture, and Society) .... MA 12FT/PGDip 12FT

Glasgow School of Art
Sound for the Moving Image .. PGCert 4FT/PGDip 8FT/MDes 12FT

University of Glasgow
Film and Television Studies .... MLitt 12FT 24PT

University of Gloucestershire
Film and Screen Enterprise .. MA 12FT/PGAdvDip 8FT/PGCert 4FT

University of Kent
Film .... MA 12FT 24PT
Film (Paris option) .... MA 12FT

King's College London
Film Studies .... MA 12FT 24PT

Kingston University
Film Studies .... MA 12FT 24PT

Leeds Metropolitan University
Filmmaking .... MA 18FT
Music for the Moving Image .... MA 12FT 24PT

University of Leeds
World Cinemas .... MA 12FT 24PT

Manchester Metropolitan University
English Studies: Contemporary Literature and Film .... MA 16FT 36PT/PGDip 12FT 24PT

University of Manchester
Screen Studies .... MA 12FT 24PT

Newcastle University
Film: Theory and Practice .... MA 12FT 24PT

University of Northampton
Screen Studies .... MA 12FT 24PT

Norwich University of the Arts
Moving Image and Sound .... MA 12FT 24PT

University of Nottingham
American Studies (Visual Culture) .... MA 12FT 24-48PT

Oxford Brookes University
Film Studies: Popular Cinema .... MA 12FT 24PT/PGDip 8FT 6-8PT/PGCert 4FT 6PT

University of Portsmouth
Film and Television Studies .... MA 12FT 24PT

Queen Mary, University of London
Film Studies .... MA 12FT 24PT

Ravensbourne
Moving Image .... MA 12FT 24PT

University of Reading
Film Studies .... MA (Res) 12FT 24PT
Television Studies .... MA (Res) 12FT 24PT
Theatre Studies .... MA (Res) 12FT 24PT

University of Salford
Film Screenwriting .... MA 15FT/PGDip 12FT/PGCert 6FT

School of Oriental and African Studies - SOAS
Global Cinemas and the Transcultural .... MA 12FT 24-36PT

Sheffield Hallam University
Film Studies .... MA 12FT 36-72PT MPhil 36FT 84PT/PhD by taught 36FT 84PT
Film Studies with Screenwriting .... MA 12FT 24PT

University of Southampton
Film Studies .... MA 12FT 24PT
Film and Cultural Management .... MA 12FT 24PT

University of St Andrews
Film Studies .... MLitt 12FT 24PT/PGDip 9FT
Modern Hispanic Literature And Film .... MLitt 12FT/MPhil 24FT

University of Stirling
Film Studies: Theory and Practice .... MLitt 12FT 27PT/PGDip 9FT 21PT/PGCert 3FT 6PT

University of Sunderland
Film & Cultural Studies .... MA 12FT 24PT

University of Sussex
Film Studies .... MA 12FT 24PT
Media and Cultural Studies .... MA 12FT 24PT

Trinity College Dublin - the University of Dublin
Film Theory and History .... MPhil 12FT

UCL - University College London
Film Studies .... MA 12FT 24PT

University of Warwick
Film and Television Studies .... MA 12FT
Research in Film and Television Studies .... MA 12FT

University of West London
Film Finance .... MA 12FT 24PT
Finance and Risk Management .... MSc 12FT 24PT
Video Production and Film Studies .... MA 12FT 24PT

University of Westminster
Film and Television: Theory, Culture and Industry .... MA 12FT 24-48PT

University of Winchester
Film Studies .... MA 12FT 24PT/PGDip 12FT 24PT/PGCert 12FT 24PT

University of Wolverhampton
Film Studies .... MA 24-36PT

University of York
Contemporary Cinema and Television .... MA 12FT 24PT
Film and Literature .... MA 12FT 24PT

Cinema
Research Courses

Aberystwyth University
Theatre, Film and Television Studies .... MPhil 12FT 24PT PhD 36FT 60PT

Bangor University
Creative and Critical Writing, Film and Media, Professional Writing .... MPhil 24FT 48PT/PhD 36FT 72PT
Creative and Critical Writing, Film and Media, Professional Writing: Practice-Led Research .... MPhil 24FT 48PT/PhD 36FT 72PT

University of Bedfordshire
Journalism, Media, Cinema or Television .... PDJMCT 36PT

Birkbeck, University of London
Arts and Humanities .... MPhil 24FT 36PT/PhD 36-48FT 60-84PT
Film and Screen Media .... MPhil 36FT 48PT/PhD 36FT 48PT

University of Birmingham
Film Studies .... MRes 12FT 24PT

Brunel University
Film and Television Studies .... PhD 36FT 48PT/MPhil 12FT 24PT

University of Central Lancashire
Film and Media ... PhD 18-36FT 42-60PT/MPhil 18-36FT 42-60PT/MA by research 12FT 24PT

University of East Anglia
Film, Television and Media Studies .... PhD 36FT 72PT/MPhil 24FT 48PT

University of Edinburgh
Film Studies .... PhD 36FT 72PT/MSc by research 12FT 24PT

University of Exeter
Film Studies .... MPhil 24FT 48PT/PhD 36-48FT 72PT
Interdisciplinary Studies .... MPhil 36FT 60PT/PhD 48FT 84PT

University of Glasgow
Film/TV .... MPhil 12FT/MLitt by research 12FT 24PT

University of Hull
Film Studies .... PhD 36FT 60PT/MPhil 24FT 36PT

University of Kent
Film .... PhD 36FT 60PT/MPhil 24FT 36PT/MA by research 12FT 24PT
Film (Practice by Research) .... MA by research 12FT 24PT/MPhil 24FT 36PT/PhD 36FT 60PT

King's College London
Film Studies Research .... PhD 36FT 48-72PT

Lancaster University
Media, Film and Cultural Studies .... PhD 36FT 48PT/MPhil 24FT 36PT

Newcastle University
Film Studies .... MLitt by research 12FT 24PT PhD 36FT 72PT/MPhil 12FT 24PT

University of Nottingham
Film and Television Studies .... PhD 36FT 72PT/MPhil 24FT 48PT/MRes 12FT

Queen's University Belfast
Film Studies .... PhD 36FT 72PT/MPhil 24FT 48PT

School of Oriental and African Studies - SOAS
Media and Film Studies .... PhD 36-48FT

University of Southampton
Film Studies .... PhD 48FT 84PT/MPhil 48FT 84PT

University of St Andrews
Film Studies .... PhD 36FT 72-84PT/MPhil 24FT 48PT
Modern Hispanic Literature And Film .... PhD 36FT 72PT/MPhil 24FT 48PT

University of Sussex
Film Studies Research Programme .. PhD 24-48FT 36-72PT/MPhil 12-36FT 24-48PT

University of Wales Trinity Saint David
Film and Media .... PhD 36FT 48-72PT/MPhil 12-36FT

UCL - University College London
Film Studies .... PhD 36FT 60PT

University of Warwick
European Cinema .... MPhil 24FT 48PT/PhD 36-48FT 60PT
Film and Television Studies .... PhD 36FT 60PT/MPhil 36FT/MA by research 12FT

University of York
Theatre, Film and Television .... MPhil 24FT 48PT/PhD 36FT 72PT

Contemporary art
Taught Courses

Aberystwyth University
Fine Art .... MA 12FT 24PT/PGDip 9FT 18PT
Fine Art and Art History .... MA 12FT 24PT

Anglia Ruskin University
Children's Book Illustration .... MA 18FT 30PT
Fine Art .... MA 12FT 24PT

University of the Arts London - Central Saint Martins College of Art and Design
Art and Science .... MA 24FT
Fine Art .... MA 24FT

University of the Arts London - Chelsea College of Art and Design
Fine Art .... MA 12FT 24PT

University of the Arts London - Wimbledon College of Art
Fine Art: Drawing .... MA 15FT 15PT
Fine Art: Painting .... MA 15FT 15PT
Fine Art: Sculpture .... MA 15FT 15PT

Bangor University
Fine Art .... MA 36PT

Bath Spa University
Fine Art .... MFA 12FT 24PT/PGDip 9FT 18PT/PGCert 4FT 9PT

Birmingham City University
Design and Visualisation .... MA 12FT 24PT
Fine Art .... MA 12FT 24PT

University of Bolton
Fine Art .... MA 12FT

Arts University Bournemouth
Fine Art .... MA 12FT 24PT

University of Brighton
Sequential Design/Illustration .... MA 12FT 24PT

City and Guilds of London Art School
Fine Art .... MA 12FT 24PT/Diploma 12FT 18PT

Canterbury Christ Church University
Fine and Applied Arts .... MA 12FT 24PT

Cardiff Metropolitan University
Fine Art .... MFA 12FT 24PT

University of Central Lancashire
Children's Book Illustration .... MA 12FT/PGDip 12FT/PGCert 12FT
Fine Art: Site and Archive Interventions .... MA 12FT 24PT/PGDip 12FT 24PT/PGCert 12FT 24PT
Fine Art: Studio Practice .... MA 12FT 24PT/PGDip 12FT/PGCert 12FT

University of Chichester
Fine Art .... MA 12FT 24PT

Coventry University
Contemporary Arts Practice .... MA 12FT 24PT
Illustration and Animation .... MA 12FT 24PT

University for the Creative Arts
Fine Art .... MA 12FT 24PT
Graphic Storytelling and Comic Art .... MA 12FT 24PT

University of Cumbria
Contemporary Fine Art .... MA 12FT

De Montfort University
Fine Art .... MA 12FT 24PT

University of Derby
Art Therapy .... MA 24FT
Art and Design: Applied Practice and Theories (ADAPT) .... MA 17FT 34PT

Art and design

Visual Communication (illustration) ... MDes 48FT

University of Dundee
Art and Humanities ... MFA 12FT
Fine Art ... MFA 12FT

University of East Anglia
World Art Studies ... PGDip 12FT 24PT

University of East London
Fine Art ... MA 12FT 24PT/PGDip 8FT 16PT/PGCert 4FT 8PT
PhD by taught 36FT 60PT

University of Edinburgh
Contemporary Art Painting ... MA 12FT 24PT/MFA 24FT
Contemporary Art Photography ... MA 12FT 24PT/MFA 24FT
Contemporary Art Practice ... MA 12FT 24PT/MFA 24FT
Contemporary Art Sculpture ... MA 12FT 24PT/MFA 24FT
Contemporary Art Theory ... MA 12FT 24PT/MFA 24FT

University of Essex
Art History and Theory ... MA 12FT 24PT/GradDip 9FT
Curating Contemporary Art ... MA 12FT 24PT
Curating Latin American Art ... MA 12FT 24PT
Gallery Studies and Critical Curating ... MA 12FT
Gallery Studies with Dissertation ... MA 12FT 24PT

Falmouth University
Fine Art: Contemporary Practice ... MA 12FT
Illustration: Authorial Practice ... MA 12FT 24PT
MFA ... MFA 12FT 24PT

National University of Ireland Galway
Fine Arts ... MA 24FT 24PT/PGDip 12FT/HDip 12FT

Glasgow School of Art
Fine Art ... PGCert 4FT/PGDip 8FT/MFA 24FT
Fine Art Practice ... MLitt 12FT 24PT
Illustration ... PGCert 4FT/PGDip 8FT/MDes 12FT

University of Glasgow
Arts of China ... MLitt 12FT
Arts of Europe ... MLitt 12FT/PGDip 9FT
Modern & Contemporary Art ... MLitt 12FT/PGDip 9FT

University of Gloucestershire
Fine Art ... MA 12FT 24PT/PGDip 8FT 20PT/PGCert 4FT 8PT

University of Hertfordshire
Applied Arts ... MA 12FT 24PT/PGDip 12FT 24PT
Digital and Lens Art ... MA 12FT 24PT/PGDip 12FT 24PT/PGCert 12FT 24PT
Fine Art ... MA 12FT 24PT/PGDip 12FT 24PT

University of Huddersfield
Fine Art ... MA 12/16FT

University of Kent
Curating ... MA 12FT 24PT
Fine Art ... MA 12FT 24PT
History and Philosophy of Art ... MA 12FT 24PT
History and Philosophy of Art (Paris option) ... MA 12FT 24PT

Kingston University
Communication Design: Illustration ... MA 12FT 24PT
Fine Art ... MFA 24FT 48PT
Fine Art with Learning and Teaching in Higher Education ... MA 12FT 24PT

Lancaster University
Contemporary Arts Research (With Pathways) ... MA 12FT 24PT

University of Leeds
Fine Art ... MFA 12FT 24PT MA 18FT

University of Lincoln
Fine Art ... MFA 24FT 48PT

Liverpool John Moores University
Fine Art ... MA 12FT

London Metropolitan University
Applied Art (MA by Project) ... MA 12FT 24PT
Drawing (MA by project) ... MA 12FT 24PT
Fine Art (MA by project) ... MA 12FT 24PT
Fine Art (Specialism) ... MA 12FT 24PT

University of the Arts London - London College of Communication
Graphic Branding & Identity ... MA 12FT

Loughborough University
Art & the Public Sphere ... MA 12FT 24PT

Manchester Metropolitan University
Contemporary Arts ... MA 12FT 24-36PT

Middlesex University
Fine Art .. MFA 18FT 36PT/MA 12FT 24PT/PGDip 6FT 12PT/PGCert 3FT 6PT

Newcastle University
Fine Art ... MFA 24FT

University of Northampton
Fine Art ... MA 12FT 24PT/PGDip 12PT

Northumbria University
Fine Art and Education ... MA 24PT

Norwich University of the Arts
MA Fine Art ... MA 12FT 24PT

Nottingham Trent University
Fine Art ... MA 12FT/PGDip 7FT/PGCert 4FT

Oxford Brookes University
Contemporary Arts ... MA 12FT 24PT/PGDip 9FT 18PT
Contemporary Arts and Music ... MA 12FT 24PT/PGDip 9FT 18PT
Fine Art: Drawing for Fine Art Practice (at Swindon College) ... MA 18FT 36PT

University of Oxford
Islamic Art and Archaeology (Research Methods) ... MSt 9FT

Plymouth University
Contemporary Art Practice ... MA 12FT

University of Portsmouth
Fine Art ... MA 12FT 24PT

Prince's Drawing School
The Drawing Year ... PGDip 12FT 12PT

University of Reading
Fine Art ... MFA 21FT

Royal College of Art
Curating Contemporary Art ... MA 24FT
Painting ... MA 24FT
Printmaking ... MA 24FT
Sculpture ... MA 24FT

University of Salford
Art and Design: Communication Design ... MA 12FT 24PT/PGDip 8FT 15PT
Art and Design: Contemporary Fine Art ... MA 12FT 36PT/PGDip 8FT 24PT

Sheffield Hallam University
Fine Art ... MA 18FT 36PT

Sotheby's Institute of Art
Contemporary Art ... MA 14FT/PGDip 9FT
Contemporary Design ... MA 14FT/PGDip 9FT

University of Southampton
Fine Art ... MA 12FT 24PT

University of Sunderland
Fine Art ... MA 12FT 24PT/PGDip 10FT 15PT/PGCert 7FT 7PT

Swansea Metropolitan University
Fine Art ... MA 24FT 36PT

Teesside University
Fine Art ... MA 12FT 24PT/PGDip 8FT 16PT/PGCert 4FT 8PT

Trinity College Dublin - the University of Dublin
Fine Art ... MFA 12FT 24PT

University of Wales Trinity Saint David
Applied Arts ... MA 12FT 24PT/PGCert 12FT 24PT/PGDip 12FT 24PT

University of Ulster
Fine Art ... MFA 18FT/PGDip 9FT

UCL - University College London
Fine Art ... MA 24FT MFA 24FT

West Herts College
Printmaking/Illustration ... PGDip 8-16PT

University of the West of England, Bristol
Fine Art ... MA 12FT 24PT

University of Wolverhampton
Fine Art ... MA 12FT 24PT

Writtle College
Fine Art and the Environment ... MA 12FT

York St John University
Fine Arts ... MA 12FT 24 - 60PT

Contemporary art
Research Courses

Aberystwyth University
Fine Art (PhDFA) ... PhD 36FT 60PT

Anglia Ruskin University
Fine Art ... MPhil 24FT/PhD 36FT
Children's Book Illustration ... MPhil 24FT/PhD 36FT

University of the Arts London - Central Saint Martins College of Art and Design
Fine Art ... PhD 24-48FT 36-96PT/MPhil 15-36FT 24-72PT

Bath Spa University
Contemporary Art ... PhD 24 - 60FT 36 - 72PT/MPhil 18 - 36FT 30 - 48PT
Fine Art ... PhD 24 - 60FT 36 - 72PT/MPhil 18 - 36FT 30 - 48PT

University of Central Lancashire
Fine Art, Fashion & Performing Arts ... PhD 30-48FT 66-84PT/MPhil 18-36FT 42-60PT/MA by research 12FT 24PT

University for the Creative Arts
Fine Art ... PhD 36FT 60PT/MPhil 24FT 36PT

De Montfort University
Fine Art ... MPhil 12-24FT 24-48PT/PhD 24-36FT 36-72PT

University of Essex
Art History and Theory ... PhD 36FT 72PT/MPhil 24FT 48PT

Goldsmiths, University of London
Art ... MPhil 24FT 36PT/PhD 36-48FT 48-72PT

University of Kent
Fine Art ... PhD 36FT 60PT
History & Philosophy of Art ... MA by research 12FT 24PT/MPhil 24FT 36PT/PhD 36FT 60PT

Lancaster University
Art ... PhD 36FT 48-60PT/MPhil 24FT 36PT
Contemporary Arts ... PhD 36FT 48PT/MPhil 24FT 36PT

Newcastle University
Fine Art ... PhD 36FT 72PT/MPhil 12FT 24PT

The Open University
Religion in Material, Visual and Performance Culture ... PhD 36FT 72PT variableDL/MPhil 15FT 24PT variableDL

Oxford Brookes University
Arts ... MPhil/PhD 36-60FT 48-72PT/PhD 24-60FT 36-72PT/MPhil 24-36FT 36-48PT

University of Oxford
Fine Art ... DPhil 48FT 96PT

Prince's School of Traditional Arts
Visual Islamic and Traditional Arts ... PhD 24-36FT 36-72PT/MPhil 12FT 24PT

Royal College of Art
Centre for Drawing Research ... PhD/MPhil
Centre for Drawing Research ... PhD/MPhil
Painting ... PhD/MPhil/MA by research
Printmaking ... PhD/MPhil/MA by research
Sculpture ... PhD/MPhil/MA by research

School of Oriental and African Studies - SOAS
Art and Archaeology ... PhD 36FT/MPhil 24FT
Department of Art and Archaeology ... PhD 36FT 72PT/MPhil 24FT 36PT

Southampton Solent University
Fine Art ... PhD 36FT 60PT/MPhil 24FT 48PT

University of Southampton
Fine Art ... PhD 48FT 84PT

UCL - University College London
Fine Art ... PhD 36FT 60PT

Contemporary crafts
Taught Courses

University of the Arts London - Camberwell College of Arts
Designer Maker ... MA 12FT 24PT

University of the Arts London - Central Saint Martins College of Art and Design
Design: Ceramics, Furniture or Jewellery ... MA 24FT

Bath Spa University
Design: Ceramics ... MA 12FT 24PT 24DL/PGDip 9FT 18PT 18DL/PGCert 4FT 9PT 9DL
Investigating Crafts ... MA 12FT 24PT/PGDip 9FT 18PT/PGCert 4FT 9PT

Birmingham City University
Jewellery, Silversmithing and Related Products ... MA 12FT 24PT

University for the Creative Arts
Contemporary Crafts (Ceramics, Glass, Jewellery) ... MA 12FT 24PT
Contemporary Crafts (Textiles) ... MA 12FT 24PT
Contemporary Jewellery ... MA 12FT 24PT
Design: Design Crafts ... MA 12FT 24PT

University of Edinburgh
Jewellery ... MA 12FT/MFA 24FT

University of Glasgow
Art History: Dress & Textile Histories ... MLitt 12FT 24PT

Lancaster University
Contemporary Arts Research (With Pathways) ... MA 12FT 24PT

London Metropolitan University
Furniture ... MA 12FT 24PT
Furniture MA by Project ... MA 12FT 24PT
Jewellery ... MA 12FT 24PT
Jewellery (MA by project) ... MA 12FT 24PT
Metal MA by Project ... MA 12FT 24PT
Silversmithing (MA by project) ... MA 12FT 24PT

Manchester Metropolitan University
Design (with pathways in design and contemporary craft practice) ... MA 12FT 24PT
MA by Research ... MA by Research 12FT 24PT

Oxford Brookes University
Social Sculpture ... MA 12FT 24PT/PGDip 9FT 18PT

Plymouth University
Design ... MA 12FT 24PT

University of Roehampton
Craft and Design Education ... PGCert 6FT 24PT PGDip 9FT 24PT

Royal College of Art
Ceramics and Glass ... MA 24FT

Art and design

Goldsmithing, Silversmithing, Metalwork and Jewellery .... MA 24FT 36PT PhD by taught/MPhil/MA 24FT

University of Salford
Art and Design: Product Design .. MA 12FT 24PT/PGDip 9FT 15PT

School of Oriental and African Studies - SOAS
History of Art and/or Archaeology.................... MA 12FT 24-36PT
Study of Contemporary Pakistan .... MA 12FT 24PT

Sheffield Hallam University
Design (Metalwork and Jewellery) .... MA 12-16FT 36PT/ PGDip 12FT 24PT/PGCert 6FT 12PT

Sotheby's Institute of Art
Contemporary Design .... MA 14FT/PGDip 9FT

University of Wales Trinity Saint David
Applied Arts .... MA 12FT 24PT/PGCert 12FT 24PT/ PGDip 12FT 24PT

Contemporary crafts
Research Courses

University of the Arts London - Central Saint Martins College of Art and Design
Fashion, Textiles and Jewellery .... PhD 24-48FT 36-96PT/MPhil 15-36FT 24-72PT

Birmingham City University
Art and Design .... MA by research 18FT 24PT

University of Central Lancashire
Design ....PhD 18-36FT 42-60PT/MPhil 18-36FT 42-60PT/MA by research 12FT 24PT

University for the Creative Arts
Contemporary Crafts .... MPhil 24FT 36PT/PhD 36FT 60PT

University of Dundee
Duncan of Jordanstone College of Art & Design .... MPhil 24FT PhD 36FT

Royal College of Art
Ceramics and Glass ....PhD/MPhil/MA by research

School of Oriental and African Studies - SOAS
Art and Archaeology....................................... PhD 36FT/MPhil 24FT

University of Southampton
Design .... PhD 48FT 84PT

Digital media
Taught Courses

Aberystwyth University
3D Imaging, Analysis and Applications ... MRes 12FT 24PT/PGDip 9FT 21PT/PGCert 5FT 17PT
Digital Marketing .... MSc 12FT 24PT

University of the Arts London - Camberwell College of Arts
Fine Art Digital ....MA 12FT 24PT 24DL

University of the Arts London - London College of Fashion
Digital Fashion .... MA 15FT 30PT

Bangor University
Creative Practice .... MRes 12FT 24PT
International Media Management.......................... MSc 12FT 24PT

University of Bedfordshire
Art Design and Internet Technology.......................... MA 12FT 24PT
Media, Culture and Technology .... MA 12FT 24PT

Birkbeck, University of London
Creative Industries (Arts and Media)....................... MA 12FT 24PT
Creative Industries (Computing) .... MSc 12FT 24PT
Creative Industries (Management)....................... MSc 12FT 24PT
Digital Media Management .... PGCert 12PT

Birmingham City University
Digital Arts in Performance .... MA 12FT 24PT
Interactive Media .... PGCert 5FT 9PT/PGDip 9FT 21PT/ MSc 16/19FT 28PT
Video Game Enterprise and Production .... MSc 12FT

Arts University Bournemouth
Interactive Media .... MA 12FT 24PT
Design Interaction .... MA 12FT 24PT

Bournemouth University
Creative and Media Education................................MA 18PT
Digital Effects ....MA 12FT

University of Bradford
Digital Arts and Media............................ MA 12FT 24PT/PGDip 9FT

University of Brighton
Creative Media .... MA 12FT 24PT/PGDip 12FT variesPT/ PGCert 12FT variesPT
Digital Media Arts .... PGDip 12FT 24PT/MA 12FT 24PT
Digital Media Production .... MSc 12FT 24-60PT/PGDip 12FT 24-60PT/PGCert 12FT 24-60PT

University of Central Lancashire
Broadcast Journalism ....PGDip 9FT/MA 12FT
Digital Marketing (CAM)................................Diploma 7.5DL
Film Production.............MA 12FT 24PT/PGDip 9FT 24PT/ PGCert 9FT 24PT

University College Cork
Interactive Media .... MSc 12FT 24PT

University for the Creative Arts
Design: Digital Design............................... MA 12FT 24PT

Dublin Institute of Technology
Digital Media Technologies........... MA 12FT 24PT/PGDip 9FT 21PT

University of Edinburgh
Design and Digital Media........................MSc 12FT 24PT
Digital Animation............................MSc(Res) 12FT 24PT
Digital Media and Culture............................MSc(Res) 12FT 24PT
Digital Studio Practice ....MSc(Res) 12FT 24PT

National University of Ireland Galway
Digital Media .... MA 12FT/PGDip 12FT

Glasgow Caledonian University
3D Design for Virtual Environments... MA 12FT 24PT/PGDip 12FT 24PT
Digital Forensics.. MSc 12FT

Glasgow School of Art
Digital Culture.............. MDes 12FT 24PT/PGDip 9FT 21PT/ PGCert 4FT 9PT
Medical Visualisation and Human Anatomy ... PGCert 4FT/PGDip 8FT/MSc 12FT

University of Gloucestershire
Media and Creative Enterprise....MA 12FT/AdvPGDip 8FT/PGCert 4FT

Glyndwr University
Creative Media .... MA 12FT 24PT
Creative Media Technology......................... MSc 12FT

Goldsmiths, University of London
Computational Studio Arts...........................MFA 24FT
Creating Social Media ....MA 12FT 24PT/MSc 12FT 24PT
Digital Entrepreneurship.................................. MSc 12FT
Digital Journalism .... MA 12FT/MSc 12FT
Digital Media: Technology and Cultural Form .... MA 12FT 24PT
Digital Sociology.....................MA 12FT 24PT/MSc 12FT 24PT
Interactive Media: Critical Theory and Practice...... MA 12FT 24PT
Media and Communications......................................GradDip 12FT

University of Hertfordshire
Animation ....MA 12FT 24PT/PGDip 12FT 24PT/PGCert 12FT 24PT
Digital and Lens Art ....MA 12FT 24PT/PGDip 12FT 24PT/PGCert 12FT 24PT
Two Dimensional Digital Animation .. MA 12FT 24PT/PGDip 12FT 24PT

University of Huddersfield
3D Digital Design .... MA 12/16FT
Digital Media .... MA 12/16FT

University of Hull
Business Technology Management .... MSc 12FT

Imperial College London
Science Media Production.. MSc 12FT

University of Kent
Advanced Electronic Systems Engineering ....PGDip 12FT 24PT/ MSc 12FT 24PT
Architectural Visualisation...MA 12FT
Broadband and Mobile Communication Networks.....PGDip 12FT 24PT/MSc 12FT 24PT
Computer Animation .... MSc 12FT
Digital Visual Effects.........................MSc 12FT/PGDip 12FT
Embedded Systems and Instrumentation ....PGDip 12FT 24PT/ MSc 12FT 24PT
Wireless Communications and Signal Processing ....PGDip 12FT 24PT/MSc 12FT 24PT

King's College London
Digital Asset & Media Management .... MA 12FT 24PT
Digital Culture and Society .... MA 12FT 24PT

Leeds Metropolitan University
Creative Technology................................MSc 12FT 24PT
Digital Visual Effects ....MSc 12FT 24PT
Information Management.............................MSc 12FT 36PT

University of Limerick
Interactive Media .... MA 12FT/MSc 12FT

University of Lincoln
Digital Media .... MA 12FT 24PT

London Metropolitan University
Digital Media .... MA 12FT 24PT

London South Bank University
Creative Media Industries: Journalism ....MA 13FT
Digital Film..MA 24PT
Digital Photography...MA 24PT
Media Arts...MA 12FT
New Media ....MA 24PT

University of the Arts London - London College of Communication
Digital Media Futures..MA 12FT

Loughborough University
Digital Media and Society ....MA 12FT

Manchester Metropolitan University ....
Digital Media Computing..........................MSc 12FT 36PT

Middlesex University
Creative Technology.........................MA 12FT 24PT/MSc 12FT 24PT
Digital Media .... MA 12FT 24PT
Film, Television, Animation............................. MA 12FT 24PT
Creative Technology....................................MSc 12FT 36PT

Newcastle University
Creative Arts Practice .... MA 12FT 24PT
Digital Architecture ....MSc 12FT 24PT

Nottingham Trent University
Film Practice.................................. MA 12FT/PGDip 7FT/PGCert 4FT
Interaction Design........................ MA 12FT/PGCert 7FT/PGDip 4FT
Product Design....................... MA 12FT/PGDip 7FT/PGCert 4FT
Product Design Innovation Management ....MA 12FT

Oxford Brookes University
Digital Media Production .... MSc 12FT 24PT
Digital Publishing .... MA 12FT 24PT/PGDip 9FT 18PT
Film Studies: Popular Cinema ....MA 12FT 24PT/ PGDip 8FT 6-8PT/PGCert 4FT 6PT

Plymouth University
Contemporary Art Practice ....MA 12FT
Digital Art and Technology ....MRes 12FT

University of Portsmouth
Design for Digital Media......................... MA 12FT 24PT
Digital Marketing ....MA 12FT
Digital Media .... MSc 12FT 36PT

Queen Mary, University of London
Computer Vision ....MSc 12FT 24PT
Media and Arts Technology .... MSc(Res) 12FT

Ravensbourne
3D Stereoscopic Media.....................MSc 12FT 24PT/MA 12FT 24PT
Animation Futures .... MA 12FT 24PT
Applied Technologies, Rapid Prototyping and Digital Technologies..MSc 12FT 24PT
Interactive Digital Media.............................. MA 12FT 24PT
Professional Media Practice .... MA 12FT 24PT

Royal College of Art
Animation .... PhD by taught 72PT/MPhil 24FT 48PT/MA 24FT

University of Salford
Animation ....MA 12FT
Children's Digital Media Production ....MA 12FT/PGDip 9FT
International and Online Journalism .... MA 12FT 36PT

School of Oriental and African Studies - SOAS
Critical Media and Cultural Studies.................... MA 12FT 24-36PT
Global Media and Postnational Communication.............MA 12FT 24-36PT

Sheffield Hallam University
Animation and Special Effects .... MA 12FT 36PT
Animation for Computer Games.............................. MA 12FT 36PT
Film Studies ....MPhil 36FT 84PT/PhD by taught 36FT 84PT
Film Studies with Screenwriting .... MA 12FT 24PT
Research Degrees - Cultural, Communication and Computing Research Institute ....MPhil 24-36FT 48-60PT/PhD by taught 36-48FT 60-72PT

University of Sheffield
Sonic Arts.. MA 12FT 24PT
Web Journalism ....MA 12FT/PGDip 9FT

University of South Wales
Visual Effects .... MA 12FT 24PT

Southampton Solent University
Digital Marketing and Media.....................................MA 12FT

University of Southampton
Digital Marketing .... MSc 12FT
Sound and Vibration Studies.............................. MSc 12FT 36PT

Staffordshire University
Film Production Technology ....MSc 12-18FT
Film Production and Visual Cultures ....MA 12FT
Film Production: Theory and Practice ....MA 12FT

University of Strathclyde
Digital Creativity...............MSc 12FT 24PT/PGDip 9FT 18PT

University of Sunderland
Animation and Design... MA 12FT 24PT

University of Sussex
Computing with Digital Media.................... MSc 12FT 24PT
Creative Media Practice .... MA 12FT 24PT
Digital Media .... MA 12FT 24PT
Embedded Digital Systems .... MSc 12FT 24PT

Swansea University
Digital Media .... MA 12FT 36PT

Swansea Metropolitan University
3D Computer Animation.............................. MA 12FT 24PT

Teesside University
Concept Art for Games and Animation .... MA 12FT 36PT
Digital Arts and Design... MA 12FT 24PT/PGDip 8FT 16PT/PGCert 4FT 8PT

Art and design

Digital Effects for Film and Television .... MA 12FT 36PT
Future Design.....MA 12FT 24PT/PGDip 8FT 16PT/PGCert 4FT 8PT

Trinity College Dublin - the University of Dublin
Interactive Digital Media.. MSc 12FT

University of Ulster
Digital Media Communication ....PGCert 10PT

UCL - University College London
Film Studies .... MA 12FT 24PT

University of Winchester
Digital Media Practice...MA 12FT 24PT/PGDip 12FT 24PT/PGCert 12FT 24PT

University of Wolverhampton
Digital and Visual Communications........................ MA 12FT 24PT

University of Worcester
Creative Digital Media .... MA 36FT 72PT/MSc 36FT 72PT/PGDip 24FT 48PT/PGCert 12FT 24PT

University of York
Human-Centred Interactive Technologies .... MSc 12FT
Social Media and Interactive Technologies...................... MSc 12FT

Digital media
Research Courses

Bangor University
Creative and Critical Writing, Film and Media, Professional Writing .... MPhil 24FT 48PT/PhD 36FT 72PT
Creative and Critical Writing, Film and Media, Professional Writing: Practice-Led Research ....MPhil 24FT 48PT/PhD 36FT 72PT

University of Bath
Digital Media .... EngD 48FT

University of Bradford
Electronic Imaging and Media Communications.PhD 36FT 48PT/MPhil 12FT 24PT

Cardiff University
Distributed and Scientific Computing ....PhD 36FT/MPhil 12FT

University of Central Lancashire
Arts and Media....PhD 30-48FT 66-84PT/MPhil 18-36FT 42-60PT/MA by research 12FT 24PT
Fine Art, Fashion & Performing Arts.......... PhD 30-48FT 66-84PT/MPhil 18-36FT 42-60PT/MA by research 12FT 24PT

University for the Creative Arts
Arts & Media .... PhD 36FT 60PT/MPhil 24FT 36PT

University of Edinburgh
Digital Communications ...PhD 36FT 72PT/MPhil 24FT 48PT/MSc by research 12FT 24PT

University of Gloucestershire
Art and Design .... PhD 30-48FT

Goldsmiths, University of London
Arts & Computational Technology ....MPhil 24FT 36PT/PhD 36-48FT 48-72PT

Heriot-Watt University
Digital Tools and Technologies.. EngD 48FT

University of Hertfordshire
Centre for Research in Electronic Art and Communication (CREAC)........... PhD 36FT 72PT/MPhil 24FT 48PT/MRes 12FT 24PT

University of Kent
Digital Arts ....MSc(Res) 12FT 24PT/MPhil 24FT 36PT/PhD 36FT 60PT
Electronic Engineering.... MSc by research 12FT 24PT/MPhil 24FT 36PT/PhD 36FT 60PT
Film (Practice by Research).........MA by research 12FT 24PT/MPhil 24FT 36PT/PhD 36FT 60PT

Newcastle University
Digital Media .... PhD 36FT 72PT
Film Studies .... MLitt by research 12FT 24PT PhD 36FT 72PT/MPhil 12FT 24PT

Newman University
Creative Arts .... PhD 36FT 72PT/MPhil 24FT 48PT

University of Portsmouth
Creative Technologies................. MPhil 24FT 48PT/PhD 36FT 72PT

Queen's University Belfast
Film Studies .... PhD 36FT 72PT/MPhil 24FT 48PT

School of Oriental and African Studies - SOAS
Media and Film Studies .... PhD 36-48FT

University of Southampton
Digital Arts and Design...MRes 12FT 24PT

UCL - University College London
Film Studies .... PhD 36FT 60PT

Fashion and textile design
Taught Courses

University of Aberdeen
Art in Scotland..MLitt 12FT 24PT

University of the Arts London - Central Saint Martins College of Art and Design
Design: Ceramics, Furniture or Jewellery ....MA 24FT
Fashion ....MA 18FT
Textile Futures ....MA 24FT

University of the Arts London - Chelsea College of Art and Design
Textile Design ....MA 12FT

University of the Arts London - London College of Fashion
Costume Design for Performance............................ MA 15FT 30PT
Digital Fashion .... MA 15FT 30PT
Fashion Artefact .... MA 15FT 30PT
Fashion Curation.. MA 15FT 30PT
Fashion Design & Technology .... MA 15FT 30PT
Fashion Entrepreneurship .... MA 15FT 30PT
Fashion Footwear .... MA 15FT 30PT
Fashion Photography... MA 15FT 30PT
Fashion and Film... MA 15FT 30PT
Fashion by Independent Project .... MA 15FT 30PT
Fashion: Buying And Merchandising...... PGCert 4FT/PGCert 30PT
Fashion: Creative Pattern Cutting For The Industry .... PGCert 3FT
Fashion: Fashion & Lifestyle Journalism .... PGCert 4FT
History and Culture of Fashion .... MA 15FT 30PT
Fashion and the Environment.................................. MA 15FT 30PT
Pattern Design and Garment Technology ....PGDip 7.5FT

Bath Spa University
Design: Brand Development ....MA 12FT 24PT/PGDip 9FT 18PT/PGCert 4FT 9PT
Design: Fashion and Textiles ....MA 12FT 24PT/PGDip 9FT 18PT/PGCert 4FT 9PT
Design: Investigating Fashion Design.. MA 12FT 24PT/PGDip 9FT 18PT/PGCert 4FT 9PT

University of Bedfordshire
Fashion Design, Styling & Promotion/ .... MA 12FT 24PT

Birmingham City University
Design Management.. MA 12FT 24PT
Fashion Accessory Design .... MA 12FT 24PT
Fashion Design.. MA 12FT 24PT
Fashion Promotion.. MA 12FT 24PT
Fashion Styling.. MA 12FT 24PT
Textile Design .... MA 12FT 24PT
Product Design.. MA 12FT 24PT

Arts University Bournemouth
Costume.. MA 12FT 24PT
Fashion... MA 12FT 24PT

University of Central Lancashire
Fashion & Lifestyle Brand Studies....... MA 12FT 30PT/PGDip 12FT 30PT/PGCert 12FT 30PT
Fashion Brand Management..MBA 12FT 30PT/PGDip 12FT 30PT/PGCert 12FT 30PT
Fashion Design .... MA 12FT/PGDip 12FT/PGCert 12FT
Fashion Shaping............. MA 12FT 24PT/PGDip 12FT/PGCert 12FT
Fashion and Lifestyle Promotion .... MA 12FT 30PT/PGDip 12FT 30PT/PGCert 12FT 30PT
Interior Design .... MA 12FT 24PT/PGDip 12FT/PGCert 12FT

University of Chichester
Fine Art... MA 12FT 24PT

University for the Creative Arts
Contemporary Crafts (Textiles) .... MA 12FT 24PT
Fashion .... MA 12FT 24PT
Fashion & Lifestyle Journalism .... MA 12FT
Fashion Management & Marketing .... MA 12FT 24PT
Fashion: Design and Atelier.. MA 12FT
Fashion: Fashion Theory .... MA 12FT
Fashion: Manufacture and Management .... MA 12FT
Fashion: Promotion, Marketing and Branding.................. MA 12FT

De Montfort University
Fashion Management .... MA 12FT 24PT
Fashion and Bodywear.. MA 12FT 24PT
Textile Design .... MA 12FT 24PT

University Centre Doncaster
Creative Pattern Cutting...PGDip 12FT

University of East London
Fashion ....MA 12FT 24PT/PGDip 8FT 16PT/PGCert 4FT 8PT
International Fashion Management .... MA 12FT 24PT/PGDip 8FT 16PT/PGCert 4FT 8PT

Edinburgh Napier University
Design (Interdisciplinary) .... MA/MDes 12FT

University of Edinburgh
Fashion ....MA 12FT/MFA 24FT
Performance Costume ....MA 12FT/MFA 24FT
Textiles ....MA 12FT/MFA 24FT

GCU London
International Fashion Marketing (London)............MSc 12FT/MSc 12-15FT
Luxury Retail Management .... MSc 12FT

Glasgow Caledonian University
International Fashion Marketing .... MSc 12FT/PGDip 9FT

Glasgow School of Art
Fashion and Textiles....................PGCert 4FT 8PT/PGDip 8FT 16PT/MDes 12FT 24PT

University of Glasgow
Art History: Dress & Textile Histories....................MLitt 12FT 24PT

Goldsmiths, University of London
Fashion .... MA 12FT

Heriot-Watt University
Fashion and Textile Innovation and New Applications.. MA 12FT/MSc 12FT/PGDip 9FT
Fashion and Textile Management................. MSc 12FT/PGDip 9FT
Fashion and Textiles Design.............................MA 12FT/PGDip 9FT
International Fashion Marketing ....MSc 12FT 24PT/PGDip 9FT 21PT
Strategic Innovation Management Fashion and Textiles........ MSc 12FT/PGDip 9FT

University of Hertfordshire
Applied Arts ....MA 12FT 24PT/PGDip 12FT 24PT
Contemporary Textiles ....MA 12FT 24PT/PGDip 12FT 24PT
Fashion ....MA 12FT 24PT/PGDip 12FT 24PT/PGCert 12FT 24PT

University of Huddersfield
Costume.. MA 12-16FT
International Fashion Design .... MA 12/16FT
International Fashion Management .... MA 12/16FT
International Fashion Promotion .... MA 12/16FT
Textiles .... MA 12/16FT
Textiles with Professional Engagement .... MA 16FT

Kingston University
Fashion .... MA 12FT 24PT
Fashion and the Creative Economy.......................... MA 12FT 24PT

University of Leeds
Advanced Textiles and Performance Clothing ...... MSc 12FT 24PT

Manchester Metropolitan University
Clothing Product Development..........................MSc 12FT 36-60PT
Strategic Fashion Buying.....................................MSc 12FT 36-60PT

University of Northampton
Design (Footwear)... MA 12FT 24PT
Fashion & Textiles .... MA 12FT 24PT
Fashion Marketing .... MA 12FT 24PT
Fashion and Textiles...............................MA 12FT 24PT/PGDip 12PT

Northumbria University
Design .... MA 12FT

Norwich University of the Arts
Fashion.. MA 12FT 24PT
Textile Design .... MA 12FT 24PT

Nottingham Trent University
Fashion Business........................... MA 12FT/PGDip 7FT/PGCert 4FT
Fashion Design............................. MA 12FT/PGDip 7FT/PGCert 4FT
Fashion Knitwear Design............ MA 12FT/PGCert 7FT/PGDip 4FT
Fashion Marketing & Communication .... MA 12FT
International Fashion Business... MA 12FT
Technology Integrated Knit Design .... MA 12FT/MSc 12FT
Textile Design & Innovation .... MA 12FT/PGDip 7FT/PGCert 4FT

Ravensbourne
Fashion .... MA 12FT 24PT

Robert Gordon University
Fashion Management ....MSc 12FT/PGDip 8FT/PGCert 4FT

Royal College of Art
Menswear... MA 24FT
Printed Textiles.. MA 24FT
Womenswear .... MA 24FT

University of Westminster
Fashion Business Management... MA 12FT

Fashion and textile design
Research Courses

University of the Arts London - Central Saint Martins College of Art and Design
Fashion, Textiles and Jewellery......... PhD 24-48FT 36-96PT/MPhil 15-36FT 24-72PT
Interdisciplinary Projects....PhD 24-48FT 36-96PT/MPhil 16-36FT 24-72PT

University of the Arts London - London College of Fashion
Research Degree .... MPhil 24PT/PhD 36FT 60PT

Bath Spa University
Fashion and Textiles....... PhD 24 - 60FT 36 - 72PT/MPhil 18 - 36FT 30 - 48PT

University of Central Lancashire
Fine Art, Fashion & Performing Arts.......... PhD 30-48FT 66-84PT/MPhil 18-36FT 42-60PT/MA by research 12FT 24PT

University for the Creative Arts
Fashion .... MPhil 24FT 36PT/PhD 36FT 60PT
Fashion and Textiles..................... PhD 36FT 60PT/MPhil 24FT 36PT

Heriot-Watt University
Textiles .... PhD 36FT 48PT/MPhil 12FT 24PT

Art and design

University of Leeds
Textile Industries, School of Design.. PhD 36+FT/MPhil 24FT/MSc by research 12FT

Manchester Metropolitan University
Department of Clothing Design and Technology .... PhD variableFT variablePT/MPhil variableFT variablePT/MSc by research 12FT 24PT
Research in Clothing Design and Technology .... PhD VariableFT VariablePT/MPhil VariableFT VariablePT

University of Manchester
Textile Design, Fashion and Management.. PhD 36FT 72PT/MPhil 12FT 24PT/MS by research 12FT 24PT
Textiles and Fashion.. MEnt 12FT

The Open University
Design ... PhD 36FT 72PT variableDL/MPhil 15FT 24PT variableDL

Royal College of Art
Fashion and Textiles.............................. PhD/MPhil/MA by research

Film making
Taught Courses

Anglia Ruskin University
Film and Television Production .... MA 12FT 24PT

Bangor University
Creative Practice .... MRes 12FT 24PT
Film and Visual Culture... MRes 12FT 24PT
Filmmaking: Concept to Screen................................. MA 12FT 24PT

Bath Spa University
Feature Filmmaking... MA 12FT 24PT

University of Bedfordshire
Creative Digital Film Production/.............................. MA 12FT 24PT
Digital Film Technologies & Production/ .... MA 12FT 24PT

Birmingham City University
Film Distribution and Marketing (Film Futures: Pro) .... MA 12FT 12DL

University of Birmingham
Film and Television: Research and Production........ MA 12FT 24PT

Arts University Bournemouth
Film Production.. MA 14FT

Bournemouth University
Cinematography for Digital Film and Television .... MA 12FT
Directing Digital Film and Television................................... MA 12FT
Post Production Editing .... MA 12FT
Producing Film and Television.. MA 12FT

University of Bradford
Digital Filmmaking .... MA 12FT/PGDip 9FT
Film Studies .... MSc 12FT 24PT

University of Bristol
Composition of Music for Film and Television .... MA 12FT
Film and Television Production .... MA 12FT

University of Central Lancashire
Film Production............................... MA 12FT 24PT/PGDip 9FT 24PT/PGCert 9FT 24PT
Scriptwriting... MA 12FT 24PT

University for the Creative Arts
Artists' Film, Video and Photography................................... MA 12FT

De Montfort University
Film/Media Studies by Independent Study................ MA 12-24DL

University of Dundee
Film Studies .... MLitt 12FT

University of East Anglia
Film Studies .... MA 12FT 24PT
Film, Television and Creative Practice .... MA 12FT 24PT

University of East London
Independent Film, Video and New Screen Media .... MA 12FT 24PT/PGDip 8FT 16PT/PGCert 4FT 8PT

Edinburgh Napier University
Advanced Film Practice .... MFA 12FT
Film .... MA 12FT 24PT
Screen Project Development .... MA 12FT 24PT

University of Edinburgh
Composition for Screen .... MSc 12FT 24PT
Film Directing.. MA 12FT/MFA 21FT
Film Studies .... MSc 12FT 24PT
Film, Exhibition and Curation.. MSc 12FT 24PT
Transdisciplinary Documentary Film Practice......... MSc(Res) 12FT

University of Essex
Filmmaking... MA 12FT

University of Exeter
Independent Film Business... MA 12FT 24PT

GCU London
TV Fiction Writing .... MA 12FT

National University of Ireland Galway
Production and Direction .... MA 12FT/PGDip 12FT

University of Gloucestershire
Film and Screen Enterprise .. MA 12FT/PGAdvDip 8FT/PGCert 4FT

Goldsmiths, University of London
Film and Screen Studies... MA 12FT 24PT
Filmmaking... MA 12FT
Screen Documentary .... MA 12FT
Script Writing .... MA 12FT
Visual Anthropology... MA 12FT 24PT

University of Hertfordshire
Animation .... MA 12FT 24PT/PGDip 12FT 24PT/PGCert 12FT 24PT
Film and Television....................... MA 12FT 24PT/PGDip 12FT 24PT
Model Design and Model Effects......... MA 12FT 24PT/PGDip 12FT 24PT/PGCert 12FT 24PT
Screen Cultures............................. MA 12FT 24PT/PGDip 12FT 24PT
Special Effects................................ MA 12FT 24PT/PGDip 12FT 24PT

University of Kent
Film .... MA 12FT 24PT
Film (Paris option) .... MA 12FT
Sound and Image (Medway)...

King's College London
Film Studies .... MA 12FT 24PT

Kingston University
Experimental Film .... MA 12FT 24PT
Film Making .... MA 12FT 24PT
Film Making and the Creative Economy.................. MA 12FT 24PT
Production Design for Film and Television........................ MA 12FT

Leeds Metropolitan University
Digital Visual Effects.. MSc 12FT 24PT
Filmmaking .... MA 18FT
Music for the Moving Image .... MA 12FT 24PT

London Metropolitan University
Film and Animation .... MA 12FT

London South Bank University
Independent Film (Editing And Montage) .... MA 12FT

Manchester Metropolitan University
Design (with pathways in design and contemporary craft practice) .... MA 12FT 24PT

Middlesex University
Film .... MA 12FT 24PT
Film, Television, Animation .... MA 12FT 24PT

Newcastle University
Creative Arts Practice .... MA 12FT 24PT
Film: Theory and Practice .... MA 12FT 24PT

Norwich University of the Arts
Moving Image and Sound .... MA 12FT 24PT

Nottingham Trent University
Design for Film, Television and Events.......... MA 12FT/PGDip 7FT/PGCert 4FT
Film Practice.................................... MA 12FT/PGDip 7FT/PGCert 4FT

Oxford Brookes University
Film Studies: Popular Cinema ... MA 12FT 24PT/PGDip 8FT 6-8PT/PGCert 4FT 6PT

University of Oxford
Film Aesthetics... MSt 9FT

Plymouth University
Contemporary Art Practice .... MA 12FT
Contemporary Film Practice .... MA 12FT
Film and Video.. MRes 12FT

Queen's University Belfast
Film and Visual Studies...................................... MA 12FT up to 31PT

Ravensbourne
Moving Image .... MA 12FT 24PT

University of Reading
Film Studies .... MA (Res) 12FT 24PT
Television Studies .... MA (Res) 12FT 24PT
Theatre Studies .... MA (Res) 12FT 24PT

Royal College of Music
Composition and Composition for Screen .... MMus 13FT

Royal Holloway, University of London
Documentary by Practice .... MA 12FT 24PT
Producing Film and Television................................... MA 12FT 24PT

University of Salford
Audio Production.. MSc 12FT 36PT
Fiction Film Production...................................... MA 12FT/PGDip 9FT
Film Screenwriting..................... MA 15FT/PGDip 12FT/PGCert 6FT
Post Production for TV and Film .... MA 12FT

Sheffield Hallam University
Film Studies .... MA 12FT 36-72PT MPhil 36FT 84PT/PhD by taught 36FT 84PT
Film Studies with Screenwriting .... MA 12FT 24PT

University of South Wales
Film .... MA 12FT 24PT/MFA 24FT 36PT
Film Producing .... MA 12FT 24PT

University of Southampton
Film Studies .... MA 12FT 24PT
Film and Cultural Management................................ MA 12FT 24PT

University of St Andrews
Film Studies.. MLitt 12FT 24PT/PGDip 9FT

Staffordshire University
Digital Feature Film Production.................................... MSc 12-18FT
Film Production Technology .... MSc 12-18FT
Film Production and Visual Cultures .... MA 12FT
Film Production: Theory and Practice .... MA 12FT

University of Stirling
Film Studies: Theory and Practice ...... MLitt 12FT 27PT/PGDip 9FT 21PT/PGCert 3FT 6PT

University of Sussex
Film Studies .... MA 12FT 24PT

Teesside University
Digital Effects for Film and Television .... MA 12FT 36PT

UCL - University College London
Film Studies .... MA 12FT 24PT

University of Warwick
Film and Television Studies.. MA 12FT
Research in Film and Television Studies .... MA 12FT

University of West London
Art Direction for Film and TV...................................... MA 12FT 24PT
Video Production and Film Studies........................... MA 12FT 24PT

University of the West of England, Bristol
Wildlife Filmmaking .... MA 12FT

University of Winchester
Film Studies .... MA 12FT 24PT/PGDip 12FT 24PT/PGCert 12FT 24PT

York St John University
Documentary Production.. MA 24FT 12PT
Film Production.. MA 12FT 24PT

Film making
Research Courses

Anglia Ruskin University
Film and Television Production .... MPhil 24FT/PhD 36FT

Bangor University
Creative and Critical Writing, Film and Media, Professional Writing................................. MPhil 24FT 48PT/PhD 36FT 72PT
Creative and Critical Writing, Film and Media, Professional Writing: Practice-Led Research .... MPhil 24FT 48PT/PhD 36FT 72PT

University of Edinburgh
Film Studies .... PhD 36FT 72PT/MSc by research 12FT 24PT
Transdisciplinary Documentary Film.................................. PhD 36FT

University of Exeter
Film Studies .... MPhil 24FT 48PT/PhD 36-48FT 72PT
Interdisciplinary Studies............ MPhil 36FT 60PT/PhD 48FT 84PT

Goldsmiths, University of London
Visual Anthropology......... MRes 12FT 24PT MPhil 24FT 36PT/PhD 36-48FT 48-72PT

University of Hull
Film Studies .... PhD 36FT 60PT/MPhil 24FT 36PT

University of Kent
Film .... PhD 36FT 60PT/MPhil 24FT 36PT/MA by research 12FT 24PT
Film (Practice by Research)......... MA by research 12FT 24PT/MPhil 24FT 36PT/PhD 36FT 60PT

King's College London
Film Studies Research.. PhD 36FT 48-72PT

Newcastle University
Film Studies .... MLitt by research 12FT 24PT PhD 36FT 72PT/MPhil 12FT 24PT

Queen's University Belfast
Film Studies .... PhD 36FT 72PT/MPhil 24FT 48PT

University of Roehampton
Film and TelevisionPhD 24-48FT 36-60PT/MPhil 21-36FT 33-48PT

University of Southampton
Film Studies .... PhD 48FT 84PT/MPhil 48FT 84PT

University of St Andrews
Film Studies .... PhD 36FT 72-84PT/MPhil 24FT 48PT

University of Wales Trinity Saint David
Film and Media .... PhD 36FT 48-72PT/MPhil 12-36FT

UCL - University College London
Film Studies .... PhD 36FT 60PT

Graphic design
Taught Courses

Aberystwyth University
3D Imaging, Analysis and Applications ... MRes 12FT 24PT/PGDip 9FT 21PT/PGCert 5FT 17PT

Anglia Ruskin University
Graphic Design and Typography.................................. MA 12FT 24PT

University of the Arts London - Chelsea College of Art and Design
Graphic Design Communication .... MA 12FT

Art and design

Birmingham City University
Design and Visualisation ... MA 12FT 24PT
Visual Communication ... MA 12FT 24PT

Arts University Bournemouth
Graphic Design ... MA 12FT 24PT
Illustration ... MA 12FT 24PT

University of Brighton
Sequential Design/Illustration ... MA 12FT 24PT

University of Bristol
Advanced Computing - Character Animation ... MSc 12FT 24PT
Image and Video Communications and Signal Processing ... MSc 12FT

Cardiff Metropolitan University
Design (Master of) ... MDes 12FT 24PT

University of Central Lancashire
Graphic Design ... MA 12FT 24PT/PGDip 12FT/PGCert 12FT

Coventry University
Graphic design ... MA 12FT 24PT
Illustration and Animation ... MA 12FT 24PT

University for the Creative Arts
Design ... MA 12FT 24PT
Graphic Design ... MA 14FT
Graphic Design and Communication ... MA 12FT 24PT
Graphic Storytelling and Comic Art ... MA 12FT 24PT

University of Derby
Computer Graphics Production ... MSc 12FT 36PT
Visual Communication (Animation) ... MDes 48FT
Visual Communication (Graphic Design) ... MDes 48FT
Visual Communication (illustration) ... MDes 48FT

Dublin Institute of Technology
Professional Design Practice (Visual Communications) .. MA 12FT

University of Dundee
Animation and Visualisation ... MSc 12FT
Product Design ... MSc 12FT

University of East London
Graphic Design ... MA 12FT 24PT/PGDip 8FT 16PT/PGCert 4FT 8PT
Print Design ... MA 12FT 24PT/PGDip 8FT 16PT/PGCert 4FT 8PT

Edinburgh Napier University
Design (Lighting) ... MA/MDes 12FT

University of Edinburgh
Graphic Design ... MA 12FT/MFA 24FT
Illustration ... MA 12FT/MFA 24FT

Glasgow Caledonian University
3D Design for Virtual Environments ... MA 12FT 24PT/PGDip 12FT 24PT

Glasgow School of Art
Communication Design ... PGCert 4FT/PGDip 8FT/MDes 24FT
Design Innovation ... PGCert 4FT 8PT/PGDip 8FT 16PT/MDes 12FT 24PT
Graphic Design ... PGCert 4FT/PGDip 8FT/MDes 12FT
Illustration ... PGCert 4FT/PGDip 8FT/MDes 12FT

Goldsmiths, University of London
Innovation in Practice ... MA 12FT
Photography: The Image and Electronic Arts ... MA 12FT

University of Hertfordshire
Character Creation and Technical Effects ... MA 12FT 24PT/PGDip 12FT 24PT
Graphic Design ... MA 12FT 24PT 24DL/PGDip 12FT 24PT 24DL
Illustration ... MA 12FT 24PT 12-24DL/PGDip 12FT 24PT 12-24DL

University of Huddersfield
International Graphic Design Practice ... MA 12/16FT

Kingston University
Communication Design: Graphic Design ... MA 12FT

Leeds Metropolitan University
Art & Design ... MA 12FT 24PT

London Metropolitan University
Graphic Design ... MA 12FT 24PT

University of the Arts London - London College of Communication
Graphic Branding & Identity ... MA 12FT
Graphic Design ... MA 12FT 24PT
Graphic Moving Image ... MA 12FT

Loughborough University
2D & 3D Visualisation ... MA 12FT/MSc 12FT

Manchester Metropolitan University
International Creative Advertising ... MSc 12FT 24PT

University of Northampton
Design (Graphic Communication) ... MA 12FT 24PT

Norwich University of the Arts
Communication Design ... MA 12FT 24PT

Nottingham Trent University
Branding and Identity Design ... MA 12FT/PGDip 7FT/PGCert 4FT
Graphic Design ... MA 12FT/PGDip 7FT/PGCert 4FT
Illustration ... MA 12FT/PGDip 7FT/PGCert 4FT

University of Portsmouth
Graphic Design ... MA 12FT 24PT

Ravensbourne
Communication Design ... MA 12FT 24PT
Visual Effects ... MA 12FT 24PT

University of Reading
Book Design ... MA 12FT 24PT
Information Design ... MA 12FT
Typeface Design ... MA 12FT 24PT
Typography and Graphic Communication ... MA (Res) 12FT 24PT

Royal College of Art
Communication Art and Design ... MA 24FT

University of Salford
Art and Design: Communication Design ... MA 12FT 24PT/PGDip 8FT 15PT
Art and Design: Product Design ... MA 12FT 24PT/PGDip 9FT 15PT
Professional Sound and Video Technology MSc 12FT 36PT/PGDip 9FT 24PT

Sheffield Hallam University
Design (Graphic Design) ... MA 12-16FT 24-36PT

University of South Wales
Graphic Communication ... MA 12FT 24PT
Visual Effects ... MA 12FT 24PT

Southampton Solent University
Illustration ... MA 12FT

Swansea Metropolitan University
Visual Communication ... MA 24FT 36PT

University of Ulster
Design for Creative Practice ... MDes 12FT 28PT/PGDip 10FT 20PT

University of the West of England, Bristol
Graphic Arts ... MA 18FT 36PT/PGDip 12FT 24PT

University of Westminster
Design for Communication ... MA 12FT/MA 12FT

University of Wolverhampton
Digital and Visual Communications ... MA 12FT 24PT

Graphic design
Research Courses

Anglia Ruskin University
Graphic Design and Typography ... MPhil 24FT/PhD 36FT

University of the Arts London - Central Saint Martins College of Art and Design
Graphic and Industrial Design ... PhD 24-48FT 36-96PT/MPhil 15-36FT 24-72PT

University for the Creative Arts
Design ... MPhil 24FT 36PT/PhD 36FT 60PT

Glasgow School of Art
Art and Design ... PhD 36FT 60PT/MPhil 12FT 24PT

Lancaster University
Design ... PhD 36FT 48PT/MPhil 24FT 36PT

Loughborough University
Design Practice ... PhD 36FT 60PT/MPhil 24FT 36PT

The Open University
Design ... PhD 36FT 72PT variableDL/MPhil 15FT 24PT variableDL

Royal College of Art
Communication Art and Design ... PhD/MPhil/MA by research

History of art
Taught Courses

University of Aberdeen
Art and Business ... MLitt 12FT 24PT

Aberystwyth University
Art History ... MA 12FT 24PT/PGDip 9FT 18PT
Fine Art and Art History ... MA 12FT 24PT

University of the Arts London - Central Saint Martins College of Art and Design
Art: Moving Image ... MRes 24FT

University of the Arts London - Chelsea College of Art and Design
Art Theory ... MA 12FT

University of the Arts London - London College of Fashion
History and Culture of Fashion ... MA 15FT 30PT

Bangor University
Fine Art ... MA 36PT

Birkbeck, University of London
History of Art ... MA 12FT 24PT
History of Art and Architecture ... GradCert 12PT
History of Art with Photography ... MA 12FT 24PT
Museum Cultures ... MA 12FT 24PT/MRes 12FT 24PT/PGDip 12FT 24PT/PGCert 6FT 12PT
Renaissance Studies ... MA 12FT 24PT
Victorian Studies ... MA 12FT 24PT

Birmingham City University
History of Art and Design ... MA 12FT 24PT
Queer Studies in Arts and Culture ... MA 12FT 24PT

University of Birmingham
History of Art ... MA 12FT 24PT

University of Brighton
History of Design and Material Culture ...

University of Bristol
Classical Reception ... MA 12FT 24PT
History of Art: Histories and Interpretations ... MA 12FT 24PT

University of Buckingham
Decorative Arts and Historic Interiors ... MA 12FT

University of Cambridge
History of Art and Architecture ... MPhil 9FT

University of Central Lancashire
Antiques ... MA 30-36DL
Fine Art: Site and Archive Interventions ... MA 12FT 24PT/PGDip 12FT 24PT/PGCert 12FT 24PT

Christie's Education London
Art, Style and Design: Renaissance to Modernism ... MLitt 12FT/PGDip 9FT
Arts of Europe: Antiquity, Middle Ages, Renaissance .. MLitt 12FT/PGDip 9FT
Modern and Contemporary Art: Beyond Modernism . MLitt 12FT/PGDip 9FT
The Arts of China: Cultural Crossroads in Asia ... MLitt 12FT/PGDip 9FT

University College Cork
Aesthetics and History of Art ... MA 12FT
Arts (Folklore) ... HDip 9FT
Arts (Greek & Roman Civilisation) ... HDip 9FT 18PT
History of Art ... HDip 9FT 18PT MA 12FT 24PT

Courtauld Institute of Art
History of Art ... MA 9FT

University of East Anglia
History of Art ... MA 12FT 24PT
The Arts of Africa, Oceania and the Americas ... MA 12FT 24PT
World Art Studies ... PGDip 12FT 24PT

University of East London
Architecture: Interpretation and Theories ... MA 12FT 24PT/PGDip 8FT 16PT/PGCert 4FT 8PT

University of Edinburgh
Art in the Global Middle Ages ... MSc 12FT 24PT
History of Art, Theory and Display ... MSc 12FT 24PT
Modern and Contemporary Art: History, Curating, Criticism ... MSc 12FT 24PT

University of Essex
Art History and Theory ... MA 12FT 24PT/GradDip 9FT
Art History and Theory with English for Academic Purposes ... Diploma 9FT
Curating Contemporary Art ... MA 12FT 24PT
Curating Latin American Art ... MA 12FT 24PT
Gallery Studies and Critical Curating ... MA 12FT
Gallery Studies with Dissertation ... MA 12FT 24PT
Human Rights and Arts ... MA 12FT 24PT

Glasgow School of Art
Photography ... PGCert 4FT/PGDip 8FT/MDes 12FT

University of Glasgow
Art History: Art: Politics: Transgression: 20th Century Avant-Gardes ... MLitt 12FT 24PT
Art History: Dress & Textile Histories ... MLitt 12FT 24PT
Art, Style & Design: Renaissance to Modernism ... MLitt 12FT/PGDip 12FT
Arts of China ... MLitt 12FT
Arts of Europe ... MLitt 12FT/PGDip 9FT
Technical Art History: Making & Meaning ... MLitt 12FT 24PT
Textile Conservation ... MPhil 24FT 48PT
Theatre History ... MLitt 12FT 24PT

Goldsmiths, University of London
Contemporary Art Theory ... MA 12FT 24PT
Global Arts ... MA 12FT 24PT

University of Kent
Arts Criticism ... MA 12FT 24PT
History and Philosophy of Art ... MA 12FT 24PT
History and Philosophy of Art (Paris option) ... MA 12FT 24PT
Medieval and Early Modern Studies ... MA 12FT 24PT

King's College London
Classical Art & Archaeology ... MA 12FT 24PT

Kingston University
Art Market Appraisal (Professional Practice) ... MA 12FT 24PT
Art and Design History ... MA 12FT 24PT

Leeds Metropolitan University
Art & Design ... MA 12FT 24PT

University of Leeds
History of Art ... MA 12FT 24PT

University of Limerick
History of Art and Architecture ... MA 12FT

Art and design

Liverpool Hope University
Art History and Curating .... MA 12FT 24PT

University of Liverpool
Art, Aesthetics and Cultural Institutions .... MA 12FT 24PT
Modern Architectural Heritage - London Based .... MSc 12FT 24PT

London Metropolitan University
Architectural History Theory and Interpretation ... MA 12FT 24PT

University of Manchester
Art History .... MA 12FT 24PT

Northumbria University
Arts .... MRes 12FT 24PT
Conservation of Fine Art .... MA 18FT

University of Nottingham
Art History .... MA 12FT 24PT
Art History (by Research) .... MA 12FT 24PT
The Visual Culture of Classical Antiquity .... MA 12FT 24PT

The Open University
Art History .... MA variableDL
Humanities .... MA variableDL/PGDip variableDL/PGCert variableDL

University of Oxford
Celtic Studies .... MPhil 21FT/MSt 9FT
History of Art and Visual Culture .... MSt 9FT
Late Antique and Byzantine Studies .... MPhil 21FT/MSt 9FT

Plymouth University
Design Thinking .... MRes 12FT 24PT

Prince's School of Traditional Arts
Visual Islamic and Traditional Arts .... MA 24FT/PED 12FT 12PT

University of Reading
Classics .... MA (Res) 12FT 24PT 60BM
History of Art and Architecture .... MA 12FT 24PT

Richmond, The American International University in London
Art History and Visual Culture .... MA 12FT 24PT

Royal College of Art
History of Design .... MA 24FT

School of Oriental and African Studies - SOAS
History of Art and/or Archaeology .... MA 12FT 24-36PT

Sotheby's Institute of Art
Art Business .... MA 14FT/PGDip 9FT
East Asian Art .... MA 14FT/PGDip 9FT
Fine and Decorative Art .... MA 14FT/PGDip 9FT

University of St Andrews
Art History .... MLitt 12FT 24PT/PGDip 9FT 18PT
Central and East European Studies .... MLitt 12FT 24PT/PGDip 9FT 18PT
History of Photography .... PGDip 9FT 18PT/MLitt 12FT 24PT
Theology, Imagination and the Arts .... MLitt 12FT/PGDip 9FT

Staffordshire University
Clinical Photography .... GradCert 12DL

University of Sussex
Art History .... MA 12FT 24PT

Trinity College Dublin - the University of Dublin
Textual and Visual Studies: 19th and 20th Century France .... MPhil 12FT

University of Wales Trinity Saint David
Applied Arts . MA 12FT 24PT/PGCert 12FT 24PT/PGDip 12FT 24PT
Fine Art .... MA 12FT 24PT/PGCert 12FT 24PT/PGDip 12FT 24PT

UCL - University College London
Architectural History .... MA 12FT 24-60PT/PGDip 9FT
History of Art .... MA 12FT 24PT/PGDip 9FT

University of Warwick
History of Art .... MA 12FT 24PT/PGDip 12FT 24PT

University of York
History of Art .... MA 12FT 24PT

History of art
Research Courses

University of Aberdeen
History of Art .... PhD 36FT 60PT/MLitt by research 12FT 24PT

Aberystwyth University
Art History .... MPhil 12FT 24PT PhD 36FT 60PT

University of the Arts London - Central Saint Martins College of Art and Design
The History and Theory of Art & Design ... PhD 24-48FT 36-96PT/MPhil 15-36FT 24-72PT

University of Bath
Architectural History and Theory .... MPhil 12-36FT 24-48PT

Birkbeck, University of London
History of Art .... PhD 36FT 48PT/MPhil 36FT 48PT

University of Birmingham
History of Art .... PhD 36FT 72PT/MPhil(B) 12FT 24PT

University of Bristol
History of Art .... PhD 36FT 72PT/MPhil 12FT 24PT/MLitt by research 24FT 48PT

University of Cambridge
History of Art .... PhD 36FT

University of Central Lancashire
Fine Art, Fashion & Performing Arts .... PhD 30-48FT 66-84PT/MPhil 18-36FT 42-60PT/MA by research 12FT 24PT

Courtauld Institute of Art
MPhil/PhD .... MPhil 24FT 48PT/PhD 36FT 84PT

University of Dundee
Duncan of Jordanstone College of Art & Design .... MPhil 24FT PhD 36FT

University of East Anglia
Sainsbury Research Unit for the Arts of Africa, Oceania and the Americas .... PhD 36FT 72PT/MPhil 24FT 48PT/MA by research 12FT 24PT

University of Edinburgh
History of Art .... PhD 36FT 72PT/MPhil 24FT 48PT/MSc by research 12FT 24PT
History of Art .... MSc by research 12FT 24PT

University of Essex
Art History and Theory .... PhD 36FT 72PT/MPhil 24FT 48PT

University of Exeter
Art History and Visual Culture .... MPhil 36FT 60PT 60DL/PhD 48FT 84PT 84DL

Glasgow School of Art
Art and Design .... PhD 36FT 60PT/MPhil 12FT 24PT

University of Glasgow
History of Art .... PhD 36FT/MPhil 12FT/MLitt by research 12FT

Goldsmiths, University of London
Art .... MPhil 24FT 36PT/PhD 36-48FT 48-72PT
Art History .... MRes 12FT 24PT
Visual Cultures .... PhD 36-48FT 48-72PT/MPhil 24FT 36PT

University of Kent
History & Philosophy of Art .... MA by research 12FT 24PT/MPhil 24FT 36PT/PhD 36FT 60PT
Medieval and Early Modern Studies ... PhD 36FT 60PT/MPhil 24FT 36PT/MA by research 12FT 24PT

Lancaster University
Art .... PhD 36FT 48-60PT/MPhil 24FT 36PT

University of Leicester
History of Art .... PhD 48FT/MPhil 36FT

Loughborough University
History of Art, Architecture and Design .... PhD 36FT 60PT/MPhil 24FT 36PT

Manchester Metropolitan University
History of Art and Design .... PhD/MPhil

University of Manchester
Art History and Visual Studies .... PhD 36FT 72PT

University of Nottingham
Art History .... PhD 36FT 72PT/MPhil 24FT 48PT
Social Sciences Research Methodology .... MPhil 24FT 48PT/PhD 36-48FT 72-96PT

The Open University
Art History .... PhD 36FT 72PT variableDL/MPhil 15FT 24PT variableDL
Artistic networks, 1300-1550 .... PhD 36FT 72PT variableDL/MPhil 15FT 24PT variableDL
Eighteenth Century Visual Cultures .. PhD 36FT 72PT variableDL/MPhil 15FT 24PT variableDL
Modern art theory and practice .... PhD 36FT 72PT variableDL/MPhil 15FT 24PT variableDL

Oxford Brookes University
Arts ... MPhil/PhD 36-60FT 48-72PT/PhD 24-60FT 36-72PT/MPhil 24-36FT 36-48PT
History of Art .... PhD 24-60FT 36-72PT/MPhil 24-36FT 36-48PT

Plymouth University
Art History .... MRes 12FT
Design Thinking .... MRes 12FT 24PT

Prince's School of Traditional Arts
Visual Islamic and Traditional Arts ... PhD 24-36FT 36-72PT/MPhil 12FT 24PT

Royal College of Art
History of Design .... PhD 24-36FT 48-60PT/MPhil 24FT 36-48PT

Sheffield Hallam University
Art and Design Research Centre: History of Art and Design .. PhD 36-48FT 60-72PT

University of Southampton
History of Art and Design .... MPhil 24FT 48PT/PhD 36FT 72PT

University of St Andrews
Art History .... PhD 36FT 72PT/MPhil 12-24FT 24-48PT
History of Photography .... PhD 36FT 72PT/MPhil 24FT 48PT
National Trust of Scotland Studies .... MPhil 12-24FT 24-48PT

University of Sussex
Art History Research Programme ..... PhD 24-48FT 36-72PT/MPhil 12-36FT 24-48PT

UCL - University College London
History of Art .... PhD 36FT 60PT

University of Warwick
History of Art .... PhD 48FT 72PT/MPhil 12FT 24PT

University of York
History of Art ... PhD 36FT 72PT/MPhil 24FT 48PT/MA by research 12FT 24PT

Industrial design
Taught Courses

University of the Arts London - Central Saint Martins College of Art and Design
Industrial Design .... MA 24FT

Aston University
Product Design Enterprise .... MSc 12FT
Product Design Innovation .... MSc 12FT

University of Bath
Engineering Design .... MSc 12FT

Birmingham City University
Design Management .... MA 12FT 24PT

University of Bolton
Advanced Composites Design .... MSc 12FT 36PT

Bournemouth University
Engineering Design Innovation .... MSc 24PT
Product Design .... MSc 12FT/MSc 24-60PT
Product Design Management .... MA 12FT/MSc 24-60PT

University of Brighton
Product Innovation and Development ..... MSc 12FT/PGDip 12FT/PGCert 12FT

Brunel University
Advanced Engineering Design .... MSc 12FT 24PT
Design Strategy and Innovation .... MA 12FT
Integrated Product Design .... MSc 12FT

Bucks New University
Engineering Management and Design .... MSc 12FT 24PT

University of Cambridge
Industrial Systems, Manufacturing and Management .... MPhil 9FT

Cardiff Metropolitan University
Advanced Product Design .... MSc 12FT
Product Development Management .... MBA 12FT 24PT

University of Central Lancashire
Consumer Product Design ..... MA 12FT 24PT/PGDip 12FT/PGCert 12FT

Coventry University
Design and Transport .... MSc 12FT 24PT
Industrial Product Design .... MSc 12FT 24PT
Vehicle Interiors .... MA 12FT 24PT

Cranfield University
Global Product Development and Management .... MSc 12FT 24-60PT/PGDip 6FT 24PT/PGCert 5FT 24PT
Innovation and Creativity in Industry .... MDes 12FT 24-60PT/PGCert 12FT 24-26PT/PGDip 12FT 24-36PT/MTech 24FT

University for the Creative Arts
Design .... MA 12FT 24PT
Design: Product Design .... MA 12FT 24PT
Sustainable Product Design .... MA 24PT

De Montfort University
Design Management .... MA 12FT 24PT/PGDip 9FT 18PT
Product Design .... MA 12FT 24PT

University of Dundee
Advanced Sustainable Urban Design .... MSc 12FT
Product Design .... MSc 12FT

Edinburgh Napier University
Advanced Materials Engineering .... MSc 12FT 24PT
Design (Interaction) .... MA/MDes 12FT
Interaction Design .... MDes 12FT
Interdisciplinary Design .... MDes 12FT 24PT

University of Edinburgh
Product Design .... MA 12FT/MFA 24FT

National University of Ireland Galway
Engineering .... HDip 12FT 24PT
Engineering Design .... MED 12 - 24FT 24PT

Glasgow School of Art
Product Design Engineering ...... PGCert 4FT 8PT/PGDip 8FT 20PT/MSc 12FT 24PT

Goldsmiths, University of London
Design: Interaction Research .... MA 15FT 30PT

University of Hertfordshire
Product Design .... MA 12FT 24PT/PGDip 12FT 24PT

Imperial College London
Innovation Design Engineering .... MA 12FT/MSc 9FT

Kingston University
Advanced Industrial and Manufacturing Systems .... MSc 12FT 24-36PT

Art and design

Advanced Product Design Engineering .... MSc 12FT 24PT
Design: Product and Space & the Creative Economy....... MA 12FT 24PT

Leeds Metropolitan University
Advanced Engineering Management .... MSc 12FT 24PT/PGCert 12PT/PGDip 12FT 24PT

Liverpool John Moores University
Sustainable Built Environment .... MSc 12FT

University of Liverpool
Product Design and Management........ MSc 12FT

London Metropolitan University
Product Design........ MA 12FT 24PT

University of the Arts London - London College of Communication
Service Design Innovation........ MDes 12FT

Loughborough University
Design and Innovation for Sustainability .... MSc 12FT 24PT
Engineering Design........ MSc 12FT 24 - 72PT
Engineering Design and Manufacture........ MSc 36- 72DL
Industrial Design and Technology........ MA 12FT 24PT
Interaction Design........ MA 12FT 24PT

Manchester Metropolitan University
Three Dimensional Design........ MA 12FT 24PT

Newcastle University
Design and Manufacturing Engineering........ MSc 12FT

Northumbria University
Design Management........ MA 12FT

Nottingham Trent University
Advanced Product Design Engineering .... MSc 12FT
Smart Design........ MA 12FT/MSc 12FT

Plymouth University
Design .... MA 12FT 24PT

Ravensbourne
Interactive Product Futures ..... MA 12FT 24PT/MSc 12FT 24-36PT

Royal College of Art
Design Products........ MA 24FT
Industrial Design Engineering........ MA 24FT
Vehicle Design........ MA 24FT

University of Salford
BIM and Integrated Design........ MSc 12FT 28PT 28DL/PGDip 8FT 20PT 20DL/PGCert 4FT 8PT 8DL
Built Environment .... DBEnv 60PT
Industrial and Commercial Combustion Engineering .MSc 36DL/PGDip 12DL/PGCert 12DL

Sheffield Hallam University
Built Environment.....MPhil 24FT 36PT/PhD by taught 24FT 60PT
Design (Industrial Design)..... MA 12-16FT 36PT/PGDip 9FT 24PT/PGCert 6FT 12PT

University of Strathclyde
Global Innovation Management........ MSc 24FT
Product Engineering Design........ MSc 12FT 24PT/PGDip 9FT 21PT

University of Sunderland
3D Design Innovation.... MA 12FT 24PT/PGDip 15FT 10PT/PGCert 7FT 7PT

Swansea Metropolitan University
Industrial Design........ MSc 12FT 24PT
Product Design and Innovation .... MA 12FT 24PT

Trinity College Dublin - the University of Dublin
Engineering (M.A.I.) .... MAI 12FT
Engineering (M.A.I.) Recurrent Education .... MAI 12FT

UCL - University College London
Built Environment: Environmental Design and Engineering........ MSc 12FT 24-60PT/PGDip 9FT
Built Environment: Heritage Science .... MRes 12FT 24-60PT/PGCert 6FT
Built Environment: Sustainable Heritage....... MSc 12FT 24-60PT/PGDip 9FT

University of Wolverhampton
Advanced Technology Management........ MSc 12FT 24PT

Industrial design
Research Courses

University of the Arts London - Central Saint Martins College of Art and Design
Graphic and Industrial Design .... PhD 24-48FT 36-96PT/MPhil 15-36FT 24-72PT

University of Birmingham
Engineering, Sustainability and Resilience .... MRes 12FT

University of Brighton
Technology and Innovation Management PhD 24-60FT 36-72PT/MPhil 18-36FT 30-48PT

Brunel University
Industrial Design........ PhD/MPhil

University for the Creative Arts
Design .... MPhil 24FT 36PT/PhD 36FT 60PT

De Montfort University
Design and New Product Development. MPhil 12-24FT 24-48PT/PhD 24-36FT 36-72PT

University of Leeds
Institute of Engineering Systems and Design.... PhD 36+FT/MPhil 24FT

Loughborough University
Design Practice........ PhD 36FT 60PT/MPhil 24FT 36PT

Middlesex University
Design and Engineering...PhD 36FT 60PT/EngD 36FT 60PT/MPhil 18FT 36PT

The Open University
Complexity Science and Design........ PhD 36FT 72PT variableDL/MPhil 15FT 24PT variableDL
Design ... PhD 36FT 72PT variableDL/MPhil 15FT 24PT variableDL
Design Processes and Products........ PhD 36FT 72PT variableDL/MPhil 15FT 24PT variableDL
Sustainable Design........ PhD 36FT 72PT variableDL/MPhil 15FT 24PT variableDL

Plymouth University
Design Thinking........ MRes 12FT 24PT

Royal College of Art
Design Products........ PhD/MPhil/MA by research
Industrial Design Engineering........ PhD/MPhil/MA by research
Interaction Design........ PhD/MPhil/MA by research
Vehicle DesignPhD 36-48FT 48-72PT/MPhil 12-36FT 24-48PT/MA by research 24FT

University of Salford
Institute for Materials ResearchPhD 36FT/MSc by research 12FT/MPhil 12FT

University of Strathclyde
Advanced Manufacturing: Forging and Forming........ EngD 48FT/PGCert by research 9FT

Swansea Metropolitan University
Research Degrees .... PhD 36FT 60PT/MPhil 12FT 24PT

University of Wolverhampton
School of Engineering and the Built Environment: Engineering Division .... MPhil/PhD

Interior design
Taught Courses

University of the Arts London - Chelsea College of Art and Design
Interior and Spatial Design........ MA 12FT

Birmingham City University
Interior Design .... MA 12FT 24PT

University of Brighton
Interior Design ....

Cardiff University
Environmental Design of Buildings........ MSc 12FT 24PT 42DL

University of Central Lancashire
Interior Design .... MA 12FT 24PT/PGDip 12FT/PGCert 12FT
Transdisciplinary Design........ MA 12FT 24PT

Coventry University
Interior Design .... MA 12FT 24PT

University for the Creative Arts
Design .... MA 12FT 24PT
Design: Architectural and Interior Design .... MA 12FT 24PT
Interior Design .... MA 12FT 24PT

De Montfort University
Interior Design .... MA 12FT 24PT

University of Dundee
Design for Services (MDes) .... MDes 12FT

Edinburgh Napier University
Design (Interior Architecture) .... MA/MDes 12FT
Design (Lighting) .... MA/MDes 12FT
Interior Architecture........ MDes 12FT

University of Edinburgh
Interior Architectural Design........ MA 12FT/MFA 24FT
Interior Design .... MA 12FT

Glasgow School of Art
Interior Design .... MDes 12FT 24PT

Goldsmiths, University of London
Design - Critical Practice........ MA 12FT 24PT
Research Architecture .... MA 12FT 24PT

University of Hertfordshire
Interior and Spatial Design .... MA 12FT 24PT/PGDip 12FT 24PT

University of Huddersfield
Spatial Design .... MA 12/16FT

Inchbald School of Design
Architectural Interior Design........ PGDip 12FT/MA 12FT 12PT

Kingston University
Design: Product and Space & the Creative Economy....... MA 12FT 24PT
Design: Product+Space........ MA 12FT 24PT

Leeds Metropolitan University
Architecture........ MA 12FT 24PT

University of Lincoln
Interior Architecture & Design........ MA 12FT 24PT

London Metropolitan University
Interior Design .... MA 12FT 24PT
Interior Design MA by Project .... MA 12FT 24PT

Manchester Metropolitan University
Architecture........ MArch 24FT 48PT
Architecture and Urbanism .... MA 12FT 24PT
MA by Research........ MA by Research 12FT 24PT

Middlesex University
Interior Architecture........ MA 12FT 24PT

University of Northampton
Design (Product and Spatial Innovation) .... MA 12FT 24PT

Nottingham Trent University
Interior Architecture and Design........ MA 12FT 24PT

Oxford Brookes University
Applied Design in Architecture .... MArchD 24FT

Plymouth University
Design .... MA 12FT 24PT

University of Portsmouth
Interior Design .... MA 12FT 24PT

University of Sheffield
Sustainable Architectural Studies........ MSc 12FT 24PT

UCL - University College London
Light and Lighting .... MSc 12FT 24-60PT

University of Westminster
Interior Design .... MA 12FT 24PT

Interior design
Research Courses

University for the Creative Arts
Design .... MPhil 24FT 36PT/PhD 36FT 60PT

De Montfort University
Design and New Product Development. MPhil 12-24FT 24-48PT/PhD 24-36FT 36-72PT

University of Dundee
Architecture .... MPhil 24FT MSc by research 12FT PhD 36FT

Goldsmiths, University of London
Research Architecture ..... PhD 36-48FT 48-72PT/MPhil 24FT 36PT

Royal College of Art
Architecture and Interiors........ PhD/MPhil/MA by research 24FT

Medical illustration
Taught Courses

Cardiff University
Medical Illustration........ PGCert 14DL

University of Central Lancashire
Photography........ MA 12FT 24PT/PGDip 12FT 24PT/PGCert 12FT 24PT

University of Cumbria
Medical Imaging........ MSc 36 - 60PT
Photography........ MA 12FT 24PT

University of Derby
Medical Ultrasound .... MSc 36-72PT

University of Dundee
Advanced Practice (Medical Imaging) .... MSc 36DL
Anatomy and Advanced Forensic Anthropology .... MSc 12FT
Forensic Art .... MSc 12FT
Forensic Facial Identification .... MSc 12FT
Medical Art .... MSc 12FT MSc 48PT
Medical Imaging .... MSc 12FT
Minimal Access Surgery........ MMAS 12FT
Primary Care .... MSc 36-60PT
Prosthodontics .... MDentSci 24FT

Glasgow School of Art
Medical Visualisation and Human Anatomy ... PGCert 4FT/PGDip 8FT/MSc 12FT

University of Glasgow
Medical Visualisation & Human Anatomy .... MSc 12FT

University of Nottingham
Biological Photography and Imaging........ MSc 12FT

University of Oxford
Diagnostic Imaging........ MSc 12FT 24PT

Queen Mary, University of London
Media and Arts Technology .... MSc(Res) 12FT

Queen's University Belfast
Clinical Anatomy ......MSc 12FT TBCPT/PGDip 12FT TBCPT/PGCert 12FT TBCPT

University of Salford
Advanced Medical Imaging .... MSc 24-60PT/PGDip 18-36PT/PGCert 12-24PT

Art and design

University of Sheffield
Cognitive Neuroscience and Human Neuroimaging ...... MSc(Res) 12FT

Staffordshire University
Clinical Photography .... GradCert 12DL

Medical illustration
Research Courses

University for the Creative Arts
Photography .... MPhil 24FT 36PT/PhD 36FT 60PT

University of Oxford
Clinical Neurosciences .... DPhil 48FT/MSc by research 24-36FT

Photography and cinematics
Taught Courses

Anglia Ruskin University
Photography .... MA 12FT 24PT

University of the Arts London - Central Saint Martins College of Art and Design
Art and Science .... MA 24FT
Art: Moving Image .... MRes 24FT
Photography .... MA 24FT

University of the Arts London - London College of Fashion
Fashion Photography .... MA 15FT 30PT

Bangor University
Creative Practice .... MRes 12FT 24PT
Film and Visual Culture .... MRes 12FT 24PT
Filmmaking: Concept to Screen .... MA 12FT 24PT
Fine Art .... MA 36PT

Birkbeck, University of London
History of Art with Photography .... MA 12FT 24PT

Birmingham City University
Freelance Photography .... MA 12FT 24PT

University of Bolton
Photography .... MA 12FT 24-36PT

Arts University Bournemouth
Photography .... MA 12FT 24PT

University of Brighton
Photography .... MA 12FT 24-72PT

University of Central Lancashire
Photography .... MA 12FT 24PT/PGDip 12FT 24PT/PGCert 12FT 24PT

University College Cork
English (American Literature & Film) .... MA 12FT
Film Studies .... MA 9FT

Coventry University
Photography .... MA 12FT 24PT

University for the Creative Arts
Artists' Film, Video and Photography .... MA 12FT
Photography .... MA 12FT 24PT MA 24FT

University of Cumbria
Photography .... MA 12FT 24PT

De Montfort University
Photographic History and Practice .... MA 12FT 24PT
Photography .... MA 12FT 24PT/PGDip 9FT 18PT

University of Derby
Still and Moving Image .... MA 12FT

University of East Anglia
Film Studies .... MA 12FT 24PT
Film Studies with Archiving .... MA 12FT 24PT
Film, Television and Creative Practice .... MA 12FT 24PT

University of East London
Photography .... MA 12FT 24PT/PGDip 8FT 16PT/PGCert 4FT 8PT

Edinburgh Napier University
Film .... MA 12FT 24PT

University of Edinburgh
Composition for Screen .... MSc 12FT 24PT
Film Studies .... MSc 12FT 24PT
Film, Exhibition and Curation .... MSc 12FT 24PT
Transdisciplinary Documentary Film Practice .... MSc(Res) 12FT

University of Exeter
Independent Film Business .... MA 12FT 24PT

National University of Ireland Galway
Film Studies (Film, Culture, and Society) ..... MA 12FT/PGDip 12FT
Production and Direction .... MA 12FT/PGDip 12FT

Glasgow School of Art
Photography .... PGCert 4FT/PGDip 8FT/MDes 12FT

Goldsmiths, University of London
Aural and Visual Cultures .... MA 12FT 24PT
Contemporary Art History .... GradDip 12FT 24PT
Global Arts .... MA 12FT 24PT
Photography and Urban Cultures .... MA 12FT 24PT
Photography: The Image and Electronic Arts .... MA 12FT

University of Hertfordshire
Digital and Lens Art .... MA 12FT 24PT/PGDip 12FT 24PT/PGCert 12FT 24PT
Photographic Media .... MA 12FT 24PT/PGDip 12FT 24PT

University of Kent
Fine Art .... MA 12FT 24PT
Visual Anthropology .... MA 12FT 24PT

Kingston University
Photography .... MA 12FT 24PT

University of Leeds
World Cinemas .... MA 12FT 24PT

London Metropolitan University
Photography .... MA 12FT 24PT

London South Bank University
Digital Photography .... MA 24PT
Photographic Cultures .... MA 12FT

University of the Arts London - London College of Communication
Photography .... MA 12FT 24PT
Photography Portfolio Development .... PGDip 30 weeksFT
Photojournalism & Documentary Photography .... MA 12FT

Middlesex University
Film, Television, Animation .... MA 12FT 24PT
Photography .... MA 12FT 24PT

Newcastle University
Film: Theory and Practice .... MA 12FT 24PT

University of Northampton
Design (Photographic Communication) .... MA 12FT 24PT

Nottingham Trent University
Film Practice .... MA 12FT/PGDip 7FT/PGCert 4FT
Photography .... MA 12FT/PGDip 7FT/PGCert 4FT

Oxford Brookes University
Film Studies: Popular Cinema .... MA 12FT 24PT/PGDip 8FT 6-8PT/PGCert 4FT 6PT

University of Oxford
Film Aesthetics .... MSt 9FT

Plymouth University
Contemporary Art Practice .... MA 12FT
Photographic Arts .... MFA 18FT
Photography .... MA 12FT

Queen's University Belfast
Film and Visual Studies .... MA 12FT up to 31PT

University of Roehampton
Media, Culture and Identity .... PGDip 9FT 24PT

Royal College of Art
Photography .... MA 24FT

University Campus Suffolk
Photographic Practice .... MA 12FT 24PT

University of Salford
Fiction Film Production .... MA 12FT/PGDip 9FT
Film Screenwriting .... MA 15FT/PGDip 12FT/PGCert 6FT

Sheffield Hallam University
Film Studies .... MA 12FT 36-72PT MPhil 36FT 84PT/PhD by taught 36FT 84PT
Film Studies with Screenwriting .... MA 12FT 24PT

Sotheby's Institute of Art
Photography: Contemporary & Historical ..... MA 14FT/PGDip 9FT

University of Southampton
Film Studies .... MA 12FT 24PT
Film and Cultural Management .... MA 12FT 24PT

University of St Andrews
Film Studies .... MLitt 12FT 24PT/PGDip 9FT

Staffordshire University
Clinical Photography .... GradCert 12DL
Film Production Technology .... MSc 12-18FT
Film Production and Visual Cultures .... MA 12FT

University of Stirling
Film Studies: Theory and Practice ...... MLitt 12FT 27PT/PGDip 9FT 21PT/PGCert 3FT 6PT

University of Sunderland
Photography .... MA 12FT 24PT/PGDip 10FT 15PT/PGCert 7FT 7PT

University of Sussex
Creative Media Practice .... MA 12FT 24PT
Literature, Film and Visual Culture .... MA 12FT 24PT

Swansea University
Communication, Media Practice and Public Relations .... MA 12FT 24-36PT

Swansea Metropolitan University
Photography .... MA 24FT 36PT

University of Ulster
Photography .... MFA 9FT

UCL - University College London
Film Studies .... MA 12FT 24PT

University of West London
Film Finance .... MA 12FT 24PT
Photography .... MA 12FT 24PT

University of Westminster
Photographic Studies .... MA 12FT 24-60PT

Photography and cinematics
Research Courses

Bangor University
Creative and Critical Writing, Film and Media, Professional Writing .... MPhil 24FT 48PT/PhD 36FT 72PT
Creative and Critical Writing, Film and Media, Professional Writing: Practice-Led Research . MPhil 24FT 48PT/PhD 36FT 72PT

University of Bolton
Film and Media Studies Specialisms .. PhD 36FT 72PT/MPhil 18FT 36PT

University for the Creative Arts
Media Arts and Communications Design ... PhD 36FT 60PT/MPhil 24FT 36PT
Photography .... MPhil 24FT 36PT/PhD 36FT 60PT

De Montfort University
Photographic Studies and Creative Imaging .... MPhil 12-24FT 24-48PT/PhD 24-36FT 36-72PT

University of Edinburgh
Film Studies .... PhD 36FT 72PT/MSc by research 12FT 24PT
Transdisciplinary Documentary Film .... PhD 36FT
Visual and Cultural Studies .... PhD 24FT 36PT/MPhil 12FT 24PT

University of Exeter
Art History and Visual Culture .. MPhil 36FT 60PT 60DL/PhD 48FT 84PT 84DL
Film Studies .... MPhil 24FT 48PT/PhD 36-48FT 72PT

University of Gloucestershire
Art and Design .... PhD 30-48FT

Goldsmiths, University of London
Visual Sociology .... MPhil 24FT 36PT/PhD 36-48FT 48-72PT

University of Kent
Fine Art .... PhD 36FT 60PT

Lancaster University
Media, Film and Cultural Studies .... PhD 36FT 48PT/MPhil 24FT 36PT

Newcastle University
Film Studies .... MLitt by research 12FT 24PT PhD 36FT 72PT/MPhil 12FT 24PT

Queen's University Belfast
Film Studies .... PhD 36FT 72PT/MPhil 24FT 48PT

Royal College of Art
Photography .... PhD/MPhil/MA by research
Photography .... PhD/MPhil/MA by research

University of Southampton
Film Studies .... PhD 48FT 84PT/MPhil 48FT 84PT

University of St Andrews
Film Studies .... PhD 36FT 72-84PT/MPhil 24FT 48PT
History of Photography .... PhD 36FT 72PT/MPhil 24FT 48PT

UCL - University College London
Film Studies .... PhD 36FT 60PT

Photojournalism
Taught Courses

Anglia Ruskin University
Photography .... MA 12FT 24PT

Arts University Bournemouth
Photography .... MA 12FT 24PT

University of Central Lancashire
Broadcast Journalism .... PGDip 9FT/MA 12FT
Journalism .... MA 12FT 36PT
Journalism Practice .... MA 12FT 24-36PT/PGDip 9FT 18-24PT
Journalism Studies .... MA 12FT 24PT
Photography .... MA 12FT 24PT/PGDip 12FT 24PT/PGCert 12FT 24PT

University of Cumbria
Photography .... MA 12FT 24PT

University of Derby
Still and Moving Image .... MA 12FT

London Metropolitan University
Photography .... MA 12FT 24PT

University of the Arts London - London College of Communication
Photography Portfolio Development .... PGDip 30 weeksFT
Photojournalism & Documentary Photography .... MA 12FT
Photojournalism & Documentary Photography (Online Mode) ... MA 24PT

University of South Wales
Contemporary Photography Practice .... MFA 18FT
Documentary Photography ... MA 12 - 18FT 24PT/MFA 24FT 36PT

Art and design

Staffordshire University
Clinical Photography ....GradCert 12DL

University of Ulster
Documentary Practice.................................... MA 12FT 24PT

University of Westminster
Photographic Studies .... MA 12FT 24-60PT
Photojournalism.. MA 12FT 24PT

Photojournalism
Research Courses

University for the Creative Arts
Photography .... MPhil 24FT 36PT/PhD 36FT 60PT

University of Manchester
Ethnographic Documentary ....MPhil 12FT 24PT
Social Anthropology with Visual Media ......PhD 48FT 84PT/MPhil 12FT 24PT

Printing
Taught Courses

Anglia Ruskin University
Children's Book Illustration............................ MA 18FT 30PT
Graphic Design and Typography............................ MA 12FT 24PT
Illustration and Book Arts ....MA 12FT 24PT/PGCert 12FT 24PT/PGDip 12FT 24PT
Printmaking .... MA 12FT 24-36PT
Publishing..MA 12FT

University of the Arts London - Camberwell College of Arts
Book Arts .... MA 12FT 24PT
Printmaking .... MA 12FT 24PT

University of Central Lancashire
Publishing......... MA 12FT 24PT/PGDip 9FT 18PT/PGCert 9FT 18PT

University of East London
Print Design ....MA 12FT 24PT/PGDip 8FT 16PT/PGCert 4FT 8PT

Edinburgh Napier University
Publishing..MSc 12FT 24PT

London Metropolitan University
Product Design .... MA 12FT 24PT

University of the Arts London - London College of Communication
Contemporary Typographic Media ....MA 12FT
Graphic Branding & Identity ....MA 12FT
Publishing..MA 12FT

Manchester Metropolitan University
Design (with pathways in design and contemporary craft practice) .... MA 12FT 24PT

Plymouth University
Publishing.......................MA 12FT 24PT/PGDip 12FT 24PT

University of Roehampton
Art, Craft and Design Education .... PGCert 6FT 24PT PGDip 9FT 24PT

University of Salford
Art and Design: Product Design .. MA 12FT 24PT/PGDip 9FT 15PT
Masters in Research (Journalism) ....MRes 12FT 24PT

University of Sheffield
Print Journalism...........................MA 12FT/PGDip 9FT

University of Stirling
Publishing Studies .... MLitt 12FT 27PT/PGDip 9FT 21PT
MRes 12FT 27PT/PGCert 9FT 18PT

West Herts College
Printmaking/Illustration .... PGDip 8-16PT

University of the West of England, Bristol
Multidisciplinary Printmaking ...MA 18FT 36PT/PGDip 12FT 24PT

Printing
Research Courses

Anglia Ruskin University
Children's Book Illustration...........................MPhil 24FT/PhD 36FT
Graphic Design and Typography...................MPhil 24FT/PhD 36FT
Publishing...MPhil 24FT/PhD 36FT

University of Central Lancashire
Fine Art, Fashion & Performing Arts........... PhD 30-48FT 66-84PT/MPhil 18-36FT 42-60PT/MA by research 12FT 24PT

University of Dundee
Duncan of Jordanstone College of Art & Design .... MPhil 24FT PhD 36FT

Reformation history
Taught Courses

University of East Anglia
Early Modern History.............................. MA 12FT 24PT
History....................................... GradDip 12FT 24PT
History of Art.. MA 12FT 24PT

University of St Andrews
Reformation Studies....... MLitt 12FT 24PT/MPhil 24FT/PGDip 9FT 24PT

Swansea University
Early Modern History.................................. MA 12FT 24PT

Reformation history
Research Courses

University of East Anglia
School of History .... PhD 36FT 72PT/MPhil 24FT 48PT

Restoration
Taught Courses

Anglia Ruskin University
Conservation of Buildings ....MSc 12FT 24 - 30PT

University of Bath
Conservation of Historic Buildings ......MSc 12FT 28PT/PGDip 9FT 20PT
Conservation of Historic Gardens and Cultural Landscapes .. MSc 12FT 28PT/PGDip 9FT 20PT

University of Bolton
Regeneration and Sustainable Communities MA 15FT/MSc 15FT/PGDip 12FT/PGCert 6FT

Bucks New University
Conservation of Furniture and Decorative Arts...... MA 12FT 24PT

College of Estate Management
Conservation of Historic Environment ......PGDip 24DL/MSc 36DL

Cardiff University
Conservation Practice....................................... MSc 24FT
Professional Conservation................................. MSc 12FT 24PT

Cranfield University
Land Reclamation and Restoration ....MSc 12FT 60PT/PGCert 12FT 60PT/PGDip 12FT 60PT

University of Dundee
Renewable Energy and Sustainable Building in a Global Context .... MSc 12FT

Durham University
Conservation of Archaeological and Museum Objects (Dissertation)... MA 24FT 36PT
Conservation of Archaeological and Museum Objects (Professional Practice)................................... MA 24FT 36PT

Edinburgh Napier University
Architectural Technology & Building Performance .... MSc 12FT 24PT 36DL
Timber Engineering ....MSc 12FT 36DL
Timber Industry Management...................... MSc 12FT 36PT 36DL

University of Edinburgh
Architectural Conservation....................................MSc 12FT 24PT

University of Greenwich
Building Rehabilitation...MSc 12FT 24PT

Heriot-Watt University
Building Conservation (Technology and Management).......... MSc 24-84DL/PGDip 24-84DL

Kingston University
Historic Building Conservation ....MSc 12FT 24PT

University of Leicester
Country House ....MA 24-48DL
Urban Conservation.........................MA 12FT 24PT/MSc 12FT 24PT

University of Lincoln
Conservation Studies....................... GradDip 12FT 24PT
Conservation of Historic Objects.............................. MA 12FT 24PT

London Metropolitan University
Restoration and Conservation MA by Project .... MA 12FT 24PT

Oxford Brookes University
Historic Conservation ....MSc 12FT 24PT/PGDip 12FT 24PT/PGCert 12PT

Plymouth University
Architectural Conservation.. MA 12FT 24PT/PGDip 10FT 12-60PT

University of Portsmouth
Historic Building Conservation .... MSc 12FT 24PT

University of Reading
Geoarchaeology .... MSc 12FT 24PT/PGDip 12FT 24PT

Royal College of Art
Conservation................................PhD by taught/MPhil/MA 24FT

School of Oriental and African Studies - SOAS
History of Art and/or Archaeology...................... MA 12FT 24-36PT

University of Sheffield
Conservation and Regeneration .... MA 12FT 24PT
Sustainable Architectural Studies............................ MSc 12FT 24PT

University of Sussex
International Trade Law............................. LLM 12FT 24PT

Trinity College Dublin - the University of Dublin
Applied Building Repair and Conservation .... PGDip 12PT

UCL - University College London
Built Environment: Sustainable Heritage .... MSc 12FT 24-60PT/PGDip 9FT
Conservation..................................MSc 12FT/PGDip 9FT/PGCert 3FT

University of York
Conservation Studies (Historic Buildings)........... MA 12FT 24-36PT
Stained Glass Conservation and Heritage Management............... MA 24FT

Restoration
Research Courses

Birmingham City University
Birmingham School of Architecture and Landscape....PhD/MPhil

School of Oriental and African Studies - SOAS
Department of Art and Archaeology ....PhD 36FT 72PT/MPhil 24FT 36PT

Set design
Taught Courses

University of the Arts London - Central Saint Martins College of Art and Design
Creative Practice for Narrative Environments....................MA 24FT
Performance Design and Practice ....MA 24FT
Screen: Directing, Writing - Drama Centre London ....MA 12FT

University of Bristol
Archaeology for Screen Media .... MA 12FT 24PT

University of Central Lancashire
Transdisciplinary Design.................................. MA 12FT 24PT

Central School of Speech and Drama, University of London
Scenography ....MA 12FT

City University London
Scenography (Dance)................................... MA 12FT 24PT

University for the Creative Arts
Design for Performance and Events .... MA 12FT 24PT

Edinburgh Napier University
Screen Project Development .... MA 12FT 24PT

University of Glasgow
Art, Style & Design: Renaissance to Modernism..........MLitt 12FT/PGDip 12FT
Modern & Contemporary Art........................MLitt 12FT/PGDip 9FT

University of Hertfordshire
Model Design and Model Effects.........MA 12FT 24PT/PGDip 12FT 24PT/PGCert 12FT 24PT

University of Lincoln
Design for Museum and Exhibition................MA 12FT 24PT 24DL

London Metropolitan University
Curating the Contemporary....................................MA 24FT

Northumbria University
Multidisciplinary Design Innovation............... MA 12FT/MSc 12FT

Nottingham Trent University
Design for Film, Television and Events..........MA 12FT/PGDip 7FT/PGCert 4FT

Ravensbourne
Environment Design... MA 12FT 24PT

Rose Bruford College
Ensemble Theatre....................................... MA 12FT/PGDip 10FT

Royal Welsh College of Music and Drama
Theatre Design... MA 12FT 12PT

Set design
Research Courses

University of the Arts London - Central Saint Martins College of Art and Design
Theatre Design and Scenography .... PhD 24-48FT 36-96PT/MPhil 15-36FT 24-72PT

Goldsmiths, University of London
Curatorial/Knowledge ....MPhil 24FT 36PT/PhD 36-48FT 48-72PT

Sustainable development
Taught Courses

University of Abertay Dundee
Energy Industry Economics..............................MSc 12FT/PGDip 9FT

Anglia Ruskin University
Sustainability: Working for Positive Change....MSc 12FT 24-30PT

Aston University
Social Responsibility & Sustainability......................MSc 12FT 24PT

Bangor University
Conservation and Land Management ....MSc 12FT/PGDip 9FT
Environmental Management................................ MBA 12FT
Forestry (Distance Learning with International Commonwealth Scholarship) ....MSc 12DL
Rheolaeth Amgylcheddol Gynaliadwy (Sustainable Environmental Management)........MSc 12FT 24PT/MA 12FT 24PT
Sustainable Tropical Forestry (SUTROFOR) (Erasmus Mundus course).. MSc 24FT
Tropical Frorestry................... MSc 36PT/PGDip 24PT/PGCert 12PT

Birmingham City University
Environmental Sustainability...... PGCert 4FT 8PT/PGDip 4FT 8PT/MSc 4FT 8PT

Art and design

Environmental Sustainability (Design and Construction) .... PGCert 4FT 8PT/PGDip 4FT 8PT/MSc 4FT 8PT

University of Birmingham
Materials for Sustainable Energy Technologies...MRes 12FT 24PT
Resilience and Urban Living........MSc 12FT 24PT/MRes 12FT 24PT

University of Bolton
Regeneration and Sustainable CommunitiesMA 15FT/MSc 15FT/PGDip 12FT/PGCert 6FT

Bournemouth University
Green Economy....................MSc 12DL

University of Bradford
Applied Management and Sustainability.................... MSc 12FT
Applied Management and Sustainability.................... MSc 12FT

University of Brighton
Sustainability of the Built Environment.....MSc 12FT 24PT/PGDip 12FT 24PT/PGCert 12FT 24PT
Sustainable Design ....MA 12FT 24-60PT/PGDip 12FT 24-60PT/PGCert 12FT 24-60PT

Brunel University
Building Services Engineering with Sustainable Energy................ MSc 12FT 36-60DL
Renewable Energy Engineering.................... MSc 12FT
Sustainable Electrical Power.................... MSc 12FT 24PT
Sustainable Energy : Technologies and Management... MSc 12FT

University of Cambridge
Engineering for Sustainable Development.................. MPhil 11FT
Sustainability Leadership.................... MSt 24PT

Cardiff University
Sustainability, Planning and Environmental Policy.................... MSc 12FT 24PT
Sustainable Energy and Environment...............MSc 12FT 24-36PT
Theory and Practice of Sustainable Design .... MSc 12FT 24PT

University of Chester
Sustainability for Community and Business.........MSc 12FT 24PT/PGDip 12FT 24PT/PGCert 12FT 12-24PT

University College Cork
Planning & Sustainable Development .... MPlan 24FT
Sustainable Energy....................MEngSci 12FT

Cranfield University
Design and Innovation for Sustainability .... MDes 12FT 24-60PT/PGDip 6FT 12PT/PGCert 5FT 12PT
Environment and Public Policy.......... MSc 12FT 60PT/PGCert 12FT 60PT/PGDip 12FT 60PT
Environmental Informatics......MSc 12FT 60PT/PGDip 12FT 60PT/PGCert 12FT 60PT
Through-life System Sustainment....................MSc 24-36PT

University for the Creative Arts
Sustainable Product Design ....MA 24PT

University of Cumbria
Greening Outdoor Practice....................PGCert 24-36PT

De Montfort University
Architecture and Sustainability.................... MSc 12FT 24PT
Energy and Industrial Sustainability .... MSc 12FT 24PT 36DL/PGDip 32DL/PGCert 16DL

University of Derby
Sustainable Architecture and Healthy Environments .....MA 12FT
Sustainable Design and Innovation...................MSc 12FT 36-72PT

Dublin Institute of Technology
Sustainable Development.................... MSc 12FT
Sustainable Electrical Energy Systems.................. MEng 12FT 24PT

University of Dundee
Advanced Sustainability of the Built Environment .... MSc 12FT
Advanced Sustainable Urban Design .... MSc 12FT
Renewable Energy and Sustainable Building in a Global Context .... MSc 12FT
Spatial Planning with Marine Spatial Planning .... MSc 12FT
Spatial Planning with Sustainable Urban Design .... MSc 12FT
Spatial Planning with Urban Conservation .... MSc 12FT

University of East Anglia
Environmental Assessment and Management..... MSc 12FT 24PT
Sustainable Business.................... MSc 12FT

University of East London
Architecture: Advanced Environmental and Energy Studies MSc.................... MSc 12FT 24PT
Architecture: Sustainability And Design .... MA 12FT 24PT/PGDip 8FT 16PT/PGCert 4FT 8PT
Renewable Energy and the Built Environment ..... MSc 12FT 24PT
Sustainability and Energy Management .... MBA 12FT 24PT

Edinburgh Napier University
Design (Sustainability)....................MA/MDes 12FT
Energy and Environmental Engineering.................. MSc 12FT 36PT
Environmental Sustainability.... MSc 12FT 36PT/PGDip 9FT 24PT/PGCert 6FT 12PT
Polymer Engineering .... MSc 12FT
Renewable Energy.................... MSc 12FT 24PT
Safety and Environmental Management..... MSc 12FT 36PT 36DL

University of Edinburgh
Advanced Sustainable Design.................... MSc 12FT 24PT
Environmental Sustainability..........MSc 12FT 24-36PT/PGDip 9FT
Global Development Challenges (Online Distance Learning)....... PGCert 12-24DL
Global Environment Challenges Certificate (Online distance learning) ....PGCert 9DL
Soils and Sustainability.................... MSc 12FT
Sustainable Energy Systems.................... MSc 12FT/PGDip 9FT

University of Exeter
Applied Ecology.................... MSc 12FT
Food Security and Sustainable Agriculture............ MSc 12FT 24PT

Forum for the Future
Leadership for Sustainable Development.................... MA 10.5FT

Glasgow Caledonian University
Sustainable Energy Technology.................... MSc 12FT 24PT

University of Glasgow
Environment & Sustainable Development.................... MSc 12FT
Sustainable Energy .... MSc 12FT

Glyndwr University
Renewable Energy Systems and Sustainability.............. MSc 12FT 24-36PT/MRes 12FT

Goldsmiths, University of London
Design & Environment .... MA 12FT 24PT
Design Futures .... MA 12FT 24PT

University of Greenwich
Natural Resources .... MSc 12FT 24PT/PGDip 12FT 24PT
Sustainable Futures .... MSc 12FT

Harper Adams University
International Agri-business and Food Chain Management... MSc 12FT 48PT/PGDip 12FT 48PT/PGCert 6FT 48PT

Heriot-Watt University
Climate Change: Impacts and Mitigation..MSc 12FT 24PT/PGDip 9FT 21PT
Climate Change: Managing The Marine Environment.. MSc 12FT 24PT/PGDip 9FT 21PT
Energy.............MSc 12FT 24PT 24-84DL/PGDip 9FT 21PT 21-84DL
Int'nl Business Management with Finance / HRM / Logistics / Marketing /Sustainability Mgmt. ....MSc 12FT 24PT/PGDip 9FT 21PT
Marine Resource Development and Protection....MSc 12FT 24PT/PGDip 9FT 21PT
Materials for Sustainable and Renewable Energies....... MSc 12FT 24PT/PGDip 9FT 21PT/PGCert 6FT 12PT
Renewable Energy Engineering..MSc 12FT 24PT/PGDip 9FT 21PT
Smart Grid and Demand Management......MSc 12FT 24PT/PGDip 9FT 18PT
Sustainability Engineering......... MSc 12FT 24PT/PGDip 9FT 21PT/PGCert 6FT 12PT

University of Hertfordshire
Water and Environmental Management..........MSc 12FT 24-60PT 24DL/PGDip 12FT 18-48PT 18DL/PGCert 12FT 18-48PT 18DL

University of Huddersfield
Architecture/Architecture (International) (RIBA Part 2)......MArch 24FT
Sustainable Architecture.................... MSc 12FT 24PT

University of Hull
Environmental Technology .... MSc 12FT 24PT
Environmental Technology (renewable energy).... MSc 12FT 24PT

Imperial College London
Transport, also with Business Management or Sustainable Development....................MSc 12FT 24-36PT

Keele University
Environmental Sustainability and Green Technology..... Cert 4FT/Diploma 8FT/MSc 12FT

University of Kent
Environmental Anthropology.........MA 12FT 24PT/MSc 12FT 24PT

King's College London
Sustainable Cities.................... MSc 12FT 24PT

Kingston University
Sustainability & Environmental Change................ MSc 12FT 24PT
Sustainability for Built Environment PracticeMA 12FT/MSc 12FT/PGCert 6FT 12PT/PGDip 12FT
Sustainable Environmental Development with Management Studies.................... MSc 12FT 24PT

Leeds Metropolitan University
Sustainable Computing.................... MSc 12FT 24PT

University of Leeds
Sustainability (Business, Environment and Corporate Responsibility)....................MA 12FT 48PT/PGDip 12FT 48PT
Sustainability (Climate Change).................... MSc 12FT
Sustainability (Ecological Economics) .... MSc 12FT 48PT
Sustainability (Environment and Development)............ MSc 12FT 12-48PT
Sustainability (Environmental Consultancy)....MSc 12FT 12-48PT
Sustainability (Environmental Politics and Policy).......... MSc 12FT 12-48PT
Sustainability (Transport) MSc 12FT 24-36PT/PGDip 9FT 18-24PT

Sustainability Research.................... MRes 12FT 12-48PT
Water, Sanitation and Health Engineering.............MSc(Eng) 12FT

University of Leicester
Environmental Informatics..........MSc 12FT 24PT/PGDip 9FT 18PT
Sustainable Management of Natural Resources..MSc 12FT 24PT/PGDip 9FT 18PT

London Metropolitan University
Planning and Sustainable Communities................ MSc 12FT 24PT
Sustainable Cities....................MSc 12FT 24+PT

London School of Economics and Political Science (LSE)
Environment and Development .... MSc 12FT 24PT

Loughborough University
Design and Innovation for Sustainability .... MSc 12FT 24PT
Low Carbon Building Design and Modelling.. MSc 12FT 24-60PT/PGDip 12FT 24-60PT/PGCert 12FT 24-60PT
Sustainable Engineering.................... MSc 12FT 96PT

Manchester Metropolitan University
Environment, Management and Sustainable Development......... MSc 12FT 36PT
Sustainable Aviation....................MSc 12FT 12-36PT

University of Manchester
Competition, Regulation and Development .... MSc 12FT 12PT
Environment and Sustainable Technology .MSc 12FT/PGDip 9FT/PGCert 6FT

Middlesex University
Sustainable Development......... MA 12FT 24PT/PGDip 12FT 24PT/PGCert 12FT 24PT
Sustainable Environmental Management...... MA 12FT 24PT/MSc 12FT 24PT

Newcastle University
Environmental Regulation and Sustainable Development.....LLM 12FT 24PT
Hydrology and Climate Change.................... MSc 12FT 48PT
Planning for Sustainability and Climate Change............ MSc 12FT
Sustainable Buildings and Environments.................... MSc 12FT

University of Northampton
Sustainable Urban Environments .... PGCert 6PT

Northumbria University
Disaster Management and Sustainable Development .... PGCert 4FT 8DL/PGDip 8FT 12DL/MSc 12FT 36-60DL
Electrical Power Engineering.................... MSc 12-16FT
Renewable and Sustainable Energy Technologies.................... MSc 12 or 16FT

Nottingham Trent University
Planning, Urban Design and Sustainable Development.... PGCert 12PT

University of Nottingham
Energy Conversion and Management (Nottingham/ Ningbo)...... MSc 12FT
Environmental Design....................MArch 12FT 24PT
Renewable Energy and Architecture .MSc 12FT 24PT/PGDip 12FT 24PT
Sustainable Bioenergy .... MSc 12FT 36PT
Sustainable Bioenergy ....MRes 12-36PT
Sustainable Building Technology (Nottingham/ Ningbo) ...... MSc 12FT 24PT
Sustainable Building Technology (collaborative) .... MSc 12FT
Sustainable Energy Engineering.................... MSc 12FT
Sustainable Energy and Entrepreneurship .... MSc 12FT
Sustainable Tall Buildings ....MArch 12FT
Sustainable Transportation and Electrical Power Systems (Erasmus Mundus) .... MSc 24FT

The Open University
Conflict and Development.................... PGCert variableDL
Development Management ....MSc variableDL/PGDip variableDL/PGCert 12DL
Human Rights and Development Management........PGCert 12DL

Oxford Brookes University
Sustainable Building: Performance and Design...MSc 12FT 27PT/PGDip 9FT 18PT

Plymouth University
Design .... MA 12FT 24PT
Marine Renewable Energy ....MSc 12FT/MRes 12FT

Queen's University Belfast
Environmental Law and Sustainable Development........LLM 12FT
Leadership for Sustainable Rural Development .... MSc 12FT
Sustainable Design .... MSc 12FT/PGDip 9FT
Sustainable Electrical Energy Systems.................... MSc 12FT

Ravensbourne
Environment Design .... MA 12FT 24PT

University of Reading
Agricultural Economics .... MSc 12FT 24PT
Agriculture and Development .... MSc 12FT 24PT
Construction Management .... MSc 12FT
Project Management .... MSc 24PT
Renewable Energy ....MSc 12FT 24PT/PGDip 9FT 21PT
Social Development and Sustainable Livelihoods ....MA 12FT

Art and design

Reseau Universitaire Transmanche
Transmanche Environment Programme .... MSc 24FT

Robert Gordon University
Energy and Sustainability ...MSc 42DL/PGDip 24DL/PGCert 12DL

Royal Holloway, University of London
Practising Sustainable Development ..... MSc 12FT 24PT/Diploma 6FT 12PT
Sustainability and Management................................ MSc 12FT 24PT

University Campus Suffolk
Sustainable Business....................................... MA 12FT 24PT

University of Salford
Real Estate Development ....MSc 12FT 28DL/PGDip 8FT 20DL
Sustainable Building Design...... MSc 12FT 28PT/PGDip 8FT 20PT/ PGCert 4FT 8PT

School of Oriental and African Studies - SOAS
Environmental Law and Sustainable Development
.... MA 12FT 24PT

Schumacher College
Economics for Transition ....MA 12FT

University of Sheffield
Planning and Development......................................MA 12FT

University of South Wales
Sustainable Power Technology .... MSc 12FT 36PT

University of Southampton
Sustainable Energy Technologies........................MSc 12FT 24PT

University of St Andrews
Sustainable Aquaculture .MSc 12FT 24PT/PGDip 9FT 24PT 24DL/ Cert 12DL
Sustainable Development................................ MSc 12FT/PGDip 9FT

Staffordshire University
Governance and Sustainable Development..........MA 36PT 36DL/ PGCert 36PT 20DL/PGDip 36PT 9DL
Regeneration .... MA 24FT 60PT

University of Stirling
Energy and the Environment ... MSc 12FT 27PT/MRes 12FT 27PT/ PGDip 9FT/PGCert 4FT

University of Strathclyde
International Law and Sustainable Development ....LLM 12FT 24PT/PGDip 9FT 21PT/PGCert 4FT 8PT
Sustainability and Environmental Studies ....MSc 12FT 24PT/ PGDip 9FT 18PT
Sustainable Engineering............. MSc 12FT 24PT/PGDip 9FT 18PT/ PGCert 9FT 18PT
Sustainable Engineering: Building Design and Management...... MSc 12FT 24PT/PGDip 9FT 18PT/PGCert 6FT 12PT
Sustainable Engineering: Sustainable Product Development...... MSc 12FT 24PT/PGDip 9FT 21PT/PGCert 6FT 12PT

University of Surrey
Sustainable Development................................MSc 12FT 12-48PT

University of Sussex
Climate Change and Development..........................MSc 12FT 24PT

Climate Change and Policy .... MSc 12FT 24PT
Energy Policy for Sustainability .... MSc 12FT 24PT
Innovation and Sustainability for International Development ..... MSc 12FT 24PT

Trinity College Dublin - the University of Dublin
Environment and Development.. MSc 12FT

University of the Highlands and Islands
Developing Low Carbon Communities ....MSc 12FT 36PT/PGDip 12FT 24PT/PGCert 12FT 12PT
Managing Sustainable Mountain Development MSc 36PT 36DL/ PGDip 24PT 24DL/PGCert 24PT 12DL
Managing Sustainable Rural Development...........MSc 24FT 36PT/ PGDip 12FT 24PT/PGCert 12FT 24PT

UCL - University College London
Energy and Resources: Policy and Practice, Australia .... MSc 24FT 36-48PT
Environment and Sustainable Development . MSc 12FT 24-60PT/ PGDip 9FT
Sustainable Urbanism.....................MSc 12FT 24-60PT/PGDip 9FT

University of West London
Development and Management of Sustainable Built Environment......................................MSc 12FT 24PT

University of the West of England, Bristol
Environmental Law and sustainable development
.... LLM 12FT 36PT

University of Worcester
Sustainable Development Advocacy (Professional Practice) ...MA 12FT 36PT

University of York
Green Chemistry and Sustainable Industrial Technology....... MSc 12FT 24-36PT

Sustainable development
Research Courses

Anglia Ruskin University
Sustainability..................................PhD 24 - 60FT 36 - 72PT

Bangor University
Renewable Materials.................. MPhil 24FT 36PT/PhD 36FT 60PT

University of Birmingham
Engineering, Sustainability and Resilience ....MRes 12FT

Cardiff University
Institute of Environment and Sustainability........ PhD 36FT/MPhil 60PT
Institute of Green Electronic Systems; Communications, Sensors and Materials .... EngD 48FT/PhD 36FT/MPhil 12FT
Sustainable Engineering.......................................PhD 36FT

Cranfield University
Sustainable Systems Research Opportunities ....PhD 36FT/ Integrated PhD 36-45FT/MTech 24FT

De Montfort University
Energy and Sustainable Development Research ...MPhil 12-24FT 24-48PT/PhD 36-48FT 48-72PT

University of Gloucestershire
Sustainability..PhD 36FT

University of Greenwich
Development Studies - Research...... MPhil 18-36FT 30-48PT/PhD 33-60FT 45-72PT
Environmental and Earth Sciences Research .....MPhil 36FT 72PT/ PhD 36FT 72PT
Natural Resources by Research ....MSc by research 12FT 24PT

University of Hertfordshire
Agriculture and the Environment .... PhD 36FT 72PT/MRes 12FT 24PT

University of Leeds
Environmental Sustainability....PhD 36FT 60PT 60DL/MPhil 24FT 48PT 48DL

University of Manchester
Environment and Sustainable Technology ....PhD 36FT 72PT/ MPhil 12FT 24PT
Sustainable Consumption..................................PhD 48FT

Newcastle University
Sustainability.. MPhil variesFT/PhD variesFT

University of Nottingham
Sustainable Energy Technology ....PhD 36FT

The Open University
Asian drivers and Africa ... PhD 36FT 72PT variableDL/MPhil 15FT 24PT variableDL
Environment, governance and justicePhD 36FT 72PT variableDL/ MPhil 15FT 24PT variableDL
Sustainable Design .... PhD 36FT 72PT variableDL/ MPhil 15FT 24PT variableDL

Oxford Brookes University
Sustainable Development MPhil/PhD .... PhD 24-60FT 36-72PT/ MPhil 24-36FT 36-48PT

School of Oriental and African Studies - SOAS
Development Studies...PhD 36FT 48-60PT

Sheffield Hallam University
Environment and Development .... MPhil 36PT
Environment and Development - Facilities Management.......PhD 33FT 45PT/MPhil 18FT 30PT
School of Environment and Development.....................PhD/MPhil

University of Strathclyde
Building Design and Management for Sustainability .... MRes 12FT 36PT

University of Surrey
Sustainability for Engineering and Energy Systems (SEES) .... EngD 48FT

University of the Highlands and Islands
Sustainability Studies... MPhil 24FT 48PT/PhD 36FT 72PT/MSc by research 12FT 24PT

Classics

Ancient greek
Taught Courses

University of Bristol
Classical Reception.. MA 12FT 24PT

Cardiff University
Late Antique and Byzantine Studies.......................... MA 12FT 24PT

Durham University
Greece. Rome and the Near East .... MA 12FT 24PT

University of Exeter
Classics and Ancient History .... MA 12FT 24PT

University of Kent
Hellenic and Hellenic Near East.................................. MA 12FT 24PT

King's College London
Late Antique & Byzantine Studies .... GradDip 12FT 24PT

National University of Ireland, Maynooth
Greek & Roman Civilization.............................. MA 12FT 24PT

Newcastle University
Greek and Byzantine Archaeology.......................... MA 12FT 24PT
Greek and Roman Archaeology .... MA 12FT 24PT

The Open University
Classical Studies ....MA variableDL

University of Oxford
Classical Archaeology....................................... MPhil 21FT/MSt 9FT
Greek and/or Roman History.......................... MSt 9FT/MPhil 24FT

University of Reading
The Classical Tradition .... MA(Res) 12FT 24PT 60BM

Royal Holloway, University of London
Classics .... MA 12FT 24PT

University of St Andrews
Classical Studies ....PGDip 9FT/MLitt 12FT 24PT
Greek ....PGDip 9FT 18PT/MLitt 12FT 24PT
Greek and Latin..........................PGDip 9FT/MLitt 12FT 24PT

Trinity College Dublin - the University of Dublin
Classics.. MPhil 12FT

University of Wales Trinity Saint David
Ancient History ....MA 12FT 24PT 12-24DL
Classical Studies ....MA 12FT 24PT 12-24DL
Greek ....PGCert 12PT 12-36DL/PGDip 24PT 12-36DL

UCL - University College London
Classics.. MA 12FT 24PT

Ancient greek
Research Courses

University of Birmingham
Greek Archaeology...MRes 12FT 24PT

University of Cambridge
Modern Greek .... PhD 36FT 60PT

University of Exeter
Classics and Ancient History ..... PhD 36FT 72PT/MPhil 24FT 48PT

Newcastle University
Classics.. MLitt by research 12FT 24PT

The Open University
Ancient and Modern Reception of Antiquity .... PhD 36FT 72PT
variableDL/MPhil 15FT 24PT variableDL
Classical Studies ...... PhD 36FT 72PT variableDL/MPhil 15FT 24PT
variableDL
Greek and Latin texts .... PhD 36FT 72PT variableDL/MPhil 15FT
24PT variableDL

University of St Andrews
Classics...PhD 36FT 72PT/MPhil 24FT

Swansea University
Greek .... MPhil 24FT 48PT/PhD 36FT 72PT

UCL - University College London
Greek, Latin and the Classical World....................... PhD 36FT 60PT

Classics
Taught Courses

Birkbeck, University of London
Classical Civilisation/Classics..................................... MA 12FT 24PT

University of Birmingham
Ancient History and Classics ....MRes 12FT 24PT/PhD by taught
36FT 72PT
Antiquity.. MA 12FT 24PT

University of Bristol
Classical Reception.. MA 12FT 24PT
Classics and Ancient History .... MA 12FT 24PT

University of Cambridge
Classics...MPhil 9FT

Cardiff University
History and Archaeology of the Greek & Roman World..MA 12FT
24PT

University College Cork
Arts (Greek & Roman Civilisation) ....HDip 9FT 18PT

Greek & Roman Civilisation.. MA 12FT 24PT

Durham University
Classical Tradition................................ MA 12FT 24PT
Classics... MA 12FT 24PT
Greece. Rome and the Near East .... MA 12FT 24PT

University of Edinburgh
Ancient Philosophy.................................MSc 12FT 24PT
Classics..MSc 12FT 24PT
Hellenistic World ....MSc 12FT 24PT

University of Exeter
Classics and Ancient History .... MA 12FT 24PT

National University of Ireland Galway
Classical Civilisation ....MA 12FT

University of Glasgow
Classics..MLitt 12FT 24PT

King's College London
Classical Studies ....GradDip 12FT 24PT
Classics .... MA 12FT 24PT

Leeds Metropolitan University
Social History... MA 12FT 24PT

University of Leeds
Classical Studies .... MA 12FT 24PT

University of Liverpool
Classics .... MA 12FT 24PT

University of Manchester
Classics and Ancient History .... MA 12FT 24PT

Newcastle University
Art Museum and Gallery Studies (with specialist pathways in:
Curatorship, and Education).........MA 12FT 24PT/PGDip 9FT 18PT
Classics and Ancient History .... MA 12FT 24PT
Greek and Byzantine Archaeology.......................... MA 12FT 24PT
Greek and Roman Archaeology .... MA 12FT 24PT
Heritage Practice ....MHPrac 24FT 48PT
Roman Frontier Studies .... MA 12FT 24PT

University of Nottingham
Classical Literature .... MA 12FT 24PT
The Visual Culture of Classical Antiquity .... MA 12FT 24PT

The Open University
Classical Studies ....MA variableDL

Humanities .... MA variableDL/PGDip variableDL/
PGCert variableDL

University of Oxford
Classical Archaeology... MPhil 21FT/MSt 9FT
Greek and/or Latin Languages and Literature ..... MPhil 21FT/MSt
9FT
Greek and/or Roman History.......................... MSt 9FT/MPhil 24FT
Islamic Studies and History .... MPhil 21FT

University of Reading
Classics .... MA (Res) 12FT 24PT 60BM
Medieval Studies .... MA (Res) 12FT 24-60PT
The City of Rome .... MA(Res) 12FT 24PT 60BM
The Classical Tradition .... MA(Res) 12FT 24PT 60BM

University of Roehampton
Classical Research.. MRes 12FT 24-36PT
Contemporary Catholicism.. MA 12FT 24PT

Royal Holloway, University of London
Ancient History .... MA 12FT 24PT
Classical Art and Archaeology.............................. MA 12FT 24PT
Classics.. MA 12FT 24PT
History: Hellenic Studies .... MA 12FT 24PT

University of Sheffield
Classical and Ancient World ....MA 12FT 24PT/PGDip 9FT 18PT/
PGCert 6FT 12PT

University of St Andrews
Art History .... MLitt 12FT 24PT/PGDip 9FT 18PT
Classical Studies ....PGDip 9FT/MLitt 12FT 24PT

Swansea University
Ancient History and Classical Culture...................... MA 12FT 36PT
Ancient Narrative Literature................................. MA 12FT 36PT
Classics.. MA 12FT 24PT

Trinity College Dublin - the University of Dublin
Classics .... MPhil 12FT

University of Wales Trinity Saint David
Classical Studies ....MA 12FT 24PT 12-24DL
Classics ....MA 12FT 24PT 12-60DL

UCL - University College London
Ancient History .... MA 12FT 24PT
Classics... MA 12FT 24PT
Reception of the Classical World............................. MA 12FT 24PT

Classics

University of Warwick
Ancient Visual and Material Culture ....MA 12FT 24PT/ Diploma 9FT 21PT/PGCert 9FT 21PT

Classics
Research Courses

Anglia Ruskin University
Philosophy..MPhil 24FT/PhD 36FT

University of Birmingham
Classics .... MRes 12-36FT 24PT
Classics and Ancient History ....PhD 36FT 72PT/MA by research 12FT 24PT

University of Bristol
Classics and Ancient History ....PhD 36FT 72PT/MPhil 12FT 24PT/ MLitt by research 24FT 48PT

University of Cambridge
Classics... PhD 36FT 60PT

Durham University
Classics and Ancient History ....PhD 36FT 72PT/MLitt by research 24FT 48PT/MA by research 12FT 24PT

University of Edinburgh
Classical Art & Archaeology .... MSc 12FT 24PT
Classics.. PhD 36FT 72PT/MPhil 24FT 48PT/MSc by research 12FT 24PT

University of Exeter
Classics and Ancient History ..... PhD 36FT 72PT/MPhil 24FT 48PT

University of Glasgow
Classics..PhD 36FT 60PT/MPhil 12FT 24PT/ MLitt by research 24FT 36PT

University of Kent
Classical and Archaeological Studies ....PhD 36FT 60PT/ MPhil 24FT 36PT/MA by research 12FT 24PT

King's College London
Classics Research .... PhD 36FT 48-72PT/MPhil 24FT 36PT

University of Leeds
Classics........................... PhD 36FT 60PT/MA by research 12FT 24PT

University of Liverpool
Classics and Ancient History .... MPhil 12FT 24-48PT/PhD 36FT 36-72PT

University of Manchester
Classics and Ancient History .... PhD 36FT 72PT

Newcastle University
Classics... PhD 36FT 72PT/MPhil 12FT 24PT MLitt by research 12FT 24PT

University of Nottingham
Classics Research Areas....PhD 36FT 72PT/MPhil 24FT 48PT/MRes 12FT 24PT

The Open University
Ancient and Modern Reception of Antiquity .... PhD 36FT 72PT variableDL/MPhil 15FT 24PT variableDL
Classical Studies ...... PhD 36FT 72PT variableDL/MPhil 15FT 24PT variableDL
Digital classics .... PhD 36FT 72PT variableDL/MPhil 15FT 24PT variableDL
Greek and Latin texts .... PhD 36FT 72PT variableDL/MPhil 15FT 24PT variableDL
Greek and Roman Material Culture... PhD 36FT 72PT variableDL/ MPhil 15FT 24PT variableDL

University of Oxford
Ancient History .... DPhil 48FT
Classical Languages and Literature.................................. DPhil 48FT

Queen's University Belfast
Ancient History .... PhD 36FT 72PT/MPhil 24FT 48PT

University of Roehampton
Classics.................. PhD 24-48FT 36-60PT/MPhil 21-36FT 33-48PT

Royal Holloway, University of London
Classics.................. PhD 36-48FT 72-96PT/MPhil 36-48FT 72-96PT

School of Oriental and African Studies - SOAS
Art and Archaeology... PhD 36FT/MPhil 24FT

University of St Andrews
Classics...PhD 36FT 72PT/MPhil 24FT

Swansea University
Classics....MA by research 12FT 24PT/MPhil 24FT 48PT/PhD 36FT 72PT
Classics, Ancient History and Egyptology ...PhD 36FT 60PT/MPhil 12FT 24PT

University of Wales Trinity Saint David
Ancient History .... PhD 36FT 36-72PT/MPhil 12-36FT
Classics .... PhD 36-60FT/MPhil 12-36FT

UCL - University College London
Greek, Latin and the Classical World .... PhD 36FT 60PT

University of Warwick
Classics and Ancient History ....PhD 36FT 60PT/MPhil 24FT 48PT/ MA by research 12FT 24PT

Latin
Taught Courses

University of Exeter
Classics and Ancient History .... MA 12FT 24PT

National University of Ireland, Maynooth
Greek & Roman Civilization.. MA 12FT 24PT

University of Oxford
Greek and/or Latin Languages and Literature ..... MPhil 21FT/MSt 9FT

University of Reading
Early Modern History ....MA (Res) 12FT 24PT
Medieval Archaeology ....MA 12FT
Research in Archaeology... MA 12FT 24PT
The City of Rome .... MA(Res) 12FT 24PT 60BM
The Classical Tradition .... MA(Res) 12FT 24PT 60BM

University of St Andrews
Book History .... MLitt 12FT 24PT/MPhil 24FT/PGDip 9FT
Classical Studies ....PGDip 9FT/MLitt 12FT 24PT
Greek and Latin......................................PGDip 9FT/MLitt 12FT 24PT
Latin ....PGDip 12-24FT 24PT/MLitt 12FT 24PT

Swansea University
Ancient Narrative Literature...................................... MA 12FT 36PT

University of Wales Trinity Saint David
Ancient History ....MA 12FT 24PT 12-24DL
Latin ....PGCert 12PT 12-36DL/PGDip 24PT 12-36DL

Latin
Research Courses

The Open University
Greek and Latin texts .... PhD 36FT 72PT variableDL/MPhil 15FT 24PT variableDL

University of St Andrews
Classics...PhD 36FT 72PT/MPhil 24FT

UCL - University College London
Greek, Latin and the Classical World .... PhD 36FT 60PT

History

American history
Taught Courses

University of Aberdeen
Cultural History........ MLitt 12FT 24PT/PGDip 9FT 18PT

University of East Anglia
American History........ MA 12FT 24PT
American Studies........ MA 12FT 24PT
American Studies and Film Studies........ MA 12FT 24PT
Modern History........ MA 12FT 24PT

University of Edinburgh
American History........ MSc 12FT 24PT

University of Glasgow
American Studies........ MLitt 12FT 24PT

University of Kent
American Studies........ MA 12FT 24PT

Northumbria University
History........ MRes 12FT 24PT/MA 12FT 24PT

University of Nottingham
American Studies (History)........ MA 12FT 24-36PT

University of Oxford
US History........ MSt 9FT

Plymouth University
History........ MA 12FT 24PT

Queen Mary, University of London
History of Political Thought and Intellectual History....... MA 12FT 24PT

University of Reading
History........ MA(Res) 12FT 24PT 36-60BM

University of Sheffield
American History........ MA 12FT 24PT
Eighteenth-Century Studies (History)........ MA 12FT 24PT

University of Stirling
Historical Research........ MRes 12FT 24PT

University of Warwick
History of Race in the Americas........ MA 12FT 24PT/PGDip 12FT 24PT

American history
Research Courses

University of Aberdeen
Cultural History...... MLitt by research 12FT/MPhil 24FT/PhD 36FT

Canterbury Christ Church University
History........ PhD 48FT 60PT/MPhil 24FT 48PT

University of Chichester
History........ PhD 36FT 84PT

University of East Anglia
American Studies........ PhD 36FT 72PT/MPhil 24FT 48PT/MA by research 12FT

Institute for the Study of the Americas, School of Advanced Study, University of London
US Presidency........ PhD 36FT/MPhil 12FT

University of Kent
American Studies........ PhD 36FT 60PT/MPhil 24FT 36PT/MA by research 12FT 24PT

Swansea University
American Studies ...MA by research 12FT 24PT/MPhil 24FT 48PT/PhD 36FT 72PT

Ancient history
Taught Courses

University of Aberdeen
Materialising the Past........ MSc 12FT 24PT

Birkbeck, University of London
History........ GradCert 12PT

University of Birmingham
Ancient History and Classics....... MRes 12FT 24PT/PhD by taught 36FT 72PT
Antiquity........ MA 12FT 24PT

University of Bristol
Classical Reception........ MA 12FT 24PT
Classics and Ancient History........ MA 12FT 24PT

Cardiff University
Ancient History........ MA 12FT 24PT
Ancient and Medieval Warfare........ MA 12FT 24PT
Early Medieval Society and Culture........ MA 12FT 24PT
History and Archaeology of the Greek & Roman World.. MA 12FT 24PT

University of Chester
Archaeology and Heritage Practice..... MSc 12FT 24 - 36PT/PGDip 12FT 24 - 36PT/PGCert 12FT 12 - 24PT
Archaeology of Death and Memory..... MA 12FT 24 - 36PT/PGDip 12FT 24 - 36PT/PGCert 12FT 12 - 24PT

University College Cork
Arts (Greek & Roman Civilisation)........ HDip 9FT 18PT
Greek & Roman Civilisation........ MA 12FT 24PT

Durham University
Ancient Philosophy........ MA 12FT
Classics........ MA 12FT 24PT

University of East Anglia
History........ GradDip 12FT 24PT

University of Edinburgh
Classics........ MSc 12FT 24PT

University of Exeter
Archaeology........ MA 12FT 24PT 36DL
Bioarchaeology........ MSc 12FT 24PT
Classics and Ancient History........ MA 12FT 24PT
Experimental Archaeology........ MA 12FT 24PT

University of Kent
Ancient History........ MA 12FT
Ancient History with a term in Rome........ MA 12FT 24PT

King's College London
Ancient History........ MA 12FT 24PT
Classical Studies........ GradDip 12FT 24PT
Classics........ MA 12FT 24PT

University of Leeds
Classical Studies........ MA 12FT 24PT

University of Leicester
Archaeology of the Roman World........ MA 12FT 24PT/PGDip 9FT 18PT
Archaeology: Historical Archaeology........ MA 12FT 24PT 24DL/PGDip 9FT 18PT 18DL
Archaeology: The Classical Mediterranean........ MA 12FT 24PT 24DL/PGDip 9FT 18PT

University of Liverpool
Ancient History........ MA 12FT 24PT/PGDip 12FT/PGCert 12FT

Manchester Metropolitan University
English Studies: The Gothic........ PGDip 12FT 24PT/MA 15FT 30PT

University of Manchester
Classics and Ancient History........ MA 12FT 24PT

Newcastle University
Archaeology........ MA 12FT 24PT
Classics and Ancient History........ MA 12FT 24PT
Greek and Byzantine Archaeology........ MA 12FT 24PT
Greek and Roman Archaeology........ MA 12FT 24PT
History........ MA 12FT 24PT
Roman Frontier Studies........ MA 12FT 24PT

Newman University
History........ MPhil 24FT 48PT

Nottingham Trent University
History........ MA 12FT 24PT/PGDip 12FT 24PT/PGCert 9FT

University of Nottingham
Ancient History........ MA 12FT 24PT

The Open University
Classical Studies........ MA variableDL

Oxford Brookes University
History........ MA 12FT 24PT/PGDip 9FT 20PT/PGCert 4FT 8PT

University of Oxford
Classical Archaeology........ MPhil 21FT/MSt 9FT
Eastern Christian Studies........ MPhil 21FT
Islamic Studies and History........ MPhil 21FT

Queen's University Belfast
Archaeology and EnvironmentMSc 12FT 24PT/PGDip 12FT 24PT/PGCert 12FT 24PT

University of Reading
Classics........ MA (Res) 12FT 24PT 60BM
Research in Archaeology........ MA 12FT 24PT
The City of Rome........ MA(Res) 12FT 24PT 60BM

Royal Holloway, University of London
Ancient History........ MA 12FT 24PT
Classics........ MA 12FT 24PT

School of Oriental and African Studies - SOAS
History........ MA 12FT 24PT

Sheffield Hallam University
History........ MPhil 36FT 84PT

University of Sheffield
Classical and Ancient World........ MA 12FT 24PT/PGDip 9FT 18PT/PGCert 6FT 12PT
Experimental Archaeology........ MSc 12FT 24PT

University of St Andrews
Ancient History........ PGDip 9FT/MLitt 12FT 24PT
Classical Studies........ PGDip 9FT/MLitt 12FT 24PT

Swansea University
Ancient History and Classical Culture........ MA 12FT 36PT
Classics........ MA 12FT 24PT

Trinity College Dublin - the University of Dublin
Classics........ MPhil 12FT

University of Wales Trinity Saint David
Ancient History........ MA 12FT 24PT 12-24DL
Classical Studies........ MA 12FT 24PT 12-24DL
Classics........ MA 12FT 24PT 12-60DL

UCL - University College London
Ancient History........ MA 12FT 24PT
Archaeology........ MA 12FT 24PT
Archaeology and Heritage of Asia........ MA 12FT 24PT
Archaeology of the Arab and Islamic World........ MA 24FT
Archaeology of the Middle East........ MA 12FT 24PT
Artefact Studies........ MA 12FT 24PT
Classics........ MA 12FT 24PT
History........ MA 12FT 24PT
History (Central and East European)........ MA 12FT 24PT
Late Antique and Byzantine Studies........ MA 12FT 24PT

University of Warwick
Ancient Visual and Material Culture........ MA 12FT 24PT/Diploma 9FT 21PT/PGCert 9FT 21PT

Ancient history
Research Courses

Birkbeck, University of London
Archaeology........ MPhil 24FT 36PT/PhD 36FT 48PT
Classical Archaeology and Ancient History........ MPhil 24FT 36PT/PhD 24FT 36PT
History........ PhD 24FT 36PT/MPhil 24FT 36PT

University of Birmingham
Classics........ MRes 12-36FT 24PT

University of Bristol
Classics and Ancient History.... PhD 36FT 72PT/MPhil 12FT 24PT/MLitt by research 24FT 48PT

Cardiff University
Ancient History........ MPhil 12FT/PhD 36FT

University of Chichester
History........ PhD 36FT 84PT

Durham University
Classics and Ancient History.... PhD 36FT 72PT/MLitt by research 24FT 48PT/MA by research 12FT 24PT

University of East Anglia
School of History........ PhD 36FT 72PT/MPhil 24FT 48PT

University of Edinburgh
Classical Art & Archaeology........ MSc 12FT 24PT
Classics.. PhD 36FT 72PT/MPhil 24FT 48PT/MSc by research 12FT 24PT

University of Exeter
Archaeology..... PhD 36FT 72PT/MPhil 24FT 48PT/MA by research 12FT 24PT
Classics and Ancient History..... PhD 36FT 72PT/MPhil 24FT 48PT

University of Liverpool
Classics and Ancient History........ MPhil 12FT 24-48PT/PhD 36FT 36-72PT

University of Manchester
Classics and Ancient History........ PhD 36FT 72PT

Newcastle University
Archaeology........ MPhil 12FT 24PT/PhD 36FT 72PT
Classics........ MLitt by research 12FT 24PT
History........ MLitt by research 12FT 24PT

Newman University
History........ MPhil 24FT 48PT

The Open University
Ancient and Modern Reception of Antiquity........ PhD 36FT 72PT variableDL/MPhil 15FT 24PT variableDL
Classical Studies...... PhD 36FT 72PT variableDL/MPhil 15FT 24PT variableDL
Greek and Roman Material Culture... PhD 36FT 72PT variableDL/MPhil 15FT 24PT variableDL

Oxford Brookes University
History........ PhD 24-60FT 36-72PT/MPhil 24-36FT 36-48PT

University of Oxford
Ancient History........ DPhil 48FT

Queen's University Belfast
Ancient History........ PhD 36FT 72PT/MPhil 24FT 48PT

University of St Andrews
Ancient History........ MPhil 24FT/PhD 36FT 72PT
Classics........ PhD 36FT 72PT/MPhil 24FT

Swansea University
Ancient History........ MA by research 12FT 24PT
Classics, Ancient History and Egyptology... PhD 36FT 60PT/MPhil 12FT 24PT
Greek........ MPhil 24FT 48PT/PhD 36FT 72PT

University of Wales Trinity Saint David
Ancient History........ PhD 36FT 36-72PT/MPhil 12-36FT

University of Warwick
Classics and Ancient History.... PhD 36FT 60PT/MPhil 24FT 48PT/MA by research 12FT 24PT

History

Atlantic history
Taught Courses

University of East Anglia
American History... MA 12FT 24PT

University of Liverpool
International Slavery Studies .... MA 12FT 24PT

University of Oxford
Global and Imperial History ....MSt 9FT

University of Sheffield
Eighteenth-Century Studies (History)...................... MA 12FT 24PT

University of Strathclyde
North Atlantic World, c900-c1800 .... MSc 12FT 24PT/PGDip 9FT 18PT

Atlantic history
Research Courses

University of Chichester
History... PhD 36FT 84PT

University of East Anglia
American Studies .... PhD 36FT 72PT/MPhil 24FT 48PT/MA by research 12FT

British history
Taught Courses

Aberystwyth University
Eighteenth Century Britain .... MA 12FT 24PT/PGDip 9FT 18PT
Modern British History (Political Culture)... MA 12FT 24PT/PGDip 9FT 18PT

Bangor University
Medieval Studies .... MA 12FT 24-36PT
Medieval and Early Modern Literature .... MA 12FT 24-36PT/PGDip 9FT

Birkbeck, University of London
History of the British Isles .... MA 12FT 24PT

University of Birmingham
British Second World War Studies.........................MA 24PT
Cultural Heritage of Shakespeare's England........... MA 12FT 24PT
Twentieth-Century British History.........................MRes 12FT 24PT
West Midlands History ....MA 24PT

University of Cambridge
Early Modern History.......................................MPhil 9FT

University of Central Lancashire
Public History.........MA 12FT 36PT/PGDip 12FT 24PT/PGCert 12FT 24PT

University of Dundee
Greater Britain in the Twentieth Century .... MLitt 12FT

University of East Anglia
History .... GradDip 12FT 24PT
Modern British History.............................. MA 12FT 24PT
Modern History .... MA 12FT 24PT

University of Edinburgh
Modern British and Irish History ....MSc 12FT 24PT
The Second World War in Europe ....MSc 12FT 24PT

University of Essex
Cultural and Social History ....MA 12FT 24PT/PGCert 9FT 21PT
Local, Community and Family History MA 12FT 24PT/PGCert 9FT 21PT

University of Glasgow
Medieval History...MLitt 12FT 24PT

University of Hull
Imperial History .... MA 12FT 24PT

King's College London
Contemporary British History .... MA 12FT 24PT

Leeds Metropolitan University
English: Contemporary Literatures........................ MA 12FT 24PT

University of Leeds
Eighteenth Century Studies...............................MA 12FT
Romantic Formations .... MA 12FT 24PT

Manchester Metropolitan University
Local and Regional History.......................... MA 12FT 24PT

Newcastle University
British History .... MA 12FT 24PT

Northumbria University
History............................. MRes 12FT 24PT/MA 12FT 24PT

University of Oxford
Modern British and European History .... MPhil 21FT/MSt 9FT

Plymouth University
History... MA 12FT 24PT

Queen Mary, University of London
Modern and Contemporary British History............. MA 12FT 24PT

Queen's University Belfast
Modern History................................... MA 12FT max 31PT

University of Reading
Early Modern History ....MA (Res) 12FT 24PT
Franco-British History .... MA (Res) 12FT 24-60PT
History ....MA(Res) 12FT 24PT 36-60BM
Medieval Archaeology ....MA 12FT
Nineteenth-Century Literature and Culture .... MA 12FT 24PT

University of Sheffield
Cultures of the British Isles............................. MA 12FT 24PT
Early Modern History....................................... MA 12FT 24PT
Eighteenth-Century Studies (English Literature) ... MA 12FT 24PT
Eighteenth-Century Studies (History)..................... MA 12FT 24PT
Nineteenth-Century Studies (English Literature)... MA 12FT 24PT

University of Sussex
Contemporary History.................................... MA 12FT 24PT

Swansea University
Early Modern History .... MA 12FT 24PT
Gender and Culture .... MA 12FT 24-36PT
History .... MA 12FT 24-36PT
Modern History .... MA 12FT 24PT

Teesside University
Local and Regional History.................................. MA 12FT 24-36PT

University of Warwick
Modern History........................MA 12FT 24PT/PGDip 12FT 24PT

University of Winchester
Regional and Local History...........MA 12FT 24PT/PGDip 9FT 18PT/PGCert 9FT 18PT

British history
Research Courses

University of Aberdeen
Cultural History......MLitt by research 12FT/MPhil 24FT/PhD 36FT

Bangor University
Heritage ....MPhil 12-24FT 24-48PT/PhD 36FT 48-72PT

Birkbeck, University of London
History... PhD 24FT 36PT/MPhil 24FT 36PT

University of Birmingham
Twentieth Century British History ....MPhil(B) 12FT 24PT

University of Cambridge
British Literature Post-1830...................................PhD 36FT

University of Chichester
History.. PhD 36FT 84PT

University of East Anglia
School of History .... PhD 36FT 72PT/MPhil 24FT 48PT

University of Edinburgh
Second World War Studies.. PhD 36FT 72PT
Study of the Two World Wars ....

University of Exeter
Medical History........PhD 48FT 84PT 84DL/MPhil 36FT 60PT 60DL

King's College London
Contemporary History........... MPhil 24FT 36PT/PhD 36FT 48-72PT

University of Leicester
English Local History........................MPhil 24FT/PhD 36FT

The Open University
Early modern Britain and Europe .... PhD 36FT 72PT variableDL/MPhil 15FT 24PT variableDL
Social and economic history of Britain and Ireland 18th-20th centuries .... PhD 36FT 72PT variableDL/MPhil 15FT 24PT variableDL

Queen's University Belfast
Modern History........................... PhD 36FT 72PT/MPhil 24FT 48PT

Swansea University
History.....PhD 36FT 72PT/MPhil 24FT 48PT/MA by research 12FT 24PT

Teesside University
Cultural Studies .... PhD 24-60FT 36PT/MPhil 18FT 30PT

Economic history
Taught Courses

University of Aberdeen
Economics... MSc 12FT

University of Birmingham
Social Research (Economic and Social History)....... MA 12FT 24PT

University of Cambridge
Economic and Social History .... MPhil 11FT

City University London
Social Research Methods................................MSc 12FT 24PT

University of Dundee
Global Empires ....MLitt 12FT

Durham University
Social and Economic History (Research Methods)............MA 12FT

University of East Anglia
Economics.............................. MSc 12FT PGDip 10FT
Modern History..................................... MA 12FT 24PT
Social Science Research Methods: Business........MRes 12FT 24PT
Social Science Research Methods: Education.......MRes 12FT 24PT
Social Science Research Methods: Law.................MRes 12FT 24PT
Social Science Research Methods: Psychology ....MRes 12FT 24PT
Social Science Research Methods: Social Work ...MRes 12FT 24PT

University of Edinburgh
Economic and Social History ....MSc by research 12FT 24PT

University of Exeter
Economic and Social History ....MRes 12FT 24PT

Glasgow Caledonian University
Social Research..MSc 12FT 24PT
Social Research (Policy Analysis)..............................MSc 12FT 24PT

University of Liverpool
Research Methodology (Economic and Social History) ...MA 12FT 24PT

London Metropolitan University
Economics..MSc 12FT 24 - 48PT

London School of Economics and Political Science (LSE)
Economic History.................................MSc 12FT 24PT

Manchester Metropolitan University
History... MA 12FT 24PT

University of Oxford
Economic and Social History ....MPhil 21FT/MSc 12FT

University of Reading
Economic Development in Emerging Markets .....MSc 12FT 24PT

University of Sheffield
Early Modern History..................................... MA 12FT 24PT

University of Southampton
Economics..................................MSc 12FT 24PT/PGDip 9FT 21PT

University of Surrey
Economics.. MA 12FT 24PT

Economic history
Research Courses

University of Dundee
Economics ....MPhil 24FT MSc by research 12FT

University of Edinburgh
Economic and Social History ....PhD 36FT 72PT/MPhil 24FT 48PT/MSc by research 12FT 24PT

University of Glasgow
Economic and Social History ...... PhD 36FT 48PT/MSc by research 24FT 36PT

London School of Economics and Political Science (LSE)
Economic History................................. PhD 36-48FT/MPhil 36-48FT

University of Manchester
Economic and Social History ....PhD 36FT

The Open University
Social and economic history of Britain and Ireland 18th-20th centuries .... PhD 36FT 72PT variableDL/MPhil 15FT 24PT variableDL

University of Oxford
History (for Economic & Social History, and History of Science)...DPhil 48FT

University of York
Economic and Social History ....MSc by research 12FT 24PT

Egyptology
Taught Courses

University of Aberdeen
Archaeology of the North............MSc 12FT 24PT/PGDip 9FT 18PT

University of Birmingham
Antiquity.. MA 12FT 24PT
Egyptology ....MRes 12FT 24PT

University of Central Lancashire
Archaeology of Death...MA 12FT

University of Exeter
Archaeology...............................MA 12FT 24PT 36DL
Experimental Archaeology................................. MA 12FT 24PT

University of Liverpool
Egyptology .... MA 12FT 24PT

University of Manchester
Biomedical and Forensic Studies in Egyptology ....MSc 12FT 24PT

University of Oxford
Egyptology .... MPhil 21FT

University of Sheffield
Experimental Archaeology....................................MSc 12FT 24PT

Swansea University
Ancient Egyptian Culture .... MA 12FT 24-36PT

UCL - University College London
Archaeology...GradDip 9FT 18PT
Egyptian Archaeology .... MA 12FT 24PT

History

Egyptology
Research Courses

University of Aberdeen
Archaeology.............MSc by research 12FT/MPhil 24FT/PhD 36FT

University of Birmingham
Egyptology ....MSc by research 12FT 24PT

University of Exeter
Archaeology.....PhD 36FT 72PT/MPhil 24FT 48PT/MA by research 12FT 24PT

University of Liverpool
Egyptology ....MPhil 12FT/PhD 36FT

University of Manchester
Egyptology ....PhD 36-48FT 72-96PT/MPhil 12FT 24PT

Swansea University
Ancient History..MA by research 12FT 24PT
Egyptology ....MPhil 12FT 24PT/PhD 36FT 60PT/MA by research 12FT 24PT

European history
Taught Courses

Bangor University
Celtic Archaeology .... MA 12FT 24PT/PGDip 8FT
Welsh History ....PhD by taught 24-36FT 48-72PT/MPhil 12FT 24PT

University of Birmingham
Modern East Mediterranean History ....MRes 12FT 24PT

University of Cambridge
Modern European History...MPhil 10FT

University of Dundee
Global Empires ....MLitt 12FT

University of East Anglia
History.. GradDip 12FT 24PT
Medieval History.. MA 12FT 24PT
Modern British History.. MA 12FT 24PT
Modern European History.................................... MA 12FT 24PT
Modern History... MA 12FT 24PT

University of Edinburgh
The Second World War in Europe ....MSc 12FT 24PT

University of Glasgow
European Studies: Cultures, Societies & Languages.... MLitt 12FT 24PT
Medieval History...MLitt 12FT 24PT

King's College London
Middle East & Mediterranean Studies...................... MA 12FT 24PT
Non-Proliferation & International Security .... MA 12FT 24PT

University of Leeds
Eighteenth Century Studies..MA 12FT

Newcastle University
European History.. MA 12FT 24PT
Later European Prehistory................................... MA 12FT 24PT

Northumbria University
History............................... MRes 12FT 24PT/MA 12FT 24PT

University of Oxford
Global and Imperial History ....MSt 9FT
Modern British and European History .... MPhil 21FT/MSt 9FT
Russian and East European Studies.............MPhil 21FT/MSc 12FT

Plymouth University
History.. MA 12FT 24PT

Queen Mary, University of London
Leo Baeck MA in European Jewish History.............. MA 12FT 24PT

University of Reading
Archaeology .... MA 12FT 24PT
Early Modern History ....MA (Res) 12FT 24PT
Franco-British History .... MA (Res) 12FT 24-60PT
History ....MA(Res) 12FT 24PT 36-60BM
Medieval Archaeology ....MA 12FT
Military History and Strategic Studies...................MA 12FT 72PT/PGDip 9FT/PGCert 6FT
Research in Archaeology... MA 12FT 24PT

Royal Holloway, University of London
Holocaust Studies .... MA 12FT 24PT

University of Sheffield
American History.. MA 12FT 24PT
Nineteenth-Century Studies (English Literature)... MA 12FT 24PT

University of St Andrews
Early Modern History................PGDip 9FT/MLitt 12FT/MPhil 24FT

University of Stirling
Renaissance Studies .....MRes 12FT 27PT/PGDip 8FT 21PT/PGCert 4FT 9PT

University of Strathclyde
Renaissance Studies .....MLitt 12FT 24PT/PGDip 9FT 21PT/PGCert 4FT 9PT

University of Sussex
Contemporary European Studies .... MA 12FT 24PT

Modern European History.. MA 12FT 24PT

Swansea University
Early Modern History .... MA 12FT 24PT
Gender and Culture .... MA 12FT 24-36PT
History.. MA 12FT 24-36PT
Modern History.. MA 12FT 24PT

Teesside University
European History .... MA 12FT 24-36PT

UCL - University College London
East European Studies...MRes 24FT
European History .... MA 12FT 24PT
History (Central and East European) .... MA 12FT 24PT
Holocaust Studies .... MA 12FT 24PT

European history
Research Courses

Aberystwyth University
French ....MPhil 12FT 24PT

Bangor University
Heritage.......................MPhil 12-24FT 24-48PT/PhD 36FT 48-72PT

University of Birmingham
Modern European History..................................MPhil(B) 12FT 24PT

University of Chichester
History... PhD 36FT 84PT

University of East Anglia
School of History .... PhD 36FT 72PT/MPhil 24FT 48PT

University of Edinburgh
Second World War Studies .... PhD 36FT 72PT
Study of the Two World Wars ....

The Open University
Early modern Britain and Europe .... PhD 36FT 72PT variableDL/MPhil 15FT 24PT variableDL
Empire and Postcolonial studies .... PhD 36FT 72PT variableDL/MPhil 15FT 24PT variableDL
History... PhD 36FT 72PT variableDL/MPhil 15FT 24PT variableDL
Policing and Criminal Justice.....PhD 36FT 72PT variableDL/MPhil 15FT 24PT variableDL
War, conflict and politics in Europe ... PhD 36FT 72PT variableDL/MPhil 15FT 24PT variableDL

University of Salford
Centre for Contemporary History & Politics...................PhD/MPhil

Swansea University
European Cultures...................................MA by research 12FT 24PT
History.....PhD 36FT 72PT/MPhil 24FT 48PT/MA by research 12FT 24PT

UCL - University College London
East European History.. PhD 36FT 60PT
East European Society and National Identity........ PhD 36FT 60PT

History
Taught Courses

Aberystwyth University
History and Heritage ....MA 12FT 24PT/PGDip 9FT 18PT
International History (Specialist) ....MA 12FT
Media History..................................MA 12FT 24PT/PGDip 9FT 18PT

School of Advanced Study, University of London
Historical Research .... MA 12FT 24PT
History of the Book .... MA 12FT 24PT

Bangor University
Archaeology.............PhD by taught 36FT 48-72PT/MPhil 12-24FT 24-48PT
Celtic Archaeology .... MA 12FT 24PT/PGDip 8FT
Heritage.... PhD by taught 36FT 48-72PT/MPhil 12-24FT 24-48PT
History.............................. MA 12FT 24PT/PGDip 8FT
PhD by taught 24-36FT 48-72PT/MPhil 12FT 24PT
Medieval Studies .... MA 12FT 24-36PT
Medieval and Early Modern Literature ..MA 12FT 24-36PT/PGDip 9FT
Welsh History ....PhD by taught 24-36FT 48-72PT/MPhil 12FT 24PT
Women's Studies.....................MA 24PT/PGDip 24PT/PGCert 12PT

Birkbeck, University of London
Contemporary History and Politics........................... MA 12FT 24PT
Early Modern History... MA 12FT 24PT
European History .... MA 12FT 24PT
Film, Television and Screen Media .... MA 12FT 24PT
Historical Research... MA 12FT 24PT
History..GradCert 12PT
History of Ideas .... MA 12FT 24PT
Medieval History.. MA 12FT 24PT
Psychoanalysis, History and Culture....................... MA 12FT 24PT
Renaissance Studies .... MA 12FT 24PT
World History .... MA 12FT 24PT

University of Birmingham
Film and Television: Research and Production........ MA 12FT 24PT
West Midlands History ....MA 24PT

University of Bristol
History.. MA 12FT 24PT
Russian History .... MA 12FT 24PT

University of Buckingham
Biography .... MA 12FT 24PT
Decorative Arts and Historic Interiors...............................MA 12FT

University of Cambridge
Archaeology ....MPhil 11-15FT
Early Modern History ....MPhil 9FT
Historical Studies ....MPhil 9FT
Modern European History...................................MPhil 10FT
Modern South Asian Studies .... MPhil(A) 9FT

Cardiff University
History.. MA 12FT 24PT

University of Central Lancashire
Archaeology of Death...MA 12FT
Public History........MA 12FT 36PT/PGDip 12FT 24PT/PGCert 12FT 24PT
Rhetoric .... MA 12FT 24PT

University of Chester
Archaeology of Death and Memory .....MA 12FT 24 - 36PT/PGDip 12FT 24 - 36PT/PGCert 12FT 12 - 24PT
Military History...........MA 12FT 24 - 36PT/PGDip 12FT 24 - 36PT/PGCert 12FT 12 - 24PT

University College Cork
Arts (History) ....HDip 9FT 18PT
History...MA 12FT

De Montfort University
History by Independent Study ....MA 12-24DL
Sport History and Culture ....MA 12-24DL

University of Dundee
Global Empires ....MLitt 12FT
History ....MLitt 12FT
Non-Graduating Taught Postgraduate in School of Humanities..
PG module variableFT
Scottish History (MLitt by distance learning)......... MLitt 24-60DL
Scottish History (MLitt)..MLitt 12FT
Twentieth Century Studies (MLitt)........................MLitt 12FT

Durham University
Medieval and Renaissance Studies.......................... MA 12FT 24PT
Modern History...MA 12FT

University of East Anglia
American History.. MA 12FT 24PT
Early Modern History... MA 12FT 24PT
History.. GradDip 12FT 24PT
History of Art .... MA 12FT 24PT
Landscape History .... MA 12FT 24PT
Medieval History.. MA 12FT 24PT
Modern British History.. MA 12FT 24PT
Modern European History.................................... MA 12FT 24PT
Modern History.. MA 12FT 24PT

University of East London
Heritage Studies..........................MA 12FT 24PT/PGCert 8FT 16PT/PGDip 4FT 8PT

Edge Hill University
History...MRes 12FT 24PT
History and Culture .... MA 12FT 24PT

University of Edinburgh
African Studies...MSc 12FT 24PT
American History...MSc 12FT 24PT
Art in the Global Middle Ages..............................MSc 12FT 24PT
Celtic and Scottish Studies..................................MSc 12FT 24PT
Chinese Studies...MA 24FT
Classics..MSc 12FT 24PT
Contemporary History...MSc 12FT 24PT
Diaspora and Migration History ....MSc 12FT 24PT
Economic and Social History ....MSc by research 12FT 24PT
Eighteenth-Century Cultures ....MSc 12FT 24PT
English Literature: Material Cultures and the History of the Book
MSc 12FT 24PT
Gender History..MSc 12FT 24PT
Hellenistic World ....MSc 12FT 24PT
History..................................MSc 12FT 24PT MSc(Res) 12FT 24PT
History (by online distance learning)....MSc 12FT 48PT 12/48DL/Diploma 12FT 36PT 12/36DL/Cert 12FT 24PT 12/24DL
History of Art, Theory and Display..........................MSc 12FT 24PT
Intellectual History ....MSc 12FT 24PT
Islamic and Middle Eastern Studies......................MSc 12FT 24PT
Late Antique, Islamic and Byzantine Studies ....MSc 12FT 24PT
Medieval History...MSc 12FT 24PT
Medieval Literatures and Cultures...........................MSc 12FT 24PT
Middle Eastern Diasporas ....MSc 12FT 24PT
Modern British and Irish History ....MSc 12FT 24PT
Modern and Contemporary Art: History, Curating, Criticism........
MSc 12FT 24PT
The Second World War in Europe ....MSc 12FT 24PT
Theology in History...............MTh 12FT 24PT/MSc 12FT 24PT

University of Essex
Cultural and Social History ....MA 12FT 24PT/PGCert 9FT 21PT
Digital History ....MA 12FT 24PT/PGCert 9FT

History

Historical Studies ....MA 36-60PT/PGCert 36-60PT
History......................MA 12FT 24PT/PGCert 9FT 21PT/PGDip 12FT
History with English for Academic Purposes..............Diploma 9FT
Local, Community and Family History ....MA 12FT 24PT/
PGCert 9FT 21PT

University of Exeter
Classics and Ancient History .... MA 12FT 24PT
Economic and Social History ....MRes 12FT 24PT
History.. MA 12FT 24PT
History of Political Thought .... MA 12FT 24PT

National University of Ireland Galway
History...MA 12FT

University of Glasgow
Art History: History of Collecting and Collections .... MLitt 12FT 24PT
History...............MLitt 12FT 24PT/PGDip 9FT 18PT/MSc 12FT 24PT
Social and Cultural History ....MSc 12FT 24PT/PGDip 9FT 21PT

Goldsmiths, University of London
History .... MA 12FT 24PT

University of Greenwich
Science (Open)..MSc 12FT 24-36PT

University of Hertfordshire
History: Communities and Cultures 1660-2000 ..MA 12FT 24PT/
PGDip 12FT 24PT/PGCert 12FT 24PT

University of Huddersfield
History.. MA 12FT 24-36PT

University of Hull
Historical Studies .... MA 12FT 24PT

Institute of Education
History of Education.. MA 12FT 24-48PT

University of Kent
Modern History .... MA 12FT 24PT
Modern History (Paris option).............................. MA 12FT 24PT
Roman History and Archaeology................................ MA 12FT 24PT
Roman History and Archaeology with a Term in Rome...MA 12FT 24PT
Science, Communication and Society ....MSc 12FT 24PT
War, Media and Society .... MA 12FT 24PT

King's College London
History ....MRes 12FT 24PT

Kingston University
History.. MA 12FT 24PT

Lancaster University
History .... MA 12FT 24PT

Leeds Metropolitan University
Social History .... MA 12FT 24PT

University of Leeds
Eighteenth Century Studies.......................................MA 12FT
History and Philosophy of Science........................... MA 12FT 24PT
Race and Resistance... MA 12FT 24PT
Social and Cultural History .... MA 12FT 24PT

University of Leicester
English Local History...MA 12FT 24PT/
MA by Individual Supervised Study 15FT 22PT
European Urbanisation...MA 12FT
History..MA 12FT 24PT/PGDip 9FT 21PT
Urban History .... MA 12FT 24PT

University of Limerick
History..MA 12FT
History of Art and Architecture ....MA 12FT
History of the Family .... MA 12FT 24PT 12/24DL

University of Lincoln
Historical Studies .... MA 12FT 24PT
Medieval Studies .... MA 12FT 24PT

Liverpool Hope University
History............MA 12FT 24PT/PGDip 12FT 24PT/PGCert 6FT 12PT
Museum & Heritage Studies.................................... MA 12FT 24PT
Music Since 1900.... MA 12FT 24PT/PGDip 12FT 24PT/PGCert 6FT
Peace Studies .... MA 12FT 24PT

University of Liverpool
Cultural History... MA 12FT 24PT
Eighteenth Century Worlds ....MA 12FT

London School of Economics and Political Science (LSE)
Global History .... MSc 12FT 24PT

University of Manchester
History.. MA 12FT 24PT

National University of Ireland, Maynooth
History... MA 12FT 24PT

Newcastle University
British History .... MA 12FT 24PT
History... MA 12FT 24PT
History of Medicine .... MA 12FT 24PT

Newman University
History...MPhil 24FT 48PT

University of Northampton
Social and Cultural History ....MA 12FT 24PT/PGDip 12PT

Northumbria University
History.. MRes 12FT 24PT/MA 12FT 24PT

Nottingham Trent University
History......................MA 12FT 24PT/PGDip 12FT 24PT/PGCert 9FT

University of Nottingham
Environmental History ....MSc 12FT 24PT
History .... MA 12FT 24PT
MATILDA Women's and Gender History (European Master)....MA 24FT
Politics and Contemporary History........................... MA 12FT 24PT

The Open University
History...MA variableDL
Humanities .... MA variableDL/PGDip variableDL/
PGCert variableDL

Oxford Brookes University
Book History and Publishing Culture ... MA 12FT 24PT/PGDip 9FT 18PT
History ....MA 12FT 24PT/PGDip 9FT 20PT/PGCert 4FT 8PT
History of Medicine ....MA 12FT 24PT/PGDip 9FT 20PT/
PGCert 4FT 8PT

University of Oxford
Architectural History ....PGCert 12PT
Classical Archaeology .... MPhil 21FT/MSt 9FT
Eastern Christian Studies .... MPhil 21FT
English Language ....MSt 9FT
Global and Imperial History ....MSt 9FT
Greek and/or Roman History.......................... MSt 9FT/MPhil 24FT
Historical Research..MSt 9-12FT
History of Art and Visual Culture ....MSt 9FT
History of Science, Medicine & Technology MPhil 24FT/MSc 12FT
History of Science: Instruments, Museums, Sci., Tech. ... MSc 12FT
Islamic Studies and History .... MPhil 21FT
Jewish Studies ....MSt 9FT
Medieval History...MSt 11FT

Plymouth University
History .... MA 12FT 24PT
History ....MRes 12FT

Queen Mary, University of London
History of Political Thought and Intellectual History.......MA 12FT 24PT
Islam and the West .... MA 12FT 24PT
Legal Theory and History.. LLM 12FT 24PT
Modern and Contemporary British History .... MA 12FT 24PT

Queen's University Belfast
Irish Local History (By Research)....................MRes 12FT up to 31PT

University of Reading
Early Modern Literature & Drama ....MA (Res) 12FT 24PT
Franco-British History .... MA (Res) 12FT 24-60PT
French Studies ....MA (Res) 12FT
German Studies ....MA (Res) 12FT 24PT
History ....MA(Res) 12FT 24PT 36-60BM
History (Secondary Teaching).................................... PGCE 10FT
Italian Studies ....MA (Res) 12FT 24PT
Legal History ....MA (Res) 12FT 24PT
Military History and Strategic Studies....................MA 12FT 72PT/
PGDip 9FT/PGCert 6FT
Philosophy .... MA 12FT 24PT

University of Roehampton
Classical Research .... MRes 12FT 24-36PT
Contemporary Catholicism...................................... MA 12FT 24PT
Historical Research................................. MA 12FT 24-48PT 24-48DL

Royal Holloway, University of London
History: Hellenic Studies .... MA 12FT 24PT
Holocaust Studies .... MA 12FT 24PT
History.. MA 12FT 24PT
Public History .... MA 12FT 24PT

Ruskin College
Public History .... MA 12FT 24PT

School of Oriental and African Studies - SOAS
History.. MA 12FT 24PT
History: Asia/Africa .... MA 12FT 24-36PT

Sheffield Hallam University
History...MPhil 36FT 84PT
History : Imperialism and Culture.MA 36DL/PGDip 36DL/PGCert 36DL
History: the Local and the Global.......................... MA 12FT 24PT

University of Sheffield
Early Modern History... MA 12FT 24PT
English Language Studies .... MA 12FT 24PT
Historical Research... MA 12FT 24PT
International History .... MA 12FT 24PT
Medieval History... MA 12FT 24PT
Nineteenth-Century Studies (English Literature)... MA 12FT 24PT
Nineteenth-Century Studies (History)..................... MA 12FT 24PT
Social Scientific Biblical Studies................................. MA 12FT 24PT

University of South Wales
History by Research .... MA 12FT 24-36PT

Regional History and Heritage................................... MA 12FT 36PT

University of Southampton
Eighteenth Century Studies..................................... MA 12FT 24PT
History .... MA 12FT 24PT/MRes 12FT 24PT
Jewish History and Culture.......... MA 12FT 24PT/MRes 12FT 24PT

University of St Andrews
Ancient History ....PGDip 9FT/MLitt 12FT 24PT
Art History..................................... MLitt 12FT 24PT/PGDip 9FT 18PT
Book History .... MLitt 12FT 24PT/MPhil 24FT/PGDip 9FT
Classical Studies ....PGDip 9FT/MLitt 12FT 24PT
Early Modern History...........PGDip 9FT/MLitt 12FT/MPhil 24FT
Environmental History ...MLitt 12FT 24PT/PGDip 9FT 24PT/MPhil 24FT
Middle Eastern History & Culture....PGDip 9FT/MLitt 12FT/MPhil 24FT
Reformation Studies....... MLitt 12FT 24PT/MPhil 24FT/PGDip 9FT 24PT

University of Stirling
English Language and Linguistics ......MLitt 12FT 27PT/PGDip 9FT 21PT/PGCert 3FT 9PT
Environment, Heritage and Policy...........................MSc 12FT 24PT
Historical Research...MRes 12FT 24PT
Renaissance Studies .....MRes 12FT 27PT/PGDip 8FT 21PT/PGCert 4FT 9PT

University of Strathclyde
Genealogical, Palaeographic and Heraldic Studies........MSc 12PT/
PGDip 10PT/PGCert 10PT
Historical Studies ....MSc 12FT 24PT/PGDip 9FT 18PT
North Atlantic World, c900-c1800.......MSc 12FT 24PT/PGDip 9FT 18PT

University of Sunderland
History...........MA 12FT 24PT/PGDip 12FT 24PT/PGCert 12FT 24PT

University of Sussex
Intellectual History .... MA 12FT 24PT

Swansea University
Ancient Egyptian Culture ....MA 12FT 24-36PT
Ancient History and Classical Culture...................... MA 12FT 36PT
Ancient Narrative Literature.................................... MA 12FT 36PT
Classics .... MA 12FT 24PT
Early Modern History... MA 12FT 24PT
Gender and Culture .... MA 12FT 24-36PT
History... MA 12FT 24-36PT
Modern History .... MA 12FT 24PT

Teesside University
European History...MA 12FT 24-36PT
HistoryMA 12FT 24-36PT/PGDip 8FT 12-24PT/PGCert 4FT 8-12PT

Trinity College Dublin - the University of Dublin
Early Modern History..MPhil 12FT
Medieval History.. MPhil 12FT
Public History and Cultural Heritage.................... MPhil 12FT 24PT
Texts, Contexts and Cultures (Doctorate) ...... PhD by taught 48FT

UCL - University College London
Early Modern Studies .... MA 12FT 24PT
History.. MA 12FT 24PT
History (Central and East European) .... MA 12FT 24PT
History of Art.. MA 12FT 24PT/PGDip 9FT
History of Medicine ....MSc 12FT 24PT
History of Political Thought and Intellectual History.......MA 12FT 24PT
History of Science, Medicine and Technology........MSc 12FT 24PT
Holocaust Studies .... MA 12FT 24PT
Jewish History .... MA 12FT 24PT
Language, Culture and History .... MA 12FT 24PT
Late Antique and Byzantine Studies......................... MA 12FT 24PT
Medieval and Renaissance Studies........................... MA 12FT 24PT

University of Warwick
Eighteenth-Century Studies ....MA 12FT 24PT/PGDip 12FT 24PT
Global History ....MA 12FT 24PT/PGDip 12FT 24PT
History..MA 12FT 24PT/PGDip 12FT 24PT
Religious, Social and Cultural History, 1500-1750 MA 12FT 24PT/
PGDip 12FT 24PT

University of Winchester
Historical Studies .... MA 12FT 24PT/PGDip 12FT 24PT/
PGCert 12FT 24PT
Regional and Local History and Archaeology........MA 12FT 24PT/
PGDip 12FT 24PT/PGCert 12FT 24PT

University of Wolverhampton
History.. MA 24-36PT

University of York
Contemporary History and International Politics .. MA 12FT 24PT
Cultures of Empire, Resistance and Postcoloniality .... MA 12FT 24PT
Early Modern History............................... MA 12FT 24PT/PGDip 9FT
Eighteenth Century Studies: Representations and Contexts 1750-1850... MA 12FT 24PT
Eighteenth Century Studies: Representations and Contexts, 1750-1850.. MA 12FT 24PT
Public History... MA 12FT 24PT

The University Of Sheffield.

Department Of History.

Uncover the past. Understand the world today.

Why choose Sheffield?

A leading university and department

- History was ranked joint 4th for world-leading research in the official Research Assessment Exercise
- Ranked joint 2nd for high-quality facilities*
- £24.5m investment in state-of-the-art resources
- 2nd in the Russell Group for student experience*

A stimulating postgraduate environment

- Innovative and intellectually stimulating teaching with leading experts in the field
- Modules that are career-focused enhancing your skills in areas like public history and historical writing
- An active community. Our students run a postgraduate forum and organise regular discussion groups

*Times Higher Education Student Survey 2013

We offer MA degrees and research supervision in the following main areas:

- Late antique and medieval history
- Early modern history
- Modern British and European history
- American history
- International history

Scholarships available

We have a variety of funding available ranging from MA fee scholarships to full Research Council awards for PhD students.

"From the quality of the teaching to the vibrant postgraduate community, the History Department is outstanding."

Alan Rowley, MA in Historical Research

Contact us to find out more

Call: 0114 22 22552
Email: history@sheffield.ac.uk
Visit: www.sheffield.ac.uk/history/prospectivepg

Download our brochure

View our upcoming open days

Find out about funding

History

History
Research Courses

University of Aberdeen
History......PhD 36FT/MPhil 24FT/MLitt by research 12FT

Aberystwyth University
History ...... PhD 36FT 60PT

School of Advanced Study, University of London
History...... PhD 36-48FT 60-72PT/MPhil 24-36FT 48-60PT MPhil 24FT 48PT/PhD 36FT 72PT
History - Commonwealth or member statePhD 36FT 72PT/MPhil 12FT 36PT

Anglia Ruskin University
History...... PhD 36FT 72PT/MPhil 24FT 48PT

Bangor University
Archaeology......PhD 36FT 48-72PT/MPhil 12-24FT 24-48PT
Heritage......MPhil 12-24FT 24-48PT/PhD 36FT 48-72PT
History......MPhil 12FT 24PT/PhD 24-36FT 48-72PT

Bath Spa University
History and Culture:Research ...... PhD 24 - 60FT 36 - 72PT/MPhil 18 - 36FT 30 - 48PT

Birkbeck, University of London
History...... PhD 24FT 36PT/MPhil 24FT 36PT

University of Bristol
History......PhD 36FT 72PT/MPhil 12FT 24PT/ MLitt by research 24FT 48PT

Brunel University
Doctoral Programme in Politics, History & International Relations ...... PhD 36FT 60PT/MPhil 12FT 24PT/MRes 12FT 24PT

University of Buckingham
Garden History......MA by research 12FT 24PT
History of Art: Renaissance to Modernism.. MA by research 12FT
Military History...... MA by research 12FT
Modern War Studies...... MA by research 12FT

University of Cambridge
Archaeological Research...... MPhil 12FT
History...... PhD 36FT 60PT

Canterbury Christ Church University
MA by Research (in History)......MA by research 12FT 24PT

Cardiff University
History and Memory...... PhD 36FT 60PT
Welsh History...... PhD 36FT possiblePT/MPhil 12FT possiblePT

University of Chichester
History...... PhD 36FT 84PT

Coventry University
History......MA by research 12FT 24PT

University of Cumbria
History...... PhD 48FT 72PT/MPhil 24FT 60PT

De Montfort University
International Centre for Sports History and Culture PhD 36-48FT 48-72PT/MPhil 12-24FT 24-48PT

University of Dundee
History...... MPhil 24FT PhD 36FT
Philosophy ...... MPhil 24FT PhD 36FT

Durham University
History....PhD 36FT/MLitt by research 24FT/MA by research 12FT

University of East Anglia
American Studies ...... PhD 36FT 72PT/MPhil 24FT 48PT/MA by research 12FT
School of History ...... PhD 36FT 72PT/MPhil 24FT 48PT

University of Edinburgh
African Studies...... PhD 36FT 72PT/MPhil 24FT 48PT
Canadian Studies...... PhD 36FT 72PT/MPhil 24FT 48PT
Celtic and Scottish Studies......PhD 36FT 72PT/MPhil 24FT 48PT/ MSc by research 12FT 24PT
Classical Art & Archaeology ...... MSc 12FT 24PT
Classics......PhD 36FT 72PT/MPhil 24FT 48PT/ MSc by research 12FT 24PT
Ecclesiastical History ...... PhD 36FT 72PT/MPhil 24FT/MTh by research 12FT 24PT/MSc by research 12FT 24PT
Economic and Social History ....PhD 36FT 72PT/MPhil 24FT 48PT/ MSc by research 12FT 24PT
History...... PhD 36FT 72PT/MPhil 24FT 48PT
History of Art..PhD 36FT 72PT/MPhil 24FT 48PT/MSc by research 12FT 24PT
History of Art (MSc by Research)......MSc by research 12FT 24PT
Islamic and Middle Eastern Studies...... PhD 36FT 72PT/MSc by research 12FT 24PT/MPhil 24FT 48PT
Medieval Studies ......PhD 36FT 72PT/MSc by research 12FT 24PT
Second World War Studies...... PhD 36FT 72PT
Study of the Two World Wars......

University of Essex
History.....PhD 36FT 72PT/MPhil 24FT 48PT/MA by research 12FT 24PT

European University Institute
History and Civilisation......PhD 48FT

University of Exeter
Classics and Ancient History ..... PhD 36FT 72PT/MPhil 24FT 48PT
History......PhD 48FT 84PT 84DL/MPhil 36FT 60PT 60DL
Maritime Historical Studies......PhD 48FT 84PT 84DL/MPhil 36FT 60PT 60DL
Medical History......PhD 48FT 84PT 84DL/MPhil 36FT 60PT 60DL
Medieval Studies ...... MPhil 36FT 60PT/PhD 48FT 84PT

University of Glasgow
History...... MPhil 24FT 36PT/PhD 36FT 48PT

University of Gloucestershire
History......PhD 30-48FT 48-84PT/MPhil 18-36FT 30-60PT/MA by research 12-24FT 18-36PT

Goldsmiths, University of London
History......PhD 36-48FT 48-72PT/MPhil 24FT 36PT MRes 12FT 24PT

University of Hull
Historical Studies ......MA by research 12FT 24PT
History...... PhD 36FT 60PT/MPhil 24FT 36PT

Keele University
History...... PhD 24-48FT 48-84PT/MPhil 12-24FT 24-36PT

University of Kent
History.....PhD 36FT 60PT/MPhil 24FT 36PT/MA by research 12FT 24PT

King's College London
History Research......MPhil 24FT 36PT/PhD 36FT 48-72PT
Palaeography & Manuscript Studies......PhD 36FT 48-72PT/MPhil 36FT 48-72PT

Kingston University
Centre for Local History StudiesPhD 48FT 72PT/MPhil 24FT 48PT/ MA by research 12FT 24PT
Historical Studies ......PhD 48FT 72PT/MPhil 24FT 48PT/MA by research 12FT 24PT

Lancaster University
History...... PhD 36FT 48PT/MPhil 24FT 36PT

University of Leeds
Division of History and Philosophy of Science...PhD 36+FT/MPhil 24FT/MA by research 12+FT
PhD, MA by Research, MPhil ...... PhD 36+FT 60-84PT/MPhil 24FT 48-72PT/MA by research 12FT 24PT

University of Leicester
Centre for Urban History ...... PhD 36FT 72PT/MPhil 24FT 48PT
School of Historical Studies...... PhD 36FT 72PT/MPhil 24FT 48PT

University of Liverpool
History...... PhD 36FT 48PT/MPhil 12FT 24PT/MRes 12FT 24PT

Loughborough University
History ...... MPhil 12FT 24PT/PhD 36FT 60PT

Manchester Metropolitan University
Department of History......PhD 24-48FT 42-84PT 42-84DL/MPhil 18-36FT 36-72PT 36-72DL/MA by research 12-24FT 24-42PT 24-42DL

University of Manchester
History...... PhD 36FT 72PT

Newcastle University
Classics...... MLitt by research 12FT 24PT
History...... PhD 36FT 72PT/MPhil 12FT 24PT MLitt by research 12FT 24PT

Newman University
History...... MPhil 24FT 48PT

University of Northampton
History...... PhD 36FT 48PT/MPhil 24FT 36PT

Nottingham Trent University
History...... PhD 48FT 96PT/MPhil 36FT 72PT

University of Nottingham
History (Research Areas)...... MPhil 24FT/MRes 12FT/PhD 36FT

The Open University
Empire and Postcolonial studies ...... PhD 36FT 72PT variableDL/ MPhil 15FT 24PT variableDL
Heritage...... PhD 36FT 72PT variableDL/MPhil 15FT 24PT variableDL
Historical and contemporary study of musical texts, contexts, and performance..... PhD 36FT 72PT variableDL/MPhil 15FT 24PT variableDL
History... PhD 36FT 72PT variableDL/MPhil 15FT 24PT variableDL
History of Mathematics... PhD 36FT 72PT variableDL/MPhil 15FT 24PT variableDL
Policing and Criminal Justice.....PhD 36FT 72PT variableDL/MPhil 15FT 24PT variableDL
Religious history and its application ...... PhD 36FT 72PT variableDL/MPhil 15FT 24PT variableDL

Oxford Brookes University
History ...... PhD 24-60FT 36-72PT/MPhil 24-36FT 36-48PT
History of Art ...... PhD 24-60FT 36-72PT/MPhil 24-36FT 36-48PT
History of Medicine ......PhD 24-60FT 36-72PT/MPhil 24-36FT 36-48PT

University of Oxford
English Local History...... DPhil 96PT
History...... DPhil 48FT

University of Portsmouth
Social, Historical and Literary Studies......MPhil 24FT 48PT/ PhD 36FT 72PT

Queen Mary, University of London
History......PhD/MA by research/MPhil

Queen's University Belfast
Past Cultural Change...... PhD 36FT 72PT/MPhil 24FT 48PT

University of Roehampton
Classics...... PhD 24-48FT 36-60PT/MPhil 21-36FT 33-48PT
History...... PhD 24-48FT 36-60PT/MPhil 21-36FT 33-48PT

Royal Holloway, University of London
Department of History...... PhD 36FT 72PT/MPhil 36FT 72PT
History...... PhD 36FT 72PT/MPhil 24FT 48PT
Research in History for degrees of MPhil and PhD ... PhD 36-48FT 72-96PT/MPhil 24FT 48PT

School of Oriental and African Studies - SOAS
History...... PhD 36FT 72PT/MPhil 24FT 36PT

Sheffield Hallam University
Humanities Research Centre: History......PhD 36-48FT 60-72PT

Southampton Solent University
History of Collecting Research Centre......PhD 36FT 60PT/ MPhil 24FT 48PT

University of Southampton
History...... MPhil 48FT 84PT/PhD 48FT 84PT
Jewish History and Culture...... PhD 48FT 84PT/MPhil 48FT 84PT
Science and Heritage......MRes 12FT

University of St Andrews
Ancient History ......MPhil 24FT/PhD 36FT 72PT
History......PhD 36-48FT 72-96PT/MPhil 12-24FT 48PT
History of Photography...... PhD 36FT 72PT/MPhil 24FT 48PT

St Mary's University College, Twickenham
History...... PhD 36FT 72PT/MPhil 24FT 48PT

University of Sunderland
History... PhD 36-48FT 48-72PT 48-72DL/MPhil 12-36FT 24-48PT 24-48DL

University of Sussex
History Research Programme...... PhD 24-48FT 36-72PT/MPhil 12-36FT 24-48PT
Intellectual History Research Programme PhD 24-48FT 36-72PT/ MPhil 12-36FT 24-48PT

Swansea University
Classics, Ancient History and Egyptology ... PhD 36FT 60PT/MPhil 12FT 24PT
Egyptology ......MPhil 12FT 24PT/PhD 36FT 60PT/MA by research 12FT 24PT
History.....PhD 36FT 72PT/MPhil 24FT 48PT/MA by research 12FT 24PT

Teesside University
History...... PhD 24-60FT 36PT/MPhil 18FT 30PT

University of Wales Trinity Saint David
History......MPhil 36FT 48-72PT/PhD 12-36FT

University of the Highlands and Islands
History...... MPhil 24FT 48PT/PhD 36FT 72PT

University of Ulster
History...... PhD 36FT 72PT/MPhil 24FT 48PT

UCL - University College London
History...... PhD 36FT 60PT
History of Medicine ...... PhD 36FT 60PT
Jewish History ...... PhD 36FT 60PT

University of Warwick
History.....PhD 36FT 60PT/MPhil 24FT 36PT/MA by research 12FT 24PT

University of Wolverhampton
History Division......PhD/MPhil

University of Worcester
History...... PhD 48FT 70PT/MPhil 24FT 48PT

University of York
History (MA by Research)PhD 36FT 72PT/MPhil 24FT 48PT/MA by research 12FT 24PT

York St John University
Historical Studies ... PhD 12-36FT/MPhil 12-36FT/MA by research 12-36FT

History of art
Taught Courses

University of Aberdeen
Art and Business......MLitt 12FT 24PT

Aberystwyth University
Art History...... MA 12FT 24PT/PGDip 9FT 18PT
Fine Art and Art History...... MA 12FT 24PT

University of the Arts London - Central Saint Martins College of Art and Design
Art: Moving Image ...... MRes 24FT

History

University of the Arts London - Chelsea College of Art and Design
Art Theory .... MA 12FT

University of the Arts London - London College of Fashion
History and Culture of Fashion .... MA 15FT 30PT

Bangor University
Fine Art .... MA 36PT

Birkbeck, University of London
History of Art .... MA 12FT 24PT
History of Art and Architecture .... GradCert 12PT
History of Art with Photography .... MA 12FT 24PT
Museum Cultures.... MA 12FT 24PT/MRes 12FT 24PT/PGDip 12FT 24PT/PGCert 6FT 12PT
Renaissance Studies .... MA 12FT 24PT
Victorian Studies .... MA 12FT 24PT

Birmingham City University
History of Art and Design .... MA 12FT 24PT
Queer Studies in Arts and Culture .... MA 12FT 24PT

University of Birmingham
History of Art .... MA 12FT 24PT

University of Brighton
History of Design and Material Culture ....

University of Bristol
Classical Reception .... MA 12FT 24PT
History of Art: Histories and Interpretations .... MA 12FT 24PT

University of Buckingham
Decorative Arts and Historic Interiors .... MA 12FT

University of Cambridge
History of Art and Architecture .... MPhil 9FT

University of Central Lancashire
Antiques .... MA 30-36DL
Fine Art: Site and Archive Interventions...... MA 12FT 24PT/PGDip 12FT 24PT/PGCert 12FT 24PT

Christie's Education London
Art, Style and Design: Renaissance to Modernism......MLitt 12FT/PGDip 9FT
Arts of Europe: Antiquity, Middle Ages, Renaissance..MLitt 12FT/PGDip 9FT
Modern and Contemporary Art: Beyond Modernism .MLitt 12FT/PGDip 9FT
The Arts of China: Cultural Crossroads in Asia .MLitt 12FT/PGDip 9FT

University College Cork
Aesthetics and History of Art .... MA 12FT
Arts (Folklore) .... HDip 9FT
Arts (Greek & Roman Civilisation) .... HDip 9FT 18PT
History of Art .... HDip 9FT 18PT MA 12FT 24PT

Courtauld Institute of Art
History of Art .... GradDip 9FT MA 9FT

University of East Anglia
History of Art .... MA 12FT 24PT
The Arts of Africa, Oceania and the Americas .... MA 12FT 24PT
World Art Studies .... PGDip 12FT 24PT

University of East London
Architecture: Interpretation and Theories .... MA 12FT 24PT/PGDip 8FT 16PT/PGCert 4FT 8PT

University of Edinburgh
Art in the Global Middle Ages .... MSc 12FT 24PT
History of Art, Theory and Display .... MSc 12FT 24PT
Modern and Contemporary Art: History, Curating, Criticism MSc 12FT 24PT

University of Essex
Art History and Theory .... MA 12FT 24PT/GradDip 9FT
Art History and Theory with English for Academic Purposes .... Diploma 9FT
Curating Contemporary Art .... MA 12FT 24PT
Curating Latin American Art .... MA 12FT 24PT
Gallery Studies and Critical Curating .... MA 12FT
Gallery Studies with Dissertation .... MA 12FT 24PT
Human Rights and Arts .... MA 12FT 24PT

Glasgow School of Art
Photography .... PGCert 4FT/PGDip 8FT/MDes 12FT

University of Glasgow
Art History: Art: Politics: Transgression: 20th Century Avant-Gardes .... MLitt 12FT 24PT
Art History: Dress & Textile Histories .... MLitt 12FT 24PT
Art, Style & Design: Renaissance to Modernism .... MLitt 12FT/PGDip 12FT
Arts of China .... MLitt 12FT
Arts of Europe .... MLitt 12FT/PGDip 9FT
Technical Art History: Making & Meaning .... MLitt 12FT 24PT
Textile Conservation .... MPhil 24FT 48PT
Theatre History .... MLitt 12FT 24PT

Goldsmiths, University of London
Contemporary Art Theory .... MA 12FT 24PT
Global Arts .... MA 12FT 24PT

University of Kent
Arts Criticism .... MA 12FT 24PT
History and Philosophy of Art .... MA 12FT 24PT
History and Philosophy of Art (Paris option) .... MA 12FT 24PT
Medieval and Early Modern Studies .... MA 12FT 24PT

King's College London
Classical Art & Archaeology .... MA 12FT 24PT

Kingston University
Art Market Appraisal (Professional Practice) .... MA 12FT 24PT
Art and Design History .... MA 12FT 24PT

Leeds Metropolitan University
Art & Design .... MA 12FT 24PT

University of Leeds
History of Art .... MA 12FT 24PT

University of Limerick
History of Art and Architecture .... MA 12FT

Liverpool Hope University
Art History and Curating .... MA 12FT 24PT

University of Liverpool
Art, Aesthetics and Cultural Institutions .... MA 12FT 24PT
Modern Architectural Heritage - London Based.... MSc 12FT 24PT

London Metropolitan University
Architectural History Theory and Interpretation ... MA 12FT 24PT

University of Manchester
Art History .... MA 12FT 24PT

Northumbria University
Arts .... MRes 12FT 24PT
Conservation of Fine Art .... MA 18FT

University of Nottingham
Art History .... MA 12FT 24PT
Art History (by Research) .... MA 12FT 24PT
The Visual Culture of Classical Antiquity .... MA 12FT 24PT

The Open University
Art History .... MA variableDL
Humanities .... MA variableDL/PGDip variableDL/PGCert variableDL

University of Oxford
Celtic Studies .... MPhil 21FT/MSt 9FT
History of Art and Visual Culture .... MSt 9FT
Late Antique and Byzantine Studies .... MPhil 21FT/MSt 9FT

Plymouth University
Design Thinking .... MRes 12FT 24PT

Prince's School of Traditional Arts
Visual Islamic and Traditional Arts .... MA 24FT/PED 12FT 12PT

University of Reading
Classics .... MA (Res) 12FT 24PT 60BM
History of Art and Architecture .... MA 12FT 24PT

Richmond, The American International University in London
Art History and Visual Culture .... MA 12FT 24PT

Royal College of Art
History of Design .... MA 24FT

School of Oriental and African Studies - SOAS
History of Art and/or Archaeology .... MA 12FT 24-36PT

Sotheby's Institute of Art
Art Business .... MA 14FT/PGDip 9FT
East Asian Art .... MA 14FT/PGDip 9FT
Fine and Decorative Art .... MA 14FT/PGDip 9FT

University of St Andrews
Art History .... MLitt 12FT 24PT/PGDip 9FT 18PT
Central and East European Studies....MLitt 12FT 24PT/PGDip 9FT 18PT
History of Photography .... PGDip 9FT 18PT/MLitt 12FT 24PT
Theology, Imagination and the Arts .... MLitt 12FT/PGDip 9FT

Staffordshire University
Clinical Photography .... GradCert 12DL

University of Sussex
Art History .... MA 12FT 24PT

Trinity College Dublin - the University of Dublin
Textual and Visual Studies: 19th and 20th Century France .... MPhil 12FT

University of Wales Trinity Saint David
Applied Arts .... MA 12FT 24PT/PGCert 12FT 24PT/PGDip 12FT 24PT
Fine Art .... MA 12FT 24PT/PGCert 12FT 24PT/PGDip 12FT 24PT

UCL - University College London
Architectural History .... MA 12FT 24-60PT/PGDip 9FT
History of Art .... MA 12FT 24PT/PGDip 9FT

University of Warwick
History of Art .... MA 12FT 24PT/PGDip 12FT 24PT

University of York
History of Art .... MA 12FT 24PT

History of art
Research Courses

University of Aberdeen
History of Art .... PhD 36FT 60PT/MLitt by research 12FT 24PT

Aberystwyth University
Art History .... MPhil 12FT 24PT PhD 36FT 60PT

University of the Arts London - Central Saint Martins College of Art and Design
The Hisotry and Theory of Art & Design ... PhD 24-48FT 36-96PT/MPhil 15-36FT 24-72PT

University of Bath
Architectural History and Theory .... MPhil 12-36FT 24-48PT

Birkbeck, University of London
History of Art .... PhD 36FT 48PT/MPhil 36FT 48PT

University of Birmingham
History of Art .... PhD 36FT 72PT/MPhil(B) 12FT 24PT

University of Bristol
History of Art .... PhD 36FT 72PT/MPhil 12FT 24PT/MLitt by research 24FT 48PT

University of Cambridge
History of Art .... PhD 36FT

University of Central Lancashire
Fine Art, Fashion & Performing Arts .... PhD 30-48FT 66-84PT/MPhil 18-36FT 42-60PT/MA by research 12FT 24PT

University of Dundee
Duncan of Jordanstone College of Art & Design .... MPhil 24FT PhD 36FT

University of East Anglia
Sainsbury Research Unit for the Arts of Africa, Oceania and the Americas .PhD 36FT 72PT/MPhil 24FT 48PT/MA by research 12FT 24PT

University of Edinburgh
History of Art .... PhD 36FT 72PT/MPhil 24FT 48PT/MSc by research 12FT 24PT

University of Essex
Art History and Theory .... PhD 36FT 72PT/MPhil 24FT 48PT

University of Exeter
Art History and Visual Culture ..MPhil 36FT 60PT 60DL/PhD 48FT 84PT 84DL

Glasgow School of Art
Art and Design .... PhD 36FT 60PT/MPhil 12FT 24PT

University of Glasgow
History of Art .... PhD 36FT/MPhil 12FT/MLitt by research 12FT

Goldsmiths, University of London
Art .... MPhil 24FT 36PT/PhD 36-48FT 48-72PT
Art History .... MRes 12FT 24PT
Visual Cultures .... PhD 36-48FT 48-72PT/MPhil 24FT 36PT

University of Kent
Cartoons and Caricature .... PhD 36FT 60PT/MPhil 24FT 36PT/MA by research 12FT 24PT
History & Philosophy of Art .... MA by research 12FT 24PT/MPhil 24FT 36PT/PhD 36FT 60PT
Medieval and Early Modern Studies...PhD 36FT 60PT/MPhil 24FT 36PT/MA by research 12FT 24PT

Lancaster University
Art .... PhD 36FT 48-60PT/MPhil 24FT 36PT

University of Leicester
History of Art .... PhD 48FT/MPhil 36FT

Loughborough University
History of Art, Architecture and Design .... PhD 36FT 60PT/MPhil 24FT 36PT

Manchester Metropolitan University
History of Art and Design .... PhD/MPhil

University of Manchester
Art History and Visual Studies .... PhD 36FT 72PT

University of Nottingham
Art History .... PhD 36FT 72PT/MPhil 24FT 48PT
Social Sciences Research Methodology .... MPhil 24FT 48PT/PhD 36-48FT 72-96PT

The Open University
Art History .... PhD 36FT 72PT variableDL/MPhil 15FT 24PT variableDL
Artistic networks, 1300-1550....PhD 36FT 72PT variableDL/MPhil 15FT 24PT variableDL
Eighteenth Century Visual Cultures .... PhD 36FT 72PT variableDL/MPhil 15FT 24PT variableDL
Gender in the Humanities .... PhD 36FT 72PT variableDL/MPhil 15FT 24PT variableDL
Modern art theory and practicePhD 36FT 72PT variableDL/MPhil 15FT 24PT variableDL

Oxford Brookes University
Arts ... MPhil/PhD 36-60FT 48-72PT/PhD 24-60FT 36-72PT/MPhil 24-36FT 36-48PT
History of Art .... PhD 24-60FT 36-72PT/MPhil 24-36FT 36-48PT

History

Plymouth University
Art History....MRes 12FT
Design Thinking....MRes 12FT 24PT

Prince's School of Traditional Arts
Visual Islamic and Traditional Arts... PhD 24-36FT 36-72PT/MPhil 12FT 24PT

Royal College of Art
History of Design....PhD 24-36FT 48-60PT/MPhil 24FT 36-48PT
History of Design....PhD/MPhil/MA by research

Sheffield Hallam University
Art and Design Research Centre: History of Art and Design..PhD 36-48FT 60-72PT

University of Southampton
History of Art and Design....MPhil 24FT 48PT/PhD 36FT 72PT

University of St Andrews
Art History....PhD 36FT 72PT/MPhil 12-24FT 24-48PT
History of Photography....PhD 36FT 72PT/MPhil 24FT 48PT
National Trust of Scotland Studies....MPhil 12-24FT 24-48PT

University of Sussex
Art History Research Programme..... PhD 24-48FT 36-72PT/MPhil 12-36FT 24-48PT

UCL - University College London
History of Art....PhD 36FT 60PT

University of Warwick
History of Art....PhD 48FT 72PT/MPhil 12FT 24PT

University of York
History of Art...PhD 36FT 72PT/MPhil 24FT 48PT/MA by research 12FT 24PT

History of science
Taught Courses

University of Aberdeen
History and Philosophy of Science.....MLitt 12FT 24PT/PGDip 9FT 18PT

Bangor University
Medical Sciences....MRes 12FT 24PT/PGCert 3FT 15PT

University of Bristol
Philosophy and History of Science....MA 12FT 24PT

University of Cambridge
History, Philosophy and Sociology of Science, Technology and Medicine....MPhil 9FT

Durham University
History and Philosophy of Science and Medicine .. MA 12FT 24PT
Social and Economic History (Research Methods)....MA 12FT

University of Exeter
History and Philosophy of Biology....MA 12FT 24PT
Philosophy and Sociology of Science....MA 12FT 24PT
Science and Technology Studies....MRes 12FT 24PT

University of Glasgow
History (with an emphasis on History of Medicine).....MLitt 12FT 24PT/MSc 12FT 24PT

Imperial College London
History of Science, Medicine and Technology / Science, Technology and Medicine in Society....MSc 12FT 24PT

University of Kent
History of Science, Medicine, Environment and Technology ...MA 12FT 24PT
Medical Humanities....MA 12FT 24PT
Science, Communication and Society....MSc 12FT 24PT

University of Leeds
Science Communication....MA 12FT 24PT

University of Leicester
Medical Humanities....MA 12FT 24PT/PGDip 12FT 24PT

London School of Economics and Political Science (LSE)
Philosophy of Science....MSc 12FT 24PT
Philosophy of the Social Sciences....MSc 12FT 24PT

University of Manchester
History of Science Technology and Medicine....MSc 12FT 24PT

Newcastle University
History of Medicine....MA 12FT 24PT

University of Nottingham
Research Methods Science and Technology Studies........MA 12FT 24PT

Oxford Brookes University
History of Medicine....MA 12FT 24PT/PGDip 9FT 20PT/PGCert 4FT 8PT

University of Oxford
Economic and Social History....MPhil 21FT/MSc 12FT
History of Science, Medicine & Technology....MPhil 24FT/MSc 12FT
History of Science: Instruments, Museums, Sci., Tech.. MSc 12FT

University of Strathclyde
Health History....MSc 12FT 24PT/PGDip 9FT 18PT/PGDip 9FT 9PT

Swansea University
Early Modern History....MA 12FT 24PT
Modern History....MA 12FT 24PT

UCL - University College London
History of Medicine....MSc 12FT 24PT
History of Science, Medicine and Technology....MSc 12FT 24PT
Science, Technology, Medicine and Society....MSc 12FT 24PT

University of Warwick
History of Medicine....MA 12FT 24PT/PGDip 12FT 24PT

History of science
Research Courses

University of Birmingham
History of Medicine....PhD 36FT 72PT/MPhil 12FT 24PT

University of Cambridge
History and Philosophy of Science....PhD 36FT 60PT

University of Exeter
Medical History....PhD 48FT 84PT 84DL/MPhil 36FT 60PT 60DL
Sociology....PhD 36FT 72PT 72DL/MPhil 24FT 48PT 48DL

Imperial College London
Centre for the History of Science, Technology and Medicine..PhD 36FT 72PT/MPhil 24FT 48PT

University of Kent
History of Science, Technology and Medicine....MA by research 12FT 24PT/MPhil 24FT 36PT/PhD 36FT 60PT

University of Manchester
History of Science, Technology and Medicine.......PhD 36FT 72PT/MPhil 12FT 24PT

The Open University
History... PhD 36FT 72PT variableDL/MPhil 15FT 24PT variableDL
History of Mathematics... PhD 36FT 72PT variableDL/MPhil 15FT 24PT variableDL
History of Medicine PhD 36FT 72PT variableDL/MPhil 15FT 24PT variableDL
Mathematics....PhD 36FT 72PT variableDL/MPhil 15FT 24PT variableDL
Philosophy....PhD 36FT 72PT variableDL/MPhil 15FT 24PT variableDL

Oxford Brookes University
History of Medicine....PhD 24-60FT 36-72PT/MPhil 24-36FT 36-48PT

University of Oxford
History (for Economic & Social History, and History of Science)... DPhil 48FT

UCL - University College London
History of Medicine....PhD 36FT 60PT
Philosophy of Science....PhD 36FT 60PT
Science and Technology Studies....PhD 36FT 60PT

International history
Taught Courses

Aberystwyth University
International History (Research Training)....MA 12FT

Brunel University
Modern World History....MA 12FT 24PT

University of Cambridge
Modern European History....MPhil 10FT

University of Chester
Faiths and Public Policy....MA 12FT 36PT 36DL/PGDip 12FT 24-36PT 24-36DL/PGCert 12FT 12-24PT 12-24DL

University of Dundee
Global Empires (MLitt)....MLitt 12FT

University of East Anglia
History....GradDip 12FT 24PT
Modern European History....MA 12FT 24PT
Modern History....MA 12FT 24PT

University of Essex
Digital History....MA 12FT 24PT/PGCert 9FT
History....MA 12FT 24PT/PGCert 9FT 21PT/PGDip 12FT

King's College London
World History & Cultures....MA 12FT 24PT

University of Limerick
International Studies....MA 12FT

London School of Economics and Political Science (LSE)
Empires, Colonialism and Globalisation....MSc 12FT 24PT
Global Studies: A European Perspective....MA 24FT
History of International Relations....MSc 12FT 24PT
International and World History (Double Degree)....MA 11FT/MA 11FT
Theory and History of International Relations....MSc 12FT 24PT

Newcastle University
European History....MA 12FT 24PT

University of Oxford
African Studies....MSc 9FT
Egyptology....MPhil 21FT
Global and Imperial History....MSt 9FT
Jewish Studies....MSt 9FT
Late Antique and Byzantine Studies....MPhil 21FT/MSt 9FT

Queen's University Belfast
Modern History....MA 12FT max 31PT

University of Reading
Military History and Strategic Studies MA 12FT 72PT/PGDip 9FT/PGCert 6FT

School of Oriental and African Studies - SOAS
History....MA 12FT 24PT
History: Asia/Africa....MA 12FT 24-36PT

Sheffield Hallam University
History: the Local and the Global....MA 12FT 24PT

University of Sheffield
American History....MA 12FT 24PT
Archaeology, Bible and Ancient Cultures....MA 12FT 24PT
International History....MA 12FT 24PT
Religion, Conflict and the Media....MA 12FT 24PT

University of Southampton
Jewish History and Culture....MA 12FT 24PT/MRes 12FT 24PT

University of St Andrews
Book History....MLitt 12FT 24PT/MPhil 24FT/PGDip 9FT
Central and East European Studies....MLitt 12FT 24PT/PGDip 9FT 18PT
Middle Eastern History & Culture....PGDip 9FT/MLitt 12FT/MPhil 24FT
Peace and Conflict Studies....MLitt 12FT

UCL - University College London
European History....MA 12FT 24PT

University of Warwick
Global History....MA 12FT 24PT/PGDip 12FT 24PT

International history
Research Courses

University of Birmingham
Modern European History....MPhil(B) 12FT 24PT

University of Chichester
History....PhD 36FT 84PT

University of East Anglia
School of History....PhD 36FT 72PT/MPhil 24FT 48PT

University of Essex
History.....PhD 36FT 72PT/MPhil 24FT 48PT/MA by research 12FT 24PT

London School of Economics and Political Science (LSE)
International History....PhD 36-48FT/MPhil 36-48FT

The Open University
History... PhD 36FT 72PT variableDL/MPhil 15FT 24PT variableDL

Queen's University Belfast
Modern History....PhD 36FT 72PT/MPhil 24FT 48PT

School of Oriental and African Studies - SOAS
History....PhD 36FT 72PT/MPhil 24FT 36PT

University of Southampton
Jewish History and Culture....PhD 48FT 84PT/MPhil 48FT 84PT

Swansea University
Ancient History....MA by research 12FT 24PT

Irish history
Taught Courses

University of Aberdeen
Modern Historical Studies....MLitt 12FT 24PT/PGDip 6FT 16PT

University of Dundee
Greater Britain in the Twentieth Century....MLitt 12FT

University of East Anglia
Modern British History....MA 12FT 24PT

University of Edinburgh
Modern British and Irish History....MSc 12FT 24PT

University of Liverpool
Understanding Conflict....MA 12FT 24PT

National University of Ireland, Maynooth
Irish History....HDip 12FT
Local History....MA 12FT 24PT

University of Oxford
Celtic Studies....MPhil 21FT/MSt 9FT

Queen's University Belfast
Irish History....MA 12FT max 31PT
Modern History....MA 12FT max 31PT

University of Sheffield
Eighteenth-Century Studies (History)....MA 12FT 24PT

St Mary's University College, Twickenham
Irish Studies....MA 12FT 24PT

Trinity College Dublin - the University of Dublin
Irish Art History....MPhil 12FT
Modern Irish History....MPhil 12FT

History

University of Ulster
Irish History and Society................ MA 14FT 27PT/PGDip 9FT 18PT

Irish history
Research Courses

The Open University
Religious history and its application . PhD 36FT 72PT variableDL/
MPhil 15FT 24PT variableDL
Social and economic history of Britain and Ireland 18th-20th
centuries.................... PhD 36FT 72PT variableDL/MPhil 15FT 24PT
variableDL

Queen's University Belfast
Modern History............................ PhD 36FT 72PT/MPhil 24FT 48PT

Maritime history
Taught Courses

Bournemouth University
Maritime Archaeology ....MSc 12FT 24PT

University of East Anglia
Modern British History.............................. MA 12FT 24PT

University of Greenwich
Maritime History .... MA 12FT 24PT

University of Hull
Maritime History...MA 12FT

London School of Economics and Political Science (LSE)
Empires, Colonialism and Globalisation.................. MSc 12FT 24PT

University of Oxford
Global and Imperial History ....MSt 9FT

University of Sheffield
Cultures of the British Isles............................. MA 12FT 24PT

Maritime history
Research Courses

University of Exeter
Maritime Historical Studies.......PhD 48FT 84PT 84DL/MPhil 36FT
60PT 60DL

The Open University
Empire and Postcolonial studies .... PhD 36FT 72PT variableDL/
MPhil 15FT 24PT variableDL
History... PhD 36FT 72PT variableDL/MPhil 15FT 24PT variableDL

Medieval history
Taught Courses

University of Aberdeen
Medieval Studies .... MLitt 12FT 24PT/PGDip 8FT 16PT

Aberystwyth University
Medieval Britain and Europe .... MA 12FT 24PT/PGDip 9FT 18PT

Bangor University
Archaeology.............PhD by taught 36FT 48-72PT/MPhil 12-24FT
24-48PT
Medieval Studies .... MA 12FT 24-36PT
Medieval and Early Modern Literature ..MA 12FT 24-36PT/PGDip
9FT

Birkbeck, University of London
Medieval History.................................. MA 12FT 24PT

University of Birmingham
Medieval History................................. MA 12FT 24PT

University of Bristol
Medieval History .... MA 12FT 24PT

University of Cambridge
Medieval History.. MPhil 12FT

Cardiff University
Early Medieval Society and Culture .... MA 12FT 24PT
Medieval British Studies.................................. MA 12FT 24PT

Durham University
Medieval History..MA 12FT

University of East Anglia
History... GradDip 12FT 24PT
Medieval History.. MA 12FT 24PT
Medieval and Early Modern Textual Cultures, 1381 - 1688......MA
12FT 24PT

University of Edinburgh
Medieval History................................. MSc 12FT 24PT

University of Exeter
History .... MA 12FT 24PT
Medieval Studies .... MA 12FT 24PT

National University of Ireland Galway
Medieval Studies ....MA 24FT

University of Glasgow
Medieval History..............................MLitt 12FT 24PT
Medieval and Renaissance Studies.....................MLitt 12FT 24PT

University of Hull
Medieval History.............................. MA 12FT 24PT

King's College London
Medieval History.............................. MA 12FT 24PT
Medieval Studies .... MA 12FT 24PT

University of Leeds
Medieval History.............................. MA 12FT 24PT
Medieval Studies .... MA 12FT 24PT

University of Liverpool
Medieval and Renaissance Studies....MA 12FT 24PT/PGCert 12FT
24PT/PGDip 12FT 24PT

University of Manchester
Medieval History .... MA 12FT 24PT

University of Oxford
Celtic Studies .... MPhil 21FT/MSt 9FT
Islamic Studies and History .... MPhil 21FT
Medieval Arabic Thought .... MPhil 21FT
Medieval Studies ....MSt 11FT
Medieval Studies .... MSt 9FT

University of Reading
Medieval Archaeology ....MA 12FT
Medieval History .... MA (Res) 12FT 24-60PT
Research in Archaeology.............................. MA 12FT 24PT

Royal Holloway, University of London
Crusader Studies.. MA 12FT 24PT
Medieval Studies .... MA 12FT 24PT

University of Sheffield
Eighteenth-Century Studies (History) .... MA 12FT 24PT
Medieval Archaeology .... MA 12FT 24PT
Medieval History .... MA 12FT 24PT

University of Southampton
Medieval & Renaissance Studies.....................MRes 12FT 24PT
Medieval and Renaissance Culture.......................... MA 12FT 24PT

University of St Andrews
Mediaeval History ....MLitt 12FT 24PT/PGDip 9FT 24PT/
MPhil 24FT
Medieval Studies ....MLitt 12FT/PGDip 9FT

University of Stirling
Historical Research...............................MRes 12FT 24PT

University of Strathclyde
Historical Studies ....MSc 12FT 24PT/PGDip 9FT 18PT

Swansea University
Medieval Studies ......MA 12FT 24-36PT/PGDip 12FT 24PT/PGCert
12FT 12PT

Trinity College Dublin - the University of Dublin
Medieval History.................................. MPhil 12FT
Medieval Language, Literature and Culture .... MPhil 12FT

University of Wales Trinity Saint David
Medieval Studies ....MA 12FT 24PT 12-24DL

UCL - University College London
Medieval and Renaissance Studies.......................... MA 12FT 24PT

University of Winchester
Historical Studies .MA 12FT 24PT/PGDip 12FT 24PT/PGCert 12FT
24PT

University of York
Medieval History........................... MA 12FT 24PT/PGDip 9FT
Medieval Studies .... MA 12FT 18PT/PGDip 9FT

Medieval history
Research Courses

University of Birmingham
History (Medieval)...................PhD 36FT 60PT/MPhil(B) 12FT 24PT
History of Christianity.......................................MPhil(B) 12FT 24PT

University of Bristol
Medieval Studies MPhil 12FT 24PT/MLitt by research 24FT 48PT/
PhD 36FT 72PT

University of Chichester
History.. PhD 36FT 84PT

University of East Anglia
School of History .... PhD 36FT 72PT/MPhil 24FT 48PT

University of Edinburgh
Medieval Studies .... PhD 36FT 72PT/MSc by research 12FT 24PT

University of Exeter
History........................PhD 48FT 84PT 84DL/MPhil 36FT 60PT 60DL
Medieval Studies .... MPhil 36FT 60PT/PhD 48FT 84PT

University of Leeds
Medieval Studies .... PhD 36FT 48PT
Medieval Studies .... PhD 36FT 48PT

The Open University
Early modern Britain and Europe .... PhD 36FT 72PT variableDL/
MPhil 15FT 24PT variableDL
History... PhD 36FT 72PT variableDL/MPhil 15FT 24PT variableDL

University of York
Medieval Studies .... PhD 36FT 72PT/MPhil 24FT 48PT

Military history
Taught Courses

University of Aberdeen
Cultural History........................... MLitt 12FT 24PT/PGDip 9FT 18PT

Aberystwyth University
War Studies (Research Training) ....MA 12FT
War Studies (Specialist) ....MA 12FT

University of Birmingham
Air Power: History, Theory and Practice..........................MA 24PT
British First World War Studies.............................MA 24PT
British Second World War Studies............................MA 24PT
History of Warfare ....MA 12FT

University of Bradford
Conflict, Security and Development.......MA 12FT 12-36PT/PGDip
24FT 24-36PT

Brunel University
War and Conflict in the Modern World.................... MA 12FT 30PT

Cardiff University
Ancient and Medieval Warfare .... MA 12FT 24PT

University of Central Lancashire
Conflict and Violence Minimisation ....PGCert 24PT

University of Chester
Military History...........MA 12FT 24 - 36PT/PGDip 12FT 24 - 36PT/
PGCert 12FT 12 - 24PT

University of East Anglia
Medieval History................................. MA 12FT 24PT

University of Edinburgh
The Second World War in Europe .... MSc 12FT 24PT

University of Glasgow
War Studies ....MLitt 12FT 24PT

University of Hull
Military History .... MA 12FT 24PT

University of Kent
War, Media and Society .... MA 12FT 24PT

King's College London
Air Power in the Modern World ....MA 24 - 72DL
History of Warfare................................... MA 12FT 24PT
Non-Proliferation & International Security .... MA 12FT 24PT
Terrorism, Security & Society .... MA 12FT 24PT
War & Psychiatry ....MSc 12FT 24PT/PGDip 12FT 24PT
War Studies.. MA 12FT 24PT
War in the Modern World (by e-learning).................. MA 24-72DL

London School of Economics and Political Science (LSE)
Empires, Colonialism and Globalisation.................. MSc 12FT 24PT

University of Nottingham
War and Contemporary Conflict............................... MA 12FT 24PT

University of Oxford
Global and Imperial History ....MSt 9FT

Plymouth University
History.. MA 12FT 24PT

University of Portsmouth
History of War, Culture and Society.......................... MA 12FT 24PT

University of Reading
Diplomacy ....MA 12FT 72PT/PGDip 12FT 72PT/PGCert 12FT 72PT
Diplomacy .... MA 12FT 24-72PT/PGCert 12FT 24-72PT/
PGDip 12FT 24-72PT
History ....MA(Res) 12FT 24PT 36-60BM
International Relations ....MA (res) 12FT 24-72PT 72BM
International Relations (Strategic Studies) ......MA 12FT 24-72PT/
PGDip 24-72PT/PGCert 12FT 24PT
Military History and Strategic Studies....................MA 12FT 72PT/
PGDip 9FT/PGCert 6FT

University of St Andrews
Peace and Conflict Studies...MLitt 12FT

Swansea University
War and Society.. MA 12FT 24PT

University of Wolverhampton
Conflict Studies...MA 12FT 24-36PT
Military History by distance learning.............MA 12FT 24PT 12DL

Military history
Research Courses

University of Aberdeen
Cultural History......MLitt by research 12FT/MPhil 24FT/PhD 36FT

University of Buckingham
Military History ....MA by research 12FT
Modern War Studies.................................. MA by research 12FT

University of Edinburgh
Second World War Studies............................... PhD 36FT 72PT
Study of the Two World Wars...

King's College London
War Studies Research .... PhD 36FT 72PT/MPhil 24FT 48PT

History

The Open University
War, conflict and politics in Europe ... PhD 36FT 72PT variableDL/ MPhil 15FT 24PT variableDL

Modern history
Taught Courses

University of Aberdeen
Cultural History............................ MLitt 12FT 24PT/PGDip 9FT 18PT

Bangor University
Early Modern Literature..................... MA 12FT 24-36PT/PGDip 9FT

University of Birmingham
Contemporary History .... MA 12FT 24PT
Early Modern History...MRes 12FT 24PT
Modern European History...MRes 12FT 24PT

University of Bradford
Human Trafficking and Contemporary Slavery...MSc 24PT/PGDip 21PT/PGCert 9PT

University of Brighton
Histories and Cultures...MA 12FT 24PT/PGDip 12FT 24PT/PGCert 12FT 24PT

University of Cambridge
Early Modern History...MPhil 9FT
Modern European History.. MPhil 10FT

Durham University
Early Modern History...MA 12FT

University of East Anglia
Early Modern History .... MA 12FT 24PT
History..GradDip 12FT 24PT
Modern British History.................................... MA 12FT 24PT
Modern European History .... MA 12FT 24PT
Modern History.................................... MA 12FT 24PT

University of Edinburgh
Eighteenth-Century Cultures ....MSc 12FT 24PT
Modern British and Irish History ....MSc 12FT 24PT

University of Essex
Cultural and Social History ....MA 12FT 24PT/PGCert 9FT 21PT
Digital History ....MA 12FT 24PT/PGCert 9FT
Historical Studies ....MA 36-60PT/PGCert 36-60PT
History..MA 12FT 24PT/PGCert 9FT 21PT/PGDip 12FT
Local, Community and Family History ....MA 12FT 24PT/ PGCert 9FT 21PT

University of Glasgow
Early Modern History..MLitt 12FT 24PT
Modern History..MLitt 12FT 24PT
Modernities: Literature, Theory & Culture ....MLitt 12FT 24PT

University of Hull
Early Modern History.. MA 12FT 24PT

Keele University
Humanities (Victorian Studies)..............................MRes 12FT 24PT

University of Kent
Modern History.. MA 12FT 24PT
Modern History (Paris option)..................................... MA 12FT 24PT

King's College London
Early Modern History.. MA 12FT 24PT
Modern History.. MA 12FT 24PT
Politics & Contemporary History............................ MA 12FT 24PT

University of Leeds
Modern History.. MA 12FT 24PT
Social and Cultural History .... MA 12FT 24PT

Liverpool John Moores University
Modern History..MRes 12FT 36PT

University of Liverpool
Twentieth-Century History .... MA 12FT 24PT

Manchester Metropolitan University
English Studies: The Gothic ....PGDip 12FT 24PT/MA 15FT 30PT

Plymouth University
History.. MA 12FT 24PT

Queen's University Belfast
Modern History.. MA 12FT max 31PT

University of Reading
Early Modern History ....MA (Res) 12FT 24PT
Military History and Strategic Studies..................... MA 12FT 72PT /PGDip 9FT/PGCert 6FT
Modern Italian History ....MA (Res) 12FT 24PT

Royal Holloway, University of London
Victorian Literature, Art, & Culture........................... MA 12FT 24PT

University of Sheffield
Early Modern History.. MA 12FT 24PT
Modern History.. MA 12FT 24PT

University of St Andrews
Early Modern History................PGDip 9FT/MLitt 12FT/MPhil 24FT
Modern History......PGDip 9FT 18PT/MLitt 12FT 24PT/MPhil 24FT

Swansea University
Early Modern History.. MA 12FT 24PT
Modern History.. MA 12FT 24PT

Trinity College Dublin - the University of Dublin
Early Modern History..MPhil 12FT

UCL - University College London
Early Modern Studies .... MA 12FT 24PT

University of Warwick
Global History ....MA 12FT 24PT/PGDip 12FT 24PT

University of York
Culture and Thought after 1945 .... MA 12FT 24PT
Early Modern History............................ MA 12FT 24PT/PGDip 9FT
Modern History.. MA 12FT 24PT/PGDip 9FT

Modern history
Research Courses

University of Aberdeen
Cultural History......MLitt by research 12FT/MPhil 24FT/PhD 36FT

University of Birmingham
Early Modern History...MRes 12FT 24PT
Modern History........................... PhD 36FT 72PT/MPhil 12FT 24PT
Twentieth Century British History ....MPhil(B) 12FT 24PT

University of Chichester
History.. PhD 36FT 84PT

University of East Anglia
School of History .... PhD 36FT 72PT/MPhil 24FT 48PT

University of Essex
History.....PhD 36FT 72PT/MPhil 24FT 48PT/MA by research 12FT 24PT

University of Exeter
Medical History........PhD 48FT 84PT 84DL/MPhil 36FT 60PT 60DL

The Open University
Book History .... PhD 36FT 72PT variableDL/MPhil 15FT 24PT variableDL
Early modern Britain and Europe .... PhD 36FT 72PT variableDL/ MPhil 15FT 24PT variableDL
History... PhD 36FT 72PT variableDL/MPhil 15FT 24PT variableDL
The changing nature of contemporary and historical welfarePhD 36FT 72PT variableDL/MPhil 15FT 24PT variableDL

Queen's University Belfast
Modern History........................... PhD 36FT 72PT/MPhil 24FT 48PT

Reformation history
Taught Courses

University of East Anglia
Early Modern History.. MA 12FT 24PT
History..GradDip 12FT 24PT
History of Art .... MA 12FT 24PT

University of St Andrews
Reformation Studies....... MLitt 12FT 24PT/MPhil 24FT/PGDip 9FT 24PT

Swansea University
Early Modern History.. MA 12FT 24PT

Reformation history
Research Courses

University of East Anglia
School of History .... PhD 36FT 72PT/MPhil 24FT 48PT

Renaissance history
Taught Courses

University of Aberdeen
Cultural History............................ MLitt 12FT 24PT/PGDip 9FT 18PT
Philosophical Research...MLitt 12FT 24PT
Renaissance & Early Modern Studies.................... MLitt 12FT 24PT/ PGDip 9FT

School of Advanced Study, University of London
Cultural and Intellectual History 1300-1650 ....MA 12FT

Birkbeck, University of London
History of Art and Architecture ....GradCert 12FT
Renaissance Studies .... MA 12FT 24PT

University of Birmingham
Shakespeare, Stratford-upon-Avon and the Cultural History of Renaissance England.. MA 12FT 24PT

University of Cambridge
Modern European History.. MPhil 10FT

Durham University
Medieval and Renaissance Literary Studies............. MA 12FT 24PT

University of East Anglia
Early Modern History.. MA 12FT 24PT
History of Art .... MA 12FT 24PT
Modern European History.. MA 12FT 24PT

University of Edinburgh
Renaissance and Early Modern Studies...................MSc 12FT 24PT

University of Glasgow
Art, Style & Design: Renaissance to Modernism..........MLitt 12FT/ PGDip 12FT

European Studies: Cultures, Societies & Languages.... MLitt 12FT 24PT
Medieval and Renaissance Studies........................MLitt 12FT 24PT

University of Kent
Medieval and Early Modern Studies........................ MA 12FT 24PT

King's College London
Early Modern English Literature: Text & Transmission....MA 12FT 24PT

University of Leeds
English Renaissance Literature .... MA 12FT 24PT

University of Liverpool
Contemporary Literature..MA 12FT
Medieval and Renaissance Studies....MA 12FT 24PT/PGCert 12FT 24PT/PGDip 12FT 24PT

Manchester Metropolitan University
English Studies: The Gothic ....PGDip 12FT 24PT/MA 15FT 30PT

Queen Mary, University of London
Renaissance and Early Modern Studies.................... MA 12FT 24PT

Queen's University Belfast
Modern History.. MA 12FT max 31PT

University of Reading
Archaeology .... MA 12FT 24PT
History..MA(Res) 12FT 24PT 36-60BM
Medieval Archaeology ....MA 12FT
Research in Archaeology.. MA 12FT 24PT

Sheffield Hallam University
Shakespeare and Renaissance Literature........... MA 12FT 24-72PT

University of Southampton
Medieval & Renaissance Studies........................MRes 12FT 24PT
Medieval and Renaissance Culture........................... MA 12FT 24PT

University of St Andrews
Reformation Studies....... MLitt 12FT 24PT/MPhil 24FT/PGDip 9FT 24PT
Shakespeare and Renaissance Literary Culture . MLitt 12FT 24PT/ PGDip 9FT 24PT

University of Stirling
Renaissance Studies .....MRes 12FT 27PT/PGDip 8FT 21PT/PGCert 4FT 9PT

University of Strathclyde
Renaissance Studies .....MLitt 12FT 24PT/PGDip 9FT 21PT/PGCert 4FT 9PT

University of Sussex
Early Modern Literature and Culture........................ MA 12FT 24PT

Swansea University
Early Modern History.. MA 12FT 24PT
Medieval Studies ......MA 12FT 24-36PT/PGDip 12FT 24PT/PGCert 12FT 12PT

Teesside University
European History.. MA 12FT 24-36PT

UCL - University College London
Medieval and Renaissance Studies........................... MA 12FT 24PT

University of Warwick
Culture of the European Renaissance .. MA 12FT 24PT/PGDip 6FT 12PT
Culture of the European Renaissance .... MA 12FT 24PT

University of York
Renaissance and Early Modern Studies................... MA 12FT 24PT

Renaissance history
Research Courses

University of Aberdeen
Cultural History......MLitt by research 12FT/MPhil 24FT/PhD 36FT

University of Chichester
History.. PhD 36FT 84PT

University of Edinburgh
English Literature: Renaissance Literature..MSc by research 12FT 24PT

University of Kent
Medieval and Early Modern Studies...PhD 36FT 60PT/MPhil 24FT 36PT/MA by research 12FT 24PT

The Open University
Artistic networks, 1300-1550....PhD 36FT 72PT variableDL/MPhil 15FT 24PT variableDL

University of Oxford
English (to 1550) .... DPhil 48FT

Queen's University Belfast
Modern History........................... PhD 36FT 72PT/MPhil 24FT 48PT

University of Warwick
Renaissance Studies ....MPhil 12FT/PhD 36FT
PhD 36FT 60PT/MPhil 24FT 36PT

History

Roman empire
Taught Courses

University of Birmingham
Antiquity .... MA 12FT 24PT
Byzantine Studies .... MRes 12FT 24PT

Cardiff University
Early Medieval Society and Culture .... MA 12FT 24PT
Late Antique and Byzantine Studies .... MA 12FT 24PT
Religious Studies: Religion in Late Antiquity .... MA 12FT 24PT

Durham University
Greece. Rome and the Near East .... MA 12FT 24PT

University of Kent
Roman History and Archaeology .... MA 12FT 24PT
Roman History and Archaeology with a Term in Rome ...MA 12FT 24PT

King's College London
Late Antique & Byzantine Studies .... MA 12FT 24PT

University of Leicester
Archaeology of the Roman World .... MA 12FT 24PT/
PGDip 9FT 18PT
Archaeology: The Classical Mediterranean .MA 12FT 24PT 24DL/
PGDip 9FT 18PT

Newcastle University
Greek and Roman Archaeology .... MA 12FT 24PT
Roman Frontier Studies .... MA 12FT 24PT
Roman and Byzantine Archaeology .... MA 12FT 24PT

The Open University
Classical Studies .... MA variableDL

University of Oxford
Late Antique and Byzantine Studies .... MPhil 21FT/MSt 9FT

University of Reading
Archaeology .... MA 12FT 24PT
The City of Rome .... MA(Res) 12FT 24PT 60BM
The Classical Tradition .... MA(Res) 12FT 24PT 60BM

Royal Holloway, University of London
History: Hellenic Studies .... MA 12FT 24PT
Late Antique and Byzantine Studies .... MA 12FT 24PT

Swansea University
Ancient History and Classical Culture .... MA 12FT 36PT

UCL - University College London
Late Antique and Byzantine Studies .... MA 12FT 24PT

Roman empire
Research Courses

University of Birmingham
Byzantine Studies .... PhD 36FT 72PT/MA by research 12FT 24PT
Late Antiquity .... MPhil(B) 12FT 24PT

The Open University
Ancient and Modern Reception of Antiquity .... PhD 36FT 72PT
variableDL/MPhil 15FT 24PT variableDL

Swansea University
Ancient History .... MA by research 12FT 24PT

Scottish history
Taught Courses

University of Aberdeen
Church History .... MTh 12FT 24PT
Pastoral Studies .... DPS 12FT 24PT

University of Dundee
Scottish History (by distance learning) .... MLitt 24-60DL

University of Edinburgh
Scottish History .... MSc 12FT 24PT
Scottish History .... MSc(Res) 12FT 24PT
Scottish Studies .... MSc 12FT 24PT

University of Nottingham
Church History (distance learning) .... MA 12DL

University of St Andrews
National Trust for Scotland Studies .... MPhil 24FT 48PT
Reformation Studies .... MLitt 12FT 24PT/MPhil 24FT/PGDip 9FT
24PT
Scottish Historical Studies ....MLitt 12FT 24PT/MPhil 24FT/PGDip
9FT 24PT

University of Stirling
Historical Research .... MRes 12FT 24PT
Renaissance Studies .....MRes 12FT 27PT/PGDip 8FT 21PT/PGCert
4FT 9PT

University of the Highlands and Islands
History of the Highlands and Islands .... MLitt 12FT 24PT/PGDip
12FT 24PT/PGCert 12FT 24PT
Orkney and Shetland Studies ....MLitt 12FT 24PT/PGCert 12FT
24PT/PGDip 12FT 24PT

Scottish history
Research Courses

University of Edinburgh
Scottish History ....PhD 36FT 72PT/MPhil 24FT 48PT/MSc by
research 12FT 24PT
Scottish History .... MSc by research 12FT 24PT

Transport history
Taught Courses

University of York
Railway Studies .... GradCert 24+DL
Railway Studies and Transport History MA 12FT 24PT/PGDip 9FT
18PT
Transport History .... GradCert 24+DL

Transport history
Research Courses

University of York
Railway Studies and Transport History ....PhD 36FT 72PT/MPhil
24FT 48PT/MA by research 12FT 24PT

Welsh history
Taught Courses

University of Aberdeen
Ethnology and Folklore .... MLitt 12FT 24PT

Aberystwyth University
History of Wales / Hanes Cymru .... MA 12FT 24PT/
PGDip 9FT 18PT

Bangor University
Archaeology .... PhD by taught 36FT 48-72PT/MPhil 12-24FT
24-48PT
Celtic Archaeology .... MA 12FT 24PT/PGDip 8FT
Celts, The / Celtiaid, Y .... MA 12FT 36PT
Cymraeg (Welsh) (Welsh medium) .... MA 12FT 24PT/PGDip 8FT
Heritage .... PhD by taught 36FT 48-72PT/MPhil 12-24FT 24-48PT
History .... PhD by taught 24-36FT 48-72PT/MPhil 12FT 24PT
Medieval Studies .... MA 12FT 24-36PT
Medieval and Early Modern Literature ..MA 12FT 24-36PT/PGDip
9FT
Welsh History ....PhD by taught 24-36PT 48-72PT/
MPhil 12FT 24PT
Welsh History .... MA 12FT 24PT/PGDip 8FT

Cardiff University
Welsh History .... MA 12FT 24PT
Welsh and Celtic Studies .... MA 12FT 24PT

University College Cork
Arts (Folklore) .... HDip 9FT
Folklore .... MA 12FT

University of Oxford
Celtic Studies .... MPhil 21FT/MSt 9FT

University of South Wales
Regional History and Heritage .... MA 12FT 36PT

Swansea University
Early Modern History .... MA 12FT 24PT
Gender and Culture .... MA 12FT 24-36PT
History .... MA 12FT 24-36PT
Modern History .... MA 12FT 24PT

University of Wales Trinity Saint David
Local History: South West Wales since 1800 .... MA 12FT 24PT
12-24DL/PGDip 12FT 24PT 12-24DL/PGCert 12FT 24PT 12-24DL

Welsh history
Research Courses

Aberystwyth University
History .... MPhil 12FT 24PT
Welsh History ....MPhil 12FT 24PT PhD 36FT 60PT

Bangor University
Archaeology ....PhD 36FT 48-72PT/MPhil 12-24FT 24-48PT
Astudiaethau Celtaidd (Celtic Studies) (Welsh medium)... MA by
research 12FT/MPhil 24FT 48-60PT/PhD 24-36FT 60-72PT
Heritage ....MPhil 12-24FT 24-48PT/PhD 36FT 48-72PT
Llenyddiaeth Gymraeg (Welsh Literature) (Welsh medium).........
MPhil 24FT 48-60PT/PhD 24-36FT 60-72PT
Welsh History ....MPhil 12FT 24PT/PhD 24-36FT 48-72PT

Cardiff University
Welsh History .... PhD 36FT possiblePT/MPhil 12FT possiblePT

Swansea University
History .....PhD 36FT 72PT/MPhil 24FT 48PT/MA by research 12FT
24PT

Humanities

Humanities
Taught Courses

Bath Spa University
Advertising Practice..MA 12FT 12DL

Birkbeck, University of London
Cultural Enquiry..MRes 12FT 24PT
Cultural and Critical Studies .... MA 12FT 24PT
Medical Humanities ....MA 24PT/PGCert 24PT/PGDip 24PT

University of Bradford
Analytical Sciences....... MSc 12FT 60PT/PGDip 12FT 60PT/PGCert 12FT 60PT

University of Brighton
Arts and Cultural Research..............................MRes 12FT 24PT
Histories and Cultures...MA 12FT 24PT/PGDip 12FT 24PT/PGCert 12FT 24PT

University of Central Lancashire
Advancing Equality, Diversity and Inclusion ....MA 12FT 36PT/
PGDip 12FT 36PT/PGCert 12FT 24PT

University of Derby
Humanities ....MA 12FT 24+PT

University of Dundee
Art and Humanities ....MFA 12FT
Humanities ....MLitt 12FT
Non-Graduating Taught Postgraduate in School of Humanities..
PG module variableFT
Non-Graduating Taught Postgraduate in School of Law............PG
module variableFT
Pre-sessional English Language Programme 3+1+1 - 8 weeksCert 2FT
Twentieth Century Studies ....MLitt 12FT

Durham University
Community and Youth Work.................................. MA 12FT 24PT

University of East Anglia
Broadcast Journalism: Theory and Practice............. MA 12FT 24PT
Environmental Sciences and Humanities ....MA 12FT 24PT/MSc 12FT 24PT
Environmental Sciences and Humanities ....MA 12FT 24PT/MSc 12FT 24PT
Environmental Sciences and Humanities ....MA 12FT 24PT/MSc 12FT 24PT
International Public Policy, Regulation and Competition
.... MA 12FT 24PT
Public Policy and the Environment .... MA 12FT 24PT

University of East London
Narrative Research ...MA 12FT 24PT/PGDip 8FT 16PT/PGCert 4FT 8PT

Edge Hill University
Humanities ....MRes 12FT 24PT

University of Edinburgh
Cultural Studies ....MSc 12FT 24PT
East Asian Relations..MSc 12FT 24PT
Eighteenth-Century Cultures.............................MSc 12FT 24PT
Interdisciplinary Creative Practices......................MSc 12FT 24PT
Islamic and Middle Eastern Studies......................MSc 12FT 24PT
Japanese Society and Culture ....MSc 12FT 24PT
Late Antique, Islamic and Byzantine Studies ....MSc 12FT 24PT
Literature & Transatlanticism ....MSc 12FT 24PT
Media, Culture & Practice ....MSc 12FT
Medieval Literatures and Cultures.......................MSc 12FT 24PT
Middle Eastern Diasporas ....MSc 12FT 24PT
Modern Chinese Cultural Studies ....MSc 12FT 24PT
Nationalism Studies ....MSc 12FT 24PT
Persian Civilisation..MSc 12FT 24PT

University of Essex
Cultural and Social History ....MA 12FT 24PT/PGCert 9FT 21PT
Digital History ....MA 12FT 24PT/PGCert 9FT
Historical Studies ....MA 36-60PT/PGCert 36-60PT
History.......................MA 12FT 24PT/PGCert 9FT 21PT/PGDip 12FT
Local, Community and Family History ....MA 12FT 24PT/
PGCert 9FT 21PT

University of Exeter
Applied Security Strategy......................................MA 12FT
History...MA 12FT 24PT

Keele University
Humanities (American Studies)............................MRes 12FT 24PT
Humanities (English)..MRes 12FT 24PT
Humanities (History)..MRes 12FT 24PT
Humanities (Medical Humanities)........................MRes 12FT 24PT
Humanities (Music)..MRes 12FT 24PT
Humanities (Russian Studies) ....MRes 12FT 24PT

University of Kent
Medical Humanities .... MA 12FT 24PT

King's College London
Digital Humanities..MA 12FT 24PT
Medical Humanities ....MSc 12FT 24PT

Kingston University
History... MA 12FT 24PT

Lancaster University
Professional Development ....PGCert 3 - 60PT

University of Leicester
Humanities .... MA 12FT 24PT/Diploma 12FT 24PT/PGCert 12FT 24PT
Medical Humanities ....MA 12FT 24PT/PGDip 12FT 24PT

University of Lincoln
Arts Journalism .... MA 12FT 24PT
English Studies .... MA 12FT 24PT
Medieval Studies .... MA 12FT 24PT

Liverpool Hope University
Education & English Language ....MA 36PT
Peace Studies .... MA 12FT 24PT
Popular Literatures .... MA 12FT 24PT

London Consortium
Humanities and Cultural Studies.....................................MRes 12FT

Manchester Metropolitan University
Humanities ....MA 12FT 24PT/PGDip 12PT

University of Manchester
Human Resource Management and Development (International Development) by Distance Learning .... MSc 33PT

Northumbria University
International Development with Philanthropy ....MSc 12-16FT 24-28PT
International Development with Policy Analysis .....MSc 12-16FT 24-28PT
Public Policy ....MSc 12FT 28PT

The Open University
Humanities .... MA variableDL/PGDip variableDL/ PGCert variableDL

Oxford Brookes University
Two Year Master's Degree - Humanities and Social Sciences ....
MSc 21-24FT/MA 21-24FT

University of Oxford
Traditional East Asia .... MPhil 21FT

University of Reading
Advanced Legal Studies .... LLM 12FT 24PT
International Law and World Order ...LLM 12FT 24PT/PGDip 9FT/ PGCert 6FT
Law ....M (Res) 12FT 24PT/PGDip 9FT/PGCert 9FT
Legal History ....MA (Res) 12FT 24PT

University of Roehampton
Post Graduate Diploma- Media, Culture and Identity ..PGDip 9FT 24PT

School of Oriental and African Studies - SOAS
Critical Media and Cultural Studies....................MA 12FT 24-36PT
Ethnomusicology..MMus 12FT 24-36PT

Schumacher College
Economics for Transition ....MA 12FT

University of Sheffield
Crossways European Humanities (Mundus) ....MA 24FT
Public Humanities .... MA 12FT 24PT

University of South Wales
Regional History and Heritage .... MA 12FT 36PT
Social and Cultural History .... MA 12FT 24PT

University of Southampton
Arts (General) .... MA 12FT 24PT

University of St Andrews
Crossways in Cultural Narratives Mundus Masters (EU)..Mundus Masters 12-24FT

University of Stirling
Humanities ....MRes 12FT 24PT/PGCert 9FT 21PT

University of Strathclyde
Health History ....MSc 12FT 24PT/PGDip 9FT 18PT/PGDip 9FT 9PT

Trinity College Dublin - the University of Dublin
Digital Humanities and Culture ....MPhil 12FT 24PT

UCL - University College London
Digital Humanities.... MA 12FT 24PT/MSc 12FT 24PT/PGDip 12FT 24PT/PGCert 3FT 24PT
European Culture and Thought: Culture ..... MA 12FT 24PT/PGDip 9FT 18PT/PGCert 3FT 6PT
European Culture and Thought: Thought... MA 12FT 24PT/PGDip 9FT 18PT/PGCert 3FT 6PT
Language, Culture and History .... MA 12FT 24PT

University of Warwick
Public Policy .... MA 12FT 24PT/PGDip 9FT

University of Westminster
Cultural and Critical Studies....................................MA 12FT 24PT

University of Winchester
Modern Liberal Arts ....MA 12FT 24PT/PGDip 12FT 24PT/PGCert 12FT 24PT

University of Wolverhampton
English..MA 24-36PT
Human Sciences ....MRes 12FT 24PT

University of York
Women's Studies (Humanities) .... MA 12FT 24PT

Humanities
Research Courses

School of Advanced Study, University of London
English Studies..PhD 36FT 72PT

Anglia Ruskin University
English Language and Intercultural Communication MPhil 24FT/ PhD 36FT
English Language and Linguistics ....MPhil 24FT/PhD 36FT

Birkbeck, University of London
Arts and Humanities ....MPhil 24FT 36PT/PhD 36-48FT 60-84PT
English and Humanities .... PhD 36-48FT 60-84PT/ MPhil 24FT 36PT
Humanities and Cultural Studies.................PhD 36FT/MPhil 36FT

University of Bradford
Department of Social Sciences and Humanities....... PhD 36-48FT 48-60PT/MPhil 12-24FT 24-48PT

University of Chester
Higher Degrees by Research.......... MPhil 12 - 48FT 24 - 72PT/PhD 24 - 48FT 48 - 84PT

University of Edinburgh
Cultural Studies .... PhD 36FT 72PT MSc by research 12FT 24PT
Hispanic Studies ....PhD 36FT 72PT/MPhil 24FT 48PT/MSc by research 12FT 24PT
Islamic and Middle Eastern Studies........... PhD 36FT 72PT/MSc by research 12FT 24PT/MPhil 24FT 48PT
Medieval Studies ....PhD 36FT 72PT/MSc by research 12FT 24PT

University of Essex
History.....PhD 36FT 72PT/MPhil 24FT 48PT/MA by research 12FT 24PT

University of Exeter
History.......................PhD 48FT 84PT 84DL/MPhil 36FT 60PT 60DL
Security, Conflict and Justice..... MPhil 26FT 60PT/PhD 48FT 84PT

University of Greenwich
Humanities ....MA by research 12FT 24PT
Humanities - Research MPhil 24FT 36 - 48PT/PhD 36FT 48 - 60PT

King's College London
Digital Humanities Research......... PhD 36FT 48-72PT/MPhil 36FT 48-72PT

Liverpool Hope University
Postgraduate Research .... PhD 24FT 48PT/MPhil 12FT 24PT

London Consortium
Humanities and Cultural Studies......................................PhD 36FT

London Metropolitan University
Dept of Humanities, Arts and Languages.......PhD Max 60FT Max 96PT/MPhil Max 36FT Max 54PT

London South Bank University
Faculty of Arts & Human Sciences......PhD 36FT 60PT/MPhil 24FT 36PT

Manchester Metropolitan University
Department of Humanities and Applied Social Studies ..... MA by research
Humanities and Applied Social Studies.......PhD 36FT 54PT/MPhil 24FT 36PT/MA by research 12FT 24PT

Middlesex University
School of Humanities and Cultural Studies.......... PhD 36FT/MPhil 12-24FT/MA by research 12-24FT

The Open University
Public engagement in science.............. PhD 36FT 72PT variableDL

University of Southampton
Transnational Studies: Society, Culture, Language.............. MA by research 12FT 24PT/MPhil 48FT 84PT/PhD 48FT 84PT

University of Strathclyde
Humanities - Research .... MPhil 12FT/MRes 12FT/PhD 33FT

Swansea University
Digital Humanities.................................MA by research 12FT 24PT
Global Migration ....MSc by research 12FT 24PT

University of the West of England, Bristol
Faculty of Creative Arts, Humanities and Education.......... PhD .FT
School of Humanities, Languages and Social Sciences......PhD -FT

University of Westminster
Social Sciences, Humanities and Languages...........MPhil 18-36FT 30-60PT

University of Wolverhampton
School of Humanities, Languages and Social Sciences....................
MPhil/PhD

Languages

Arabic
Taught Courses

University of Aberdeen
Modern Thought ....MLitt 12FT 24PT

Durham University
Arabic/English Translation and Interpreting........... MA 12FT 24PT

University of East Anglia
Applied Translation Studies.. MA 12FT 24PT

University of Edinburgh
International Relations of the Middle East with Arabic ....
MSc 24FT

University of Exeter
Middle East and Islamic Studies................................ MA 12FT 24PT

Heriot-Watt University
Arabic-English Translating and Conference Interpreting ....
MSc 12FT 24PT/PGDip 9FT 21PT
Arabic-English Translation and Computer-Assisted Translation
Tools...MSc 12FT 24PT/PGDip 9FT 21PT

University of Leeds
Middle Eastern and Islamic Studies........................... MA 12FT 24PT

University of Nottingham
Literatures in English Translation ....MA 12FT

University of Oxford
Medieval Arabic Thought .... MPhil 21FT
Modern Middle Eastern Studies .... MPhil 21FT
Syriac Studies ....MSt 9FT

School of Oriental and African Studies - SOAS
Arabic Language Teaching...MA 12FT 24PT
Arabic Literature .... MA 12FT 24-36PT

Arabic
Research Courses

University of Central Lancashire
Translation, English as a Foreign Language, Learning & Teaching
Methodology, Language.....PhD 30-48FT 66-84PT/MPhil 18-36FT
42-60PT/MA by research 12FT 24PT

University of Exeter
Arab and Islamic Studies ...... PhD 36-48FT 72PT/MPhil 24FT 48PT
Middle East Politics...................................... MPhil 24FT 48PT 48DL/
PhD 36FT 72PT 72DL

Armenian
Taught Courses

University of Bristol
Classical Reception.. MA 12FT 24PT

University of Oxford
Classical Armenian Studies..MSt 9FT

Celtic studies
Taught Courses

University of Aberdeen
Celtic Studies .... MLitt 12FT 24PT/PGDip 9FT 18PT
Irish and Scottish Studies.......... MLitt 12FT 24PT/PGDip 9FT 18PT

Bangor University
Archaeology.............PhD by taught 36FT 48-72PT/MPhil 12-24FT
24-48PT
Celtic Archaeology .... MA 12FT 24PT/PGDip 8FT
Celts, The / Celtiaid, Y.................................. MA 12FT 36FT
Cymraeg (Welsh) (Welsh medium)....... MA 12FT 24PT/PGDip 8FT
Welsh History ....PhD by taught 24-36FT 48-72PT/
MPhil 12FT 24PT

University of Cambridge
Anglo-Saxon, Norse and Celtic...MPhil 9FT

Cardiff University
Early Celtic Studies... MA 12FT 24PT

Cliff College
Celtic Mission and SpiritualityPGCert 12PT/PGDip 12FT 24PT/MA
12-18FT 24-30PT

University College Cork
Arts (Folklore) ....HDip 9FT
Folklore...MA 12FT

University of Glasgow
Celtic Studies ....MLitt 12FT 24PT

University of Oxford
Celtic Studies... MPhil 21FT/MSt 9FT

Queen's University Belfast
Irish Translation ....MA 12FT max 31PT/PGDip 12FT max 31PT

Swansea University
Welsh... MA 12FT 24PT
Welsh Writing in English .... MA 12FT 24PT

University of Wales Trinity Saint David
Astudiaethau Celtaidd .... MA 12FT 24PT 12-24DL/PGCert 12FT
24PT 12-24DL/PGDip 12FT 24PT 12-24DL
Celtic Studies ....MA 12FT 24PT 12-24DL/PGCert 12FT 24PT
12-24DL/PGDip 12FT 24PT 12-24DL

Celtic studies
Research Courses

University of Aberdeen
Celtic Studies .... PhD 36FT 60PT/MLitt by research 12FT 24PT/
MPhil 24FT 48PT

Aberystwyth University
Celtic Studies ....MPhil 12FT 24PT PhD 36FT 60PT

Bangor University
Astudiaethau Celtaidd (Celtic Studies) (Welsh medium).... MA by
research 12FT/MPhil 24FT 48-60PT/PhD 24-36FT 60-72PT
Llenyddiaeth Gymraeg (Welsh Literature) (Welsh medium).........
MPhil 24FT 48-60PT/PhD 24-36FT 60-72PT

University of Cambridge
Anglo-Saxon, Norse and Celtic...PhD 36FT

University of Edinburgh
Celtic and Scottish Studies PhD 36FT 72PT/MPhil 24FT 48PT/MSc
by research 12FT 24PT

University of Exeter
Cornish Studies .... PhD 36FT 72PT/MPhil 24FT 48PT

National University of Ireland Galway
College of Arts, Social Sciences & Celtic Studies ..PhD 48FT 72PT/
MLitt by research 24FT 48PT/Structured PhD 48FT 72PT

University of Glasgow
Celtic ....PhD 36FT/MPhil 12FT/MLitt by research 12FT

Queen's University Belfast
Irish and Celtic Studies................ PhD 36FT 72PT/MPhil 24FT 48PT

Swansea University
Welsh.......PhD 36FT 60PT/MPhil 12FT 24PT/MA by research 12FT
24PT

University of Ulster
Celtic Studies .... PhD 36FT 72PT/MPhil 24FT 48PT

Chinese
Taught Courses

Bangor University
Translation Studies .... MA 12FT 24PT

Goldsmiths, University of London
Critical Asian Studies.. MA 12FT 24PT

Heriot-Watt University
Chinese-English Translating and Conference Interpreting..... MSc
12FT 24PT/PGDip 9FT 21PT
Chinese-English Translation and Computer-Assisted Translation
Tools...MSc 12FT 24PT/PGDip 9FT 21PT

University of Leeds
Chinese...MA 12FT/PGDip 9FT/PGCert 6FT
Chinese Business and the Asia Pacific...................... MA 12FT 24PT
Chinese Studies.. MA 12FT 24PT
Chinese and Business.. MA 12FT 24PT

Newcastle University
Interpreting...MA 12FT/MA 24FT

University of Nottingham
Chinese/English Translation & Interpreting.......................MA 12FT

University of Oxford
Chinese Studies ....MSt 9FT
Modern Chinese Studies.. MPhil 21FT

School of Oriental and African Studies - SOAS
Chinese Studies.. MA 12FT 24-36PT

University of Sheffield
Chinese Studies..MA 12FT
Teaching Chinese as a Foreign Language...........................MA 12FT

Swansea University
Chinese-English Translation and Language Teaching......MA 12FT
Translation and Interpreting ....MA 12FT

UCL - University College London
Chinese Health and Humanity..MA 12FT
Chinese Studies (Health and Humanity)............................MA 24FT

Chinese
Research Courses

Bangor University
Translation Studies ....PhD 36FT/MPhil 12FT
Translation Studies (by Practice) ....
PhD 36FT 72PT/MPhil 24FT 48PT

University of Edinburgh
Chinese.. PhD 36FT 72PT/MPhil 24FT 48PT/MSc by research 12FT
24PT

Czech
Taught Courses

University of Oxford
Slavonic Studies... MPhil 24FT/MSt 9FT

Czech
Research Courses

University of Bristol
Russian and Czech. PhD 36FT 72PT/MLitt by research 24FT 48PT/
MPhil 12FT 24PT

Dutch
Taught Courses

UCL - University College London
Dutch Studies.. MA 12FT 24PT

Dutch
Research Courses

University of Cambridge
Old Dutch ....PhD 36FT 60PT

UCL - University College London
Dutch... PhD 36FT 60PT

English as a foreign language
Taught Courses

Belfast Metropolitan College
Cambridge ESOL Level 5 Certificate in Teaching English to
Speakers of Other Languages ....Cert 5PT

University of Central Lancashire
Interpreting & Translation ....MA 12FT
Teaching English to Speakers of Other Languages (TESOL) with
Applied Linguistics .... MA 12FT 24-60PT 24-60DL

Coventry University
English Language Teaching.. MA 12FT 30PT

University for the Creative Arts
English Language for the Creative Arts .... Pre-Masters 2FT 3FT

University of Cumbria
TESOL (Teaching English to Speakers of Other Languages)......MA
12FT

University of Dundee
Pre-Sessional Programme for Postgraduates (10 weeks)........ Cert
2.5FT

University of Essex
Accounting with English for Academic Purposes.......Diploma 9FT
Applied Linguistics with English for Academic Purposes...............
Diploma 9FT
Art History and Theory with English for Academic Purposes ....
Diploma 9FT
Biotechnology with English for Academic Purposes.......................
Diploma 9FT
Cambridge Certificate in English Language Teaching to Adults ...
GradCert 9FT
Computer Science with English for Academic Purposes ....
Diploma 9FT
Economics with English for Academic Purposes ....Diploma 9FT
Electronic Engineering with English for Academic Purposes.........
Diploma 9FT
Entrepreneurship and Innovation with English for Academic
Purposes...Diploma 9FT
Finance with English for Academic Purposes..............Diploma 9FT
History with English for Academic Purposes...............Diploma 9FT
Management with English for Academic Purposes...Diploma 9FT
Politics with English for Academic Purposes ....Diploma 9FT
Psychoanalytic Studies with English for Academic Purposes ....
Diploma 9FT
Psychological Studies with English for Academic Purposes...........
Diploma 9FT
Teaching English as a Foreign Language .... MA 12FT 24PT
Teaching English to Speakers of Other Languages ....
MA 12FT 24PT

University of Huddersfield
English Language Proficiency and British Culture .....PGCert 12PT

King's College London
Biomedical Sciences & Scientific English ....GradDip 12FT
International Pre-Master's Programme................ Diploma 6-12FT
International Studies & Academic English ....GradDip 12FT

Kingston University
Marketing with English ....MA 12FT

Leeds Metropolitan University
10-week Pre-Sessional .... 10-week Pre-Sessional 2FT
4-Week Pre-Sessional .... 4-Week Pre-Sessional 1FT
International Masters ....Academic English and masters
programme unknownFT

University of Leeds
English as an Additional Language and Education.........MA 36PT/
PGDip 36PT

Northumbria University
Applied Linguistics - TESOL .... MA 12FT 36PT

Oxford Brookes University
Education (TESOL) .... MA 12FT/MA 24-36FT

Languages

University of Reading
English Language Teaching .MA 12FT 24PT 24-48DL/PGDip 12FT 24PT/PGCert 12FT 24PT

Royal Holloway, University of London
Bridging Diploma for International Students ....Diploma 9FT

University of Salford
TESOL and Applied Linguistics ..... MA 12FT 36PT/PGDip 9FT 24PT

University of Southampton
English Language Teaching.........MA 12FT 24PT/PGCert 12DL/MA 28DL

University of St Andrews
Pre Masters (for Business-Related Masters Programmes).............. Cert 9FT

University of Stirling
Teaching English to Speakers of other Languages (TESOL) and Computer Assisted Language Learning......MSc 12FT 24PT/PGDip 9FT 18PT/PGCert 6FT 12PT

Swansea University
Certificate in English Language Teaching to Adults (CELTA)... Cert 1FT 3PT

University of West London
Pre-Masters Studies..GradCert 4FT

French
Taught Courses

Bangor University
European Languages and Cultures........................... MA 12FT 24PT
Translation Studies .... MA 12FT 24PT

University College Cork
French ....MA 12FT
French - Linguistics..MA 12FT
Translation Studies (French) ....MA 12FT

National University of Ireland Galway
French...MA 12FT

University of Kent
Graduate Diploma in Humanities (French) ....GradDip 12FT

King's College London
French Literature & Culture .... MA 12FT 24PT

Liverpool John Moores University
French Extension Course ....Extension course 3PT
Modern Languages: French, Spanish, German, French & Spanish or French & German .... PGCE 10FT

National University of Ireland, Maynooth
French...MA 12FT

University of Nottingham
Early Modern French Studies................................ MA 12FT 24-36PT
French... MA 12FT 24-36PT

University of Portsmouth
Francophone Africa .... MA 12FT 24PT

University of Reading
French (Conversion Course) (Secondary)........................ PGCE 24FT
French Studies..MA (Res) 12FT
Modern Languages (Secondary Teaching)...................... PGCE 10FT
Primary Teaching with French Specialism...................... PGCE 10FT

Royal Holloway, University of London
French .... MA 12FT 24PT

University of Sheffield
French Studies (Research Track)............................... MA 12FT 24PT

University of St Andrews
French Language Studies.........MLitt 12FT 24PT/PGDip 9FT 24PT/MPhil 24FT
French Studies........MLitt 12FT 24PT/PGDip 9FT 24PT/MPhil 24FT

Swansea University
Literary Translation (French) .... MA 12FT 24-36PT
Translation and Interpreting ....MA 12FT
Translation with Language Technology................... MA 12FT 24PT

French
Research Courses

Aberystwyth University
French ....MPhil 12FT 24PT PhD 36FT 60PT

Bangor University
French .... PhD 36FT/MPhil 12FT
Translation Studies .... PhD 36FT/MPhil 12FT
Translation Studies (PhD by Practice).PhD 36FT 72PT/MPhil 24FT 48PT

Birkbeck, University of London
French.. PhD 36FT 48PT/MPhil 24FT 36PT

University of Bristol
French..PhD 36FT 72PT/MLitt by research 24FT 48PT/MPhil 12FT 24PT

University of Cambridge
French.. PhD 36FT 60PT

Durham University

Modern Languages and Cultures ....PhD 36FT 72PT/MA by research 12FT 24PT

University of Edinburgh
French.... PhD 36FT 72PT/MPhil 24FT 48PT/MSc by research 12FT 24PT

University of Exeter
French Studies............................. PhD 36FT 60PT/MPhil 48FT 89PT

University of Glasgow
French Language and Literature...PhD 36FT/MPhil 12FT/MLitt by research 12FT

University of London Institute in Paris
French and Comparative Studies.........PhD 36FT 72PT/MPhil 24FT 48PT

University of Kent
French......PhD 36FT 60PT/MPhil 24FT 36PT/MA by research 12FT 24PT

King's College London
French Research .... PhD 36FT 48-72PT/MPhil 24FT 36PT

University of Leicester
French.. PhD 36FT 48PT/MPhil 24FT 36PT

University of Liverpool
French .... PhD 24-48FT 48-84PT/MPhil 12-48FT 48-72PT

University of Nottingham
French ....MA by research 12FT 24PT PhD 36FT 72PT/MPhil 24FT 48PT

Oxford Brookes University
Modern Languages .....MPhil/Phil 36-60FT 48-72PT/PhD 24-60FT 36-72PT/MPhil 24-36FT 36-48PT

Queen Mary, University of London
French...PhD

Royal Holloway, University of London
French ....PhD 36FT

University of St Andrews
French Language Studies.........PhD 36FT 72PT/DLang 36FT 72PT/MPhil 12-24FT 48PT
French Studies........................PhD 36FT 72PT/MPhil 12-24FT 48PT

Swansea University
European Cultures..........................MA by research 12FT 24PT
French .... PhD 36FT 72PT/MPhil 24FT 36PT

UCL - University College London
French .... PhD 36FT 60PT

University of Warwick
French Studies...........................PhD 36FT 60PT/MPhil 24FT 36PT/MA by research 12FT 24PT

German
Taught Courses

Bangor University
European Languages and Cultures........................... MA 12FT 24PT
Translation Studies .... MA 12FT 24PT

University College Cork
Arts (German)...HDip 9FT 18PT
German Studies .... MA 12FT 24PT

National University of Ireland Galway
German Literature/ Language ....MA 12FT

University of Kent
Graduate Diploma in Humanities (German).............GradDip 12FT
Modern German and Comparative Literature .... MA 12FT 24PT

University of Limerick
Irish and German Studies...MA 12FT

Liverpool John Moores University
Modern Languages: French, Spanish, German, French & Spanish or French & German .... PGCE 10FT

National University of Ireland, Maynooth
German .... MA 12FT 24PT

University of Oxford
Yiddish Studies...MSt 9FT

University of Reading
German Studies ....MA (Res) 12FT 24PT
Modern Languages (Secondary Teaching) .... PGCE 10FT

Royal Holloway, University of London
German .... MA 12FT 24PT

University of Sheffield
Germanic Studies (Research Track)........................... MA 12FT 24PT

University of St Andrews
German Studies .....MLitt 12FT 24PT/PGDip 9FT 24PT/MPhil 24FT

Swansea University
Translation and Interpreting ....MA 12FT
Translation with Language Technology................... MA 12FT 24PT

University of Warwick
German Cultural Studies..............MA 12FT 24PT/PGDip 9FT 21PT/PGCert 3-6FT 6PT

German
Research Courses

Aberystwyth University
German ....MPhil 12FT 24PT PhD 36FT 60PT

Bangor University
German .... PhD 36FT/MPhil 12FT
Translation Studies .... PhD 36FT/MPhil 12FT
Translation Studies (by Practice) ....PhD 36FT 72PT/MPhil 24FT 48PT

Birkbeck, University of London
German .... PhD 36FT 48PT/MPhil 24FT 36PT

University of Bristol
German .... PhD 36FT 72PT/MLitt by research 24FT 48PT/MPhil 12FT 24PT

University of Cambridge
German .... PhD 36FT 60PT

University of Edinburgh
German..PhD 36FT 72PT/MPhil 24FT 48PT
MSc by research 12FT 24-36PT

University of Exeter
German Studies .... PhD 48FT 84PT/MPhil 36FT 60PT

University of Glasgow
German Language and Literature .... PhD 36FT/MPhil 12FT/MLitt by research 12FT

King's College London
German Research .... PhD 36FT 48-72PT/MPhil 24FT 36PT

University of Leeds
German ....PhD 36+FT/MPhil 24FT/MA by research 12+FT

University of Liverpool
German .... PhD 24-48FT 48-84PT/MPhil 12-48FT 24-72PT

University of Nottingham
German ....MA by research 12FT 24-36PT

Queen Mary, University of London
German .... PhD 36FT 72PT/MPhil 24FT 48PT

Royal Holloway, University of London
German .... PhD 36FT/MPhil 24FT/MA by research 12FT

University of St Andrews
German Studies ....PhD 36FT 72PT/DLang 36FT 72PT/MPhil 12-24FT 48PT

Swansea University
European Cultures..........................MA by research 12FT 24PT
German .... PhD 36FT 72PT/MPhil 24FT 48PT

University of Ulster
German .... PhD 36FT 72PT/MPhil 24FT 48PT

UCL - University College London
German .... PhD 36FT 60PT

Greek
Taught Courses

University of Aberdeen
Sociolinguistics .... MLitt 12FT 24PT/PGDip 9FT 21PT

Bangor University
Translation Studies .... MA 12FT 24PT

King's College London
Modern Greek Studies (Sociolinguistics)................. MA 12FT 24PT

University of Oxford
Eastern Christian Studies .... MPhil 21FT
Greek and/or Latin Languages and Literature ..... MPhil 21FT/MSt 9FT
Greek and/or Roman History.......................... MSt 9FT/MPhil 24FT

University of St Andrews
Greek ....PGDip 9FT 18PT/MLitt 12FT 24PT
Greek and Latin.............................PGDip 9FT/MLitt 12FT 24PT

Greek
Research Courses

Bangor University
Translation Studies .... PhD 36FT/MPhil 12FT
Translation Studies (PhD by Practice).PhD 36FT 72PT/MPhil 24FT 48PT

University of Cambridge
Modern Greek .... PhD 36FT 60PT

Swansea University
Greek .... MPhil 24FT 48PT/PhD 36FT 72PT

Hebrew
Taught Courses

University of Aberdeen
Jewish Studies............................ MLitt 12FT 24PT/PGDip 9FT 18PT
Pastoral Studies ....DPS 12FT 24PT

King's College London
Bible and Ministry.. MA 12FT 24PT

Languages

Oxford Centre for Hebrew and Jewish Studies
Jewish Studies ...... MSt 9FT

University of Oxford
Classical Hebrew Studies ...... MSt 9FT
Jewish Studies ...... MSt 9FT
Yiddish Studies ...... MSt 9FT

School of Oriental and African Studies - SOAS
Israeli Studies ...... MA 12FT 24-36PT
MA in the Study of Contemporary Pakistan ...... MA 12FT 24PT

UCL - University College London
Hebrew and Jewish Studies ...... MA 12FT 24PT

Hebrew
Research Courses

University of Edinburgh
Hebrew and Old Testament Studies. MPhil 24FT/PhD 36FT 72PT/MTh by research 12FT 24PT/MSc by research 12FT 24PT

UCL - University College London
Hebrew and Jewish Studies ...... PhD 36FT 60PT

Indian
Research Courses

University of Edinburgh
Sanskrit. PhD 36FT 72PT/MPhil 24FT 48PT/MSc by research 12FT 24PT

Irish gaelic
Taught Courses

Aberystwyth University
Irish/Gwyddeleg ...... MA 12FT 24PT

University College Cork
Modern Irish ...... MA 12FT 24PT

Dublin Institute of Technology
Applied Irish/Ghaeilge Fheidhmeach ...... MA 24PT

National University of Ireland Galway
Ateangaireacht Chomhdhála ...... MA 12FT/PGDip 9FT
Nua-Ghaeilge ...... MA 12FT
Old and Middle Irish ...... MA 12FT

National University of Ireland, Maynooth
sa Nua-Ghaeilge (Modern Irish) ...... MA 12FT

Trinity College Dublin - the University of Dublin
Old Irish ...... PGDip 12FT

University of Ulster
Modern Irish ...... MA 27PT/PGDip 18PT

Italian
Taught Courses

Bangor University
European Languages and Cultures ...... MA 12FT 24PT
Translation Studies ...... MA 12FT 24PT

University College Cork
Arts (Italian) ...... HDip 9FT 18PT
Italian ...... MA 12FT

University of Kent
Graduate Diploma in Humanities (Italian) ...... GradDip 12FT

University of Reading
Italian Studies ...... MA (Res) 12FT 24PT
Modern Italian History ...... MA (Res) 12FT 24PT
The City of Rome ...... MA(Res) 12FT 24PT 60BM

Royal Holloway, University of London
Italian ...... MA 12FT 24PT

University of St Andrews
Italian Studies ...... MLitt 12FT 24PT/PGDip 9FT 24PT/MPhil 24FT

Swansea University
Translation and Interpreting ...... MA 12FT
Translation with Language Technology ...... MA 12FT 24PT

University of Warwick
Italian Studies: Culture and Communication ...... MA 12FT 24PT

Italian
Research Courses

Bangor University
Italian ...... MPhil 12FT/PhD 36FT
Translation Studies ...... PhD 36FT/MPhil 12FT
Translation Studies (PhD by Practice). PhD 36FT 72PT/MPhil 24FT 48PT

University of Bristol
Italian .. PhD 36FT 72PT/MLitt by research 24FT 48PT/MPhil 12FT 24PT

University of Edinburgh
Italian .... PhD 36FT 72PT/MPhil 24FT 48PT/MSc by research 12FT 24PT

University of Exeter
Italian Studies ...... PhD 48FT 84PT/MPhil 36FT 60PT

University of Kent
Italian ...... PhD 36FT 60PT/MPhil 24FT 36PT/MA by research 12FT 24PT

University of Leicester
Modern languages (Italian) ...... PhD 36FT 48PT/MPhil 24FT 36PT

Royal Holloway, University of London
Italian ...... PhD 36FT 72PT/MPhil 24FT 48PT

University of St Andrews
Italian Studies ...... PhD 36FT 72PT/MPhil 24FT 48PT

Swansea University
European Cultures ...... MA by research 12FT 24PT
Italian ...... PhD 36FT 72PT/MPhil 24FT 48PT

University of Warwick
Italian ...... PhD 36FT 60PT/MPhil 24FT 48PT/MA by research 12FT 24PT

Japanese
Taught Courses

University of East Anglia
Applied Translation Studies ...... MA 12FT 24PT

University of Edinburgh
Japanese Society and Culture ...... MSc 12FT 24PT

University of Greenwich
Language Learning and Japanese Language Teaching ...... MA 12FT
Management of Language Learning ...... MA 12FT

University of Leeds
Japanese Studies ...... MA 12FT 24PT

Newcastle University
Interpreting ...... MA 12FT/MA 24FT

University of Oxford
Japanese Studies ...... MSt 10FT
Modern Japanese Studies ...... MPhil 24FT/MSc 12FT

School of Oriental and African Studies - SOAS
Applied Linguistics and Language Pedagogy (Japanese, Korean, Chinese or Tibetan) ...... MA 12FT 24-36PT
Japanese Studies ...... MA 12FT 24-36PT

Japanese
Research Courses

Birkbeck, University of London
Japanese ...... PhD 36FT 48PT/MPhil 24FT 36PT

University of Central Lancashire
Translation, English as a Foreign Language, Learning & Teaching Methodology, Language ..... PhD 30-48FT 66-84PT/MPhil 18-36FT 42-60PT/MA by research 12FT 24PT

University of Edinburgh
Japanese ...... PhD 36FT 72PT/MPhil 24FT 48PT/MSc by research 12FT 24PT

Languages
Taught Courses

University of Aberdeen
Language Policy and Planning. MLitt 12FT 24PT/PGDip 9FT 18PT

Bangor University
Cymraeg (Welsh) (Welsh medium) ...... MA 12FT 24PT/PGDip 8FT
European Languages and Cultures ...... MA 12FT 24PT

University of Bath
Interpreting and Translating ..... MA 12FT/PGDip 9FT 21PT/PGCert 4FT 16PT

Birkbeck, University of London
Modern Languages: Combined Language StudiesMA 12FT 24PT/MRes 12FT 24PT/PGDip 12FT 24PT
Spanish, Portuguese and Latin American Cultural Studies ...... MA 12FT 24PT/MRes 12FT 24PT

University of Cambridge
Russian Studies ...... MPhil 9FT

University of Central Lancashire
Interpreting & Translation ...... MA 12FT

University of Dundee
Language & Communication ...... MSc 12FT
Pre-Sessional Programme for Postgraduates (4 weeks) ... Cert 1FT

Durham University
TESOL ...... MA 12FT

University of East Anglia
Applied Translation Studies ...... MA 12FT 24PT
Communication and Language Studies ...... MA 12FT 24PT
Language and Intercultural Communication ...... MA 12FT 24PT

University of Edinburgh
Advanced Arabic ...... MSc 12FT
Arab World Studies ...... MSc 24FT
Celtic and Scottish Studies ...... MSc 12FT 24PT
Chinese Studies ...... Master of Chinese Studies 24FT
Classics ...... MSc 12FT 24PT
International Relations of the Middle East with Arabic ...... MSc 24FT
Islamic and Middle Eastern Studies ...... MSc 12FT 24PT
Japanese Society and Culture ...... MSc 12FT 24PT
Law and Chinese ...... LLM 24FT
Literary Translation as Creative Practice ...... MSc 12FT 24PT

University of Essex
Chinese-English Translation and Interpreting ..... MA 9-12FT 24PT
Teaching English as a Foreign Language ...... MA 12FT 24PT
Translation and Literature ...... MA 9-12FT 24PT
Translation, Interpreting and Subtitling ...... MA 9-12FT 24PT

University of Exeter
European Languages and Cultures ...... MA 12FT 24PT/MRes 12FT 24PT

National University of Ireland Galway
Advanced Language Skills (French or German or Italian or Spanish) ...... MA 12FT

Goldsmiths, University of London
Critical Asian Studies ...... MA 12FT 24PT
Education: Culture, Language and Identity ...... MA 12FT 24-60PT
Multilingualism, Linguistics and Education ...... MA 12FT 24PT

Heriot-Watt University
Arabic-English Translating and Conference InterpretingMSc 12FT 24PT/PGDip 9FT 21PT
Arabic-English Translation and Computer-Assisted Translation Tools ...... MSc 12FT 24PT/PGDip 9FT 21PT
Chinese-English Translating and Conference Interpreting ..... MSc 12FT 24PT/PGDip 9FT 21PT
Chinese-English Translation and Computer-Assisted Translation Tools ...... MSc 12FT 24PT/PGDip 9FT 21PT
International Management and Business Communication... MSc 12FT 24PT/PGDip 9FT 21PT
Interpreting and Translating ...... MSc 12FT/PGDip 9FT
Translation and Computer Assisted Translation Tools ... MSc 12FT 24PT/PGDip 9FT 21PT

University of Hull
Modern Languages ...... MRes 12FT 24PT

University of Kent
Contemporary ...... MA 12FT 24PT

Leeds Metropolitan University
English Language & Education Studies (Pre-Masters) ...... GradDip 12FT

University of Limerick
English ...... MA 12FT
Irish and German Studies ...... MA 12FT
Languages ...... GradDip 9FT
Modern Language Studies ...... MA 12FT
Teaching English to Speakers of Other Languages ...... MA 12FT

Liverpool John Moores University
Modern Languages: French, Spanish, German, French & Spanish or French & German ...... PGCE 10FT

University of Liverpool
Modern Languages (by Directed Research) ...... MA 12FT 24PT

London Metropolitan University
PGCE Secondary Modern Languages ...... PGCE 12FT

University of Manchester
American Studies (Literature and Culture) ...... MA 12FT
Languages and Cultures (research route) ...... MA 12FT 24PT

Middlesex University
Interpreting ...... MA 12FT

Newcastle University
Professional Translating for European Languages. MA 12FT 24PT
Translating ...... MA 12 or 24FT
Translating and Interpreting ...... MA 12 or 24FT
Translation Studies ...... MLitt 12FT 24PT

Newman University
PGCE Primary with Modern Foreign Languages .. PGCE(QTS) 12FT
PGCE Secondary Modern Foreign Languages ...... PGCE(QTS) 12FT

Nottingham Trent University
English Language Teaching ...... MA 12FT 24PT
English Literary Research ...... MA 12FT 24PT/PGDip 12FT 21PT/PGCert 9FT 21PT

University of Nottingham
Communication and Entrepreneurship ...... MSc 12FT 24PT
Digital Technologies for Language Teaching (Distance Learning) MA 24DL
Modern Languages and Critical Theory ...... MA 12FT 24PT

Oxford Brookes University
English ...... MA 12FT 24PT/PGDip 9FT 20PT/PGCert 4FT 8PT
Publishing and Language ...... MA 12FT 24PT/PGDip 9FT 18PT

Oxford Centre for Hebrew and Jewish Studies
Jewish Studies ...... MSt 9FT

University of Oxford
Cuneiform Studies ...... MPhil 21FT
Greek and/or Latin Languages and Literature ..... MPhil 21FT/MSt 9FT
Greek and/or Roman History ...... MSt 9FT/MPhil 24FT
Japanese Studies ...... MSt 10FT
Modern Languages ...... MPhil 21FT/MSt 9FT

Languages

University of Portsmouth
Modern Foreign Languages: French and Mandarin................ PGCE (Postgraduate) 12FT/PGCE (Professional) 12FT

Queen Mary, University of London
Applied Linguistics for English Language Teaching MA 12FT 24PT

Queen's University Belfast
English (Broadcast Literacy)... MA 12FT 24PT
Languages .... MA 12FT 30PT
Translation .... MA 12FT 12PT

University of Reading
Applied Linguistics ..MA 12FT 24-48PT/PGCert 12FT/PGDip 12FT
Applied Linguistics - Research Pathway ... MA (Res) 12FT 24-72PT

Royal Holloway, University of London
English Literature .... MA 12FT 24PT
French... MA 12FT 24PT
German .... MA 12FT 24PT
Hispanic Studies .... MA 12FT 24PT
Italian .... MA 12FT 24PT

University of Salford
Interpreting and Translating........ MA 12FT 36PT/PGDip 9FT 24PT
Translating ....MA 12FT 36PT/PGDip 9FT 24PT
Translating for International Business. MA 12FT 36PT/PGDip 9FT 24PT

School of Oriental and African Studies - SOAS
Ancient Near Eastern Languages .... MA 12FT 24-36PT
Arabic Language Teaching.. MA 12FT 24PT
Language Documentation and Description ...... MA 12FT 24-36PT
Languages and literatues of South East Asia .... MA 12FT 24-36PT

Sheffield Hallam University
English..........................MPhil 36FT 84PT/PhD by taught 36FT 84PT
English Language Teaching...MA 12FT
English Language and Linguistics .... MA 12FT 24-72PT
Modern and Contemporary Literature............... MA 12FT 24-72PT

University of Sheffield
Germanic Studies (Research Track).......................... MA 12FT 24PT
Hispanic Studies .... MA 12FT 24PT
Language and Communication Impairment in Children PGDip 24 PTDL/PGCert 12 PTDL

University of St Andrews
French Language Studies MLitt 12FT 24PT/PGDip 9FT 24PT/MPhil 24FT

French Studies........ MLitt 12FT 24PT/PGDip 9FT 24PT/MPhil 24FT
German Studies ..... MLitt 12FT 24PT/PGDip 9FT 24PT/MPhil 24FT
Greek .... PGDip 9FT 18PT/MLitt 12FT 24PT
Greek and Latin.......................................PGDip 9FT/MLitt 12FT 24PT
Italian Studies .... MLitt 12FT 24PT/PGDip 9FT 24PT/MPhil 24FT
Language and Linguistics......... MLitt 12FT 24PT/PGDip 9FT 18PT/ MPhil 24FT

University of Stirling
Teaching English to Speakers of Other Languages (on-line).. MSc 36PT
Teaching English to Speakers of other Languages (TESOL) and Computer Assisted Language Learning......MSc 12FT 24PT/PGDip 9FT 18PT/PGCert 6FT 12PT
Teaching of English to Speakers of Other Languages (TESOL)....... MSc 12FT 24PT/PGDip 9FT 18PT/PGCert 6FT 12PT
Teaching of English to Speakers of Other Languages (TESOL) and Applied Linguistics.. MSc 12FT 24PT/PGDip 9FT 18PT/PGCert 6FT 12PT
Translation Studies .... MRes 12FT 27PT/PGCert 9FT 21PT
Translation Studies with TESOL MSc 12FT 27PT/PGDip 9FT 21PT/ PGCert 9FT 9PT

University of Sunderland
News Journalism ....MA 12FT

Swansea University
Chinese-English Translation and Language Teaching......MA 12FT
Translation Technology..PGCert 12FT
Welsh... MA 12FT 24PT
Welsh Writing in English .... MA 12FT 24PT

Trinity College Dublin - the University of Dublin
English Language Teaching.......................MPhil 12FT/PGDip 12FT

UCL - University College London
English Linguistics.................................... MA 12FT 24PT/PGDip 9FT
Translation Theory and Practice .... MA 12FT 24PT

University of Warwick
Drama Education and English Language Teaching (ELT) .MA 12FT 24-36PT

Languages
Research Courses

Aberystwyth University
European Languages .... PhD 36FT 60PT
French .... MPhil 12FT 24PT

German ....MPhil 12FT 24PT
Spanish ....MPhil 12FT 24PT PhD 36FT 60PT

School of Advanced Study, University of London
Modern Languages (French, German, Italian and Spanish) . MRes 12FT 24PT

Anglia Ruskin University
English Language and Intercultural Communication MPhil 24FT/ PhD 36FT
English Language and Linguistics ....MPhil 24FT/PhD 36FT

Aston University
Languages and European Studies......PhD 36FT 60PT 60DL/MPhil 24FT 48PT 48DL
School of Languages and European Studies......... PhD 36FT/MPhil 24FT/MSc by research 12FT

Bangor University
French ....PhD 36FT/MPhil 12FT
German...PhD 36FT/MPhil 12FT
Llenyddiaeth Gymraeg (Welsh Literature) (Welsh medium).......... MPhil 24FT 48-60PT/PhD 24-36FT 60-72PT
Spanish...MPhil 12FT/PhD 36FT

University of Bath
Politics, Languages and International Studies........... PhD 24-48FT 36-72PT/MPhil 12-36FT 24-48PT

Birkbeck, University of London
Iberian and Latin American Studies....PhD 36FT 60PT/MPhil 36FT 60PT
Japanese .... PhD 36FT 48PT/MPhil 24FT 36PT

University of Bradford
Department of Languages and European Studies.... PhD 36-48FT 48-60PT/MPhil 12-24FT 24-48PT

University of Buckingham
Biography ....MA by research 12FT 24PT/MPhil 24FT 48PT/DPhil 36FT 72PT

University of Cambridge
Portuguese.. PhD 36FT 60PT
Slavonic Studies.. PhD 36FT 60PT
Spanish... PhD 36FT 60PT

University of Central Lancashire
Languages and International Studies.....................................
MA by research 12FT 24PT/MPhil 18-36FT 42-60PT/PhD 30-48FT 66-84PT

University of Edinburgh
Celtic and Scottish Studies........PhD 36FT 72PT/MPhil 24FT 48PT/ MSc by research 12FT 24PT
Chinese.. PhD 36FT 72PT/MPhil 24FT 48PT/MSc by research 12FT 24PT
Classics.. PhD 36FT 72PT/MPhil 24FT 48PT/MSc by research 12FT 24PT
French.... PhD 36FT 72PT/MPhil 24FT 48PT/MSc by research 12FT 24PT
German . PhD 36FT 72PT/MPhil 24FT 48PT/MSc by research 12FT 24-36PT
Hebrew and Old Testament Studies. MPhil 24FT/PhD 36FT 72PT/ MTh by research 12FT 24PT/MSc by research 12FT 24PT
Hispanic Studies ....PhD 36FT 72PT/MPhil 24FT 48PT/MSc by research 12FT 24PT
Islamic and Middle Eastern Studies........... PhD 36FT 72PT/MSc by research 12FT 24PT/MPhil 24FT 48PT
Italian .... PhD 36FT 72PT/MPhil 24FT 48PT/MSc by research 12FT 24PT
Japanese ....PhD 36FT 72PT/MPhil 24FT 48PT/ MSc by research 12FT 24PT

University of Essex
English Language Teaching........PhD 36FT 60PT 48DL/MPhil 24FT 48PT

University of Exeter
Russian Studies .... PhD 36FT 72PT/MPhil 24FT 48PT

Goldsmiths, University of London
English, Comparative Literature or Modern Languages ....PhD 36-48FT 48-72PT/MPhil 24FT 36PT

University of Hull
Modern Languages ....PhD 36FT 60PT/MPhil 24FT 36PT/ MRes 12FT 24PT

Kingston University
European Research Centre (ERC) ....PhD 48FT 72PT/MPhil 24FT 48PT/MA by research 12FT 24PT

Lancaster University
European Languages and Cultures.....PhD 36FT 48PT/MPhil 24FT 36PT

University of Leicester
French.. PhD 36FT 48PT/MPhil 24FT 36PT
Modern languages (Italian) .... PhD 36FT 48PT/MPhil 24FT 36PT

University of Liverpool
Modern Languages ....MRes 12FT 24PT

Manchester Metropolitan University
Department of Languages...PhD 24-48FT 42-84PT 42-84DL/MPhil 18-36FT 36-72PT 36-72DL/MA by research 12-24FT 24-42PT 24-42DL

Languages

Newcastle University
English Language and/or LinguisticsMLitt by research 12FT 24PT
English Literature .... MLitt by research 12FT 24PT
Modern Languages .... MLitt by research 12FT 24PT
Translating and Interpreting ..... MPhil 12FT 24PT/PhD 36FT 72PT

Newman University
English... PhD 36FT 72PT/MPhil 24FT 48PT

University of Nottingham
Modern Languages (Masters by Research).. MA by research 12FT 24PT
Modern Languages and Cultures Research Areas MA by research 12FT 24PT

The Open University
Discourse and Social IssuesPhD 36FT 72PT variableDL/EdD 36PT/MRes 12FT
Languages and Applied Linguistics.... PhD 36FT 72PT variableDL/MPhil 15FT 24PT variableDL

Oxford Brookes University
English ....MPhil/PhD 36-60FT 48-72PT/PhD 24-60FT 36-72PT/MPhil 24-36FT 36-48PT
Modern Languages ....MPhil/Phil 36-60FT 48-72PT/PhD 24-60FT 36-72PT/MPhil 24-36FT 36-48PT

University of Oxford
Medieval and Modern Language and Literature .... DPhil 48FT

University of Portsmouth
Languages and Area Studies ..... MPhil 24FT 48PT/PhD 36FT 72PT

Robert Gordon University
Aberdeen Business School ...PhD 12FT 36PT 36DL/MSc(Res) 12FT 36PT 36DL

University of Roehampton
Modern Languages (French, Spanish and/or Translation) ....PhD 24-48FT 36-60PT/MPhil 21-36FT 33-48PT

University of Salford
Centre for Language and Linguistics .... PhD/MPhil

School of Oriental and African Studies - SOAS
Linguistics...................................... PhD 36FT 72PT/MPhil 24FT 36PT

University of Southampton
Languages, Culture and Society PhD 36FT 72PT/MPhil 24FT 48PT
Modern Languages .... PhD 48FT 84PT/MPhil 48FT 84PT

University of St Andrews
Cultural Identity Studies....... PhD 36FT 72PT/MPhil 12-24FT 48PT
French Language StudiesPhD 36FT 72PT/DLang 36FT 72PT/MPhil 12-24FT 48PT
Italian Studies .... PhD 36FT 72PT/MPhil 24FT 48PT
Language and Linguistics.........PhD 36FT 72PT/DLang 36FT 72PT/MPhil 24FT 48PT

Swansea University
Applied Language Studies (Vocabulary Acquisition).....PhD 60PT/MPhil 12FT 24PT
Applied Linguistics ...PhD 36FT 90PT/MPhil 12-18FT 24-36PT/MA by research 12FT 24PT
French .... PhD 36FT 72PT/MPhil 24FT 36PT
German .... PhD 36FT 72PT/MPhil 24FT 48PT
Hispanic Studies .... PhD 36FT 72PT/MPhil 24FT 48PT
Italian .... PhD 36FT 72PT/MPhil 24FT 48PT
Welsh.......PhD 36FT 60PT/MPhil 12FT 24PT/MA by research 12FT 24PT

UCL - University College London
Languages and Culture of Eastern Europe.............. PhD 36FT 60PT
Translation Studies .... PhD 36FT 60PT

University of the West of England, Bristol
School of Humanities, Languages and Social Sciences......PhD -FT

University of Wolverhampton
School of Humanities, Languages and Social Sciences....................MPhil/PhD

University of York
Language and Linguistic Science.........PhD 36FT 72PT/MPhil 24FT 48PT/MA by research 12FT 24PT

York St John University
Languages Studies & LinguisticsPhD 12-36FT/MPhil 12-36FT/MA by research 12-36FT

Polish
Taught Courses

University of Oxford
Slavonic Studies................................... MPhil 24FT/MSt 9FT

Portuguese
Research Courses

University of Cambridge
Portuguese.. PhD 36FT 60PT

Russian
Taught Courses

University of Glasgow
Russian Language ....PGCert 9FT PGDip 12FT/PGCert 9FT

Russian for Social Sciences .... PGDip 12FT/PGCert 9FT
Russian for Social Scientists.. PGCert 9FT
Russian, Central & East European Studies (Erasmus Mundus International Masters)........International Masters (double/single degree) 24FT
Russian, Central and East European Studies ....MSc 12FT 24PT/PGDip 9FT

University of Nottingham
Russian...PGDip 9FT 24PT

University of Oxford
Russian and East European Studies..............MPhil 21FT/MSc 12FT
Slavonic Studies................................... MPhil 24FT/MSt 9FT

University of St Andrews
Central and East European Studies....MLitt 12FT 24PT/PGDip 9FT 18PT
Russian Studies .... MLitt 12FT 24PT/PGDip 9FT 24PT

Russian
Research Courses

University of Bristol
Russian and Czech. PhD 36FT 72PT/MLitt by research 24FT 48PT/MPhil 12FT 24PT

University of Edinburgh
Russian..............................PhD 36FT 72PT/MPhil 24FT 48PT/MSc by research 12FT 24PT
Russian Studies (by Research) ....MSc by research 12FT 24/36PT

University of Exeter
Russian Studies .... PhD 36FT 72PT/MPhil 24FT 48PT

Queen Mary, University of London
Russian ....PhD/MPhil

University of St Andrews
Russian Studies ....PhD 36FT 72PT/DLang 36FT 72PT/MPhil 12-24FT 48PT

UCL - University College London
Russian .... PhD 36FT 60PT

Scottish gaelic
Taught Courses

University of Aberdeen
Gaelic Medium Education .... PGCert 12PT

University of St Andrews
Reformation Studies....... MLitt 12FT 24PT/MPhil 24FT/PGDip 9FT 24PT

University of the Highlands and Islands
Orkney and Shetland Studies..........MLitt 12FT 24PT/PGCert 12FT 24PT/PGDip 12FT 24PT

Serbo-croatian
Taught Courses

University of Nottingham
Serbian/ Croatian ....PGDip 9FT

Slovene
Taught Courses

University of Nottingham
Slovene...PGDip 9FT

University of Oxford
Slavonic Studies................................... MPhil 24FT/MSt 9FT

Spanish
Taught Courses

Bangor University
European Languages and Cultures .... MA 12FT 24PT
Translation Studies .... MA 12FT 24PT

Birkbeck, University of London
Spanish, Portuguese and Latin American Cultural Studies ......MA 12FT 24PT/MRes 12FT 24PT

University of Dundee
Spanish for Teachers ....PGDip 24DL

National University of Ireland Galway
Spanish..MA 12FT

University of Kent
Graduate Diploma in Humanities (Hispanic Studies).......GradDip 12FT
Hispanic and Comparative Literature .... MA 12FT 24PT
Modern Hispanic Studies ....MA 24FT

Liverpool John Moores University
Modern Languages: French, Spanish, German, French & Spanish or French & German .... PGCE 10FT
Spanish Extension Course ....Pre Course 3FT

University of Reading
Modern Languages (Secondary Teaching) .... PGCE 10FT

Royal Holloway, University of London
Hispanic Studies .... MA 12FT 24PT

University of St Andrews
Modern Hispanic Literature And Film ....MLitt 12FT/MPhil 24FT
Spanish and Latin American Studies.MLitt 12FT 24PT/PGDip 9FT 24PT

Swansea University
Literary Translation ....MA 24FT
Translation and Interpreting ....MA 12FT
Translation with Language Technology .... MA 12FT 24PT

Spanish
Research Courses

Aberystwyth University
Spanish ....MPhil 12FT 24PT PhD 36FT 60PT

Bangor University
Spanish................................MPhil 12FT/PhD 36FT
Translation Studies ....PhD 36FT/MPhil 12FT
Translation Studies (by Practice)PhD 36FT 72PT/MPhil 24FT 48PT

Birkbeck, University of London
Iberian and Latin American Studies....PhD 36FT 60PT/MPhil 36FT 60PT

University of Cambridge
Spanish.. PhD 36FT 60PT

University of Kent
Hispanic Studies ....PhD 36FT 60PT/MPhil 24FT 36FT/MA by research 12FT 24PT

University of Leicester
Spanish... PhD 36FT 48PT/MPhil 24FT 36FT

University of St Andrews
Modern Hispanic Literature And Film PhD 36FT 72PT/MPhil 24FT 48FT

Swansea University
European Cultures.................................MA by research 12FT 24PT
Hispanic Studies .... PhD 36FT 72PT/MPhil 24FT 48PT

University of Ulster
Spanish................................MPhil 24FT 48PT/PhD 36FT 72PT 60DL

Welsh
Taught Courses

Aberystwyth University
Translation (English-Welsh) / Cyfieithu (Cymraeg-Saesneg).......... PGCert 8PT

Bangor University
Celtic Archaeology .... MA 12FT 24PT/PGDip 8FT
Celts, The / Celtiaid, Y....................................... MA 12FT 36FT
Cymraeg (Welsh) (Welsh medium) .... MA 12FT 24PT/PGDip 8FT
European Languages and Cultures .... MA 12FT 24PT
Forensic Linguistics ....MSc 12FT 24PT
Language Development ....MSc 12FT 36FT
Translation Studies .... MA 12FT 24PT
Welsh History PhD by taught 24-36FT 48-72PT/MPhil 12FT 24PT

Swansea University
Literary Translation ....MA 24FT
Translation and Interpreting ....MA 12FT
Translation with Language Technology .... MA 12FT 24PT
Welsh .... MA 12FT 24PT

University of Wales Trinity Saint David
Bilingualism and Multilingualism ....MA 24FT 48PT 24-48DL/PGCert 24FT 48PT 24-48DL/PGDip 24FT 48PT 24-48DL
Dwyieithrwydd ac Amlieithrwydd...........MA 24FT 48PT 24-48DL/PGCert 24FT 48PT 24-48DL/PGDip 24FT 48PT 24-48DL

Welsh
Research Courses

Aberystwyth University
Welsh Literature ....MPhil 12FT 24PT PhD 36FT 60PT

Bangor University
Astudiaethau Celtaidd (Celtic Studies) (Welsh medium).... MA by research 12FT/MPhil 24FT 48-60PT/PhD 24-36FT 60-72PT
Llenyddiaeth Gymraeg (Welsh Literature) (Welsh medium).......... MPhil 24FT 48-60PT/PhD 24-36FT 60-72PT
Translation Studies ....PhD 36FT/MPhil 12FT
Translation Studies (PhD by Practice).PhD 36FT 72PT/MPhil 24FT 48PT

Cardiff University
Welsh.........................PhD 36FT possiblePT/MPhil 12FT possiblePT

Swansea University
Welsh.......PhD 36FT 60PT/MPhil 12FT 24PT/MA by research 12FT 24PT

University of Wales Trinity Saint David
Centre for Bilingualism and Welsh Studies ....PhD 36FT/MPhil 12-24FT

Linguistics

Bilingualism
Taught Courses

University of Aberdeen
Plurilingual Education ....MEd 24PT/PGCert 12PT

Bangor University
Bilingualism .... MA 12FT 24PT
Bilingualism ....PhD by taught 36-48FT 60-84PT/MPhil 24FT
Cognitive Linguistics .... MA 12FT 24PT
Language, Policy and Planning ....MA 12FT 24-48PT/PGDip 8FT/PGCert 4FT
Linguistics .... MA 12FT 24PT
Linguistics and Applied Linguistics ....PhD by taught 36-48FT 60-84PT/MPhil 24FT
Translation Studies .... MA 12FT 24PT

University of Birmingham
Bilingualism in Education ....PGCert 12DL/PGDip 24DL/MEd 24-76DL

University of East Anglia
Communication and Language Studies .... MA 12FT 24PT
Forensic Linguistics and Translation .... MA 12FT 24PT

University of East London
Multilingualism ....MA 12FT 24PT/PGDip 8FT 16PT/PGCert 4FT 8PT

University of Edinburgh
Additional Support for Learning (Bilingual Learners) .. MEd 72PT/PGDip 48PT/PGCert 24PT

Institute of Education
Bilingual Learners .... MA 12FT 24PT

King's College London
Language & Cultural Diversity .... MA 12FT 24PT

University of Wales Trinity Saint David
Bilingualism and Multilingualism ....MA 24FT 48PT 24-48DL/PGCert 24FT 48PT 24-48DL/PGDip 24FT 48PT 24-48DL
Dwyieithrwydd ac Amlieithrwydd ....MA 24FT 48PT 24-48DL/PGCert 24FT 48PT 24-48DL/PGDip 24FT 48PT 24-48DL

University of Westminster
Bilingual Translation .... MA 12FT 24PT

Bilingualism
Research Courses

Bangor University
Bilingualism ....MPhil 24FT/PhD 36-48FT 60-84PT
Linguistics .... PhD 36-48FT 60-84PT/MPhil 24FT
Translation Studies ....PhD 36FT/MPhil 12FT
Translation Studies (by Practice) ....PhD 36FT 72PT/MPhil 24FT 48PT

University of Wales Trinity Saint David
Bilingualism and MultilingualismPhD 12FT 24PT/MA by research 12FT 24PT
Centre for Bilingualism and Welsh Studies ....PhD 36FT/MPhil 12-24FT

Linguistics
Taught Courses

University of Aberdeen
English Linguistics for Advanced Teachers of English (ELATE).... MLitt 12FT 24PT/PGDip 9FT 18PT
Plurilingual Education ....MEd 24PT/PGCert 12PT
Sociolinguistics .... MLitt 12FT 24PT/PGDip 9FT 21PT

Anglia Ruskin University
Applied Linguistics and TESOL (Teaching English to Speakers of Other Languages) ....MA 12FT 24PT 12-24DL

Aston University
Applied Linguistics (Corpus Linguistics, Forensic Linguistics, Literary Linguistics, ... MA 12FT 24 - 36PT
Applied Linguistics ....MSc 24 - 36DL
Forensic Linguistics .... MSc 24 -60DL/PGDE 24 - 60DL/PGCert 24 - 60DL/Diploma 24-60DL

Bangor University
Bilingualism ....PhD by taught 36-48FT 60-84PT/MPhil 24FT MA 12FT 24PT
Cognitive Linguistics .... MA 12FT 24PT
Forensic Linguistics .... MSc 12FT 24PT
Language Development .... MSc 12FT 36PT
Linguistics .... MA 12FT 24PT
Linguistics and Applied Linguistics ....PhD by taught 36-48FT 60-84PT/MPhil 24FT

University of Bedfordshire
Applied Linguistics ....MA 12FT
Applied Linguistics (TEFL) .... MA 12FT 24PT
Intercultural Communication .... MA 12FT 24PT

Birkbeck, University of London
Applied Linguistics .... MA 12FT 24PT
Intercultural Communication for Business and Professions .... MA 12FT 24PT
International Field Leadership ....PGCert 12PT
Language Teaching .... MA 12FT 24PT
Linguistic Studies ....GradCert 12PT
Teaching English to Speakers of Other Languages (TESOL) ....MA 12FT 24PT

Birmingham City University
English Linguistics (Distance Learning) .... MA 24-84DL/PGDip 24-84DL

University of Birmingham
Applied Corpus Linguistics ....MA 12FT
Applied Linguistics ....MA 12FT
Applied Linguistics (by Distance Learning) .... MA 30FT 30DL
Language and Linguistics (Philosophy of) .... MA 12FT 24PT
Literary Linguistics .... MA 12FT 24PT
Philosophy of Language and Linguistics .... MA 12FT 24PT
Special Applications of Linguistics ....MA 12FT

University of Brighton
English Language .... MA 12FT 24PT/PGDip 12FT 24PT/PGCert 12FT 24PT
Linguistics.... MRes 12FT 24PT/MA 12FT 24PT/PGDip 12FT 24PT/PGCert 12FT 24PT
Philosophy of Language .... MA 12FT 24-72PT

University of Cambridge
English and Applied Linguistics ....MPhil 9FT
Linguistics ....MPhil 9FT

Cardiff University
Applied Linguistics .... MA 12FT 24PT/PGDip 9FT 18PT
Forensic Linguistics .... MA 12FT 24PT/Diploma 12FT 18PT
Language and Communication Research.... MA 12FT 24PT/PGDip 9FT 18PT

University of Central Lancashire
Intercultural Business Communication .... MA 12FT 24-36PT
Rhetoric .... MA 12FT 24PT

University College Cork
Applied Linguistics ....MA 12FT
French - Linguistics ....MA 12FT

University of Dundee
Language & Communication .... MSc 12FT

University of East Anglia
Applied Translation Studies .... MA 12FT 24PT
Communication and Language Studies .... MA 12FT 24PT
Conflicts in Intercultural Communication .... MA 12FT 24PT
Forensic Linguistics and Translation .... MA 12FT 24PT
Language and Intercultural Communication .... MA 12FT 24PT

University of East London
Narrative Research (Postgraduate Associate Certificate) by distance learning .... Postgraduate Associate Certificate 5DL

Edge Hill University
English Language ....MRes 12FT 24PT

University of Edinburgh
Applied Linguistics .... MSc 12FT 24PT
Cognitive Science .... MSc 12FT 36PT
Developmental Linguistics .... MSc 12FT 24PT
Education: Language, Theory, Practice & LiteracyMSc 12FT 72PT/PGDip 9FT 48PT/PGCert 4FT 24PT
English Language .... MSc 12FT 24PT
Evolution of Language & Cognition .... MSc 12FT 24PT
Mind, Language and Embodied Cognition .... MSc 12FT 24PT
Psychology of Language .... MSc 12FT 24PT
Theoretical Linguistics ....

University of Essex
Applied Linguistics ....MA 9-12FT 24PT
Applied Linguistics with English for Academic Purposes Diploma 9FT
Chinese-English Translation and Interpreting ....MA 9-12FT 24PT
English Language ....MA 9-12FT 24PT
English Language and Linguistics ....MA 9-12FT 24PT
Linguistic Studies ....MA 9-12FT 24PT
Linguistics ....MA 9-12FT 24PT/MRes 12FT 24PT
Phonology ....MA 9-12FT 24PT
Psycholinguistics and Neurolinguistics ....MA 9-12FT 24PT
Sociolinguistics ....MA 9-12FT 24PT
Sociolinguistics of the Arab World ....MA 12FT
Syntax ....MA 9-12FT 24PT
Teaching English as a Foreign Language .... MA 12FT 24PT
Translation and Literature ....MA 9-12FT 24PT
Translation, Interpreting and Subtitling ....MA 9-12FT 24PT

National University of Ireland Galway
Teagasc Teangacha (An Ghaeilge) Páirtaimseartha ....MA 24PT

University of Glasgow
English Language & English Linguistics: Applied.. MSc 12FT 24PT
English Language and English Linguistics .... MSc 12FT 24PT

Glyndwr University
Advanced English for Speakers of Other Languages ....MA 12FT 24PT/PGDip 12FT 24PT/PGCert 12FT 24PT

Goldsmiths, University of London
Multilingualism, Linguistics and Education .... MA 12FT 24PT
Sociocultural Linguistics .... MA 12FT 24PT

University of Greenwich
Language Learning and Japanese Language Teaching ....MA 12FT

University of Huddersfield
English Language Proficiency and British Culture ....PGCert 12PT
Modern English Language .... MA 12FT 24PT

University of Hull
English by Research .... MA 12FT 24PT
Modern Languages ....MRes 12FT 24PT

University of Kent
Humanities (English Language and Linguistics) ....GradDip 12FT
Linguistics .... MA 12FT 24PT

King's College London
English Language Teaching & Applied Linguistics .... MA 12FT 24PT
Language & Cultural Diversity .... MA 12FT 24PT

Kingston University
Applied Linguistics for Language Teaching .... MA 12FT 24PT

Lancaster University
Language Testing (distance) ....MA 24PT 24DL

Leeds Metropolitan University
English Language & Education Studies (Pre-Masters) ....GradDip 12FT
English Language Teaching ....MA 12FT 24PT 24DL/PGDip 12FT 24PT

University of Leeds
English Language and World Englishes .... MA 12FT 24PT
Linguistics .... MA 12FT 24PT
Linguistics and English Language Teaching .... MA 12FT 24PT
Professional Language and Intercultural Studies ....MA 12FT

University of Leicester
Applied Linguistics and TESOL ...MA 12FT 24PT 30DL/PGCert 4FT 8PT 12DL

University of Lincoln
Science and Environmental Journalism .... MA 12FT 24PT

Liverpool Hope University
English Language ....MA 12FT 24-36PT

University of Liverpool
Applied Linguistics ....MA 12FT

Manchester Metropolitan University
Applied Linguistics .... MA 12FT 24PT

University of Manchester
English Language .... MA 12FT 24PT
Intercultural Communication .... MA 12FT 24PT
Languages and Linguistics .... MA 12FT 24PT/PGDip 9FT
Linguistics .... MA 12FT 24PT/PGDip 9FT

Newcastle University
Applied Linguistics Research .... MA 12FT 24PT
Applied Linguistics and TESOL .... MA 12FT 24PT
Cross-Cultural Communication and Applied Linguistics.... MA 12FT 24PT
Linguistics (with specialist pathways in English Language, Language Acquisition, and European Languages) .... MA 12FT 24PT

Northumbria University
Applied Linguistics - TESOL .... MA 12FT 36PT

University of Nottingham
Applied Linguistics .... MA 12FT 24-36PT
Applied Linguistics and English Language Teaching ....MA 12FT 24-36PT
Applied Linguistics and English Language Teaching by web-based distance learning ....MA 24-48DL
Applied Linguistics by web-based distance learning MA 24-48DL
English Studies .... MA 12FT 24-36PT/PGDip 12FT 24-36PT
Literary Linguistics .... MA 12FT 24-36PT
Literary Linguistics by Web Based Distance Learning .... MA 24-48DL
Modern English Language by web-based distance learning ... MA 24-48DL
Translation Studies .... MA 12FT 24PT

Oxford Brookes University
English Language and Study SkillsGraduate Preparation Diploma 9FT
English Language and Study Skills ....Graduate Preparation Certificate 3-6FT

University of Oxford
Applied Linguistics and Second Language Acquisition.. MSc 12FT 24PT
English (1550-1700) ....MSt 9FT
English (1660-1830) ....MSt 9FT
English (1800-1914) ....MSt 12FT
English (1900-Present) ....MSt 9FT
English (650-1550) ....MSt 9FT
English Language ....MSt 9FT
English Studies (Medieval Period) .... MPhil 21FT
General Linguistics and Comparative Philology.. MPhil 21FT/MSt 9FT

University of Portsmouth
Applied Linguistics and TESOL (DL) .... MA 36DL
Communication and Language Skills .... MA 12FT 24PT

Linguistics

Queen Mary, University of London
Applied Linguistics for English Language Teaching MA 12FT 24PT

Queen's University Belfast
English (Speech and Language) ... MA 12FT 24PT/PGDip 9FT 18PT

University of Reading
Applied Linguistics ... MA 12FT 24-48PT/PGCert 12FT/PGDip 12FT
Applied Linguistics - Research Pathway ... MA (Res) 12FT 24-72PT
English Language Teaching ... MA 12FT 24PT 24-48DL/PGDip 12FT 24PT/PGCert 12FT 24PT
Neuroscience of Language ... MSc 12FT 24PT
Speech and Language Therapy ... MSc 24FT

University of Roehampton
Applied Linguistics and TESOL ... MA 12FT 24PT/PGDip 9FT 18PT

University of Salford
TESOL and Applied Linguistics ... MA 12FT 36PT/PGDip 9FT 24PT

School of Oriental and African Studies - SOAS
Applied Linguistics and Language Pedagogy (Japanese, Korean, Chinese or Tibetan) ... MA 12FT 24-36PT
Language Documentation and Description ... MA 12FT 24-36PT
Linguistics ... MA 12FT 24-36PT
Sinology ... MA 12FT 24-36PT

Sheffield Hallam University
English Language and Linguistics ... MA 12FT 24-72PT

University of Sheffield
Applied Linguistics with TESOL MA 12FT 24PT/Diploma 9FT 18PT
Cognitive Studies ... MA 12FT 24PT
English Language Studies ... MA 12FT 24PT
English Literature ... MA 12FT 24PT
Hispanic Studies ... MA 12FT 24PT
Intercultural Communication ... MA 12FT 24PT
Language Acquisition ... MA 12FT 24PT/PGDip 9FT 18PT
Language and Communication Impairment in Children ... PGDip 24 PTDL/PGCert 12 PTDL

University of Southampton
Applied Linguistics (Research Methodology) ... MA 12FT 24PT
Applied Linguistics for Language Teaching ... MA 12FT 24PT
Applied Linguistics for Language Teaching ... MA 12FT 24PT
English Language Teaching Innovation ... PGDip 4PT

University of St Andrews
English Studies ... PGDip 9FT/MLitt 12FT
Language and Linguistics ... MLitt 12FT 24PT/PGDip 9FT 18PT/MPhil 24FT

St Mary's University College, Twickenham
Applied Linguistics and English Language Teaching ... MA 12FT 24PT/PGDip 12FT 24PT/PGCert 6FT 12PT

University of Stirling
English Language and Linguistics ... MLitt 12FT 27PT/PGDip 9FT 21PT/PGCert 3FT 9PT
Teaching of English to Speakers of Other Languages (TESOL) and Applied Linguistics .. MSc 12FT 24PT/PGDip 9FT 18PT/PGCert 6FT 12PT

University of Sussex
Applied Linguistics ... MA 12FT 24PT

Trinity College Dublin - the University of Dublin
Applied Linguistics ... MPhil 12FT 24PT
Linguistics ... MPhil 12FT 24PT

University of Ulster
English Language and Linguistics ... PGDip 10FT 16PT/MSc 12FT 36PT

UCL - University College London
English Linguistics ... MA 12FT 24PT/PGDip 9FT
Linguistics ... MA 12FT 24PT
Linguistics with specialisation in Phonology ... MRes 12FT
Linguistics with specialisation in Pragmatics ... MRes 12FT
Linguistics with specialisation in Syntax ... MRes 12FT
Neuroscience, Language and Communication ... MSc 12FT 24PT
Phonetics ... MA 12FT 24PT

University of the West of England, Bristol
Intercultural Communication ... MA 12FT

University of Westminster
Linguistics and English Language ... MA 12FT 24PT

University of Wolverhampton
Language and Information Processing ... MA 12FT 24PT

University of York
Applied Linguistics for English Language Teaching ... MA 12FT/PGDip 9FT/PGCert 7FT
Forensic Speech Science ... MSc 12FT 24PT
Linguistics ... MA 12FT 24PT
Phonetics and Phonology ... MA 12FT 24PT
Sociolinguistics ... MA 12FT 24PT
Syntax and Semantics ... MA 12FT 24PT

York St John University
Applied Linguistics: Teaching English to Speakers of Other Languages (TESOL) ... MA 12FT 60PT
English Language & Linguistics ... MA 12FT 60PT

Linguistics
Research Courses

Anglia Ruskin University
English Language and Intercultural Communication MPhil 24FT/PhD 36FT
English Language and Linguistics ... MPhil 24FT/PhD 36FT

Bangor University
Bilingualism ... MPhil 24FT/PhD 36-48FT 60-84PT
Linguistics ... PhD 36-48FT 60-84PT/MPhil 24FT

Birkbeck, University of London
Applied Linguistics ... New Route PhD 36FT 58PT
Applied Linguistics ... PhD 36FT 60PT/MPhil 12FT 24PT
Intercultural Communication ... New Route PhD 36FT 56PT
Language Teaching ... New Route PhD 36FT 56PT
Teaching English to Speakers of Other Languages (TESOL) ... New Route PhD 36FT 56PT

Birmingham City University
English ... PhD 84FT/MPhil 84FT

University of Birmingham
Applied Linguistics with Integrated Study ... PhD 48FT 48-72PT
Corpus Linguistics ... MRes 12FT 24PT
English Language and Applied Linguistics ... PhD 36FT 72PT/MLitt by research 24FT 48PT/MA by research 12FT 24PT

University of Brighton
Education and Languages Research Division ... PhD 24-60FT 36-72PT/MPhil 18-36FT 30-48PT

University of Cambridge
English and Applied Linguistics ... PhD 36FT

Canterbury Christ Church University
Applied Linguistics ... MPhil 24FT 36PT

Cardiff University
Language and Communication ... PhD 36FT/MPhil 12FT

University of Central Lancashire
English Literature/English Language & Linguistics ... MPhil 18-36FT 42-60PT/MA by research 12FT 24PT/PhD 18-36FT 42-60PT

City University London
Human Communication ... PhD/MPhil

University of East Anglia
Language and Communication Studies ... PhD 36FT 72PT/MPhil 24FT 48PT/MA by research 12FT 24PT

University of Edinburgh
English Language (by Research) ... MSc by research 12FT 24PT
Linguistics & English Language ... PhD 36FT 72PT
Linguistics (by Research) ... MSc by research 12FT 24PT
Theoretical Linguistics (by Research) ... MS by research 12FT

University of Essex
Analysing Language Use . PhD 36FT 60PT 48DL/MPhil 24FT 48PT
Applied Linguistics ... PhD 36FT 60PT 48DL/MPhil 24FT 48PT
English Language Teaching ... PhD 36FT 60PT 48DL/MPhil 24FT 48PT
Experimental Linguistics . PhD 36FT 60PT 48DL/MPhil 24FT 48PT
Linguistics ... PhD 36FT 60PT 48DL/MPhil 24FT 48PT
Psycholinguistics and Neurolinguistics ... PhD 36FT 60PT 48DL/MPhil 24FT 48PT
Sociolinguistics ... PhD 36FT 60PT 48DL/MPhil 24FT 48PT

University of Glasgow
English Language and English Literature .. PhD 36FT/MPhil 12FT/MLitt by research 12FT

University of Hull
Modern Languages ... PhD 36FT 60PT/MPhil 24FT 36PT/MRes 12FT 24PT

University of Kent
English Language and Linguistics ... MA by research 12FT 24PT/MPhil 24FT 36PT/PhD 36-48FT 60-72PT

Kingston University
Linguistics and Language Studies ... PhD 48FT 72PT/MPhil 24FT 48PT/MA by research 12FT 24PT

Lancaster University
Applied Linguistics by Thesis and Coursework ... PhD 36FT 60PT 60DL/MPhil 30FT 48PT 48DL
Linguistics ... PhD 36FT 48PT/MPhil 24FT 36PT

University of Leeds
Department of Linguistics and Phonetics PhD 36+FT/MPhil 24FT/MA by research 12+FT
School of English ..PhD 36+FT/MA by research 12+FT/MPhil 24FT

University of Liverpool
English ... PhD 24-48FT 48-84PT/MPhil 12-48FT 48-72PT

Loughborough University
English Language and Literature PhD 36FT 60PT/MPhil 24FT 36PT

University of Manchester
English Language ... PhD 36FT 72PT
Linguistics ... PhD 36FT 72PT/MPhil 12FT 24PT/Integrated PhD 36-48FT
Linguistics and English Language ... Integrated PhD 36-48FT

Newcastle University
Education and Communication ... Integrated PhD 36-48FT
Educational and Applied Linguistics ... Integrated PhD 48FT
English Language and/or Linguistics MLitt by research 12FT 24PT
English Literature, Language and Creative Writing ... PhD 36FT 72PT/MPhil 12FT 24PT/MLitt by research 12FT 24PT
Linguistics ... MLitt by research 12FT 24PT
Linguistics and English Language ... Integrated PhD 48FT 72PT
Phonetics and Phonology ... Integrated PhD 48FT 96PT

The Open University
Academic and Professional Communication Literacies ... PhD 36FT 72PT variableDL/EdD 36PT variableDL/MRes 12FT
Discourse and Social Issues PhD 36FT 72PT variableDL/EdD 36PT/MRes 12FT
Language Learning and Teaching ... PhD 36FT 72PT variableDL/MRes 12FT/EdD 36PT
Language Policy ... PhD 36FT 72PT variableDL/EdD 36PT/MRes 12FT
Language, Multimedia and Knowledge Technologies ... MPhil 15FT 24PT/PhD 36FT 72PT variableDL
Languages and Applied Linguistics ... PhD 36FT 72PT variableDL/MPhil 15FT 24PT variableDL
Mind, Meaning and Rationality ... PhD 36FT 72PT variableDL/MPhil 15FT 24PT variableDL
Multimodal meaning making ... PhD 36FT 72PT variableDL/EdD 36PT/MRes 12FT

University of Oxford
Comparative Philology & General Linguistics ... DPhil 48FT
English ... DPhil 48FT

Queen Mary, University of London
English ... PhD/MPhil
Linguistics ... PhD/MPhil/MA by research 24PT

University of Roehampton
English Language & Linguistics ... PhD 24-48FT 36-60PT/MPhil 21-36FT 33-48PT
English Literature PhD 24-48FT 36-60PT/MPhil 21-36FT 33-48PT
Language Testing and Assessment .. PhD 24-48FT 36-60PT/MPhil 21-36FT 33-48PT

University of Salford
Centre for Language and Linguistics ... PhD/MPhil

School of Oriental and African Studies - SOAS
Linguistics ... PhD 36FT 72PT/MPhil 24FT 36PT

Sheffield Hallam University
Communication and Computing Research Centre ... PhD 36-48FT 48-60PT/MPhil 24-36FT 48-60PT

University of Southampton
English ... PhD 48FT 84PT/MPhil 48FT 84PT
Integrated PhD in Applied Linguistics/English Language Teaching ... Integrated PhD 60FT

University of St Andrews
English ... PhD 36FT 72PT/MPhil 24FT 48PT
Language and Linguistics ... PhD 36FT 72PT/DLang 36FT 72PT/MPhil 24FT 48PT

St Mary's University College, Twickenham
English ... PhD 36FT 72PT/MPhil 24FT 48PT

University of Surrey
Translation Studies ... PhD 21-72FT 33-96PT/MPhil 18-33FT

Swansea University
Applied Language Studies (Vocabulary Acquisition) ... PhD 60PT/MPhil 12FT 24PT
Applied Linguistics ... PhD 36FT 90PT/MPhil 12-18FT 24-36PT/MA by research 12FT 24PT
English ... PhD 36FT 72PT/MPhil 24FT 48PT/MA by research 12FT 24PT

University of Ulster
Linguistics ... PhD 36FT 72PT 60DL/MPhil 24FT 48PT 48DL

UCL - University College London
English Language and Literature ... PhD 36FT 60PT
Human Communication Science ... PhD 36FT 60PT
Linguistics ... PhD 36FT 60PT
Speech, Hearing and Phonetic Sciences ... PhD 36FT 60PT

University of York
Language and Linguistic Science ... PhD 36FT 72PT/MPhil 24FT 48PT/MA by research 12FT 24PT

York St John University
Languages Studies & Linguistics PhD 12-36FT/MPhil 12-36FT/MA by research 12-36FT

Natural language processing
Taught Courses

Bangor University
Bilingualism ... MA 12FT 24PT
Bilingualism ... PhD by taught 36-48FT 60-84PT/MPhil 24FT
Cognitive Linguistics ... MA 12FT 24PT
Linguistics ... MA 12FT 24PT
Linguistics and Applied Linguistics ... PhD by taught 36-48FT 60-84PT/MPhil 24FT

Linguistics

Psychological Research ..MSc 12FT 24PT/PGDip 8FT 16PT/PGCert 4FT 8PT
Psychology..........MA 12FT 24PT/PGDip 9FT 18PT/PGCert 4FT 8PT

University of Central Lancashire
Rhetoric........ MA 12FT 24PT

University of Cumbria
The Research Process........PGCert 12 - 18PT

University of Dundee
Non-Graduating Taught Postgraduate in School of Psychology .... PG module variableFT

University of Edinburgh
Cognitive Science........MSc 12FT 36PT
Speech and Language Processing .... MSc 12FT/PGDip 9FT

Heriot-Watt University
Artificial Intelligence ....MSc 12FT 24PT/PGDip 9FT

University of Limerick
Interactive Media .... MA 12FT/MSc 12FT

University of Roehampton
Specialised Translation........ MA 12FT 24PT/PGDip 9FT 24PT

School of Oriental and African Studies - SOAS
Linguistics........ MA 12FT 24-36PT

University of Sheffield
Computer Science with Speech and Language Processing..... MSc 12FT

Staffordshire University
Advanced Technology........MSc 12-24FT 24-60PT

Trinity College Dublin - the University of Dublin
Speech and Language Processing ....MPhil 12FT 24PT

Natural language processing
Research Courses

Bangor University
Bilingualism........MPhil 24FT/PhD 36-48FT 60-84PT
Doctorate by Research ....PhD 36FT/MPhil 24FT
Linguistics........ PhD 36-48FT 60-84PT/MPhil 24FT

Cardiff University
Language and Translation Studies......PhD 36FT 60PT/MPhil 24FT 48PT

University of Central Lancashire
Translation, English as a Foreign Language, Learning & Teaching Methodology, Language.....PhD 30-48FT 66-84PT/MPhil 18-36FT 42-60PT/MA by research 12FT 24PT

University of Edinburgh
Speech Technology Research (Centre for) ....PhD 36FT

Sign language
Taught Courses

University of Central Lancashire
British Sign Language/English Interpreting and Translation...MA 36PT
British Sign Language/English Interpreting and Translation .... PGDip 24PT

Sheffield Hallam University
Advanced Communication Skills........PGCert 4PT 4DL

UCL - University College London
Language Sciences........MSc 12FT 24PT

Translating
Taught Courses

Aberystwyth University
Applied Translation .... MA 12FT 24PT
Translation (English-Welsh) / Cyfieithu (Cymraeg-Saesneg)........ PGCert 8PT

Aston University
TESOL and Translation Studies........ MA 12FT 24 -36PT
Translation Studies .... MA 12FT 24 - 36PT
Translation in a European Context .... MA 12FT 24 - 36PT

Bangor University
Language, Policy and Planning ....MA 12FT 24-48PT/PGDip 8FT/PGCert 4FT
Translation Studies .... MA 12FT 24PT

University of Bath
Interpreting and Translating.....MA 12FT/PGDip 9FT 21PT/PGCert 4FT 16PT
Translation and Professional Language SkillsMA 12FT/PGDip 9FT

University of Bedfordshire
Chartered Institute of Linguistics (IoL) Diploma in Public Service Interpreting (DPSI)........DPSI 12PT

University of Birmingham
Translation Studies .... MA 12FT 24PT
Translation Studies by distance learning .... MA 30DL

University of Bristol
Translation .... MA 12-36DL/PGDip 12-24DL

Cardiff University
Translation Studies ....

University of Central Lancashire
British Sign Language/English Interpreting and Translation...MA 36PT
British Sign Language/English Interpreting and Translation .... PGDip 24PT
Interpreting & Translation ....MA 12FT

City University London
Principles and Practice of Translation ....PGCert 12PT
Translating Popular Culture........ MA 12FT 24PT

University College Cork
Translation Studies (French) ....MA 12FT

Durham University
Arabic/English Translation and Interpreting........ MA 12FT 24PT
Translation Studies .... MA 12FT 24PT

University of East Anglia
Applied Translation Studies........ MA 12FT 24PT
Conflicts in Intercultural Communication .... MA 12FT 24PT
Forensic Linguistics and Translation........ MA 12FT 24PT
Language and Intercultural Communication........ MA 12FT 24PT
Literary Translation .... MA 12FT 24PT

University of Edinburgh
Literary Translation as Creative Practice........MSc 12FT 24PT
Translation Studies ....MSc 12FT 24PT

University of Essex
Chinese-English Translation and Interpreting .....MA 9-12FT 24PT
Translation and Literature........MA 9-12FT 24PT
Translation, Interpreting and Subtitling........MA 9-12FT 24PT

University of Exeter
Translation .... MA 12FT 24PT

National University of Ireland Galway
Léann Teanga........ MA 24FT/HDip 12FT
Translations Studies........MA 12FT

University of Glasgow
Translation Studies: Translation & Professional PracticeMSc 12FT 24PT

Glyndwr University
Advanced English for Speakers of Other Languages........MA 12FT 24PT/PGDip 12FT 24PT/PGCert 12FT 24PT

Heriot-Watt University
Arabic-English Translating and Conference Interpreting ....MSc 12FT 24PT/PGDip 9FT 21PT
Arabic-English Translation and Computer-Assisted Translation Tools........MSc 12FT 24PT/PGDip 9FT 21PT
Chinese-English Translating and Conference Interpreting..... MSc 12FT 24PT/PGDip 9FT 21PT
Chinese-English Translation and Computer-Assisted Translation Tools........MSc 12FT 24PT/PGDip 9FT 21PT
Interpreting and Translating........ MSc 12FT/PGDip 9FT
Translating and Conference Interpreting...MSc 12FT 24PT/PGDip 9FT 21PT
Translation and Computer Assisted Translation Tools... MSc 12FT 24PT/PGDip 9FT 21PT

University of Hull
TESOL with Translation Studies .... MA 12FT 24PT
Translation Studies .....MA 12FT 24PT/PGCert 3FT 6PT/PGDip 6FT 12PT
Translation Studies with TESOL .... MA 12FT 24PT

Imperial College London
Scientific, Technical and Medical Translation with Translation Technology........MSc 12FT 24PT

King's College London
Language & Cultural Diversity........ MA 12FT 24PT

Kingston University
Translation Studies .... MA 12FT 24PT

Leeds Metropolitan University
Vocational Diploma in Interpreting.......Vocational Diploma 12DL

University of Leeds
Applied Translation Studies.........MA 12FT 24PT/PGDip 9FT 18PT
Audiovisual Translation Studies .... MA 12FT 24PT
Conference Interpreting ....PGDip 9FT
Conference Interpreting and Translation Studies........MA 12FT

London Metropolitan University
Conference Interpreting ....MA 12FT
Interpreting........ MA 12FT 24PT
Interpreting (Health) ....PGDip variousFT
Interpreting (Legal) ....PGDip variousFT
Public Service Interpreting........ MA 12FT 24PT
Public Service Interpreting (Health & Legal) .... MA 12FT 24PT
Specialised Translation........ PGCert 12FT 24+PT
Translation .... MA 12FT 24PT
Translation and Technology........ PGCert 12FT 24+PT

University of Manchester
Conference Interpreting ....MSc 12FT 24PT/PGDip 9FT 24PT
Translation and Interpreting Studies ... MA 12FT 24PT/PGDip 9FT

Middlesex University
Theory and Practice of Translation........ MA 12FT 24PT

Newcastle University
Interpreting........MA 12FT/MA 24FT
Translating ....MA 12 or 24FT
Translating and Interpreting ....MA 12 or 24FT
Translation Studies ....MLitt 12FT 24PT

University of Nottingham
Chinese/English Translation & Interpreting........MA 12FT
Literatures in English Translation........MA 12FT

University of Portsmouth
Translation Studies .... MA 12FT 24PT
Translation Studies (DL)........ MA 36DL

Queen Mary, University of London
Comparative Literature........MSc 12FT 24PT

Queen's University Belfast
Interpreting........ MA 12FT 24PT
Translation .... MA 12FT 12PT

University of Roehampton
Audiovisual Translation .... MA 12FT 24PT PGDip 9FT 24PT
Specialised Translation........ MA 12FT 24PT/PGDip 9FT 24PT

University of Salford
Interpreting and Translating......... MA 12FT 36PT/PGDip 9FT 24PT
Translating .... MA 12FT 36PT/PGDip 9FT 24PT
Translating for International Business. MA 12FT 36PT/PGDip 9FT 24PT

School of Oriental and African Studies - SOAS
Ancient Near Eastern Languages .... MA 12FT 24-36PT

University of Sheffield
Screen Translation........ MA 12FT 24PT
Translation Studies .... MA 12FT 24PT

University of St Andrews
Book History .... MLitt 12FT 24PT/MPhil 24FT/PGDip 9FT
Language and Linguistics.........MLitt 12FT 24PT/PGDip 9FT 18PT/MPhil 24FT

University of Stirling
Translation Studies ....MRes 12FT 27PT/PGCert 9FT 21PT
Translation Studies with TESOL MSc 12FT 27PT/PGDip 9FT 21PT/PGCert 9FT 9PT

University of Surrey
Audiovisual Translation ....MA 12FT
Business Translation and Interpreting.........MA 12FT/PGCert 9FT/Diploma 9FT
Monolingual Subtitling and Audio Description ....MA 12FT
Public Service Interpreting......MA 12FT/Diploma 9FT/PGCert 9PT
Translation ....MA 12FT/PGDip 9FT
Translation Studies .... MA 12FT/Diploma 9FT
Translation Studies with Intercultural Communication MA 12FT/Diploma 9FT

Swansea University
Chinese-English Translation and Language Teaching......MA 12FT
European Master's in Translation with Language Technology MA 48FT
Literary Translation ....MA 24FT
Literary Translation (French)........ MA 12FT 24-36PT
Literary Translation (German) .... MA 12FT 24-36PT
Literary Translation (Spanish)........ MA 12FT 24-36PT
Translation Technology ....PGCert 12FT
Translation and Interpreting ....MA 12FT
Translation with Language Technology........ MA 12FT 24PT

Trinity College Dublin - the University of Dublin
Literary Translation .... MPhil 12FT

University of Ulster
Professional Translation........ MA 12FT 24PT

UCL - University College London
Translation Theory and Practice .... MA 12FT 24PT

University of Warwick
Translation Studies .... MA 12FT 24PT/PGDip 12FT/PGCert 3FT
Translation, Media and Cultural Transfer MA 12FT 24PT/Diploma 9FT 18PT
Translation, Writing and Cultural Difference.........MA 12FT 24PT/PGDip 9FT 18PT

University of Westminster
Bilingual Translation........ MA 12FT 24PT
Interpreting........ MA 12FT 24PT
Technical and Specialised Translation........ MA 12FT 24PT
Translation and Interpreting .... MA 12FT 24PT
Translation and Linguistics .... MA 12FT 24PT

Translating
Research Courses

University of Aberdeen
Translational Medicine...PhD 36FT/MPhil 24FT/MD 24FT/ChM by research 24FT

Aston University
Translation Studies .... PhD 36FT 60PT

Bangor University
French........PhD 36FT/MPhil 12FT

Linguistics

German .... PhD 36FT/MPhil 12FT
Spanish.. MPhil 12FT/PhD 36FT
Translation Studies .... PhD 36FT/MPhil 12FT
Translation Studies (PhD by Practice).PhD 36FT 72PT/MPhil 24FT 48PT

University of Bristol
German .... PhD 36FT 72PT/MLitt by research 24FT 48PT/MPhil 12FT 24PT

Cardiff University
Language and Translation Studies......PhD 36FT 60PT/MPhil 24FT 48PT

University of Edinburgh
Translation Studies .... PhD 36FT 72PT

Heriot-Watt University
Translation and Interpreting ..... PhD 36FT 48PT/MPhil 12FT 24PT

University of Manchester
Interpreting Studies...PhD 36FT
Translation and Intercultural Studies..............................PhD 36FT/MPhil 12FT 24PT

Newcastle University
Translating and Interpreting ..... MPhil 12FT 24PT/PhD 36FT 72PT

University of St Andrews
Language and Linguistics.........PhD 36FT 72PT/DLang 36FT 72PT/MPhil 24FT 48PT

University of Surrey
Translation Studies ....PhD 21-72FT 33-96PT/MPhil 18-33FT

UCL - University College London
Translation Studies .... PhD 36FT 60PT

University of Warwick
Translation Studies .... PhD 36FT 60PT/MPhil 24FT 36PT
Translation Studies and Comparative Literature..PhD 36FT 60PT/MPhil 24FT 36PT

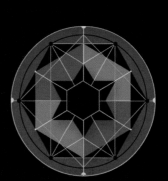

Literature and creative writing

African literature
Taught Courses

School of Oriental and African Studies - SOAS
African Literature.............................. MA 12FT 24-36PT
African Studies.................................. MA 12FT 24-36PT
Comparative Literature (Asia/Africa)................... MA 12FT 24-36PT

American literature
Taught Courses

Aberystwyth University
Literary Studies (American Literature)...................... MA 12FT 24PT

University of Cambridge
American Literature..................................MPhil 9FT

University College Cork
English (American Literature & Film).....................MA 12FT

University of East Anglia
American Literature.............................. MA 12FT 24PT
American Studies................................. MA 12FT 24PT
American Studies and Film Studies............ MA 12FT 24PT

University of Edinburgh
American Literature...MSc(Res) 12FT 24PT
English Literature: US Literature - Cultural Values from
Revolution to Empire.....................................MSc 12FT 24PT

University of Essex
Literature...................................... MA 12FT 24PT

University of Glasgow
American Studies...MLitt 12FT 24PT

University of Kent
English and American Literature................................ MA 12FT 24PT
English and American Literature (Paris option)................MA 12FT

Leeds Metropolitan University
English: Contemporary Literatures........................... MA 12FT 24PT

University of Leeds
American Literature and Culture............................... MA 12FT 24PT

University of Nottingham
American Studies (Literature)............................ MA 12FT 24-36PT
American Studies with Canadian Literature...... MA 12FT 24-36PT
English and American Studies........................... MA 12FT 24-36PT

University of Sheffield
English Literature (American Literature pathway). MA 12FT 24PT

Trinity College Dublin - the University of Dublin
Literatures of the Americas....................................MPhil 12FT

American literature
Research Courses

University of Kent
American Studies............PhD 36FT 60PT/MPhil 24FT 36PT/MA by
research 12FT 24PT

King's College London
American Studies Research.. MPhil 24FT 36PT/PhD 36FT 48-72PT

University of Leeds
American Studies...................... PhD 36-42FT/MPhil 24FT/
MA by research 12FT

University of Nottingham
American and Canadian Studies Research Areas.PhD 36FT 72PT/
MPhil 24FT 48PT/MRes 12FT 24PT

Arabic literature
Taught Courses

University of Leeds
Middle Eastern and Islamic Studies.......................... MA 12FT 24PT

University of Oxford
Modern Middle Eastern Studies... MPhil 21FT
Syriac Studies..MSt 9FT

School of Oriental and African Studies - SOAS
Arabic Literature... MA 12FT 24-36PT

Caribbean literature
Taught Courses

UCL - University College London
Caribbean and Latin American Studies................... MA 12FT 24PT

University of Warwick
Humanities (Caribbean Studies)............................. MA 12FT 24PT

Caribbean literature
Research Courses

University of Birmingham
Caribbean Literature...MRes 12FT 24PT

University of Warwick
Caribbean Studies...........PhD 36FT 60PT/MPhil 24FT 36PT/MA by
research 12FT 24PT

Childrens literature
Taught Courses

Bangor University
Arthurian Literature............................... MA 12FT 24-36PT

Bath Spa University
Writing for Young People............................... MA 12FT 24PT

University of Bolton
Children's Literature and Culture.................................MA 24PT
Safeguarding and Promoting Children's Welfare.... MSc 36-60PT/
PGDip 24PT/PGCert 12PT

Canterbury Christ Church University
English: Children's Literature ....MA 12FT

University of Central Lancashire
Writing for Children..MA 12FT 24PT/PGDip 9FT 24PT/PGCert 9FT
24PT

University of Dundee
Writing Practice & Study .... MLitt 12FT

University of Glasgow
Childrens's Literature & Literacies.................... MEd 12FT 24-36PT

Institute of Education
Children's Media Culture...............................30 Credit Module 3PT

University of Reading
Children's Literature ....MA (Res) 12FT 24PT

University of Roehampton
Children's Literature .... MA 12FT 24PT
Children's Literature Distance Learning ....MA 24PT 24DL
Children's Literature.....................................PGDip 9FT 24PT
Children's Literature Distance Learning ....PGDip 24PT 24DL

Rose Bruford College
MA Theatre for Young Audiences........MA 12FT 24PT/PGDip 10FT
22PT

Trinity College Dublin - the University of Dublin
Children's Literature .... MPhil 12FT

Childrens literature
Research Courses

University of Roehampton
Children's Literature .... PhD 24-48FT 48PT/MPhil 21-36FT
33-48PT

Comparative literary studies
Taught Courses

University of Aberdeen
Comparative Literature.............. MLitt 12FT 24PT/PGDip 9FT 18PT

Bangor University
Early Modern Literature......................MA 12FT 24-36PT/PGDip 9FT
English............. PhD by taught 36FT 72-96PT/MPhil 24FT 48-60PT

Birkbeck, University of London
Comparative Literature....................................... MA 12FT 24PT

University College Cork
French (French & Comparative Literature)...................MA 12FT

Durham University
Twentieth-Century Literary Studies.................... MA 12FT 24PT

University of East Anglia
Literary Translation .... MA 12FT 24PT

University of Edinburgh
Comparative and General Literature.....................MSc 12FT 24PT

University of Essex
Creative Writing .... MA 12FT 24PT
English Language and Literature............................. MA 12FT 24PT
Film Studies .... MA 12FT 24PT
Film and Literature .... MA 12FT 24PT
Literature .... MA 12FT 24PT
Myth, Literature and the Unconscious .... MA 12FT 24PT
Theatre.. MA 12FT 24PT
Wild Writing: Literature and the Environment........ MA 12FT 24PT

University of Exeter
Creative Writing .... MA 11FT 23PT
English Literary Studies.................................. MA 11FT 23PT

Goldsmiths, University of London
Comparative Literary Studies................................. MA 12FT 24PT

University of Hertfordshire
English Literature: Modern Literary Cultures.........MA 12FT 24PT/
PGDip 12FT 24PT/PGCert 12FT 24PT

University of Huddersfield
Literary Studies .... MA 12FT 24PT

University of Kent
Comparative Literature .... MA 12FT 24PT
Comparative Literature (Paris option)..................MA 12FT
French and Comparative Literature .... MA 12FT 24PT
French and Comparative Literature (Paris option)............MA 12FT
Graduate Diploma in Humanities (Comparative Literature).........
GradDip 12FT
Hispanic and Comparative Literature .... MA 12FT 24PT
Modern German and Comparative Literature .... MA 12FT 24PT

King's College London
Comparative Literature.............................. MA 12FT 24PT
German & Comparative Literature .... MA 12FT 24PT
German & Comparative Literature ....MRes 12FT 24PT

University of Limerick
Comparative Literature & Cultural Studies .... MA 12FT 24PT

University of Nottingham
Comparative Literature....................................MA 12FT
Literary Linguistics .... MA 12FT 24-36PT
Literatures in English Translation ....MA 12FT

Plymouth University
English and Culture.............................. MA 12FT 24PT

University of Reading
Children's Literature (MA Res)...........................MA (Res) 12FT 24PT

School of Oriental and African Studies - SOAS
Comparative Literature (Asia/Africa)................... MA 12FT 24-36PT

University of Sheffield
Nineteenth-Century Studies (English Literature)... MA 12FT 24PT

University of St Andrews
Crossways in Cultural Narratives Mundus Masters (EU)..Mundus
Masters 12-24FT
Evolutionary and Comparative Psychology: The Origins of Mind.
MSc 12FT 24PT

University of Strathclyde
Literary Journalism..................... MLitt 12FT 24PT/PGDip 9FT 21PT

University of Sunderland
English... MA 12FT 24PT

Trinity College Dublin - the University of Dublin
Comparative Literature .... MPhil 12FT

UCL - University College London
Comparative Literature .... MA 12FT 24PT

University of Warwick
Comparative Cultural Studies ..MA 12FT 24PT/PGCert 3FT/PGDip
12FT
Comparative Literary and Cultural Studies.............. MA 12FT 24PT
English...PGDip 12FT
English Literature .... MA 12FT 24PT
Pan-Romanticisms .... MA 12FT 24PT

Comparative literary studies
Research Courses

School of Advanced Study, University of London
French or Comparative/Interdisciplinary Studies PhD 36FT 60PT/
MPhil 12FT 24PT
Germanic or Comparative/Interdisciplinary Studies ......PhD 36FT
60PT/MPhil 12FT 24PT

University of East Anglia
Creative and Critical Writing ..... PhD 36FT 72PT/MPhil 24FT 48PT
Life Writing................................... PhD 36FT 72PT/MPhil 24FT 48PT
Literary Cultures pre-1900 .... PhD 36FT 72PT/MPhil 24FT 48PT
Literary Translation .... PhD 36FT 72PT/MPhil 24FT 48PT

University of Edinburgh
Comparative Literature.................................. PhD 36FT 72PT

University of Essex
Creative Writing.............PhD 36FT 72PT/MPhil 24FT 48PT/MA by
research 12FT 24PT
Film Studies .....PhD 36FT 72PT/MPhil 24FT 48PT/MA by research
12FT 24PT
Film Studies (Creative Practices)PhD 36FT 72PT/MPhil 24FT 48PT
Literature PhD 36FT 72PT/MPhil 24FT 48PT/MA by research 12FT
24PT
Theatre StudiesPhD 36FT 72PT/MPhil 24FT 48PT/MA by research
12FT 24PT
Theatre Studies (Playwriting).... PhD 36FT 72PT/MPhil 24FT 48PT

University of Exeter
EnglishPhD 36-48FT 72PT/MPhil 24FT 48PT/MA by research 12FT
24PT

Goldsmiths, University of London
English, Comparative Literature or Modern Languages...........PhD
36-48FT 48-72PT/MPhil 24FT 36PT

University of Kent
Comparative Literature..PhD 36FT 60PT/MPhil 24FT 36PT/MA by
research 12FT 24PT

King's College London
Comparative Literature Research . PhD 36FT 48-72PT/MPhil 36FT
48-72PT

University of Salford
Centre for Literary and Cultural Studies.........................PhD/MPhil

UCL - University College London
Comparative Literature.................................. PhD 36FT 60PT

University of Warwick
Comparative and Literary Cultural Studies.PhD 36FT 60PT/MPhil
24FT 36PT
English.....PhD 36FT 60PT/MPhil 24FT 36PT/MA by research 12FT
24PT

Literature and creative writing

Translation Studies and Comparative Literature..PhD 36FT 60PT/MPhil 24FT 36PT

Creative writing
Taught Courses

University of Aberdeen
Creative Writing.......................... MLitt 12FT 24PT/PGDip 9FT 21PT

Aberystwyth University
Creative Writing.......... MA 12FT 24PT
Scriptwriting (Screen and Radio)..........MA 12FT 24PT/PGDip 9FT 20PT

Anglia Ruskin University
Creative Writing.......... MA 12FT 24PT

University of the Arts London - Central Saint Martins College of Art and Design
Creative Practice for Narrative Environments..........MA 24FT

Bangor University
Creative Practice..........MRes 12FT 24PT
Creative Writing............PhD by taught 36FT 72-96PT/MPhil 24FT 48-60PT

Bath Spa University
Creative Writing..........MA 12FT
Scriptwriting.......... MA 12FT 24PT
Travel and Nature Writing..........MA 12FT 24PT 12DL
Writing for Young People.......... MA 12FT 24PT

Birkbeck, University of London
Creative Writing.......... MA 12FT 24PT
Screenwriting..........PGCert 12PT/MA 24PT

Birmingham City University
Writing.......... MA 12FT 24-60PT

University of Birmingham
Creative Writing .... MA 12FT 24PT

University of Bolton
Writing and Producing.......... MA 12FT 24PT

Bournemouth University
Screenwriting.......... MA 24FT 24DL
Scriptwriting..........MA 12FT

Brunel University
Creative Writing.......... MA 1 yearFT 2 yearsPT
Creative Writing: The Novel.......... MA 12FT 24PT

University of Cambridge
Creative Writing.......... MSt 24PT

Canterbury Christ Church University
Creative Writing: Prose Fiction..........MA 24PT

Cardiff Metropolitan University
Creative Writing.......... MA 12FT 24PT
English and Creative Writing.......... MA 12FT 24PT

Cardiff University
Creative Writing..........MA 12FT

University of Central Lancashire
Playwriting.......... MA 12FT 24PT
Scriptwriting.......... MA 12FT 24PT
Writing for Children..........MA 12FT 24PT/PGDip 9FT 24PT/PGCert 9FT 24PT

Central School of Speech and Drama, University of London
Writing for Stage and Broadcast Media..........MA 12FT 24PT/MFA 24FT

University of Chichester
Creative Writing.....MA 12+FT 24-36PT/PGDip 24PT/PGCert 12PT

City University London
Creative Writing (Non-Fiction)..........MA 24PT
Creative Writing (Novels)..........MA 24PT
Creative Writing (Playwriting & Screenwriting)..... MA 24FT 24PT

De Montfort University
Television Scriptwriting..........MA 24PT

University of Dundee
Comics Studies..........MLitt 12FT
Creative Writing (Module)..........Module 3PT
Writing Practice & Study..........MLitt 12FT

University of East Anglia
Biography and Creative Non-Fiction.......... MA 12FT 24PT
Creative Entrepreneurship..........MA 12FT
Creative Writing: Poetry.......... MA 12FT 24PT
Creative Writing: Prose.......... MA 12FT 24PT
Creative Writing: Scriptwriting.......... MA 12FT 24PT
Writing the Modern World.......... MA 12FT 24PT

University of East London
Writing: Imaginative Practice..........PGCert 12PT
Writing: Imaginative Practice (by distance learning).......MA 24PT

Edge Hill University
Creative Writing.......... MA 12FT 24PT
Scriptwriting.......... MA 12FT 24PT

Edinburgh Napier University
Creative WritingMA 12FT 24PT/PGDip 9FT 18PT/PGCert 6FT 12PT
Flexible Managed Programme (FECCI)...MA 12FT 24PT/MSc 12FT 24PT/PGCert 12FT 24PT
Screenwriting..... MA 12FT 24PT/PGDip 9FT 18PT 9-18DL/PGCert 6FT 12PT

University of Edinburgh
Creative Writing (Online Distance Learning)..........MSc 36DL

University of Essex
Creative Writing.......... MA 12FT 24PT
Wild Writing: Literature and the Environment....... MA 12FT 24PT

University of Exeter
Creative Writing.......... MA 11FT 23PT
English Literary Studies.......... MA 11FT 23PT
Theatre Practice: Applied Theatre.......... MA 12FT 24PT
Theatre Practice: Directing and Actor Training....... MA 12FT 24PT
Theatre Practice: General Programme.......... MA 12FT 24PT
Theatre Practice: Physical Performance & Actor TrainingMA 12FT 24PT
Theatre Practice: Staging Shakespeare..MA 12FT 24PT/MFA 24FT

Falmouth University
Professional Writing..........MA 12FT 24PT 24DL

GCU London
TV Fiction Writing..........MA 12FT

National University of Ireland Galway
Screenwriting.......... MA 12FT/PGDip 12FT

Glasgow Caledonian University
Television Fiction Writing.......... MA 12FT 24PT

University of Glasgow
Creative Writing..........MFA 24FT MLitt 12FT 24PT 12DL
Playwriting & Dramaturgy..........MLitt 12FT

University of Gloucestershire
Creative and Critical Writing.......MA 12FT 24PT/PGDip 8FT 20PT/PGCert 4FT 8PT

Goldsmiths, University of London
Creative and Cultural Industries..........GradDip 12FT
Creative and Life Writing.......... MA 12FT 24PT
Script Writing..........MA 12FT
Writer/Teacher.......... MA 12FT 24PT
Writing for Performance.......... MA 12FT 24PT

University of Hull
Creative Writing.......... MA 12FT 24PT

Keele University
Creative Writing..........MA 12-15FT 24-27PT

University of Kent
Creative Writing.......... MA 12FT 24PT
Creative Writing (Paris option)..........MA 12FT

King's College London
Life Writing.......... MA 12FT 24PT

Kingston University
Creative Writing..........MA 12FT 24PT MFA 24FT 48PT
Creative Writing Low Residency.......... MA 12FT 24PT
Creative Writing Low Residency..........MFA 24FT 48PT
Creative Writing and Pedagogy.......... MA 12FT 24PT
Creative Writing and Publishing.......... MA 12FT 24PT
Creative Writing and the Creative Economy.......... MA 12FT 24PT
Managing in the Creative Economy.......... MA 12FT 24PT
Playwriting.......... MA 12FT 24PT

University of Leeds
Writing for Performance and Production.... MA 12FT 24PT/PGDip 12FT 24PT/PGCert 12FT 24PT

University of Lincoln
Creative Writing.......... MA 12FT 24PT

Liverpool John Moores University
Screenwriting..........MA 24PT/PGDip 12PT/PGCert 20PT
Writing..........MA 24PT/PGCert 20PT/PGDip 12PT

London Metropolitan University
Creative Industries.......... MA 12FT 24PT
Creative Writing.......... MA 12FT 24PT
Screenwriting..........MA 12FT

London South Bank University
Creative Writing..........MA 24PT

University of the Arts London - London College of Communication
Screenwriting..........MA 24PT

Loughborough University
Creative Writing.......... MA 12FT 24PT

Manchester Metropolitan University
Creative Writing.......... MA 24FT 36PT/PGDip 12FT 24PT/MA 24DL

University of Manchester
Creative Writing.......... MA 12FT 24PT

Middlesex University
Creative Writing..........MA 24PT

Newcastle University
Creative Writing.......... MA 12FT 24PT
Creative Writing..........PGCert 12FT 24PT

Northumbria University
Creative Writing.......... MA 12FT 24PT
Creative Writing in the Classroom..........PGCert 12PT

Nottingham Trent University
Creative Writing.......... MA 12FT 24PT
Language & Culture Bridging Programme, School of Art & Design..........Language and Culture Bridging Programme 3FT

University of Nottingham
Creative Writing.......... MA 12FT 24PT

Oxford Brookes University
Creative Writing.......... MA 12FT 24PT/PGDip 8FT 6-8PT/PGCert 4FT 6PT

University of Oxford
Creative Writing.......... MSt 24PT

Plymouth University
Creative Writing.......... MA 12FT 24PT

University of Portsmouth
Creative Writing.......... MA 12FT 24PT

Queen's University Belfast
English (Creative Writing)..........MA 12FT 24PT/PGDip 12FT 24PT

University of Roehampton
Post Graduate Diploma- Creative and Professional WritingPGDip 9FT 24PT

Royal Holloway, University of London
Creative Writing.......... MA 12FT 24PT

University of Salford
Art and Design: Creative Education...... MA 12FT 24PT/PGDip 8FT 15PT
Creative Writing: Innovation and Experiment.......MA 12FT 36PT/PGDip 8FT 24PT/PGCert 4FT 12PT
Film Screenwriting..........MA 15FT/PGDip 12FT/PGCert 6FT
Television and Radio Scriptwriting MA 27PT/PGDip 24PT/PGCert 12PT

Sheffield Hallam University
Writing.......... MA 12FT 24PT

University of Sheffield
English Literature: Creative Writing.......... MA 12FT 24PT

University of South Wales
Scriptwriting.......... MA 12FT 24PT
Scriptwriting for Screen, Media and Stage.......... MA 12FT 24PT
Writing..........MPhil 48PT

University of Southampton
Creative Writing.......... MA 12FT 24PT

University of St Andrews
Creative Writing.......... MLitt 12FT 24PT/PGDip 9FT 24PT

University of Stirling
Creative Writing.....MLitt 12FT 27PT/PGDip 9FT 21PT/PGCert 3FT 3PT

University of Sussex
Creative and Critical Writing.......... MA 12FT 24PT
Writing History.......... MA 12FT 24PT

Swansea University
Creative Writing..........MA 12FT 24-36PT

Teesside University
Creative WritingMA 12FT 24PT/PGDip 9FT 18PT/PGCert 6FT 12PT

Trinity College Dublin - the University of Dublin
Creative Writing.......... MPhil 12FT

University of Wales Trinity Saint David
Creative and Script Writing......MA 12FT 24PT/PGCert 12FT 24PT/PGDip 12FT 24PT

University of Westminster
Creative Writing: Writing the City.......... MA 12FT 24PT

University of Winchester
Creative and Critical Writing.... MA 12FT 24PT/PGDip 12FT 24PT/PGCert 12FT 24PT
Doctor of Creative Arts (Creative Writing)..... PhD by taught 48FT 72PT
Writing for Children.......MA 12FT 24PT/PGDip 12FT 24PT/PGCert 12FT 24PT

University of Wolverhampton
Transmedia Screenwriting.......... MA 12FT 24PT

University of York
Theatre: Writing, Directing and Performance.......... MA 12FT 24PT

York St John University
Creative Writing.......... MA 12FT 24PT

Creative writing
Research Courses

Aberystwyth University
Creative Writing (PhD).......... PhD 36FT 60PT

Anglia Ruskin University
Creative Writing..........MPhil 24FT/PhD 36FT

Bangor University
Creative Writing.......... MPhil 24FT 48PT/PhD 36FT 72PT

Literature and creative writing

Creative and Critical Writing, Film and Media, Professional Writing ... MPhil 24FT 48PT/PhD 36FT 72PT
Creative and Critical Writing, Film and Media, Professional Writing: Practice-Led Research . MPhil 24FT 48PT/PhD 36FT 72PT

Bath Spa University
Creative Writing ... PhD 24 - 60FT 36 - 72PT

University of Birmingham
Creative Writing (by Distance Learning) ... PhD 36FT 72PT

University of Bolton
Creative Writing Specialisms ... PhD 36FT 72PT/MPhil 24FT 36PT

Cardiff University
Creative and Critical Writing ... PhD 36FT

University of Essex
Creative Writing ... PhD 36FT 72PT/MPhil 24FT 48PT/MA by research 12FT 24PT

University of Exeter
Drama ... PhD 48FT 89PT/MPhil 36FT 60PT
EnglishPhD 36-48FT 72PT/MPhil 24FT 48PT/MA by research 12FT 24PT
Film Studies ... MPhil 24FT 48PT/PhD 36-48FT 72PT

University of Gloucestershire
Creative Writing ... PhD 30-48FT

University of Kent
The Contemporary Novel: Practice as Research ... MA by research 12FT 24PT/PhD 36FT 60PT

Lancaster University
Creative Writing ... PhD 36FT 48PT/MPhil 24FT 36PT

University of Manchester
Creative Writing ... PhD 36FT 72PT

The Open University
Academic and Professional Communication Literacies..PhD 36FT 72PT variableDL/EdD 36PT variableDL/MRes 12FT
English... PhD 36FT 72PT variableDL/MPhil 15FT 24PT variableDL

University of Strathclyde
Creative Writing ... MRes 12FT 24PT

University of Sussex
Creative Writing Research Programme ... PhD 24-48FT 36-72PT/MPhil 12-36FT 24-48PT
Creative and Critical Practice Research Programme. PhD 24-48FT 36-72PT/MPhil 12-36FT 24-48PT

Swansea University
Creative Writing ... MPhil 24FT 48PT/PhD 36FT 72PT

Critical theory
Taught Courses

University of Brighton
Cultural and Critical Theory (Aesthetics and Cultural Theory) ... MA 12FT 24PT/PGDip 12FT 24PT/PGCert 12FT 24PT
Cultural and Critical Theory (Globalisation, Politics and Culture) ... MA 12FT 24PT/PGDip 12FT 24PT/PGCert 12FT 24PT
Cultural and Critical Theory (Philosophy and Critical Theory) ... MA 12FT 24PT/PGDip 12FT 24PT/PGCert 12FT 24PT

Cardiff University
Critical and Cultural Theory ... MA 12FT 24PT

University of Derby
Systemic Thinking and Practice ... PGCert 12PT

University of Dundee
Art and Humanities ... MFA 12FT
Writing Practice & Study ... MLitt 12FT

Durham University
Studies in Poetry ... MA 12FT 24PT

University of East Anglia
Biography and Creative Non-Fiction ... MA 12FT 24PT
Creative Writing: Poetry ... MA 12FT 24PT
Creative Writing: Prose ... MA 12FT 24PT
Creative Writing: Scriptwriting ... MA 12FT 24PT
Culture and Modernity ... MA 12FT 24PT
Philosophy and Literature ... MA 12FT 24PT
Writing the Modern World ... MA 12FT 24PT

Edge Hill University
Critical Screen Practice ... MA 12FT 24PT

University of Exeter
Creative Writing ... MA 11FT 23PT
English Literary Studies ... MA 11FT 23PT

Glasgow School of Art
Writing and Criticism ... PGCert 4FT 8PT/PGDip 8FT 16PT/MLitt 12FT 24PT

University of Glasgow
Arts of China ... MLitt 12FT
Arts of Europe ... MLitt 12FT/PGDip 9FT
Creative Writing ... MFA 24FT

Goldsmiths, University of London
Creative and Cultural Industries ... GradDip 12FT
Critical & Creative Analysis ... MA 12FT 24PT

University of Kent
Arts Criticism ... MA 12FT 24PT
Critical Theory (taught jointly with the School of European Culture and Languages) ... MA 12FT 24PT

King's College London
Critical Methodologies ... MA 12FT 24PT

Kingston University
Aesthetics and Art Theory ... MA 12FT 24PT
Criticism, Literature, Theory ... MA 12FT 24PT
Philosophy and Contemporary Critical Theory ... MA 12FT 24PT

University of Northampton
Modern English Studies ... MA 12FT 24PT/PGDip 12PT

University of Nottingham
Critical Theory ... MA 12FT 24-36PT/PGDip 9FT 24PT
Critical Theory ... MA 12FT 24-36PT
Critical Theory and Cultural Studies ... MA 12FT 24-36PT
Critical Theory and Politics ... MA 12FT 24PT
Modern Languages and Critical Theory ... MA 12FT 24PT

University of Roehampton
Film and Screen Cultures ... MA 12FT 24-36PT

School of Oriental and African Studies - SOAS
African Literature ... MA 12FT 24-36PT
Arabic Literature ... MA 12FT 24-36PT
Comparative Literature (Asia/Africa) ... MA 12FT 24-36PT
Critical Media and Cultural Studies ... MA 12FT 24-36PT
Global Media and Postnational Communication ... MA 12FT 24-36PT
Languages and literatues of South East Asia ... MA 12FT 24-36PT

University of Sussex
Creative and Critical Writing ... MA 12FT 24PT
Critical Theory ... MA 12FT 24PT

Critical theory
Research Courses

Bangor University
Creative and Critical Writing, Film and Media, Professional Writing ... MPhil 24FT 48PT/PhD 36FT 72PT
Creative and Critical Writing, Film and Media, Professional Writing: Practice-Led Research . MPhil 24FT 48PT/PhD 36FT 72PT

Cardiff University
Creative and Critical Writing ... PhD 36FT
Critical and Cultural Theory ... PhD 36FT/MPhil 12-24FT

University of Kent
The Contemporary Novel: Practice as Research ... MA by research 12FT 24PT/PhD 36FT 60PT

Lancaster University
Ruskin Studies ... MPhil 24FT 36PT/PhD 36FT 48PT

University of Nottingham
Critical Theory and Cultural Studies ... PhD 36FT 72PT/MPhil 24FT 48PT
Cultural Studies and Critical Theory ... New Route PhD 48FT 96PT

The Open University
Modern art theory and practicePhD 36FT 72PT variableDL/MPhil 15FT 24PT variableDL

University of Salford
Centre for Literary and Cultural Studies ... PhD/MPhil

School of Oriental and African Studies - SOAS
Art and Archaeology ... PhD 36FT/MPhil 24FT
Development Studies ... PhD 36FT 48-60PT
Economics ... PhD 36FT 72PT/MPhil 24FT 36PT
Languages and Cultures of South Asia ... PhD 36FT 72PT/MPhil 24FT 48PT
Media and Film Studies ... PhD 36-48FT
Politics ... PhD 36FT 72PT/MPhil 24FT 36PT
Social Anthropology ... PhD 36FT/MPhil 24FT

University of Sussex
English Research Programme ... PhD 24-48FT 36-72PT/MPhil 12-36FT 24-48PT
Social and Political Thought ... DPhil 24-48FT 36-72PT/MPhil 12-36FT 24-48PT

English literature
Taught Courses

University of Aberdeen
English Literary Studies ... MLitt 12FT 24PT/PGDip 9FT 18PT

Anglia Ruskin University
English Literature ... MA 12FT 24PT

Bangor University
Arthurian Literature ... MA 12FT 24-36PT
Creative Writing ... PhD by taught 36FT 72-96PT/MPhil 24FT 48-60PT
Early Modern Literature ... MA 12FT 24-36PT/PGDip 9FT
English ... PhD by taught 36FT 72-96PT/MPhil 24FT 48-60PT
English ... MA 12FT 24-36PT
Women's Studies ... MA 24PT/PGDip 24PT/PGCert 12PT

Birkbeck, University of London
Comparative Literature ... MA 12FT 24PT
Contemporary Literature and Culture ... MA 12FT 24PT
Medieval Literature and Culture ... MA 12FT 24PT
Renaissance Studies ... MA 12FT 24PT
Romantic Studies..MA 12FT 24PT/PGDip 12FT 24PT/PGCert 12FT 24PT
Victorian Studies ... MA 12FT 24PT

University of Birmingham
English Literature ... MA 12FT 24PT
Literary Linguistics ... MA 12FT 24PT
Literature and Film ... MRes 12FT 24PT
Literature and Modernity ... MPhil(B) 12FT 24PT
Literature, Culture and Modernity: Victorian and Modernity..MA 12FT 24PT

University of Bristol
English Literature ... MA 12FT 24PT

Brunel University
English Literature ... MA 12FT 24PT

University of Cambridge
English Studies: 18th Century and Romantic Studies ... MPhil 9FT
English Studies: Culture & Criticism ... MPhil 9FT

Canterbury Christ Church University
English Literature ... MA 12FT
English: Literatures Victorian and Modern ... MA 12FT

Cardiff Metropolitan University
English ... MA 12FT 24PT

Cardiff University
English Literature ... MA 12FT

University of Central Lancashire
English Language and Literature ... MA 12FT 24PT
Modern and Contemporary Literature ... MA 12FT 24PT

University of Chester
Nineteenth Century Literature and Culture ... MA 12FT/PGDip 12FT/PGCert 12FT

University College Cork
Arts (English) ... HDip 9FT 18PT
English (Modernities, Romanticism, Modernism, & Post Modernism) ... MA 12FT
English (Texts & Contexts: Medieval to Renaissance) ... MA 12FT

University of Cumbria
Literature, Romanticism and the English Lake District ... MA 12FT 24PT

University of Dundee
English Studies ... MLitt 12FT
Writing Practice & Study ... MLitt 12FT

University of East Anglia
Culture and Modernity ... MA 12FT 24PT
Medieval and Early Modern Textual Cultures, 1381 - 1688 ... MA 12FT 24PT
Writing the Modern World ... MA 12FT 24PT

Edge Hill University
English ... MA 12FT 24PT
English Literature ... MRes 12FT 24PT

University of Edinburgh
English Literature: Literature and Modernity:1900 to the Present ... MSc 12FT 24PT
English Literature: Creative Writing ... MSc 12FT/PGDip 9FT
English Literature: Literature and Society: Enlightenment, Romantic and Victorian ... MSc 12FT 24PT
English Literature: Material Cultures and the History of the Book MSc 12FT 24PT
English Literature: US Literature - Cultural Values from Revolution to Empire ... MSc 12FT 24PT

University of Exeter
English Literary Studies ... MA 11FT 23PT

University of Glasgow
Modernities: Literature, Theory & Culture ... MLitt 12FT 24PT

University of Hertfordshire
English Literature: Modern Literary Cultures ... MA 12FT 24PT/PGDip 12FT 24PT/PGCert 12FT 24PT

University of Hull
English Literature ... MA 12FT 24PT
English by Research ... MA 12FT 24PT

Keele University
Humanities (English) ... MRes 12FT 24PT

University of Kent
Dickens and Victorian Culture ... MA 12FT 24PT
Eighteenth Century Studies ... MA 12FT 24PT
Eighteenth-Century Studies (Paris option) ... MA 12FT 24PT
English and American Literature ... MA 12FT 24PT
English and American Literature (Paris option) ... MA 12FT
Postcolonial Studies ... MA 12FT 24PT
Postcolonial Studies (Paris option) ... MA 12FT
Shakespeare ... MA 12FT 24PT

King's College London
Early Modern English Literature: Text & Transmission ... MA 12FT 24PT
English: 1850 - Present ... MA 12FT 24PT

Literature and creative writing

Kingston University
English Literature .... MA 12FT 24PT

University of Leeds
English Language and World Englishes .... MA 12FT 24PT
English Literature .... MA 12FT 24PT
English Renaissance Literature .... MA 12FT 24PT

University of Lincoln
English Studies .... MA 12FT 24PT

Liverpool John Moores University
Literature and Cultural History .... MRes 24PT

University of Liverpool
Directed Research in English .... MA 12FT
Renaissance and 18th Century Literature .... MA 12FT 24PT

Manchester Metropolitan University
English Studies: Contemporary Literature and Film .... MA 16FT 36PT/PGDip 12FT 24PT
English Studies: The Gothic .... PGDip 12FT 24PT/MA 15FT 30PT

University of Manchester
English and American Studies .... MA 12FT 24PT

Northumbria University
English Literature .... MRes 12FT 24PT

Nottingham Trent University
English Literary Research .... MA 12FT 24PT/PGDip 12FT 21PT/PGCert 9FT 21PT

University of Nottingham
English Studies .... MA 12FT 24-36PT/PGDip 12FT 24-36PT
English Studies by web-based distance learning .... MA 24-48PT 24-48DL
English and American Studies .... MA 12FT 24-36PT

The Open University
English .... MA variableDL

Oxford Brookes University
English .... MA 12FT 24PT/PGDip 9FT 20PT/PGCert 4FT 8PT

University of Oxford
English (1550-1700) .... MSt 9FT
English (1660-1830) .... MSt 9FT
English (1800-1914) .... MSt 12FT
English (1900-Present) .... MSt 9FT
English (650-1550) .... MSt 9FT
English (English and American Studies) .... MSt 9FT
English Language .... MSt 9FT
English Studies (Medieval Period) .... MPhil 21FT

Plymouth University
English .... MRes 12FT 24PT
English and Culture .... MA 12FT 24PT

University of Portsmouth
Literature, Culture and Identity .... MA 12FT 24PT

Queen Mary, University of London
English Studies: Eighteenth Century Literature and Romanticism MA 12FT 24PT
English Studies: English Literature .... MA 12FT 24PT

Queen's University Belfast
English (Broadcast Literacy) .... MA 12FT 24PT
English (Creative Writing) .... MA 12FT 24PT/PGDip 12FT 24PT

University of Reading
Children's Literature .... MA (Res) 12FT 24PT
Early Modern History .... MA (Res) 12FT 24PT
Early Modern Literature & Drama .... MA (Res) 12FT 24PT
English .... MA (Res) 12FT 24PT

Royal Holloway, University of London
English Literature .... MA 12FT 24PT
Literatures of Modernity: Modernism, Postmodernism, Postcolonialism .... MA 12FT 24PT

Sheffield Hallam University
English .... MPhil 36FT 84PT/PhD by taught 36FT 84PT

University of Sheffield
Eighteenth-Century Studies (English Literature) ... MA 12FT 24PT
English Literature .... MA 12FT 24PT
English Literature (American Literature pathway). MA 12FT 24PT
English Literature: Creative Writing .... MA 12FT 24PT
English Studies (online) .... MA 12/24DL
Nineteenth-Century Studies (English Literature)... MA 12FT 24PT

University of Southampton
Eighteenth Century Studies .... MA 12FT 24PT
English .... MA 12FT 24PT/MRes 12FT 24PT

University of St Andrews
English Studies .... PGDip 9FT/MLitt 12FT
Shakespeare and Renaissance Literary Culture. MLitt 12FT 24PT/PGDip 9FT 24PT
Women, Writing and Gender .. MLitt 12FT 24PT/PGDip 9FT 24PT/MPhil 24FT

St Mary's University College, Twickenham
Gothic: Culture, Subculture, Counterculture .... MA 12FT 24PT

University of Stirling
English Language and Linguistics ...... MLitt 12FT 27PT/PGDip 9FT 21PT/PGCert 3FT 9PT
Renaissance Studies ..... MRes 12FT 27PT/PGDip 8FT 21PT/PGCert 4FT 9PT

University of Strathclyde
Renaissance Studies ..... MLitt 12FT 24PT/PGDip 9FT 21PT/PGCert 4FT 9PT

University of Sussex
English Studies .... MA 12FT 24PT

Swansea University
English Literature .... MA 12FT 24-36PT

Trinity College Dublin - the University of Dublin
Children's Literature .... MPhil 12FT

UCL - University College London
English: Issues in Modern Culture .... MA 12FT 24PT

University of Warwick
Colonial and Post-Colonial Literature in English .... PGDip 12FT/MA 12FT 24PT
English Literature .... MA 12FT 24PT
Pan-Romanticisms .... MA 12FT 24PT

University of Westminster
English Literature .... MA 12FT 24PT

University of Winchester
English Studies: Literature in Context MA 12FT 24PT/PGDip 12FT 24PT/PGCert 12FT 24PT

University of Wolverhampton
English .... MA 24-36PT

English literature
Research Courses

University of Aberdeen
English .... PhD 36FT 60PT/MLitt by research 12FT 24PT/MPhil 24FT 48PT

Aberystwyth University
English Literature (PhD) .... PhD 36FT 60PT

Birkbeck, University of London
Arts and Humanities .... MPhil 24FT 36PT/PhD 36-48FT 60-84PT
English and Humanities .... PhD 36-48FT 60-84PT/MPhil 24FT 36PT

Birmingham City University
English .... PhD 84FT/MPhil 84FT

University of Birmingham
Literature and Modernity 1880-1940 (English) .... MPhil(B) 12FT 24PT

University of Bolton
English Specialisms .... PhD 36FT 72PT/MPhil 18FT 36PT

University of Bristol
English Literature .... PhD 36FT 72PT/MPhil 12FT 24PT/MLitt by research 24FT 48PT

Brunel University
English .... PhD 36FT 48PT/MPhil 12FT 24PT

University of Buckingham
English Literature ...MA by research 12FT 24PT/MPhil 24FT 48PT/DPhil 36FT 72PT

University of Cambridge
English .... PhD 36FT

Canterbury Christ Church University
English Literature .... PhD 48FT 60PT/MPhil 24FT 48PT

Cardiff University
English Literature .... PhD 36FT/MPhil 12-24FT

University of Central Lancashire
English Literature/English Language & Linguistics .... MPhil 18-36FT 42-60PT/MA by research 12FT 24PT/PhD 18-36FT 42-60PT

University of Cumbria
English and Drama..PhD 48FT 72PT 72DL/MPhil 36FT 60PT 60DL

De Montfort University
English .... PhD 36-48FT 48-72PT/MPhil 12-24FT 24-48PT

University of Dundee
English .... MPhil 24FT PhD 36FT

Durham University
English Studies .... MA by research 12FT 24PT/MLitt by research 24FT 48PT/PhD 36FT 72PT

University of Edinburgh
English Literature .... PhD 36FT 72PT/MPhil 24FT 48PT/MSc by research 12FT 24PT
English Literature: Medieval Literature .... MSc by research 12FT 24PT
English Literature: Postcolonial Literature..MSc by research 12FT 24PT
English Literature: Renaissance Literature..MSc by research 12FT 24PT
English Literature: Romanticism .... MSc by research 12FT 24PT
English Literature: Scottish Literature .... MSc by research 12FT 24PT
English Literature: Victorian Literature .... MSc by research 12FT 24PT

University of Exeter
EnglishPhD 36-48FT 72PT/MPhil 24FT 48PT/MA by research 12FT 24PT

University of Glasgow
English Language and English Literature .. PhD 36FT/MPhil 12FT/MLitt by research 12FT

University of Gloucestershire
English .... PhD 30-48FT 48-84PT/MPhil 18-36FT 30-60PT/MA by research 12-24FT 18-36PT

Goldsmiths, University of London
English .... MRes 12FT 24PT
English, Comparative Literature or Modern Languages .... PhD 36-48FT 48-72PT/MPhil 24FT 36PT

University of Hull
English .... PhD 36FT 60PT/MPhil 24FT 36PT

Keele University
English .... PhD 24-48FT 48-84PT/MPhil 12-24FT 24-36PT

University of Kent
English ..... PhD 36FT 60PT/MPhil 24FT 36PT/MA by research 12FT 24PT
Poetry: Practice as Research .... PhD 36FT 60PT
Postcolonial StudiesMA by research 12FT 24PT/MPhil 24FT 36PT/PhD 36FT 60PT
Text and Event in Early Modern Europe (TEEME): An Erasmus Mundus Joint Doctorate .... PhD 36FT 60PT
Text and Practice .... PhD 36FT 60PT
The Contemporary Novel: Practice as Research ... MA by research 12FT 24PT/PhD 36FT 60PT

King's College London
English Research .... PhD 36FT 48-72PT/MPhil 24FT 36PT
Palaeography & Manuscript Studies ...... PhD 36FT 48-72PT/MPhil 36FT 48-72PT

Kingston University
Centre for Iris Murdoch StudiesPhD 48FT 72PT/MPhil 24FT 48PT/MA by research 12FT 24PT
English Literature .... PhD 48FT 72PT/MPhil 24FT 48PT/MA by research 12FT 24PT

Lancaster University
Ruskin Studies .... MPhil 24FT 36PT/PhD 36FT 48PT

University of Leeds
School of English .... PhD 36+FT/MA by research 12+FT/MPhil 24FT

University of Leicester
Department of English .... PhD 36FT 72PT/MPhil 36FT 72PT

University of Liverpool
English .... PhD 24-48FT 48-84PT/MPhil 12-48FT 48-72PT

Loughborough University
English Language and Literature .... PhD 36FT 60PT/MPhil 24FT 36PT

Manchester Metropolitan University
Department of English .... PhD 24-48FT 42-84PT 42-84DL/MPhil 18-36FT 36-72PT 36-72DL/MA by research 12-24FT 24-42PT 24-42DL

University of Manchester
English and American Studies .... PhD 36FT

Middlesex University
English Literary Studies .... PhD/MPhil/MA by research

Newcastle University
English Literature .... MLitt by research 12FT 24PT
English Literature, Language and Creative Writing .... PhD 36FT 72PT/MPhil 12FT 24PT/MLitt by research 12FT 24PT

Newman University
English .... PhD 36FT 72PT/MPhil 24FT 48PT

Nottingham Trent University
English .... PhD 48FT 96PT/MPhil 36FT 72PT

University of Nottingham
CELE Research Staff and Interests .... PhD 36FT 72PT/MPhil 24FT 48PT
English Studies research opportunities .... PhD 36FT 72PT/MPhil 24FT 48PT

The Open University
English... PhD 36FT 72PT variableDL/MPhil 15FT 24PT variableDL

Oxford Brookes University
English .... MPhil/PhD 36-60FT 48-72PT/PhD 24-60FT 36-72PT/MPhil 24-36FT 36-48PT

University of Oxford
English .... DPhil 48FT
English (to 1550) .... DPhil 48FT

Queen Mary, University of London
English .... PhD/MPhil

University of Roehampton
English Literature PhD 24-48FT 36-60PT/MPhil 21-36FT 33-48PT

Royal Holloway, University of London
English .... PhD 36FT/MPhil 24FT

Literature and creative writing

Sheffield Hallam University
Humanities Research Centre: English.........PhD 36-48FT 60-72PT

University of Southampton
English.............................. PhD 48FT 84PT/MPhil 48FT 84PT

University of St Andrews
English.............................. PhD 36FT 72PT/MPhil 24FT 48PT

St Mary's University College, Twickenham
English.............................. PhD 36FT 72PT/MPhil 24FT 48PT

University of Surrey
English..............................PhD 21-72FT 33-96PT

University of Sussex
English Research Programme............ PhD 24-48FT 36-72PT/MPhil 12-36FT 24-48PT

Swansea University
English.....PhD 36FT 72PT/MPhil 24FT 48PT/MA by research 12FT 24PT

Teesside University
English...................... PhD 24-60FT 36PT/MPhil 18FT 30PT

University of Wales Trinity Saint David
English.............................. PhD 36FT 48-72PT/MPhil 12 - 36FT

University of Ulster
English.............................. PhD 36FT 72PT/MPhil 24FT 48PT

UCL - University College London
English Language and Literature.............................. PhD 36FT 60PT

University of Warwick
English.....PhD 36FT 60PT/MPhil 24FT 36PT/MA by research 12FT 24PT

University of Worcester
English Literature .... PhD 48FT 70PT/MPhil 24FT 48PT

University of York
English.....MA by research 12FT 24PT/PhD 36FT 72PT/MPhil 24FT 48PT

European literature
Taught Courses

Bangor University
Arthurian Literature................................... MA 12FT 24-36PT
European Languages and Cultures............................ MA 12FT 24PT

University of Bristol
European Literatures .... MA 12FT 24PT

University of Cambridge
European Literature and Culture...................................MPhil 9FT
Medieval and Renaissance Literature ....MPhil 9FT
Modern European History................................. MPhil 10FT

University of East Anglia
Modern European History .... MA 12FT 24PT
Writing the Modern World .... MA 12FT 24PT

University of Exeter
English Literary Studies.............................. MA 11FT 23PT

National University of Ireland Galway
International Contemporary Literatures and Media........MA 12FT 24PT

University of Glasgow
European Studies: Cultures, Societies & Languages.... MLitt 12FT 24PT
Russian, Central & East European Studies (Erasmus Mundus International Masters) ....International Masters (double/single degree) 24FT
Russian, Central and East European Studies ....MSc 12FT 24PT/ PGDip 9FT

University of Kent
Comparative Literature........................... MA 12FT 24PT
Comparative Literature (Paris option)................................MA 12FT
French and Comparative Literature .... MA 12FT 24PT
French and Comparative Literature (Paris option)............MA 12FT
Modern European Literature .... MA 12FT 24PT
Postcolonial Studies................................... MA 12FT 24PT
Postcolonial Studies (Paris option)................................MA 12FT

University of Liverpool
Contemporary Literature ....MA 12FT

University of Oxford
Classical Armenian Studies...MSt 9FT
Slavonic Studies .... MPhil 24FT/MSt 9FT

University of Portsmouth
European Studies .... MA 12FT 24PT

University of Sheffield
Hispanic Studies.............................. MA 12FT 24PT

University of St Andrews
Russian Studies .... MLitt 12FT 24PT/PGDip 9FT 24PT

Staffordshire University
Community & Participatory Arts............................... MA 12FT 24PT

University of Stirling
Renaissance Studies .....MRes 12FT 27PT/PGDip 8FT 21PT/PGCert 4FT 9PT

University of Strathclyde
Literary Journalism...................... MLitt 12FT 24PT/PGDip 9FT 21PT
Renaissance Studies .....MLitt 12FT 24PT/PGDip 9FT 21PT/PGCert 4FT 9PT

UCL - University College London
Russian and East European Literature and Culture .... MA 12FT 24PT

University of York
Renaissance Literature, 1500-1700 .... MA 12FT 24PT
Romantic and Sentimental Literature, 1770-1830 .... MA 12FT 24PT

European literature
Research Courses

Bangor University
French...PhD 36FT/MPhil 12FT
German ....PhD 36FT/MPhil 12FT
Spanish ....MPhil 12FT/PhD 36FT

University of Edinburgh
English Literature: Renaissance Literature..MSc by research 12FT 24PT
English Literature: Romanticism ....MSc by research 12FT 24PT

University of Exeter
English...PhD 36-48FT 72PT/MPhil 24FT 48PT/MA by research 12FT 24PT

Keele University
European Studies .... MPhil 24FT 36PT/PhD 48FT 84PT

University of Kent
Comparative Literature..PhD 36FT 60PT/MPhil 24FT 36PT/MA by research 12FT 24PT
French......PhD 36FT 60PT/MPhil 24FT 36PT/MA by research 12FT 24PT
Postcolonial StudiesMA by research 12FT 24PT/MPhil 24FT 36PT/ PhD 36FT 60PT

University of Salford
Centre for Literary and Cultural Studies ....PhD/MPhil

University of St Andrews
Russian StudiesPhD 36FT 72PT/DLang 36FT 72PT/MPhil 12-24FT 48PT

Swansea University
European Cultures...................................MA by research 12FT 24PT

French literature
Taught Courses

University College Cork
French ....MA 12FT
French (French & Comparative Literature).........................MA 12FT
French Creativity/Literature & Film................................MA 12FT

National University of Ireland Galway
French..MA 12FT

University of Kent
French and Comparative Literature .... MA 12FT 24PT
French and Comparative Literature (Paris option)............MA 12FT
Graduate Diploma in Humanities (French) ....GradDip 12FT
Modern French Studies (Paris option)................................MA 12FT
Modern French Studies: Writing, Theory and Visual Culture...MA 12FT 24PT

National University of Ireland, Maynooth
French..MA 12FT

University of Nottingham
Twentieth and Twenty-First Century French Thought .....MA 12FT 24-36PT

University of Reading
French Studies ....MA (Res) 12FT

University of Sheffield
French Studies (Research Track)................................. MA 12FT 24PT

University of St Andrews
French Language Studies.........MLitt 12FT 24PT/PGDip 9FT 24PT/ MPhil 24FT
French Studies........MLitt 12FT 24PT/PGDip 9FT 24PT/MPhil 24FT

Trinity College Dublin - the University of Dublin
Textual and Visual Studies: 19th and 20th Century France .... MPhil 12FT

UCL - University College London
French and Francophone Studies .... MA 12FT 24PT

French literature
Research Courses

Bangor University
French...PhD 36FT/MPhil 12FT

University of Bristol
French..PhD 36FT 72PT/MLitt by research 24FT 48PT/MPhil 12FT 24PT

University of Cambridge
French... PhD 36FT 60PT

University of Edinburgh
French.... PhD 36FT 72PT/MPhil 24FT 48PT/MSc by research 12FT 24PT

University of Glasgow
French Language and Literature...PhD 36FT/MPhil 12FT/MLitt by research 12FT

University of London Institute in Paris
French and Comparative Studies.........PhD 36FT 72PT/MPhil 24FT 48PT

University of Kent
French......PhD 36FT 60PT/MPhil 24FT 36PT/MA by research 12FT 24PT

King's College London
French Research .... PhD 36FT 48-72PT/MPhil 24FT 36PT

University of Nottingham
French............. MRes 12FT 24PT/MPhil 24FT 48PT/PhD 36FT 72PT
French (by Research)..............................MA by research 12FT 24PT
French .... PhD 36FT 72PT/MPhil 24FT 48PT

Royal Holloway, University of London
French...PhD 36FT

University of St Andrews
French Language Studies.........PhD 36FT 72PT/DLang 36FT 72PT/ MPhil 12-24FT 48PT

Swansea University
European Cultures...................................MA by research 12FT 24PT
French .... PhD 36FT 72PT/MPhil 24FT 36PT

University of Ulster
French.. PhD 36FT 72PT/MPhil 24FT 48PT

UCL - University College London
French .... PhD 36FT 60PT

University of Warwick
French Studies.........PhD 36FT 60PT/MPhil 24FT 36PT/ MA by research 12FT 24PT

German literature
Taught Courses

University College Cork
German Studies .... MA 12FT 24PT

National University of Ireland Galway
German Literature/ Language ....MA 12FT

University of Kent
Graduate Diploma in Humanities (German)............GradDip 12FT
Modern German and Comparative Literature .... MA 12FT 24PT

King's College London
German & Comparative Literature ....MRes 12FT 24PT
MA 12FT 24PT

National University of Ireland, Maynooth
German .... MA 12FT 24PT

University of Nottingham
Modern and Contemporary German Studies.... MA 12FT 24-36PT

University of Reading
German Studies ....MA (Res) 12FT 24PT

University of Sheffield
Germanic Studies (Research Track) .... MA 12FT 24PT

University of St Andrews
German Studies .....MLitt 12FT 24PT/PGDip 9FT 24PT/MPhil 24FT

University of Warwick
German Cultural Studies..............MA 12FT 24PT/PGDip 9FT 21PT/ PGCert 3-6FT 6PT

German literature
Research Courses

Aberystwyth University
German ....MPhil 12FT 24PT

School of Advanced Study, University of London
Germanic or Comparative/Interdisciplinary Studies ......PhD 36FT 60PT/MPhil 12FT 24PT

Bangor University
German ....PhD 36FT/MPhil 12FT

University of Cambridge
German .... PhD 36FT 60PT

University of Edinburgh
German ....PhD 36FT 72PT/MPhil 24FT 48PT/ MSc by research 12FT 24-36PT

University of Glasgow
German Language and Literature .... PhD 36FT/MPhil 12FT/ MLitt by research 12FT

University of Kent
German Literature...........PhD 36FT 60PT/MPhil 24FT 36PT/MA by research 12FT 24PT
German and Comparative Literature .... PhD 36FT 60PT

King's College London
German Research .... PhD 36FT 48-72PT/MPhil 24FT 36PT

Literature and creative writing

University of Nottingham
German .... MPhil 12-36FT 24-72PT/PhD 24-48FT 48-96PT

Queen Mary, University of London
German .... PhD 36FT 72PT/MPhil 24FT 48PT

Royal Holloway, University of London
German .... PhD 36FT/MPhil 24FT/MA by research 12FT

Swansea University
European Cultures...................................MA by research 12FT 24PT
German .... PhD 36FT 72PT/MPhil 24FT 48PT

University of Ulster
German .... PhD 36FT 72PT/MPhil 24FT 48PT

UCL - University College London
German .... PhD 36FT 60PT

Irish literature
Taught Courses

Aberystwyth University
Irish/Gwyddeleg.. MA 12FT 24PT
Literary Studies (Eighteenth Century Writing and Romanticism)
MA 12FT 24PT/PGDip 9FT 18PT

Bangor University
Early Modern Literature.................... MA 12FT 24-36PT/PGDip 9FT

University College Cork
English (Irish Writing, Theories & Traditions)....................MA 12FT
Modern Irish .... MA 12FT 24PT

National University of Ireland Galway
Old and Middle Irish ....MA 12FT

King's College London
Early Modern English Literature: Text & Transmission ....MA 12FT
24PT

National University of Ireland, Maynooth
English (Narrative Modernity Ireland) .... MA 12FT 24PT
sa Nua-Ghaeilge (Modern Irish) ....MA 12FT

Queen's University Belfast
English (Irish Writing)..................MA 12FT 24PT/PGDip 12FT 24PT

Trinity College Dublin - the University of Dublin
Irish Writing .... MPhil 12FT/PGDip 9FT

University of Ulster
Irish Literature in English................ MA 12FT 30PT/PGDip 9FT 18PT
Modern Irish .... MA 27PT/PGDip 18PT

Irish literature
Research Courses

University of Ulster
English............................... PhD 36FT 72PT/MPhil 24FT 48PT

Italian literature
Taught Courses

University College Cork
Arts (Italian)...HDip 9FT 18PT
Italian ....MA 12FT

University of Kent
Humanities (Italian)...GradDip 12FT

University of Reading
Italian Studies ....MA (Res) 12FT 24PT
Modern Italian History ....MA (Res) 12FT 24PT

University of St Andrews
Italian Studies ....MLitt 12FT 24PT/PGDip 9FT 24PT/MPhil 24FT

UCL - University College London
Italian Studies .... MA 12FT 24PT

University of Warwick
Italian Studies: Culture and Communication .... MA 12FT 24PT

Italian literature
Research Courses

Bangor University
Italian ....MPhil 12FT/PhD 36FT

University of Bristol
Italian ..PhD 36FT 72PT/MLitt by research 24FT 48PT/MPhil 12FT
24PT

University of Edinburgh
Italian .... PhD 36FT 72PT/MPhil 24FT 48PT/MSc by research 12FT
24PT

University of Glasgow
Italian ....PhD 36FT/MPhil 12FT/MLitt by research 12FT

University of Kent
Italian ......PhD 36FT 60PT/MPhil 24FT 36PT/MA by research 12FT
24PT

University of Leeds
Department of Italian ...PhD 36+FT/MA by research 12+FT/MPhil
24FT

Royal Holloway, University of London
Italian .... PhD 36FT 72PT/MPhil 24FT 48PT

University of St Andrews
Italian Studies .... PhD 36FT 72PT/MPhil 24FT 48PT

Swansea University
European Cultures...................................MA by research 12FT 24PT
Italian .... PhD 36FT 72PT/MPhil 24FT 48PT

University of Warwick
Italian ......PhD 36FT 60PT/MPhil 24FT 48PT/MA by research 12FT
24PT

Japanese literature
Taught Courses

University of Oxford
Japanese Studies ....MSt 10FT
Modern Japanese Studies ....MPhil 24FT/MSc 12FT

School of Oriental and African Studies - SOAS
Comparative Literature (Asia/Africa)................... MA 12FT 24-36PT
Japanese Literature................................... MA 12FT 24-36PT
Japanese Studies .... MA 12FT 24-36PT

Korean literature
Taught Courses

University of Oxford
Korean Studies ....MSt 9FT

School of Oriental and African Studies - SOAS
Comparative Literature (Asia/Africa)................... MA 12FT 24-36PT
Korean Literature... MA 12FT 24-36PT
Korean Studies .... MA 12FT 24-36PT

Literature and creative writing
Taught Courses

University of Aberdeen
Creative Writing.......................... MLitt 12FT 24PT/PGDip 9FT 21PT
Language Policy and Planning .... MLitt 12FT 24PT/
PGDip 9FT 18PT
Modern Thought ....MLitt 12FT 24PT
The Novel..................................... MLitt 12FT 24PT/PGDip 9FT 21PT

Aberystwyth University
Literary Studies .... MA 12FT 24PT
Literary Studies (Eighteenth Century Writing and Romanticism)...
.... MA 12FT 24PT/PGDip 9FT 18PT
Literary Studies (Medieval and Renaissance Writing)......MA 12FT
24PT/PGDip 9FT 24PT
Literary Studies (Postmodern Writing) .... MA 12FT 24PT
Literature and Creative Writing .... MA 12FT 24PT

School of Advanced Study, University of London
History of the Book .... MA 12FT 24PT

Bangor University
Creative Writing............ PhD by taught 36FT 72-96PT/MPhil 24FT
48-60PT

Bath Spa University
Ecocriticism and Environmental Writing ....MA 12FT
Environmental management.......................................MA 12FT
Literature, Landscape and Environment................... MA 12FT 24PT
Writing Poetry ....MA 12FT

Birkbeck, University of London
Contemporary Literature and Culture...................... MA 12FT 24PT
Modern & Contemporary Literature .... MA 12FT 24PT

Bournemouth University
Literary Media .... MA 12FT 24PT

Brunel University
Contemporary Literature and Culture...................... MA 12FT 24PT
Creative Writing................................ MA 1 yearFT 2 yearsPT
Creative Writing... MA 12FT 24PT

University of Buckingham
Biography .... MA 12FT 24PT

University of Cambridge
Creative Writing .... MSt 24PT

Cardiff Metropolitan University
English and Creative Writing.................................... MA 12FT 24PT

University of Central Lancashire
English Language and Literature............................... MA 12FT 24PT
Modern and Contemporary Literature.................... MA 12FT 24PT

University of Chester
Nineteenth Century Literature and Culture .... MA 12FT/PGDip
12FT/PGCert 12FT

University College Cork
Arts (English)..HDip 9FT 18PT
English (American Literature & Film)..............................MA 12FT

University of Cumbria
Literature, Romanticism and the English Lake District....MA 12FT
24PT

De Montfort University
English by Independent Study ....MA 12FT 24PT 12-24DL

University of Dundee
Creative Writing (Module)...................................Module 3PT
Philosophy and Literature ....MLitt 12FT

Twentieth Century Studies .... MLitt 12FT
Writing Practice & Study .... MLitt 12FT

Durham University
English Literary Studies................................. MA 12FT 24PT
Studies in Poetry....................................... MA 12FT 24PT
Twentieth-Century Literary Studies................... MA 12FT 24PT

University of East Anglia
American Literature................................. MA 12FT 24PT
Biography and Creative Non-Fiction .... MA 12FT 24PT
Creative Writing: Poetry .... MA 12FT 24PT
Creative Writing: Prose .... MA 12FT 24PT
Creative Writing: Scriptwriting..................... MA 12FT 24PT
Culture and Modernity .... MA 12FT 24PT
Literary Translation .... MA 12FT 24PT
Philosophy and Literature .... MA 12FT 24PT
Writing the Modern World .... MA 12FT 24PT

University of East London
Narrative Research ...MA 12FT 24PT/PGDip 8FT 16PT/PGCert 4FT
8PT

University of Edinburgh
American Literature................................MSc(Res) 12FT 24PT
Comparative and General Literature.................... MSc 12FT 24PT
Creative Writing (Online Distance Learning)...................MSc 36DL
English Literature: Creative Writing .... MSc 12FT/PGDip 9FT
English Literature: Literature and Society: Enlightenment,
Romantic and Victorian ....MSc 12FT 24PT
English Literature: Material Cultures and the History of the Book
MSc 12FT 24PT
English Literature: US Literature - Cultural Values from
Revolution to Empire.............................MSc 12FT 24PT
Literary Translation as Creative Practice.................MSc 12FT 24PT
Literature & Transatlanticism .... MSc 12FT 24PT
Medieval Literatures and Cultures .... MSc 12FT 24PT
Playwriting...MSc 12FT 24PT
Writing for Theatre and Performance ....MSc 12FT 24PT

University of Essex
Creative Writing..................................... MA 12FT 24PT
English Language and Literature.................... MA 12FT 24PT
Film and Literature .... MA 12FT 24PT
Literature .... MA 12FT 24PT
Myth, Literature and the Unconscious .... MA 12FT 24PT
Wild Writing: Literature and the Environment........ MA 12FT 24PT

University of Exeter
Creative Writing..................................... MA 11FT 23PT
English Literary Studies.............................. MA 11FT 23PT
European Languages and Cultures ....MA 12FT 24PT/MRes 12FT
24PT

National University of Ireland Galway
International Contemporary Literatures and Media........MA 12FT
24PT
Literature and Publishing ....MA 12FT
Writing..MA 12FT

University of Glasgow
Creative Writing...MFA 24FT
Modernities: Literature, Theory & Culture ....MLitt 12FT 24PT
Playwriting & Dramaturgy.................................MLitt 12FT

University of Huddersfield
Literary Studies .... MA 12FT 24PT

University of Hull
Creative Writing..................................... MA 12FT 24PT
English by Research .... MA 12FT 24PT
Modern and Contemporary Literature.................. MA 12FT 24PT

University of Kent
Creative Writing..................................... MA 12FT 24PT
Creative Writing (Paris option)...........................MA 12FT
Critical Theory (taught jointly with the School of European
Culture and Languages)........................... MA 12FT 24PT
Contemporary .... MA 12FT 24PT

King's College London
Early Modern English Literature: Text & Transmission ....MA 12FT
24PT
Life Writing...MA 12FT 24PT

Kingston University
Criticism, Literature, Theory .... MA 12FT 24PT

Lancaster University
Creative Writing (Campus based or distance learning) ...MA 12FT
24PT 24DL
English Language and Contemporary Literary Studies....MA 12FT
24/36PT
English Literary Research .... MA 12FT 24PT

Leeds Metropolitan University
English: Contemporary Literatures .... MA 12FT 24PT

University of Leeds
Postcolonial Literary and Cultural Studies ....MA 12PT
Romantic Formations .... MA 12FT 24PT
Twentieth-century Literature .... MA 12FT 24PT

University of Leicester
Modern Literature (and Creative Writing)................ MA 12FT 24PT

Literature and creative writing

University of Lincoln
Creative Writing...MA 12FT 24PT
Science and Environmental Journalism...MA 12FT 24PT
Sports Journalism...MA 12FT 24PT

Liverpool Hope University
Creative Practice...MA 12FT 24PT/PGDip 12FT 24PT
Education & English Language...MA 36PT
Education & English Literature...MA 36PT
English Language...MA 12FT 24-36PT
English Literature...MA 12FT 24-36PT
Popular Literatures...MA 12FT 24PT

Liverpool John Moores University
Writing...MA 24PT/PGCert 20PT/PGDip 12PT

University of Liverpool
Reading in Practice...MA 24PT
Science Fiction Studies...MA 12FT

London Metropolitan University
Creative Writing...MA 12FT 24PT

Loughborough University
Creative Writing...MA 12FT 24PT
English...MA 12FT 24PT

Manchester Metropolitan University
English Studies: The Gothic...PGDip 12FT 24PT/MA 15FT 30PT

University of Manchester
Contemporary Literature and Culture...MA 12FT 24PT
Literature and Culture 1200-1700...MA 12FT 24PT

Middlesex University
Creative Writing...MA 24PT

Newcastle University
Creative Writing...MA 12FT 24PT
Creative Writing...PGCert 12FT 24PT
English Literature, 1500-1900...MA 12FT 24PT
Modern and Contemporary Studies...MA 12FT 24PT

Newman University
Colonial and Postcolonial Literature...MA 24DL

University of Northampton
Modern English Studies...MA 12FT 24PT/PGDip 12PT

Northumbria University
Creative Writing...MA 12FT 24PT
Creative Writing in the Classroom...PGCert 12PT

Nottingham Trent University
Creative Writing...MA 12FT 24PT

University of Nottingham
Classical Literature...MA 12FT 24PT
Communication and Entrepreneurship...MSc 12FT 24PT
Literary Linguistics by Web Based Distance Learning MA 24-48DL

The Open University
Humanities...MA variableDL/PGDip variableDL/PGCert variableDL

Oxford Brookes University
Creative Writing...MA 12FT 24PT/PGDip 8FT 6-8PT/PGCert 4FT 6PT

University of Oxford
Creative Writing...MSt 24PT
English (English and American Studies)...MSt 9FT

Plymouth University
Creative Writing...MA 12FT 24PT

Queen Mary, University of London
Applied Linguistics for English Language Teaching...MA 12FT 24PT
English Studies: Eighteenth Century Literature and Romanticism...MA 12FT 24PT
English Studies: Writing in the Modern Age...MA 12FT 24PT

Queen's University Belfast
English (Poetry: Creativity and Criticism)...MA 12FT 24PT/PGDip 9FT 18PT
English (Reconceiving the Renaissance- Literatures, Places, Cultures)...MA 12FT 24PT/PGDip 12FT 24PT
English Literary Studies (Modern Literary Studies) MA 12FT 24PT/PGDip 12FT 24PT

University of Reading
English...MA (Res) 12FT 24PT
Nineteenth-Century Literature and Culture...MA 12FT 24PT

Royal Holloway, University of London
Creative Writing...MA 12FT 24PT
Comparative Literature and Culture...MA 12FT 24PT
Poetic Practice...MA 12FT 24PT

University of Salford
Creative Writing: Innovation and Experiment...MA 12FT 36PT/PGDip 8FT 24PT/PGCert 4FT 12PT
Literature, Culture and Modernity MA 12FT 36PT/PGDip 8FT 24PT

School of Oriental and African Studies - SOAS
African Literature...MA 12FT 24-36PT
Arabic Literature...MA 12FT 24-36PT
Chinese Literature...MA 12FT 24-36PT
Comparative Literature (Asia/Africa)...MA 12FT 24-36PT
Japanese Literature...MA 12FT 24-36PT
Korean Literature...MA 12FT 24-36PT
Languages and literatues of South East Asia...MA 12FT 24-36PT

Sheffield Hallam University
Modern and Contemporary Literature...MA 12FT 24-72PT

University of Sheffield
English Literature: Creative Writing...MA 12FT 24PT

University of South Wales
English by Research...MA 12FT 24PT
Literature, Culture and Society...MA 12FT 24PT

University of Southampton
20th and 21st Century Literature...MA 12FT 24PT

University of St Andrews
Creative Writing...MLitt 12FT 24PT/PGDip 9FT 24PT
Romantic/Victorian Studies...MLitt 12FT 24PT/PGDip 9FT 24PT

St Mary's University College, Twickenham
Gothic: Culture, Subculture, Counterculture...MA 12FT 24PT

University of Stirling
Creative Writing...MLitt 12FT 27PT/PGDip 9FT 21PT/PGCert 3FT 3PT
Gothic Imagination (The)...MLitt 12FT 27PT/PGDip 9FT 21PT/PGCert 3FT 9PT
Modern Scottish Writing...MLitt 12FT 27PT/PGDip 9FT 21PT/PGCert 4FT 9PT
Renaissance Studies...MRes 12FT 27PT/PGDip 8FT 21PT/PGCert 4FT 9PT

University of Strathclyde
Literature, Culture and Place...MLitt 12FT 24PT/PGDip 9FT 21PT/PGCert 4FT 9PT

University of Sussex
Literature and Culture 1700-1900...MA 12FT 24PT
Literature and Philosophy...MA 12FT 24PT
Literature, Film and Visual Culture...MA 12FT 24PT
Modern and Contemporary Literature, Culture and Thought...MA 12FT 24PT
Sexual Dissidence in Literature and Culture...MA 12FT 24PT

Swansea University
Ancient Narrative Literature...MA 12FT 36PT
Creative Writing...MA 12FT 24-36PT
English Literature...MA 12FT 24-36PT
Welsh Writing in English...MA 12FT 24PT

Trinity College Dublin - the University of Dublin
Creative Writing...MPhil 12FT
Literary Translation...MPhil 12FT
Popular Literature...MPhil 12FT
Texts, Contexts and Cultures...PhD by taught 48FT

University of Wales Trinity Saint David
Creative Writing...MA 12FT 24PT
Modern Literature...MA 12FT 36PT/PGDip 12FT 36PT

University of Warwick
MA Drama Education and English Language Teaching (ELT)...MA 12FT 24-36PT
Philosophy and Literature...MA 12FT 24PT
Translation, Writing and Cultural Difference...MA 12FT 24PT/PGDip 9FT 18PT
Writing...MA 12FT

University of Winchester
Creative and Critical Writing...MA 12FT 24PT/PGDip 12FT 24PT/PGCert 12FT 24PT

University of York
English Literary Studies...MA 12FT
Film and Literature...MA 12FT 24PT
Modern and Contemporary Literature and Culture MA 12FT 24PT

York St John University
Contemporary Literature...MA 12FT 24PT

Literature and creative writing
Research Courses

Anglia Ruskin University
Creative Writing...MPhil 24FT/PhD 36FT

Bangor University
Creative Writing...MPhil 24FT 48PT/PhD 36FT 72PT
English...MPhil 24FT 48PT/PhD 36FT 72PT

University of Buckingham
Biography...MA by research 12FT 24PT/MPhil 24FT 48PT/DPhil 36FT 72PT
English Literature...MA by research 12FT 24PT/MPhil 24FT 48PT/DPhil 36FT 72PT

University of Chichester
English...PhD 36FT 84PT/MPhil 24FT 84PT

University of Edinburgh
Canadian Studies...PhD 36FT 72PT/MPhil 24FT 48PT
Comparative Literature...PhD 36FT 72PT
English Literature...PhD 36FT 72PT/MPhil 24FT 48PT/MSc by research 12FT 24PT
English Literature: Critical Theory...MSc by research 12FT 24PT
English Literature: Medieval Literature...MSc by research 12FT 24PT
English Literature: Postcolonial Literature..MSc by research 12FT 24PT
English Literature: Renaissance Literature..MSc by research 12FT 24PT
English Literature: Romanticism...MSc by research 12FT 24PT
English Literature: Scottish Literature MSc by research 12FT 24PT
English Literature: Victorian Literature...MSc by research 12FT 24PT
European Theatre...PhD 36FT 72PT
Medieval Studies...PhD 36FT 72PT/MSc by research 12FT 24PT

University of Essex
Creative Writing...PhD 36FT 72PT/MPhil 24FT 48PT/MA by research 12FT 24PT
Film Studies...PhD 36FT 72PT/MPhil 24FT 48PT/MA by research 12FT 24PT
Film Studies (Creative Practices) PhD 36FT 72PT/MPhil 24FT 48PT
Literature PhD 36FT 72PT/MPhil 24FT 48PT/MA by research 12FT 24PT
Theatre Studies (Playwriting)...PhD 36FT 72PT/MPhil 24FT 48PT

University of Exeter
English PhD 36-48FT 72PT/MPhil 24FT 48PT/MA by research 12FT 24PT
Interdisciplinary Research...MPhil 36FT 60PT/PhD 48FT 84PT
Interdisciplinary Studies...MPhil 36FT 60PT/PhD 48FT 84PT

University of Gloucestershire
Creative Writing...PhD 30-48FT

Goldsmiths, University of London
Creative Writing...PhD 36-48FT 48-72PT/MPhil 24FT 36PT

University of Kent
Text and Practice...PhD 36FT 60PT
The Contemporary Novel: Practice as Research...MA by research 12FT 24PT/PhD 36FT 60PT

Lancaster University
English...PhD 36FT 48PT/MPhil 24FT 36PT

University of Leicester
Creative Writing...PhD 36FT 48PT

Liverpool John Moores University
Media, Critical and Creative Arts MPhil 36FT 84PT/PhD 36FT 84PT

University of Northampton
Literary and Cultural Studies...PhD 36FT 48PT/MPhil 24FT 36PT

The Open University
Book History...PhD 36FT 72PT variableDL/MPhil 15FT 24PT variableDL
Postcolonial Literatures...PhD 36FT 72PT variableDL/MPhil 15FT 24PT variableDL

University of Oxford
English (to 1550)...DPhil 48FT
Medieval and Modern Language and Literature...DPhil 48FT

University of Portsmouth
Social, Historical and Literary Studies...MPhil 24FT 48PT/PhD 36FT 72PT

Queen's University Belfast
English...PhD 36FT 72PT/MPhil 24FT 48PT

University of Strathclyde
Creative Writing...MRes 12FT 24PT

University of Sussex
Creative and Critical Writing Research Programme...PhD 24-48FT 36-72PT/MPhil 12-36FT 24-48PT

Swansea University
American Studies...MA by research 12FT 24PT/MPhil 24FT 48PT/PhD 36FT 72PT
English...PhD 36FT 72PT/MPhil 24FT 48PT/MA by research 12FT 24PT

University of Ulster
Arts...MRes 12FT 24PT

University of Warwick
Philosophy and Literature..PhD 36FT 60PT/MPhil 24FT 36PT/MA by research 12FT 24PT

University of Worcester
English Literature...PhD 48FT 70PT/MPhil 24FT 48PT

University of York
English...MA by research 12FT 24PT/PhD 36FT 72PT/MPhil 24FT 48PT

York St John University
Arts & Literature...PhD 12-36FT/MPhil 12-36FT/MA by research 12-36FT

Medieval literature
Taught Courses

Aberystwyth University
Medieval Welsh Literature (English Medium only)...MA 12FT 24PT

Bangor University
Arthurian Literature...MA 12FT 24-36PT

Literature and creative writing

Early Modern Literature....................... MA 12FT 24-36PT/PGDip 9FT
Medieval Studies.. MA 12FT 24-36PT
Medieval and Early Modern Literature ..MA 12FT 24-36PT/PGDip 9FT

University of Cambridge
Medieval and Renaissance Literature ....MPhil 9FT

Cardiff University
Medieval British Studies.............................. MA 12FT 24PT

University College Cork
English (Texts & Contexts: Medieval to Renaissance) .....MA 12FT

Durham University
Medieval and Renaissance Literary Studies.............. MA 12FT 24PT

University of East Anglia
Medieval and Early Modern Textual Cultures, 1381 - 1688......MA 12FT 24PT

University of Edinburgh
Medieval Literatures and Cultures............................MSc 12FT 24PT

University of Exeter
English Literary Studies................................ MA 11FT 23PT

University of Glasgow
Medieval History..MLitt 12FT 24PT

University of Hull
Medieval Vernacular Language and Literature....... MA 12FT 24PT

University of Kent
Medieval and Early Modern Studies........................ MA 12FT 24PT

King's College London
Early Modern English Literature: Text & Transmission ....MA 12FT 24PT
Medieval English: Sex, Gender & Culture .... MA 12FT 24PT

University of Nottingham
English Studies.................. MA 12FT 24-36PT/PGDip 12FT 24-36PT

University of Oxford
Celtic Studies... MPhil 21FT/MSt 9FT
English (English and American Studies) ....MSt 9FT
English Language...MSt 9FT
English Studies (Medieval Period)................................. MPhil 21FT
Medieval Studies..MSt 9FT

Queen's University Belfast
English Literary Studies (Medieval Literature) ....MA 12FT 24PT/PGDip 12FT 24PT

University of Reading
Classics .... MA (Res) 12FT 24PT 60BM
Medieval Archaeology ....MA 12FT
Medieval Studies .... MA (Res) 12FT 24-60PT

University of Roehampton
Historical Research............................ PGDip 9FT 24-48PT 24-28DL

University of Southampton
Medieval & Renaissance Studies............................MRes 12FT 24PT
Medieval and Renaissance Culture........................... MA 12FT 24PT

University of St Andrews
Mediaeval English ....MLitt 12FT/PGDip 9FT/MPhil 24FT
Mediaeval Studies..............................MLitt 12FT/PGDip 9FT

Swansea University
Medieval Studies ......MA 12FT 24-36PT/PGDip 12FT 24PT/PGCert 12FT 12PT

Trinity College Dublin - the University of Dublin
Medieval Language, Literature and Culture .... MPhil 12FT

University of Wales Trinity Saint David
Medieval and Early Modern LiteratureMA 12FT 36PT/PGDip 12FT 36PT

University of York
Medieval Literatures................................ MA 12FT 24PT

Medieval literature
Research Courses

Aberystwyth University
Welsh Literature ....MPhil 12FT 24PT
PhD 36FT 60PT

University of Birmingham
Medieval History......................... PhD 36FT 72PT/MPhil 12FT 24PT
Medieval Studies.......................................MPhil(B) 12FT 24PT

University of Edinburgh
English Literature: Medieval Literature ....MSc by research 12FT 24PT
Medieval Studies ....PhD 36FT 72PT/MSc by research 12FT 24PT

University of Exeter
EnglishPhD 36-48FT 72PT/MPhil 24FT 48PT/MA by research 12FT 24PT

University of Kent
Medieval and Early Modern Studies...PhD 36FT 60PT/MPhil 24FT 36PT/MA by research 12FT 24PT

University of Oxford
English (to 1550)...DPhil 48FT
Medieval and Modern Language and Literature..........DPhil 48FT

University of Edinburgh
Scandinavian Studies ....MSc(Res) 12FT 24PT

Scandinavian literature
Research Courses

University of Edinburgh
Scandinavian Studies ....PhD 36FT 72PT/MPhil 24FT 48PT/MSc by research 12FT 24PT
Scandinavian Studies (Masters by Research).......MSc by research 12FT 24/36PT

Scottish literature
Taught Courses

University of Aberdeen
Art in Scotland..MLitt 12FT 24PT
Irish and Scottish Studies.......... MLitt 12FT 24PT/PGDip 9FT 18PT

Bangor University
Arthurian Literature.. MA 12FT 24-36PT
Early Modern Literature................... MA 12FT 24-36PT/PGDip 9FT

University of Dundee
Scottish Internship Graduate Certificate ....GradCert 8FT

University of Nottingham
Literatures in English Translation.........................MA 12FT

University of Sheffield
Cultures of the British Isles............................... MA 12FT 24PT

University of St Andrews
National Trust for Scotland Studies......................MPhil 24FT 48PT
Reformation Studies........MLitt 12FT 24PT/MPhil 24FT/PGDip 9FT 24PT

University of Stirling
Modern Scottish Writing (MLitt) ....MLitt 12FT 27PT/PGDip 9FT 21PT/PGCert 4FT 9PT

University of the Highlands and Islands
Highlands & Islands Literature .... MLitt 12FT 24PT/PGDip 12FT 24PT/PGCert 12FT 24PT
History of the Highlands and Islands....... MLitt 12FT 24PT/PGDip 12FT 24PT/PGCert 12FT 24PT

Scottish literature
Research Courses

University of Aberdeen
Irish and Scottish Studies...PhD 36FT

University of Edinburgh
English Literature: Medieval Literature ....MSc by research 12FT 24PT
English Literature: Scottish LiteratureMSc by research 12FT 24PT

University of Glasgow
Scottish Literature.PhD 36FT/MPhil 12FT/MLitt by research 12FT

Shakespeare
Taught Courses

Bangor University
English............. PhD by taught 36FT 72-96PT/MPhil 24FT 48-60PT

Bath Spa University
Performing Shakespeare .... MA 12FT 24PT/MFA 12FT 24PT

Birkbeck, University of London
Shakespeare and Contemporary Performance....... MA 12FT 24PT

University of Birmingham
Cultural Heritage of Shakespeare's England........... MA 12FT 24PT
Shakespeare Studies..................................... MA 12FT 24PT
Shakespeare and Education.MA 12FT 24PT 24-72DL/PGDip 12FT 24PT 24-72DL
Shakespeare and Theatre.MA 12FT 72PT 72DL/PGDip 12FT 72PT 72DL
Shakespeare, Stratford-upon-Avon and the Cultural History of Renaissance England.......................... MA 12FT 24PT

University of Central Lancashire
Playwriting .... MA 12FT 24PT

University of Kent
Shakespeare.. MA 12FT 24PT

King's College London
Shakespeare Studies............................. MA 12FT 24PT

Leeds Metropolitan University
English: Contemporary Literatures............................ MA 12FT 24PT

Queen's University Belfast
English (Reconceiving the Renaissance- Literatures, Places, Cultures) ....MA 12FT 24PT/PGDip 12FT 24PT

Royal Holloway, University of London
Shakespeare... MA 12FT 24PT

Royal Conservatoire of Scotland
Classical and Contemporary Text (Directing)...................MA 12FT

Sheffield Hallam University
Shakespeare and Renaissance Literature........... MA 12FT 24-72PT

University of St Andrews
Shakespeare and Renaissance Literary Culture. MLitt 12FT 24PT/PGDip 9FT 24PT

University of Stirling
Renaissance Studies .....MRes 12FT 27PT/PGDip 8FT 21PT/PGCert 4FT 9PT

University of Strathclyde
Renaissance Studies .....MLitt 12FT 24PT/PGDip 9FT 21PT/PGCert 4FT 9PT

UCL - University College London
English: Shakespeare in History .... MA 12FT 24PT

Shakespeare
Research Courses

University of Birmingham
PhD with Integrated Study (Shakespeare Studies)........Integrated PhD 48FT 96PT/MLitt by research 36FT 72PT/MPhil 24FT 48PT
Shakespeare Studies.........PhD 36FT 72PT/MLitt by research 24FT 48PT/MPhil 12FT 24PT

University of Oxford
English (to 1550)... DPhil 48FT

Spanish literature
Taught Courses

Birkbeck, University of London
Comparative Literature............................... MA 12FT 24PT

University College Cork
Arts (Hispanic Studies)..............................HDip 9FT 18PT
Hispanic Studies..................................... MA 12FT 24PT

University of Kent
Hispanic Studies ....GradDip 12FT
Hispanic and Comparative Literature .... MA 12FT 24PT
Modern Hispanic Studies......................................MA 24PT

University of St Andrews
Modern Hispanic Literature And Film........MLitt 12FT/MPhil 24FT

Spanish literature
Research Courses

Bangor University
Spanish...MPhil 12FT/PhD 36FT

University of Cambridge
Spanish... PhD 36FT 60PT

University of Kent
Hispanic Studies..............PhD 36FT 60PT/MPhil 24FT 36PT/MA by research 12FT 24PT

University of St Andrews
Modern Hispanic Literature And Film ....PhD 36FT 72PT/MPhil 24FT 48PT

Swansea University
European Cultures................................MA by research 12FT 24PT

Theatre studies
Taught Courses

Aberystwyth University
Politics, Media and Performance............................... MA 12FT 24PT
Practising Theatre and Performance.... MA 12FT 24PT/PGDip 9FT 18PT

University of the Arts London - Central Saint Martins College of Art and Design
Acting (formerly MA European Classical Acting) Drama Centre London ....MA 12FT
Collaborative Performance ....MA 12FT

University of the Arts London - London College of Fashion
Costume Design for Performance............................ MA 15FT 30PT

University of the Arts London - Wimbledon College of Art
Theatre: Interdisciplinary Performance.............................MA 12FT

Bangor University
Creative Practice...MRes 12FT 24PT

Bath Spa University
Performing Shakespeare .... MA 12FT 24PT/MFA 12FT 24PT
Theatre for Young Audiences .... MA 12FT 24PT

Birkbeck, University of London
Creative Producing...MA 12FT
Shakespeare and Contemporary Performance....... MA 12FT 24PT
Text and Performance (with RADA) .... MA 12FT 24PT
Theatre Directing..MFA 24FT

Birmingham City University
Acting .... MA 12FT/PGDip 10FT
Acting: The British Tradition ....MA 12FT/PGDip 9FT

Arts University Bournemouth
Costume.. MA 12FT 24PT

University of Bristol
Performance Research .... MA 12FT 24PT

Literature and creative writing

University of Central Lancashire
Performance ....MA 12FT 24-30PT/PGDip 12FT 24PT/PGCert 12FT

Central School of Speech and Drama, University of London
Advanced Theatre Practice....MA 12FT
Applied Theatre (Drama in the Community and Drama Education).... MA 12FT 24PT
Creative Producing....MA 12FT 24PT/MFA 24FT
PG Certificate in Applied Theatre with Young PeoplePGCert 12FT
Scenography....MA 12FT
Theatre Studies (Performance and the City).... MA 12FT 24PT

University of Chester
Dance...... MA 12FT 24PT/PGDip 12FT 24PT/PGCert 12FT 12-24PT
Dental Practice Management (Work Based and Integrative Studies)....MA 24-72PT/PGDip 24-60PT/PGCert 12-36PT
Developing RPL Policy and Practice (Work Based and Integrative Studies)....MA 24-72PT/PGDip 24-60PT/PGCert 12-36PT

University of Chichester
Theatre Collectives....MA 12FT 24PT 12DL

University College Cork
Drama & Theatre Studies....MA 12FT

University of Dundee
Theatre Studies (MLitt)....MLitt 12FT

University of East Anglia
Film, Television and Creative Practice.... MA 12FT 24PT
Theatre Directing: Text and Production.... MA 12FT 24PT

Edinburgh Napier University
Film.... MA 12FT 24PT

University of Edinburgh
Theatre and Performance Studies.... MSc 12FT
Writing for Theatre and Performance....MSc 12FT 24PT

University of Exeter
Independent Film Business.... MA 12FT 24PT
Theatre Practice: Applied Theatre.... MA 12FT 24PT
Theatre Practice: Directing and Actor Training.... MA 12FT 24PT
Theatre Practice: General Programme.... MA 12FT 24PT
Theatre Practice: Physical Performance & Actor TrainingMA 12FT 24PT
Theatre Practice: Staging Shakespeare..MA 12FT 24PT/MFA 24FT

National University of Ireland Galway
Drama & Theatre Studies....MA 12FT

University of Glasgow
Historically Informed Performance Practice.......MMus 12FT 24PT
Playwriting & Dramaturgy....MLitt 12FT
Theatre History....MLitt 12FT 24PT
Theatre Practices....MLitt 12FT 24PT
Theatre Studies....MLitt 12FT 24PT

Goldsmiths, University of London
Applied Theatre: Drama in Educational, Community & Social Contexts.... MA 12FT 24PT
Black British Writing, Drama and Performance...... MA 12FT 24PT
Contemporary African Theatre & Performance....MA 12FT
Performance and Culture: Interdisciplinary PerspectivesMA 12FT 24PT

University of Huddersfield
Performance....PGDip 12FT

University of Hull
Drama and Theatre Practice.... MA 12FT 24PT

University of Kent
Arts Criticism.... MA 12FT 24PT
Drama and Theatre.... MA 12FT 24PT
Drama and Theatre: Physical Actor Training and PerformanceMA 12FT
Drama and Theatre: Physical Actor Training and Performance with a term in Moscow....MA 12FT
Shakespeare.... MA 12FT 24PT

King's College London
Theatre & Performance Studies.... MA 12FT 24PT

Leeds Metropolitan University
Performance.... MA 12FT 24PT

University of Leeds
Performance, Culture and Context....... MA 12FT 24PT/PGDip 9FT 21PT/PGCert 6FT 12PT
Theatre Making: Critical Engagement with Creative Practice.MA 12FT
Theatre and Development Studies....MA 12FT

London South Bank University
Theatre Practice....MA 28PT

Loughborough University
Performance and Multi-Media.... MA 12FT 24PT

Manchester Metropolitan University
Movement Practice for Theatre....MA 12FT

University of Manchester
Applied Theatre (pathway of Theatre and Performance)MA 12FT 24PT
Theatre & Performance.... MA 12FT 24PT

Newcastle University
Creative Arts Practice.... MA 12FT 24PT
Film: Theory and Practice.... MA 12FT 24PT

Oxford Brookes University
Film Studies: Popular Cinema .. MA 12FT 24PT/PGDip 8FT 6-8PT/PGCert 4FT 6PT

Plymouth University
Theatre and Performance....MRes 12FT

Queen's University Belfast
Drama.... MA 12FT 24PT

University of Reading
Early Modern Literature & Drama (MA Res)...MA (Res) 12FT 24PT
Film Studies (MA Res)....MA (Res) 12FT 24PT
Television Studies (MA Res)....MA (Res) 12FT 24PT
Theatre Studies (MA Res)....MA (Res) 12FT 24PT

Rose Bruford College
MA Ensemble Theatre.... MA 12FT/PGDip 10FT
MA Theatre for Young Audiences........ MA 12FT 24PT/PGDip 10FT 22PT
PG Certificate in Learning and Teaching in Higher Education (Theatre & Performing Arts)....PGCHE 12PT

Royal College of Music
Performance....RCM Artist Diploma 10FT

Royal Holloway, University of London
Research (Drama).... MA 12FT 24PT
Theatre.... MA 12FT 24PT

Royal Conservatoire of Scotland
Classical and Contemporary Text (Acting)....MA 12FT
Classical and Contemporary Text (Directing)....MA 12FT
Musical Theatre (Directing)....MA 12FT
Musical Theatre (Performance)....MA 12FT

Royal Welsh College of Music and Drama
Musical Theatre....MA 12FT
Theatre Design.... MA 12FT 12PT

University of Salford
Digital Performance.... MA 12FT 36PT/PGDip 8FT 24PT

School of Oriental and African Studies - SOAS
Performance....MMus 12FT 24PT

Sheffield Hallam University
Film Studies.... MA 12FT 36-72PT
Film Studies ....MPhil 36FT 84PT/PhD by taught 36FT 84PT
Film Studies with Screenwriting.... MA 12FT 24PT

University of Sheffield
Theatre and Performance Studies.... MA 12FT 24PT

University of Southampton
Film Studies.... MA 12FT 24PT

University of St Andrews
Film Studies....MLitt 12FT 24PT/PGDip 9FT

St Mary's University College, Twickenham
Physical Theatre....MA 12FT

University of Stirling
Film Studies: Theory and Practice......MLitt 12FT 27PT/PGDip 9FT 21PT/PGCert 3FT 6PT

University of Surrey
Dance Cultures....MA 12FT 24 or 36PT
Theatre Studies....MA 12FT 24 or 36PT

Trinity College Dublin - the University of Dublin
Theatre and Performance.... MPhil 12FT

University of Wales Trinity Saint David
Theatre and Society.... MA 12FT/PGDip 9FT/PGCert 6FT

UCL - University College London
Film Studies.... MA 12FT 24PT

University of York
Theatre: Writing, Directing and Performance........ MA 12FT 24PT

York St John University
Applied Theatre.... MA 12FT 24PT
Theatre and Performance.... MA 12FT 24PT

Theatre studies
Research Courses

Aberystwyth University
Theatre, Film and Television Studies (MPhil).......MPhil 12FT 24PT
Theatre, Film and Television Studies (PhD).... PhD 36FT 60PT

University of Birmingham
Directing and Dramaturgy....MRes 12FT 24PT
Drama and Theatre PhD/ PhD by Distance PhD 36FT 72PT/MA by research 12FT 24PT/MPhil 12FT 24PT
Drama and Theatre Studies....MRes 12FT 24PT
Drama and Theatre Studies Practice-Based PhD (Dramaturgy, Playwriting or Performance).... PhD 36FT 72PT

University of Bristol
Drama: Theatre, Film, Television.... PhD 36FT 72PT/MLitt by research 24FT 48PT/MPhil 12FT 24PT

Central School of Speech and Drama, University of London
Drama, Performing, Theatre Studies, and Design for Theatre PhD 36 (min)FT 72 (min)PT

University of Edinburgh
European Theatre.... PhD 36FT 72PT

University of Exeter
Drama.... PhD 48FT 89PT/MPhil 36FT 60PT

University of Glasgow
Theatre....PhD 36FT/MPhil 12FT/MLitt by research 12FT

University of Hull
Theatre and Contemporary Studies ...PhD 36FT 60PT/MPhil 24FT 36PT/MA by research 12FT 24PT

University of Kent
Drama.... MA by research 12FT 24PT/PhD 36FT 60PT
Drama (Practice as Research).... MA by research 12FT 24PT

Lancaster University
Theatre Studies.... PhD 36PT

Loughborough University
Drama and Theatre Studies....... PhD 36FT 60PT/MPhil 24FT 36PT

University of Manchester
Applied Theatre Professional Doctorate....Professional Doctorate 36FT 72PT

Newcastle University
Film Studies.... MLitt by research 12FT 24PT
Film Studies.... PhD 36FT 72PT/MPhil 12FT 24PT

Queen's University Belfast
Drama Studies.... PhD 36FT 72PT/MPhil 24FT 48PT
Film Studies.... PhD 36FT 72PT/MPhil 24FT 48PT

University of Roehampton
Drama, Theatre and Performance.... PhD 24-48FT 36-60PT/MPhil 21-36FT 33-48PT

Royal Academy of Music
Performance Practice....MPhil 24FT/PhD 36FT

Royal Holloway, University of London
Drama and Theatre Studies....MPhil 12FT/PhD 36FT

Royal Conservatoire of Scotland
PhD (Drama).... PhD 36FT 72PT

University of Southampton
Film Studies.... PhD 48FT 84PT/MPhil 48FT 84PT

University of St Andrews
Film Studies.... PhD 36FT 72-84PT/MPhil 24FT 48PT

University of Sussex
Drama, Theatre and Performance.... PhD 24-48FT 36-72PT/MPhil 12-36FT 24-48PT

UCL - University College London
Film Studies.... PhD 36FT 60PT

University of Warwick
Theatre StudiesPhD 36FT 60PT/MPhil 24FT 36PT/MA by research 12FT 24PT

University of York
Theatre, Film and Television...... MPhil 24FT 48PT/PhD 36FT 72PT

Victorian literature
Taught Courses

Bangor University
English.... PhD by taught 36FT 72-96PT/MPhil 24FT 48-60PT

Birkbeck, University of London
Romantic Studies..MA 12FT 24PT/PGDip 12FT 24PT/PGCert 12FT 24PT
Victorian Studies.... MA 12FT 24PT

University of Birmingham
Literature and Modernity....MPhil(B) 12FT 24PT
Literature, Culture and Modernity: Victorian and Modernity..MA 12FT 24PT

Canterbury Christ Church University
English: Literatures Victorian and Modern....MA 12FT

University of Chester
Nineteenth Century Literature and Culture........ MA 12FT/PGDip 12FT/PGCert 12FT

University College Cork
English (Modernities, Romanticism, Modernism, & Post Modernism)....MA 12FT

Durham University
Romantic and Victorian Literary Studies.... MA 12FT 24PT

University of Exeter
English Literary Studies.... MA 11FT 23PT

University of Glasgow
Victorian Literature....MLitt 12FT 24PT

University of Kent
Dickens and Victorian Culture.... MA 12FT 24PT

Leeds Metropolitan University
English: Contemporary Literatures.... MA 12FT 24PT

Literature and creative writing

Leeds Trinity University
Victorian Studies .... MA 12FT 24-48PT/PGDip 12FT 24-48PT

University of Leeds
Victorian Literature....................................... MA 12FT 24PT

University of Leicester
Victorian Studies .... MA 12FT 24PT

Liverpool John Moores University
Literature and Cultural History...................................MRes 24PT

University of Liverpool
Victorian Literature....................................... MA 12FT 24PT

University of Reading
Children's Literature ....MA (Res) 12FT 24PT
Nineteenth-Century Literature and Culture .... MA 12FT 24PT

Royal Holloway, University of London
Victorian Literature, Art, & Culture........................... MA 12FT 24PT

St Mary's University College, Twickenham
Gothic: Culture, Subculture, Counterculture .... MA 12FT 24PT

University of Sussex
Literature and Culture 1700-1900 .... MA 12FT 24PT

University of York
Nineteenth-Century Literature and Culture............ MA 12FT 24PT

Victorian literature
Research Courses

University of Birmingham
Literature and Modernity 1880-1940 (English) .... MPhil(B) 12FT 24PT

University of Edinburgh
English Literature: Victorian Literature........MSc by research 12FT 24PT

University of Exeter
EnglishPhD 36-48FT 72PT/MPhil 24FT 48PT/MA by research 12FT 24PT

University of Oxford
English (to 1550).. DPhil 48FT

Welsh literature
Taught Courses

Aberystwyth University
Literary Studies (Medieval and Renaissance Writing)......MA 12FT 24PT/PGDip 9FT 24PT
Literary Studies (Welsh Writing in English) ....MA 12FT 24PT/PGDip 9FT 18PT
Medieval Welsh Literature (English Medium only)..........................MA 12FT 24PT

Bangor University
Arthurian Literature... MA 12FT 24-36PT
Celtic Archaeology .... MA 12FT 24PT/PGDip 8FT
Celts, The / Celtiaid, Y.. MA 12FT 36PT
Creative Writing............ PhD by taught 36FT 72-96PT/MPhil 24FT 48-60PT
Cymraeg (Welsh) (Welsh medium)....... MA 12FT 24PT/PGDip 8FT
Early Modern Literature.................... MA 12FT 24-36PT/PGDip 9FT
English............. PhD by taught 36FT 72-96PT/MPhil 24FT 48-60PT
Welsh History ....PhD by taught 24-36FT 48-72PT/MPhil 12FT 24PT

University of East Anglia
Culture and Modernity .... MA 12FT 24PT

Swansea University
Creative Writing.. MA 12FT 24-36PT
Welsh... MA 12FT 24PT

Welsh literature
Research Courses

Aberystwyth University
Welsh Literature .... PhD 36FT 60PT

Bangor University
Astudiaethau Celtaidd (Celtic Studies) (Welsh medium).... MA by research 12FT/MPhil 24FT 48-60PT/PhD 24-36FT 60-72PT
Creative Writing........................... MPhil 24FT 48PT/PhD 36FT 72PT
Llenyddiaeth Gymraeg (Welsh Literature) (Welsh medium)MPhil 24FT 48-60PT/PhD 24-36FT 60-72PT

Cardiff University
Welsh.......................... PhD 36FT possiblePT/MPhil 12FT possiblePT

Swansea University
Welsh.......PhD 36FT 60PT/MPhil 12FT 24PT/MA by research 12FT 24PT

World literature
Taught Courses

University of East Anglia
Culture and Modernity .... MA 12FT 24PT
Writing the Modern World .... MA 12FT 24PT

University of Edinburgh
Literature & Transatlanticism .... MSc 12FT 24PT

Newman University
Colonial and Postcolonial Literature................................. MA 24DL

School of Oriental and African Studies - SOAS
Chinese Literature .... MA 12FT 24-36PT
Chinese Studies.. MA 12FT 24-36PT
Comparative Literature (Asia/Africa)............. MA 12FT 24-36PT
Japanese Literature.. MA 12FT 24-36PT
Korean Literature... MA 12FT 24-36PT
Postcolonial Studies... MA 12FT 24PT

World literature
Research Courses

University of Cambridge
British Literature Post-1830...PhD 36FT

University of Central Lancashire
Languages and International Studies MA by research 12FT 24PT/MPhil 18-36FT 42-60PT/PhD 30-48FT 66-84PT

University of Edinburgh
English Literature: Postcolonial Literature..MSc by research 12FT 24PT

The Open University
Postcolonial Literatures ... PhD 36FT 72PT variableDL/MPhil 15FT 24PT variableDL

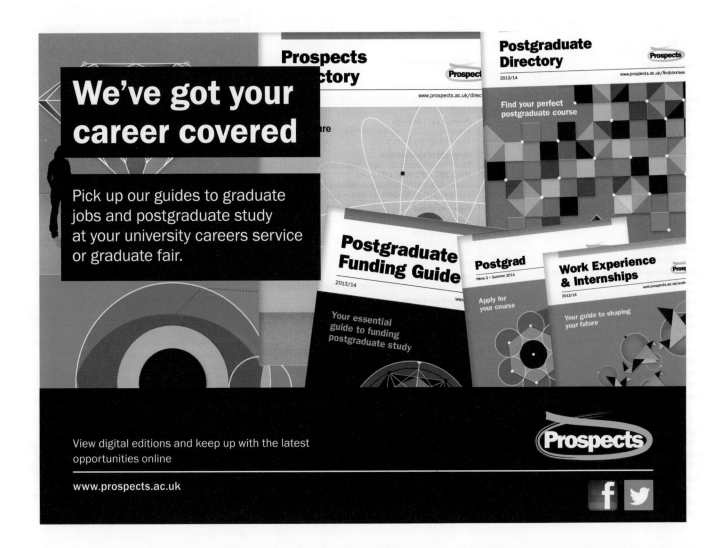

Media studies and publishing

Audio engineering
Taught Courses

Bangor University
Composition/Electroacoustic Composition/Sonic ArtMMus 12FT 24PT
Music .... MA 12FT 24PT/PGDip 9FT

Bath Spa University
Creative Sound and Media Technology . MMus 12FT 24PT/PGDip 9FT 18PT/PGCert 4FT 9PT

Birmingham City University
Radio and Audio Production .... MA 12FT 24PT

Bournemouth University
Digital Music and Audio Production........MSc 12FT/MSc 24PT
Sound Production for Film and Television........MA 12FT

Cardiff University
Computing with Placement .... MSc 12FT

Edinburgh Napier University
Design (Digital Arts) ....MA/MDes 12FT
Sound Production........ MA 12FT 24PT

University of Edinburgh
Acoustics and Music Technology........MSc 12FT 24PT
Musical Instrument Research........MMus 12FT 24PT
Sound Design ....MSc 12FT 24PT
Sound Environments........MSc 12FT 24PT

Glasgow School of Art
Sound for the Moving Image..PGCert 4FT/PGDip 8FT/MDes 12FT

University of Glasgow
Composition ....PGDip 12FT 24PT/PGCert 12FT 24PT
Sonic Arts........ PGDip 12FT 24PT

Glyndwr University
Creative Audio Technology........MSc 12FT/MRes 12FT

Goldsmiths, University of London
Aural and Visual Cultures........ MA 12FT 24PT
Computational Arts ....MA 24-36FT 36-48PT
Innovation in Practice........MA 12FT
Music ....GradDip 12FT
Music including specialist pathways........MMus 12FT 24PT

University of Hertfordshire
Music Composition for Film and Media .....MSc 12FT 24PT/PGDip 12FT 24PT/PGCert 12FT 24PT
Music and Sound Design Technology (Audio Engineering).... MSc 12FT 24PT/PGDip 12FT 24PT/PGCert 12FT 24PT
Music and Sound Technology (Audio Programming)..... MSc 12FT 24PT/PGDip 12FT 24PT/PGCert 12FT 24PT

University of Hull
Creative Music Technology ....MRes 12FT 24PT
Sonic Art ....MRes 12FT 24PT

University of Kent
Music Technology........ MA 24FT 48PT
Sound and Image (Medway)........

Leeds College of Music
Music Production .... MA 12FT 28PT

Leeds Metropolitan University
Music Technology........MSc 12FT 24PT
Sound & Music for Interactive Games........MSc 12FT 24PT
Sound Design ....MSc 12FT 24PT

University of Leeds
Music Technology and Computer Music ....MMus 12FT 24PT

University of Limerick
Music Technology........MA 12FT

London Metropolitan University
Music Technology (by project) .... MA 12FT 24PT

University of the Arts London - London College of Communication
Service Design Innovation........ MDes 12FT
Sound Arts........MA 12FT

National University of Ireland, Maynooth
Music Technology........HDip 12FT

North East Surrey College of Technology
Acoustics and Noise Control........IOA Diploma 9PT
Applied Acoustics and Noise Control ....MSc 9PT

Norwich University of the Arts
Moving Image and Sound .... MA 12FT 24PT

Oxford Brookes University
Composition and Sonic Art .... MA 12FT 24PT/PGDip 9FT 18PT
Music .... MA 12FT 24PT

Plymouth University
Computer Music........MRes 12FT

University of Portsmouth
Computational Sound........MSc 12FT 24PT

Queen Margaret University, Edinburgh
Audiology (Pre-Registration) ....PGDip 24FT/MSc 30FT

Queen Mary, University of London
Digital Music Processing........MSc 12FT 24PT

Queen's University Belfast
Music .... MA 12FT 32PT
Sonic Arts........MA 12FT

Royal College of Music
Composition .... PGDip 10FT/AdvPGDip 10FT/MMus 13FT
Composition and Composition for Screen ....MMus 13FT

Royal Welsh College of Music and Drama
Composition ....PGDip 12FT/PGDip 24PT/MA 24PT/MMus 24PT
Music Performance. MA 24PT/MA 12FT/PGDip 12FT/MMus 12FT

University of Salford
Animation ....MA 12FT
Audio Production........MSc 12FT 36PT
Professional Sound and Video Technology MSc 12FT 36PT/PGDip 9FT 24PT

School of Oriental and African Studies - SOAS
Music and Development .... MA 12FT 24PT

University of Sheffield
Sonic Arts........ MA 12FT 24PT

University of South Wales
Music Engineering and Production........MSc 12FT 24-36PT

University of Southampton
Audiology ....MSc 12FT 24PT/PGDip 9FT 18PT/PGCert 9FT 18PT
Sound and Vibration Studies........MSc 12FT 36PT

Staffordshire University
Music Technology........MSc 12-18FT

University of Sunderland
Animation and Design .... MA 12FT 24PT

University of Surrey
Monolingual Subtitling and Audio Description ....MA 12FT

University of Sussex
Music and Sonic Media .... MA 12FT 24PT

Trinity College Dublin - the University of Dublin
Music and Media Technologies........ MPhil 24FT

UCL - University College London
Audiological Science........ MSc 12FT/PGDip 9FT

University of West London
Advanced Music Technology .... MA 12FT 24PT/PGDip 12FT 24PT/PGCert 12FT 24PT
Electronic / Electro-acoustic Composition........MMus 12FT 24PT
Record Production .... MA 12FT 24PT

University of Westminster
Audio Production........ MA 12FT 24PT

Audio engineering
Research Courses

De Montfort University
Music, Technology and Innovation .. PhD 36-48FT 48-72PT/MPhil 12-24FT 24-48PT

University of Edinburgh
Acoustics........PhD 36FT/MPhil 24FT/MSc by research 12FT
Sound Design (by Research) ....MSc 12FT 24PT

University of Hertfordshire
Centre for Research in Electronic Media (CREM)..PhD 36FT 72PT/MPhil 24FT 48PT/MRes 12FT 24PT
Composition and Performance as Research Practice (CAPARP)..... PhD 36FT 72PT/MPhil 24FT 48PT/MRes 12FT 24PT

University of Hull
Sonic Art ....MRes 12FT 24PT

University of Kent
Electronic Engineering.... MSc by research 12FT 24PT/MPhil 24FT 36PT/PhD 36FT 60PT
Music Technology........ MPhil 36FT 60PT/PhD 36FT 60PT

University of Leeds
Music .... PhD 36FT/MPhil 24FT/MA by research 12FT

Newcastle University
Music ....by research 12FT 24PT/PGDip by research 9FT 18PT

The Open University
Acoustics........ PhD 36FT 72PT variableDL/MPhil 15FT 24PT variableDL
Environmental acoustics .... PhD 36FT 72PT/MPhil 15FT 24PT
Interdisciplinary themes in music research including film and literature........ PhD 36FT 72PT variableDL/MPhil 15FT 24PT variableDL
Music computing and acousticsPhD 36FT 72PT variableDL/MPhil 15FT 24PT variableDL
Musical acoustics .... PhD 36FT 72PT/MPhil 15FT 24PT

Oxford Brookes University
Music .... PhD 24-60FT 48-72PT/MPhil 24-36FT 36-48PT

Royal Academy of Music
Composition........MPhil 24FT/PhD 36FT

University of Surrey
Sound Recording........ PhD 33-48FT 45-96PT/MPhil 21-36FT 33-72PT

University of York
Music Technology....... PhD 36FT 72PT/MA by research 12FT 24PT

Cinema
Taught Courses

Aberystwyth University
Film Studies .... MA 12FT 24PT

University of the Arts London - London College of Fashion
Fashion and Film........ MA 15FT 30PT

Bangor University
Creative Practice ....MRes 12FT 24PT
Film and Visual Culture........MRes 12FT 24PT
Filmmaking: Concept to Screen........ MA 12FT 24PT

University of Bedfordshire
International Cinema .... MA 12FT 24PT

Birkbeck, University of London
World Cinema........ MA 12FT 24PT

University of Birmingham
Literature and Film........MRes 12FT 24PT

University of Bradford
Film Studies ....MSc 12FT 24PT

University of Central Lancashire
Film Production........MA 12FT 24PT/PGDip 9FT 24PT/PGCert 9FT 24PT

University College Cork
English (American Literature & Film)........MA 12FT
Film Studies .... MA 9FT
French Creativity/Literature & Film........MA 12FT

University of Dundee
Film Studies ....MLitt 12FT

University of East Anglia
Film Studies .... MA 12FT 24PT
Film Studies with Archiving........ MA 12FT 24PT
Film, Television and Creative Practice .... MA 12FT 24PT

University of East London
Independent Film, Video and New Screen Media
........MA 12FT 24PT/PGDip 8FT 16PT/PGCert 4FT 8PT

Edge Hill University
Film Studies ....MRes 12FT 24PT

Edinburgh Napier University
Film .... MA 12FT 24PT
International Journalism for Media Professionals (Distance Learning)........ MA 12FT 24PT

University of Edinburgh
Film Studies ....MSc 12FT 24PT
Film, Exhibition and Curation........MSc 12FT 24PT

University of Exeter
Independent Film Business........ MA 12FT 24PT

National University of Ireland Galway
Film Studies (Film, Culture, and Society)..... MA 12FT/PGDip 12FT

Glasgow School of Art
Sound for the Moving Image..PGCert 4FT/PGDip 8FT/MDes 12FT

University of Glasgow
Film and Television Studies........MLitt 12FT 24PT

University of Gloucestershire
Film and Screen Enterprise ..MA 12FT/PGAdvDip 8FT/PGCert 4FT

University of Kent
Film .... MA 12FT 24PT
Film (Paris option) ....MA 12FT

King's College London
Film Studies .... MA 12FT 24PT

Kingston University
Film Studies .... MA 12FT 24PT

Leeds Metropolitan University
Filmmaking........MA 18FT
Music for the Moving Image .... MA 12FT 24PT

University of Leeds
World Cinemas........ MA 12FT 24PT

Manchester Metropolitan University
English Studies: Contemporary Literature and Film........MA 16FT 36PT/PGDip 12FT 24PT

University of Manchester
Screen Studies........ MA 12FT 24PT

Newcastle University
Film: Theory and Practice .... MA 12FT 24PT

University of Northampton
Screen Studies........ MA 12FT 24PT

Norwich University of the Arts
Moving Image and Sound .... MA 12FT 24PT

University of Nottingham
American Studies (Visual Culture)........ MA 12FT 24-48PT

Media studies and publishing

Oxford Brookes University
Film Studies: Popular Cinema ... MA 12FT 24PT/PGDip 8FT 6-8PT/PGCert 4FT 6PT

University of Portsmouth
Film and Television Studies ... MA 12FT 24PT

Queen Mary, University of London
Film Studies ... MA 12FT 24PT

Ravensbourne
Moving Image ... MA 12FT 24PT

University of Reading
Film Studies ... MA (Res) 12FT 24PT

University of Salford
Film Screenwriting ... MA 15FT/PGDip 12FT/PGCert 6FT

School of Oriental and African Studies - SOAS
Global Cinemas and the Transcultural ... MA 12FT 24-36PT

Sheffield Hallam University
Film Studies ... MA 12FT 36-72PT
MPhil 36FT 84PT/PhD by taught 36FT 84PT
Film Studies with Screenwriting ... MA 12FT 24PT

University of Southampton
Film Studies ... MA 12FT 24PT
Film and Cultural Management ... MA 12FT 24PT

University of St Andrews
Film Studies ... MLitt 12FT 24PT/PGDip 9FT
Modern Hispanic Literature And Film ... MLitt 12FT/MPhil 24FT

University of Stirling
Film Studies: Theory and Practice ... MLitt 12FT 27PT/PGDip 9FT 21PT/PGCert 3FT 6PT

University of Sunderland
Film & Cultural Studies ... MA 12FT 24PT

University of Sussex
Film Studies ... MA 12FT 24PT
Media and Cultural Studies ... MA 12FT 24PT

Trinity College Dublin - the University of Dublin
Film Theory and History ... MPhil 12FT

UCL - University College London
Film Studies ... MA 12FT 24PT

University of Warwick
Film and Television Studies ... MA 12FT
Research in Film and Television Studies ... MA 12FT

University of West London
Film Finance ... MA 12FT 24PT
Finance and Risk Management ... MSc 12FT 24PT
Video Production and Film Studies ... MA 12FT 24PT

University of Westminster
Film and Television: Theory, Culture and Industry ... MA 12FT 24-48PT

University of Winchester
Film Studies ... MA 12FT 24PT/PGDip 12FT 24PT/PGCert 12FT 24PT

University of Wolverhampton
Film Studies ... MA 24-36PT

University of York
Contemporary Cinema and Television ... MA 12FT 24PT
Film and Literature ... MA 12FT 24PT

Cinema
Research Courses

Aberystwyth University
Theatre, Film and Television Studies ... MPhil 12FT 24PT PhD 36FT 60PT

Bangor University
Creative and Critical Writing, Film and Media, Professional Writing ... MPhil 24FT 48PT/PhD 36FT 72PT
Creative and Critical Writing, Film and Media, Professional Writing: Practice-Led Research ... MPhil 24FT 48PT/PhD 36FT 72PT

University of Bedfordshire
Journalism, Media, Cinema or Television ... PDJMCT 36PT

Birkbeck, University of London
Arts and Humanities ... MPhil 24FT 36PT/PhD 36-48FT 60-84PT
Film and Screen Media ... MPhil 36FT 48PT/PhD 36FT 48PT

University of Birmingham
Film Studies ... MRes 12FT 24PT

Brunel University
Film and Television Studies ... PhD 36FT 48PT/MPhil 12FT 24PT

University of Central Lancashire
Film and Media ... PhD 18-36FT 42-60PT/MPhil 18-36FT 42-60PT/MA by research 12FT 24PT

University of East Anglia
Film, Television and Media Studies ... PhD 36FT 72PT/MPhil 24FT 48PT

University of Edinburgh
Film Studies ... PhD 36FT 72PT/MSc by research 12FT 24PT

University of Exeter
Film Studies ... MPhil 24FT 48PT/PhD 36-48FT 72PT
Interdisciplinary Studies ... MPhil 36FT 60PT/PhD 48FT 84PT

University of Glasgow
Film/TV ... MPhil 12FT/MLitt by research 12FT 24PT

University of Hull
Film Studies ... PhD 36FT 60PT/MPhil 24FT 36PT

University of Kent
Film PhD 36FT 60PT/MPhil 24FT 36PT/MA by research 12FT 24PT
Film (Practice by Research) ... MA by research 12FT 24PT/MPhil 24FT 36PT/PhD 36FT 60PT

King's College London
Film Studies Research ... PhD 36FT 48-72PT

Lancaster University
Media, Film and Cultural Studies ... PhD 36FT 48PT/MPhil 24FT 36PT

Newcastle University
Film Studies ... MLitt by research 12FT 24PT
Film Studies ... PhD 36FT 72PT/MPhil 12FT 24PT

University of Nottingham
Film and Television Studies ... PhD 36FT 72PT/MPhil 24FT 48PT/MRes 12FT

Queen's University Belfast
Film Studies ... PhD 36FT 72PT/MPhil 24FT 48PT

School of Oriental and African Studies - SOAS
Media and Film Studies ... PhD 36-48FT

University of Southampton
Film Studies ... PhD 48FT 84PT/MPhil 48FT 84PT

University of St Andrews
Film Studies ... PhD 36FT 72-84PT/MPhil 24FT 48PT
Modern Hispanic Literature And Film ... PhD 36FT 72PT/MPhil 24FT 48PT

University of Sussex
Film Studies Research Programme .. PhD 24-48FT 36-72PT/MPhil 12-36FT 24-48PT

University of Wales Trinity Saint David
Film and Media ... PhD 36FT 48-72PT/MPhil 12-36FT

UCL - University College London
Film Studies ... PhD 36FT 60PT

University of Warwick
European Cinema ... MPhil 24FT 48PT/PhD 36-48FT 60PT
Film and Television Studies ... PhD 36FT 60PT/MPhil 36FT/MA by research 12FT

University of York
Theatre, Film and Television ... MPhil 24FT 48PT/PhD 36FT 72PT

Creative writing
Taught Courses

University of Aberdeen
Creative Writing ... MLitt 12FT 24PT/PGDip 9FT 21PT

Aberystwyth University
Creative Writing ... MA 12FT 24PT
Scriptwriting (Screen and Radio). MA 12FT 24PT/PGDip 9FT 20PT

Anglia Ruskin University
Creative Writing ... MA 12FT 24PT

University of the Arts London - Central Saint Martins College of Art and Design
Creative Practice for Narrative Environments ... MA 24FT

Bangor University
Creative Practice ... MRes 12FT 24PT
Creative Writing ... PhD by taught 36FT 72-96PT/MPhil 24FT 48-60PT
English ... PhD by taught 36FT 72-96PT/MPhil 24FT 48-60PT

Bath Spa University
Creative Writing ... MA 12FT
Scriptwriting ... MA 12FT 24PT
Travel and Nature Writing ... MA 12FT 24PT 12DL
Writing for Young People ... MA 12FT 24PT

Birkbeck, University of London
Creative Writing ... MA 12FT 24PT
Screenwriting ... PGCert 12PT/MA 24PT

Birmingham City University
MA Writing ... MA 12FT 24-60PT

University of Birmingham
Creative Writing MA ... MA 12FT 24PT

University of Bolton
Writing and Producing ... MA 12FT 24PT

Bournemouth University
Screenwriting ... MA 24FT 24DL
Scriptwriting ... MA 12FT

Brunel University
Creative Writing ... MA 1 yearFT 2 yearsPT
Creative Writing: The Novel ... MA 12FT 24PT

University of Cambridge
Creative Writing ... MSt 24PT

Canterbury Christ Church University
Creative Writing: Prose Fiction ... MA 24PT

Cardiff Metropolitan University
Creative Writing ... MA 12FT 24PT
English and Creative Writing ... MA 12FT 24PT

Cardiff University
Creative Writing ... MA 12FT

University of Central Lancashire
Playwriting ... MA 12FT 24PT
Scriptwriting ... MA 12FT 24PT
Writing for Children..MA 12FT 24PT/PGDip 9FT 24PT/PGCert 9FT 24PT

Central School of Speech and Drama, University of London
Writing for Stage and Broadcast Media MA 12FT 24PT/MFA 24FT

University of Chichester
Creative Writing ..... MA 12+FT 24-36PT/PGDip 24PT/PGCert 12PT

City University London
Creative Writing (Non-Fiction) ... MA 24PT
Creative Writing (Novels) ... MA 24PT
Creative Writing (Playwriting & Screenwriting) ..... MA 24FT 24PT

De Montfort University
Television Scriptwriting ... MA 24PT

University of Dundee
Comics Studies (MLitt) ... MLitt 12FT
Creative Writing (Module) ... Module 3PT
Writing Practice & Study (MLitt) ... MLitt 12FT

University of East Anglia
Biography and Creative Non-Fiction ... MA 12FT 24PT
Creative Entrepreneurship ... MA 12FT
Creative Writing: Poetry ... MA 12FT 24PT
Creative Writing: Prose ... MA 12FT 24PT
Creative Writing: Scriptwriting ... MA 12FT 24PT
Writing the Modern World ... MA 12FT 24PT

University of East London
Writing: Imaginative Practice (PG Cert) ... PGCert 12PT
Writing: Imaginative Practice MA by distance learning..MA 24PT

Edge Hill University
Creative Writing ... MA 12FT 24PT
Scriptwriting ... MA 12FT 24PT

Edinburgh Napier University
Creative WritingMA 12FT 24PT/PGDip 9FT 18PT/PGCert 6FT 12PT
Flexible Managed Programme (FECCI) ... MA 12FT 24PT/MSc 12FT 24PT/PGCert 12FT 24PT
Screenwriting ..... MA 12FT 24PT/PGDip 9FT 18PT 9-18DL/PGCert 6FT 12PT

University of Edinburgh
Creative Writing (Online Distance Learning) ... MSc 36DL

University of Essex
Creative Writing ... MA 12FT 24PT
Wild Writing: Literature and the Environment ... MA 12FT 24PT

University of Exeter
Creative Writing ... MA 11FT 23PT
English Literary Studies ... MA 11FT 23PT
Theatre Practice: Applied Theatre ... MA 12FT 24PT
Theatre Practice: Directing and Actor Training ... MA 12FT 24PT
Theatre Practice: General Programme ... MA 12FT 24PT
Theatre Practice: Physical Performance & Actor TrainingMA 12FT 24PT
Theatre Practice: Staging Shakespeare..MA 12FT 24PT/MFA 24FT

Falmouth University
Professional Writing ... MA 12FT 24PT 24DL

GCU London
TV Fiction Writing ... MA 12FT

National University of Ireland Galway
Screenwriting ... MA 12FT/PGDip 12FT

Glasgow Caledonian University
Television Fiction Writing ... MA 12FT 24PT

University of Glasgow
Creative Writing ... MFA 24FT
Creative Writing ... MLitt 12FT 24PT 12DL
Playwriting & Dramaturgy ... MLitt 12FT

University of Gloucestershire
Creative and Critical Writing ... MA 12FT 24PT/PGDip 8FT 20PT/PGCert 4FT 8PT

Goldsmiths, University of London
Creative and Cultural Industries ... GradDip 12FT
Creative and Life Writing ... MA 12FT 24PT
Script Writing ... MA 12FT
Writer/Teacher ... MA 12FT 24PT
Writing for Performance ... MA 12FT 24PT

University of Hull
Creative Writing ... MA 12FT 24PT

Media studies and publishing

Keele University
Creative Writing ... MA 12-15FT 24-27PT

University of Kent
Creative Writing ... MA 12FT 24PT
Creative Writing (Paris option) ... MA 12FT

King's College London
Life Writing ... MA 12FT 24PT

Kingston University
Creative Writing ... MA 12FT 24PT
Creative Writing ... MFA 24FT 48PT
Creative Writing Low Residency ... MA 12FT 24PT
Creative Writing Low Residency ... MFA 24FT 48PT
Creative Writing and Pedagogy ... MA 12FT 24PT
Creative Writing and Publishing ... MA 12FT 24PT
Creative Writing and the Creative Economy ... MA 12FT 24PT
Managing in the Creative Economy ... MA 12FT 24PT
Playwriting ... MA 12FT 24PT

University of Leeds
Writing for Performance and Production ... MA 12FT 24PT/PGDip 12FT 24PT/PGCert 12FT 24PT

University of Lincoln
Creative Writing ... MA 12FT 24PT

Liverpool John Moores University
Screenwriting ... MA 24PT/PGDip 12PT/PGCert 20PT
Writing ... MA 24PT/PGCert 20PT/PGDip 12PT

London Metropolitan University
Creative Industries ... MA 12FT 24PT
Creative Writing ... MA 12FT 24PT
Screenwriting ... MA 12FT

London South Bank University
Creative Writing ... MA 24PT

University of the Arts London - London College of Communication
Screenwriting ... MA 24PT

Loughborough University
Creative Writing ... MA 12FT 24PT

Manchester Metropolitan University
Creative Writing ... MA 24FT 36PT/PGDip 12FT 24PT/MA 24DL

University of Manchester
Creative Writing ... MA 12FT 24PT

Middlesex University
Creative Writing ... MA 24PT

Newcastle University
Creative Writing ... MA 12FT 24PT
Creative Writing ... PGCert 12FT 24PT

Northumbria University
Creative Writing ... MA 12FT 24PT
Creative Writing in the Classroom ... PGCert 12PT

Nottingham Trent University
Creative Writing ... MA 12FT 24PT
Language & Culture Bridging Programme, School of Art & Design ... Language and Culture Bridging Programme 3FT

University of Nottingham
Creative Writing ... MA 12FT 24PT

Oxford Brookes University
Creative Writing MA 12FT 24PT/PGDip 8FT 6-8PT/PGCert 4FT 6PT

University of Oxford
Creative Writing ... MSt 24PT

Plymouth University
Creative Writing ... MA 12FT 24PT

University of Portsmouth
Creative Writing ... MA 12FT 24PT

Queen's University Belfast
English (Creative Writing) ... MA 12FT 24PT/PGDip 12FT 24PT

University of Roehampton
Post Graduate Diploma- Creative and Professional WritingPGDip 9FT 24PT

Royal Holloway, University of London
Creative Writing ... MA 12FT 24PT

University of Salford
Art and Design: Creative Education ... MA 12FT 24PT/PGDip 8FT 15PT
Creative Writing: Innovation and Experiment ... MA 12FT 36PT/PGDip 8FT 24PT/PGCert 4FT 12PT
Film Screenwriting ... MA 15FT/PGDip 12FT/PGCert 6FT
Television and Radio Scriptwriting MA 27PT/PGDip 24PT/PGCert 12PT

Sheffield Hallam University
Writing ... MA 12FT 24PT

University of Sheffield
English Literature: Creative Writing ... MA 12FT 24PT

University of South Wales
Scriptwriting ... MA 12FT 24PT
Scriptwriting for Screen, Media and Stage ... MA 12FT 24PT
Writing ... MPhil 48PT

University of Southampton
Creative Writing ... MA 12FT 24PT

University of St Andrews
Creative Writing ... MLitt 12FT 24PT/PGDip 9FT 24PT

University of Stirling
Creative Writing ... MLitt 12FT 27PT/PGDip 9FT 21PT/PGCert 3FT 3PT

University of Sussex
Creative and Critical Writing ... MA 12FT 24PT
Writing History ... MA 12FT 24PT

Swansea University
Creative Writing ... MA 12FT 24-36PT

Teesside University
MA Creative Writing .MA 12FT 24PT/PGDip 9FT 18PT/PGCert 6FT 12PT

Trinity College Dublin - the University of Dublin
Creative Writing ... MPhil 12FT

University of Wales Trinity Saint David
Creative and Script Writing ... MA 12FT 24PT/PGCert 12FT 24PT/PGDip 12FT 24PT

University of Westminster
Creative Writing: Writing the City ... MA 12FT 24PT

University of Winchester
Creative and Critical Writing ... MA 12FT 24PT/PGDip 12FT 24PT/PGCert 12FT 24PT
Doctor of Creative Arts (Creative Writing) ... PhD by taught 48FT 72PT
Writing for Children ... MA 12FT 24PT/PGDip 12FT 24PT/PGCert 12FT 24PT

University of Wolverhampton
Transmedia Screenwriting ... MA 12FT 24PT

University of York
Theatre: Writing, Directing and Performance ... MA 12FT 24PT

York St John University
Creative Writing ... MA 12FT 24PT

Creative writing
Research Courses

Aberystwyth University
Creative Writing (PhD) ... PhD 36FT 60PT

Anglia Ruskin University
Creative Writing ... MPhil 24FT/PhD 36FT

Bangor University
Creative Writing ... MPhil 24FT 48PT/PhD 36FT 72PT
Creative and Critical Writing, Film and Media, Professional Writing ... MPhil 24FT 48PT/PhD 36FT 72PT
Creative and Critical Writing, Film and Media, Professional Writing: Practice-Led Research . MPhil 24FT 48PT/PhD 36FT 72PT

Bath Spa University
Creative Writing ... PhD 24 - 60FT 36 - 72PT

University of Birmingham
Creative Writing PhD/PhD by Distance Learning.. PhD 36FT 72PT

University of Bolton
Creative Writing Specialisms ... PhD 36FT 72PT/MPhil 24FT 36PT

Cardiff University
Creative and Critical Writing ... PhD 36FT

University of Essex
Creative Writing ... PhD 36FT 72PT/MPhil 24FT 48PT/MA by research 12FT 24PT

University of Exeter
Drama ... PhD 48FT 89PT/MPhil 36FT 60PT
EnglishPhD 36-48FT 72PT/MPhil 24FT 48PT/MA by research 12FT 24PT
Film Studies ... MPhil 24FT 48PT/PhD 36-48FT 72PT

University of Gloucestershire
Creative Writing ... PhD 30-48FT

University of Kent
The Contemporary Novel: Practice as Research ... MA by research 12FT 24PT/PhD 36FT 60PT

Lancaster University
Creative Writing ... PhD 36FT 48PT/MPhil 24FT 36PT

University of Manchester
Creative Writing ... PhD 36FT 72PT

The Open University
Academic and Professional Communication Literacies..PhD 36FT 72PT variableDL/EdD 36PT variableDL/MRes 12FT
English... PhD 36FT 72PT variableDL/MPhil 15FT 24PT variableDL

University of Strathclyde
Creative Writing ... MRes 12FT 24PT

University of Sussex
Creative Writing Research Programme ... PhD 24-48FT 36-72PT/MPhil 12-36FT 24-48PT
Creative and Critical Practice Research Programme. PhD 24-48FT 36-72PT/MPhil 12-36FT 24-48PT

Swansea University
Creative Writing ... MPhil 24FT 48PT/PhD 36FT 72PT

Digital media
Taught Courses

University of Abertay Dundee
Games Development ... MProf 12FT

Aberystwyth University
3D Imaging, Analysis and Applications ... MRes 12FT 24PT/PGDip 9FT 21PT/PGCert 5FT 17PT
Cyfryngau Creadigol Ymarferol ... MA 12FT 24PT/PGDip 9FT 18PT
Digital Marketing ... MSc 12FT 24PT
Information Technology Law ... LLM 12FT
International Politics of the Internet ... MA 12FT
InternationalTechnology Law (Distance-Learning) ... LLM 36DL/PGDip 24DL
Management and Digital Business ... MSc 12FT 24PT

University of the Arts London - Camberwell College of Arts
Fine Art Digital ... MA 12FT 24PT 24DL

University of the Arts London - London College of Fashion
Digital Fashion ... MA 15FT 30PT

Bangor University
Creative Practice ... MRes 12FT 24PT
International Media Management ... MSc 12FT 24PT

University of Bedfordshire
Art Design and Internet Technology ... MA 12FT 24PT
Media, Culture and Technology ... MA 12FT 24PT

Birkbeck, University of London
Creative Industries (Arts and Media) ... MA 12FT 24PT
Creative Industries (Computing) ... MSc 12FT 24PT
Creative Industries (Management) ... MSc 12FT 24PT
Digital Media Management ... PGCert 12PT

Birmingham City University
Digital Arts in Performance ... MA 12FT 24PT
Interactive Media PGCert 5FT 9PT/PGDip 9FT 21PT/MSc 16/19FT 28PT
Social Media ... MA 12FT 24PT 12-36DL
Video Game Enterprise and Production ... MSc 12FT

Arts University Bournemouth
Interactive Media ... MA 12FT 24PT
Design Interaction ... MA 12FT 24PT

Bournemouth University
Creative and Media Education ... MA 18PT
Digital Effects ... MA 12FT

University of Bradford
Digital Arts and Media ... MA 12FT 24PT/PGDip 9FT

University of Brighton
Creative MediaMA 12FT 24PT/PGDip 12FT variesPT/PGCert 12FT variesPT
Digital Media Arts ... PGDip 12FT 24PT/MA 12FT 24PT
Digital Media Production ... MSc 12FT 24-60PT/PGDip 12FT 24-60PT/PGCert 12FT 24-60PT

University of Central Lancashire
Digital Marketing (CAM) ... Diploma 7.5DL
Film Production ... MA 12FT 24PT/PGDip 9FT 24PT/PGCert 9FT 24PT

City University London
Social Media ... MSc 12FT 24PT

University College Cork
Interactive Media ... MSc 12FT 24PT

University for the Creative Arts
Design: Digital Design ... MA 12FT 24PT

Dublin Institute of Technology
Digital Media Technologies ... MA 12FT 24PT/PGDip 9FT 21PT

University of Dundee
Film Studies ... MLitt 12FT

University of Edinburgh
Design and Digital Media ... MSc 12FT 24PT
Digital Animation ... MSc(Res) 12FT 24PT
Digital Media and Culture ... MSc(Res) 12FT 24PT
Digital Studio Practice (MSc by Research) ... MSc(Res) 12FT 24PT

National University of Ireland Galway
Digital Media ... MA 12FT/PGDip 12FT

Glasgow Caledonian University
3D Design for Virtual Environments ... MA 12FT 24PT/PGDip 12FT 24PT
Digital Forensics ... MSc 12FT

Glasgow School of Art
Digital Culture ... MDes 12FT 24PT/PGDip 9FT 21PT/PGCert 4FT 9PT
Medical Visualisation and Human Anatomy ... PGCert 4FT/PGDip 8FT/MSc 12FT

University of Gloucestershire
Media and Creative Enterprise ... MA 12FT/AdvPGDip 8FT/PGCert 4FT

Media studies and publishing

Glyndwr University
Creative Media ... MA 12FT 24PT
Creative Media Technology ... MSc 12FT

Goldsmiths, University of London
Computational Studio Arts ... MFA 24FT
Creating Social Media ... MA 12FT 24PT/MSc 12FT 24PT
Digital Entrepreneurship ... MSc 12FT
Digital Journalism ... MA 12FT/MSc 12FT
Digital Media: Technology and Cultural Form ... MA 12FT 24PT
Digital Sociology ... MA 12FT 24PT/MSc 12FT 24PT
Interactive Media: Critical Theory and Practice ... MA 12FT 24PT
Media and Communications ... GradDip 12FT

University of Hertfordshire
Animation ... MA 12FT 24PT/PGDip 12FT 24PT/PGCert 12FT 24PT
Digital and Lens Art ... MA 12FT 24PT/PGDip 12FT 24PT/PGCert 12FT 24PT
Two Dimensional Digital Animation .. MA 12FT 24PT/PGDip 12FT 24PT

University of Huddersfield
3D Digital Design ... MA 12/16FT
Digital Media ... MA 12/16FT

University of Hull
Business Technology Management ... MSc 12FT

Imperial College London
Science Media Production ... MSc 12FT

University of Kent
Advanced Electronic Systems Engineering ... PGDip 12FT 24PT/MSc 12FT 24PT
Architectural Visualisation ... MA 12FT
Broadband and Mobile Communication Networks ... PGDip 12FT 24PT/MSc 12FT 24PT
Computer Animation ... MSc 12FT
Digital Visual Effects ... MSc 12FT/PGDip 12FT
Embedded Systems and Instrumentation ... PGDip 12FT 24PT/MSc 12FT 24PT
Wireless Communications and Signal Processing ... PGDip 12FT 24PT/MSc 12FT 24PT

King's College London
Digital Asset & Media Management ... MA 12FT 24PT
Digital Culture and Society ... MA 12FT 24PT

Leeds Metropolitan University
Creative Technology ... MSc 12FT 24PT
Digital Visual Effects ... MSc 12FT 24PT
Information Management ... MSc 12FT 36PT

University of Leicester
New Media and Society ... MA 12FT

University of Limerick
Interactive Media ... MA 12FT/MSc 12FT

University of Lincoln
Digital Media ... MA 12FT 24PT

London Metropolitan University
Digital Media ... MA 12FT 24PT

London South Bank University
Creative Media Industries: Journalism ... MA 13FT
Digital Film ... MA 24PT
Digital Photography ... MA 24PT
Media Arts ... MA 12FT
New Media ... MA 24PT

University of the Arts London - London College of Communication
Digital Media Futures ... MA 12FT

Loughborough University
Digital Media and Society ... MA 12FT

Middlesex University
Creative Technology ... MA 12FT 24PT/MSc 12FT 24PT
Creative Technology ... MA 12FT
Digital Media ... MA 12FT 24PT
Film, Television, Animation ... MA 12FT 24PT
Creative Technology ... MSc 12FT 36PT

Newcastle University
Creative Arts Practice ... MA 12FT 24PT
Digital Architecture ... MSc 12FT 24PT
Film: Theory and Practice ... MA 12FT 24PT

Nottingham Trent University
Film Practice ... MA 12FT/PGDip 7FT/PGCert 4FT
Interaction Design ... MA 12FT/PGCert 7FT/PGDip 4FT
Product Design ... MA 12FT/PGDip 7FT/PGCert 4FT
Product Design Innovation Management ... MA 12FT

Oxford Brookes University
Digital Media Production ... MSc 12FT 24PT
Digital Publishing ... MA 12FT 24PT/PGDip 9FT 18PT
Film Studies: Popular Cinema ... MA 12FT 24PT/PGDip 8FT 6-8PT/PGCert 4FT 6PT

Plymouth University
Contemporary Art Practice ... MA 12FT
Digital Art and Technology ... MRes 12FT

University of Portsmouth
Design for Digital Media ... MA 12FT 24PT
Digital Marketing ... MA 12FT
Digital Media ... MSc 12FT 36PT

Queen Mary, University of London
Computer Vision ... MSc 12FT 24PT
Media and Arts Technology (MSc by Research) ... MSc(Res) 12FT

Ravensbourne
3D Stereoscopic Media ... MSc 12FT 24PT/MA 12FT 24PT
Animation Futures ... MA 12FT 24PT
Applied Technologies, Rapid Prototyping and Digital Technologies ... MSc 12FT 24PT
Interactive Digital Media ... MA 12FT 24PT
Professional Media Practice ... MA 12FT 24PT

Royal College of Art
Animation ... MA 24FT PhD by taught 72PT/MPhil 24FT 48PT/MA 24FT

University of Salford
Animation ... MA 12FT
Children's Digital Media Production ... MA 12FT/PGDip 9FT
International and Online Journalism ... MA 12FT 36PT
Social Media ... MA 9FT/PGDip 9FT

School of Oriental and African Studies - SOAS
Critical Media and Cultural Studies ... MA 12FT 24-36PT
Global Media and Postnational Communication ... MA 12FT 24-36PT

Sheffield Hallam University
Animation and Special Effects ... MA 12FT 36PT
Animation for Computer Games ... MA 12FT 36PT
Research Degrees - Cultural, Communication and Computing Research Institute ... MPhil 24-36FT 48-60PT/PhD by taught 36-48FT 60-72PT

University of Sheffield
Sonic Arts ... MA 12FT 24PT
Web Journalism ... MA 12FT/PGDip 9FT

University of South Wales
Visual Effects ... MA 12FT 24PT

Southampton Solent University
Digital Marketing and Media ... MA 12FT

University of Southampton
Digital Marketing ... MSc 12FT
Sound and Vibration Studies ... MSc 12FT 36PT

Staffordshire University
Film Production Technology ... MSc 12-18FT
Film Production and Visual Cultures ... MA 12FT
Film Production: Theory and Practice ... MA 12FT

University of Strathclyde
Digital Creativity ... MSc 12FT 24PT/PGDip 9FT 18PT

University of Sunderland
Animation and Design ... MA 12FT 24PT

University of Sussex
Computing with Digital Media ... MSc 12FT 24PT
Creative Media Practice ... MA 12FT 24PT
Digital Media ... MA 12FT 24PT
Embedded Digital Systems ... MSc 12FT 24PT

Swansea University
Digital Media ... MA 12FT 36PT

Swansea Metropolitan University
3D Computer Animation ... MA 12FT 24PT

Teesside University
Concept Art for Games and Animation ... MA 12FT 36PT
Digital Arts and Design ... MA 12FT 24PT/PGDip 8FT 16PT/PGCert 4FT 8PT
Digital Effects for Film and Television ... MA 12FT 36PT
Future Design ... MA 12FT 24PT/PGDip 8FT 16PT/PGCert 4FT 8PT
Mass Communications ... MA 12FT 24PT

Trinity College Dublin - the University of Dublin
Interactive Digital Media ... MSc 12FT

University of Ulster
Digital Media Communication ... PGCert 10PT

University of Winchester
Digital Media Practice ... MA 12FT 24PT/PGDip 12FT 24PT/PGCert 12FT 24PT

University of Wolverhampton
Digital and Visual Communications ... MA 12FT 24PT

University of Worcester
Creative Digital Media ... MA 36FT 72PT/MSc 36FT 72PT/PGDip 24FT 48PT/PGCert 12FT 24PT

University of York
Human-Centred Interactive Technologies ... MSc 12FT
Social Media and Interactive Technologies ... MSc 12FT

Digital media
Research Courses

University of Bath
Digital Media ... EngD 48FT

University of Bradford
Electronic Imaging and Media Communications. PhD 36FT 48PT/MPhil 12FT 24PT

Cardiff University
Distributed and Scientific Computing ... PhD 36FT/MPhil 12FT

University of Central Lancashire
Arts and Media ... PhD 30-48FT 66-84PT/MPhil 18-36FT 42-60PT/MA by research 12FT 24PT

University for the Creative Arts
Arts & Media ... PhD 36FT 60PT/MPhil 24FT 36PT

University of Edinburgh
Digital Communications ... PhD 36FT 72PT/MPhil 24FT 48PT/MSc by research 12FT 24PT

University of Gloucestershire
Art and Design ... PhD 30-48FT

Goldsmiths, University of London
Arts & Computational Technology ... MPhil 24FT 36PT/PhD 36-48FT 48-72PT

Heriot-Watt University
Digital Tools and Technologies ... EngD 48FT

University of Hertfordshire
Centre for Research in Electronic Art and Communication (CREAC) ... PhD 36FT 72PT/MPhil 24FT 48PT/MRes 12FT 24PT

University of Kent
Digital Arts ... MSc(Res) 12FT 24PT/MPhil 24FT 36PT/PhD 36FT 60PT
Electronic Engineering ... MSc by research 12FT 24PT/MPhil 24FT 36PT/PhD 36FT 60PT

Newcastle University
Digital Media ... PhD 36FT 72PT

University of Portsmouth
Creative Technologies ... MPhil 24FT 48PT/PhD 36FT 72PT

School of Oriental and African Studies - SOAS
Media and Film Studies ... PhD 36-48FT

University of Southampton
Digital Arts and Design ... MRes 12FT 24PT

Film making
Taught Courses

Anglia Ruskin University
Film and Television Production ... MA 12FT 24PT

Bangor University
Creative Practice ... MRes 12FT 24PT
Film and Visual Culture ... MRes 12FT 24PT
Filmmaking: Concept to Screen ... MA 12FT 24PT

Bath Spa University
Feature Filmmaking ... MA 12FT 24PT

University of Bedfordshire
Creative Digital Film Production/ ... MA 12FT 24PT
Digital Film Technologies & Production/ ... MA 12FT 24PT

Birmingham City University
Film Distribution and Marketing (Film Futures: Pro) ... MA 12FT 12DL

University of Birmingham
Film and Television: Research and Production ... MA 12FT 24PT

Arts University Bournemouth
MA Film Production ... MA 14FT

Bournemouth University
Cinematography for Digital Film and Television ... MA 12FT
Directing Digital Film and Television ... MA 12FT
Post Production Editing ... MA 12FT
Producing Film and Television ... MA 12FT

University of Bradford
Digital Filmmaking ... MA 12FT/PGDip 9FT
Film Studies ... MSc 12FT 24PT

University of Bristol
Composition of Music for Film and Television ... MA 12FT
Film and Television Production ... MA 12FT

University of Central Lancashire
Film Production ... MA 12FT 24PT/PGDip 9FT 24PT/PGCert 9FT 24PT
Scriptwriting ... MA 12FT 24PT

University for the Creative Arts
Artists' Film, Video and Photography ... MA 12FT

De Montfort University
Film/Media Studies by Independent Study ... MA 12-24DL

University of Dundee
Film Studies ... MLitt 12FT

University of East Anglia
Film Studies ... MA 12FT 24PT
Film, Television and Creative Practice ... MA 12FT 24PT

University of East London
Independent Film, Video and New Screen Media ... MA 12FT 24PT/PGDip 8FT 16PT/PGCert 4FT 8PT

Media studies and publishing

Edinburgh Napier University
Advanced Film Practice .... MFA 12FT
Film .... MA 12FT 24PT
Screen Project Development .... MA 12FT 24PT

University of Edinburgh
Composition for Screen .... MSc 12FT 24PT
Film Directing .... MA 12FT/MFA 21FT
Film Studies .... MSc 12FT 24PT
Film, Exhibition and Curation .... MSc 12FT 24PT
Transdisciplinary Documentary Film Practice .... MSc(Res) 12FT

University of Essex
Filmmaking .... MA 12FT

University of Exeter
Independent Film Business .... MA 12FT 24PT

GCU London
TV Fiction Writing .... MA 12FT

National University of Ireland Galway
Production and Direction .... MA 12FT/PGDip 12FT

University of Gloucestershire
Film and Screen Enterprise .. MA 12FT/PGAdvDip 8FT/PGCert 4FT

Goldsmiths, University of London
Film and Screen Studies .... MA 12FT 24PT
Filmmaking .... MA 12FT
Screen Documentary .... MA 12FT
Script Writing .... MA 12FT
Visual Anthropology .... MA 12FT 24PT

University of Hertfordshire
Animation .... MA 12FT 24PT/PGDip 12FT 24PT/PGCert 12FT 24PT
Film and Television .... MA 12FT 24PT/PGDip 12FT 24PT
Model Design and Model Effects .... MA 12FT 24PT/PGDip 12FT 24PT/PGCert 12FT 24PT
Screen Cultures .... MA 12FT 24PT/PGDip 12FT 24PT
Special Effects .... MA 12FT 24PT/PGDip 12FT 24PT

University of Kent
Film .... MA 12FT 24PT
Film (Paris option) .... MA 12FT
Sound and Image (Medway) ....

King's College London
Film Studies .... MA 12FT 24PT

Kingston University
Experimental Film .... MA 12FT 24PT
Film Making .... MA 12FT 24PT
Film Making and the Creative Economy .... MA 12FT 24PT
Production Design for Film and Television .... MA 12FT

Leeds Metropolitan University
Digital Visual Effects .... MSc 12FT 24PT
Filmmaking .... MA 18FT
Music for the Moving Image .... MA 12FT 24PT

London Metropolitan University
Film and Animation .... MA 12FT

London South Bank University
Independent Film (Editing And Montage) .... MA 12FT

Manchester Metropolitan University
Design (with pathways in design and contemporary craft practice) .... MA 12FT 24PT

Middlesex University
Film .... MA 12FT 24PT
Film, Television, Animation .... MA 12FT 24PT

Newcastle University
Creative Arts Practice .... MA 12FT 24PT
Film: Theory and Practice .... MA 12FT 24PT

Norwich University of the Arts
Moving Image and Sound .... MA 12FT 24PT

Nottingham Trent University
Design for Film, Television and Events .... MA 12FT/PGDip 7FT/PGCert 4FT
Film Practice .... MA 12FT/PGDip 7FT/PGCert 4FT

Oxford Brookes University
Film Studies: Popular Cinema .... MA 12FT 24PT/PGDip 8FT 6-8PT/PGCert 4FT 6PT

University of Oxford
Film Aesthetics .... MSt 9FT

Plymouth University
Contemporary Art Practice .... MA 12FT
Contemporary Film Practice .... MA 12FT
Film and Video .... MRes 12FT

Queen's University Belfast
Film and Visual Studies .... MA 12FT up to 31PT

Ravensbourne
Moving Image .... MA 12FT 24PT

University of Reading
Film Studies .... MA (Res) 12FT 24PT
Television Studies .... MA (Res) 12FT 24PT
Theatre Studies .... MA (Res) 12FT 24PT

Royal College of Music
Composition and Composition for Screen .... MMus 13FT

Royal Holloway, University of London
Documentary by Practice .... MA 12FT 24PT
Producing Film and Television .... MA 12FT 24PT

University of Salford
Audio Production .... MSc 12FT 36PT
Fiction Film Production .... MA 12FT/PGDip 9FT
Film Screenwriting .... MA 15FT/PGDip 12FT/PGCert 6FT
Post Production for TV and Film .... MA 12FT

Sheffield Hallam University
Film Studies .... MA 12FT 36-72PT
MPhil 36FT 84PT/PhD by taught 36FT 84PT
Film Studies with Screenwriting .... MA 12FT 24PT

University of South Wales
Film .... MA 12FT 24PT/MFA 24FT 36PT
Film Producing .... MA 12FT 24PT

University of Southampton
Film Studies .... MA 12FT 24PT
Film and Cultural Management .... MA 12FT 24PT

University of St Andrews
Film Studies .... MLitt 12FT 24PT/PGDip 9FT

Staffordshire University
Digital Feature Film Production .... MSc 12-18FT
Film Production Technology .... MSc 12-18FT
Film Production and Visual Cultures .... MA 12FT
Film Production: Theory and Practice .... MA 12FT

University of Stirling
Film Studies: Theory and Practice ...... MLitt 12FT 27PT/PGDip 9FT 21PT/PGCert 3FT 6PT

University of Sussex
Film Studies .... MA 12FT 24PT

Teesside University
Digital Effects for Film and Television .... MA 12FT 36PT

UCL - University College London
Film Studies .... MA 12FT 24PT

University of Warwick
Film and Television Studies .... MA 12FT
Research in Film and Television Studies .... MA 12FT

University of West London
Art Direction for Film and TV .... MA 12FT 24PT
Video Production and Film Studies .... MA 12FT 24PT

University of the West of England, Bristol
Wildlife Filmmaking .... MA 12FT

University of Winchester
Film Studies .... MA 12FT 24PT/PGDip 12FT 24PT/PGCert 12FT 24PT

York St John University
Documentary Production .... MA 24FT 12PT
Film Production .... MA 12FT 24PT

Film making
Research Courses

Anglia Ruskin University
Film and Television Production .... MPhil 24FT/PhD 36FT

Bangor University
Creative and Critical Writing, Film and Media, Professional Writing .... MPhil 24FT 48PT/PhD 36FT 72PT
Creative and Critical Writing, Film and Media, Professional Writing: Practice-Led Research .... MPhil 24FT 48PT/PhD 36FT 72PT

University of Edinburgh
Film Studies .... PhD 36FT 72PT/MSc by research 12FT 24PT
Transdisciplinary Documentary Film .... PhD 36FT

University of Exeter
Film Studies .... MPhil 24FT 48PT/PhD 36-48FT 72PT
Interdisciplinary Studies .... MPhil 36FT 60PT/PhD 48FT 84PT

Goldsmiths, University of London
Visual Anthropology .... MRes 12FT 24PT
MPhil 24FT 36PT/PhD 36-48FT 48-72PT

University of Hull
Film Studies .... PhD 36FT 60PT/MPhil 24FT 36PT

University of Kent
Film .... PhD 36FT 60PT/MPhil 24FT 36PT/MA by research 12FT 24PT
Film (Practice by Research) .... MA by research 12FT 24PT/MPhil 24FT 36PT/PhD 36FT 60PT

King's College London
Film Studies Research .... PhD 36FT 48-72PT

Newcastle University
Film Studies .... MLitt by research 12FT 24PT
PhD 36FT 72PT/MPhil 12FT 24PT

Queen's University Belfast
Film Studies .... PhD 36FT 72PT/MPhil 24FT 48PT

University of Roehampton
Film and Television PhD 24-48FT 36-60PT/MPhil 21-36FT 33-48PT

University of Southampton
Film Studies .... PhD 48FT 84PT/MPhil 48FT 84PT

University of St Andrews
Film Studies .... PhD 36FT 72-84PT/MPhil 24FT 48PT

University of Wales Trinity Saint David
Film and Media .... PhD 36FT 48-72PT/MPhil 12-36FT

UCL - University College London
Film Studies .... PhD 36FT 60PT

Journalism
Taught Courses

University of the Arts London - London College of Fashion
Fashion Journalism .... MA 15FT 30PT
Fashion: Fashion & Lifestyle Journalism .... PGCert 4FT

Bangor University
Creative Practice .... MRes 12FT 24PT

University of Bedfordshire
International Journalism .... MA 12FT

Birkbeck, University of London
Journalism .... PGCert 12PT/MA 12FT 24PT

Birmingham City University
Broadcast Journalism .... PGDip 6FT
Freelancing and Journalism Enterprise .... MA 12FT 24PT
International Broadcast Journalism .... MA 12FT
International Journalism .... MA 12FT 24PT
Online Journalism .... MA 12FT 24PT 12-36DL

Bournemouth University
International Journalism .... MA 12FT
Journalism and New Media .... MA 12FT
Multimedia Journalism .... MA 12FT

University of Brighton
Media Ethics .... MA 12FT 24PT/PGDip 12FT 24PT/PGCert 12FT 24PT

Brunel University
Documentary Practice .... MA 12FT 24PT
International Journalism .... MA 12FT
Journalism (NCTJ accredited) .... MA 12FT 24PT

Cardiff University
International Journalism .... MA 12FT 36PT
Journalism .... PGDip 9FT
Journalism, Media and Communications .... MA 12FT

University of Central Lancashire
Broadcast Journalism .... PGDip 9FT/MA 12FT
Film Production MA 12FT 24PT/PGDip 9FT 24PT/PGCert 9FT 24PT
International Journalism .... MA 12FT
Journalism .... MA 12FT 36PT
Journalism Leadership .... MA 12FT 24PT/PGDip 9FT 18PT/PGCert 9FT 18PT
Journalism Practice .... MA 12FT 24-36PT/PGDip 9FT 18-24PT
Journalism Studies .... MA 12FT 24PT
Magazine Journalism .... MA 12FT/PGDip 9FT
Newspaper Journalism .... PGDip 9FT/MA 12FT

City University London
Broadcast Journalism/Television Journalism.. MA 10FT 24PT/MA 12FT
Erasmus Mundus Global Journalism Masters .... MA 24FT
Financial Journalism .... MA 10FT
Interactive Journalism .... MA 10FT
International Journalism .... MA 12FT
Investigative Journalism .... MA 10FT
Magazine Journalism .... MA 10FT
Newspaper Journalism .... MA 10FT
Political Journalism .... MA 12FT
Science Journalism .... MA 10FT

Coventry University
Automotive Journalism .... MA 12FT 24PT
Global Journalism .... MA 12FT 24PT
Health Journalism .... MA 12FT 24PT
Specialist Journalism .... MA 12FT 24PT

University for the Creative Arts
Fashion & Lifestyle Journalism .... MA 12FT

Dublin Institute of Technology
International Journalism .... MA 12FT
Journalism .... MA 12FT

Edinburgh Napier University
International Journalism for Media Professionals (Distance Learning) .... MA 12FT 24PT
Journalism .... MSc 12FT 24PT/PGDip 9FT 18PT

Falmouth University
International Journalism .... MA 12FT
Multimedia Broadcast Journalism .... MA 12FT

Farnborough College of Technology
Radio .... MA 12FT 24PT

National University of Ireland Galway
Journalism .... MA 12FT

Media studies and publishing

Glasgow Caledonian University
Creative and Cultural Business .... MA 12FT
Multimedia Communication .... MSc 12FT
Multimedia Journalism .... MA 12FT/PGDip 9PT

University of Glasgow
Film Journalism .... MLitt 12FT 24PT

University of Gloucestershire
Journalism .... MA 12FT/AdvPGDip 8FT/PGCert 4FT

Goldsmiths, University of London
Digital Journalism .... MA 12FT/MSc 12FT
Journalism .... MA 12FT
Television Journalism .... MA 12FT

Griffith College Dublin
Journalism and Media Communications .... PGDip 12FT 18PT

University of Kent
Arts Criticism .... MA 12FT 24PT
International Multimedia Journalism .... MA 12FT
Multimedia Journalism .... MA 12FT

Kingston University
Journalism .... MA 12FT 24PT/PGDip 12FT 24PT MFA 24FT 48PT
Journalism and the Creative Economy .... MA 12FT 24PT
Journalism in Open Societies .... MA 12FT 24PT

Leeds Trinity University
Broadcast Journalism .... MA 12-24PT/PGDip 10FT
Radio Journalism .... MA 12PT/PGDip 10FT
Print Journalism .... MA 12PT/PGDip 10FT

University of Leeds
International Journalism .... MA 12FT

University of Limerick
Journalism .... PGDip 9FT 18PT/MA 24FT

University of Lincoln
Journalism .... MA 12FT
Journalism, War and International Human Rights .... MA 12FT 24PT

Liverpool John Moores University
International Journalism ... PGCert 6FT/PGDip 9FT 21PT/MA 12FT 24PT

London Metropolitan University
Journalism .... MA 12FT 24-48PT

London South Bank University
Creative Media Industries: Journalism .... MA 13FT

University of the Arts London - London College of Communication
Broadcast Journalism .... PGDip 12FT
Documentary Film .... MA 12FT
Journalism - Print/Online Pathway .... MA 45 weeksFT
Journalism - Television Pathway .... MA 45 weeksFT

Manchester Metropolitan University
Multimedia Journalism .... MA 12FT 24PT

Middlesex University
Media and Communications Management .... MA 12FT 24PT

Newcastle University
International Multimedia Journalism .... MA 12FT
Media and Journalism .... MA 12FT 24PT

Nottingham Trent University
Newspaper Journalism .... MA 12FT 24PT/PGDip 9FT 21PT

Robert Gordon University
Journalism .... MSc 12FT

University Campus Suffolk
Journalism .... MA 12FT 24PT

University of Salford
International and Online Journalism .... MA 12FT 36PT
Journalism .... MA 12FT/PGDip 9FT MRes 12FT 24PT

Sheffield Hallam University
International Broadcast Journalism .... MA 15FT/PGDip 10FT/PGCert 5FT
Sports Journalism .... MA 12FT 36PT

University of Sheffield
Broadcast Journalism .... MA 12FT/PGDip 9FT
Global Journalism .... MA 12FT
International Political Communication .... MA 12FT
Journalism Studies (Broadcast) .... MA 12FT
Journalism Studies (Web) .... MA 12FT
Magazine Journalism .... MA 12FT/PGDip 9FT
Print Journalism .... MA 12FT/PGDip 9FT
Religion, Conflict and the Media .... MA 12FT 24PT
Web Journalism .... MA 12FT/PGDip 9FT

University of South Wales
Journalism .... MA 12FT 24PT
Journalism (International) .... MA 12FT 24PT

St Mary's University College, Twickenham
Sports Journalism .... MA 12FT/PGCert 12FT/PGA 12FT

Staffordshire University
Broadcast Journalism .... MA 12FT
Journalism .... MA 12FT 48PT
Sports Broadcast Journalism .... MA 12FT 48PT

University of Stirling
Media Research .... MRes 12FT/PGDip 9FT

University of Strathclyde
Digital Journalism .... MSc 12FT/PGDip 9FT
Investigative Journalism .... MSc 12FT 24PT/PGDip 9FT 21PT
Journalism .... MLitt 12FT/PGDip 9FT
Literary Journalism .... MLitt 12FT 24PT/PGDip 9FT 21PT

University of Sussex
International Journalism .... MA 12FT 24PT
Journalism and Documentary Practice .... MA 12FT 24PT
Journalism and Media Studies .... MA 12FT 24PT
Multimedia Journalism .... MA 12FT 24PT

Swansea University
Comparative Journalism .... MA 12FT 36PT
Journalism, Media and Globalization .... MA 24FT

Teesside University
Journalism .... MA 12FT 24PT

University of Ulster
Journalism .... MA 12FT

University of the West of England, Bristol
Journalism .... MA 12FT 28PT

University of Westminster
Medical Journalism .... GradDip 9FT
Multimedia Journalism (Broadcast) .... MA 12FT
Multimedia Journalism (Broadcast) .... PGDip 9PT
Multimedia Journalism (Print and Online) .... MA 12FT
Multimedia Journalism (Print and Online) .... PGDip 9PT

University of Winchester
Journalism .... MA 12FT/PGDip 12FT/PGCert 12FT

Journalism
Research Courses

Bangor University
Creative and Critical Writing, Film and Media, Professional Writing .... MPhil 24FT 48PT/PhD 36FT 72PT
Creative and Critical Writing, Film and Media, Professional Writing: Practice-Led Research . MPhil 24FT 48PT/PhD 36FT 72PT

University of Bedfordshire
Professional Doctorate in Journalism, Media, Cinema or Television .... PDJMCT 36PT

Cardiff University
Journalism Studies Group .... PhD 36FT possiblePT/MPhil 24FT possiblePT
Mediatized Conflict Group .... PhD 36FT possiblePT/MPhil 24FT possiblePT
Race, Representation and Cultural Identity Group .... PhD 36FT possiblePT/MPhil 24FT possiblePT
Risk, Science, Health and Media Group .... PhD 36FT possiblePT/MPhil 24FT possiblePT

University of Central Lancashire
Journalism .... PhD/MPhil/MA by research

City University London
Journalism .... PhD/MPhil

University of Kent
Journalism (Medway) .... MA by research 12FT 24PT/MPhil 24FT 36PT/PhD 36FT 60PT

Newcastle University
Media, Journalism and Public Relations .... PhD 36FT 72PT

Magazine journalism
Taught Courses

Cardiff University
Journalism .... PGDip 9FT

University of Central Lancashire
Broadcast Journalism .... PGDip 9FT/MA 12FT
Journalism .... MA 12FT 36PT
Journalism Practice .... MA 12FT 24-36PT/PGDip 9FT 18-24PT
Journalism Studies .... MA 12FT 24PT
Magazine Journalism .... MA 12FT/PGDip 9FT
Publishing .... MA 12FT 24PT/PGDip 9FT 18PT/PGCert 9FT 18PT

University of East London
Magazines ... MA 12FT 24PT/PGDip 12FT 24PT/PGCert 12FT 24PT

Edinburgh Napier University
International Journalism for Media Professionals (Distance Learning) .... MA 12FT 24PT
Journalism .... MSc 12FT 24PT/PGDip 9FT 18PT
Magazine Publishing .... MSc 12FT 24PT
Publishing .... MSc 12FT 24PT

Falmouth University
Professional Writing .... MA 12FT 24PT 24DL

Goldsmiths, University of London
Digital Journalism .... MA 12FT/MSc 12FT

Kingston University
Magazine Journalism .... MA 12FT 24PT/PGDip 12FT 24PT

Leeds Trinity University
Magazine Journalism .... PGDip 10FT/MA 12PT

University of Limerick
Journalism .... PGDip 9FT 18PT/MA 24FT

Nottingham Trent University
Magazine Journalism .... MA 12FT/PGDip 9FT

Plymouth University
Publishing .... MA 12FT 24PT/PGDip 12FT 24PT

Robert Gordon University
Journalism .... MSc 12FT

University of Salford
International and Online Journalism .... MA 12FT 36PT
Journalism .... MA 12FT/PGDip 9FT MRes 12FT 24PT

University of Sheffield
Web Journalism .... MA 12FT/PGDip 9FT

University of Strathclyde
Journalism .... MLitt 12FT/PGDip 9FT

University of Sunderland
Magazine Journalism .... MA 12FT 24PT

University of Sussex
Multimedia Journalism .... MA 12FT 24PT

University of the West of England, Bristol
Journalism .... MA 12FT 28PT

University of Westminster
Multimedia Journalism (Print and Online) .... MA 12FT
Multimedia Journalism (Print and Online) .... PGDip 9PT

Magazine journalism
Research Courses

Cardiff University
Journalism Studies Group .... PhD 36FT possiblePT/MPhil 24FT possiblePT

Media production
Taught Courses

Aberystwyth University
Cyfryngau Creadigol Ymarferol .... MA 12FT 24PT/PGDip 9FT 18PT
Scriptwriting (Screen and Radio). MA 12FT 24PT/PGDip 9FT 20PT

University of the Arts London - Central Saint Martins College of Art and Design
Screen: Directing, Writing - Drama Centre London .... MA 12FT

Bangor University
Creative Practice .... MRes 12FT 24PT
Filmmaking: Concept to Screen .... MA 12FT 24PT
International Media Management .... MSc 12FT 24PT

University of Bedfordshire
Documentary .... MA 12FT

Birmingham City University
Future Media .... MA 12FT/MSc 12FT

University of Birmingham
Film and Television: Research and Production .... MA 12FT 24PT

Arts University Bournemouth
Interactive Media .... MA 12FT 24PT

Bournemouth University
Scriptwriting .... MA 12FT
Sound Production for Film and Television .... MA 12FT

University of Bradford
Music Video Creation .... MA 12FT 24PT

University of Brighton
Digital Media Production .... MSc 12FT 24-60PT/PGDip 12FT 24-60PT/PGCert 12FT 24-60PT

University of Bristol
Archaeology for Screen Media .... MA 12FT 24PT

Brunel University
Documentary Practice .... MA 12FT 24PT

University of Cambridge
Screen Media and Cultures .... MPhil 9FT

Canterbury Christ Church University
Film Production .... MA 12FT

University of Central Lancashire
Film Production .... MA 12FT 24PT/PGDip 9FT 24PT/PGCert 9FT 24PT
Interaction Design .... MRes 12FT 24-36PT

Central School of Speech and Drama, University of London
Music Theatre .... MA 12FT

University of Chester
Popular Music ..... MA 12FT 24-72PT/PGDip 12FT 24-60PT/PGCert 12FT 12-36PT
Television Production ...... MA 12FT 24-72PT/PGDip 12FT 24-60PT

City University London
Audiovisual Translation / Audio Description .... MA 24PT

Coventry University
Media Production .... MA 12FT 24PT

Media studies and publishing

University of Dundee
Comics Studies ... MLitt 12FT
Film Studies ... MLitt 12FT
Product Design ... MSc 12FT

Edge Hill University
Media Production Management ... Executive MA 12FT 24PT

Edinburgh Napier University
Screen Project Development ... MA 12FT 24PT

University of Edinburgh
Media, Culture & Practice ... MSc 12FT
Transdisciplinary Documentary Film Practice ... MSc(Res) 12FT

Farnborough College of Technology
MA IN RADIO ... MA 12FT 24PT

National University of Ireland Galway
Production and Direction ... MA 12FT/PGDip 12FT
Screenwriting ... MA 12FT/PGDip 12FT

University of Gloucestershire
Film and Screen Enterprise .. MA 12FT/PGAdvDip 8FT/PGCert 4FT
Professional Media Practice ... MA 24PT

Goldsmiths, University of London
Creating Social Media ... MA 12FT 24PT/MSc 12FT 24PT
Design: Interaction Research ... MA 15FT 30PT
Screen Documentary ... MA 12FT

University of Hertfordshire
Animation ... MA 12FT 24PT/PGDip 12FT 24PT/PGCert 12FT 24PT
Film and Television ... MA 12FT 24PT/PGDip 12FT 24PT
Screen Cultures ... MA 12FT 24PT/PGDip 12FT 24PT
Special Effects ... MA 12FT 24PT/PGDip 12FT 24PT

Kingston University
Production Design for Film and Television ... MA 12FT

University of Leeds
Audiovisual Translation Studies ... MA 12FT 24PT

University of Limerick
Interactive Media ... MA 12FT/MSc 12FT

University of Lincoln
Media, Film and TV Production ... MA 12FT 24PT

London Metropolitan University
Product Design ... MA 12FT 24PT

University of the Arts London - London College of Communication
Broadcast Journalism ... PGDip 12FT
Documentary Film ... MA 12FT
Interactive Media ... MA 12FT

Newcastle University
Film: Theory and Practice ... MA 12FT 24PT

Newman University
Business and Media Production Foundation Degree ... FdA 24FT

Nottingham Trent University
Design for Film, Television and Events ... MA 12FT/PGDip 7FT/PGCert 4FT
Film Practice ... MA 12FT/PGDip 7FT/PGCert 4FT

Oxford Brookes University
Digital Media Production ... MSc 12FT 24PT
Digital Publishing ... MA 12FT 24PT/PGDip 9FT 18PT
Film Studies: Popular Cinema ... MA 12FT 24PT/PGDip 8FT 6-8PT/PGCert 4FT 6PT

University of Oxford
Film Aesthetics ... MSt 9FT

Plymouth University
Contemporary Film Practice ... MA 12FT
Film and Video ... MRes 12FT

Queen's University Belfast
Educational Multimedia ... MSc 12FT 24PT
English (Broadcast Literacy) ... MA 12FT 24PT
Film and Visual Studies ... MA 12FT up to 31PT

Ravensbourne
3D Stereoscopic Media ... MSc 12FT 24PT/MA 12FT 24PT
Broadcast Futures ... MA 12FT 24PT/MSc 12FT 24PT
Professional Media Practice ... MA 12FT 24PT

Rose Bruford College
Ensemble Theatre ... MA 12FT/PGDip 10FT

Royal Holloway, University of London
Documentary by Practice ... MA 12FT 24PT

University of Salford
Audio Production ... MSc 12FT 36PT
Children's Digital Media Production ... MA 12FT/PGDip 9FT
Fiction Film Production ... MA 12FT/PGDip 9FT
Film Screenwriting ... MA 15FT/PGDip 12FT/PGCert 6FT
International and Online Journalism ... MA 12FT 36PT
Post Production for TV and Film ... MA 12FT
Professional Sound and Video Technology ... MSc 12FT 36PT/PGDip 9FT 24PT
Television Documentary Production ... MA 12FT/PGDip 9FT
Wildlife Documentary Production ... MA 12FT

Sheffield Hallam University
Film Studies ... MA 12FT 36-72PT MPhil 36FT 84PT/PhD by taught 36FT 84PT
Film Studies with Screenwriting ... MA 12FT 24PT
Film and Media Production ... MA 18FT 36PT

University of Sheffield
Broadcast Journalism ... MA 12FT/PGDip 9FT
Global Journalism ... MA 12FT
Screen Translation ... MA 12FT 24PT
Sonic Arts ... MA 12FT 24PT

University of South Wales
Visual Effects ... MA 12FT 24PT

Southampton Solent University
Interactive Production ... MA 12FT 18PT/PGDip 9FT 12PT

University of Southampton
Film Studies ... MA 12FT 24PT
Film and Cultural Management ... MA 12FT 24PT

University of St Andrews
Film Studies ... MLitt 12FT 24PT/PGDip 9FT

Staffordshire University
Film Production Technology ... MSc 12-18FT
Film Production and Visual Cultures ... MA 12FT
Film Production: Theory and Practice ... MA 12FT

University of Stirling
Film Studies: Theory and Practice ... MLitt 12FT 27PT/PGDip 9FT 21PT/PGCert 3FT 6PT

University of Sunderland
Media Production (TV/Video) ... MA 12FT 24PT/PGDip 8FT 16PT/PGCert 4FT 8PT

University of Sussex
Creative Media Practice ... MA 12FT 24PT
Digital Documentary ... MA 12FT 24PT
Journalism and Documentary Practice ... MA 12FT 24PT
Music and Sonic Media ... MA 12FT 24PT

University of Ulster
Documentary Practice ... MA 12FT 24PT

UCL - University College London
Film Studies ... MA 12FT 24PT

University of West London
Film Finance ... MA 12FT 24PT
Video Production and Film Studies ... MA 12FT 24PT

York St John University
Documentary Production ... MA 24FT 12PT
Film Production ... MA 12FT 24PT

Media production
Research Courses

University of the Arts London - Central Saint Martins College of Art and Design
Theatre Design and Scenography ... PhD 24-48FT 36-96PT/MPhil 15-36FT 24-72PT

Bangor University
Creative and Critical Writing, Film and Media, Professional Writing ... MPhil 24FT 48PT/PhD 36FT 72PT
Creative and Critical Writing, Film and Media, Professional Writing: Practice-Led Research ... MPhil 24FT 48PT/PhD 36FT 72PT

University of Bedfordshire
Media ... MA by research 12FT/MPhil 24FT/PhD 36FT

University for the Creative Arts
Visual Identity and New Media MPhil 24FT 36PT/PhD 36FT 60PT

De Montfort University
Media Studies ... PhD 36-48FT 48-72PT/MPhil 12-24FT 24-48PT

University of Edinburgh
Transdisciplinary Documentary Film ... PhD 36FT

Newcastle University
Film Studies ... MLitt by research 12FT 24PT
Film Studies ... PhD 36FT 72PT/MPhil 12FT 24PT

Queen's University Belfast
Film Studies ... PhD 36FT 72PT/MPhil 24FT 48PT

University of Southampton
Film Studies ... PhD 48FT 84PT/MPhil 48FT 84PT

University of St Andrews
Film Studies ... PhD 36FT 72-84PT/MPhil 24FT 48PT

UCL - University College London
Film Studies ... PhD 36FT 60PT

Media studies
Taught Courses

Bangor University
Creative Practice ... MRes 12FT 24PT
Film and Visual Culture ... MRes 12FT 24PT
Filmmaking: Concept to Screen ... MA 12FT 24PT
International Media Management ... MSc 12FT 24PT

University of Bedfordshire
Intercultural Communication ... MA 12FT 24PT
Performing Before the Camera ... PGCert 3FT

Birkbeck, University of London
Creative Industries (Arts and Media) ... MA 12FT 24PT
Cultural Enquiry ... MRes 12FT 24PT
Japanese Cultural Studies/Japanese Creative Industries Studies. MA 12FT 24PT
Journalism ... PGCert 12PT/MA 12FT 24PT
Screenwriting ... PGCert 12PT/MA 24PT

Birmingham City University
Creative Industries and Cultural Policy ... MA 12FT 24PT 12-36DL
Future Media ... MA 12FT/MSc 12FT
Media Arts Philosophy Practice ... MA 12FT 24PT

Bournemouth University
Adaptation ... MA 12FT 24PT
Creative and Media Education ... MA 18PT
Journalism and New Media ... MA 12FT
Literary Media ... MA 12FT 24PT

University of Bradford
Media Studies ... MA 12FT 24PT 12DL

Brunel University
Media and Communications ... MSc 12FT
Media and Public Relations ... MA 12FT 24PT

University of Cambridge
Screen Media and Cultures ... MPhil 9FT

University of Central Lancashire
Broadcast Journalism ... PGDip 9FT/MA 12FT
International Journalism ... MA 12FT
Journalism ... MA 12FT 36PT
Journalism Practice ... MA 12FT 24-36PT/PGDip 9FT 18-24PT
Journalism Studies ... MA 12FT 24PT
Scriptwriting ... MA 12FT 24PT

City University London
Media and Communications ... MA 12FT 24PT
Translating Popular Culture ... MA 12FT 24PT
Transnational Media and Globalisation ... MA 12FT 24PT

Coventry University
Communication, Culture and Media ... MA 12FT 24PT

De Montfort University
Film/Media Studies by Independent Study ... MA 12-24DL

Dublin Institute of Technology
Media Studies ... MA 24PT

University of Dundee
Film Studies ... MLitt 12FT
Non-Graduating Taught Postgraduate in School of Humanities ... PG module variableFT

University of East Anglia
Media Economics ... MA 12FT
Media Law, Policy and Practice ... LLM 12FT 24PT
Media and Cultural Politics ... MA 12FT 24PT
Media and International Development ... MA 12FT 24PT
Media, Culture and Society ... MA 12FT 24PT

Edge Hill University
Critical Screen Practice ... MA 12FT 24PT
Media ... MRes 12FT 24PT

Edinburgh Napier University
Screen Project Development ... MA 12FT 24PT

University of Edinburgh
Media, Culture & Practice ... MSc 12FT
Science Communication and Public Engagement ... MSc 36DL/PGDip 24DL/PGCert 12DL

University of Exeter
European Media Studies with Integrated Study Abroad Option .. MA 12FT 24PT

National University of Ireland Galway
International Contemporary Literatures and Media ... MA 12FT 24PT
Public Advocacy and Activism ... MA 12FT/PGDip 12FT

Glasgow Caledonian University
Creative and Cultural Business ... MA 12FT
Multimedia Communication ... MSc 12FT

Glasgow School of Art
Digital Culture ... MDes 12FT 24PT/PGDip 9FT 21PT/PGCert 4FT 9PT

University of Gloucestershire
Media and Creative Enterprise ... MA 12FT/AdvPGDip 8FT/PGCert 4FT
Professional Media Practice ... MA 24PT

Goldsmiths, University of London
Creating Social Media ... MA 12FT 24PT/MSc 12FT 24PT
Film and Screen Studies ... MA 12FT 24PT
Gender, Media & Culture ... MA 12FT 24PT
Media and Communications ... MA 12FT 24PT
Media and Communications ... GradDip 12FT

Media studies and publishing

University of Greenwich
Media and Communication....MA 12FT 24PT
Media, Arts, Philosophy and Practice....MA 12FT 24PT

Griffith College Dublin
Journalism and Media Communications....PGDip 12FT 18PT

University of Hertfordshire
Special Effects....MA 12FT 24PT/PGDip 12FT 24PT

University of Hull
Advertising and Marketing....MSc 12FT

Institute of Education
Children's Media Culture....30 Credit Module 3PT
Computer Games, Culture and Education..30 Credit Module 3PT
Media, Culture and Education....MA 12FT 24-48PT
Youth Culture, Media and Education....30 Credit Module 3PT

Keele University
Global Media and Culture.MA 12 - 15FT 24 - 27PT/PGDip 9-12FT 21-24PT/PGCert 9-12FT 21-24PT
Media, Communications and Culture....MRes 12FT 24PT

University of Kent
International Multimedia Journalism....MA 12FT
Multimedia Journalism....MA 12FT

Kingston University
Corporate Communications....MA 12FT
Media and Communications....MA 12FT 24PT

Leeds Metropolitan University
Corporate Communications....MSc 36PT

University of Leeds
Communications Studies....MA 12FT
Media Management....MA 36PT

University of Leicester
Communications, Media and Public Relations (by Distance Learning)....MA 24FT/PGDip 20FT
Globalization and Communications....MA 12FT
Media and Communication Research....MSc 12FT
New Media and Society....MA 12FT
New Media, Governance and Democracy....MA 12FT

University of Lincoln
Media and Cultural Studies....MRes 12FT 24PT

London Metropolitan University
Media and Communications....MA 12FT

London School of Economics and Political Science (LSE)
Double Degree in Global Media and Communications MSc 12FT/MA 12FT
Media and Communications....MSc 12FT 24PT
Media and Communications (Media and Communication Governance)....MSc 12FT 24PT
Media, Communication and Development....MSc 12FT 24PT
Politics and Communication....MSc 12FT 24PT

London South Bank University
Media Writing....MA 24PT

Loughborough University
Global Media and Cultural Industries....MA 12FT
Media And Cultural Analysis....MA 12FT

University of Manchester
Corporate Communications and Reputation Management .. MSc 12FT

Middlesex University
Creative Technology....MA 12FT 24PT/MSc 12FT 24PT
Media Management....MSc 12FT 24PT

Newcastle University
Cross-Cultural Communication and Media StudiesMA 12FT 24PT

Newman University
Business and Media Production Foundation Degree....FdA 24FT

University of Nottingham
Health Communication by Web Based Distance Learning....MA 24-48DL

University of Oxford
Film Aesthetics....MSt 9FT

Queen's University Belfast
Communication....MSc 12FT 36PT/PGDip 12FT 24PT/PGCert 6FT 12PT/AdvPGDip 4FT 12PT

University of Roehampton
Film and Screen Cultures....MA 12FT 24-36PT

Royal College of Art
Communication Art and Design....MA 24FT

University of Salford
Digital Architectural Design....MSc 12FT 28PT/PGDip 8FT 16PT
Fiction Film Production....MA 12FT/PGDip 9FT
Film Screenwriting....MA 15FT/PGDip 12FT/PGCert 6FT
International and Online Journalism....MA 12FT 36PT
Journalism....MA 12FT/PGDip 9FT MRes 12FT 24PT
Research (Media)....MRes 12FT 24PT
Media Psychology....MSc 12FT 36PT/PGDip 8FT 24PT/PGCert 4FT 9PT
Post Production for TV and Film....MA 12FT
Social Media....MA 9FT/PGDip 9FT

School of Oriental and African Studies - SOAS
Anthropology of Media....MA 12FT 24-36PT
Global Media and Postnational Communication....MA 12FT 24-36PT
Media in the Middle East....MA 12FT

Sheffield Hallam University
Corporate Communication....MA 12-18FT 18-60PT 18-60DL/PGDip 8-12FT 24-36PT 24-26DL/PGCert 6FT 12-18PT 12-18DL

University of Sheffield
Broadcast Journalism....MA 12FT/PGDip 9FT
Global Journalism....MA 12FT
Journalism Studies (Broadcast)....MA 12FT
Journalism Studies (Web)....MA 12FT
Religion, Conflict and the Media....MA 12FT 24PT

University of South Wales
Visual Effects....MA 12FT 24PT

Southampton Solent University
Digital Marketing and Media....MA 12FT

University of Southampton
Film Studies....MA 12FT 24PT
Film and Cultural Management....MA 12FT 24PT

University of St Andrews
Film Studies....MLitt 12FT 24PT/PGDip 9FT

University of Stirling
Film Studies: Theory and Practice....MLitt 12FT 27PT/PGDip 9FT 21PT/PGCert 3FT 6PT
Media Management....MSc 12FT/PGDip 9FT
Media Research....MRes 12FT/PGDip 9FT

University of Strathclyde
Journalism....MLitt 12FT/PGDip 9FT

University of Sussex
Gender and Media Studies....MA 12FT 24PT
Media and Cultural Studies....MA 12FT 24PT

Swansea University
Communication, Media Practice and Public Relations....MA 12FT 24-36PT

University of Ulster
Communication, Advertising and Public Relations....MSc 12FT 36PT/PGDip 9FT 18PT
Media Management and Policy....MA 12FT 24PT

Webster Graduate School London
Media Communications....MA 14FT

University of West London
Corporate Communication....MSc 12FT 24PT
Media....MPhil 12FT 18-36PT/PhD by taught 36FT 36-60PT

University of the West of England, Bristol
Media Practice and Culture....MA 12FT

University of Westminster
Applied Sound for Interactive Media....MA 12FT 24PT
Communication Policy....MA 12FT 24-48PT
Diversity and the Media....MA 12FT
Global Media....MA 12FT
International Media Business....MA 12FT 24PT
Media Management....MA 12FT 24PT
Media and Development....MA 12FT
Social Media....MA 12FT 24PT

York St John University
MBA: Media Management....MBA 12FT 24 - 60PT

Media studies
Research Courses

University of the Arts London - Central Saint Martins College of Art and Design
Media and Communication Studies....PhD 24-48FT 36-96PT/MPhil 15-36FT 24-72PT

Bangor University
Creative and Critical Writing, Film and Media, Professional Writing....MPhil 24FT 48PT/PhD 36FT 72PT
Creative and Critical Writing, Film and Media, Professional Writing: Practice-Led Research....MPhil 24FT 48PT/PhD 36FT 72PT

University of Bedfordshire
Professional Doctorate in Journalism, Media, Cinema or Television....PDJMCT 36PT

Birkbeck, University of London
Arts and Humanities....MPhil 24FT 36PT/PhD 36-48FT 60-84PT
Film and Screen Media....MPhil 36FT 48PT/PhD 36FT 48PT

Birmingham City University
Media Research Degrees....PhD 36-42FT 48-72PT/MPhil 24-30FT 36-48PT

University of Bolton
Film and Media Studies Specialisms..PhD 36FT 72PT/MPhil 18FT 36PT

Brunel University
Doctoral Programme in Sociology & Communications....MPhil 12FT 24PT/MRes 12FT 24PT/PhD 36FT 60PT

Canterbury Christ Church University
Media and Cultural Studies....PhD 48FT 60PT/MPhil 24FT 48PT

Cardiff University
Centre for Global Communications Management Research..PhD 36FT
Feminist Media Studies....PhD 36FT possiblePT/MPhil 24FT possiblePT
Mediatized Conflict Group....PhD 36FT possiblePT/MPhil 24FT possiblePT
Race, Representation and Cultural Identity Group....PhD 36FT possiblePT/MPhil 24FT possiblePT
Risk, Science, Health and Media Group....PhD 36FT possiblePT/MPhil 24FT possiblePT

University of Central Lancashire
Arts and Media....PhD 30-48FT 66-84PT/MPhil 18-36FT 42-60PT/MA by research 12FT 24PT
Film and Media...PhD 18-36FT 42-60PT/MPhil 18-36FT 42-60PT/MA by research 12FT 24PT

De Montfort University
Media Studies....PhD 36-48FT 48-72PT/MPhil 12-24FT 24-48PT

Falmouth University
Research Art, Design, Media or Performance....PhD 24 -60FT 36-72PT

University of Gloucestershire
Media, Film and Communication Studies. PhD 30-48FT 48-84PT/MPhil 18-36FT 30-60PT/MA by research 12-24FT 18-36PT

Goldsmiths, University of London
Media and Communications...PhD 36-48FT 48-72PT/MPhil 24FT 36PT
Media and Communications....MRes 12FT 24PT

Keele University
Cultural and Media StudiesPhD 24-48FT 48-84PT/MPhil 12-24FT 24-36PT

University of Kent
Journalism (Medway)....MA by research 12FT 24PT/MPhil 24FT 36PT/PhD 36FT 60PT

Kingston University
Media, Film and Drama....PhD 48FT 72PT/MPhil 24FT 48PT/MA by research 12FT 24PT

Lancaster University
Media, Film and Cultural Studies....PhD 36FT 48PT/MPhil 24FT 36PT

University of Leeds
Institute of Communications Studies....PhD 36+FT/MPhil 24FT/MA by research 12FT/MSc by research 12FT

University of Leicester
Media and Communication....PhD 36FT/MPhil 24FT

Liverpool John Moores University
Media and Cultural Studies....MPhil 36FT 84PT/DPhil 36FT 84PT

University of Liverpool
Communication and Media....MPhil 24FT 36-60PT/PhD 12-48FT 48-84PT

London School of Economics and Political Science (LSE)
Media and Communications....PhD 36-48FT/MPhil 36-48FT

Loughborough University
Communication and Media Studies...PhD 36FT 60PT/MPhil 24FT 36PT

Manchester Metropolitan University
Communication Media....PhD/MPhil
Communication, Cultural and Media Studies....PhD 36FT 48PT 48DL/MPhil 18FT 36PT 36DL/MA by research 12FT 24PT 24DL
Department of Information and Communications....PhD 24-48FT 42-84PT 42-84DL/MPhil 18-36FT 36-72PT 36-72DL/MA by research 12-24FT 24-42PT 24-42DL

Newcastle University
Education and Communication....Integrated PhD 36-48FT

Nottingham Trent University
Communications, Cultural and Media Studies....PhD 48FT 96PT/MPhil 36FT 72PT

The Open University
Culture, Media and the Social...PhD 36FT 72PT variableDL/MPhil 15FT 24PT variableDL

University of Portsmouth
Creative Arts, Film and Media...MPhil 24FT 48PT/PhD 36FT 72PT

University of Salford
Media, Music and Performing Arts Research Centre....PhD/MPhil

University of Southampton
Film Studies....PhD 48FT 84PT/MPhil 48FT 84PT

University of St Andrews
Film Studies....PhD 36FT 72-84PT/MPhil 24FT 48PT

University of Sunderland
Media....PhD 30-48FT 42-72PT/MPhil 18-36FT 30-48PT

University of Sussex
Media and Cultural Studies Research Programme...PhD 24-48FT 36-72PT/MPhil 12-36FT 24-48PT

Media studies and publishing

Swansea University
Media and Communication Studies...MPhil 24FT 48PT/PhD 36FT 72PT

University of Ulster
Communication .... PhD 36FT 72PT/MPhil 24FT 48PT
Media Studies .... PhD 36FT 72PT/MPhil 24FT 48PT

University of Westminster
Media, Art and Design .... MPhil 18-36FT 30-60PT

University of York
Language and Communication .... PhD 36FT 72PT/MPhil 24FT 48PT

Media studies and publishing
Taught Courses

Aberystwyth University
Cyfryngau Creadigol Ymarferol.... MA 12FT 24PT/PGDip 9FT 18PT
Politics, Media and Performance .... MA 12FT 24PT

Anglia Ruskin University
Publishing .... MA 12FT

Bath Spa University
Advertising Practice .... MA 12FT 12DL

University of Bedfordshire
MA Mass Communications .... MA 12FT 24PT

Birkbeck, University of London
Creative Industries (Management) .... MSc 12FT 24PT
Film, Television and Screen Media .... MA 12FT 24PT

Birmingham City University
Media and Creative Enterprise .... MA 12FT 24PT

University of Birmingham
Critical Discourse, Culture and Communication .... MA 12FT

University of Brighton
Creative Media .... MA 12FT 24PT/PGDip 12FT variesPT/PGCert 12FT variesPT

Brunel University
Advanced Multimedia Design and 3D Technologies...... MSc 12FT 24PT
Digital Design and Branding .... MSc 12FT

University of Cambridge
Screen Media and Cultures .... MPhil 9FT

University of Central Lancashire
Publishing......... MA 12FT 24PT/PGDip 9FT 18PT/PGCert 9FT 18PT

City University London
Transnational Media and Globalisation .... MA 12FT 24PT

University of East Anglia
Broadcast Journalism: Theory and Practice .... MA 12FT 24PT
Media Economics .... MA 12FT

Edinburgh Napier University
Publishing .... MSc 12FT 24PT

University of Edinburgh
Digital Media and Culture .... MSc(Res) 12FT 24PT
Film Studies .... MSc 12FT 24PT
Film, Exhibition and Curation .... MSc 12FT 24PT
Media, Culture & Practice .... MSc 12FT

Glasgow Caledonian University
Multimedia Communication .... MSc 12FT

University of Glasgow
Media Management .... MSc 12FT

University of Gloucestershire
Professional Media Practice .... MA 24PT

Goldsmiths, University of London
Global Media and Transnational Communications MA 12FT 24PT

Lancaster University
Contemporary Arts (With pathways) .. MA 12FT 24PT/PGCert 6FT 12PT

University of Leicester
Mass Communications .... MA 12FT
Mass Communications (by Distance Learning) .. MA 24DL/PGDip 20DL/PGCert 12DL
New Media and Society (by Distance Learning).. MA 24FT/PGDip 20FT

University of Limerick
Journalism .... PGDip 9FT 18PT/MA 24FT
Technical Communication and E-Learning .... MA 12FT/PGDip 9FT 18PT/GradCert 9DL

University of Lincoln
Community Radio .... MA 12FT 24PT
Digital Journalism .... MA 12FT 24PT
Digital Media .... MA 12FT 24PT
Journalism .... MA 12FT
Journalism, War and International Human Rights MA 12FT 24PT
Media and Cultural Studies .... MRes 12FT 24PT
Media, Film and TV Production .... MA 12FT 24PT
Science and Environmental Journalism .... MA 12FT 24PT
Sports Journalism .... MA 12FT 24PT
Studies in Media and Culture .... MA 12FT 24PT

University of Liverpool
Politics and the Mass Media.. MA 12FT 24PT/PGDip 12FT/PGCert 12FT

London South Bank University
Cultural and Media Studies .... MA 24PT

University of the Arts London - London College of Communication
Media, Communications & Critical Practice .... MA 12FT

Manchester Metropolitan University
Film and Media Studies .... MA/MFA 12/24FT 24/48PT
Filmmaking .... MA/MFA 12/24FT 24/48PT
Media Arts .... MA/MFA 12/24FT 24/48PT
Photography .... MA/MFA 12/24FT 24/48PT

Middlesex University
Media and Communications Management .... MA 12FT 24PT

Newcastle University
Media and Journalism .... MA 12FT 24PT
Media and Public Relations .... MA 12FT 24PT

Newman University
Business and Media Production Foundation Degree ..... FdA 24FT

Norwich University of the Arts
Communication Design .... MA 12FT 24PT

Nottingham Trent University
Media and Globalisation .... MA 12FT 27PT/PGDip 9FT 18PT/PGCert 9FT

Oxford Brookes University
Digital Publishing .... MA 12FT 24PT/PGDip 9FT 18PT
Publishing .... MA 12FT 24PT/PGDip 9FT 18PT
Publishing (by distance learning)/........ MA 24PT/PGDip 18PT/PGCert 12PT

Queen Mary, University of London
Computer and Communications Law .... LLM 12FT 24PT
Media Law .... LLM 12FT 24PT

Queen's University Belfast
Irish-Medium Film and Script Production ...... MA 12FT up to 31PT

Ravensbourne
Communication Design .... MA 12FT 24PT
Professional Media Practice .... MA 12FT 24PT

University of Roehampton
Audiovisual Translation .... MA 12FT 24PT

Royal College of Art
Communication Art and Design .... MA 24FT

University of Salford
Art and Design: Communication Design .... MA 12FT 24PT/PGDip 8FT 15PT
Children's Digital Media Production .... MA 12FT/PGDip 9FT
Post Production for TV and Film .... MA 12FT
Television Documentary Production .... MA 12FT/PGDip 9FT

School of Oriental and African Studies - SOAS
Global Media and Postnational Communication .... MA 12FT 24-36PT
Media in the Middle East .... MA 12FT

Sheffield Hallam University
Communication and Media .... MA 12FT 36PT

University of Sheffield
Print Journalism .... MA 12FT/PGDip 9FT

University of South Wales
Media, Culture and Communication .... MA 12FT 24PT

University of Southampton
Digital Marketing .... MSc 12FT

Staffordshire University
Digital Feature Film Production .... MSc 12-18FT
Film Production Technology .... MSc 12-18FT
Film Production and Visual Cultures .... MA 12FT
Film Production: Theory and Practice .... MA 12FT
Journalism .... MA 12FT 48PT
Sports Broadcast Journalism .... MA 12FT 48PT

University of Stirling
Film Studies: Theory and Practice ...... MLitt 12FT 27PT/PGDip 9FT 21PT/PGCert 3FT 6PT
Media Management .... MSc 12FT/PGDip 9FT
Media Research .... MRes 12FT/PGDip 9FT
Media and Communications Management (Vietnam) . MSc 16FT 27PT
Publishing Studies .... MLitt 12FT 27PT/PGDip 9FT 21PT MRes 12FT 27PT/PGCert 9FT 18PT
Strategic Communication & Public Relations (Joint Degree)......... MSc 12FT/PGDip 9FT/PGCert 3FT
Strategic Public Relations & Communication Management .... MSc 12FT 24PT/PGDip 9FT 21PT
Strategic Public Relations (Double Degree with Lund University).. .... MSc 16/21FT/PGCert 3FT
Strategic Public Relations (Online) .... MSc 30DL/PGDip 20DL

University of Sunderland
Media & Cultural Studies .... MA 12FT 24PT/PGDip 15FT 10PT/PGCert 7FT 7PT
Media Production (TV/Video)...... MA 12FT 24PT/PGDip 8FT 16PT/PGCert 4FT 8PT
News Journalism .... MA 12FT

University of Sussex
Media Practice for Development and Social Change .... MA 12FT 24PT

Swansea University
Communication, Media Practice and Public Relations .... MA 12FT 24-36PT
Comparative Journalism .... MA 12FT 36PT
Journalism, Media and Globalization .... MA 24FT

Teesside University
Mass Communications .... MA 12FT 24PT

University of Warwick
Creative and Media Enterprises .... MA 12FT 24PT
Translation, Media and Cultural Transfer .... MA 12FT 24PT/Diploma 9FT 18PT

University of Westminster
Media and Development .... MA 12FT

University of Winchester
Theatre and Media for Development .... MA 12FT 24PT/PGDip 12FT 24PT/PGCert 12FT 24PT

University of York
Contemporary Cinema and Television .... MA 12FT 24PT
Digital Film and Television Production .... MA 12FT
Postproduction with Sound Design .... MA 12FT/MSc 12FT
Postproduction with Visual Effects .... MA 12FT/MSc 12FT

Media studies and publishing
Research Courses

Anglia Ruskin University
Children's Book Illustration .... MPhil 24FT/PhD 36FT
Creative Writing .... MPhil 24FT/PhD 36FT
Film Studies and Media Studies .... MPhil 24FT/PhD 36FT
Film and Television Production .... MPhil 24FT/PhD 36FT
Graphic Design and Typography .... MPhil 24FT/PhD 36FT
Publishing .... MPhil 24FT/PhD 36FT
Sound and Audio Engineering ...... MPhil 18 - 36FT 30 - 48PT/PhD 24 - 60FT 36 - 72PT

University of Bedfordshire
Research in Media .... MA by research 12FT/MPhil 24FT/PhD 36PT

Birmingham City University
Media Research Degrees .... PhD 36-42FT 48-72PT/MPhil 24-30FT 36-48PT

Cardiff University
Audience and Fan Studies .... PhD 36FT possiblePT/MPhil 24FT possiblePT

University of Central Lancashire
Arts and Media.... PhD 30-48FT 66-84PT/MPhil 18-36FT 42-60PT/MA by research 12FT 24PT

University for the Creative Arts
Media Arts and Communications Design .... PhD 36FT 60PT/MPhil 24FT 36PT
Visual Identity and New Media MPhil 24FT 36PT/PhD 36FT 60PT

University of Edinburgh
Film Studies .... PhD 36FT 72PT/MSc by research 12FT 24PT

University of Exeter
Film Studies .... MPhil 24FT 48PT/PhD 36-48FT 72PT

King's College London
Culture, Media & Creative Industries Research... PhD 36FT/MPhil 36FT

University of Lincoln
Journalism .... MPhil 12FT 24PT/PhD 12FT 24PT

Liverpool John Moores University
Media, Critical and Creative ArtsMPhil 36FT 84PT/PhD 36FT 84PT

London Metropolitan University
Sir John Cass Department of Art Media and Design....... PhD Max 60FT Max 96PT/MPhil Max 36FT Max 54PT

Newcastle University
Media, Journalism and Public Relations .... PhD 36FT 72PT

Oxford Brookes University
Publishing .... MPhil/PhD 36-60FT 48-72PT/PhD 24-60FT 36-72PT/MPhil 24-36FT 36-48PT

University of Portsmouth
Art, Design and Media .... MPhil 24FT 48PT/PhD 36FT 72PT

Royal College of Art
Communication Art and Design......... PhD/MPhil/MA by research

Royal Holloway, University of London
Media Arts .... PhD 36FT 48PT/MPhil 24FT 36PT

Southampton Solent University
Media Arts Research Centre .... PhD/MPhil

Media studies and publishing

Swansea University
Digital Humanities.....MA by research 12FT 24PT
Digital Media...MA by research 12FT 24PT/MPhil 24FT 48PT/PhD 36FT 72PT

University of Worcester
Film Studies .....PhD 48FT 70PT/MPhil 24FT 48PT

University of York
Language and Communication .....PhD 36FT 72PT/MPhil 24FT 48PT

Music management
Taught Courses

Birmingham City University
Music Industries.....MA 12FT 24PT 12-36DL

Bucks New University
Music and Entertainment Management .....MA 12FT 24PT

University of Central Lancashire
Music Industry Management and Promotion .....MSc 12FT 24PT

University of Chester
Popular Music..... MA 12FT 24-72PT/PGDip 12FT 24-60PT/PGCert 12FT 12-36PT

University for the Creative Arts
Creative Industries Management .....MBA 12FT

Goldsmiths, University of London
Creative and Cultural Industries.....GradDip 12FT
Music.....GradDip 12FT
Music (MMus) including specialist pathways....MMus 12FT 24PT

University of Huddersfield
MMus.....MMus 12FT 24PT
Performance .....PGDip 12FT

Kingston University
Production of Popular Music.....MMus 12FT 24PT

Leeds Metropolitan University
Music Production .....MA 12FT 24PT

University of Liverpool
Music Industry Studies .....MA 12FT 24PT
Popular Music Studies.....MA 12FT 24PT

Northumbria University
Business with Music Management .....MSc 12FT
Master of Fine Art .....MFA 24FT 48PT
Music Management .....MA 12/18FT 24/28PT 24/28DL

University of Salford
Children's Digital Media Production .....MA 12FT/PGDip 9FT
Digital Performance.....MA 12FT 36PT/PGDip 8FT 24PT
Media.....MRes 12FT 24PT
Music .....MRes 12FT 24PT
Performance .....MRes 12FT 24PT
Music .....MA 12FT 24PT
Social Media.....MA 9FT/PGDip 9FT
Television Documentary Production .....MA 12FT/PGDip 9FT

School of Oriental and African Studies - SOAS
Music and Development .....MA 12FT 24PT

University of Sheffield
Music Management .....MA 12FT 24PT
Music Performance.....MA 12FT 24PT

University of Southampton
Music .....MRes 12FT 24PT

University of St Andrews
Managing in the Creative Industries (collab).....MLitt 12FT

University of West London
Music Industry Management and Artist Development ..MA 12FT 24PT/PGDip 12FT 24PT/PGCert 12FT 24PT
Record Production .....MA 12FT 24PT

University of Westminster
Music Business Management.....MA 12FT 24-48PT

Music management
Research Courses

University of Aberdeen
Music .....PhD 36FT/MPhil 24FT

University of Bolton
Supply Chain, Business IT, Music and Creative Industries Management Specialisms........... MPhil 18FT 24 - 42PT/PhD 36FT 48 - 72PT

University of Oxford
Music .....DPhil 48FT

University of Salford
Media, Music and Performing Arts Research Centre....PhD/MPhil

Photography and cinematics
Taught Courses

Anglia Ruskin University
Photography .....MA 12FT 24PT

University of the Arts London - Central Saint Martins College of Art and Design
Art and Science .....MA 24FT
Art: Moving Image .....MRes 24FT
Photography .....MA 24FT

University of the Arts London - London College of Fashion
Fashion Photography.....MA 15FT 30PT

Bangor University
Creative Practice .....MRes 12FT 24PT
Film and Visual Culture.....MRes 12FT 24PT
Filmmaking: Concept to Screen.....MA 12FT 24PT
Fine Art.....MA 36PT

Birkbeck, University of London
History of Art with Photography.....MA 12FT 24PT

Birmingham City University
Freelance Photography .....MA 12FT 24PT

University of Bolton
Photography .....MA 12FT 24-36PT

Arts University Bournemouth
Photography .....MA 12FT 24PT

University of Brighton
Photography .....MA 12FT 24-72PT

University of Central Lancashire
Photography MA 12FT 24PT/PGDip 12FT 24PT/PGCert 12FT 24PT

University College Cork
English (American Literature & Film).....MA 12FT
Film Studies .....MA 9FT

Coventry University
Photography .....MA 12FT 24PT

University for the Creative Arts
Artists' Film, Video and Photography.....MA 12FT
Graduate Certificate in Contemporary Practice ....GradCert 3FT
Photography .....MA 12FT 24PT
Photography .....MA 24FT

University of Cumbria
Photography .....MA 12FT 24PT

De Montfort University
Photographic History and Practice .....MA 12FT 24PT
Photography .....MA 12FT 24PT/PGDip 9FT 18PT

University of Derby
Still and Moving Image.....MA 12FT

University of East Anglia
Film Studies .....MA 12FT 24PT
Film Studies with Archiving.....MA 12FT 24PT
Film, Television and Creative Practice .....MA 12FT 24PT

University of East London
Photography .....MA 12FT 24PT/PGDip 8FT 16PT/PGCert 4FT 8PT

Edinburgh Napier University
Film .....MA 12FT 24PT

University of Edinburgh
Composition for Screen .....MSc 12FT 24PT
Film Studies .....MSc 12FT 24PT
Film, Exhibition and Curation.....MSc 12FT 24PT
Transdisciplinary Documentary Film Practice......... MSc(Res) 12FT

University of Exeter
Independent Film Business.....MA 12FT 24PT

National University of Ireland Galway
Film Studies (Film, Culture, and Society)..... MA 12FT/PGDip 12FT
Production and Direction .....MA 12FT/PGDip 12FT

Glasgow School of Art
Photography .....PGCert 4FT/PGDip 8FT/MDes 12FT

Goldsmiths, University of London
Aural and Visual Cultures .....MA 12FT 24PT
Contemporary Art History.....GradDip 12FT 24PT
Global Arts .....MA 12FT 24PT
Photography and Urban Cultures .....MA 12FT 24PT
Photography: The Image and Electronic Arts.....MA 12FT

University of Hertfordshire
Digital and Lens Art ....MA 12FT 24PT/PGDip 12FT 24PT/PGCert 12FT 24PT
Photographic Media .....MA 12FT 24PT/PGDip 12FT 24PT

University of Kent
Fine Art.....MA 12FT 24PT
Visual Anthropology.....MA 12FT 24PT

Kingston University
Photography .....MA 12FT 24PT

University of Leeds
World Cinemas.....MA 12FT 24PT
World Cinemas.....MA 12FT 24PT

London Metropolitan University
Photography .....MA 12FT 24PT

London South Bank University
Digital Photography.....MA 24PT
Photographic Cultures .....MA 12FT

University of the Arts London - London College of Communication
Photography .....MA 12FT 24PT
Photography Portfolio Development .....PGDip 30 weeksFT
Photojournalism & Documentary Photography .....MA 12FT

Middlesex University
Film, Television, Animation .....MA 12FT 24PT
Photography .....MA 12FT 24PT

Newcastle University
Film: Theory and Practice .....MA 12FT 24PT

University of Northampton
Design (Photographic Communication).....MA 12FT 24PT

Nottingham Trent University
Film Practice.....MA 12FT/PGDip 7FT/PGCert 4FT
Photography .....MA 12FT/PGDip 7FT/PGCert 4FT

Oxford Brookes University
Film Studies: Popular Cinema .....MA 12FT 24PT/PGDip 8FT 6-8PT/PGCert 4FT 6PT

University of Oxford
Film Aesthetics.....MSt 9FT

Plymouth University
Contemporary Art Practice .....MA 12FT
Photographic Arts .....MFA 18FT
Photography .....MA 12FT

Queen's University Belfast
Film and Visual Studies.....MA 12FT up to 31PT

University of Roehampton
Media, Culture and Identity.....PGDip 9FT 24PT

Royal College of Art
Photography .....MA 24FT

University Campus Suffolk
Photographic Practice .....MA 12FT 24PT

University of Salford
Fiction Film Production .....MA 12FT/PGDip 9FT
Film Screenwriting.....MA 15FT/PGDip 12FT/PGCert 6FT

Sheffield Hallam University
Film Studies .....MA 12FT 36-72PT MPhil 36FT 84PT/PhD by taught 36FT 84PT
Film Studies with Screenwriting .....MA 12FT 24PT

Sotheby's Institute of Art
Photography: Contemporary & Historical .....MA 14FT/PGDip 9FT

University of Southampton
Film Studies .....MA 12FT 24PT
Film and Cultural Management .....MA 12FT 24PT

University of St Andrews
Film Studies .....MLitt 12FT 24PT/PGDip 9FT

Staffordshire University
Clinical Photography .....GradCert 12DL
Film Production Technology .....MSc 12-18FT
Film Production and Visual Cultures .....MA 12FT

University of Stirling
Film Studies: Theory and Practice ......MLitt 12FT 27PT/PGDip 9FT 21PT/PGCert 3FT 6PT

University of Sunderland
Photography.... MA 12FT 24PT/PGDip 10FT 15PT/PGCert 7FT 7PT

University of Sussex
Creative Media Practice .....MA 12FT 24PT
Literature, Film and Visual Culture .....MA 12FT 24PT

Swansea University
Communication, Media Practice and Public Relations ....MA 12FT 24-36PT

Swansea Metropolitan University
Photography .....MA 24FT 36PT

University of Ulster
Photography .....MFA 9FT

UCL - University College London
Film Studies .....MA 12FT 24PT

University of West London
Film Finance.....MA 12FT 24PT
Photography .....MA 12FT 24PT

University of Westminster
Photographic Studies .....MA 12FT 24-60PT

Photography and cinematics
Research Courses

Bangor University
Creative and Critical Writing, Film and Media, Professional Writing .....MPhil 24FT 48PT/PhD 36FT 72PT
Creative and Critical Writing, Film and Media, Professional Writing: Practice-Led Research . MPhil 24FT 48PT/PhD 36FT 72PT

University of Bolton
Film and Media Studies Specialisms ..PhD 36FT 72PT/MPhil 18FT 36PT

Media studies and publishing

University for the Creative Arts
Media Arts and Communications Design...PhD 36FT 60PT/MPhil 24FT 36PT
Photography.......MPhil 24FT 36PT/PhD 36FT 60PT

De Montfort University
Photographic Studies and Creative Imaging.......MPhil 12-24FT 24-48PT/PhD 24-36FT 36-72PT

University of Edinburgh
Film Studies.......PhD 36FT 72PT/MSc by research 12FT 24PT
Transdisciplinary Documentary Film.......PhD 36FT
Visual and Cultural Studies.......PhD 24FT 36PT/MPhil 12FT 24PT

University of Exeter
Art History and Visual Culture..MPhil 36FT 60PT 60DL/PhD 48FT 84PT 84DL
Film Studies.......MPhil 24FT 48PT/PhD 36-48FT 72PT

University of Gloucestershire
Art and Design.......PhD 30-48FT

Goldsmiths, University of London
Visual Sociology.......MPhil 24FT 36PT/PhD 36-48FT 48-72PT

University of Kent
Fine Art.......PhD 36FT 60PT

Lancaster University
Media, Film and Cultural Studies.......PhD 36FT 48PT/MPhil 24FT 36PT

Newcastle University
Film Studies.......MLitt by research 12FT 24PT
Film Studies.......PhD 36FT 72PT/MPhil 12FT 24PT

Queen's University Belfast
Film Studies.......PhD 36FT 72PT/MPhil 24FT 48PT

Royal College of Art
Photography.......PhD/MPhil/MA by research
Photography.......PhD/MPhil/MA by research

University of Southampton
Film Studies.......PhD 48FT 84PT/MPhil 48FT 84PT

University of St Andrews
Film Studies.......PhD 36FT 72-84PT/MPhil 24FT 48PT
History of Photography.......PhD 36FT 72PT/MPhil 24FT 48PT

UCL - University College London
Film Studies.......PhD 36FT 60PT

Photojournalism
Taught Courses

Anglia Ruskin University
Photography.......MA 12FT 24PT

Arts University Bournemouth
Photography.......MA 12FT 24PT

University of Central Lancashire
Broadcast Journalism.......PGDip 9FT/MA 12FT
Journalism.......MA 12FT 36PT
Journalism Practice.......MA 12FT 24-36PT/PGDip 9FT 18-24PT
Journalism Studies.......MA 12FT 24PT
Photography.......MA 12FT 24PT/PGDip 12FT 24PT/PGCert 12FT 24PT

University of Cumbria
Photography.......MA 12FT 24PT

University of Derby
Still and Moving Image.......MA 12FT

London Metropolitan University
Photography.......MA 12FT 24PT

University of the Arts London - London College of Communication
Photography Portfolio Development.......PGDip 30 weeksFT
Photojournalism & Documentary Photography.......MA 12FT
Photojournalism & Documentary Photography (Online Mode)...MA 24PT

University of South Wales
Contemporary Photography Practice.......MFA 18FT
Documentary Photography...MA 12 - 18FT 24PT/MFA 24FT 36PT

Staffordshire University
Clinical Photography.......GradCert 12DL

University of Ulster
Documentary Practice.......MA 12FT 24PT

University of Westminster
Photographic Studies.......MA 12FT 24-60PT
Photojournalism.......MA 12FT 24PT

Photojournalism
Research Courses

University for the Creative Arts
Photography.......MPhil 24FT 36PT/PhD 36FT 60PT

University of Manchester
Ethnographic Documentary.......MPhil 12FT 24PT
Social Anthropology with Visual Media......PhD 48FT 84PT/MPhil 12FT 24PT

Political communication
Taught Courses

Aberystwyth University
Politics, Media and Performance.......MA 12FT 24PT

University of Bath
Global Political Economy: transformations and policy analysis ... MRes 12FT 24-36PT

Brunel University
Public Affairs & Lobbying.......MSc 15FT 30PT

Cardiff University
Legal and Political Aspects of International Affairs.......LLM 12FT
Political Communications.......MA 12FT

University of Central Lancashire
Global Communication Studies.......MA 12FT 24-36PT

University of Chester
Faiths and Public PolicyMA 12FT 36PT 36DL/PGDip 12FT 24-36PT 24-36DL/PGCert 12FT 12-24PT 12-24DL

City University London
International Communications and Development.......MA 12FT 24PT
Media and Communications.......MA 12FT 24PT
Political Communication.......MA 12FT 24PT

University College Cork
Government.......MBS 12FT 24PT
Politics.......MA 12FT

Coventry University
Communication, Culture and Media.......MA 12FT 24PT
Global Journalism.......MA 12FT 24PT

Dublin Institute of Technology
Public Affairs and Political Communications.......MA 12FT

University College Dublin
Politics.......MA 12FT/MLitt 24FT

University of East Anglia
International Public Policy and Public Management...MRes 12FT 24PT
International Relations.......MA 12FT 24PT
Media Economics.......MA 12FT
Media Law, Policy and Practice.......LLM 12FT 24PT
Media and Cultural Politics.......MA 12FT 24PT
Media, Culture and Society.......MA 12FT 24PT
Public Policy and Public Management.......MRes 12FT 24PT

University of Edinburgh
Science Communication and Public Engagement.......MSc 12FT

University of Essex
Global Project Management.......MSc 12FT 24PT

University of Exeter
Food Security and Sustainable Agriculture.......MSc 12FT 24PT

National University of Ireland Galway
Public Advocacy and Activism.......MA 12FT/PGDip 12FT

Glasgow Caledonian University
Multimedia Communication.......MSc 12FT

University of Glasgow
Political Communication...MSc 12FT 24PT/PGDip 9FT MRes 12FT 24PT

Goldsmiths, University of London
Media and Communications.......GradDip 12FT MA 12FT 24PT
Political Communications.......MA 12FT 24PT

University of Hull
Global Communication and International Politics.......MA 12FT 24PT

University of Kent
International Relations (Brussels).......MA 12FT 24PT/PGDip 12FT 24PT
International Relations (international double award) (Canterbury, Moscow).......MA 24FT
International Relations with International Law....MA 12FT 24PT/PGDip 12FT 24PT
International Security and the Politics of TerrorPGDip 12FT 24PT/MA 12FT 24PT
Peace and Conflict Studies (International Double Award).......MA 24FT
Political Strategy and Communication (Brussels).. MA 12FT 24PT
Political Theory and Practices of ResistancePGDip 12FT 24PT/MA 12FT 24PT

Kingston University
International Political Communication, Advocacy and Campaigning.......MSc 12FT 24PT
Political Communication, Advocacy and Campaigning. MSc 12FT 24PT

Leeds Metropolitan University
International Communication.......MA 12FT

University of Leeds
Global Development.......MA 12FT 24PT
Global Development and Education.......MA 12FT 24PT
Global Development and International Political Economy......MA 12FT 24PT

International Communications.......MA 12FT
Political Communication.......MA 12FT
Politics.......MA 12FT 24PT
Politics (Political Theory).......MA 12FT 24PT

University of Leicester
New Media, Governance and Democracy (by Distance Learning) MA 24FT/PGDip 20FT
Political Research.......MSc 12FT 24PT/PGDip 9FT 18PT

University of Limerick
Politics.......MA 12FT

University of Liverpool
Politics and the Mass Media.. MA 12FT 24PT/PGDip 12FT/PGCert 12FT

London School of Economics and Political Science (LSE)
Double Degree in Global Media and Communications MSc 12FT/MA 12FT
Media and Communications.......MSc 12FT 24PT
Media and Communications (Media and Communication Governance).......MSc 12FT 24PT
Media, Communication and Development.......MSc 12FT 24PT
Politics and Communication.......MSc 12FT 24PT

Newcastle University
International Politics (Global Justice and Ethics)... MA 12FT 24PT

Nottingham Trent University
Politics.......MA 12FT 24PT

The Open University
Systems Thinking in Practice.......MSc variableDL/PGCert variableDL/PGDip variableDL

University of Oxford
Global Governance and Diplomacy.......MSc 12FT
International Relations.......MPhil 21FT
International Summer School in Forced Migration.......Cert less than 1FT

Queen Mary, University of London
Health Systems and Global Policy.......MSc 12FT 24-48PT

Queen's University Belfast
Political Psychology.......MSc 12FT 24PT
Politics.......MA 12FT 24PT

University of Reading
Communication for Innovation and Development.......MSc 12FT 24PT
Diplomacy....MA 12FT 72PT/PGDip 12FT 72PT/PGCert 12FT 72PT
Public Policy.......MA 12FT 24PT 72BM

Royal Holloway, University of London
New Political Communication.......MSc 12/9FT 24/20PT
Political Research.......MSc 12/9FT 24/20PT
Political Theory.......MSc 12/9FT 24/20PT

University of Salford
International Relations and Globalisation...MA 12FT 36PT 36DL/PGDip 8FT 24PT 36DL
Terrorism and Security......MA 12FT 36PT 36DL/PGDip 12FT 36PT 36DL

School of Oriental and African Studies - SOAS
African Politics.......MSc 12FT 24-36PT
Anthropology of Media.......MA 12FT 24-36PT
Asian Politics.......MSc 12FT 24PT
Dispute and Conflict Resolution.......MA 12FT 24PT
International Politics.......MSc 12FT 24PT
International Studies and Diplomacy....MA 12FT 24-36PT/PGDip 12FT 24PT
Media in the Middle East.......MA 12FT
Middle East Politics.......MSc 12FT 24PT
Politics of China.......MSc 12FT 24PT
Postcolonial Studies.......MA 12FT 24PT
Violence, Conflict and Development.......MSc 12FT 24PT

University of Sheffield
Comparative Governance and Public Policy.......MA 12FT 24PT
European Governance and Politics.......MA 12FT 24PT
European Law, Politics and Governance.......MA 12FT
European and Global Affairs.......MA 24FT
Global Justice.......MA 12FT 24PT
Global Politics and Law.......MA 12FT 24PT
Global Politics and Law (Doshisha Pathway).......MA 24FT
Globalisation and Development.......MA 12FT 24PT
International Political Communication.......MA 12FT

University of Southampton
European Law.......LLM 12FT 24PT
Global Politics.......MSc 12FT 24PT/PGDip 9FT 21PT
Global Politics (Research).......MSc 12FT 24PT/PGDip 9FT 21PT
Global Security.......MSc 12FT 24PT/PGDip 9FT 21PT

University of St Andrews
International Political Theory.......MLitt 12FT 24PT/MPhil 24FT

University of Stirling
Strategic Communication & Public Relations (Joint Degree)....... MSc 12FT/PGDip 9FT/PGCert 3FT
Strategic Public Relations & Communication Management....... MSc 12FT 24PT/PGDip 9FT 21PT

Media studies and publishing

Strategic Public Relations (Double Degree with Lund University).. ...MSc 16/21FT/PGCert 3FT
Strategic Public Relations (Online)...MSc 30DL/PGDip 20DL

University of Surrey
International Politics...MA 12FT 24PT
Politics...MA 12FT 24PT

Swansea University
Communication, Media Practice and Public Relations....MA 12FT 24-36PT
Politics...MA 12FT 24PT

Teesside University
Mass Communications...MA 12FT 24PT

Trinity College Dublin - the University of Dublin
International Politics...MSc 12FT 24PT
Political Science...MSc 12FT 24PT

University of Ulster
Political Lobbying and Public Affairs....MSc 12FT 36PT/PGDip 9FT 24PT

UCL - University College London
Institutions, Development and Globalisation...MA 12FT 24PT
Politics, Security and Integration...MA 12FT 24PT

University of Westminster
Communication Policy...MA 12FT 24-48PT
International Liaison and Communication...MA 12FT 24PT

Political communication
Research Courses

School of Advanced Study, University of London
Politics and International Studies.......PhD 36FT 72PT/MPhil 12FT 36PT

University of Bath
Global Political Economy: transformations and policy analysis (delivered collaboratively w...MRes 12FT 24-36PT

University of Cambridge
Politics and International Studies...PhD 36FT

Cardiff University
Centre for Global Communications Management Research ..PhD 36FT

University College Dublin
Politics...PhD 36FT/MLitt by research 24FT

University of East Anglia
Political, Social and International Studies...PhD 36FT 72PT/MPhil 24FT 48PT/MA by research 12FT 24PT

Goldsmiths, University of London
Media and Communications...MRes 12FT 24PT

University of Kent
International Relations (Brussels or Canterbury).PhD 36FT 60PT/MPhil 24FT 36PT/MA by research 12FT 24PT

University of Liverpool
Politics...PhD 24-48FT 48-84PT/MPhil 12-48FT 24-72PT

Manchester Metropolitan University
Politics...PhD 24-48FT 42-84PT 42-84DL/MPhil 18-36FT 36-72PT 36-72DL/MA by research 12-24FT 24-42PT 24-42DL

Newcastle University
Politics...PhD 36FT 72PT/MPhil 12FT 24PT

University of Nottingham
School of Politics MRes...MRes 12FT 24PT

The Open University
Comparative Politics...PhD 36FT 72PT variableDL/MPhil 15FT 24PT variableDL
Political Theory.........PhD 36FT 72PT variableDL/MPhil 15FT 24PT variableDL
Political ideas, policies and actions...PhD 36FT 72PT variableDL/MPhil 15FT 24PT variableDL

University of Oxford
International Relations...DPhil 48FT/MPhil 21FT

School of Oriental and African Studies - SOAS
Politics...PhD 36FT 72PT/MPhil 24FT 36PT

University of Sussex
Politics Research Programme...PhD 24-48FT 36-72PT/MPhil 12-36FT 24-48PT

Swansea University
International Development...MA by research 12FT 24PT
Media and Communication Studies...MPhil 24FT 48PT/PhD 36FT 72PT

Printing
Taught Courses

Anglia Ruskin University
Children's Book Illustration...MA 18FT 30PT
Graphic Design and Typography...MA 12FT 24PT
Illustration and Book Arts........MA 12FT 24PT/PGCert 12FT 24PT/PGDip 12FT 24PT
Printmaking...MA 12FT 24-36PT
Publishing...MA 12FT

University of the Arts London - Camberwell College of Arts
Book Arts...MA 12FT 24PT
Printmaking...MA 12FT 24PT

University of Central Lancashire
Publishing.........MA 12FT 24PT/PGDip 9FT 18PT/PGCert 9FT 18PT

University of East London
Print Design ....MA 12FT 24PT/PGDip 8FT 16PT/PGCert 4FT 8PT

Edinburgh Napier University
Publishing...MSc 12FT 24PT

London Metropolitan University
Product Design...MA 12FT 24PT

University of the Arts London - London College of Communication
Contemporary Typographic Media...MA 12FT
Graphic Branding & Identity...MA 12FT
Publishing...MA 12FT

Plymouth University
Publishing...MA 12FT 24PT/PGDip 12FT 24PT

University of Roehampton
Art, Craft and Design Education...PGCert 6FT 24PT PGDip 9FT 24PT

University of Salford
Art and Design: Product Design..MA 12FT 24PT/PGDip 9FT 15PT
Journalism...MRes 12FT 24PT

University of Sheffield
Print Journalism...MA 12FT/PGDip 9FT

University of Stirling
Publishing Studies...MLitt 12FT 27PT/PGDip 9FT 21PT MRes 12FT 27PT/PGCert 9FT 18PT

West Herts College
Printmaking/Illustration...PGDip 8-16PT

University of the West of England, Bristol
Multidisciplinary Printmaking...MA 18FT 36PT/PGDip 12FT 24PT

Printing
Research Courses

Anglia Ruskin University
Children's Book Illustration...MPhil 24FT/PhD 36FT
Graphic Design and Typography...MPhil 24FT/PhD 36FT
Publishing...MPhil 24FT/PhD 36FT

Publishing studies
Taught Courses

Anglia Ruskin University
Publishing...MA 12FT

University of Central Lancashire
Journalism Practice...MA 12FT 24-36PT/PGDip 9FT 18-24PT
Publishing.........MA 12FT 24PT/PGDip 9FT 18PT/PGCert 9FT 18PT

City University London
Electronic Publishing...MSc 12FT/MA 12FT/PGDip 9FT
International Publishing Studies...MA 12FT
Publishing Studies...MA 12FT/PGDip 9FT

University of Dundee
Design for Services...MDes 12FT

Edinburgh Napier University
International Journalism for Media Professionals (Distance Learning)...MA 12FT 24PT
Magazine Publishing...MSc 12FT 24PT
Publishing...MSc 12FT 24PT

National University of Ireland Galway
Literature and Publishing...MA 12FT

Glasgow Caledonian University
Multimedia Communication...MSc 12FT

Kingston University
Publishing...MA 12FT 24PT
Publishing and the Creative Economy...MA 12FT 24PT

University of the Arts London - London College of Communication
Publishing...MA 12FT

Oxford Brookes University
Book History and Publishing Culture ..MA 12FT 24PT/PGDip 9FT 18PT
Digital Publishing...MA 12FT 24PT/PGDip 9FT 18PT
European Master in Publishing...EM 24FT
International Publishing...MA 12FT 24PT/PGDip 9FT 18PT
Publishing...MA 12FT 24PT/PGDip 9FT 18PT
Publishing (by distance learning)...MA 24PT/PGDip 18PT/PGCert 12PT
Publishing and Language...MA 12FT 24PT/PGDip 9FT 18PT

Plymouth University
Publishing...MA 12FT 24PT/PGDip 12FT 24PT

University of Salford
Journalism...MRes 12FT 24PT

School of Oriental and African Studies - SOAS
MA in the Study of Contemporary Pakistan...MA 12FT 24PT

University of Southampton
Digital Marketing...MSc 12FT

University of Stirling
Publishing Studies...MLitt 12FT 27PT/PGDip 9FT 21PT MRes 12FT 27PT/PGCert 9FT 18PT

UCL - University College London
Electronic Communication and Publishing......MA 12FT 24-60PT/PGDip 9FT 18-45PT/PGCert 4FT 24PT
Publishing...MA 12FT 60PT/PGCert 2FT 24PT/PGDip 9FT 18-45PT

Publishing studies
Research Courses

Anglia Ruskin University
Publishing...MPhil 24FT/PhD 36FT

The Open University
Book History...PhD 36FT 72PT variableDL/MPhil 15FT 24PT variableDL

Oxford Brookes University
Publishing...MPhil/PhD 36-60FT 48-72PT/PhD 24-60FT 36-72PT/MPhil 24-36FT 36-48PT

Radio production
Taught Courses

Birmingham City University
Music Radio...MA 12FT 24PT
Radio and Audio Production...MA 12FT 24PT

Bournemouth University
Radio Production...MA 12FT

University of Central Lancashire
Scriptwriting...MA 12FT 24PT

Farnborough College of Technology
Radio...MA 12FT 24PT

Goldsmiths, University of London
Radio...MA 12FT

University of Lincoln
Community Radio...MA 12FT 24PT

University of Salford
Television and Radio Scriptwriting...MA 27PT/PGDip 24PT/PGCert 12PT

University of Sheffield
Broadcast Journalism...MA 12FT/PGDip 9FT

University of South Wales
Radio...MA 12FT 24PT

University of Sunderland
Radio...MA 12FT 24PT/PGDip 10FT 15PT/PGCert 7FT 7PT

University of Winchester
Global Radio Production...MA 12FT 24PT/PGDip 9FT 18PT/PGCert 9FT 18PT

Technical communication
Taught Courses

Cardiff University
Science, Media and Communication...MSc 12FT

Cranfield University
Information Capability Management...MSc(Eng) 12FT 60PT/PGCert 3FT 36PT/PGDip 6FT 48PT

De Montfort University
Communications Engineering H64071...MSc 12FT 24-72PT

University of Derby
Mobile Device Software Development...MSc 12FT 36PT
Visual Communication (Animation)...MDes 48FT
Visual Communication (Graphic Design)...MDes 48FT
Visual Communication (illustration)...MDes 48FT

Dublin Institute of Technology
Electronics and Communications Engineering......MSc 12FT 24PT

University of Dundee
User Experience Engineering...MSc 12FT

Glasgow Caledonian University
Multimedia Communication...MSc 12FT
Voice Over IP and Unified Communications...MSc 12FT 27PT/PGDip 9FT
Wireless Communication Technologies......MSc 12FT 24PT/PGDip 9FT 18PT
Wireless Networking...MSc 13FT 36PT/PGDip 9FT 12PT

University of Glasgow
Environmental Science, Technology & Society (Dumfries Campus)...MSc 12FT 24PT
Search Engine Technologies ....MRes 12FT 24PT/PGDip 9FT 21PT/PGCert 9FT 9PT
Search Engine Technologies ......MSc 12FT 24PT/PGDip 9FT 21PT/PGCert 9FT 9PT

Goldsmiths, University of London
Media and Communications...GradDip 12FT
Professional Media Practice...MA variableFT variablePT

Media studies and publishing

University of Greenwich
Information and Communications Technology.....MSc 12FT 24PT
Information and Communications Technology (Operations Technology)....MSc 12FT 24PT
Information and Communications Technology (e-Technology).... MSc 12FT 24PT
Wireless Mobile Communications Systems Engineering........ MSc 12FT 24PT

Heriot-Watt University
Arabic-English Translation and Computer-Assisted Translation Tools....MSc 12FT 24PT/PGDip 9FT 21PT
Chinese-English Translation and Computer-Assisted Translation Tools....MSc 12FT 24PT/PGDip 9FT 21PT
Translation and Computer Assisted Translation Tools... MSc 12FT 24PT/PGDip 9FT 21PT

University of Hertfordshire
Data Communications and Networks..........MSc 12-16FT 36-48PT
Human Computer Interaction (Online)............MSc 12FT 24-36PT 12-36DL

University of Hull
Wireless Systems....MSc 12FT
Wireless Systems and Logistics Technology....MSc 12FT

Imperial College London
Science Communication....MSc 12FT 24PT
Scientific, Technical and Medical Translation with Translation Technology....MSc 12FT 24PT

University of Kent
Science, Communication and Society....MSc 12FT 24PT

Kingston University
Media and Communications....MA 12FT 24PT

University of Limerick
Technical Communication and E-Learning....MA 12FT/PGDip 9FT 18PT/GradCert 9DL

London Metropolitan University
Translation and Technology....PGCert 12FT 24+PT

Loughborough University
Digital Communication Systems....MSc 12FT 36PT
Networked Comunications....MSc 12FT 36PT

The Open University
Science....MSc variableDL
Science and Society....MSc variableDL/PGDip variableDL

University of Portsmouth
Science with Physics....PGCE (Postgraduate) 12FT/PGCE (Professional) 12FT

Ravensbourne
3D Stereoscopic Media....MSc 12FT 24PT/MA 12FT 24PT

University of Salford
Art and Design: Communication Design .... MA 12FT 24PT/PGDip 8FT 15PT

School of Oriental and African Studies - SOAS
Global Media and Postnational Communication.............MA 12FT 24-36PT

Sheffield Hallam University
Technical Communication....MA 36DL/PGDip 24DL/PGCert 12DL

University of Sheffield
Science Communication....MSc 12FT

University of the West of England, Bristol
Practical Science Communication....PGCert 12PT
Science Communication....MSc 12FT 24PT
Science Communication....... MSc 24PT/PGDip 24PT/PGCert 12PT

University of Westminster
Technical and Specialised Translation....MA 12FT 24PT

University of Worcester
Medical Communications....PGCert 12PT

University of York
Human-Centred Interactive Technologies....MSc 12FT

Technical communication
Research Courses

The Open University
Materialities, Space and Power........... PhD 36FT 72PT variableDL/ MPhil 15FT 24PT variableDL
Technology, communication and education .... PhD 36FT 72PT variableDL/MPhil 15FT 24PT variableDL

Television production
Taught Courses

Anglia Ruskin University
Film and Television Production....MA 12FT 24PT

University of the Arts London - Central Saint Martins College of Art and Design
Screen: Directing, Writing - Drama Centre London..........MA 12FT

University of Bedfordshire
Documentary....MA 12FT

Birmingham City University
Broadcast Journalism....PGDip 6FT
Television Production....MA 12FT

Bournemouth University
Directing Digital Film and Television....MA 12FT
Post Production Editing....MA 12FT
Producing Film and Television....MA 12FT

University of Bristol
Film and Television Production....MA 12FT

Brunel University
Documentary Practice....MA 12FT 24PT

University of Central Lancashire
Film Production....MA 12FT 24PT/PGDip 9FT 24PT/ PGCert 9FT 24PT
Scriptwriting....MA 12FT 24PT

University of Chester
Television Production ...... MA 12FT 24-72PT/PGDip 12FT 24-60PT

City University London
Broadcast Journalism/Television Journalism.. MA 10FT 24PT/MA 12FT

University of East Anglia
Film, Television and Creative Practice....MA 12FT 24PT

Edinburgh Napier University
Screen Project Development....MA 12FT 24PT

University of Edinburgh
Transdisciplinary Documentary Film Practice......... MSc(Res) 12FT

Falmouth University
Television Production....MA 12FT

GCU London
TV Fiction Writing....MA 12FT

University of Hertfordshire
Film and Television....MA 12FT 24PT/PGDip 12FT 24PT
Interactive Media....MA 12FT 24PT/PGDip 12FT 24PT

University of Leeds
Audiovisual Translation Studies....MA 12FT 24PT

University of the Arts London - London College of Communication
Documentary Film....MA 12FT
Journalism - Television Pathway....MA 45 weeksFT

University of Oxford
Film Aesthetics....MSt 9FT

Queen Mary, University of London
Documentary Practice....MA 12FT 24PT

Royal Holloway, University of London
Documentary by Practice....MA 12FT 24PT
Producing Film and Television....MA 12FT 24PT

University of Salford
Audio Production....MSc 12FT 36PT
Fiction Film Production....MA 12FT/PGDip 9FT
Film Screenwriting....MA 15FT/PGDip 12FT/PGCert 6FT
Television Documentary Production ....MA 12FT/PGDip 9FT
Television and Radio Scriptwriting .... MA 27PT/PGDip 24PT/ PGCert 12PT
Wildlife Documentary Production....MA 12FT

University of Sheffield
Broadcast Journalism....MA 12FT/PGDip 9FT

University of Southampton
Film Studies....MA 12FT 24PT
Film and Cultural Management....MA 12FT 24PT

University of St Andrews
Film Studies....MLitt 12FT 24PT/PGDip 9FT

Staffordshire University
Sports Broadcast Journalism....MA 12FT 48PT

University of Stirling
Film Studies: Theory and Practice......MLitt 12FT 27PT/PGDip 9FT 21PT/PGCert 3FT 6PT

Teesside University
Digital Effects for Film and Television....MA 12FT 36PT

University of West London
Art Direction for Film and TV....MA 12FT 24PT

Television production
Research Courses

Anglia Ruskin University
Film and Television Production....MPhil 24FT/PhD 36FT

University of Edinburgh
Transdisciplinary Documentary Film....PhD 36FT

University of Southampton
Film Studies....PhD 48FT 84PT/MPhil 48FT 84PT

University of St Andrews
Film Studies....PhD 36FT 72-84PT/MPhil 24FT 48PT

Television studies
Taught Courses

Aberystwyth University
Politics, Media and Performance....MA 12FT 24PT

Bournemouth University
Cinematography for Digital Film and Television....MA 12FT

University of Bristol
Film and Television Studies....MA 12FT 24PT

University of Central Lancashire
Broadcast Journalism....PGDip 9FT/MA 12FT
Journalism....MA 12FT 36PT
Journalism Practice.............MA 12FT 24-36PT/PGDip 9FT 18-24PT
Journalism Studies....MA 12FT 24PT
Performance ....MA 12FT 24-30PT/PGDip 12FT 24PT/PGCert 12FT
Scriptwriting....MA 12FT 24PT

University of Chester
Television Production ...... MA 12FT 24-72PT/PGDip 12FT 24-60PT

University College Cork
Film Studies....MA 9FT

University of East Anglia
American Studies and Film Studies....MA 12FT 24PT
Film Studies....MA 12FT 24PT
Film, Television and Creative Practice....MA 12FT 24PT

Edinburgh Napier University
Film....MA 12FT 24PT

University of Exeter
Independent Film Business....MA 12FT 24PT

Glasgow Caledonian University
Television Fiction Writing....MA 12FT 24PT

University of Glasgow
Film and Television Studies....MLitt 12FT 24PT

Goldsmiths, University of London
Television Journalism....MA 12FT

King's College London
Film Studies....MA 12FT 24PT

Newcastle University
Film: Theory and Practice....MA 12FT 24PT

Oxford Brookes University
Film Studies: Popular Cinema .. MA 12FT 24PT/PGDip 8FT 6-8PT/ PGCert 4FT 6PT

University of Oxford
Film Aesthetics....MSt 9FT

University of Portsmouth
Film and Television Studies....MA 12FT 24PT

University of Reading
Film Studies....MA (Res) 12FT 24PT
Television Studies....MA (Res) 12FT 24PT
Theatre Studies....MA (Res) 12FT 24PT

University of Salford
Fiction Film Production....MA 12FT/PGDip 9FT
Film Screenwriting....MA 15FT/PGDip 12FT/PGCert 6FT

Sheffield Hallam University
Film Studies....MA 12FT 36-72PT MPhil 36FT 84PT/PhD by taught 36FT 84PT
Film Studies with Screenwriting....MA 12FT 24PT

University of Southampton
Film Studies....MA 12FT 24PT
Film and Cultural Management....MA 12FT 24PT

University of St Andrews
Film Studies....MLitt 12FT 24PT/PGDip 9FT

University of Stirling
Film Studies: Theory and Practice......MLitt 12FT 27PT/PGDip 9FT 21PT/PGCert 3FT 6PT

UCL - University College London
Film Studies....MA 12FT 24PT

University of Warwick
Film and Television Studies....MA 12FT
Research in Film and Television Studies....MA 12FT

University of Westminster
Film and Television: Theory, Culture and Industry...........MA 12FT 24-48PT

University of York
Contemporary Cinema and Television....MA 12FT 24PT

Television studies
Research Courses

Aberystwyth University
Theatre, Film and Television Studies (MPhil).......MPhil 12FT 24PT
Theatre, Film and Television Studies (PhD)............ PhD 36FT 60PT

Birkbeck, University of London
Film and Screen Media............... MPhil 36FT 48PT/PhD 36FT 48PT

Brunel University
Film and Television Studies........ PhD 36FT 48PT/MPhil 12FT 24PT

Media studies and publishing

Cardiff University
Audience and Fan Studies .... PhD 36FT possiblePT/MPhil 24FT possiblePT

University of Central Lancashire
Film and Media ...PhD 18-36FT 42-60PT/MPhil 18-36FT 42-60PT/ MA by research 12FT 24PT

King's College London
Film Studies Research .... PhD 36FT 48-72PT

Newcastle University
Film Studies .... MLitt by research 12FT 24PT PhD 36FT 72PT/MPhil 12FT 24PT

University of Nottingham
Film and Television Studies....... PhD 36FT 72PT/MPhil 24FT 48PT/ MRes 12FT

Queen's University Belfast
Film Studies .... PhD 36FT 72PT/MPhil 24FT 48PT

University of Roehampton
Film and TelevisionPhD 24-48FT 36-60PT/MPhil 21-36FT 33-48PT

School of Oriental and African Studies - SOAS
Media and Film Studies .... PhD 36-48FT

University of Southampton
Film Studies .... PhD 48FT 84PT/MPhil 48FT 84PT

University of St Andrews
Film Studies .... PhD 36FT 72-84PT/MPhil 24FT 48PT

UCL - University College London
Film Studies .... PhD 36FT 60PT

University of Warwick
Film and Television Studies..... PhD 36FT 60PT/MPhil 36FT/MA by research 12FT

University of York
Theatre, Film and Television ...... MPhil 24FT 48PT/PhD 36FT 72PT

Theatre studies
Taught Courses

Aberystwyth University
Politics, Media and Performance .... MA 12FT 24PT
Practising Theatre and Performance.... MA 12FT 24PT/PGDip 9FT 18PT

University of the Arts London - Central Saint Martins College of Art and Design
Acting (formerly MA European Classical Acting) Drama Centre London .... MA 12FT
Collaborative Performance .... MA 12FT

University of the Arts London - London College of Fashion
Costume Design for Performance .... MA 15FT 30PT

University of the Arts London - Wimbledon College of Art
Theatre: Interdisciplinary Performance .... MA 12FT

Bangor University
Creative Practice .... MRes 12FT 24PT

Bath Spa University
Performing Shakespeare .... MA 12FT 24PT/MFA 12FT 24PT
Theatre for Young Audiences .... MA 12FT 24PT

Birkbeck, University of London
Creative Producing .... MA 12FT
Shakespeare and Contemporary Performance....... MA 12FT 24PT
Text and Performance (with RADA) .... MA 12FT 24PT
Theatre Directing .... MFA 24FT

Birmingham City University
Acting .... MA 12FT/PGDip 10FT
Acting: The British Tradition .... MA 12FT/PGDip 9FT

Arts University Bournemouth
Costume .... MA 12FT 24PT

University of Bristol
Performance Research .... MA 12FT 24PT

University of Central Lancashire
Performance ....MA 12FT 24-30PT/PGDip 12FT 24PT/PGCert 12FT

Central School of Speech and Drama, University of London
Advanced Theatre Practice .... MA 12FT
Applied Theatre (Drama in the Community and Drama Education) .... MA 12FT 24PT
Creative Producing .... MA 12FT 24PT/MFA 24FT
PG Certificate in Applied Theatre with Young PeoplePGCert 12FT
Scenography .... MA 12FT
Theatre Studies (Performance and the City) .... MA 12FT 24PT

University of Chester
Dance...... MA 12FT 24PT/PGDip 12FT 24PT/PGCert 12FT 12-24PT
Dental Practice Management (Work Based and Integrative Studies) .... MA 24-72PT/PGDip 24-60PT/PGCert 12-36PT
Developing RPL Policy and Practice (Work Based and Integrative Studies) .... MA 24-72PT/PGDip 24-60PT/PGCert 12-36PT

University of Chichester
Theatre Collectives .... MA 12FT 24PT 12DL

University College Cork
Drama & Theatre Studies .... MA 12FT

University of Dundee
Theatre Studies (MLitt) .... MLitt 12FT

University of East Anglia
Film, Television and Creative Practice .... MA 12FT 24PT
Theatre Directing: Text and Production .... MA 12FT 24PT

Edinburgh Napier University
Film .... MA 12FT 24PT

University of Edinburgh
Theatre and Performance Studies .... MSc 12FT
Writing for Theatre and Performance .... MSc 12FT 24PT

University of Exeter
Independent Film Business .... MA 12FT 24PT
Theatre Practice: Applied Theatre .... MA 12FT 24PT
Theatre Practice: Directing and Actor Training....... MA 12FT 24PT
Theatre Practice: General Programme .... MA 12FT 24PT
Theatre Practice: Physical Performance & Actor Training .... MA 12FT 24PT
Theatre Practice: Staging Shakespeare .... MA 12FT 24PT/ MFA 24FT

National University of Ireland Galway
Drama & Theatre Studies .... MA 12FT

University of Glasgow
Historically Informed Performance Practice....... MMus 12FT 24PT
Playwriting & Dramaturgy .... MLitt 12FT
Theatre History .... MLitt 12FT 24PT
Theatre Practices .... MLitt 12FT 24PT
Theatre Studies .... MLitt 12FT 24PT

Goldsmiths, University of London
Applied Theatre: Drama in Educational, Community & Social Contexts .... MA 12FT 24PT
Black British Writing, Drama and Performance...... MA 12FT 24PT
Contemporary African Theatre & Performance .... MA 12FT
Performance and Culture: Interdisciplinary Perspectives .... MA 12FT 24PT

University of Huddersfield
Performance .... PGDip 12FT

University of Hull
Drama and Theatre Practice .... MA 12FT 24PT

University of Kent
Arts Criticism .... MA 12FT 24PT
Drama and Theatre .... MA 12FT 24PT
Drama and Theatre: Physical Actor Training and Performance..... MA 12FT
Drama and Theatre: Physical Actor Training and Performance with a term in Moscow .... MA 12FT
Shakespeare .... MA 12FT 24PT

King's College London
Theatre & Performance Studies .... MA 12FT 24PT

Leeds Metropolitan University
Performance .... MA 12FT 24PT

University of Leeds
Performance, Culture and Context....... MA 12FT 24PT/PGDip 9FT 21PT/PGCert 6FT 12PT
Theatre Making: Critical Engagement with Creative Practice...... MA 12FT
Theatre and Development Studies .... MA 12FT

London South Bank University
Theatre Practice .... MA 28PT

Loughborough University
Performance and Multi-Media .... MA 12FT 24PT

Manchester Metropolitan University
Movement Practice for Theatre .... MA 12FT

University of Manchester
Applied Theatre (pathway of Theatre and Performance) .... MA 12FT 24PT
Theatre & Performance .... MA 12FT 24PT

Newcastle University
Creative Arts Practice .... MA 12FT 24PT
Film: Theory and Practice .... MA 12FT 24PT

Oxford Brookes University
Film Studies: Popular Cinema .. MA 12FT 24PT/PGDip 8FT 6-8PT/ PGCert 4FT 6PT

Plymouth University
Theatre and Performance .... MRes 12FT

Queen's University Belfast
Drama .... MA 12FT 24PT

University of Reading
Early Modern Literature & Drama .... MA (Res) 12FT 24PT
Film Studies (MA Res) .... MA (Res) 12FT 24PT
Television Studies (MA Res) .... MA (Res) 12FT 24PT
Theatre Studies (MA Res) .... MA (Res) 12FT 24PT

Rose Bruford College
MA Ensemble Theatre .... MA 12FT/PGDip 10FT
MA Theatre for Young Audiences........ MA 12FT 24PT/PGDip 10FT 22PT

PG Certificate in Learning and Teaching in Higher Education (Theatre & Performing Arts) .... PGCHE 12PT

Royal College of Music
Performance .... RCM Artist Diploma 10FT

Royal Holloway, University of London
Research (Drama) .... MA 12FT 24PT
Theatre .... MA 12FT 24PT

Royal Conservatoire of Scotland
Classical and Contemporary Text (Acting) .... MA 12FT
Classical and Contemporary Text (Directing) .... MA 12FT
Musical Theatre (Directing) .... MA 12FT
Musical Theatre (Performance) .... MA 12FT

Royal Welsh College of Music and Drama
Musical Theatre .... MA 12FT
Theatre Design .... MA 12FT 12PT

University of Salford
Digital Performance .... MA 12FT 36PT/PGDip 8FT 24PT

School of Oriental and African Studies - SOAS
Performance .... MMus 12FT 24PT

Sheffield Hallam University
Film Studies .... MA 12FT 36-72PT
Film Studies .... MPhil 36FT 84PT/PhD by taught 36FT 84PT
Film Studies with Screenwriting .... MA 12FT 24PT

University of Sheffield
Theatre and Performance Studies .... MA 12FT 24PT

University of Southampton
Film Studies .... MA 12FT 24PT

University of St Andrews
Film Studies .... MLitt 12FT 24PT/PGDip 9FT

St Mary's University College, Twickenham
Physical Theatre .... MA 12FT

University of Stirling
Film Studies: Theory and Practice ......MLitt 12FT 27PT/PGDip 9FT 21PT/PGCert 3FT 6PT

University of Surrey
Dance Cultures .... MA 12FT 24 or 36PT
Theatre Studies .... MA 12FT 24 or 36PT

Trinity College Dublin - the University of Dublin
Theatre and Performance .... MPhil 12FT

University of Wales Trinity Saint David
Theatre and Society .... MA 12FT/PGDip 9FT/PGCert 6FT

UCL - University College London
Film Studies .... MA 12FT 24PT

University of York
Theatre: Writing, Directing and Performance .... MA 12FT 24PT

York St John University
Applied Theatre .... MA 12FT 24PT
Theatre and Performance .... MA 12FT 24PT

Theatre studies
Research Courses

Aberystwyth University
Theatre, Film and Television Studies .... MPhil 12FT 24PT PhD 36FT 60PT

University of Birmingham
Directing and Dramaturgy .... MRes 12FT 24PT
Drama and Theatre PhD/ PhD by Distance .... PhD 36FT 72PT/ MA by research 12FT 24PT/MPhil 12FT 24PT
Drama and Theatre Studies .... MRes 12FT 24PT
Drama and Theatre Studies Practice-Based PhD (Dramaturgy, Playwriting or Performance) .... PhD 36FT 72PT

University of Bristol
Drama: Theatre, Film, Television .... PhD 36FT 72PT/MLitt by research 24FT 48PT/MPhil 12FT 24PT

Central School of Speech and Drama, University of London
Drama, Performing, Theatre Studies, and Design for Theatre....... PhD 36 (min)FT 72 (min)PT

University of Edinburgh
European Theatre .... PhD 36FT 72PT

University of Exeter
Drama .... PhD 48FT 89PT/MPhil 36FT 60PT

University of Glasgow
Theatre .... PhD 36FT/MPhil 12FT/MLitt by research 12FT

University of Hull
Theatre and Contemporary Studies ...PhD 36FT 60PT/MPhil 24FT 36PT/MA by research 12FT 24PT

University of Kent
Drama .... MA by research 12FT 24PT/PhD 36FT 60PT
Drama (Practice as Research) .... MA by research 12FT 24PT

Lancaster University
Theatre Studies .... PhD 36PT

Loughborough University
Drama and Theatre Studies....... PhD 36FT 60PT/MPhil 24FT 36PT

Media studies and publishing

University of Manchester
Applied Theatre Professional Doctorate....Professional Doctorate
36FT 72PT

Newcastle University
Film Studies .... MLitt by research 12FT 24PT
Film Studies .... PhD 36FT 72PT/MPhil 12FT 24PT

Queen's University Belfast
Drama Studies............................... PhD 36FT 72PT/MPhil 24FT 48PT
Film Studies .... PhD 36FT 72PT/MPhil 24FT 48PT

University of Roehampton
Drama, Theatre and Performance.... PhD 24-48FT 36-60PT/MPhil
21-36FT 33-48PT

Royal Academy of Music
Performance Practice .... MPhil 24FT/PhD 36FT

Royal Holloway, University of London
Drama and Theatre Studies .... MPhil 12FT/PhD 36FT

Royal Conservatoire of Scotland
PhD (Drama) .... PhD 36FT 72PT

University of Southampton
Film Studies .... PhD 48FT 84PT/MPhil 48FT 84PT

University of St Andrews
Film Studies .... PhD 36FT 72-84PT/MPhil 24FT 48PT

University of Sussex
Drama, Theatre and Performance.... PhD 24-48FT 36-72PT/MPhil
12-36FT 24-48PT

UCL - University College London
Film Studies .... PhD 36FT 60PT

University of Warwick
Theatre StudiesPhD 36FT 60PT/MPhil 24FT 36PT/MA by research
12FT 24PT

University of York
Theatre, Film and Television ...... MPhil 24FT 48PT/PhD 36FT 72PT

Music and performing arts

Composing
Taught Courses

Aberystwyth University
Gwleidyddiaeth a Chymdeithas Cymru (Arbenigol).........MA 12FT 24PT/PGDip 9FT 18PT
Gwleidyddiaeth a Chymdeithas Cymru (Hyfforddiant Ymchwil).... .... MA 12FT 24PT/PGDip 9FT 18PT

Bangor University
Composition/Electroacoustic Composition/Sonic ArtMMus 12FT 24PT
Music .... MA 12FT 24PT/PGDip 9FT
Performance (Music) .... MA 12FT 24PT/PGDip 9FT

Bath Spa University
Composition . MMus 12FT 24PT/PGDip 9FT 18PT/PGCert 4FT 9PT
Songwriting .... MMus 12FT 24PT 12 - 24DL

Birmingham City University
Music (Intensive) .... MMus 13FT
Music .... MMus 22FT 33PT PGDip 12FT 24PT

University of Bristol
Composition of Music for Film and Television .... MA 12FT

Cardiff University
Composition .... MMus 12FT 24PT

University of Central Lancashire
Music Industry Management and Promotion .... MSc 12FT 24PT
Music Practice .... MA 12FT 24PT
Playwriting .... MA 12FT 24PT

University of Chester
Popular Music..... MA 12FT 24-72PT/PGDip 12FT 24-60PT/PGCert 12FT 12-36PT

University of Chichester
Music PerformanceMA 12-15FT 24-36PT/PGDip 9-12FT 18-24PT/PGCert 6-9FT 12-18PT

City University London
Music Composition (Validated) .... MMus 12FT

University College Cork
Arts (Music) .... HDip 9FT 18PT
Composition .... MA 12FT

Durham University
Composition .... MA 12FT 24PT

University of Edinburgh
Composition .... MMus 12FT 24PT
Digital Composition and Performance .... MSc 12FT 24PT
Musicology .... MMus 12FT 24PT

University of Glasgow
Composition .... PGDip 12FT 24PT/PGCert 12FT 24PT
Musicology .... PGDip 12FT 24PT/PGCert 12FT 24PT
Sonic Arts .... PGDip 12FT 24PT

Goldsmiths, University of London
Music .... GradDip 12FT
Music including specialist pathways .... MA 12FT 24PT MMus 12FT 24PT

University of Huddersfield
Music .... MMus 12FT 24PT

University of Hull
Sonic Art .... MRes 12FT 24PT

Kingston University
Composing for Film and Television .... MMus 12FT 24PT
Production of Popular Music .... MMus 12FT 24PT
Sonic Arts .... MMus 12FT 24PT

University of Leeds
Composition .... MMus 12FT 24PT

University of Manchester
Composition .... MusM 12FT 24PT
Electroacoustic Music Composition .... MusM 12FT 24PT

National University of Ireland, Maynooth
Composition .... MA 12FT 24PT

Middlesex University
Popular Music .... MMus 12FT 24PT

Oxford Brookes University
Composition and Sonic Art .... MA 12FT 24PT/PGDip 9FT 18PT
Music .... MA 12FT 24PT

Queen's University Belfast
Music .... MA 12FT 32PT

University of Reading
Music Teaching in Professional Practise ..... MA 12FT 36PT/PGDip 24FT 48PT

Royal Academy of Music
Composition .... MMus 12-24FT

Royal College of Music
Composition .... PGDip 10FT/AdvPGDip 10FT/MMus 13FT
Composition and Composition for Screen .... MMus 13FT

Royal Northern College of Music
Master of Music (1 year intensive) .... MMus 12FT
Master of Music (2 years) .... MMus 21FT

Royal Conservatoire of Scotland
Master of Music (all specialims) .... MMus 12FT/MMus 24FT Music(Perf/Opera/Comp/Conducting/Accompaniment/Jazz/Piano for Dance/Repetiteur/Scot Music) ...... PGDip 12FT 24-60PT

Royal Welsh College of Music and Drama
Composition ....PGDip 12FT/PGDip 24PT/MA 24PT/MMus 24PT
Music Performance. MA 24PT/MA 12FT/PGDip 12FT/MMus 12FT

University of Salford
Digital Performance .... MA 12FT 36PT/PGDip 8FT 24PT
Media .... MRes 12FT 24PT
Music .... MRes 12FT 24PT
Performance .... MRes 12FT 24PT

School of Oriental and African Studies - SOAS
Music and Development .... MA 12FT 24PT

Staffordshire University
Music Technology .... MSc 12-18FT

University of Surrey
Musicology .... MRes 12FT 24PT

Trinity College Dublin - the University of Dublin
Music and Media Technologies .... MPhil 24FT

Trinity Laban Conservatoire of Music and Dance
Performance; Jazz; Composition; Creative Practice ... MMus 12FT 24PT

University of West London
Composing for Film and Television .... MMus 12FT 24PT
Electronic / Electro-acoustic Composition .... MMus 12FT 24PT

University of Wolverhampton
Music .... MA 12FT 24-36PT

York St John University
Music Composition .... MA 12FT 24PT

Composing
Research Courses

Bangor University
Music (including Composition) .... PhD 24-36FT 48-60PT/MPhil 12FT 24PT/MA by research 12FT
Performance .... PhD 36FT 72PT/MPhil 24FT 48PT

Birmingham City University
Music .... MPhil appx. 24FT appx. 36PT PhD appx. 36FT appx. 60PT

University of Birmingham
Musical Composition .... PhD 36FT 72PT/MPhil 12FT 24PT

Cardiff University
Composition .... PhD 36FT possiblePT/MPhil 12FT possiblePT

Durham University
Music (Composition) .... MMus (comp) 24FT 48PT/PhD (comp) 36FT 72PT

University of Edinburgh
Creative Music Practice .... PhD 36FT 72PT
Music..... PhD 36FT 72PT/MPhil 24FT 48PT/MSc by research 12FT 24PT

University of Hertfordshire
Composition and Performance as Research Practice (CAPARP)..... PhD 36FT 72PT/MPhil 24FT 48PT/MRes 12FT 24PT

Lancaster University
Music .... PhD 36FT 48PT/MPhil 24FT 36PT

University of Liverpool
Popular Music .... PhD 36FT 72PT/MPhil 24FT 48PT

University of Manchester
Composition .... PhD 36FT 72PT
Electroacoustic Composition .... PhD 36FT 72PT

Newcastle University
Music .... MMus by research 12FT 24PT/PGDip by research 9FT 18PT

University of Nottingham
Music composition .... PhD 36FT 72PT/MPhil 24FT 48PT/AMusD 36FT 72PT/AMusM by research 12FT 24PT

The Open University
Interdisciplinary themes in music research including film and literature .... PhD 36FT 72PT variableDL/MPhil 15FT 24PT variableDL

Oxford Brookes University
Music .... PhD 24-60FT 48-72PT/MPhil 24-36FT 36-48PT

Royal Academy of Music
Composition .... MPhil 24FT/PhD 36FT

Royal College of Music
Music .... DMus 36-48FT 48-72PT

Royal Conservatoire of Scotland
Drama .... PhD 36FT 72PT
Music .... PhD 48FT

University of Salford
Media, Music and Performing Arts Research Centre....PhD/MPhil

University of Surrey
Music .... PhD 33-48FT 45-96PT/MPhil 21-36FT 33-72PT

University of Sussex
Musical Composition Research Programme .... PhD 24-48FT 36-72PT/MPhil 12-36FT 24-48PT

University of West London
Composition .... MPhil 12FT 24PT/DMA 36FT 72PT
Popular Music .... MPhil 12FT 24PT/DMA 36FT 72PT

Dance
Taught Courses

University of the Arts London - Central Saint Martins College of Art and Design
Collaborative Performance .... MA 12FT

Bath Spa University
Dance .... MA 12FT 24PT

University of Bedfordshire
Community Dance Leadership .... MA 12FT 24PT
Dance Performance & Choreography .... MA 12FT 24PT
Dance Science .... MSc 12FT 24PT

Arts University Bournemouth
Contemporary Performance .... MA 12FT 24PT

University of Central Lancashire
Dance and Somatic Well-being....... MA 24PT/PGDip 24PT/PGCert 24PT
Performance ....MA 12FT 24-30PT/PGDip 12FT 24PT/PGCert 12FT

University of Chester
Dance...... MA 12FT 24PT/PGDip 12FT 24PT/PGCert 12FT 12-24PT

University of Chichester
Performance: Dance .... MA 16FT 24-36PT

City University London
Choreography .... MA 12FT 24PT
Dance Management and Development...... MA 24PT/PGDip 24PT
Dance Performance .... MA 12FT
Dance Science .... MSc 12FT 24PT
Dance Studies .... MA 13FT 23-33PT
European Dance Theatre Practice .... MA 12FT 24PT
Scenography (Dance) .... MA 12FT 24PT

De Montfort University
Performance by Independent Study .... MA 12FT 24PT 12-24DL

University of East Anglia
Creative Entrepreneurship .... MA 12FT

University of Edinburgh
Dance Science and Education .....MSc 12FT 72PT/PGDip 9FT 48PT

University of Glasgow
Historically Informed Performance Practice....... MMus 12FT 24PT

Goldsmiths, University of London
Performance and Culture: Interdisciplinary PerspectivesMA 12FT 24PT

University of Huddersfield
Performance .... PGDip 12FT

University of Leeds
Performance, Culture and Context....... MA 12FT 24PT/PGDip 9FT 21PT/PGCert 6FT 12PT

University of Limerick
Dance .... GradDip 12PT/MA 12PT
Dance Performance (Irish Traditional/Contemporary Dance) .... MA 12FT
Ethnochoreology .... MA 12FT
Ritual Chant & Song .... MA 12FT

London Contemporary Dance School
Contemporary Dance .... PGDip 12FT 24PT

Middlesex University
Choreography .... MA 16FT 28PT
Professional Practice (Dance Technique Pedagogy) .... MA 16PT

University of Roehampton
Ballet Studies .... MA 12FT 24PT
Choreography .... MFA 24FT 48PT
Community Dance .... MA 12FT 24-36PT
Dance Anthropology .... MA 12FT 24PT
Dance Studies .... MA 12FT 24PT
Global Dance .... MA 12FT 24PT
Choreography and Performance .... MRes 12FT 24PT
Ballet Studies .... PGDip 9FT 24PT
Dance Anthropology .... PGDip 9FT 24PT
Dance Studies .... PGDip 9FT 24PT
South Asian Dance Studies .... PGDip 9FT 24PT

Rose Bruford College
Theatre for Young Audiences .....MA 12FT 24PT/PGDip 10FT 22PT

Royal Academy of Music
Musical Theatre .... PGDip 9FT

Royal College of Music
Performance .... RCM Artist Diploma 10FT

School of Oriental and African Studies - SOAS
Performance .... MMus 12FT 24PT

University of Sheffield
Theatre and Performance Studies .... MA 12FT 24PT

Music and performing arts

University of Surrey
Dance Cultures.................................MA 12FT 24 or 36PT

Trinity Laban Conservatoire of Music and Dance
Choreography...MA 12FT
Creative Practice: Dance Professional Practice Pathway.MA 12FT 24PT
Creative Practice: Self Selected Pathway.................MA 12FT 24PT
Dance Performance (Transitions Dance Company)..........MA 12FT
Dance Theatre: The Body in Performance............MA 12FT 24PT
Performance Design.................................PGDip 12FT 24PT
Creative Practice...MFA 18FT
Dance Science.....................................MSc 12FT 24PT

University of Winchester
Dance: Practice and Production..MA 12FT 24PT/PGDip 9FT 18PT/ PGCert 9FT 18PT

University of Wolverhampton
Dance Science.................................MSc 12FT 24-36PT
Dance...MA 24PT

Dance
Research Courses

University of Chichester
Dance......................... PhD 36FT 84PT/MPhil 24FT 84PT

City University London
Laban Centre London.......PhD 24FT 36-84PT/MPhil 12FT 24-60PT

University of Hull
Theatre and Contemporary Studies ...PhD 36FT 60PT/MPhil 24FT 36PT/MA by research 12FT 24PT

University of Manchester
Anthropology, Media & Performance...................PhD 36FT 72PT

Plymouth University
Dance..MRes 12FT

University of Roehampton
Dance...................PhD 24-48FT 36-60PT/MPhil 21-36FT 33-48PT

Royal Academy of Music
Performance Practice..........................MPhil 24FT/PhD 36FT

Royal Conservatoire of Scotland
Drama..PhD 36FT 72PT

University of Surrey
Dance, Film and Theatre.....PhD 33-48FT 45-96PT/MPhil 21-36FT 33-72PT

Trinity Laban Conservatoire of Music and Dance
Research Degree Programme......PhD min. 24FT min. 36PT/MPhil min. 12FT min. 24PT

Drama
Taught Courses

Aberystwyth University
Politics, Media and Performance.................MA 12FT 24PT
Practising Theatre and Performance.... MA 12FT 24PT/PGDip 9FT 18PT
Scriptwriting (Screen and Radio). MA 12FT 24PT/PGDip 9FT 20PT

University of the Arts London - Central Saint Martins College of Art and Design
Acting (formerly MA European Classical Acting) Drama Centre London..MA 12FT
Collaborative Performance............................MA 12FT
Screen: Acting - Drama Centre London................MA 24FT

University of the Arts London - Wimbledon College of Art
Theatre: Interdisciplinary Performance.................MA 12FT

University of Bedfordshire
PgCert Performing Before the Camera...............PGCert 3FT

Birkbeck, University of London
Creative Producing.....................................MA 12FT
Shakespeare and Contemporary Performance.......MA 12FT 24PT
Text and Performance (with RADA)...............MA 12FT 24PT
Theatre Directing..MFA 24PT

Birmingham City University
Acting.............................. MA 12FT/PGDip 10FT
Acting: The British Tradition.............MA 12FT/PGDip 9FT
Professional Voice Practice.............MA 12FT 12PT/PGDip 9FT 9PT

Bournemouth University
Directing Digital Film and Television...................MA 12FT

University of Brighton
Performance and Visual Practices .... MA 12FT 24PT

University of Bristol
Performance Research .... MA 12FT 24PT

University of Central Lancashire
Performance ....MA 12FT 24-30PT/PGDip 12FT 24PT/PGCert 12FT

Central School of Speech and Drama, University of London
Acting .... MA 12FT 24-36PT
Acting for Screen ....MA 12FT
Actor Training and Coaching .... MA 12FT 24PT
Advanced Theatre Practice............................MA 12FT
Applied Theatre (Drama in the Community and Drama Education) .... MA 12FT 24PT

University of Chester
Education: Singing in the Curriculum.................PGCert 12 - 36PT

University of Chichester
Theatre Collectives............................MA 12FT 24PT 12DL

City University London
Acting..MA 12FT

University College Cork
Drama & Theatre Studies.............................MA 12FT

De Montfort University
Performance Practices .... MA 12FT 24PT
Performance by Independent Study..........MA 12FT 24PT 12-24DL

University of Dundee
Theatre Studies ....MLitt 12FT

University of East Anglia
Creative Entrepreneurship.............................MA 12FT
Theatre Directing: Text and Production...............MA 12FT 24PT

University of East London
Acting MA...........MA 12FT 24PT/PGDip 8FT 16PT/PGCert 4FT 8PT
Theatre Directing MAMA 12FT 24PT/PGDip 8FT 16PT/PGCert 4FT 8PT

University of Essex
Acting..MA 12FT/MFA 20FT
Acting (International)........................MA 12FT/MFA 20FT
Theatre Directing...........................MA 12FT/MFA 12FT

University of Exeter
Theatre Practice: Applied Theatre.............. MA 12FT 24PT
Theatre Practice: Directing and Actor Training....... MA 12FT 24PT
Theatre Practice: General Programme................. MA 12FT 24PT
Theatre Practice: Physical Performance & Actor Training.............. MA 12FT 24PT
Theatre Practice: Staging Shakespeare................MA 12FT 24PT/ MFA 24FT

National University of Ireland Galway
Drama & Theatre Studies.............................MA 12FT

University of Glasgow
Historically Informed Performance Practice.......MMus 12FT 24PT
Playwriting & Dramaturgy.............................MLitt 12FT

Goldsmiths, University of London
Applied Theatre: Drama in Educational, Community & Social Contexts...MA 12FT 24PT
Black British Writing, Drama and Performance....... MA 12FT 24PT
Contemporary African Theatre & Performance................MA 12FT
Performance Making...............................MA 12FT 24PT

University of Huddersfield
Performance..PGDip 12FT

University of Kent
Drama and Theatre............................ MA 12FT 24PT
Drama and Theatre: Physical Actor Training and Performance.....MA 12FT
Drama and Theatre: Physical Actor Training and Performance with a term in Moscow...........................MA 12FT
Shakespeare...................................... MA 12FT 24PT

Kingston University
Playwriting .... MA 12FT 24PT

University of Leeds
Performance, Culture and Context....... MA 12FT 24PT/PGDip 9FT 21PT/PGCert 6FT 12PT
Theatre Making: Critical Engagement with Creative Practice....... MA 12FT

Loughborough University
Performance and Multi-Media .... MA 12FT 24PT

University of Manchester
Applied Theatre (pathway of Theatre and Performance)..............MA 12FT 24PT
Theatre & Performance .... MA 12FT 24PT

University of Northampton
Performance Arts.....................MA 12FT 24PT/PGDip 12PT

University of Oxford
Musicology and Performance.........................MPhil 21FT

Plymouth University
Theatre and Performance............................MRes 12FT

Queen's University Belfast
Drama.. MA 12FT 24PT

University of Reading
Early Modern Literature & Drama ....MA (Res) 12FT 24PT

Rose Bruford College
Theatre for Young Audiences .....MA 12FT 24PT/PGDip 10FT 22PT

Royal Academy of Music
Musical Theatre ....PGDip 9FT

Royal College of Music
Performance..............................RCM Artist Diploma 10FT

Royal Holloway, University of London
Research (Drama) .... MA 12FT 24PT
Theatre.. MA 12FT 24PT

Royal Conservatoire of Scotland
Classical and Contemporary Text (Acting) ....MA 12FT
Classical and Contemporary Text (Directing)....................MA 12FT
Musical Theatre (Directing).............................MA 12FT
Musical Theatre (Performance) ....MA 12FT

Royal Welsh College of Music and Drama
Acting for Stage Screen and Radio.......................MA 14FT
Musical Theatre.......................................MA 12FT
Theatre Design .... MA 12FT 12PT

University of Sheffield
Theatre and Performance Studies............. MA 12FT 24PT

University of South Wales
Drama.. MA 12FT 24PT

St Mary's University College, Twickenham
Theatre Directing.................................. MA 12FT 24PT

Trinity College Dublin - the University of Dublin
Theatre and Performance .... MPhil 12FT

University of Wales Trinity Saint David
Advanced Vocal Studies ....MA 12FT
Theatre and Society .... MA 12FT/PGDip 9FT/PGCert 6FT

UCL - University College London
Performing Arts Medicine............MSc 12FT 24PT/PGDip 9FT 24PT

University of Winchester
Devised Performance ....MA 12FT 24PT/PGDip 12FT 24PT/PGCert 12FT 24PT

University of Wolverhampton
Drama..MA 24PT

University of Worcester
Drama............... MA 12FT 24PT/PGDip 9FT 18PT/PGCert 6FT 12PT

University of York
Theatre: Writing, Directing and Performance .... MA 12FT 24PT

York St John University
Applied Theatre.............................. MA 12FT 24PT
Theatre and Performance..................... MA 12FT 24PT

Drama
Research Courses

Aberystwyth University
Theatre, Film and Television Studies ....MPhil 12FT 24PT PhD 36FT 60PT

University of Birmingham
Directing and Dramaturgy.........................MRes 12FT 24PT
Drama and Theatre.............................PhD 36FT 72PT/ MA by research 12FT 24PT/MPhil 12FT 24PT
Drama and Theatre Studies ....MRes 12FT 24PT
Drama and Theatre Studies Practice-Based (Dramaturgy, Playwriting or Performance)......................... PhD 36FT 72PT
Playwriting Studies.............................MPhil(B) 12FT 24PT

University of Bristol
Drama: Theatre, Film, Television...............PhD 36FT 72PT/MLitt by research 24FT 48PT/MPhil 12FT 24PT

Central School of Speech and Drama, University of London
Drama, Performing, Theatre Studies, and Design for Theatre PhD 36 (min)FT 72 (min)PT

University of Cumbria
English and Drama..PhD 48FT 72PT 72DL/MPhil 36FT 60PT 60DL

University of Edinburgh
European Theatre .... PhD 36FT 72PT

University of Exeter
Drama................................. PhD 48FT 89PT/MPhil 36FT 60PT

Goldsmiths, University of London
Drama..............................PhD 36-48FT 48-72PT/MPhil 24FT 36PT

University of Hull
Drama .... PhD 36FT 60PT/MPhil 24FT 36PT
Theatre and Contemporary Studies ...PhD 36FT 60PT/MPhil 24FT 36PT/MA by research 12FT 24PT

University of Kent
Drama.................... MA by research 12FT 24PT/PhD 36FT 60PT
Drama (Practice as Research) .... MA by research 12FT 24PT

Kingston University
Media, Film and Drama .PhD 48FT 72PT/MPhil 24FT 48PT/MA by research 12FT 24PT

Liverpool John Moores University
Media, Critical and Creative ArtsMPhil 36FT 84PT/PhD 36FT 84PT

Loughborough University
Drama and Theatre Studies....... PhD 36FT 60PT/MPhil 24FT 36PT

University of Manchester
Applied Theatre Professional Doctorate....Professional Doctorate 36FT 72PT
Drama .... PhD 36FT 72PT

Queen Mary, University of London
Drama...PhD/MPhil

Queen's University Belfast
Drama Studies............................ PhD 36FT 72PT/MPhil 24FT 48PT

Music and performing arts

University of Roehampton
Drama, Theatre and Performance.... PhD 24-48FT 36-60PT/MPhil 21-36FT 33-48PT

Royal Academy of Music
Performance Practice .... MPhil 24FT/PhD 36FT

Royal Holloway, University of London
Drama and Theatre Studies .... MPhil 12FT/PhD 36FT

Royal Conservatoire of Scotland
Drama........ PhD 36FT 72PT

University of Sussex
Drama, Theatre and Performance.... PhD 24-48FT 36-72PT/MPhil 12-36FT 24-48PT

University of Ulster
Drama........ PhD 36FT 72PT

Dramatherapy
Taught Courses

Anglia Ruskin University
Dramatherapy........ MA 24FT

Central School of Speech and Drama, University of London
Applied Theatre (Drama in the Community and Drama Education) .... MA 12FT 24PT
Drama and Movement Therapy (Sesame) .... MA 18FT

University of Derby
Drama Therapy........ MA 24FT

University of Exeter
Theatre Practice: Applied Theatre........ MA 12FT 24PT
Theatre Practice: Directing and Actor Training....... MA 12FT 24PT
Theatre Practice: General Programme........ MA 12FT 24PT
Theatre Practice: Physical Performance & Actor Training........ MA 12FT 24PT
Theatre Practice: Staging Shakespeare..MA 12FT 24PT/MFA 24FT

University of Glasgow
Primary Expressive Arts .... PGCert 12PT

Manchester Metropolitan University
Movement Practice for Theatre .... MA 12FT

University of Roehampton
Dramatherapy........ MA 24FT 36PT

UCL - University College London
Performing Arts Medicine........ MSc 12FT 24PT/PGDip 9FT 24PT

University of Worcester
Dramatherapy........ MA 36PT
Psychodrama PsychotherapyMSc 60PT/PGDip 48PT/PGCert 24PT

Dramatherapy
Research Courses

University of Exeter
Drama........ PhD 48FT 89PT/MPhil 36FT 60PT

Music
Taught Courses

University of Aberdeen
Vocal Music........ MMus 12FT 24PT/PGDip 9FT/PGCert 4FT

Bangor University
Composition/Electroacoustic Composition/Sonic Art........ MMus 12FT 24PT
Music........ MA 12FT 24PT/PGDip 9FT
Performance (Music) .... MA 12FT 24PT/PGDip 9FT

Birmingham City University
Advanced Postgraduate Diploma (Professional Performance)...... AdvPGDip 12FT 24PT
Music (Intensive) .... MMus 13FT
Music .... MMus 22FT 33PT PGCert 12FT PGDip 12FT 24PT
Music Radio........ MA 12FT 24PT

University of Birmingham
Music .... MA 12FT 24PT

Arts University Bournemouth
Contemporary Performance........ MA 12FT 24PT

Bournemouth University
Digital Music and Audio Production........ MSc 12FT/MSc 24PT

Canterbury Christ Church University
Music .... MMus 12FT 24PT/PGDip 12FT 24PT

Cardiff University
Ethnomusicology........ MA 12FT 24PT
Music, Culture and Politics........ MA 12FT 24PT
Musicology........ MA 12FT 24PT
Performance Studies .... MMus 12FT 24PT

University of Central Lancashire
Music Industry Management and Promotion .... MSc 12FT 24PT
Music Practice .... MA 12FT 24PT
Performance ....MA 12FT 24-30PT/PGDip 12FT 24PT/PGCert 12FT

University of Chester
Education: Singing in the Curriculum........ PGCert 12 - 36PT
Performance Practice .MA 12FT 24 - 72PT/PGDip 12FT 24 - 60PT/PGCert 12FT 12 - 36PT
Popular Music..... MA 12FT 24-72PT/PGDip 12FT 24-60PT/PGCert 12FT 12-36PT

University of Chichester
Choral Studies ....MA 12-15FT 24-36PT/PGDip 9-12FT 18-24PT/PGCert 6-9FT 12-18PT
Music PerformanceMA 12-15FT 24-36PT/PGDip 9-12FT 18-24PT/PGCert 6-9FT 12-18PT

City University London
Music........ MA 12FT 24PT
Music Performance (Validated) .... MMus 12FT 24PT
Musicology (Ethnomusicology) .... MA 12FT 24PT

University College Cork
Arts (Music)........ HDip 9FT 18PT
Composition........ MA 12FT
Ethnomusicology........ MA 12FT
Music and Cultural History........ MA 12FT

Dublin Institute of Technology
Music (Performance) .... PGDip 9FT/MMus 12FT

Durham University
Ethnomusicology........ MA 12FT 24PT

University of East Anglia
Creative Entrepreneurship........ MA 12FT

University of Edinburgh
Digital Composition and Performance .... MSc 12FT 24PT
Early Keyboard Performance Studies .... MMus 12FT 24PT
Musical Instrument Research........ MMus 12FT 24PT
Musicology........ MMus 12FT 24PT

University of Glasgow
Historically Informed Performance Practice....... MMus 12FT 24PT
Popular Music........ MLitt 12FT 24PT
Popular Music: Creative Practice .... MLitt 12FT 24PT
Popular Music: Music Industries .... MLitt 12FT 24PT

Goldsmiths, University of London
Graduate Diploma in Music........ GradDip 12FT
Music........ GradDip 12FT
Music including specialist pathways........ MA 12FT 24PT
Music including specialist pathways........ MMus 12FT 24PT

University of Hertfordshire
Music Composition for Film and Media .....MSc 12FT 24PT/PGDip 12FT 24PT/PGCert 12FT 24PT
Music and Sound Design Technology (Audio Engineering).... MSc 12FT 24PT/PGDip 12FT 24PT/PGCert 12FT 24PT
Music and Sound Technology (Audio Programming)..... MSc 12FT 24PT/PGDip 12FT 24PT/PGCert 12FT 24PT

University of Huddersfield
MMus .... MMus 12FT 24PT
Performance .... PGDip 12FT

University of Hull
Creative Music Technology .... MRes 12FT 24PT
Music........ MMus 12FT 24PT
Sonic Art .... MRes 12FT 24PT

University of Kent
Music Composition........ MA 24FT 48PT
Music Technology........ MA 24FT 48PT

King's College London
Advanced Musical Studies .... PGCert 12FT 24PT
Music........ MMus 12FT 24PT

Kingston University
Music........ MA 12FT 24PT
Music and the Creative Economy........ MA 12FT 24PT
Production of Popular Music........ MMus 12FT 24PT

Lancaster University
Music by research........ MMus 12FT

Leeds College of Music
Community Music........ MA 12FT 28PT
Jazz........ MA 12FT 28PT
Music........ MA 12FT 28PT
Music Production .... MA 12FT 28PT

Leeds Metropolitan University
Music Production .... MA 12FT 24PT
Music Technology........ MSc 12FT 24PT

University of Leeds
Music........ PGDip 12FT 24PT
Music Technology and Computer Music .... MMus 12FT 24PT
Musicology........ MMus 12FT 24PT

University of Limerick
Classical String Performance........ MA 24FT
Community Music........ MA 12FT
Education Music .... Professional Diploma 12FT
Ethnomusicology........ MA 12FT
Irish Traditional Music Performance........ MA 12FT
Music Technology........ MA 12FT
Ritual Chant & Song........ MA 12FT

Liverpool Hope University
Music Since 1900.... MA 12FT 24PT/PGDip 12FT 24PT/PGCert 6FT
The Beatles, Popular Music and Society .... MA 12FT 24PT

University of Liverpool
Music........ MMus 12FT 24PT
Popular Music Studies........ MA 12FT 24PT

London Metropolitan University
Music Technology (by project) .... MA 12FT 24PT

University of Manchester
Musicology........ MMus 12FT 24PT

National University of Ireland, Maynooth
Music Technology........ HDip 12FT

Middlesex University
Music........ MA 12FT 24PT

Northumbria University
Master of Fine Art .... MFA 24FT 48PT
Music Management .... MA 12/18FT 24/28PT 24/28DL

The Open University
HumanitiesMA variableDL/PGDip variableDL/PGCert variableDL
Music........ MA variableDL

Oxford Brookes University
Composition and Sonic Art .... MA 12FT 24PT/PGDip 9FT 18PT
Contemporary Arts and Music .... MA 12FT 24PT/PGDip 9FT 18PT
Music .... MA 12FT 24PT

University of Oxford
Musicology........ MSt 10FT
Musicology and Performance .... MPhil 21FT

Queen Mary, University of London
Digital Music Processing........ MSc 12FT 24PT

Queen's University Belfast
Music........ MA 12FT 32PT

University of Reading
Education (Music Education)........ MA 12FT 24-84PT/PGDip 12FT
Music (Secondary Teaching) .... PGCE 10FT
Music Education .... MA 12FT 24-60PT/PGDip 12FT 24-60PT

University of Roehampton
Applied Music Education........ PGCert 6FT 24PT
Applied Music Psychology........ PGCert 6FT 24PT

Royal Academy of Music
Musical Theatre .... PGDip 9FT
Performance .... MA 12-24FT MMus 12-24FT

Royal College of Music
Composition .... PGDip 10FT/AdvPGDip 10FT/MMus 13FT
Composition and Composition for Screen........ MMus 13FT
Performance .... RCM Artist Diploma 10FT
Vocal Performance .....GradDip 10FT/PGDip 10FT/AdvPGDip 10FT

Royal Holloway, University of London
Advanced Musical Studies .... MMus 12FT 24PT

Royal Northern College of Music
Master of Music (1 year intensive)........ MMus 12FT
Master of Music (2 years)........ MMus 21FT
Master of Performance (1 year)........ MPerf 12FT
RNCM Postgraduate International Artist Diploma........ RNCM Postgraduate International Artist Diploma 9FT

Royal Conservatoire of Scotland
Music (all specialims) .... MMus 12FT/MMus 24FT
Music(Perf/Opera/Comp/Conducting/Accompaniment/Jazz/Piano for Dance/Repetiteur/Scot Music)...... PGDip 12FT 24-60PT
Musical Theatre (Directing)........ MA 12FT
Musical Theatre (Performance) .... MA 12FT

Royal Welsh College of Music and Drama
Brass Band ConductingPGDip 12FT/PGDip 24PT/MA 24PT/MMus 24PT
Choral Conducting .. MA 24PT/MA 12FT/PGDip 12FT/MMus 12FT
Composition ....PGDip 12FT/PGDip 24PT/MA 24PT/MMus 24PT
Historical PerformancePGDip 12FT/PGDip 24PT/MA 24PT/MMus 24PT
Jazz........ MA 24PT/MA 12FT/PGDip 12FT/MMus 12FT
Music Performance. MA 24PT/MA 12FT/PGDip 12FT/MMus 12FT
Musical Theatre .... MA 12FT
Opera Performance........ MA 24PT
Orchestral Conducting PGDip 12FT/PGDip 24PT/MA 24PT/MMus 24PT
Orchestral Performance........ PGDip 12FT/PGDip 24PT/MA 12FT/MMus 12FT
Repetiteurship.....PGDip 12FT/PGDip 24PT/MA 24PT/MMus 24PT

University of Salford
Digital Performance........ MA 12FT 36PT/PGDip 8FT 24PT
Media........ MRes 12FT 24PT
Music........ MRes 12FT 24PT
Performance .... MRes 12FT 24PT
Music........ MA 12FT 24PT

School of Oriental and African Studies - SOAS
Ethnomusicology........ MMus 12FT 24-36PT
Music and Development .... MA 12FT 24PT
Performance .... MMus 12FT 24PT

University of Sheffield
Ethnomusicology........ MA 12FT 24PT
Music Management .... MA 12FT 24PT
Music Performance........ MA 12FT 24PT

Music and performing arts

Music Psychology in Education .... MA 24 PTDL
Psychology for Musicians .... MA 24 PTDL
World Music Studies .... MA 24 PTDL

University of Southampton
Music .... MMus 12FT 24PT
Music .... MRes 12FT 24PT

Staffordshire University
Music Technology .... MSc 12-18FT

University of Surrey
Music .... MMus 12FT 24PT
Musicology .... MRes 12FT 24PT

Trinity College Dublin - the University of Dublin
Music and Media Technologies .... MPhil 24FT

Trinity Laban Conservatoire of Music and Dance
Creative Practice: Self Selected Pathway .... MA 12FT 24PT
Performance; Jazz; Composition; Creative Practice ... MMus 12FT 24PT
PGCE 'Musicians In Education' .... PGCE 12FT

University of Wales Trinity Saint David
Advanced Vocal Studies .... MA 12FT

University of Ulster
Music .... MMus 12FT 24PT

University of West London
Music .... MPhil 72FT 96PT
Performance (Work Based Learning) .... MMus 12FT 24PT/PGDip 9FT 18PT/PGCert 6FT 12PT

University of Wolverhampton
Music .... MA 12FT 24-36PT

University of York
Community Music .... MA 12FT 36PT
Music .... MA 12FT 24PT

York St John University
Music Composition .... MA 12FT 24PT

Music
Research Courses

University of Aberdeen
Music .... PhD 36FT/MPhil 24FT

Bangor University
Music (including Composition) .... PhD 24-36FT 48-60PT/MPhil 12FT 24PT/MA by research 12FT
Performance .... PhD 36FT 72PT/MPhil 24FT 48PT

Birmingham City University
Music .... PhD appx. 36FT appx. 60PT MPhil appx. 24FT appx. 36PT

University of Birmingham
Music .... MPhil 12FT 24PT
Musical Composition .... PhD 36FT 72PT/MPhil 12FT 24PT
Musicology .... PhD 36FT 72PT/MPhil 12FT 24PT

University of Cambridge
Music .... PhD 36FT

Canterbury Christ Church University
Music .... PhD 48FT 60PT/MPhil 24FT 48PT

Cardiff University
Performance .... PhD 36FT possiblePT/MPhil 12FT possiblePT
Thesis (Musicology) .... PhD 36FT possiblePT/MPhil 12FT possiblePT

University of Cumbria
Music .... PhD 48FT 72PT 72DL/MPhil 36FT 60PT 60DL

De Montfort University
Music, Technology and Innovation .. PhD 36-48FT 48-72PT/MPhil 12-24FT 24-48PT

Durham University
Music (Composition) .... MMus (comp) 24FT 48PT/PhD (comp) 36FT 72PT

University of Edinburgh
Music ..... PhD 36FT 72PT/MPhil 24FT 48PT/MSc by research 12FT 24PT

University of Glasgow
Music ..... PhD 36FT/MPhil 12FT/MLitt by research 12FT/MMus by research 12FT

Goldsmiths, University of London
Music (Research, Composition or Performance Practice) .... PhD 36-48FT 48-72PT/MPhil 24FT 36PT

University of Kent
Music Technology .... MPhil 36FT 60PT/PhD 36FT 60PT

King's College London
Music Research .... PhD 36FT 48PT/MPhil 36FT 48PT

Kingston University
Music .... MA by research 12FT 24PT/MPhil 24FT 48PT/PhD 48FT 72PT

Lancaster University
Music .... PhD 36FT 48PT/MPhil 24FT 36PT

University of Leeds
Music .... PhD 36FT/MPhil 24FT/MA by research 12FT

University of Liverpool
Music .... PhD 36FT 60PT/MPhil 24FT 48PT
Popular Music .... PhD 36FT 72PT/MPhil 24FT 48PT

University of Manchester
Music .... PhD 36FT 72PT
Musicology .... PhD 36FT 72PT

Newcastle University
Music .... MMus by research 12FT 24PT/PGDip by research 9FT 18PT

University of Nottingham
Music composition .... PhD 36FT 72PT/MPhil 24FT 48PT/AMusD 36FT 72PT/AMusM by research 12FT 24PT
Music research areas .... PhD tbcFT/MPhil tbcFT
Music research events .... PhD 36FT/MPhil 24FT
Musicology and Music Theory .. PhD 36FT 72PT/MPhil 24FT 48PT

The Open University
Acoustics .... PhD 36FT 72PT variableDL/MPhil 15FT 24PT variableDL
Environmental acoustics .... PhD 36FT 72PT/MPhil 15FT 24PT
Historical and contemporary study of musical texts, contexts, and performance ..... PhD 36FT 72PT variableDL/MPhil 15FT 24PT variableDL
Interdisciplinary themes in music research including film and literature .... PhD 36FT 72PT variableDL/MPhil 15FT 24PT variableDL
Music ..... PhD 36FT 72PT variableDL/MPhil 15FT 24PT variableDL
Music computing and acoustics .... PhD 36FT 72PT variableDL/MPhil 15FT 24PT variableDL
Musical acoustics .... PhD 36FT 72PT/MPhil 15FT 24PT
Non-invasive monitoring .... PhD 36FT 72PT/MPhil 15FT 24PT
The social and cultural study of music .... PhD 36FT 72PT variableDL/MPhil 15FT 24PT variableDL

Oxford Brookes University
Music .... PhD 24-60FT 48-72PT/MPhil 24-36FT 36-48PT

University of Oxford
Music .... DPhil 48FT

Queen's University Belfast
Ethnomusicology .... PhD 36FT 72PT/MPhil 24FT 48PT
Music and Sonic Arts .... PhD 36FT 72PT/MPhil 24FT 48PT

Royal Academy of Music
Composition .... MPhil 24FT/PhD 36FT
Performance Practice .... MPhil 24FT/PhD 36FT

Royal College of Music
Music .... DMus 36-48FT 48-72PT

Royal Holloway, University of London
Music .... PhD 36FT 72PT/MPhil 24FT 48PT

Royal Conservatoire of Scotland
Drama .... PhD 36FT 72PT
Music .... PhD 48FT

School of Oriental and African Studies - SOAS
Music .... PhD 36FT 72PT/MPhil 24FT 36PT

University of Southampton
Music .... PhD 48FT 84PT/MPhil 48FT 84PT

University of Surrey
Music .... PhD 33-48FT 45-96PT/MPhil 21-36FT 33-72PT

University of Sussex
Musical Composition Research Programme .... PhD 24-48FT 36-72PT/MPhil 12-36FT 24-48PT

University of Ulster
Music .... PhD 36FT 72PT/MPhil 24FT 48PT

University of West London
Classical Music Performance .... MPhil 24FT 36PT/DMA 36FT 72PT
Popular Music .... MPhil 12FT 24PT/DMA 36FT 72PT

University of York
Music .... PhD 36FT 72PT/MPhil 24FT 48PT
Music by Research .... MA by research 12FT 24PT

Music and performing arts
Taught Courses

University of Aberdeen
Music .... MMus 12FT 24PT

Bangor University
Composition/Electroacoustic Composition/Sonic Art .... MMus 12FT 24PT
Music .... MA 12FT 24PT/PGDip 9FT
Performance (Music) .... MA 12FT 24PT/PGDip 9FT

Bath Spa University
Performance .... MMus 12FT 24PT/PGDip 9FT 18PT/PGCert 4FT 9PT

Birmingham City University
Digital Arts in Performance .... MA 12FT 24PT
Performance and Pedagogy .... MMus 24FT 36PT
Professional Voice Practice .... MA 12FT 12PT/PGDip 9FT 9PT

University of Birmingham
Music .... MA 12FT 24PT

University of Brighton
Performance and Visual Practices .... MA 12FT 24PT

University of Bristol
Music .... MA 12FT 24PT

Brunel University
Contemporary Performance Making .... MA 12FT 24PT

Bucks New University
Performing Arts .... MA 12FT 24PT

University of Central Lancashire
Dance and Somatic Well-being .... MA 24PT/PGDip 24PT/PGCert 24PT
Music Industry Management and Promotion .... MSc 12FT 24PT
Music Practice .... MA 12FT 24PT
Performance .... MA 12FT 24-30PT/PGDip 12FT 24PT/PGCert 12FT

Central School of Speech and Drama, University of London
Music Theatre .... MA 12FT
Performance Practices and Research .... MA 12FT

University of Chester
Dance...... MA 12FT 24PT/PGDip 12FT 24PT/PGCert 12FT 12-24PT
Performance Practice .MA 12FT 24 - 72PT/PGDip 12FT 24 - 60PT/PGCert 12FT 12 - 36PT

University of Chichester
Music PerformanceMA 12-15FT 24-36PT/PGDip 9-12FT 18-24PT/PGCert 6-9FT 12-18PT

University College Cork
Arts (Music) .... HDip 9FT 18PT
Music and Cultural History .... MA 12FT

Durham University
Musicology .... MA 12FT 24PT

University of East Anglia
Creative Entrepreneurship .... MA 12FT
Theatre Directing: Text and Production .... MA 12FT 24PT

Edge Hill University
Making Performance .... MA 12FT 24PT

University of Edinburgh
Acoustics and Music Technology .... MSc 12FT 24PT
Composition .... MMus 12FT 24PT
Composition for Screen .... MSc 12FT 24PT
Digital Composition and Performance .... MSc 12FT 24PT
Early Keyboard Performance Studies .... MMus 12FT 24PT
Musical Instrument Research .... MMus 12FT 24PT
Musicology .... MMus 12FT 24PT
Theatre and Performance Studies .... MSc 12FT

University of Exeter
Theatre Practice: Applied Theatre .... MA 12FT 24PT
Theatre Practice: Directing and Actor Training .... MA 12FT 24PT
Theatre Practice: General Programme .... MA 12FT 24PT
Theatre Practice: Physical Performance & Actor Training .... MA 12FT 24PT
Theatre Practice: Staging Shakespeare .... MA 12FT 24PT/MFA 24FT

University of Glasgow
Historically Informed Performance Practice .... MMus 12FT 24PT
Musicology .... PGDip 12FT 24PT/PGCert 12FT 24PT
Popular Music: Creative Practice .... MLitt 12FT 24PT
Popular Music: Music Industries .... MLitt 12FT 24PT
Theatre History .... MLitt 12FT 24PT
Theatre Practices .... MLitt 12FT 24PT
Theatre Studies .... MLitt 12FT 24PT

Goldsmiths, University of London
Art & Politics .... MA 12FT 24PT
Fine Art .... MFA 24FT 36ft&ptPT/MFA 48PT/PGDip 12FT
Music (MMus) including specialist pathways .... MMus 12FT 24PT
Musical Theatre .... MA 12FT 24PT

University of Hertfordshire
Music Composition for Film and Media ..... MSc 12FT 24PT/PGDip 12FT 24PT/PGCert 12FT 24PT
Music and Sound Design Technology (Audio Engineering) .... MSc 12FT 24PT/PGDip 12FT 24PT/PGCert 12FT 24PT
Music and Sound Technology (Audio Programming) ..... MSc 12FT 24PT/PGDip 12FT 24PT/PGCert 12FT 24PT

University of Huddersfield
MMus .... MMus 12FT 24PT
Performance .... PGDip 12FT

University of Hull
Drama and Theatre Practice .... MA 12FT 24PT
Music .... MMus 12FT 24PT

University of Kent
Drama and Theatre: Physical Actor Training and Performance ..... MA 12FT
Drama and Theatre: Physical Actor Training and Performance with a term in Moscow .... MA 12FT

King's College London
Creative Arts in the Classroom .... MA 12FT 24-48PT
Theatre & Performance Studies .... MA 12FT 24PT

Music and performing arts

Kingston University
Music Performance ....MMus 12FT 24PT
Sonic Arts...MMus 12FT 24PT

Lancaster University
Theatre and Performance by Research .... MA 12FT 24PT

Leeds College of Music
Music .... MA 12FT 28PT

Leeds Metropolitan University
Audio Engineering...MSc 12FT 24PT
Music Production .... MA 12FT 24PT
Music Technology ....MSc 12FT 24PT

University of Leeds
Performance ....MMus 12FT 24PT
Performance, Culture and Context....... MA 12FT 24PT/PGDip 9FT
21PT/PGCert 6FT 12PT

University of Limerick
Classical String Performance..MA 24FT
Community Music..MA 12FT
Education Music ....Professional Diploma 12FT
Ethnochoreology ....MA 12FT
Ethnomusicology ....MA 12FT
Festive Arts..MA 12FT
Irish Traditional Music Performance.............................MA 12FT
Music Therapy ....MA 24FT
Ritual Chant & Song ....MA 12FT

University of Lincoln
Advanced Performance Practice.............................. MA 12FT 24PT
Choreographing Live Art...MFA 12FT 24PT
Choreography .... MA 12FT 24PT
Choreographing Live Art................. MA 12FT 24PT/MFA 12FT 24PT

Liverpool Hope University
Contemporary Popular Theatres ....MA 24PT
Creative Practice.................MA 12FT 24PT/PGDip 12FT 24PT
Education & Music...MA 36PT
Music Since 1900.... MA 12FT 24PT/PGDip 12FT 24PT/PGCert 6FT
Sacred Music .... MA 12FT 36PT

Manchester Metropolitan University
Design for Performance.......................MA/MFA 12/24FT 24/48PT
Theatre Studies ....MA/MFA 12/24FT 24/48PT

University of St Mark and St John
Creative Conflict Transformation through the Arts..........MA 20FT

Middlesex University
Choreography.. MA 16FT 28PT
Popular Music..MMus 12FT 24PT

Newcastle University
Music ....MMus 12FT 24PT/PGDip 9FT 18PT

University of Northampton
Performance Arts..............................MA 12FT 24PT/PGDip 12PT

University of Nottingham
Music .... MA 12FT 24PT

Oxford Brookes University
Contemporary Arts .... MA 12FT 24PT/PGDip 9FT 18PT
Contemporary Arts and Music .... MA 12FT 24PT/PGDip 9FT 18PT
Music .... MA 12FT 24PT

Plymouth University
Performance Practice .... MA 12FT 24PT
Performance Training...........................MA 12FT 24PT/MFA 18FT
Theatre and Performance.......................................MRes 12FT

Queen Mary, University of London
Theatre and Performance........................ MA 12FT 24PT

Queen's University Belfast
Drama.. MA 12FT 24PT
Music .... MA 12FT 32PT
Sonic Arts...MA 12FT

University of Roehampton
Dance Studies.. MA 12FT 24PT
Performance and Creative Research...............................MRes 12FT

Rose Bruford College
Learning and Teaching in Higher Education (Theatre &
Performing Arts) ....PGCHE 12PT

Royal Academy of Music
Performance .... MA 12-24FT
Performance ....MMus 12-24FT

Royal College of Music
Composition .... PGDip 10FT/AdvPGDip 10FT/MMus 13FT
Composition and Composition for Screen...................MMus 13FT
Integrated Masters Programme .... MMus 13FT/PGDip 10FT/
AdvPGDip 10FT
Performance ....RCM Artist Diploma 10FT

Royal Holloway, University of London
Advanced Musical Studies ....MMus 12FT 24PT

Royal Conservatoire of Scotland
Classical and Contemporary Text (Directing)....................MA 12FT
Musical Theatre (Directing) ....MA 12FT
Musical Theatre (Performance) ....MA 12FT

Royal Welsh College of Music and Drama
Acting for Stage Screen and Radio......................................MA 14FT
Brass Band ConductingPGDip 12FT/PGDip 24PT/MA 24PT/MMus
24PT
Choral Conducting .. MA 24PT/MA 12FT/PGDip 12FT/MMus 12FT
Composition ....PGDip 12FT/PGDip 24PT/MA 24PT/MMus 24PT
Historical PerformancePGDip 12FT/PGDip 24PT/MA 24PT/MMus
24PT
Jazz....................... MA 24PT/MA 12FT/PGDip 12FT/MMus 12FT
Music Performance . MA 24PT/MA 12FT/PGDip 12FT/MMus 12FT
Musical Theatre ....MA 12FT
Opera Performance ....MA 24PT
Orchestral Conducting PGDip 12FT/PGDip 24PT/MA 24PT/MMus
24PT
Orchestral Performance.......... PGDip 12FT/PGDip 24PT/MA 12FT/
MMus 12FT
Repetiteurship.....PGDip 12FT/PGDip 24PT/MA 24PT/MMus 24PT
Stage & Event Management .... MA 12FT 12PT
Theatre Design .... MA 12FT 12PT

University of Salford
Digital Performance.......................MA 12FT 36PT/PGDip 8FT 24PT
Music ....MRes 12FT 24PT
Performance ....MRes 12FT 24PT
Music .... MA 12FT 24PT

School of Oriental and African Studies - SOAS
Ethnomusicology...MMus 12FT 24-36PT
Music and Development .... MA 12FT 24PT
Performance ....MMus 12FT 24PT

University of Sheffield
Music Management .... MA 12FT 24PT
Music Performance .... MA 12FT 24PT
Music Psychology in Education.............................MA 24 PTDL
Theatre and Performance Studies............................MA 12FT 24PT
World Music Studies..MA 24 PTDL

University of Southampton
Music ....MRes 12FT 24PT

Staffordshire University
Community & Participatory Arts............................. MA 12FT 24PT
Music Technology ....MSc 12-18FT

Trinity College Dublin - the University of Dublin
Music and Media Technologies.......................... MPhil 24FT

Trinity Laban Conservatoire of Music and Dance
Creative Practice: Dance Professional Practice Pathway.MA 12FT
24PT
Creative Practice: Self Selected Pathway................. MA 12FT 24PT
PGCE 'Musicians In Education' ....PGCE 12FT

University of West London
PerformanceMMus 12FT 24PT 12-24DL/PGDip 9FT 18PT 9-18DL/
PGCert 6FT 12PT 6-12DL

University of Winchester
Doctor of Creative Arts (Performing Arts)...... PhD by taught 48FT
72PT
Popular Performances...MA 12FT 24PT/PGDip 12FT 24PT/PGCert
12FT 24PT
Theatre and Media for Development.MA 12FT 24PT/PGDip 12FT
24PT/PGCert 12FT 24PT

University of York
Community Music.. MA 12FT 36PT

Music and performing arts
Research Courses

University of Aberdeen
Music ....PhD 36FT/MPhil 24FT

Anglia Ruskin University
Music, Theatre and Performance, Music Therapy, Dramatherapy..
.... PhD 36FT 72PT/MPhil 24FT 48PT

Bangor University
Creative and Critical Writing, Film and Media, Professional
Writing .... MPhil 24FT 48PT/PhD 36FT 72PT
Creative and Critical Writing, Film and Media, Professional
Writing: Practice-Led Research ....MPhil 24FT 48PT/
PhD 36FT 72PT
Music (including Composition)................... PhD 24-36FT 48-60PT/
MPhil 12FT 24PT/MA by research 12FT
Performance .... PhD 36FT 72PT/MPhil 24FT 48PT

Bath Spa University
Centre for Musical Research .... PhD 24 - 60FT 36 - 72PT/MPhil
18 - 36FT 30 - 48PT

University of Birmingham
Music ....MPhil 12FT 24PT

University of Bristol
Music ....PhD 36FT 72PT/MMus by research 24FT 48PT/MLitt by
research 24FT 48PT/MPhil 12FT 24PT

Brunel University
Contemporary Drama and Performing ArtsPhD 36FT 48PT/MPhil
12FT 24PT
Music .... PhD 36FT 48PT/MPhil 12FT 24PT

University of Central Lancashire
Arts and Media....PhD 30-48FT 66-84PT/MPhil 18-36FT 42-60PT/
MA by research 12FT 24PT

University of Chichester
Dance.. PhD 36FT 84PT/MPhil 24FT 84PT

City University London
Music ....PhD 36FT/MPhil 24FT/DMA

University of Cumbria
A programme of research may be proposed in any relevant field
of study ....PhD xFT/MA by research xFT/MPhil xFT/MRes xFT

De Montfort University
Performance Studies ....PhD 36-48FT 48-72PT/MPhil 12-24FT
24-48PT

Durham University
Music .... PhD 36FT 72PT/MMus by research 24FT 48PT/MA by
research 12FT 24PT

University of Edinburgh
Creative Music Practice..................................... PhD 36FT 72PT
Music ..... PhD 36FT 72PT/MPhil 24FT 48PT/MSc by research 12FT
24PT

University of Exeter
Drama.. PhD 48FT 89PT/MPhil 36FT 60PT

University of Hertfordshire
Composition and Performance as Research Practice (CAPARP).....
PhD 36FT 72PT/MPhil 24FT 48PT/MRes 12FT 24PT

University of Hull
Music .... PhD 36FT 60PT/MPhil 24FT 36PT
Theatre and Contemporary Studies ...PhD 36FT 60PT/MPhil 24FT
36PT/MA by research 12FT 24PT

Keele University
Music .... PhD 24-48FT 48-84PT/MPhil 12-24FT 24-36PT

Kingston University
Media, Film and Drama .PhD 48FT 72PT/MPhil 24FT 48PT/MA by
research 12FT 24PT

Liverpool Hope University
Postgraduate Research .... PhD 24FT 48PT/MPhil 12FT 24PT

Manchester Metropolitan University
Department of Arts, Design and Performance ....PhD/MPhil/
MA by research

Newcastle University
Music .... MMus by research 12FT 24PT/PGDip by
research 9FT 18PT
Music .... PhD 36FT 72PT/MPhil 12FT 24PT

Oxford Brookes University
Music .... PhD 24-60FT 48-72PT/MPhil 24-36FT 36-48PT

University of Oxford
Music...DPhil 48FT

Plymouth University
Dance...MRes 12FT

Queen's University Belfast
Ethnomusicology........................ PhD 36FT 72PT/MPhil 24FT 48PT

University of Roehampton
Drama, Theatre and Performance.... PhD 24-48FT 36-60PT/MPhil
21-36FT 33-48PT

Royal Academy of Music
Composition ....MPhil 24FT/PhD 36FT
Performance Practice ....MPhil 24FT/PhD 36FT

Royal Conservatoire of Scotland
Drama.. PhD 36FT 72PT
Music ....PhD 48FT

Royal Welsh College of Music and Drama
Arts Management ....MA by research 12FT 24PT

University of Salford
Media, Music and Performing Arts Research Centre....PhD/MPhil

School of Oriental and African Studies - SOAS
Music .... PhD 36FT 72PT/MPhil 24FT 36PT

University of Sussex
Music Research ProgrammePhD 24-48FT 36-72PT/MPhil 12-36FT
24-48PT
Music Theatre Research ProgrammePhD 24-48FT 36-72PT/MPhil
12-36FT 24-48PT

University of Ulster
Master of Research, Arts (MRes)...........................MRes 12FT 24PT
Music .... PhD 36FT 72PT/MPhil 24FT 48PT

University of West London
Classical Music Performance....MPhil 24FT 36PT/DMA 36FT 72PT

University of Worcester
Drama... MPhil 24FT 48PT/PhD 48FT 70PT

University of York
Music Technology .... PhD 36FT 72PT/MA by research 12FT 24PT

Music and performing arts

Music therapy
Taught Courses

University of Aberdeen
Studies in Mindfulness .... MSc 36PT/PGDip 24PT/PGCert 12PT

Anglia Ruskin University
Music Therapy .... MA 24FT

City University London
Music Therapy .... MMT 24FT

Goldsmiths, University of London
Music, Mind and Brain .... MSc 12FT 24PT

Leeds Metropolitan University
Psychological Therapies .... MA 48PT

University of Limerick
Music Therapy .... MA 24FT

University of Roehampton
Applied Music Psychology .... MA 12FT 24PT
Music Therapy .... MA 24FT 36PT
Applied Music Psychology .... PGCert 6FT 24PT PGDip 9FT 24PT

University of Sheffield
Music Psychology in Education .... MA 24 PTDL
Psychology of Music .... MA 12FT 24PT

University of South Wales
Art Psychotherapy .... MA 36PT
Buddhist Studies .... PGCert 12DL/PGDip 24DL/MA 36DL
Evaluation Studies .... PGCert 9-12DL
Music Therapy .... MA 36PT

University of the West of England, Bristol
Music Therapy .... MA 36PT

Theatre studies
Taught Courses

Aberystwyth University
Politics, Media and Performance .... MA 12FT 24PT
Practising Theatre and Performance .... MA 12FT 24PT/PGDip 9FT 18PT

University of the Arts London - Central Saint Martins College of Art and Design
Acting (formerly MA European Classical Acting) Drama Centre London .... MA 12FT
Collaborative Performance .... MA 12FT

University of the Arts London - London College of Fashion
Costume Design for Performance .... MA 15FT 30PT

University of the Arts London - Wimbledon College of Art
Theatre: Interdisciplinary Performance .... MA 12FT

Bangor University
Creative Practice .... MRes 12FT 24PT

Bath Spa University
Performing Shakespeare .... MA 12FT 24PT/MFA 12FT 24PT
Theatre for Young Audiences .... MA 12FT 24PT

Birkbeck, University of London
Creative Producing .... MA 12FT
Shakespeare and Contemporary Performance .... MA 12FT 24PT
Text and Performance (with RADA) .... MA 12FT 24PT
Theatre Directing .... MFA 24FT

Birmingham City University
Acting .... MA 12FT/PGDip 10FT
Acting: The British Tradition .... MA 12FT/PGDip 9FT

Arts University Bournemouth
Costume .... MA 12FT 24PT

University of Bristol
Performance Research .... MA 12FT 24PT

University of Central Lancashire
Performance ....MA 12FT 24-30PT/PGDip 12FT 24PT/PGCert 12FT

Central School of Speech and Drama, University of London
Advanced Theatre Practice .... MA 12FT
Applied Theatre (Drama in the Community and Drama Education) .... MA 12FT 24PT
Creative Producing .... MA 12FT 24PT/MFA 24FT
Applied Theatre with Young People .... PGCert 12FT
Scenography .... MA 12FT
Theatre Studies (Performance and the City) .... MA 12FT 24PT

University of Chester
Dance...... MA 12FT 24PT/PGDip 12FT 24PT/PGCert 12FT 12-24PT

University of Chichester
Theatre Collectives .... MA 12FT 24PT 12DL

University College Cork
Drama & Theatre Studies .... MA 12FT

University of Dundee
Theatre Studies .... MLitt 12FT

University of East Anglia
Film, Television and Creative Practice .... MA 12FT 24PT
Theatre Directing: Text and Production .... MA 12FT 24PT

University of Edinburgh
Theatre and Performance Studies .... MSc 12FT
Writing for Theatre and Performance .... MSc 12FT 24PT

University of Exeter
Theatre Practice: Applied Theatre .... MA 12FT 24PT
Theatre Practice: Directing and Actor Training .... MA 12FT 24PT
Theatre Practice: General Programme .... MA 12FT 24PT
Theatre Practice: Physical Performance & Actor TrainingMA 12FT 24PT
Theatre Practice: Staging Shakespeare..MA 12FT 24PT/MFA 24FT

National University of Ireland Galway
Drama & Theatre Studies .... MA 12FT

University of Glasgow
Historically Informed Performance Practice....... MMus 12FT 24PT
Playwriting & Dramaturgy .... MLitt 12FT
Theatre History .... MLitt 12FT 24PT
Theatre Practices .... MLitt 12FT 24PT
Theatre Studies .... MLitt 12FT 24PT

Goldsmiths, University of London
Applied Theatre: Drama in Educational, Community & Social Contexts .... MA 12FT 24PT
Black British Writing, Drama and Performance...... MA 12FT 24PT
Contemporary African Theatre & Performance .... MA 12FT
Performance and Culture: Interdisciplinary PerspectivesMA 12FT 24PT

University of Huddersfield
Performance .... PGDip 12FT

University of Hull
Drama and Theatre Practice .... MA 12FT 24PT

University of Kent
Arts Criticism .... MA 12FT 24PT
Drama and Theatre .... MA 12FT 24PT
Drama and Theatre: Physical Actor Training and PerformanceMA 12FT
Drama and Theatre: Physical Actor Training and Performance with a term in Moscow .... MA 12FT
Shakespeare .... MA 12FT 24PT

King's College London
Theatre & Performance Studies .... MA 12FT 24PT

Leeds Metropolitan University
Performance .... MA 12FT 24PT

University of Leeds
Performance, Culture and Context .... MA 12FT 24PT/PGDip 9FT 21PT/PGCert 6FT 12PT
Theatre Making: Critical Engagement with Creative Practice. MA 12FT
Theatre and Development Studies .... MA 12FT

London South Bank University
Theatre Practice .... MA 28PT

Loughborough University
Performance and Multi-Media .... MA 12FT 24PT

Manchester Metropolitan University
Movement Practice for Theatre .... MA 12FT

University of Manchester
Applied Theatre (pathway of Theatre and Performance)MA 12FT 24PT
Theatre & Performance .... MA 12FT 24PT

Newcastle University
Creative Arts Practice .... MA 12FT 24PT
Film: Theory and Practice .... MA 12FT 24PT

Plymouth University
Theatre and Performance .... MRes 12FT

Queen's University Belfast
Drama .... MA 12FT 24PT

University of Reading
Early Modern Literature & Drama .... MA (Res) 12FT 24PT
Theatre Studies .... MA (Res) 12FT 24PT

Rose Bruford College
Ensemble Theatre .... MA 12FT/PGDip 10FT
Theatre for Young Audiences .....MA 12FT 24PT/PGDip 10FT 22PT
Learning and Teaching in Higher Education (Theatre & Performing Arts) .... PGCHE 12PT

Royal College of Music
Performance .... RCM Artist Diploma 10FT

Royal Holloway, University of London
Research (Drama) .... MA 12FT 24PT
Theatre .... MA 12FT 24PT

Royal Conservatoire of Scotland
Classical and Contemporary Text (Acting) .... MA 12FT
Classical and Contemporary Text (Directing) .... MA 12FT
Musical Theatre (Directing) .... MA 12FT
Musical Theatre (Performance) .... MA 12FT

Royal Welsh College of Music and Drama
Musical Theatre .... MA 12FT
Theatre Design .... MA 12FT 12PT

University of Salford
Digital Performance .... MA 12FT 36PT/PGDip 8FT 24PT

School of Oriental and African Studies - SOAS
Performance .... MMus 12FT 24PT

SUniversity of Sheffield
Theatre and Performance Studies .... MA 12FT 24PT

St Mary's University College, Twickenham
Physical Theatre .... MA 12FT

University of Surrey
Dance Cultures .... MA 12FT 24 or 36PT
Theatre Studies .... MA 12FT 24 or 36PT

Trinity College Dublin - the University of Dublin
Theatre and Performance .... MPhil 12FT

University of Wales Trinity Saint David
Theatre and Society .... MA 12FT/PGDip 9FT/PGCert 6FT

University of York
Theatre: Writing, Directing and Performance .... MA 12FT 24PT

York St John University
Applied Theatre .... MA 12FT 24PT
Theatre and Performance .... MA 12FT 24PT

Theatre studies
Research Courses

Aberystwyth University
Theatre, Film and Television Studies .... MPhil 12FT 24PT PhD 36FT 60PT

University of Birmingham
Directing and Dramaturgy .... MRes 12FT 24PT
Drama and Theatre PhD by Distance .... PhD 36FT 72PT/MA by research 12FT 24PT/MPhil 12FT 24PT
Drama and Theatre Studies .... MRes 12FT 24PT
Drama and Theatre Studies Practice-Based (Dramaturgy, Playwriting or Performance) .... PhD 36FT 72PT

University of Bristol
Drama: Theatre, Film, Television .... PhD 36FT 72PT/MLitt by research 24FT 48PT/MPhil 12FT 24PT

Central School of Speech and Drama, University of London
Drama, Performing, Theatre Studies, and Design for Theatre PhD 36 (min)FT 72 (min)PT

University of Edinburgh
European Theatre .... PhD 36FT 72PT

University of Exeter
Drama .... PhD 48FT 89PT/MPhil 36FT 60PT

University of Glasgow
Theatre .... PhD 36FT/MPhil 12FT/MLitt by research 12FT

University of Hull
Theatre and Contemporary Studies ...PhD 36FT 60PT/MPhil 24FT 36PT/MA by research 12FT 24PT

University of Kent
Drama .... MA by research 12FT 24PT/PhD 36FT 60PT
Drama (Practice as Research) .... MA by research 12FT 24PT

Lancaster University
Theatre Studies .... PhD 36PT

Loughborough University
Drama and Theatre Studies .... PhD 36FT 60PT/MPhil 24FT 36PT

University of Manchester
Applied Theatre Professional Doctorate....Professional Doctorate 36FT 72PT

Queen's University Belfast
Drama Studies .... PhD 36FT 72PT/MPhil 24FT 48PT

University of Roehampton
Drama, Theatre and Performance.... PhD 24-48FT 36-60PT/MPhil 21-36FT 33-48PT

Royal Academy of Music
Performance Practice .... MPhil 24FT/PhD 36FT

Royal Holloway, University of London
Drama and Theatre Studies .... MPhil 12FT/PhD 36FT

Royal Conservatoire of Scotland
Drama .... PhD 36FT 72PT

University of Sussex
Drama, Theatre and Performance.... PhD 24-48FT 36-72PT/MPhil 12-36FT 24-48PT

University of Warwick
Theatre Studies .... PhD 36FT 60PT/MPhil 24FT 36PT/MA by research 12FT 24PT

University of York
Theatre, Film and Television ...... MPhil 24FT 48PT/PhD 36FT 72PT

Philosophy

Aesthetics
Taught Courses

University of Central Lancashire
Non-Surgical Facial Aesthetics for Registered Healthcare Professionals....MSc 36PT/PGDip 24PT

University College Cork
Aesthetics and History of Art....MA 12FT

University of Edinburgh
Contemporary Art Theory....MA 12FT 24PT/MFA 24FT

University of Hertfordshire
Applied Arts....MA 12FT 24PT/PGDip 12FT 24PT

University of Kent
History and Philosophy of Art....MA 12FT 24PT
History and Philosophy of Art (Paris option)....MA 12FT 24PT
Modern French Studies: Writing, Theory and Visual Culture...MA 12FT 24PT

Kingston University
Aesthetics and Art Theory....MA 12FT 24PT

Lancaster University
Contemporary Arts Research (With Pathways)....MA 12FT 24PT

University of Liverpool
Art, Aesthetics and Cultural Institutions....MA 12FT 24PT

Oxford Brookes University
Contemporary Arts and Music....MA 12FT 24PT/PGDip 9FT 18PT

University of Oxford
Film Aesthetics....MSt 9FT

Sotheby's Institute of Art
Contemporary Art....MA 14FT/PGDip 9FT
Contemporary Design....MA 14FT/PGDip 9FT

University of Southampton
Aesthetics....MA 12FT 24PT

Aesthetics
Research Courses

University of Kent
History & Philosophy of Art....MA by research 12FT 24PT/MPhil 24FT 36PT/PhD 36FT 60PT

Lancaster University
Contemporary Arts....PhD 36FT 48PT/MPhil 24FT 36PT

School of Oriental and African Studies - SOAS
Art and Archaeology....PhD 36FT/MPhil 24FT

Epistemology
Taught Courses

University of Aberdeen
Philosophical Research....MLitt 12FT 24PT

Bangor University
Philosophy and Religion....MA 12FT 36PT
Philosophy and Religion....MRes 12FT 36PT

Durham University
Ancient Philosophy....MA 12FT

University of East Anglia
Philosophy....MRes 12FT 24PT/MA 24PT

University of Kent
Anthropology and Conservation....MA 12FT 24PT

University of Roehampton
Attachment Studies....MSc 18-24FT 24-36PT

Schumacher College
Holistic Science....MSc 12FT

University of Sheffield
Social Research....MA 12FT 24PT

Epistemology
Research Courses

Bangor University
Theology and Religious Studies....MPhil 24FT 36PT/PhD 24-36FT 60PT

University of East Anglia
Philosophy....PhD 36FT 72PT/MPhil 24FT 48PT

University of Exeter
Philosophy....MA by research 12FT 24PT/MPhil 24FT 48PT/PhD 48FT 72PT

Ethics
Taught Courses

Aston University
Social Responsibility & Sustainability....MSc 12FT 24PT

Bangor University
Medical Sciences....MRes 12FT 24PT/PGCert 3FT 15PT

Birkbeck, University of London
Corporate Governance and Business Ethics....MSc 12FT 24PT/MRes 12FT 24PT/PGCert 12PT

University of Birmingham
Global Ethics...MSc 12FT 24PT/PGDip 6FT 36PT/PGCert 4FT 24PT
Human Rights and Human Values....MSc 12FT 24-48PT/PGDip 9FT 36PT/PGCert 4FT 24PT
International Law, Ethics and Politics....MA 12FT 24PT
Philosophy of Religion and Ethics....MA 12FT 24PT/Diploma 8FT 16PT/Cert 4FT 8PT

University of Brighton
Applied Ethics....MA 12FT 24PT/PGDip 12FT 24PT/PGCert 12FT 24PT
Ethics of Art and Design....MA 12FT 24PT/PGDip 12FT 24PT/PGCert 12FT 24PT
Ethics of Education....MA 12FT 24PT/PGDip 12FT 24PT/PGCert 12FT 24PT
Healthcare Ethics....MA 12FT 24 - 72PT/PGCert 12FT 24 - 72PT/PGDip 12FT 24 - 72PT
Medical Ethics....MA 12FT 24PT/PGDip 12FT 24PT/PGCert 12FT 24PT
Philosophy of Language....MA 12FT 24-72PT
Politics and Ethics....MA 12FT 24PT/PGDip 12FT 24PT/PGCert 12FT 24PT

University of Bristol
Health Care Ethics and Law..MSc 24PT/Diploma 24PT/Cert 24PT
Philosophy and Law....MA 12FT 24PT

Cardiff University
Ethics and Social Philosophy....MA 12FT 24PT
Legal Aspects of Medical Practice....LLM 12FT 24PT

University of Central Lancashire
Medical Law and Bioethics....LLM 12FT 24PT/PGDip 12FT 24PT
Personality Disorder (Practice Development)....MSc 36-60PT/PGDip 24PT
Personality Disorder (Research)....MSc 36-60PT/PGDip 12-24PT

University of Chester
Faiths and Public Policy....MA 12FT 36PT 36DL/PGDip 12FT 24-36PT 24-36DL/PGCert 12FT 12-24PT 12-24DL

De Montfort University
Medical Law and Ethics....PGDip 15DL/LLM 15-27DL

University of Dundee
Healthcare Law and Ethics (LLM by distance learning)....LLM 36DL

University of East Anglia
Philosophy and Literature....MA 12FT 24PT

Edge Hill University
Mental Health Law and Ethics....PGCert 12FT 36PT

University of Edinburgh
Ethics....MTh 12FT 24PT/MSc 12FT 24PT
Medical Law and Ethics (Online Distance Learning)....LLM 12FT 20 - 36PT 20 - 36DL
Philosophy....MSc 12FT 24PT
Philosophy (MSc by Research)....MSc(Res) 12FT 24PT

University of Essex
Ethics, Politics and Public Policy....MA 12FT 24PT

University of Exeter
Ethics, Religion and Society....MA 12FT 24PT

National University of Ireland Galway
Ethics, Culture and Global Change....MA 12FT 24PT

University of Glasgow
Animal Welfare Science, Ethics & Law....MSc 12FT/PGDip 9FT
Applied Medical Science....MSc 12FT
Quantitative Methods in Biodiversity, Conservation and Epidemiology....MSc 12FT/PGDip 9FT

Heythrop College
Contemporary Ethics....MA 12FT 24PT

University of Hull
Applied Ethics....MA 12FT 24PT

Keele University
Ethics of Policing and Criminal JusticeMA 12FT 24PT/PGDip 12PT
Humanities (Philosophy)....MRes 12FT 24PT
Medical Ethics and Law....MA 12FT 24PT 24DL/PGDip 12PT 12DL
Research Ethics....MA 12FT 24DL/PGDip 12DL/PGCert 12DL

University of Kent
Medical Humanities....MA 12FT 24PT
Medical Law and Ethics....LLM 12FT 24PT/PGDip 12FT 24PT
Science, Communication and Society....MSc 12FT 24PT

King's College London
Global Ethics & Human Values....MA 12FT
Health & Society....MSc 12FT 24-48PT
Jewish Studies....MA 12FT 24PT
Medical Ethics & Law....MA 12FT 24PT

Leeds Metropolitan University
Applied Biomedical Sciences Research....MSc 12FT
Biomedical Sciences....MSc 12FT unknownPT

University of Leeds
Healthcare Ethics....MA 12FT 24PT

Manchester Metropolitan University
European Philosophy....MA 12FT 24PT

Middlesex University
Ethics and Law in Healthcare Practice....MA 24PT/PGDip 18PT/PGCert 12PT

Newcastle University
International Politics (Global Justice and Ethics)...MA 12FT 24PT

Nottingham Trent University
Health Law....LLM 12FT 24PT
Philosophy....MA 12FT 24PT/PGDip 12FT 24PT

University of Nottingham
Public Procurement Law and Policy....PGDip 21PT/LLM 24PT/PGCert 12-21PT

University of Oxford
Philosophy....BPhil 48FT/MLitt 36FT/MSt 11FT
Philosophy of Physics....MSt 12FT
Politics: Political Theory....MPhil 21FT

University of Reading
Ethics & Political Theory....MA 12FT 24PT
Philosophy....MA 12FT 24PT

University of Salford
Health Care Law..LLM 27DL/MA 27DL/PGDip 20DL/PGCert 12DL

University of Sheffield
Biotechnology Law and Ethics....LLM 12FT 24PT
Philosophy....MA 12FT 24PT
Religion, Conflict and the Media....MA 12FT 24PT
Reproductive and Developmental Medicine....MSc 12FT
Stem Cell and Regenerative Medicine....MSc 12FT

University of Southampton
Philosophy....MA 12FT 24PT

St Mary's University College, Twickenham
Bioethics and Medical Law....MA 12FT 36PT/PGDip 12FT 24PT/PGCert 6FT 12PT

Staffordshire University
Healthcare Law and Ethics....LLM 18FT 36PT

University of Stirling
Philosophy....MLitt 12FT

Swansea University
Healthcare Law and Ethics....MA 36PT

University of Wales Trinity Saint David
Applied Philosophy....MA 48PT/PGCert 48PT/PGDip 48PT
Philosophy....MA 48PT/PGDip 48PT/PGCert 48PT

UCL - University College London
Global Governance and Ethics....MSc 12FT 24PT
Philosophy....MA 12FT 24PT
Philosophy, Politics and Economics of Health...MA 12FT 36-60PT

University of Warwick
Philosophy and Ethics of Mental Health....MSc 12FT 24PT 36DL/MA 12FT 24PT 36DL/PGA 6FT
Philosophy and Ethics of Mental Health....MSc 12FT 24PT 36DL/MA 12FT 24PT 36DL/PGDip 12FT 24PT 36DL/PGA 6FT

University of Winchester
Religion, Ethics and Society....MTh 12FT 24PT 12/24DL/PGDip 12FT 24PT 12/24DL/PGCert 12FT 24PT 12/24DL
Theology, Religion and Ethics....GradDip 12FT 24PT

University of York
Philosophy, Theology and Ethics....MA 12FT 24PT
Political Philosophy....MA 12FT 24PT/PGDip 12FT

Ethics
Research Courses

Barts and the London School of Medicine and Dentistry
Department of Human Science and Medical Ethics...PhD/MPhil/MA by research

University of Birmingham
Biomedical Ethics by research....PhD 36FT 72PT/MSc by research 12FT 24PT
Global Ethics....PhD 36FT 72PT

Cardiff University
Philosophy....PhD 36FT on offerPT/MPhil 12FT on offerPT

University of Central Lancashire
Bioethics....MProf by research 12FT 24PT/MPhil 24FT 36-48PT/PhD 36FT 60PT/MD 36FT 60PT

University of Cumbria
Religion and Ethics..PhD 48FT 72PT 72DL/MPhil 36FT 60PT 60DL

University of Dundee
Philosophy....MPhil 24FT PhD 36FT

University of Edinburgh
Philosophy....PhD 36FT 72PT/MPhil 24FT 48PT

University of Exeter
Philosophy....MA by research 12FT 24PT/MPhil 24FT 48PT/PhD 48FT 72PT

University of Gloucestershire
Philosophy and Ethics....PhD 30-48FT

University of Hull
Philosophy....PhD 36FT 60PT/MPhil 24FT 36PT

Philosophy

Keele University
Ethics .... PhD 24-48FT 48-84PT/MPhil 12-24FT 24-36PT
Medical Ethics ....MRes 36PT 36DL/DMedEth 48-84PT 48-84DL
Medical Ethics Professional Doctorate .. DMedEth 48-84PT/MRes 24-36PT

Manchester Metropolitan University
Philosophy............PhD 24-48FT 42-84PT 42-84DL/MPhil 18-36FT 36-72PT 36-72DL/MA by research 12-24FT 24-42PT 24-42DL

University of Manchester
Bioethics and Medical Jurisprudence....................... PhD 36FT 72PT
Science Ethics ....PhD 36FT

Newcastle University
Philosophical Studies .... PhD 36FT 72PT/MPhil 12FT 24PT

The Open University
Mind, Meaning and Rationality.......... PhD 36FT 72PT variableDL/MPhil 15FT 24PT variableDL
Philosophy................ PhD 36FT 72PT variableDL/MPhil 15FT 24PT variableDL
Value...... PhD 36FT 72PT variableDL/MPhil 15FT 24PT variableDL

Metaphysics
Taught Courses

University of Aberdeen
Philosophical Research..MLitt 12FT 24PT
Plurilingual Education...................................MEd 24PT/PGCert 12PT
Studies in Mindfulness .... MSc 36PT/PGDip 24PT/PGCert 12PT

University of Bradford
Analytical Sciences....... MSc 12FT 60PT/PGDip 12FT 60PT/PGCert 12FT 60PT

University of Leeds
Philosophy of Physics .... MA 12FT 24PT

University of Liverpool
Metaphysics, Language and the Mind..................... MA 12FT 24PT

University of St Andrews
Philosophy (collaborative)........MLitt 12FT 24PT/PGDip 9FT 21PT/Conversion Diploma 9FT 21PT

Metaphysics
Research Courses

University of Hull
Philosophy of Mind and Body ....MA by research 12FT 24PT

University of Liverpool
Advanced Science (Physical Science Pathway - Nanoscale and Condensed Matter Physics) ....MRes 12FT

The Open University
Philosophy................ PhD 36FT 72PT variableDL/MPhil 15FT 24PT variableDL

Philosophy
Taught Courses

University of Aberdeen
History and Philosophy of Science.....MLitt 12FT 24PT/PGDip 9FT 18PT
Philosophical Research..MLitt 12FT 24PT
Philosophy.................................... MLitt 12FT 24PT/PGDip 9FT 18PT

Bangor University
Philosophy and Religion ....MA 12FT 36PT MRes 12FT 36PT

Birkbeck, University of London
History of Ideas... MA 12FT 24PT
Philosophy.............................. MA 12FT 24PT/PGCert 12FT

Birmingham City University
MA Media Arts Philosophy Practice.......................... MA 12FT 24PT

University of Birmingham
Philosophy... MA 12FT 24PT
Philosophy of Health and Happiness........................ MA 12FT 24PT
Philosophy of Health and Happiness (Distance learning)........MA 12FT 36PT
Philosophy of Language and Linguistics .... MA 12FT 24PT
Philosophy of Mind and Cognitive Science............. MA 12FT 24PT
Philosophy of Religion and Ethics.....MA 12FT 24PT/Diploma 8FT 16PT/Cert 4FT 8PT
Philosophy of Religion and Ethics MA (Distance Learning)......MA 12FT 36PT

University of Brighton
Philosophy of Language... MA 12FT 24-72PT

University of Bristol
Logic and Philosophy of Mathematics .... MA 12FT 24PT
Philosophy ....Diploma 12FT 24PT MA 12FT 24PT
Philosophy and History of Science............................ MA 12FT 24PT
Philosophy and Law... MA 12FT 24PT
Philosophy of Biological and Cognitive Sciences ... MA 12FT 24PT

Cardiff University
Analytic and Modern European Philosophy........... MA 12FT 24PT

University of Central Lancashire
Creative Thinking... MA 30DL

Philosophy & Mental Health.......................MA 36DL/PGDip 24DL/PGCert 12DL

University College Cork
Arts (Philosophy) ....HDip 9FT 18PT
Philosophy..MA 12FT

University of Dundee
Continental Philosophy ....MLitt 12FT
Non-Graduating Taught Postgraduate in School of Humanities.. PG module variableFT
Philosophy and Literature ....MLitt 12FT

Durham University
History and Philosophy of Science and Medicine .. MA 12FT 24PT
Philosophy..GradDip 9FT
Philosophy.. MA 12FT 24PT

University of East Anglia
Philosophy.. MRes 12FT 24PT/MA 24PT
Philosophy and Literature.. MA 12FT 24PT
Philosophy, Politics and Economics of Public Choice........MA 12FT 24PT

University of Edinburgh
Ancient Philosophy..MSc 12FT 24PT
Ethics ....MTh 12FT 24PT/MSc 12FT 24PT
Evolution of Language & Cognition ....MSc 12FT 24PT
Intellectual History ....MSc 12FT 24PT
Philosophy...MSc 12FT 24PT
Philosophy (MSc by Research)..........................MSc(Res) 12FT 24PT

University of Essex
Continental Philosophy .... MA 12FT 24PT
Ethics, Politics and Public Policy................................ MA 12FT 24PT
Philosophy... MA 12FT 24PT
Philosophy and Psychoanalysis .... MA 12FT 24PT

University of Exeter
History and Philosophy of Biology............................ MA 12FT 24PT
Philosophy and Sociology of Science........................ MA 12FT 24PT
Science and Technology Studies.............................MRes 12FT 24PT
Social and Political Philospohy.................................. MA 12FT 24PT

University of Glasgow
Philosophy..MLitt 12FT 24PT
Philosophy (Conversion Programme)....................MLitt 12FT 24PT

University of Greenwich
Media, Arts, Philosophy and Practice .... MA 12FT 24PT
Philosophy.................................MA 24PT/PGDip 24PT/PGCert 24PT

Heythrop College
Contemporary Ethics... MA 12FT 24PT
Philosophy... MA 12FT 24PT
Philosophy and Religion .... MA 12FT 24PT
Philosophy in Education .... MA 12FT 24PT

University of Hull
Philosophy..MRes 12FT 24PT
Spirituality Studies... MA 12FT 24PT

Institute of Education
English, Globalization and Language Policy (formerly World Englishes) .... MA 12FT 24-48PT
Philosophy of Education.. MA 12FT 24-48PT

Islamic College for Advanced Studies
Islam and the West: A Comparative Study ..MA 12FT 24PT 36DL/PGDip 12FT 24PT
Islam and the West: A Comparative Study - via Distance Learning ....MA 12FT 24PT 36-48DL

Keele University
Humanities (Philosophy)..MRes 12FT 24PT

University of Kent
Graduate Diploma in Humanities (Philosophy) ....GradDip 12FT
History and Philosophy of Art.................................... MA 12FT 24PT
History and Philosophy of Art (Paris option)........... MA 12FT 24PT
Philosophy... MA 12FT 24PT
Reasoning.. MA 12FT 24PT

King's College London
History of Philosophy.. MA 12FT 24PT
Language & Cognition... MA 12FT 24PT
Philosophy... MA 12FT 24PT
Philosophy of Medicine .... MA 12FT 24PT
Philosophy of Mental Disorder.................................MSc 12FT 24PT
Philosophy of Psychology.. MA 12FT 24PT
Philosophy of Religion... MA 12FT 24PT

Kingston University
Contemporary European Philosophy .... MA 18FT 36PT
Modern European Philosophy.................................... MA 12FT 24PT
Philosophy and Contemporary Critical Theory....... MA 12FT 24PT

Lancaster University
Philosophy.................................... MA 12FT 24PT/PGCert 12FT 24PT MPhil 24FT/PhD by taught 24FT
Philosophy and Religion .... MA 12FT 24PT
Politics and Philosophy... MA 12FT 24PT
Politics, Philosophy and Religion .... MA 12FT 24PT

University of Leeds
History and Philosophy of Science............................ MA 12FT 24PT
Philosophy... MA 12FT 24PT

Philosophy of Physics .... MA 12FT 24PT
Philosophy of Religion.. MA 12FT 24PT

University of Liverpool
Metaphysics, Language and the Mind...................... MA 12FT 24PT
Philosophy... MA 12FT 24PT
Philosophy as a Way of Life.. MA 12FT 24PT

London School of Economics and Political Science (LSE)
Economics and Philosophy...MSc 13FT 25PT
Philosophy and Public Policy ....MSc 12FT 24PT
Philosophy of Science..MSc 12FT 24PT
Philosophy of the Social Sciences..............................MSc 12FT 24PT

University of Manchester
Philosophy..MRes 12FT 24PT

Nottingham Trent University
Philosophy..................................MA 12FT 24PT/PGDip 12FT 24PT

University of Nottingham
Philosophical Theology .... MA 12FT 24-48PT
Philosophy... MA 12FT 24PT
Philosophy (by Research).. MA 12FT 24PT
Systematic and Philosophical Theology (distance learning)....MA 12FT 24-48DL

The Open University
Humanities .... MA variableDL/PGDip variableDL/PGCert variableDL
Philosophy...MA variableDL
Systems Thinking in PracticeMSc variableDL/PGCert variableDL/PGDip variableDL

University of Oxford
Ancient Philosophy..MSt 9FT
Philosophical Theology..................................... MPhil 21FT/MSt 9FT
Philosophy......................................BPhil 48FT/MLitt 36FT/MSt 11FT
Philosophy of Physics ....MSt 12FT
Politics: Political Theory ....MPhil 21FT

Queen's University Belfast
Moral, Legal and Political Philosophy....................... MA 12FT 24PT

University of Reading
Neuroscience of Language ....MSc 12FT 24PT
Philosophy .... MA 12FT 24PT

University of Sheffield
Philosophy... MA 12FT 24PT

University of Southampton
Aesthetics.. MA 12FT 24PT
Philosophy... MA 12FT 24PT

University of St Andrews
Philosophy (collaborative)........MLitt 12FT 24PT/PGDip 9FT 21PT/Conversion Diploma 9FT 21PT

University of Stirling
Philosophy...MLitt 12FT

University of Sussex
Literature and Philosophy .... MA 12FT 24PT
Philosophy... MA 12FT 24PT

University of Wales Trinity Saint David
Applied Philosophy ....MA 48PT/PGCert 48PT/PGDip 48PT
European Philosophy.........MA 24-60PT 24-60DL/PGCert 24-60PT 24-60DL/PGDip 24-60PT 24-60DL
Philosophy.................................MA 48PT/PGDip 48PT/PGCert 48PT

UCL - University College London
Philosophy... MA 12FT 24PT
Philosophy, Politics and Economics of Health... MA 12FT 36-60PT

University of Warwick
Continental Philosophy .... MA 12FT 24PT
Philosophy...Diploma 12FT 24PT
Philosophy and Ethics of Mental HealthMSc 12FT 24PT 36DL/MA 12FT 24PT 36DL/PGA 6FT
Philosophy and Literature .... MA 12FT 24PT
Philosophy and Social Theory..................................... MA 12FT 24PT
Philosophy of Mind... MA 12FT 24PT

University of Winchester
Modern Liberal Arts ....MA 12FT 24PT/PGDip 12FT 24PT/PGCert 12FT 24PT

University of York
Philosophy.....................................GradDip 9FT 18PT MA 12FT 24PT
Philosophy, Politics and Economics.......................................MA 12FT
Political Philosophy: the Idea of Toleration.............MA 12FT 24PT/PGDip 12FT
Politics, Philosophy and Economics: Economics and Development...MA 12FT
Politics, Philosophy and Economics: Economics and Politics ...MA 12FT
Politics, Philosophy and Economics: Politics and Development.... MA 12FT
Politics, Philosopy and Economics: Economics and Philosophy..... MA 12FT

Philosophy

Philosophy
Research Courses

University of Aberdeen
Philosophy...............PhD 36FT/MPhil 24FT/MLitt by research 12FT

Anglia Ruskin University
Philosophy...MPhil 24FT/PhD 36FT

Bangor University
Theology and Religious Studies.... MPhil 24FT 36PT/PhD 24-36FT 60PT

Birkbeck, University of London
Philosophy....... PhD 36FT 60PT/MPhil 24FT 36PT/MPhilStud 24FT 36PT

University of Birmingham
Philosophy.......MPhil(B) 12FT 24PT/MLitt by research 24FT 48PT/PhD 36FT 72PT/MPhil 12FT 24PT

Bournemouth University
Philosophy.......... PhD 36FT/MPhil 20FT MPhil 24+FT/DPhil 24+FT

University of Bristol
Philosophy.... PhD 36FT 72PT/MLitt by research 24FT 48PT/MPhil 24FT 48PT

University of Cambridge
Philosophy...PhD 36FT/MPhil 10FT

Cardiff University
Philosophy.................. PhD 36FT on offerPT/MPhil 12FT on offerPT

University of Chester
Research Degrees at the University of Chester .... MPhil 12 - 48FT 24 - 72PT/PhD 24 - 48FT 48 - 84PT

University of Dundee
Philosophy .... MPhil 24FT PhD 36FT

Durham University
Philosophy......MA by research 12FT 24PT/MLitt by research 24FT 48PT/PhD 36FT 72PT

University of East Anglia
Philosophy.................................... PhD 36FT 72PT/MPhil 24FT 48PT

University of Edinburgh
Christian Ethics and Practical Theology.......MPhil 24FT/PhD 36FT 72PT/MTh by research 12FT 24PT/MSc by research 12FT 24PT
Philosophy.................................... PhD 36FT 72PT/MPhil 24FT 48PT

University of Essex
Philosophy........PhD 36FT 72PT/MPhil 24FT 48PT/MA by research 12FT 24PT

University of Exeter
Philosophy........MA by research 12FT 24PT/MPhil 24FT 48PT/PhD 48FT 72PT

University of Glasgow
Philosophy.... PhD 36FT 60PT/MPhil 24FT 48PT/MLitt by research 12FT 24PT

University of Gloucestershire
Philosophy and Ethics .... PhD 30-48FT

Heythrop College
Philosophy (MRes)...MRes 12FT 24PT

University of Hull
Philosophy................................... PhD 36FT 60PT/MPhil 24FT 36PT
Philosophy of Mind and Body .... MA by research 12FT 24PT

Keele University
Philosophy............. PhD 24-48FT 48-84PT/MPhil 12-24FT 24-36PT

University of Kent
History & Philosophy of Art.......MA by research 12FT 24PT/MPhil 24FT 36PT/PhD 36FT 60PT
Philosophy........PhD 36FT 60PT/MPhil 24FT 36PT/MA by research 12FT 24PT

King's College London
Philosophy Research...... MPhil 24FT 36PT/PhD 24-36FT 48-72PT/MPhilStud 24FT 36PT

Lancaster University
Philosophy...................................... PhD 36FT 48PT/MPhil 24FT 36PT
Ruskin Studies.............................. MPhil 24FT 36PT/PhD 36FT 48PT

University of Leeds
Division of History and Philosophy of Science...PhD 36+FT/MPhil 24FT/MA by research 12+FT
School of Philosophy .... PhD 36+FT/MPhil 24FT/MA by research 12FT

University of Liverpool
Philosophy... PhD 36FT/MPhil 12FT

London School of Economics and Political Science (LSE)
Philosophy, Logic and Scientific Method........PhD 36-48FT/MPhil 36-48FT

Manchester Metropolitan University
Philosophy.............PhD 24-48FT 42-84PT 42-84DL/MPhil 18-36FT 36-72PT 36-72DL/MA by research 12-24FT 24-42PT 24-42DL

University of Manchester
Philosophy..PhD 36-48FT 72PT
Politics .... PhD 36FT 72PT

Newcastle University
Philosophical Studies .... PhD 36FT 72PT/MPhil 12FT 24PT

University of Nottingham
Philosophy........MPhil 24FT 48PT/PhD 36FT 72PT/MA by research 12FT 24PT
Social Sciences Research Methodology ....MPhil 24FT 48PT/PhD 36-48FT 72-96PT

The Open University
Materialities, Space and Power PhD 36FT 72PT variableDL/MPhil 15FT 24PT variableDL
Mind, Meaning and Rationality PhD 36FT 72PT variableDL/MPhil 15FT 24PT variableDL
Philosophy.................. PhD 36FT 72PT variableDL/MPhil 15FT 24PT variableDL
Value...... PhD 36FT 72PT variableDL/MPhil 15FT 24PT variableDL

Oxford Brookes University
Religion, Theology and Philosophy (MPhil/PhD)....... PhD 24-60FT 36-72PT/MPhil 24-36FT 36-48PT

University of Oxford
Philosophy.. DPhil 48FT

University of Southampton
Philosophy.................................... PhD 48FT 84PT/MPhil 48FT 84PT

University of St Andrews
Philosophy..........................PhD 36FT 72PT/MPhil 12-24FT 24-48PT

University of Sussex
Philosophy Research Programme..... PhD 24-48FT 36-72PT/MPhil 12-36FT 24-48PT

University of Wales Trinity Saint David
Philosophy... PhD 36-60FT/MPhil 12-36FT

UCL - University College London
Philosophy.......................... PhD 36FT 60PT/MPhil Stud 24FT 48PT/PhD 24FT 48PT
Philosophy of Science.. PhD 36FT 60PT

University of Warwick
Philosophy.................. PhD 36FT/MPhil 24FT/MA by research 12FT
Philosophy and Literature .. PhD 36FT 60PT/MPhil 24FT 36PT/MA by research 12FT 24PT

University of York
History of Philosophy (by Research) .... MA by research 12FT 24PT
Philosophy........PhD 36FT 72PT/MPhil 24FT 48PT/MA by research 12FT 24PT

Theology and religious studies

Buddhism
Taught Courses

University of Aberdeen
Anthropology of Religion .... MSc 12FT 24PT
Practical Theology .... MTh 12FT 24PT
Religion and Politics .... MSc 12FT 24PT

Bangor University
Philosophy and Religion .... MA 12FT 36PT
Philosophy and Religion .... MRes 12FT 36PT

Cardiff University
Religious Studies: Asian Religions .... MA 12FT 24PT

University of Oxford
Classical Indian Religion .... MPhil 21FT
Study of Religion .... MSt 12FT

School of Oriental and African Studies - SOAS
Religions .... MA 12FT 24-36PT

University of South Wales
Buddhist Studies .... PGCert 12DL/PGDip 24DL/MA 36DL

Buddhism
Research Courses

Bangor University
Theology and Religious Studies.... MPhil 24FT 36PT/PhD 24-36FT 60PT

University of Edinburgh
Sanskrit . PhD 36FT 72PT/MPhil 24FT 48PT/MSc by research 12FT 24PT

School of Oriental and African Studies - SOAS
Study of Religions .... PhD 36FT 72PT/MPhil 24FT 36PT

Christianity
Taught Courses

University of Aberdeen
Divinity and Religious Studies .... MTh 12FT 24PT
Pastoral Studies .... DPS 12FT 24PT
Practical Theology .... MTh 12FT 24PT

Anglia Ruskin University
Pastoral Theology .... MA 12FT 60 (max)PT

Bangor University
Philosophy and Religion .... MA 12FT 36PT MRes 12FT 36PT

University of Birmingham
Evangelical and Charismatic Studies........ MA 12FT 36PT/Diploma 12FT 36PT/Cert 12FT 36PT
History of Christianity .... MA 12FT 24PT

Cardiff University
Theology: Christian Ethics .... MTh 12FT 24PT
Theology: Christian Doctrine .... MTh 12FT 24PT

University of Chester
Faiths and Public Policy .... MA 12FT 36PT 36DL/PGDip 12FT 24-36PT 24-36DL/PGCert 12FT 12-24PT 12-24DL
Practical and Contextual Theology.... MA 12FT 36PT 36DL/PGDip 12FT 24 - 36PT 24 - 36DL/PGCert 12FT 12 - 24PT 12 - 24DL
Religious Studies .... MA 12FT 36PT 36DL/PGDip 12FT 24 - 36PT 24 - 36DL/PGCert 12FT 12 - 24PT 12 - 24DL
Theology ..MA 12FT 36PT 36DL/PGDip 12FT 24 - 36PT 24 - 36DL/PGCert 12FT 12 - 24PT 12 - 24DL

Durham University
Biblical Studies .... MA 12FT
Christian Theology .... MA 12FT 24PT
Christian Theology (Anglican Studies) .... MA 12FT 24PT
Christian Theology (Catholic Studies) .... MA 12FT 24PT

University of Edinburgh
World Christianity .... MTh 12FT 24PT/MSc 12FT 24PT

University of Exeter
Biblical Studies .... MA 12FT 24PT

University of Gloucestershire
Sport and Christian Outreach (Sports Chaplaincy)MA 12FT 24PT/PGDip 8FT 20PT/PGCert 4FT 8PT

Heythrop College
Biblical Studies .... MA 24FT 12PT
Christian Theology .... MA 24FT 12PT
Contemporary Ethics .... MA 12FT 24PT

King's College London
Bible and Ministry .... MA 12FT 24PT
Biblical Studies .... MA 12FT 24PT
Christian Education .... MA 12FT 24PT
Christianity & the Arts .... MA 12FT 24PT
Contemporary Ecclesiology .... MA 12FT 24PT
Theology, Politics & Faith-Based Organisations .... MA 12FT 24-48PT

University of Manchester
Biblical Studies .... MA 12FT 24PT

Oxford Brookes University
Ministry .... MA 24FT 60PT

University of Oxford
Applied Theology .... MTh 12FT 48PT/PGDip 12FT 48PT
Eastern Christian Studies .... MPhil 21FT
Judaism and Christianity in the Graeco-Roman World .... MPhil 21FT
Study of Religion .... MSt 12FT
Theology .... MPhil 21FT/MSt 9FT/PGDip 12FT

University of Roehampton
Contemporary Catholicism PGDip .... PGDip 12FT 24PT

School of Oriental and African Studies - SOAS
Religions .... MA 12FT 24-36PT
Religions: Christianities of Asia and Africa Pathway........ MA 12FT 24-36PT

University of Sheffield
Archaeology, Bible and Ancient Cultures .... MA 12FT 24PT
Biblical Studies Research .... MA 12FT 24PT
Biblical Studies by Distance Learning .... MA flexibleDL/PGDip flexibleDL/PGCert flexibleDL
Liturgy .... MA 12FT 24PT
Ministry and Biblical Studies .... MA 12FT 24PT
Ministry and Theology .... MA 12FT 24PT
Social Scientific Biblical Studies .... MA 12FT 24PT

University of St Andrews
Biblical Language and Literature .... MLitt 12FT/PGDip 9FT
Book History .... MLitt 12FT 24PT/MPhil 24FT/PGDip 9FT
Scripture and Theology .... MLitt 12FT 24PT/PGDip 9FT 18PT
Systematic and Historical Theology .... PGDip 9FT/MLitt 12FT

St Mary's University College, Twickenham
Catholic School Leadership: Principles and Practice........ MA 12FT 36PT/PGDip 24PT/PGCert 12PT

University of Wales Trinity Saint David
Christian Theology .... MTh 12FT 24PT

University of Winchester
Orthodox Studies ....MTh 12FT 24PT/PGDip 9FT 18PT/PGCert 9FT 18PT

Christianity
Research Courses

Bangor University
Ministry .... DMin 24-36FT 60PT
Theology and Religious Studies.... MPhil 24FT 36PT/PhD 24-36FT 60PT

University of Birmingham
History of Christianity .... MPhil(B) 12FT 24PT

University of Chester
Theology and Religious Studies .... DProf 24 - 48FT 24 - 84PT

Cliff College
Mission; Evangelism; Church Leadership; Biblical Studies; Wesley & Methodist Studies.....MPhil 12FT 24PT 24DL/PhD 36FT 72PT 72DL

University of Edinburgh
Christian Ethics and Practical Theology....... MPhil 24FT/PhD 36FT 72PT/MTh by research 12FT 24PT/MSc by research 12FT 24PT
New Testament Language, Literature and Theology....... PhD 36FT 72PT/MTh by research 12FT 24PT/MSc by research 12FT 24PT/MPhil 24FT
World Christianity ...PhD 36FT 72PT/MPhil 24FT/MSc by research 12FT 24PT/MTh by research 12FT 24PT

Heythrop College
Christianity and Interreligious Relations .... MRes 12FT 24PT
Pastoral Theology .... MRes 12FT 24PT

School of Oriental and African Studies - SOAS
Study of Religions .... PhD 36FT 72PT/MPhil 24FT 36PT

Hinduism
Taught Courses

Cardiff University
Religious Studies: Asian Religions .... MA 12FT 24PT

School of Oriental and African Studies - SOAS
Religions .... MA 12FT 24-36PT

Hinduism
Research Courses

University of Edinburgh
Sanskrit . PhD 36FT 72PT/MPhil 24FT 48PT/MSc by research 12FT 24PT

School of Oriental and African Studies - SOAS
Study of Religions .... PhD 36FT 72PT/MPhil 24FT 36PT

Islamic studies
Taught Courses

University of Aberdeen
Bayt al-Maqdis and Jerusalem Studies.... MLitt 12FT 24PT/PGDip 9FT 18PT
Islamic Studies .... MLitt 12FT 24PT/PGDip 9FT 18PT

Bangor University
Islamic Banking and Finance .... MBA 12FT

Birkbeck, University of London
Middle East in Global Politics: Islam, Conflict and Development .... MSc 12FT 24PT

University of Birmingham
Islamic Studies ...PGDip 8FT 16PT/MA 12FT 24PT/PGCert 3FT 6PT

Cardiff University
Islam in Contemporary Britain........ MA 12FT 24PT/Diploma 36PT
Religious Studies: Asian Religions .... MA 12FT 24PT

University of East London
Islamic and Middle Eastern Studies .... LLM 12FT 24PT/PGDip 8FT 16PT/PGCert 4FT 8PT

University of Edinburgh
Islamic and Middle Eastern Studies .... MSc 12FT 24PT

University of Exeter
Islamic Studies .... MA 12FT 24PT
Middle East and Islamic Studies .... MA 12FT 24PT

Islamic College for Advanced Studies
Islam and the West: A Comparative Study .. MA 12FT 24PT 36DL/PGDip 12FT 24PT
Islam and the West: A Comparative Study - via Distance Learning .... MA 12FT 24PT 36-48DL
Islamic Finance........ MSc 12FT 24PT 24DL/PGDip 12FT 24PT 24DL
Islamic Studies .... MA 12FT 24PT 12-36DL
Islamic Studies - Via Distance Learning .... MA 12FT 24PT 36DL

Markfield Institute of Higher Education
Islamic Banking, Finance and Management .... MA 12FT 24PT/PGDip 12FT 24PT/PGCert 6FT 12PT
Islamic StudiesMA 12FT 24PT/PGDip 12FT 24PT/PGCert 6FT 12PT
Muslim Community Studies..... MA 12FT 24PT/PGDip 12FT 24PT/PGCert 6FT 12PT

Newcastle University
Finance and Law with Islamic Finance .... MSc 12FT

University of Oxford
Islamic Art and Archaeology (Research Methods) .... MSt 9FT
Islamic Studies and History .... MPhil 21FT
Study of Religion .... MSt 12FT

Queen Mary, University of London
Islam and the West .... MA 12FT 24PT

University of Salford
Islamic Banking and Finance..... MSc 12FT 36PT/PGDip 8FT 24PT/PGCert 4FT 9PT

School of Oriental and African Studies - SOAS
Islamic Societies and Cultures .... MA 12FT 24-36PT
Islamic Studies .... MA 12FT 24-36PT
Religions .... MA 12FT 24-36PT

University of St Andrews
Middle East and Central Asian Security Studies .... PGDip 9FT/MLitt 12FT/MPhil 24FT
Middle Eastern History & Culture....PGDip 9FT/MLitt 12FT/MPhil 24FT

University of Wales Trinity Saint David
Islamic Studies .... MA 12FT 24PT 12-60DL/PGCert 12FT 24PT 12-60DL/PGDip 12FT 24PT 12-60DL

UCL - University College London
Archaeology of the Arab and Islamic World .... MA 24FT
Archaeology of the Middle East .... MA 12FT 24PT

University of Warwick
Applied Social Research with Specialism in Islam in Contemporary Societies .... MA 12FT/MA 24PT
Islam in Contemporary Society .... MA 12FT

Islamic studies
Research Courses

University of Birmingham
Islam and Christian/Muslim Relations .... PhD 36FT 72PT 48DL/MPhil 12FT 24PT
Islamic Studies .... MPhil(B) 12FT 24PT 24DL

University of Edinburgh
Islamic and Middle Eastern Studies .... PhD 36FT 72PT/MSc by research 12FT 24PT/MPhil 24FT 48PT

University of Exeter
Arab and Islamic Studies ...... PhD 36-48FT 72PT/MPhil 24FT 48PT
Kurdish Studies .... MPhil 36FT 60PT 60DL/PhD 48FT 84PT 84DL
Palestine Studies ..... MPhil 36FT 60PT 60DL/PhD 48FT 84PT 84DL

Prince's School of Traditional Arts
Visual Islamic and Traditional Arts... PhD 24-36FT 36-72PT/MPhil 12FT 24PT

School of Oriental and African Studies - SOAS
Study of Religions .... PhD 36FT 72PT/MPhil 24FT 36PT

University of Wales Trinity Saint David
Islamic Studies .... PhD 36FT 48-72PT/MPhil 12-36FT

Jainism
Taught Courses

School of Oriental and African Studies - SOAS
Religions .... MA 12FT 24-36PT

Theology and religious studies

Jainism
Research Courses

University of Edinburgh
Sanskrit. PhD 36FT 72PT/MPhil 24FT 48PT/MSc by research 12FT 24PT

School of Oriental and African Studies - SOAS
Study of Religions .... PhD 36FT 72PT/MPhil 24FT 36PT

Jewish studies
Taught Courses

University of Aberdeen
Jewish Studies .... MLitt 12FT 24PT/PGDip 9FT 18PT

King's College London
Jewish Studies .... MA 12FT 24PT

University of Manchester
Jewish Studies .... MA 12FT 24PT

Oxford Centre for Hebrew and Jewish Studies
Jewish Studies .... MSt 9FT

University of Oxford
Jewish Studies .... MSt 9FT
Jewish Studies in the Graeco-Roman Period .... MPhil 21FT/MSt 9FT
Judaism and Christianity in the Graeco-Roman World .... MPhil 21FT
Modern Jewish Studies .... MPhil 21FT/MSt 9FT
Study of Religion .... MSt 12FT
Yiddish Studies .... MSt 9FT

Queen Mary, University of London
Leo Baeck MA in European Jewish History .... MA 12FT 24PT

Royal Holloway, University of London
Holocaust Studies .... MA 12FT 24PT

School of Oriental and African Studies - SOAS
Israeli Studies .... MA 12FT 24-36PT
Religions .... MA 12FT 24-36PT

University of Southampton
Jewish History and Culture .... MA 12FT 24PT/MRes 12FT 24PT

UCL - University College London
Hebrew and Jewish Studies .... MA 12FT 24PT
Holocaust Studies .... MA 12FT 24PT
Jewish History .... MA 12FT 24PT

Jewish studies
Research Courses

University of Birmingham
Jewish and Holocaust Studies .. PhD 36FT 72PT/MPhil 12FT 24PT

School of Oriental and African Studies - SOAS
Study of Religions .... PhD 36FT 72PT/MPhil 24FT 36PT

University of Southampton
Jewish History and Culture .... PhD 48FT 84PT/MPhil 48FT 84PT

UCL - University College London
Hebrew and Jewish Studies .... PhD 36FT 60PT
Jewish History .... PhD 36FT 60PT

Sikhism
Taught Courses

Cardiff University
Religious Studies: Asian Religions .... MA 12FT 24PT

Sikhism
Research Courses

School of Oriental and African Studies - SOAS
Study of Religions .... PhD 36FT 72PT/MPhil 24FT 36PT

Theology and religious studies
Taught Courses

University of Aberdeen
Biblical Studies .... MTh 12FT 24PT
Church History .... MTh 12FT 24PT
Pastoral Studies .... DPS 12FT 24PT
Practical Theology .... MTh 12FT 24PT
Religion and Society .... MSc 12FT 24PT/PGDip 9FT 18PT/PGCert 6FT 12PT
Social Anthropology of Religion .... MLitt 12FT 24PT
Systematic Theology .... MTh 12FT 24PT
Theology and Religious Studies .... MTh 12FT 24PT

Anglia Ruskin University
Christian Theology .... MA 60FT 60PT/PGDip 60FT 60PT/PGCert 60FT 60PT
Pastoral Theology .... MA 12FT 60 (max)PT

Bangor University
Philosophy and Religion .... MA 12FT 36PT MRes 12FT 36PT

University of Birmingham
Evangelical and Charismatic Studies .... MA 12FT 36PT/Diploma 12FT 36PT/Cert 12FT 36PT
Inter-religious Relations .... MRes 12FT 24PT
Philosophy of Religion and Ethics ..... MA 12FT 24PT/Diploma 8FT 16PT/Cert 4FT 8PT
Philosophy of Religion and Ethics (Distance Learning) .... MA 12FT 36PT
Quaker Studies .... PGCert 3FT 6PT/PGDip 16PT/MA 12FT 24PT

University of Bristol
Religion .... MA 12FT 24PT

University of Cambridge
Theology and Religious Studies .... Diploma 9FT MPhil 9FT

Cardiff University
Religious Studies: Religion in Late Antiquity .... MA 12FT 24PT
Theology: Church History .... MTh 12FT 24PT
Theology: Chaplaincy Studies .... MTh 36PT
Theology: Practical Theology .... MTh 12FT 24PT

University of Central Lancashire
Creative Thinking .... MA 30DL

University of Chester
Practical and Contextual Theology .... MA 12FT 36PT 36DL/PGDip 12FT 24 - 36PT 24 - 36DL/PGCert 12FT 12 - 24PT 12 - 24DL
Religious Studies .... MA 12FT 36PT 36DL/PGDip 12FT 24 - 36PT 24 - 36DL/PGCert 12FT 12 - 24PT 12 - 24DL
Theology .. MA 12FT 36PT 36DL/PGDip 12FT 24 - 36PT 24 - 36DL/PGCert 12FT 12 - 24PT 12 - 24DL

University of Chichester
Theology .... MA 15FT 30PT/PGDip 12FT 24PT/PGCert 9FT 15PT

Cliff College
Celtic Mission and Spirituality PGCert 12PT/PGDip 12FT 24PT/MA 12-18FT 24-30PT
Emerging Church ...... PGCert 12PT/PGDip 12FT 24PT/MA 12-18FT 24-30PT
Leadership: Renewal and Mission ... PGCert 6FT 12PT/PGDip 12FT 24PT/MA 12-18FT 24-30PT
Mission and Evangelism. PGCert 6FT 12PT/PGDip 12FT 24PT/MA 12-18FT 24-30PT
Mission and Religious Pluralism .. PGCert 12PT/PGDip 12FT 24PT/MA 12-18FT 24-30PT
Mission and the World of Work ... PGCert 12PT/PGDip 12FT 24PT/MA 12-18FT 24-30PT
Wesleyan Theology and Spirituality ...... PGCert 12PT/PGDip 12FT 24PT/MA 12-18FT 24-30PT

University of Cumbria
Theology .... MA 12FT 36PT/PGDip 6FT 24PT/PGCert 3FT 12PT

De Montfort University
Inter-religious Relations .... MA 24PT

Durham University
Religion and Society .... MA 12FT 24PT
Spirituality, Theology and Health. MA 12FT 24 to 36PT/MSc 12FT 24 to 36PT
Theology and Religion .... MA 12FT 24PT GradDip 9FT 21PT

University of Edinburgh
Asian Religions .... MSc 12FT 24PT
Biblical Studies .... MSc 12FT 24PT/MTh 12FT 24PT
Ministry .... MTh 12FT 24PT/MSc 12FT 24PT
Religious Studies .... MSc 12FT 24PT
Science and Religion .... MSc 12FT
Theology in History .... MTh 12FT 24PT/MSc 12FT 24PT
World Christianity .... MTh 12FT 24PT/MSc 12FT 24PT

University of Exeter
Biblical Studies .... MA 12FT 24PT
Ethics, Religion and Society .... MA 12FT 24PT
Theology .... MA 12FT 24PT

University of Glasgow
Religion, Education and Culture .... MEd 24 - 36PT
Religion, Theology & Culture ...... MLitt 12FT 24PT/MTh 12FT 24PT
Religious Education by Distance Learning .... PGCert 24DL

University of Gloucestershire
Theology .... GradDip 24PT MTh 24PT

Glyndwr University
Psychology of Religion .... MSc 36PT

Heythrop College
Abrahamic Religions .... MA 12FT 24PT
Biblical Studies .... MA 24FT 12PT
Canon Law .... MA 12FT 24PT
Christian Spirituality .... MA 12FT 24PT
Christian Theology .... MA 24FT 12PT
Christianity and Interreligious Relations .... MA 12FT 24PT
Contemporary Ethics .... MA 12FT 24PT
Ignatian Spirituality .... PGCert 12FT
Pastoral Ministry .... PGCert 12PT
Pastoral Theology .... MA 12FT 24PT
Psychology of Religion .... MA 12FT 24PT

University of Hull
Spirituality Studies .... MA 12FT 24PT
Theology .... MA 12FT 24PT

University of Kent
Humanities (Religious Studies) .... GradDip 12FT
Study of Mysticism and Religious Experience .... MA 12FT 24PT
Theory and Method in the Study of Religion .... MA 12FT 24PT/PGCert 12FT 24PT

King's College London
Abrahamic Religions .... MA 12FT 24PT
Bible and Ministry .... MA 12FT 24PT
Christianity & the Arts .... MA 12FT 24PT
Contemporary Ecclesiology .... MA 12FT 24PT
Contemporary Ministry & Apologetics .... MA 12FT 24PT
Doctorate in Theology and Ministry .... DMin min 60PT
Philosophy of Religion .... MA 12FT 24PT
Religion in Contemporary Society .... MA 12FT 24PT
Systematic Theology .... MA 12FT 24PT
Theology & Religious Studies .... GradDip 12FT 24PT
Theology, Politics & Faith-Based Organisations MA 12FT 24-48PT

Lancaster University
Diplomacy and Religion .... MA 12FT 24PT
Philosophy and Religion .... MA 12FT 24PT
Politics, Philosophy and Religion .... MA 12FT 24PT
Religion and Conflict .... MA 12FT 24PT
Religious Studies .... MA 12FT 24-36PT/PGDip 12FT 24PT MPhil 24FT/PhD by taught 24FT

Leeds Metropolitan University
Health & Social Care Chaplaincy .... PGCert 12PT

University of Leeds
Religion and Public Life .... MA 12FT 24PT/PGDip 12FT 24PT/PGCert 12FT 24PT
Religious Studies and Development Studies .... MA 12FT 24PT
Theology and Pastoral Studies .... MA 12FT 24PT
Theology or Religious Studies and Development Studies .... MA 12FT 24PT

Liverpool Hope University
Biblical Studies .... PGCert 12PT
Christian Theology .... PGCert 12PT
Jewish Studies .... PGCert 12PT
Sacred Music .... MA 12FT 36PT
Theology and Religious Studies MA 12FT 24PT/PGDip 12FT 24PT/PGCert 6FT 12PT

Luther King House Theological College
Contextual Theology ..... MA 12FT 60PT/PGCert 12FT 12PT/PGDip 12FT 24PT

University of Manchester
Religion and Political Life .... MA 12FT 24PT
Religions and Theology .... MA 12FT 24PT

National University of Ireland, Maynooth
Culture, Religion and Society in Modern Ireland .... MA 12FT

Newman University
Contemporary Christian Theology ..... MA 36PT 36DL/PGDip 24PT 24DL/PGCert 12PT 12DL
PGCE Secondary Religious Education .... PGCE(QTS) 12FT

University of Nottingham
Church History (distance learning) .... MA 12DL
Jewish History and Thought (Distance Learning) .... MA 12FT 24-48PT
Philosophical Theology .... MA 12FT 24-48PT
Systematic and Philosophical Theology (distance learning) .... MA 12FT 24-48DL
Theology and Religious Studies .... MA 12FT 24-48PT

Oxford Brookes University
Ministry .... MA 24FT 60PT

Oxford Centre for Hebrew and Jewish Studies
Jewish Studies .... MSt 9FT

University of Oxford
Applied Theology .... MTh 12FT 48PT/PGDip 12FT 48PT
Classical Indian Religion .... MPhil 21FT
Development Studies .... MPhil 36FT
Eastern Christian Studies .... MPhil 21FT
Islamic Studies and History .... MPhil 21FT
Philosophical Theology .... MPhil 21FT/MSt 9FT
Study of Religion .... MSt 12FT
Theology .... MPhil 21FT/MSt 9FT/PGDip 12FT

Queen's University Belfast
Divinity .... MDiv 24FT 36-60PT
Theology .... MTh 12FT 24-48PT/PGDip 12FT 24-48PT/GradDip 12FT 24-48PT

University of Roehampton
Christian Ministry .... MA 12FT 24-48PT
Contemporary Catholicism PGDip .... PGDip 12FT 24PT
Religion and Gender .... MA 12FT 24PT
Religion and Gender PGDip .... PGDip 12FT 24PT
Theology and Religious Studies .... MA 12FT 24PT
Theology and Religious Studies PGDip .... PGDip 12FT 24PT

School of Oriental and African Studies - SOAS
Islamic Societies and Cultures .... MA 12FT 24-36PT
Religions .... MA 12FT 24-36PT
Religions: Christianities of Asia and Africa Pathway .... MA 12FT 24-36PT
Religions: Japanese Religions Pathway .... MA 12FT 24-36PT

University of Sheffield
Biblical Studies Research .... MA 12FT 24PT

Theology and religious studies

Biblical Studies by Distance Learning .... MA flexibleDL/PGDip flexibleDL/PGCert flexibleDL
Classical and Ancient World ....MA 12FT 24PT/PGDip 9FT 18PT/PGCert 6FT 12PT
Ministry and Biblical Studies.......................................MA 12FT 24PT
Ministry and Theology..MA 12FT 24PT
Religion, Conflict and the Media ....MA 12FT 24PT
Social Scientific Biblical Studies..................................MA 12FT 24PT

Spurgeon's College
Advanced Christian Studies.......................................MTh 24PT 60PT
Applied Theology...MTh 36+DL
Biblical and Theological Studies ....MTh 24PT 60PT
Christian Thought and Practice .... MA 24FT 60PT
Preaching...MTh NAFT NAPT 30+DL

University of St Andrews
Bible and the Contemporary World (Distance Learning) ...... MLitt 24DL/PGDip 18DL
Bible and the Contemporary World (Full-time, campus-based).... MLitt 12FT
Biblical Language and Literature...................MLitt 12FT/PGDip 9FT
Scripture and Theology............. MLitt 12FT 24PT/PGDip 9FT 18PT
Systematic and Historical Theology .... PGDip 9FT/MLitt 12FT
Theology, Imagination and the Arts...........MLitt 12FT/PGDip 9FT

St Mary's University College, Twickenham
Religion, Politics and Conflict Resolution.. MA 24PT/PGDip 24PT/PGCert 12PT
Theology ....MA 12FT 36PT/PGDip 12FT 24PT/PGCert 6FT 12PT

Trinity College Dublin - the University of Dublin
Divinity ....BD 60PT
Intercultural Theology and Interreligious Studies .... MPhil 12FT 24PT
Master in Theological Studies ....MTheol 36/72PT

University of Wales Trinity Saint David
Biblical Interpretation ...MA 12FT 24PT/PGCert 12FT 24PT/PGDip 12FT 24PT

University of the Highlands and Islands
Theological studies ....MTh 12FT 24PT

University of Winchester
Death Religion and Culture....... MA 12FT 36PT/PGDip 12FT 24PT/PGCert 12FT 24PT
Religion, Ethics and Society .... MTh 12FT 24PT 12/24DL/PGDip 12FT 24PT 12/24DL/PGCert 12FT 24PT 12/24DL
Theology, Religion and Ethics............................GradDip 12FT 24PT

University of York
Philosophy, Theology and Ethics .... MA 12FT 24PT

York St John University
Theology & Religious Studies................................MA 12FT 24-48PT

Theology and religious studies
Research Courses

University of Aberdeen
Divinity and Religious Studies........PhD 36FT/MPhil 24FT/MTh by research 12FT/MRes 12FT

Bangor University
Theology and Religious Studies.... MPhil 24FT 36PT/PhD 24-36FT 60PT

University of Birmingham
Inter-Religious Relations.....................................MPhil(B) 12FT 24PT
Pentecostal and Charismatic Studies.....................PhD 36FT 72PT/MPhil 12FT 24PT
Quaker Studies............................... PhD 36FT 72PT/MPhil 12FT 24PT

Theology...PhD 36FT 72PT 48DL

University of Bristol
Theology and Religious Studies...............................PhD 36FT 72PT/MLitt by research 24FT 48PT/MPhil 12FT 24PT

University of Cambridge
Theology and Religious Studies................................ PhD 36FT 60PT
MLitt by research 24FT

Canterbury Christ Church University
Religious Studies or Theology ... PhD 48FT 60PT/MPhil 24FT 48PT

University of Chichester
Theology.. PhD 36FT 84PT/DPhil 24FT 84PT

Cliff College
Mission; Evangelism; Church Leadership; Biblical Studies; Wesley & Methodist Studies.....MPhil 12FT 24PT 24DL/PhD 36FT 72PT 72DL

University of Cumbria
Religion and Ethics..PhD 48FT 72PT 72DL/MPhil 36FT 60PT 60DL

Durham University
Doctor of Theology and Ministry ....DThM 36FT 72PT
Theology and Religion...........Integrated PhD 48FT 96PT PhD 36FT 72PT/MLitt by research 24FT 48PT/MA by research 12FT 24PT

University of East Anglia
Spirituality and Religion in Education....................PhD 36FT 72PT/MPhil 24FT 48PT/MA by research 12FT 24PT

University of Edinburgh
Christian Ethics and Practical Theology.......MPhil 24FT/PhD 36FT 72PT/MTh by research 12FT 24PT/MSc by research 12FT 24PT
Ecclesiastical History .... PhD 36FT 72PT/MPhil 24FT/MTh by research 12FT 24PT/MSc by research 12FT 24PT
Hebrew and Old Testament Studies.MPhil 24FT/PhD 36FT 72PT/MTh by research 12FT 24PT/MSc by research 12FT 24PT
New Testament Language, Literature and Theology.......PhD 36FT 72PT/MTh by research 12FT 24PT/MSc by research 12FT 24PT/MPhil 24FT
Religious Studies .... MTh by research 12FT 24PT/MSc by research 12FT 24PT/MPhil 24FT 24PT/PhD 36FT 24PT
Systematic Theology............... MPhil 24FT/PhD 36FT 72PT/MTh by research 12FT 24PT/MSc by research 12FT 24PT
World Christianity ...PhD 36FT 72PT/MPhil 24FT/MSc by research 12FT 24PT/MTh by research 12FT 24PT

University of Exeter
Theology and Religion...... PhD 48FT 84PT 48DL/MPhil 36FT 60PT 36DL/MA by research 12FT 24PT

University of Glasgow
Theology and Religious Studies................................PhD 36FT 72PT/MLitt by research 24FT 36PT/MTh by research 12FT 24PT

University of Gloucestershire
Theology & Religious Studies............ PhD 30-48FT 48-84PT/MPhil 18-36FT 30-60PT/MA by research 12-24FT 18-36FT

Heythrop College
Biblical Studies ....MRes 12FT 24PT
Pastoral Theology ....MRes 12FT 24PT
Theology....................................... PhD 36FT 72PT/MPhil 24FT 48PT

University of Kent
Theology and Religious StudiesPhD 36FT 60PT/MPhil 24FT 36PT/MA by research 12FT 24PT

King's College London
Doctorate in Theology and Ministry.....................DThMin 36-84PT
Theology & Ministry...........................MPhil 36-72PT/PhD 36-72PT

Theology & Religious Studies Research.PhD 36FT 48-72PT/MPhil 24FT 36PT

Lancaster University
Religious Studies .... PhD 36FT 48PT/MPhil 24FT 36PT

University of Leeds
Department of Theology and Religious Studies...........PhD 36+FT/MPhil 24FT/MA by research 12+FT

Liverpool Hope University
Postgraduate Research .... PhD 24FT 48PT/MPhil 12FT 24PT

University of Manchester
Religions and Theology...PhD 36FT 72PT

Newman University
Theology, Religion and/or Religious Education ... PhD 36FT/MPhil 24FT

University of Nottingham
Theology and Religious Studies research areas....PhD 36FT 72PT/MPhil 24FT 48PT/MA by research 12FT 24PT/MRes 12FT

The Open University
Contemporary Religions and Spiritualities............. PhD 36FT 72PT variableDL/MPhil 15FT 24PT variableDL
Religion and Locality............................. PhD 36FT 72PT variableDL/MPhil 15FT 24PT variableDL
Religion in Material, Visual and Performance Culture....PhD 36FT 72PT variableDL/MPhil 15FT 24PT variableDL
Religion, identities, cultures and citizenship.......... PhD 36FT 72PT variableDL/MPhil 15FT 24PT variableDL
Religious Studies ..... PhD 36FT 72PT variableDL/MPhil 15FT 24PT variableDL
Religious history and its application .... PhD 36FT 72PT variableDL/MPhil 15FT 24PT variableDL

Oxford Brookes University
Religion, Theology and Philosophy (MPhil/PhD)....... PhD 24-60FT 36-72PT/MPhil 24-36FT 36-48PT

University of Oxford
Theology ....DPhil 48FT 96PT

Queen's University Belfast
Theology.. PhD 36FT 72PT/MPhil 24FT 48PT

University of Roehampton
Theology and Religious Studies........ PhD 24-48FT 36-60PT/MPhil 21-36FT 33-48PT

School of Oriental and African Studies - SOAS
Study of Religions......................... PhD 36FT 72PT/MPhil 24FT 36PT

Spurgeon's College
DMin..DMin 54+DL
MPhil...MPhil 36FT 108PT 36+DL
PhD..PhD 36FT 108PT 36+DL

University of St Andrews
Divinity...PhD 36FT/MPhil 12-24FT

University of Wales Trinity Saint David
Centre for Theology and Education ....PhD/MPhil
Religious Studies .... PhD 36FT 48-72PT 36-72DL/MPhil 12FT 18-24PT 12-24DL
Theology..PhD 36FT 48-72PT/MPhil 12-36FT

University of the Highlands and Islands
Theology .... PhD 36FT 60PT/MPhil 24FT 48PT

York St John University
Theology and Religious Studies........ PhD 12-36FT 24-60PT/MPhil 12-36FT 24-60PT/MA by research 12-36FT 24-60PT

The blueprint for postgraduate success

Everything you need to make the right postgraduate choice

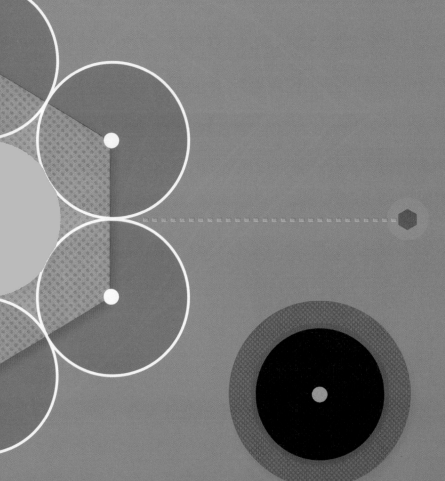

For when you mean business.

Whether it's a general, executive or specialist MBA, we'll find you the right course.

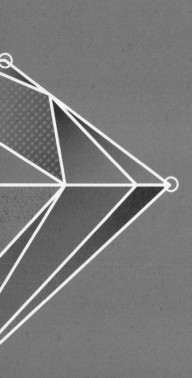
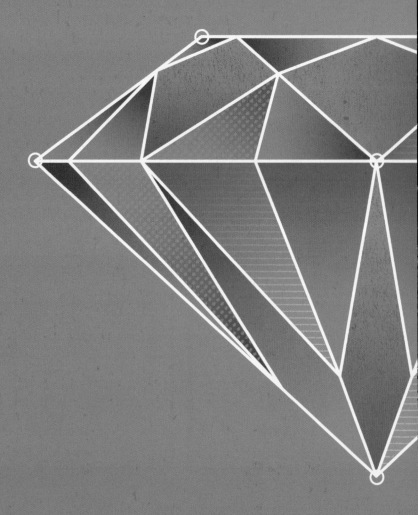

Prospects MBA Directory

The essential guide to MBA study

www.prospects.ac.uk/mba

Business and social sciences

GOING TO APPLY? MENTION PROSPECTS' ADVICE ON YOUR APPLICATION

This section includes articles and profiles specifically relating to the business and social sciences subject areas. There are student and graduate case studies, advice from an expert in the field and features on new and popular courses. Browse the following pages to gain a greater understanding of your chosen subject field and hear from other people who have been in a similar position

Invest in your future

Studying a postgraduate degree could give you the momentum you need to make a splash in the world of business. Find out how further study could pay dividends and propel you up the career ladder

Make no bones about it, the UK economy remains in the doldrums. As economists mention terms like 'double-dip' and even 'triple-dip recession', attention is drawn to the nation's businesspeople as they try to find a way to navigate out of these choppy financial waters.

Business is key to getting the economy firing again – even opposing political parties agree on that. This is clear when you consider that 80% of the whole of the UK's labour force work in the service – or tertiary – sector, which contains industries such as banking, insurance, media, financial services and real estate. What's more, almost 80% of the country's gross domestic product (GDP) comes from this sector too.

As a result, improving the knowledge, skills and work experience of the UK's budding business professionals is vital to a blossoming economy, and postgraduate courses can play an integral part.

Postgraduate business courses
Three distinct types of postgraduate course exist in business and management: general programmes that are open to undergraduates from unrelated disciplines; those that are subject specific and build on first-degree specialisation; and high-level courses that require years of on-the-job experience in business.

General courses are increasingly popular, allowing people to make the first step into a career in business even if their first degree was in a different discipline. These kinds of programmes tend to focus on the likes of management, marketing, advertising, and human resources (HR), but make sure you check the entry requirements for each programme, as they will differ from institution to institution. Some may actually request a degree in a related subject.

Programmes specifically aimed at business graduates provide students with the opportunity to specialise within a particular area of business. Postgraduates in this category desire an extra qualification and better skills in order to distinguish themselves from undergraduates competing for the same jobs. Examples of courses of this kind include accounting, financial analysis, insurance, risk management and supply chain management.

MBAs
The third kind of business qualification is a Master of Business Administration (MBA). This prestigious degree is aimed at business professionals who have years of industry experience. Course admission is extremely competitive at the top universities, with business leaders from around the globe applying for these world-renowned programmes.

There are three kinds of MBA: general, executive and specialist. Each is aimed at candidates with varying levels of experience and different career goals.

Tuition fees can be expensive. For example, the MBA programme at the University of Oxford's Saïd Business School will set you back £59,750. This is clearly not a degree for the novice.

However, for top-level business leaders, an MBA is worth it. According to the Association of MBAs' (AMBA) Careers Survey 2013, the mean salary of MBA graduates from AMBA-accredited business schools working in the UK is now over £82,000.

What's more, it found that within ten years, more than half of all graduates surveyed were either in chief executive officer (CEO), directorship or senior management positions.

For many business students, a postgraduate course is their first serious investment.

To find out more about MBAs, visit *www.prospects.ac.uk/postgraduate_qualifications_mba.htm*

STUDENT VIEW

OMAR ANWAR IS A MANAGING PARTNER AT XCELERATE MANAGEMENT CONSULTANTS. HE STUDIED FOR AN MBA AT THE UNIVERSITY OF BOLTON

I decided to undertake the MBA programme at the University of Bolton to further my business and leadership skills and to challenge myself academically at a high level.

I had been a successful senior business manager for a number of years and felt I needed to be proactive in developing my leadership and business skills to stay one step ahead of the competition and to progress my career. I felt a postgraduate degree, especially the MBA, would give me an advantage in the workplace.

Studying at Masters level allows you to open your mind to new thought processes and challenge concepts that already exist. The experience and expertise of the lecturers and fellow students offers a direct insight into the business world, which gives you confidence to utilise the knowledge and skills you have developed in the workplace.

The MBA has enabled me to look at the business world from a different perspective and has allowed me to broaden my horizons and skills. All of which has given me the confidence to start my own management consultancy business.

The big society

The social sciences delve into the very nature of our society and help us understand more about our behaviour and the world in which we live. Find out more about postgraduate study in this extensive discipline

The term social scientist can be applied to a vast number of roles, across a range of sectors. Lawyers are social scientists. Linguists are social scientists. Anthropologists are social scientists. Economists are social scientists. The list goes on.

Each job requires the ability to gather information about the world in which we live and analyse and interpret the data to produce conclusions. A social scientist then implements these findings for the greater good of the community in which they work, whether it's a large financial institution or a deprived social group.

Margaret Cox, from King's College London's department of education and professional studies, says, 'The study of social science, which is the study of society and how people behave, is fundamental to improving society and the wellbeing of people.

'It will involve developing an understanding of the psychology of how people learn and behave and the sociology of how people's behaviours influence others and the society in which they live.

'The outcomes from social science research will inform policy makers and practitioners and influence the directions into which societies are drawn and flourish. A qualification in these areas will give you the skills and knowledge to make a valuable contribution to society anywhere in the world.'

Employability
As this is a discipline that covers many fields of study and work, you can find a huge range of postgraduate programmes that all have very different goals.

For instance, while many postgraduate courses in the social sciences are aimed at specialising a student's previous academic knowledge, some will focus solely on providing the skills required to work in that field. These tend to be taught courses and often include a placement, which can, in some cases, be given more prominence than face-to-face teaching.

Just a couple of examples of courses that ready postgraduates for the world of work include heritage centre management, social work, law, librarianship and psychology.

Unprecedented freedom
Postgraduate courses in social sciences also give people the chance to pursue a career in academia and add to the research that exists around the subject that they love.

Professor Malcolm D. MacLeod, provost of St Leonard's College and dean of graduate studies at the University of St Andrews, says, 'Research degree programmes allow students an unprecedented level of freedom to devote their time to their subject and to work at their own pace without the need to face exams or interact with people who don't share their passion for academic discovery'.

Whether you opt for a research programme or a taught course, it's clear postgraduate qualifications in social sciences are extremely popular with graduates. The degrees cover a range of fundamental issues in humanity and society – how we coexist with others and how we interact with the world around us.

FIVE SOCIAL SCIENCE SUBJECTS

LAW AND CRIMINOLOGY
Researches crime and criminals

SOCIOLOGY
Investigates the development of human society and how we function

ECONOMICS
Deals in the production, consumption and transfer of wealth

LINGUISTICS
Studies language and its nature, structure and variation

ANTHROPOLOGY
Specialises in the study of humankind

Thomas Mason studied MSc Economics at The University of Manchester

STUDENT VIEW

I really enjoyed my undergraduate studies in economics and politics and was always open to the possibility of studying for a Masters degree in economics.

I was aware that obtaining a scientific postgraduate degree of a high standard was a minimum requirement of employers advertising vacancies for professional economists. This applies to both private and public sector positions. Economists who wish to study for a PhD will often require a Masters degree for successful enrolment.

Postgraduate study is challenging as a result of the increased difficulty of the material and the significantly increased workloads. The decision to undertake postgraduate study should be based on a genuine devotion to the discipline and not as a 'stopgap'. Devoted students find working at the requisite levels of motivation much easier.

Prospects speaks to **Simon Hallsworth**, head of the School of Applied Social Sciences at University Campus Suffolk (UCS)

What makes UCS a popular institution for postgraduates?

At UCS, undergraduates and postgraduates are surrounded by inspiring people, from experienced academic staff and acclaimed visiting professors to fellow students. As UCS is a relatively small institution, all students enjoy excellent contact time with their tutors and more personalised support.

The School of Applied Social Sciences at UCS has a track record in uniting high academic standards with real-world professionalism. It works closely with national and local government agencies, such as the Teaching Agency, the Health and Care Professions Council, and the College of Social Work, to transform and professionalise the workforce, and brings the academic rigour required to challenge and push boundaries.

The research-active staff includes national and international experts in fields including criminology and gang policy, international adoption, social care for older people, poverty and living standards, prison law and policy, and the implications of new technologies for childhood.

What courses are on offer in the School of Applied Social Sciences?

Our MA Childhood and Youth Studies is based on an informed and critical approach to the academic study of childhood and youth and is intended to reflect both the desires and ambitions of postgraduate students, and the philosophical traditions and current developments in the social studies of childhood and youth. In line with recent international developments, the MA is transdisciplinary in approach but has a strong emphasis on perspectives drawn from sociology, social policy, geography, anthropology and history.

The MA Learning and Teaching has been developed for postgraduates and professionals interested in specialised or advanced study within the field of education. It enables teachers to formally engage in focused study and to refine their goals in the profession and their work within an educational setting.

The MA meets the needs of those that teach across the early years, primary, secondary and post-compulsory sectors, including NQTs and those in the early stages of their teaching career. The programme offers strong leadership modules that enable experienced teachers to develop the ability to meet the challenges of education.

What facilities does the school offer its students?

The school has its main base in the UCS Waterfront Building, the campus hub, where most teaching and tutorials take place. It has a large auditorium, several lecture theatres and teaching rooms for small and large groups, all with state-of-the-art audio-visual equipment.

The library at UCS Ipswich recently benefited from a £2.5million renovation and now boasts a modern, IT-rich study environment including group study pods equipped with iMacs and a completely silent study area.

The graduate school manages research degrees and delivers professional development and training for all postgraduate students that supports the development of transferable skills and knowledge and fosters interaction between students of different academic disciplines.

> *The School of Applied Social Sciences at UCS has a track record in uniting high academic standards with real-world professionalism*

Does the school have good links with industry?

Staff are active in research and engage with a wide range of external partners in the delivery and development of projects; these have included West Midlands Police, The Co-operative, the Suffolk Foundation, Nominet and the Institute of Education.

One recent study has seen Dr Wendy Lecluyse, lecturer in early childhood studies, develop a free mobile hearing aid application in collaboration with Professor Ray Meddis and Dr Nick Clark of the department of psychology at the University of Essex.

What do you look for in prospective students?

Students should be highly enthusiastic about their subject and aware of current research within the general area. Postgraduate groups at UCS attend lectures and seminars and are expected to contribute fully to discussions.

How does the school prepare postgraduates for life after university?

The school runs conferences, seminars and professional-training sessions that bring undergraduates and postgraduates into regular contact with academics, early-career researchers, Doctoral candidates, police, teachers and social workers, among others. These range from guest speakers participating as part of teaching programmes, to conferences, talks and seminars covering a wide range of topics, such as children and childhoods, social work practice or social justice and the big society.

What careers do your alumni go on to pursue?

UCS has an excellent track record of graduate employability, with more than 90% of students going on to secure work or progress to further study. Our Masters degrees prepare students for senior roles in the voluntary sector and public sector, as well as for the private sector and in some cases to establish their own business. Many students also progress to PhD study.

Study for a postgraduate qualification with UCS in a stunning waterfront location

Why study at UCS?

- Learn from the experts with our experienced academic staff, visiting professors and guest lecturers

- Strong links with industry and direct connections with employers

- Surrounded by beautiful countryside but only an hour from London

- Support from the Graduate School with dedicated social and learning space

- Excellent contact time and support from tutors

We offer a wide range of postgraduate courses in the following areas:

- Applied Social Sciences

- Arts and Humanities

- Business, Leadership and Enterprise

- Nursing and Midwifery

- Science, Technology and Health

Find out more

+44 (0)1473 338833

infozone@ucs.ac.uk

www.ucs.ac.uk

CASE STUDY

Mindaugas Vaiciulis is approaching completion of the MSc in Investment Analysis at Aston Business School, Aston University, Birmingham. He discusses his programme and how it has prepared him for employment

Why did you choose this degree and institution?

I completed my BSc in International Business and Economics at Aston University. It was incredible for gaining a good understanding of how businesses work but was a very broad programme. At MSc level, I wanted to study something more specific and mathematical; I also wanted to do a finance-related course that would be really applied.

My preference was to stay in a familiar environment to help me to achieve high standards from the start. Aston also has a reputation for producing highly employable graduates.

Tell us a bit about the content of the course...

The programme is comprehensive and practical and prepares students to go into industry as an investment analyst. It covers many aspects of the investment industry, from a theoretical understanding of financial theory to short-term investing principles taught in the trading techniques modules and long-term investment matters in security analysis.

What facilities are available at the institution?

The business school's postgraduate suite, available to business-school MSc students, has computer labs and workshop rooms. There's also the university library and, for investment analysis and finance and investment students, the Reuters trading room, where trading seminars take place, with software including Reuters Eikon.

How has the programme helped you prepare for employment?

It develops your confidence as it covers crucial elements of the investment analysis sector. Now, I wouldn't find it daunting to be asked technical questions in interviews or in the workplace.

What are the main differences between undergraduate and postgraduate life?

The main difference is the commitment needed and the amount of information to process. At times it can be really busy and you have less time for revision and exams. It's important to be committed and passionate about your subject area, to be prepared and to start working early.

What advice would you give to students considering taking this programme?

You have to demonstrate a good level of quantitative and analytical skills to get onto the course. I'd advise students to gain knowledge of at least the basics of finance and maths; otherwise it might be a struggle to keep up with the curriculum, especially at the start of the course.

University of Brighton

Brighton Business School

Fast-track your career

Brighton Business School offers a range of postgraduate courses to strengthen your existing qualifications and support your career progression.

- Many of our courses are accredited by professional bodies.
- According to the latest Research Assessment Exercise 70% of our business and management research is of international standing.
- Guest speakers from industry give practical insights into contemporary business issues.
- Most of our staff have commercial experience so they can pass on practical know-how which helps with your employability.
- There is always something interesting happening in Brighton. Situated on the south coast, the city is bright, upbeat and unconventional.

Postgraduate opportunities include:
- Economics and Finance MSc
- Finance and Investment MSc
- Human Resource Management MSc
- Law PGDip/CPE
- Logistics and Supply Chain Management MSc
- Management MSc
- Managing Change and Innovation MSc
- Marketing MSc
- Retail Management MSc
- MBA

Get in touch
+44 (0)1273 642197
postgrad.business@brighton.ac.uk
www.brighton.ac.uk/bbs

CASE STUDY

Andrew Graham Jones is studying for the LLM International Law at Bangor University, specialising in international human rights and international criminal law

Why did you choose this course and institution?

I have had a passion for international law since the second year of my undergraduate studies. While the course only involved a small amount of international studies, this area always caught my attention and, where possible, I took that direction with my coursework. I studied international human rights in my final year and I thought it was by far the most interesting module. When choosing a Masters, my decision was easy.

I chose Bangor as I had a friend studying here for the past six years. I visited him on a number of occasions prior to applying and very much enjoyed both the city and the surrounding areas – especially since I engage in outdoor sports and activities. The university also appealed to me because it carries a good name and reputation, while the course itself is unique in its speciality. The law department also offers other opportunities that make the chance to study here appealing, such as participation in the prestigious Telders Moot Court Competition, held at the seat of the International Court of Justice in The Hague in the Netherlands.

What are the benefits of studying at Bangor?

The university and course offer an incredible studying environment, the likes of which I hadn't experienced before. Having completed my undergraduate degree at a much larger university, I was used to bigger classes and a less personal approach. At Bangor I have felt much closer to my lecturers because classes are smaller. There has been a real chance to engage with my learning and to discuss study topics and issues with colleagues, rather than feeling like just another face in a crowded lecture hall.

What does the course involve?

The most wide-reaching area of the subject is public international law, which focuses on the law between nations, encompassing everything

The main difference between undergraduate and postgraduate study has been the increased workload, but more importantly, my increased ability to handle it

from law of treaties to the legality of nuclear weapons.

International human rights law involves studying the international framework of the laws that regulate the rights of people. This is one of the areas the course specialises in, offering an in-depth look at the law's workings, successes and issues from its beginnings to the present day.

International humanitarian law, also known as the law of armed conflict, has been my favourite module from the beginning of the course. The module on legacies of war and repression has been interactive and involved much more critical thinking than a straightforward law class.

What are the main differences between undergraduate and postgraduate study?

For me the main difference has been the increased workload, but more importantly, my increased ability to handle it. I'm aware of how much more work I'm required to do, but at the same time, I'm more willing to complete it. I'm much more enthusiastic about the course and the work I do – I made the decision to study for my Masters because I wanted to continue in academia, not just because I felt it was the next step after school.

What facilities are available for law students at Bangor?

Bangor Law School offers a fantastic library with everything you need both in the building and online. The lecturers are available at all times and are more than happy to help you in any way they can, not only regarding issues with the course but with personal and developmental matters as well.

I have developed so much during a short time and the course has given me the knowledge to continue with a career in law. The entire experience has given me a feel for what I may face in the future, and it has left me feeling more prepared.

What advice would you give to others considering further study?

Approach postgraduate study with an open mind – there are so many opportunities that can be taken during the course and at the university as a whole that you should always be open to trying new things. The lecturers have been amazing and supportive throughout and the way classes are taught is engaging and innovative – as are the assessments. The course needs real commitment, but I have got so much out of it and every second with my head in a book has been worth it.

CASE STUDY

Charlotte Deans is studying for the MA International Development: Social Policy and Social Development at the Institute for Development Policy and Management (IDPM) at The University of Manchester

Why did you choose this degree and institution?

During the last year of my undergraduate degree in sociology at Durham University, when I was able to specialise in topics that really grasped my interests (something that was encouraged within my dissertation module), I began to really enjoy academic study and research and wanted to pursue it further.

I chose this course because the content sounded partly familiar; consisting of social and political theory I'd previously touched on, and also totally foreign. My undergraduate course was UK-centric and I wanted to branch out and study development policy in other areas of the world, focusing on less-developed states. Manchester has an excellent reputation for social development studies, and is logistically convenient for me as I'm living at home in Cheshire while studying.

Tell us a bit about the content of the course…

After every seminar and lecture, my mind is racing with the contrasting agendas of different development agents, and with the fact of how injustices to the world's poor are perpetuated through corrupt governance. However, it's not all doom and gloom – the whole point of development is to acknowledge these inequalities and empower citizens to rise above them.

In the first term I learned about theoretical perspectives of development. I found the next term more practical, putting theory into practice to prepare us for our dissertations. The teaching element of the course culminated with a once-in-a-lifetime opportunity to conduct fieldwork in Masindi, Uganda – an amazing trip I'll never forget.

What facilities are available at the institution?

Facilities for postgraduate students are outstanding. We have access to all buildings after hours – useful

for the run-up to deadlines. One computer room within my department building is restricted to postgraduates so we have access to computers at all times. The library is massive and you can always find a study space. The new Learning Commons is a beautiful place to work, with a great café.

What are the main differences between undergraduate and postgraduate life?

To be brutally honest, you have to change your entire work ethic if, like me, you're coming straight from undergraduate study – although a lot of people on my course came from years of employment, so their organisational skills were probably better honed than mine! It's wise to treat a Masters like a 9-to-5 job as the workload is heavy and expectations are high.

Saying that, the tutors are very welcoming and you see them much more on a one-to-one basis than at undergraduate level. Even though you're encouraged to take your own approach to topics when writing assignments, tutors do appreciate how overwhelming the first term can be and are eager to assist.

The university emphasises the need to achieve a work/life balance from the Welcome Week onwards. I also love the multinational feel

I'm much more focused in my work and timekeeping, which I think will benefit me in whatever industry I go into

of IDPM – many of my postgraduate friends and colleagues are from different parts of the world and it has been great to forge links and learn about other cultures. They've all really enjoyed their time in Manchester and felt welcomed by the university.

How has the course helped you prepare for employment?

I'm much more focused in my work and timekeeping, which I think will benefit me in whatever industry I go into. It has also made me question the world around me, and taught me not to take any information, be it a UN report or a piece of editorial, at face value.

What advice would you give to other students considering doing your course?

Get stuck in from the start! I found it hard to adjust from undergraduate to postgraduate levels of study regarding what was expected from me and there was quite a workload, with a third of the course being assessed before January.

I would also advise students to seek help and advice from tutors, who are down to earth and approachable.

What are your plans for after you graduate?

The practical fieldwork module confirmed my desire to go into the development industry, and the social implications of HIV really interest me, so I'll be looking for roles with non-governmental organisations (NGOs) within this sector.

MANCHESTER
1824
The University of Manchester

School of Environment, Education and Development

Make a difference!

Masters and PhD study with world-class thinkers at one of the most prestigious universities in the world

GEOGRAPHY | PLANNING AND ENVIRONMENTAL MANAGEMENT

Masters programmes and PhD research in:

Environmental Governance | GIS | Environmental Modelling and Monitoring
Environmental Impact Assessment | Global Urbanism | Urban Regeneration
Planning | Real Estate Management & Development | International Planning *

EDUCATION
Manchester Institute of Education

Masters programmes , professional doctorates and PhD research in:

Education | Counselling | Learning Disabilities | TESOL | Educational Leadership
Educational and Child Psychology *

INTERNATIONAL DEVELOPMENT
Institute for Development Policy and Management (IDPM)

Masters programmes and PhD research in:

Poverty | Social Development | Development Studies | Development Economics | Politics
Public Policy | Development Informatics | Human Resource Management and Development
Environment | Globalisation *

*Please check our website for specific programmes and options available

Scholarships and bursaries available | www.seed.manchester.ac.uk
Contact us: +44 (0) 0161 275 0969 | sed.admissions@manchester.ac.uk

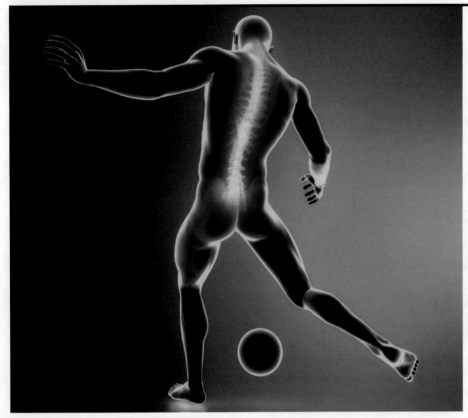

A sporting chance

Science is now a core element of elite sport, helping athletes break boundaries once thought impossible. We find out how postgraduate study can help you into a career working alongside top sportspeople

Despite having a history stretching back to the ancient Greeks, it's only in the last 20 years or so that sports science has become such an integral part of sport, particularly at the highest level.

It is now commonplace for professional clubs to have sports science teams as big as their starting line-ups working behind the scenes to boost athletes' performances.

This demand for skilled sports scientists, as well as the worldwide popularity of sport and the consequent fact that millions of people would love to work in the sector, means that postgraduate sports science courses are in demand at UK universities.

What does it cover?
At first only very general courses existed, which aimed to cover the breadth of the discipline. Today, however, there is a huge variety of programmes available, ranging from the generic and interdisciplinary to the highly specialised.

Sports science can be divided into three branches: biomechanics, which examines the causes and consequences of human movement; physiology, which is concerned with how the body reacts to exercise and training; and psychology, which looks at how the mind works in sport and exercise settings.

Within those, you could study anything from strength and conditioning, sport psychology and sport nutrition to sport performance enhancement and sport therapy.

Core practitioner skills
But why would a graduate choose to continue their studies in this area?

Firstly, it gives you the chance to improve your understanding of a subject you love, or carve out a niche for yourself by specialising in a specific topic within your area of expertise.

In addition, a postgraduate course in sports science aims to develop the key skills required to move into the world of work, especially as the industry is becoming more and more competitive.

Sandy Willmott, programme leader for the University of Lincoln's MSc Sport Science, explains, 'It is essential to be able to demonstrate relevant practical experience to potential employers. Our course is designed to allow our students to compile a diverse portfolio of graduate-level skills and real-world experience.'

Dr Robin Jackson, who leads Brunel University's MSc Sport and Exercise Psychology, explains that this programme 'gives students a comprehensive understanding of different theoretical frameworks used by practitioners, which is crucial in ensuring students have the knowledgebase to provide high-quality, evidence-based practice when fully qualified.

'The course also gives students a comprehensive understanding of core practitioner skills, as well as oral, written, presentation, and group work skills that are attractive to any prospective employer.'

Not only that, but in sports psychology a postgraduate qualification is essential in order to become a practitioner. To work in this field, it's obligatory to have either chartered status from the British Psychological Society (BPS) or accredited status from the British Association of Sport and Exercise Sciences (BASES). Both require an undergraduate and postgraduate degree, followed by two years of supervised practice and registration with the Health Care and Professions Council (HCPC).

Increasing demand
There is currently a high demand for sport and exercise scientists, as Dr Keith Tolfrey, senior lecturer at Loughborough University's School of Sport, Exercise and Health Sciences, explains.

'We've seen the global sport and exercise industry continue to thrive despite the economic downturn, while the success of the 2012 Olympics has increased both the appetite for sporting events and also public participation in sport and exercise.

'Health and fitness is also high on the political agenda so there really are numerous opportunities for people with skills not just in sport and exercise science, but also in sport management, nutrition, physiotherapy and so on.'

As a result, Loughborough's sports science graduates go on to work in a range of roles.

'For us, there's no such thing as a typical graduate career. We have graduates working as performance analysts for national sporting bodies, as sports scientists for companies like GlaxoSmithKline, as management specialists for leisurewear companies, as physiotherapists, teachers and lecturers, dieticians, coaches and researchers,' Dr Tolfrey adds.

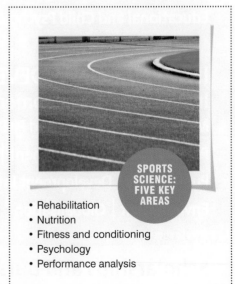

SPORTS
SCIENCE:
FIVE KEY
AREAS

• Rehabilitation
• Nutrition
• Fitness and conditioning
• Psychology
• Performance analysis

CASE STUDY

Tara Cronin studied for the MSc Public Relations at Manchester Metropolitan University (MMU). During her studies she won a year's paid internship with a scientific and medical publishing company

Why this course and why MMU?

I realised towards the end of my undergraduate studies that I would need to learn something practical if I was going to find work. The interest in PR came from the experience of promoting my own art exhibitions and shows during that time.

I chose MMU Business School for a number of reasons. The first was the reputation of the course, which was better than any other I had seen. It had also been recommended by a friend of the family who had worked with a number of former MMU students and was full of praise for the quality of their work.

I was a little hesitant when I first arrived in Manchester from Ireland and slightly worried about how a sculpture and combined media graduate would fit in on a very business-focused Masters degree. I remember thinking in my first lecture, 'How on earth am I going to cope with this?' However, I persevered and the opportunities I have enjoyed through taking the course have just been incredible.

Winning the Chartered Institute of Public Relations (CIPR) student representative competition really kick-started my career. The prize was an internship with BioMed Central, which began in the middle of the Masters programme. The business school extended my dissertation deadline by six months to allow me to work full time in London. I know MMU has a very high employment rate for its students, but to be encouraged to take up a position before the end of the course, and for them to then continue to support me through it, was incredible.

How did your studies prepare you for your future career?

If I'd have stayed in Ireland, I know I wouldn't have had access to the same level of experience that I had at MMU. People now see my CV and, considering my age and level, they're amazed I've packed so much into three years.

You learn at MMU what the workplace is all about. I think of my time in Manchester as providing a bridge between

In times like these, you have to be exceptional to stand out from the crowd, and a Masters does this for you – it gives you the edge

study and work. It's been hard work but it has paid off tenfold. I got to do so much more than I could have imagined and it's all due to the opportunities MMU created for me – it was a great foot on the ladder.

What advice would you give to others breaking into your industry?

In times like these, you have to be exceptional to stand out from the crowd, and a Masters does this for you – it gives you the edge. Working full time and writing my dissertation did mean that my social life was non-existent for a while. I was at my desk until 10pm and spent weekends writing up chapters that I then emailed to my tutors – not a great deal of fun but well worth it. My tutors would always be there at the end of the phone and they would always reply to my many emails. All of the hard work eventually paid off because at the end of the internship I was offered and took up a full-time position with BioMed Central.

CASE STUDY

Olly Strawbridge studied the LLM Corporate Governance and Law/Grad ICSA course at the University of Portsmouth and now works in a successful global company. He tells us more about his route from further study to the world of work

Why did you take this course?

I didn't know what career I wanted to pursue following A-levels. I decided it was best to go to university to study something I was good at and enjoyed, so I enrolled at Portsmouth to read history.

I really enjoyed the undergraduate degree, but towards the end of my course it dawned on me that I was about to enter the real world and didn't really have a plan. All I knew was that I wanted to be successful, both in terms of having a rewarding career and financially.

My tutor suggested I should stay on and enrol on the Masters programme. However, although I liked the subject, I couldn't see myself pursuing history as a career. A friend told me about the corporate governance and law/grad ICSA (Institute of Chartered Secretaries and Administrators) course, which I soon viewed as a 'golden gateway'.

It was a way of accessing the corporate world and therefore provided the potential for the sort of career I was looking for.

How has the course helped your career so far?

The course carried with it the professionally recognised chartered secretary qualification, which meant I managed to secure a job as a company secretarial assistant for Chemring Group PLC before graduating, initially working part

Everything I learned on my Masters is directly relevant to the work I do now

time to allow me to complete my dissertation.

I now work in the head office of a Financial Times Stock Exchange (FTSE) 250 global corporate; something I am pleased to have achieved so early in my career. Everything I learned on my Masters is directly relevant to the work I do now. In this respect, choosing a career-specific postgraduate course really was beneficial.

I know some people at university who struggled to get work, others who got work related to their degree, and others who secured jobs unrelated to their education. The corporate governance and law course was good in this respect as the ICSA accreditation provided a route into a fulfilling and financially rewarding profession. As with any job, it helped that I had relevant work experience that I had undertaken throughout my Masters year.

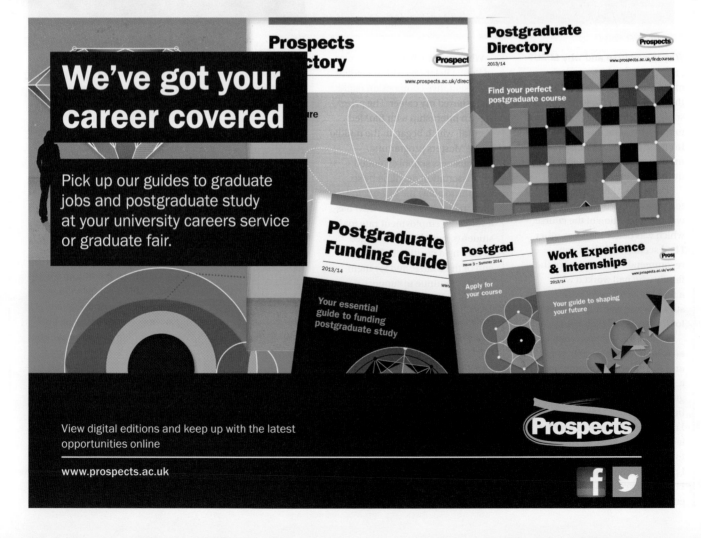

CASE STUDY

Sarah Yates completed the MSc Finance at Imperial College Business School

Why did you choose this course and institution?

I chose MSc Finance to gain an in-depth understanding of key financial concepts as a strong foundation for a career in banking. After completing a quantitative undergraduate degree in BSc Economics and Finance, I wanted a challenging finance Masters to build on what I'd already learned. The MSc Finance programme is one of the most quantitative finance Masters in the UK.

I also chose Imperial College Business School because of its excellent global reputation and strong career and professional development service – staff provide CV advice, one-to-one consultations with career advisers, mock interviews and practice assessment centres. I also liked that the school is in London and has strong links with the finance industry, providing students with considerable exposure to companies in this sector.

Lastly, I wanted the opportunity to work in a multicultural environment and build a network with people from varied backgrounds.

How do you think the course will benefit your career?

Completing the MSc Finance at the business school has equipped me with a number of beneficial skills. I learned about theoretical financial concepts through taking courses such as advanced econometrics and asset pricing and derivatives, and I also acquired practical skills through the more applied subjects (e.g. applied corporate finance), as well as strengthening my technical skills.

The classes taught by Adjunct Professor Andreas Angelopoulos (venture capital finance and innovation and private equity and entrepreneurial finance) were extremely valuable, allowing me to improve my analytical and financial modelling skills through the completion of an investment proposal, investment model and term sheet.

Furthermore, I had the opportunity to work with a diverse range of people through various projects and pieces of coursework

Partake in public speaking and presentation skills workshops – worthwhile skills that make you more employable

and found learning about new cultures and methods of working particularly enjoyable.

What were the best aspects of your course?

It was challenging but also rewarding – I was constantly being pushed to work harder and take on more things. The peer group in the MSc Finance programme is extremely driven, motivated and ambitious and I found I had common goals with many people.

When I look back to the start of the programme I think I have grown a lot, both in an academic sense, in terms of developing a more sophisticated thought process and a more advanced knowledge of finance, and personally, in that I have made a lot of friends and become more independent through living in a new city.

Another aspect I really enjoyed is the diverse range of people I got to work with on a daily basis. The first group I was assigned consisted of people from Germany, Turkey, Singapore and Hong Kong, and we all had different approaches yet came together to work as a very effective group. The quality of the lecturers was also a highlight for me, with Andreas Angelopoulos and Robert Stefanowski making a particularly strong impression on me.

What advice would you give to people starting a similar course?

Starting a Masters is very daunting, especially given the workload expected of you in the first semester at the school. You also have to adapt to working with a new network of people, living in a new city and trying to obtain an internship/job. So I think it's really important to set clear personal, career and academic objectives from the outset. When I moved to London from Ireland, I didn't know anyone else doing the programme, so I went out of my way to talk to as many people as possible and be sociable.

Make the most of the resources and opportunities available to you, such as alumni and company networking events and optional courses, and partake in public speaking and presentation skills workshops – worthwhile skills that make you more employable.

What are your plans?

My immediate plan is to participate in the Morgan Stanley IBD Summer Analyst programme. I am focused on putting all my effort into this internship in the hope that it will convert to a full-time position on completion. I plan to work in investment banking for the next three to five years and then perhaps complete a Masters in Business Administration.

Become a market leader

A popular sector among graduates, marketing involves identifying, anticipating and satisfying customer demand. Could postgraduate study help you build your own brand and give you a leg up in the industry?

Marketing is an integral part of any business or organisation across every sector in the UK economy. Its aim is to manage and enhance brands, and ultimately give customers what they want.

Despite economic conditions meaning many companies have had to cut marketing budgets in recent years, its continued importance to the business world means the industry offers employment opportunities in a variety of roles. For example, a graduate could work as anything from a marketing executive or copywriter to a social media consultant or account manager.

Marketing attracts graduates from an array of disciplines because many transferable skills gained while studying can be utilised in marketing roles. These include: research; writing; teamwork; organisation; and communication skills.

Transferable skills

Studying marketing to Masters level has a number of benefits, which mostly revolve around readying you for a career in the sector.

Many courses have good links with industry, as well as tutors who have spent years as marketing professionals themselves. This all means that students get to work on assignments and projects that are true to real life and, as a result, develop specialised employability skills to help them hit the ground running once they start work.

Dr Fernando Fastoso, director of studies for the MSc International Marketing and MSc Strategic Marketing at the Bradford University School of Management, says, 'With increased competition in both business-to-consumer (B2C) and business-to-business (B2B) markets, companies need to make sure that they choose and implement the right marketing strategy to succeed. They need graduates with good knowledge and understanding of current best practice, and the personal skills to make a contribution from the outset.

'The students at Bradford enjoy the benefit of learning from an internationally diverse faculty whose research is at the forefront of current academic thinking in marketing. Many of our faculty also have substantial experience of devising and implementing marketing strategies in organisations both big and small. This provides a rich learning experience of leading theory supported by practical know-how.'

Let's get digital

Studying marketing at postgraduate level allows you to specialise in a specific area, such as digital marketing, which is one of the fastest growing areas in the sector. This is due to increasing numbers of companies seeing the benefits of investing more of their budget in increasing their online visibility.

The main branches of digital marketing are: search engine optimisation (SEO), which aims to improve the visibility of websites in search engines; digital content marketing, which involves creating and sharing content with a view to gaining more customers; and social media marketing, through which organisations can build their reputation, engage with customers and build up a following.

As a result of this shift by businesses towards marketing on the web, a growing number of graduates are able to find employment opportunities in the sector. And, with a growing number of digital marketing-based postgraduate courses on offer at universities across the UK, those job prospects can be boosted further.

According to Dave Edmundson-Bird, principal lecturer in digital marketing and enterprise at Manchester Metropolitan University (MMU), 'A postgraduate digital marketer is very hot property in marketing – much more than someone who has avoided it. Few marketing jobs these days exist in a world without digital.

'Employers like postgrads, because they think strategically and critically about employing communication tools in whole marketing campaigns.'

Dave stresses that courses at MMU aim to cover the whole spectrum of digital marketing, such as SEO, mobile, social media marketing and analytics.

Whichever aspect of marketing you choose to study, you should find that a postgrad course will give you the return on investment that you're looking for.

MARKETING MAKE-UP

Marketing is a big sector. Here are three of the biggest components of modern-day marketing:

ADVERTISING
The more traditional side of marketing, this involves placing adverts in newspapers, magazines, on television and on billboards.

DIGITAL MARKETING
Encompasses SEO, social media, digital content marketing, mobile, analytics, pay-per-click (PPC), email marketing and more.

PR
Managing clients' reputations, influencing people's behaviour and opinions to try and gain custom, and seeking out potential coverage in national press for clients.

The University of Manchester
Manchester Business School

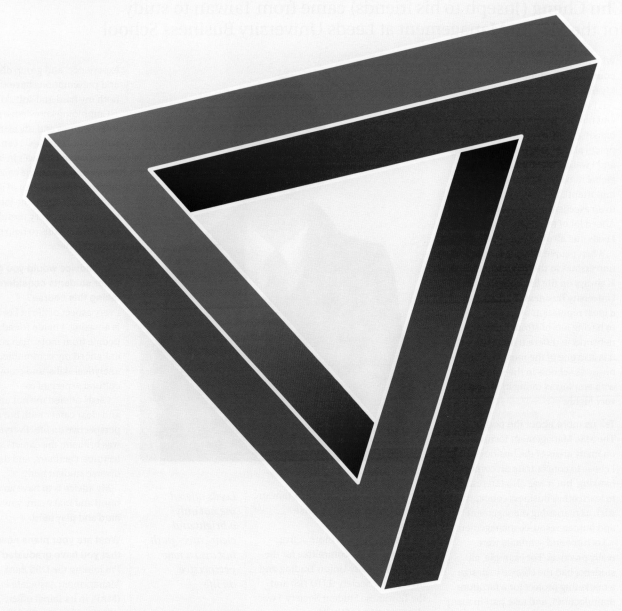

Think you can find a postgraduate
course to change your perspective
on business?

Think world class lecturers.
Think specialised programmes.
Think Manchester Business School.

You can.

MBS Postgraduate Courses

Apply now for 2014
Limited scholarships available

go.mbs.ac.uk/postgraduate

Original Thinking Applied

CASE STUDY

Chu Cheng (Joseph to his friends) came from Taiwan to study for the MSc in Management at Leeds University Business School

Why did you choose this course and institution?

My first degree was in economics but I wanted a career in banking and finance, specifically corporate banking. I was eager to acquire more practical knowledge about business and I wanted to build a strong global network. It was also very important that I had access to an excellent careers service. After a lot of research, I found that Leeds met all of my requirements.

When people talk about good universities in the UK, Leeds is always on the list. Leeds University Business School has a great reputation in Asia due to having lots of strong alumni networks in different industries; it is also one of the most famous business schools in the world, with employers rating its students very highly.

Tell us more about the course...

The MSc Management focuses on many areas of the business world. I chose to concentrate on corporate banking, but it was also interesting to learn other business concepts, such as marketing management and human resource management.

Lectures and seminars were really practical. For example, all students had the chance to design a marketing project for a furniture manufacturer, and take part in many presentations and group projects based on real-life case studies.

In seminars, there was opportunity to debate with students from different backgrounds and different countries. These experiences helped to develop my leadership and teamwork skills, which have enhanced my employability.

What facilities are available at this institution?

Leeds has a computer cluster, a library, a gym, a common room, a cafe and a careers service.

What are the main differences between undergraduate and postgraduate life?

Gaining international and cross-cultural experience was the major difference between

my undergraduate course in Taiwan and my postgraduate course at Leeds.

My social life was more active, too. I was on the committee for the Leeds University Union Trading and Investment Society (LUUTIS) and the Taiwanese Student Society. I was also a member of the Hong Kong Society basketball team.

These societies gave me the opportunity to participate in many events throughout the year, such as a visit to the Bank of America Merrill Lynch with LUUTIS, a Halloween party with the Taiwanese Student Society, and a trip to York to play with the basketball team.

In my postgraduate course at Leeds, I met and worked with people from all around the world. The impact of the new cultures made my thinking process more dynamic and enhanced my social skills.

How did the course help you prepare for employment?

The experience and skills I've gained at Leeds are definitely helpful. The MSc Management focuses not only on theories but also on practical

Leeds offered me not only a bright and clear career path but also a new perspective on life

experience, and group discussions and presentations have shaped both my hard and soft skills.

Combining knowledge gained from lectures and my extra-curricular activities, I can give an impressive answer in interviews. Also, our programme careers adviser provided a lot of important information about the job market and taught me very useful networking skills to help me interact with recruiters.

What advice would you give other students considering taking this course?

Every aspect of life in Leeds is amazing. I made friends with people from more than 20 nations, enhanced my communication and analytical skills, and enjoyed cross-cultural experiences.

Leeds offered me not only a bright and clear career path but also a new perspective on life. Everything was brilliant: the careers service; lectures; seminars; and the diverse student body.

My advice is to have an open mind and make sure you work hard and play hard.

What are your plans now that you have graduated?

I'm joining the DBS Bank Management Associate Program (MAP) in its Taipei office. The MAP will provide me with a two-year cross-function rotation in the Institutional Banking Group in order to gain a well-rounded understanding of corporate banking.

It's a great start for my career and I am very grateful to the business school for their support in finding me such a remarkable opportunity.

Discover your potential.
Then exceed it.

People from all over the world choose Leeds University Business School for their Masters degree. We are one of the most influential business schools in the UK and have received global recognition for the quality of our teaching and research. We hold EQUIS and AMBA accreditation and are ranked in the top 100 universities in the world (QS World Rankings 2012).

We are also ranked in the UK top 10 for research by the most recent Research Assessment Exercise.

So, if you are interested in studying a Masters in Economics, Enterprise, Finance, HR, International Business, Management or Marketing, find out more by visiting **www.business.leeds.ac.uk/masters/prospects-uk** or email **masters@lubs.leeds.ac.uk**

Leeds University Business School

UNIVERSITY OF LEEDS

Business and social sciences
Course and research opportunities

This section sets out every UK and Ireland postgraduate opportunity in the area of business and social sciences. Use the following pages to browse the taught courses and research opportunities at each institution. The listings are divided into subject chapters which are subsequently divided into related subject areas.

Taught courses and research opportunities are listed separately, each entry containing university name, course name, mode of study and type of study information. Please see the full A-Z index of all subjects in this publication on page 557. Further details of each course can be found at *www.prospects.ac.uk/findcourses*

BUSINESS AND SOCIAL SCIENCES SUBJECT CHAPTERS LIST

Business and social sciences
368 POSTGRADUATE DIRECTORY www.prospects.ac.uk/findcourses

Section sponsored by BPP UNIVERSITY COLLEGE

Accounting and finance

Accounting
Taught Courses

University of Abertay Dundee
Finance .... MSc 12FT/PGDip 9FT
Oil and Gas Accounting .... MSc 12FT/PGDip 9FT

Anglia Ruskin University
Accounting and Financial Analysis .... MSc 18FT 24PT
Association of Chartered Certified Accountants .... ACCA professional qualification 36-48PT
Corporate Governance .... MA 18FT 24PT

Bangor University
ACCA (Professional Development) .... ACCA 48PT
Accounting and Finance .... MSc 12FT
Accounting and Finance - LondonCentre .... MSc 12FT
Banking and Finance ....MSc 12FT MA 12FT/PGDip 9FT MBA 12FT
Banking and Finance - London Centre .... MSc 12FT
Business and Finance .... MSc 12FT/PGDip 9FT MA 12FT/PGDip 9FT
Business and Marketing .... MA 12FT/PGDip 9FT
CIMA (Professional Development) .... CIMA 12PT
Finance....... MBA 12FT MA 12FT/PGDip 9FT MSc 12FT/PGDip 9FT
Finance - London Centre .... MBA 12FT MSc 12FT
International Banking and Development Finance .... MSc 12FT/PGDip 9FT
International Banking and Development Finance - London Centre .... MSc 12FT
Islamic Banking and Finance .... MA 12FT/PGDip 9FT MSc 12FT/PGDip 9FT
Islamic Banking and Finance - London Centre .... MBA 12FT
Management .... MBA 12FT 36PT
Management and Finance .... MSc 12FT/MA 12FT

University of Bedfordshire
Association of Chartered Certified Accountants ....ACCA 24-36PT
Chartered Institute of Management Accountants .... CIMA 24-36PT

Belfast Metropolitan College
ACCA Stage 1 .... ACCA 10PT
ACCA Stage 2 .... ACCA 10PT
ACCA Stage 3 .... ACCA 10PT
CIMA Foundation .... CIMA 10PT
CIMA Managerial Level .... CIMA 10PT
CIMA Strategic Level .... CIMA 10PT

Birkbeck, University of London
Accounting and Financial Management .... MSc 12FT 24PT

Birmingham City University
Association of Chartered Certified Accountants Course (ACCA) - Full-time & Part-time .... ACCA 12FT 36-60PT
Audit Management and Consultancy .... MSc 12FT 36PT 36DL/PGDip 24PT 24DL

University of Bolton
Accountancy (Advanced Standing) .... MA 18 - 24PT
Accountancy and Financial Strategy .... MA 12FT 24 - 42PT

Bournemouth University
Corporate Governance .... MSc 12FT/MSc 24PT

University of Bradford
Finance, Accounting and Management .... MSc 12FT/PGDip 9FT

Brunel University
Accounting and Business Management .... MSc 12FT

University of Central Lancashire
Finance and Management .... MSc 12FT
Financial Analysis .... MSc 12FT

City University London
Charity Accounting and Financial Management .... PGDip 13FT/MSc 19FT

University College Cork
Management Information and Managerial Accounting Systems .... MBS 15FT

Coventry University
Accounting and Financial Management .... MSc 12FT 24PT

De Montfort University
ACCA - Association of Chartered Certified Accountants .ACCA Up to 48PT
CIMA - Chartered Institute of Management Accountants ... CIMA Up to 48PT
Forensic Accounting .... MSc 12FT

University of Derby
MBA Advanced Standing (ACCA and CIMA) .... MBA 12FT

Dublin Institute of Technology
Accounting .... MSc 12FT 24PT
Accounting .... PGDip 9FT

University of Dundee
Accounting and Finance .... MSc 12FT
International Accounting .... MSc 12FT
Professional Accountancy .... MSc 12FT

University of East Anglia
Advanced Business Management .... MSc 12FT
Business Management .... MSc 12FT
International Accounting and Financial Management . MSc 12FT
Investment and Financial Management .... MSc 12FT
MBA (full-time) .... MBA 12FT

Edinburgh Napier University
Wealth Management .... MSc 24-36DL

University of Edinburgh
Accounting and Finance .... MSc 12FT 24PT

University of Essex
Accounting .... MSc 12FT 24PT/MRes 12FT 24PT
Accounting and Finance .... MSc 12FT 24PT
Accounting and Financial Management .... MSc 12FT 24PT
Accounting and Management ... MSc 12FT 24PT/MRes 12FT 24PT
Accounting with English for Academic Purposes .... Diploma 9FT
International Accounting .... MSc 12FT 24PT
Work, Organisation and Society .... MSc 12FT 24PT/MRes 12FT 24PT

GCU London
Accounting and Finance (Fast Track) .... MSc 6FT

National University of Ireland Galway
Accounting .... MAcc 12FT

Glasgow Caledonian University
Association of Chartered Certified Accountants .... ACCA 36PT
Chartered Institute of Management Accountants .... CIMA 48PT
Master of Accounting .... MAcc 12FT FlexiblePT
Master of Accounting (Oil and Gas Accounting) .... MAcc 12FT FlexiblePT
Master of Accounting (Public Sector Financial Management) ...... MAcc 12FT FlexiblePT

University of Glasgow
International Accounting and Financial Management .... MAcc 12FT
International Financial Analysis .... MSc 12FT

University of Gloucestershire
Accounting and Finance (Top up) .... MSc 4FT 12PT
Accounting and Financial Management ....MSc 12FT 24PT/PGDip 8FT 20PT/PGCert 4FT 8PT

University of Greenwich
Accounting and Finance .... MSc 12FT 24PT

Heriot-Watt University
International Accounting and Finance .... MSc 12FT 24PT/PGDip 9FT 21PT
International Accounting and Management .... MSc 12FT 24PT/PGDip 9FT 21PT

University of Hertfordshire
Accounting and Financial Management .. MSc 12FT/PGDip 12FT/PGCert 12FT
CIMA Operational and Management Level .... Diploma 18M
CIMA Strategic Level .... Diploma 18M

University of Huddersfield
Accounting .... MSc 12FT
Accounting and Finance by Distance Learning .... MA 9FT 15PT

University of Hull
Accounting and Finance .... MSc 12FT

ifs School of Finance
Banking Practice and Management and Chartered Fellowship.... MSc 24PT 36DL/PGDip 16PT 28DL/PGCert 8PT 12DL

University of Kent
Financial Markets .... MSc 12FT
Financial Services in Banking .... MSc 12FT
International Accounting and Finance .... MSc 12FT

King's College London
Accounting, Accountability & Financial Management.. MSc 12FT

Leeds Metropolitan University
Accounting .... MSc 12FT 24PT
Accounting and Finance .... MSc 12FT 24PT
Association of Chartered Certified Accountants - Fundementals Level (ACCA) .... ACCA 12PT
Association of Chartered Certified Accountants - Knowledge Level (ACCA) .... ACCA 12PT
Association of Chartered Certified Accountants - Professional Level (ACCA) .... ACCA 24PT
Association of Chartered Certified Accountants Professional (ACCA) .... ACCA 12FT

University of Leeds
Accounting and Finance .... MA 12FT

University of Leicester
Accounting and Finance .... MSc 12FT
Management, Finance and Accounting .... MSc 12FT

University of Lincoln
Chartered Institute of Management Accounting .... CIMA 8PT

University of Liverpool
Accounting - London Based .... MSc 15FT
International Accounting and Finance (Online Degree) MSc 24FT 24+PT

London School of Economics and Political Science (LSE)
Accounting and Finance .... MSc 9FT 21PT PGDip 9FT
Accounting, Organisations and Institutions .... MSc 10FT

London South Bank University
Charity Finance & Accounting .... CIPFA Certificate 12PT
Charity Finance & Accounting - Blended ... CIPFA Certificate 12PT

Manchester Metropolitan University
Association of Chartered Certified Accountants (ACCA) Professional Qualification .... ACCA FlexiblePT
Financial Management .... MSc 12FT 24-36PT

Newcastle University
Banking and Finance .... MSc 12FT
Operations Management, Logistics and Accounting ..... MSc 12FT
Operations and Supply Chain Management .... MSc 12FT

Nottingham Trent University
CIPFA - Professional Accountancy Qualification (PAQ) .... CIPFA 30-42PT

Oxford Brookes University
Accounting .... MSc 12FT 24PT

University of Portsmouth
Forensic Accounting .... MSc 12FT 36PT

Queen Mary, University of London
Accounting and Finance .... MSc 12FT

Queen's University Belfast
Accounting and Finance .... MSc 12FT

University of Reading
Accounting and Financial Management .... MSc 12FT
International Management and Accounting .... MSc 12FT 24PT

Robert Gordon University
Accounting and Finance .... MSc 12FT/PGDip 8FT/PGCert 4FT
Oil and Gas Accounting .... MSc 12FT/PGDip 8FT/PGCert 4FT

Royal Holloway, University of London
International Accounting .... MSc 12FT

University of Salford
Accounting and Finance .... MSc 12FT 36PT/PGDip 8FT 24PT/PGCert 4FT 9PT
International Banking and FInance ..... MSc 12FT 36PT/PGDip 8FT 24PT/PGCert 4FT 9PT
International Corporate FInanceMSc 12FT 36PT/PGDip 8FT 24PT/PGCert 4FT 9PT

Sheffield Hallam University
Accounting and Finance .... MA 12FT
Banking and Finance .... MA 12FT
Charity Resource Management ..... MSc 30PT/PGDip 18PT/PGCert 12PT

University of South Wales
Accounting .... MSc 12FT
Association of Chartered Certified Accountants (ACCA) .... ACCA 24-48PT
Chartered Institute of Management Accountants (CIMA) ... CIMA 6FT 12PT
Forensic Audit and Accounting .... MSc 12FT

University of Southampton
Accounting and Finance .... MSc 12FT/PGDip 9FT
Accounting and Management .... MSc 12FT/PGDip 9FT
International Banking and Financial StudiesMSc 12FT/PGDip 9FT

University of Stirling
International Accounting & FinanceMSc 12FT/PGDip 9FT/PGCert 6FT

University of Strathclyde
International Accounting and FinanceMSc 12FT 24PT/PGDip 9FT 21PT
International Banking and Finance ..... MSc 12FT 24PT/PGDip 9FT 21PT

Swansea Metropolitan University
Chartered Institute of Management Accountants ...... CIMA 12FT
The Association of Chartered Certified Accountants ... ACCA 48FT

Teesside University
Accounting and Finance .... MSc 12FT 24PT

University of Ulster
ACCA - Association of Chartered Certified Accountants (Professional Scheme) .... ACCA 9PT
Accounting .... GradDip 9FT
Advanced Accounting (full time) .... MSc 12FT

University of West London
Association of Chartered Certified Accountants (ACCA) .... ACCA 36PT/ACCA 36FT

Accounting
Research Courses

Bangor University
Accounting, Banking, Economics, Finance, Management Studies. .... MPhil 24FT/PhD 36FT

University of Dundee
Accountancy and Business Finance .... MAcc 12FT MPhil 24FT MSc by research 12FT PhD 36FT

University of East Anglia
Business Management .... PhD 36FT 72PT/MPhil 24FT 48PT

Accounting and finance

Business, Accountability, Regulation and Development .... PhD 36FT 72PT/MPhil 24FT 48PT

University of Essex
Accounting ......PhD 36FT 72PT/MPhil 24FT 48PT/MSc by research 12FT 24PT
Finance ....PhD 36FT/MRes 12FT 24PT/MPhil 24FT 48PT
Finance and Accounting .... PhD 36FT 72PT

University of Exeter
Accountancy .... PhD 36FT 72PT/MPhil 24FT 48PT

Heriot-Watt University
Accountancy and Finance.....................PhD 36FT 48PT/MPhil 12FT

University of Kent
Accounting & Finance .... PhD 36FT 60PT

London School of Economics and Political Science (LSE)
Accounting... MPhil 36-48FT/PhD 36-48FT

The Open University
Accounting............... PhD 36FT 72PT variableDL/MPhil 15FT 24PT variableDL

Queen's University Belfast
Accounting.. PhD 36FT 72PT/MPhil 24FT 48PT

Accounting and finance
Taught Courses

University of Aberdeen
Accounting and Finance .... MSc 12FT 24PT/MRes 12FT

Aberystwyth University
International Finance and Accounting .... MSc 12FT 24PT

Aston University
Accounting & Finance .... MSc 12FT

Bangor University
ACCA (Professional Development)..................................ACCA 48PT
Accounting and Finance .... MSc 12FT
Accounting and Finance - LondonCentre .... MSc 12FT
Accounting, Banking, Economics, Finance, Management Studies MPhil 24FT/PhD by taught 36FT
Banking and Finance ....MSc 12FT MA 12FT/PGDip 9FT MBA 12FT
Banking and Finance - London Centre .... MSc 12FT
Business and Finance ...MSc 12FT/PGDip 9FTMA 12FT/PGDip 9FT
Business and Marketing...MA 12FT/PGDip 9FT
CIMA (Professional Development)..................................CIMA 12PT
Finance.........MBA 12FTMA 12FT/PGDip 9FT MSc 12FT/PGDip 9FT
Finance - London Centre .... MBA 12FT MSc 12FT
International Banking and Development Finance.........MSc 12FT/PGDip 9FT
International Banking and Development Finance - London Centre.. MSc 12FT
Islamic Banking and Finance........ MA 12FT/PGDip 9FT MSc 12FT/PGDip 9FT MBA 12FT
Islamic Banking and Finance - London Centre............... MBA 12FT
Management...MBA 12FT 36PT
Management and Finance................................ MSc 12FT/MA 12FT

Bath Spa University
Business and Management: Accounting .... MA 12FT 32PT

University of Bath
Accounting and Finance .... MSc 12FT
Economics and Finance..MSc 12FT 30PT/PGDip 9FT 21PT/PGCert 4FT

University of Bedfordshire
Accounting and Finance .... MSc 12FT
Finance and Business Management........................... MSc 12-15FT

Birkbeck, University of London
Accounting and Financial Management .... MSc 12FT 24PT
Corporate Governance and Business Ethics ....MSc 12FT 24PT/MRes 12FT 24PT/PGCert 12PT

Birmingham City University
Accountancy and Finance (ACCA, CIMA + Top Up pathways). MSc 12FT

University of Birmingham
Accounting and Finance ....MSc(Res) 12FT/MPhil 24FT/PhD by taught 36FT
International Accounting and Finance .... MSc 12FT

University of Bolton
Accountancy and Financial Strategy .... MA 12FT 24 - 42PT

University of Brighton
Economics and Finance. MSc see siteFT/PGDip see siteFT/PGCert see siteFT

University of Bristol
Accounting, Finance and Management .... MSc 12FT
Economics, Accounting and Finance .... MSc 12FT

Brunel University
Accounting and Business Management.......................... MSc 12FT
Finance and Accounting .... MSc 12FT
Accounting and Business Management.......................... MSc 12FT

University of Buckingham
Accounting and Finance .... MSc 12FT
Finance and Investment .... MSc 12FT
Financial Service Management .... MSc 12FT

Bucks New University
International Accounting and Finance .... MSc 12-15FT

University of Cambridge
Master of Finance ....MFin 12FT

Cardiff University
Accounting and Finance .... MSc 12FT

University of Central Lancashire
Finance and Development.. MSc 12FT
Finance and Investment .... MSc 12FT
Finance and Management.. MSc 12FT
Financial Analysis .... MSc 12FT
Master of Business Administration .... MBA 12FT
Master of Business Administration - Part-time............. MBA 36PT
Postgraduate Certificate in Management ....PGCert 18PT

City University London
International Accounting and Finance .... MSc 9-12FT

University College Cork
Accounting and Corporate Finance.................................... HDip 9FT
Corporate Finance and Accounting....................................MBS 12FT

University of Cumbria
Master of Business Administration .... MBA 12FT 36PT

De Montfort University
Accounting and Finance .... MSc 12FT 24PT
Accounting and Finance, Fast track, DL ....MSc 12DL

University of Dundee
Accounting and Finance ....MRes 12FT MSc 12FT
Finance .... MSc 12FT
Financial Economics ....PGDip 9FT
International Accounting .... MSc 12FT
Non-Graduating Taught Postgraduate in School of Business... PG module variableFT

Durham University
Finance (Accounting and Finance) .... MSc 12FT

University of East Anglia
Finance and Economics.. MSc 12FT
International Accounting and Financial Management . MSc 12FT
International Business Finance and Economics ....MA 12FT
Investment and Financial Management .... MSc 12FT

University of East London
Finance and Risk ..... MSc 12FT 24PT/PGDip 8FT 16PT/PGCert 4FT 8PT
International Accounting and Finance ....MSc 12FT 24PT/PGDip 8FT 16PT/PGCert 4FT 8PT

Edinburgh Napier University
Accounting and Finance .... MSc 12FT 36PT
Strategic Risk Management and Finance............... MSc 12FT 24PT

University of Edinburgh
Accounting and Finance .... MSc 12FT 24PT
Banking and Risk .... MSc 12FT
Carbon Finance .... MSc 12FT
Finance and Investment .... MSc 12FT
Financial Management.. MSc 12FT
Financial Modelling and Optimization ....MSc 12FT 24PT/PGDip 9FT
Financial Operational Research .... MSc 12FT/PGDip 9FT

University of Essex
Accounting ....MSc 12FT 24PT/MRes 12FT 24PT
Accounting and Finance .... MSc 12FT 24PT
Accounting and Financial Management .... MSc 12FT 24PT
Accounting and Management ...MSc 12FT 24PT/MRes 12FT 24PT
Banking .... MSc 12FT 24PT
Banking and Finance .... MSc 12FT 24PT
Finance..MSc 12FT 24PT/MRes 12FT 24PT
Finance and Investment .... MSc 12FT 24PT
Finance and Management.. MSc 12FT 24PT
International Accounting .... MSc 12FT 24PT
International Finance .... MSc 12FT 24PT

University of Exeter
Finance ....GradDip 9FT
Finance and Management..MSc 9FT

GCU London
International Banking, Finance and Risk Management .... MSc 12FT

National University of Ireland Galway
Electronic Commerce.. MBS 18approxFT

Glasgow Caledonian University
Master of Accounting....................................MAcc 12FT FlexiblePT
Master of Accounting (Oil and Gas Accounting) ....MAcc 12FT FlexiblePT
Master of Accounting (Public Sector Financial Management) ...... MAcc 12FT FlexiblePT

University of Glasgow
International Accounting and Financial ManagementMAcc 12FT
Quantitative Finance.. MSc 12FT

University of Gloucestershire
Accounting and Finance (Top up) .... MSc 4FT 12PT
Accounting and Financial Management ....MSc 12FT 24PT/PGDip 8FT 20PT/PGCert 4FT 8PT

Glyndwr University
Accounting and Financial Management .... MSc 12FT

University of Greenwich
Accounting and Finance .... MSc 12FT 24PT
Finance (Executive Part-time) ....PGDip 24PT/MSc 24PT
Finance and Financial Information Systems..........MSc 12FT 24PT/PGDip 12FT 24PT
Financial Management............. MSc 12FT 24PT/PGDip 12FT 24PT

Heriot-Watt University
Finance..MSc 12FT 24PT/PGDip 9FT 21PT
Finance and Management...........MSc 12FT 24PT/PGDip 9FT 21PT
Financial Management ....MSc 84DL
International Accounting and FinanceMSc 12FT 24PT/PGDip 9FT 21PT
International Accounting and Management ....MSc 12FT 24PT/PGDip 9FT 21PT
Investment Management ....MSc 12FT 24PT/PGDip 9FT 21PT

University of Hertfordshire
Accounting and Financial Management .. MSc 12FT/PGDip 12FT/PGCert 12FT
CIMA Operational and Management Level .... Diploma 1BM
CIMA Strategic Level .... Diploma 1BM
Financial Market Analysis .... MSc 12FT

University of Huddersfield
Accounting .... MSc 12FT
Accounting and Finance .... MA 12FT 6PT
Accounting and Finance by Distance Learning..........MA 9FT 15PT
Banking and Finance .... MSc 12FT
Finance... MSc 12FT
International Finance with Law .... MSc 12FT

University of Hull
Accounting and Finance .... MSc 12FT
Finance and Investment .... MSc 12FT
Financial Management.. MSc 12FT

Imperial College London
Finance .... MSc 12FT

Kingston University
Accounting and Finance .... MSc 12FT
Finance .... MSc 12FT

Leeds Metropolitan University
Accounting and Finance .... MSc 12FT 24PT
Association of Chartered Certified Accountants - Fundementals Level (ACCA) ....ACCA 12PT
Association of Chartered Certified Accountants - Knowledge Level (ACCA) ....ACCA 12PT
Association of Chartered Certified Accountants - Professional Level (ACCA) ....ACCA 24PT

University of Leeds
Accounting and Finance ....MA 12FT

University of Leicester
Accounting and Finance .... MSc 12FT
Banking and Finance .... MSc 12FT 24PT
Business Analysis and Finance............................... MSc 12FT 24PT
Finance .... MSc 12FT 24-60DL
Management, Finance and Accounting.......................... MSc 12FT

University of Lincoln
Accounting .... MSc 15FT 12PT
Finance .... MBA 12-15FT

University of Liverpool
Business Finance and Management....................... MBA 12FT 24PT
Finance........ MSc 12FT 24PT/PGDip 12FT 24PT/PGCert 12FT 24PT

London Metropolitan University
Business Economics .... MA 12FT 24PT
Finance ....GradDip 12FT 24PT MSc 12FT 24PT

London School of Economics and Political Science (LSE)
Accounting and Finance ....MSc 9FT 21PT PGDip 9FT
Accounting, Organisations and Institutions .... MSc 10FT
Finance (Part-Time) .... MSc 21PT
Finance and Economics.. MSc 10FT
Law and Accounting .... MSc 12FT 24PT

London South Bank University
ACCA International Summer School - Fundamental Papers ACCA 4FT
Accounting with Finance.. MSc 10FT 14PT
Fundamental Papers .... ACCA 4PT
International Finance .... MSc 12FT 24PT
International Finance & Accounting .... MSc 18FT
Management in Civil Society (Accounting & Finance) .. MSc 30PT
Management in Civil Society (Accounting & Finance) - Blended.. MSc 30PT
Professional Papers - Revision Only .... ACCA 4PT
Professional Papers - Tuition & Revision .... ACCA 4PT
Professional Papers - Tuition Only .... ACCA 4PT

Loughborough University
Finance and Management (for non-finance graduates) MSc 12FT

Manchester Metropolitan University
Accounting and Finance .... MSc 12FT
Association of Chartered Certified Accountants Professional Qualification .... ACCA FlexiblePT

Accounting and finance

MSc Accounting and Finance ... MSc 12FT

University of Manchester
Accounting and Finance ... MSc 12FT

Middlesex University
Financial Management ... MSc 14FT 26PT

Newcastle University
Banking and Finance ... MSc 12FT
Finance ... MSc 12FT
Finance and Economics (Research) ... MA 12FT 24PT
Finance and Financial Regulation ... MSc 12FT
Finance and Law with Islamic Finance ... MSc 12FT
Finance, Accounting and Business ... GradDip 9FT
Operations Management, Logistics and Accounting ... MSc 12FT

University of Northampton
Accounting and Finance ... MSc 12FT 24PT/PGCert 12PT
Accounting and Finance (top-up from ACCA, CIMA, CPA and AIA)) MSc 12PT 12DL

Nottingham Trent University
Economics and Finance/International Finance ... MSc 12FT
International Real Estate Investment and Finance MSc 12FT 24PT
Strategic Accounting and Finance ... MSc 12FT

The Open University
Accounting ... Professional Certificate variableDL

Oxford Brookes University
Accounting ... MSc 12FT 24PT
Finance ... MSc 12FT 24PT

University of Oxford
Financial Economics ... MSc 9FT

Plymouth University
Finance ... MSc 12FT 24PT
Masters in Business Administration ... MBA 12FT
The Global MBA ... MBA 12FT

University of Portsmouth
Finance ... MSc 12FT
Financial Decision Analysis ... MSc 12FT 36PT
Forensic Accounting (DL) ... MSc 36DL

Queen Mary, University of London
Accounting and Finance ... MSc 12FT
Accounting and Management ... MSc 12FT
Business Finance ... MSc 12FT 24PT
International Business ... MSc 12FT
Management ... MSc 12FT 24PT
Mathematical Finance ... MSc 12FT 24PT
Tax Law ... LLM 12FT 24PT

Queen's University Belfast
Accounting and Finance ... MSc 12FT
Computational Finance and Trading ... MSc 12FT

University of Reading
Accounting and Financial Management ... MSc 12FT
Construction Cost Management ... MSc 24PT
Construction Management ... MSc 12FT
Development Finance ... MSc 12FT
Economics of International Business and Finance ... MSc 12FT 24PT
International Business and Finance ... MSc 12FT
Project Management ... MSc 24PT

Richmond, The American International University in London
Masters in Business Administration ... MBA 12FT 24PT

Robert Gordon University
Accounting and Finance ... MSc 12FT/PGDip 8FT/PGCert 4FT
Oil and Gas Accounting ... MSc 12FT/PGDip 8FT/PGCert 4FT
Strategic Accounting (with CIMA) ... MSc 24DL

Royal Holloway, University of London
Financial and Industrial Economics ... MSc 12FT
International Accounting ... MSc 12FT

University of Salford
Accounting and Finance ... MSc 12FT 36PT/PGDip 8FT 24PT/PGCert 4FT 9PT
International Banking and Finance ... MSc 12FT 36PT/PGDip 8FT 24PT/PGCert 4FT 9PT
International Corporate Finance MSc 12FT 36PT/PGDip 8FT 24PT/PGCert 4FT 9PT

School of Oriental and African Studies - SOAS
Development Economics ... MSc 12FT 24-36PT
Finance and Development ... MSc 24-60DL/PGDip 12-60DL

Sheffield Hallam University
Accounting and Finance ... MA 12FT
Banking and Finance ... MA 12FT
Charity Resource Management ... MSc 30PT/PGDip 18PT/PGCert 12PT
Forensic Accounting ... MSc 12FT 24PT

University of Sheffield
Business Finance and Economics ... MSc 12FT 24PT
Economics ... MSc 12FT 24PT
Finance ... MSc 12FT 24PT
Finance and Accounting ... MSc 12FT
Financial Economics ... MSc 12FT 24PT
International Finance and Economics ... MSc 12FT 24PT

University of South Wales
ACA - Institute of Chartered Accountants in England and Wales (ICAEW) ... ACA 36PT
Accounting and Finance/Accounting and Financial Management/ ... MSc 12FT 24PT
Islamic Banking and Finance ... MSc 12FT
Management and Development of International Financial Systems ... MSc 12FT

University of Southampton
Accounting and Finance ... MSc 12FT/PGDip 9FT
Accounting and Management ... MSc 12FT/PGDip 9FT
Finance and Economics ... MSc 12FT 24PT/PGDip 9FT 21PT
International Banking and Financial Studies MSc 12FT/PGDip 9FT
International Financial Markets ... MSc 12FT/PGDip 9FT
LLM Finance and Law (1 yrs) ... LLM 12FT

University of St Andrews
Finance & Management ... MLitt 12FT
Finance (FIN) ... PGDip 9FT/MSc 12FT/MPhil 24FT

Staffordshire University
Accounting and Finance ... MA 12FT
Accounting for Professionals ... MSc 12FT
Islamic Finance ... MSc 12FT

University of Stirling
Finance ... MSc 12FT/PGDip 9FT/PGCert 6FT
International Accounting & Finance MSc 12FT/PGDip 9FT/PGCert 6FT

University of Strathclyde
European Financial Management ... MSc 12FT
Finance ... MSc 12FT 24PT/PGDip 9FT 21PT
International Accounting and Finance MSc 12FT 24PT/PGDip 9FT 21PT
International Banking and Finance ... MSc 12FT 24PT/PGDip 9FT 21PT
Quantitative Finance ... MSc 12FT/PGDip 9FT

Swansea University
Accounting and Finance ... MSc 12FT
Business Economics with Finance ... MSc 12FT
Finance ... MSc 12FT
International Banking and Finance ... MSc 12FT
International Banking, Finance and Economics ... MSc 12FT

Swansea Metropolitan University
Association of Taxation Technicians ... ATT 12FT
Chartered Institute of Management Accountants ... CIMA 12FT

Teesside University
Accounting and Finance ... MSc 12FT 24PT

Trinity College Dublin - the University of Dublin
Finance ... MSc 12FT 24PT

University of Ulster
Financial Services ... MSc 12FT/PGDip 9FT

UCL - University College London
Financial Risk Management ... MSc 12FT

University of Warwick
Accounting and Finance in Health Service Organisations ... PGA 12PT/CPDMod 1PT
Business (Finance & Accounting) ... MSc 12FT
Finance ... MSc 12FT
Finance & Information Technology ... MSc 12FT
Accounting & Finance ... MSc 12FT
Finance & Behavioural Science ... MSc 12FT

Webster Graduate School London
Finance ... MS 14FT

University of West London
Finance and Accounting ... MSc 12FT 24PT

University of the West of England, Bristol
Accounting and Financial Management ... LLM 12FT 36PT
Finance ... MSc 12FT

University of Westminster
Finance Banking and Insurance ... MSc 12FT
Finance and Accounting ... MSc 12FT
Property Finance ... MSc 12FT 24PT

University of Winchester
Accounting and Finance ... MSc 12FT 24PT/PGDip 9FT 18PT/PGCert 9FT 18PT

University of Wolverhampton
Finance and Accounting ... MSc 12FT

University of York
Accounting and Financial Management ... MSc 12FT
Management with Business Finance ... MSc 12FT

York St John University
Master of Business Administration Managing Finance ... MBA 12FT 60PT

Accounting and finance
Research Courses

University of Aberdeen
Accountancy ... PhD 36FT/MPhil 24FT
Finance ... PhD 36FT/MPhil 24FT/MRes 12FT

Aberystwyth University
Accounting and Finance ... MPhil 12FT 24PT PhD 36FT 60PT
Economics (MPhil) ... MPhil 12FT 24PT

Bangor University
Accounting, Banking, Economics, Finance, Management Studies ... MPhil 24FT/PhD 36FT

University of Birmingham
Accounting and Finance ... PhD 36FT 72PT/MPhil 24FT 48PT/MSc by research 12FT 24PT

University of Bristol
Accounting and Finance ... MPhil 12FT 24PT/PhD 36FT 72PT

Cardiff University
Accounting and Finance ... PhD 36-48FT possiblePT

De Montfort University
Accounting and Finance ... PhD 24 - 36FT 36 - 72PT/MPhil 12 - 24FT 24 - 48PT

University of Dundee
Accountancy and Business Finance (by research) ... MAcc 12FT
Accountancy and Business Finance ... MPhil 24FT
Accountancy and Business Finance (by research) ... MSc by research 12FT
Accountancy and Business Finance ... PhD 36FT

University of East Anglia
Accounting, Finance and Governance ... PhD 36FT 72PT/MPhil 24FT 48PT

University of Essex
Accounting ... PhD 36FT 72PT/MPhil 24FT 48PT/MSc by research 12FT 24PT
Banking ... PhD 36FT 72PT/MPhil 24FT 48PT/MSc by research 12FT 24PT
Finance ... PhD 36FT/MRes 12FT 24PT/MPhil 24FT 48PT
Finance and Accounting ... PhD 36FT 72PT

University of Exeter
Accountancy ... PhD 36FT 72PT/MPhil 24FT 48PT
Finance ... PhD 36FT 72PT/MPhil 24FT 48PT

University of Glasgow
Accounting and Finance ... PhD 36FT

Heriot-Watt University
Accountancy and Finance ... PhD 36FT 48PT/MPhil 12FT

University of Hertfordshire
Centre for Research in Finance and Accounting (CFiFA) . PhD 36FT 72PT/MPhil 24FT 48PT/MRes 12FT 24PT

University of Hull
Centre for International Accounting and Finance PhD 36FT 60PT/MPhil 24FT 36PT

University of Kent
Accounting & Finance ... PhD 36FT 60PT

Lancaster University
Accounting & Finance ... PhD 36FT 48PT/MPhil 24FT 36PT

London School of Economics and Political Science (LSE)
Accounting ... MPhil 36-48FT/PhD 36-48FT
Finance ... MPhil 36-48FT/PhD 36-48FT

Manchester Metropolitan University
Accounting and Finance .. PhD 48FT 90PT/MPhil 36FT 72PT/MRes 12FT 24PT/MA or MSc by Research 18FT 36PT

University of Manchester
Accounting and Finance ... PhD 36FT 72PT/MPhil 12FT 24PT

Newcastle University
Finance and Accounting ... PhD 36FT 72PT/MPhil 12FT 24PT

University of Portsmouth
Accounting and Financial Management ... MPhil 24FT 48PT/PhD 36FT 72PT

Queen's University Belfast
Accounting ... PhD 36FT 72PT/MPhil 24FT 48PT
Finance ... PhD 36FT 72PT/MPhil 24FT 48PT

University of Southampton
School of Management: Accounting, Accountability and Governance ... PhD 36FT 72PT/MPhil 24FT 48PT

University of St Andrews
Finance ... PhD 36FT 72PT/MPhil 24FT 48PT

University of Strathclyde
Accounting and Finance - Research ... PhD 33FT/MPhil 12FT/DBA 33FT

Actuarial science
Taught Courses

University of Aberdeen
Mathematics ... MSc 12FT

Bangor University
ACCA (Professional Development) ... ACCA 48PT
Accounting and Finance ... MSc 12FT
Accounting and Finance - London Centre ... MSc 12FT
Banking and Finance ... MSc 12FT MA 12FT/PGDip 9FT MBA 12FT
Banking and Finance - London Centre ... MSc 12FT
Business and Finance .. MSc 12FT/PGDip 9FT MA 12FT/PGDip 9FT

Section sponsored by
BPP UNIVERSITY COLLEGE
Business and social sciences
www.prospects.ac.uk/findcourses POSTGRADUATE DIRECTORY 371

Accounting and finance

Business and Marketing .... MA 12FT/PGDip 9FT
CIMA (Professional Development) .... CIMA 12PT
Finance .... MBA 12FT MA 12FT/PGDip 9FT MSc 12FT/PGDip 9FT
Finance - London Centre .... MBA 12FT MSc 12FT
International Banking and Development Finance .... MSc 12FT/PGDip 9FT
International Banking and Development Finance - London Centre .... MSc 12FT
Islamic Banking and Finance .... MA 12FT/PGDip 9FT MSc 12FT/PGDip 9FT
Islamic Banking and Finance - London Centre .... MBA 12FT
Management .... MBA 12FT 36PT
Management and Finance .... MSc 12FT/MA 12FT

Birkbeck, University of London
Mathematics .... GradCert 12PT/GradDip 24PT MSc 24PT

Birmingham City University
Risk Management .... MSc 36PT 36DL 36BM

Brunel University
Modelling and Management of Risk .... MSc 12FT

University of Cambridge
Management Science & Operations .... MPhil 9FT

University of Central Lancashire
Finance and Management .... MSc 12FT

University of Chester
Chester Business Masters ProgrammeMSc 12FT 24 - 72PT/PGDip 12FT 24 - 60PT/PGCert 12FT 12 - 36PT

City University London
Actuarial Management .... PGDip 6FT 12PT/MSc 9FT 18PT
Actuarial Science .... PGDip 6FT 12PT/MSc 9FT 18PT
Project Management, Finance and Risk .... MSc 12-18FT 24-30PT

Edinburgh Napier University
Wealth Management .... MSc 24-36DL

University of Edinburgh
Financial Operational Research .... MSc 12FT/PGDip 9FT

University of Essex
Global Project Management .... MSc 12FT 24PT

University of Exeter
Financial Mathematics .... MSc 9FT/MSc 12FT

Glasgow Caledonian University
Banking, Finance and Risk Management .... MSc 12FT 24PT
Master of Finance .... MFin 12FT FlexiblePT

University of Glasgow
Financial Forecasting and Investment .... MSc 12FT
Financial Modelling .... MSc 12FT
Financial Risk Management .... MSc 12FT

Heriot-Watt University
Actuarial Management .... MSc 12FT 48PT/PGDip 9FT 48PT
Actuarial Science .... MSc 12FT 24PT/PGDip 9FT 18PT
Financial Mathematics .... MSc 12FT
Graduate Certificate in Mathematical Sciences .... GradCert 9FT
Quantitative Finance and Mathematics .... MSc 12FT 24PT/Diploma 9FT 21PT
Quantitative Financial Engineering .... MSc 12FT 24PT/Diploma 9FT 21PT
Quantitative Financial Risk Management ... MSc 12FT/PGDip 9FT

Imperial College London
Actuarial Finance .... MSc 24PT

University of Kent
Actuarial Science .... PGDip 9FT
Applied Actuarial Science .... MSc 12FT 24PT
Finance, Investment and Risk .... MSc 12FT/PGDip 12FT
Applied Actuarial Science .... MSc 24FT/PGDip 24FT
Mathematics and its Applications .... MSc 24FT
Statistics with Finance .... MSc 24FT/GradDip 24FT
Statistics .... GradDip 24FT/MSc 24FT
Mathematics and its Applications .... MSc 12FT 24PT
Statistics with Finance .... MSc 12FT

Kingston University
Investment and Financial Risk Management .... MSc 12FT

Lancaster University
Management Science .... MRes 12FT/PhD by taught 36FT

University of Leeds
Financial Mathematics .... MSc 12FT
Financial Risk Management .... MSc 12FT

University of Leicester
Actuarial Science .... PGDip 24DL/MSc 36DL
Financial Mathematics and Computation . MSc 12FT 24PT/PGDip 9FT

University of Liverpool
Financial Mathematics .... MSc 12FT

London School of Economics and Political Science (LSE)
Statistics (Financial Statistics) .... MSc 9 or 12FT 21 or 24PT

University of Manchester
Actuarial Science .... MSc 12FT 24PT

University of Sheffield
Statistics with Financial Mathematics .... MSc 12FT 24-36 PTDL

University of Sussex
Financial Mathematics .... MSc 12FT

University of Warwick
Financial Mathematics .... MSc 12FT

Actuarial science
Research Courses

University of Aberdeen
Mathematical Sciences .... PhD 36FT/MPhil 24FT/MSc by research 12FT

Bangor University
Accounting, Banking, Economics, Finance, Management Studies .... MPhil 24FT/PhD 36FT

University of Birmingham
Management Mathematics .... PhD 36FT/MPhil 24FT

City University London
Actuarial Science and Statistics .... MPhil 12FT/PhD 24-36FT

University of Kent
Actuarial Science .... PhD 36FT 60PT

University of Manchester
Actuarial Science .... PhD 36FT

The Open University
Applied Mathematics .... PhD 36FT 72PT variableDL/MPhil 15FT 24PT variableDL

Swansea University
Mathematical Ecology .... MSc by research 12FT 24PT
Mathematics .... MSc by research 12FT 24PT

Finance and banking
Taught Courses

University of Aberdeen
Economics of Health .... MSc 12FT/PGDip 9FT
Finance and Investment Management .... MSc 12FT/PGDip 9FT/PGCert 6FT
International Health and Management ..... MSc 12FT 24PT/PGDip 9FT 18PT
Management Economics and International Relations . MSc 12FT/PGDip 9FT/PGCert 6FT
Petroleum, Energy Economics and Finance .... MSc(Econ) 12FT

University of Abertay Dundee
Finance .... MSc 12FT/PGDip 9FT
Oil and Gas Finance .... MSc 12FT

Aberystwyth University
International Finance .... MSc 12FT 24PT
International Finance and Accounting .... MSc 12FT 24PT
International Finance and Banking .... MSc 12FT 24PT
Management and Finance .... MSc 12FT 24PT/PGDip 9FT 18PT

Anglia Ruskin University
Accounting and Financial Analysis .... MSc 18FT 24PT
Financial Management Practice .... MSc 12FT/PGDip 12FT/PGCert 12FT

Aston University
Finance & Financial Regulation .... MSc 12FT
Finance & Investments .... MSc 12FT

BPP Business School
Finance .... MSc 12FT 24+PT

Bangor University
ACCA (Professional Development) .... ACCA 48PT
Accounting and Finance .... MSc 12FT
Accounting and Finance - LondonCentre .... MSc 12FT
Accounting, Banking, Economics, Finance, Management Studies MPhil 24FT/PhD by taught 36FT
Banking and Finance .... MA 12FT/PGDip 9FT MBA 12FT MSc 12FT
Banking and Finance - London Centre .... MSc 12FT MBA 12FT
Banking and Law .... MA 12FT/PGDip 9FT MBA 12FT/PGDip 9FT
Business and Finance .. MA 12FT/PGDip 9FT MSc 12FT/PGDip 9FT
Business and Marketing .... MA 12FT/PGDip 9FT
CIMA (Professional Development) .... CIMA 12PT
Chartered Banker .... MBA 6DL
Finance .... MA 12FT/PGDip 9FT MSc 12FT/PGDip 9FT MBA 12FT
Finance - London Centre .... MSc 12FT MBA 12FT
International Banking and Development Finance .... MSc 12FT/PGDip 9FT
International Banking and Development Finance - London Centre .... MSc 12FT
Islamic Banking and Finance .... MBA 12FT MA 12FT/PGDip 9FT MSc 12FT/PGDip 9FT
Islamic Banking and Finance - London Centre .... MBA 12FT
Management .... MBA 12FT 36PT
Management and Finance .... MSc 12FT/MA 12FT

University of Bath
Accounting and Finance .... MSc 12FT
International Money & Banking .... MSc 12FT
Management with Finance .... MSc 12FT

University of Bedfordshire
International Finance and Banking .... MSc 12FT
Investment and Finance .... MSc 12FT
Islamic Banking and Finance .... MSc 12FT

Birkbeck, University of London
Computing for the Financial Services .... MSc 24PT
Corporate Responsibility and Sustainability .... MSc 12FT 24PT
Finance .... MSc 12FT 24PT GradDip 12-24PT
Financial Engineering .... GradDip 12FT 24PT MSc 12FT 24PT
Financial Risk Management .... MSc 12FT 24PT
Investment Management .... MSc 12FT 24PT

University of Birmingham
Financial Engineering .... MSc 12FT
Global Banking and Finance .... MBA 12FT
International Money and Banking .... MSc 12FT
Money, Banking and Finance .... MSc 12FT

Bournemouth University
Finance with Risk Management .... MSc 12-15FT
International Business with Economics .... MA 12-15FT

University of Bradford
Finance .... MSc 12FT/PGDip 9FT
Finance, Accounting and Management .... MSc 12FT/PGDip 9FT
Global Finance and Banking .... MSc 12FT

University of Brighton
Economics and Finance .... MSc see siteFT/PGDip see siteFT/PGCert see siteFT
Finance and Management .... MSc see siteFT/PGDip see siteFT/PGCert see siteFT

University of Bristol
Economics and Finance .... MSc 12FT
Economics, Finance and Management .... MSc 12FT
Finance and Investment .... MSc 12FT

British Institute of Technology & E-commerce
Banking & Finance .... PGCert 3FT/DipHE 6FT 12PT/MBA 12FT 24PT

Brunel University
Business Finance .... MSc 12FT
International Money, Finance and Investment .... MSc 12FT

University of Buckingham
Finance and Investment .... MSc 12FT

University of Cambridge
Finance .... MPhil 9FT MFin 12FT

Cardiff Metropolitan University
Finance .... MSc 12FT 24PT
Financial Management .... MSc 12FT 24PT

Cardiff University
Finance .... MSc 12FT
Financial Economics .... MSc 12FT 24PT
International Economics, Banking and Finance ..... MSc 12FT 24PT

University of Central Lancashire
Finance and Development .... MSc 12FT
Finance and Investment .... MSc 12FT
Finance and Management .... MSc 12FT
Financial Analysis .... MSc 12FT
International Business Economics .... MA 12FT

City University London
Banking and International Finance .... MSc 10FT
Charity Accounting and Financial Management PGDip 13FT/MSc 19FT
Finance .... MSc 12FT
Finance and Investment .... MSc 18-24PT
Financial Mathematics .... MSc 12FT

University College Cork
Accounting and Corporate Finance .... HDip 9FT
Corporate Finance and Accounting .... MBS 12FT

Coventry University
Accounting and Financial Management .... MSc 12FT 24PT
Finance .... MSc 12FT 26PT MBA 12FT 26PT

Cranfield University
Finance and Management .... MSc 11FT

De Montfort University
Finance & Investment .... MSc 12FT 24PT

University of Derby
Business and Payroll Management .... MSc 36PT
Corporate and Financial Law .... LLM 12FT 36PT
International Business and Finance .... MSc 12FT
International Financial Markets .... MSc 12FT 36PT

Dublin Institute of Technology
Finance .... PGDip 9FT

University of Dundee
Finance .... MSc 12FT
Financial Economics .... PGDip 9FT
Strategic Management .... MSc 12FT

Durham University
Finance .... MSc 12FT
Finance (Corporate and International Finance) .... MSc 12FT
Finance (Economics and Finance) .... MSc 12FT
Finance (Finance and Investment) .... MSc 12FT
Finance (International Banking and Finance) .... MSc 12FT
Finance (International Money, Finance and Investment) .... MSc 12FT

Accounting and finance

Islamic Finance........MSc 12FT
Islamic Finance........MA 12FT
Management (Finance)........MSc 12FT

University of East Anglia
Finance and Economics........MSc 12FT
Finance and Management........MSc 12FT
International Accounting and Financial Management . MSc 12FT
International Business Finance and Economics ....MA 12FT
Investment and Financial Management........MSc 12FT
Sustainable Business........MSc 12FT

University of East London
Finance ....MBA 12-15FT 24PT
Financial Management .... MSc 12FT 24PT/PGDip 8FT 16PT/ PGCert 4FT 8PT
International Law and Financial Markets... LLM 12FT 24PT/PGDip 8FT 16PT/PGCert 4FT 8PT
Islamic Banking and Finance..... MSc 12FT 24PT/PGDip 8FT 16PT/ PGCert 4FT 8PT

Edge Hill University
Finance........MBA 12FT

Edinburgh Napier University
Banking and Financial Regulation........MSc 12FT
Corporate Strategy and Finance . MSc(Eng) 12FT 36PT/PGDip 9FT 12-60DL/PGCert 5FT 12-60DL
Global Investment Banking........MSc 12FT
International Banking and Finance........MSc 12FT
International Business Management........MSc 12FT
International Finance........MSc 12FT/PGDip 9FT
Wealth Management........MSc 24-36DL

University of Edinburgh
Accounting and Finance........MSc 12FT 24PT
Banking and Risk........MSc 12FT
Carbon Finance........MSc 12FT
Finance and Investment........MSc 12FT
Financial Management........MSc 12FT

University of Essex
Accounting and Finance........MSc 12FT 24PT
Accounting and Financial Economics........MSc 12FT 24PT
Accounting and Financial Management........MSc 12FT 24PT
Banking........MSc 12FT 24PT
Banking and Finance........MSc 12FT 24PT
Computational Economics, Financial Markets and Policy....... MSc 12FT 24PT
Computational Finance........MSc 12FT 24PT
Finance........MSc 12FT 24PT/MRes 12FT 24PT
Finance and Investment........MSc 12FT 24PT
Finance and Management........MSc 12FT 24PT
Finance with English for Academic Purposes........Diploma 9FT
Financial Decision Making with Applications.......MSc 12FT 24PT/ PGDip 9-12FT
Financial Econometrics........MSc 12FT
Financial Engineering and Risk Management.......MSc 12FT 24PT
Financial Software Engineering........MSc 12FT 24PT
High Frequency Finance and Trading........MSc 12FT 24PT
International Finance........MSc 12FT 24PT
Mathematics and Finance........MSc 12FT 24PT/PGDip 9FT

European Business School London
Global Banking & Finance........MSc 12-16FT

University of Exeter
Finance........GradDip 9FT
Finance and Investment........MSc 9FT
Finance and Management........MSc 9FT
Financial Analysis and Fund Management........MSc 12FT
Marketing and Financial Services........MSc 9FT

Futex Investment & Trading Academy
Proprietary Trading........MSc 12FT

GCU London
Accounting and Finance (Fast Track) ....MSc 6FT
International Banking, Finance and Risk Management .... MSc 12FT
International Economics and Finance........MSc 12FT

National University of Ireland Galway
Finance and Information Systems........MSc 12FT
International Finance........MEconSci 9 approxFT

Glasgow Caledonian University
Banking, Finance and Risk Management........MSc 12FT 24PT
Financial Services, Risk and Operations......MSc 12FT 24PT/PGDip 9FT 24PT
International Banking and Finance ..MSc 12FT 24PT/PGCert 9FT/ PGDip 6FT
International Economics and Finance........MSc 12FT
Finance........MFin 12FT FlexiblePT

University of Glasgow
Banking and Financial Services........MSc 12FT
Economics, Banking and Finance........MSc 12FT
Finance and Economic Development........MSc 12FT
Financial Forecasting and Investment........MSc 12FT
International Banking and Finance........MSc 12FT
International Corporate Finance & Banking........MSc 12FT
International Finance........MFin 12FT

International Finance and Economic Policy........MSc 12FT
International Financial Analysis........MSc 12FT
International Trade & Finance........MSc 12FT
Investment Banking & Finance........MSc 12FT
Management with International Finance........MSc 12FT
Quantitative Finance........MSc 12FT

University of Gloucestershire
Accounting and Finance (Top up)........MSc 4FT 12PT
Accounting and Financial Management....MSc 12FT 24PT/PGDip 8FT 20PT/PGCert 4FT 8PT

University of Greenwich
Accounting and Finance........MSc 12FT 24PT
Finance (Executive Part-time)........PGDip 24PT/MSc 24PT
Finance and Investment Analysis........MSc 12FT 24PT
Financial Services........MBA 12FT 24PT
International Banking and Finance........MSc 12FT 24PT

Heriot-Watt University
Finance........MSc 12FT 24PT/PGDip 9FT 21PT
Finance and Management........MSc 12FT 24PT/PGDip 9FT 21PT
Int'nl Business Management with Finance / HRM / Logistics / Marketing /Sustainability Mgmt........MSc 12FT 24PT/PGDip 9FT 21PT
International Accounting and Finance MSc 12FT 24PT/PGDip 9FT 21PT
Investment Management........MSc 12FT 24PT/PGDip 9FT 21PT
Quantitative Financial Engineering........MSc 12FT 24PT/ Diploma 9FT 21PT
Quantitative Financial Risk Management ... MSc 12FT/PGDip 9FT

University of Hertfordshire
Accounting and Financial Management .. MSc 12FT/PGDip 12FT/ PGCert 12FT
Finance and Investment Management MSc 12FT 24-36PT/PGDip 12FT 24-36PT/PGCert 12FT 24-36PT

University of Huddersfield
Accounting........MSc 12FT
Accounting and Finance by Distance Learning........MA 9FT 15PT
Banking and Finance........MSc 12FT
Finance........MSc 12FT
International Business with Financial Services ..... MSc 12FT 24PT

University of Hull
Accounting and Finance........MSc 12FT
Finance and Investment........MSc 12FT
Financial Systems Development (.NET)........MSc 12FT
Money, Banking and Finance........MSc 12FT

ifs School of Finance
Banking Practice and Management and Chartered Fellowship.... MSc 24PT 36DL/PGDip 16PT 28DL/PGCert 8PT 12DL

Imperial College London
Economics & Strategy for Business........MSc 12FT
Finance........MSc 12FT
Mathematics and Finance........MSc 12FT
Metals and Energy Finance........MSc 12FT

Islamic College for Advanced Studies
Islamic Finance........MSc 12FT 24PT 24DL/PGDip 12FT 24PT 24DL

Keele University
Finance and Information Technology........MSc 12FT/PGDip 9FT/ PGCert 9FT
Finance and Management........MSc 12FT/PGDip 9FT/PGCert 9FT

University of Kent
Financial Markets........MSc 12FT
Financial Services in Banking........MSc 12FT
International Accounting and Finance........MSc 12FT
International Finance and Economic Development....... MSc 12FT 24PT

King's College London
Financial Mathematics........MSc 12FT 24PT

Kingston University
Banking and Finance........MSc 12FT 24PT
Finance........MSc 12FT
Financial and Business Management........MSc 12FT
Law with Finance........LLM 12FT

Lancaster University
Finance........MSc 12FT/MRes 12FT
Money, Banking and Finance........MSc 12FT/MRes 12FT

Leeds Metropolitan University
Applied Finance (top-up)........BA (Hons) 12FT
Finance........MSc 12FT 24PT
International Trade and Finance........MA 12FT

University of Leeds
Accounting and Finance........MA 12FT
Banking and Finance........MSc 12FT
Finance and Investment........MSc 12FT
Financial Risk Management........MSc 12FT
International Finance........MSc 12FT

University of Leicester
Accounting and Finance........MSc 12FT
Banking and Finance........MSc 12FT 24PT
Finance........MSc 12FT 24-60DL
Management, Finance and Accounting........MSc 12FT

Money and Banking........MSc 12FT

University of Limerick
Financial Services........MSc 12FT

University of Lincoln
Finance........MBA 12-15FT

University of Liverpool
Corporate Finance (Online Degrees)........MSc 24FT 24+PT
Economics and Finance........MSc 12FT 24PT

London Business School
Finance........MSc 10FT 22PT

London Metropolitan University
Finance........GradDip 12FT 24PT
Finance........MSc 12FT 24PT

London School of Economics and Political Science (LSE)
Finance (Full-Time)........MSc 10FT
Finance and Economics........MSc 10FT
Finance and Private Equity........MSc 10FT

London South Bank University
Charity Finance & Accounting........CIPFA Certificate 12PT
Charity Finance & Accounting - Blended ...CIPFA Certificate 12PT
International Banking & Finance........MSc 12FT
International Investment & Finance........MSc 12FT 24PT
Management in Civil Society (Accounting & Finance) - Blended.. MSc 30PT

Loughborough University
Banking and Finance........MSc 12FT
Banking and Financial Markets........MSc 12FT
Finance and Management (for non-finance graduates)........ MSc 12FT
International Financial and Political Relations........MSc 12FT
Money, Banking and Finance........MSc 12FT

Manchester Metropolitan University
Finance and Business........MSc 12FT
Financial Management........MSc 12FT 24-36PT
Financial Planning and Wealth Management........MSc 12FT
Strategic Financial Management........MSc 12FT

University of Manchester
Development Finance........MSc 12FT 24PT
Finance........MSc 12FT

Markfield Institute of Higher Education
Islamic Banking, Finance and Management........MA 12FT 24PT/ PGDip 12FT 24PT/PGCert 6FT 12PT

Middlesex University
Banking and Finance........MSc 12FT 24PT
Financial Management........MSc 14FT 26PT
International Finance........MSc 12FT

Newcastle University
Banking and Finance........MSc 12FT
Finance........MSc 12FT
Finance and Economics (Research)........MA 12FT 24PT
Finance and Financial Regulation........MSc 12FT
Finance and Law with Islamic Finance........MSc 12FT
Finance, Accounting and Business........GradDip 9FT
International Economics and Finance........MSc 12FT
International Financial Analysis........MA 12FT
Quantitative Finance and Risk Management........MSc 12FT

University of Northampton
International Banking and Finance........MSc 12FT

Northumbria University
Business with Financial Management........MSc 12FT
Global Financial Management........MSc 12FT

Nottingham Trent University
Economics and Finance/International Finance........MSc 12FT

University of Nottingham
Banking and Financial Markets in Contemporary China........ MSc 12FT
Business and Economy of Contemporary China........MSc 12FT
Corporate Finance in Contemporary China........MSc 12FT
Finance and Investment........MSc 12FT
Numerical Techniques for Finance........MSc 12FT

Oxford Brookes University
Finance........MSc 12FT 24PT

University of Oxford
Financial Economics........MSc 9FT
Mathematical & Computational Finance........MSc 10FT

Plymouth University
Finance........MSc 12FT 24PT

Queen Mary, University of London
Accounting and Finance........MSc 12FT
Banking........MSc 12FT
Banking and Finance........MSc 12FT 24PT
Finance........MSc 12FT
International Financial Management........MA 12FT
Investment and Finance (optional pathway: CISI specialist pathway in Wealth Management)........MSc 12FT 24PT
EAP and Economics & Finance........GradDip 12FT

Section sponsored by
BPP UNIVERSITY COLLEGE
Business and social sciences
www.prospects.ac.uk/findcourses POSTGRADUATE DIRECTORY 373

Accounting and finance

Queen's University Belfast
Finance .... MSc 12FT

University of Reading
Banking and Finance in Emerging Economies .... MSc 12FT 24PT
Banking and Financial Systems in the Global Economy .... MSc 12FT
Corporate Finance .... MSc 10FT 24PT
Financial Engineering .... MSc 10FT
Financial Risk Management .... MSc 10FT 24PT 24DL
International Business and Finance .... MSc 12FT
International Financial Regulation .... LLM 12FT
International Management .... MSc 12FT
International Securities, Investment and Banking .... MSc 12FT
International Shipping and Finance .... MSc 12FT
Investment Banking and Islamic Finance .... MSc 12FT
Real Estate Finance .... MSc 12FT
The Economics of International Business and Finance .... MSc 12FT

Regent's Business School London
Global Management (Finance) .... MA 12 - 16FT

Robert Gordon University
Financial Management..MSc 12FT 36PT/PGDip 8FT 24PT/PGCert 4FT 12PT

University of Roehampton
International Management .... MSc 12FT 24PT
International Management with Finance .... MSc 12FT 24PT PGDip 9FT 24PT

Royal Holloway, University of London
Financial and Industrial Economics .... MSc 12FT

University of Salford
Accounting and Finance .... MSc 12FT 36PT/PGDip 8FT 24PT/PGCert 4FT 9PT
International Banking and FInance ..... MSc 12FT 36PT/PGDip 8FT 24PT/PGCert 4FT 9PT
International Corporate FInanceMSc 12FT 36PT/PGDip 8FT 24PT/PGCert 4FT 9PT
Islamic Banking and FInance ..... MSc 12FT 36PT/PGDip 8FT 24PT/PGCert 4FT 9PT

School of Oriental and African Studies - SOAS
Finance and Financial Law .... MSc 12FT 24-36PT

Sheffield Hallam University
Banking and Finance .... MA 12FT
Financial Management .... MA 12FT

University of Sheffield
Business Finance and Economics .... MSc 12FT 24PT
Economics .... MSc 12FT 24PT
Finance .... MSc 12FT 24PT
Finance and Accounting .... MSc 12FT
Financial Economics .... MSc 12FT 24PT
International Finance and Economics .... MSc 12FT 24PT
Money, Banking & Finance .... MSc 12FT 24PT

University of South Wales
Finance .... MSc 12FT 24PT
Finance and Investment .... MSc 12FT 24PT

University of Southampton
Accounting and Finance .... MSc 12FT/PGDip 9FT
Finance and Economics .... MSc 12FT 24PT/PGDip 9FT 21PT
International Banking and Financial Studies .... MSc 12FT/PGDip 9FT
International Financial Markets .... MSc 12FT/PGDip 9FT
Management Science and Finance .... MSc 12FT/PGDip 9FT

University of St Andrews
Finance & Management .... MLitt 12FT
Finance (FIN) .... PGDip 9FT/MSc 12FT/MPhil 24FT
Money Banking & Finance .... MSc 12FT/PGDip 9FT/MPhil 24FT

University of Stirling
Banking and Finance .... MSc 12FT/PGDip 9FT
Computing for Financial Markets ... MSc 12FT/PGDip 9FT/PGCert 9FT
Finance .... MSc 12FT/PGDip 9FT/PGCert 6FT
International Accounting & Finance .... MSc 12FT/PGDip 9FT/PGCert 6FT

University of Strathclyde
European Financial Management .... MSc 12FT
Finance .... MSc 12FT 24PT/PGDip 9FT 21PT
International Accounting and Finance .... MSc 12FT 24PT/PGDip 9FT 21PT
International Banking and Finance ..... MSc 12FT 24PT/PGDip 9FT 21PT
Investment and Finance .... MSc 12FT 24PT 24DL/PGDip 9FT 21PT 21DL
Quantitative Finance .... MSc 12FT/PGDip 9FT

University of Surrey
International Financial Management .... MSc 12FT 24PT

University of Sussex
Banking and Finance .... MSc 12FT 24PT
International Accounting and Corporate Governance... MSc 12FT 24PT

Swansea University
Business Economics with Finance .... MSc 12FT
Economics with International Banking .... MSc 12FT
Finance .... MSc 12FT
International Banking and Finance .... MSc 12FT
International Banking, Finance and Economics .... MSc 12FT
Management (Finance) .... MSc 12FT
Mathematics and Computing for Finance .... MSc 12FT 24/36PT

Swansea Metropolitan University
Chartered Institute of Management Accountants ...... CIMA 12FT

Trinity College Dublin - the University of Dublin
Finance .... MSc 12FT 24PT

UCL - University College London
Engineering with Finance .... MSc 12FT/PGDip 9FT
Financial Risk Management .... MSc 12FT

University of Warwick
Finance .... MSc 12FT
Finance & Economics .... MSc 12FT
Finance & Information Technology .... MSc 12FT
Accounting & Finance .... MSc 12FT

University of West London
Finance and Global Capital Markets .... MSc 12FT 24PT
International Banking and Finance Law .... LLM 12FT 24PT

University of the West of Scotland
Financial Services .... MSc 12FT/Diploma 9FT

University of Westminster
Global Finance .... MA 12FT
Investment and Risk Finance .... MSc 12FT

University of Worcester
Finance & Management .... MSc 12FT/PGDip 10FT/PGCert 6FT

University of York
Economics and Finance .... MSc 12FT
Finance .... MSc 12FT
Finance and Econometrics .... MSc 12FT
Project Analysis, Finance and Investment .... MSc 12FT

Finance and banking
Research Courses

University of Aberdeen
Finance .... PhD 36FT/MPhil 24FT/MRes 12FT

Aberystwyth University
Management and Business .... MPhil 12FT 24PT PhD 36FT 60PT

Bangor University
Accounting, Banking, Economics, Finance, Management Studies .... MPhil 24FT/PhD 36FT

Birkbeck, University of London
Economics/Finance .... PhD 24FT 36PT/MPhil 24FT 36PT

Birmingham City University
Financial .... MPhil 24FT 36PT/PhD 48FT 72PT

Brunel University
Economics and Finance .... PhD 36FT 72PT/MPhil 24FT 48PT

University of Dundee
Accountancy and Business Finance (by research) .... MAcc 12FT
Accountancy and Business Finance .... MPhil 24FT
Accountancy and Business Finance (by research)MSc by research 12FT
Accountancy and Business Finance .... PhD 36FT
Economics .... PhD 36FT

Durham University
Islamic Economics and Finance .... PhD 36FT

University of Essex
Banking .... PhD 36FT 72PT/MPhil 24FT 48PT/MSc by research 12FT 24PT
Computational Finance .... PhD 36FT
Finance .... PhD 36FT/MRes 12FT 24PT/MPhil 24FT 48PT
Finance and Accounting .... PhD 36FT 72PT

University of Exeter
Finance .... PhD 36FT 72PT/MPhil 24FT 48PT

Heriot-Watt University
Accountancy and Finance .... PhD 36FT 48PT/MPhil 12FT

University of Kent
Accounting & Finance .... PhD 36FT 60PT

Newcastle University
Finance and Accounting .... PhD 36FT 72PT/MPhil 12FT 24PT

The Open University
Finance.. PhD 36FT 72PT variableDL/MPhil 15FT 24PT variableDL

Queen's University Belfast
Finance .... PhD 36FT 72PT/MPhil 24FT 48PT

University of Southampton
School of Management: International Finance.... PhD 36FT 72PT/MPhil 24FT 48PT

University of St Andrews
Finance .... PhD 36FT 72PT/MPhil 24FT 48PT

University of Surrey
Finance .... PhD 36FT 48PT/MPhil 24FT 36PT

Insurance studies
Taught Courses

City University London
Insurance and Risk Management .... MSc 9-12FT 24PT

University of Exeter
Climate Change and Risk Management .... MSc 12FT 24PT

University of Glasgow
Financial Risk Management .... MSc 12FT

Heriot-Watt University
Actuarial Management .... MSc 12FT 48PT/PGDip 9FT 48PT
Actuarial Science .... MSc 12FT 24PT/PGDip 9FT 18PT
Financial Mathematics .... MSc 12FT
Quantitative Finance and Mathematics .... MSc 12FT 24PT/Diploma 9FT 21PT
Quantitative Financial Engineering .... MSc 12FT 24PT/Diploma 9FT 21PT
Quantitative Financial Risk Management ... MSc 12FT/PGDip 9FT

Leeds Metropolitan University
Association of Chartered Certified Accountants - Professional Level .... ACCA 24PT

UCL - University College London
Natural Hazards for Insurers .... PGCert 4PT

University of Westminster
Finance Banking and Insurance .... MSc 12FT

Investments and commodities
Taught Courses

University of Aberdeen
Finance and Investment Management .... MSc 12FT/PGDip 9FT/PGCert 6FT

Aston University
Finance & Investments .... MSc 12FT
Investment Analysis .... MSc 12FT

Bangor University
Banking and Finance - London Centre .... MBA 12FT

University of Bath
International Money & Banking .... MSc 12FT

University of Bedfordshire
Investment and Finance .... MSc 12FT

University of Birmingham
Investments .... MSc 12FT

University of Bristol
Finance and Investment .... MSc 12FT

British Institute of Technology & E-commerce
Banking & Finance .... PGCert 3FT/DipHE 6FT 12PT/MBA 12FT 24PT

Brunel University
Finance and Investment .... MSc 12FT

University of Buckingham
Finance and Investment .... MSc 12FT

College of Estate Management
Property Investment .... PGDip 24DL/MSc 36DL

University of Cambridge
Master of Finance .... MFin 12FT

Cardiff Metropolitan University
Finance .... MSc 12FT 24PT

Cardiff University
Finance .... MSc 12FT

University of Central Lancashire
Finance and Investment .... MSc 12FT
Finance and Management .... MSc 12FT
Financial Analysis .... MSc 12FT
International Business and Management .... MSc 12FT

City University London
Banking and International Finance .... MSc 10FT
Finance and Investment .... MSc 18-24PT
Investment Management .... MSc 9-12FT
Mathematical Trading and Finance .... MSc 9FT 24PT

Coventry University
Finance .... MSc 12FT 26PT
Finance .... MBA 12FT 26PT
Investment Management .... MSc 12FT 24-30PT

University of Cumbria
International Business Management .... MA 12FT

De Montfort University
Finance & Investment .... MSc 12FT 24PT
International Business and Finance .... MSc 12FT

University of Derby
International Business and Finance .... MSc 12FT
International Financial Markets .... MSc 12FT 36PT

Durham University
Finance (Corporate and International Finance) .... MSc 12FT
Finance (Finance and Investment) .... MSc 12FT
Finance (International Banking and Finance) .... MSc 12FT

Accounting and finance

Finance (International Money, Finance and Investment) .... MSc 12FT

University of East Anglia
Finance and Management .... MSc 12FT
International Accounting and Financial Management . MSc 12FT
Investment and Financial Management .... MSc 12FT

Edinburgh Napier University
Global Investment Banking .... MSc 12FT
International Banking and Finance .... MSc 12FT
Wealth Management .... MSc 24-36DL

University of Edinburgh
Banking and Risk .... MSc 12FT
Carbon Finance .... MSc 12FT
Finance and Investment .... MSc 12FT

European Business School London
Global Banking & Finance .... MSc 12-16FT

University of Exeter
Finance and Investment .... MSc 9FT
Finance and Management .... MSc 9FT
Financial Analysis and Fund Management .... MSc 12FT
Money and Banking .... MSc 12FT

Glasgow Caledonian University
International Banking and Finance .. MSc 12FT 24PT/PGCert 9FT/PGDip 6FT

University of Glasgow
Financial Forecasting and Investment .... MSc 12FT
Financial Modelling .... MSc 12FT
International Corporate Finance & Banking .... MSc 12FT
International Finance .... MFin 12FT
International Financial Analysis .... MSc 12FT
Investment Banking & Finance .... MSc 12FT

University of Greenwich
Finance and Investment Analysis .... MSc 12FT 24PT
Information Technology with e-Business / with Security....... MSc 12FT 24PT

Heriot-Watt University
Actuarial Management .... MSc 12FT 48PT/PGDip 9FT 48PT
Actuarial Science .... MSc 12FT 24PT/PGDip 9FT 18PT
Investment Management .... MSc 12FT 24PT/PGDip 9FT 21PT
Quantitative Finance and Mathematics .... MSc 12FT 24PT/Diploma 9FT 21PT
Quantitative Financial Engineering .... MSc 12FT 24PT/Diploma 9FT 21PT
Quantitative Financial Risk Management ... MSc 12FT/PGDip 9FT

University of Hertfordshire
Finance and Investment Management .... MSc 12FT 24-36PT/PGDip 12FT 24-36PT/PGCert 12FT 24-36PT

University of Hull
Finance and Investment .... MSc 12FT
Money, Banking and Finance .... MSc 12FT

University of Kent
Finance, Investment and Risk .... MSc 12FT/PGDip 12FT
Financial Services in Banking .... MSc 12FT

Lancaster University
Money, Banking and Finance .... MSc 12FT/MRes 12FT

University of Leeds
Finance and Investment .... MSc 12FT

London Metropolitan University
Finance .... GradDip 12FT 24PT MSc 12FT 24PT

London South Bank University
International Banking & Finance .... MSc 12FT
International Investment & Finance .... MSc 12FT 24PT

Loughborough University
Money, Banking and Finance .... MSc 12FT

Middlesex University
International Finance .... MSc 12FT
Investment and Finance .... MSc 12FT 24PT

Newcastle University
Banking and Finance .... MSc 12FT
Finance .... MSc 12FT
Finance and Economics (Research) .... MA 12FT 24PT
Finance and Financial Regulation .... MSc 12FT
Finance and Law with Islamic Finance .... MSc 12FT
Finance, Accounting and Business .... GradDip 9FT
International Financial Analysis .... MA 12FT
Quantitative Finance and Risk Management .... MSc 12FT

Nottingham Trent University
International Real Estate Investment and FinanceMSc 12FT 24PT

University of Nottingham
Finance and Investment .... MSc 12FT

Oxford Brookes University
Finance .... MSc 12FT 24PT
International Trade and Logistics .... MSc 12FT 24PT

Plymouth University
Finance .... MSc 12FT 24PT

Queen Mary, University of London
Investment and Finance (optional pathway: CISI specialist pathway in Wealth Management) .... MSc 12FT 24PT

University of Reading
Capital Markets, Regulation and Compliance .... MSc 10FT 24DL
Intelligent Buildings: Design, Construction and Management .... MSc 24PT
International Financial Regulation .... LLM 12FT
International Securities, Investment and Banking .... MSc 12FT
Investment Banking and Islamic Finance .... MSc 12FT
Investment Management .... MSc 10FT 24DL
Real Estate .... MSc 12FT
Real Estate (part time) .... MSc 24-72PT
Real Estate Investment and Finance .... MSc 24-72PT

Robert Gordon University
Asset Integrity Management .... MSc 36-60DL
International Trade .... LLM 12FT/MSc 9FT/PGDip 6FT

University of Roehampton
International Management with Finance .... MSc 12FT 24PT

Royal Holloway, University of London
Financial and Industrial Economics .... MSc 12FT

University of Salford
International Banking and Finance ..... MSc 12FT 36PT/PGDip 8FT 24PT/PGCert 4FT 9PT
International Corporate Finance .... MSc 12FT 36PT/PGDip 8FT 24PT/PGCert 4FT 9PT
Procurement, Logistics and Supply Chain Management .... MSc 12FT 36PT/PGDip 8FT 24PT/PGCert 4FT 9PT

School of Oriental and African Studies - SOAS
MA Globalisation and Multinational Corporations .... MA 12FT 24PT

Sheffield Hallam University
Banking and Finance .... MA 12FT
Charity Resource Management ..... MSc 30PT/PGDip 18PT/PGCert 12PT

University of South Wales
Finance and Investment .... MSc 12FT 24PT

University of Southampton
International Banking and Financial StudiesMSc 12FT/PGDip 9FT

University of St Andrews
Money Banking & Finance .... MSc 12FT/PGDip 9FT/MPhil 24FT

University of Stirling
Investment Analysis .... MSc 12FT/PGDip 9FT/PGCert 6FT

University of Strathclyde
International Banking and Finance ..... MSc 12FT 24PT/PGDip 9FT 21PT
Investment and Finance .... MSc 12FT 24PT 24DL/PGDip 9FT 21PT 21DL
Quantitative Finance .... MSc 12FT/PGDip 9FT

University of Sussex
Financial Risk and Investment Analysis .... MSc 12FT 24PT
International Finance .... MSc 12FT 24PT
Management and Finance .... MSc 12FT 24PT

Swansea University
International Banking and Finance .... MSc 12FT
Mathematics and Computing for Finance .... MSc 12FT 24/36PT

Trinity College Dublin - the University of Dublin
Finance .... MSc 12FT 24PT

UCL - University College London
Financial Risk Management .... MSc 12FT

University of Warwick
Accounting & Finance .... MSc 12FT

University of West London
International Banking and Finance Law .... LLM 12FT 24PT

University of the West of Scotland
International Financial Management .... MSc 12FT 36PT/Diploma 9FT 24PT

University of Westminster
Investment and Risk Finance .... MSc 12FT

University of York
Project Analysis, Finance and Investment .... MSc 12FT

Investments and commodities

Research Courses

University of Exeter
Finance .... PhD 36FT 72PT/MPhil 24FT 48PT

Heriot-Watt University
Accountancy and Finance .... PhD 36FT 48PT/MPhil 12FT

Newcastle University
Finance and Accounting .... PhD 36FT 72PT/MPhil 12FT 24PT

Queen's University Belfast
Finance .... PhD 36FT 72PT/MPhil 24FT 48PT

Risk management

Taught Courses

University of Aberdeen
Patient Safety: A Clinical Human Factors Approach..... MRes 12FT
Safety and Reliability Engineering .... MSc 12FT 24-36PT

Bangor University
Risk Management in Health and Social Care ...... MSc 36PT/PGDip 24PT/PGCert 12PT

University of Bath
Environment, Energy & Resilience .... MRes 12FT 24-36PT

Birmingham City University
Risk Management .... MSc 36PT 36DL 36BM

Bournemouth University
Finance with Risk Management .... MSc 12-15FT

Brunel University
Modelling and Management of Risk .... MSc 12FT

University of Central Lancashire
Fire Investigation .... MSc 12FT/PGDip 9FT/PGCert 6FT
Fire Safety Engineering .... MSc 12FT 24PT
Fire Scene Investigation .... MSc 24-36PT
Fire and Rescue Service Management .... MSc 12FT 24PT
Management Studies .... DMS 18PT
Project Management...... MSc 12FT 36PT/PGDip 6FT 12PT/PGCert 3FT 6PT

University of Chester
Programme and Project Management .... MSc 12FT 24 - 48PT/PGDip 12FT 24 - 48PT/PGCert 12FT 12 - 24PT

City University London
Insurance and Risk Management .... MSc 9-12FT 24PT

Cranfield University
Environmental Risk Management .... MSc 12FT 24-60PT/PGDip 6FT 24PT/PGCert 5FT 24PT
Offshore and Ocean Technology with Risk Management .... MSc 12FT 24-60PT/MTech 24FT/PGDip 6FT 24PT/PGCert 5FT 24PT

Cranfield University, Shrivenham
Resilience .... MSc 30PT/PGDip 24PT/PGCert 12PT
Security Sector Management .... MSc 12FT 30PT

University of Cumbria
Leadership and Management in Policing .... MBA 36PT/PGDip 36PT/PGCert 36PT
Management Studies .... GradDip 24PT/GradCert 12PT

De Montfort University
Risk Management .... MSc 12FT 24PT

University of Dundee
Advanced Practice (Clinical Governance) .... MSc 36DL

Durham University
Risk and Environmental Hazards .... MA 12FT
Risk and Security .... MA 12FT

University of East Anglia
Advanced Management .... MSc 12FT
MBA (full-time) .... MBA 12FT
Management .... MSc 12FT

University of East London
Finance and Risk ..... MSc 12FT 24PT/PGDip 8FT 16PT/PGCert 4FT 8PT

Edinburgh Napier University
Strategic Risk Management and Finance .... MSc 12FT 24PT

University of Edinburgh
Banking and Risk .... MSc 12FT
Operational Research with Risk .... MSc 12FT 24PT/PGDip 9FT

University of Exeter
Climate Change and Risk Management .... MSc 12FT 24PT

GCU London
Risk Management .... MSc 12FT/PGDip 9FT

Glasgow Caledonian University
Banking, Finance and Risk Management .... MSc 12FT 24PT
Financial Services, Risk and Operations ...... MSc 12FT 24PT/PGDip 9FT 24PT
Management .... MSc 12FT FlexiblePT/PGDip 9FT FlexiblePT/PGCert 6FT FlexiblePT
Risk Management ..... MSc 12FT FlexiblePT FlexibleDL/PGDip 9FT FlexiblePT FlexibleDL

University of Glasgow
Financial Risk Management .... MSc 12FT
Management .... MSc 12FT

University of Greenwich
Finance and Financial Information Systems .... MSc 12FT 24PT/PGDip 12FT 24PT

Heriot-Watt University
Actuarial Management .... MSc 12FT 48PT/PGDip 9FT 48PT
Actuarial Science .... MSc 12FT 24PT/PGDip 9FT 18PT
Climate Change: Impacts and Mitigation..MSc 12FT 24PT/PGDip 9FT 21PT

Section sponsored by

BPP
UNIVERSITY
COLLEGE

Business and social sciences
www.prospects.ac.uk/findcourses **POSTGRADUATE DIRECTORY 375**

Accounting and finance

Climate Change: Managing The Marine Environment.. MSc 12FT 24PT/PGDip 9FT 21PT
Financial Mathematics.................................... MSc 12FT
Food Science, Safety and Health MSc 12FT 24PT 24-84DL/PGDip 9FT 21PT 24-84DL
Food and Beverage Science..........MSc 12FT 24PT/PGDip 9FT 21PT
Investment Management ....MSc 12FT 24PT/PGDip 9FT 21PT
Quantitative Finance and Mathematics.................MSc 12FT 24PT/ Diploma 9FT 21PT
Quantitative Financial Engineering.........................MSc 12FT 24PT/ Diploma 9FT 21PT
Quantitative Financial Risk Management ... MSc 12FT/PGDip 9FT
Safety and Risk Management (Distance Learning Only)......... MSc 24-84DL/PGDip 21-84DL
Safety, Risk and Reliability Engineering (Distance Learning Only) ....MSc 24-84DL/PGDip 24-84DL

University of Hull
Financial Mathematics.................................... MSc 12FT

Imperial College London
Risk Management & Financial Engineering .... MSc 12FT

Keele University
Management.................... MA 12FT/PGDip 9FT/PGCert 9FT

University of Kent
Applied Actuarial Science...MSc 12FT 24PT
Finance, Investment and Risk........................MSc 12FT/PGDip 12FT

King's College London
Risk Analysis ....MA 12FT 24PT/MSc 12FT 24PT

Lancaster University
Safety Engineering (Industry-Based)................................. MSc 24PT

University of Leeds
Financial Mathematics... MSc 12FT
Financial Risk Management .... MSc 12FT
Patient Safety and Clinical Risk Management.............. PGCert 4FT

University of Leicester
Financial Mathematics and Computation .MSc 12FT 24PT/PGDip 9FT
Security and Risk Management... MSc 24DL/PGDip 18DL/PGCert 12DL

University of Limerick
Financial Services .... MSc 12FT

University of Liverpool
Financial Mathematics.. MSc 12FT

London School of Economics and Political Science (LSE)
Management and Regulation of Risk................................ MSc 12FT

Loughborough University
Security Management ....MSc 24-36DL/PGDip 12-24DL/PGCert 12DL

University of Manchester
Quantitative Finance: Risk Management .... MSc 12FT

Middlesex University
Risk Management ....MSc 12FT 24PT

Newcastle University
Quantitative Finance and Risk Management .... MSc 12FT

University of Nottingham
Corporate Strategy and Governance................................ MSc 12FT
Risk Management .... MSc 12FT

The Open University
Management..Professional Diploma 12DL

Oxford Brookes University
Environmental Assessment and Management ...MSc 12FT 24PT/ PGDip 9FT 21PT

University of Portsmouth
Risk Management .... MSc 12FT 36FT

Queen's University Belfast
Risk Management and Financial Regulation.................... MSc 12FT

University of Reading
Construction Management .... MSc 12FT
Corporate Finance ....MSc 10FT 24PT
Financial Risk Management .... MSc 10FT 24PT 24DL
International Securities, Investment and Banking .... MSc 12FT
Project Management .... MSc 24PT

Robert Gordon University
Asset Integrity Management ....MSc 36-60DL
Health Safety and Risk Management ....MSc 36PT 36DL

Royal Veterinary College
Risk Analysis in Health and Food Safety - PGCert .... PGCert 6FT

University of Salford
Environmental Assessment and Management ....MSc 12FT 36PT/ PGDip 8FT 24PT
Management.... MSc 12FT 36PT/PGDip 8FT 24PT/PGCert 4FT 9PT
Quantity Surveying (Mechanical and Electrical) .MSc 12FT 28DL/ PGDip 8FT 16DL

School of Oriental and African Studies - SOAS
Environmental Management.............................MSc 12FT 24-36PT
Finance and Financial Law ....MSc 12FT 24-36PT
International Management (China) ....MSc 12FT 24-36PT
International Management (Japan) ....MSc 12FT 24-36PT
International Management (Middle East and North Africa).. MSc 12FT 24PT
Public Policy and Management (Distance Learning)....MSc 24DL/ PGDip 12DL

Sheffield Hallam University
Environmental Management..........................MSc 12-24FT 24-36PT
Environmental Management (International Resource and Climate Management).................................MSc 12-18FT 24-36PT
Environmental Management (Wildlife and Landscape Conservation) ....MSc 12-18FT 24-36PT
Risk Management .... MA 12FT/PGDip 9FT/PGCert 4FT 8PT

University of Sheffield
Management.. MSc 12FT
Management (Creative and Cultural Industries) .... MSc 12FT
Management (International Business)............................ MSc 12FT

University of South Wales
Sustainable Business Risk Management............... MSc 12/FT 36PT
Sustainable Business Risk Management (Distance Learning)MSc 36DL

University of Southampton
Corporate Risk and Security Management MSc 12FT 27PT/PGDip 9FT 21PT
Environmental Monitoring and Assessment ....MSc 12FT 27PT
Maritime Engineering Science: Nuclear Safety ManagementMSc 12FT
Risk Management ....MSc 12FT 27PT/PGDip 9FT 21PT

University of St Andrews
Management...................................MLitt 12FT 24PT
Management (Human Resource Management) ....MLitt 12FT
Management and Information Technology ....MSc 12FT/ PGDip 9FT

University of Stirling
Management................................MSc 12FT 27PT/PGDip 9FT 21PT

University of Strathclyde
European Financial Management........................... MSc 12FT
Global Energy Management ....MSc 12FT 24PT
Safety and Risk Management ....PGCert 12PT/PGDip 12PT/MSc 24PT

University of Sussex
Corporate and Financial Risk Management ....MSc 12FT 24PT
Financial Risk and Investment Analysis...................MSc 12FT 24PT

Swansea University
Finance... MSc 12FT
International Banking and Finance .... MSc 12FT
International Banking, Finance and Economics .... MSc 12FT

Trinity College Dublin - the University of Dublin
Environmental Sciences .... MSc 12FT

UCL - University College London
Financial Risk Management .... MSc 12FT
Natural Hazards for Insurers .... PGCert 4PT
Risk and Disaster Reduction .... MRes 12FT 24PT PGCert 12PT
Risk, Disaster and Resilience ....MSc 12FT 24PT/PGDip 9FT 24PT

University of Warwick
Clinical Quality Improvement and Risk Management......................
PGA 12PT/CPDMod 1PT

University of West London
Health and Social Care Leadership....................... MSc 24PT

Risk management
Research Courses

Aston University
Environmental Systems and Safety Management Research Group...PhD 36FT/MPhil 24FT

University of Birmingham
Environmental Science and Risk Management..............PhD 36FT/ MSc by research 12FT

University of Cambridge
Management Studies...PhD 36FT

University of Hertfordshire
Condition Monitoring and Asset Management ...PhD 36FT 72PT/ MPhil 24FT 48PT/MRes 12FT 24PT

Newcastle University
Environmental Science............... MPhil 12FT 24PT/PhD 36FT 72PT
Integrated PhD 48FT

Oxford Brookes University
Safety Technology ....PhD 24-60FT 36-72PT/ MPhil 24-36FT 36-48PT

University of Sheffield
Management.................................. PhD 36FT 72PT/MPhil 24FT 48PT

University of Southampton
School of Management: Centre for Risk Research..........PhD 36FT 72PT/MPhil 24FT 48PT
School of Management: Health ....MPhil 24FT 48PT/ PhD 26FT 72PT
School of Management: Management Sciences .... MPhil 24FT 48PT/PhD 36FT 72PT
School of Management: Organisation and Management... MPhil 24FT 48PT/PhD 36FT 72PT

Business and management studies

Actuarial science
Taught Courses

University of Aberdeen
Mathematics .... MSc 12FT

Bangor University
ACCA (Professional Development) .... ACCA 48PT
Accounting and Finance .... MSc 12FT
Accounting and Finance - LondonCentre .... MSc 12FT
Banking and Finance ....MSc 12FT MA 12FT/PGDip 9FT MBA 12FT
Banking and Finance - London Centre .... MSc 12FT
Business and Finance .... MSc 12FT/PGDip 9FT MA 12FT/PGDip 9FT
Business and Marketing .... MA 12FT/PGDip 9FT
CIMA (Professional Development) .... CIMA 12PT
Finance....... MBA 12FT MA 12FT/PGDip 9FT MSc 12FT/PGDip 9FT
Finance - London Centre .... MBA 12FT MSc 12FT
International Banking and Development Finance .... MSc 12FT/PGDip 9FT
International Banking and Development Finance - London Centre .... MSc 12FT
Islamic Banking and Finance .... MA 12FT/PGDip 9FT MSc 12FT/PGDip 9FT
Islamic Banking and Finance - London Centre .... MBA 12FT
Management .... MBA 12FT 36PT
Management and Finance .... MSc 12FT/MA 12FT

Birkbeck, University of London
Mathematics .... MSc 24PT

Birmingham City University
Risk Management .... MSc 36PT 36DL 36BM

Brunel University
Modelling and Management of Risk .... MSc 12FT

University of Cambridge
Management Science & Operations .... MPhil 9FT

University of Central Lancashire
Finance and Management .... MSc 12FT

University of Chester
Chester Business Masters Programme .... MSc 12FT 24 - 72PT/PGDip 12FT 24 - 60PT/PGCert 12FT 12 - 36PT

City University London
Actuarial Management .... PGDip 6FT 12PT/MSc 9FT 18PT
Actuarial Science .... PGDip 6FT 12PT/MSc 9FT 18PT
Project Management, Finance and Risk ......MSc 12-18FT 24-30PT

Edinburgh Napier University
Wealth Management .... MSc 24-36DL

University of Edinburgh
Financial Operational Research .... MSc 12FT/PGDip 9FT

University of Essex
Global Project Management .... MSc 12FT 24PT

University of Exeter
Financial Mathematics .... MSc 9FT/MSc 12FT

Glasgow Caledonian University
Banking, Finance and Risk Management .... MSc 12FT 24PT
Master of Finance .... MFin 12FT FlexiblePT

University of Glasgow
Financial Forecasting and Investment .... MSc 12FT
Financial Modelling .... MSc 12FT
Financial Risk Management .... MSc 12FT

Heriot-Watt University
Actuarial Management .... MSc 12FT 48PT/PGDip 9FT 48PT
Actuarial Science .... MSc 12FT 24PT/PGDip 9FT 18PT
Financial Mathematics .... MSc 12FT
Quantitative Finance and Mathematics .... MSc 12FT 24PT/Diploma 9FT 21PT
Quantitative Financial Engineering .... MSc 12FT 24PT/Diploma 9FT 21PT
Quantitative Financial Risk Management ... MSc 12FT/PGDip 9FT

Imperial College London
Actuarial Finance .... MSc 24PT

University of Kent
Actuarial Science .... PGDip 9FT
Applied Actuarial Science .... MSc 12FT 24PT
Finance, Investment and Risk .... MSc 12FT/PGDip 12FT
International Master's in Applied Actuarial Science ..... MSc 24FT/PGDip 24FT
International Master's in Mathematics and its Applications .... MSc 24FT
International Master's in Statistics with Finance .... MSc 24FT/GradDip 24FT
International Masters in Statistics .... GradDip 24FT/MSc 24FT
Mathematics and its Applications .... MSc 12FT 24PT
Statistics with Finance .... MSc 12FT

Kingston University
Investment and Financial Risk Management .... MSc 12FT

Lancaster University
Management Science .... MRes 12FT/PhD by taught 36FT

University of Leeds
Financial Mathematics .... MSc 12FT
Financial Risk Management .... MSc 12FT

University of Leicester
Actuarial Science .... PGDip 24DL/MSc 36DL
Financial Mathematics and Computation .... MSc 12FT 24PT/PGDip 9FT

University of Liverpool
Financial Mathematics .... MSc 12FT

London School of Economics and Political Science (LSE)
Statistics (Financial Statistics) .... MSc 9 or 12FT 21 or 24PT

University of Manchester
Actuarial Science .... MSc 12FT 24PT

University of Roehampton
Obesity: Risks and Prevention ....MSc 12FT 24PT PGCert 6FT 12PT PGDip 9FT 24PT

University of Sheffield
Statistics with Financial Mathematics .... MSc 12FT 24-36 PTDL

University of Sussex
Financial Mathematics .... MSc 12FT

University of Warwick
Financial Mathematics .... MSc 12FT

Actuarial science
Research Courses

University of Aberdeen
Mathematical Sciences.... PhD 36FT/MPhil 24FT/MSc by research 12FT

Bangor University
Accounting, Banking, Economics, Finance, Management Studies. .... MPhil 24FT/PhD 36FT

University of Birmingham
Management Mathematics .... PhD 36FT/MPhil 24FT

City University London
Actuarial Science and Statistics .... MPhil 12FT/PhD 24-36FT

University of Kent
Actuarial Science .... PhD 36FT 60PT

University of Manchester
Actuarial Science .... PhD 36FT

The Open University
Applied Mathematics....... PhD 36FT 72PT variableDL/MPhil 15FT 24PT variableDL

Swansea University
Mathematical Ecology .... MSc by research 12FT 24PT
Mathematics .... MSc by research 12FT 24PT

Airport management
Taught Courses

Bucks New University
Air Transport Management .... MSc 15FT 27PT

City University London
Air Safety Management .... MSc 12FT 36PT
Air Transport Management .... MSc 12FT 36PT

Cranfield University
Air Transport Management .... MSc 12FT
Air Transport Management (Executive) .... MSc 24-48PT
Airport Planning and Management .... MSc 12FT
Airport Planning and Management - Executive .... MSc 36PT

University of West London
Airline and Airport Management .... MA 12FT 24PT

University of Westminster
Air Transport Planning and Management .... MSc 12FT 24PT

Arts management
Taught Courses

Anglia Ruskin University
Arts Management .... MA 18FT 24PT

University of the Arts London - Central Saint Martins College of Art and Design
Art: Exhibition Studies .... MRes 24FT

Birkbeck, University of London
Arts Management .... GradDip 12PT/PGDip 12FT 24PT
Arts Policy and Management .... MA 12FT 24PT/PGCert 12PT
Creative Industries (Arts and Media) .... MA 12FT 24PT

Birmingham City University
Arts and Project Management .... MA 12FT 24PT

University of Brighton
Arts and Cultural Research .... MRes 12FT 24PT

University of Central Lancashire
Arts Project Management .... PGCert 3PT
Transdisciplinary Design .... MA 12FT 24PT

City University London
Culture, Policy and Management Pathways Programme .... MA 12FT 24PT

University for the Creative Arts
Creative Industries Management .... MBA 12FT

De Montfort University
Cultural Events Management .... MA 12FT 24PT/MSc 12FT 24PT

University of Derby
Art and Design: Applied Practice and Theories (ADAPT) .... MA 17FT 34PT
Arts Practice .... PGCert 12PT

University of East Anglia
Museum Studies .... MA 12FT

Falmouth University
MFA .... MFA 12FT 24PT

National University of Ireland Galway
Arts Policy and Practice .... MA 12FT/PGDip 12FT

Glasgow Caledonian University
Creative and Cultural Business .... MA 12FT
Design Practice & Management .... MA 12FT 24PT/PGDip 9FT
Social Enterprise .... PGCert 6PT

University of Glasgow
Arts of China .... MLitt 12FT
Arts of Europe .... MLitt 12FT/PGDip 9FT
Composition .... PGDip 12FT 24PT/PGCert 12FT 24PT
Sonic Arts .... PGDip 12FT 24PT

Glyndwr University
Creative Media .... MA 12FT 24PT

Goldsmiths, University of London
Arts Administration and Cultural Policy .... MA 12FT 24PT
Creative and Cultural Industries .... GradDip 12FT

University of Kent
Curating .... MA 12FT 24PT

Kingston University
Managing in the Creative Economy .... MA 12FT 24PT

Lancaster University
Design Management .... MA 12FT 24PT

London South Bank University
Critical Arts Management .... MA 24PT
Cultural and Media Studies .... MA 24PT

University of Manchester
Arts Management, Policy & Practice .... MA 12FT 24PT

Middlesex University
Media Management .... MSc 12FT 24PT

Newcastle University
Art Museum and Gallery Practice .... MPrac 24FT 48PT
Art Museum and Gallery Studies (with specialist pathways in: Curatorship, and Education) .... MA 12FT 24PT/PGDip 9FT 18PT
Arts, Business and Creativity .... MA 12FT 24PT

Northumbria University
Arts and Media Management .... MA 12/16FT 24/28PT 24/28DL
Business with Arts Management .... MSc 12FT
Conservation of Fine Art .... MA 18FT
Fine Art and Education .... MA 24PT

Nottingham Trent University
Design for Publication .... MA 12FT

Plymouth University
Creativity and Enterprise .... MA 12FT 24PT

University of Roehampton
Performance and Creative Research .... MRes 12FT

University of Salford
Art and Design: Design Management .... MSc 12FT 24PT/PGDip 8FT 15PT
Creative Writing: Innovation and Experiment .... MA 12FT 36PT/PGDip 8FT 24PT/PGCert 4FT 12PT

Sotheby's Institute of Art
Art Business .... MA 14FT/PGDip 9FT

University of St Andrews
Managing in the Creative Industries (collab) .... MLitt 12FT

Staffordshire University
Community & Participatory Arts .... MA 12FT 24PT

University of Sunderland
Applied Management .... MSc 24PT

Swansea Metropolitan University
Visual Arts Enterprise .... MA 24FT 36PT/PGCert 9FT

University of Wales Trinity Saint David
Professional Arts Management .... MBA 12FT 24PT

University of Ulster
Cultural Management.... MSc 12FT 30PT/PGDip 9FT 18PT/PGCert 4FT 8PT
Management in Creative Industries .... MSc 24FT 12PT

University of Warwick
Creative and Media Enterprises .... MA 12FT 24PT

University of Winchester
Cultural and Arts ManagementMA 12FT 24PT/PGDip 12FT 24PT/PGCert 12FT 24PT

Section sponsored by

BPP
UNIVERSITY
COLLEGE

Business and social sciences
www.prospects.ac.uk/findcourses **POSTGRADUATE DIRECTORY 377**

Business and management studies

York St John University
MBA Design Management...................................MBA 12FT 24 - 60PT

Arts management
Research Courses

Birkbeck, University of London
Arts Management.......................... PhD 36FT 60PT/MPhil 24FT 36PT

City University London
Arts Policy and Management...PhD/MPhil
Department of Arts Policy and Management................PhD/MPhil

Goldsmiths, University of London
Art............................MPhil 24FT 36PT/PhD 36-48FT 48-72PT

University of Manchester
Arts Management & Cultural Policy .... PhD 36FT 72PT
Arts and Cultural Management Professional Doctorate.................
Professional Doctorate 36FT 72PT

Oxford Brookes University
Arts ... MPhil/PhD 36-60FT 48-72PT/PhD 24-60FT 36-72PT/MPhil
24-36FT 36-48PT

University of Roehampton
Media & Cultural Studies...PhD 24-48FT 36-60PT/MPhil 21-36FT
33-48PT

Royal Welsh College of Music and Drama
Arts Management.....................................MA by research 12FT 24PT

University of Salford
Media, Music and Performing Arts Research Centre....PhD/MPhil

Business and management studies
Taught Courses

University of Aberdeen
Business Administration ....MBA 12FT/PGDip 9FT/PGCert 6FT
Marketing.. MBA 12FT

University of Abertay Dundee
Management... MSc 12FT/PGDip 9FT

Aberystwyth University
Enterprise and Innovation Management................ MSc 12FT 24PT
Management and Corporate Leadership .... MSc 12FT 24PT
Management and Digital Business .... MSc 12FT 24PT
Management and Finance...........MSc 12FT 24PT/PGDip 9FT 18PT
Management and Tourism Management...............MSc 12FT 24PT

Management with Marketing ....MSc 12FT 24PT/PGDip 9FT 18PT
Managment and Project Management..................MSc 12FT 24PT
Marketing...................................MSc 12FT 24PT/PGDip 9FT 21PT

Anglia Ruskin University
Information Systems Management ....MBA 12FT 24PT
Project Management...MSc 12FT 24-30PT

Aston University
Human Resource Management & Business...........MSc 12FT 24PT
Marketing Management ....MSc 12FT

Bangor University
Accounting, Banking, Economics, Finance, Management Studies
MPhil 24FT/PhD by taught 36FT
Chartered Banker .... MBA 6DL
Islamic Banking and Finance ....MBA 12FT

Bath Spa University
Advertising Practice..MA 12FT 12DL
Business and Management .... MA 12FT 32PT/PGDip 9FT 18PT
Business and Management: Accounting .... MA 12FT 32PT
Business and Management: Enterprise................... MA 12FT 32PT
Business and Management: Marketing .... MA 12FT 32PT

University of Bath
Advanced Management Practice ....MSc 12FT

University of Bedfordshire
Business Web Analytics and Management ....MSc 12-18FT
Business and Management ....MSc 12-15FT
Finance and Business Management............................MSc 12-15FT
International Business and Management ....MSc 12-15FT
Marketing and Business Management ....MSc 12-15FT

Belfast Metropolitan College
Human Resource Management CIPD Advanced Diploma
Level 7.. CIPD 9PT
Purchasing and Supply CIPS Graduate Diploma Level 6.................
CIPS 9PT

Birkbeck, University of London
Business Innovation with E-business......................MSc 12FT 24PT/
MRes 12FT 24PT
Business Innovation with Entrepreneurship and Innovation
Management..................................MSc 12FT 24PT/MRes 12FT 24PT
Business Innovation with International Technology
Management..................................MSc 12FT 24PT/MRes 12FT 24PT
Career Management and Coaching.....................................MSc 24PT
Corporate Responsibility and Sustainability ....MSc 12FT 24PT

Creative Industries (Management).........................MSc 12FT 24PT
International Business and the European Union.............................
MSc 12FT 24PT/MRes 12FT 24PT
International Management......................................MSc 12FT 24PT
Investment Management ....MSc 12FT 24PT
Management.............................. MSc 12FT 24PT/MRes 12FT 24PT/
PGCert 12FT 24PT

Birmingham City University
MSc Leadership and Organisational Performance.......... MSc 12FT
MSc Multi Unit Leadership and Strategy ....MSc 12FT

University of Birmingham
MSc programmes ? flexible route ....Flexible Entry Route 24FT
Pharmaceutical Enterprise...MSc 12FT 24PT

University of Brighton...
Learning Objectives ..... MSc 12FT 24PT/PGCert 12FT 24PT/PGDip
12FT 24PT

Brunel University
Accounting and Business Management..........................MSc 12FT
Applied Corporate Brand Management ....MSc 12FT
Business Intelligence and Social Media...........................MSc 12FT
Global Supply Chain Management.....................................MSc 12FT
Human Resource Management and Employment Relations. MSc
12FT
International Business .... MSc 12FT
Accounting and Business Management..........................MSc 12FT
Business Intelligence and Social Media..........................MSc 12FT
Management..MSc 12FT
Marketing..MSc 12FT
Sustainability, Entrepreneurship and Design (with Professional
Development)..MSc 18FT

University of Buckingham
Lean Enterprise .... MSc 24PT
Management in a Global Service Economy.....................MSc 12FT
Management in a Service Economy ....MSc 12FT 24PT
Master of Business Administration ....MBA 12FT

Bucks New University
Leadership in Multi-Agency Settings ....PGCert 9PT

Canterbury Christ Church University
Business and Management ....MSc 12-15FT

Cardiff Metropolitan University
Marketing...MSc 12FT 24PT

Section sponsored by BPP University College

Business and social sciences

378 POSTGRADUATE DIRECTORY www.prospects.ac.uk/findcourses

Business and management studies

University of Central Lancashire
Business Management .... MSc 12FT
Diploma in Human Resource Management.. Diploma 12PT/CIPD 12PT
Human Resource Management/Development..... MSc 12FT 24PT
International Business and Management .... MSc 12FT
Logistics and Supply Chain Management .... MSc 12FT
Human Resource Management/Development...... MA 12PT 12DL
Internal Communication Management .... MSc 24+PT
Management Studies........ DMS 18PT
Master of Business Administration .... MBA 12FT MBA 36PT
Master of Business Administration - Health........ MBA 36PT
Postgraduate Certificate in Management (PGCM)....PGCert 18PT
Postgraduate Diploma in Human Resource Management/ Development........ PGDip 24PT/CIPD 24PT
Sport Business Management .... MSc 12FT up to 36PT
Sports Marketing and Business Management..... MSc 12FT up to 36PT
Strategic Marketing Leadership (Advanced Entry) .... MA 12PT

University of Chester
Business Administration .... MBA 12FT MBA 24PT
Business Development (Work Based and Integrative Studies) .... MA 24-72PT/MSc 24-72PT/PGDip 24-60PT/PGCert 12-36PT
Business and Administration (Work Based and Integrative Studies) .... MA 24-72PT/MSc 24-72PT/PGDip 24-60PT/PGCert 12-36PT
Personal Leadership Development (Work Based and Integrative Studies) .... MA 24-72PT/PGDip 24-60PT/PGCert 12-36PT
Work Based Learning Facilitation........ PGCert 12-36PT
Work Based and Integrative StudiesMA 24 - 72PT/MSc 24 - 72PT/ PGDip 24 - 60PT/PGCert 12 - 36PT

City University London
Advanced Organisational Consultancy (validated) ...PGDip 24PT/ MA 24PT
Professional Development (Through Work-Based Learning)...MA 12-36FT 12-72PT

University College Cork
Business Information Systems........ MBS 12FT
Electronic Business........ MBS 12FT
Management Business Administration........ MBA 48PT
Management Information and Managerial Accounting Systems........ MBS 15FT
Third Sector Management........ MSocSci 24PT

Cranfield University
Design, Strategy and Leadership...MDes 12FT 36PT/PGDip 36PT/ PGCert 36PT

University of Cumbria
International Business .... MBA 12FT
International Business Management .... MA 12FT
Master of Business Administration .... MBA 12FT 36PT

University of Derby
Business and Payroll Management .... MSc 36PT
International Business .... MSc 12FT 36PT
International Business and Finance .... MSc 12FT
MA Management .... MSc 12FT 36PT/PGDip 12FT/PGCert 9FT

University Centre Doncaster
Business Administration .... MBA 24PT

University of Dundee
Advanced Practice (Organisational Leadership) .... MSc 36DL
Business Intelligence .... MSc 12FT
Non-Graduating Taught Postgraduate in School of Business... PG module variableFT

University of East Anglia
Advanced Business Management........ MSc 12FT
Advanced Management .... MSc 12FT
Business Management .... MSc 12FT
Executive MBA........ MBA 27PT
MBA (full-time) .... MBA 12FT
Management........ MSc 12FT
Public Policy and the Environment .... MA 12FT 24PT
Sustainable Business........ MSc 12FT

University of East London
Business Psychology .... MSc 12FT 24PT/PGDip 8FT 16PT/ PGCert 4FT 8PT

Edge Hill University
Master of Business Administration (Information Technology) ..... MBA 12-18FT

Edinburgh Napier University
Business Management .... MSc 12FT
Business Management with Entrepreneurship........ MSc 12FT
Business Management with Human Resource Management (HRM) .... MSc 12FT
Business Management with Marketing........ MSc 12FT
Flexibly-managed programme (Business School)........ MSc 12FT 24-36PT 24-36DL/PGDip 9FT 18-27PT 18-27DL/PGCert 6FT 12-18PT 12-18DL
Strategic ICT Leadership .... MSc 24PT

University of Edinburgh
Architectural Project Management........ MSc 84DL
Banking and Risk .... MSc 12FT
Business Administration .... MBA 12-16FT
Carbon Capture & Storage........ MSc 12FT 36PT
Carbon Finance .... MSc 12FT
Carbon Management .... MSc 12FT
Competition Law and Innovation........ LLM 12FT 24PT
Developing Educational Leadership and Learning.....PGCert 24PT
Executive Master of Business Administration .... MBA 24PT
Finance and Investment .... MSc 12FT
Financial Management........ MSc 12FT
Human Resource Management........ MSc 12FT
International Business and Emerging Markets .... MSc 12FT
Management........ MSc 12FT
Management of Bioeconomy, Innovation and Governance... MSc 12FT 24PT
Sport and Recreation Business ManagementPGDip 9FT 24-48PT/ MSc 12FT 24-72PT

University of Essex
Accounting and Financial Management .... MSc 12FT 24PT
Accounting and Management...MSc 12FT 24PT/MRes 12FT 24PT
Environmental Governance: the Natural World, Science and Society........ MSc 12FT 24PT/MA 12FT 24PT
Environmental Resource Management........ MSc 12FT 24PT
Finance and Management........ MSc 12FT 24PT
International Business and Entrepreneurship........ MSc 12FT 24PT
International Management........ MSc 12FT 24PT
Organisational Studies and International Human Resource Management........ MSc 12FT 24PT
Work, Organisation and Society MSc 12FT 24PT/MRes 12FT 24PT

University of Exeter
Biotechnology and Enterprise........ MSc 12FT
Finance and Management........ MSc 9FT
Human Resource Management........ MSc 12FT 30PT/ PGDip 9FT 21PT
Independent Film Business........ MA 12FT 24PT
Information Technology Management for Business...... MSc 12FT
International Supply Chain Management .... MSc 12FT
Management........ MRes 12FT

GCU London
International Business Management .... MSc 12FT

National University of Ireland Galway
Business Studies .... HDip 12FT
Electronic Commerce........ MBS 18approxFT

Glasgow Caledonian University
Creative and Cultural Business .... MA 12FT
Entrepreneurship........ MSc 12FT
Global Business Law and Regulation .... LLM 12FT
International Sports Management........ MSc 12FT
Management........ MSc 12FT FlexiblePT/PGDip 9FT FlexiblePT/ PGCert 6FT FlexiblePT
Master of Research .... MRes 12FT
Operations and Business Management .... MSc 12FT

University of Glasgow
International Management & Design Innovation........ MSc 12FT
Management........ MSc 12FT
Management with Enterprise & Business Growth .... MSc 12FT/ PGDip 9FT/PGCert 6FT

Glyndwr University
Business Administration .... MBA 12FT 24-36PT
Executive MBA........ Executive MBA 24PT
Human Resource Management........ MA 12FT 36PT
Management........ MSc 12FT/PGCert 12FT/PGDip 12FT
Marketing Management .... MSc 12FT/PGCert 12FT/PGDip 12FT

Goldsmiths, University of London
Consumer Behaviour........ MSc 12FT

University of Greenwich
Business Administration .... MBA 12FT
Business and Financial EconomicsMA 12FT 24PT/MSc 12FT 24PT/ PGDip 12FT 24PT

Griffith College Dublin
International Business Management .... PGCert 6FT 12PT PGDip 12FT 24PT MSc 12FT 24PT

Grimsby Institute of Further and Higher Education
Professional Development........ MA 24FT 36PT

Heriot-Watt University
Actuarial Management........ MSc 12FT 48PT/PGDip 9FT 48PT
Actuarial Science .... MSc 12FT 24PT/PGDip 9FT 18PT
Business Administration .... MBA 12FT 24PT 84DL
Business Management .... MSc 12FT 24PT/PGDip 9FT 18PT
European Master in Strategic Project Management...... MSc 16FT
Financial Management .... MSc 84DL
Financial Mathematics........ MSc 12FT
Human Resource Management........ MSc 84DL
Int'nl Business Management with Finance / HRM / Logistics / Marketing /Sustainability Mgmt. .... MSc 12FT 24PT/PGDip 9FT 21PT
International Accounting and Management .... MSc 12FT 24PT/ PGDip 9FT 21PT
International Fashion Marketing .... MSc 12FT 24PT/ PGDip 9FT 21PT
International Management and Business Communication... MSc 12FT 24PT/PGDip 9FT 21PT
International Marketing .... PGDip 9FT 21PT/MSc 12FT 24PT
Logistics and Supply Chain Management........ MSc 12FT 24PT/ PGDip 9FT 24PT
Maritime Logistics and Supply Chain Management...... MSc 12FT 24PT/PGDip 9FT 21PT
Marketing........ MSc 84DL
Quantitative Finance and Mathematics........ MSc 12FT 24PT/ Diploma 9FT 21PT
Quantitative Financial Engineering........ MSc 12FT 24PT/ Diploma 9FT 21PT
Quantitative Financial Risk Management... MSc 12FT/PGDip 9FT
Strategic Planning .... MSc 84DL
Strategic Project Management...MSc 12FT 24PT/PGDip 9FT 21PT

University of Hertfordshire
Business Administration .... DBA by taught 48-60PT
Business Psychology .... MSc 12FT 48PT
Management..... MSc 12FT 24-30PT/PGDip 12FT 24-30PT/PGCert 12FT 24-30PT
Organisational Change .... DMan 36PT/MA by Research 24PT

University of Huddersfield
Business .... MSc 12FT 24PT
Legal Practice Management .... MBA 12FT 36PT
Management........ MSc 12/18FT 15BM
Marketing Management .... MSc 12FT 24PT

University of Hull
Business Analytics and Consulting Practice .... MSc 12FT
Business Management .... MSc 12FT
Business and Management .... MRes 12FT
Marketing Management .... MSc 12FT

Imperial College London
Imperial MBA........ MBA 12FT/EMBA 24PT/EMBA 21PT
Management........ MSc 12FT

Keele University
Finance and Management .... MSc 12FT/PGDip 9FT/PGCert 9FT

University of Kent
Computing and Entrepreneurship........ MSc 12FT 36PT
Conservation and Business........ MSc 12FT 24PT
Human Resource Management........ MSc 12FT
International Management (or with Management English)........ GradDip 12FT
Management (General) .... MSc 12FT
Management (International Business)........ MSc 12FT
Management (Marketing) .... MSc 12FT
Management Science........ MSc 12FT
Management Science (Business Analytics) .... MSc 12FT
The Kent MBA........ MBA 12FT 24PT
Value Chain Management .... MSc 12FT

Kingston University
Business........ PhD by taught 36-48FT 72-96PT
Clinical Leadership .... MSc 24PT
Digital Image & Signal Processing with Management Studies .... MSc 12FT 24-36PT
Financial and Business Management .... MSc 12FT
International Human Resource Management..PGDip 12FT 24PT/ MA 12FT 24PT
Logistics and Supply Chain Management........ MSc 12FT
Management........ MA 24PT MA top-up 12FT/PGDip 24PT
Management Consultancy .... MSc 12FT
Software Engineering (Web) with Management Studies....... MSc 12FT 24-36PT
Strategic Project Management........ MSc 12FT

Leeds Metropolitan University
Association of Chartered Certified Accountants - Fundementals Level (ACCA) .... ACCA 12PT
Association of Chartered Certified Accountants - Knowledge Level (ACCA) .... ACCA 12PT
Business (IPOS)........ MA 12FT 60PT
Business Intelligence (SAS) .... MSc 12FT 24PT
Contract Management .... MSc 24PT/PGDip 24PT
Corporate Governance........ MSc 4FT 36PT
Finance........ MSc 12FT 24PT
Human Resource Management........ MA 12FT 24PT/PGDip 24PT
Leadership & Change Management .... MSc unknownPT
MBA (Executive) E-Learning........ MBA 24DL
MBA (Graduate) .... MBA 12FT

Leeds Trinity University
Business Studies......MBS 15FT 24PT/PGDip 9FT 18PT/PGCert 6FT 6PT

University of Leeds
Culture, Creativity and Entrepreneurship... MA 12FT 24PT/PGDip 9FT 21PT/PGCert 6FT 12PT
Japanese Business........ MA 12FT 24PT
Management........ MSc 12FT

University of Leicester
Management........ MSc 12FT 24-60DL/PGDip 24-48DL/PGCert 12-36DL
Management, Finance and Accounting........ MSc 12FT

University of Limerick
Business Administration Corporate .... MBA 24PT
Business Management .... MA 12FT
Computational Finance .... MSc 12FT

Section sponsored by

BPP
UNIVERSITY
COLLEGE

Business and social sciences
www.prospects.ac.uk/findcourses **POSTGRADUATE DIRECTORY 379**

Business and management studies

Financial Services .... MSc 12FT
Human Resource Management.................................. MA 12FT 24PT
International Entrepreneurship Management...............MBS 12FT
International Management and Global Business......... MSc 12FT
International Tourism... MA 12FT 24PT
Project Management... MSc 12FT
Risk Management and Insurance........................... MSc 12FT
Software Engineering and Entrepreneurship Management.. MSc 12FT
Sustainable Resource Management: Policy and Practice .... MSc 12FT
Taxation...MA 12FT

University of Lincoln
Business Administration .... MBA 12PT
Events Management .... MSc 12FT 24PT
Hospitality and Tourism Services Management .... MSc 12FT
Human Resource Development (CIPD) .... MSc 12FT 36PT
Human Resource Management .... MSc 12FT 24PT
International Business.. MSc 12FT 24PT
Logistics Management....................................... MSc 12FT 24PT
Marketing... MSc 12-15FT

Liverpool Hope University
Business Management .... MA 12FT 24PT/PGDip 12FT 24PT/ PGCert 6FT 12PT
International MBA........................... International MBA 12FT 24PT
MBA (Information Technology)..........................MBA 12FT 24PT

Liverpool John Moores University
Entrepreneurship .... MSc 12FT 24PT
International News Journalism .... MA 12FT 24PT
Maritime Management .... MBA 12FT 24PT
Mass Communications .... MA 12FT 24PT

University of Liverpool
Doctor of Business Administration (Online Degree)...........DBA by taught 24FT 24+PT

London Business School
Masters in Management................................... MSc 12FT
PhD... PhD by taught 48FT/MRes 24FT

London College UCK
Marketing Management .... PGDip 12FT 24PT

London Metropolitan University
Business Economics....................................... MA 12FT 24PT
Doctor of Business Administration.......DBA by taught 36FT 48PT

London School of Hygiene and Tropical Medicine
Public Health (Health Services Management)....... MSc 12FT 24PT
Public Health (Health Services Research)................ MSc 12FT 24PT

London South Bank University
Business Project Management .... MSc 15FT 24PT
Management in Civil Society .... MSc 24PT

Loughborough University
Business Analysis and Management (for non-business graduates) .... MSc 12FT
Finance and Management (for non-finance graduates)MSc 12FT
Management (for non-business graduates).................. MSc 12FT
Security Management ....MSc 24-36DL/PGDip 12-24DL/PGCert 12DL

Manchester Metropolitan University
Business Management ....MSc 12FT 24PT/PGDip 12FT 24PT/ PGCert 12FT 24PT
Business Management (Top up programme)........MSc 12FT 36PT/ PGDip 24PT/PGCert 12PT
Digital Business Management............................ MSc 12FT
MSc Strategic Financial Management .... MSc 12FT
Management .... MSc 12FT/PGDip 18-24PT
PgCert/PgDip/MSc Digital Business Management .... MSc 12FT

University of Manchester
Business Analytics: Operational Research and Risk Analysis. MSc 12FT
Information Systems: Business IT .... MSc 12FT

Middlesex University
Business Practice, MProf.................................MA 24PT
Financial Management..................................... MSc 14FT 26PT
Management... MSc 12FT 24PT
Public Works Professional Practice DProf....DProf by taught 36PT
Research Methods for Business & Management........... MSc 12FT 24PT/PGCert 12FT 24PT/PGDip 12FT 24PT

Newcastle University
Architectural Practice and Management .... PGDip 12PT
Art Museum and Gallery Studies (with specialist pathways in: Curatorship, and Education)........ MA 12FT 24PT/PGDip 9FT 18PT
Arts, Business and Creativity...................................... MA 12FT 24PT
Banking and Finance .... MSc 12FT
Doctor of Business Administration.................DBA by taught 60PT
E-Business .... MSc 12FT
E-Business (Information Systems) .... MSc 12FT
Finance, Accounting and Business..........................GradDip 9FT
Human Resource Management...............................MA 12FT

Northumbria University
Business Administration .... MBA 12FT
Business with Arts Management .... MSc 12FT

Business with Entrepreneurship .... MSc 12FT
Business with Financial Management.......................... MSc 12FT
Business with Hospitality and Tourism Management... MSc 12FT
Business with Human Resource Management .... MSc 12FT
Business with Information Management...................... MSc 12FT
Business with Logistics and Supply Chain Management .... MSc 12FT
Business with Management.................................... MSc 12FT
Business with Marketing Management........................ MSc 12FT
Business with Music Management .... MSc 12FT
Business with Pipeline Integrity Management .... MSc 12FT
Global Business Management.................................. MSc 12FT
Global Financial Management................................. MSc 12FT
Global Logistics, Operations and Supply Chain ManagementMSc 12FT
Human Resource Management and Development. MA 24/36PT/ PGDip 24PT
International Human Resource Management................ MSc 12FT
Music Management ....MA 12/18FT 24/28PT 24/28DL

Nottingham Trent University
Human Resource Management (FT)........................... MSc 12FT
Management... MSc 12FT
Management and Human Resource Management........ MSc 12FT
Management and International Business .... MSc 12FT
Management and Marketing................................. MSc 12FT

University of Nottingham
Business Administration ....PGDip 9FT
Business Administration (Executive)........................MBA 24PT
Business Administration (Executive) - Corporate Social
Responsibility..MBA 24PT
Administration (Executive) - Healthcare ....MBA 24PT
Administration - Corporate Social Responsibility .... MBA 12FT 24-48PT
Administration - Entrepreneurship..................MBA 12FT 24-48PT
Administration - Finance..............................MBA 12FT 24-48PT
Administration - General.............................MBA 12FT 24-48PT
Administration - Singapore ....MBA 24-48PT

The Open University
Business Administration ....MBA variableDL/PGCert 12DL

Oxford Brookes University
Business Management (January Entry)..........................MSc 12FT
Business Management (January or Sept Entry).....MSc 12FT 24PT
Human Resource Management (MA, DHRM and CHRM)........MA 24PT/PGDip 24PT/PGCert 12PT
Human Resource Management .... MSc 12FT 24PT
Management (Certificate) - Online........................... CM 12DL
Management (Certificate) - Online (Solihull College)..... CM 12DL
Management, Certificate in (Corporate Online)............... CM 12DL

University of Oxford
Business Administration ....EMBA 21PT
Business Administration .... MBA 12FT

Plymouth University
Business and Management .... MSc 12FT
Doctor of Business Administration.................DBA by taught 60PT
International Procurement and Supply Chain Management MSc 12FT 24PT
Masters in Business Administration .... MBA 12FT
Professional Leadership....................................MSc 12FT 24PT
Public Administration and Leadership..................... MA 12FT 24PT
The Executive MBA ....MBA 24PT
The Global MBA .... MBA 12FT

University of Portsmouth
Business and Management .... MSc 12FT
Partnership Masters Programme....................MA 12PT/MSc 12PT

Queen Margaret University, Edinburgh
Human Resources for Health .... MSc 12FT 24PT/PGDip 8FT 16PT/ PGCert 4FT 8PT

Queen Mary, University of London
Accounting and Management .... MSc 12FT
International Business .... MSc 12FT
Management... MSc 12FT 24PT
Public Administration .... MPA 12FT 24PT

Queen's University Belfast
Business Administration - International .... MBA 12FT
Business Administration Executive ....MBA 24PT
Human Resouce Management ....MA 36PT/PGDip 24PT MSc 12FT
Marketing .... MSc 12FT

Ravensbourne
Design Management.................................MDes 12FT 24PT
Service Design .... MDes 12FT 24PT

University of Reading
Accounting and Financial Management .... MSc 12FT
Business Information Management .... MSc 12FT
Business and Management in Emerging Markets
.... MA 12FT 24PT
International Human Resource Management .... MSc 12FT
International Management and Accounting ....MSc 12FT 24PT
Rural Land and Business Management .... MSc 12FT

Richmond, The American International University in London
Masters in Business Administration (MBA)...........MBA 12FT 24PT

Robert Gordon University
Asset Integrity Management ....MSc 36-60DL
Design Management..MSc 36DL
Human Resource Management.................... MSc 12FT 36PT 36DL/ PGDip 8FT 24PT 24DL/PGCert 4FT 12PT 12DL
IT Management ....MSc 12FT 36DL
Management........................MSc 12FT/PGDip 9FT/PGCert 6FT

Royal Agricultural University
Business Management ....MSc 12FT 24PT
Business Management in the Food Industries .....MBA 15FT 24PT
Property Agency and Management................................. MSc 12FT
Sustainable Business.......................................MSc 12FT 24PT

Royal Holloway, University of London
Asia Pacific Business ....MA 12FT

University Campus Suffolk
Human Resource Management.......................PGDip 12FT 24PT
Sustainable Business .... MA 12FT 24PT

University of Salford
Global Management ....MSc 12FT 36PT/PGDip 8FT 24PT/ PGCert 4FT 9PT
Human Resource Management and Development........ MSc 12FT 24PT/PGDip 8FT 24PT/PGCert 4FT 9PT
Information Systems Management ....MSc 12FT 36PT/PGDip 8FT 24PT/PGCert 4FT 9PT
International Business ...MSc 12FT 36PT/PGDip 8FT 24PT/PGCert 4FT 9PT
International Business Law and Regulation................... LLM 12FT/ PGDip 8FT/PGCert 4FT
Leadership and Management for Healthcare Practice ....
MSc 12FT 36PT/PGDip 8FT 24PT/PGCert 4FT 9PT
MBA, The Salford ....MBA 12FT 36PT
Management.... MSc 12FT 36PT/PGDip 8FT 24PT/PGCert 4FT 9PT

School of Oriental and African Studies - SOAS
Environmental Management........................MSc 12FT 24-36PT
Finance and Development ....MSc 24-60DL/PGDip 12-60DL
Finance and Financial Law ....MSc 12FT 24-36PT
International Management (China) ....MSc 12FT 24-36PT
International Management (Japan) ....MSc 12FT 24-36PT
International Management (Middle East and North Africa).. MSc 12FT 24PT
Globalisation and Multinational Corporations ...... MA 12FT 24PT
Public Policy and Management (Distance Learning)....MSc 24DL/ PGDip 12DL

Sheffield Hallam University
Business...MRes 12FT 36PT
Human Resource Leadership............................... MSc 12PT
Human Resource Management/Development.............. MSc 12FT 24-36PT/PGDip 24PT
Managing Global Business ....MSc 12FT/PGDip 6FT/PGCert 3FT

University of Sheffield
Business Administration .... MBA 12FT
Entrepreneurship.. MSc 12FT
Global Marketing Management................................ MSc 12FT
PGDip 9FT/PGCert 6FT
Human Resource Management........................... MSc 12FT
Information Management.........................MSc 12FT 24-36PT
Information Management (Professional Enhancement
Programme).... MSc Up to 12FT 24-36PT/PGDip 9FT 18PT/PGCert 6FT 12PT
Information Systems Management .... MSc 12FT
International Commercial Law and Practice .... LLM 12FT 24PT
International Management................................ MSc 12FT
Leadership and Management............................... MSc 12FT
Management.. MSc 12FT
Management (Creative and Cultural Industries) .... MSc 12FT
Management (International Business)........................ MSc 12FT
Marketing Management Practice .... MSc 12FT

University of South Wales
ACA - Institute of Chartered Accountants in England and Wales (ICAEW) ....ACA 36PT
Chartered Institute of Purchasing and Supply (CIPS) Diplomas in Procurement and Supply....................Diploma in Procurement and Supply 8PT/Advanced Diploma in Procurement and Supply 8PT/ Professional Diploma in Procurement and Supply 8PT
Human Resource Management..................PGDip 24PT MSc 24PT
International Management.................................MSc 12FT 30PT
Learning and Development NVQ 3, 4, 5 ...NVQ Level 3 18 maxPT/ NVQ Level 4 18 maxPT/NVQ Level 5 18 maxPT
Project Management......................................MSc 15FT 36PT
Sustainable Business Risk Management.............. MSc 12/FT 36PT

Southampton Solent University
Business Studies .... MA 24-72PT 24-72DL
Human Resource Management.............................MA 12FT

University of Southampton
Business Analytics and Management Sciences....MSc 12FT 27PT/ PGDip 9FT 21PT
Human Resource Management .... MSc 12FT/PGDip 9FT
International Business Law........................... LLM 12FT 24PT
International Management..........................MSc 12FT/PGDip 9FT

Business and management studies

LLM Insurance Law (1 yrs)....................................LLM 12FT
MBA (Part-time)................................. MBA 39PT/PGDip 33PT
Digital Marketing (1 yrs)....................................MSc 12FT
Finance (1 yrs)..MSc 12FT
Organisation Development and Facilitation....................MSc 36FT
Risk and Finance (1 yrs)....................................MSc 12FT
Strategy and Innovation (1 yrs)...............................MSc 12FT
Marketing Management................................ MSc 12FT/PGDip 9FT

University of South Wales
Evaluation Studies...................................PGCert 9-12DL

University of St Andrews
Business and English (Diploma) ....Diploma 9FT
Finance & Management ....MLitt 12FT
International Business ....MLitt 12FT
Management...MLitt 12FT 24PT
Management (Human Resource Management) ....MLitt 12FT
Management Studies..MRes 12FT 24PT
Management and Information Technology ....MSc 12FT/
PGDip 9FT

St Mary's University College, Twickenham
Charity Management....PGCert 12PT/PGDip 24PT/MA 12FT 24PT

Staffordshire University
Health Management and Policy (Distance Learning) ....PGCert
12PT/PGDip 24PT/MA 36PT
Human Resource Management...............................PGDip 24PT
Management... MSc 24FT
Masters in Business Administration........MBA 12FT/International
MBA 12FT/Finance MBA 12FT

University of Stirling
Aquaculture: Sustainable Aquaculture ....MSc 12FT
Business and Management ....MRes 12FT
Computing for Business ....MSc 12FT
Human Resource Management..................... MSc 12FT/PGDip 9FT
Human Resource Management and Socio Economic
Development....................MSc 12FT/PGDip 9FT/PGCert 6FT
International Business .... MSc 12FT/PGDip 9FT
International Business and Socio Economic Development .... MSc
12FT/PGDip 9FT/PGCert 6FT
Investment Analysis ....MSc 12FT/PGDip 9FT/PGCert 6FT
MBA Retailing...MBA 30DL
MBA in Finance (Vietnam) ....MBA 18PT
Management...................................MSc 12FT 27PT/PGDip 9FT 21PT
Master of Business Administration .... MBA 12FT

Retail Management............................... MSc 12FT/PGDip 9FT

University of Strathclyde
Business Analysis and Consulting......................... MSc 12FT
Business and Management........MSc 12FT 30PT/PGDip 9FT 20PT
Human Resource Management..MSc 12FT 24PT/PGDip 9FT 24PT
Information Management........MSc 12FT/PGDip 9FT/PGCert 4FT
International Human Resource Management................. MSc 12FT
International Management..............................MA 12FT/PGDip 9FT
Management of Information Technology Systems.......MSc 12FT/
PGDip 9FT
Master in Business Administration ..... MBA 12FT 36PT 30-60DL/
PGDip 9FT 24PT 36DL
Research Methodology in Business and Management ....
MRes 12FT 24PT/PGDip 9FT 21PT/PGCert 4FT 9PT

University of Sunderland
Business Management ....MA 12FT
Human Rights ....LLM 12FT

University of Surrey
Management..MSc 12FT 24DL

University of Sussex
International Accounting and Corporate Governance... MSc 12FT
24PT
Management and Finance .... MSc 12FT 24PT

Swansea University
MBA.. MBA 12FT
Management... MSc 12FT
Management (Finance)....................................... MSc 12FT
Management (Human Resource Management) .... MSc 12FT
Management (International Management)................... MSc 12FT
Management (International Standards)..................... MSc 12FT
Management (Marketing) .... MSc 12FT

Teesside University
Business Administration .... MBA 12FT 24PT
Management.............................MSc 12FT 24PT PGCert 12PT
Service Improvement .... MSc 36PT

Trinity College Dublin - the University of Dublin
Business and Management .... MSc 12FT

University of the Highlands and Islands
Enterprise and eMarketing ....PGCert 12-24PT

UCL - University College London
Management.. MSc 12FT 24PT

Management Science and Innovation...........................MRes 12FT

University of Warwick
Engineering Business ManagementMSc 12FT 36PT/PGDip 24PT/
PGCert 18PT
Management & Organizational Analysis................ MA 12FT 24PT

University of the West of Scotland
Entrepreneurship and Economic Development........ PGCert 24FT/
MSc 12FT
Management.............................. MSc 12FT 36PT/Diploma 9FT 24PT

University of the West of England, Bristol
Leadership and Management (Coaching and Mentoring)...... MSc
12FT

University of Westminster
Media Management.. MA 12FT 24PT
Purchasing and Supply Chain Management.......... MSc 12FT 24PT

University of Winchester
Business Management ....MSc 12FT 24PT/PGDip 12FT 24PT/
PGCert 12FT 24PT
Sustainable Business......MSc 12FT 18PT/PGDip 9FT 18PT/PGCert
9FT 18PT

University of Wolverhampton
Healthcare Leadership .... PGCert 12PT/MSc 24PT
Human Resource Development and Organisational Change........
MSc 24PT/PGDip 24PT
Human Resource Development and Organisational Change (top-
up)... MSc 12PT
Human Resource Management (top-up)................... MSc 12PT
Innovation and Entrepreneurship............................ MSc 12FT 24PT
Leadership................................. MA 24PT/PGCert 12PT
Master of Business Administration (top-up).................. MBA 12PT
Medical Education..PGCert 12PT
Oil and Gas Management .... MSc 12FT 24PT
Sales Management ....PGCert 12PT

University of York
Corporate Social Responsibility with Environmental
Management... MSc 12FT

Business and management studies
Research Courses

Aberystwyth University
Management and Business ....MPhil 12FT 24PT PhD 36FT 60PT
Marketing .... MPhil 12FT 24PT

Anglia Ruskin University
Business and Management .... MPhil 36FT 72PT/PhD 36FT 72PT
Professional Doctorate in Business and Management....................
DBA 36FT 72PT
Professional Doctorate in Education .... EdD 36FT 36 - 72PT
Professional Doctorate in Health and Social Care........DProf 36FT
36 - 72PT
Professional Doctorate in Laws......................DProf 36 PT
Sustainability...............................PhD 24 - 60FT 36 - 72PT

Aston University
ABS Research Degrees (Business & Management / Management
Research) ...... PhD 36-48FT 48-60PT/MPhil 24FT/MSc by research
12FT

University of Bath
Knowledge Transfer.. MPhil 24PT

University of Bedfordshire
Research in Business.......................... MA by research 12FT 24PT/
MSc by research 12FT 24PT

Birkbeck, University of London
Management................................ PhD 24FT 36PT/MPhil 24FT 36PT

University of Birmingham
Business Administration ....DBA 48-72PT
Doctorate in Business Administration.......................DBA 48-72PT
Integrated Study (Business and Management)...............PhD 48FT

University of Bolton
Supply Chain, Business IT, Music and Creative Industries
Management Specialisms............ MPhil 18FT 24 - 42PT/PhD 36FT
48 - 72PT

University of Bradford
Management........ PhD 36-48FT 48-60PT/MPhil 12-24FT 24-48PT

Brunel University
Doctoral Programme in Business and Management ......PhD 36FT
72PT/MPhil 24FT 48PT

University of Buckingham
Business.................................. DPhil 36FT 72PT/MPhil 24FT 48PT
Economics and International Studies ....DPhil 36FT 72PT/MPhil
24FT 48PT

University of Cambridge
Management Studies...PhD 36FT

University of Chester
Higher Degrees by Research .... MPhil 12 - 48FT 24 - 72PT/PhD
24 - 48FT 48 - 84PT
Work Related Studies ....DProf 24-84PT

Section sponsored by

BPP
UNIVERSITY
COLLEGE

Business and social sciences
www.prospects.ac.uk/findcourses POSTGRADUATE DIRECTORY 381

Business and management studies

City University London
Business School..PhD/MPhil

University of Dundee
Accountancy and Business Finance ....MAcc 12FT MPhil 24FT
MSc by research 12FT PhD 36FT

University of East Anglia
Business Management .... PhD 36FT 72PT/MPhil 24FT 48PT
Business, Accountability, Regulation and Development.................
PhD 36FT 72PT/MPhil 24FT 48PT

University of Edinburgh
Management............................PhD 36FT 72PT/MPhil 24FT/MSc by
research 12FT

University of Essex
Environmental Governance......PhD 36FT 72PT/MPhil 24FT 48PT/
MSc by research 12FT 24PT
Management............PhD 36FT/MRes 12FT 24PT/MPhil 24FT 48PT

University of Exeter
Management................................ PhD 48FT 84PT/MPhil 36FT 60PT

University of Gloucestershire
Doctorate in Business Administration..........................DBA 30-48FT

Goldsmiths, University of London
Management...MPhil 36FT/PhD 36FT

Heriot-Watt University
Management...PhD 36FT/MPhil 12FT

University of Hertfordshire
Business Administration (Professional Doctorate)..........................
DBA 48FT 72PT

University of Kent
Accounting & Finance....................................... PhD 36FT 60PT
Management...PhD 36FT 60PT/MPhil 24FT 36PT/MA by research
12FT 24PT
Management Science.................. PhD 36FT 60PT/MPhil 24FT 36PT

Kingston University
Research.. PhD 36FT 72PT

Lancaster University
Management.. PhD 36FT 48PT

University of Leeds
Leeds University Business School..............PhD 36+FT/MPhil 24FT/
MA by research 12+FT

University of Leicester
Management................................. PhD 36FT 48PT/MPhil 24FT 36PT

University of Lincoln
Business ....MPhil 24FT 48PT/PhD 18-24FT 30-36PT

Liverpool Hope University
Postgraduate Research .... PhD 24FT 48PT/MPhil 12FT 24PT

University of Liverpool
Management.................... PhD 24-48FT 48-84PT/MPhil 12FT 24PT/
MRes 12FT 24PT

London Business School
Business and Management ....PhD 48FT/MRes 24FT

Loughborough University
Business and Management Studies...PhD 36FT 60PT/MPhil 24FT
36PT

Manchester Metropolitan University
Business Information Technology, Management Science, Policy
Modelling ......PhD 48FT 90PT/MPhil 36FT 72PT/MRes 12FT 24PT/
MA or MSc by Research 18FT 36PT

University of Manchester
Business and Management ......PhD 36FT 72PT/MPhil 12FT 24PT/
MRes 12FT

Middlesex University
Middlesex University Business School...............PhD/MPhil/MA by
research

Newcastle University
Biotechnology and Business Enterprise ....MRes 12FT
Business and Management .... PhD 36FT 72PT/MPhil 12FT 24PT

Nottingham Trent University
Business & Management Research ....MPhil 24FT 36PT/PhD 48FT
72PT

University of Nottingham
Business and Management ......MRes 12FT/MPhil 24FT/PhD 36FT

The Open University
Business and Management ...... MPhil 15FT 24PT variableDL/PhD
36FT 72PT variableDL/MRes 12FT variableDL
Marketing.................PhD 36FT 72PT variableDL/MPhil 15FT 24PT
variableDL
Surveillance................................... MPhil 15FT 24PT/PhD 36FT 72PT

Oxford Brookes University
Business Doctoral Programmes .... PhD 24-60FT 36-72PT/MPhil
24-36FT 36-48PT

University of Oxford
Management Studies... DPhil 48FT

University of Portsmouth
Operations and Systems Management.......MPhil 24FT 48PT/PhD
36FT 72PT
Organisation Studies and Human Resource Management...........
MPhil 24FT 48PT/PhD 36FT 72PT
Professional Doctorate in Business Administration.......DBA 48PT
Strategy, Enterprise and Innovation...MPhil 24FT 48PT/PhD 36FT
72PT

Queen's University Belfast
Economics... PhD 36FT 72PT/MPhil 24FT 48PT
Management................................ PhD 36FT 72PT/MPhil 24FT 48PT

Robert Gordon University
Aberdeen Business School ...PhD 12FT 36PT 36DL/MSc(Res) 12FT
36PT 36DL

Royal Welsh College of Music and Drama
Arts Management...................................MA by research 12FT 24PT

Sheffield Hallam University
Business and Management Programme................. PhD 36FT 48PT

University of Sheffield
Management........................... PhD 36FT 72PT/MPhil 24FT 48PT

Southampton Solent University
Southampton Business School..PhD/MPhil

University of Southampton
Doctor of Business Administration ....DBA 48PT
School of Management .... PhD 36FT 72PT/MPhil 24FT 48PT
School of Management: Accounting, Accountability and
Governance................................... PhD 36FT 72PT/MPhil 24FT 48PT
School of Management: Centre for Risk ResearchPhD 36FT 72PT/
MPhil 24FT 48PT
School of Management: Information Systems.....PhD 36FT 72PT/
MPhil 24FT 48PT
School of Management: International Finance....PhD 36FT 72PT/
MPhil 24FT 48PT

University of St Andrews
Management.....................PhD 36-48FT 72-84PT/MPhil 24FT 48PT

Business and management studies

Staffordshire University
Business School.......PhD 36FT 60PT/MPhil 18FT 36PT
Doctorate in Business Administration.......DBA 48PT

University of Strathclyde
Hunter Centre for Entrepreneurship - Research.......PhD 33FT/MPhil 12FT/MRes 12FT
Management - Research....PhD 36FT 48PT/MPhil 36FT 48PT/DBA 36FT 48PT/MRes 12FT

University of Sunderland
Business & Management.......PhD 36-48FT 48-72PT 48-72DL/MPhil 12-36FT 24-48PT 24-48DL

University of Surrey
Management.......PhD 36FT 48PT/PhD 48FT 96PT
School of Management.......PhD 18 maxFT 30 maxPT/DBA 48PT 48DL

Swansea University
Business Management.......MPhil 12FT 24PT/PhD 36FT 60PT

Teesside University
Business or Management Studies.......PhD min 24FT min 36PT/MPhil min 18FT min 30PT

University of Wales Trinity Saint David
Business Management.......PhD 36FT 48-72PT/MPhil 12-36FT

University of Ulster
Business & Management Studies.......PhD 36FT 72PT/MPhil 24FT 48PT

UCL - University College London
Management Science and Innovation.......PhD 36FT 60PT

University of West London
School of Business.......PhD 36FT 72PT/MPhil 24FT 48PT

University of the West of England, Bristol
Faculty of Business and Law.......PhD .FT

University of Westminster
Westminster Business School.......MPhil 18-36FT 30-60PT

University of Worcester
Business Management and I.T.......PhD 48FT 70PT/MPhil 24FT 48PT
Doctor of Business Administration.......DBA 36PT

Business formation
Taught Courses

University of Aberdeen
Business Research.......MRes 12FT 24PT

Cardiff University
Business Strategy & Entrepreneurship.......MSc 12FT

University of Central Lancashire
Business Management.......MSc 12FT

University of Cumbria
International Business.......MBA 12FT
International Business Management.......MA 12FT

University of Derby
Business and Payroll Management.......MSc 36PT
International Business.......MSc 12FT 36PT

University of Dundee
Non-Graduating Taught Postgraduate in School of Business... PG module variableFT

University of East Anglia
Creative Entrepreneurship.......MA 12FT
Entrepreneurship and Strategy.......MSc 12FT

National University of Ireland Galway
Business Studies.......HDip 12FT

Glasgow Caledonian University
Social Enterprise.......PGCert 6PT

University of Glasgow
International Business & Entrepreneurship.......MSc 12FT
International Management & Design Innovation.......MSc 12FT

Goldsmiths, University of London
Creating Social Media.......MA 12FT 24PT/MSc 12FT 24PT

Leeds Metropolitan University
Business (IPOS).......MA 12FT 60PT

Middlesex University
Business Enterprise and Entrepreneurship.......MA 12-15FT 24-27PT

Newcastle University
E-Business.......MSc 12FT
E-Business (E-Marketing).......MSc 12FT
Innovation, Creativity and Entrepreneurship.......MSc 12FT
Management and Business Studies (Research).....MA 12FT 24PT/PGDip 9FT 21PT

Nottingham Trent University
International Fashion Business.......MA 12FT
Management.......MSc 12FT
Management and Human Resource Management.......MSc 12FT
Management and International Business.......MSc 12FT
Management and Marketing.......MSc 12FT

Oxford Brookes University
Management (Certificate) - Online.......CM 12DL
Management (Certificate) - Online (Solihull College).....CM 12DL
Management, Certificate in (Corporate Online).......CM 12DL

Robert Gordon University
Management.......MSc 12FT/PGDip 9FT/PGCert 6FT

Sheffield Hallam University
Managing Global Business.......MSc 12FT/PGDip 6FT/PGCert 3FT

Southampton Solent University
Business Studies.......MA 24-72PT 24-72DL

Staffordshire University
Creative Futures.......MA 12FT

University of Stirling
Business and Management.......MRes 12FT

University of Strathclyde
Business and Management.......MSc 12FT 30PT/PGDip 9FT 20PT

Teesside University
Innovation and Transformational Change.......PGCert 12PT
Management.......PGCert 12PT MSc 12FT 24PT

University of Wales Trinity Saint David
Entrepreneurship.......MBA 12FT 24PT/PGDip 12FT 24PT/PGCert 12FT 24PT
Social Entrepreneurship.......MBA 12FT 24PT/PGCert 12FT 24PT/PGDip 12FT 24PT

UCL - University College London
Engineering with Innovation and Entrepreneurship....MSc 12FT/PGDip 9FT
Management.......MSc 12FT 24PT
Management Science and Innovation.......MRes 12FT

University of the West of Scotland
Entrepreneurship and Economic Development.......PGCert 24FT/MSc 12FT

University of Westminster
Business Innovation for the Digital Economy.......MSc 12FT

Business formation
Research Courses

University of Chester
Business.......DBA 24-84PT

University of Dundee
Non-Graduating Research in School of Business (6 months or more).......Non-Grad 6-24FT
Non-Graduating Research in School of Business (less than 6 months).......Non-Grad 1-5FT

Queen's University Belfast
Management.......PhD 36FT 72PT/MPhil 24FT 48PT

UCL - University College London
Management Science and Innovation.......PhD 36FT 60PT

Business studies
Taught Courses

University of Aberdeen
Business Research.......MRes 12FT 24PT

Aberystwyth University
International Business.......MSc 12FT 24PT/PGDip 9FT 18PT
International Business Management.......MSc 12FT 24PT/PGDip 9FT 18PT/PGCert 6FT 12PT

Anglia Ruskin University
Corporate Governance.......MA 18FT 24PT

Aston University
MSc Business & Management.......MSc 12FT
MSc Organisational Psychology & Business.......MSc 12FT

Bangor University
Accounting and Finance.......MSc 12FT
Accounting and Finance - LondonCentre.......MSc 12FT
Banking and Finance....MSc 12FT MA 12FT/PGDip 9FT MBA 12FT
Banking and Finance - London Centre.......MSc 12FT
Business and Finance.......MSc 12FT/PGDip 9FT MA 12FT/PGDip 9FT
Business and Marketing.......MA 12FT/PGDip 9FT
Business with Consumer Psychology.......MA 12FT/PGDip 9FT MSc 12FT/PGDip 9FT
Consumer Psychology with Business.......MSc 12FT/PGDip 9FT MA 12FT/PGDip 9FT
Environmental Management.......MBA 12FT
Finance.......MBA 12FT MA 12FT/PGDip 9FT MSc 12FT/PGDip 9FT
Finance - London Centre.......MBA 12FT MSc 12FT
International Banking and Development Finance.......MSc 12FT/PGDip 9FT
International Banking and Development Finance - London Centre.......MSc 12FT
Islamic Banking and Finance.......MA 12FT/PGDip 9FT MSc 12FT/PGDip 9FT
Islamic Banking and Finance - London Centre.......MBA 12FT
Management.......MBA 12FT 36PT
Management and Finance.......MSc 12FT/MA 12FT
Rheolaeth Amgylcheddol Gynaliadwy (Sustainable Environmental Management).......MSc 12FT 24PT/MA 12FT 24PT

University of Bath
Business and Community....MSc 12FT 24-60PT/PGDip 9FT 21PT/PGCert 4FT

University of Bedfordshire
Finance and Business Management.......MSc 12-15FT
Pre-Masters in Business.......International Pre-Masters 24FT

Birmingham City University
MA Human Resource Management (CIPD).......MA 36PT/PGDip 24PT

University of Birmingham
Social Research (Business).......MA 12FT 24PT
Strategic Marketing and Consulting.......MSc 12FT

University of Bolton
Accountancy and Financial Strategy.......MA 12FT 24 - 42PT

Bournemouth University
Corporate Governance.......MSc 12FT/MSc 24PT

University of Bradford
Professional Studies.......MSc 24DL/PGDip 24DL/PGCert 24DL

Brunel University
Accounting and Business Management.......MSc 12FT
Business Intelligence and Social Media.......MSc 12FT
Human Resource Management.......MSc 12FT
Human Resource Management and Employment Relations. MSc 12FT
International Business.......MSc 12FT

University of Cambridge
Innovation, Strategy and Organisation.......MPhil 9FT

Cardiff University
Business Strategy & Entrepreneurship.......MSc 12FT

University of Central Lancashire
Business Management.......MSc 12FT
Global Communication Studies.......MA 12FT 24-36PT
Human Resource Management/Development.....MSc 12FT 24PT
International Business Economics.......MA 12FT
International Business and Management.......MSc 12FT
Logistics and Supply Chain Management.......MSc 12FT
Human Resource Management/Development.......MA 12PT 12DL
Management Studies.......DMS 18PT
Marketing and PR.......MA 12FT
Master of Business Administration.......MBA 12FT
Master of Business Administration - Health.......MBA 36PT
Master of Business Administration - Part-time.......MBA 36PT
Postgraduate Certificate in Management (PGCM)....PGCert 18PT
Postgraduate Diploma in Human Resource Management/Development.......PGDip 24PT/CIPD 24PT
Strategic Marketing Leadership (Advanced Entry).......MA 12PT

University of Chester
Action Research and Appreciative Inquiry (Work Based and Integrative Studies)...MSc 24-72PT/MA 24-72PT/PGDip 24-60PT/PGCert 12-36PT
Business and Personal Coaching (Work Based and Integrative Studies).......MA 24-72PT/PGDip 24-60PT/PGCert 12-36PT

University College Cork
Contemporary Chinese Culture & Business.......MA 12FT
Food Business.......MSc 24FT

University of Cumbria
International Business.......MBA 12FT
International Business Management.......MA 12FT
Management Studies.......GradDip 24PT/GradCert 12PT
Master of Business Administration.......MBA 12FT 36PT

University of Derby
Business and Payroll Management.......MSc 36PT
International Business.......MSc 12FT 36PT
International Business and Finance.......MSc 12FT
MA Management.......MSc 12FT 36PT/PGDip 12FT/PGCert 9FT

University Centre Doncaster
Human Resource Management.......MSc 36PT

Dublin Institute of Technology
Business and Entrepreneurship.......MSc 12FT
Strategic Management.......MSc 12FT 30PT

University of Dundee
Finance.......MSc 12FT
Non-Graduating Taught Postgraduate in School of Business... PG module variableFT

Durham University
Management (Innovation Technology and Operations Management).......MSc 12FT
The Durham EBS Executive Master of Business Administration... MBA 24PT

University of East Anglia
Advanced Business Management.......MSc 12FT
Business Management.......MSc 12FT
International Business Economics.......MA 12FT
International Business Finance and Economics.......MA 12FT
Sustainable Business.......MSc 12FT

Section sponsored by
BPP UNIVERSITY COLLEGE

Business and management studies

Edinburgh Napier University
Business Management with Marketing ..... MSc 12FT
Flexibly-managed programme (Business School) ..... MSc 12FT 24-36PT 24-36DL/PGDip 9FT 18-27PT 18-27DL/PGCert 6FT 12-18PT 12-18DL
Intercultural Business Communication ..... MSc 12FT
International Human Resource Management ..... MSc 12FT

University of Edinburgh
Human Resource Management ..... MSc 12FT

University of Exeter
Biotechnology and Enterprise ..... MSc 12FT
Finance ..... GradDip 9FT
Independent Film Business ..... MA 12FT 24PT
Management ..... GradDip 9FT MRes 12FT

GCU London
International Business Management ..... MSc 12FT

National University of Ireland Galway
Business Studies ..... HDip 12FT
Technology Commercialisation ..... PGDip 12DL
Technology Management ..... MSc 24PT 24DL

Glasgow Caledonian University
Biotechnology with Business ..... MSc 12FT
Global Business Law and Regulation ..... LLM 12FT
Human Resource Management ..... PGDip 9FT 24PT/MSc 12FT 24-36PT
International Sports Management ..... MSc 12FT
Management ..... MSc 12FT FlexiblePT/PGDip 9FT FlexiblePT/PGCert 6FT FlexiblePT
Master of Research ..... MRes 12FT

University of Glasgow
Management with Human Resources ..... MSc 12FT

Glyndwr University
Executive MBA ..... Executive MBA 24PT

Goldsmiths, University of London
Digital Entrepreneurship ..... MSc 12FT

University of Greenwich
Business and Financial Economics MA 12FT 24PT/MSc 12FT 24PT/PGDip 12FT 24PT

University of Hertfordshire
Business Administration ..... DBA by taught 48-60PT
Business Computing ..... MSc 12-16FT

University of Huddersfield
Business ..... MSc 12FT 24PT

University of Hull
Business Analytics and Consulting Practice ..... MSc 12FT

Imperial College London
Economics & Strategy for Business ..... MSc 12FT

University of Kent
Management (General) ..... MSc 12FT
Management (International Business) ..... MSc 12FT
Management Science ..... MSc 12FT
Management Science (Business Analytics) ..... MSc 12FT

Leeds Metropolitan University
Association of Chartered Certified Accountants - Fundementals Level ..... ACCA 12PT
Association of Chartered Certified Accountants - Knowledge Level ..... ACCA 12PT
Finance ..... MSc 12FT 24PT
Human Resource Management ..... MA 12FT 24PT/PGDip 24PT
Leadership & Change Management ..... MSc unknownPT
MBA (Executive) E-Learning ..... MBA 24DL
MBA (Graduate) ..... MBA 12FT
Supply Chain Management & Logistics ..... MSc 12FT

University of Lincoln
Business Administration ..... MBA 12PT

Liverpool Hope University
Business Management ..... MA 12FT 24PT/PGDip 12FT 24PT/PGCert 6FT 12PT

London Metropolitan University
Human Resource Management ..... MA 24PT PGDip 12FT 24PT

London School of Economics and Political Science (LSE)
Management and Strategy ..... MSc 12FT

London South Bank University
Business Project Management ..... MSc 15FT 24PT

Manchester Metropolitan University
Finance and Business ..... MSc 12FT

Middlesex University
Human Rights and Business ..... MA 24PT/PGCert 12PT/PGDip 15PT
Masters in Work Based Studies ..... MA 12-24DL

Newcastle University
E-Business ..... MSc 12FT
E-Business (E-Marketing) ..... MSc 12FT

Northumbria University
Business Administration ..... MBA 12FT
Business with Arts Management ..... MSc 12FT
Business with Financial Management ..... MSc 12FT
Business with Hospitality and Tourism Management ..... MSc 12FT
Business with Human Resource Management ..... MSc 12FT
Business with Information Management ..... MSc 12FT
Business with Legal Management ..... MSc 12/16FT
Business with Management ..... MSc 12FT
Business with Marketing Management ..... MSc 12FT
Business with Music Management ..... MSc 12FT
Business with Public Administration ..... MSc 12FT
Global Business Management ..... MSc 12FT
Human Resource Management and Development. MA 24/36PT/PGDip 24PT
International Human Resource Management ..... MSc 12FT

Nottingham Trent University
Management ..... MSc 12FT
Management and Human Resource Management ..... MSc 12FT
Management and International Business ..... MSc 12FT
Management and Marketing ..... MSc 12FT

University of Nottingham
Public Procurement Law and Policy ..... PGDip 21PT/LLM 24PT/PGCert 12-21PT

The Open University
Systems Thinking in Practice MSc variableDL/PGCert variableDL/PGDip variableDL

Oxford Brookes University
Biotechnology with Business ..... MSc 12FT 24PT/PGDip 8FT 20PT
Business Management (January Entry) ..... MSc 12FT
Business Management (January or Sept Entry) ..... MSc 12FT 24PT
European Business, Culture and Languages . MA 12FT/PGDip 9FT
Management (Certificate) - Online ..... CM 12DL
Management (Certificate) - Online (Solihull College) ..... CM 12DL
Management, Certificate in (Corporate Online) ..... CM 12DL
Two Year Master's Degree - Business ..... MSc 21-24FT

University of Oxford
Business Administration ..... EMBA 21PT MBA 12FT

University of Reading
Accounting and Financial Management ..... MSc 12FT
Business Economics ..... MSc 12FT 24PT
Economics of International Business and Finance ..... MSc 12FT 24PT
Environmental Management ..... MSc 12FT 24PT
International Business and Finance ..... MSc 12FT
International Human Resource Management ..... MSc 12FT
Public Policy ..... MA 12FT 24PT 72BM
Rural Land and Business Management ..... MSc 12FT

Robert Gordon University
Management ..... MSc 12FT/PGDip 9FT/PGCert 6FT

University of Roehampton
Post Graduate Diploma- International Management with Finance ..... PGDip 9FT 24PT
Post Graduate Diploma- International Management with Human Resource Management ..... PGDip 9FT 24PT
Post Graduate Diploma- International Management with Marketing ..... PGDip 9FT 24PT
Project Management ..... MSc 12FT

Royal Agricultural University
Business Management ..... MSc 12FT 24PT

University Campus Suffolk
Business and Management ..... MSc 12FT 24PT

University of Salford
Global Management ..... MSc 12FT 36PT/PGDip 8FT 24PT/PGCert 4FT 9PT
International Business ... MSc 12FT 36PT/PGDip 8FT 24PT/PGCert 4FT 9PT
International Business Law and Regulation LLM 12FT/PGDip 8FT/PGCert 4FT
Leadership and Management for Healthcare Practice ..... MSc 12FT 36PT/PGDip 8FT 24PT/PGCert 4FT 9PT
MBA, The Salford ..... MBA 12FT 36PT
Social Media ..... MA 9FT/PGDip 9FT

School of Oriental and African Studies - SOAS
International Management (China) ..... MSc 12FT 24-36PT
International Management (Japan) ..... MSc 12FT 24-36PT
International Management (Middle East and North Africa).. MSc 12FT 24PT
Public Policy and Management (Distance Learning) .... MSc 24DL/PGDip 12DL

Sheffield Hallam University
Managing Global Business ..... MSc 12FT/PGDip 6FT/PGCert 3FT
Organisation Development and Consultancy ..... MSc 24PT/PGDip 18PT/PGCert 12PT

University of Sheffield
Business Administration ..... MBA 12FT
Business Finance and Economics ..... MSc 12FT 24PT
Global Marketing Management ..... MSc 12FT
Global Marketing Management ..... MSc 12FT/PGDip 9FT/PGCert 6FT
Leadership and Management ..... MSc 12FT

Southampton Solent University
Business Studies ..... MA 24-72PT 24-72DL

University of Southampton
Business Analytics and Management Sciences .... MSc 12FT 27PT/PGDip 9FT 21PT
International Business Law ..... LLM 12FT 24PT
MBA (Part-time) ..... MBA 39PT/PGDip 33PT

University of St Andrews
International Business ..... MLitt 12FT

St Mary's University College, Twickenham
Charity Management .... PGCert 12PT/PGDip 24PT/MA 12FT 24PT

Staffordshire University
Economics for Business Analysis ..... MSc 12-16FT

University of Stirling
Business and Management ..... MRes 12FT
International Business ..... MSc 12FT/PGDip 9FT
International Business and Socio Economic Development ..... MSc 12FT/PGDip 9FT/PGCert 6FT
Master of Business Administration ..... MBA 12FT

University of Strathclyde
Business Analysis and Consulting ..... MSc 12FT
Business and Management ..... MSc 12FT 30PT/PGDip 9FT 20PT
Master in Business Administration ..... MBA 12FT 36PT 30-60DL/PGDip 9FT 24PT 36DL

University of Surrey
Doctor of Business Administration ..... DBA by taught 48-72PT

University of Sussex
Digital Communication Systems with Business Management ..... MSc 12FT 24PT
Management and Entrepreneurship ..... MSc 12FT 24PT

Swansea University
Business Economics ..... MSc 12FT
Business Economics with Computing ..... MSc 12FT
Business Economics with Finance ..... MSc 12FT
MBA ..... MBA 12FT
Management ..... MSc 12FT
Management (Finance) ..... MSc 12FT
Management (Human Resource Management) ..... MSc 12FT
Management (International Management) ..... MSc 12FT
Management (International Standards) ..... MSc 12FT
Management (Marketing) ..... MSc 12FT

Teesside University
Management ..... PGCert 12PT MSc 12FT 24PT

Trinity College Dublin - the University of Dublin
Business and Management ..... MSc 12FT

University of Wales Trinity Saint David
Leadership ..... MBA 12FT 24PT
Professional Practice ..... MA FlexibleFT FlexiblePT FlexibleDL/PGDip FlexibleFT FlexiblePT/PGCert FlexibleFT FlexiblePT

University of Ulster
Business Studies ..... MBS 12FT

UCL - University College London
Management ..... MSc 12FT 24PT
Management Science and Innovation ..... MRes 12FT
Telecommunications with Business ..... MSc 12FT 36-60PT

University of Warwick
Business (Behavioural Science) ..... MSc 12FT
Business (Finance & Accounting) ..... MSc 12FT
Business (Marketing) ..... MSc 12FT
Business Analytics & Consulting ..... MSc 12FT

University of West London
Corporate Communication ..... MSc 12FT 24PT

University of the West of England, Bristol
Family Business Advising ..... PGCert 12PT

University of Winchester
Doctor of Business Administration ..... DBA by taught 48PT
Sustainable Business ..... MSc 12FT 18PT/PGDip 9FT 18PT/PGCert 9FT 18PT

University of York
Development Economics and Emerging Markets ..... MSc 12FT

Business studies
Research Courses

Bangor University
Accounting, Banking, Economics, Finance, Management Studies ..... MPhil 24FT/PhD 36FT

University of Bolton
Business Management Specialisms ..... PhD 36FT 72PT

University of Brighton
Business School Research Division ..... PhD 24-60FT 36-72PT/MPhil 18-36FT 30-48PT

University of Cambridge
Management Studies ..... PhD 36FT

University of Chester
Business ..... DBA 24-84PT

Business and management studies

De Montfort University
Strategy and Management (Research)MPhil 12 - 24FT 24 - 48PT/ PhD 24 - 36FT 36 - 72PT

University of Dundee
Economics (by research) .... MPhil 24FT
Economics (by research) ....MSc by research 12FT

Durham University
Business... PhD 36FT 72PT
The Durham DBA.. DBA 36PT

University of East Anglia
Business Management .... PhD 36FT 72PT/MPhil 24FT 48PT

University of Exeter
Management.................................. PhD 48FT 84PT/MPhil 36FT 60PT

National University of Ireland Galway
College of Business, Public Policy & Law ....PhD 48FT 72PT/MPhil 24FT 48PT/MComm by research 24FT 48PT/MSc by research 24FT 48PT
College of Business, Public Policy & Law .....MSc by research 24FT 48PT

University of Greenwich
Business - Research..........PhD 36FT 48-60PT/MPhil 24FT 36-48PT
Business MA by Research .... MA by research 12 - 24FT

University of Hertfordshire
Business Administration (Professional Doctorate)...........................
DBA 48FT 72PT

University of Hull
Centre for Management and Organisational Learning ....
PhD 36FT 60PT/MPhil 24FT 36PT

Imperial College London
Doctoral Programme ....PhD 36FT

University of Lincoln
Business ....MPhil 24FT 48PT/PhD 18-24FT 30-36PT

Manchester Metropolitan University
Human Resource Management and Organisational Behaviour ...
PhD 48FT 90PT/MPhil 36FT 72PT/MRes 12FT 24PT/MA or MSc by Research 18FT 36PT

University of Manchester
EntD Business...EntD 48FT 96PT
MEnt Business.......................................MEnt 12FT 24PT

Newcastle University
Business and Management .... PhD 36FT 72PT/MPhil 12FT 24PT

The Open University
Human resources and organisation studies........... PhD 36FT 72PT variableDL/MPhil 15FT 24PT variableDL
Social Marketing...... PhD 36FT 72PT variableDL/MPhil 15FT 24PT variableDL

Oxford Brookes University
Business Doctoral Programmes .... PhD 24-60FT 36-72PT/MPhil 24-36FT 36-48PT

Queen's University Belfast
Management................................. PhD 36FT 72PT/MPhil 24FT 48PT

University of Roehampton
Business & Management...PhD 24-48FT 36-60PT/MPhil 21-36FT 33-48PT

Sheffield Hallam University
Business and Management Programme.................. PhD 36FT 48PT

Staffordshire University
Business School........................... PhD 36FT 60PT/MPhil 18FT 36PT

University of Sunderland
Business & Management.............PhD 36-48FT 48-72PT 48-72DL/ MPhil 12-36FT 24-48PT 24-48DL

Swansea University
Business Management .... MPhil 12FT 24PT/PhD 36FT 60PT

Teesside University
Business or Management Studies ....PhD min 24FT min 36PT/ MPhil min 18FT min 30PT

UCL - University College London
Management Science and Innovation..................... PhD 36FT 60PT

University of Warwick
Business Studies.......................PhD 36FT 60PT/MPhil 24FT

Consumer science
Taught Courses

Bangor University
Business with Consumer Psychology.............MA 12FT/PGDip 9FT MSc 12FT/PGDip 9FT

Cardiff Metropolitan University
Marketing..MSc 12FT 24PT

University of Chester
Action Research and Appreciative Inquiry (Work Based and Integrative Studies)...MSc 24-72PT/MA 24-72PT/PGDip 24-60PT/ PGCert 12-36PT

University of East Anglia
Brand Leadership..MSc 12FT

Marketing... MSc 12FT
Marketing and Management.. MSc 12FT

GCU London
Luxury Brand Marketing (London) .... MBA 12FT/MBA 12-15FT

Glasgow Caledonian University
Creative and Cultural Business ....MA 12FT

University of Liverpool
Consumer Marketing .... MSc 12FT 24PT

University of Warwick
Finance & Behavioural Science.. MSc 12FT

Consumer science
Research Courses

Manchester Metropolitan University
Research in Consumer Marketing, Consumer Protection and Trading Standards ... PhD VariableFT VariablePT/MPhil VariableFT VariablePT/MSc by research 12FT 24PT

Customer service
Taught Courses

University of Buckingham
Management in a Service Economy .... MSc 12FT 24PT

University of Central Lancashire
Chartered Institute of Marketing Chartered PG Diploma in Marketing (Stage 1)................................. CIM Diploma 12PT
Chartered Institute of Marketing Chartered PG Diploma in Marketing (Stage 2).................................. CIM Diploma 12PT
Chartered Institute of Marketing Professional Certificate in Marketing..................................... CIM AdvCert 12PT
Chartered Institute of Marketing Professional Diploma in Marketing.. CIM Diploma 12PT
Marketing and PR...MA 12FT
Strategic Communication ....MA 24PT

Cranfield University
Strategic Marketing .... MSc 11FT

Edinburgh Napier University
Strategic ICT Leadership .... MSc 24PT

University of Exeter
Management...MRes 12FT

Glasgow Caledonian University
Biotechnology with Business ....MSc 12FT

University of Glasgow
Organisational Leadership (Oman)............MSc 24PT/PGDip 18PT/ PGCert 12PT
Strategic Leadership (PgCert) .... PGCert 9FT 12PT

Goldsmiths, University of London
Curating .... MFA 24FT 36ft&ptPT
Global Leadership.. MSc 12FT

University of Kent
Logistics ....MSc 12FT 24PT

Manchester Metropolitan University
Combined Studies.....................................MSc 12FT 24-36PT
Leadership................................MSc 24PT/PGDip 18PT/PGCert 8PT
MSc Strategic Financial Management .... MSc 12FT
Management and Leadership..Cert 6PT

Queen Margaret University, Edinburgh
International Management and Leadership with Hospitality....... MSc 12FT 24PT/PGDip 9FT 18PT/PGCert 3FT 6PT

Queen Mary, University of London
Marketing.. MSc 12FT

University of Warwick
Service Leadership..Diploma 15PT

Customer service
Research Courses

University of Aberdeen
Molecular and Cell Biology ....PhD 36FT/MPhil 24FT/MSc by research 12FT

University of Exeter
Management..................................... PhD 48FT 84PT/MPhil 36FT 60PT

Goldsmiths, University of London
Curating ....PhD 36-48FT 48-72PT/MPhil 24FT 36PT

London Metropolitan University
Dept of Computing.....PhD Max 60FT Max 96PT/MPhil Max 36FT Max 54PT
Dept of Computing.....PhD Max 60FT Max 96PT/MPhil Max 36FT Max 54PT

The Open University
Marketing...................PhD 36FT 72PT variableDL/MPhil 15FT 24PT variableDL
Social Marketing...... PhD 36FT 72PT variableDL/MPhil 15FT 24PT variableDL

Disaster management
Taught Courses

University of Bradford
Integrated Emergency Management .... MA 32 - 60PT

Bucks New University
Business Continuity, Security and Emergency Management .... MSc 18PT

University of Central Lancashire
Fire Investigation..........................MSc 12FT/PGDip 9FT/PGCert 6FT
Fire Safety Engineering ....MSc 12FT 24PT
Fire Scene Investigation................................MSc 24-36PT
Fire and Rescue Service Management .... MSc 12FT 24PT

Coventry University
Disaster Management ....MSc 12FT 24PT
Emergency Planning and Management...........MSc 12FT 24-30PT

University of Huddersfield
Risk, Disaster and Environmental Management...MSc 12FT 24PT

University of Hull
Disaster and Emergency Management ....PGCert 24PT

King's College London
Disasters, Adaptation & Development...................MA 12FT 24PT/ MSc 12FT 24PT

Kingston University
Hazards and Disaster Management..................MSc 12FT 24PT

University of Leicester
Emergency Planning Management .... MSc 24DL/PGDip 18DL/ PGCert 18DL

Loughborough University
Infrastructure in Emergencies by Distance Learning....................
PGCert 36PT 60DL

Manchester Metropolitan University
Emergency Management..................................PGCert up to 60PT
Emergency Medicine .... MSc 72PT

University of Manchester
International Disaster Management .... MA 12FT 24PT

Newcastle University
Sustainable Buildings and Environments .... MSc 12FT

Northumbria University
Disaster Management and Sustainable Development ....
PGCert 4FT 8DL/PGDip 8FT 12DL/MSc 12FT 36-60DL

Oxford Brookes University
Development and Emergency Practice
..........................MA 12FT 24PT/PGDip 9FT 21PT/PGCert 3-9FT 9PT
Shelter After Disaster .... PGCert 4FT

University of Portsmouth
Crisis and Disaster Management ....MSc 12FT 24PT

Queen Mary, University of London
Trauma Sciences ....MSc 12FT 24PT

Royal Veterinary College
Control of Infectious Diseases in Animals .... MSc 24PT

Sheffield Hallam University
Sustainable Communities and Environments ....MSc 12-18FT 24-36PT

University of South Wales
Disaster Management for Environmental Hazards........ MSc 14FT 24-36PT

UCL - University College London
Earthquake Engineering with Disaster Management ... MSc 12FT 24PT
Geophysical Hazards .... MSc 12FT 24PT
Risk and Disaster Reduction .... MRes 12FT 24PT PGCert 12PT
Risk, Disaster and Resilience ....MSc 12FT 24PT/PGDip 9FT 24PT

University of Warwick
Major Incident Management .... PGA 12PT/CPDMod 1PT
Models of Emergency Care .... PGA 12PT/CPDMod 1PT

University of York
Development Economics and Emerging Markets........... MSc 12FT

Disaster management
Research Courses

Coventry University
Disaster Management .... MSc by research 12FT 24-36PT
Disaster Relief and Development Engineering....MSc by research 12FT 24-36PT
Emergency Planning.......................MSc by research 12FT 24-36PT

Oxford Brookes University
Safety Technology ....
PhD 24-60FT 36-72PT/MPhil 24-36FT 36-48PT

Education management
Taught Courses

University of Aberdeen
Advanced Educational Studies.. MEd 12FT 24PT 48DL/PGDip 9FT 18PT 36DL

Business and management studies

Advanced Professional Studies......MEd 12FT/PGDip 12FT/PGCert 12FT
Community Learning and Development....MSc 36PT/PGDip 24PT
Effective Teaching in Numeracy....PGCert 12PT
Leadership in Professional Contexts....MSc 24PT
Learning and Development (Primary)....PGCert 12PT

Bath Spa University
Education Studies....MA 12FT

Belfast Metropolitan College
CIPD Level 7 Postgraduate Diploma in Personnel and Development....GradDip 9PT

Birkbeck, University of London
Education, Power and Social Change....MSc 12FT 24PT/PGDip 6FT 15PT/PGCert 3FT 6PT
Higher Education ....PGCert 12PT

University of Birmingham
Management of Special Education in Developing Countries MEd 12FT 24PT/PGDip 12FT 24PT
Professional Studies.....MEd 12FT 24PT/PGDip 12FT 24PT/PGCert 3FT 12PT/AdvCert 3FT 12PT
School Improvement and Educational Leadership.... MA 12-24FT 24-48PT/PGDip 24-48PT/PGCert 12-24PT

University of Bolton
Educational Management .... MA 12FT 24-60PT

University of Brighton
Doctorate in Education....MA 48PT/MSc 48PT
Education (International Education)....MA 12FT 36PT/PGDip 24PT/PGCert 12PT
Education (Leadership and Management) MA.... MA 24PT/PGDip 24PT/PGCert 12PT
Professional Education Studies....PGCert 12PT

University of Bristol
Education: Educational Leadership, Policy & Development...MEd 12FT 24-60PT

Brunel University
Education (Educational Management).... MA 12FT 24PT

University of Buckingham
Educational Leadership....MEd 18FT

Bucks New University
Leadership & Management in the Public Sector....MA 24PT

Canterbury Christ Church University
Leadership and Management for Learning....MA 36PT
Literacy and Learning....MA 36PT

University of Chester
Education and Teaching Studies (Work Based and Integrative Studies)....MA 24-72PT/MSc 24-72PT/PGDip 24-60PT/PGCert 12-36PT
Education: Leadership and Management.....MA 24 - 72PT/PGDip 24 - 60PT/PGCert 12 - 36PT
Educational Leadership (Work Based and Integrative Studies)..... MA 24-72PT/MSc 24-72PT/PGDip 24-60PT/PGCert 12-36PT
Leadership Development (Work Based and Integrative Studies)....MA 24-72PT/MSc 24-72PT/PGDip 24-60PT/PGCert 12-36PT
Leadership and Management (Work Based and Integrative Studies)....MA 24-72PT/MSc 24-72PT/PGDip 24-60PT/PGCert 12-36PT
Learning and Development (Work Based and Integrative Studies)....MA 24-72PT/MSc 24-72PT/PGDip 24-60PT/PGCert 12-36PT
Personal Leadership Development (Work Based and Integrative Studies)....MA 24-72PT/PGDip 24-60PT/PGCert 12-36PT
Transpersonal Leadership (Work Based and Integrative Studies)....MA 24-72PT/MSc 24-72PT/PGDip 24-60PT/PGCert 12-36PT

University College Cork
Educational Administration....PGDip 24PT

University of Derby
Education....EdD by taught 36-72PT

University Centre Doncaster
Education In-Service....PGCE 24PT
Education Pre-Service....PGCE 12FT
Education, Innovation & Enterprise .... MA 12FT 24PT

University of Dundee
Advanced Practice (Organisational Leadership) ....MSc 36DL
Education (Chartered Teacher)....MEd 18PT/PGDip 9PT/PGCert 6PT
Educational Psychology .... MSc 24FT

Durham University
Education.... MA 12FT 36PT

University of East Anglia
Adult Literacy, Lifelong Learning & Development ....MA 12FT
Advanced Educational Practice.... MA 36PT/MA 48PT
Education....MA 12FT
Mathematics Education....MA 12FT
Social Science Research Methods: Psychology ....MRes 12FT 24PT
Social Science Research Methods: Social Work ...MRes 12FT 24PT

University of East London
Creative Leadership in Education... MA 24PT/PGCert 16PT/PGDip 8PT

Edge Hill University
Management of International Higher Education ....MA 24PT

Edinburgh Napier University
Managerial Leadership .... MSc 12FT

University of Edinburgh
Developing Educational Leadership and Learning.....PGCert 24PT
Educational Leadership and Management (including the Scottish Qualification for Headship Diploma)... PGDip 27PT/MEd 33PT/PGCert 15PT

University of Exeter
Education Taught Doctorate........ EdD by taught 24FT 48PT 48DL
Educational Research ....MSc 12FT 24PT 12-24DL
Professional Studies....MEd 36PT

National University of Ireland Galway
Education: Master of....MEd 12PT
Professional Education Studies.... PGDip 12PT
Professional Education Studies [School Planning]...... PGDip 12PT

Glasgow Caledonian University
Health and Social Care Education .... MSc 12FT

University of Glasgow
Community Learning & Development....MEd 12FT 24PT/PGDip 9FT 18PT
International Management and Leadership .... MSc 12FT
Learning and Teaching in Higher Education.......MEd 36DL/PGDip 24DL
Middle Leadership & Management in Schools (Inservice Programme).... PGCert 24+PT
Organisational Leadership....MSc 12FT 24PT
Organisational Leadership (Oman)....MSc 24PT/PGDip 18PT/PGCert 12PT
Professional Development in Education .... PGCert 60 maxPT
School Leadership & Management (Scottish Qualification for Headship) (inservice programme).... PGDip 24PT

University of Gloucestershire
Educational Leadership.......... MEd 24PT/PGDip 20PT/PGCert 8PT

Glyndwr University
Education.... PGCE 12FT 24-36PT/CertEd 24-36PT
Professional Education.......... MSc 12FT 24-60PT/DipMedEd 24FT 24-36PT/CertMedEd 6FT 12PT

Goldsmiths, University of London
Education: School-Based Explorations.... MA 24-60PT
Global Leadership.... MSc 12FT

University of Hertfordshire
Leading Learning ....MA 12FT 24PT/MEd 12FT 24PT/PGDip 12FT 24PT/PGCert 12FT 24PT

University of Huddersfield
Action Research for Education .... MA 36PT/PGDip 24PT/PGCert 12PT
Leadership in Education and Public Services.......... MA 12FT 36PT
Learning & Development Managment .... MA 12FT 36PT
Professional Work-Based Learning Suite....MA 36PT

University of Hull
Education....MEd 12FT 24-72PT/AdvDip 12FT 24-72PT/AdvCert 6FT 12-36PT
Leadership and Learning ....MEd 12FT 24PT

Institute of Education
Development Education .... MA 12FT 24PT
Educational Leadership (International)....MBA 24-48PT
Educational Planning, Economics and International Development.... MA 12FT 24-48PT
European Masters: Lifelong Learning Policy and Management.... MA 12FT
Harris Academy Leadership ....MA 24PT
Higher Education Management....MBA 24PT
Intensive Course in Education Management Information Systems (EMIS).... Intensive Course 3FT
Leadership .... MA 12FT 24-48PT
Lifelong Learning: Policy and Management.... European Master's 24FT
National Professional Qualification for Headship (NPQH).... Headship Qualification 4-18DL
School Effectiveness and School Improvement.... MA 12FT 24-48PT

Keele University
Education MBA........ MBA 28PT 28DL/DBA by taught 20PT 20DL/PGCert 15PT
Educational Leadership, Management and Learning .... MA 24PT/PGDip 18PT/Cert 10PT
Leadership and Management....PGCert 12PT

University of Kent
Higher Education....PGDip 12FT 24PT/MA 12FT 24PT
Higher Education (PGCHE).... PGCHE 24FT

King's College London
Education Management.... MA 12FT 24-48PT
Further Education Management....MBA 12FT 24-48PT

Lancaster University
Human Resources and Consulting....MA 12FT
Management Learning and Leadership.... MA 12FT 24PT

Leeds Metropolitan University
Leadership & Management....MSc 36PT/PGDip 36PT
Multi Unit Leadership ....MSc 12FT 24PT
Professional Development....PGCert 12PT

University of Leeds
International Educational Management..... MA 12FT/PGDip 12FT

University of Leicester
Educational Leadership....MSc 24-48DL

Liverpool John Moores University
Advanced Educational Practice (Leadership and Management)... PGCert 12PT

Loughborough University
Management and Leadership (Higher Education Administration)....MSc 30PT/PGDip 18PT

Manchester Metropolitan University
Doctor of Education....EdD by taught 48-72PT
Education Business Management ....MSc 24-72PT
Education Studies.... MA 12FT 24PT
Educational Leadership and Management....MSc 36-60PT
Management and Leadership....Cert 6PT
Teaching and Learning.... MA 12-18PT

University of Manchester
Educational Leadership and Improvement....MA 24PT
Educational Leadership and School Improvement ....MA 12FT
Educational Leadership and School Improvement (Inclusive Education) MA....MA 12FT

National University of Ireland, Maynooth
Educational Management ....HDip 12FT

Middlesex University
Education... MA 36PT 36DL/PGCert 12PT 12DL/PGDip 24PT 24DL
Education: Leadership, Management and Change.... MA 18FT 24PT

Northumbria University
Education with Leadership ....MEd 12FT

Nottingham Trent University
Doctorate in Business Administration ....DBA by taught 36PT

University of Nottingham
Educational Leadership and Management....MA 12FT 24PT/PGDip 9FT 18PT/PGCert 6FT 12PT
International Higher Education.... MA 12FT 24PT

University of Oxford
Education (Child Development and Education).... MSc 12FT

University of Reading
Education (Leadership and Management)........MA 12FT 24-84PT/PGDip 12FT

University of Roehampton
Education.... MA 12FT 24PT
Education Leadership and Management .... MA 12FT 24+PT PGCert 6FT 12+PT PGDip 9FT 18+PT

Sheffield Hallam University
Advanced Professional Development ....MSc VAFT/PGDip VAFT/PGCert VAFT
Leadership and Management in Education....MSc 12FT 36PT/PGDip 12FT 24PT/PGCert 12FT 12PT

University of Sheffield
Applied Professional Studies in Education....MA 24-36DL
Education....MA 12FT

University of South Wales
Leadership and Management (Education) .... MA 12FT 36PT
Leadership and Management (FE/PCET).... MA 36- 60PT
Leadership and Management (Health Promotion & Education) .... MA 36-60PT

University of Southampton
Education Management and Leadership ....MSc 12FT 24PT

St Mary's University College, Twickenham
Catholic School Leadership: Principles and Practice........MA 12FT 36PT/PGDip 24PT/PGCert 12PT

University of Stirling
Educational Leadership and Educational Leadership (SQH)... MSc 36PT/PGDip 15PT/PGCert 6PT
Professional Learning and Leadership .... MSc 36PT

University of Strathclyde
Education..............EdD by taught 36-72PT/MEd 24-36PT 24-36DL
Management and Leadership in EducationMSc max 60PT/PGDip max 48PT/PGCert max 24PT
School Leadership and Management (SQH)....PGDip 12FT

Trinity College Dublin - the University of Dublin
Master in Education .... MSc 12FT 24/36PT

University of Warwick
Educational Studies .... MA 12FT 24-48PT

University of West London
Management Studies (Health and Social Care) - Top up.... MA 12PT

Section sponsored by
BPP UNIVERSITY COLLEGE
Business and social sciences
www.prospects.ac.uk/findcourses POSTGRADUATE DIRECTORY 387

Business and management studies

Education management
Research Courses

Bath Spa University
Education Policy in Practice .... PhD 24 - 60FT 36 - 72PT

University of Bath
Higher Education Management .... DBA 36-96PT

Birkbeck, University of London
Education/Lifelong Learning ..... MPhil 24FT 36PT/PhD 24FT 36PT

University of Birmingham
Leaders and Leadership in Education .... EdD 36FT 72PT

University of Dundee
Education ....MPhil 24FT MSc by research 12FT PhD 36FT

Durham University
Education.................................EdD 36FT 72PT 72DL PhD 36FT 72PT

University of East Anglia
Applied Research in Education.................................PhD 36FT 72PT/MPhil 24FT 48PT/MA by research 12FT 24PT
Counselling Studies........PhD 36FT 72PT/MPhil 24FT 48PT/MA by research 12FT 24PT
Higher Education and Society..................................PhD 36FT 72PT/MPhil 24FT 48PT/MA by research 12FT 24PT
Literacy and Development Group.......PhD 36FT 72PT/MPhil 24FT 48PT/MA by research 12FT 24PT
Mathematics Education...PhD 36FT 72PT/MPhil 24FT 48PT/MA by research 12FT 24PT
Pedagogy and Engagement with Learning............PhD 36FT 72PT/MPhil 24FT 48PT/MA by research 12FT 24PT
Physical Education Pedagogy Group.......................PhD 36FT 72PT/MPhil 24FT 48PT/MA by research 12FT 24PT
Spirituality and Religion in Education....................PhD 36FT 72PT/MPhil 24FT 48PT/MA by research 12FT 24PT

Keele University
Education Professional Doctorate.... EdD 48-84PT 48-84DL/MRes 24-36PT 24-36DL

University of Kent
Higher Education.. PhD 36FT 60PT

London Metropolitan University
Education...EdD 60PT

University of Nottingham
Educational Leadership...EdD 48PT

The Open University
Doctorate in Education ....EdD 36PT
Educational studies............. PhD 36FT 72PT/EdD 36PT/MRes 12FT
Language Policy .... PhD 36FT 72PT variableDL/EdD 36PT/MRes 12FT

University of Southampton
Doctorate in Education EdD....................................... EdD 36FT 48PT

University of Warwick
Education..........MA by research 12FT 24PT/MSc by research 12FT 24PT/MPhil 24FT 36PT/PhD 36FT 60PT

Entrepreneurship
Taught Courses

University of Aberdeen
Management, Enterprise & Innovation.......MSc 12FT/PGDip 9FT/PGCert 6FT

Anglia Ruskin University
Marketing and Innovation ....MA 18FT 24PT/PGCert 18FT 24PT/PGDip 18FT 24PT

University of the Arts London - Central Saint Martins College of Art and Design
Innovation Management ....MA 24FT

University of the Arts London - London College of Fashion
Fashion Entrepreneurship .... MA 15FT 30PT

Aston University
Industrial Enterprise Management .... MSc 12FT
MSc Entrepreneurship & International Business........... MSc 12FT

University of Bath
Innovation and Technology Management..MSc 12FT/PGDip 6FT/PGCert 3FT

Birmingham City University
Media and Creative Enterprise.................................... MA 12FT 24PT

University of Birmingham
Digital Entrepreneurship..MSc 12FT 24PT
Pharmaceutical Enterprise..MSc 12FT 24PT

University of Bradford
Applied Management and Enterprise................................ MSc 12FT
Employability and Entrepreneurship ....PGCert 12PT
MSc Applied Managment and Enterprise .... MSc 12FT
Professional Studies.............MSc 24DL/PGDip 24DL/PGCert 24DL

University of Brighton
Management (Innovation)... MSc 12FT

British Institute of Technology & E-commerce
Innovative Management .... PGCert 3FT/DipHE 6FT 12PT/MBA 12FT 24PT

Brunel University
Accounting and Business Management............................ MSc 12FT
Business Intelligence and Social Media............................ MSc 12FT
Design Strategy and Innovation ....MA 12FT
Human Resource Management.. MSc 12FT
Human Resource Management and Employment Relations......... MSc 12FT
Management.. MSc 12FT

University of Cambridge
Bioscience Enterprise .... MPhil 10FT

Cardiff University
Business Strategy & Entrepreneurship............................. MSc 12FT

Coventry University
Digital Games and Business Innovation..... MSc 12FT 36PT 12DL/PGDip 6FT 18PT 6DL/PGCert 3FT 9PT 3DL

Cranfield University
Design, Strategy and Leadership...MDes 12FT 36PT/PGDip 36PT/PGCert 36PT
Innovation and Creativity in Industry .... MDes 12FT 24-60PT/PGCert 12FT 24-26PT/PGDip 12FT 24-36PT/MTech 24FT
Knowledge Management for Innovation........ MSc 12FT 24-60PT/PGDip 6FT 24PT/PGCert 5FT 24PT/MTech 24FT

De Montfort University
Design Entrepreneurship.............. MA 12FT 24PT/PGDip 9FT 18PT
International Business and Entrepreneurship .... MSc 12FT

University Centre Doncaster
Education, Innovation & Enterprise .... MA 12FT 24PT

Dublin Institute of Technology
Business and Entrepreneurship.. MSc 12FT

Durham University
Executive MA Entrepreneurship .... MA 30DL
Management (Entrepreneurship) .... MSc 12FT

University of East Anglia
Creative Entrepreneurship..MA 12FT
Entrepreneurship and Strategy .... MSc 12FT
MBA .... MBA 12FT

Edinburgh Napier University
Business Management with Entrepreneurship.............. MSc 12FT

University of Edinburgh
Competition Law and Innovation............................. LLM 12FT 24PT

University of Essex
Entrepreneurship and Innovation............................MSc 12FT 24PT
Entrepreneurship and Innovation with English for Academic Purposes...Diploma 9FT
International Business and Entrepreneurship.......MSc 12FT 24PT
International Marketing and Entrepreneurship....MSc 12FT 24PT
Social Entrepreneurship...MSc 12FT 24PT

European Business School London
Entrepreneurial Management ....MA 12 - 16FT

University of Exeter
Biotechnology and Enterprise... MSc 12FT

National University of Ireland Galway
Technology Commercialisation ....PGDip 12DL
Technology Management ....MSc 24PT 24DL

Glasgow Caledonian University
Biotechnology with Business .... MSc 12FT
Entrepreneurship... MSc 12FT
Management of IT Innovation .... MSc 12FT
Social Enterprise .... PGCert 6PT

University of Glasgow
International Business & Entrepreneurship..................... MSc 12FT
International Management & Design Innovation.......... MSc 12FT
Management with Enterprise & Business Growth ....MSc 12FT/PGDip 9FT/PGCert 6FT

Goldsmiths, University of London
Creative & Cultural Entrepreneurship .... MA 12FT 24PT
Digital Entrepreneurship... MSc 12FT
Innovation in Practice...MA 12FT
Management of Innovation .... MSc 12FT
Social Entrepreneurship................. MA 12FT 24PT/PGDip 6FT 12PT

University of Hertfordshire
Organisational Change............DMan 36PT/MA by Research 24PT

Imperial College London
Innovation, Entrepreneurship & Management.............. MSc 12FT

University of Kent
Computing and Entrepreneurship...........................MSc 12FT 36PT

Lancaster University
Contemporary Arts (With pathways) ....MA 12FT 24PT/PGCert 6FT 12PT
Entrepreneurship, Innovation and Practice .... MSc 12FT

Leeds Metropolitan University
Doctorate of Business Administration.............................. DBA 48PT
Sport Business.. MA 12FT 24PT

University of Leeds
Culture, Creativity and Entrepreneurship... MA 12FT 24PT/PGDip 9FT 21PT/PGCert 6FT 12PT
Culture, Creativity, and Entrepreneurship .... MA 12FT 24PT/PGDip 12FT 24PT/PGCert 9FT 18PT

University of Limerick
International Entrepreneurship Management................MBS 12FT

University of Liverpool
Architecture and Entrepreneurship - London Based ...... MSc 12FT 24PT
Entrepreneurship..MSc 12FT 24PT

University of the Arts London - London College of Communication
Service Design Innovation.. MDes 12FT

University of Manchester
Biotechnology and Enterprise... MSc 12FT

Middlesex University
Business Enterprise and Entrepreneurship................. MA 12-15FT 24-27PT

Newcastle University
Arts, Business and Creativity...................................... MA 12FT 24PT
E-Business .... MSc 12FT
E-Business (E-Marketing) .... MSc 12FT
Innovation, Creativity and Entrepreneurship.................. MSc 12FT

Northumbria University
Business with Entrepreneurship .... MSc 12FT
Fashion Management and Entrepreneurship....................MA 12FT

Nottingham Trent University
International Fashion Business...MA 12FT

University of Nottingham
Applied Biopharmaceutical Biotechnology and Entrepreneurship ....MSc 12FT 24PT
Computer Science and Entrepreneurship.........MSc 12FT 24-48PT
Cultural Industries and Entrepreneurship........MSc 12FT 24-36PT
Cultural Studies and Entrepreneurship........................ MSc 12FT
Electrical and Electronic Engineering and Entrepreneurship........ MSc 12FT 24PT
Entrepreneurship.. MSc 12FT

Oxford Brookes University
Business Management (January Entry)............................ MSc 12FT
Business Management (January or Sept Entry)..... MSc 12FT 24PT

Plymouth University
Design Thinking ....MRes 12FT 24PT

University of Portsmouth
Innovation Management and Entrepreneurship.. MSc 12FT 24PT

Queen Mary, University of London
Management and Organisational Innovation...................MA 12FT

Ravensbourne
Enabling Creative Innovation.........MA 12FT 24PT/MSc 12FT 24PT
M Innovation/MFA Master of Innovation ....MFA 12FT 24PT

University of Reading
Business Technology Consulting .... MSc 12FT
Entrepreneurship and Management .... MSc 12FT
Environmental Management ....MSc 12FT 24PT

Richmond, The American International University in London
Entrepreneurship...MSc 12FT 24PT

Royal Agricultural University
Business Management ....MSc 12FT 24PT

Royal Holloway, University of London
Entrepreneurship.. MSc 12FT

University of Salford
Project Management......MSc 12FT 36PT/PGDip 8FT 24PT/PGCert 4FT 9PT

Schumacher College
Economics for Transition ....MA 12FT

Sheffield Hallam University
Technology Enhanced Learning, Innovation and Change....... MSc 36PT/PGDip 24PT/PGCert 12PT

University of Sheffield
Entrepreneurship.. MSc 12FT

Southampton Solent University
Management Programme... MA 12FT 12DL

University of Southampton
Global Enterprise and Entrepreneurship...... MSc 12FT/PGDip 9FT

University of St Andrews
Mediaeval Studies ....MLitt 12FT/PGDip 9FT

Staffordshire University
Computing Soluttions for Business .... MSc 12-18FT
Creative Futures..MA 12FT

University of Strathclyde
Environmental Entrepreneurship......... MSc 12FT 24PT/PGDip 9FT 18PT/PGCert 6FT 12PT

University of Sunderland
Applied Management .... MSc 24PT

University of Surrey
Entrepreneurship.. MSc 12FT

Business and management studies

University of Sussex
Management and Entrepreneurship........................MSc 12FT 24PT

Swansea University
Management (Entrepreneurship)..MSc 12FT

Teesside University
Innovation and Transformational Change...................PGCert 12PT

University of Wales Trinity Saint David
Entrepreneurship........................MBA 12FT 24PT/PGDip 12FT 24PT/PGCert 12FT 24PT
Social Entrepreneurship.........MBA 12FT 24PT/PGCert 12FT 24PT/PGDip 12FT 24PT

University of the Highlands and Islands
Enterprise and eMarketing..PGCert 12-24PT

University of Ulster
Business Development and Innovation......MSc 12FT 24PT/PGDip 9FT 18PT/PGCert 4FT 9PT

UCL - University College London
Engineering with Innovation and Entrepreneurship....MSc 12FT/PGDip 9FT
Management Science and Innovation.............................MRes 12FT
Technology Entrepreneurship...............MSc 12FT 24PT/PGDip 9FT

University of the West of Scotland
Entrepreneurship and Economic Development PGCert 24FT/MSc 12FT

York St John University
Leading Innovation & Change....................................MA 12FT 24PT

Entrepreneurship
Research Courses

University of Bolton
Innovation...MPhil 18FT

University of Brighton
Technology and Innovation Management PhD 24-60FT 36-72PT/MPhil 18-36FT 30-48PT

University of Edinburgh
Science, Technology and Innovation Studies.......MSc by research 12FT 24PT/PhD 36FT 72PT

University of Essex
Entrepreneurship............PhD 36FT 72PT/MPhil 24FT 48PT/MSc by research 12FT 24PT

Goldsmiths, University of London
Creative and Cultural Entrepreneurship......MPhil 24FT 36PT/PhD 36-48FT 48-72PT

University of Manchester
Business...EntD 48FT 96PT MEnt 12FT 24PT

Newcastle University
Biotechnology and Business Enterprise..........................MRes 12FT

University of Nottingham
Computer Science and Entrepreneurship.........MSc 12FT 24-48PT

The Open University
Managing Knowledge and Innovation....................PhD 36FT 72PT variableDL/MPhil 15FT 24PT variableDL

Plymouth College of Art
Entrepreneurship for Creative Practice.........MA by research 24PT

University of Southampton
School of Management: Health............................MPhil 24FT 48PT/PhD 26FT 72PT
School of Management: Management Sciences.........MPhil 24FT 48PT/PhD 36FT 72PT
School of Management: Organisation and Management... MPhil 24FT 48PT/PhD 36FT 72PT

University of Strathclyde
Hunter Centre for Entrepreneurship - Research............PhD 33FT/MPhil 12FT/MRes 12FT

University of Sussex
Technology and Innovation Management PhD 24-48FT 36-72PT/MPhil 12-36FT 24-48PT

Teesside University
Business or Management Studies..........PhD min 24FT min 36PT/MPhil min 18FT min 30PT

UCL - University College London
Management Science and Innovation.....................PhD 36FT 60PT

Environmental policy
Taught Courses

University of Aberdeen
Climate Change Law and Sustainable Development......LLM 12FT 24--36PT

University of Abertay Dundee
Energy & Environmental Management............................MSc 12FT

Aberystwyth University
Remote Sensing & Geographical Information Systems (GIS)........MSc 12FT 24PT/PGDip 9FT 18PT/PGCert 5FT 10PT
Remote Sensing and GeographyMSc 12FT 24PT/PGDip 9FT 18PT/PGCert 5FT 10PT

School of Advanced Study, University of London
Advanced Legislative Studies..........................LLM 12FT 24PT 24DL

Bangor University
Conservation and Land Management..........MSc 12FT/PGDip 9FT
Environmental Forestry...MSc 12FT
Environmental Management..MBA 12FT
Forestry and Environmental Management degrees (TRANSFOR-M)..MSc 24FT
Marine Biology...................................MSc 12FT 24-36PT/PGDip 9FT
Marine Environmental Protection......................MSc 12FT 24-36PT
Physical Oceanography.....................MSc 12FT 24-36PT/PGDip 9FT
Rheolaeth Amgylcheddol Gynaliadwy (Sustainable Environmental Management)........MSc 12FT 24PT/MA 12FT 24PT

University of Bath
Environment, Energy & Resilience ....MRes 12FT 24-36PT

University of Bedfordshire
Environmental Management..............................MSc 12-18FT 36PT

Birmingham City University
Environmental Sustainability......PGCert 4FT 8PT/PGDip 4FT 8PT/MSc 4FT 8PT
Environmental Sustainability (Design and Construction).............PGCert 4FT 8PT/PGDip 4FT 8PT/MSc 4FT 8PT

University of Birmingham
Development Management (Human Resources and Development Management)...MSc 12FT 24PT/GradDip 9FT 24PT
Environmental and Natural Resource Economics............................MSc 12FT 24PT

University of Brighton
Environmental Assessment and Management....MSc 12FT 24PT/PGCert 12FT 24PT/PGDip 12FT 24PT

University of Bristol
Climate Change Science and Policy..........................MSc 12FT 24PT
Environmental Policy and Management................MSc 12FT 24PT/PGCert 12FT 24PT/PGDip 12FT 24PT

Brunel University
Climate Change Impacts and Sustainability..........MSc 12FT 24PT
Environmental Science: Legislation and Management...................MSc 12FT 24PT

University of Cambridge
Environmental Policy..MPhil 10FT
Land Economy Research ....MPhil 10FT

Cardiff University
Sustainability, Planning and Environmental Policy.........................MSc 12FT 24PT

University of Central Lancashire
Energy and Environmental Management.............MSc 12FT 24PT/PGDip 9FT 18PT/PGCert 6FT 12PT

University of Chester
Regeneration for Practitioners.....MA 12FT 24 - 72PT/PGDip 12FT 24 - 60PT/PGCert 12FT 12 - 36PT
Sustainability for Community and Business.........MSc 12FT 24PT/PGDip 12FT 24PT/PGCert 12FT 12-24PT

Cranfield University
Economics for Natural Resource & Environmental Management MSc 12FT 24-60PT/PGCert 5FT 24PT/PGDip 6FT 24PT
Environment and Public Policy..........MSc 12FT 60PT/PGCert 12FT 60PT/PGDip 12FT 60PT
Environmental Informatics......MSc 12FT 60PT/PGDip 12FT 60PT/PGCert 12FT 60PT
Environmental Risk Management...................MSc 12FT 24-60PT/PGDip 6FT 24PT/PGCert 5FT 24PT

University of Cumbria
Leadership and Management in Policing.......................MBA 36PT/PGDip 36PT/PGCert 36PT

University of Dundee
Climate Change Economics and Policy ....MSc 12FT
Climate Change and Energy Law and Policy.....................LLM 12FT
Energy Studies with Specialisation in Energy Policy .....MSc 12FT
Environmental Law..LLM 12FT
Environmental Law and Policy ....LLM 12FT
Mineral Law and Policy ....LLM 12FT LLM 60DL
Natural Resources Law and Policy (LLM by distance learning)..LLM 60DL
Non-Graduating Taught Postgrad Grad School of Natural Resources Law, Policy & Management....... PG module variableFT
Petroleum Law and Policy (LLM Full/Part Time)............LLM 12FT/PGDip 9FT
Petroleum Law and Policy (LLM by distance learning).............LLM 24-60DL
Spatial Planning with Environmental Assessment........MSc 12FT
Spatial Planning with Marine Spatial Planning..............MSc 12FT
Supplementary Studies in Graduate School of Natural Resources, Law, Policy and Management..........Masters Level Modules 6-9FT

University of East Anglia
Climate Change..MSc 12FT
Climate Change and International Development............................MSc 12FT 24PT
Energy Engineering with Environmental ManagementMSc 12FT/MSc 24PT/MSc 36PT/MSc 48PT
Environment and International Development......MSc 12FT 24PT
Environmental Sciences...MSc 12FT 24PT
Environmental Sciences and Humanities.......MA 12FT 24PT/MSc 12FT 24PT
Impact Evaluation for International DevelopmentMSc 12FT 24PT
Public Policy and Public Management...................MRes 12FT 24PT

University of Edinburgh
Carbon Capture & Storage..MSc 12FT 36PT
Carbon Finance...MSc 12FT
Carbon Management..MSc 12FT
Environmental Protection and Management.......MSc 12FT 24PT/PGDip 9FT
Environmental Sustainability..........MSc 12FT 24-36PT/PGDip 9FT
Global Environment Challenges Certificate (Online distance learning)...PGCert 9DL
Global Environment and Climate Change Law...... LLM 12FT 24PT
Integrated Resource Management.....................................MSc 12FT

University of Exeter
Climate Change Impacts and Feedbacks...............MRes 12FT 24PT
Climate Change and Risk Management..................MSc 12FT 24PT
Conservation Science and Policy..MSc 11FT
Critical Human Geographies..MRes 12FT
Energy Policy...MSc 12FT 24PT
Environment, Energy and Resilience......................MRes 12FT 24PT
Sustainable Development..MSc 12FT 24PT

National University of Ireland Galway
Economic and Environmental Modelling...MEconSci 10approxFT

University of Glasgow
Applied Carbon Management (Dumfries Campus)........MSc 12FT 24PT
Environmental Science, Technology & Society (Dumfries Campus)..MSc 12FT 24PT
Environmental Statistics ....MSc 12FT

Goldsmiths, University of London
Design & Environment ....MA 12FT 24PT

Heriot-Watt University
Climate Change: Impacts and Mitigation..............MSc 12FT 24PT/PGDip 9FT 21PT
Climate Change: Managing The Marine Environment...................MSc 12FT 24PT/PGDip 9FT 21PT
Environmental Analysis and Assessment ....MRes 12FT 24PT/PGDip 9FT 18PT/PGCert 9FT 18PT
Marine Resource Development and Protection....MSc 12FT 24PT/PGDip 9FT 21PT

Institute of Education
Educational Planning, Economics and International Development..MA 12FT 24-48PT

Keele University
Climate Change Studies - Policy, Justice and Global Politics....MA 12FT 24PT

University of Kent
Agri-Environmental Economics and Policy............MSc 12FT 24PT
Anthropology and Conservation...............................MA 12FT 24PT
Conservation and Business..MSc 12FT 24PT
Environmental Law and Policy.................................LLM 12FT 24PT/PGDip 12FT 24PT

Kingston University
Sustainability & Environmental Change................MSc 12FT 24PT

University of Leeds
Sustainability (Climate Change)...MSc 12FT
Sustainability (Environment and Development).............MSc 12FT 12-48PT
Sustainability (Environmental Politics and Policy)..........MSc 12FT 12-48PT

London School of Economics and Political Science (LSE)
Environmental Economics and Climate Change...MSc 12FT 24PT
Environmental Policy and Regulation......................MSc 12FT 24PT

London South Bank University
Management in Civil Society - Blended...........................MSc 24PT

Loughborough University
Sustainable Engineering...MSc 12FT 96PT

Middlesex University
Global Governance and Public Policy........................MA 12FT 24PT
Sustainable Environmental Management......MA 12FT 24PT/MSc 12FT 24PT

Newcastle University
Environmental Law and Policy (Research)..............LLM 12FT 24PT
Environmental Regulation and Sustainable Development.....LLM 12FT 24PT
Sustainable Buildings and Environments.........................MSc 12FT

Nottingham Trent University
Human Security and Environmental Change.........MA 12FT 24PT/PGDip 9FT 18PT/PGCert 9FT

University of Nottingham
Economic Development and Policy Analysis....................MSc 12FT

The Open University
Science and Society....................MSc variableDL/PGDip variableDL

The next step for top-performing graduates

Masters in Management

Designed for high-achieving graduates across all disciplines, London Business School's Masters in Management provides specific and tangible foundations for a successful career in business.

This 12-month, full-time programme is a business qualification with impact. In 2012, our MiM employment rate was 95% within 3 months of graduation*.

As well as a renowned qualification from a world-class business school, you also gain access to the School's network of more than 35,000 global alumni – a community that offers support and opportunities throughout your career.

Find out more from our current students and admissions staff at one of our on-campus information events **www.london.edu/events**

For more information **www.london.edu/mim/**
Email **mim@london.edu** | Call **+44 (0)20 7000 7573**

London Business School
Regent's Park
London NW1 4SA
United Kingdom

www.london.edu

*Figures taken from London Business School's Masters in Management 2012 employment report

Business and management studies

Oxford Brookes University
Environmental Assessment and Management ....MSc 12FT 24PT/PGDip 9FT 21PT

University of Oxford
Environmental Change & Management .... MSc 12FT
Nature, Society and Environmental Policy .... MSc 12FT
Water Science, Policy and Management .... MSc 12FT

Queen Mary, University of London
Environmental Science: Integrated Management of Freshwater Environments .... MSc 12FT 24-36PT

Queen's University Belfast
Environmental Planning .... MSc 12FT
Sustainable Design .... MSc 12FT/PGDip 9FT

Ravensbourne
Environment Design .... MA 12FT 24PT

University of Reading
Applied Development Studies .... MSc 12FT 24PT
Climate Change & Development .... MSc 12FT 24PT
Economics of Climate Change .... MSc 12FT 24PT
Environment and Development .... MSc 12FT
The Economics of Climate Change .... MSc 12FT

Robert Gordon University
Energy Management.... MSc 12FT 36DL/PGDip 8FT 24DL/PGCert 4FT 12DL
Energy and Sustainability ...MSc 42DL/PGDip 24DL/PGCert 12DL

Royal Holloway, University of London
Global Health: Pathogens and Policy .... MSc 12FT 24PT/PGDip 9FT

University of Salford
Environmental Assessment and Management....MSc 12FT 36PT/PGDip 8FT 24PT
Environmental and Public Health .... MSc 12FT 24-36PT/PGDip 8FT 24PT

School of Oriental and African Studies - SOAS
Environmental Law and Sustainable Development .... MA 12FT 24PT
Environmental Management .... MSc 12FT 24-36PT
Global Energy and Climate Policy .... MSc 12FT 24PT
Globalisation and Multinational Corporations .... MA 12FT 24PT

Schumacher College
Holistic Science .... MSc 12FT

Sheffield Hallam University
Environmental Management .... MSc 12-24FT 24-36PT
Environmental Management (International Resource and Climate Management) .... MSc 12-18FT 24-36PT
Environmental Management (Wildlife and Landscape Conservation) .... MSc 12-18FT 24-36PT
Sustainable Communities and Environments .... MSc 12-18FT 24-36PT

University of South Wales
Environmental Conservation Management .... MSc 12FT 36PT

University of Southampton
Environmental Monitoring and Assessment .... MSc 12FT 27PT
Environmental Pollution Control .... MSc 12FT 27PT

University of St Andrews
Sustainable Aquaculture. MSc 12FT 24PT/PGDip 9FT 24PT 24DL/Cert 12DL

Staffordshire University
Habitat Management and Conservation ...MSc 15FT/PGDip 12FT

University of Stirling
Environmental Policy and Governance .... LLM 12FT/MSc 12FT

University of Strathclyde
Applied Economics ... MSc 12FT 24PT 24DL/PGDip 9FT 18PT 18DL
Sustainability and Environmental Studies .... MSc 12FT 24PT/PGDip 9FT 18PT

University of Surrey
Environmental Strategy .... MSc 12FT 12-60PT

University of Sussex
Environment, Development and Policy .... MA 12FT 24PT

Swansea University
Environmental Dynamics and Climate Change..... MSc 12FT 36PT
Geographic Information and Climate Change......MSc 12FT 36PT/PGCert 12FT 12PT

Teesside University
Energy and Environmental Management.........MSc 12-16FT 24PT

Trinity College Dublin - the University of Dublin
Environment and Development .... MSc 12FT
Environmental Sciences .... MSc 12FT

UCL - University College London
Anthropology, Environment and Development .... MSc 12FT 24PT
Biodiversity, Evolution and Conservation MRes .... MRes 12FT
Climate Change .... MSc 12FT 24PT
Energy Demand Studies .... MRes 12FT
Energy and Resources: Policy and Practice, Australia .... MSc 24FT 36-48PT
Global Health and Development: tropEd programme .... MSc 12FT 24-60PT

University of the West of England, Bristol
Environmental Consultancy .... MSc 36-60DL

Environmental policy
Research Courses

Aberystwyth University
Earth Sciences .... MPhil 12FT 24PT PhD 36FT 60PT
Human Geography .... PhD 36FT 60PT

Bangor University
Biodiversity Conservation .... MPhil 24FT 36PT/PhD 36FT 60PT
Ocean Sciences .... MPhil 24FT/PhD 36FT

University of Bedfordshire
Environmental Studies .... PhD 36FT 72PT

Brunel University
Environmental Issues and Environmental Change.....MPhil 12FT/PhD 36FT

University of Cambridge
Land Economy (by thesis) .... MPhil 11FT

Cardiff University
Environment .... PhD 36FT 60PT/MPhil 36FT 60PT
Institute of Environment and Sustainability........ PhD 36FT/MPhil 60PT

Coventry University
Environmental & Climate Change......MSc by research 12FT 24PT

University of Dundee
Town and Regional Planning .... MPhil 24FT

University of East Anglia
Copy of Environmental Sciences: Geosciences and Natural Hazards .... PhD 36FT 72PT/MPhil 24FT 48PT
Environmental Sciences: Climate, Ocean and Atmospheric Sciences .... PhD 36FT 72PT/MPhil 24FT 48PT
Environmental Sciences: Resources, Sustainability and Governance .... PhD 36FT 72PT/MPhil 24FT 48PT

University of Exeter
Environment, Energy and Resilience .... MPhil 36FT 60PT/PhD 36FT 84PT
Human Geography.........PhD 48FT 84PT/MPhil 36FT 60PT/MSc by research 12FT 24PT

University of Gloucestershire
Sustainability .... PhD 36FT

University of Kent
Biodiversity Management .... PhD 36FT 60PT/MSc by research 12FT 24PT

London School of Economics and Political Science (LSE)
Environmental Policy and Development.........MPhil 36-48FT/PhD 36-48FT

Manchester Metropolitan University
Environmental and Geographical Sciences .... MSc by research/MPhil/PhD

Newcastle University
Energy .... PhD 36FT 72PT/MPhil 12FT 24PT
Environmental Science .... MPhil 12FT 24PT/PhD 36FT 72PT
Environmental Science .... Integrated PhD 48FT

University of Nottingham
Environmental and Geomorphological Sciences .PhD 36FT 72PT/MPhil 24FT 48PT

The Open University
Environment, governance and justicePhD 36FT 72PT variableDL/MPhil 15FT 24PT variableDL
Geography .... PhD 36FT 72PT variableDL/MPhil 15FT 24PT variableDL
Political ideas, policies and actions.... PhD 36FT 72PT variableDL/MPhil 15FT 24PT variableDL

Oxford Brookes University
Impact Assessment MPhil/PhD ...... MPhil/PhD 36-60FT 48-72PT/PhD 24-60FT 36-72PT/MPhil 24-36FT 36-48PT

Queen's University Belfast
Environmental Change .... PhD 36FT 72PT/MPhil 24FT 48PT

Sheffield Hallam University
Centre for Regional Economic and Social Research Applied Social Research .... PhD 36FT 60PT
Environment and Development .... MPhil 36PT
Environment and Development - Facilities Management.......PhD 33FT 45PT/MPhil 18FT 30PT

Swansea University
Environmental Sustainability..............MSc by research 12FT 24PT
Sustainable Resources .... MSc by research 12FT

European business
Taught Courses

Aston University
European Master in Management .... MSc 24FT
IT Project Management .... MSc 12FT
European Union and International Relations .... MA 12FT 24 - 36PT
Strategy & International Business .... MSc 12FT

University of Bradford
European and International Business Management..... MSc 12FT

University of Central Lancashire
Business Management .... MSc 12FT
Global Communication Studies .... MA 12FT 24-36PT

University of Cumbria
International Business .... MBA 12FT
International Business Management .... MA 12FT

University of Derby
Business and Payroll Management .... MSc 36PT
International Business .... MSc 12FT 36PT

ESCP Europe Business School
European Business .... MEB Master in European Business 12FT
Management .... Master in Management 24+FT

Edinburgh Napier University
Strategic Risk Management and Finance .... MSc 12FT 24PT

University of Exeter
European Media Studies with Integrated Study Abroad Option .... MA 12FT 24PT
Finance .... GradDip 9FT
Management .... MRes 12FT

Heriot-Watt University
European Master in Strategic Project Management...... MSc 16FT
Finance and Management...........MSc 12FT 24PT/PGDip 9FT 21PT

Leeds Metropolitan University
Business (IPOS) .... MA 12FT 60PT
Strategic Project Management .... MSc 12FT 24PT

Manchester Metropolitan University
Combined Studies .... MSc 12FT 24-36PT
Strategic Financial Management .... MSc 12FT
Business Administration .... MBA 24-30PT 30BM

Oxford Brookes University
European Business, Culture and Languages .MA 12FT/PGDip 9FT

Royal Holloway, University of London
European Business .... MA 12FT

University of Salford
Project Management......MSc 12FT 36PT/PGDip 8FT 24PT/PGCert 4FT 9PT

University of Sheffield
Europubhealth: European Masters Programme in Public Health. MPH 24FT

University of Stirling
Business and Management .... MRes 12FT

University of Strathclyde
Business and Management ....MSc 12FT 30PT/PGDip 9FT 20PT

University of Surrey
European Politics, Business and Law .... MA 12FT 24PT

European business
Research Courses

University of Chester
Business .... DBA 24-84PT

University of Exeter
European Studies .... PhD 48FT 89PT/MPhil 36FT 60PT
Management .... PhD 48FT 84PT/MPhil 36FT 60PT

Manchester Metropolitan University
Research Business .... MRes 12FT 30PT

Facilities management
Taught Courses

University of Aberdeen
Urban Planning and Real Estate .... MSc 12FT/PGDip 12FT

University of Brighton
Facilities Management ....MSc 12FT 24PT/PGDip 12FT 24PT/PGCert 12FT 24PT

College of Estate Management
Facilities Management .... MSc 36DL/PGDip 24DL

University of Cambridge
Real Estate Finance .... MPhil 10FT

University of Central Lancashire
Construction Management (Facilities Management) .... MSc 24DL/PGDip 12DL/PGCert 6DL

Edinburgh Napier University
Facilities Management .... MSc 12FT 24PT 24DL

Glasgow Caledonian University
Building Services Engineering .... MSc 12FT 24PT
Management..............MSc 12FT FlexiblePT/PGDip 9FT FlexiblePT/PGCert 6FT FlexiblePT
Real Estate Management .... MSc 12FT 24PT

University of Glasgow
Healthcare Chaplaincy .... PGCert 12PT

Business and management studies

Real Estate (PgCert)........PGCert 12FT

University of Greenwich
Facilities Management........MSc 12FT 24PT

Heriot-Watt University
Carbon Management.. MSc 12FT 24PT 24-84DL/PGDip 9FT 21PT 24-84DL
MRes Courses in Urban Studies/Housing/Planning Studies/Real Estate Research........MSc(Res) 12FT

Kingston University
Real Estate........MSc 12-24FT 24-48PT

Leeds Metropolitan University
Facilities Management........MSc 24DL

Liverpool John Moores University
Applied Facilities Management........MSc 12FT 24PT

Manchester Metropolitan University
Digital Business Management........MSc 12FT

Northumbria University
International Real Estate Management........MSc 12FT

Nottingham Trent University
Real Estate........MSc 12FT 24PT

Oxford Brookes University
Real Estate........MSc 12FT 24PT
Real Estate Management........MSc 12FT/PGDip 9FT

Queen's University Belfast
Advanced Concrete Technology.....MSc 24PT/PGDip 24PT/PGCert 24PT

Royal Agricultural University
Rural Estate Management........MSc 12FT

University of Salford
Corporate Real Estate and Facilities Management.......MSc 28DL/PGDip 20DL/PGCert 8DL
Management.... MSc 12FT 36PT/PGDip 8FT 24PT/PGCert 4FT 9PT
Real Estate and Property Management.....MSc 12FT 28DL/PGDip 8FT 20DL

School of Oriental and African Studies - SOAS
Globalisation and Multinational Corporations...... MA 12FT 24PT

Sheffield Hallam University
Facilities Management........MBA 36PT
Real Estate........MSc 12FT 24PT
Real Estate - International........MSc 12FT

University of Sheffield
Management........MSc 12FT
Management (Creative and Cultural Industries)........MSc 12FT
Management (International Business)........MSc 12FT

University of St Andrews
Management........MLitt 12FT 24PT
Management (Human Resource Management)........MLitt 12FT
Management and Information Technology........MSc 12FT/PGDip 9FT

University of Stirling
Management........MSc 12FT 27PT/PGDip 9FT 21PT

Swansea Metropolitan University
Facilities Management........MSc 12FT 24PT

UCL - University College London
Facility and Environment Management.......... MSc 12FT 24-60PT/PGDip 9FT

University of the West of England, Bristol
Real Estate Management........MA 12FT 28PT/PGDip 9FT 21PT/PGCert 9FT 21PT
Real Estate Management........MA 12FT 28PT

University of Westminster
Facilities and Property Management........MSc 12FT 24PT

Facilities management
Research Courses

University of Aberdeen
Real Estate........PhD 36FT/MPhil 24FT

University of Nottingham
Social Sciences Research Methodology.......MPhil 24FT 48PT/PhD 36-48FT 72-96PT

Oxford Brookes University
Real Estate and Construction MPhil/PhD . PhD 24-60FT 36-72PT/MPhil 24-36FT 36-48PT

Sheffield Hallam University
Environment and Development - Facilities Management.......PhD 33FT 45PT/MPhil 18FT 30PT
Facilities and Property Management........DBA 48PT 48DL

University of Sheffield
Management........PhD 36FT 72PT/MPhil 24FT 48PT

Food marketing management
Taught Courses

BPP Business School
Professional Marketing........MSc 12FT 24+PT

Bangor University
Marketing........MBA 12FT/PGDip 9FT

University of Brighton
Food Services and Wellbeing Management... MSc 12FT 24-72PT/PGDip 12FT 24-72PT/PGCert 12FT 24-72PT

Cardiff Metropolitan University
Food Technology for Industry........MSc 24-60DL

University of Central Lancashire
Marketing Management........MSc 12FT
Marketing and PR........MA 12FT

University College Cork
Co-operative Organisation Food Marketing & Rural Development........PGDip 12FT
Food Business........MSc 24FT

Cranfield University
Food Chain Systems.........MSc 12FT 24-36PT/PGDip 6FT 24-36PT/PGCert 4FT 24-36PT

University of Derby
Marketing Management........MSc 12FT

University of East Anglia
Marketing and Management........MSc 12FT
Supply Chain Management........MSc 12FT
Sustainable Agriculture and Food Security........MSc 12FT

University of Exeter
Food Security and Sustainable Agriculture........MSc 12FT 24PT
International Supply Chain Management........MSc 12FT
Management........MRes 12FT
Marketing........MSc 12FT

Glasgow Caledonian University
Marketing........MSc 12FT/PGDip 9FT

Harper Adams University
European Masters in Regional Food Production & Global Marketing........MSc 24FT
Food Industry Management.. PGCert 12FT 24PT/MSc 12FT 24PT/PGDip 12FT 24PT
Meat Business Management (PgD & MSc are /subject to validation)........PGCert 12FT 24PT/PGDip 12FT 24PT/MSc 12FT 24PT

Manchester Metropolitan University
International Food Management........MSc 12FT 24-60PT
Logistics and Supply Chain Management........MSc 12FT

Newcastle University
Advanced Food Marketing........MSc 12FT

University of Nottingham
Food Production Management.......MSc 12FT 24PT/PGDip 9-12FT 18-24PT

University of Reading
Food Economics and Marketing........MSc 12FT

University of Roehampton
Marketing........MSc 12FT 24PT

University of Salford
Marketing.......... MSc 12FT 36PT/PGDip 8FT 24PT/PGCert 4FT 9PT

University of Sheffield
Marketing Management Practice........MSc 12FT

University of Southampton
Marketing Management........MSc 12FT/PGDip 9FT

University of St Andrews
Marketing........MLitt 12FT

University of Stirling
Marketing........MSc 12FT/PGDip 9FT

University of Strathclyde
Marketing........MSc 12FT 24PT/PGDip 9FT 18PT

University of Surrey
Food Management........MSc 12FT
Marketing Management........MSc 12FT

University of West London
Gastronomy and Food Management........GradDip 12FT MA 12FT 24PT

Food marketing management
Research Courses

University of Exeter
Management........PhD 48FT 84PT/MPhil 36FT 60PT

The Open University
Marketing........PhD 36FT 72PT variableDL/MPhil 15FT 24PT variableDL

Sheffield Hallam University
School of Leisure and Food Management........PhD/MPhil
School of Leisure and Food Management........PhD/MPhil

Health and safety management
Taught Courses

University of Bedfordshire
Health Studies........MSc 24PT/PGCert 24PT/PGDip 24PT

University of Birmingham
Occupational Health........MSc 12FT 24PT/PGDip 12FT 24PT
Science of Occupational Health, Safety and Environment..... MSc 12FT 24PT/PGDip 12PT

University of Central Lancashire
Fire Investigation........MSc 12FT/PGDip 9FT/PGCert 6FT
Fire Safety Engineering........MSc 12FT 24PT
Fire Scene Investigation........MSc 24-36PT
Fire and Rescue Service Management........MSc 12FT 24PT

Cranfield University
Health and the Environment........ MSc 12FT 24-36PT/PGDip 12FT 24-36PT

Dublin Institute of Technology
Environmental Health and Safety Management........MSc 12FT 24PT
Health Care Risk Management........MSc 12FT 24PT

University of Dundee
Concrete Engineering and Environmental Management...... MSc 12FT
Epidemiology and Global Health International Prevention Research Institute Summer School........Cert 1FT
Geotechnical Engineering........MSc 12FT
Global Health and Wellbeing........MSc 36DL
Structural Engineering........MSc 12FT

Durham University
Risk, Health and Public Policy........MA 12FT

University of Edinburgh
Structural & Fire Safety Engineering........MSc 12FT

National University of Ireland Galway
Occupational Health & Safety........MSc 12FT 24PT/HDipAppSc 12FT 24PT
Occupational Safety Engineering and Ergonomics........MAppSci 12FT 24PT

Glyndwr University
Construction Health and Safety........NEBOSH NGC 4PT

University of Greenwich
Professional Practice in Health & Social Care......... MA 12FT 24PT 27DL/PGDip 12FT 24PT 27DL
Safety, Health and Environment......... PGCert 24DL/PGDip 24DL/MSc 24DL

Heriot-Watt University
Safety and Risk Management (Distance Learning Only)......... MSc 24-84DL/PGDip 21-84DL

Imperial College London
Quality and Safety in Healthcare........MSc 24PT

Leeds Metropolitan University
Public Health (Health Promotion and Environmental Health) Zambia........MSc 36PT
Specialist Community Public Health Nursing - Occupational Health Nursing........MSc 24PT/PGDip 12FT 24PT

Loughborough University
Occupational Health and Safety Management....... MSc 24-36PT/PGDip 12-24PT/PGCert 12PT

University of Manchester
Occupational Medicine....MSc 36DL/AdvDip 24DL/PGCert 12DL/CPD 6DL

Middlesex University
Occupational Safety & Health Management........MSc 12-18FT 24minPT/PGDip 12-18FT 24minPT/PGCert 12-18FT 24PT

Nottingham Trent University
Occupational Health and Safety Management..MSc 24PT/PGDip 12PT

University of Portsmouth
Occupational Health and Safety Management..........PGCert 12DL

Robert Gordon University
Health Safety and Risk Management........MSc 36PT 36DL

University of Salford
Environmental Assessment and Management....MSc 12FT 36PT/PGDip 8FT 24PT
Environmental and Public Health........MSc 12FT 24-36PT/PGDip 8FT 24PT
Occupational Safety and Health........MSc 12FT 36PT/PGDip 8FT 24PT
Safety, Health and Environment........MSc 12FT 36PT/PGDip 8FT 24PT

University of Sheffield
Process Safety and Loss Prevention ... MSc(Eng) 12FT 24PT/PGDip 9FT

University of Southampton
Environmental Monitoring and Assessment......... MSc 12FT 27PT
Maritime Engineering Science: Nuclear Safety ManagementMSc 12FT

University of Strathclyde
Safety and Risk Management........PGCert 12PT/PGDip 12PT/MSc 24PT

Business and management studies

University of Sunderland
Environment, Health and Safety .... MSc 12FT 24-28PT/PGDip 12FT 24PT/PGCert 12FT 24PT
Environmental Management and Assessment - Health and Safety .... MSc 12DL/MSc 24DL

Swansea Metropolitan University
Non Destructive Testings and Evaluation .... MSc 12FT 24PT

Trinity College Dublin - the University of Dublin
Health and Safety in Construction .... PGDip 12PT

University of West London
Health and Social Care Leadership .... MSc 24PT

University of the West of Scotland
Occupational Safety & Health .... Diploma 24PT
Occupational Safety & Health .... DipHE 24PT/BSc 36PT

Health and safety management
Research Courses

University of Aberdeen
Environmental and Occupational Medicine .... PhD 36FT/MSc by research 12FT/MPhil 24FT
Patient Safety .... PhD 36FT/MPhil 24FT/MSc by research 12FT

University of Birmingham
Occupational and Environmental Medicine .... PhD 36FT 72PT/MPhil 12FT 24PT

University of Nottingham
Institute of Work, Health and Organisations Research Areas .... PhD 36FT 72PT/MPhil 24FT 48PT

University of Southampton
School of Management: Health .... MPhil 24FT 48PT/PhD 26FT 72PT
School of Management: Management Sciences .... MPhil 24FT 48PT/PhD 36FT 72PT
School of Management: Organisation and Management .... MPhil 24FT 48PT/PhD 36FT 72PT

Health services management
Taught Courses

University of Aberdeen
Health Services and Public Health Research .... MSc 12FT 24PT/PGDip 9FT 21PT
International Healthcare Management .... MBA 12FT/PGDip 9FT/PGCert 6FT
Public Health Nutrition .... MSc 12FT 24PT/PGDip 9FT 18PT

Anglia Ruskin University
Advanced Practice .... MSc 12FT 24PT
Healthcare Management .... MSc 24DL
Hospital Management .... MBA 12FT 24PT

Bangor University
Health Science .... MSc 12FT 24 - 60PT/PGDip 9FT
Health Studies/Health Science, Nursing, Midwifery, Radiography and Allied Health Professio... PhD by taught 36FT 48-60PT/MPhil 24FT 36PT
Health and Social Care Leadership .... MSc 12FT 24 - 60PT/PGDip 9FT
Policy Research and Evaluation .... MA 12FT 21-30PT/PGDip 9FT 17-21PT/PGCert 5FT 12-21PT
Public Health and Health Promotion .... MSc 12FT 24 - 60PT/PGDip 9FT
Risk Management in Health and Social Care .... MSc 36PT/PGDip 24PT/PGCert 12PT
Social Policy, Sociology .... PhD by taught 36FT 60PT/MPhil 12-24FT 24-36PT

University of Bedfordshire
Enhancing Quality Through Patient Safety .... MSc 12FT 24PT/PGCert 12FT 24PT/PGDip 12FT 24PT
Leadership in Healthcare Practice .... MSc 24PT
Medical Education Leadership .... PGCert 12-36PT
Medical Stimulation .... PGCert 12-36PT

Birmingham City University
Dimensions in Healthcare .... PGCert 12PT/PGCert 36PT
Health and Social Care (Leadership) .... PGDip 12PT/PGDip 36PT

University of Birmingham
Health Care Policy and Management .... MSc 12FT 24PT/GradDip 9FT 21PT
Leadership and Management for Social Care .... MA 36PT/PGDip 24PT
Leadership and Management for Social Work .... PGDip 18PT/MA 36PT
Leadership for Health Services Improvement .... MSc 24PT
Managing Integration for Health and Well-being MSc 12FT 24PT/PGDip 12FT 24PT

University of Bolton
Leadership in Health and Social Care.. MSc 36-60PT/PGDip 24PT/PGCert 12PT

Bournemouth University
Leadership and Management in Health and Social Care .... GradDip 24PT
Leading and Developing Services .... MA 36PT

University of Bradford
Diversity Management .... MSc 24PT
Health and Social Care Management .... MSc 24-36PT/PGDip 12-24PT/PGCert 9-12PT
Leadership, Management and Change .... MSc 12FT 24 - 60PT

University of Brighton
Clinical Studies and Management .... MSc 12FT 24 - 72PT/PGCert 12FT 24 - 72PT/PGDip 12FT 24 - 72PT
Food Services and Wellbeing Management ... MSc 12FT 24-72PT/PGDip 12FT 24-72PT/PGCert 12FT 24-72PT
Health Promotion and Management ... MA 12FT 24 - 72PT/PGDip 12FT 24 - 72PT
Physiotherapy and Management .... MSc 12 - 24FT 24 - 72PT/PGCert 12 - 24FT 24 - 72PT/PGDip 12 - 24FT 24 - 72PT
Public Service Management ... MBA 18FT 36PT/PGDip 18FT 24PT/PGCert 18FT 24PT

Brunel University
MSc Ageing Studies .... PGCert 12PT/PGDip 24PT/MSc 36PT

Bucks New University
Leadership & Management in the Public Sector .... MA 24PT

University of Central Lancashire
Advanced Practice (Health and Social Care) .... MSc 24PT
Advanced Stroke Practice .... MSc 36FT 60PT/PGDip 24PT/PGCert 12PT
Clinical Leadership for Practice Innovation .... Module 4PT
Integrated Healthcare by elearning .... MSc 36-48PT/PGDip 24PT/PGCert 12PT

University of Chester
Health Care Leadership (Work Based and Integrative Studies) .... MA 24-72PT/MSc 24-72PT/PGDip 24-60PT/PGCert 12-36PT
Health and Social Care - Commissioning .... PGCert 12 - 36PT
Public Services Management (Work Based and Integrative Studies) .... MA 24-72PT/PGDip 24-60PT/PGCert 12-36PT

University of Chichester
Management (Health and Social Care Services) . MA 27PT/PGDip 18PT/PGCert 12PT

City University London
Clinical Leadership for Allied Health Professionals .... MSc 24PT/PGCert 12PT/PGDip 24PT
Health Management in Strategic Management and Leadership .... MSc 12FT 24PT
Health Services Research .... MSc 12FT 24PT/MRes 12FT 24PT

Cranfield University
Clinical Research .... MSc 12FT 36PT/PGCert 9FT 24PT/PGDip 6FT 24PT
Clinical Research Executive .... MSc 36PT/PGDip 9FT 24-36PT/PGCert 6FT 12-24PT
Clinical Research Management .... MSc 12FT 36PT/PGDip 12FT 36PT
Health Administration ... MSc 12FT 24-36PT/PGDip 12FT 24-36PT

University of Cumbria
Advanced Practice in Health and Social Care .... MSc 24 - 60PT
Leadership in Health and Social Care .... MBA 12FT 36PT/PGDip 12FT 36PT/PGCert 12FT 36PT

De Montfort University
Clinically-Led Commissioning .... PGCert 12PT
Foundation In Professional Practice .... PGCert 12PT/PGCert 12PT

University of Derby
Clinical Supervision .... PGCert 12PT 12DL
Community Specialist Practice .... MSc 12FT 24PT
Management of Long Term Conditions .... PGCert 12PT

University of Dundee
Clinical Audit and Research for Allied Healthcare Professionals .... PGCert 6DL
Quality Improvement .... MSc 36DL PGCert 12DL PGDip 24DL

University of East London
Leadership and Team Development .... PGCert 5FT 12 - 36PT
Planning and Developing Health Care .... PGCert 5FT 12-36PT

Edge Hill University
Leadership Development (Clinical Leadership / Leadership and Management) .... MSc 36-72PT

University of Edinburgh
Health Systems and Public Policy .... MSc 12FT 24-36PT
Integrated Service Improvement: Health and Social Care .... MSc 24-36PT/PGDip 20PT/PGCert 12PT

University of Essex
Health Care Management .... Diploma 18-60PT/MSc 24-60PT
Health Services Management .... Prof Doc 48-84PT
Public Health Management .... MSc 24-60PT/Diploma 18-60PT/Cert 12-60PT
Social Care Practice Management .... Prof Doc 48-84PT
Social Services Management .... Prof Doc 48-84PT

National University of Ireland Galway
Health Services Research .... MHSc 24PT/PGDip 24PT

Glasgow Caledonian University
Advanced Practice with Older People .... MSc 12FT
Advancing Practice in Primary Care .... MSc 24FT
Counselling Skills in Health and Social Care .... PGCert 12-24FT
Diagnostic Imaging .... MSc 12-24FT
Musculoskeletal Management .... MSc 36-72PT
Optimal Heart Failure Care .... MSc 12FT
Perinatal Mental Health .... MSc 12FT
Professional Doctorate for Health, Social Care Sector and Nursing Professionals .... DProf by taught 48FT
Public Health with Social Action .... MSc 12FT
Radiatiotherapy and Oncology .... MSc 12-24FT
Telehealthcare .... MSc 12FT

University of Glasgow
Mental Health, Global .... MSc 12FT 24PT/PGDip 9FT 18PT/PGCert 9FT 18PT
Public Policy & Management ... MSc 12FT 24PT 60BM/PGDip 9FT 21PT

University of Greenwich
Professional Practice in Health & Social Care .... MA 12FT 24PT 27DL/PGDip 12FT 24PT 27DL

Imperial College London
International Health Management .... MSc 12FT

Institute of Education
Advanced Educational Practice - Graduate Diploma .... GradDip 12-24FT 36-60PT/GradCert 12-24FT 36-60PT

Keele University
Health Executive MBA .... MBA 30PT
Health Services Management .... PGDip 24PT

King's College London
Advanced Practice (Leadership) .... MSc 36-72PT/PGDip 24-72PT/PGCert 12-72PT
Public Services Policy & Management .... MSc 12FT 24PT

Kingston University
Biomedical Science with Management Studies .... MSc 12FT 24PT
Clinical Leadership .... MSc 24PT
Leadership and Management in Health .... MSc 12FT 24-48PT/PGDip 12FT 24-48PT/PGCert 12FT 24-48PT

Lancaster University
Medical Leadership .... PGCert 12PT
Organisational Change (Health Care) .... PGCert 12PT

Leeds Metropolitan University
Environmental Health .... MSc 12FT 36PT
Public Health (Health Promotion and Environmental Health) Zambia .... MSc 36PT

University of Leeds
Health Management, Planning and PolicyPGCert 3FT/PGDip 9FT/MA 12FT
Hospital Management .... PGCert 3FT/PGDip 9FT/MA 12FT
Patient Safety and Clinical Risk Management .... PGCert 4FT

Liverpool John Moores University
Advanced Healthcare Practice .... MSc 36PT
International Public Health .... MSc 12FT 24PT

London College UCK
Leadership and Management in the Health and Social Care Sector .... PGDip 12FT 24PT

London School of Economics and Political Science (LSE)
Health Policy, Planning and Financing .... MSc 12FT 24PT
International Health Policy .... MSc 12FT 24PT
Public Management and Governance .... MSc 12FT

London School of Hygiene and Tropical Medicine
Health Policy, Planning and Financing .... MSc 12FT 24PT
Public Health (Environment & Health) .... MSc 12FT 24PT
Public Health (Health Economics) .... MSc 12FT 24PT
Public Health (Health Services Management) .... MSc 12FT 24PT
Public Health (Health Services Research) .... MSc 12FT 24PT

London South Bank University
Construction Project Management (Health Care) .... MSc 24PT
International Health Services and Hospital Management .... MSc 15FT

University of Manchester
Healthcare Management .... MSc 12FT

Middlesex University
Development with Work Experience .... MA 12-15FT 24PT
Development with Work-based Learning .... MA 12-15FT 24PT
Leading and Developing Public and Community Services, ... PGCert 12PT/AdvDip 12PT
Managing Major Projects .... PGCert 9DL
Managing Major Projects and Programmes .... MSc 24PT

University of Northampton
Healthcare Management .... MBA 24PT
Leadership for Health and Social Care .... PGCert 12PT

Northumbria University
Clinical Practice (Advanced Critical Care Practice) .... MA 36FT
Systemic Teaching, Training and Supervision .... MA 24PT

Nottingham Trent University
Public Services Management .... MSc 12PT/PGDip 12PT/PGCert 12PT

University of Nottingham
Clinical Leadership for Innovative Practice Certificate .... PGCert 12-24PT

Business and management studies

The Open University
Advancing Healthcare Practice..PGCert 12DL/PGDip variableDL/MSc variableDL
Advancing Professional Practice................................MSc variableDL
Clinical Leadership ....PGCert 12DL

Oxford Brookes University
Management in Health and Social Care .... MSc 12FT 30-36PT/PGCert 12FT 12PT/PGDip 12FT 12-18PT

University of Oxford
Biomedical Engineering .... MSc 12FT

Plymouth University
Healthcare Strategy & Performance .... MSc 24PT

University of Portsmouth
Leadership in Health and Wellbeing .... MSc 36PT

Queen Margaret University, Edinburgh
Human Resources for Health .... MSc 12FT 24PT/PGDip 8FT 16PT/PGCert 4FT 8PT
Public Services Governance .... PGCert 12FT 24-84PT

Queen Mary, University of London
Health Systems and Global Policy......................MSc 12FT 24-48PT

Royal College of Nursing
Advancing Healthcare Pratice ....MSc 23-50DL

Royal Holloway, University of London
Leadership & Management in Health .... MSc 12FT 24PT
Medical Sociology .... MSc 12FT 24PT

University of Salford
Advanced Practice (Health and Social Care)........MSc 24PT/PGDip 18PT/PGCert 12PT
International Hospital and Health Service Leadership and Management.........................MSc 12FT/PGDip 8FT/PGCert 4FT
Leadership and Management for Healthcare Practice ....
MSc 12FT 36PT/PGDip 8FT 24PT/PGCert 4FT 9PT
Public Health .... MSc 12FT 36PT/PGDip 8FT 24PT/PGCert 9PT

Sheffield Hallam University
Health and Social Care Leadership.............MSc 36PT/PGDip 24PT/PGCert 12PT
Nutrition with Public Health Management .... MSc 12FT

University of Sheffield
International Development (Masters in Public Health) ....
MPH 12FT 24PT
International Health Technology Assessment..... MSc 24-60 PTDL
Public Health ....MPH 12FT 24-36PT
Public Health (Health Services Research).........MPH 12FT 24-36PT
Public Health (Management and Leadership) ....
MPH 12FT 24-36PT

University of South Wales
Health & Public Service Management.....................MSc 12FT 36PT/PGCert 4FT 12PT/PGDip 8FT 24PT
Leadership and Management (Health Promotion & Education) ....MA 36-60PT

University of Southampton
Clinical Leadership in Cancer, Palliative and End of Life Care........
MSc 24FT 48PT
Leadership and Management Health and Social Care... MSc 12FT 48PT

Staffordshire University
Health Management and Policy (Distance Learning) .... PGCert 12PT/PGDip 24PT/MA 36PT

University of Stirling
Applied Studies (Management and Leadership in Social Services) .... MSc 30PT/PGDip 24PT/PGCert 12PT

University of Surrey
Advanced Practice ....MSc 12FT 24PT
Health Care Management .... MSc 12FT 24PT 24DL

University of Sussex
Leadership and Management in Integrated Children's Services... MA 60PT/PGDip 60PT/PGCert 60PT

Swansea University
Healthcare Management...MSc 12FT 36PT
Public Health and Partnerships in Care .... MSc 12FT 36PT

Teesside University
Leadership in Health and Social Care.........................PGCert 12PT
Transformational Leadership in Health and Social CareMSc 36PT

Trinity College Dublin - the University of Dublin
Health Services Management .... MSc 24PT

University of the Highlands and Islands
Chartered Management Institute - Diploma Public Service Leadership.......................Chartered Management Institute 12PT

University of Ulster
Health Communication ....PGDip 9FT 18PT/MSc 12FT 24PT

UCL - University College London
CYP IAPT Management ....PGCert 12FT
International Health Euro .... MSc 12FT

University of Warwick
Accounting and Finance in Health Service Organisations.......PGA 12PT/CPDMod 1PT

Child Health Services: Management, Organisations and Data Systems.. PGA 12PT/CPDMod 1PT
Clinical Quality Improvement and Risk Management...................
PGA 12PT/CPDMod 1PT
Health Sciences: Health Services Management.............................
MSc 36PT/PGDip 24PT/PGCert 12PT/PGA 12PT
Health Services Management........MSc 36PT/PGDip 24PT/PGCert 12PT
International Health Policy ....PGA 12PT/cpdmod 1PT
Introduction to Management in Health Service Organisations....
PGA 12PT/CPDMod 1PT
Managing People in Health Service Organisations ....PGA 12PT/CPDMod 1PT
Models of Emergency Care .... PGA 12PT/CPDMod 1PT
Organisational Behaviour and Health Service Policy ....PGA 12PT/CPDMod 1PT

University of West London
Health and Social Care Leadership................................ MSc 24PT
Management Studies (Health and Social Care)........... PGDip 24PT
Management Studies (Health and Social Care) - Top up.MA 12PT

University of the West of England, Bristol
Leadership and Management in Health and Social Care................
MSc 33PT

University of Westminster
Integrated Governance in Health in Healthcare Communities.....
MSc 24-60PT

University of Worcester
MBA in Executive Leadership & Management (Health & Social Care)...MBA 12FT 36PT

Health services management
Research Courses

Anglia Ruskin University
Health Social Care and Education ......MPhil 24FT 24DL/PhD 36FT

Bangor University
Health Studies/Health Science, Nursing, Midwifery, Radiography & Allied Health Professions ....MPhil 24FT 36PT/PhD 36FT 48-60PT
Social Policy......................PhD 36FT 60PT/MPhil 12-24FT 24-36PT

University of Birmingham
Health Services Management..PhD 36FT 72PT/MPhil 24FT 48PT/MSc by research 12FT

University of Brighton
Applied Social Sciences Division....... PhD 24-60FT 36-72PT/MPhil 18-36FT 30-48PT
School of Service Management Research Student Division....PhD 48FT 60PT/MPhil 24FT 36PT

University of Bristol
Social Science (Policy Studies Doctorate) .... DSocSci 36FT 96PT

City University London
Health Management and Food Policy..MSc by research/MHM by research

University of Dundee
Social Dimensions of Health Institute .... MPhil 24FT PhD 36FT

Keele University
Health Management Professional Doctorate ....DBA 48-84PT
Health Policy and Governance/Public Policy............. PhD 24-48FT 48-96PT/MPhil 12-24FT 24-36PT

King's College London
Health Service & Population Research Department ....PhD 36FT

University of Leeds
Nuffield Institute for Health........... PhD 36+FT/MPhil 24FT/MA by research 12+FT
Professional Doctorate in Public Management ..... PhD 36FT 60PT

London School of Hygiene and Tropical Medicine
Public Health & Policy (Research).........DrPH 42FT 42PT/PhD 42FT 42PT/MPhil 12FT 12PT

University of Nottingham
Public Policy - Professional Doctorate in Public Policy ....
PDPP 48-96PT

The Open University
Public Leadership and Social Enterprise .... PhD 36FT 72PT variableDL/MPhil 15FT 24PT variableDL

University of Oxford
Public Health .... DPhil 48FT/MSc by research 24FT

Plymouth University
Professional and Organisational Issues........................MPhil tbcFT

University of Sheffield
Public Health: Integrated Studies ....New Route PhD 48FT

University of Surrey
Health Care .... PhD 36FT 48PT/MPhil 24FT 36PT
Health Care Management .... PhD 36FT 48PT/MPhil 24FT 36PT

University of West London
Service Management (Health and Social Care) .... Professional Doctorate (PD) 33FT 45PT

University of Westminster
Health Sciences... DProf 48-96PT

Hotel and catering management
Taught Courses

Bath Spa University
Travel and Nature Writing...............................MA 12FT 24PT 12DL

University of Bedfordshire
International Tourism Management.... MSc 12-15FT 24PT/PGDip 12FT/PGCert 12FT
Tourism and Environmental Management .... MSc 12-15FT 24PT/PGDip 12FT/PGCert 12FT

University College Birmingham
Hospitality Management.............MA 12FT 24PT/PGDip 9FT 18PT/PGCert 5FT 9PT
Hospitality with Tourism Management .....MSc 12FT 24PT/PGDip 12FT 24PT
Professional Hospitality and Tourism Management..... MA 30DL/PGDip 24DL/PGCert 12DL
Tourism Business Administration ....MA 12FT 24PT 18-30DL/PGDip 9FT 18PT 24DL/PGCert 5FT 9PT 12DL
Tourism Destination Management ...... MA 12FT 24PT/PGDip 9FT 12PT
UCB MBA / MBA (Hospitality and Tourism pathway) ... MBA 12FT

Bournemouth University
Hotel and Food Services Management..............MSc 12-15FT 24PT

Cardiff Metropolitan University
Hospitality Management.........MSc 24FT 36PT/PGDip 18FT 36PT/PGCert 9FT 36PT

University of Central Lancashire
International Hospitality and Event Management .... MSc 12FT 24PT/PGDip 12FT 24PT
International Hospitality and Tourism Management.... MSc 12FT 24PT/PGDip 12FT 24PT
International Tourism Management....................MSc 12FT 24PT/PGDip 12FT 24PT
International Tourism and Attraction Management ..... MSc 12FT 24PT/PGDip 12FT 24PT
Internship in International Tourism, Hospitality and Event Management.. MA 12FT 24PT

University College Cork
Food Business .... MSc 24FT

University of Derby
International Hospitality Management ......MA 12FT 36PT/PGDip 12FT/PGCert 9FT
International Spa Management.......................................MA 36FT

Dublin Institute of Technology
Hospitality Management ....MSc 12FT 24PT

Edinburgh Napier University
International Human Resource Management................. MSc 12FT
Tourism and Hospitality Management...................MSc 12FT 24PT

University of Exeter
International Tourism Management................................ MSc 12FT

Glasgow Caledonian University
International Tourism Management..MSc 12FT 24PT FlexibleDL/PGDip 9FT

University of Glasgow
Management with Human Resources.............................. MSc 12FT

University of Gloucestershire
MBA Hospitality .... MBA 12FT

University of Huddersfield
International Hospitality Management ....MSc 12FT 24PT

Leeds Metropolitan University
International Hospitality Management......MSc 12FT 24PT/PGDip 12FT 24PT/PGCert 4FT 12PT
International Tourism & Hospitality Management........ MSc 12FT 24PT
Multi Unit Leadership ....MSc 12FT 24PT

University of Lincoln
Hospitality and Tourism Services Management .... MSc 12FT

London College UCK
Hospitality and Tourism Management......PGDip 12FT 24PT 24DL

Manchester Metropolitan University
Hospitality Management.....................................MSc 12FT 24-60PT
International Tourism Management.................MSc 12FT 24-60PT

Middlesex University
International Tourism and Hospitality Management......MA 12FT 24PT

Northumbria University
Business with Hospitality and Tourism Management... MSc 12FT

Oxford Brookes University
International Hospitality and Tourism Management ... MSc 12FT 24PT/MSc-Sandwich Mode 24FT

Plymouth University
Tourism and Hospitality Management........MSc 12FT/PGDip 12FT

Section sponsored by BPP UNIVERSITY COLLEGE

Business and social sciences
394 POSTGRADUATE DIRECTORY www.prospects.ac.uk/findcourses

Business and management studies

Queen Margaret University, Edinburgh
International Management and Leadership with Hospitality....... MSc 12FT 24PT/PGDip 9FT 18PT/PGCert 3FT 6PT
Hospitality Management............ MBA 12FT 24-84PT/PGDip 12FT 24-84PT/PGCert 12FT 24-84PT

Regent's Business School London
Business Management in International Travel & Tourism ....MA 21PT

Robert Gordon University
International Tourism and Hospitality Management.... MSc 12FT 36PT/PGDip 9FT 24PT/PGCert 6FT 12PT

University of Roehampton
International Management....................................... MSc 12FT 24PT

School of Oriental and African Studies - SOAS
Anthropology of Travel, Tourism and Pilgrimage ... MA 12FT 24PT

Sheffield Hallam University
International Hospitality Management.................MSc 12FT 36DL
International Hospitality and Tourism Management.... MSc 12FT

St Mary's University College, Twickenham
International Tourism Development......................... MA 12FT 24PT

University of Strathclyde
International Hospitality and Tourism Management.... MSc 12FT 24PT/PGDip 9FT 21PT

University of Sunderland
Tourism and Hospitality ....MSc 12FT 24PT

University of Surrey
International Hotel Management .... MSc 12FT
Master of Business Administration (MBA) .... MBA 12FT

Swansea Metropolitan University
International Tourism...MBA 12FT 24 - 48PT

University of Ulster
International Hotel and Tourism Management .... MSc 12FT 30PT

University of West London
Gastronomy and Food Management........................ MA 12FT 24PT GradDip 12FT
Hospitality Management.. MA 12FT 24PT

University of Wolverhampton
Hospitality Management...................................... MA 12FT 24-36PT

Hotel and catering management
Research Courses

Manchester Metropolitan University
Research in Hospitality and Tourism Management .... PhD VariableFT VariablePT/MPhil VariableFT VariablePT/MSc by research 12FT 24PT

Oxford Brookes University
Hospitality, Leisure and Tourism Management .... PhD 24-60FT 36-72PT/MPhil 24-36FT 36-48PT

Robert Gordon University
Aberdeen Business School ...PhD 12FT 36PT 36DL/MSc(Res) 12FT 36PT 36DL

University of Surrey
Hospitality..................................... PhD 36FT 48PT/MPhil 24FT 36PT

University of West London
London School of Hospitality & Tourism.....PhD 36FT 72PT/MPhil 24FT 48PT

Human resource management
Taught Courses

University of Aberdeen
Human Resource Management....................MBA 12FT/PGDip 9FT/PGCert 6FT

University of Abertay Dundee
Human Resource Management...................... MSc 12FT/PGDip 9FT

Anglia Ruskin University
Chartered Institute of Personnel and Development (CIPD) - Human Resource ....CIPD 24PT
HRM (Block Delivery).. PGDip 30PT
Human Resource Management.................. MA 12FT/PGDip 12FT
Human Resource Management stage 3 only (Top-Up).. MA 12PT/PGDip 12PT

Aston University
MSc Human Resource Management & Business............................ MSc 12FT 24PT

BPP Business School
MSc Professional Human Resources.......MSc 18+FT 24+PT/PGDip 24+PT/PGCert 12+PT

University of Bath
Management with Human Resource Management...... MSc 12FT

University of Bedfordshire
Chartered Institute of Personnel and Development .... CIPD 36PT
Human Resource Management (CIPD accredited) .... MSc 24PT
International Human Resource Management........... MA 12-18FT
Managing Business Creativity and Innovation............... MSc 24PT
Postgraduate Diploma in Human Resource Management (CIPD accredited)..PGDip 24FT

Belfast Metropolitan College
CIPD L5 Intermediate Diploma in HRM ....CIPD 10PT
CIPD Level 7 Postgraduate Diploma in Personnel and Human Resource Management CIPD Advanced Diploma Level 7CIPD 9PT

Birkbeck, University of London
Career Management and Coaching.................................... MSc 24PT
Corporate Responsibility and Sustainability .... MSc 12FT 24PT
Human Resource Development and Consultancy MSc 12FT 24PT
Human Resource Management................................ MSc 12FT 24PT
International Management....................................... MSc 12FT 24PT
Management............................... MSc 12FT 24PT/MRes 12FT 24PT/PGCert 12FT 24PT

Birmingham City University
MA Human Resource Management (CIPD) .... MA 36PT/PGDip 24PT
MSc International Human Resource Management (CIPD) ..... MSc 12FT

University of Birmingham
Development Management (Human Resources and Development Management)... MSc 12FT 24PT/GradDip 9FT 24PT
Human Resource Management.. MSc 12FT
Human Resource Management with CIPD pathway ..... MSc 12FT

Bournemouth University
Management with Human Resources.............................. MSc 12FT
Professional Development (Human Resource Management) MSc 27PT

University of Bradford
Human Resource Management.. MSc 12FT
Human and Organisational Capacity Building for Development. MSc 12FT 24 - 60PT/PGDip 9FT 21PT/PGCert 9PT
Human Resource Management..............MSc 36PT/Post Graduate Diploma 24PT

University of Brighton
Human Resource Management........ MSc 12FT 36PT/PGCert 12FT 36PT/PGDip 12FT 36PT

Brunel University
Human Resource Management.. MSc 12FT
Human Resource Management and Employment Relations......... MSc 12FT

Bucks New University
Human Resource Management................................. MA 12FT 24PT

Canterbury Christ Church University
Human Resource Management, Business Partnership ... MA 30PT

Cardiff University
Human Resource Management................................ MSc 12FT 24PT

University of Central Lancashire
Diploma in Human Resource Management....................................... Diploma 12PT/CIPD 12PT
Human Resource Management/Development..... MSc 12FT 24PT
MA Human Resource Management/Development .... MA 12PT 12DL
Master of Business Administration.................................. MBA 12FT
Master of Business Administration - Health.................. MBA 36PT
Master of Business Administration - Part-time............. MBA 36PT
Postgraduate Certificate in Management (PGCM)....PGCert 18PT
Postgraduate Diploma in Human Resource Management/Development...PGDip 24PT/CIPD 24PT

University of Chester
Business Development (Work Based and Integrative Studies)...... MA 24-72PT/MSc 24-72PT/PGDip 24-60PT/PGCert 12-36PT
Chester Business Masters Programme.......... MSc 12FT 24 - 72PT/PGDip 12FT 24 - 60PT/PGCert 12FT 12 - 36PT
Coach-Mentoring and Facilitation in Organisations (Work Based and Integrative Studies)............MA 24-72PT/MSc 24-72PT/PGDip 24-60PT/PGCert 12-36PT
Human Resource Development (Work Based and Integrative Studies) ....MA 24-72PT/MSc 24-72PT/PGDip 24-60PT/PGCert 12-36PT
Wellbeing in the Workplace (Work Based and Integrative Studies) ....MA 24-72PT/PGDip 24-60PT/PGCert 12-36PT

City University London
Advanced Organisational Consultancy (validated) ...PGDip 24PT/MA 24PT

Coventry University
Human Resource Management.....MA 12FT 24PT/PGDip 24-60PT
Human Resource Management (Top-up)............................ MA 7PT

Cranfield University
International Human Resource Management................ MSc 24PT

University of Cumbria
Master of Business Administration .... MBA 12FT 36PT

De Montfort University
Human Resource Management...........MA 12FT 24PT/PGDip 12PT
International Business and HRM.. MSc 12FT

University of Derby
Human Resource Management (CIPD accredited) .... MA 12-14FT 36PT

University Centre Doncaster
Human Resource Management.. MSc 36PT

Durham University
Executive MA Human Resource Management .... MA 30DL
Human Resource Management..MA 12FT
Management (Human Resource Management) .... MSc 12FT

University of East Anglia
Advanced Business Management....................................... MSc 12FT
Advanced Management .... MSc 12FT
Business Management .... MSc 12FT
Entrepreneurship and Strategy .... MSc 12FT
Human Resource Management.. MSc 12FT
Management... MSc 12FT

University of East London
Human Resource Management................................MA 12FT 24PT/PGDip 8FT 16PT/PGCert 4FT 8PT
International Human Resource Management ...... MA 12FT 24PT/PGDip 8FT 16PT/PGCert 4FT 8PT

Edge Hill University
Master of Business Administration (Human Resource Management) .... MBA 12FT

Edinburgh Napier University
Business Management with Human Resource Management (HRM) .... MSc 12FT
Human Resource Management...MSc 12FT 24/36PT/PGDip 12FT 24/36PT
International Human Resource Management................ MSc 12FT

University of Edinburgh
Human Resource Management.. MSc 12FT

European Business School London
Human Resources... MA 12 - 16FT

University of Exeter
Human Resource Management...............................MSc 12FT 30PT/PGDip 9FT 21PT
International Tourism Management................................. MSc 12FT

National University of Ireland Galway
Industrial Relations & Human Resource Management........ MSc 9 approxFT
Strategy Innovation and People Management.....MSc 9 approxFT

Glasgow Caledonian University
Human Resource Management........... PGDip 9FT 24PT/MSc 12FT 24-36PT
International Human Resource Management....... MSc 12FT 24PT

University of Glasgow
Management with Human Resources............................... MSc 12FT

University of Gloucestershire
Human Resource Management (International) ....MSc 12FT/PGDip 8FT/PGCert 4FT
Human Resource Management (Strategic)MA 12PT/PGDip 20PT/PGCert 8PT

Glyndwr University
Human Resource Management................................. MA 12FT 36PT

University of Greenwich
International Human Resource Management....... MA 12FT 36PT/PGDip 12FT 36PT
Leadership and Management (CIPD) .... Cert 12PT
Personnel and Development...MA 24PT

Heriot-Watt University
Human Resource Management...MSc 84DL
Int'nl Business Management with Finance / HRM / Logistics / Marketing /Sustainability Mgmt. .... MSc 12FT 24PT/PGDip 9FT 21PT

University of Hertfordshire
Business Psychology.. MSc 12FT 48PT
Human Resource ManagementMA 12FT 24PT/PGDip 12FT 24PT/PGCert 12FT 24PT
Human Resource Management and Employment Relations... MA 12FT 24PT/PGCert 12FT 24PT/PGDip 12FT 24PT
Leadership and Management in Public Services...MSc variousPT/PGDip variousPT/PGCert variousPT

University of Huddersfield
Human Resource Management / Development ....MA 12PT
International Human Resource Management...................MA 12FT
Learning & Development Managment .... MA 12FT 36PT

University of Hull
Human Resource Management.. MSc 12FT

Keele University
European Industrial Relations and Human Resource Management............................MA 24PT/PGDip 18PT/PGCert 18PT
Human Resource Management...................... MA 12FT/PGDip 9FT/PGCert 9FT
Industrial Relations..................MA 24PT/PGDip 18PT/PGCert 18PT
Industrial Relations and Human Resource Management......... MA 24PT/PGDip 18PT/PGCert 18PT

University of Kent
Human Resource Management.. MSc 12FT

Business and social sciences
www.prospects.ac.uk/findcourses POSTGRADUATE DIRECTORY 395

Business and management studies

King's College London
Human Resource Management & Organisational Analysis... MSc 12FT 24PT

Kingston University
Human Resource Management....MA top-up 6-12PT PGDip 24PT MA 12FT 24PT
International Human Resource Management..PGDip 12FT 24PT/ MA 12FT 24PT

Lancaster University
Human Resource and Knowledge Management.... MSc 12FT
Human Resources and Consulting....MA 12FT

Leeds Metropolitan University
Chartered Institute of Marketing (CIM)....Diploma 12PT
Human Resource Management....MA 12FT 24PT/PGDip 24PT
International Business.... MA 12FT 24PT
Project Management....MSc 12FT 24PT
Strategic Project Management....MSc 12FT 24PT

University of Leeds
Diversity Management.... MA 12FT 24PT
Human Resource Management.... MA 12FT 24PT

University of Leicester
Human Resource Management and Training....MSc 24-36DL/ GradDip 18DL/PGCert 12DL
Industrial Relations and Workplace Learning....MSc 24-36DL/ GradDip 18DL/PGCert 12DL
Performance Management and Workplace Learning.... MSc 24-36DL/PGDip 18DL/PGCert 12DL

University of Limerick
Human Resource Management.... MA 12FT 24PT
Quality Management.... PGDip 9FT/MSc 12FT

University of Lincoln
Human Resource Development (CIPD)....MSc 12FT 36PT

Liverpool Hope University
Human Resource Management and Development.... MSc 12FT 24PT

Liverpool John Moores University
Personnel and Development....MA 24PT

University of Liverpool
Global Human Resource Management (Online Degree).... MSc 24FT 24+PT
Human Resource Management....MSc 12FT 24PT

London College UCK
International Human Resource Management... PGDip 12FT 24PT

London Metropolitan University
Human Resource Management.... MA 24PT PGDip 12FT 24PT
Human Resources and Employment Management.... MA 12FT 24PT

London School of Economics and Political Science (LSE)
Development Management....MSc 12FT 24PT
International Employment Relations and Human Resource Management....MSc 12FT
Management and Human Resources....MSc 12FT
Organisational Behaviour.... MSc 12FT

London South Bank University
Human Resource Practice....Cert 6PT
Human Resources Development....MSc 30PT
Human Resources Management....MSc 30PT
Human Resources Management - Fast Track (Final Level).... MSc 18PT
International Human Resources.... MSc 12FT
Learning and Development Practice....Cert 6PT

Loughborough University
Management and Leadership (part-time for Working Professionals)....MSc 24-36PT/PGDip 18PT/PGCert 12PT

Manchester Metropolitan University
Digital Business Management.... MSc 12FT
Human Resource Management....MSc 12FT 24PT
International Human Resource Management.... MSc 12FT
PgCert/PgDip/MSc Digital Business Management.... MSc 12FT

University of Manchester
Human Resource Development (International Development).... MSc 12FT 24PT
Human Resource Management (International Development).... MSc 12FT 24PT/PGDip 9FT 21PT
Human Resource Management and Industrial Relations.... MSc 12FT
International Human Resource Management and Comparative Industrial Relations.... MSc 12FT

Middlesex University
Human Resource Management (Chartered Institute of Personnel and Development).... MA 12FT 24PT/PGDip 12FT 24PT/ PGCert 12FT 24PT
International Human Resource Management....MA 12FT 24PT/ PGDip 12FT 24PT
Personal and Professional Development....AdvDip 2 weeksBM
Recruitment Practice....MA 12-36DL/PGDip 12-36DL/PGCert 12-36DL

Newcastle University
Human Resource Management....MA 12FT
International Human Resource Management....MA 12FT

University of Northampton
Human Resource Management....MA 12FT PGDip 24PT
Human Resource Management (CIPD top up)....MA 15PT 15DL

Northumbria University
Business with Human Resource Management.... MSc 12FT
Human Resource Management and Development. MA 24/36PT/ PGDip 24PT
International Human Resource Management.... MSc 12FT

Nottingham Trent University
CIPD Certificate in Human Resources Practice (CHRP)....Cert 9PT
Human Resource Management....MSc 24PT MSc 12FT
Management and Human Resource Management.... MSc 12FT
Postgraduate Diploma Human Resource Management (PDHRM).... PGDip 24PT

Oxford Brookes University
Human Resource Management (MA, DHRM and CHRM)....MA 24PT/PGDip 24PT/PGCert 12PT
Human Resource Management ....MSc 12FT 24PT

Plymouth University
Human Resource Management....PGDip 24PT/MA 12FT 36PT

University of Portsmouth
Human Resource Development (Top-up).... MSc 6FT 12PT
Human Resource Management.... PGDip 24PT MSc 12FT
Human Resource Management (Top-up).... MSc 6FT 12PT
International Human Resource Management.... MSc 12FT

Queen Margaret University, Edinburgh
Human Resources for Health.... MSc 12FT 24PT/PGDip 8FT 16PT/ PGCert 4FT 8PT

Queen Mary, University of London
International Human Resource Management and Employment Relations.... MSc 12FT

Queen's University Belfast
Human Resouce Management ....MA 36PT/PGDip 24PT MSc 12FT

University of Reading
Applied Management....MA 36PT/PGDip 24PT
Construction Management .... MSc 12FT
International Human Resource Management .... MSc 12FT
Project Management .... MSc 24PT

Robert Gordon University
Human Resource Management.... MSc 12FT 36PT 36DL/ PGDip 8FT 24PT 24DL/PGCert 4FT 12PT 12DL

University of Roehampton
International Management with Human Resource Management MSc 12FT
Post Graduate Diploma- International Management with Human Resource Management....PGDip 9FT 24PT

Royal Holloway, University of London
International HRM.... MSc 12FT

University Campus Suffolk
Human Resource Management.... PGDip 12FT 24PT
MA Human Resource Strategy....MA Approx15FT

University of Salford
Human Resource Management and Development.... MSc 12FT 24PT/PGDip 8FT 24PT/PGCert 4FT 9PT

Sheffield Hallam University
Human Resource Leadership.... MSc 12PT
Human Resource Management/Development.... MSc 12FT 24-36PT/PGDip 24PT
International Human Resource Management.... MSc 12FT
Organisational Psychology ....MSc 12FT 24PT

University of Sheffield
Human Resource Management.... MSc 12FT

University of South Wales
Human Resource Management....PGDip 24PT MSc 12FT 36PT MSc 24PT

Southampton Solent University
Human Resource Management....MA 12FT

University of Southampton
Human Resource Management.... MSc 12FT/PGDip 9FT

University of St Andrews
Management (Human Resource Management)....MLitt 12FT

University of Stirling
Human Resource Management.... MSc 12FT/PGDip 9FT
Human Resource Management and Socio Economic Development....MSc 12FT/PGDip 9FT/PGCert 6FT

University of Strathclyde
Human Resource Management....MSc 12FT 24PT/ PGDip 9FT 24PT
International Human Resource Management.... MSc 12FT

University of Sunderland
Human Resource Management....MSc 12FT 24-36PT

University of Surrey
Human Resource Management.... MSc 12FT 24PT 24DL
Intercultural Communication with International Business....MA 12FT 24PT

Swansea University
Management (Human Resource Management).... MSc 12FT

Swansea Metropolitan University
Certificate in Personnel Practice....CPP 12PT
Chartered Institute of Personnel and Development (CIPD) - Professional Development Scheme....CIPD 36PT

Teesside University
Human Resource Management.... MA 12FT 24PT

Trinity College Dublin - the University of Dublin
European Employment Studies....MSc 12FT 24PT

University of Wales Trinity Saint David
Human Resource Managemant....MBA 12FT 24PT/PGCert 12FT 24PT/PGDip 12FT 24PT

University of Ulster
Human Resource Management.... MSc 24PT

University of Warwick
Industrial Relations & Managing Human Resources....MA 12FT 24PT

West Herts College
Chartered Institute of Personnel and Development.. PGDip 24PT

University of West London
Human Resource Management.... PGDip 24PT
Human Resource Management (Top-up)....MA 12PT

University of the West of Scotland
Human Resource Management....MSc 33PT/PGDip 24PT

University of the West of England, Bristol
Human Resources Management.... MA 12FT 18-24PT
International Human Resource Management....MA 12FT

University of Westminster
Human Resource Management.... MA 12FT 24PT
Human Resource Management (Evening Study)....MA 24PT
International Human Resource Management....MA 12FT
Personnel and Development (Evening Study)....MA 24PT

University of Winchester
Human Resource Management CIPD (top-up)....MSc 6PT

University of Wolverhampton
Human Resource Development and Organisational Change MSc 24PT/PGDip 24PT
Human Resource Development and Organisational Change (top-up).... MSc 12PT
Human Resource Management....MA 12FT 24PT/PGDip 24PT
Human Resource Management (top-up).... MSc 12PT

University of Worcester
Human Resource Management....MA 36FT 72PT/ PGDip 24FT 48PT/PGCert 12FT 24PT
Management & Human Resources.... MSc 12FT/PGDip 10FT/ PGCert 6FT

University of York
Human Resource Management....MA 12FT

York St John University
Strategic Human Resource Management .... MA 12FT 24PT

Human resource management
Research Courses

Birmingham City University
Human Resources.... MPhil 24FT 36PT/PhD 24FT 36PT

Cardiff University
Human Resource Management.... PhD 36-48FT possiblePT

De Montfort University
Human Resource Management (Research).... MPhil 12 - 24FT 24 - 48PT/PhD 24 - 36FT 36 - 72PT

University of Dundee
Non-Graduating Research in School of Humanities (6 months or more)....Non-Grad 6-24FT
Non-Graduating Research in School of Humanities (less than 6 months).... Non-Grad 1-5FT

University of East Anglia
Business Management .... PhD 36FT 72PT/MPhil 24FT 48PT

University of Hertfordshire
Centre for Research in Employment Studies....PhD 36FT 72PT/ MPhil 24FT 48PT/MRes 12FT 24PT

Lancaster University
Organisation, Work and Technology ....PhD 36FT 48PT/ MPhil 24FT 36PT

London School of Economics and Political Science (LSE)
Employment Relations and Organisational Behaviour.... MPhil 36-48FT/PhD 36-48FT

Manchester Metropolitan University
Human Resource Management and Organisational Behaviour... PhD 48FT 90PT/MPhil 36FT 72PT/MRes 12FT 24PT/MA or MSc by Research 18FT 36PT

Business and social sciences
396 POSTGRADUATE DIRECTORY www.prospects.ac.uk/findcourses

Section sponsored by

BPP
UNIVERSITY
COLLEGE

Business and management studies

The Open University
Human resources and organisation studies........... PhD 36FT 72PT variableDL/MPhil 15FT 24PT variableDL

Oxford Brookes University
Business Doctoral Programmes .... PhD 24-60FT 36-72PT/MPhil 24-36FT 36-48PT

University of Portsmouth
Marketing and Sales.................... MPhil 24FT 48PT/PhD 36FT 72PT

University of Strathclyde
Human Resource Management - Research .... PhD 33FT/ MPhil 12FT/DBA 33FT/MRes 12FT

University of Sunderland
Business & Management............. PhD 36-48FT 48-72PT 48-72DL/ MPhil 12-36FT 24-48PT 24-48DL

Inclusive education
Taught Courses

University of Aberdeen
Bayt al-Maqdis and Jerusalem Studies.... MLitt 12FT 24PT/PGDip 9FT 18PT
Community Learning and Development....MSc 36PT/PGDip 24PT
Effective Teaching in Numeracy......................................PGCert 12PT
Inclusive Practice ....MEd 24PT
Plurilingual Education................................MEd 24PT/PGCert 12PT

University of Birmingham
Inclusion and Special Educational Needs...MEd 12FT 24PT 72DL/ MA 12FT 24PT 72DL/Diploma 12FT 24PT 48DL
Management of Special Education in Developing Countries .... MEd 12FT/PGDip 12FT/B/Phil 12FT
Special Educational Needs Coordination (National Award for SENC) ....PGCert 12/24PT

University of Bolton
Inclusive Education .... MA 12FT 24-60PT

University of Brighton
Inclusive Arts Practice ....MA 24-72PT/PGCert 24-72PT

University of Bristol
Disability Studies: Inclusive Theory and Research .... MSc 12FT 12-60PT/PGDip 12FT 12-60PT/PGCert 12FT 12-60PT
Education: Special and Inclusive Education .... MEd 12FT 24-60PT

Brunel University
Education (Gifted Education) .... MA 12FT 24PT

University of Central Lancashire
Excellence in Leadership for Inclusion and Community..... PGCert 12-24PT

University of Chester
Education: Inclusion and Marginalisation ......MA 36-72PT/PGDip 36-60PT/PGCert 12-36PT

University College Cork
Special Educational Needs ....PGDip 9FT

University of Dundee
Advanced Practice (Practice Education) ....MSc 36DL

Edge Hill University
Special Educational Needs Coordination ....National Award 12-36DL

University of Edinburgh
Additional Support for Learning (Inclusive Education) MEd 72PT/ PGDip 48PT/PGCert 24PT
Inclusive and Special Education...MSc 12FT

University of Exeter
Education Taught Doctorate........ EdD by taught 24FT 48PT 48DL
Educational Research .... MSc 12FT 24PT 12-24DL
Special Educational Needs Masters...........PGDip 12FT/MEd 12FT/ PGCert 6FT

University of Glasgow
Inclusive Education: Research, Policy & Practice...MEd 12FT 72PT
Professional Development in Education .... PGCert 60 maxPT

University of Gloucestershire
Inclusive Education .... MA 24PT/PGDip 20PT/PGCert 8PT
Teacher Training (Primary) .... PGCE 12FT
Teacher Training (Secondary)...PGCE 12FT

University of Hull
Inclusive Education .. MEd 18FT 36PT/AdvDip 12FT 24PT/AdvCert 6FT 12PT

Institute of Education
Change to Teach .... Change to Teach Scheme 10PT
Developing SEN Co-ordination - SENCO .... PGCert 12PT 12DL
Development Education....................................... MA 12FT 24PT
Special and Inclusive Education............................... MA 12FT 24PT
Special and Inclusive Education (SINGAPORE)GradDip 12FT 24PT
Transnational Perspectives on Democratic Education.....30 credit module 3FT

King's College London
Inclusive Education & Technology .... MA 12FT 24-48PT
Language, Ethnicity & Education .... MA 12FT 24-48PT

University of Leeds
Co-ordinating Inclusive Provision for Children with Learning Difficulties...PGCert 12PT
Disability and Special Education .... MA 12FT 24PT
Provision for Children with Developmental Disorders .... PGCert 12FT
Special Educational Needs ....MA 12FT 24PT/PGDip 12FT 24PT

London Metropolitan University
Assessment for Specific Learning Difficulties in FE and HE............ PGDip 12PT

London South Bank University
Teachers of Adults with Learning Difficulties ....PGCert 12-24PT

Manchester Metropolitan University
Autistic Spectrum Conditions .... MA 12-60PT
Urban Education................................... MA 12FT 24 - 60PT

University of Manchester
Profound and Complex Learning Disability................ MSc 12-15FT 24-36DL/PGDip 12-15FT 18DL/PGCert 12DL

Middlesex University
Inclusive Education ....MA 36PT 36DL

University of Northampton
Special Educational Needs ....MA 24PT

Northumbria University
Special Educational Needs and Inclusion....................PGCert 12PT

Queen's University Belfast
Inclusion and Special Needs Education .... DASE 12FT 60PT/MEd 12FT 60PT

University of Reading
Education (Inclusive Education).....MA 12FT 24-84PT/PGDip 12FT
Inclusive Education .... MA 12FT 24-60PT

University of Roehampton
Special and Inclusive Education.......................PGCert 6FT 12-24PT
Post Graduate Diploma- Special and Inclusive Education ...PGDip 9FT 24-48PT
Special and Inclusive Education .... MA 12FT 24-48PT

Sheffield Hallam University
Inclusion ....MA 12FT 36PT/PGDip 24PT

University of South Wales
SEN Developmental Co-ordination Disorder (Dyspraxia) .... PGCert 12DL
SEN Hearing Impairment .... PGDip leading to MA SEN 24PT
Special Educational Needs .... MA 12FT 36PT

Teesside University
Promoting Inclusive Practice in Education............. PGDip 24 - 36PT

University of Wales Trinity Saint David
Inclusive Studies ...MA 12FT 24PT/PGCert 12FT 24PT/PGDip 12FT 24PT
Inclusive Studies (Neuro-diversity)....MA 12FT 24PT/PGCert 12FT 24PT/PGDip 12FT 24PT
Special Educational Needs ....GradCert 12PT

Inclusive education
Research Courses

Bath Spa University
Children and the Environment ....PhD 24 - 60FT 36 - 72PT

University of Nottingham
Cognitive Development and LearningPhD 36FT 72PT/MPhil 24FT 48PT

The Open University
Children, young people, families, and personal relationships .... PhD 36FT 72PT/MPhil 15FT 24PT
Doctorate in Education ....EdD 36PT
Education and Educational Technology.............................EdD 36PT variableDL/PhD 36FT 72PT variableDL/MRes 12FT/MPhil 15FT 24PT variableDL
Multimodal meaning making......PhD 36FT 72PT variableDL/EdD 36PT/MRes 12FT
Technology Enhanced Learning ...PhD 36FT 72PT variableDL/EdD 36PT/MRes 12FT

Industrial relations
Taught Courses

Birmingham City University
Public Relations.. MA 12FT 24PT

Brunel University
Human Resource Management and Employment Relations........ MSc 12FT

University of Cambridge
Industrial Systems, Manufacturing and Management .... MPhil 9FT

University of Central Lancashire
International Relations ....MA 12FT

University of East Anglia
Employment Law............................... LLM 12FT 24PT/PGCert 12FT
Industrial Economics .... MSc 12FT

National University of Ireland Galway
Industrial Relations & Human Resource Management........ MSc 9 approxFT

University of Hertfordshire
Human Resource Management and Employment Relations...MA 12FT 24PT/PGCert 12FT 24PT/PGDip 12FT 24PT

Keele University
Industrial Relations and Employment LawMA 24PT/PGDip 18PT/ PGCert 18PT

Leeds Metropolitan University
Specialist Community Public Health Nursing - Health Visiting .... MSc 24PT/PGDip 12FT 24PT

University of Leicester
Industrial Relations and Workplace Learning ....MSc 24-36DL/ GradDip 18DL/PGCert 12DL

London School of Economics and Political Science (LSE)
Management, Organisations and Governance .... MSc 12FT

University of Manchester
International Human Resource Management and Comparative Industrial Relations... MSc 12FT

Nottingham Trent University
Employment Law................................. LLM 12FT 24PT

University of Nottingham
Public Procurement Law and Policy .... PGDip 21PT/LLM 24PT/ PGCert 12-21PT

Ruskin College
International Labour and Trade Union Studies....... MA 12FT 24PT

University of Salford
Industrial and Commercial Combustion Engineering .MSc 36DL/ PGDip 12DL/PGCert 12DL

School of Oriental and African Studies - SOAS
Labour, Social Movements and Development .... MSc 12FT 24PT
MA Globalisation and Multinational Corporations......................... MA 12FT 24PT

University of Warwick
Certificate in Employment Research ....CER 12PT
Industrial Relations & Managing Human Resources.......MA 12FT 24PT
International Employment Relations...................... MA 12FT 24PT
Social Research with Specialism in Comparative Labour Studies... MA 12FT 24PT

University of Westminster
Public Relations...MA 12FT 24-48PT

Industrial relations
Research Courses

Cardiff University
Work, Employment and Globalisation.........PhD 36FT possiblePT/ MPhil 12FT possiblePT

University of Hertfordshire
Centre for Research in Employment Studies.........PhD 36FT 72PT/ MPhil 24FT 48PT/MRes 12FT 24PT

Keele University
Employment policy and Equalities .. PhD 24-48FT 48-96PT/MPhil 12-24FT 24-36PT

University of Kent
Industrial Relations.... PhD 36FT 60PT/MA by research 12FT 24PT

Lancaster University
Organisation, Work and Technology ..PhD 36FT 48PT/MPhil 24FT 36PT

London Metropolitan University
Dept of Law Governance and International Relations.... PhD Max 60FT Max 96PT/MPhil Max 36FT Max 54PT

London School of Economics and Political Science (LSE)
Employment Relations and Organisational Behaviour .... MPhil 36-48FT/PhD 36-48FT

University of Salford
Institute for Materials ResearchPhD 36FT/MSc by research 12FT/ MPhil 12FT

School of Oriental and African Studies - SOAS
Development Studies...PhD 36FT 48-60PT
Economics .... PhD 36FT 72PT/MPhil 24FT 36PT
Politics .... PhD 36FT 72PT/MPhil 24FT 36PT

University of Warwick
Employment Research .... PhD 36FT 60PT

Insurance studies
Taught Courses

City University London
Insurance and Risk Management.........................MSc 9-12FT 24PT

University of Exeter
Climate Change and Risk Management.................MSc 12FT 24PT

Glasgow School of Art
Sound for the Moving Image......................PGCert 4FT/PGDip 8FT/ MDes 12FT

A journalist at heart, I was blown away by the fascinating picture this programme has painted of the business world. Now I'm converted.

Monica Molesa, International Marketing MSc

Find out more about our marketing programmes including:

- **International Marketing MSc**
- **E-Business (E-Marketing) MSc**
- **Advanced International Business Management and Marketing MSc/MSc**

#vibrant

ncl.ac.uk/nubs

A New Perspective

Business and management studies

University of Glasgow
Financial Risk Management ... MSc 12FT

Heriot-Watt University
Actuarial Management ... MSc 12FT 48PT/PGDip 9FT 48PT
Actuarial Science ... MSc 12FT 24PT/PGDip 9FT 18PT
Financial Mathematics ... MSc 12FT
Quantitative Finance and Mathematics MSc 12FT 24PT/Diploma 9FT 21PT
Quantitative Financial Engineering ... MSc 12FT 24PT/Diploma 9FT 21PT
Quantitative Financial Risk Management ... MSc 12FT/PGDip 9FT

Leeds Metropolitan University
Association of Chartered Certified Accountants - Professional Level (ACCA) ... ACCA 24PT

Manchester Metropolitan University
English Studies: The Gothic ... PGDip 12FT 24PT/MA 15FT 30PT

University of Strathclyde
Quantum Information and Coherence ... MSc 12FT 24PT/PGDip 9FT

Swansea University
Mathematics and Computing for Finance ... MSc 12FT 24/36PT

UCL - University College London
Natural Hazards for Insurers ... PGCert 4PT

University of Westminster
Finance Banking and Insurance ... MSc 12FT

International business
Taught Courses

University of Aberdeen
Business Research ... MRes 12FT 24PT

Anglia Ruskin University
International Business ... MA 18FT 24PT/PGCert 18FT 24PT/PGDip 18FT 24PT
International Business Economics .. MSc 18FT 24PT/PGCert 18FT/PGDip 18FT 24PT
International Logistics ... MSc 18FT

Aston University
Entrepreneurship & International Business ... MSc 12FT
International Business ... MSc 12FT
Strategy & International Business ... MSc 12FT

Bangor University
Accounting and Finance ... MSc 12FT
Accounting and Finance - LondonCentre ... MSc 12FT
Accounting, Banking, Economics, Finance, Management Studies MPhil 24FT/PhD by taught 36FT
Banking and Finance ... MSc 12FT MA 12FT/PGDip 9FTMBA 12FT
Banking and Finance - London Centre ... MSc 12FT
Business and Finance ... MSc 12FT/PGDip 9FT MA 12FT/PGDip 9FT
Business and Marketing ... MA 12FT/PGDip 9FT
Finance ... MBA 12FT MA 12FT/PGDip 9FT MSc 12FT/PGDip 9FT
Finance - London Centre ... MBA 12FT MSc 12FT
International Banking and Development Finance ... MSc 12FT/PGDip 9FT
International Banking and Development Finance - London Centre ... MSc 12FT
Islamic Banking and Finance ... MA 12FT/PGDip 9FT MSc 12FT/PGDip 9FT MBA 12FT
Islamic Banking and Finance - London Centre ... MBA 12FT
Management ... MBA 12FT 36PT
Management and Finance ... MSc 12FT/MA 12FT

University of Bedfordshire
International Human Resource Management ... MA 12-18FT

Birkbeck, University of London
Corporate Responsibility and Sustainability ... MSc 12FT 24PT
Intercultural Communication for Business and Professions ... MA 12FT 24PT
International Business ... MSc 12FT 24PT/MRes 12FT 24PT
International Business and Development ... MSc 12FT 24PT/MRes 12FT 24PT
International Business and the European Union .MSc 12FT 24PT/MRes 12FT 24PT
International Management ... MSc 12FT 24PT

University of Birmingham
International Business ... MSc 12FT
International Marketing ... MSc 12FT

Bournemouth University
International Business Finance ... MSc 12-15FT

University of Bradford
European and International Business Management ... MSc 12FT
Global Finance and Banking ... MSc 12FT
International Business and Management ... MSc 12FT/PGDip 9FT

British Institute of Technology & E-commerce
International Business & Commercial Law ... PGCert 3FT/DipHE 6FT 12PT/MBA 12FT 24PT

Brunel University
International Business ... MSc 12FT
Management ... MSc 12FT

Bucks New University
International MBA ... MBA 15FT

Cardiff Metropolitan University
International Business Management ... MSc 12FT 24PT

University of Central Lancashire
Global Communication Studies ... MA 12FT 24-36PT
Intercultural Business Communication ... MA 12FT 24-36PT
International Business Economics ... MA 12FT
International Business and Management ... MSc 12FT

City University London
Energy Trade and Finance ... MSc 12FT 24PT
Shipping Trade and Finance ... MSc 9-12FT 24PT

Coventry University
International Business ... MSc 12FT 24PT MBA 12FT 30PT

University of Cumbria
International Business ... MBA 12FT
International Business Management ... MA 12FT

De Montfort University
Graduate Certificate in International Business (Pre-Masters) ... GradCert 5-9FT
Intercultural Business Communication ... MSc 12FT 36PT/PGDip 12FT 36PT/PGCert 12FT 36PT
International Business and Corporate Social Responsibility .. MSc 12FT
International Business and Entrepreneurship ... MSc 12FT
International Business and Finance ... MSc 12FT
International Business and HRM ... MSc 12FT
International Business and Management ... MSc 12FT

University of Derby
International Business ... MSc 12FT 36PT
International Business and Finance ... MSc 12FT

Dublin Institute of Technology
International Business ... MSc 12FT

University of Dundee
International Business ... MSc 12FT

Durham University
Management (International Business) ... MSc 12FT

University of East Anglia
International Business Economics ... MA 12FT
International Business Finance and Economics ... MA 12FT
International Commercial and Business Law ... LLM 12FT 24PT
International Public Policy and Public Management ... MRes 12FT 24PT
Sustainable Business ... MSc 12FT

University of East London
International Business Management ... MSc 12FT 24PT/PGDip 8FT 16PT/PGCert 4FT 8PT

Edinburgh Napier University
Business Management with Human Resource Management (HRM) ... MSc 12FT
Corporate Strategy and Finance ... MSc(Eng) 12FT 36PT/PGDip 9FT 12-60DL/PGCert 5FT 12-60DL
International Banking and Finance ... MSc 12FT
International Business Management ... MSc 12FT
International Human Resource Management ... MSc 12FT
Strategic Risk Management and Finance ... MSc 12FT 24PT

University of Edinburgh
International Business and Emerging Markets ... MSc 12FT

European Business School London
International Business ... MA 12 - 16FT MBA 12 - 16FT
Luxury Brand Management ... MA 12 - 16FT

University of Exeter
Finance ... GradDip 9FT
One Planet MBA ... MBA 12FT 30PT

Futex Investment & Trading Academy
Proprietary Trading ... MSc 12FT

Glasgow Caledonian University
International Business ... MSc 12FT
International Development ... MSc 12FT

University of Glasgow
International Business & Entrepreneurship ... MSc 12FT
International Business and Economic Development ... MSc 12FT
International Finance ... MFin 12FT
Management with International Real Estate ... MSc 12FT

University of Greenwich
International Business ... MA 12FT 36PT
International Business in China ... MA 12FT
International Business in India ... MBA 12FT 36PT
International Human Resource Management ... MA 12FT 36PT/PGDip 12FT 36PT

Griffith College Dublin
International Business Management ... PGCert 6FT 12PT PGDip 12FT 24PT MSc 12FT 24PT
MBA (International Business) ... MBA 12FT 24PT

Heriot-Watt University
Finance and Management ... MSc 12FT 24PT/PGDip 9FT 21PT
International Business Management with Finance / HRM / Logistics /Marketing /Sustainability Mgmt. ... MSc 12FT 24PT/PGDip 9FT 21PT
International Management and Business Communication ... MSc 12FT 24PT/PGDip 9FT 21PT
International Marketing ... PGDip 9FT 21PT/MSc 12FT 24PT

University of Hertfordshire
Global Business ... MSc 12FT
International Business ... MSc 12FT/PGDip 12FT/PGCert 12FT

Holborn College
International Business Management ... MSc 12-18FT

University of Huddersfield
International Business Management ... MSc 12FT 24PT
International Business with Financial Services ... MSc 12FT 24PT
International Human Resource Management ... MA 12FT

University of Hull
International Business ... MSc 12FT

Imperial College London
International Health Management ... MSc 12FT

Keele University
International Business ... MA 12FT/PGDip 9FT/PGCert 9FT

University of Kent
Management (International Business) ... MSc 12FT

Kingston University
International Business Management ... MSc 12FT

Lancaster University
Business Administration ... MBA 12FT 24PT
International Business ... MSc 12FT/MRes 12FT/PGDip 12FT

Leeds Metropolitan University
Business (IPOS) ... MA 12FT 60PT
International Business ... MA 12FT 24PT
International Communication ... MA 12FT
International Trade and Finance ... MA 12FT
Responsible Tourism Management ... MSc 12FT 36PT 36DL/PGDip 12FT 24PT 24DL/PGCert 4FT 24PT 24DL

University of Leeds
International Business ... MSc 12FT
International Finance ... MSc 12FT

University of Limerick
International Entrepreneurship Management ... MBS 12FT
International Studies ... MA 12FT

University of Lincoln
International Business ... MSc 12FT 24PT

Liverpool Hope University
International MBA ... International MBA 12FT 24PT

University of Liverpool
International Business ... MSc 12FT 24PT

London Business School
Sloan Masters in Leadership and Strategy ... MSc 12FT

London Metropolitan University
International Business ... MA 12FT 24PT

London South Bank University
Business Administration - Chinese Business Practice ... MBA 12FT
Eur-Asian Business Management ... MBA 18FT
International Business ... MSc 15FT 24PT

Manchester Metropolitan University
International Business Management ... MSc 12FT/PGDip 9FT

University of Manchester
Global Business Analysis ... MBus 12FT
International Business and Management ... MSc 12FT

Middlesex University
International Business and Trade (Top-up) ... MA 15FT

Newcastle University
Advanced International Business Management and Marketing ... MSc/MSc (Dual Award) 17FT
Advanced International Business and Management ... MA/MSc (Dual Award) 17FT
International Business Law ... LLM 12FT 24PT
International Business Management ... MA 12FT

University of Northampton
International Environmental Management ... MSc 24PT 24DL
International Political Economy ... MA 12FT 24PT

Nottingham Trent University
International Business ... MSc 12FT
Management ... MSc 12FT
Management and Human Resource Management ... MSc 12FT
Management and International Business ... MSc 12FT
Management and Marketing ... MSc 12FT

University of Nottingham
International Business ... MSc 12FT

Oxford Brookes University
International Business Economics ... MSc 12FT 24PT
Management (Certificate) - Online ... CM 12DL
Management (Certificate) - Online (Solihull College) ... CM 12DL
Management, Certificate in (Corporate Online) ... CM 12DL

Section sponsored by
BPP UNIVERSITY COLLEGE

Business and social sciences
www.prospects.ac.uk/findcourses POSTGRADUATE DIRECTORY 399

Business and management studies

Plymouth University
International Logistics and International Supply Chain Management....MSc 12FT 24PT

University of Portsmouth
International Business and English....MA 12FT

Queen Mary, University of London
Accounting and Finance....MSc 12FT
Business Finance....MSc 12FT 24PT
International Business and Politics....MSc 12FT 24PT

Queen's University Belfast
International Business....MSc 12FT

University of Reading
Business Economics....MSc 12FT 24PT
Economics of International Business and Finance....MSc 12FT 24PT
Entrepreneurship and Management....MSc 12FT
International Business....MSc 12FT 24PT
International Business and Economic Development....MSc 12FT 24PT
International Business and Finance....MSc 12FT
International Human Resource Management....MSc 12FT
International Management....MSc 12FT
Marketing and International Management....MSc 12FT 24PT
Marketing and International Management....MSc 12FT

Regent's Business School London
MA Global Management....MA 12-16FT

Robert Gordon University
International Business....MSc 12FT 36DL/PGDip 8FT 24DL
Management....MSc 12FT/PGDip 9FT/PGCert 6FT

University of Salford
International Business...MSc 12FT 36PT/PGDip 8FT 24PT/PGCert 4FT 9PT
International Business Law and RegulationLLM 12FT/PGDip 8FT/PGCert 4FT
International Corporate FInanceMSc 12FT 36PT/PGDip 8FT 24PT/PGCert 4FT 9PT
International Events Management....MSc 12FT 36PT/PGDip 8FT 24PT/PGCert 4FT 9PT
Translating for International Business. MA 12FT 36PT/PGDip 9FT 24PT

School of Oriental and African Studies - SOAS
Economics (with Reference to the Asia Pacific Region)....MSc 12FT 24PT
Finance and Financial Law....MSc 12FT 24-36PT
Global Energy and Climate Policy....MSc 12FT 24PT
International Management (China)....MSc 12FT 24-36PT
International Management (Japan)....MSc 12FT 24-36PT
International Management (Middle East and North Africa).. MSc 12FT 24PT
International Studies and Diplomacy....MA 12FT 24-36PT/PGDip 12FT 24PT
Labour, Social Movements and Development....MSc 12FT 24PT
Law, Development and Globalisation....MA 12FT 24PT
MA Globalisation and Multinational CorporationsMA 12FT 24PT
Public Policy and Management (Distance Learning)....MSc 24DL/PGDip 12DL

Sheffield Hallam University
International Business Management....MSc 12FT/PGDip 9FT/PGCert 6FT
Managing Global Business....MSc 12FT/PGDip 6FT/PGCert 3FT

University of Sheffield
East Asian Business....MSc 12FT
International Commercial Law and Practice....LLM 12FT 24PT
International Development and Planning....MA 12FT
International Management....MSc 12FT

Southampton Solent University
Business Studies....MA 24-72PT 24-72DL

University of Southampton
International Business Law....LLM 12FT 24PT
International Management....MSc 12FT/PGDip 9FT

University of St Andrews
International Business....MLitt 12FT

Staffordshire University
International Business....MSc 12-16FT

University of Stirling
International Business....MSc 12FT/PGDip 9FT
International Business and Socio Economic Development.... MSc 12FT/PGDip 9FT/PGCert 6FT

University of Strathclyde
International Economic Law....LLM 12FT 24PT/PGDip 9FT 21PT/PGCert 4FT 8PT
International Management....MA 12FT/PGDip 9FT
International Marketing....MSc 12FT 24PT/PGDip 9FT 18PT

University of Surrey
Intercultural Communication with International Business....MA 12FT 24PT
International Financial Management....MSc 12FT 24PT

Teesside University
Management....PGCert 12PT
Management....MSc 12FT 24PT

University of Ulster
International Business....MSc 12FT 36PT/PGDip 9FT 18PT
International Business by e-learning....MSc 24PT 12DL/PGDip 18PT 18DL/PGCert 12PT 12DL

UCL - University College London
Management....MSc 12FT 24PT
Management Science and Innovation....MRes 12FT

Webster Graduate School London
International Business....MA 14FT

University of West London
International Business Management....MSc 12FT/MA 12FT

University of the West of Scotland
International Business....MSc 12FT 36PT/Diploma 9FT 24PT

University of Westminster
International Business and Management....MA 12FT

University of Wolverhampton
International Business Management....MA 12FT

University of York
International Business & Strategic Management....MSc 12FT

York St John University
International Business....MA 12FT 60PT

International business
Research Courses

Bangor University
Accounting, Banking, Economics, Finance, Management Studies....MPhil 24FT/PhD 36FT

University of Central Lancashire
International Business....PhD/MPhil/MA by research

University of Chester
Business....DBA 24-84PT

University of Dundee
Non-Graduating Research in School of Business (6 months or more)....Non-Grad 6-24FT
Non-Graduating Research in School of Business (less than 6 months)....Non-Grad 1-5FT

Manchester Metropolitan University
Strategy, Enterprise and International Business....PhD 48FT 90PT/MPhil 36FT 72PT/MRes 12FT 24PT/MA or MSc by Research 18FT 36PT

Queen's University Belfast
Management....PhD 36FT 72PT/MPhil 24FT 48PT

UCL - University College London
Management Science and Innovation....PhD 36FT 60PT

International management
Taught Courses

University of Aberdeen
Business Research....MRes 12FT 24PT

Aberystwyth University
International Business Management....MSc 12FT 24PT/PGDip 9FT 18PT/PGCert 6FT 12PT

Anglia Ruskin University
International Management Practice....MSc 18FT/PGDip 18FT/PGCert 18FT

Aston University
Strategy & International Business....MSc 12FT

Bangor University
Accounting and Finance....MSc 12FT
Accounting and Finance - LondonCentre....MSc 12FT
Accounting, Banking, Economics, Finance, Management Studies MPhil 24FT/PhD by taught 36FT
Banking and Finance....MSc 12FT MA 12FT/PGDip 9FT MBA 12FT
Banking and Finance - London Centre....MSc 12FT
Business and Finance ..MSc 12FT/PGDip 9FT MA 12FT/PGDip 9FT
Business and Marketing....MA 12FT/PGDip 9FT
Finance.... MBA 12FT MA 12FT/PGDip 9FT MSc 12FT/PGDip 9FT
Finance - London Centre....MBA 12FT MSc 12FT
International Banking and Development Finance....MSc 12FT/PGDip 9FT
International Banking and Development Finance - London Centre....MSc 12FT
International Media Management....MSc 12FT 24PT
Islamic Banking and Finance....MA 12FT/PGDip 9FT IMSc 12FT/PGDip 9FT MBA 12FT
Islamic Banking and Finance - London Centre....MBA 12FT
Management....MBA 12FT 36PT
Management and Finance....MSc 12FT/MA 12FT

University of Bath
International Management....MSc 12FT

University of Bedfordshire
International Business and Management....MSc 12-15FT

University of Birmingham
International Accounting and Finance....MSc 12FT

University College Birmingham
Tourism Business Administration....MA 12FT 24PT 18-30DL/PGDip 9FT 18PT 24DL/PGCert 5FT 9PT 12DL
Tourism Destination Management....MA 12FT 24PT/PGDip 9FT 12PT

University of Bradford
European and International Business Management....MSc 12FT
International Business and Management... MSc 12FT/PGDip 9FT
International Development Management....MA 12FT 24PT/PGDip 9FT 21PT/PGCert 9PT
International Marketing....MSc 12FT

University of Brighton
International Event Management....MSc 12FT 24-72PT/PGCert 12FT 24-72PT/PGDip 12FT 24-72PT
International Hospitality Management....MSc 12FT 24-72PT/PGDip 12FT 24-72PT/PGCert 12FT 24-72PT
International Management....MSc 15FT/PGCert 15FT/PGDip 15FT
International Management....MBA 18FT 36PT/PGDip 18FT 36PT/PGCert 18FT 36PT
International Tourism Management.... MSc 12FT 24-72PT/PGDip 12FT 24-72PT/PGCert 12FT 24-72PT
Tourism and International Development....MSc 12FT 24-72PT/PGDip 12FT 24-72PT/PGCert 12FT 24-72PT

Brunel University
Accounting and Business Management....MSc 12FT
Global Supply Chain Management....MSc 12FT
Human Resource Management....MSc 12FT
International Business....MSc 12FT
Marketing....MSc 12FT

University of Central Lancashire
International Business and Management....MSc 12FT
International Tourism Management....MSc 12FT 24PT/PGDip 12FT 24PT

University of Chester
Coaching for Internal Business Solutions and Team Development (WBIS)....MA 24-72PT/PGDip 24-60PT/PGCert 12-36PT

Coventry University
International Marketing....MSc 12FT 24PT
International Tourism Management....MSc 12FT 24-30PT

University of Cumbria
International Business....MBA 12FT
International Business Management....MA 12FT

De Montfort University
International Business and Corporate Social Responsibility.. MSc 12FT
International Business and Management....MSc 12FT

University of Derby
Business and Payroll Management....MSc 36PT

University of Dundee
International Mineral Resources Management....MBA 18DL 12FT

University of East Anglia
Advanced Business Management....MSc 12FT
Advanced Management....MSc 12FT
Business Management....MSc 12FT
Entrepreneurship and Strategy....MSc 12FT
Finance and Management....MSc 12FT
Human Resource Management....MSc 12FT
International Public Policy and Public Management...MRes 12FT 24PT
Management....MSc 12FT
Marketing and Management....MSc 12FT

University of East London
International Business Management....MSc 12FT 24PT/PGDip 8FT 16PT/PGCert 4FT 8PT
International Marketing Management MSc....MSc 12FT 24PT/PGDip 8FT 16PT/PGCert 4FT 8PT

Edinburgh Napier University
International Business Management....MSc 12FT
International Tourism Management.... MSc 12FT 24-36PT/PGDip 9FT 24-36PT

University of Essex
Accounting and Financial Management....MSc 12FT 24PT
Accounting and Management...MSc 12FT 24PT/MRes 12FT 24PT
Finance and Management....MSc 12FT 24PT
Global Project Management....MSc 12FT 24PT
International Management....MSc 12FT 24PT
Marketing and Brand Management....MA 12FT 24PT

University of Exeter
International Management....MSc 9FT/MSc 12FT
International Tourism Management....MSc 12FT

National University of Ireland Galway
International Management....MSc 12FT

Business and management studies

Glasgow Caledonian University
Global Supply Chain and Logistics Management .... MSc 12FT 24PT
International Business .... MSc 12FT
International Events Management .... MSc 12FT 24DL
International Human Resource Management .... MSc 12FT 24PT
International Project Management .... MSc 12FT 24PT 24-48DL/PGDip 12FT 24PT
International Tourism Management ..MSc 12FT 24PT FlexibleDL/PGDip 9FT
Management .... MSc 12FT FlexiblePT/PGDip 9FT FlexiblePT/PGCert 6FT FlexiblePT

University of Glasgow
International Management & Design Innovation .... MSc 12FT
International Management and Leadership .... MSc 12FT
International Strategic Marketing .... MSc 12FT
Management .... MSc 12FT
Organisational Leadership (Oman) .... MSc 24PT/PGDip 18PT/PGCert 12PT

Heriot-Watt University
International Management and Business Communication... MSc 12FT 24PT/PGDip 9FT 21PT

University of Huddersfield
International Business Management .... MSc 12FT 24PT

Imperial College London
Economics & Strategy for Business .... MSc 12FT

King's College London
International Management .... MSc 12FT

Kingston University
Internal Communication Management .... MA top-up 11PT/PGDip 12PT
International Business Management .... MSc 12FT

Lancaster University
Management .... MSc 12FT/PhD by taught 36FT

Leeds Metropolitan University
International Business .... MA 12FT 24PT
International Events Management....MSc 12FT 24PT/PGDip 12FT 24PT/PGCert unknownFT 12PT

University of Leeds
International Business .... MSc 12FT
International Marketing Management .... MSc 12FT

University of Liverpool
International Management (Online Degree) .... MSc 24FT 24+PT

London Metropolitan University
International Business .... MA 12FT 24PT

London School of Economics and Political Science (LSE)
Development Management .... MSc 12FT 24PT
Global Management .... MSc 17PT 17BM
International Management .... MSc 12FT
Management and Strategy .... MSc 12FT
TRIUM Global Executive .... MBA 16PT

London South Bank University
International Business .... MSc 15FT 24PT
International Management .... MA 12FT

Loughborough University
International Management (for non-business graduates)..... MSc 12FT

Manchester Metropolitan University
International Business Management .... MSc 12FT/PGDip 9FT
International Tourism Management .... MSc 12FT 24-60PT

University of Manchester
Chinese Business and Management .... MSc 12FT

Newcastle University
Advanced International Business Management and Marketing .... MSc/MSc (Dual Award) 17FT
Advanced International Business and Management .... MA/MSc (Dual Award) 17FT
Cross-Cultural Communication and International Management .... MA 12FT 24PT
International Business Management .... MA 12FT
International Marketing .... MSc 12FT

Northumbria University
Business with International Management .... MSc 12FT
Global Business Management .... MSc 12FT
International Development .... MSc 12FT

Nottingham Trent University
Human Resource Management .... MSc 24PT
International Business .... MSc 12FT
Management .... MSc 12FT
Management and Human Resource Management .... MSc 12FT
Management and International Business .... MSc 12FT
Management and Marketing .... MSc 12FT

The Open University
Development Management ..MSc variableDL/PGDip variableDL/PGCert 12DL

Oxford Brookes University
International Management .... MSc 12FT
International Management and International Relations ...... MSc 12FT 24PT
Management (Certificate) - Online .... CM 12DL
Management (Certificate) - Online (Solihull College) ..... CM 12DL
Management, Certificate in (Corporate Online) .... CM 12DL

Queen Margaret University, Edinburgh
International Management and Leadership .... MSc 12FT 24PT/PGDip 9FT 18PT/PGCert 3FT 6PT
International Management and Leadership with HospitalityMSc 12FT 24PT/PGDip 9FT 18PT/PGCert 3FT 6PT

Queen Mary, University of London
International Financial Management .... MA 12FT
International Human Resource Management and Employment Relations .... MSc 12FT
Modern and Contemporary British History .... MA 12FT 24PT

Queen's University Belfast
International Business .... MSc 12FT

University of Reading
Entrepreneurship and Management .... MSc 12FT
International Business .... MSc 12FT 24PT
International Human Resource Management .... MSc 12FT
International Management .... MSc 12FT
Marketing and International Management .... MSc 12FT 24PT
Marketing and International Management .... MSc 12FT

Regent's Business School London
Business Management in International Travel & Tourism .... MA 21PT

Reseau Universitaire Transmanche
International Management (Consulting) .... MSc 24FT

Robert Gordon University
International Business .... MSc 12FT 36DL/PGDip 8FT 24DL
International Marketing Management ..... MSc 12FT 36DL/PGDip 8FT 24DL/PGCert 4FT 12DL
International Tourism and Hospitality Management .... MSc 12FT 36PT/PGDip 9FT 24PT/PGCert 6FT 12PT
Management .... MSc 12FT/PGDip 9FT/PGCert 6FT

University of Roehampton
International Management .... MSc 12FT 24PT
International Management with Human Resource Management MSc 12FT
International Management with Marketing .... MSc 12FT
International Management .... PGDip 9FT 24PT
International Management with Finance .... PGDip 9FT 24PT
International Management with Human Resource Management .... PGDip 9FT 24PT

Royal Holloway, University of London
International Management .... MBA 12FT
International Management .... MSc 12FT
MBA International Management .... MBA 12FT 24PT

University of Salford
Global Management .... MSc 12FT 36PT/PGDip 8FT 24PT/PGCert 4FT 9PT
International Business ... MSc 12FT 36PT/PGDip 8FT 24PT/PGCert 4FT 9PT
International Business Law and RegulationLLM 12FT/PGDip 8FT/PGCert 4FT
International Hospital and Health Service Leadership and Management .... MSc 12FT/PGDip 8FT/PGCert 4FT

School of Oriental and African Studies - SOAS
Anthropology of Travel, Tourism and Pilgrimage ... MA 12FT 24PT
Environmental Management .... MSc 12FT 24-36PT
International Management (China) .... MSc 12FT 24-36PT
International Management (Japan) .... MSc 12FT 24-36PT
Research for International Development .... MSc 12FT 24PT

Sheffield Hallam University
Global Strategic Marketing .... MSc 12FT
International Business Management .... MSc 12FT/PGDip 9FT/PGCert 6FT
International Marketing .... MSc 12FT
International Tourism Management .... MSc 12FT
Managing Global Business .... MSc 12FT/PGDip 6FT/PGCert 3FT

University of Sheffield
Global Marketing Management .... MSc 12FT/PGDip 9FT/PGCert 6FT
International Commercial Law and Practice .... LLM 12FT 24PT
International Management .... MSc 12FT
Management (International Business) .... MSc 12FT

Southampton Solent University
International Maritime Studies - Shipping and Logistics........ MSc 12FT 24PT
International Maritime Studies: Ship and Shipping Management .... MSc 12FT 24PT

University of Southampton
International Business Law .... LLM 12FT 24PT
International Management .... MSc 12FT/PGDip 9FT

University of St Andrews
International Business .... MLitt 12FT

St Mary's University College, Twickenham
International Tourism Development .... MA 12FT 24PT

Staffordshire University
International Business .... MSc 12-16FT

University of Stirling
Business and Management .... MRes 12FT
International Business .... MSc 12FT/PGDip 9FT
International Business and Socio Economic Development .... MSc 12FT/PGDip 9FT/PGCert 6FT

University of Strathclyde
Business and Management .... MSc 12FT 30PT/PGDip 9FT 20PT
International Management .... MA 12FT/PGDip 9FT

University of Sunderland
International Management .... MA 12FT

University of Surrey
International Business Management .... MSc 12FT/PGDip 9FT

University of Sussex
International Management .... MSc 12FT 24PT

Swansea University
Management (International Management) .... MSc 12FT

Teesside University
International Management .... MSc 12FT 24PT
Management .... PGCert 12PT MSc 12FT 24PT

Trinity College Dublin - the University of Dublin
International Management .... MSc 12FT 24PT

UCL - University College London
Management .... MSc 12FT 24PT
Management Science and Innovation .... MRes 12FT

University of West London
International Business Management .... MSc 12FT/MA 12FT

University of the West of England, Bristol
International Management .... MSc 12FT
International Tourism Management .... MSc 12-18FT 24-36PT

University of Westminster
International Business and Management .... MA 12FT
International Development Management .... MA 12FT

University of Winchester
Managing Contemporary Global Issues ...... MA 12FT 24PT/PGDip 12FT 24PT/PGCert 12FT 24PT

University of York
International Business & Strategic Management .... MSc 12FT

International management
Research Courses

Bangor University
Accounting, Banking, Economics, Finance, Management Studies. .... MPhil 24FT/PhD 36FT

De Montfort University
Strategy and Management (Research)MPhil 12 - 24FT 24 - 48PT/PhD 24 - 36FT 36 - 72PT

University of East Anglia
Business Management .... PhD 36FT 72PT/MPhil 24FT 48PT

University of Essex
Management .... PhD 36FT/MRes 12FT 24PT/MPhil 24FT 48PT

Manchester Metropolitan University
Strategy, Enterprise and International Business .... PhD 48FT 90PT/MPhil 36FT 72PT/MRes 12FT 24PT/MA or MSc by Research 18FT 36PT

The Open University
Strategic management .... PhD 36FT 72PT variableDL/MPhil 15FT 24PT variableDL

Queen's University Belfast
Management .... PhD 36FT 72PT/MPhil 24FT 48PT

UCL - University College London
Management Science and Innovation .... PhD 36FT 60PT

Local governance
Taught Courses

School of Advanced Study, University of London
Advanced Legislative Studies .... LLM 12FT 24PT 24DL

University of the Arts London - Central Saint Martins College of Art and Design
Architecture: Cities and Innovation .... MA 24FT

Bangor University
Language, Policy and Planning .... MA 12FT 24-48PT/PGDip 8FT/PGCert 4FT

University of Bath
Global Political Economy: transformations and policy analysis ... MRes 12FT 24-36PT

Birkbeck, University of London
Global Governance and Emerging Powers .... MSc 12FT 24PT

University of Birmingham
Development Management .... MSc 12FT 24PT/PGDip 9FT 24PT
Local Policy and Politics .... MSc 12FT 24PT
Local and Regional Economic Development .... MSc 12FT 24PT/PGDip 9FT 21PT/GradDip 9FT 21PT/GradCert 9FT 21PT

Section sponsored by

BPP
UNIVERSITY
COLLEGE

Business and social sciences
www.prospects.ac.uk/findcourses **POSTGRADUATE DIRECTORY 401**

Business and management studies

Public Management (with specialist pathways) .... MSc 12FT 24PT/PGDip 12FT 24PT/PGCert 12FT 15PT
Social Research (Local Government and Public Policy) ....MA 12FT 24PT

University of Cambridge
Politics .... MPhil 10FT

Cardiff University
Governance and Devolution..LLM 12FT

University of Central Lancashire
Advancing Equality, Diversity and Inclusion ....MA 12FT 36PT/ PGDip 12FT 36PT/PGCert 12FT 24PT
Equality and Community Leadership............................PGCert 24PT

University of Chester
Conflict Transformation (Work Based and Integrative Studies)....MA 24-72PT/MSc 24-72PT/PGDip 24-60PT/PGCert 12-36PT

University College Cork
Government .... MBS 12FT 24PT

University of Dundee
Advanced Practice (Clinical Governance) ....MSc 36DL

University of East Anglia
Conflict, Governance and International Development....MA 12FT 24PT

University of East London
NGO and Development Management ....MSc 12FT 24PT/ PGDip 8FT 16PT/PGCert 4FT 8PT

University of Exeter
Applied Ecology.. MSc 12FT

London School of Economics and Political Science (LSE)
Local Economic Development .... MSc 12FT
Political Science and Political Economy .... MSc 12FT 24PT

Northumbria University
Public Administration.. MPA 12FT 24PT

University of Oxford
Global Governance and Diplomacy .... MSc 12FT

Queen's University Belfast
Legislative Studies and Practice..MA 12FT

University of Reading
Law ....M (Res) 12FT 24PT/PGDip 9FT/PGCert 9FT
Public Policy .... MA 12FT 24PT 72BM

University of Salford
Intelligence and Security Studies.............................MA 12FT 36PT/ PGDip 9FT 20PT

School of Oriental and African Studies - SOAS
Asian Politics .... MSc 12FT 24PT
Chinese Law .... MA 12FT 24PT
Development Studies with Special Reference to Central Asia....... MSc 12FT 24PT
Environmental Law and Sustainable Development .... MA 12FT 24PT
Global Energy and Climate Policy .... MSc 12FT 24PT
Human Rights Law .... MA 12FT 24PT
International Politics .... MSc 12FT 24PT
International Studies and Diplomacy ....MA 12FT 24-36PT/PGDip 12FT 24PT
Islamic Law... MA 12FT 24PT
Middle East Politics...MSc 12FT 24PT
Near and Middle Eastern Studies........................ MA 12FT 24-36PT
Policy Studies.. PGCert 9FT
Political Economy of Development....................MSc 12FT 24-36PT
Politics of China .... MSc 12FT 24PT
State, Society and Development .... MSc 12FT 24PT
Turkish Studies .... MA 12FT 24PT
Violence, Conflict and Development...................MSc 12FT 24PT

University of Sheffield
Globalisation and Development .... MA 12FT 24PT

University of Stirling
Environmental Policy and Governance........... LLM 12FT/MSc 12FT

University of Sussex
Corruption and Governance .... MA 12FT 24PT

UCL - University College London
Urban Economic Development ....MSc 12FT 24-60PT/PGDip 9FT

Local governance
Research Courses

University of Bath
Global Political Economy: transformations and policy analysis (delivered collaboratively w............................... MRes 12FT 24-36PT

University of Birmingham
Local Government Studies .... PhD 36FT 72PT/MPhil 24FT 48PT

London School of Economics and Political Science (LSE)
Government... PhD 36-48FT/MPhil 36-48FT

School of Oriental and African Studies - SOAS
Development Studies..................................PhD 36FT 48-60PT

Logistics and supply chain management
Taught Courses

Anglia Ruskin University
International Logistics.. MSc 18FT

Aston University
MSc Supply Chain Management .... MSc 12FT

University of Bedfordshire
Logistics and Supply Chain Management........................ MSc 12FT

Belfast Metropolitan College
CIPS Level 4 Diploma in Purchasing and Supply......Diploma 10PT
CIPS Level 5 Advanced Diploma in Purchasing and SupplyAdvDip 10PT
CIPS Level 6 Graduate Diploma in Purchasing and Supply ..... CIPS 10PT

Birmingham City University
International Logistics and Supply Chain ....MSc 24DL
Logistics and Supply Chain Management..............MSc 13FT 30PT

University of Birmingham
MBA (Strategy and Procurement Management) .... MBA 15FT 24-48PT

University of Brighton
Logistics and Supply Chain Management...MSc see siteFT/PGDip see siteFT/PGCert see siteFT

Brunel University
Global Supply Chain Management..................................... MSc 12FT

Bucks New University
International Logistics and Supply Chain Management......... MSc 12-15FT

Cardiff University
International Transport... MSc 12FT 24PT
Logistics and Operations Management .... MSc 12FT
Marine Policy..MSc 12FT 24PT

University of Central Lancashire
Logistics and Supply Chain Management........................ MSc 12FT
Operations Management.. MSc 12FT

City University London
Shipping Trade and Finance....................................MSc 9-12FT 24PT

Section sponsored by BPP UNIVERSITY COLLEGE

Business and social sciences

402 POSTGRADUATE DIRECTORY www.prospects.ac.uk/findcourses

Business and management studies

Supply Chain, Trade and Finance........................... MSc 9-12FT 24PT

Coventry University
Logistics.. MSc 12FT 24-36PT
Supply Chain Management................................ MSc 12FT 24-30PT

Cranfield University
Airport Planning and Management .... MSc 12FT
Airport Planning and Management - Executive............. MSc 36PT
Logistics and Supply Chain Management..MSc 24PT/PGDip 24PT
Logistics and Supply Chain Management - Executive part-time .... MSc 24-60PT/PGDip 24-36PT
Operations Leadership - Fellowship in Operations Leadership ..... PGCert 9FT

Dublin Institute of Technology
Supply Chain Management................................... MSc 36PT

University of East Anglia
Advanced Management .... MSc 12FT
Management.. MSc 12FT
Supply Chain Management..................................... MSc 12FT

University of Exeter
Engineering and Management.. MSc 12FT
International Supply Chain Management....................... MSc 12FT

GCU London
International Operations and Supply Chain Management.... MSc 12FT

Glasgow Caledonian University
Design Practice & Management .... MA 12FT 24PT/PGDip 9FT
Global Supply Chain and Logistics Management .... MSc 12FT 24PT
Particulate Solids Handling .... MSc 30DL/PGDip 30DL

University of Greenwich
Engineering Management (Enterprise Engineering) ..... MSc 12FT 24PT
Engineering Management (Supply Chain Management)....... MSc 12FT 24PT
Global Manufacturing.. MSc 12FT 24PT
Project Management for Logistics .... MSc 12FT
Transport and Logistics Management .... MA 12FT 24PT/PGDip 12FT 24PT
e-Logistics and Supply Chain Management...................... MA 12FT

Heriot-Watt University
Int'nl Business Management with Finance / HRM / Logistics / Marketing /Sustainability Mgmt......... MSc 12FT 24PT/PGDip 9FT 21PT
Logistics and Supply Chain Management.............MSc 12FT 24PT/PGDip 9FT 24PT
Maritime Logistics and Supply Chain Management...... MSc 12FT 24PT/PGDip 9FT 21PT

University of Hertfordshire
Manufacturing Management .... MSc 12-16FT 36PT
Operations and Supply Chain Management....MSc 12-16FT 36PT

University of Huddersfield
Engineering Management.. MSc 12FT
Global Logistics and Supply Chain Management .... MSc 12FT

University of Hull
Logistics and Supply Chain Management........................ MSc 12FT

University of Kent
Logistics... MSc 12FT 24PT
Value Chain Management .... MSc 12FT

Kingston University
Logistics and Supply Chain Management........................ MSc 12FT

Lancaster University
Logistics and Supply Chain Management........................ MSc 12FT

Leeds Metropolitan University
Supply Chain Management & Logistics .... MSc 12FT

University of Lincoln
Logistics Management.. MSc 12FT 24PT

Liverpool John Moores University
International Transport, Trade and Logistics .... MSc 12FT 24PT

University of Liverpool
Operations and Supply Chain Management (Online Degree)....... MSc 24FT 24+PT

Manchester Metropolitan University
Logistics and Supply Chain Management........................ MSc 12FT

University of Manchester
Operations, Project and Supply Chain Management.... MSc 12FT

Middlesex University
MBA Shipping and Logistics .... MBA 24PT

Newcastle University
Dual Award in Operations Management (Newcastle and Groningen)... MSc/MSc (Dual Award) 17FT
Marine Transport with Management .... MSc 12FT
Operations Management, Logistics and Accounting..... MSc 12FT
Operations and Supply Chain Management.................... MSc 12FT
Rail Freight and Logistics.. MSc 12FT

Northumbria University
Business with Logistics and Supply Chain Management .... MSc 12FT
Global Logistics, Operations and Supply Chain Management ...... MSc 12FT

University of Nottingham
Food Production Management.......MSc 12FT 24PT/PGDip 9-12FT 18-24PT
Global Supply Chain Management (Executive)............... MSc 24PT
Logistics and Supply Chain Management......................... MSc 12FT
Public Procurement Law and Policy........... PGDip 21PT/LLM 24PT/PGCert 12-21PT
Supply Chain and Operations Management.................... MSc 12FT

Oxford Brookes University
International Trade and Logistics .... MSc 12FT 24PT

Plymouth University
International Logistics and International Supply Chain Management... MSc 12FT 24PT
International Procurement and Supply Chain Management MSc 12FT 24PT
International Shipping..................................... MSc 12FT/PGDip 9FT
International Supply Chain Management ... MSc 12FT/PGDip 9FT

University of Portsmouth
Logistics and Supply Chain Management............... MSc 12FT 36PT

University of Reading
International Shipping and Finance .... MSc 12FT

Robert Gordon University
International Trade ....LLM 12FT/MSc 9FT/PGDip 6FT
Purchasing and Supply Chain Management.......... MSc 12FT 36PT 36DL/PGDip 9FT 24PT 24DL/PGCert 6FT 12PT 12DL

University of Roehampton
International Management...................................... MSc 12FT 24PT

University of Salford
Manufacturing Systems and Management .... MSc 12FT/PGDip 9FT
Procurement, Logistics and Supply Chain Management .... MSc 12FT 36PT/PGDip 8FT 24PT/PGCert 4FT 9PT

Sheffield Hallam University
Logistics and Supply Chain Management..MSc 12FT 36PT/PGDip 8FT 24PT/PGCert 4FT 12PT

University of Sheffield
Logistics and Supply Chain Management......................... MSc 12FT

University of South Wales
International Logistics and Supply Chain Management................. MSc 12FT 36PT
Strategic Procurement Management .... MSc 12FT 36PT

Southampton Solent University
International Maritime Studies - Shipping and Logistics........ MSc 12FT 24PT
International Maritime Studies: Ship and Shipping Management MSc 12FT 24PT
Shipping Operations..MSc 12-24DL

University of Strathclyde
Supply Chain Management.........MSc 12FT 24PT/PGDip 9FT 18PT

University of Surrey
Operations and Logistics Management .... MSc 12FT

University of Sussex
Global Supply Chain and Logistics Management .... MSc 12FT

Swansea University
Management (Operations, Supply Chain and Project Management) .... MSc 12FT

Swansea Metropolitan University
Food Logistics .... MSc 24PT
Institute of Logistics Qualifications........... Cert 12-36PT/Diploma 12-36PT/AdvDip 12-36PT
Lean and Agile Manufacturing .... MSc 12FT 24PT
Logistics .... MSc 24PT

University of Warwick
Supply Engineering and Logistics............................. MSc 12FT 24PT

University of West London
Chartered Institute of Purchasing and Supply ....CIPS 12-36PT 12-36DL

University of the West of Scotland
Logistics and Supply Chain Management..............MSc 12FT 36PT/Diploma 9FT 24PT

University of Westminster
Logistics and Supply Chain Management......................... MSc 12FT
Purchasing and Supply Chain Management.......... MSc 12FT 24PT

Logistics and supply chain management
Research Courses

University of Bolton
Supply Chain, Business IT, Music and Creative Industries Management Specialisms........... MPhil 18FT 24 - 42PT/PhD 36FT 48 - 72PT

Cardiff University
Logistics and Operations Management .... PhD 36-48FT possiblePT

Cranfield University
Complex Supply Network Dynamics...................................PhD 36FT
Modeling and Optimization in Complex FMCG Supply Networks...PhD 36FT

University of Hull
Centre for Logistics Research..... PhD 36FT 60PT/MPhil 24FT 36PT

London School of Economics and Political Science (LSE)
Management Science......................... MPhil 36-48FT/PhD 36-48FT

Management economics
Taught Courses

University of Central Lancashire
Construction Management (Construction Economics)MSc 24DL/PGDip 12DL/PGCert 6DL

City University London
Business Economics... MSc 12FT
International Business Economics .... MSc 12FT

University of East Anglia
International Business Economics ....MA 12FT

University of Essex
Management Economics.. MSc 12FT

University of Exeter
Economics... MSc 12FT
Economics and Experimental Economics.......................... MSc 12FT

Glasgow Caledonian University
Management..............MSc 12FT FlexiblePT/PGDip 9FT FlexiblePT/PGCert 6FT FlexiblePT

University of Huddersfield
Business Economics.. MSc 12FT

Leeds Metropolitan University
Project Management.. MSc 12FT 24PT
Strategic Project Management................................ MSc 12FT 24PT

London School of Economics and Political Science (LSE)
Economics and Management.. MSc 10FT

University of Reading
Applied Management ....MA 36PT/PGDip 24PT

Royal Holloway, University of London
Economics.. MSc 12FT

School of Oriental and African Studies - SOAS
Environmental Law and Sustainable DevelopmentMA 12FT 24PT
Finance and Development ....MSc 24-60DL/PGDip 12-60DL
International Management (China) ....MSc 12FT 24-36PT
International Management (Japan) ....MSc 12FT 24-36PT
International Management (Middle East and North Africa).. MSc 12FT 24PT
PGDip Policy Studies... PGCert 9FT

Schumacher College
Economics for Transition ....MA 12FT

Staffordshire University
Economics for Business Analysis .... MSc 12-16FT

University of Sussex
Science and Technology Policy.................................. MSc 12FT 24PT

Trinity College Dublin - the University of Dublin
Economic Policy Studies... MSc 24PT
Economics.. MSc(Econ) 12FT 24PT

UCL - University College London
Comparative Business Economics............................ MA 12FT 24PT
Construction Economics and Management... MSc 12FT 24-60PT/PGDip 9FT
Economic Policy.. MSc 12FT

Management economics
Research Courses

University of Bristol
Management................................... MPhil 12FT 24PT/PhD 36FT 72PT

University of Buckingham
Economics and International Studies ....DPhil 36FT 72PT/MPhil 24FT 48PT

University of Exeter
Economics....................................... PhD 48FT 89PT/MPhil 36FT 60PT

Newcastle University
Economics....................................... PhD 36FT 72PT/MPhil 12FT 24PT

University of Salford
Centre for Marketing and Communication ....PhD/MPhil

Management studies
Taught Courses

University of Aberdeen
Management, Enterprise & Innovation.......MSc 12FT/PGDip 9FT/PGCert 6FT

Business and social sciences
www.prospects.ac.uk/findcourses POSTGRADUATE DIRECTORY 403

Business and management studies

University of Abertay Dundee
Energy & Environmental Management .... MSc 12FT
Industrial Environmental Management.....MSc 12FT 24PT/PGDip 9FT 18PT
Management............ MSc 12FT/PGDip 9FT
Oil and Gas Management .... MSc 12FT/PGDip 9FT

Aberystwyth University
Information Management and Leadership ....MSc 12FT 24PT/PGDip 9FT 21PT
International Business ....MSc 12FT 24PT/PGDip 9FT 18PT
Management............ MSc 12FT/PGDip 9FT

Anglia Ruskin University
Business Management of Waste and Resources.......MSc 12-24DL
Engineering Management............MSc 12 - 15FT 24 - 30PT
HRM (Block Delivery)............ PGDip 30PT
Healthcare Management............MSc 24DL
Hospital Management............MBA 12FT 24PT
International Management Practice......... MSc 18FT/PGDip 18FT/PGCert 18FT
Leadership............MA 36DL/PGCert 36DL/PGDip 36DL
Management....... MSc 18FT 24PT/PGDip 18FT 24PT/PGCert 18FT 24PT
Management ....PGCert (CiM) 12PT PGDip (DMS) 12PT
Management Practice............ MSc 18PT
Marketing Management Practice ....MSc 18FT/PGCert 18FT/PGDip 18FT
Solution Focused Thinking & Leadership............ MSc 18PT

Aston University
Doctor of Business Administration........DBA by taught 24FT 48PT 48DL
Engineering Management............ MSc 12FT
Operational Research & Management Studies............ MSc 12FT

BPP Business School
Management............MSc 12FT 24+PT

BPP Law School
Financial Regulation and Compliance............ LLM 12FT 24PT

Bangor University
ACCA (Professional Development)............ACCA 48PT
Accounting and Finance .... MSc 12FT
Accounting and Finance - LondonCentre .... MSc 12FT
Accounting, Banking, Economics, Finance, Management Studies MPhil 24FT/PhD by taught 36FT
Banking and Finance ....MA 12FT/PGDip 9FT MBA 12FT MSc 12FT
Banking and Finance - London Centre .... MSc 12FT
Business and Finance ....MA 12FT/PGDip 9FT MSc 12FT/PGDip 9FT
Business and Marketing ....MA 12FT/PGDip 9FT
CIMA (Professional Development)............CIMA 12PT
Environmental Management............ MBA 12FT
Finance............MA 12FT/PGDip 9FT MSc 12FT/PGDip 9FT MBA 12FT
Finance - London Centre .... MSc 12FT
Finance - London Centre .... MBA 12FT
International Banking and Development Finance.........MSc 12FT/PGDip 9FT
International Banking and Development Finance - London Centre .... MSc 12FT
International Media Management............MSc 12FT 24PT
Islamic Banking and Finance.........MBA 12FT MA 12FT/PGDip 9FT MSc 12FT/PGDip 9FT
Islamic Banking and Finance - London Centre .... MBA 12FT
Law and Management............ MBA 12FT/PGDip 9FT
Management............MBA 12FT 36PT
Management and Finance............ MSc 12FT/MA 12FT
Rheolaeth Amgylcheddol Gynaliadwy (Sustainable Environmental Management)........MSc 12FT 24PT/MA 12FT 24PT

University of Bath
Advanced Management Practice .... MSc 12FT
Management............ MSc 12FT
Management with Finance .... MSc 12FT
Management with Human Resource Management...... MSc 12FT
Management with Marketing .... MSc 12FT
Management with Operations Management .... MSc 12FT

University of Bedfordshire
Chartered Management Institute - Executive Diploma in Management............Executive Diploma in Management 12PT
Doctor of Business Administration............PhD by taught 48-60PT
Engineering Business Management............ MSc 12FT
Managing Business Creativity and Innovation............ MSc 24PT
Postgraduate Certificate in Management ....PGCert 12PT
Telecommunications Management............MSc 12-15FT

Birkbeck, University of London
Accounting and Financial Management ....MSc 12FT 24PT
Business Innovation with E-business............MSc 12FT 24PT/MRes 12FT 24PT
Career Management and Coaching............ MSc 24PT
Corporate Governance and Business Ethics ....MSc 12FT 24PT/MRes 12FT 24PT/PGCert 12PT
Creative Industries (Management)............MSc 12FT 24PT
Human Resource Management............MSc 12FT 24PT
Information Systems and Management....MSc 12FT 24PT/PGDip 12FT 24PT
International Business ....MSc 12FT 24PT/MRes 12FT 24PT
International Business and Development ....MSc 12FT 24PT/MRes 12FT 24PT
International Field Leadership ....PGCert 12PT
International Management............MSc 12FT 24PT
Management............ MSc 12FT 24PT/MRes 12FT 24PT/PGCert 12FT 24PT PGDip 12FT 24PT/PGCert 12PT
Management Consultancy and Organisational Change............ MSc 12FT 24PT
Management in the Public Sector....... MSc 12FT 24PT/MRes 12FT 24PT
Marketing............MSc 12FT 24PT/MRes 12FT 24PT
Marketing Communications ....MSc 12FT 24PT
Medical Leadership............ MSc 24-60PT/PGDip 24-60PT/PGCert 24-60PT
Services and Retail Marketing............ MSc 12FT
Sport Governance............PGCert 12PT 12DL
Sport Management ...... PGCert 12PT 12DL/MSc 12FT 24PT/MRes 12FT 24PT
Sport Management and Marketing............MSc 12FT 24PT
Sport Management and the Business of Football .... MSc 12FT 24PT/MRes 12FT 24PT
Sport Marketing............MSc 12FT 24PT

Birmingham City University
Doctorate in Business Administration............DBA by taught 36PT
IT for Strategic Management ....MSc 12/18FT
Management (+ named pathways in Finance, International Business & Marketing)............ MSc 12FT
Quality Management............ MSc 30PT

University of Birmingham
Business Administration ....PGDip 9FT
Development Management MSc/Graduate Diploma ... MSc 12FT 24PT/PGDip 9FT 24PT
Leadership and Management for Social Care...... MA 36PT/PGDip 24PT
Public Management (with specialist pathways)..MSc 12FT 24PT/PGDip 12FT 24PT/PGCert 12FT 15PT

University College Birmingham
Marketing Management (Events, Hospitality or Tourism) ....MA 15FT 21PT/PGCert 6FT 12PT/PGDip 9FT 18PT
Professional Hospitality and Tourism Management..... MA 30DL/PGDip 24DL/PGCert 12DL
Tourism Business Administration ....MA 12FT 24PT 18-30DL/PGDip 9FT 18PT 24DL/PGCert 5FT 9PT 12DL
Tourism Destination Management...... MA 12FT 24PT/PGDip 9FT 12PT
UCB MBA / MBA (Hospitality and Tourism pathway) ... MBA 12FT

University of Bolton
International Management............ MSc 12FT
Management............MA 12 - 18FT

Bournemouth University
International Business Management ....MSc 12-15FT
Management............MSc 12-15FT
Management with Human Resources .... MSc 12FT
Management with Marketing ....MSc 12-15FT

Bradford College
Management............MA 12FT

University of Bradford
Applied Management and Enterprise............ MSc 12FT
Applied Management and Sustainability .... MSc 12FT
European and International Business Management..... MSc 12FT
Finance, Accounting and Management........ MSc 12FT/PGDip 9FT
MSc Applied Management and Sustainability............ MSc 12FT
MSc Applied Managment and Enterprise .... MSc 12FT
Management............ International Master's 12FT
Management............ MSc 12FT/PGDip 9FT
Marketing and Management............ MSc 12FT/PGDip 9FT
Sustainable Operations and Management .... MSc 12FT

University of Brighton
Advanced Social Work and Management............
Change Management............MSc 24PT/PGDip 24PT
Chartered Management Institute .... CMI Diploma see siteFT
Doctor of Business Administration............MA 48 - 76PT/MSc 48 - 76PT
Finance and Management.........MSc see siteFT/PGDip see siteFT/PGCert see siteFT
Health and Management............ MSc 12FT 24 - 72PT/PGDip 12FT 24 - 72PT
Management............MSc 12FT/PGCert 12FT/PGDip 12FT
Management (Innovation)............ MSc 12FT
Management Practice............ MSc 36PT
Podiatry and Management............ MSc 12 - 24FT 24 - 72PT/PGCert 12FT 24PT/PGDip 12 - 24FT 24 - 48PT

University of Bristol
Management............ MSc 12FT

British Institute of Technology & E-commerce
Innovative Management............ PGCert 3FT/DipHE 6FT 12PT/MBA 12FT 24PT

Brunel University
Accounting and Business Management............ MSc 12FT
Applied Corporate Brand Management .... MSc 12FT
Business Intelligence and Social Media............ MSc 12FT
Design Strategy and Innovation ....MA 12FT
Human Resource Management............ MSc 12FT
International Business .... MSc 12FT
Management............ MSc 12FT
Marketing............ MSc 12FT

University of Buckingham
Lean Enterprise .... MSc 24PT
Management in a Service Economy ....MSc 12FT 24PT

Bucks New University
Leadership and Management ....MA 26PT
Online Executive .... MBA 27PT

University of Cambridge
Innovation, Strategy and Organisation ....MPhil 9FT
Management............MPhil 9FT
Technology Policy ....MPhil 9FT

Canterbury Christ Church University
Management Studies............ MA 36PT/DMS 24PT/CMS 12PT

Cardiff Metropolitan University
International Business Management ....MSc 12FT 24PT

Cardiff University
Media Management .... MBA 12FT
Port and Shipping Administration ....PGDip 9FT
Strategic Marketing ....MSc 12FT 24PT

University of Central Lancashire
Business Management .... MSc 12FT
Diploma in Human Resource Management........... Diploma 12PT/CIPD 12PT
Fire and Rescue Service Management ....MSc 12FT 24PT
Human Resource Management/Development..... MSc 12FT 24PT
International Business and Management .... MSc 12FT
Journalism Leadership ....MA 12FT 24PT/PGDip 9FT 18PT/PGCert 9FT 18PT
Logistics and Supply Chain Management............ MSc 12FT
MA Human Resource Management/Development .... MA 12PT 12DL
MSc Internal Communication Management ....MSc 24+PT
Management Studies............ DMS 18PT
Master of Business Administration .... MBA 12FT
Master of Business Administration - Health............ MBA 36PT
Master of Business Administration - Part-time............ MBA 36PT
Postgraduate Certificate in Management (PGCM)....PGCert 18PT
Postgraduate Diploma in Human Resource Management/Development............PGDip 24PT/CIPD 24PT
Project Management......MSc 12FT 36PT/PGDip 6FT 12PT/PGCert 3FT 6PT
Urban Environmental Management... MSc 12FT 24PT/PGDip 9FT 18PT/PGCert 6FT 12PT

University of Chester
Action Research and Appreciative Inquiry (Work Based and Integrative Studies)...MSc 24-72PT/MA 24-72PT/PGDip 24-60PT/PGCert 12-36PT
Change Management (Work Based and Integrative Studies)........ MSc 24-72PT/MA 24-72PT/PGDip 24-60PT/PGCert 12-36PT
Coaching Supervision (Work Based and Integrative Studies) .... MA 24-72PT/PGDip 24-60PT/PGCert 12-36PT
Conflict Transformation (Work Based and Integrative Studies).... MA 24-72PT/MSc 24-72PT/PGDip 24-60PT/PGCert 12-36PT
Dental Practice Management (Work Based and Integrative Studies) ....MA 24-72PT/PGDip 24-60PT/PGCert 12-36PT
Enterprise Facilitation (Work Based and Integrative Studies)........ MA 24-72PT/PGDip 24-60PT/PGCert 12-36PT
Executive Coaching (Work Based and Integrative Studies) ......MA 24-72PT/MSc 24-72PT/PGDip 24-60PT/PGCert 12-36PT
Facilitation (Work Based and Integrative Studies)....MA 24-72PT/MSc 24-72PT/PGDip 24-60PT/PGCert 12-36PT
Innovation Facilitation (Work Based and Integrative Studies) ...... MA 24-72PT/PGDip 24-60PT/PGCert 12-36PT
Leadership Development (Work Based and Integrative Studies).... ....MA 24-72PT/MSc 24-72PT/PGDip 24-60PT/PGCert 12-36PT
Leadership and Management (Work Based and Integrative Studies) ....MA 24-72PT/MSc 24-72PT/PGDip 24-60PT/PGCert 12-36PT
Leading RPL Policy and Practice (Work Based and Integrative Studies) ....MA 24-72PT/PGDip 24-60PT/PGCert 12-36PT
Management............MSc 12FT 24PT
Negotiation and Mediation Skills (Work Based and Integrative Studies) ....MA 24-72PT/MSc 24-72PT/PGDip 24-60PT/PGCert 12-36PT
Professional Studies and Development (Work Based and Integrative Studies)...MA 24-72PT/MSc 24-72PT/PGDip 24-60PT/PGCert 12-36PT
Transpersonal Leadership (Work Based and Integrative Studies)... ....MA 24-72PT/MSc 24-72PT/PGDip 24-60PT/PGCert 12-36PT
Wellbeing in the Workplace (Work Based and Integrative Studies) ....MA 24-72PT/PGDip 24-60PT/PGCert 12-36PT

University of Chichester
Strategic Management............MA 12FT

Business and management studies

Management (Health and Social Care Services) .... MA 27PT/PGDip 18PT/PGCert 12PT

City University London
Information Leadership .... MIL 28PT
Management .... MSc 9-12FT
Maritime Operations and Management .... MSc 12FT 24-36PT
Masters in Innovation, Creativity and Leadership .... MSc 24PT/MInnov 28PT
NGO Management .... MSc 18FT/PGDip 12FT
Voluntary Sector Management .... PGDip 14PT/MSc 24PT

University College Cork
Food Business .... MSc 24FT
Third Sector Management .... MSocSci 24PT

Cornwall College
Management NVQ5 8PT
Management Studies .... DMS 12PT/CMS 12PT

Coventry University
Management by Work Based Learning .... MA 12PT

Cranfield University
Environmental Management for Business ..... MSc 12FT 24-60PT/PGDip 6FT 24PT/PGCert 5FT 24PT
Finance and Management .... MSc 11FT
Global Product Development and Management .... MSc 12FT 24-60PT/PGDip 6FT 24PT/PGCert 5FT 24PT
Management .... MSc 12FT
Management .... PhD by taught 48FT 72PT
Managing Organisational Performance .... MSc 24PT
Managing Performance Improvement .... PGCert 9FT
Operations Leadership - Fellowship in Operations Leadership ..... PGCert 9FT

Cranfield University, Shrivenham
Defence Leadership .... MSc 12FT 60PT/PGDip 6FT 48PT/PGCert 3FT 36PT

University of Cumbria
Events Leadership and Management .... MBA 12FT 36PT/PGCert 12FT 36PT/PGDip 12FT 36PT
Leadership and Management in Policing .... MBA 36PT/PGDip 36PT/PGCert 36PT
Management Studies .... GradDip 24PT/GradCert 12PT
Master of Business Administration .... MBA 12FT 36PT

De Montfort University
Management Studies (CMS) .... PGCert 12PT
Management Studies (DMS) .... PGDip 12PT

University of Derby
International Hospitality Management ...... MA 12FT 36PT/PGDip 12FT/PGCert 9FT
International Spa Management .... MA 36FT
Leadership Coaching .... MA 36PT
MA Management .... MSc 12FT 36PT/PGDip 12FT/PGCert 9FT
Pre MBA/Management Masters Foundation Programme....... ILM Introductory Certificate 2FT
Strategic Management Online .... MSc 12FT 26PT

University Centre Doncaster
Business Administration .... MBA 24PT

University of Dundee
Advanced Practice (Organisational Leadership) .... MSc 36DL
Catchment Hydrology & Management .... MSc 12FT
Information Technology and International Business .... MSc 12FT
International Mineral Resources Management (MBA by distance learning) .... MBA 18DL
International Mineral Resources Management .... MBA 12FT
International Oil and Gas Management (MBA by distance learning) .... MBA 24DL
International Oil and Gas Management ...... MBA 12FT MSc 12FT
Non-Graduating Taught Postgrad Grad School of Natural Resources Law, Policy & Management .... PG module variableFT

Durham University
Executive MA in Management .... MA 30DL
Management .... MSc 12FT
Management .... MA 18FT 48PT
Management (Consulting and Organisational Change) .... MSc 12FT
Management (Innovation Technology and Operations Management) .... MSc 12FT
The Durham EBS Executive Master of Business Administration... MBA 24PT

University of East Anglia
Advanced Business Management .... MSc 12FT
Advanced Management .... MSc 12FT
Business Management .... MSc 12FT
Entrepreneurship and Strategy .... MSc 12FT
Environmental Assessment and Management ..... MSc 12FT 24PT
Finance and Management .... MSc 12FT
Human Resource Management .... MSc 12FT
Investment and Financial Management .... MSc 12FT
Management .... MSc 12FT
Marketing and Management .... MSc 12FT
Supply Chain Management .... MSc 12FT

University of East London
Leadership .... MBA 12FT 24PT/PGDip 8FT 16PT/PGCert 4FT 8PT
Sports Management MSc .... MSc 12FT 24PT/PGDip 8FT 16PT/PGCert 4FT 8PT
Strategic Leadership and Management MA .... MA 36PT/PGCert 12PT/Diploma 24PT

Edge Hill University
Civil Society Leadership .... MA 12-24DL
Critical Management Research .... MRes 12FT 24PT
Management .... MA 12FT 24PT
Management Development .... MSc 24PT
Voluntary and Third Sector Management .... MA 24PT

Edinburgh Napier University
Advanced Leadership Practice (Distance Learning) .... MSc 24PT
Managerial Leadership .... MSc 12FT

University of Edinburgh
Financial Management .... MSc 12FT
Management .... MSc 12FT
Management of Bioeconomy, Innovation and Governance... MSc 12FT 24PT

University of Essex
Management and Organisational Dynamics .... MA 12FT 24PT
Sociology and Management .... MA 12FT 24PT

European Business School London
Creative Leadership .... MA 16-20PT
International Business .... MA 12 - 16FT MBA 12 - 16FT

University of Exeter
Information Technology Management for Business...... MSc 12FT
Leadership and Change .... MA 24PT 24DL/PGDip 20PT/PGCert 9PT
Management .... MRes 12FT GradDip 9FT
One Planet MBA .... MBA 12FT 30PT

Forum for the Future
Leadership for Sustainable Development .... MA 10.5FT

GCU London
International Business Management .... MSc 12FT

National University of Ireland Galway
Enterprise Systems .... MAppSci 12FT 24PT
Innovation Management .... PGDip 12PT 12DL
Strategy Innovation and People Management .... MSc 9 approxFT

Glasgow Caledonian University
Design Practice & Management .... MA 12FT 24PT/PGDip 9FT
Global Supply Chain and Logistics Management .... MSc 12FT 24PT
International Human Resource Management .... MSc 12FT 24PT
International Sports Management .... MSc 12FT
Management .... MSc 12FT FlexiblePT/PGDip 9FT FlexiblePT/PGCert 6FT FlexiblePT
Management of IT Innovation .... MSc 12FT
Operations and Business Management .... MSc 12FT

University of Glasgow
Historically Informed Performance Practice .... MMus 12FT 24PT
Management .... MSc 12FT
Management with Enterprise & Business Growth .... MSc 12FT/PGDip 9FT/PGCert 6FT
Management with Human Resources .... MSc 12FT
Organisational Leadership (Oman) .... MSc 24PT/PGDip 18PT/PGCert 12PT
Strategic Leadership .... PGCert 9FT 12PT

University of Gloucestershire
Computing (IT Management) ... MSc 12FT 24PT/PGDip 8FT 20PT/PGCert 4FT 8PT

Glyndwr University
Executive MBA .... Executive MBA 24PT

Goldsmiths, University of London
Creative & Cultural Entrepreneurship .... MA 12FT 24PT
Global Leadership .... MSc 12FT
Management of Innovation .... MSc 12FT
Social Entrepreneurship .... MA 12FT 24PT/PGDip 6FT 12PT

University of Greenwich
Doctorate in Business Administration (Leadership and Management) .... DBA by taught 48 - 72PT
Management Studies / Management .... PGDip 24PT/MA 12PT

Grimsby Institute of Further and Higher Education
Leadership and Management .... MSc 12FT 24PT

Heriot-Watt University
Business Administration .... MBA 12FT 24PT 84DL
Business Management .... MSc 12FT 24PT/PGDip 9FT 18PT
Business Psychology .... MSc 12FT 24-84PT 12-84DL/PGDip 9FT 15-48PT 9-48DL/PGCert 6FT 12-48PT 6-48DL
European Master in Strategic Project Management...... MSc 16FT
Financial Management .... MSc 84DL
Human Resource Management .... MSc 84DL
Strategic Planning .... MSc 84DL
Strategic Project Management... MSc 12FT 24PT/PGDip 9FT 21PT

University of Hertfordshire
Organisational Change .... DMan 36PT/MA by Research 24PT

University of Hull
Business Management .... MSc 12FT

Keele University
Leadership and Management .... PGCert 12PT
Management .... MA 12FT/PGDip 9FT/PGCert 9FT

University of Kent
Human Resource Management .... MSc 12FT
International Management (or with Management English) .... GradDip 12FT
Management (General) .... MSc 12FT
Management (International Business) .... MSc 12FT
Management (Marketing) .... MSc 12FT
Management Science .... MSc 12FT
Management Science (Business Analytics) .... MSc 12FT

King's College London
Engineering with Management .... MSc 12FT

Kingston University
Analytical Chemistry with Management Studies .... MSc 12FT 24PT
Digital Image & Signal Processing with Management Studies .... MSc 12FT 24-36PT
Doctor of Business Administration .... DBA by taught 48-96PT
Embedded Systems with Management Studies .... MSc 12FT 24-36PT
Management .... MA 24PT
Management Consultancy .... MSc 12FT
Management .... MA top-up 12FT/PGDip 24PT
Network and Information Security with Management Studies... MSc 12FT 24-36PT
Networking and Data Communications with Management Studies .... MSc 12FT 24-36PT
Organisational Development and Change Management ...... MSc 24PT/PGDip 24PT
Pharmaceutical Analysis with Management Studies.... MSc 12FT 24PT
Pharmaceutical Science with Management Studies ..... MSc 12FT
Software Engineering (Web) with Management Studies....... MSc 12FT 24-36PT
Software Engineering with Management Studies .... MSc 12FT 24-36PT
Sustainable Environmental Development with Management Studies .... MSc 12FT 24PT

Lancaster University
Information Technology, Management and Organisational Change .... MSc 12FT/PGDip 12FT/MRes 12FT
Management (With pathways) .... MSc 12FT
Management Learning and Leadership .... MA 24PT
Management Learning and Leadership .... MA 12FT 24PT
Management Science .... MRes 12FT/PhD by taught 36FT
Management Science and Marketing Analytics .... MSc 12FT
Operational Research and Management Science .... MSc 12FT
Organisational Change .... PGCert 12PT
Project Management .... MSc 12FT

Leeds Metropolitan University
Association of Chartered Certified Accountants - Fundementals Level (ACCA) .... ACCA 12PT
Association of Chartered Certified Accountants - Knowledge Level (ACCA) .... ACCA 12PT
Association of Chartered Certified Accountants - Professional Level (ACCA) .... ACCA 24PT
Chartered Institute of Marketing (CIM) .... Diploma 12PT
Chartered Institute of Marketing (CIM).... Professional Certificate 12PT
Coaching Psychology .... PGDip 24PT
Coaching Supervision .... PGDip 24PT
Corporate Communications .... MSc 36PT
Corporate Governance .... MSc 4FT 36PT
Doctorate of Business Administration .... DBA 48PT
Events Management - Distant Learning MSc 24PT/PGCert 12PT/PGDip 24PT
Finance .... MSc 12FT 24PT
International Trade and Finance .... MA 12FT
Leadership & Change Management .... MSc unknownPT
MBA (Executive) E-Learning .... MBA 24DL
MBA (Graduate) .... MBA 12FT
Management .... MSc 12FT 24PT/PGCert 12PT
Marketing .... MSc 12FT
Project Management .... MSc 12FT 24PT
Specialist Community Public Health Nursing - Health Visiting .... MSc 24PT/PGDip 12FT 24PT
Sport Business .... MA 12FT 24PT
Sports Event Management .... MSc 12FT 24PT/PGCert 12FT 24PT/PGDip 12FT 24PT
Strategic Project Management .... MSc 12FT 24PT
Supply Chain Management & Logistics .... MSc 12FT

University of Leicester
Business Administration .... MBA 12FT 24-60DL
Police Leadership & Management .... PGDip 18DL/MSc 24DL/PGCert 12DL

University of Limerick
Business Management .... MA 12FT

Liverpool Hope University
Business Management .... MA 12FT 24PT/PGDip 12FT 24PT/PGCert 6FT 12PT

Section sponsored by

BPP
UNIVERSITY
COLLEGE

Business and social sciences
www.prospects.ac.uk/findcourses POSTGRADUATE DIRECTORY 405

Business and management studies

Liverpool John Moores University
Port Management.. MSc 12FT

University of Liverpool
Management..MSc 12FT 24PT
The Liverpool MBA ....MBA 12FT 24PT

London College UCK
Strategic Management and Leadership (DMS)..................................
PGDip 12FT 24PT 24DL/PGCert 6FT 12PT

London Metropolitan University
Corporate Social Responsibility .... MA 12FT 24-36PT
Creative Industries Management .... Professional Doctorate 36FT 48PT
Management Studies (in company) .... PGDip 24PT

London School of Economics and Political Science (LSE)
Management.. MSc 24FT

London South Bank University
Charity Management....................................ICSA Certificate 12PT
Charity Management - Blended ....ICSA Certificate 12PT
Diploma in Management Studies ....DMS 12PT
Management (Final Level)... MA 6PT
Management in Civil Society - Blended..........................MSc 24PT
Public Administration.......................................MPA 28PT

Loughborough University
Management (for non-business graduates)............. MSc 12FT
Management and Leadership (part-time for Working
Professionals) .... MSc 24-36PT/PGDip 18PT/PGCert 12PT
Management for Engineers (ECITB)......................PGCert 12-24PT
Marketing and Management (for non-business graduates).. MSc 12FT

Manchester Metropolitan University
Business Management (Top up programme)........MSc 12FT 36PT/
PGDip 24PT/PGCert 12PT
Human Resource Management...............................MSc 12FT 24PT
International Human Resource Management................. MSc 12FT
Leadership in Health and Social Care.......................MSc 18-24PT
Management...............................MSc 12FT/PGDip 18-24PT
Place Management................ MSc 36PT/PGDip 24PT/PGCert 12PT
Strategic Leadership and Change.......................MSc 12FT 24-36PT

University of Manchester
Innovation Management and Entrepreneurship ....
MSc 12FT 24PT
Management .... MSc 12FT
Organisational Change and Development MSc 12FT 24PT/PGDip 9FT 21PT

Middlesex University
Doctorate in Professional Studies ....DProf by taught 36DL
Engineering Management ....MSc 12FT 36PT
Enterprise Practice, MProf.......................................MA 24PT
Management Practice, MProf.....................................MA 24PT
Management Studies..AdvDip 2.5FT
Management for Personal Assistants..............................MA 24DL
Masters in Professional Studies..............................MProf 12-24DL
Masters/Doctorate by Public Works (DProf PW) ....
DProf by taught 24-36DL

Newcastle University
Doctor of Business Administration.................DBA by taught 60PT
Innovation, Creativity and Entrepreneurship................... MSc 12FT
Management and Business Studies (Research).....MA 12FT 24PT/
PGDip 9FT 21PT
Marine Transport with Management .... MSc 12FT
Strategic Planning and Investment ....MSc 12FT
Subsea Engineering and Management ....MSc 12FT 24-36PT
Transport Planning and Business Management .... MSc 12FT 24-48PT

Newman University
Business and Media Production Foundation Degree....... FdA 24FT

University of Northampton
Business Leadership...MBA 24PT
Corporate Governance and Leadership ......MSc 12FT 24PT/PGDip 12PT
Corporate Governance and Leadership (top up from ICSA).... MSc 12PT 12DL
Leadership and Management..................................... MA 36DL
Management.............MA 12FT 24PT PGCert 12PT MSc 12FT 24PT
Management Studies...DMS 24PT 24DL
Professional Leadership (Management)........................... MA 24DL

Northumbria University
Business Information Systems Management...........MSc 12/16FT
Business with Legal Management.......................MSc 12/16FT
Business with Management................................. MSc 12FT
Business with Marketing Management.......................... MSc 12FT
Business with Public Administration .... MSc 12FT
Housing Policy and Management................................MA 12FT
Housing Policy and Management with Professional Practice .... MA 36PT/PGDip 24PT
Leadership and Management in Integrated Childrens Services ... MA 36PT/PGDip 24PT/PGCert 12PT

Nottingham Trent University
Engineering Management..............................MSc 12FT 24PT
Environmental Management...........................MRes 12-24DL

Management .... MSc 12FT
Management and Human Resource Management........ MSc 12FT
Management and International Business .... MSc 12FT
Management and Investment Strategy .... MSc 12FT
Management and Marketing.................................... MSc 12FT
Product Design Innovation Management ....MA 12FT
Sport and Leisure Management............................MRes 12FT 24PT
Structural Engineering with Management ....MSc 12FT 24PT

University of Nottingham
Corporate Social Responsibilty............................ MSc 12FT
Corporate Strategy and Governance .... MSc 12FT
Energy Conversion and Management (Nottingham/ Ningbo)......
MSc 12FT
Management.. MSc 12FT
Management in Contemporary China and Emerging Markets.....
MSc 12FT
Management of Information Technology.........MSc 12FT 24-48PT

The Open University
Management...Professional Diploma 12DL
Systems Thinking in PracticeMSc variableDL/PGCert variableDL/
PGDip variableDL
Technology Management .... MSc variableDL/PGCert variableDL/
PGDip variableDL

Oxford Brookes University
Business Management (January Entry)...................... MSc 12FT
Business Management (January or Sept Entry).....MSc 12FT 24PT
Management (Certificate) - Online............................. CM 12DL
Management (Certificate) - Online (Solihull College)..... CM 12DL
Management, Certificate in (Corporate Online)............... CM 12DL
Strategic Management and Leadership (MA and DML) MA 24PT/
PGDip 12PT

University of Oxford
Major Programme Management .... MSc 24PT

University of Portsmouth
Leadership and Management....................... MSc 12PT PGDip 12PT PGCert 12PT

Queen Mary, University of London
International Human Resource Management and Employment
Relations .... MSc 12FT
Management and Organisational Innovation..................MA 12FT

Queen's University Belfast
Leadership for Sustainable Rural Development .... MSc 12FT
Management .... MSc 12FT
Organisation and Management ....MSSc 36PT

Ravensbourne
Design Management..MDes 12FT 24PT
Luxury Brand Management..................................MDes 12FT 24PT
Service Design ....MDes 12FT 24PT

University of Reading
Applied Management ....MA 36PT/PGDip 24PT
Applied Meteorology and Climate with Management
.... MSc 12FT 24PT
Business Information Management .... MSc 12FT
Communication for Innovation and Development .... MSc 12FT 24PT
Entrepreneurship and Management .... MSc 12FT
Informatics (MSc - Beijing).................. MSc 18FT 36PT/PGDip 9FT/
PGCert 6FT
Information Management & Systems ....MSc 12FT 36PT/PGDip 9FT/PGCert 6FT
International Human Resource Management .... MSc 12FT
Investment Management ....MSc 10FT 24DL

Regent's Business School London
Creative Leadership.. MA 16-20PT

Robert Gordon University
Design Management..MSc 36DL
Graduate Certificate in Management Studies..........GradCert 9DL
IT Management ....MSc 12FT 36DL
Leadership and Management..MSc 12FT 36DL/PGDip 8FT 24DL/
PGCert 4FT 12DL
Management.........................MSc 12FT/PGDip 9FT/PGCert 6FT

University of Roehampton ....
International Management with Marketing ....PGDip 9FT 24PT

Royal Agricultural University
Business Management ....MSc 12FT 24PT
Business Management in the Food Industries .....MBA 15FT 24PT

Royal Holloway, University of London
Sustainability and Management ....MSc 12FT 24PT

University Campus Suffolk
Community Leadership..MA 12FT
Leadership and Service Innovation .... MA TBCPT
Business and Management ....MSc 12FT 24PT

University of Salford
Global ManagementMSc 12FT 36PT/PGDip 8FT 24PT/PGCert 4FT 9PT
Human Resource Management and Development........ MSc 12FT 24PT/PGDip 8FT 24PT/PGCert 4FT 9PT
Information Systems Management ....MSc 12FT 36PT/PGDip 8FT 24PT/PGCert 4FT 9PT

International Business ...MSc 12FT 36PT/PGDip 8FT 24PT/PGCert 4FT 9PT
International Business Law and RegulationLLM 12FT/PGDip 8FT/
PGCert 4FT
Leadership and Management for Healthcare Practice....................
MSc 12FT 36PT/PGDip 8FT 24PT/PGCert 4FT 9PT
MBA, The Salford ....MBA 12FT 36PT
Management.... MSc 12FT 36PT/PGDip 8FT 24PT/PGCert 4FT 9PT
Transport Engineering and Planning...................MSc 12FT 36PT

School of Oriental and African Studies - SOAS
International Management (China) ....MSc 12FT 24-36PT
International Management (Japan) ....MSc 12FT 24-36PT
International Management (Middle East and North Africa).. MSc 12FT 24PT

Sheffield Hallam University
Business Administration ....DBA by taught 48PT
Business and English (pre-masters course) ....GradDip 7FT
Charity Resource Management .....MSc 30PT/PGDip 18PT/PGCert 12PT
Information Technology and Management .... MSc 30DL/PGDip 24DL/PGCert 12DL
Leading and Managing Physical Education and Youth Sport. MSc 3PT
Leading and Managing Sport Development ....MSc 24PT/PGDip 16PT/PGCert 8PT
Managing Global Business ....MSc 12FT/PGDip 6FT/PGCert 3FT
Organisation Development and Consultancy.....MSc 24PT/PGDip 18PT/PGCert 12PT
Sport Business Management .... MSc 12FT 24PT/PGDip 8FT 16PT/
PGCert 4FT 8PT

University of Sheffield
Architecture and Town and Regional Planning...........MArch 24FT
Global Marketing Management.................MSc 12FT/PGDip 9FT/
PGCert 6FT
Human Resource Management.............................. MSc 12FT
Information Management ....MSc 12FT 24-36PT
Information Management (Professional Enhancement
Programme) .... MSc Up to 12FT 24-36PT/PGDip 9FT 18PT/PGCert 6FT 12PT
Information Systems Management .... MSc 12FT
Leadership and Management .... MSc 12FT
Management... MSc 12FT
Management (Creative and Cultural Industries) .... MSc 12FT
Management (International Business).......................... MSc 12FT

University of South Wales
Doctor of Business Administration........... DBA by taught 36-48PT
Management.. MSc 12FT
Management NVQ Level 3, 5, 7NVQ Level 3 18 maxPT/NVQ Level 5 18 maxPT/NVQ Level 7 18 maxPT

Southampton Solent University
Management Programme.....................................MA 12FT 12DL
Marketing Management .... MA 12FT 32PT

University of Southampton
Accounting and Management ....MSc 12FT/PGDip 9FT
Business Analytics and Management Sciences....MSc 12FT 27PT/
PGDip 9FT 21PT
Human Resource Management ....MSc 12FT/PGDip 9FT
International Business Law.................................. LLM 12FT 24PT
MBA .... MBA 39PT/PGDip 33PT
Leadership and Management Health and Social Care... MSc 12FT 48PT
Management Science and Finance................ MSc 12FT/PGDip 9FT
Transportation Planning and Engineering.............MSc 12FT 24PT/
PGDip 12FT

University of St Andrews
International Business ....MLitt 12FT
Management..MLitt 12FT 24PT
Management (Human Resource Management) ....MLitt 12FT
Management Studies..MRes 12FT 24PT
Management and Information Technology MSc 12FT/PGDip 9FT
Managing in the Creative Industries (collab)................MLitt 12FT

St Mary's University College, Twickenham
Charity Management....PGCert 12PT/PGDip 24PT/MA 12FT 24PT

University of Stirling
Applied Studies (Management and Leadership in Social Services)
.... MSc 30PT/PGDip 24PT/PGCert 12PT
Energy Management..MSc 12FT
Environmental Management.... MSc 12FT 27PT/PGDip 9FT 18PT/
PGCert 6FT 12PT
Human Resource Management..................... MSc 12FT/PGDip 9FT
Human Resource Management and Socio Economic
Development....................MSc 12FT/PGDip 9FT/PGCert 6FT
International Business ....MSc 12FT/PGDip 9FT
International Business and Socio Economic Development .... MSc 12FT/PGDip 9FT/PGCert 6FT
Management....................MSc 12FT 27PT/PGDip 9FT 21PT
Master of Business Administration .... MBA 12FT
Media Management.............................MSc 12FT/PGDip 9FT
Publishing Studies ....MLitt 12FT 27PT/PGDip 9FT 21PT
MRes 12FT 27PT/PGCert 9FT 18PT
Sport Management ...MSc 9FT 24PT/PGDip 9FT 24PT/PGCert 6FT 12PT

Business and social sciences
406 POSTGRADUATE DIRECTORY www.prospects.ac.uk/findcourses

Section sponsored by

BPP
UNIVERSITY
COLLEGE

Business and management studies

University of Strathclyde
Applied Economics...MSc 12FT 24PT 24DL/PGDip 9FT 18PT 18DL
European Financial Management...MSc 12FT
Global Energy Management ....MSc 12FT 24PT
Global Innovation Management...................................MSc 24FT
Human Resource Management.......................MSc 12FT 24PT/
PGDip 9FT 24PT
Information Management.........MSc 12FT/PGDip 9FT/PGCert 4FT
Management of Information Technology Systems.......MSc 12FT/
PGDip 9FT
Master in Business Administration ..... MBA 12FT 36PT 30-60DL/
PGDip 9FT 24PT 36DL
School Leadership and Management (SQH)..................PGDip 12FT

University of Sunderland
Applied Management ....MSc 24PT

University of Surrey
Corporate Environmental Management ....MSc 12FT 12-60PT
Doctor of Business Administration .... DBA by taught 48-72PT

University of Sussex
Engineering Business Management.........................MSc 12FT 24PT
Management ....MSc 12FT
Technology and Innovation Management...............MSc 12FT 24PT

Swansea University
MBA...MBA 12FT
Management..MSc 12FT
Management (Finance)..MSc 12FT
Management (Human Resource Management) ....MSc 12FT
Management (International Management)...................MSc 12FT
Management (International Standards) ....MSc 12FT
Management (Marketing) ....MSc 12FT

Swansea Metropolitan University
Graduate Certificate/Postgraduate Certificate in
Management.............................GradCert 6FT 12PT/PGCert 12PT

Teesside University
Doctorate in Business Administration...........DBA by taught 48PT
Engineering Management..............MSc 12-18FT 24PT/PGDip 8FT
Innovation and Transformational Change.................PGCert 12PT
Leadership in Health and Social Care........................PGCert 12PT
Management ....MSc 12FT 24PT
Management...PGCert 12PT
Marketing Management ....MSc 12FT 24PT
Service Improvement ....MSc 36PT

Trinity College Dublin - the University of Dublin
Business and Management ....MSc 12FT

University of Wales Trinity Saint David
Information Management.... MBA 12FT 24PT/PGCert 12FT 24PT/
PGDip 12FT 24PT
Management.............. MSc 12-24FT 18-48PT/PGDip 9FT 18-36PT/
PGCert 9FT 18-36PT

University of the Highlands and Islands
Interpretation: Management and Practice...... PGCert 12FT 24PT/
PGDip 12FT 24PT/MSc 12FT 24PT
Leadership and Management........MSc 36PT/PGCert 12PT/PGDip
24PT

University of Ulster
Applied Management ....MSc 12FT 36PT/PGDip 9FT 18PT
Business Improvement ....MSc 27PT
Executive Leadership...MSc 24PT
Management..MSc 12FT 24PT
Management and Corporate Governance/Grad ICSA.... MSc 12FT
24-36PT/PGDip 9FT 18PT
Management and Corporate Governance/Grad ICSA - Dublin......
PGDip 24-36PT

UCL - University College London
Management...MSc 12FT 24PT
Management Science and Innovation ....MRes 12FT
Managing Archaeological Sites ....MA 12FT 24PT
Professional Practice and Management in Architecture (Part 3)..
Cert 6-12PT
Project and Enterprise Management... MSc 12FT 24-60PT/PGDip
9FT
Strategic Management of Projects.......MSc 24-60PT/PGDip 24PT

University of Warwick
Applied Management ....Diploma 18PT
E-Business Management..MSc 12FT 36PT
Management..MSc 12FT
Marketing & Strategy...MSc 12FT
Service Leadership..Diploma 15PT

Webster Graduate School London
International Non-Governmental Organisations ....MA 14FT
Management & Leadership...MA 14FT

West Herts College
Management Studies..PGDip 24PT

University of West London
Managing Human Resources...MA 24PT

University of the West of Scotland
Management of eBusiness ....MSc 12FT/Diploma 12-24FT/Cert
12-24FT

University of the West of England, Bristol
Management..MSc 12FT 24-33PT

University of Westminster
Business Intelligence and Analytics ....MSc 12FT 24-48PT
Management....................MA 12FT 24PT PGCert 12PT PGDip 18PT
Management (Advanced Standing)........................PGDip 12-24PT
MA 12-24PT

University of Winchester
Doctor of Business Administration ....DBA by taught 48PT
Master of Business Administration ....MBA 12FT 24-72PT

University of Wolverhampton
Advanced Technology Management.......................MSc 12FT 24PT
Corporate Direction ....MSc 24PT
Management .... MA 12FT 24PT/PGCert 12PT
Management Studies ....DMS 24PT
Master of Business Administration (top-up)...................MBA 12PT

University of Worcester
Diploma in Management Studies........................PGDip 12FT 24PT
Finance & Management.......... MSc 12FT/PGDip 10FT/PGCert 6FT
Management........................ MSc 12FT/PGDip 10FT/PGCert 6FT
Management & Human ResourcesMSc 12FT/PGDip 10FT/PGCert
6FT
Management Studies..Diploma 24PT
Marketing Management ....MA 12FT 24PT

University of York
Corporate Social Responsibility with Environmental
Management................................MSc 12FT MA 12FT/MRes 12FT
Management with Business Finance ....MSc 12FT

York St John University
Leadership & Management...................................MA 12FT 24-60PT

Management studies
Research Courses

University of Aberdeen
Management..................................PhD 36FT/MPhil 24FT/MRes 12FT

Anglia Ruskin University
Health Social Care and Education ......MPhil 24FT 24DL/PhD 36FT

Aston University
Executive DBA in Management .... DBA 48PT 48DL

Bangor University
Accounting, Banking, Economics, Finance, Management Studies
MPhil 24FT/PhD 36FT
Forest Ecology and Management........MPhil 24FT 36PT/PhD 36FT
60PT

University of Bath
Management........ PhD 24-48FT 36-72PT/MPhil 12-36FT 24-48PT

Birkbeck, University of London
Management..................................PhD 24FT 36PT/MPhil 24FT 36PT

Birmingham City University
Doctorate of Business Administration ....DBA 60PT

University of Bradford
PhD at School of Management......... PhD 36-48FT 48-60PT/MPhil
12-24FT 24-48PT

University of Brighton
School of Service Management Research Student Division....PhD
48FT 60PT/MPhil 24FT 36PT

University of Bristol
Management.................................. MPhil 12FT 24PT/PhD 36FT 72PT

University of Cambridge
Management Studies...PhD 36FT

Canterbury Christ Church University
Business and Management.......PhD 48FT 60PT/MPhil 24FT 48PT

Cardiff Metropolitan University
Management...PhD 12-60FT 12-60PT

Cranfield University
Management..................................PhD 36 - 48FT 48 - 72PT

University of Dundee
Accountancy and Business Finance ....MAcc 12FT MPhil 24FT
MSc by research 12FT hD 36FT

Durham University
The Durham DBA...DBA 36PT

University of East Anglia
Business Management .... PhD 36FT 72PT/MPhil 24FT 48PT

University of Edinburgh
Management......................... PhD 36FT 72PT/MPhil 24FT/
MSc by research 12FT

University of Exeter
Leadership Studies....................... PhD 48FT 84PT/MPhil 36FT 60PT
Management................................. PhD 48FT 84PT/MPhil 36FT 60PT

University of Glasgow
Management Studies.................. PhD 36FT/MLitt by research 12FT

Goldsmiths, University of London
Creative and Cultural Entrepreneurship......MPhil 24FT 36PT/PhD
36-48FT 48-72PT

Heriot-Watt University
Management.......................................PhD 36FT/MPhil 12FT

University of Hertfordshire
Centre for Research in Finance and Accounting (CFiFA)................
PhD 36FT 72PT/MPhil 24FT 48PT/MRes 12FT 24PT
Complexity and Management Centre ....PhD 36FT 72PT/
MPhil 24FT 48PT/MRes 12FT 24PT

University of Hull
Centre for Management and Organisational Learning ....
PhD 36FT 60PT/MPhil 24FT 36PT

Keele University
Management........ PhD 24-48FT 48-96PT/MPhil 12-24FT 24-36PT

University of Kent
Management...PhD 36FT 60PT/MPhil 24FT 36PT/MA by research
12FT 24PT
Management Science................. PhD 36FT 60PT/MPhil 24FT 36PT

King's College London
Management Research.............. MPhil 24FT 48PT/PhD 36FT 72PT

Lancaster University
Management... PhD 36FT 48PT
Management Learning and Leadership.......PhD 36FT 48PT/MPhil
24FT 36PT
Management Science................. MRes 12FT/MPhil 24FT/PhD 48FT

University of Leicester
Management............................... PhD 36FT 48PT/MPhil 24FT 36PT

Liverpool John Moores University
Doctor of Business Administration...........................DBA 36FT 84PT

London School of Economics and Political Science (LSE)
Management.. PhD 36-48FT/MPhil 36-48FT

Manchester Metropolitan University
Doctor of Business Administration ....DBA 54-90PT

Newcastle University
Business and Management........ PhD 36FT 72PT/MPhil 12FT 24PT

University of Northampton
Faculty of Management and Business............................PhD/MPhil

Nottingham Trent University
Doctorate of Business Administration...............................DBA 36PT

University of Nottingham
Risk Analysis, Social Processes and Health ....MPhil 36FT/
PhD 24FT

The Open University
Human resources and organisation studies........... PhD 36FT 72PT
variableDL/MPhil 15FT 24PT variableDL
Strategic management.... PhD 36FT 72PT variableDL/MPhil 15FT
24PT variableDL
Technology Management .... PhD 36FT 72PT variableDL/
MPhil 15FT 24PT variableDL

Oxford Brookes University
Business Doctoral Programmes .... PhD 24-60FT 36-72PT/MPhil
24-36FT 36-48PT

University of Oxford
Management Studies..DPhil 48FT

Queen's University Belfast
Management........................ PhD 36FT 72PT/MPhil 24FT 48PT

Royal Holloway, University of London
School of Management .... PhD 36FT 72PT/MPhil 18FT 36PT

School of Pharmacy, University of London
Practice and Policy...PhD 36FT 60PT

Sheffield Hallam University
Business and Management Programme.................PhD 36FT 48PT
Doctorate in Business Administration ....DBA 48PT
Organisation and ManagementPhD 36FT 60PT/MPhil 24FT 42PT

University of Sheffield
Management.................................PhD 36FT 72PT/MPhil 24FT 48PT

University of Southampton
Management Sciences................. PhD 36FT 62PT/MPhil 24FT 48PT
School of Management: Organisation and Management... MPhil
24FT 48PT/PhD 36FT 72PT

University of St Andrews
Management........................PhD 36-48FT 72-84PT/MPhil 24FT 48PT

University of Strathclyde
Management Science - Research .... PhD 33FT/MPhil 12FT/DBA
33FT/MRes 12FT

University of Surrey
Business Administration ....PhD 48PT
School of Management ....PhD 18 maxFT 30 maxPT/
DBA 48PT 48DL

University of Sussex
Technology and Innovation Management PhD 24-48FT 36-72PT/
MPhil 12-36FT 24-48PT

Teesside University
Business or Management Studies ....PhD min 24FT min 36PT/
MPhil min 18FT min 30PT

Section sponsored by BPP UNIVERSITY COLLEGE
Business and social sciences
www.prospects.ac.uk/findcourses POSTGRADUATE DIRECTORY 407

Business and management studies

UCL - University College London
Management Science and Innovation ... PhD 36FT 60PT

University of the West of Scotland
Department of Management and Marketing ... PhD/MPhil

University of Worcester
Business Management and I.T. ... PhD 48FT 70PT/MPhil 24FT 48PT

University of York
Management Studies ... MPhil 24FT 48PT/PhD 36FT 72PT

York St John University
Management Studies ... PhD 12-36FT/MPhil 12-36FT/MA by research 12-36FT

MBA
Taught Courses

University of Abertay Dundee
Master of Business Administration ... MBA 12FT 18PT

Anglia Ruskin University
Master of Business Administration ... MBA 15FT 24PT

Aston University
Master of Business Administration ... MBA 12FT 27PT 27DL

Bangor University
Chartered Banker ... MBA 6DL
Environmental Management ... MBA 12FT
Law and Management ... MBA 12FT/PGDip 9FT

University of Bath
The Bath MBA ... MBA 12FT 24PT

University of Bedfordshire
Executive Master of Business Administration ... MBA 24PT
Master of Business Administration ... MBA 12-18FT

Birmingham City University
Executive MBA ... MBA 24PT
Master of Business Administration ... MBA 12FT

University of Birmingham
Executive MBA ... MBA 24-48PT
Global Banking and Finance ... MBA 12FT
Global MBA ... MBA 12FT
MBA (Strategy and Procurement Management) ... MBA 15FT 24-48PT
MBA ... MBA 12FT 21-24PT
MBA Corporate Governance and Responsibility ... MBA 12FT

University College Birmingham
Professional Hospitality and Tourism Management ... MA 30DL/PGDip 24DL/PGCert 12DL
UCB MBA / MBA (Hospitality and Tourism pathway) ... MBA 12FT

University of Bolton
Master of Business Administration ... MBA 12FT 36PT

Bournemouth University
Master of Business Administration ... MBA 12FT/MBA 24PT

University of Bradford
Accelerated MBA ... MBA 10FT
Distance Learning MBA ... MBA 12FT
Doctorate in Business Administration ... DBA by taught 48PT
Executive MBA in Dubai ... MBA 12FT
Executive MBA in Manila ... MBA 12FT
Executive MBA in the UK ... MBA 12FT
MBA in Italy ... MBA 12FT
MBA in the UK ... MBA 12FT
The Bradford Accelerated MBA ... MBA 10FT
The Bradford Distance-learning MBA ... MBA 24-72DL
The Bradford Executive MBA in Dubai ... MBA 24BM
The Bradford MBA - Executive Part-time ... MBA 24-72PT
The Bradford MBA - Full-time ... MBA 12FT
The Bradford-Perugia MBA in Italy ... MBA 12FT

University of Brighton
General Management ... MBA 12FT 36PT/PGDip 12FT 24PT/PGCert 12FT 24PT

Brunel University
Business Administration ... MBA 12FT
MBA ... MBA 12FT

University of Buckingham
Master of Business Administration ... MBA 12FT

Bucks New University
Executive Master of Business Administration ... MBA 15FT

University of Cambridge
Executive MBA ... EMBA 20PT
Master in Business Administration ... MBA 12FT

Canterbury Christ Church University
Business Administration, MBA (Executive) ... MBA 24PT
Business Administration, MBA (International) ... MBA 15FT/MBA 12FT

Cardiff Metropolitan University
Executive MBA ... MBA 24PT
Master of Business Administration ... MBA 12FT

Cardiff University
Business Administration ... MBA 12FT 27PT MBA 28PT

Media Management MBA ... MBA 12FT

University of Central Lancashire
Business Management ... MSc 12FT
Master of Business Administration ... MBA 12FT
Master of Business Administration - Health ... MBA 36PT
Master of Business Administration - Part-time ... MBA 36PT

University of Chester
Business Administration ... MBA 12FT MBA 24PT

City University London
Executive MBA Dubai ... MBA 24PT
Executive MBA Evening ... MBA 24PT
Executive MBA Weekend ... MBA 24PT
MBA ... MBA 12FT 24-48PT

University College Cork
Management Business Administration ... MBA 48PT

Coventry University
General Management ... MBA 12FT 30PT

Cranfield University
Executive Doctorate ... DBA by taught 48PT
Executive MBA Masters in Business Administration ... MBA 24PT
Master of Business Administration ... MBA 12FT 24PT

Cranfield University, Shrivenham
Master of Business Administration (Defence) ... MSc 12FT 24PT

University for the Creative Arts
Creative Industries Management ... MBA 12FT

University of Cumbria
Master of Business Administration ... MBA 12FT 36PT

De Montfort University
MBA ... MBA 12FT
MBA (Executive) ... MBA 24PT
MBA (Finance) ... MBA 12FT 24PT
MBA (Global) ... MBA 15FT

University of Derby
MBA with Accredited Chartered Manager status ... MBA 12FT 36PT/PGCert 24PT/PGDip 12PT

University Centre Doncaster
Business Administration ... MBA 24PT

Dublin Institute of Technology
MBA ... MBA 30PT

University of Dundee
International Mineral Resources Management ... MBA 18DL IMBA 12FT
International Oil and Gas Management ... MBA 24DL MBA 12FT

Durham University
Business Administration (Finance) (Global) ... MBA 24FT 60PT
Business Administration (Global) ... PGCert 24FT 60PT
Business Administration (Global) ... MBA 24FT 60PT
Executive Master of Business Administration ... MBA 24PT
Master of Business Administration ... MBA 24PT
Master of Business Administration ... MBA 12FT

University of East Anglia
MBA (full-time) ... MBA 12FT

University of East London
Finance MBA ... MBA 12-15FT 24PT
International Business MBA ... MBA 12-15FT 24PT
Sustainability and Energy Management MBA ... MBA 12FT 24PT

Edge Hill University
Master of Business Administration ... MBA 12FT
Master of Business Administration (Distance Learning) ... MBA 12DL
Master of Business Administration (Finance) ... MBA 12FT
Master of Business Administration (Human Resource Management) ... MBA 12FT
Master of Business Administration (Marketing) ... MBA 12FT

Edinburgh Napier University
International Business Management ... MSc 12FT
Masters Business Administration ... MBA 12/18FT 36PT 36DL

University of Edinburgh
Business Administration ... MBA 12-16FT

University of Essex
MBA ... MBA 12FT 24PT

European Business School London
International Business ... MBA 12 - 16FT

University of Exeter
One Planet MBA ... MBA 12FT 30PT

Farnborough College of Technology
Business Administration ... MBA 24 monthPT

GCU London
Luxury Brand Marketing (London) ... MBA 12FT/MBA 12-15FT

National University of Ireland Galway
Executive Master of Business Administration ... EMBA 24PT/PGDip 12PT

Falmouth University
World First MBA ... MBA 12FT 24PT

Glasgow Caledonian University
MBA ... MBA 12FT 24PT

University of Glasgow
MBA (Master of Business Administration ... MBA 12FT

University of Gloucestershire
MBA Business Administration ... MBA 12FT 24PT
MBA Hospitality ... MBA 12FT

Glyndwr University
Executive MBA ... Executive MBA 24PT

University of Greenwich
Business Administration ... MBA 12FT
Executive Master of Business Administration ... MBA 36PT 36DL
Financial Services ... MBA 12FT 24PT
Maritime Management ... MBA 12FT 24PT
Masters in Business Administration ... MBA 12FT

Griffith College Dublin
MBA (International Business) ... MBA 12FT 24PT

Grimsby Institute of Further and Higher Education
Master of Business Administration ... MBA 24PT

Heriot-Watt University
Business Administration ... MBA 12FT 24PT 84DL

University of Hertfordshire
Master of Business Administration ... MBA 12FT 30PT

Holborn College
MBA ... MBA 12-18FT

University of Huddersfield
MBA ... MBA 12FT 24-36BM
Master of Business Administration with Creative Industries ... MBA 12FT 12BM

University of Hull
MBA - the Hull MBA ... MBA 12FT
MBA Executive ... MBA 24PT
MBA by overseas study - the Hull MBA ... MBA 24PT

Keele University
Business Administration ... MBA 24PT/PGDip 18PT/PGCert 18PT
Education MBA ... MBA 28PT 28DL/DBA by taught 20PT 20DL/PGCert 15PT
Health Executive MBA ... MBA 30PT

University of Kent
The Kent MBA ... MBA 12FT 24PT

Kingston University
Business Administration ... MBA 12FT 24PT
Business Administration ... DBA by taught 48-96PT
Master of Business Administration ... MBA 12FT 24PT

Lancaster University
Business Administration (Executive MBA) ... MBA 24PT
International Masters for Practising Management ... MA 26PT

Leeds Metropolitan University
Doctorate of Business Administration ... DBA 48PT
MBA (Executive) ... MBA 12FT 24PT
MBA (Executive) E-Learning ... MBA 24DL
MBA (Graduate) ... MBA 12FT

University of Leeds
Master of Business Administration ... MBA 12FT

Liverpool Hope University
International MBA ... International MBA 12FT 24PT
MBA (Information Technology) ... MBA 12FT 24PT

Liverpool John Moores University
MBA in Business Management ... MBA 12FT

University of Liverpool
Football Industries ... MBA 12FT 24PT
Master of Business Administration ... MBA 12FT 24PT
Master of Business Administration (Online Degree) ... MBA 24FT 24+PT

London Business School
EMBA-Global Americas and Europe ... MBA 20PT
EMBA-Global Asia ... MBA 16-20PT
Executive MBA (Dubai) ... MBA 20PT
Executive MBA (London) ... MBA 20PT
Masters in Business Administration ... MBA 15-21FT

London Metropolitan University
MBA ... MBA 12FT 24PT
MBA (with Executive Development) ... MBA 18FT 36PT

London School of Economics and Political Science (LSE)
TRIUM Global Executive MBA ... MBA 16PT

London South Bank University
Business Administration - Executive FT ... MBA 12FT
Business Administration - Executive PT ... MBA 30PT
Eur-Asian Business Management ... MBA 18FT

Loughborough University
International Sports Management MBA ... MBA 24BM
Master of Business Administration ... MBA 12FT 24-36PT

Section sponsored by BPP UNIVERSITY COLLEGE

Business and social sciences

408 POSTGRADUATE DIRECTORY www.prospects.ac.uk/findcourses

Business and management studies

Manchester Metropolitan University
Digital Business Management ... MSc 12FT
Master of Business Administration ... MBA 24-30PT 30BM
Digital Business Management ... MSc 12FT

University of Manchester
Business Administration ... MBA 18FT
Manchester Global MBA ... MBA 36PT 36DL
Manchester Global MBA (Accelerated) ... MBA 24PT
Manchester Global MBA (Engineering) ... MBA 36PT
Manchester Global MBA (Finance) ... MBA 36PT
Manchester Global MBA (Finance) (Accelerated) ... MBA 36PT
Part Time/Blended Learning MBAs ... MBA 24PT/MBA 30DL/MBA 36DL/MBA 36DL

Middlesex University
Doctor of Business Administration ... DBA by taught 48PT
MBA Business Informatics ... MBA 24PT
MBA Oil and Gas ... MBA 24PT
MBA Shipping and Logistics ... MBA 24PT
Master of Business Administration ... MBA 12FT 24PT

Newcastle University
Advanced International Business Management and Marketing ... MSc/MSc (Dual Award) 17FT
Advanced International Business and Management ... MA/MSc (Dual Award) 17FT
Doctor of Business Administration ... DBA by taught 60PT
Master of Business Administration ... MBA 12FT

University of Northampton
Business Administration ... MBA 12FT 30PT
Business Administration (1 year top up from DMS) ... MBA 12PT 12DL

Northumbria University
Business Administration ... MBA 12FT
Business with International Management ... MSc 12FT

Nottingham Trent University
Doctorate in Business Administration ... DBA by taught 36PT
Executive Master of Business Administration ... MBA 24PT
Master of Business Administration ... MBA 12FT

University of Nottingham
MBA Programmes in Singapore ... MBA 24-48PT
Master of Business Administration ... MBA 12FT 24-48PT

The Open University
Business Administration ... MBA variableDL/PGCert 12DL

Oxford Brookes University
Broadband Networks ... MSc 12FT 24PT
Business Management (January Entry) ... MSc 12FT
Business Management (January or Sept Entry) ... MSc 12FT 24PT
MBA ... MBA 12FT 12-30PT 30DL

University of Oxford
Business Administration ... EMBA 21PT
Business Administration ... MBA 12FT

Plymouth University
Masters in Business Administration ... MBA 12FT
The Global MBA ... MBA 12FT

University of Portsmouth
Master of Business Administration ... MBA 12FT
Master of Business Administration (Executive) ... MBA 30PT
Master of Business Administration (with Business Placement) ... MBA 24FT

Queen Margaret University, Edinburgh
Hospitality Management ... MBA 12FT 24-84PT/PGDip 12FT 24-84PT/PGCert 12FT 24-84PT
Master of Business Administration MBA 12FT 24-84PT 24-48DL/PGDip 12FT 24-84PT/PGCert 12FT 24-84PT

Queen's University Belfast
Business Administration Executive MBA (part-time) ... MBA 24PT

Robert Gordon University
MBA Information Management ... MBA 36DL
Master of Business Administration ... MBA 12FT

University of Roehampton
Master of Business Administration ... MBA 12FT 24PT

Royal Agricultural University
Business Management ... MSc 12FT 24PT

Royal Holloway, University of London
MBA International Management ... MBA 12FT 24PT

University Campus Suffolk
MBA ... MBA 12FT 30PT/PGDip 18PT/PGCert 12PT

University of Salford
International Business ... MSc 12FT 36PT/PGDip 8FT 24PT/PGCert 4FT 9PT
International Business Law and Regulation LLM 12FT/PGDip 8FT/PGCert 4FT
MBA, The Salford ... MBA 12FT 36PT

Sheffield Hallam University
Business Administration ... DBA by taught 48PT
Business Administration (full-time) ... MBA 12FT 36PT/PGDip 24PT/PGCert 12PT
Business Administration (part-time) ... MBA 36PT

University of Sheffield
Business Administration ... MBA 12FT

University of South Wales
International Management ... MSc 12FT 30PT
Master of Business Administration ... MBA 12FT 36PT/EMBA 24-30PT
Master of Business Administration ... MBA 12FT 30PT
Project Management ... MSc 15FT 36PT
Regional History and Heritage ... MA 12FT 36PT

Southampton Solent University
Master of Business Administration ... MBA 12FT 48PT

University of Southampton
Accounting and Management ... MSc 12FT/PGDip 9FT
International Business Law ... LLM 12FT 24PT
MBA ... MBA 12FT MBA 39PT/PGDip 33PT

University of St Andrews
International Business ... MLitt 12FT

Staffordshire University
Masters in Business Administration ... MBA 12FT/International MBA 12FT/Finance MBA 12FT

University of Stirling
International Business ... MSc 12FT/PGDip 9FT
International Business and Socio Economic Development ... MSc 12FT/PGDip 9FT/PGCert 6FT
MBA Retailing ... MBA 30DL
Master of Business Administration ... MBA 12FT

University of Strathclyde
Business Analysis and Consulting ... MSc 12FT
Master in Business Administration ... MBA 12FT 36PT 30-60DL/PGDip 9FT 24PT 36DL

University of Sunderland
Master of Business Administration ... MBA 12FT

University of Surrey
Master of Business Administration ... MBA 12FT

University of Sussex
MBA ... MBA 36PT

Swansea University
MBA ... MBA 12FT

Swansea Metropolitan University
Business Administration ... MBA 15FT 36PT
MBA (International Tourism) ... MBA 12FT 24 - 48PT

Trinity College Dublin - the University of Dublin
Business and Management ... MSc 12FT
Master in Business Administration ... MBA 12FT 24PT

University of Wales Trinity Saint David
Entrepreneurship ... MBA 12FT 24PT/PGDip 12FT 24PT/PGCert 12FT 24PT
Human Resource Managemant ... MBA 12FT 24PT/PGCert 12FT 24PT/PGDip 12FT 24PT
Information Management ... MBA 12FT 24PT/PGCert 12FT 24PT/PGDip 12FT 24PT
Information Security Management ... MBA 12FT 24PT
Leadership ... MBA 12FT 24PT
Marketing ... MBA 12FT 24PT/PGCert 12FT 24PT/PGDip 12FT 24PT
Social Entrepreneurship ... MBA 12FT 24PT/PGCert 12FT 24PT/PGDip 12FT 24PT
Tourism Management ... MBA 12-24FT 18-48PT/PGDip 9FT 18-36PT/PGCert 9FT 18-36PT

University of Ulster
Business Administration ... MBA 12FT 24-60PT

University of Warwick
Business Administration (MBA) Executive ... MBA 36-96PT
Business Administration (MBA) by distance learning ... MBA 36-96DL
Business Administration (MBA) by full time study ... MBA 12FT

Webster Graduate School London
MBA ... MBA 14FT 28PT

University of West London
MBA ... MBA 18FT 24PT

University of the West of Scotland
Executive Master of Business Administration ... EMBA 24-60PT
Quality Management ... MBA 36DL

University of the West of England, Bristol
Executive MBA ... MBA 36PT
Business Administration / Finance / Global Operations MBA 12FT

University of Westminster
Business Administration ... MBA 12FT 24PT

University of Winchester
Business Administration ... MBA 12FT 24-72PT

University of Wolverhampton
Master of Business Administration ... MBA 12FT 24PT

University of Worcester
MBA ... MBA 12FT 30PT

York St John University
Design Management ... MBA 12FT 24 - 60PT
Media Management ... MBA 12FT 24 - 60PT
Master of Business Administration ... MA 12FT 60PT
Master of Business Administration Managing Finance ... MBA 12FT 60PT

MBA
Research Courses

University of Birmingham
Business Administration ... DBA 48-72PT
Doctorate in Business Administration ... DBA 48-72PT

University of Gloucestershire
Doctorate in Business Administration ... DBA 30-48FT

Kingston University
Business Administration ... DBA 48PT/MSc by research 24PT

Newcastle University
Business and Management ... PhD 36FT 72PT/MPhil 12FT 24PT

Nottingham Trent University
Doctorate of Business Administration ... DBA 36PT

Sheffield Hallam University
Business and Management Programme ... PhD 36FT 48PT
Doctorate in Business Administration ... DBA 48PT

University of Sunderland
Business & Management ... PhD 36-48FT 48-72PT 48-72DL/MPhil 12-36FT 24-48PT 24-48DL

Teesside University
Business or Management Studies ... PhD min 24FT min 36PT/MPhil min 18FT min 30PT

Music management
Taught Courses

Birmingham City University
Music Industries ... MA 12FT 24PT 12-36DL

Brunel University
Management ... MSc 12FT

Bucks New University
Music and Entertainment Management ... MA 12FT 24PT

University of Central Lancashire
Music Industry Management and Promotion ... MSc 12FT 24PT

University of Chester
Popular Music ... MA 12FT 24-72PT/PGDip 12FT 24-60PT/PGCert 12FT 12-36PT

University for the Creative Arts
Creative Industries Management ... MBA 12FT

Goldsmiths, University of London
Creative and Cultural Industries ... GradDip 12FT
Music ... GradDip 12FT
Music (MMus) including specialist pathways ... MMus 12FT 24PT

University of Huddersfield
MMus ... MMus 12FT 24PT
Performance ... PGDip 12FT

Kingston University
Production of Popular Music ... MMus 12FT 24PT

Leeds Metropolitan University
Music Production ... MA 12FT 24PT

University of Liverpool
Music Industry Studies ... MA 12FT 24PT
Popular Music Studies ... MA 12FT 24PT

Northumbria University
Business with Music Management ... MSc 12FT
Master of Fine Art ... MFA 24FT 48PT
Music Management ... MA 12/18FT 24/28PT 24/28DL

University of Salford
Children's Digital Media Production ... MA 12FT/PGDip 9FT
Digital Performance ... MA 12FT 36PT/PGDip 8FT 24PT
Masters in Research (Media) ... MRes 12FT 24PT
Masters in Research (Music) ... MRes 12FT 24PT
Masters in Research (Performance) ... MRes 12FT 24PT
Music ... MA 12FT 24PT
Social Media ... MA 9FT/PGDip 9FT
Television Documentary Production ... MA 12FT/PGDip 9FT

School of Oriental and African Studies - SOAS
Music and Development ... MA 12FT 24PT

University of Sheffield
Music Management ... MA 12FT 24PT
Music Performance ... MA 12FT 24PT

University of Southampton
Music ... MRes 12FT 24PT

University of St Andrews
Managing in the Creative Industries (collab) ... MLitt 12FT

University of West London
Music Industry Management and Artist Development ... MA 12FT 24PT/PGDip 12FT 24PT/PGCert 12FT 24PT
Record Production ... MA 12FT 24PT

Section sponsored by
BPP UNIVERSITY COLLEGE

Business and social sciences
www.prospects.ac.uk/findcourses POSTGRADUATE DIRECTORY 409

Business and management studies

University of Westminster
Music Business Management.......MA 12FT 24-48PT

Music management
Research Courses

University of Aberdeen
Music.......PhD 36FT/MPhil 24FT

University of Bolton
Supply Chain, Business IT, Music and Creative Industries Management Specialisms.......MPhil 18FT 24 - 42PT/PhD 36FT 48 - 72PT

University of Oxford
Music.......DPhil 48FT

University of Salford
Media, Music and Performing Arts Research Centre....PhD/MPhil

Project management
Taught Courses

University of Aberdeen
Project Management.......MSc 36PT 36DL/PGDip 24PT 24DL/PGCert 12PT 12DL

Aberystwyth University
Managment and Project Management.......MSc 12FT 24PT

Anglia Ruskin University
Construction Project Management.......MSc 12FT 24-30PT
Project Management.......MSc 12FT 24-30PT

University of the Arts London - Central Saint Martins College of Art and Design
Innovation Management.......MA 24FT

Aston University
IT Project Management.......MSc 12FT

University of Bedfordshire
Engineering Business Management.......MSc 12FT
Project Management.......MSc 12FT 24PT

Birmingham City University
International Project Management.......MSc 24DL
Project Management.......MSc 12FT 24PT

University of Birmingham
Industrial Project Management......MSc 36PT/Diploma 12-24PT/Cert 12-24PT
Project Management.......MSc 12FT 24PT

Bournemouth University
Engineering Project Management.......MSc 12FT/MSc 24-60PT
Management with Project Management.......MSc 12-15FT

University of Bradford
Development and Project Planning.....MSc 12FT 24PT/PGDip 9FT 21PT/PGCert 9PT
Project Planning and Management.....MSc 12FT 24PT/PGDip 9FT 21PT/PGCert 9PT

Brunel University
Global Supply Chain Management.......MSc 12FT

Cardiff Metropolitan University
Technology Project Management....MSc 12FT 24PT/PGDip 24PT/PGCert 12PT

University of Central Lancashire
Agile Software Projects.......MSc 36PT/PGDip 24PT/PGCert 12PT
Arts Project Management.......PGCert 3PT
Construction Management (Project Management).....MSc 24DL/PGDip 12DL/PGCert 6DL
Construction Project Management.....MSc 12FT 24PT/PGDip 6FT 12PT/PGCert 3FT 6PT
Project Management......MSc 12FT 36PT/PGDip 6FT 12PT/PGCert 3FT 6PT

University of Chester
Programme and Project Management.......MSc 12FT 24 - 48PT/PGDip 12FT 24 - 48PT/PGCert 12FT 12 - 24PT

City University London
Project Management, Finance and Risk......MSc 12-18FT 24-30PT

Coventry University
Engineering Project Management.......MSc 12FT 24-36PT

Cranfield University
Programme and Project Management 2 year Executive.......MSc 24PT

Cranfield University, Shrivenham
Programme and Project Management Executive.......MSc 36FT

De Montfort University
Project Management.......MSc 12FT 24PT

University of Derby
MA Management.......MSc 12FT 36PT/PGDip 12FT/PGCert 9FT

University of East Anglia
Advanced Business Management.......MSc 12FT
Advanced Management.......MSc 12FT
Business Management.......MSc 12FT
Finance and Management.......MSc 12FT
Management.......MSc 12FT

University of East London
Project Management.....MSc 12FT 24PT/PGDip 8FT 16PT/PGCert 4FT 8PT

Edinburgh Napier University
Timber Industry Management.......MSc 12FT 36PT 36DL

University of Edinburgh
Architectural Project Management.......MSc 84DL

GCU London
International Project Management (London).....MSc 12FT/PGDip 9FT

Glasgow Caledonian University
International Project Management.......MSc 12FT 24PT 24-48DL/PGDip 12FT 24PT
Management.......MSc 12FT FlexiblePT/PGDip 9FT FlexiblePT/PGCert 6FT FlexiblePT

University of Greenwich
Project Management for Logistics.......MSc 12FT

Heriot-Watt University
Biotechnology.......MSc 12FT 24PT/PGDip 9FT 20PT
Brewing and Distilling.......MSc 12FT 24PT/PGDip 9FT 21PT
Carbon Management.. MSc 12FT 24PT 24-84DL/PGDip 9FT 21PT 24-84DL
Strategic Project Management...MSc 12FT 24PT/PGDip 9FT 21PT

University of Hertfordshire
Project Management.......MSc 12FT 24-60PT

University of Huddersfield
Business Project Management.......MSc 12FT 36PT

Keele University
Management.......MA 12FT/PGDip 9FT/PGCert 9FT
Project Management.......MSc 12FT

University of Kent
Conservation Project Management.......MSc 12FT 24PT

King's College London
Computing, IT Law & Management.......MSc 12FT

Leeds Metropolitan University
Project Management.......MSc 12FT 24PT

University of Leeds
Engineering Project Management.......MSc(Eng) 12FT
Environmental Engineering & Project Management.....MSc(Eng) 12FT

University of Leicester
Agile Software Engineering Techniques.......MSc 12FT/PGDip 9FT

Liverpool John Moores University
Construction Project Management.......MSc 12FT 24PT

University of Liverpool
Programme and Project Management.......MSc 12FT 24PT
Project Management (Online Degree).......MSc 24FT 24+PT

London South Bank University
Business Project Management.......MSc 15FT 24PT

Manchester Metropolitan University
Project Management.......MSc 12FT 24PT

University of Manchester
Management and Implementation of Development Projects......MSc 12FT 24PT
Management of Projects.......MSc 12FT 36PT
Management of Projects: Commercial Project Management.......MSc 12FT 36PT
Management of Projects: Construction Project Management.....MSc 12FT 36PT
Management of Projects: Engineering Project ManagementMSc 12FT 36PT
Project Management.......MSc 36-72FT

Middlesex University
Managing Major Projects.......PGCert 9DL
Managing Major Projects and Programmes.......MSc 24PT
Project Management.......MSc 12-15FT 24-27PT

Newcastle University
Advanced Computer Science.......MSc 12FT 24PT

Northumbria University
Construction Project Management...MSc 12FT 30PT/PGDip 12FT 24PT/PGCert 12FT 24PT
Project Management.......MSc 16FT 36PT 36DL/PGDip 12FT 24PT 24DL
Project Management (Chalmers Dual Award).......MSc 24FT
Project Management/Management de projets de construction a l'international - dual award.......MSc 15FT

Nottingham Trent University
Construction Management.......MSc 12FT 24-60PT 24-60DL
Engineering Management.......MSc 12FT 24PT
Project Management (Construction) MSc 24FT 24-60PT 24-60DL

University of Nottingham
Geospatial Intelligence.......MSc(Res) 12FT 24PT

The Open University
Development Management..MSc variableDL/PGDip variableDL/PGCert 12DL
Management.......Professional Diploma 12DL

Oxford Brookes University
Project Management in the Built Environment.......MSc 12FT 24DL/PGDip 9FT 21DL/PGCert 9FT 9DL

University of Portsmouth
Project Management.......MSc 12FT
Project Management and Leadership.......MSc 36PT

Queen's University Belfast
Construction and Project Management/ Cionstruction and Project Management with Industrial Internship.......MSc 12FT 24-36PT/PGDip 9FT 18PT

University of Reading
Applied Management.......MA 36PT/PGDip 24PT
Construction Cost Management.......MSc 24PT
Construction Management.......MSc 12FT
Intelligent Buildings: Design, Construction and Management.... MSc 24PT
Project Management.......MSc 24PT
Renewable Energy.......MSc 12FT 24PT/PGDip 9FT 21PT

Robert Gordon University
Construction Project Management.MSc 12FT 28-36PT 28-36DL/PGDip 9FT 18-24PT 18-24DL/PGCert 4FT 9-12PT 9-12DL
Graduate Certificate Project Management.......GradCert 9DL
Project Management.... MSc 12FT 36DL/PGDip 8FT 24DL/PGCert 4FT 12DL

University of Roehampton
Project Management.......MSc 12FT

University of Salford
Project Management......MSc 12FT 36PT/PGDip 8FT 24PT/PGCert 4FT 9PT

Sheffield Hallam University
Construction Management.......MSc 12FT 24-36PT
Project Management.......MSc 12FT 24-36PT
Project Management.......MSc 12FT 24-36PT/PGDip 12FT 24PT/PGCert 6-12FT 12PT

University of Sheffield
Public Humanities.......MA 12FT 24PT

University of Southampton
MSc Leadership and Management Health and Social Care.... MSc 12FT 48PT

University of Sunderland
Project Management.......MSc 14FT/PGDip 9FT/PGCert 5FT

University of Sussex
Managing Innovation and Projects.......MSc 12FT

Teesside University
Advanced Computer Science.......MSc 12FT 36PT
Engineering Management.......MSc 12-18FT 24PT/PGDip 8FT
Information Technology Project Management.......MSc 12FT 24-36PT/PGDip 8FT 24PT/PGCert 4FT 12PT
Project Management.......MSc 12-16FT/PGDip 8FT

Trinity College Dublin - the University of Dublin
Project Management.......PGDip 12PT

UCL - University College London
Engineering with Finance.......MSc 12FT/PGDip 9FT
Project and Enterprise Management... MSc 12FT 24-60PT/PGDip 9FT
Strategic Management of Projects.......MSc 24-60PT/PGDip 24PT

University of Warwick
Programme and Project Management.......MSc 12FT 36PT

University of West London
Project Management.......MSc 12FT 24PT

University of Westminster
Project Management.......MSc 12FT 24PT

University of Winchester
Project Management... MSc 12FT 24PT/PGDip 12FT 24PT/PGCert 12FT 24PT

University of Wolverhampton
Construction Project Management.......MSc 12FT 24PT/PGCert 12FT 24PT

University of York
Project Analysis, Finance and Investment.......MSc 12FT

Project management
Research Courses

University of East Anglia
Business Management.......PhD 36FT 72PT/MPhil 24FT 48PT

Heriot-Watt University
International Centre for Brewing and Distilling (ICBD)..PhD 36FT 48PT/MPhil 24FT

University of Manchester
Management of Projects...MPhil 12FT 24PT/PhD 36FT 72PT/MSc by research 12FT/MEnt 12FT 24PT

Oxford Brookes University
Construction and Project Management Group MPhil/PhD ....PhD 24-60FT 36-72PT/MPhil 24-36FT 36-48PT

Section sponsored by BPP UNIVERSITY COLLEGE

Business and social sciences

410 POSTGRADUATE DIRECTORY www.prospects.ac.uk/findcourses

Business and management studies

Public administration
Taught Courses

University of Bath
International Public Policy Analysis.............MSc 12FT/PGDip 9FT/PGCert 6FT
Security, Conflict & Justice .... MRes 12FT 24-36PT

University of Bedfordshire
Applied Public Policy: Children's and Young People's Services MA 24PT

Birkbeck, University of London
Management in the Public Sector....... MSc 12FT 24PT/MRes 12FT 24PT
Public Policy and Management ....MSc 12FT 24PT/MRes 12FT 24PT

University of Birmingham
Public Service.. MBA 24PT
Public Administration... MPA 12FT 24PT
Public Management (with specialist pathways)..MSc 12FT 24PT/PGDip 12FT 24PT/PGCert 12FT 15PT
Public Service Commissioning..........MSc 12FT 24PT/PGDip 21PT/PGCert 9FT 21PT
Social Research (Local Government and Public Policy) ....MA 12FT 24PT

University of Bradford
Leadership, Management and Change............MSc 12FT 24 - 60PT
Public Policy and Programme Management ....MSc 12FT 24PT/PGDip 9FT 21PT/PGCert 9PT

University of Brighton
Public Administration MA.............MPA 12FT 24-72PT/PGDip 12FT 24-72PT/PGCert 12FT 24-72PT
Public Service Management...MBA 18FT 36PT/PGDip 18FT 24PT/PGCert 18FT 24PT

University of Bristol
Economics and Public Policy.. MSc 12FT
Public Policy...MSc 12FT 24PT

Bucks New University
Leadership & Management in the Public Sector..............MA 24PT

Cardiff University
Governance and Devolution...LLM 12FT
Politics and Public Policy...MSc 12FT 24PT
Public Administration..MPA 24PT
Regeneration Studies ....MSc 12FT 24PT

University of Chester
Action Research and Appreciative Inquiry (Work Based and Integrative Studies)...MSc 24-72PT/MA 24-72PT/PGDip 24-60PT/PGCert 12-36PT
Public Services Management (Work Based and Integrative Studies) ....MA 24-72PT/PGDip 24-60PT/PGCert 12-36PT

University College Cork
Government.. MBS 12FT 24PT

Cranfield University, Shrivenham
Information Assurance for the Public Sector.......MSc 36FT/PGDip 24FT/PGCert 12FT

De Montfort University
Public Finance...MSc 12FT 24PT

Durham University
Public Policy and Health ....PGCert 10PT MSc 12FT 24PT

University of East Anglia
International Public Policy and Public Management ... MRes 12FT 24PT
International Public Policy, Regulation and CompetitionMA 12FT 24PT
Public Policy and Public Management..................... MA 12FT 24PT MRes 12FT 24PT

Edge Hill University
Master of Public Administration ....MPA 12FT
Voluntary and Third Sector Management ....MA 24PT

University of Edinburgh
Health Systems and Public Policy........................MSc 12FT 24-36PT
Public Policy (Master of) ....MPP 15FT

University of Exeter
INTO Diploma in Public Administration ....GradDip 9FT
Master of Public Administration ....MA 12FT 24PT 36DL 21BM

Glasgow Caledonian University
Master of Accounting (Public Sector Financial Management)...... MAcc 12FT FlexiblePT

University of Glasgow
Public Policy ....MSc 12FT 24PT 60BM/PGDip 9FT 18PT 48BM/PGCert 4FT 8PT 48BM
Public Policy & Management ... MSc 12FT 24PT 60BM/PGDip 9FT 21PT
Public Policy Research................ MRes 12FT 24PT/PGDip 9FT 18PT
Urban Research.......................... MRes 12FT 24PT/PGDip 9FT 18PT

University of Greenwich
Masters in Public Administration............................ MPA 12FT 36PT

Institute of Education
Educational Planning, Economics and International Development... MA 12FT 24-48PT

University of Kent
European Public Policy (Brussels) .... MA 12FT 24PT
International Social Policy.. MA 12FT 24PT
Social and Public Policy: Commissioning (Distance Learning, Medway)..MA 24DL/PGDip 24DL

King's College London
Public Policy .... MA 12FT 24PT
Public Services Policy & Management.....................MSc 12FT 24PT
Risk Analysis ....MA 12FT 24PT/MSc 12FT 24PT

Leeds Metropolitan University
Public Health - Health Promotion......MSc 12FT 30PT/PGDip 12FT 24PT/PGCert 4FT 12PT
Specialist Community Public Health Nursing - Health Visiting .... MSc 24PT/PGDip 12FT 24PT

University of Leicester
Police Leadership & Management...........PGDip 18DL/MSc 24DL/PGCert 12DL

University of Limerick
Public Administration..PGDip 9FT/MA 12FT

London Metropolitan University
Public Administration...MPA 12FT 24+PT

London School of Economics and Political Science (LSE)
Double Degree in Public Administration and Government.... MSc 12FT/MSc 12FT
European Public and Economic Policy...............................MPA 21FT
International Migration and Public Policy..............MSc 12FT 24PT
Management, Organisations and Governance .... MSc 12FT
Philosophy and Public Policy ....MSc 12FT 24PT
Public Management and Governance.............................. MSc 12FT
Public Policy and Administration..............................MSc 12FT 24PT
Public Policy and Management ....MPA 21FT
Public and Economic Policy...MPA 21FT
Public and Social Policy ....MPA 21FT
Regulation ....MSc 12FT 24PT

London South Bank University
Charity Finance & Accounting ....CIPFA Certificate 12PT
Charity Finance & Accounting - Blended ...CIPFA Certificate 12PT
Charity Management......................................ICSA Certificate 12PT
Management in Civil Society .... MSc 24PT
Public Administration..MPA 28PT
Public Administration - Executive ....MPA 28PT

University of Manchester
International Development: Public Policy and Management........ MA 12FT 24PT
Political Science - Governance and Public Policy ... MA 12FT 24PT/PGDip 9FT 24PT

Middlesex University
Development with Work Experience.................. MA 12-15FT 24PT
Development with Work-based Learning .... MA 12-15FT 24PT
Global Governance and Public Policy ....MSc 12FT 24PT

Newcastle University
Skills, Technology, Research and Management for the UK Water Sector (STREAM)..EngD by taught 48FT

Northumbria University
Business with Public Administration .... MSc 12FT
Public Administration.. MPA 12FT 24PT

Nottingham Trent University
Public Services Management ....MSc 12PT/PGDip 12PT/PGCert 12PT

University of Nottingham
International Social Policy..................................... MA 12FT 24-48PT
Public Administration.................. MPA 12FT 24PT/PGDip 9FT 18PT
Public Policy ....MA 12FT 24-48PT/PGDip 9FT 24PT
Public Procurement Law and Policy.......... PGDip 21PT/LLM 24PT/PGCert 12-21PT
Research Methods (Public Policy).............................. MA 12FT 24PT

Plymouth University
Public Administration... DPA by taught 36PT
Public Administration and Leadership..................... MA 12FT 24PT

University of Portsmouth
Public Administration .... MPA 12FT 24PT

Queen Margaret University, Edinburgh
Public Services Governance .... PGCert 12FT 24-84PT

University of Reading
Public Policy .... MA 12FT 24PT 72BM

Robert Gordon University
Master of Public Administration .....MPA 12FT/PGDip 8FT/PGCert 4FT

School of Oriental and African Studies - SOAS
PGDip Policy Studies.. PGCert 9FT
Public Policy and Management .... MSc 24DL/PGDip 12DL

University of Sheffield
Comparative Governance and Public Policy .... MA 12FT 24PT
International Development (Masters in Public Health) .... MPH 12FT 24PT

University of South Wales
Health & Public Service Management....................MSc 12FT 36PT/PGCert 4FT 12PT/PGDip 8FT 24PT
Public Service Management .....MSc 12FT 36PT/PGCert 4FT 12PT/PGDip 8FT 24PT

University of Strathclyde
Public Policy ....MSc 12FT 24PT

University of the Highlands and Islands
Chartered Management Institute - Diploma Public Service Leadership.........................Chartered Management Institute 12PT

University of Ulster
Food Regulatory Affairs by e-Learning .....PGCert 8PT/PGDip 10PT 8DL/MSc 18-20PT 10DL
Public Administration...MPA 24PT

UCL - University College London
Public Policy .... MSc 12FT 24PT

University of Warwick
Accounting and Finance in Health Service Organisations.......PGA 12PT/CPDMod 1PT
Organisational Behaviour and Health Service Policy....PGA 12PT/CPDMod 1PT

University of York
Economic and Social Policy Analysis.................................. MSc 12FT
Public Administration..... MPA 12FT 24PT 12+DL/MPA 12FT 36PT/PGDip 12FT 24PT/PGCert 12PT
Public Administration and Public Policy ...... MA 12FT 24PT/PGDip 12FT
Public Administration in International Development .....MA 12FT 24PT 12+DL/MPA 12FT/PGDip 12FT
Public Policy and Management .....MA 36DL/PGDip 24DL/PGCert 12DL

Public administration
Research Courses

University of Birmingham
Management Mathematics............................PhD 36FT/MPhil 24FT

Cardiff University
Urban and Regional Governance.............................. PhD 36FT 60PT

De Montfort University
Public Policy (Research)........................... MPhil 12 - 24FT 24 - 48PT/PhD 24 - 36FT 36 - 72PT

National University of Ireland Galway
College of Business, Public Policy & Law ....PhD 48FT 72PT/MPhil 24FT 48PT/MComm by research 24FT 48PT/MSc by research 24FT 48PT
College of Business, Public Policy & Law .....MSc by research 24FT 48PT

Keele University
Management........ PhD 24-48FT 48-96PT/MPhil 12-24FT 24-36PT

King's College London
Public Policy Research........... MPhil 24FT 36PT/PhD 36FT 48-72PT

University of Leeds
Professional Doctorate in Public Management..... PhD 36FT 60PT

University of Nottingham
Public Policy - Professional Doctorate in Public Policy (PDPP)PDPP 48-96PT
Social Policy and Administration..........MA by research 12FT 24PT

The Open University
Citizenship and Governance......PhD 36FT 72PT variableDL/MPhil 15FT 24PT variableDL
Public Leadership and Social Enterprise .... PhD 36FT 72PT variableDL/MPhil 15FT 24PT variableDL
The changing nature of contemporary and historical welfarePhD 36FT 72PT variableDL/MPhil 15FT 24PT variableDL

University of Southampton
Doctor of Business Administration .... DBA 48PT

UCL - University College London
Public Policy .... PhD 36FT 60PT

Retail management
Taught Courses

University of the Arts London - London College of Fashion
Design Management for the Fashion Industries.... MA 15FT 30PT
Fashion Curation... MA 15FT 30PT
Fashion: Buying And Merchandising...... PGCert 4FT/PGCert 30PT
Strategic Fashion Marketing....................................... MA 15FT 30PT

University of Bedfordshire
Fashion Design, Styling & Promotion/ .... MA 12FT 24PT

Bournemouth University
Retail Management...MSc 12-15FT 24PT

University of Central Lancashire
Fashion Brand Management ..MBA 12FT 30PT/PGDip 12FT 30PT/PGCert 12FT 30PT

Business and social sciences
www.prospects.ac.uk/findcourses POSTGRADUATE DIRECTORY 411

Business and management studies

Fashion and Lifestyle Promotion .... MA 12FT 30PT/PGDip 12FT 30PT/PGCert 12FT 30PT
International Business and Management .... MSc 12FT
Marketing and PR .... MA 12FT

University of Chester
Action Research and Appreciative Inquiry (Work Based and Integrative Studies)...MSc 24-72PT/MA 24-72PT/PGDip 24-60PT/PGCert 12-36PT
Coaching for Internal Business Solutions and Team Development (WBIS) .... MA 24-72PT/PGDip 24-60PT/PGCert 12-36PT

Cranfield University
Retail Management .... MSc 12FT

University for the Creative Arts
Fashion .... MA 12FT 24PT
Fashion Management & Marketing .... MA 12FT 24PT
Fashion Promotion and Imaging ....
Fashion: Manufacture and Management .... MA 12FT
Fashion: Promotion, Marketing and Branding .... MA 12FT

Dublin Institute of Technology
Fashion Buying and Management .... PGDip 12FT
MBS (Retail Management) .... MBS 12FT 24PT

University of East Anglia
Advanced Management .... MSc 12FT
Management .... MSc 12FT
Marketing .... MSc 12FT
Supply Chain Management .... MSc 12FT

Edinburgh Napier University
International Business Management .... MSc 12FT

GCU London
International Fashion Marketing (London) .... MSc 12FT/MSc 12-15FT

Glasgow Caledonian University
International Fashion Marketing .... MSc 12FT/PGDip 9FT

University of Glasgow
International Strategic Marketing .... MSc 12FT

Heriot-Watt University
International Fashion Marketing .... MSc 12FT 24PT/PGDip 9FT 21PT

University of Huddersfield
International Fashion Management .... MA 12/16FT
International Fashion Promotion .... MA 12/16FT

Kingston University
Fashion Retailing .... MA 12FT 24PT
Retail Management and Marketing .... MSc 12FT

Leeds Metropolitan University
Multi Unit Leadership .... MSc 12FT 24PT

Loughborough University
Automotive Retail Management .... MSc 48PT/PGDip 36PT/PGCert 18PT
Strategic Automotive Dealership Management .... MSc 33PT

Manchester Metropolitan University
International Fashion Marketing .... MSc 12FT 36-60PT
Internet Retailing .... MSc 12-30PT/PGDip 12-30PT/PGCert 12-30PT
Marketing Communications .... MSc 12FT 30PT/PGDip 24PT/PGCert 12PT
Marketing Management .... MSc 12FT 12-36PT
Strategic Fashion Buying .... MSc 12FT 36-60PT

University of Manchester
International Fashion Retailing .... MSc 12FT
International Fashion Retailing (Business Process Improvement).. .... MSc 12FT
International Fashion Retailing (Multichannel Management)...... MSc 12FT

Nottingham Trent University
Fashion Business .... MA 12FT/PGDip 7FT/PGCert 4FT
Fashion Marketing & Communication .... MA 12FT

University of Portsmouth
Sales Management .... MA 12PT

Queen Mary, University of London
Marketing .... MSc 12FT

Ravensbourne
Fashion .... MA 12FT 24PT

Robert Gordon University
Fashion Management .... MSc 12FT/PGDip 8FT/PGCert 4FT

University of Stirling
MBA Retailing .... MBA 30DL
Retail Management .... MSc 12FT/PGDip 9FT

University of Surrey
International Retail Marketing .... MSc 12FT

University of Westminster
Fashion Business Management .... MA 12FT

Retail management
Research Courses

University for the Creative Arts
Fashion .... MPhil 24FT 36PT/PhD 36FT 60PT

Manchester Metropolitan University
Marketing and Retail .... PhD 48FT 90PT/MPhil 36FT 72PT/MRes 12FT 24PT/MA or MSc by Research 18FT 36PT

The Open University
Marketing .... PhD 36FT 72PT variableDL/MPhil 15FT 24PT variableDL
Social Marketing...... PhD 36FT 72PT variableDL/MPhil 15FT 24PT variableDL

Robert Gordon University
Aberdeen Business School ...PhD 12FT 36PT 36DL/MSc(Res) 12FT 36PT 36DL

University of Surrey
Retail and Marketing .... PhD 36FT 48PT/MPhil 24FT 36PT

Risk management
Taught Courses

University of Aberdeen
Patient Safety: A Clinical Human Factors Approach..... MRes 12FT
Safety and Reliability Engineering .... MSc 12FT 24-36PT

Bangor University
Risk Management in Health and Social Care ...... MSc 36PT/PGDip 24PT/PGCert 12PT

University of Bath
Environment, Energy & Resilience .... MRes 12FT 24-36PT

Birmingham City University
Risk Management .... MSc 36PT 36DL 36BM

Bournemouth University
Finance with Risk Management .... MSc 12-15FT

Brunel University
Modelling and Management of Risk .... MSc 12FT

University of Central Lancashire
Fire Investigation .... MSc 12FT/PGDip 9FT/PGCert 6FT
Fire Safety Engineering .... MSc 12FT 24PT
Fire Scene Investigation .... MSc 24-36PT
Fire and Rescue Service Management .... MSc 12FT 24PT
Management Studies .... DMS 18PT
Project Management...... MSc 12FT 36PT/PGDip 6FT 12PT/PGCert 3FT 6PT

University of Chester
Programme and Project Management .... MSc 12FT 24 - 48PT/PGDip 12FT 24 - 48PT/PGCert 12FT 12 - 24PT

City University London
Insurance and Risk Management .... MSc 9-12FT 24PT

Cranfield University
Environmental Risk Management .... MSc 12FT 24-60PT/PGDip 6FT 24PT/PGCert 5FT 24PT
Offshore and Ocean Technology with Risk Management MSc...... MSc 12FT 24-60PT/MTech 24FT/PGDip 6FT 24PT/PGCert 5FT 24PT

Cranfield University, Shrivenham
Resilience .... MSc 30PT/PGDip 24PT/PGCert 12PT
Security Sector Management .... MSc 12FT 30PT

University of Cumbria
Leadership and Management in Policing MBA 36PT/PGDip 36PT/PGCert 36PT
Management Studies .... GradDip 24PT/GradCert 12PT

De Montfort University
Risk Management .... MSc 12FT 24PT

University of Dundee
Advanced Practice (Clinical Governance) .... MSc 36DL

Durham University
Risk and Environmental Hazards .... MA 12FT
Risk and Security .... MA 12FT

University of East Anglia
Advanced Management .... MSc 12FT
MBA .... MBA 12FT
Management .... MSc 12FT

University of East London
Finance and Risk MSc ..... MSc 12FT 24PT/PGDip 8FT 16PT/PGCert 4FT 8PT

Edinburgh Napier University
Strategic Risk Management and Finance .... MSc 12FT 24PT

University of Edinburgh
Banking and Risk .... MSc 12FT
Operational Research with Risk .... MSc 12FT 24PT/PGDip 9FT

University of Exeter
Climate Change and Risk Management .... MSc 12FT 24PT

GCU London
Risk Management .... MSc 12FT/PGDip 9FT

Glasgow Caledonian University
Banking, Finance and Risk Management .... MSc 12FT 24PT
Financial Services, Risk and Operations...... MSc 12FT 24PT/PGDip 9FT 24PT
Management .... MSc 12FT FlexiblePT/PGDip 9FT FlexiblePT/PGCert 6FT FlexiblePT
Risk Management ..... MSc 12FT FlexiblePT FlexibleDL/PGDip 9FT FlexiblePT FlexibleDL

University of Glasgow
Financial Risk Management .... MSc 12FT
Management .... MSc 12FT

University of Greenwich
Finance and Financial Information Systems.......... MSc 12FT 24PT/PGDip 12FT 24PT

Heriot-Watt University
Actuarial Management .... MSc 12FT 48PT/PGDip 9FT 48PT
Actuarial Science .... MSc 12FT 24PT/PGDip 9FT 18PT
Climate Change: Impacts and Mitigation .... MSc 12FT 24PT/PGDip 9FT 21PT
Climate Change: Managing The Marine Environment .... MSc 12FT 24PT/PGDip 9FT 21PT
Financial Mathematics .... MSc 12FT
Food Science, Safety and Health .... MSc 12FT 24PT 24-84DL/PGDip 9FT 21PT 24-84DL
Food and Beverage Science .... MSc 12FT 24PT/PGDip 9FT 21PT
Investment Management .... MSc 12FT 24PT/PGDip 9FT 21PT
Quantitative Finance and Mathematics .... MSc 12FT 24PT/Diploma 9FT 21PT
Quantitative Financial Engineering .... MSc 12FT 24PT/Diploma 9FT 21PT
Quantitative Financial Risk Management ... MSc 12FT/PGDip 9FT
Safety and Risk Management (Distance Learning Only)......... MSc 24-84DL/PGDip 21-84DL
Safety, Risk and Reliability Engineering (Distance Learning Only) .... MSc 24-84DL/PGDip 24-84DL

University of Hull
Financial Mathematics .... MSc 12FT

Imperial College London
Risk Management & Financial Engineering .... MSc 12FT

Keele University
Management .... MA 12FT/PGDip 9FT/PGCert 9FT

University of Kent
Applied Actuarial Science .... MSc 12FT 24PT
Finance, Investment and Risk .... MSc 12FT/PGDip 12FT

King's College London
Risk Analysis .... MA 12FT 24PT/MSc 12FT 24PT

Lancaster University
Safety Engineering (Industry-Based) .... MSc 24PT

Leeds Metropolitan University
Events Management .... MSc 24PT/PGCert 12PT/PGDip 24PT
Sports Event Management .... MSc 12FT 24PT/PGCert 12FT 24PT/PGDip 12FT 24PT

University of Leeds
Financial Mathematics .... MSc 12FT
Financial Risk Management .... MSc 12FT
Patient Safety and Clinical Risk Management .... PGCert 4FT

University of Leicester
Financial Mathematics and Computation .... MSc 12FT 24PT/PGDip 9FT
Security and Risk Management... MSc 24DL/PGDip 18DL/PGCert 12DL

University of Limerick
Financial Services .... MSc 12FT

University of Liverpool
Financial Mathematics .... MSc 12FT

London School of Economics and Political Science (LSE)
Management and Regulation of Risk .... MSc 12FT

Loughborough University
Security Management .... MSc 24-36DL/PGDip 12-24DL/PGCert 12DL

University of Manchester
Quantitative Finance: Risk Management .... MSc 12FT

Middlesex University
Risk Management .... MSc 12FT 24PT

Newcastle University
Quantitative Finance and Risk Management .... MSc 12FT

University of Nottingham
Corporate Strategy and Governance .... MSc 12FT
Risk Management .... MSc 12FT

The Open University
Management .... Professional Diploma 12DL

Oxford Brookes University
Environmental Assessment and Management ...MSc 12FT 24PT/PGDip 9FT 21PT

University of Portsmouth
Risk Management .... MSc 12FT 36PT

Business and management studies

Queen's University Belfast
Risk Management and Financial Regulation.................... MSc 12FT

University of Reading
Construction Management .... MSc 12FT
Corporate Finance .... MSc 10FT 24PT
Financial Risk Management .... MSc 10FT 24PT 24DL
International Securities, Investment and Banking .... MSc 12FT
Project Management .... MSc 24PT

Robert Gordon University
Asset Integrity Management......................................MSc 36-60DL
Health Safety and Risk Management ....MSc 36PT 36DL

Royal Veterinary College
Risk Analysis in Health and Food Safety .... PGCert 6FT

University of Salford
Environmental Assessment and Management....MSc 12FT 36PT/
PGDip 8FT 24PT
Management.... MSc 12FT 36PT/PGDip 8FT 24PT/PGCert 4FT 9PT
Quantity Surveying (Mechanical and Electrical).MSc 12FT 28DL/
PGDip 8FT 16DL

School of Oriental and African Studies - SOAS
Environmental Management..............................MSc 12FT 24-36PT
Finance and Financial Law ....MSc 12FT 24-36PT
International Management (China) ....MSc 12FT 24-36PT
International Management (Japan) ....MSc 12FT 24-36PT
International Management (Middle East and North Africa)..........
MSc 12FT 24PT
Public Policy and Management (Distance Learning)....MSc 24DL/
PGDip 12DL

Sheffield Hallam University
Environmental Management.........................MSc 12-24FT 24-36PT
Environmental Management (International Resource and
Climate Management)....................................MSc 12-18FT 24-36PT
Environmental Management (Wildlife and Landscape
Conservation) ....MSc 12-18FT 24-36PT
Risk Management .... MA 12FT/PGDip 9FT/PGCert 4FT 8PT

University of Sheffield
Management .... MSc 12FT
Management (Creative and Cultural Industries) .... MSc 12FT

Management (International Business)............................. MSc 12FT

University of South Wales
Sustainable Business Risk Management............... MSc 12/FT 36PT
MSc 36DL

University of Southampton
Corporate Risk and Security Management............MSc 12FT 27PT/
PGDip 9FT 21PT
Environmental Monitoring and Assessment .... MSc 12FT 27PT
Maritime Engineering Science: Nuclear Safety Management ......
MSc 12FT
Risk Management ....MSc 12FT 27PT/PGDip 9FT 21PT

University of St Andrews
Management..MLitt 12FT 24PT
Management (Human Resource Management) ....MLitt 12FT
Management and Information Technology ....MSc 12FT/
PGDip 9FT

University of Stirling
Management.................................MSc 12FT 27PT/PGDip 9FT 21PT

University of Strathclyde
European Financial Management...................................... MSc 12FT
Global Energy Management .... MSc 12FT 24PT
Safety and Risk Management ....PGCert 12PT/PGDip 12PT/MSc
24PT

University of Sussex
Corporate and Financial Risk Management .... MSc 12FT 24PT
Financial Risk and Investment Analysis................... MSc 12FT 24PT

Swansea University
Finance.. MSc 12FT
International Banking and Finance .... MSc 12FT
International Banking, Finance and Economics .... MSc 12FT

Trinity College Dublin - the University of Dublin
Environmental Sciences... MSc 12FT

UCL - University College London
Financial Risk Management .... MSc 12FT
Natural Hazards for Insurers .... PGCert 4PT
Risk and Disaster Reduction .... MRes 12FT 24PT PGCert 12PT
Risk, Disaster and Resilience ....MSc 12FT 24PT/PGDip 9FT 24PT

University of Warwick
Clinical Quality Improvement and Risk Management..PGA 12PT/
CPDMod 1PT

University of West London
Health and Social Care Leadership.......................................MSc 24PT

Risk management
Research Courses

Aston University
Environmental Systems and Safety Management Research
Group...PhD 36FT/MPhil 24FT

University of Birmingham
Environmental Science and Risk Management.............PhD 36FT/
MSc by research 12FT

University of Cambridge
Management Studies...PhD 36FT

University of Hertfordshire
Condition Monitoring and Asset Management ...PhD 36FT 72PT/
MPhil 24FT 48PT/MRes 12FT 24PT

Newcastle University
Environmental Science............... MPhil 12FT 24PT/PhD 36FT 72PT
Integrated PhD 48FT

Oxford Brookes University
Safety Technology ....PhD 24-60FT 36-72PT/MPhil 24-36FT
36-48PT

University of Sheffield
Management................................. PhD 36FT 72PT/MPhil 24FT 48PT

University of Southampton
School of Management: Centre for Risk ResearchPhD 36FT 72PT/
MPhil 24FT 48PT
School of Management: Health ....MPhil 24FT 48PT/
PhD 26FT 72PT
School of Management: Management Sciences .... MPhil 24FT
48PT/PhD 36FT 72PT
School of Management: Organisation and Management... MPhil
24FT 48PT/PhD 36FT 72PT

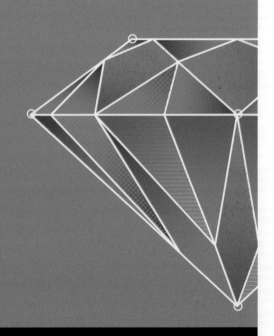

Economics

Econometrics
Taught Courses

Bangor University
Banking and Finance - London Centre ... MBA 12FT

Birkbeck, University of London
Econometrics ... PGCert 12PT
Financial Economics ... MSc 12FT 24PT
Financial Engineering ... MSc 12FT 24PT GradDip 12FT 24PT

University of Bristol
Economics and Econometrics ... MSc 12FT

University of Dundee
Financial Economics ... PGDip 9FT

University of East Anglia
Development Economics ... MSc 12FT 24PT
Economics ... MSc 12FT PGDip 10FT
Economics and International Relations ... MA 12FT
Experimental Economics ... MSc 12FT
Finance and Economics ... MSc 12FT
Health Economics ... MSc 12FT 36PT/PGDip 12FT 24PT/PGCert 12PT
Impact Evaluation for International Development ... MSc 12FT 24PT
Industrial Economics ... MSc 12FT
Media Economics ... MA 12FT
Statistics ... MSc 12FT 24PT

University of Essex
Accounting and Financial Economics ... MSc 12FT 24PT
Applied Economics and Data Analysis ... MA 12FT 24PT
Computational Economics, Financial Markets and Policy ... MSc 12FT 24PT
Economics ... MSc 12FT/PGDip 9FT
Economics and Econometrics ... MSc 12FT 24PT
Financial Econometrics ... MSc 12FT
Financial Economics ... MSc 12FT
Financial Economics and Econometrics ... MSc 12FT
International Economics ... MSc 12FT 24PT

European Business School London
Global Banking & Finance ... MSc 12-16FT

University of Exeter
Economics ... MSc 12FT
Economics and Econometrics ... MSc 12FT
Economics and Experimental Economics ... MSc 12FT

National University of Ireland Galway
Economic and Environmental Modelling ... MEconSci 10approxFT

Heriot-Watt University
Quantitative Financial Engineering ... MSc 12FT 24PT/Diploma 9FT 21PT
Quantitative Financial Risk Management ... MSc 12FT/PGDip 9FT

University of Hull
Energy Markets ... MSc 12FT

University of Kent
Economics Conversion ... MSc 24FT
Economics and Econometrics ... MSc 12FT 24PT
Economics and Finance ... MSc 12FT 24PT
Finance and Econometrics ... MSc 12FT 24PT
International Finance and Economic Development ... MSc 12FT 24PT

Kingston University
Applied Econometrics ... MSc 12FT 24PT

University of Leeds
Economics ... MA 12FT

University of Leicester
Banking and Finance ... MSc 12FT 24PT
Financial Economics ... MSc 12FT 24PT

London School of Economics and Political Science (LSE)
Econometrics and Mathematical Economics ... MSc 10 or 22FT

Loughborough University
Banking and Finance ... MSc 12FT
Economics and Finance ... MSc 12FT

University of Manchester
Econometrics ... MSc 12FT 24PT

University of Nottingham
Economics and Econometrics ... MSc 12FT

University of Oxford
Financial Economics ... MSc 9FT

Queen Mary, University of London
Banking and Finance ... MSc 12FT 24PT
Finance ... MSc 12FT
Finance and Econometrics ... MSc 12FT 24PT

University of Reading
Agricultural Development Economics ... MSc 12FT 24PT
Agricultural Economics ... MSc 12FT 24PT
Banking and Finance in Emerging Economies ... MSc 12FT 24PT
Business Economics ... MSc 12FT 24PT
Food Economics and Marketing ... MSc 12FT
Real Estate Finance ... MSc 12FT
Real Estate Investment and Finance ... MSc 24-72PT
The Economics of International Business and Finance ... MSc 12FT

Royal Holloway, University of London
Financial and Industrial Economics ... MSc 12FT

School of Oriental and African Studies - SOAS
Development Economics ... MSc 12FT 24-36PT
International Management (Japan) ... MSc 12FT 24-36PT

University of Sheffield
Financial Economics ... MSc 12FT 24PT

University of Southampton
Economics and Econometrics ... MSc 12FT 24PT/PGDip 9FT 21PT
Finance and Economics ... MSc 12FT 24PT/PGDip 9FT 21PT

Swansea University
Economics ... MSc 12FT
Economics with International Banking ... MSc 12FT
International Banking, Finance and Economics ... MSc 12FT

Swansea Metropolitan University
Chartered Institute of Management Accountants ... CIMA 12FT

University of York
Finance and Econometrics ... MSc 12FT
Financial Engineering ... MSc 12FT

Econometrics
Research Courses

University of Dundee
Economics ... MPhil 24FT MSc by research 12FT

University of East Anglia
Applied and Financial Economics ... PhD 36FT 72PT/MPhil 24FT 48PT
Experimental Economics ... PhD 36FT 72PT/MPhil 24FT 48PT
Industrial Economics ... PhD 36FT 72PT/MPhil 24FT 48PT

University of Essex
Economics ... PhD 36FT 72PT/MPhil 24FT 48PT

University of Exeter
Economics ... PhD 48FT 89PT/MPhil 36FT 60PT

Heriot-Watt University
Economics, including CERT (Centre for Economic Reform & Transformation) ... PhD 36FT/MPhil 12FT

Loughborough University
Economics ... PhD 36FT 60PT/MPhil 24FT 36PT

The Open University
Economics of Innovation and Development ... PhD 36FT 72PT variableDL/MPhil 15FT 24PT variableDL

Swansea University
Economics ... PhD 36FT 60PT/MPhil 12FT 24PT

Economic history
Taught Courses

University of Aberdeen
Economics ... MSc 12FT

University of Birmingham
Social Research (Economic and Social History) ... MA 12FT 24PT

University of Cambridge
Economic and Social History ... MPhil 11FT

City University London
Social Research Methods ... MSc 12FT 24PT

University of Dundee
Global Empires (MLitt) ... MLitt 12FT

Durham University
Social and Economic History (Research Methods) ... MA 12FT

University of East Anglia
Economics ... MSc 12FT
Economics ... PGDip 10FT
Modern History ... MA 12FT 24PT
Social Science Research Methods: Business ... MRes 12FT 24PT
Social Science Research Methods: Education ... MRes 12FT 24PT
Social Science Research Methods: Law ... MRes 12FT 24PT
Social Science Research Methods: Psychology ... MRes 12FT 24PT
Social Science Research Methods: Social Work ... MRes 12FT 24PT

University of Edinburgh
Economic and Social History ... MSc by research 12FT 24PT

University of Exeter
Economic and Social History ... MRes 12FT 24PT

Glasgow Caledonian University
Social Research ... MSc 12FT 24PT
Social Research (Policy Analysis) ... MSc 12FT 24PT

University of Liverpool
Research Methodology (Economic and Social History) ... MA 12FT 24PT

London Metropolitan University
Economics ... MSc 12FT 24 - 48PT

London School of Economics and Political Science (LSE)
Economic History ... MSc 12FT 24PT

Manchester Metropolitan University
History ... MA 12FT 24PT

University of Oxford
Economic and Social History ... MPhil 21FT/MSc 12FT

University of Reading
Economic Development in Emerging Markets ... MSc 12FT 24PT

University of Sheffield
Early Modern History ... MA 12FT 24PT

University of Southampton
Economics ... MSc 12FT 24PT/PGDip 9FT 21PT

University of Surrey
Economics ... MA 12FT 24PT

Economic history
Research Courses

University of Dundee
Economics ... MPhil 24FT MSc by research 12FT

University of Edinburgh
Economic and Social History ... PhD 36FT 72PT/MPhil 24FT 48PT/MSc by research 12FT 24PT

University of Glasgow
Economic and Social History ... PhD 36FT 48PT/MSc by research 24FT 36PT

London School of Economics and Political Science (LSE)
Economic History ... PhD 36-48FT/MPhil 36-48FT

University of Manchester
Economic and Social History ... PhD 36FT

The Open University
Social and economic history of Britain and Ireland 18th-20th centuries ... PhD 36FT 72PT variableDL/MPhil 15FT 24PT variableDL

University of Oxford
History (for Economic & Social History, and History of Science) ... DPhil 48FT

University of York
Economic and Social History ... MSc by research 12FT 24PT

Economics
Taught Courses

University of Aberdeen
Economics ... MSc 12FT
Management Economics and International Relations . MSc 12FT/PGDip 9FT/PGCert 6FT

University of Abertay Dundee
Energy Industry Economics ... MSc 12FT/PGDip 9FT

University of Bath
Economics ... MSc 12FT 24PT MRes 12FT 24PT MSc 12FT 24PT/PGDip 9FT 24PT/PGCert 4FT
Economics (Development) ... MSc 12FT 24PT/PGDip 9FT 21PT/PG Cert Microeconomics (Development) 4FT/PG Cert Macroeconomics (Development) 4FT
Economics and Finance .. MSc 12FT 30PT/PGDip 9FT 21PT/PGCert 4FT

Birkbeck, University of London
Econometrics ... PGCert 12PT
Economics ... GradDip 12FT 24PT MSc 12FT 24PT
Finance ... MSc 12FT 24PT GradDip 12-24PT
Financial Economics ... MSc 12FT 24PT
Sport Governance ... PGCert 12PT 12DL
Sport Management ... PGCert 12PT 12DL/MSc 12FT 24PT/MRes 12FT 24PT

University of Birmingham
Development Economics ... MSc 12FT 24PT
Economics ... MSc 12FT
Environmental and Natural Resource Economics ... MSc 12FT 24PT
Local and Regional Economic Development ... MSc 12FT 24PT/PGDip 9FT 21PT/GradDip 9FT 21PT/GradCert 9FT 21PT

University of Brighton
Economics and Finance ... MSc see siteFT/PGDip see siteFT/PGCert see siteFT

University of Bristol
Economics ... GradDip 9FT MSc 12FT
Economics and Econometrics ... MSc 12FT
Economics and Finance ... MSc 12FT
Economics and Public Policy ... MSc 12FT
Economics, Accounting and Finance ... MSc 12FT
Economics, Finance and Management ... MSc 12FT

University of Cambridge
Economics ... MPhil 11FT/PGDip 9FT

University of Central Lancashire
Construction Management (Construction Economics) MSc 24DL/PGDip 12DL/PGCert 6DL
International Business Economics ... MA 12FT

City University London
Development Economics ... MSc 12FT 24PT

Economics

Economic Regulation and Competition .... MSc 12FT 24PT
Economics .... MSc 12FT 24PT

University College Cork
Economics .... MA 9FT 18PT

Cranfield University
Economics for Natural Resource & Environmental Management MSc 12FT 24-60PT/PGCert 5FT 24PT/PGDip 6FT 24PT

University of Dundee
Accounting and Finance .... MSc 12FT
Climate Change Economics and Policy .... MSc 12FT
Economics .... PGDip 9FT
Energy Studies with Specialisation in Energy Economics ...... MSc 12FT/PGDip 9FT
Energy Studies with Specialisation in Oil and Gas Economics ..... MSc 12FT
Managing in the Energy Industries .... MSc 12FT
Non-Graduating Taught Postgraduate in School of Business... PG module variableFT
Supplementary Studies in Graduate School of Natural Resources, Law, Policy and Management ....Masters Level Modules 6-9FT

University of East Anglia
Development Economics .... MSc 12FT 24PT
Economics .... MSc 12FT PGDip 10FT
Economics and International Relations .... MA 12FT
Environmental Economics .... MSc 12FT 24PT
Experimental Economics .... MSc 12FT
Finance and Economics .... MSc 12FT
Health Economics .... MSc 12FT 36PT/PGDip 12FT 24PT/PGCert 12PT
Industrial Economics .... MSc 12FT
Media Economics .... MA 12FT
Philosophy, Politics and Economics of Public Choice .... MA 12FT 24PT

Edinburgh Napier University
Accounting and Finance .... MSc 12FT 36PT

University of Edinburgh
Carbon Management .... MSc 12FT
Ecological Economics .... MSc 12FT 24-36PT/PGDip 9FT
Economics/Economics(Finance) - Scottish Graduate Programme MSc 12FT 24PT
Management of Bioeconomy, Innovation and Governance... MSc 12FT 24PT

University of Essex
Accounting and Financial Economics .... MSc 12FT 24PT
Applied Economics and Data Analysis .... MA 12FT 24PT
Computational Economics, Financial Markets and Policy....... MSc 12FT 24PT
Economics .... MSc 12FT/PGDip 9FT
Economics and Econometrics .... MSc 12FT 24PT
Economics with English for Academic Purposes .... Diploma 9FT
Financial Econometrics .... MSc 12FT
Financial Economics .... MSc 12FT
Financial Economics and Econometrics .... MSc 12FT
Financial and Business Economics .... MSc 12FT
International Economics .... MSc 12FT 24PT
Management Economics .... MSc 12FT
Political Economy .... MA 12FT 24PT/MSc 12FT 24PT/MRes 12FT

University of Exeter
Economics .... MSc 12FT
Economics and Econometrics .... MSc 12FT
Economics and Experimental Economics .... MSc 12FT
Financial Economics .... MSc 12FT
Money and Banking .... MSc 12FT

National University of Ireland Galway
Economic Science .... HDip 2 sem.FT
Economic and Environmental Modelling... MEconSci 10approxFT
Strategy Innovation and People Management..... MSc 9 approxFT

Glasgow Caledonian University
International Economics and Finance .... MSc 12FT

University of Glasgow
Economic Development .... MSc 12FT
Economics, Banking and Finance .... MSc 12FT
Global Economy .... MSc 12FT 24PT

University of Greenwich
Construction Management and Economics .... MSc 12FT 24PT

Heriot-Watt University
Actuarial Science .... MSc 12FT 24PT/PGDip 9FT 18PT

University of Hull
Economics and Business .... MSc 12FT
Energy Markets .... MSc 12FT

University of Kent
Actuarial Science .... PGDip 9FT
Agri-Environmental Economics and Policy .... MSc 12FT 24PT
Applied Economics and International Development ..... MSc 12FT 24PT
Diploma in Economic Analysis .... MSc 24FT
Economics .... MSc 12FT 24PT
Economics Conversion .... MSc 24FT
Economics and Econometrics .... MSc 12FT 24PT
Economics and Finance .... MSc 12FT 24PT
Finance and Econometrics .... MSc 12FT 24PT
International Development .... MSc 12FT 24PT
International Development (Brussels) .... MA 12FT 24PT
International Finance and Economic Development .... MSc 12FT 24PT
International Master's in Applied Actuarial Science ..... MSc 24FT/PGDip 24FT
International Political Economy (Brussels) .... MA 12FT 24PT

King's College London
Political Economy .... MA 12FT 24PT

Kingston University
Business and Economic Forecasting .... MSc 12FT 24PT
Economics (Political Economy) .... MA 12FT 24PT

Lancaster University
Economics .... MSc 12FT

University of Leeds
Economics .... MA 12FT
Sustainability (Ecological Economics) .... MSc 12FT 48PT

University of Leicester
Economics .... MSc 12FT 24PT

University of Limerick
Economic Analysis .... MSc(Econ) 12FT
Finance and Information Systems .... MSc 12FT

University of Liverpool
Advanced Computer Science with Internet Economics. MSc 12FT
Business Finance and Management .... MBA 12FT 24PT
Economics and Finance .... MSc 12FT 24PT

London Metropolitan University
Economics .... GradDip 12FT 24PT MSc 12FT 24 - 48PT

London School of Economics and Political Science (LSE)
Economics .... MSc 10 or 22FT
Economics and Philosophy .... MSc 13FT 25PT
Political Economy of Late Development .... MSc 12FT

London School of Hygiene and Tropical Medicine
Demography & Health .... MSc 12FT 24PT
Public Health (Health Economics) .... MSc 12FT 24PT

London South Bank University
International Finance & Accounting .... MSc 18FT

Loughborough University
Banking and Finance .... MSc 12FT
Banking and Financial Markets .... MSc 12FT

Manchester Metropolitan University
Economic and Financial Analysis .... MSc 12FT/PGDip 9FT
MSc Accounting and Finance .... MSc 12FT

University of Manchester
Development Economics and Policy .... MSc 12FT 24PT
Economics (Economics of Health) .... MSc 12FT 24PT
Economics (Environmental Economics) .... MSc 12FT 24PT
Economics .... MA 12FT 24PT MSc 12FT 24PT
Economics and Econometrics .... MSc 12FT 24PT
Law and Economics .... LLM 12FT

National University of Ireland, Maynooth
Economic Science .... HDip 12FT
Economics of Competition & Regulation .... MEconSci 12FT

Middlesex University
Banking and Finance .... MSc 12FT 24PT

Newcastle University
Banking and Finance .... MSc 12FT
E-Business .... MSc 12FT
E-Business (Information Systems) .... MSc 12FT
International Economics and Finance .... MSc 12FT

Nottingham Trent University
Economics and Finance/International Finance .... MSc 12FT

University of Nottingham
Applied Economics .... MSc 12FT
Applied Economics and Financial Economics .... MSc 12FT
Behavioural Economics .... MSc 12FT
Economic Development and Policy Analysis .... MSc 12FT
Economics .... MSc 12FT
Economics (Conversion) .... PGDip 9FT
Economics and Development Economics .... MSc 12FT
Economics and Econometrics .... MSc 12FT
Economics and Financial Economics .... MSc 12FT
Economics and International Economics .... MSc 12FT

University of Oxford
Development Studies .... MPhil 36FT
Economics .... MPhil 21FT
Economics for Development .... MSc 9-21FT
Financial Economics .... MSc 9FT

University of Portsmouth
Economics for Business .... MA 12FT

Queen Mary, University of London
Economics .... MSc 12FT

University of Reading
Agricultural Development Economics .... MSc 12FT 24PT
Agricultural Economics .... MSc 12FT 24PT
Applied Development Studies .... MSc 12FT 24PT
Banking and Finance in Emerging Economies ...... MSc 12FT 24PT
Business Economics .... MSc 12FT 24PT
Climate Change & Development .... MSc 12FT 24PT
Construction Cost Management .... MSc 24PT
Corporate Real Estate .... MSc 24-72PT
Development Finance .... MSc 12FT
Development Planning .... MSc 12FT 24PT/PGDip 12FT 24PT
Development Planning Research ......MSc 12FT 24PT/PGDip 12FT 24PT
Economic Development in Emerging Markets ..... MSc 12FT 24PT
Economics of International Business and Finance MSc 12FT 24PT
Environment and Development .... MSc 12FT
Environmental Management .... MSc 12FT 24PT
Ethics & Political Theory .... MA 12FT 24PT
Food Economics and Marketing .... MSc 12FT
International Business and Economic Development .... MSc 12FT 24PT
International Economic Development .... MSc 12FT
International Finance and Economic Development ...... MSc 12FT 24PT
International Management and Accounting .... MSc 12FT 24PT
International Planning and Sustainable Urban Management ..... MSc 12FT/PGCert 6FT/PGDip 9FT
Law and Economics .... MSc 12FT/PGDip 9FT/PGCert 6FT
Project Management .... MSc 24PT
Real Estate .... MSc 12FT
Real Estate (part time) .... MSc 24-72PT
Real Estate Finance .... MSc 12FT
Real Estate Investment and Finance .... MSc 24-72PT
The Economics of Climate Change .... MSc 12FT

Royal Holloway, University of London
Economics .... MSc 12FT

University of Salford
International Banking and FInance ..... MSc 12FT 36PT/PGDip 8FT 24PT/PGCert 4FT 9PT
International Corporate FInanceMSc 12FT 36PT/PGDip 8FT 24PT/PGCert 4FT 9PT

School of Oriental and African Studies - SOAS
Development Economics .... MSc 12FT 24-36PT
Economics (with Reference to Africa) .... MSc 12FT 24PT
Economics (with Reference to South Asia) .... MSc 12FT 24PT
Economics (with Reference to the Asia Pacific Region) . MSc 12FT 24PT
Economics (with reference to the Middle East)..... MSc 12FT 24PT
Finance and Development .... MSc 24-60DL/PGDip 12-60DL

Schumacher College
Economics for Transition .... MA 12FT PGCert

Sheffield Hallam University
Banking and Finance .... MA 12FT
Local and Regional Economic Development....... MSc 48DL/PGDip 36DL/PGCert 12DL

University of Sheffield
Development Economics and Policy .... MSc 12FT 24PT
Economics .... MSc 12FT 24PT
Economics and Health Economics .... MSc 12FT
Finance .... MSc 12FT 24PT
Finance and Accounting .... MSc 12FT
Financial Economics .... MSc 12FT 24PT
International Finance and Economics .... MSc 12FT 24PT

University of Southampton
Economics .... MSc 12FT 24PT/PGDip 9FT 21PT
Economics and Econometrics ...... MSc 12FT 24PT/PGDip 9FT 21PT
Finance and Economics .... MSc 12FT 24PT/PGDip 9FT 21PT
International Banking and Financial Studies .... MSc 12FT/PGDip 9FT
International Financial Markets .... MSc 12FT/PGDip 9FT

University of St Andrews
Finance & Management .... MLitt 12FT
Finance (FIN) .... PGDip 9FT/MSc 12FT/MPhil 24FT

Staffordshire University
Economics for Business Analysis .... MSc 12-16FT
Economics of Globalisation and European Integration .... MA 12-16FT

University of Stirling
Environmental Economics .... MSc 12FT
Finance .... MSc 12FT/PGDip 9FT/PGCert 6FT
Human Resource Management and Socio Economic Development .... MSc 12FT/PGDip 9FT/PGCert 6FT
International Accounting & FinanceMSc 12FT/PGDip 9FT/PGCert 6FT

University of Strathclyde
Applied Economics ... MSc 12FT 24PT 24DL/PGDip 9FT 18PT 18DL
Finance .... MSc 12FT 24PT/PGDip 9FT 21PT
International Accounting and FinanceMSc 12FT 24PT/PGDip 9FT 21PT
International Banking and Finance ..... MSc 12FT 24PT/PGDip 9FT 21PT

University of Surrey
Economics .... MA 12FT 24PT

Section sponsored by
BPP UNIVERSITY COLLEGE

Business and social sciences
www.prospects.ac.uk/findcourses POSTGRADUATE DIRECTORY 415

Economics

University of Sussex
Development Economics ... MSc 12FT 24PT
Economics ... MSc 12FT 24PT/GradDip 9FT
International Economics ... MSc 12FT 24PT

Swansea University
Business Economics ... MSc 12FT
Business Economics with Computing ... MSc 12FT
Business Economics with Finance ... MSc 12FT
Economics ... MSc 12FT
International Banking, Finance and Economics ... MSc 12FT

Trinity College Dublin - the University of Dublin
Economic Policy Studies ... MSc 24PT
Economics ... MSc(Econ) 12FT 24PT

UCL - University College London
Comparative Business Economics ... MA 12FT 24PT
Economic Policy ... MSc 12FT
Economics ... MSc 12FT
The Politics and Economics of Eastern Europe ... MRes 12FT
Urban Economic Development ... MSc 12FT 24-60PT/PGDip 9FT

University of Warwick
Economics ... MSc 12FT 24PT/PGDip 9FT 18PT
Economics and International Finance ... MSc 12FT
MA International Political Economy ... MA 12FT 24PT/PGDip 9FT

University of York
Development Economics and Emerging Markets ... MSc 12FT
Economic and Social Policy Analysis ... MSc 12FT
Economics ... MSc 12FT
Economics and Econometrics ... MSc 12FT
Economics and Finance ... MSc 12FT
Environmental Economics ... MSc 12FT
Environmental Economics and Environmental Management ... MSc 12FT/PGDip 9FT
Philosophy, Politics and Economics ... MA 12FT
Politics, Philosophy and Economics: Economics and Development ... MA 12FT
Politics, Philosophy and Economics: Economics and Politics ... MA 12FT
Politics, Philosophy and Economics: Politics and Development ... MA 12FT
Politics, Philosopy and Economics: Economics and PhilosophyMA 12FT
Project Analysis, Finance and Investment ... MSc 12FT
Public Economics ... MSc 12FT

Economics
Research Courses

University of Aberdeen
Economics ... PhD 36FT/MPhil 24FT

Aberystwyth University
Economics ... PhD 36FT 60PT
Management and Business ... MPhil 12FT 24PT PhD 36FT 60PT

Anglia Ruskin University
Business and Management ... MPhil 36FT 72PT/PhD 36FT 72PT

University of Bath
Economics ... MPhil 12FT 24PT/PhD 36FT 72PT

Birkbeck, University of London
Economics/Finance ... PhD 24FT 36PT/MPhil 24FT 36PT

University of Birmingham
Economics PhD ... PhD 48FT

University of Bristol
Economics ... PhD 36FT 72PT/MPhil 12FT 24PT

Brunel University
Doctoral Programme in Economics and Finance .. PhD 36FT 72PT/MPhil 24FT 48PT

University of Buckingham
Economics and International Studies ... DPhil 36FT 72PT/MPhil 24FT 48PT

University of Cambridge
Economics ... PhD 36FT

Cardiff University
Economics ... PhD 48FT

University of Dundee
Economics ... MPhil 24FT MSc by research 12FT PhD 36FT

University of East Anglia
International Development: Economic Development ... PhD 36FT 72PT/MPhil 24FT 48PT
International Development: Sustainable Development ... PhD 36FT 72PT/MPhil 24FT 48PT

University of Edinburgh
Economics ... PhD 36FT

University of Essex
Applied Social and Economic Research ... PhD 36FT 72PT/MPhil 24FT 48PT
Economics ... PhD 36FT 72PT/MPhil 24FT 48PT
Health Research ... PhD 36FT 72PT/MPhil 24FT 48PT
Survey Methodology ... PhD 36FT 72PT/MPhil 24FT 48PT

European University Institute
Economics ... PhD 48FT

University of Exeter
Economics ... PhD 48FT 89PT/MPhil 36FT 60PT

Heriot-Watt University
Economics, including CERT (Centre for Economic Reform & Transformation) ... PhD 36FT/MPhil 12FT

University of Hertfordshire
Centre for Research in Institutional Economics (CRIE) ... PhD 36FT 72PT/MPhil 24FT 48PT/MRes 12FT 24PT

University of Hull
Centre for Economic Policy ... PhD 36FT 60PT/MPhil 24FT 36PT/MRes 12FT 24PT

Institute for the Study of the Americas, School of Advanced Study, University of London
Economics ... PhD 36FT/MPhil 12FT

Keele University
Economics ... PhD 24-48FT 48-84PT/MPhil 12-24FT 24-36PT

University of Kent
Economics ... PhD 36FT 60PT/MPhil 24FT 36PT

King's College London
Political Economy Research ... MPhil 24FT 36PT/PhD 36FT 72PT

Kingston University
Economics ... PhD 48FT 72PT/MPhil 24FT 48PT/MSc by research 12FT 24PT

Lancaster University
Economics ... PhD 36FT 48PT/PGDipRes 24FT 36PT

University of Leicester
Economics ... PhD 36FT/MPhil 48FT

University of Liverpool
Management ... PhD 24-48FT 48-84PT/MPhil 12FT 24PT/MRes 12FT 24PT

London School of Economics and Political Science (LSE)
Economics ... MRes 36-48FT/PhD 36-48FT

Manchester Metropolitan University
Department of Economics ... PhD 24-48FT 42-84PT 42-84DL/MPhil 18-36FT 36-72PT 36-72DL/MA by research 12-24FT 24-42PT 24-42DL

University of Manchester
Economics ... PhD 36FT 72PT/MRes 12FT 24PT

National University of Ireland, Maynooth
Economics ... PhD 36 - 60FT/MLitt by research 12 - 36FT

Newcastle University
Economics ... PhD 36FT 72PT/MPhil 12FT 24PT

Nottingham Trent University
Economics ... PhD 24FT/MPhil 48FT

University of Nottingham
Economics ... PhD 36FT
School of Economics ... PhD 36FT/MPhil 24FT

The Open University
Economics ... PhD 36FT 72PT variableDL/MPhil 15FT 24PT variableDL
Economics of Health and Welfare ... PhD 36FT 72PT variableDL/MPhil 15FT 24PT variableDL
Economics of Innovation and Development ... PhD 36FT 72PT variableDL/MPhil 15FT 24PT variableDL
Mind, Meaning and Rationality ... PhD 36FT 72PT variableDL/MPhil 15FT 24PT variableDL
Personal finance ... PhD 36FT 72PT variableDL/MPhil 15FT 24PT variableDL

University of Oxford
Economics ... DPhil 48FT

University of Portsmouth
Economics and Finance ... MPhil 24FT 48PT/PhD 36FT 72PT

Queen Mary, University of London
Department of Economics ... PhD 36FT/MPhil

Queen's University Belfast
Economics ... PhD 36FT 72PT/MPhil 24FT 48PT

Robert Gordon University
Aberdeen Business School ... PhD 12FT 36PT 36DL/MSc(Res) 12FT 36PT 36DL

Royal Holloway, University of London
Economics ... PhD 48FT/MPhil 36FT

School of Oriental and African Studies - SOAS
Development Studies ... PhD 36FT 48-60PT
Economics ... PhD 36FT 72PT/MPhil 24FT 36PT

University of Sheffield
Economics ... PhD 36FT 72PT/MPhil 24FT 48PT

University of Southampton
Economics ... PhD 36-48FT 84PT/MPhil 24-48FT 84PT

University of St Andrews
Economics ... PhD 36FT 72PT/MPhil 24FT 36PT
Finance ... PhD 36FT 72PT/MPhil 24FT 48PT

Staffordshire University
Economics Division of Business School ... MPhil 12FT/PhD 12FT

University of Strathclyde
Economics - Research ... PhD 33FT/MPhil 12FT/DBA 33FT

University of Surrey
Economics ... PhD 33FT 45PT/MPhil 21FT 33PT

University of Sussex
Economics Research Programme ... PhD 24-48FT 36-72PT/MPhil 12-36FT 24-48PT

Swansea University
Economics ... PhD 36FT 60PT/MPhil 12FT 24PT

UCL - University College London
East European Economics ... PhD 36FT 60PT
Economics ... PhD 36FT 60PT

University of Warwick
Economics ... PhD 48FT/MPhil 12FT

University of the West of Scotland
Department of Land Economics ... PhD/MPhil

University of York
Economic and Social History ... MSc by research 12FT 24PT
Economics ... PhD 36FT/MPhil 24FT
Environmental Economics and Environmental Management (EEEM) ... PhD 36FT 72PT/MPhil 24FT 48PT

Financial economics
Taught Courses

University of Aberdeen
Economics ... MSc 12FT

Bangor University
ACCA (Professional Development) ... ACCA 48PT
Accounting and Finance ... MSc 12FT
Accounting and Finance - LondonCentre ... MSc 12FT
Accounting, Banking, Economics, Finance, Management Studies MPhil 24FT/PhD by taught 36FT
Banking and Finance ... MSc 12FT MA 12FT/PGDip 9FT MBA 12FT
Banking and Finance - London Centre ... MBA 12FTMSc 12FT
Business and Finance ... MSc 12FT/PGDip 9FT MA 12FT/PGDip 9FT
Business and Marketing ... MA 12FT/PGDip 9FT
CIMA (Professional Development) ... CIMA 12PT
Finance ... MBA 12FTMA 12FT/PGDip 9FTMSc 12FT/PGDip 9FT
Finance - London Centre ... MBA 12FTMSc 12FT
International Banking and Development Finance ... MSc 12FT/PGDip 9FT
International Banking and Development Finance - London Centre ... MSc 12FT
Islamic Banking and Finance ... MBA 12FTMA 12FT/PGDip 9FT MSc 12FT/PGDip 9FT
Islamic Banking and Finance - London Centre ... MBA 12FT
Management ... MBA 12FT 36PT
Management and Finance ... MSc 12FT/MA 12FT

Bournemouth University
International Business with Economics ... MA 12-15FT

University of Bradford
Economics and Finance for Development ... MSc 12FT 24-60PT/PGDip 9FT 21PT
European MSc in Economics ... MSc 12FT
Financial Economics ... MSc 12FT

University of Brighton
Economics and Finance ... MSc see siteFT/PGDip see siteFT/PGCert see siteFT

Bucks New University
Applied Commissioning ... PGCert 6PT

University of Cambridge
Real Estate Finance ... MPhil 10FT

Cardiff University
Financial Economics ... MSc 12FT 24PT

University of Central Lancashire
International Business Economics ... MA 12FT

City University London
Financial Economics ... MSc 12FT 24PT

University of Derby
International Financial Markets ... MSc 12FT 36PT

University of Dundee
Accounting and Finance ... MSc 12FT
Finance ... MSc 12FT
Financial Economics ... PGDip 9FT

Durham University
Finance (Economics and Finance) ... MSc 12FT

University of East Anglia
Economics ... MSc 12FT PGDip 10FT
Finance and Economics ... MSc 12FT
International Business Economics ... MA 12FT

University of Edinburgh
Economics/Economics(Finance) - Scottish Graduate Programme MSc 12FT 24PT

Section sponsored by BPP UNIVERSITY COLLEGE

Business and social sciences

416 POSTGRADUATE DIRECTORY www.prospects.ac.uk/findcourses

Economics

University of Essex
Accounting and Financial Economics ... MSc 12FT 24PT
Applied Economics and Data Analysis ... MA 12FT 24PT
Computational Economics, Financial Markets and Policy ... MSc 12FT 24PT
Economics ... MSc 12FT/PGDip 9FT
Economics and Econometrics ... MSc 12FT 24PT
Financial Econometrics ... MSc 12FT
Financial Economics ... MSc 12FT
Financial Economics and Econometrics ... MSc 12FT
Financial and Business Economics ... MSc 12FT
International Economics ... MSc 12FT 24PT
Management Economics ... MSc 12FT

University of Exeter
Economics ... MSc 12FT
Economics and Econometrics ... MSc 12FT
Economics and Experimental Economics ... MSc 12FT
Financial Economics ... MSc 12FT

GCU London
International Economics and Finance ... MSc 12FT

Glasgow Caledonian University
Financial Services, Risk and Operations ... MSc 12FT 24PT/PGDip 9FT 24PT
International Economics and Finance ... MSc 12FT

University of Glasgow
Financial Economics ... MSc 12FT
Financial Forecasting and Investment ... MSc 12FT
Real Estate ... PGCert 12FT

University of Greenwich
Business and Financial Economics MA 12FT 24PT/MSc 12FT 24PT/PGDip 12FT 24PT
Financial Services ... MBA 12FT 24PT

Heriot-Watt University
Actuarial Management ... MSc 12FT 48PT/PGDip 9FT 48PT
Actuarial Science ... MSc 12FT 24PT/PGDip 9FT 18PT
Financial Mathematics ... MSc 12FT
Quantitative Finance and Mathematics ... MSc 12FT 24PT
Quantitative Financial Engineering ... MSc 12FT 24PT
Quantitative Financial Risk Management ... MSc 12FT/PGDip 9FT

University of Huddersfield
Financial Economics ... MSc 12FT

Imperial College London
Economics & Strategy for Business ... MSc 12FT

University of Kent
Actuarial Science ... PGDip 9FT
Economics ... MSc 12FT 24PT
Economics Conversion ... MSc 24FT
Economics and Econometrics ... MSc 12FT 24PT
Economics and Finance ... MSc 12FT 24PT
Finance and Econometrics ... MSc 12FT 24PT
Finance, Investment and Risk ... MSc 12FT/PGDip 12FT
Financial Markets ... MSc 12FT
Financial Services in Banking ... MSc 12FT
International Accounting and Finance ... MSc 12FT
International Finance and Economic Development ... MSc 12FT 24PT
International Master's in Applied Actuarial Science ... MSc 24FT/PGDip 24FT
International Master's in Statistics with Finance ... MSc 24FT
International Masters in Statistics ... MSc 24FT
Statistics with Finance ... MSc 12FT

Kingston University
Financial Economics ... MA 12FT 24PT

Leeds Metropolitan University
Finance ... MSc 12FT 24PT
International Trade and Finance ... MA 12FT

University of Leeds
Economics and Finance ... MA 12FT 24PT

University of Leicester
Business Analysis and Finance ... MSc 12FT 24PT
Financial Economics ... MSc 12FT 24PT
Money and Banking ... MSc 12FT

University of Limerick
Finance and Information Systems ... MSc 12FT

London Metropolitan University
Economics ... MSc 12FT 24 - 48PT

London School of Economics and Political Science (LSE)
Econometrics and Mathematical Economics ... MSc 10 or 22FT
Finance and Economics ... MSc 10FT
Real Estate Economics and Finance ... MSc 12FT 24PT

Loughborough University
Economics and Finance ... MSc 12FT

University of Manchester
Finance and Business Economics ... MSc 12FT 24PT
Financial Economics ... MSc 12FT 24PT

National University of Ireland, Maynooth
Economics & Finance ... MA 12FT 24PT

Nottingham Trent University
Economics and Finance/International Finance ... MSc 12FT

University of Nottingham
Applied Economics and Financial Economics ... MSc 12FT
Banking and Financial Markets in Contemporary China ... MSc 12FT
Economics and Financial Economics ... MSc 12FT

University of Oxford
Financial Economics ... MSc 9FT

University of Portsmouth
Business Economics ... MSc 12FT 24PT
Business Economics, Finance and Banking ... MSc 12FT 24PT

Queen Mary, University of London
Economics ... MSc 12FT
Finance ... MSc 12FT
Finance and Econometrics ... MSc 12FT 24PT
Pre-masters Graduate Diploma in EAP and Economics & Finance GradDip 12FT

University of Reading
Accounting and Financial Management ... MSc 12FT
Banking and Finance in Emerging Economies ... MSc 12FT 24PT
Banking and Financial Systems in the Global Economy MSc 12FT
Development Finance ... MSc 12FT
Economics of International Business and Finance MSc 12FT 24PT
International Business and Finance ... MSc 12FT
International Finance and Economic Development ... MSc 12FT 24PT
International Financial Regulation ... LLM 12FT
Law and Economics ... MSc 12FT/PGDip 9FT/PGCert 6FT
Real Estate Finance ... MSc 12FT
The Economics of International Business and Finance . MSc 12FT

Royal Holloway, University of London
Economics ... MSc 12FT

School of Oriental and African Studies - SOAS
Finance and Development ... MSc 24-60DL/PGDip 12-60DL
Finance and Financial Law ... MSc 12FT 24-36PT

Schumacher College
Economics for Transition ... MA 12FT

University of Sheffield
Business Finance and Economics ... MSc 12FT 24PT
Finance ... MSc 12FT 24PT
Finance and Accounting ... MSc 12FT
Financial Economics ... MSc 12FT 24PT
Money, Banking & Finance ... MSc 12FT 24PT

University of Southampton
Finance and Economics ... MSc 12FT 24PT/PGDip 9FT 21PT

University of St Andrews
Finance & Management ... MLitt 12FT
Finance (FIN) ... PGDip 9FT/MSc 12FT/MPhil 24FT

Staffordshire University
Economics for Business Analysis ... MSc 12-16FT

University of Stirling
Computing for Financial Markets ... MSc 12FT/PGDip 9FT/PGCert 9FT
Finance ... MSc 12FT/PGDip 9FT/PGCert 6FT

University of Strathclyde
Finance ... MSc 12FT 24PT/PGDip 9FT 21PT

University of Surrey
Economics ... MA 12FT 24PT

Swansea University
Business Economics with Finance ... MSc 12FT
International Banking, Finance and Economics ... MSc 12FT

Trinity College Dublin - the University of Dublin
Economic Policy Studies ... MSc 24PT
Economics ... MSc(Econ) 12FT 24PT

UCL - University College London
Comparative Business Economics ... MA 12FT 24PT
Economic Policy ... MSc 12FT

University of Warwick
Finance & Economics ... MSc 12FT

Financial economics
Research Courses

University of Aberdeen
Finance ... PhD 36FT/MPhil 24FT/MRes 12FT

Bangor University
Accounting, Banking, Economics, Finance, Management Studies MPhil 24FT/PhD 36FT

University of Dundee
Accountancy and Business Finance ... MAcc 12FT
MPhil 24FT MSc by research 12FT PhD 36FT

University of Essex
Economics ... PhD 36FT 72PT/MPhil 24FT 48PT

University of Exeter
Economics ... PhD 48FT 89PT/MPhil 36FT 60PT

University of Hertfordshire
Centre for Research in Finance and Accounting (CFiFA) ... PhD 36FT 72PT/MPhil 24FT 48PT/MRes 12FT 24PT

Newcastle University
Economics ... PhD 36FT 72PT/MPhil 12FT 24PT

The Open University
Economics of Innovation and Development ... PhD 36FT 72PT variableDL/MPhil 15FT 24PT variableDL

School of Oriental and African Studies - SOAS
Development Studies ... PhD 36FT 48-60PT
Economics ... PhD 36FT 72PT/MPhil 24FT 36PT

University of St Andrews
Finance ... PhD 36FT 72PT/MPhil 24FT 48PT

Health economics
Taught Courses

University of Aberdeen
Economics of Health ... MSc 12FT/PGDip 9FT
Health Economics ... PGCert 8FT

Birkbeck, University of London
Applied Statistics with Medical Applications ... MSc 24PT

University of Birmingham
Health Economics and Health Policy ... MSc 12FT 24PT/PGDip 12FT 24PT

Cardiff University
International Pharmacoeconomics and Health Economics ... MSc 36DL/Diploma 24DL

City University London
Economic Evaluation in Healthcare ... MSc 12FT 24PT
Health Economics ... MSc 12FT 24PT

University College Cork
Health Evaluation Economics ... PGDip 9FT 18PT

University of Dundee
Applied Health Statistics ... MSc 12FT

University of East Anglia
Clinical Research ... MSc 12FT 36PT/PGDip 12FT 24PT
Health Economics ... MSc 12FT 36PT/PGDip 12FT 24PT/PGCert 12PT

Edinburgh Napier University
Health Administration ... MSc 12FT 24-36PT/PGDip 9FT 18-27PT/PGCert 6FT 12-18PT

University of Exeter
Economics ... MSc 12FT
Economics and Experimental Economics ... MSc 12FT

National University of Ireland Galway
Health Economics ... MSc 12FT

University of Glasgow
Health Technology Assessment ... MSc 12FT 24PT/PGDip 9FT 18PT

Goldsmiths, University of London
Foundations in Clinical Psychology & Health Services .. MSc 12FT

King's College London
Global Health ... MSc 12FT

Leeds Metropolitan University
Health & Social Care Chaplaincy ... PGCert 12PT
Health Care Studies ... MA 24PT

London School of Economics and Political Science (LSE)
Health Economics, Policy and Management (Modular) ... PGCert 12-24PT/Diploma 18-48PT/MSc 24-60PT

University of Sheffield
Economics and Health Economics ... MSc 12FT
International Health Technology Assessment ... MSc 24-60 PTDL

UCL - University College London
Philosophy, Politics and Economics of Health ... MA 12FT 36-60PT

University of Warwick
Health Services Management ... MSc 36PT/PGDip 24PT/PGCert 12PT

University of York
Health Economics ... MSc 12FT

Health economics
Research Courses

University of Aberdeen
Health Economics ... PhD 36FT/MPhil 24FT/MSc by research 12FT

Bangor University
Health Economics ... PhD 36FT 60PT/MPhil 24FT 48PT MSc by research 12FT 24PT

University of Birmingham
Health Economics ... PhD 36FT 72PT/MSc by research 24FT 12PT

University of Exeter
Economics ... PhD 48FT 89PT/MPhil 36FT 60PT

Imperial College London
Medical Statistics ... PhD

Section sponsored by BPP UNIVERSITY COLLEGE

Business and social sciences
www.prospects.ac.uk/findcourses POSTGRADUATE DIRECTORY 417

Economics

Keele University
Statistics Group....PhD 36FT

The Open University
Economics of Health and Welfare...... PhD 36FT 72PT variableDL/MPhil 15FT 24PT variableDL

International economics
Taught Courses

University of Aberdeen
Economics....MSc 12FT

Anglia Ruskin University
International Business Economics ..MSc 18FT 24PT/PGCert 18FT/PGDip 18FT 24PT
International Finance.... MSc 12FT 24PT/PGCert 12FT 24PT/PGDip 12FT 24PT

Aston University
International Business Economics....MSc 12FT

Bangor University
Accounting, Banking, Economics, Finance, Management Studies....MPhil 24FT/PhD by taught 36FT
Islamic Banking and Finance....MBA 12FT

University of Bath
Global Political Economy: transformations and policy analysis ... MRes 12FT 24-36PT
International Public Policy Analysis....MSc 12FT/PGDip 9FT/PGCert 6FT

University of Birmingham
International Development....MSc 12FT/PGDip 9FT
International Development (Poverty, Inequality and Development)....MSc 12FT 24PT 48DL/GradDip 9FT
International Economics....MSc 12FT
Political Theory....MA 12FT 24PT

University of Cambridge
Master of Finance....MFin 12FT

Cardiff University
International Economics, Banking and Finance.....MSc 12FT 24PT

University of Central Lancashire
International Business Economics....MA 12FT

University of Chester
Coaching for Internal Business Solutions and Team Development (WBIS)....MA 24-72PT/PGDip 24-60PT/PGCert 12-36PT

City University London
International Business Economics....MSc 12FT

University College Dublin
European Economic & Public Affairs....MEconSci 12FT

University of Dundee
Financial Economics....PGDip 9FT

University of East Anglia
Development Economics....MSc 12FT 24PT
Economics....MSc 12FT PGDip 10FT
Industrial Economics....MSc 12FT
International Business Economics....MA 12FT
International Business Finance and Economics....MA 12FT
International Development....MA 12FT 24PT
MRes in International Development (by distance learning) MRes 24DL

Edinburgh Napier University
Wealth Management....MSc 24-36DL

University of Essex
Accounting and Financial Economics....MSc 12FT 24PT
Applied Economics and Data Analysis....MA 12FT 24PT
Computational Economics, Financial Markets and Policy....... MSc 12FT 24PT
Economics....MSc 12FT/PGDip 9FT
Economics and Econometrics....MSc 12FT 24PT
Financial Econometrics....MSc 12FT
Financial Economics....MSc 12FT
Financial Economics and Econometrics....MSc 12FT
Financial and Business Economics....MSc 12FT
High Frequency Finance and Trading....MSc 12FT 24PT
International Economics....MSc 12FT 24PT
Management Economics....MSc 12FT

University of Exeter
Economics....MSc 12FT
Economics and Experimental Economics....MSc 12FT

GCU London
International Economics and Finance....MSc 12FT
Luxury Brand Marketing (London).......... MBA 12FT/MBA 12-15FT

Glasgow Caledonian University
Financial Services, Risk and Operations......MSc 12FT 24PT/PGDip 9FT 24PT
International Business....MSc 12FT
International Development....MSc 12FT
International Economics and Finance....MSc 12FT

University of Glasgow
Economic & Financial Sector Policies....MSc 12FT
Europe and International Development....MSc 12FT
International Business and Economic Development..... MSc 12FT
International Finance and Economic Policy....MSc 12FT

University of Greenwich
Business and Financial EconomicsMA 12FT 24PT/MSc 12FT 24PT/PGDip 12FT 24PT

University of Hull
Global Political Economy....MA 12FT 24PT

Imperial College London
Economics & Strategy for Business....MSc 12FT

University of Kent
International Development.... MSc 12FT 24PT MA 12FT 24PT
International Finance and Economic Development....... MSc 12FT 24PT

King's College London
Emerging Economies & International Development..... MSc 12FT
International Political Economy....MA 12FT
Political Economy of Emerging Markets....MSc 12FT

Kingston University
International Politics and Economics....MA 12FT 24PT

Leeds Metropolitan University
International Business....MA 12FT 24PT
International Political Economy....MA 12FT

University of Leeds
Chinese Business and the Asia Pacific....MA 12FT 24PT
Chinese Studies....MA 12FT 24PT
Global Development and International Political Economy......MA 12FT 24PT
International Finance....MSc 12FT

London Metropolitan University
Business Economics....MA 12FT 24PT
Economics....MSc 12FT 24 - 48PT
International Business....MA 12FT 24PT

London School of Economics and Political Science (LSE)
Affaires Internationales and International Relations/International Political Economy....MSc 23FT
European Public and Economic Policy....MPA 21FT
Finance and Private Equity....MSc 10FT
Global Studies: A European Perspective....MA 24FT

Loughborough University
International Financial and Political Relations....MSc 12FT

Newcastle University
International Economics and Finance....MSc 12FT
International Political Economy....MA 12FT 24PT

Northumbria University
Global Business Management....MSc 12FT
Global Financial Management....MSc 12FT
Global Logistics, Operations and Supply Chain ManagementMSc 12FT

Nottingham Trent University
Economics and Finance/International Finance....MSc 12FT

University of Nottingham
Economics and International Economics....MSc 12FT

Oxford Brookes University
International Business Economics....MSc 12FT 24PT
International Trade and Logistics....MSc 12FT 24PT

University of Oxford
Economics for Development....MSc 9-21FT

University of Reading
Agricultural Economics....MSc 12FT 24PT
Applied Development Studies....MSc 12FT 24PT
Banking and Finance in Emerging Economies......MSc 12FT 24PT
Business Economics....MSc 12FT 24PT
Economic Development in Emerging Markets.....MSc 12FT 24PT
Economics of International Business and Finance MSc 12FT 24PT
Environment and Development....MSc 12FT
Food Economics and Marketing....MSc 12FT
International Business and Economic Development .... MSc 12FT 24PT
International Economic Development....MSc 12FT
International Finance and Economic Development...... MSc 12FT 24PT
The Economics of International Business and Finance . MSc 12FT

Robert Gordon University
International Trade....LLM 12FT/MSc 9FT/PGDip 6FT

Royal Holloway, University of London
Economics....MSc 12FT

University of Salford
International Banking and Finance..... MSc 12FT 36PT/PGDip 8FT 24PT/PGCert 4FT 9PT
International Business Law and RegulationLLM 12FT/PGDip 8FT/PGCert 4FT
International Corporate FinanceMSc 12FT 36PT/PGDip 8FT 24PT/PGCert 4FT 9PT

School of Oriental and African Studies - SOAS
Development Economics....MSc 12FT 24-36PT
Economics (with Reference to Africa)....MSc 12FT 24PT
Economics (with Reference to South Asia)....MSc 12FT 24PT
Economics (with Reference to the Asia Pacific Region).... MSc 12FT 24PT
Economics (with reference to the Middle East)..... MSc 12FT 24PT
Environmental Law and Sustainable Development.... MA 12FT 24PT
Finance and Development....MSc 24-60DL/PGDip 12-60DL
Labour, Social Movements and Development....... MSc 12FT 24PT
Law, Development and Globalisation....MA 12FT 24PT
Political Economy of Development....MSc 12FT 24-36PT
Research for International Development....MSc 12FT 24PT

Schumacher College
Economics for Transition....MA 12FT

University of Sheffield
Business Finance and Economics....MSc 12FT 24PT
Development Economics and Policy....MSc 12FT 24PT
International Commercial Law and Practice.......... LLM 12FT 24PT
International Political Economy....MA 12FT 24PT

University of Southampton
International Banking and Financial Studies....MSc 12FT/PGDip 9FT

University of St Andrews
International Strategy & Economics (ISE)...MSc 12FT/PGDip 9FT/MPhil 24FT

Staffordshire University
Economics for Business Analysis....MSc 12-16FT
Economics of Globalisation and European Integration....MA 12-16FT

University of Stirling
Computing for Financial Markets ... MSc 12FT/PGDip 9FT/PGCert 9FT
International Business and Socio Economic Development..... MSc 12FT/PGDip 9FT/PGCert 6FT

University of Strathclyde
International Banking and Finance..... MSc 12FT 24PT/PGDip 9FT 21PT

University of Surrey
Economics....MA 12FT 24PT

University of Sussex
Global Political Economy....MA 12FT 24PT
International Economics....MSc 12FT 24PT

Swansea University
Economics....MSc 12FT
International Banking, Finance and Economics....MSc 12FT

Trinity College Dublin - the University of Dublin
Economic Policy Studies....MSc 24PT
Economics....MSc(Econ) 12FT 24PT

UCL - University College London
Comparative Business Economics....MA 12FT 24PT
Economic Policy....MSc 12FT

University of Warwick
Economics and International Finance....MSc 12FT

University of West London
Finance and Global Capital Markets....MSc 12FT 24PT

University of Westminster
International Economic Policy & Analysis........MSc 12FT MA 12FT

International economics
Research Courses

University of Bath
Global Political Economy: transformations and policy analysis (delivered collaboratively w....MRes 12FT 24-36PT

University of Buckingham
Modern War Studies....MA by research 12FT

University of Essex
Economics....PhD 36FT 72PT/MPhil 24FT 48PT

University of Exeter
Economics....PhD 48FT 89PT/MPhil 36FT 60PT

University of Greenwich
Development Studies - Research...... MPhil 18-36FT 30-48PT/PhD 33-60FT 45-72PT

Newcastle University
Economics....PhD 36FT 72PT/MPhil 12FT 24PT

The Open University
Economics of Innovation and Development.......... PhD 36FT 72PT variableDL/MPhil 15FT 24PT variableDL

University of Surrey
Economics....PhD 33FT 45PT/MPhil 21FT 33PT

Macroeconomics
Taught Courses

University of East Anglia
Development Economics....MSc 12FT 24PT
Economics....MSc 12FT PGDip 10FT

University of Essex
Accounting and Financial Economics....MSc 12FT 24PT

Economics

Applied Economics and Data Analysis .... MA 12FT 24PT
Computational Economics, Financial Markets and Policy....... MSc 12FT 24PT
Economics.. MSc 12FT/PGDip 9FT
Economics and Econometrics.................................... MSc 12FT 24PT
Financial Econometrics .... MSc 12FT
Financial Economics.. MSc 12FT
Financial Economics and Econometrics........................... MSc 12FT
Financial and Business Economics .... MSc 12FT
International Economics................................ MSc 12FT 24PT
Management Economics .... MSc 12FT

University of Exeter
Economics... MSc 12FT
Economics and Experimental Economics.......................... MSc 12FT

University of Kent
Diploma in Economic Analysis................................ MSc 24FT
Economics.. MSc 12FT 24PT
Economics Conversion .... MSc 24FT
Economics and Econometrics................................ MSc 12FT 24PT

University of Nottingham
Economy, Space and Society........................MSc 12FT 24PT

University of Reading
Banking and Finance in Emerging Economies ...... MSc 12FT 24PT
Banking and Financial Systems in the Global Economy MSc 12FT
Development Finance .... MSc 12FT
International Economic Development .... MSc 12FT

Royal Holloway, University of London
Economics.. MSc 12FT

Schumacher College
Economics for Transition ....MA 12FT

Staffordshire University
Economics for Business Analysis ....MSc 12-16FT

Trinity College Dublin - the University of Dublin
Economic Policy Studies.................................... MSc 24PT
Economics.. MSc(Econ) 12FT 24PT

UCL - University College London
Economic Policy... MSc 12FT
International Master's in Economy, State and Society ....
International Master's 24FT

Macroeconomics
Research Courses

University of Essex
Economics.. PhD 36FT 72PT/MPhil 24FT 48PT

University of Exeter
Economics......................... PhD 48FT 89PT/MPhil 36FT 60PT

Heriot-Watt University
Economics, including CERT (Centre for Economic Reform & Transformation)...............................PhD 36FT/MPhil 12FT

London School of Economics and Political Science (LSE)
Economics........................MRes 36-48FT/PhD 36-48FT

Newcastle University
Economics...................... PhD 36FT 72PT/MPhil 12FT 24PT

Management economics
Taught Courses

University of Central Lancashire
Construction Management (Construction Economics)MSc 24DL/PGDip 12DL/PGCert 6DL

City University London
Business Economics .... MSc 12FT
International Business Economics .... MSc 12FT

University of East Anglia
International Business Economics ....MA 12FT

University of Essex
Management Economics.................................... MSc 12FT

University of Exeter
Economics.. MSc 12FT
Economics and Experimental Economics......................... MSc 12FT

Glasgow Caledonian University
Management MSc 12FT FlexiblePT/PGDip 9FT FlexiblePT/PGCert 6FT FlexiblePT

University of Huddersfield
Business Economics .... MSc 12FT

Leeds Metropolitan University
Project Management......................MSc 12FT 24PT
Strategic Project Management............................MSc 12FT 24PT

London School of Economics and Political Science (LSE)
Economics and Management................................ MSc 10FT

University of Reading
Applied Management ....MA 36PT/PGDip 24PT

Royal Holloway, University of London
Economics.. MSc 12FT

School of Oriental and African Studies - SOAS
Environmental Law and Sustainable Development........................
MA 12FT 24PT
Finance and Development ....MSc 24-60DL/PGDip 12-60DL
International Management (China) ....MSc 12FT 24-36PT
International Management (Japan) ....MSc 12FT 24-36PT
International Management (Middle East and North Africa)..........
MSc 12FT 24PT
PGDip Policy Studies.. PGCert 9FT

Schumacher College
Economics for Transition ....MA 12FT

Staffordshire University
Economics for Business Analysis ....MSc 12-16FT

University of Sussex
Science and Technology Policy...........................MSc 12FT 24PT

Trinity College Dublin - the University of Dublin
Economic Policy Studies...................................... MSc 24PT
Economics.. MSc(Econ) 12FT 24PT

UCL - University College London
Comparative Business Economics........................... MA 12FT 24PT
Construction Economics and Management... MSc 12FT 24-60PT/PGDip 9FT
Economic Policy... MSc 12FT

Management economics
Research Courses

University of Bristol
Management................................. MPhil 12FT 24PT/PhD 36FT 72PT

University of Buckingham
Economics and International Studies ....DPhil 36FT 72PT/MPhil 24FT 48PT

University of Exeter
Economics..................................... PhD 48FT 89PT/MPhil 36FT 60PT

Newcastle University
Economics..................................... PhD 36FT 72PT/MPhil 12FT 24PT

University of Salford
Centre for Marketing and Communication ....PhD/MPhil

Section sponsored by
BPP UNIVERSITY COLLEGE

Business and social sciences
www.prospects.ac.uk/findcourses POSTGRADUATE DIRECTORY 419

Information science and librarianship

Archive management
Taught Courses

Aberystwyth University
Archive Administration ......MA 36DL/PGDip 24DL
Archive Administration ......MA 12FT 24PT/UDip 9FT 18PT
Digital Curation ......MSc 12FT 24PT/PGDip 9FT 21PT
Digital Information Services......MSc 12FT 24PT/PGDip 9FT 21PT
Information and Library Studies ......MA 36DL/PGDip 24DL
International Archives, Records and Information Management (Distance Learning)......MA 60DL/PGDip 48DL

University of Dundee
Archives and Records Management ..... MLitt 24DL/PGDip 18DL/ Cert 6DL

University of East Anglia
Film Studies with Archiving...... MA 12FT 24PT

University of Glasgow
Information Management and Preservation (Digital) (Archives and Records Management)...MSc 12FT 24+PT/PGDip 9FT/PGCert 4FT

University of Liverpool
Archives and Records Management...... MARM 12FT
Archives and Records Management (International Pathway)...... MARM 12FT

Northumbria University
Information and Records Management......MSc 24DL

University of Reading
Early Modern Literature & Drama ......MA (Res) 12FT 24PT
Legal History ......MA (Res) 12FT 24PT

University of Sheffield
Digital Library Management (Professional Enhancement Programme).... MSc Up to 12FT 24-36PT/PGDip 9FT 18PT/PGCert 6FT 12PT
Information Management......MSc 12FT 24-36PT
Information Management (Professional Enhancement Programme).... MSc Up to 12FT 24-36PT/PGDip 9FT 18PT/PGCert 6FT 12PT
Librarianship...... MA 12FT 24-36PT
Librarianship (Professional Enhancement Programme) MA Up to 12FT 24-36PT/PGDip 9FT/PGCert 6FT

University of Strathclyde
Information Management......MSc 12FT/PGDip 9FT/PGCert 4FT

Trinity College Dublin - the University of Dublin
Digital Humanities and Culture ......MPhil 12FT 24PT

UCL - University College London
Archives and Records Management... MA 12FT 24 - 60PT/PGCert 4FT 24PT/PGDip 9FT 18-45PT
Digital Humanities.... MA 12FT 24PT/MSc 12FT 24PT/PGDip 12FT 24PT/PGCert 3FT 24PT
Records and Archives Management (International)......MA 12FT 24-60PT/PGDip 9FT 24-60PT/PGCert 4FT

Archive management
Research Courses

Aberystwyth University
Archive and Records Management ......MPhil 12FT 24PT
Archive and Records Management ...... PhD 36FT 60PT
Information and Library Studies ......MPhil 12FT 24PT

University of Liverpool
Archives and Records Management......MPhil 12FT/PhD 36FT

UCL - University College London
Library, Archive and Information Studies...... PhD 36FT 60PT

Heritage centre management
Taught Courses

Bath Spa University
Curatorial Practice.....MA 12FT 24PT/PGDip 9FT 18PT/PGCert 4FT 9PT
Heritage Management ... MA 12FT 24PT/PGDip 9FT 18PT/PGCert 4FT

University of Birmingham
Heritage Management ......MA 12FT 24DL/PGDip 3FT
Heritage and Identity...... PGCert 30DL/PGDip 30DL/MA 30DL

Bishop Grosseteste University College Lincoln
Heritage Education ...... MA 12FT 24PT

University of Central Lancashire
International Heritage and Attraction Management .... MSc 12FT 24PT/PGDip 12FT 24PT
International Heritage and Event Management..MSc 12FT 24PT/ PGDip 12FT 24PT

Durham University
Conservation of Archaeological and Museum Objects (Dissertation)...... MA 24FT 36PT
Conservation of Archaeological and Museum Objects (Professional Practice)...... MA 24FT 36PT

University of East Anglia
Cultural Heritage and International Development ...... MA 12FT 24PT
Cultural Heritage and Museum Studies...... MA 12FT 24PT
Museum Studies......MA 12FT

University of East London
Heritage Studies ...... MA 12FT 24PT/PGCert 8FT 16PT/ PGDip 4FT 8PT

University of Glasgow
Museum Studies......MSc 12FT 24PT

University of Kent
Heritage Management (Athens) ......MA 12FT

King's College London
Eighteenth-Century Studies ...... MA 12FT 24PT

Kingston University
Heritage (Contemporary Practice) ...... MA 12FT 24PT
Museums and Galleries and the Creative Economy...... MA 12FT 24PT

University of Leeds
Art Gallery and Museum Studies ...... MA 12FT 24PT

University of Leicester
Art Museum and Gallery Studies ......MA 12FT/PGDip 9FT
Country House MA/Postgraduate Diploma/Postgraduate Certificate......MA 24-48DL
Interpretation, Representation and Heritage .... MA 24DL/PGCert 18DL
Learning and Visitor Studies in Museums and Galleries...... MA 24DL/PGCert 18DL

Newcastle University
Art Museum and Gallery Practice ...... MPrac 24FT 48PT
Art Museum and Gallery Studies (with specialist pathways in: Curatorship, and Education)...... MA 12FT 24PT/PGDip 9FT 18PT
Heritage Practice ......MHPrac 24FT 48PT
Heritage Studies (specialist pathways in: Education and Interpretation, and Management)...... MA 12FT 24PT/PGDip 9FT 18PT
Museum Practice......MPrac 24FT 48PT
Museum Studies......PGCert 18PT MA 12FT 24PT/PGDip 9FT 18PT

Northumbria University
Cultural Heritage Management...MA 12/18FT 24/28PT 24/28DL

Norwich University of the Arts
MA Curation...... MA 12FT 24PT

Nottingham Trent University
Museum and Heritage Management ......MA 12FT 24PT/ PGDip 19FT 21PT

Queen Margaret University, Edinburgh
Arts and Cultural Management.....MA 12FT 24-84PT/PGDip 12FT 24-84PT/PGCert 12FT 24-84PT

Queen's University Belfast
Heritage Science......MSc 12FT 24PT/PGDip 7FT 14PT

University of Salford
Art and Design: Museum and Heritage Interpretation...MA 12FT 24PT/PGDip 8FT 15PT

University of Sheffield
Cultural Heritage Management......MA 12FT
Cultures of the British Isles...... MA 12FT 24PT

University of St Andrews
Museum and Gallery Studies... MLitt 12FT 24PT/PGDip 9FT 18PT
National Trust for Scotland Studies...... MPhil 24FT 48PT

St Mary's University College, Twickenham
Charity Management....PGCert 12PT/PGDip 24PT/MA 12FT 24PT

University of Sussex
International Trade Law...... LLM 12FT 24PT

University of Wales Trinity Saint David
Heritage Studies......MA 12FT 24PT 12-24DL

University of Ulster
Cultural Heritage and Museum Studies...... MA 12FT 36PT
Cultural Management....MSc 12FT 30PT/PGDip 9FT 18PT/PGCert 4FT 8PT

UCL - University College London
Built Environment: Heritage Science ......MRes 12FT 24-60PT/ PGCert 6FT
Built Environment: Sustainable Heritage...... MSc 12FT 24-60PT/ PGDip 9FT
Conservation......MSc 12FT/PGDip 9FT/PGCert 3FT
Conservation for Archaeology and Museums...... MSc 24FT
Museum Studies...... MA 12FT 24PT
Museum and Gallery Practice ...... MA 12FT 24PT

University of Westminster
Museums, Galleries and Contemporary Culture.... MA 12FT 24PT

University of Winchester
Cultural Heritage and Resource Management......MA 12FT 24PT/ PGDip 9FT 18PT/PGCert 5FT 10PT

University of York
Cultural Heritage Management...... MA 12FT 36PT
Digital Heritage ......MSc 12FT 24PT/PGDip 9FT
Stained Glass Conservation and Heritage Management...... MA 24FT

Heritage centre management
Research Courses

City University London
Arts Policy and Management......PhD/MPhil
Department of Arts Policy and Management......PhD/MPhil

University of Glasgow
Education......PhD 36FT 60PT/MPhil 12FT 24PT/MSc by research 12FT 24PT/EdD 36-60DL

Newcastle University
Museum, Gallery and Heritage Studies.......PhD 36FT 72PT/MPhil 12FT 24PT

The Open University
Heritage ...... PhD 36FT 72PT variableDL/MPhil 15FT 24PT variableDL

University of Southampton
MRes Science and Heritage......MRes 12FT

University of St Andrews
Museum and Gallery Studies.... PhD 36FT 72PT/MPhil 24FT 48PT

Information science
Taught Courses

Aberystwyth University
Digital Curation ......MSc 12FT 24PT/PGDip 9FT 21PT
Digital Information Services......MSc 12FT 24PT/PGDip 9FT 21PT
Information Governance and Assurance......MSc 60DL/ PGDip 48DL
Information Management and Leadership......MSc 12FT 24PT/ PGDip 9FT 21PT
Information and Library Studies ......MA 36DL/PGDip 24DL

Aston University
MSc Information Systems and Business Analysis...... MSc 12FT 24PT

Bangor University
Computer Science ...... MSc 12FT
Information Management...... MBA 12FT

Bournemouth University
Applied Data Analytics......MSc 12FT/MSc 24PT

University of Brighton
Information Management.......MSc 12FT 24PT/PGDip 12FT 24PT/ PGCert 12FT 24PT

University of Cambridge
Management Science & Operations ......MPhil 9FT

Coventry University
Management Information Systems...... MSc 12FT 24-36PT 20DL/ PGDip 8FT 16PT/PGCert 4FT 8PT

University of Cumbria
Computing and IT...... PGDip 12PT/PGCert 12PT

University of East Anglia
Information Systems ...... MSc 12FT 24PT

Edinburgh Napier University
Digital Systems ......MA/MDes 12FT 24PT

National University of Ireland Galway
Information Systems Management ...... MSc 12FT 24PT

Heriot-Watt University
Advanced Internet Applications......MSc 12FT 24PT/PGDip 9FT
Artificial Intelligence ......MSc 12FT 24PT/PGDip 9FT
Computer Services ManagementMSc 12FT 24PT/PGDip 9FT 21PT
Creative Software Systems......MSc 12FT 24PT/PGDip 9FT 21PT
Information Technology (Business) .....MSc 12FT 24PT/PGDip 9FT 21PT
Information Technology (Software Systems) ......MSc 12FT 24PT/ PGDip 9FT 21PT
Software Engineering......MSc 12FT 24PT/PGDip 9FT 21PT

Leeds Metropolitan University
Information Management......MSc 12FT 36PT

Loughborough University
Information Management and Business Technology.... MSc 12FT 24-60PT/PGDip 9FT 24-36PT/PGCert 6FT
Information and Knowledge Management ... MSc 12FT 24-33PT/ PGDip 9FT 18-27PT

Manchester Metropolitan University
Digital Business Management...... MSc 12FT
Digital Marketing Communications......MSc 30PT/PGDip 24PT/ PGCert 12PT
PgCert/PgDip/MSc Digital Business Management ...... MSc 12FT

Queen's University Belfast
Advance Wireless Communications......MSc 12FT 24PT/ PGDip 12FT 24PT/PGCert 12FT 24PT

Robert Gordon University
MBA Information Management......MBA 36DL

Royal Holloway, University of London
Information Security ......PGCert 48PT

University of Salford
Databases and Web-based Systems.... MSc 12FT 24PT/PGDip 9FT 18PT

Information science and librarianship

Information Security .... MSc 12FT 24PT/PGDip 9FT 18PT/
PGCert 9FT 18PT
Information Security Management..... MSc 12FT 24PT/PGDip 9FT
18PT/PGCert 9FT 18PT
Information Systems Management .... MSc 12FT 36PT/PGDip 8FT
24PT/PGCert 4FT 9PT

Sheffield Hallam University
Information Systems Security.................... MSc 12FT 24PT
Information Systems with SAP .... MBA 12FT 36PT

University of Sheffield
Information Management........................ MSc 12FT 24-36PT
Information Management (Professional Enhancement
Programme).... MSc Up to 12FT 24-36PT/PGDip 9FT 18PT/PGCert
6FT 12PT
Information Systems.......................... MSc 12FT 24-36PT
Information Systems (Professional Enhancement Programme)...
MSc Up to 12FT 24-36PT/PGDip 9FT 18PT/PGCert 6FT 12PT
Information Systems Management .... MSc 12FT

University of Southampton
Information Technology and Commerce................. LLM 12FT 24PT
Information Technology and Telecommunications Law.................
LLM 24DL

University of Stirling
Information Technology .... MSc 12FT/PGDip 9FT

University of Strathclyde
Information Management......... MSc 12FT/PGDip 9FT/PGCert 4FT

Trinity College Dublin - the University of Dublin
Digital Humanities and Culture .... MPhil 12FT 24PT

University of Wales Trinity Saint David
Information Management.... MBA 12FT 24PT/PGCert 12FT 24PT/
PGDip 12FT 24PT

University of Ulster
Library and Information Management..... MSc 36PT/PGDip 24PT/
PGCert 12PT

UCL - University College London
Digital Humanities.... MA 12FT 24PT/MSc 12FT 24PT/PGDip 12FT
24PT/PGCert 3FT 24PT
Information Security .... MSc 12FT/PGDip 9FT

University of Warwick
Information Systems Management & Innovation......... MSc 12FT

Information science
Research Courses

Bangor University
Communication Networks and Protocols... MPhil 24FT/PhD 36FT
Pattern Recognition / Classifiers .... MPhil 24FT/PhD 36FT

Cardiff University
Information Systems .... MRes 12FT

University of Central Lancashire
Business Information Management .... PhD/MPhil/
MSc by research 12FT

University of Hertfordshire
Algorithms .... PhD 36FT 72PT/MRes 12FT 24PT

University of Oxford
Engineering Science................... DPhil 48FT/MSc by research 24FT

Royal Holloway, University of London
Information Security .... PhD 36FT

Information science and librarianship
Taught Courses

Aberystwyth University
Digital Curation .... MSc 12FT 24PT/PGDip 9FT 21PT
Digital Information Services........ MSc 12FT 24PT/PGDip 9FT 21PT
Information Management and Leadership .... MSc 12FT 24PT/
PGDip 9FT 21PT
Information Systems .... MSc 12FT 24PT/PGDip 9FT 18PT/
PGCert 6FT 12PT
Information and Library Studies .... MA 36DL/PGDip 24DL
MA 12FT/PGDip 9FT
Management of Library and Information Services ...... MSc 36DL/
PGDip 24DL

University of Brighton
Information Studies.... MA 12FT 24 - 72PT/PGDip 12FT 24 - 72PT/
PGCert 12FT 24 - 72PT

Brunel University
Business Intelligence and Social Media............................ MSc 12FT

University of Cambridge
Management Science & Operations .... MPhil 9FT

City University London
Information Management in the Cultural Sector.......... MSc 12FT
24-36PT/MA 12FT 28PT
Library Science.................................. MSc 12FT 24-36PT

Leeds Metropolitan University
Information Management.......................... MSc 12FT 36PT

Loughborough University
Information and Library Management...... MA 12FT 24-33PT/MSc
12FT 24-33PT/PGDip 9FT 18-33PT

Manchester Metropolitan University
Library and Information Management.................... MA 15FT 36PT/
MSc 15FT 36PT

Newcastle University
Art Museum and Gallery Studies (with specialist pathways in:
Curatorship, and Education)......... MA 12FT 24PT/PGDip 9FT 18PT
Heritage Practice .... MHPrac 24FT 48PT

Northumbria University
Information and Library Management.................... MA 12FT 24PT/
MSc 12FT 24PT

Robert Gordon University
Information Management.......................... MSc 36DL/PGDip 24DL
Information and Library Studies.......... MSc 12FT 36DL/PGDip 9FT
24DL/PGCert 6FT 12DL

University of Sheffield
Digital Library Management .... MSc 12FT 24-36PT
Digital Library Management (Professional Enhancement
Programme).... MSc Up to 12FT 24-36PT/PGDip 9FT 18PT/PGCert
6FT 12PT
Librarianship .... MA 12FT 24-36PT
Librarianship (Professional Enhancement Programme) MA Up to
12FT 24-36PT/PGDip 9FT/PGCert 6FT
Multilingual Information Management................... MA 12FT 24PT

University of Strathclyde
Information and Library Studies MSc 12FT 24PT/PGDip 8FT 18PT/
PGCert 4FT 12PT

UCL - University College London
Library and Information Studies...... MA 12FT 24-60PT/PGDip 9FT
24-60PT
Library, Archive and Information Studies.............. MRes 12FT 24PT

University of West London
Information Management....................... MSc 12FT 24PT

Information science and librarianship
Research Courses

Aberystwyth University
Information and Library Studies .... MPhil 12FT 24PT
PhD 36FT 60PT

City University London
Department of Information Science .... PhD/MPhil

Loughborough University
Information Science .... PhD 36FT/MPhil 24FT

Manchester Metropolitan University
Department of Information and Communications................... PhD
24-48FT 42-84PT 42-84DL/MPhil 18-36FT 36-72PT 36-72DL/MA
by research 12-24FT 24-42PT 24-42DL

The Open University
Digital classics.......... PhD 36FT 72PT variableDL/MPhil 15FT 24PT
variableDL

University of Sheffield
Information Studies.................... PhD 36FT 72PT/MPhil 24FT 48PT

UCL - University College London
Library, Archive and Information Studies................ PhD 36FT 60PT

University of West London
Centre for Library and Information Management....... MPhil 24FT
48PT/PhD 36FT 72PT

Knowledge management
Taught Courses

Aberystwyth University
Digital Curation .... MSc 12FT 24PT/PGDip 9FT 21PT

**University of the Arts London - Central Saint Martins College of
Art and Design**
MA Culture, Criticism and Curation.................................... MA 12FT

Bangor University
Information Management .... MBA 12FT

Birmingham City University
Enterprise Systems Management...................... MSc 12/16FT 30PT

University of Brighton
Management (Innovation)........................ MSc 12FT

Brunel University
Business Intelligence and Social Media .... MSc 12FT
Human Resource Management .... MSc 12FT
International Business .... MSc 12FT
Marketing.......................... MSc 12FT

Cranfield University
Knowledge Management for Innovation........ MSc 12FT 24-60PT/
PGDip 6FT 24PT/PGCert 5FT 24PT/MTech 24FT
Management & Information Systems............. MSc 12FT 24-60PT/
PGDip 6FT 24PT/PGCert 5FT 24PT

Dublin Institute of Technology
Computing (Knowledge Management).................... MSc 12FT 24PT

Durham University
Management (Innovation Technology and Operations
Management) .... MSc 12FT

University of East Anglia
Knowledge Discovery and Data Mining .... MSc 12FT/MSc 24PT/
MSc 36PT

National University of Ireland Galway
Information Systems Management .... MSc 12FT 24PT
Innovation Management .... PGDip 12PT 12DL

Glasgow Caledonian University
Management of IT Innovation .... MSc 12FT
Social Enterprise .... PGCert 6PT

Goldsmiths, University of London
Management of Innovation .... MSc 12FT

Lancaster University
Human Resource and Knowledge Management .... MSc 12FT
Information Technology, Management and Organisational
Change .... MSc 12FT/PGDip 12FT/MRes 12FT

London School of Economics and Political Science (LSE)
Management, Information Systems and Innovation (MISI)... MSc
12FT

Loughborough University
Information Management and Business Technology.... MSc 12FT
24-60PT/PGDip 9FT 24-36PT/PGCert 6FT
Information and Knowledge Management ... MSc 12FT 24-33PT/
PGDip 9FT 18-27PT

University of Manchester
ACS: Data and Knowledge Management........................ MSc 12FT

The Open University
Technology Management .... MSc variableDL/PGCert variableDL/
PGDip variableDL

Queen Mary, University of London
Management and Organisational Innovation.................. MA 12FT

University of Reading
Law .... M (Res) 12FT 24PT/PGDip 9FT/PGCert 9FT
Legal History ....MA (Res) 12FT 24PT

University of Southampton
Knowledge and Information Systems Management..... MSc 12FT
30PT/PGDip 9FT 24PT

University of Strathclyde
Pharmaceutical Quality and Good Manufacturing Practice ....
MSc 27PT/PGDip 21PT

University of the West of Scotland
Knowledge Management .... MSc 12FT 33PT/Diploma 9FT 24PT

Knowledge management
Research Courses

University of Bolton
Innovation .... MPhil 18FT

London School of Economics and Political Science (LSE)
Information Systems and Innovation............... PhD 36-48FT/MPhil
36-48FT

The Open University
Computing .... PhD 36FT 72PT variableDL/MPhil 15FT 24PT
variableDL
Managing Knowledge and Innovation .... PhD 36FT 72PT
variableDL/MPhil 15FT 24PT variableDL
Technology Management .... PhD 36FT 72PT variableDL/
MPhil 15FT 24PT variableDL

Museum and gallery management
Taught Courses

University of Aberdeen
Museum Studies..MLitt 12FT 24PT

**University of the Arts London - Central Saint Martins College of
Art and Design**
Culture, Criticism and Curation ....MA 12FT

University of the Arts London - London College of Fashion
Fashion Curation.................................... MA 15FT 30PT

Bath Spa University
Curatorial Practice.....MA 12FT 24PT/PGDip 9FT 18PT/PGCert 4FT
9PT
Heritage Management ... MA 12FT 24PT/PGDip 9FT 18PT/PGCert
4FT

Birkbeck, University of London
Museum Cultures....MA 12FT 24PT/MRes 12FT 24PT/PGDip 12FT
24PT/PGCert 6FT 12PT

Birmingham City University
Contemporary Curatorial Practice............................ MA 12FT 24PT

University of Birmingham
Heritage and Identity............ PGCert 30DL/PGDip 30DL/MA 30DL

University of Brighton
History of Design and Material Culture.....................................

Cardiff University
Care of Collections .... MSc 12FT 24PT

Information science and librarianship

Science, Media and Communication................................. MSc 12FT

Christie's Education London
Modern and Contemporary Art: Beyond Modernism.MLitt 12FT/PGDip 9FT
The Arts of China: Cultural Crossroads in Asia ....MLitt 12FT/PGDip 9FT

City University London
Culture, Policy and Management Pathways Programme .... MA 12FT 24PT

Courtauld Institute of Art
Curating the Art Museum...MA 12FT

University of Derby
Arts Practice..PGCert 12PT

Durham University
Conservation of Archaeological and Museum Objects (Dissertation)... MA 24FT 36PT
Conservation of Archaeological and Museum Objects (Professional Practice)................................. MA 24FT 36PT
Museum and Artefact Studies................................... MA 12FT 24PT

University of East Anglia
Cultural Heritage and Museum Studies.................. MA 12FT 24PT
Museum Studies...MA 12FT
World Art Studies.. PGDip 12FT 24PT

University of Edinburgh
Modern and Contemporary Art: History, Curating, Criticism........ MSc 12FT 24PT

University of Essex
Curating Latin American Art....................................... MA 12FT 24PT
Gallery Studies and Critical Curating..................................MA 12FT
Gallery Studies with Dissertation .... MA 12FT 24PT

University of Glasgow
Art, Style & Design: Renaissance to Modernism..........MLitt 12FT/PGDip 12FT
Modern & Contemporary Art........................MLitt 12FT/PGDip 9FT
Museum Studies..MSc 12FT 24PT

Goldsmiths, University of London
Arts Administration and Cultural Policy.................. MA 12FT 24PT
Curating... MFA 24FT 36ft&ptPT

Institute of Education
Museums and Galleries in Education....................... MA 12FT 24PT

University of Kent
Curating... MA 12FT 24PT

King's College London
Eighteenth-Century Studies .... MA 12FT 24PT

Kingston University
Curating Contemporary Design (in partnership with the Design Museum) .... MA 12FT 24PT
Heritage (Contemporary Practice) .... MA 12FT 24PT
Museum and Gallery Studies....................................... MA 12FT 24PT
Museums and Galleries and the Creative Economy........................ MA 12FT 24PT

University of Leeds
Art Gallery and Museum Studies............................... MA 12FT 24PT
Culture, Creativity, and Enterpreneurship ....MA 12FT 24PT/PGDip 12FT 24PT/PGCert 9FT 18PT

University of Leicester
Art Museum and Gallery Studies...................MA 12FT/PGDip 9FT
Interpretation, Representation and Heritage ....MA 24DL/PGCert 18DL
Learning and Visitor Studies in Museums and Galleries...........MA 24DL/PGCert 18DL
Museum Studies............................MA 12FT 24DL/MSc 12FT 24DL/PGDip 9FT 18DL

Liverpool Hope University
Art History and Curating... MA 12FT 24PT

London Metropolitan University
Curating the Contemporary..MA 24FT

University of Manchester
Art Gallery and Museum Studies.............................. MA 12FT 24PT

Newcastle University
Art Museum and Gallery Practice ....MPrac 24FT 48PT
Art Museum and Gallery Studies (with specialist pathways in: Curatorship, and Education).........MA 12FT 24PT/PGDip 9FT 18PT
Heritage Practice..MHPrac 24FT 48PT
Heritage Studies (specialist pathways in: Education and Interpretation, and Management)........ MA 12FT 24PT/PGDip 9FT 18PT
Museum Practice... MPrac 24FT 48PT
Museum Studies......PGCert 18PT MA 12FT 24PT/PGDip 9FT 18PT

Northumbria University
Arts and Media Management.......MA 12/16FT 24/28PT 24/28DL

Norwich University of the Arts
Curation... MA 12FT 24PT

Nottingham Trent University
Museum and Heritage Management MA 12FT 24PT/PGDip 19FT 21PT

Queen's University Belfast
Heritage Science............................MSc 12FT 24PT/PGDip 7FT 14PT

Richmond, The American International University in London
Visual Arts Management& Curating........................ MA 12FT 24PT

Royal College of Art
Curating Contemporary Art..MA 24FT

University Campus Suffolk
Arts Practice.. MA 12FT 24PT

University of Salford
Art and Design: Museum and Heritage Interpretation...MA 12FT 24PT/PGDip 8FT 15PT

University of Sheffield
Cultures of the British Isles.. MA 12FT 24PT

University of St Andrews
Museum and Gallery Studies... MLitt 12FT 24PT/PGDip 9FT 18PT
National Trust for Scotland Studies......................MPhil 24FT 48PT

St Mary's University College, Twickenham
Charity Management....PGCert 12PT/PGDip 24PT/MA 12FT 24PT

University of Sussex
Art History and Museum Curating .... MA 12FT 24PT
Art History and Museum Curating with Photography....MA 12FT 24PT

University of Ulster
Cultural Heritage and Museum Studies.................. MA 12FT 36PT
Cultural Management....MSc 12FT 30PT/PGDip 9FT 18PT/PGCert 4FT 8PT
Museum Practice and Management..........MA 36DL/PGDip 18DL

UCL - University College London
Conservation for Archaeology and Museums................. MSc 24FT
Museum Studies.. MA 12FT 24PT
Museum and Gallery Practice .... MA 12FT 24PT

University of Westminster
Museums, Galleries and Contemporary Culture.... MA 12FT 24PT

University of Winchester
Cultural Heritage and Resource Management......MA 12FT 24PT/PGDip 9FT 18PT/PGCert 5FT 10PT

University of York
Digital Heritage ....MSc 12FT 24PT/PGDip 9FT

Museum and gallery management
Research Courses

University of Buckingham
History of Art: Renaissance to Modernism............................ MA by research 12FT

Goldsmiths, University of London
Curating.............................PhD 36-48FT 48-72PT/MPhil 24FT 36PT
Curatorial/Knowledge ....MPhil 24FT 36PT/PhD 36-48FT 48-72PT

University of Leicester
Department of Museum Studies ....PhD 36FT 72DL/MPhil 36FT 72DL

University of Manchester
Museology...... PhD 36FT 72PT/Professional Doctorate 36FT 72PT

Newcastle University
Museum, Gallery and Heritage Studies.......PhD 36FT 72PT/MPhil 12FT 24PT

The Open University
Heritage..................... PhD 36FT 72PT variableDL/MPhil 15FT 24PT variableDL

Royal College of Art
Conservation...PhD/MPhil/MA by research

Royal Welsh College of Music and Drama
Arts Management...................................MA by research 12FT 24PT

University of Southampton
Science and Heritage...MRes 12FT

University of St Andrews
Museum and Gallery Studies.... PhD 36FT 72PT/MPhil 24FT 48PT

Records management
Taught Courses

Aberystwyth University
Archive Administration ....MA 36DL/PGDip 24DL MA 12FT 24PT/UDip 9FT 18PT
Digital Curation ....MSc 12FT 24PT/PGDip 9FT 21PT
Digital Information Services........MSc 12FT 24PT/PGDip 9FT 21PT
Information Governance and Assurance ....MSc 60DL/PGDip 48DL
Information and Library Studies ....MA 36DL/PGDip 24DL
International Archives, Records and Information Management MA 60DL/PGDip 48DL

Bangor University
Information Management... MBA 12FT

University of Dundee
Archives and Records Management ..... MLitt 24DL/PGDip 18DL/Cert 6DL

University of Glasgow
Information Management and Preservation (Digital) (Archives and Records Management)...MSc 12FT 24+PT/PGDip 9FT/PGCert 4FT
Management... MSc 12FT

King's College London
Digital Asset & Media Management .... MA 12FT 24PT

University of Liverpool
Archives and Records Management............................. MARM 12FT
Archives and Records Management (International Pathway)....... MARM 12FT

Manchester Metropolitan University
Digital Business Management.. MSc 12FT

Northumbria University
Information and Records Management ....MSc 24DL

Robert Gordon University
Information Management.......................... MSc 36DL/PGDip 24DL
Information and Library Studies.......... MSc 12FT 36DL/PGDip 9FT 24DL/PGCert 6FT 12DL

University of Sheffield
Digital Library Management ....MSc 12FT 24-36PT
Digital Library Management (Professional Enhancement Programme).... MSc Up to 12FT 24-36PT/PGDip 9FT 18PT/PGCert 6FT 12PT
Information Management...................................MSc 12FT 24-36PT
Information Management (Professional Enhancement Programme).... MSc Up to 12FT 24-36PT/PGDip 9FT 18PT/PGCert 6FT 12PT
Librarianship... MA 12FT 24-36PT
Librarianship (Professional Enhancement Programme)................. MA Up to 12FT 24-36PT/PGDip 9FT/PGCert 6FT

University of Strathclyde
Information Management.........MSc 12FT/PGDip 9FT/PGCert 4FT

Trinity College Dublin - the University of Dublin
Digital Humanities and Culture ....MPhil 12FT 24PT

UCL - University College London
Archives and Records Management... MA 12FT 24 - 60PT/PGCert 4FT 24PT/PGDip 9FT 18-45PT
Digital Humanities.... MA 12FT 24PT/MSc 12FT 24PT/PGDip 12FT 24PT/PGCert 3FT 24PT
Library and Information Studies...... MA 12FT 24-60PT/PGDip 9FT 24-60PT
Records and Archives Management (International).........MA 12FT 24-60PT/PGDip 9FT 24-60PT/PGCert 4FT

Records management
Research Courses

Aberystwyth University
Archive and Records Management ....MPhil 12FT 24PT PhD 36FT 60PT
Information and Library Studies (MPhil).............MPhil 12FT 24PT

University of Liverpool
Archives and Records Management............MPhil 12FT/PhD 36FT

Restoration
Taught Courses

Anglia Ruskin University
Conservation of Buildings..................................MSc 12FT 24 - 30PT

University of Bath
Conservation of Historic Buildings ......MSc 12FT 28PT/PGDip 9FT 20PT
Conservation of Historic Gardens and Cultural Landscapes.......... MSc 12FT 28PT/PGDip 9FT 20PT

University of Bolton
Regeneration and Sustainable CommunitiesMA 15FT/MSc 15FT/PGDip 12FT/PGCert 6FT

Bucks New University
Conservation of Furniture and Decorative Arts...... MA 12FT 24PT

College of Estate Management
Conservation of Historic Environment ......PGDip 24DL/MSc 36DL

Cardiff University
Conservation Practice... MSc 24FT
Professional Conservation...MSc 12FT 24PT

Cranfield University
Land Reclamation and Restoration ....MSc 12FT 60PT/PGCert 12FT 60PT/PGDip 12FT 60PT

University of Dundee
Renewable Energy and Sustainable Building in a Global Context .... MSc 12FT

Durham University
Conservation of Archaeological and Museum Objects (Dissertation)... MA 24FT 36PT
Conservation of Archaeological and Museum Objects (Professional Practice)................................. MA 24FT 36PT

Edinburgh Napier University
Architectural Technology & Building Performance .... MSc 12FT 24PT 36DL

Information science and librarianship

Timber Engineering ....MSc 12FT 36DL
Timber Industry Management........................ MSc 12FT 36PT 36DL

University of Edinburgh
Architectural Conservation...MSc 12FT 24PT

University of Greenwich
Building Rehabilitation...MSc 12FT 24PT

Heriot-Watt University
Building Conservation (Technology and Management).......... MSc 24-84DL/PGDip 24-84DL

Kingston University
Historic Building Conservation ....MSc 12FT 24PT

University of Leicester
Country House MA/Postgraduate Diploma/Postgraduate Certificate...MA 24-48DL
Urban Conservation...........................MA 12FT 24PT/MSc 12FT 24PT

University of Lincoln
Conservation Studies...GradDip 12FT 24PT
Conservation of Historic Objects..............................MA 12FT 24PT

London Metropolitan University
Restoration and Conservation ....MA 12FT 24PT

Oxford Brookes University
Historic Conservation ....MSc 12FT 24PT/PGDip 12FT 24PT/PGCert 12PT

Plymouth University
Architectural Conservation...................MA 12FT 24PT/PGDip 10FT 12-60PT

University of Portsmouth
Historic Building Conservation ....MSc 12FT 24PT

University of Reading
Geoarchaeology .... MSc 12FT 24PT/PGDip 12FT 24PT

Royal College of Art
Conservation....................................PhD by taught/MPhil/MA 24FT

School of Oriental and African Studies - SOAS
History of Art and/or Archaeology......................MA 12FT 24-36PT

University of Sheffield
Conservation and Regeneration .... MA 12FT 24PT
Sustainable Architectural Studies...........................MSc 12FT 24PT

University of Sussex
International Trade Law..LLM 12FT 24PT

Trinity College Dublin - the University of Dublin
Applied Building Repair and Conservation .... PGDip 12PT

UCL - University College London
Built Environment: Sustainable Heritage .... MSc 12FT 24-60PT/PGDip 9FT
Conservation...............................MSc 12FT/PGDip 9FT/PGCert 3FT

University of York
Conservation Studies (Historic Buildings).......... MA 12FT 24-36PT
Stained Glass Conservation and Heritage Management...............MA 24FT

Restoration
Research Courses

Birmingham City University
Birmingham School of Architecture and Landscape....PhD/MPhil

University of Cambridge
Brain Repair...PhD 36FT

School of Oriental and African Studies - SOAS
Department of Art and Archaeology .PhD 36FT 72PT/MPhil 24FT 36PT

Section sponsored by BPP UNIVERSITY COLLEGE

Business and social sciences
www.prospects.ac.uk/findcourses POSTGRADUATE DIRECTORY 423

Law and legal studies

Administrative law
Taught Courses

Bangor University
Language, Policy and Planning.......MA 12FT 24-48PT/PGDip 8FT/PGCert 4FT
Law.......PhD by taught 36FT/MPhil 24FT

University of Birmingham
Public Management (with specialist pathways)..MSc 12FT 24PT/PGDip 12FT 24PT/PGCert 12FT 15PT

University of Bristol
Public Law....... LLM 12FT 24PT

Cardiff University
Governance and Devolution.......LLM 12FT
Law and Governance of the European Union.......LLM 12FT

University of Central Lancashire
Specialist Community Public Health Nurse - Health Visiting or School Nursing.......PGDip 12FT 24PT

City University London
Public International Law....... LLM 12FT 24PT

University of Derby
International and Comparative Law....... LLM 12FT 36PT
LLM (in an approved area of legal scholarship)..... LLM 12FT 36PT

University of East Anglia
Legal Studies.......GradDip 12FT

University of Edinburgh
Comparative and European Private Law....... LLM 12FT 24PT

University of Exeter
European Law....... LLM 12FT 24PT
INTO Diploma in Public Administration.......GradDip 9FT
Master of Laws....... LLM 12FT 24PT
Master of Public Administration..........MA 12FT 24PT 36DL 21BM

National University of Ireland Galway
Public Law....... LLM 12FT 24PT

University of Glasgow
Leadership Drugs & Alcohol Setting....... PGCert 9FT 18PT

University of Kent
Combined Title (Law).......PGDip 12FT 24PT/LLM 12FT 24PT
European Law.......LLM 12FT 24PT/PGDip 12FT 24PT
Public International Law.......PGDip 12FT 24PT/LLM 12FT 24PT

London Metropolitan University
Public Administration....... MPA 12FT 24PT

London School of Economics and Political Science (LSE)
Regulation.......MSc 12FT 24PT

London South Bank University
Public Administration - Executive.......MPA 28PT

University of Manchester
Public International & European Law.......LLM 12FT

University of Nottingham
Public International Law....... LLM 12FT 24PT
Public Procurement Law and Policy.......PGDip 21PT/LLM 24PT/PGCert 12-21PT

Queen Mary, University of London
Comparative and International Dispute Resolution LLB graduate entry 12FT
European Law.......LLB graduate entry 12FT
Public International Law.......LLB graduate entry 12FT
Public Law (UoL).......LLB graduate entry 12FT

Queen's University Belfast
Legislative Studies and Practice.......MA 12FT

School of Oriental and African Studies - SOAS
Law.......MA 12FT 2-36PT

University of Sheffield
Comparative Governance and Public Policy....... MA 12FT 24PT
Europubhealth: European Masters Programme in Public Health.......MPH 24FT

University of St Andrews
Evolutionary and Comparative Psychology: The Origins of Mind.......MSc 12FT 24PT

Administrative law
Research Courses

University of Essex
Law....... PhD 36FT 72PT/MPhil 24FT 48PT

Arbitration
Taught Courses

Anglia Ruskin University
International Management Practice.......MSc 18FT/PGDip 18FT/PGCert 18FT

College of Estate Management
Adjudication.......PGDip 24DL
Arbitration.......PGDip 24DL

University of Central Lancashire
Advanced Legal Practice.......LLM 12FT 24PT/PGDip 12FT
Conflict and Violence Minimisation.......PGCert 24PT

University of Chester
Contemporary Legal Studies.........LLM 12FT 24-36PT/PGDip 12FT 24-36PT/PGCert 12FT 12-24PT

City University London
Civil Litigation and Dispute Resolution.......LLM 12FT

Coventry University
Conflict Resolution Skills.......PGCert 6DL

University of Dundee
International Dispute Resolution and Management.....LLM 12FT
Professional Legal Practice.......PGDip 9FT

University of East Anglia
Conflicts in Intercultural Communication....... MA 12FT 24PT

University of Kent
International Conflict Analysis (Canterbury or Brussels).......MA 12FT 24PT/PGDip 12FT 24PT
International Conflict and Security....... MA 12FT 24PT
Peace and Conflict Studies (International Double Award).......MA 24FT

Kingston University
Dispute Resolution....... LLM 12FT 24PT

Lancaster University
Conflict Resolution and Peace Studies....... MA 12FT 24PT

Leeds Metropolitan University
Construction Law & Dispute Resolution.......MSc 24DL
LLM Law (top-up).......LLM 36PT
Legal Practice Course....... PGDip 12FT 24PT

University of Limerick
Peace and Development Studies.......MA 12FT

Liverpool John Moores University
Legal Practice....... LPC 12FT 24PT
egal Practice-LPC/BPTC Conversion....... LPC 10FT 16PT

University of St Mark and St John
Creative Conflict Transformation through the Arts.......MA 20FT

Queen Mary, University of London
International Commercial Arbitration (Distance Learning).......PGDip 12FT

Robert Gordon University
Construction Law and Arbitration....LLM 36DL/MSc 36DL/PGDip 24DL/PGCert 12DL
Mediation.......PGCert 12FT

School of Oriental and African Studies - SOAS
Dispute and Conflict Resolution....... MA 12FT 24PT

Trinity College Dublin - the University of Dublin
Conflict and Dispute Resolution Studies....... PGDip 12PT

University of Westminster
Conflict Prevention Dispute Resolution....... MA 12FT 24PT
International and Commercial Dispute Resolution Law LLM 12FT 24PT

University of Winchester
Reconciliation........MA 12FT 24PT/DipHE 12FT 24PT/PGCert 12FT 24PT
Reconciliation and Peacebuilding.......MA 12FT 24PT/PGDip 12FT 24PT/PGCert 12FT 24PT

Arbitration
Research Courses

University of Kent
International Conflict Analysis (Brussels or Canterbury).......PhD 36FT 60PT/MPhil 24FT 36PT/MA by research 12FT 24PT

Banking law
Taught Courses

Bangor University
Banking and Law.........MA 12FT/PGDip 9FT MBA 12FT/PGDip 9FT
Law and Banking.......LLM 12FT

University of Cambridge
Master of Finance.......MFin 12FT

University of Dundee
Law.......LLM 12FT

Edinburgh Napier University
International Banking and Finance....... MSc 12FT

University of Essex
International Business Law....... LLM 12FT 24PT
International Commercial Law....... LLM 12FT 24PT
International Trade Law....... LLM 12FT 24PT

GCU London
International Banking, Finance and Risk Management.......MSc 12FT
International Economics and Finance....... MSc 12FT

University of Glasgow
Banking and Financial Services....... MSc 12FT
Financial Forecasting and Investment....... MSc 12FT
International Corporate Finance & Banking....... MSc 12FT

Queen Mary, University of London
Banking and Finance Law.......MA 12FT
Oral Biology.......MSc 12FT 24PT

University of Reading
International Corporate Finance....... LLM 12FT 24PT
International Financial Regulation.......LLM 12FT

School of Oriental and African Studies - SOAS
Law.......MA 12FT 2-36PT

University of West London
Finance and Global Capital Markets....... MSc 12FT 24PT

Banking law
Research Courses

University of Dundee
Law....... LLM by research 12FT MPhil 24FT

Biotechnological law
Taught Courses

Edinburgh Napier University
Biotechnology..... MSc 12FT 24-36PT/PGDip 9FT 18-27PT/PGCert 6FT 12-18PT

Glasgow Caledonian University
Biotechnology....... MSc 12FT

University of Glasgow
Biotechnology....... MSc 12FT

University of Hertfordshire
Biotechnology.......MSc 12-16FT/PGCert 12-16FT/PGDip 12-16FT

Nottingham Trent University
Biotechnology.......MSc 12FT 24PT MSc(Res) 12FT 24PT

Sheffield Hallam University
Biotechnology....... MSc 12FT 24PT/PGDip 8FT 16PT/PGCert 4FT 8PT

University of Sheffield
Biotechnology Law and Ethics....... LLM 12FT 24PT

Biotechnological law
Research Courses

University of Cambridge
Biotechnology.......PhD 36FT

Newcastle University
Biotechnology....... MPhil 12FT 24PT/PhD 36FT 72PT
Biotechnology and Business Enterprise.......MRes 12FT

BVC
Taught Courses

BPP Law School
Bar Professional Course.......BVC 12FT 24PT

Cardiff University
Bar Professional Training Course (BPTC).......BVC 10FT

University of Central Lancashire
Excellence in Leadership for Inclusion and Community..... PGCert 12-24PT

University of Chester
Leadership Development (Work Based and Integrative Studies)..........MA 24-72PT/MSc 24-72PT/PGDip 24-60PT/PGCert 12-36PT
Leadership and Management (Work Based and Integrative Studies)..........MA 24-72PT/MSc 24-72PT/PGDip 24-60PT/PGCert 12-36PT

City University London
Bar Professional Training Course.......BVC 12FT 24PT

University of Glasgow
Organisational Leadership (Oman)...........MSc 24PT/PGDip 18PT/PGCert 12PT

Goldsmiths, University of London
Global Leadership....... MSc 12FT

University of Law
Bar Professional Training Course.......BVC 12FT 24PT

University of Leeds
LLB Law (graduate programme)......LLB graduate entry 12FT 24PT

London South Bank University
International Criminal Law & Procedure....... LLM 14FT 26PT
Management in Civil Society (Accounting & Finance) - Blended....... MSc 30PT
Management in Civil Society (Marketing and Fundraising - Blended)....... MSc 30PT

Manchester Metropolitan University
Bar Professional Training Course (BPTC)....... PGDip 12FT 24PT

Northumbria University
Bar Professional Training Course (BPTC)....... PGDip 12FT 24PT
Master of Laws.......MA 30-36DL
Master of Laws Bar Practice.......MA 24FT

Nottingham Trent University
Bar Professional Training Course.......BPTC 12FT

Law and legal studies

University of the West of England, Bristol
Bar Professional Training Course (BPTC)................PGDip 9FT 24PT

Civil law
Taught Courses

University of Cambridge
Master of Law............LLM 9FT

Cardiff University
Social Care Law............LPC 10FT

University of Derby
Law.......PhD by taught 36-60FT 72-96PT/MPhil 24-48FT 48-72PT

University of Dundee
Comparative & European Private International Law .....LLM 12FT
Law (General) ....LLM 12FT

National University of Ireland Galway
Bachelor of Laws............LLB graduate entry 36FT 48PT

Glasgow Caledonian University
Bachelor of Laws - Fast-track..........LLB graduate entry 24FT 39PT

University of Oxford
Civil Law............BCL 9-21FT

School of Oriental and African Studies - SOAS
Law............MA 12FT 2-36PT

University of Strathclyde
Advocacy............LLM 12FT/PGDip 9FT

Teesside University
Civil Engineering............MSc 12 - 16FT 24PT/PGDip 8FT

Civil law
Research Courses

University of Dundee
Law ....LLM by research 12FT MPhil 24FT

Civil litigation
Taught Courses

University of Strathclyde
Advocacy............LLM 12FT/PGDip 9FT

Commercial law
Taught Courses

University of Aberdeen
International Commercial Law ....LLM 12FT 36PT
International Law............LLM 12FT 24-36PT
Law and Sustainable Development............LLM 12FT 24PT
Private International Law............LLM 12FT 24PT

School of Advanced Study, University of London
International Corporate Governance, Financial Regulation & Economic Law............LLM 12FT 24PT

Anglia Ruskin University
International Commercial Law ....LLM 12FT

Aston University
LLM International Commercial Law............LLM 12FT 24-60PT

BPP Law School
Business Law .... LLB graduate entry 22-34FT 46-82PT 22-82DL
Commercial Law............LLM 12FT 24PT
International Business Law............LLM 12FT 24PT

Bangor University
Executive LLM in Public Procurement Law and Strategy..........LLM 24BM
International Commercial and Business Law............LLM 12FT/PGDip 9FT
International Law - specialising in Global Trade Law......LLM 12FT
LLM in Public Procurement Law and Strategy............LLM 12FT
Law............PhD by taught 36FT/MPhil 24FT
Law and Banking ....LLM 12FT
Public Procurement Law and Strategy............LLM 12FT 24PT

University of Bedfordshire
Corporate Law............LLM 12FT
International Commercial Law ....LLM 12FT

Birmingham City University
International Business Law........PGCert 3FT 6PT/PGDip 6FT 18PT/LLM 12FT 24PT

University of Birmingham
Commercial Law............LLM 12FT 24PT
International Commercial Law ....LLM 12FT 24PT
MBA Corporate Governance and Responsibility............MBA 12FT

Bournemouth University
International Commercial Law ....LLM 12-15FT

University of Bristol
Commercial Law............LLM 12FT 24PT
Labour Law and Corporate Governance ....LLM 12FT 24PT

British Institute of Technology & E-commerce
International Business & Commercial Law ....PGCert 3FT/DipHE 6FT 12PT/MBA 12FT 24PT

Brunel University
International Commercial Law ....LLM 12FT/PGDip 9FT

University of Buckingham
International and Commercial Law............LLM 9FT/LLM 12FT

Bucks New University
International Commercial Law ....LLM 12FT

Cardiff University
International Commercial Law ....LLM 12FT

University of Central Lancashire
Law............LLM 12FT 24PT/PGDip 12FT 24PT

City University London
International Commercial Law ....LLM 12FT

Coventry University
International Business Law............LLM 12FT 24-30PT

De Montfort University
Business Law ....LLM 12FT LLM 15-27DL
International Business Law............LLM 12FT

University of Derby
Commercial Law............LLM 12FT 24PT
Corporate and Financial Law............LLM 12FT 36PT

University of Dundee
Corporate & Commercial Law ....LLM 12FT
International Commercial Law - Dual Qualifying ProgrammeLLM 12FT
Non-Graduating Taught Postgraduate in School of Law............PG module variableFT

Durham University
European Trade and Commercial Law............LLM 12FT
International Trade and Commercial Law............LLM 12FT

University of East Anglia
International Commercial and Business Law......... LLM 12FT 24PT
International Public Policy, Regulation and Competition ....MA 12FT 24PT
International Trade Law............LLM 12FT 24PT

Edge Hill University
International Business and Commercial Law......... LLM 12FT 24PT

University of Edinburgh
Commercial Law............LLM 12FT 24PT
Corporate Law............LLM 12FT 24PT
International Commercial Law and Practice (online distance learning) ....LLM 12FT 20 - 36PT 12 - 36DL
International Economic Law............LLM 12FT 24PT

University of Exeter
International Commercial Law ....LLM 12FT 24PT
Law............GradDip 9FT

Glasgow Caledonian University
Design Practice & Management .... MA 12FT 24PT/PGDip 9FT
Global Business Law and Regulation ....LLM 12FT
International Business............MSc 12FT

University of Glasgow
International Commercial Law ....LLM 12FT 24PT

University of Gloucestershire
International Business Law............LLM -FT -PT -DL

University of Greenwich
International and Commercial Law............LLM 12FT 24PT

University of Hertfordshire
Commercial Law............LLM 12FT 24PT
Commercial and Maritime Law............LLM 12FT 24PT
Commercial and Telecommunications Law............LLM 12FT 24PT
E-Commerce Law............LLM 12FT 24PT
Maritime Law............LLM 12FT 24PT

Holborn College
Business and Commercial Law............LLM 12-18FT

University of Huddersfield
Commercial Law............LLM 12FT 24PT

University of Hull
International Business Law............LLM 12FT 24PT

Keele University
Law and Society......... LLM 12FT 24- 48PT/PGDip 12-48PT/PGCert 12-24PT

University of Kent
International Commercial Law ....LLM 12FT 24PT/PGDip 12FT 24PT

Kingston University
International Commercial Law ....LLM 12FT 24PT

Lancaster University
International Business and Corporate Law............LLM 12FT 24PT

Leeds Metropolitan University
Corporate Governance............MSc 4FT 36PT
International Business ....MA 12FT 24PT

University of Leeds
European and International Business Law ....LLM 12FT 24PT
International Business Law............LLM 12FT 24PT

University of Limerick
International Commercial Law ....LLM 12FT

London Metropolitan University
International Business............MA 12FT 24PT
International Commercial Law ....LLM 12FT 24-60PT

University of Manchester
Corporate Governance............LLM 12FT

Middlesex University
International Business Law............LLM 12FT 24PT

Newcastle University
International Business Law............LLM 12FT 24PT

Northumbria University
Commercial Law............LLM 12FT 24DL/PGDip 9FT 18DL
International Commercial Law ....LLM 12FT 24DL/PGDip 9FT 18DL
Laws............MA 30-36DL

Nottingham Trent University
Corporate Law............LLM 12FT 24PT
Insolvency Law............LLM 12FT 24PT
Intellectual Property Law............LLM 12FT 24PT

University of Nottingham
International Commercial Law ....LLM 12FT 24PT

Oxford Brookes University
International Trade and Commercial Law............LLM 12FT 24PT/PGDip 9FT 18PT

University of Portsmouth
Corporate Governance and Law/Grad ICSA............LLM 12FT 36PT

Queen Mary, University of London
Commercial and Corporate Law............MA 12FT
International Commercial Arbitration (Distance Learning)............PGDip 12FT

Queen's University Belfast
Corporate Governance............LLM 12FT 24PT
Law and International Commerce ....LLM 12FT 24PT

University of Reading
International Commercial Law ....LLM 12FT
Law and Economics ....LLM 12FT 24PT MSc 12FT/PGDip 9FT/PGCert 6FT

Robert Gordon University
International Commercial Law ....LLM 12FT/PGDip 8FT/PGCert 4FT

School of Oriental and African Studies - SOAS
Law............MA 12FT 2-36PT
MA Globalisation and Multinational Corporations............MA 12FT 24PT

University of Sheffield
Commercial Law............LLM 12FT 36PT
International Commercial Law and Practice .... LLM 12FT 24PT

University of South Wales
International Commercial Law ....LLM 12FT 24-36PT

University of Southampton
Commercial and Corporate Law............LLM 12FT 24PT
International Business Law............LLM 12FT 24PT

Staffordshire University
LLM International Trade and Commerce via Distance Larning ....LLM 16DL

University of Surrey
International Commercial Law ....LLM 12FT 24PT

University of Sussex
International Commercial Law ....LLM 12FT 24PT

Swansea University
Intellectual Property & Commercial Practice......... LLM 12FT 36PT
International Commercial Law ....LLM 12FT 36PT
International Commercial and Maritime Law .... LLM 12FT 36PT

Teesside University
Business Law ....LLM 12FT 24PT

Trinity College Dublin - the University of Dublin
Laws (International and European Business Law)..........LLM 12FT

University of Warwick
Corporate Governance and Financial Regulation.LLM 12FT 24PT/PGDip 9FT

University of West London
International Business and Commercial Law......... LLM 12FT 24PT

University of the West of England, Bristol
Commercial Law............LLM 12FT 24-36PT

University of York
International Corporate and Commercial Law ....LLM 12FT

Commercial law
Research Courses

University of East Anglia
Law..........PhD 36FT 72PT/MPhil 24FT 48PT/LLM by research 12FT 24PT

University of Exeter
Law............PhD 48FT 84PT 84DL/MPhil 36FT 60PT 60DL/MA by research 12FT 24PT

Section sponsored by

BPP
UNIVERSITY
COLLEGE

Business and social sciences
www.prospects.ac.uk/findcourses **POSTGRADUATE DIRECTORY 425**

Law and legal studies

University of Kent
Law..........PhD 36FT 60PT/MPhil 24FT 36PT/LLM by research 12FT
24PT

University of Leeds
Centre for Business Law and Practice.....PhD 36+FT/MPhil 24+FT/
MA by research 12+FT

London Metropolitan University
Dept of Law Governance and International Relations.... PhD Max
60PT Max 96PT/MPhil Max 36FT Max 54PT

Queen Mary, University of London
Centre for Commercial Law Studies ....PhD/LLM by research/
MSc by research 12FT

University of Salford
Research Opportunities at Salford Law School...Salford Centre of
Legal Research 36DL

Company law
Taught Courses

Bangor University
Executive LLM in Public Procurement Law and Strategy..........LLM
24BM
International Law - specialising in Global Trade Law......LLM 12FT
LLM in Public Procurement Law and Strategy.................LLM 12FT
Public Procurement Law and Strategy ....LLM 12FT 24PT

University of Exeter
Master of Laws .... LLM 12FT 24PT

Glasgow Caledonian University
Design Practice & Management .... MA 12FT 24PT/PGDip 9FT

Holborn College
Business and Commercial Law......................... LLM 12-18FT

Manchester Metropolitan University
Law .... LLM 12FT 24PT

Nottingham Trent University
Corporate Law .... LLM 12FT 24PT

University of Nottingham
Sustainable Bioenergy ....MRes 12-36PT

Queen Mary, University of London
International Business Law.......................... LLM 12FT 24PT

Queen's University Belfast
Corporate Governance .... LLM 12FT 24PT
Law and Governance .... LLM 12FT 24PT

University of Reading
International Corporate Finance .... LLM 12FT 24PT

Sheffield Hallam University
Law and Corporate Strategy........................ LLM 12FT 24PT

Company law
Research Courses

Manchester Metropolitan University
Master of Research Business ....MRes 12FT 30PT

Nottingham Trent University
Law...................................... MPhil 24FT 48PT/PhD 48FT 72PT

Competition law
Taught Courses

Aberystwyth University
International Commercial Law and the Environment (Distance
Learning)..LLM 12FT

Bangor University
Executive LLM in Public Procurement Law and Strategy..........LLM
24BM
LLM in Public Procurement Law and Strategy.................LLM 12FT
Public Procurement Law and Strategy .... LLM 12FT 24PT

University of Dundee
Law (General) ....LLM 12FT

University of East Anglia
International Commercial and Competition Law ....LLM 12FT

University of Edinburgh
Competition Law and Innovation............................ LLM 12FT 24PT

University of Essex
International Business Law............................... LLM 12FT 24PT
International Commercial Law .... LLM 12FT 24PT
International Trade Law.................................... LLM 12FT 24PT
Internet Law...LLM 12FT

University of Glasgow
International Competition Law & Policy................. LLM 12FT 24PT

King's College London
Competition Law .... LLM 12FT 24PT
EU Competition Law ....PGDip 24DL/MA 24DL
Economics for Competition Law..................MA 24DL/PGDip 24DL

Nottingham Trent University
Competition Law .... LLM 12FT 24PT

Queen Mary, University of London
Competition Law ....LLB graduate entry 12FT

Health Systems and Global Policy.......................MSc 12FT 24-48PT

University of Reading
International Commercial Law ....LLM 12FT

Competition law
Research Courses

University of Dundee
Law .... LLM by research 12FT MPhil 24FT

University of East Anglia
Law..........PhD 36FT 72PT/MPhil 24FT 48PT/LLM by research 12FT
24PT

Computer law
Taught Courses

Aberystwyth University
Information Technology Law......................................LLM 12FT
International Commercial Law and the Environment (Distance
Learning)..LLM 12FT
InternationalTechnology Law (Distance-Learning)....... LLM 36DL/
PGDip 24DL
Internet Commerce and Law..LLM 12FT

University College Cork
E-Law .... LLM 12FT 24PT

University of Derby
Information Security .... MSc 12FT 36PT
Intellectual Property and Information Technology Law .LLM 12FT
36PT
International Protection of Human Rights and Personal Freedom
LLM 12FT 24PT
LLM (in an approved area of legal scholarship) ..... LLM 12FT 36PT

University of Dundee
Computing .... MSc 12FT
Computing Research .... MSc 12FT
Computing with International Business .... MSc 12FT
Computing with Vision and Imaging .... MSc 12FT

University of East Anglia
Information Technology and Intellectual Property Law .LLM 12FT
24PT

University of Edinburgh
Innovation, Technology and the Law........................ LLM 12FT 24PT
Innovation, Technology and the Law (Online Distance Learning)
LLM 12FT 20-36PT 12 - 36DL

University of Exeter
Information Technology Management for Business...... MSc 12FT

National University of Ireland Galway
Law, Technology and Goverence..LLM 12FT

Glasgow Caledonian University
Management of IT Innovation .... MSc 12FT

University of Greenwich
Information Technology with e-Business / with Security....... MSc
12FT 24PT

University of Hertfordshire
Commercial Law .... LLM 12FT 24PT
Commercial and Telecommunications Law........... LLM 12FT 24PT
Telecommunications Law.................................... LLM 12FT 24PT

King's College London
Computing, IT Law & Management................... MSc 12FT

Kingston University
Cybercrime .... MA 12FT 24PT

Leeds Metropolitan University
Information & Technology.......MSc 12FT 24PT/PGDip 12FT 24PT/
PGCert 4FT 24PT

University of Leeds
CyberLaw: Information Technology, Law & Society.........LLM 12FT
24PT

University of Oxford
Software and Systems Security ....MSc 24-48PT

Queen Mary, University of London
Computer and Communications Law by Distance Learning..........
PGCert 12FT

University of Southampton
Information Technology and Commerce................. LLM 12FT 24PT
Information Technology and Telecommunications Law.................
LLM 24DL

University of Strathclyde
Internet Law and Policy ..... LLM 12FT 24PT 24DL/PGDip 9FT 21PT
21DL/PGCert 9FT

Computer law
Research Courses

University of Dundee
Computing ....MPhil 24FT MSc by research 12FT PhD 36FT
Non-Graduating Research in School of Computing (6 months or
more)..Non-Grad 6-24FT
Non-Graduating Research in School of Computing (less than 6
months)... Non-Grad 1-5FT

University of East Anglia
Law..PhD 36FT 72PT/MPhil 24FT 48PT/
LLM by research 12FT 24PT

Construction law
Taught Courses

Cardiff University
Architecture: Professional Studies...... MA 24FT 36PT/PGDip 12FT

University of Central Lancashire
Construction Law and Dispute Resolution ....MSc 24PT 24DL/
PGCert 24PT 24DL/PGDip 24PT 24DL

University of Glasgow
Contemporary Law & Practice .... LLM 12FT 24PT

King's College London
Construction Law & Dispute Resolution .... MSc 12FT 24PT

Kingston University
Management in Construction (Law) .... MSc 24PT

Leeds Metropolitan University
Construction Law & Dispute Resolution ....MSc 24DL

Northumbria University
Construction Project Management...MSc 12FT 30PT/PGDip 12FT
24PT/PGCert 12FT 24PT
Project Management/Management de projets de construction a
l'international - dual award....................................... MSc 15FT

University of Reading
Construction Cost Management .... MSc 24PT
Construction Management .... MSc 12FT
Project Management .... MSc 24PT

Robert Gordon University
Construction Law and Arbitration ....LLM 36DL/MSc 36DL/PGDip
24DL/PGCert 12DL

University of Salford
Construction Law and Practice ....LLM 24DL/MSc 24DL/PGDip
16DL/PGCert 8DL

School of Oriental and African Studies - SOAS
Law, Culture and Society .... MA 12FT 24PT
Law, Development and Globalisation .... MA 12FT 24PT

University of Strathclyde
Construction Law ....LLM 12FT 24PT/PGDip 9FT 21PT

Trinity College Dublin - the University of Dublin
Construction Law and Contract Administration .... PGDip 12FT

University of the West of England, Bristol
Construction Law ....MSc 12FT 24PT

University of Wolverhampton
Construction Law and Dispute Resolution ..... MSc 12FT 24-36PT/
PGCert 12FT 24PT

Construction law
Research Courses

University of East Anglia
Business, Accountability, Regulation and Development PhD 36FT
72PT/MPhil 24FT 48PT

Consumer law
Taught Courses

De Montfort University
Food Law... PGDip 15DL/LLM 15-27DL

Consumer law
Research Courses

Manchester Metropolitan University
Research in Consumer Marketing, Consumer Protection and
Trading Standards ... PhD VariableFT VariablePT/MPhil VariableFT
VariablePT/MSc by research 12FT 24PT

Contract law
Taught Courses

Bangor University
International Commercial and Business Law.................. LLM 12FT/
PGDip 9FT

Manchester Metropolitan University
LLM (Master of Laws)... LLM 12FT 24PT

Northumbria University
Graduate Diploma in Law/Common Professional Examination
(GDL/CPE)..CPE 12FT 24DL
Laws.. MA 30-36DL
Project Management/Management de projets de construction a
l'international - dual award.. MSc 15FT

University of Reading
International Commercial Law ....LLM 12FT
Oil and Gas ....LLM 12FT 24PT MSc 12FT 24PT

School of Oriental and African Studies - SOAS
Law...MA 12FT 2-36PT

Trinity College Dublin - the University of Dublin
Construction Law and Contract Administration .... PGDip 12FT

Section sponsored by BPP UNIVERSITY COLLEGE

Business and social sciences
426 POSTGRADUATE DIRECTORY www.prospects.ac.uk/findcourses

Law and legal studies

Conveyancing law
Taught Courses

Leeds Metropolitan University
Doctorate of Business Administration.............................. DBA 48PT

University of Liverpool
Advanced Science..........MSc 12FT 24PT/PGDip 12FT/PGCert 12FT

Nottingham Trent University
Doctorate in Business Administration...........DBA by taught 36PT

Conveyancing law
Research Courses

University of Dundee
Community Learning & Development .... MPhil 24FT

University of Greenwich
Pharmacy - Research........................... MPhil 36-72FT/PhD 36-72FT

University of Southampton
Doctor of Business Administration .... DBA 48PT

Corporate finance law
Taught Courses

University of Aberdeen
Corporate Finance .... MSc 12FT

School of Advanced Study, University of London
International Corporate Governance, Financial Regulation & Economic Law.. LLM 12FT 24PT

University of Bedfordshire
Corporate Law...LLM 12FT

University of Birmingham
Corporate Governance and Responsibility...................... MBA 12FT

University of Central Lancashire
Finance and Development .... MSc 12FT
Finance and Investment .... MSc 12FT

University College Cork
Accounting and Corporate Finance.....................................HDip 9FT
Corporate Finance and Accounting....................................MBS 12FT

De Montfort University
Business Law .... LLM 12FT LLM 15-27DL

University of Derby
Corporate and Financial Law..................................... LLM 12FT 36PT

University of Edinburgh
Corporate Law... LLM 12FT 24PT

European Business School London
Global Banking & Finance.. MSc 12-16FT

University of Glasgow
Corporate and Financial Law..................................... LLM 12FT 24PT
International Corporate Finance & Banking .... MSc 12FT

University of Leeds
Law and Finance .... MSc 12FT 24PT

London Metropolitan University
Finance.. MSc 12FT 24PT

London South Bank University
Corporate Governance (Fast Track) .... MSc 24PT
Corporate Governance with Graduate ICSA .... MSc 12FT 32PT

Newcastle University
Finance... MSc 12FT
Finance and Financial Regulation .... MSc 12FT
Finance and Law with Islamic Finance............................. MSc 12FT

Nottingham Trent University
Corporate Law .... LLM 12FT 24PT

Oxford Brookes University
Finance.. MSc 12FT 24PT

Plymouth University
Finance.. MSc 12FT 24PT

Queen Mary, University of London
Law and Finance .... MSc 12FT 24PT

Queen's University Belfast
Corporate Governance .... LLM 12FT 24PT

University of Reading
Corporate Finance .... MSc 10FT 24PT
Corporate Real Estate .... MSc 24-72PT
International Corporate Finance .... LLM 12FT 24PT
International Financial Regulation ....LLM 12FT
Law and Economics .... LLM 12FT 24PT
Law and Economics ....MSc 12FT/PGDip 9FT/PGCert 6FT

Royal Holloway, University of London
Financial and Industrial Economics .... MSc 12FT

School of Oriental and African Studies - SOAS
Finance and Financial Law ....MSc 12FT 24-36PT
MGlobalisation and Multinational Corporations.............................. MA 12FT 24PT

University of Southampton
Commercial and Corporate Law .... LLM 12FT 24PT

University of Stirling
Corporate Social Responsibility ....LLM 12FT

University of Strathclyde
European Financial Management..................................... MSc 12FT

Trinity College Dublin - the University of Dublin
Finance... MSc 12FT 24PT

UCL - University College London
Financial Risk Management .... MSc 12FT

University of Westminster
Corporate Finance Law... LLM 12FT 24PT

Corporate finance law
Research Courses

University of Aberdeen
Finance... PhD 36FT/MPhil 24FT/MRes 12FT

Newcastle University
Finance and Accounting .... PhD 36FT 72PT/MPhil 12FT 24PT

Nottingham Trent University
Law.. MPhil 24FT 48PT/PhD 48FT 72PT

Queen's University Belfast
Finance.. PhD 36FT 72PT/MPhil 24FT 48PT

Criminal law
Taught Courses

University of Aberdeen
Criminal Justice and Human Rights .... LLM 12FT 36PT
Human Rights & Criminal Justice .... LLM 12FT 24-36PT
Transitional Justice and Reconciliation..................MSc 12FT 24PT/PGDip 9FT 18PT

Aberystwyth University
Environmental Law and Management .....LLM 36DL/PGDip 24DL
Environmental and Human Rights Law ....LLM 36DL/PGDip 24DL
Human Rights and Humanitarian Law.......... LLM 12FT LLM 36DL
International Commercial Law (distance-learning)...... LLM 36DL/PGDip 24DL
International Commercial Law (full-time) ....LLM 12FT 24PT/PGDip 9FT 21PT LLM 36DL/PGDip 24DL
Research Preparation (Law) ....MRes 12FT 24PT

Bangor University
Comparative Criminology and Criminal Justice ....MA 12FT 24PT/PGDip 9FT PhD by taught 36FT 72PT/MPhil 12-24FT 24-36PT/MARes 12FT 24PT
Criminology and Law..MA 12FT
International Law - specialising in International Criminal&International Human Rights Law ....LLM 12FT
Law and Criminology..LLM 12FT

Birkbeck, University of London
Constitutional Politics, Law and Theory .... LLM 12FT 24PT
Criminal Law and Criminal Justice...........................MA 12FT 24PT/LLM 12FT 24PT
Law (General)... LLM 12FT 24PT
Qualifying Law Degree... LLM 24FT 36PT

University of Birmingham
Criminal Law... LLM 12FT 24PT

University of Bradford
Applied Criminal Justice Studies .... MA 24PT/PGDip 21PT/PGCert 9PT

Brunel University
International and Comparative Criminal Justice ....LLM 12FT

University of Cambridge
Applied Criminology and Police Management................ MSt 24PT
Applied Criminology, Penology and Management......... MSt 24PT
Criminological Research ....MPhil 9FT
Criminology ....MPhil 9FT
Master of Law.. LLM 9FT

Canterbury Christ Church University
Criminology and Criminal Justice .... MA 12FT 36PT

University of Central Lancashire
Conflict and Violence Minimisation ....PGCert 24PT

University of Chester
Contemporary Legal Studies ....LLM 12FT 24-36PT/PGDip 12FT 24-36PT/PGCert 12FT 12-24PT

University College Cork
Criminal Justice... LLM 12FT 24PT

De Montfort University
Criminology and Criminal Justice ....MA 24-36DL

University of Derby
Criminal Investigation... MSc 12FT 24PT
International and Comparative Law........................ LLM 12FT 36PT
Law.......PhD by taught 36-60FT 72-96PT/MPhil 24-48FT 48-72PT
Transnational Criminal Law .... LLM 12FT 36PT

University College Dublin
Human Rights ....MSc 12FT/MLitt 24FT

University of Dundee
International Criminal Justice & Human Rights ....LLM 12FT

Durham University
Criminology and Criminal Justice .... MSc 12FT

University of East Anglia
Legal Studies..GradDip 12FT

University of East London
International Law and Criminal Justice LLM ....LLM 12FT 24PT/PGDip 8FT 16PT/PGCert 4FT 8PT

Edge Hill University
International Justice and Human Rights Law........ LLM 12FT 24PT
Research..LLM 12-24FT 18-36PT

University of Edinburgh
Criminal Law.. LLM 12FT 24PT
Criminal Law and Criminal Justice........................... LLM 12FT 24PT
Criminology and Criminal Justice .... MSc 12FT 24PT
Global Crime, Justice and Security........................... MSc 12FT 24PT

National University of Ireland Galway
Human Rights and Criminal Justice (Cross Border).........LLM 12FT
International Criminal Law .... LLM 12FT 24PT

University of Glasgow
Criminology .... MRes 12FT 24PT/PGDip 9FT 21PT
Transnational Crime, Justice and Security .... MSc 12FT 24PT

University of Gloucestershire
Criminology ...... PGCert 4FT 8PT/PGDip 8FT 20PT/MSc 12FT 24PT

Glyndwr University
Criminology and Criminal Justice .... MA 12FT 24PT

University of Greenwich
Criminal Justice StudiesPGCert 12FT 24PT/MSc 12FT 24PT/PGDip 12FT 24PT
Criminology ....MA 12FT 24PT/PGDip 12FT 24PT

University of Hull
Restorative Justice...MA 12FT 24PT 12-24DL

University of Kent
Criminal Justice............................LLM 12FT 24PT/PGDip 12FT 24PT
Criminology .... MA 12FT 24PT
Criminology with a semester abroad........................ MA 12FT 24PT
International Criminal Justice...PGDip 12FT 24PT/LLM 12FT 24PT
Social and Public Policy: Criminal Justice (Distance Learning, Medway)...MA 24DL/PGDip 24DL

Leeds Metropolitan University
Criminology .... MSc 12FT 24PT

University of Leeds
Criminal Justice Studies... MA 12FT 24PT
Criminal Justice Studies and Policing......................MA 12FT 24PT/PGDip 12FT 24PT
Criminal Law and Criminal Justice........................... LLM 12FT 24PT
Criminological Research .... MA 12FT 24+PT
Criminology .... MA 12FT 24PT
Security and Justice .... MA 12FT 24PT

University of Leicester
Criminology .... MSc 12FT 24PT/PGDip 12FT 24PT
Criminology and Criminal Justice .... MSc 24DL/PGDip 18DL/PGCert 12DL
Terrorism, Security and Policing ....MSc 12FT 24PT/PGDip 12FT 24PT

University of Limerick
Human Rights in Criminal Justice.................... MA 12FT/LLM 12FT

Liverpool John Moores University
Criminal Justice........................MA 24PT/PGDip 18PT/PGCert 12PT

University of Liverpool
Applied Criminal Justice Research .... MA 12FT 24PT

London South Bank University
Criminology & Social Research Methods .... MSc 13FT 24PT

Manchester Metropolitan University
Criminology .... MA 12FT 24PT

University of Northampton
International Criminal Law and Security ....LLM 12FT

Northumbria University
Criminology and Criminal Justice .... MA 12FT 24PT
Graduate Diploma in Law/Common Professional Examination (GDL/CPE)..CPE 12FT 24DL
Laws ....MA 30-36DL

Nottingham Trent University
Criminology .... MA 12FT 24PT
International Criminal Justice.................................. LLM 12FT 24PT

University of Nottingham
Criminal Justice... LLM 12FT 24PT
International Criminal Justice Law and Armed Conflict................. LLM 12FT 24-48PT

University of Oxford
Criminology & Criminal Justice .... MSc 12FT
Criminology & Criminal Justice (Research Methods)..... MSc 12FT

University of Portsmouth
Criminology and Criminal Justice ....MSc 12FT 24/ 36DL
Criminology and Criminal Psychology............MSc 12FT 24/ 36DL
International Criminal Justice..................................... MSc 24 / 36DL

Section sponsored by

BPP
UNIVERSITY
COLLEGE

Business and social sciences
www.prospects.ac.uk/findcourses POSTGRADUATE DIRECTORY 427

Law and legal studies

Queen's University Belfast
Criminal Justice.............................. MSc 12FT 24PT/PGDip 12FT 24PT
Human Rights and Criminal Justice ....LLM 12FT 24PT/MSSc 12FT 24PT

University of Roehampton
Human Rights .... MA 18FT 24+PT
Human Rights and International Relations .... MA 18FT 24+PT

School of Oriental and African Studies - SOAS
Human Rights Law... MA 12FT 24PT
International Law .... MA 12FT 24PT

Sheffield Hallam University
International Criminal Justice... MA 12FT 24PT/PGCert 6FT 12PT/PGDip 3FT 6PT
International Criminal Justice.............Doctorate 36-60FT 48-84PT MA 12FT 24PT
International Criminal Justice........... MA 12FT 24PT/PGDip 12PT/PGCert 6PT

University of Sheffield
International Criminology ....MA 12FT

University of South Wales
Criminal and Social Justice .... MA 12FT 24PT
Criminology and Criminal JusticeMSc 12FT 24PT/PGDip 4FT 8PT/PGCert 8FT 16PT

Southampton Solent University
Criminology abd Criminal Justice .... MSc 12FT

University of Southampton
Crime Analysis... MSc 12FT 24PT

University of Stirling
Criminological Research .... MRes 12FT 27PT/PGDip 9FT 21PT

University of Strathclyde
Advocacy..LLM 12FT/PGDip 9FT
Criminal Justice and Penal Change........MSc 12FT 24PT/LLM 12FT 24PT/PGDip 9FT

University of Surrey
Criminology, Criminal Justice and Social Research............................ MSc 12FT 24PT

University of Sussex
Criminal Law and Criminal Justice............................ LLM 12FT 24PT
International Criminal Law... LLM 12FT 24PT

Teesside University
Criminal Investigation...MSc 12FT 24PT
Criminal Law .... LLM 12FT 24PT
Criminology .... MSc 12FT 24PT

University of Ulster
Human Rights Law and Transational Justice.......... LLM 12FT 24PT

UCL - University College London
Crime Analysis (by Distance Learning)....................PGCert 12-24PT
Crime Prevention and Community Safety ....PGCert 9FT/PGDip 9FT 18-45PT
Crime and Forensic Science .... MSc 12FT

University of West London
Criminology and Criminal Justice ....LLM 24PT

Criminal law
Research Courses

Aberystwyth University
Law & Criminology ....LLM by research 12FT 24PT

Bangor University
Criminology and Criminal Justice ....PhD 36FT 60PT/MPhil 12-24FT 24-36PT

Birmingham City University
Social Sciences.............................. PhD 36FT 60PT/MPhil 36FT 60PT

University of Cambridge
Criminology .... PhD 36FT 60PT
Legal Studies... Diploma 9FT 18PT

University College Dublin
Human Rights .... PhD 36FT/MLitt by research 24FT

University of Kent
Criminology .....MPhil 24FT 36PT/PhD 36FT 60PT/MA by research 12FT 24PT
The Doctorate in Cultural and Global Criminology (DCGC).....PhD 36FT 60PT

University of Leeds
Centre for Criminal Justice Studies.....PhD 36FT 48PT/MPhil 24FT 36PT/MA by research 12FT 24PT

Nottingham Trent University
Law... MPhil 24FT 48PT/PhD 48FT 72PT

University of Portsmouth
Criminal Justice Studies.............. MPhil 24FT 48PT/PhD 36FT 72PT

Professional Doctorate in Criminal Justice .... DCrimJ 48DL

Queen's University Belfast
Law.. PhD 36FT 72PT/MPhil 24FT 48PT

University of Salford
Research Opportunities at Salford Law School...Salford Centre of Legal Research 36DL

University of Ulster
Transitional Justice Institute ..... PhD 36FT 72PT/MPhil 24FT 48PT

Criminal litigation
Taught Courses

Bangor University
Comparative Criminology and Criminal Justice ....MA 12FT 24PT/PGDip 9FT
Criminology and Criminal Justice .... PhD by taught 36FT 72PT/MPhil 12-24FT 24-36PT/MARes 12FT 24PT

University of Cambridge
Applied Criminology and Police Management............... MSt 24PT
Applied Criminology, Penology and Management........ MSt 24PT
Criminological Research ....MPhil 9FT
Criminology ....MPhil 9FT

City University London
Criminal Litigation .... LLM 12FT 24PT

De Montfort University
Criminology and Criminal Justice ....MA 24-36DL

University of Derby
Criminal Investigation....................................MSc 12FT 24PT

University of Glasgow
Contemporary Law & Practice .... LLM 12FT 24PT

London South Bank University
International Criminal Law & Procedure................. LLM 14FT 26PT

Northumbria University
Criminology and Criminal Justice .... MA 12FT 24PT

University of Oxford
Criminology & Criminal Justice.. MSc 12FT
Criminology & Criminal Justice (Research Methods)..... MSc 12FT

University of Sheffield
International Criminology ....MA 12FT

Section sponsored by BPP UNIVERSITY COLLEGE

Business and social sciences
428 POSTGRADUATE DIRECTORY www.prospects.ac.uk/findcourses

Law and legal studies

University of Southampton
Crime Analysis ... MSc 12FT 24PT

University of Stirling
Criminological Research ... MRes 12FT 27PT/PGDip 9FT 21PT

University of Strathclyde
Advocacy ... LLM 12FT/PGDip 9FT
Criminal Justice and Penal Change ... MSc 12FT 24PT/LLM 12FT 24PT/PGDip 9FT

Criminal litigation
Research Courses

Bangor University
Criminology and Criminal Justice ... PhD 36FT 60PT/MPhil 12-24FT 24-36PT

Criminology
Taught Courses

Aberystwyth University
Research Training ... LLM 12FT 24PT

Anglia Ruskin University
Criminology (Transnational Crime) ... MA 12FT 24PT

Bangor University
Comparative Criminology and Criminal Justice ... MA 12FT 24PT/PGDip 9FT
Criminology and Criminal Justice ... PhD by taught 36FT 72PT/MPhil 12-24FT 24-36PT/MARes 12FT 24PT
Criminology and Law ... MA 12FT
Criminology and Sociology ... MA 12FT 21-30PT/PGDip 9FT 17-21PT/PGCert 5FT 12-21PT
Forensic Linguistics ... MSc 12FT 24PT
Language Development ... MSc 12FT 36PT
Law and Criminology ... LLM 12FT

Birmingham City University
Criminology ... MA 12FT 24PT/PGDip 8FT 12PT/PGCert 3FT 9PT

University of Birmingham
Clinical Criminology ... MSc 24PT/PGDip 12PT

University of Bradford
Applied Criminal Justice Studies ... MA 24PT/PGDip 21PT/PGCert 9PT
Human Trafficking and Contemporary Slavery ... MSc 24PT/PGDip 21PT/PGCert 9PT

University of Brighton
Criminology ... MA 12FT 24-72PT/PGDip 12FT 24-72PT/PGCert 12FT 24-72PT

University of Cambridge
Applied Criminology and Police Management ... MSt 24PT
Applied Criminology, Penology and Management ... MSt 24PT
Criminological Research ... MPhil 9FT
Criminology ... MPhil 9FT

Canterbury Christ Church University
Criminology and Criminal Justice ... MA 12FT 36PT

Cardiff University
Criminology and Criminal Justice ... MSc 12FT

University of Central Lancashire
Conflict and Violence Minimisation ... PGCert 24PT
Counter Terrorism ... MSc 12FT
Criminal Investigation ... MSc 12PT
Global Security and Justice ... MA 12FT

City University London
Criminology and Criminal Justice ... MA 12FT 24PT
Social Research Methods ... MSc 12FT 24PT

University of Cumbria
Leadership and Management in Policing MBA 36PT/PGDip 36PT/PGCert 36PT

De Montfort University
Criminology and Criminal Justice ... MA 24-36DL PhD

University of Derby
Criminal Investigation ... MSc 12FT 24PT
International and Comparative Law ... LLM 12FT 36PT

Dublin Institute of Technology
Criminology ... MA 12FT 24PT

University of Dundee
Forensic Odontology ... MFOdont 12FT
Forensic Toxicology ... MFTox 12FT

Durham University
Criminology and Criminal Justice ... MSc 12FT

University of East Anglia
Social Science Research Methods: Business ... MRes 12FT 24PT
Social Science Research Methods: Education ... MRes 12FT 24PT
Social Science Research Methods: Law ... MRes 12FT 24PT
Social Science Research Methods: Psychology ... MRes 12FT 24PT
Social Science Research Methods: Social Work ... MRes 12FT 24PT

Edge Hill University
Criminology ... MRes 12-24FT 18-36PT

University of Edinburgh
Criminal Law ... LLM 12FT 24PT
Criminal Law and Criminal Justice ... LLM 12FT 24PT
Criminology and Criminal Justice ... MSc 12FT 24PT
Forensic Anthropology ... MSc 12FT 24PT
Global Crime, Justice and Security ... MSc 12FT 24PT

University of Essex
Criminology and Socio-Legal Research ... MA 12FT 24PT
Organised Crime, Terrorism and Security ... MSc 12FT 24PT

University of Exeter
Security, Conflict and Justice ... MRes 12FT 24PT
Socio-Legal Research ... MRes 12FT 24PT

Glasgow Caledonian University
Social Research ... MSc 12FT 24PT

University of Glasgow
Criminology ... MRes 12FT 24PT/PGDip 9FT 21PT
Criminology & Criminal Justice ... MSc 12FT 24PT/PGDip 9FT 21PT
Sociology and Research Methods ... MRes 12FT 24PT
Transnational Crime, Justice and Security ... MSc 12FT 24PT

University of Gloucestershire
Criminology ... PGCert 4FT 8PT/PGDip 8FT 20PT/MSc 12FT 24PT

Glyndwr University
Criminology and Criminal Justice ... MA 12FT 24PT

University of Greenwich
Criminal Justice StudiesPGCert 12FT 24PT/MSc 12FT 24PT/PGDip 12FT 24PT
Criminology ... MA 12FT 24PT/PGDip 12FT 24PT
International Criminology ... MA 12FT 24PT/PGCert 12FT 24PT/PGDip 12FT 24PT

Keele University
Criminology and Criminal Justice ... MA 12FT 24PT/PGDip 12FT 24PT/PGCert 12FT 24PT/MRes 12FT 24PT

University of Kent
Criminology ... MA 12FT 24PT
Criminology with a semester abroad ... MA 12FT 24PT
Security and Terrorism ... MA 12FT 24PT/PGDip 12FT 24PT
Social and Public Policy: Criminal Justice (Distance Learning, Medway) ... MA 24DL/PGDip 24DL

Kingston University
Criminological Psychology ... MA 12FT 24PT
Criminology ... MA 12FT 24PT

Lancaster University
Criminology ... MRes 12FT 24PT

Leeds Metropolitan University
Criminology ... MSc 12FT 24PT

University of Leeds
Criminal Justice Studies ... MA 12FT 24PT
Criminal Justice Studies and Policing ... MA 12FT 24PT/PGDip 12FT 24PT
Criminal Law and Criminal Justice ... LLM 12FT 24PT
Criminological Research ... MA 12FT 24+PT
Criminology ... MA 12FT 24PT

University of Leicester
Applied Criminology ... MSc 12FT 24PT/PGDip 12FT 24PT
Clinical Criminology ... MSc 12FT 24PT/PGDip 12FT 24PT
Criminology ... MSc 12FT 24PT/PGDip 12FT 24PT
Criminology and Criminal Justice ... MSc 24DL/PGDip 18DL/PGCert 12DL
Forensic Science and Criminal Justice ... MSc 24-27DL
Security and Risk Management ... MSc 24DL/PGDip 18DL/PGCert 12DL

Liverpool Hope University
Criminal Justice ... MA 12FT 24PT/PGDip 12FT 24PT/PGCert 6FT 12PT

London Metropolitan University
Criminology ... MA 12FT 24PT
Women and Child Abuse ... MSc 12FT 24PT

London South Bank University
Crime & Litigation ... LLM 13FT 25PT
Criminology & Social Research Methods ... MSc 13FT 24PT

Manchester Metropolitan University
Criminology ... MA 12FT 24PT
Psychology and Criminology ... MSc 12FT 24-36PT/PGDip 12FT 24-36PT/PGCert 12FT 24-36PT

University of Manchester
Crime, Law and Society ... MA 12FT 24PT
Criminology & Socio-Legal Studies ... MRes 12FT 24PT

Middlesex University
Criminology ... MA 12FT 24PT
Criminology with Forensic Psychology ... MSc 12FT 24PT
Public Protection ... MA 12FT 24PT
Youth Justice, Community Safety, and Applied Criminology ... MA 12FT 24PT

University of Northampton
Criminology ... MSc 12FT 24PT/PGDip 12PT

Northumbria University
Criminology and Criminal Justice ... MA 12FT 24PT

Nottingham Trent University
Criminology ... MA 12FT 24PT
International Criminal Justice ... LLM 12FT 24PT

University of Nottingham
Criminological Psychology ... MSc 12FT 24PT
Socio-Legal and Criminological Research ... MA 12FT

The Open University
Social Policy and Criminology ... MA variableDL

University of Oxford
Criminology & Criminal Justice ... MSc 12FT
Criminology & Criminal Justice (Research Methods) ... MSc 12FT

Plymouth University
Criminology ... MSc 12FT

University of Portsmouth
Crime Science, Investigation and Intelligence ... MSc 12FT 24PT
Criminology and Community Safety ... MSc 12FT 24/ 36DL
Criminology and Criminal Justice ... MSc 12FT 24/ 36DL
Criminology and Criminal Pyschology ... MSc 12FT 24/ 36DL

Queen's University Belfast
Criminology ... MSSc 12FT 24PT/PGDip 12FT 24PT

Sheffield Hallam University
Forensic Criminolgy ... MSc 12FT 24PT
International Criminal Justice ... MA 12FT 24PT/PGCert 6FT 12PT/PGDip 3FT 6PT Doctorate 36-60FT 48-84PT MA 12FT 24PT/PGDip 12PT/PGCert 6PT

University of Sheffield
Global Justice ... MA 12FT 24PT
International Criminology ... MA 12FT

University of South Wales
Criminal and Social Justice ... MA 12FT 24PT
Criminology and Criminal JusticeMSc 12FT 24PT/PGDip 4FT 8PT/PGCert 8FT 16PT

Southampton Solent University
Criminology abd Criminal Justice ... MSc 12FT

University of Southampton
Crime Analysis ... MSc 12FT 24PT

University of Stirling
Applied Social Research (Criminology) ... MSc 12FT 30PT/PGDip 9FT 18PT MRes 12FT 30PT
Criminological Research ... MRes 12FT 27PT/PGDip 9FT 21PT

University of Strathclyde
Criminal Justice and Penal Change ... MSc 12FT 24PT/LLM 12FT 24PT/PGDip 9FT

University of Surrey
Criminology, Criminal Justice and Social Research ... MSc 12FT 24PT

Swansea University
Applied Criminal Justice and Criminology ... MA 12FT 36PT

Teesside University
Criminal Investigation ... MSc 12FT 24PT
Criminology ... MSc 12FT 24PT

UCL - University College London
Crime Analysis (by Distance Learning) ... PGCert 12-24PT
Crime Prevention and Community Safety PGCert 9FT/PGDip 9FT 18-45PT
Crime Science ... MSc 12FT 24-60PT
Crime and Forensic Science ... MSc 12FT

University of West London
Criminology and Criminal Justice ... LLM 24PT

Criminology
Research Courses

Aberystwyth University
Law & Criminology ... LLM by research 12FT 24PT MPhil 12FT 24PT PhD 36FT 60PT

Bangor University
Criminology and Criminal Justice PhD 36FT 60PT/MPhil 12-24FT 24-36PT

University of Bedfordshire
Crime, Society and the Media ... PhD 36FT 72PT

Birmingham City University
Social Sciences ... PhD 36FT 60PT/MPhil 36FT 60PT

University of Cambridge
Criminology ... PhD 36FT 60PT

Cardiff University
Crime, Security and Justice ... PhD 36FT possiblePT/MPhil 12FT possiblePT

University of Dundee
Forensic Medicine ... MPhil 24FT

University of Essex
Criminology ... PhD 36FT 72PT/MPhil 24FT 48PT/MA by research 12FT 24PT

Section sponsored by

BPP
UNIVERSITY
COLLEGE

Business and social sciences
www.prospects.ac.uk/findcourses POSTGRADUATE DIRECTORY 429

Law and legal studies

Criminology and Socio-Legal Research........PhD 36FT 72PT/MPhil 24FT 48PT/MA by research 12FT 24PT

University of Hull
Criminology .... PhD 36FT 60PT/MPhil 24FT 36PT

Keele University
Criminology .... PhD 24-48FT 48-84PT/MPhil 12-24FT 24-36PT

University of Kent
Criminology .....MPhil 24FT 36PT/PhD 36FT 60PT/MA by research 12FT 24PT
The Doctorate in Cultural and Global Criminology (DCGC).....PhD 36FT 60PT

University of Leicester
Department of Criminology...... PhD 36FT 72PT/MPhil 24FT 48PT

University of Liverpool
Criminological Research ....MRes 12FT 24PT

University of Manchester
Criminology .... PhD 36FT 72PT/MPhil 12FT 24PT

Middlesex University
Sociology and Criminology........ PhD 36FT 60PT/MPhil 24FT 48PT

Nottingham Trent University
Law .... MPhil 24FT 48PT/PhD 48FT 72PT

The Open University
Policing and Criminal Justice.....PhD 36FT 72PT variableDL/MPhil 15FT 24PT variableDL
Policing, punishment and justice....... PhD 36FT 72PT variableDL/MPhil 15FT 24PT variableDL
Social Policy and Criminology ...PhD 36FT 72PT variableDL/MPhil 15FT 24PT variableDL

University of Oxford
Legal Research.. DPhil 48FT

Queen's University Belfast
Law .... PhD 36FT 72PT/MPhil 24FT 48PT

University of Sheffield
Criminology and Socio-Legal Studies.....................PhD 36FT 72PT/MPhil 24FT 48PT

Swansea University
Criminology .... MPhil 24FT 48PT/PhD 36FT 72PT

UCL - University College London
Crime Science .... PhD 36FT 60PT

Ecclesiastical law
Taught Courses

University of Aberdeen
Pastoral Studies ....DPS 12FT 24PT

Aberystwyth University
Gwleidyddiaeth a Chymdeithas Cymru (Arbenigol).........MA 12FT 24PT/PGDip 9FT 18PT
Gwleidyddiaeth a Chymdeithas Cymru (Hyfforddiant Ymchwil)..
MA 12FT 24PT/PGDip 9FT 18PT

Cardiff University
Canon Law...LLM 24PT

Heythrop College
Canon Law.. MA 12FT 24PT

University of Winchester
Ecclesiastical Law ....LLM 24PT

Economic regulation
Taught Courses

University of Central Lancashire
Construction Management (Construction Economics)MSc 24DL/PGDip 12DL/PGCert 6DL

University of Chester
Developing RPL Policy and Practice (Work Based and Integrative Studies) .... MA 24-72PT/PGDip 24-60PT/PGCert 12-36PT

City University London
Economic Regulation and Competition.................. MSc 12FT 24PT

University of Dundee
Climate Change Economics and Policy .... MSc 12FT

National University of Ireland Galway
Economic Policy Evaluation and Planning... MEconSci 9 approxFT 18approxPT

Heriot-Watt University
Marine Resource Development and Protection....MSc 12FT 24PT/PGDip 9FT 21PT

University of Kent
Diploma in Economic Analysis.............................. MSc 24FT

Newcastle University
Finance and Financial Regulation .... MSc 12FT

University of Reading
Banking and Finance in Emerging Economies ...... MSc 12FT 24PT
Banking and Financial Systems in the Global Economy .... MSc 12FT
Economic Development in Emerging Markets ..... MSc 12FT 24PT
Economics of Climate Change .... MSc 12FT 24PT

Law and Economics .... LLM 12FT 24PT
MSc 12FT/PGDip 9FT/PGCert 6FT

School of Oriental and African Studies - SOAS
Development Economics......................................MSc 12FT 24-36PT
Economics (with Reference to Africa).....................MSc 12FT 24PT
Economics (with Reference to South Asia) ....MSc 12FT 24PT
Economics (with reference to the Middle East).....MSc 12FT 24PT

University of Sussex
Development Economics...MSc 12FT 24PT

Economic regulation
Research Courses

University of York
Economics...PhD 36FT/MPhil 24FT

Employment law
Taught Courses

Bangor University
Executive LLM in Public Procurement Law and Strategy..........LLM 24BM
LLM in Public Procurement Law and Strategy....................LLM 12FT
Law..PhD by taught 36FT/MPhil 24FT
Public Procurement Law and Strategy .... LLM 12FT 24PT

Brunel University
Human Resource Management and Employment Relations........MSc 12FT

University of Central Lancashire
Employment Law.......................LLM 12FT 24PT/PGDip 12FT 24PT/PGCert 12FT 24PT
Employment Law by distance learning .... LLM 24-36PT/PGCert 12PT/PGDip 24-36PT

University of Chester
Contemporary Legal Studies ....LLM 12FT 24-36PT/PGDip 12FT 24-36PT/PGCert 12FT 12-24PT

De Montfort University
Employment Law and Practice.............. PGDip 15DL/LLM 15-27DL

University of East Anglia
Employment Law................................. LLM 12FT 24PT/PGCert 12FT

University of Glasgow
Equality & Human Rights ....MSc 12FT 24PT

Keele University
Industrial Relations and Employment LawMA 24PT/PGDip 18PT/PGCert 18PT

University of Kent
European Law..............................LLM 12FT 24PT/PGDip 12FT 24PT

Kingston University
Employment Law... LLM 12FT 24PT

University of Leeds
Diversity Management .... MA 12FT 24PT

University of Leicester
Employment Law.. LLM 27DL

Middlesex University
Employment Law.. LLM 14FT 26PT

Northumbria University
Employment Law in Practice ....LLM 24DL/PGDip 18DL/PGCert 9DL

Nottingham Trent University
Employment Law...................................... LLM 12FT 24PT

Queen Mary, University of London
Commercial and Corporate Law ....MA 12FT
European Law...............................LLB graduate entry 12FT

University of Reading
International Commercial Law ....LLM 12FT

Robert Gordon University
Employment Law and Practice.........LLM 28-36PT 28-36DL/PGDip 24PT

Ruskin College
International Labour and Trade Union Studies....... MA 12FT 24PT

School of Oriental and African Studies - SOAS
Law..MA 12FT 2-36PT

University of Sheffield
European Gender Studies.. MA 12FT 24PT

University of Surrey
LLM Employment Law .... LLM 24DL

Trinity College Dublin - the University of Dublin
European Employment Studies ....MSc 12FT 24PT

Employment law
Research Courses

Cardiff University
Work, Employment and Globalisation......... PhD 36FT possiblePT/MPhil 12FT possiblePT

University of Hertfordshire
Centre for Research in Employment Studies........PhD 36FT 72PT/MPhil 24FT 48PT/MRes 12FT 24PT

London School of Economics and Political Science (LSE)
Employment Relations and Organisational Behaviour .... MPhil 36-48FT/PhD 36-48FT

Environmental law
Taught Courses

University of Aberdeen
Energy Law .... LLM 12FT 24PT
Pertroleum, Energy Economics and Finance..........MSc(Econ) 12FT

Aberystwyth University
Climate Change and Human Rights ....LLM 12FT
Environmental Law and Management .....LLM 36DL/PGDip 24DL
Environmental and Human Rights Law ....LLM 36DL/PGDip 24DL
International Commercial Law and the Environment ...LLM 12FT

School of Advanced Study, University of London
Advanced Legislative Studies ....LLM 12FT 24PT 24DL

Brunel University
Environmental Science: Legislation and Management...................
MSc 12FT 24PT

University of Central Lancashire
Nuclear Safety, Security and Safeguards....MSc 12FT 24PT/PGDip 9FT 18PT/PGCert 6FT 12PT

De Montfort University
Environmental Law .... PGDip 15DL/LLM 15-27DL

University of Derby
International and Comparative Law........................ LLM 12FT 36PT

University of Dundee
Climate Change and Energy Law and Policy ....LLM 12FT
Energy Law and Policy ....LLM 24-60DL
LLM 12FT
Energy Studies ....MSc 24-60DL
Energy Studies with Specialisation in Energy Economics ...... MSc 12FT/PGDip 9FT
Energy Studies with Specialisation in Energy Finance ....
MSc 12FT/PGDip 9FT
Energy Studies with Specialisation in Energy Policy .....MSc 12FT
Energy Studies with Specialisation in Energy and the Environment ....MSc 12FT
Environmental Law ....LLM 12FT
Environmental Law and Policy ....LLM 12FT
International Mineral Resources Management (MBA). MBA 12FT
Mineral Law and Policy ....LLM 12FT
LLM 60DL
Natural Resources Law and Policy ....LLM 12FT/PGDip 9FT
LLM 60DL
Petroleum Law and Policy ....LLM 12FT/PGDip 9FT
LLM 24-60DL
Petroleum Taxation and Finance ....LLM 12FT
Spatial Planning with Environmental Assessment .... MSc 12FT
Spatial Planning with Marine Spatial Planning .... MSc 12FT
Water Law (LLM Full time)... LLM 12-24FT
PGDip 18-60DL/PGCert 12-60DL/LLM 24-60DL

University of East Anglia
Energy Engineering with Environmental ManagementMSc 12FT/MSc 24FT/MSc 36FT/MSc 48FT

Edinburgh Napier University
Environmental Sustainability.... MSc 12FT 36PT/PGDip 9FT 24PT/PGCert 6FT 12PT

University of Edinburgh
Global Environment Challenges Certificate (Online distance learning) ....PGCert 9DL
Global Environment and Climate Change Law...... LLM 12FT 24PT

University of Exeter
Energy Policy ....MSc 12FT 24PT
Environment, Energy and Resilience ....MRes 12FT 24PT

University of Glasgow
Applied Carbon Management (Dumfries Campus)........ MSc 12FT 24PT

Harper Adams University
Agricultural Law...PGCert 12FT 24PT

University of Hull
International Environmental Law .... LLM 12FT 24PT

University of Kent
Environmental Law and Policy.................................LLM 12FT 24PT/PGDip 12FT 24PT
Environmental Social Science ....MSc 12FT 24PT
Ethnobotany...MSc 12FT 24PT
International Environmental Law ......PGDip 12FT 24PT/LLM 12FT 24PT

Kingston University
Environmental Law and Sustainability....................LLM 12FT 24PT

North East Surrey College of Technology
Acoustics and Noise Control....................................IOA Diploma 9PT
Applied Acoustics and Noise Control ....MSc 9PT

Business and social sciences
430 POSTGRADUATE DIRECTORY www.prospects.ac.uk/findcourses

Section sponsored by

BPP
UNIVERSITY
COLLEGE

Law and legal studies

Newcastle University
Ecological Consultancy .... MSc 12FT
Environmental Regulation and Sustainable Development .....LLM 12FT 24PT

University of Nottingham
Environmental Law .... LLM 12FT 24PT
Law and Environmental Science................................MSc 12FT 24PT
Public Procurement Law and Policy .... PGDip 21PT/LLM 24PT/
PGCert 12-21PT

Plymouth University
Environmental Consultancy .... MSc 12FT 24PT

Queen's University Belfast
Ecological Management and Conservation Biology....... MSc 12FT 24PT/PGDip 9FT
Environmental Law and Sustainable Development ....LLM 12FT

University of Reading
Climate Change & Development .... MSc 12FT 24PT
Economics of Climate Change .... MSc 12FT 24PT
Environmental Management .... MSc 12FT 24PT
International Commercial Law ....LLM 12FT
Rural Land and Business Management .... MSc 12FT
The Economics of Climate Change .... MSc 12FT

Robert Gordon University
Commercial Practice for the Energy Sector .... MSc 24DL
Energy Management.... MSc 12FT 36DL/PGDip 8FT 24DL/PGCert 4FT 12DL
Energy and Sustainability ...MSc 42DL/PGDip 24DL/PGCert 12DL
Oil and Gas Law ....LLM 12-18FT 12-18/36DL

School of Oriental and African Studies - SOAS
Environmental Law and Sustainable Development ....
MA 12FT 24PT
Global Energy and Climate Policy .... MSc 12FT 24PT
International and Comparative Commercial Law.. MA 12FT 24PT

University of Sheffield
Comparative Governance and Public Policy .... MA 12FT 24PT

University of Southampton
Ecological and Environmental Sciences........................MRes 12FT
Integrated Environmental Studies...........................MSc 12FT 27PT

Staffordshire University
Ecology and Conservation....................................... MSc 15FT

University of Stirling
Energy and the Environment ... MSc 12FT 27PT/MRes 12FT 27PT/
PGDip 9FT/PGCert 4FT
Environmental Policy and Governance........... LLM 12FT/MSc 12FT

Swansea University
International Commercial Law .... LLM 12FT 36PT

Teesside University
Energy and Environmental Management........MSc 12-16FT 24PT

UCL - University College London
Climate Change .... MSc 12FT 24PT
Energy Demand Studies ....MRes 12FT
Energy and Resources: Policy and Practice, Australia .... MSc 24FT 36-48PT

University of the West of England, Bristol
Environmental Law and sustainable development
.... LLM 12FT 36PT

Environmental law
Research Courses

University of Dundee
Energy, Petroleum and Mineral Law and Policy ....
LLM by research 12FT
Energy, Petroleum and Mineral Law and Policy .... MPhil 24FT
MSc by research 12FT
Energy, Petroleum and Mineral Law and Policy ....PhD 36FT
Water Law, Policy and Science .... LLM by
research 12FT PhD 36FT

University of Exeter
Environment, Energy and Resilience ..MPhil 36FT 60PT/PhD 36FT 84PT

University of Kent
Environmental Social Science ....PhD 36FT 60PT/
MPhil 24FT 36PT/MSc by research 12FT 24PT

Newcastle University
Energy............................... PhD 36FT 72PT/MPhil 12FT 24PT

Nottingham Trent University
Law.................................... MPhil 24FT 48PT/PhD 48FT 72PT

Queen's University Belfast
Ecology, Evolution, Behaviour and Environmental Economics
.... PhD 36FT 72PT/MPhil 24FT 48PT

European law
Taught Courses

Bangor University
International Law - specialising in European Law ....LLM 12FT
International Law - specialising in International
Criminal&International Human Rights Law ....LLM 12FT

Law......................................PhD by taught 36FT/MPhil 24FT

Birkbeck, University of London
Constitutional Politics, Law and Theory .... LLM 12FT 24PT

University of Bristol
European Legal Studies.................................... LLM 12FT 24PT

University of Cambridge
Master of Law... LLM 9FT

Cardiff University
European Legal Studies.....................................LLM 12FT
Law and Governance of the European Union ....LLM 12FT

University of Central Lancashire
Law...LLM 12FT 24PT/PGDip 12FT 24PT

University of Dundee
Comparative & European Private International Law .....LLM 12FT

University of Edinburgh
Comparative and European Private Law .... LLM 12FT 24PT
European Law... LLM 12FT 24PT

University of Essex
European Union Law .... LLM 12FT 24PT

University of Exeter
European Law... LLM 12FT 24PT
European Politics .... MA 12FT 24PT
Master of Laws.. LLM 12FT 24PT

University of Glasgow
Human Rights & International Politics ....MRes 12FT 24PT
International Law and Security................................. LLM 12FT 24PT

University of Hull
European Union Governance ....MA 12FT

University of Kent
European Law.................LLM 12FT 24PT/PGDip 12FT 24PT
Law (Erasmus-Europe)...LLM 12FT

King's College London
European Union Law .... PGDip 24DL/MA 24DL

University of Leeds
European Law.. LLM 12FT 24PT
European and International Business Law .... LLM 12FT 24PT
International and European Human Rights Law... LLM 12FT 24PT

University of Leicester
European Union (Commercial/Social Law & Policy/General)
Law ....LLM 27DL/PGDip 24DL/PGCert 12DL/Cert 5DL

University of Lincoln
European Law .... LLM 12FT 24PT

University of Liverpool
European Law .... LLM 12FT 24PT

London School of Economics and Political Science (LSE)
Politics and Government in the European Union ....
MSc 12FT 24PT

Newcastle University
European Union Studies..................................... MA 12FT 24PT
International Legal Studies...................................... LLM 12FT 24PT

Northumbria University
Graduate Diploma in Law/Common Professional Examination
(GDL/CPE) ....CPE 12FT 24DL
Laws..MA 30-36DL

Nottingham Trent University
Competition Law .... LLM 12FT 24PT

University of Nottingham
European Law.. LLM 12FT 24PT

University of Portsmouth
European Law and Policy... MA 12FT 24PT

Queen Mary, University of London
European Law...LLB graduate entry 12FT
International Business and Politics...........................MSc 12FT 24PT

University of Reading
Advanced Legal Studies .... LLM 12FT 24PT
Diplomacy .... MA 12FT 24-72PT/PGCert 12FT 24-72PT/
PGDip 12FT 24-72PT
International Relations ....MA (res) 12FT 24-72PT 72BM
International Relations (Strategic Studies) ......MA 12FT 24-72PT/
PGDip 24-72PT/PGCert 12FT 24PT

Robert Gordon University
Oil and Gas Law ....LLM 12-18FT 12-18/36DL

University of Sheffield
European Gender Studies................................... MA 12FT 24PT
European Governance and Politics .... MA 12FT 24PT
European Health Law and Policy .... LLM 12FT 24PT
European Law, Politics and Governance ....MA 12FT
European and Global Affairs..MA 24FT
International and European Law...................LLM 12FT Up to 36PT

University of Southampton
European Law.. LLM 12FT 24PT
European and Comparative Property Law .... LLM 12FT 24PT

University of Strathclyde
Human Rights Law.......................LLM 12FT 24PT/PGDip 9FT 21PT/
PGCert 9FT

University of Surrey
European Politics, Business and Law....................... MA 12FT 24PT
LLM European Law .... LLM 12FT 24PT

Trinity College Dublin - the University of Dublin
International Politics .... MSc 12FT 24PT
Laws (International and European Business Law) ....LLM 12FT

University of Westminster
European Union Law .... LLM 12FT 24PT

European law
Research Courses

European University Institute
Comparative, European and International Legal Studies ....
LLM by research 12FT

University of Exeter
European Studies .... PhD 48FT 89PT/MPhil 36FT 60PT
Law.......................PhD 48FT 84PT 84DL/MPhil 36FT 60PT 60DL/
MA by research 12FT 24PT

University of Kent
Law...PhD 36FT 60PT/MPhil 24FT 36PT/
LLM by research 12FT 24PT

University of Leeds
Centre for the Study of Law and Policy in Europe PhD 36FT 48PT/
MPhil 24FT 36PT/MA by research 12FT 24PT

London Metropolitan University
Dept of Law Governance and International Relations.... PhD Max 60FT Max 96PT/MPhil Max 36FT Max 54PT

Nottingham Trent University
Law.. MPhil 24FT 48PT/PhD 48FT 72PT

University of Surrey
Law......................... PhD 33-48FT 45-96PT/MPhil 21-36FT 33-72PT

Family law
Taught Courses

University of Aberdeen
Sex, Gender, Violence: Contemporary Critical Approaches .... MSc 12FT 24PT/PGDip 9FT 18PT

Bangor University
Law...PhD by taught 36FT/MPhil 24FT

University of Central Lancashire
Child Care Practice, PQ Specialist Award with Children, Young
People, Families & Carers..PGCert 18PT
Conflict and Violence Minimisation ....PGCert 24PT

University of Chester
Family and Child Psychology ...MSc 12FT 24PT/PGDip 12FT 24PT/
PGCert 12FT 12-24PT

University of East Anglia
Child and Family Psychology ....MSc 12FT 24PT

University of Glasgow
Contemporary Law & Practice .... LLM 12FT 24PT

Keele University
Child Care Law and Practice...........................MA 24PT/PGDip 12PT
Law and Society .... LLM 12FT 24- 48PT/PGDip 12-48PT/PGCert 12-24PT
Safeguarding Adults: Law, Policy and Practice MA 12FT 24-48PT/
PGDip 12FT 12-48PT

King's College London
Child Studies.................................MA 12FT 24PT/PGDip 12FT

London Metropolitan University
Violence Against Women.................................... PGCert 12FT 24+PT

Newman University
Children, Young People and Families................... MA 24FT 36-48PT

Oxford Brookes University
Children, Young People and Family Well-Being ....MSc 12-36DL/
PGDip 8-36DL/PGCert 4-36DL

Sheffield Hallam University
Anti-Social Behaviour Law and Strategies ....PGCert 12PT

University of Sheffield
Professional Practice with Children and Families ....MA 36PT

Trinity College Dublin - the University of Dublin
Child Protection and Welfare .... MSc 24PT PGDip 12PT

University of Warwick
Child Law and Child Protection................. PGA 12PT/CPDMod 1PT

University of Worcester
Dynamics of Domestic Violence ...... MA 24PT/PGDip 24PT/PGCert 12PT

Section sponsored by
BPP UNIVERSITY COLLEGE
Business and social sciences
www.prospects.ac.uk/findcourses POSTGRADUATE DIRECTORY 431

Law and legal studies

Financial law
Taught Courses

School of Advanced Study, University of London
International Corporate Governance, Financial Regulation & Economic Law .... LLM 12FT 24PT

Aston University
MSc Finance & Financial Regulation .... MSc 12FT

BPP Law School
Financial Regulation and Compliance .... LLM 12FT 24PT

Bangor University
Law and Banking .... LLM 12FT

University of Central Lancashire
Finance and Management .... MSc 12FT
Financial Analysis .... MSc 12FT

University of Derby
Corporate and Financial Law .... LLM 12FT 36PT

Edinburgh Napier University
Banking and Financial Regulation .... MSc 12FT
Corporate Strategy and Finance .... MSc(Eng) 12FT 36PT/PGDip 9FT 12-60DL/PGCert 5FT 12-60DL

University of Edinburgh
Corporate Law .... LLM 12FT 24PT

University of Essex
International Business Law .... LLM 12FT 24PT
International Commercial Law .... LLM 12FT 24PT
International Trade Law .... LLM 12FT 24PT

Glasgow Caledonian University
Banking, Finance and Risk Management .... MSc 12FT 24PT
Financial Services, Risk and Operations ...... MSc 12FT 24PT/PGDip 9FT 24PT
International Banking and Finance .. MSc 12FT 24PT/PGCert 9FT/PGDip 6FT
Master of Finance .... MFin 12FT FlexiblePT
Risk Management ..... MSc 12FT FlexiblePT FlexibleDL/PGDip 9FT FlexiblePT FlexibleDL

University of Glasgow
Banking and Financial Services .... MSc 12FT
Corporate and Financial Law .... LLM 12FT 24PT
Financial Risk Management .... MSc 12FT

University of Kent
International Accounting and Finance .... MSc 12FT

King's College London
International Financial Law .... LLM 12FT 24-48PT

Kingston University
Corporate and Financial Law .... LLM 12FT 24PT

Leeds Metropolitan University
Association of Chartered Certified Accountants - Professional Level (ACCA) .... ACCA 24PT

London School of Economics and Political Science (LSE)
Law and Accounting .... MSc 12FT 24PT

University of Oxford
Financial Economics .... MSc 9FT

Queen Mary, University of London
Accounting and Finance .... MSc 12FT
Banking and Finance Law (University of London) .... MA 12FT
Oral Biology .... MSc 12FT 24PT

Queen's University Belfast
Risk Management and Financial Regulation .... MSc 12FT

University of Reading
Accounting and Financial Management .... MSc 12FT
Financial Risk Management .... MSc 10FT 24PT 24DL
International Corporate Finance .... LLM 12FT 24PT
International Financial Regulation .... LLM 12FT

University of Salford
Accounting and Finance .... MSc 12FT 36PT/PGDip 8FT 24PT/PGCert 4FT 9PT

School of Oriental and African Studies - SOAS
Finance and Financial Law .... MSc 12FT 24-36PT

University of Sheffield
Finance .... MSc 12FT 24PT
Finance and Accounting .... MSc 12FT
Financial Economics .... MSc 12FT 24PT

University of Southampton
Accounting and Finance .... MSc 12FT/PGDip 9FT
Finance and Economics .... MSc 12FT 24PT/PGDip 9FT 21PT

University of St Andrews
Finance & Management .... MLitt 12FT
Finance (FIN) .... PGDip 9FT/MSc 12FT/MPhil 24FT

University of Stirling
Finance .... MSc 12FT/PGDip 9FT/PGCert 6FT

University of Strathclyde
European Financial Management .... MSc 12FT
Finance .... MSc 12FT 24PT/PGDip 9FT 21PT

University of Warwick
Corporate Governance and Financial Regulation. LLM 12FT 24PT/PGDip 9FT

University of West London
Finance and Accounting .... MSc 12FT 24PT

University of Winchester
Accounting and Finance .... MSc 12FT 24PT/PGDip 9FT 18PT/PGCert 9FT 18PT

Financial law
Research Courses

University of East Anglia
Business, Accountability, Regulation and Development .... PhD 36FT 72PT/MPhil 24FT 48PT

University of St Andrews
Finance .... PhD 36FT 72PT/MPhil 24FT 48PT

Forensics
Taught Courses

Anglia Ruskin University
Forensic Science .... MSc 12 - 15FT 24 - 30PT

Bournemouth University
Forensic Osteology .... MSc 12FT 24PT
Forensic Toxicology by Research .... MSc 12FT 24PT

University of Central Lancashire
Criminal Investigation .... MSc 12PT
DNA Profiling .... MSc 12FT 24PT
Document Analysis .... MSc 12FT 24PT
Fire Investigation .... MSc 12FT/PGDip 9FT/PGCert 6FT
Fire Scene Investigation .... MSc 24-36PT
Forensic Anthropology ..... MSc 12FT/PGDip 6FT 12PT/PGCert 3FT 6PT
Forensic Medicine and Bioethics .... MSc 36PT/PGDip 24PT
Forensic Psychology MSc 12FT 24PT/PGDip 9FT 24PT/PGCert 9FT 24PT
Forensic Toxicology .... MSc 12FT
Forensic and Legal Medicine .... LLM 36PT/MA 36PT/PGDip 24PT

Cranfield University
Safety and Accident Investigation - Air Transport .... MSc 24-36PT
Safety and Accident Investigation - Rail ... MSc 36PT/PGDip 36PT/PGCert 36PT

Cranfield University, Shrivenham
Forensic Archaeology and Anthropology .... MSc 12FT 60PT
Forensic Ballistics .... MSc 12FT 60PT/PGDip 12FT 60PT/PGCert 12FT 60PT
Forensic Engineering and Science .... MSc 12FT 60PT/PGDip 7FT 36PT/PGCert 7FT 36PT
Forensic Explosives and Explosion Investigation .... MSc 12FT 60PT/PGDip 12FT 60PT/PGCert 12FT 60PT
Forensic Investigation .... MSc 12FT 60PT/PGDip 12FT 60PT/PGCert 12FT 60PT

University of Dundee
Anatomy and Advanced Forensic Anthropology .... MSc 12FT
Forensic Art .... MSc 12FT MSc 48PT
Forensic Custody Nursing (GradCert) .... GradCert 12FT
Forensic Facial Identification .... MSc 12FT
Forensic Medicine (MFM) .... MFM 12FT
Forensic Odontology (MFOdont) .... MFOdont 12FT
Forensic Toxicology (MFTox) .... MFTox 12FT

University of East Anglia
Forensic Linguistics and Translation .... MA 12FT 24PT

University of Edinburgh
Forensic Anthropology .... MSc 12FT 24PT

University of Glasgow
Forensic Toxicology .... MSc(MedSci) 12FT

University of Huddersfield
Forensic Podiatry .... PGCert 18-24BM

University of Hull
Analytical and Forensic Chemistry .... MSc 12FT

University of Kent
Forensic Science .... MSc 12FT

King's College London
Forensic Mental Health .... MSc 12FT 24PT/PGDip 12FT 24PT
Forensic Science .... MSc 12FT/MRes 15FT

Kingston University
Forensic Analysis .... MSc 12FT

University of Leicester
Forensic Science and Criminal Justice .... MSc 24-27DL

London Metropolitan University
Forensic Science .... MSc 12FT 24PT

London South Bank University
Forensic Science .... MSc 12FT 24PT

University of Manchester
Biomedical and Forensic Studies in Egyptology .... MSc 12FT 24PT

Northumbria University
Forensic Science .... MSc 12FT 36PT

Nottingham Trent University
Forensic Science and Technology .... MSc 12FT 24PT

Queen Mary, University of London
Forensic Medical Sciences .... MSc 12FT 24-60PT

Sheffield Hallam University
Forensic Accounting .... MSc 12FT 24PT
Forensic Engineering .... MSc 12FT 24PT
Forensic Science .... MSc 12FT 24PT

University of South Wales
Analytical and Forensic Science .... MSc 24FT

Staffordshire University
Forensic Science via Distance Learning ..... MSc 12-18FT 12/36DL/PGDip 12-18FT

University of Strathclyde
Forensic Science .... MSc 12FT/PGDip 9FT/PGCert 9FT

Swansea University
Applied Analytical Science (LCMS) ..... MSc 12FT 36PT/PGDip 12FT 36PT

Teesside University
Criminal Investigation .... MSc 12FT 24PT
Forensic Radiography .... PGCert 12PT 12DL MSc 36PT 36DL
Forensic Science .... MSc 12 or 16FT 24PT

UCL - University College London
Crime Analysis (by Distance Learning) .... PGCert 12-24PT
Crime Prevention and Community Safety .... PGCert 9FT/PGDip 9FT 18-45PT
Crime and Forensic Science .... MSc 12FT

University of the West of England, Bristol
Advanced Forensic Analysis .... MSc 12FT 24PT

University of Wolverhampton
Fire Scene Investigation .... MSc 12FT 24PT
Forensic Genetics and Human Identification .... MSc 12FT 24PT
Forensic Mark Comparison in collaboration with West Midlands Police .... MSc 12FT 24PT

Forensics
Research Courses

University of Central Lancashire
Forensic and Investigative Science ...... PhD 48FT 84PT/MPhil 36FT 60PT/MD 48PT/MSc by research 24FT 36PT

University of Dundee
Forensic Medicine .... MPhil 24FT
MSc by research 12FT PhD 36FT

University of Lincoln
Forensic Science .... MSc by research 12FT 24PT/MPhil 18FT 36PT/PhD 33FT 60PT

Teesside University
Forensic Science .... PhD 24FT 36PT/MPhil 18FT 30PT

UCL - University College London
Crime Science .... PhD 36FT 60PT

Fraud
Taught Courses

University of Dundee
Energy Studies .... MSc 24-60DL

Leeds Metropolitan University
Association of Chartered Certified Accountants - Professional Level .... ACCA 24PT

University of Portsmouth
Counter Fraud and Counter Corruption Studies .... MSc 12FT 24/36DL
Forensic Accounting .... MSc 12FT 36PT

University of Roehampton
Obesity: Risks and Prevention .... MSc 12FT 24PT
PGCert 6FT 12PT PGDip 9FT 24PT

University of South Wales
Forensic Audit and Accounting .... MSc 12FT

UCL - University College London
Countering Organised Crime and Terrorism ... MSc 12FT 24-60PT/PGDip 24PT

GDL
Taught Courses

Aberystwyth University
Graduate Diploma in Law (Conversion Course) .... GDL 10FT

Aston University
GDL (Graduate Diploma in Law) .... GDL 12FT 24PT 24DL

BPP Law School
Graduate Diploma in Law .... GDL 12FT 24PT 24DL

Birmingham City University
Graduate Diploma in Law/Common Professional Examination ... GDL 12FT 24PT

Bournemouth University
Graduate Diploma in Law/CPE .... GradDip 12FT/GradDip 24PT

Law and legal studies

Brunel University
Law CPE/Graduate Diploma in Law....GradDip 9FT

Cardiff University
Graduate Diploma in Law....GDL 12FT

University of Central Lancashire
Graduate Diploma in Law/Common Professional Examination Course....CPE 12FT 24PT 24DL/GDL 12FT 24PT 24DL
Law....LLM 12FT 24PT/PGDip 12FT 24PT
Professional Skills Course....CPD 24PT

City University London
Graduate Diploma in Law....GDL 12FT

De Montfort University
Graduate Diploma in Law (GDL)....GradDip 12FT 24DL

University of Glasgow
Professional Legal Practice, Diploma in....PGDip 9FT

University of Hertfordshire
Graduate Diploma in Legal Studies....GDL 12FT 24PT 24DL

University of Huddersfield
Law (Common Professional Examination)....GradDip 12DL

Keele University
Law - Common Professional Examination....GDL 12FT 24PT

University of Law
Graduate Diploma in Law....GDL 12FT 24PT 24DL

Leeds Metropolitan University
LLM Law (top-up)....LLM 36PT

Liverpool John Moores University
Graduate Diploma in Law....GDL 12FT 24PT

London Metropolitan University
Common Professional Examination (CPE)....Diploma 12FT 24PT

London School of Economics and Political Science (LSE)
Finance and Private Equity....MSc 10FT

London South Bank University
Law Conversion Course - Legal Studies....PGDip 20PT

Manchester Metropolitan University
Graduate Diploma in Law (Common Professional Examination) - graduate conversion course....PGDip 12FT 24PT

Middlesex University
Graduate Diploma in Law (CPE)....GDL 10FT 20PT 20DL

Northumbria University
Graduate Diploma in Law/Common Professional Examination (GDL/CPE)....CPE 12FT 24DL

Nottingham Trent University
Graduate Diploma in Law....GDL 12FT 24DL

University of Roehampton
Attachment Studies....PGDip 6-12FT 12PT
Audiovisual Translation....PGDip 9FT 24PT

Royal Northern College of Music
Postgraduate Diploma....PGDip 9FT

School of Oriental and African Studies - SOAS
Law, Culture and Society....MA 12FT 24PT

Sheffield Hallam University
Law....GradDip 10FT 24PT

Staffordshire University
GDL/CPE....GDL 12FT 24PT/CPE 12FT 24PT

University of Sussex
Common Professional Examination/ Graduate Diploma in Law.. CPE 12FT/PGDip 12FT

Swansea University
Law, Graduate Diploma....GDL 9FT

Teesside University
Law....PGDip 12FT 24PT

University of the West of England, Bristol
Law: Graduate Diploma....CPE 10FT 24DL

University of Westminster
Graduate Diploma in Law (CPE) Full-time Study....GDL 12FT GDL 24PT

University of Winchester
Graduate Conversion Diploma in Psychology GradDip 12FT 24PT
Law (Graduate Diploma / Common Professional Examination (GDL/CPE) Law)....GDL 12FT 24PT

University of Wolverhampton
CPE....LLDip 12FT 24PT

GDL
Research Courses

University of Birmingham
Law....MPhil 24FT 48PT
PhD 36FT 72PT/MJur by research 12FT 24PT/MPhil 24FT 48PT

University of Westminster
Law....MPhil 18-36FT 30-60PT

Human rights
Taught Courses

University of Aberdeen
Criminal Justice....LLM 12FT 24-36PT
Criminal Justice and Human Rights....LLM 12FT 36PT
Human Rights....LLM 12FT 24-36PT
Human Rights & Criminal Justice....LLM 12FT 24-36PT
International Law....LLM 12FT 24-36PT

Aberystwyth University
Climate Change and Human Rights....LLM 12FT
Democracy, Human Security and International Law....LLM 12FT
Human Rights and Development....LLM 12FT
Human Rights and Humanitarian Law....LLM 12FT LLM 36DL
International Commercial Law and Human Rights....LLM 12FT 24PT/PGDip 9FT 21PT
Rights, Gender and International Law....LLM 12FT

School of Advanced Study, University of London
Human Rights....MA 12FT 24PT

Bangor University
Criminology and Law....MA 12FT
International Law - specialising in International Criminal&International Human Rights Law....LLM 12FT
Law....PhD by taught 36FT/MPhil 24FT
Law and Criminology....LLM 12FT

University of Bath
Security, Conflict & Justice....MRes 12FT 24-36PT

Birkbeck, University of London
Constitutional Politics, Law and Theory....LLM 12FT 24PT
Human Rights....MA 12FT 24PT/LLM 12FT 24PT
Law (General)....LLM 12FT 24PT

Birmingham City University
International Human Rights....PGDip 6-8FT 12-16PT/LLM 12FT 24PT

University of Birmingham
Human Rights and Human Values....MSc 12FT 24-48PT/ PGDip 9FT 36PT/PGCert 4FT 24PT

University of Bradford
Conflict, Security and Development....MA 12FT 12-36PT/PGDip 24FT 24-36PT

University of Bristol
Human Rights Law....LLM 12FT 24PT

Brunel University
International Human Rights Law....LLM 12FT/PGDip 9FT

Cardiff University
Human Rights....LLM 12FT

University of Central Lancashire
Global Security and Justice....MA 12FT

City University London
Human Rights....MA 12FT 24PT
International Politics and Human Rights....MA 12FT 24PT

De Montfort University
International Human Rights Law....PGDip 15DL/LLM 15-27DL

University College Dublin
Human Rights....MSc 12FT/MLitt 24FT

University of Dundee
International Criminal Justice & Human Rights....LLM 12FT
International Law....LLM 12FT

Durham University
Conflict Prevention, Sustainable Peace and Security....MSc 12FT

University of East London
Anthropology, Human Rights and Justice....MSc 12FT 24PT/ PGDip 8FT 16PT/PGCert 4FT 8PT
Human Rights ...LLM 12FT 24PT/PGDip 8FT 16PT/PGCert 4FT 8PT

Edge Hill University
International Justice and Human Rights Law....LLM 12FT 24PT

University of Edinburgh
Global Crime, Justice and Security....MSc 12FT 24PT
International Law....LLM 12FT 24PT

University of Essex
Human Rights and Arts....MA 12FT 24PT
Human Rights and Cultural Diversity....MA 12FT 24PT
Human Rights and Research Methods....MA 12FT 24PT
International Human Rights Law....LLM 12FT
International Human Rights and Humanitarian Law....LLM 12FT
Theory and Practice of Human Rights....MA 12FT 24PT
UK Human Rights and Public Law....LLM 12FT 24PT

University of Exeter
International Human Rights Law....LLM 12FT 24PT
Security, Conflict and Justice....MRes 12FT 24PT

National University of Ireland Galway
Gender, Globalisation and Rights....MA 12FT 24PT
Human Rights Law (Cross-border)....LLM 12FT
Human Rights and Criminal Justice (Cross Border)....LLM 12FT
International Human Rights Law....LLM 12FT 24PT

Glasgow Caledonian University
Citizenship and Human Rights by Learning Contract...MSc 12FT/ PGDip 12FT/PGCert 12FT

University of Glasgow
Equality & Human Rights....MRes 12FT 24PT MSc 12FT 24PT
Human Rights & International Politics....MRes 12FT 24PT MSc 12FT/PGDip 9PT
International Law and Security....LLM 12FT 24PT
Transnational Crime, Justice and Security....MSc 12FT 24PT

Goldsmiths, University of London
Development & Rights....MA 12FT 24PT

University of Hull
International Human Rights Law....LLM 12FT 24PT
International Law....LLM 12FT 24PT

Keele University
Human Rights, Globalisation and Justice ... PGDip 12FT/MA 12FT 24PT
Law and Society....LLM 12FT 24- 48PT/PGDip 12-48PT/PGCert 12-24PT

University of Kent
Human Rights....MA 12FT 24PT/PGDip 12FT 24PT
International Criminal Justice...PGDip 12FT 24PT/LLM 12FT 24PT

Kingston University
Human Rights....MA 12FT 24PT
Human Rights and Genocide Studies....Joint European MA 18FT

Lancaster University
International Human Rights and Terrorism Law... LLM 12FT 24PT

University of Leeds
International and European Human Rights Law... LLM 12FT 24PT
Security and Justice....MA 12FT 24PT

University of Leicester
International Human Rights Law....LLM 12FT 24PT

University of Limerick
Human Rights in Criminal Justice....MA 12FT/LLM 12FT

University of Lincoln
Globalising Justice....MA 12FT 24PT
Journalism, War and International Human Rights.... MA 12FT 24PT

University of Liverpool
Humanitarian Studies....MSc 12FT/Diploma 9FT/Cert 6FT
International Human Rights Law....LLM 12FT 24PT

London School of Economics and Political Science (LSE)
Human Rights....MSc 12FT 24PT

London South Bank University
Human Rights & Development....LLM 16FT 28PT
International Human Rights & Development....LLM 16FT 28PT
International Refugee Law and Policy....PGCert 16FT 28PT

University of Manchester
Human Rights....MA 12FT 24PT/PGDip 9FT 21PT
Humanitarianism and Conflict Response....MA 12FT 24PT

Middlesex University
Human Rights and Business....MA 24PT/PGCert 12PT/ PGDip 15PT
Minorities, Rights and the Law....LLM 12FT 24PT

Northumbria University
Information Rights Law and Practice....LLM 24DL/PGDip 18DL/ PGCert 9DL

Nottingham Trent University
Human Rights....LLM 12FT 24PT
International Criminal Justice....LLM 12FT 24PT

University of Nottingham
Global Citizenship, Identities and Human Rights.... MA 12FT 24PT
Human Rights Law....LLM 12FT 24-48PT
International Criminal Justice Law and Armed Conflict.... LLM 12FT 24-48PT
Social and Global Justice....MA 12FT 24PT

The Open University
Human Rights and Development Management....PGCert 12DL

Oxford Brookes University
Development and Emergency Practice....MA 12FT 24PT/ PGDip 9FT 21PT/PGCert 3-9FT 9PT
Humanitarian Action and Conflict (PGCert)....PGCert 12DL
International Human Rights Law....LLM 12FT 24PT/ PGDip 9FT 18PT

University of Oxford
Criminology & Criminal Justice....MSc 12FT
International Human Rights Law....MSt 24PT 24DL
Refugee and Forced Migration Studies....MSc 9FT

Queen Mary, University of London
Human Rights Law....LLB graduate entry 12FT

Queen's University Belfast
Human Rights Law....LLM 12FT 24PT
Human Rights Law (Cross-Border)....LLM 12FT
Human Rights and Criminal Justice ....LLM 12FT 24PT/MSSc 12FT 24PT

YOU WILL BENEFIT FROM:

- Exceptionally competitive fees
- Small class sizes and individual pastoral support
- State-of-the-art facilities including a replica Crown Courtroom and Mediation Centre
- Flexible study methods to meet your needs
- Outstanding links to the legal profession
- Innovative and wide-ranging elective choices
- A range of co-curricular activities including accredited short courses

POSTGRADUATE OPEN EVENINGS:

27 NOVEMBER
29 JANUARY
26 FEBRUARY
26 MARCH

CONTACT US:

For more information on the
LPC, GDL or LLM contact:

Steven Goulton
Postgraduate Admissions Tutor
lawadmissions@herts.ac.uk

STAND OUT FROM THE CROWD

go.herts.ac.uk/law

Shaping your life in law

Law and legal studies

Human Rights and Criminal Justice (Cross-Border)........LLM 12FT

University of Reading
Advanced Legal Studies .... LLM 12FT 24PT
International Law and World Order ...LLM 12FT 24PT/PGDip 9FT/PGCert 6FT

Richmond, The American International University in London
International Conflict& Security .... MA 12FT 24PT

University of Roehampton
Human Rights ....MA 18FT 24+PT
Human Rights Practice: Erasmus Mundus........MA 24FT
Human Rights and International Relations........MA 18FT 24+PT
Human Rights ....PGCert 10FT 12+PT
Human Rights and International Relations........PGCert 10FT
Human Rights ....PGDip 12FT 24+PT
Human Rights and International Relations........PGDip 12FT 24PT

School of Oriental and African Studies - SOAS
Human Rights Law........ MA 12FT 24PT

Sheffield Hallam University
International Criminal Justice... MA 12FT 24PT/PGCert 6FT 12PT/PGDip 3FT 6PT
International Criminal Justice........Doctorate 36-60FT 48-84PT MA 12FT 24PT PGDip 12PT/PGCert 6PT

University of Sheffield
Global Justice .... MA 12FT 24PT

University of Southampton
International Law........ LLM 12FT 24PT

University of St Andrews
Peace and Conflict Studies........MLitt 12FT

University of Strathclyde
Criminal Justice and Penal Change........MSc 12FT 24PT/LLM 12FT 24PT/PGDip 9FT
Human Rights Law...LLM 12FT 24PT/PGDip 9FT 21PT/PGCert 9FT

University of Surrey
International Intervention .... MA 12FT 24PT
LLM Justice .... LLM 12FT 24PT

University of Sussex
Conflict, Security and Development........ MA 12FT 24PT
Criminal Law and Criminal Justice........ LLM 12FT 24PT
Human Rights .... MA 12FT 24PT
International Criminal Law........ LLM 12FT 24PT

Swansea University
Development and Human Rights........ MA 12FT 36PT
International Security & Development .... MA 12FT 24PT

University of Ulster
Gender, Conflict and Human Rights........ LLM 12FT 24PT
Human Rights Law and Transational Justice........ LLM 12FT 24PT

UCL - University College London
Human Rights .... MA 12FT 24PT
Transnational Studies........ MA 12FT 24PT

University of Warwick
International Development Law and Human Rights ......LLM 12FT 24PT/PGDip 9FT

University of York
Applied Human Rights........ MA 12FT 24PT/Diploma 12FT 24PT
International Human Rights Law & Practice........LLM 12FT 24PT/PGDip 12FT 24PT

Human rights
Research Courses

School of Advanced Study, University of London
International Human Rights........PhD 36FT/MPhil 12FT

University of Central Lancashire
Sociology, Ethnicity & Human Rights, Criminology .... PhD 30-48FT 66-84PT/MPhil 18-36FT 42-60PT/MA by research 12FT 24PT

University College Dublin
Human Rights .... PhD 36FT/MLitt by research 24FT

University of Essex
Human Rights .... MPhil 24FT 48PT/PhD 36FT 72PT
Human Rights and Research MethodsPhD 36FT 72PT/MPhil 24FT 48PT

Kingston University
Helen Bamber Centre for the Study of Rights and Conflict.....PhD 48FT 72PT/MPhil 24FT 48PT/MA by research 12FT 24PT

University of Manchester
Humanitarianism and Conflict Response .... PhD 48FT 96PT

University of Nottingham
School of Law Research Areas .... PhD 36FT/MPhil 24FT/MRes 24FT

University of Salford
Research Opportunities at Salford Law School...Salford Centre of Legal Research 36DL

School of Oriental and African Studies - SOAS
Development Studies........PhD 36FT 48-60PT

University of Sussex
Human Rights Research Programme .... PhD 24-48FT 36-72PT/MPhil 12-36FT 24-48PT

Insolvency law
Taught Courses

Nottingham Trent University
Insolvency Law........ LLM 12FT 24PT

Insurance law
Taught Courses

Queen Mary, University of London
Insurance Law........ LLM 12FT 24PT

University of Reading
International Financial Regulation ....LLM 12FT

Intellectual property
Taught Courses

Bangor University
International Intellectual Property Law ....LLM 12FT

Bournemouth University
Intellectual Property........ PGCert 6PT

Brunel University
Intellectual Property Law .... PGCert 9FT
International Intellectual Property Law ....LLM 12FT/PGDip 9FT

University of Derby
Intellectual Property and Information Technology Law........ LLM 12FT 36PT

University of Dundee
Corporate & Commercial Law ....LLM 12FT

University of East Anglia
Information Technology and Intellectual Property Law........ LLM 12FT 24PT

University of Edinburgh
Intellectual Property Law ....LLM 12FT 24PT 12 - 36DL

University of Glasgow
Intellectual Property and the Digital Economy...... LLM 12FT 24PT

University of Hertfordshire
Telecommunications Law........ LLM 12FT 24PT

King's College London
UK, EU & US Copyright Law........MA 24DL/PGDip 24DL

University of Leeds
Intellectual Property Law .... LLM 12FT 24PT

University of Liverpool
Technology and Intellectual Property Law (Online Degree)....LLM 24FT 24+PT

University of Manchester
Intellectual Property Law ....LLM 12FT/PGDip 9FT

Nottingham Trent University
Intellectual Property Law .... LLM 12FT 24PT

Queen Mary, University of London
Certificate in Trade Mark Law and Practice........Cert 12FT 12PT
Intellectual Property ....MSc 12FT 24PT

University of Reading
International Commercial Law ....LLM 12FT

University of Roehampton
Attachment Studies........ MSc 18-24FT 24-36PT PGCert 6FT 12PT PGDip 6-12FT 12PT

Swansea University
Intellectual Property & Commercial Practice........ LLM 12FT 36PT

University of West London
International Studies in Intellectual Property Law........ LLM 12FT 24PT

Intellectual property
Research Courses

University of Aberdeen
Real Estate........PhD 36FT/MPhil 24FT

University of East Anglia
Law........PhD 36FT 72PT/MPhil 24FT 48PT/LLM by research 12FT 24PT

International economic law
Taught Courses

Aberystwyth University
International Commercial Law and the Environment (Distance Learning)........LLM 12FT

Anglia Ruskin University
International Business Law........ LLM 12FT 24DL

Bangor University
International Commercial and Business Law........ LLM 12FT/PGDip 9FT
International Law........LLM 12FT
International Law - specialising in European Law ....LLM 12FT
Law........PhD by taught 36FT/MPhil 24FT
Law and Banking ....LLM 12FT

Brunel University
International Economic Law........LLM 12FT/PGDip 9FT

University of Central Lancashire
International Business Economics ....MA 12FT

Coventry University
International Business Law........ LLM 12FT 24-30PT

University of East Anglia
Development Economics........MSc 12FT 24PT
International Accounting and Financial Management .... MSc 12FT
International Business Economics ....MA 12FT

University of East London
International Law and the World Economy LLM ..LLM 12FT 24PT/PGDip 8FT 16PT/PGCert 4FT 8PT

University of Edinburgh
International Commercial Law and Practice (online distance learning) .... LLM 12FT 20 - 36PT 12 - 36DL
International Economic Law........ LLM 12FT 24PT

University of Glasgow
Intellectual Property and the Digital Economy...... LLM 12FT 24PT

University of Kent
International Economic Law (Brussels)........ LLM 12FT 24PT

Manchester Metropolitan University
Top-up LLM........ LLM 12FT 24PT

Newcastle University
International Business Law........ LLM 12FT 24PT

Northumbria University
International Commercial Law .... LLM 12FT 24DL/PGDip 9FT 18DL

Oxford Brookes University
International Economic Law........ LLM 12FT 24PT/PGDip 9FT 18PT
International Trade and Logistics ....MSc 12FT 24PT

Queen Mary, University of London
Economic Regulation........ LLM 12FT 24PT

University of Reading
Law and Economics ....MSc 12FT/PGDip 9FT/PGCert 6FT
The Economics of International Business and Finance . MSc 12FT

Robert Gordon University
International Commercial Law ....LLM 12FT/PGDip 8FT/PGCert 4FT
International Trade ....LLM 12FT/MSc 9FT/PGDip 6FT

University of Sheffield
International Finance and Economics........MSc 12FT 24PT

University of Southampton
International Financial Markets .... MSc 12FT/PGDip 9FT

University of Strathclyde
International Economic Law.......LLM 12FT 24PT/PGDip 9FT 21PT/PGCert 4FT 8PT

University of Warwick
International Economic Law........ LLM 12FT 24PT/PGDip 9FT

University of the West of England, Bristol
International Trade and Economic Law........ LLM 12FT 36PT

International economic law
Research Courses

University of Cambridge
International Law........ Diploma 11FT

International financial law
Taught Courses

School of Advanced Study, University of London
International Corporate Governance, Financial Regulation & Economic Law........ LLM 12FT 24PT

Anglia Ruskin University
International Business Law........LLM 12FT 24DL
International Finance........ MSc 12FT 24PT/PGCert 12FT 24PT/PGDip 12FT 24PT

BPP Law School
International Business Law........ LLM 12FT 24PT

Bangor University
Banking and Finance - London Centre .... MBA 12FT
Banking and Law ....MA 12FT/PGDip 9FT MBA 12FT/PGDip 9FT
International Commercial and Business LawLLM 12FT/PGDip 9FT
International Law........LLM 12FT
International Law - specialising in European Law ....LLM 12FT
Law and Banking ....LLM 12FT

University of Bath
International Money & Banking........ MSc 12FT

University of Birmingham
International Accounting and Finance .... MSc 12FT

Law and legal studies

Brunel University
INTERNATIONL FINANCIAL REGULATION AND CORPORATE LAW LLM....LLM 12FT

University of Central Lancashire
International Business Economics....MA 12FT

University of Derby
Corporate and Financial Law....LLM 12FT 36PT
International Financial Markets....MSc 12FT 36PT
LLM (in an approved area of legal scholarship)....LLM 12FT 36PT

University of Dundee
Financial Economics....PGDip 9FT
International Accounting....MSc 12FT
International Law....LLM 12FT

University of East Anglia
International Business Finance and Economics....MA 12FT

Edinburgh Napier University
International Banking and Finance....MSc 12FT

European Business School London
Global Banking & Finance....MSc 12-16FT

University of Glasgow
Corporate and Financial Law....LLM 12FT 24PT
International Business and Economic Development....MSc 12FT
International Finance....MFin 12FT

University of Kent
International Economic Law (Brussels)....LLM 12FT 24PT

University of Liverpool
International Finance and Banking Law (Online Degree)....LLM 24FT 24+PT

University of Manchester
International Financial Law....LLM 12FT

Newcastle University
International Business Law....LLM 12FT 24PT

Northumbria University
International Commercial Law....LLM 12FT 24DL/PGDip 9FT 18DL

University of Nottingham
Banking and Financial Markets in Contemporary China....MSc 12FT

University of Reading
Banking and Finance in Emerging Economies....MSc 12FT 24PT
Banking and Financial Systems in the Global Economy....MSc 12FT
Capital Markets, Regulation and Compliance....MSc 10FT 24DL
International Commercial Law....LLM 12FT
International Corporate Finance....LLM 12FT 24PT
International Financial Regulation....LLM 12FT
International Securities, Investment and Banking....MSc 12FT
Law and Economics....LLM 12FT 24PT
Law and Economics....MSc 12FT/PGDip 9FT/PGCert 6FT

Robert Gordon University
International Commercial Law....LLM 12FT/PGDip 8FT/PGCert 4FT

University of Stirling
Computing for Financial Markets....MSc 12FT/PGDip 9FT/PGCert 9FT

University of Strathclyde
European Financial Management....MSc 12FT
International Economic Law....LLM 12FT 24PT/PGDip 9FT 21PT/PGCert 4FT 8PT
International Law and Sustainable Development....LLM 12FT 24PT/PGDip 9FT 21PT/PGCert 4FT 8PT

University of Warwick
International Economic Law....LLM 12FT 24PT/PGDip 9FT

University of West London
International Banking and Finance Law....LLM 12FT 24PT

University of the West of England, Bristol
International Banking and Finance Law....LLM 12FT 36PT
International Trade and Economic Law....LLM 12FT 36PT

University of Westminster
International Banking Law....LLM 12FT 24PT

University of Wolverhampton
LLM International Commercial and Financial Law (Oil and Gas)....LLM 12FT
LLM International Corporate and Financial Law....LLM 12FT 24-36PT

University of York
Development Economics and Emerging Markets....MSc 12FT

International financial law
Research Courses

University of Cambridge
International Law....Diploma 11FT

London Metropolitan University
Dept of Law Governance and International Relations....PhD Max 60FT Max 96PT/MPhil Max 36FT Max 54PT

University of Salford
Centre for Marketing and Communication....PhD/MPhil

International law
Taught Courses

University of Aberdeen
International Law and Globalisation....LLM 12FT

Aberystwyth University
Criminology and International Justice....MSc 12FT
Democracy, Human Security and International Law....LLM 12FT
Human Rights and Humanitarian Law....LLM 36DL
International Commercial Law....LLM 36DL/PGDip 24DL LLM 12FT 24PT/PGDip 9FT 21PT
International Commercial Law and the Environment....LLM 12FT
International Law and Criminology of Armed Conflict....LLM 12FT
Rights, Gender and International Law....LLM 12FT

Anglia Ruskin University
International Business Law....LLM 12FT 24DL
International Commercial Law....LLM 12FT

BPP Law School
International Business Law....LLM 12FT 24PT

Bangor University
International Commercial and Business Law....LLM 12FT/PGDip 9FT
International Intellectual Property Law....LLM 12FT
International Law....LLM 12FT
International Law - specialising in European Law....LLM 12FT
International Law - specialising in Global Trade Law....LLM 12FT
International Law - specialising in International Criminal&International Human Rights Law....LLM 12FT
Law....PhD by taught 36FT/MPhil 24FT

University of Bedfordshire
International Commercial Law....LLM 12FT

University of Birmingham
International Law, Ethics and Politics....MA 12FT 24PT

University of Bristol
International Law....LLM 12FT 24PT
Law and Globalisation....LLM 12FT 24PT

Brunel University
International Intellectual Property Law....LLM 12FT/PGDip 9FT

University of Buckingham
International and Commercial Law....LLM 9FT/LLM 12FT

Cardiff Metropolitan University
International Business (Masters in Law)....LLM 12FT 24PT

Cardiff University
European Legal Studies....LLM 12FT
Legal and Political Aspects of International Affairs....LLM 12FT

University of Central Lancashire
International Business Law....LLM 12FT 24PT/PGDip 12FT 24PT/PGCert 12FT 24PT
Law....LLM 12FT 24PT/PGDip 12FT 24PT

University of Chester
Contemporary Legal Studies....LLM 12FT 24-36PT/PGDip 12FT 24-36PT/PGCert 12FT 12-24PT

City University London
Public International Law....LLM 12FT 24PT

Coventry University
Diplomacy, Law and Global Change....MA 12FT 24-30PT
Global Development and International Law....MSc 12FT 24-30PT
International Law....LLM 12FT 24-30PT

De Montfort University
International Business Law....LLM 12FT

University of Derby
International and Comparative Law....LLM 12FT 36PT
LLM (in an approved area of legal scholarship)....LLM 12FT 36PT
Law....PhD by taught 36-60FT 72-96PT/MPhil 24-48FT 48-72PT
Transnational Criminal Law....LLM 12FT 36PT

University of Dundee
Comparative & European Private International Law....LLM 12FT
International Business Law and Transactions....LLM 12FT
International Criminal Justice & Human Rights....LLM 12FT
International Law....LLM 12FT

University of East Anglia
International Commercial and Business Law....LLM 12FT 24PT
International Commercial and Competition Law....LLM 12FT
International Trade Law....LLM 12FT 24PT

University of East London
International Business Law LLM....LLM 12FT 24PT/PGDip 8FT 16PT/PGCert 4FT 8PT
International Law LLM....LLM 12FT 24PT/PGDip 8FT 16PT/PGCert 4FT 8PT
International Law and Criminal Justice LLM....LLM 12FT 24PT/PGDip 8FT 16PT/PGCert 4FT 8PT
Terrorism Studies MSc....MSc 12FT 24PT/PGDip 8FT 16PT/PGCert 4FT 8PT

University of Edinburgh
Global Crime, Justice and Security....MSc 12FT 24PT
International Commercial Law and Practice (online distance learning)....LLM 12FT 20 - 36PT 12 - 36DL
International Economic Law....LLM 12FT 24PT
International Law....LLM 12FT 24PT

University of Exeter
International Commercial Law....LLM 12FT 24PT
International and Comparative Public Law....LLM 12FT 24PT
Law....GradDip 9FT
Master of Laws....LLM 12FT 24PT

National University of Ireland Galway
International Human Rights Law....LLM 12FT 24PT
International and Comparative Disability Law and Policy....LLM 12FT 24PT

Glasgow Caledonian University
Global Business Law and Regulation....LLM 12FT
International Business....MSc 12FT

University of Glasgow
Human Rights & International Politics (MRes)....MRes 12FT 24PT
International Law....LLM 12FT 24PT
International Law and Security....LLM 12FT 24PT

University of Gloucestershire
LLM in International Business Law....LLM -FT -PT -DL

University of Greenwich
International and Commercial Law....LLM 12FT 24PT
International and Commercial Law....LLM 12FT 24PT

University of Hertfordshire
International Law....LLM 12FT 24PT

University of Huddersfield
International Law....LLM 12FT 24PT

University of Hull
International Business Law....LLM 12FT 24PT
International Human Rights Law....LLM 12FT 24PT
International Law....LLM 12FT 24PT
International Law and Politics....MA 12FT 24PT

Keele University
LLM in International Law....LLM 12FT 24PT

University of Kent
European Law....LLM 12FT 24PT/PGDip 12FT 24PT
International Environmental Law....PGDip 12FT 24PT/LLM 12FT 24PT
International Law with International Relations (Brussels or Canterbury)....LLM 12FT 24PT/PGDip 12FT 24PT
International Relations with International Law....MA 12FT 24PT/PGDip 12FT 24PT
Public International Law....PGDip 12FT 24PT/LLM 12FT 24PT

King's College London
Geopolitics, Territory & Security....MA 12FT 24PT
International Business Law....LLM 12FT 24-48PT
International Tax....LLM 12FT 24-48PT

Lancaster University
Diplomacy and International Law....LLM 12FT 24PT/MA 12FT 24PT
International Law....LLM 12FT 24PT
International Law and International Relations....LLM 12FT 24PT/MA 12FT 24PT

University of Law
LL.M in International Legal Practice....LLM 10FT 24 - 60DL

Leeds Metropolitan University
International Business....MA 12FT 24PT
International Business Law....LLM 12FT
LLM Law (top-up)....LLM 36PT

University of Leeds
European and International Business Law....LLM 12FT 24PT
International Business Law....LLM 12FT 24PT
International Law....LLM 12FT 24PT
International and European Human Rights Law....LLM 12FT 24PT
Security and Justice....MA 12FT 24PT

University of Leicester
Public International Law....LLM 12FT 24PT

University of Limerick
International Commerical Law....LLM 12FT

University of Liverpool
International Business Law....LLM 12FT 24PT
International Business Law (Online Degree)....LLM 24FT 24+PT
International Human Rights Law....LLM 12FT 24PT

London Metropolitan University
International Commercial Law....LLM 12FT 24-60PT
International Law....LLM 12FT 24PT

University of Manchester
International Business and Commercial Law....LLM 12FT
Public International & European Law....LLM 12FT

Middlesex University
International Business Law....LLM 12FT 24PT

Law and legal studies

Newcastle University
International Business Law........ LLM 12FT 24PT
International Legal Studies........ LLM 12FT 24PT
International Politics (Global Justice and Ethics) ... MA 12FT 24PT
International Studies........ MA 12FT 24PT

Northumbria University
International Commercial Law .... LLM 12FT 24DL/PGDip 9FT 18DL
Laws........ MA 30-36DL

Nottingham Trent University
Human Rights .... LLM 12FT 24PT
Public International Law........ LLM 12FT 24PT

University of Nottingham
International Law........ LLM 12FT 24PT
International Law and Development .... LLM 12FT 24PT
International Law, Security and Terrorism .... MA 12FT 24PT
Public International Law........ LLM 12FT 24PT

Oxford Brookes University
International Economic Law........ LLM 12FT 24PT/PGDip 9FT 18PT
International Human Rights Law........ LLM 12FT 24PT/PGDip 9FT 18PT
International Law.....LLM 12FT 24PT/PGDip 9FT 18PT/PGCert 9FT 18PT
International Law and International Relations .....MA 12FT 24PT/PGDip 8FT 20PT/PGCert 4FT 16PT
International Studies MA 12FT 24PT/PGDip 9FT 18PT/PGCert 9FT 18PT
Public International Law .... LLM 12FT 24PT/PGDip 9FT 18PT

University of Oxford
Diplomatic Studies Foreign Services Programme .... PGCert 9FT/PGDip 12FT

Queen Mary, University of London
Comparative and International Dispute Resolution .... LLB graduate entry 12FT
European Law........ LLB graduate entry 12FT
International Business Law........ LLM 12FT 24PT
Public International Law........ LLB graduate entry 12FT

Queen's University Belfast
Human Rights and Criminal Justice (Cross-Border)........ LLM 12FT
Law and International Commerce .... LLM 12FT 24PT

University of Reading
Advanced Legal Studies .... LLM 12FT 24PT
Construction Management .... MSc 12FT
Diplomacy .... MA 12FT 24-72PT/PGCert 12FT 24-72PT/PGDip 12FT 24-72PT
International Commercial Law .... LLM 12FT
International Law and World Order ...LLM 12FT 24PT/PGDip 9FT/PGCert 6FT
International Relations .... MA (res) 12FT 24-72PT 72BM
International Relations (Strategic Studies) ......MA 12FT 24-72PT/PGDip 24-72PT/PGCert 12FT 24PT
Law (M Res)........ M (Res) 12FT 24PT/PGDip 9FT/PGCert 9FT
Law and Society .... M(Res) 12FT 24PT
Project Management .... MSc 24PT

Reseau Universitaire Transmanche
International Mobility, Globalisation and the Law........ LLM 15FT

Richmond, The American International University in London
International Conflict& Security .... MA 12FT 24PT

Robert Gordon University
International Commercial Law .... LLM 12FT/PGDip 8FT/PGCert 4FT
Oil and Gas Law .... LLM 12-18FT 12-18/36DL

University of Salford
International Business...MSc 12FT 36PT/PGDip 8FT 24PT/PGCert 4FT 9PT
International Business Law and RegulationLLM 12FT/PGDip 8FT/PGCert 4FT

School of Oriental and African Studies - SOAS
Chinese Law........ MA 12FT 24PT
Dispute and Conflict Resolution........ MA 12FT 24PT
Global Energy and Climate Policy .... MSc 12FT 24PT
Human Rights Law........ MA 12FT 24PT
International Law........ MA 12FT 24PT
International and Comparative Legal Studies... MA 12FT 24-36PT
Islamic Law........ MA 12FT 24PT
Labour, Social Movements and Development .... MSc 12FT 24PT
Law........ MA 12FT 2-36PT
Law, Development and Globalisation........ MA 12FT 24PT

University of Sheffield
Commercial Law........ LLM 12FT 36PT
Comparative Governance and Public Policy .... MA 12FT 24PT
Europubhealth: European Masters Programme in Public Health .... MPH 24FT
International Commercial Law and Practice .... LLM 12FT 24PT
International Criminology .... MA 12FT
International Law........ LLM 12FT Up to 36PT
International and European Law........ LLM 12FT Up to 36PT

University of Southampton
Commercial and Corporate Law .... LLM 12FT 24PT
International Business Law........ LLM 12FT 24PT
International Law .... LLM 12FT 24PT

University of St Andrews
Evolutionary and Comparative Psychology: The Origins of Mind........ MSc 12FT 24PT
International Business .... MLitt 12FT

University of Stirling
International Business .... MSc 12FT/PGDip 9FT
International Business and Socio Economic Development .... MSc 12FT/PGDip 9FT/PGCert 6FT
International Conflict and Co-operation ....MSc 12FT 27PT/PGDip 9FT 21PT/PGCert 3FT 9PT

University of Strathclyde
International Law and Sustainable DevelopmentLLM 12FT 24PT/PGDip 9FT 21PT/PGCert 4FT 8PT

University of Surrey
LLM International Law........ LLM 12FT 24PT

University of Sussex
International Law .... LLM 12FT 24PT

Swansea University
Intellectual Property & Commercial Practice........ LLM 12FT 36PT
International Commercial Law .... LLM 12FT 36PT
International Commercial and Maritime Law .... LLM 12FT 36PT
International Maritime Law .... LLM 12FT 36PT
International Trade Law........ LLM 12FT 36PT

Teesside University
International Law .... LLM 12FT 24PT

Trinity College Dublin - the University of Dublin
International Politics .... MSc 12FT 24PT
Laws (International and Comparative Law)........ LLM 12FT
Laws (International and European Business Law) .... LLM 12FT

UCL - University College London
Countering Organised Crime and Terrorism... MSc 12FT 24-60PT/PGDip 24PT
Human Rights .... MA 12FT 24PT
Transnational Studies........ MA 12FT 24PT

University of Warwick
International Development Law and Human Rights ......LLM 12FT 24PT/PGDip 9FT

University of the West of England, Bristol
International Law........ LLM 12FT

University of Westminster
International Law........ LLM 12FT 24PT

International law
Research Courses

University of Cambridge
International Law........ Diploma 11FT
Legal Studies........ Diploma 9FT 18PT

University of East Anglia
Law........ PhD 36FT 72PT/MPhil 24FT 48PT/LLM by research 12FT 24PT

European University Institute
Comparative, European and International Legal Studies .. LLM by research 12FT

University of Exeter
Law........ PhD 48FT 84PT 84DL/MPhil 36FT 60PT 60DL/MA by research 12FT 24PT

University of Kent
International Law (Brussels).....MPhil 24FT 36PT/PhD 36FT 60PT/LLM by research 12FT 24PT
Law........ PhD 36FT 60PT/MPhil 24FT 36PT/LLM by research 12FT 24PT

University of Warwick
Law........ PhD 36FT 60PT/MPhil 24FT 36PT/LLM by research 12FT 24PT

International trade law
Taught Courses

School of Advanced Study, University of London
International Corporate Governance, Financial Regulation & Economic Law........ LLM 12FT 24PT

Anglia Ruskin University
International Business Law........ LLM 12FT 24DL

Aston University
LLM International Commercial Law........ LLM 12FT 24-60PT

BPP Law School
Business Law .... LLB graduate entry 22-34FT 46-82PT 22-82DL
International Business Law........ LLM 12FT 24PT

Bangor University
Executive LLM in Public Procurement Law and Strategy........ LLM 24BM
International Commercial and Business Law........ LLM 12FT/PGDip 9FT
International Law .... LLM 12FT
International Law - specialising in European Law .... LLM 12FT
International Law - specialising in Global Trade Law......LLM 12FT
LLM in Public Procurement Law and Strategy........ LLM 12FT
Law........ PhD by taught 36FT/MPhil 24FT
Public Procurement Law and Strategy........ LLM 12FT 24PT

Birmingham City University
International Business Law........PGCert 3FT 6PT/PGDip 6FT 18PT/LLM 12FT 24PT

University of Birmingham
International Commercial Law .... LLM 12FT 24PT

British Institute of Technology & E-commerce
International Business & Commercial Law .... PGCert 3FT/DipHE 6FT 12PT/MBA 12FT 24PT

Brunel University
International Commercial Law .... LLM 12FT/PGDip 9FT
International Trade Law........ LLM 12FT/PGDip 9FT

Bucks New University
International Commercial Law .... LLM 12FT

University of Central Lancashire
International Business Law...... LLM 12FT 24PT/PGDip 12FT 24PT/PGCert 12FT 24PT
Law........ LLM 12FT 24PT/PGDip 12FT 24PT

Coventry University
International Business Law........ LLM 12FT 24-30PT

University of Dundee
International Commercial Law .... LLM 12FT
International Commercial Law - Dual Qualifying Programme..... LLM 12FT
International Law .... LLM 12FT

Durham University
European Trade and Commercial Law........ LLM 12FT
International Trade and Commercial Law........ LLM 12FT

University of East Anglia
International Trade Law........ LLM 12FT 24PT

Edge Hill University
International Business and Commercial Law........ LLM 12FT 24PT

University of Edinburgh
Corporate Law........ LLM 12FT 24PT
International Commercial Law and Practice (online distance learning) .... LLM 12FT 20 - 36PT 12 - 36DL
International Economic Law........ LLM 12FT 24PT

University of Essex
International Business Law........ LLM 12FT 24PT
International Commercial Law .... LLM 12FT 24PT
International Trade Law........ LLM 12FT 24PT

University of Exeter
International Commercial Law .... LLM 12FT 24PT
Law........ GradDip 9FT

University of Glasgow
International Business & Entrepreneurship........ MSc 12FT

Holborn College
International Trade Law........ LLM 15-18FT

University of Kent
European Law........ LLM 12FT 24PT/PGDip 12FT 24PT
International Commercial Law .... LLM 12FT 24PT/PGDip 12FT 24PT

Lancaster University
International Business and Corporate Law........ LLM 12FT 24PT

University of Leeds
International Trade Law........ LLM 12FT 24PT

University of Leicester
International Commercial Law .... LLM 12FT 24PT

University of Liverpool
International Business Law (Online Degree)........ LLM 24FT 24+PT

University of Manchester
International Trade Transactions........ LLM 12FT

Newcastle University
International Business Law........ LLM 12FT 24PT

University of Northampton
International Commercial Law .... LLM 12FT

Northumbria University
International Environmental Law .... PGDip 9FT 18DL
International Trade Law........ LLM 12FT 24DL/PGDip 9FT 18DL

Nottingham Trent University
International Trade Law........ LLM 12FT 24PT

University of Nottingham
International Commercial Law .... LLM 12FT 24PT

Oxford Brookes University
International Economic Law........ LLM 12FT 24PT/PGDip 9FT 18PT
International Trade and Commercial Law........ LLM 12FT 24PT/PGDip 9FT 18PT
International Trade and Logistics........ MSc 12FT 24PT
WTO Law .... LLM 12FT 24PT/PGDip 9FT 18PT

University of Portsmouth
International Business Law........ LLM 12FT 36PT

Law and legal studies

Queen's University Belfast
Law and International Commerce .... LLM 12FT 24PT

University of Reading
International Corporate Finance .... LLM 12FT 24PT
International Shipping and Finance .... MSc 12FT
Law and Economics ....MSc 12FT/PGDip 9FT/PGCert 6FT

Robert Gordon University
International Commercial Law .... LLM 12FT/PGDip 8FT/PGCert 4FT
International Trade ....LLM 12FT/MSc 9FT/PGDip 6FT
Oil and Gas Law ....LLM 12-18FT 12-18/36DL

Ruskin College
International Labour and Trade Union Studies....... MA 12FT 24PT

School of Oriental and African Studies - SOAS
International and Comparative Commercial Law.. MA 12FT 24PT

University of Sheffield
International Commercial Law and Practice .... LLM 12FT 24PT

University of South Wales
International Commercial Law .... LLM 12FT 24-36PT

Southampton Solent University
International Maritime Studies - Shipping and Logistics........ MSc 12FT 24PT
International Maritime Studies: Ship and Shipping Management MSc 12FT 24PT

Staffordshire University
LLM International Trade and Commerce via Distance Larning...... LLM 16DL

University of Stirling
Corporate Social Responsibility ....LLM 12FT

Swansea University
International Commercial Law .... LLM 12FT 36PT
International Commercial and Maritime Law .... LLM 12FT 36PT
International Trade Law... LLM 12FT 36PT

Teesside University
Business Law .... LLM 12FT 24PT

University of West London
International Business and Commercial Law......... LLM 12FT 24PT
International Investment and Arbitration Law ..... LLM 12FT 24PT

University of the West of England, Bristol
International Banking and Finance Law.................. LLM 12FT 36PT
International Trade and Economic Law.................... LLM 12FT 36PT

University of Westminster
International Commercial Law .... LLM 12FT 24PT

University of Wolverhampton
International Commercial and Financial Law (Oil and Gas) ....LLM 12FT
International Corporate and Financial Law ...... LLM 12FT 24-36PT

University of York
International Corporate and Commercial Law ....LLM 12FT

International trade law
Research Courses

University of East Anglia
Business, Accountability, Regulation and Development................ PhD 36FT 72PT/MPhil 24FT 48PT
Law ....PhD 36FT 72PT/MPhil 24FT 48PT/LLM by research 12FT 24PT

University of Kent
Law..PhD 36FT 60PT/MPhil 24FT 36PT/LLM by research 12FT 24PT

Islamic law
Taught Courses

Bangor University
Banking and Finance - London Centre .... MBA 12FT

University of Bedfordshire
Islamic Banking and Finance .... MSc 12FT

Durham University
Islamic Finance...MSc 12FT MA 12FT

University of East London
Islamic Banking and Finance .... MSc 12FT 24PT/PGDip 8FT 16PT/PGCert 4FT 8PT

Islamic College for Advanced Studies
Islamic Law............. MA 12FT 24PT 24DL/PGDip 12FT 18PT 18DL/PGCert 6FT 12PT 12DL

Newcastle University
Finance and Law with Islamic Finance.............................. MSc 12FT

University of Reading
International Securities, Investment and Banking .... MSc 12FT
Investment Banking and Islamic Finance .... MSc 12FT

University of Salford
Islamic Banking and FInance..... MSc 12FT 36PT/PGDip 8FT 24PT/PGCert 4FT 9PT

School of Oriental and African Studies - SOAS
Chinese Law.. MA 12FT 24PT
Islamic Law.. MA 12FT 24PT
Islamic Societies and Cultures .... MA 12FT 24-36PT
Law, Culture and Society .... MA 12FT 24PT
Law, Development and Globalisation .... MA 12FT 24PT

University of South Wales
Islamic Banking and Finance... MSc 12FT

Islamic law
Research Courses

Durham University
Islamic Economics and Finance ....PhD 36FT

Law and legal studies
Taught Courses

University of Aberdeen
General Law .... LLM 12FT 24-36PT
Law and Sustainable Development......................... LLM 12FT 24PT

Aberystwyth University
Climate Change and Human Rights ....LLM 12FT
Criminology and Criminal Justice .... MSc 12FT
Criminology and International Justice............................. MSc 12FT
Information Technology Law..LLM 12FT
International Commercial Law and Human Rights ....LLM 12FT 24PT/PGDip 9FT 21PT
International Commercial Law and the Environmental.LLM 12FT
International Law and Criminology of Armed Conflict ..LLM 12FT
Internet Commerce and Law...LLM 12FT
Law...LLM 12FT

Anglia Ruskin University
Forensic Science...MSc 12 - 15FT 24 - 30PT

BPP Law School
LLB .... LLB graduate entry 22-34FT 46-82PT 22-82DL
LLB Upgrade........................LLB graduate entry 4FT 4-60PT 4-60DL

Bangor University
Banking and Law ....MA 12FT/PGDip 9FT MBA 12FT/PGDip 9FT
Comparative Criminology and Criminal Justice.... MA 12FT 24PT/PGDip 9FT
Criminology and Criminal Justice .... PhD by taught 36FT 72PT/MPhil 12-24FT 24-36PT/MARes 12FT 24PT
Criminology and Law...MA 12FT
Executive LLM in Public Procurement Law and Strategy.........LLM 24BM
International Commercial and Business Law................. LLM 12FT/PGDip 9FT
International Intellectual Property Law ....LLM 12FT
International Law...LLM 12FT
International Law - specialising in European Law ....LLM 12FT
International Law - specialising in Global Trade Law......LLM 12FT
International Law - specialising in International Criminal&International Human Rights Law ....LLM 12FT
Public Procurement Law and Strategy...............................LLM 12FT
Law...LLM 12FT/PGDip 9FT
PhD by taught 36FT/MPhil 24FT
Law and Banking ....LLM 12FT
Law and Criminology...LLM 12FT
Law and Management.................................... MBA 12FT/PGDip 9FT
Public Procurement Law and Strategy..................... LLM 12FT 24PT

Birkbeck, University of London
Constitutional Politics, Law and Theory .... LLM 12FT 24PT
Criminal Law and Criminal Justice...........................MA 12FT 24PT/LLM 12FT 24PT
Human Rights ....MA 12FT 24PT/LLM 12FT 24PT
Human Rights (Intensive)................LLM 12FT 24PT/MA 12FT 24PT
International Economic Law, Justice and Development................. LLM 12FT 24PT
Law (General)... LLM 12FT 24PT
Law, Democracy and Human Welfare: Global Perspectives ....LLM 12FT 24PT
Qualifying Law Degree... LLM 24FT 36PT

University of Birmingham
LLB for Graduates ....LLB graduate entry 24FT
LLM General Law.. LLM 12FT 24PT

University of Bradford
Law.. GradDip 12FT 24PT

University of Brighton
Law.. CPE 24PT/PGDip 24PT

University of Bristol
General Legal Studies... LLM 12FT 24PT
Law ....MA 24FT
Socio-Legal Studies .... MSc 12FT 24PT

Brunel University
Master of Laws ....LLM 12FT/PGDip 9FT

University of Buckingham
International and Commercial Law ....LLM 9FT/LLM 12FT PGDip 9FT/PGDip 12FT

University of Cambridge
Criminological Research ....MPhil 9FT
Criminology ....MPhil 9FT
Master of Law..LLM 9FT
Politics .... MPhil 10FT

Cardiff University
Legal Practice...LLM 12PT 12DL
Law...LLM 12FT
Social Care Law ....LPC 10FT

University of Central Lancashire
Conflict and Violence Minimisation ....PGCert 24PT
Global Security and Justice ....MA 12FT
International Relations ....MA 12FT
Law...LLM 12FT 24PT/PGDip 12FT 24PT
Professional Skills Course .... CPD 24PT

City University London
Graduate Entry LLB...LLB(Hons) 24FT
Professional Legal Practice...LLM 12FT
Professional Legal Skills..LLM 12FT

University College Cork
Criminal Justice... LLM 12FT 24PT
E-Law .... LLM 12FT 24PT
LLB .... LLB graduate entry 9FT 18PT
LLM... LLM 12FT 24PT
Law.. PGDip 12FT 24PT

Coventry University
Law... LLM 12FT 24-30PT

University of Cumbria
Leadership in Equality and Diversity...................... MBA 12FT 36PT

De Montfort University
Legal Practice .... LLM 12DL

University of Derby
LLM (in an approved area of legal scholarship)..... LLM 12FT 36PT
Law.......PhD by taught 36-60FT 72-96PT/MPhil 24-48FT 48-72PT
Legal Practice Top Up.. LLM 12FT 36PT

Dublin Institute of Technology
Law... PGDip 9FT

University of Dundee
Law (General) ....LLM 12FT
Non-Graduating Taught Postgraduate in School of Law........... PG module variableFT
Professional Legal Practice ....PGDip 9FT

Durham University
Master of Laws...LLM 12FT

University of East Anglia
Employment Law................................ LLM 12FT 24PT/PGCert 12FT
Information Technology and Intellectual Property Law.LLM 12FT 24PT
International Commercial and Business Law......... LLM 12FT 24PT
International Commercial and Competition Law ....LLM 12FT
International Public Policy, Regulation and Competition .... MA 12FT 24PT
International Trade Law... LLM 12FT 24PT
Law.. LLM 12FT 24PT
Media Law, Policy and Practice .... LLM 12FT 24PT
Public Policy and the Environment .... MA 12FT 24PT

University of East London
Law General ......LLM 12FT 24PT/PGDip 8FT 16PT/PGCert 4FT 8PT

University of Edinburgh
Commercial Law.. LLM 12FT 24PT
Comparative Public Policy ....MSc 12FT 24PT
Comparative and European Private Law .... LLM 12FT 24PT
Competition Law and Innovation.............................. LLM 12FT 24PT
Corporate Law... LLM 12FT 24PT
Criminal Law.. LLM 12FT 24PT
Criminal Law and Criminal Justice............................ LLM 12FT 24PT
Criminology and Criminal Justice ....MSc 12FT 24PT
European Law... LLM 12FT 24PT
Forensic Anthropology ....MSc 12FT 24PT
Global Crime, Justice and Security..........................MSc 12FT 24PT
Global Environment and Climate Change Law...... LLM 12FT 24PT
Information Technology Law ....LLM 12-36DL
Innovation, Technology and the Law........................ LLM 12FT 24PT
Intellectual Property Law ....LLM 12FT 24PT 12 - 36DL
International Commercial Law and Practice (online distance learning) .... LLM 12FT 20 - 36PT 12 - 36DL
International Economic Law...................................... LLM 12FT 24PT
International Law... LLM 12FT 24PT
Law.................................. LLM 12FT 24PT LLM 12FT 20 - 36PT 12 - 36DL
PG Professional Development 24DL
Law PgCert ....PGCert 4-20DL
Law and Chinese...LLM 24FT

University of Essex
Economic, Social and Cultural Rights...................... LLM 12FT 24PT
European Union Law .... LLM 12FT 24PT
International Business Law.. LLM 12FT 24PT
International Commercial Law .... LLM 12FT 24PT
International Human Rights Law ....LLM 12FT
International Human Rights and Humanitarian Law.....LLM 12FT
International Trade Law .... LLM 12FT 24PT
Internet Law...LLM 12FT

Law and legal studies

UK Human Rights and Public Law............................ LLM 12FT 24PT

University of Exeter
Applied Security Strategy...MA 12FT
European Law.. LLM 12FT 24PT
International Commercial Law .... LLM 12FT 24PT
International Human Rights Law............................ LLM 12FT 24PT
International and Comparative Public Law .... LLM 12FT 24PT
Law..GradDip 9FT
Master of Laws... LLM 12FT 24PT
Security, Conflict and Justice..................................MRes 12FT 24PT
Socio-Legal Research ....MRes 12FT 24PT

National University of Ireland Galway
Law, Technology and Goverence...LLM 12FT
Public Law.. LLM 12FT 24PT

Glasgow Caledonian University
Bachelor of Laws - Fast-track...........LLB graduate entry 24FT 39PT
Global Business Law and Regulation ....LLM 12FT

University of Glasgow
Contemporary Law & Practice .... LLM 12FT 24PT
Law.. MRes 12FT LLM 12FT 24PT
Professional Legal Practice, Diploma in ....PGDip 9FT
Socio-Legal Studies ....MRes 12FT

University of Gloucestershire
Law (Top up)..LLM 6FT 12PT

University of Hertfordshire
Law... LLM 12FT 24PT
Legal Practice .... LLM 5PT

Heythrop College
Canon Law.. MA 12FT 24PT

University of Huddersfield
International Finance with Law .... MSc 12FT
LLM .... LLM 24DL
Legal Practice Management ....MBA 12FT 36PT

University of Hull
Restorative Justice...MA 12FT 24PT 12-24DL

Keele University
International Law.. LLM 12FT 24PT
Law and Society......... LLM 12FT 24- 48PT/PGDip 12-48PT/PGCert 12-24PT

University of Kent
Combined Title (Law)..................PGDip 12FT 24PT/LLM 12FT 24PT
Criminal Justice............................LLM 12FT 24PT/PGDip 12FT 24PT
European Law..............................LLM 12FT 24PT/PGDip 12FT 24PT
Graduate Diploma in Law for Postgraduate Study........................ GradDip 12FT
International Commercial Law ....LLM 12FT 24PT/ PGDip 12FT 24PT
International Criminal Justice...PGDip 12FT 24PT/LLM 12FT 24PT
International Development........... MSc 12FT 24PT MA 12FT 24PT
International Development (Brussels).................... MA 12FT 24PT
International Economic Law (Brussels)................... LLM 12FT 24PT
International Environmental Law......PGDip 12FT 24PT/LLM 12FT 24PT
International Law with International Relations (Brussels or Canterbury)..................................LLM 12FT 24PT/PGDip 12FT 24PT
Law..PGDip 12FT 24PT/LLM 12FT 24PT
Law (Erasmus-Europe)..LLM 12FT
Medical Law and Ethics...............LLM 12FT 24PT/PGDip 12FT 24PT
Public International Law............PGDip 12FT 24PT/LLM 12FT 24PT

King's College London
Intellectual Property & Information Law.......... LLM 12FT 24-48PT
Master of Laws.. LLM 12FT 24-48PT

Kingston University
Employment Law and Mediation.................................PGCert 12PT
General Law.. LLM 12FT 24PT
Law - Common Professional Examination.......... PGDip 12FT 24PT
Law joint masters degree (with Criminology or Human Rights) .. LLM 12FT 24PT/MA 12FT 24PT
Law with Finance...LLM 12FT
Legal Studies.. MA 12-24PT

Lancaster University
Environment and the Law.................................LLM 12FT/MA 12FT
Human Rights and the Environment ....LLM 12FT/MA 12FT
International Human Rights Law.......................................LLM 12FT
Law.................... PGDip 9FT 18PT/MPhil 24FT/PhD by taught 24FT

University of Law
Bar Professional Training Course..............................BVC 12FT 24PT
Graduate Diploma in Law ....GDL 12FT 24PT 24DL
Legal Practice Course...LPC 12FT 24PT 24DL
International Legal Practice..............................LLM 10FT 24 - 60DL
Professional Legal Practice...................................... LLM 24 - 60PT

Leeds Metropolitan University
Construction Law & Dispute Resolution ....MSc 24DL
International Business Law..LLM 12FT
LLM Law (top-up)..LLM 36PT
Law...PGDip 12FT 24PT
Legal Practice Course..PGDip 12FT 24PT
Paralegal Practice .... PGDip 24PT

University of Leeds
Law ....LLB graduate entry 12FT 24PT

University of Leicester
Law .... LLM 12FT 24PT

University of Limerick
Human Rights in Criminal Justice.................... MA 12FT/LLM 12FT
International Commerical Law ....LLM 12FT
Law.. LLM 12FT 24PT

University of Lincoln
Globalising Justice .... MA 12FT 24PT
Journalism, War and International Human Rights MA 12FT 24PT

Liverpool Hope University
Criminal Justice....... MA 12FT 24PT/PGDip 12FT 24PT/PGCert 6FT 12PT

Liverpool John Moores University
European Law.. LLM 12FT 24PT
Global Crime, Justice and Security.......................... LLM 12FT 24PT
Legal Practice.. LPC 12FT 24PT
Master of Laws in Legal Practice-LPC/BPTC Conversion .... LPC 10FT 16PT

University of Liverpool
LLM I(General) .... LLM 12FT 24PT

London College UCK
Paralegal Practice .... PGDip 12FT 24PT

London Metropolitan University
Law (Common Professional Examination) CPE.PGDip 12FT 24PT/ CPE 12FT 24PT

London School of Economics and Political Science (LSE)
Law...LLM 12FT 24 or 48PT
Law, Anthropology and Society .... MSc 12FT

London South Bank University
Law Conversion Course - Legal Studies........................ PGDip 20PT
Legal Studies..CPE 12FT 24PT

Manchester Metropolitan University
LLM (Master of Laws)... LLM 12FT 24PT
Top-up LLM.. LLM 12FT 24PT

University of Manchester
Health Care Ethics ....PGCert 18DL
Health Care Law .... PGCert 9-13FT
LLM Health Care Ethics and Law.......... Master of Laws 12FT 24PT
Law...LLM 12FT
Law and Development...............................MA 12FT 24PT LLM 12FT

Middlesex University
LLM.. LLM 12FT 24PT
Law Practice, MProf..MA 24PT
Minorities, Rights and the Law................................ LLM 12FT 24PT

National University of Ireland Galway ....
LLM by research ....LLM 24FT

Newcastle University
International Business Law....................................... LLM 12FT 24PT
International Legal Studies....................................... LLM 12FT 24PT

University of Northampton
Law...LLM 12PT

Northumbria University
Advanced Legal Practice .... LLM 18DL
Bar Professional Training Course (BPTC)............. PGDip 12FT 24PT
Business Law ....PGCert 9DL
Business with Legal Management..............................MSc 12/16FT
Commercial Law..........................LLM 12FT 24DL/PGDip 9FT 18DL
Employment Law in Practice.....................LLM 24DL/PGDip 18DL/ PGCert 9DL
Graduate Diploma in Law/Common Professional Examination (GDL/CPE) ....CPE 12FT 24DL
Information Rights Law and Practice.......LLM 24DL/PGDip 18DL/ PGCert 9DL
International Commercial Law .... LLM 12FT 24DL/ PGDip 9FT 18DL
International Environmental Law......................... PGDip 9FT 18DL
International Trade Law..............LLM 12FT 24DL/PGDip 9FT 18DL
Laws .... MA 30-36DL
Legal Practice Course.. PGDip 10FT 20PT
Master of Laws... MA 30-36DL
Master of Laws Bar Practice...MA 24FT
Medical Law..LLM 24DL/PGDip 18DL
Mental Health Law..LLM 24DL/PGDip 18DL
Mental Health Law Policy and Practice....LLM 24DL/PGDip 18DL/ PGCert 9DL
Planning and Environmental Law.. LLM 24DL

Nottingham Trent University
Bar Professional Training Course..BPTC 12FT
Competition Law.. LLM 12FT 24PT
Human Rights .... LLM 12FT 24PT
Insolvency Law.. LLM 12FT 24PT
Intellectual Property Law .... LLM 12FT 24PT
International Criminal Justice.................................. LLM 12FT 24PT
International Trade Law.. LLM 12FT 24PT
Law (General LLM).. LLM 12FT 24PT
Legal Practice Course... LPC 12FT 24PT

University of Nottingham
Master of Laws... LLM 12FT 24PT
Public Procurement Law and Policy........... PGDip 21PT/LLM 24PT/ PGCert 12-21PT

The Open University
Law...LLM variableDL

Oxford Brookes University
International Economic Law........ LLM 12FT 24PT/PGDip 9FT 18PT
International Human Rights Law............................LLM 12FT 24PT/ PGDip 9FT 18PT
International Law and International Relations .....MA 12FT 24PT/ PGDip 8FT 20PT/PGCert 4FT 16PT
LLM in Legal Practice - Parts 2 and 3...................................LLM 15PT
Legal Practice (LPC) PGDip...PGDip 9FT 21PT
WTO Law .... LLM 12FT 24PT/PGDip 9FT 18PT

University of Oxford
Global Governance and Diplomacy .... MSc 12FT
Legal Research...MSt 9-12FT
Magister Juris ....MJur 9-21FT

Plymouth University
Graduate Diploma in Law ....GradDip 12FT
Legal Practice..LLM 12PT PGDip 12FT

University of Portsmouth
Law... LLM 12FT 36PT

Queen Mary, University of London
Banking and Finance Law (University of London).............MA 12FT
Certificate in Trade Mark Law and Practice............Cert 12FT 12PT
Commercial and Corporate Law ....MA 12FT
Comparative and International Dispute Resolution .... LLB graduate entry 12FT
Competition Law ....LLB graduate entry 12FT
Computer and Communications Law .... LLM 12FT 24PT
Computer and Communications Law by Distance Learning......... PGCert 12FT
Energy and Natural Resources Law.......................... LLM 12FT 24PT
Environmental Law.. LLM 12FT 24PT
European Law...LLB graduate entry 12FT
Human Rights Law......................................LLB graduate entry 12FT
Intellectual Property (MSc Management of IP).....MSc 12FT 24PT
International Shipping Law .... LLM 12FT 24PT
Law.. MA 12FT 24PT
Law and Development .... LLM 12FT 24PT
Law and Finance ....MSc 12FT 24PT
Legal Theory and History... LLM 12FT 24PT
MA by Research in Law ....MA 12FT
Media Law... LLM 12FT 24PT
Mental Health and Law ....MSc 12FT 24PT 24DL/PGCert 3FT/ PGDip 12FT 24PT
Paris LLM... LLM 12FT 24PT
Public International Law............................LLB graduate entry 12FT
Public Law (UoL)..LLB graduate entry 12FT
Tax Law.. LLM 12FT 24PT

Queen's University Belfast
Human Rights and Criminal Justice (Cross-Border).........LLM 12FT
JD: Juris Doctor ....JD 36FT
Law and Governance .... LLM 12FT 24PT
Law and International Commerce .... LLM 12FT 24PT
Legal Science...MLegSc 24FT up to 60PT
Professional Legal Studies..Diploma 12FT

University of Reading
Advanced Legal Studies .... LLM 12FT 24PT
Food Technology - Quality Assurance .... MSc 12FT
International Law and World Order ...LLM 12FT 24PT/PGDip 9FT/ PGCert 6FT
Law ....M (Res) 12FT 24PT/PGDip 9FT/PGCert 9FT
Law and Economics .... LLM 12FT 24PT
Law and Society ....M(Res) 12FT 24PT
Legal History ....MA (Res) 12FT 24PT
Oil and Gas .... LLM 12FT 24PT MSc 12FT 24PT

Richmond, The American International University in London
International Conflict& Security .... MA 12FT 24PT

Robert Gordon University
Construction Law and Arbitration .... LLM 36DL/MSc 36DL/PGDip 24DL/PGCert 12DL
Diploma in Professional Legal Practice...........................PGDip 7FT
International Commercial Law . LLM 12FT/PGDip 8FT/PGCert 4FT
Mediation ....PGCert 12FT
Oil and Gas Law ....LLM 12-18FT 12-18/36DL

School of Oriental and African Studies - SOAS
Chinese Law.. MA 12FT 24PT
Dispute and Conflict Resolution............................... MA 12FT 24PT
Human Rights Law... MA 12FT 24PT
International Law.. MA 12FT 24PT
International and Comparative Commercial Law.. MA 12FT 24PT
International and Comparative Legal Studies... MA 12FT 24-36PT
Islamic Law.. MA 12FT 24PT
Law...MA 12FT 2-36PT
Law, Culture and Society .... MA 12FT 24PT
Law, Development and Globalisation .... MA 12FT 24PT

Sheffield Hallam University
Anti-Social Behaviour Law and Strategies ....PGCert 12PT

Section sponsored by

BPP
UNIVERSITY
COLLEGE

Business and social sciences
www.prospects.ac.uk/findcourses POSTGRADUATE DIRECTORY 439

Law and legal studies

International Criminal Justice............Doctorate 36-60FT 48-84PT
International Criminal Justice............ MA 12FT 24PT
International Criminal JusticeMA 12FT 24PT/PGDip 12PT/PGCert 6PT
International Criminal Justice... MA 12FT 24PT/PGCert 6FT 12PT/PGDip 3FT 6PT
Law .... GradDip 10FT 24PT
Law and Corporate Strategy..................................... LLM 12FT 24PT

University of Sheffield
Commercial Law .... LLM 12FT 36PT
Global Justice .... MA 12FT 24PT
Global Politics and Law .... MA 12FT 24PT
Global Politics and Law (Doshisha Pathway).....................MA 24FT
International Criminology ....MA 12FT
Law....................................... MA 24FT 36PT
Law.......................................GDL 12FT
Legal Practice................................MA 6FT 10PT
Legal Practice Course.....................LPC 12FT 24PT
Stem Cell and Regenerative Medicine .... MSc 12FT

University of South Wales
Masters in Law .... LLM 12FT 24PT

Southampton Solent University
LLM Masters of Law .... LLM 12FT 24PT

University of Southampton
Commercial and Corporate Law .... LLM 12FT 24PT
European and Comparative Property Law .... LLM 12FT 24PT
Global Politics.................MSc 12FT 24PT/PGDip 9FT 21PT
Global Politics (Research) ....MSc 12FT 24PT/PGDip 9FT 21PT
LLM Finance and Law (1 yrs)......................LLM 12FT
LLM Insurance Law (1 yrs).......................LLM 12FT
Law....................................... LLM 12FT 24PT

Staffordshire University
Family Law .... LLM 18FT 36PT
GDL/CPE .... GDL 12FT 24PT/CPE 12FT 24PT
Healthcare Law and Ethics.......................... LLM 18FT 36PT
LLM International Sports Law via Distance Learning..... LLM 16DL
LLM International Trade and Commerce via Distance LarningLLM 16DL
Legal Practice Course....................................LPC 12FT 24PT
Social Welfare Law, Policy and Advice Practice .... MA 28DL

University of Stirling
Corporate Social Responsibility ....LLM 12FT
International Energy Law and Policy .. LLM 12FT 27PT/PGDip 9FT 21PT/PGCert 3FT 9PT
Law: Accelerated Graduate LLB................ LLB graduate entry 24FT

University of Strathclyde
Advocacy....................................LLM 12FT/PGDip 9FT
Construction Law .... LLM 12FT 24PT/PGDip 9FT 21PT
Criminal Justice and Penal Change........MSc 12FT 24PT/LLM 12FT 24PT/PGDip 9FT
Internet Law and Policy ..... LLM 12FT 24PT 24DL/PGDip 9FT 21PT 21DL/PGCert 9FT
LLB Graduate Entry........................LLB graduate entry 24FT
Mediation and Conflict Resolution...... MSc 12FT 24PT/PGDip 9FT 21PT/PGCert 4FT 8PT
Professional Legal Practice...................................... Diploma 9FT 24PT

University of Sunderland
Human Rights ....LLM 12FT

University of Surrey
LLM Law .... LLM 12FT 24PT
Law.......................................MA 24FT

University of Sussex
Law....................................... LLM 12FT 24PT

Swansea University
Applied Criminal Justice and Criminology............... MA 12FT 36PT
Healthcare Law and Ethics.................................MA 36PT
Intellectual Property & Commercial Practice........ LLM 12FT 36PT
International Commercial Law .... LLM 12FT 36PT
International Commercial and Maritime Law .... LLM 12FT 36PT
International Maritime Law .... LLM 12FT 36PT
International Trade Law .... LLM 12FT 36PT
Law, Graduate Diploma ....GDL 9FT
Legal Practice Course (LPC)......................... LPC 12FT 24PT

Teesside University
Business Law .... LLM 12FT 24PT
Criminal Law............................... LLM 12FT 24PT
International Law .... LLM 12FT 24PT
Law .... LLM 12FT 24PT
Law (PgDip) ....PGDip 12FT 24PT
Medical Law .... LLM 12FT 24PT

Trinity College Dublin - the University of Dublin
Conflict and Dispute Resolution Studies..................... PGDip 12PT
Laws ....LLM 12FT
Laws (International and Comparative Law).....................LLM 12FT
Laws (International and European Business Law) ....LLM 12FT

UCL - University College London
Countering Organised Crime and Terrorism... MSc 12FT 24-60PT/PGDip 24PT
Human Rights .... MA 12FT 24PT
Law....................................... LLM 12FT 24PT

Legal and Political Theory..................................... MA 12FT 24PT

University of the West of Scotland
Law.......................................Cert 12PT

University of the West of England, Bristol
Advanced Legal Practice .... LLM 36FT 48PT
Professional Skills Course (Law)..........................PSC tbcPT

University of Westminster
Legal Practice..................................LLM 24PT
Legal Practice Course.......................LPC 12FT

University of Wolverhampton
Construction Law and Dispute Resolution ..... MSc 12FT 24-36PT/PGCert 12FT 24PT
LLM .... LLM 12FT 24PT

University of York
Applied Human Rights............ MA 12FT 24PT/Diploma 12FT 24PT

Law and legal studies
Research Courses

University of Aberdeen
Law ....PhD 36FT 60PT/MPhil 24FT 42PT/LLM by research 12FT 24PT

Aberystwyth University
Law & Criminology ....LLM by research 12FT 24PT MPhil 12FT 24PT PhD 36FT 60PT

School of Advanced Study, University of London
Legislative Studies.............................PhD 36 - 60FT/MPhil 12 - 36FT

Anglia Ruskin University
Law .... PhD 36FT 72PT/MPhil 24FT 48PT
Professional Doctorate in Laws...........................DProf 36 PT

Bangor University
Criminology and Criminal Justice ....PhD 36FT 60PT/MPhil 12-24FT 24-36PT
Law.................................PhD 24-36FT/MPhil 12FT

Birkbeck, University of London
Law .... PhD 24FT 36PT/MPhil 24FT 36PT

Birmingham City University
Law .... PhD 36FT 60PT/MPhil 36FT 60PT

University of Birmingham
Law........PhD 36FT 72PT/MJur by research 12FT 24PT/MPhil 24FT 48PT

University of Bristol
Law .... PhD 36FT 72PT/MPhil 12FT 24PT

Brunel University
Brunel Law School .... PhD 36FT 60PT/MPhil 24FT 36PT

University of Buckingham
Law....... DPhil 36FT 72PT/MPhil 24FT 48PT/LLM by research 12FT 24PT

University of Cambridge
Criminology .... PhD 36FT 60PT
Law....................... PhD 36FT/MLitt by research 24FT
Legal Studies................................ Diploma 9FT 18PT

Cardiff University
Law... PhD 36FT/MPhil 24FT

University of Central Lancashire
Law...........PhD 30-48FT 66-84PT/MPhil 18-36FT 42-60PT/LLM by research 12FT 24PT

City University London
Department of Law...................................PhD/LLM by research

De Montfort University
Law (Research)MPhil 12 - 24FT 24 - 48PT/PhD 24 - 36FT 36 - 72PT

University of Dundee
Law .... LLM by research 12FT MPhil 24FT PhD 36FT

Durham University
Law..........................PhD 36FT/MPhil 24FT/MJur by research 12FT

University of East Anglia
Law.................................PhD 36FT 72PT/MPhil 24FT 48PT/LLM by research 12FT 24PT

University of Edinburgh
Law................................ PhD 36FT 72PT/LLM by research 12FT 24PT

University of Essex
Human Rights and Research MethodsPhD 36FT 72PT/MPhil 24FT 48PT
Law .... PhD 36FT 72PT/MPhil 24FT 48PT

European University Institute
Law...PhD 48FT

University of Exeter
Law.............................PhD 48FT 84PT 84DL/MPhil 36FT 60PT 60DL/MA by research 12FT 24PT
Legal Practice...........PhD 36FT 72PT 72DL/MPhil 24FT 48PT 48DL
Security, Conflict and Justice ..... MPhil 26FT 60PT/PhD 48FT 84PT

National University of Ireland Galway
College of Business, Public Policy & Law ....PhD 48FT 72PT/MPhil 24FT 48PT/MComm by research 24FT 48PT/MSc by research 24FT 48PT

College of Business, Public Policy & Law .....MSc by research 24FT 48PT
School of Law............. PhD 48FT 72PT/LLM by research 24FT 48PT

University of Glasgow
Law..PhD 36FT/LLM by research 12FT

University of Greenwich
Law ....LLM by research 12FT 24PT

University of Hull
Law................................. PhD 39FT 60PT/MPhil 27FT 36PT

Keele University
Law........................ PhD 24-48FT 48-84PT/MPhil 12-24FT 24-36PT

University of Kent
International Law (Brussels).....MPhil 24FT 36PT/PhD 36FT 60PT/LLM by research 12FT 24PT
Law...............................PhD 36FT 60PT/MPhil 24FT 36PT/LLM by research 12FT 24PT
Socio-Legal Studies ....PhD 36FT 60PT/MPhil 24FT 36PT/LLM by research 12FT 24PT

King's College London
Law Research .... PhD 36FT 72PT/MPhil 24FT 36PT

Lancaster University
Law...............PhD 36FT 48PT/MPhil 24FT 36PT/LLM by research 12FT 24PT

University of Leeds
School of Law........... PhD 36+FT/MPhil 24FT/MA by research 12FT

University of Leicester
Department of Law........... PhD 36FT 60PT 72DL/MPhil 12FT 24PT

University of Lincoln
Law .... MPhil 24-36 FT 48-72PT/PhD 24-36FT 48-72PT
Master of Laws (International Law) ...LLM by research 12FT 24PT

University of Liverpool
Law...............PhD 24-48FT 48-84PT/MPhil 12-48FT 24-72PT/LLM by research 12-36FT 24-60PT

London School of Economics and Political Science (LSE)
Law/Socio-Legal Studies..................... PhD 36-48FT/MPhil 36-48FT

Manchester Metropolitan University
Law .... LLM by research 12-24FT 24-42PT 24-42DL

University of Manchester
Law .... MPhil 12FT 24PT/PhD 36FT 72PT

Newcastle University
Law ....PhD 36FT 72PT/LLM by research 12FT 24PT/MPhil 12FT 24PT

Nottingham Trent University
Law .... MPhil 24FT 48PT/PhD 48FT 72PT

University of Nottingham
Law Research Areas.......................PhD 36FT/MPhil 24FT
School of Law Research Areas .... PhD 36FT/MPhil 24FT/MRes 24FT

Oxford Brookes University
Law .... PhD 24-60FT 36-72PT/MPhil 24-36FT 36-48PT

University of Oxford
Law.................... DPhil 48FT/MStud in Legal Research 9FT
Legal Research.. DPhil 48FT

Plymouth University
Law......................... PhD 24-48FT 36-72PT/MPhil 12-36FT 24-48PT

University of Portsmouth
Law................................ MPhil 24FT 48PT/PhD 36FT 72PT

Queen Mary, University of London
Centre for Commercial Law Studies ....PhD/LLM by research/MSc by research 12FT
Law.....................................PhD 48FT 60PT/MPhil

Robert Gordon University
Aberdeen Business School ...PhD 12FT 36PT 36DL/MSc(Res) 12FT 36PT 36DL

University of Salford
Research Opportunities at Salford Law School...Salford Centre of Legal Research 36DL

School of Advanced Study, University of London.........................
Advanced Legislative Studies ....LLM 12FT 24PT 24DL

School of Oriental and African Studies - SOAS
Law................................. PhD 36FT 72PT/MPhil 24FT 36PT

Sheffield Hallam University
Social Science and Law...PhD/MPhil

University of Sheffield
Law...............................PhD 36FT 72PT/MPhil 24FT 36PT/LLM by research 12FT 24PT

Southampton Solent University
Law Research Centre..PhD/MPhil

University of Southampton
Faculty of Law.............................. PhD 36FT 72PT/MPhil 48FT 72PT

Staffordshire University
Law .... PhD 12-18FT 12-72PT/MPhil 12-18FT 12-72PT

Law and legal studies

University of Stirling
Law - Research..PhD 36FT

University of Strathclyde
Law - Research................ PhD 33FT 48PT/MPhil 12FT 21PT

University of Sunderland
Law......................... PhD 30-48FT 42-72PT/MPhil 18-36FT 30-48PT

University of Surrey
Law......................... PhD 33-48FT 45-96PT/MPhil 21-36FT 33-72PT

University of Sussex
Law Studies Research Programme... PhD 24-48FT 36-72PT/MPhil
12-36FT 24-48PT

Swansea University
Law...................................... PhD 36FT 72PT/MPhil 24FT 48PT

UCL - University College London
Law .... PhD 36FT 60PT

University of Warwick
Law................................PhD 36FT 60PT/MPhil 24FT 36PT/
LLM by research 12FT 24PT

University of West London
Ealing Law School...................... PhD 36FT 72PT/MPhil 24FT 48PT

University of the West of England, Bristol
Faculty of Business and Law .... PhD .FT

University of Westminster
Law ....MPhil 18-36FT 30-60PT

University of Wolverhampton
School of Legal Studies ....PhD/MPhil

University of York
Law ....PhD 12FT

Litigation
Taught Courses

University of Aberdeen
Creative Writing......................... MLitt 12FT 24PT/PGDip 9FT 21PT

City University London
Civil Litigation and Dispute Resolution ....LLM 12FT

LPC
Taught Courses

University of Aberdeen
Legal Practice...DipLP 9FT 21PT

Aberystwyth University
Legal Practice Course (LPC)..............................PGDip 10FT

Anglia Ruskin University
Legal Practice..LLM 6FT 12PT
Legal Practice (LPC)................................. PGDip 12FT 24PT

BPP Law School
Legal Practice Course .... LPC 12FT 16+PT
Professional Legal Practice........................ LLM 4FT 5-72PT 4-72DL

Birmingham City University
Legal Practice Course (LPC).........................PGDip 12FT 24PT

Bournemouth University
Legal Practice Course .... LPC 12FT/LPC 24PT

Cardiff University
Legal Practice Course (LPC) .... LPC 10FT 24PT

University of Central Lancashire
Advanced Legal Practice .... LLM 12FT 24PT/PGDip 12FT
Legal Practice.. PGDip 12FT 24PT

City University London
Legal Practice Course......................................LPC 12FT

De Montfort University
Legal Practice Course (LPC) Full time ....LPC 12FT LLM 24PT

University of Derby
Legal Practice Top Up...................... LLM 12FT 36PT

University of Dundee
Professional Legal Practice ....PGDip 9FT

University of Hertfordshire
Law Society's Legal Practice Course.............................LPC 12FT

University of Huddersfield
Legal Practice Course.............................. PGDip 12FT 24PT

University of Law
LL.M Legal Practice Course ....LPC 12FT 24PT 24DL
LL.M in Professional Legal Practice............................LLM 24 - 60PT

Leeds Metropolitan University
LLM Law (top-up)...LLM 36FT
Legal Practice Course.............................. PGDip 12FT 24PT

Liverpool John Moores University
Legal Practice .... LPC 12FT 24PT
Legal Practice-LPC/BPTC Conversion .... LPC 10FT 16PT

London College UCK
Paralegal Practice .... PGDip 12FT 24PT

London Metropolitan University
Barrister to Solicitor LPC .... PGDip 12FT

Legal Practice Course...LLM 12PT
Legal Practice Course (LPC)..................PGDip 12FT 24PT/LLM 36PT

London South Bank University
Management in Civil Society (Accounting & Finance) - Blended..
MSc 30PT
Management in Civil Society (Marketing and Fundraising -
Blended)..MSc 30PT

Manchester Metropolitan University
Legal Practice (LPC)..............................PGDip 12FT 16-24PT
Top-up LLM .... LLM 12FT 24PT

Nottingham Trent University
Legal Practice Course.............................. LPC 12FT 24PT

Oxford Brookes University
LLM in Legal Practice - Parts 2 and 3...................LLM 15PT
Legal Practice (LPC) PGDip..............................PGDip 9FT 21PT

Plymouth University
Legal Practice Course...PGDip 12FT

Robert Gordon University
Diploma in Professional Legal Practice...........................PGDip 7FT

University of Sheffield
Law...............................GDL 12FT MA 24FT 36PT
Legal Practice.......................................MA 6FT 10PT
Legal Practice Course.............................. LPC 12FT 24PT

University of Southampton
Law... LLM 12FT 24PT

Staffordshire University
Legal Practice Course.............................. LPC 12FT 24PT

Swansea University
Legal Practice Course (LPC).......................... LPC 12FT 24PT

University of Ulster
Professional Legal Practice.............................PGDip 24FT

University of West London
Legal Practice (Top-up)..................................LLM 12PT
Legal Practice Course (LPC)..... PGDip 12FT 24PT/PGCert 6FT 12PT

University of the West of England, Bristol
Legal Practice Course (LPC)...................................PGDip 11FT 22PT

University of Wolverhampton
Legal Practice Course.............................. LPC 12FT 24PT

LPC
Research Courses

University of Oxford
Law .... DPhil 48FT/MStud in Legal Research 9FT

University of Salford
Research Opportunities at Salford Law School...Salford Centre of
Legal Research 36DL

University of Stirling
Law - Research...PhD 36FT

Maritime law
Taught Courses

University of Bristol
Maritime Law .... LLM 12FT 24PT

Cardiff University
Marine Policy .... MSc 12FT 24PT

University of Greenwich
Maritime Policy .... MA 12FT 24PT

University of Hertfordshire
Commercial and Maritime Law .... LLM 12FT 24PT
Maritime Law .... LLM 12FT 24PT

University of Liverpool
Marine Planning and Management .... MSc 12FT 24PT

London Metropolitan University
International Trade, Transport and Maritime Law...........LLM 12FT
24-60PT
Maritime Law ....PGDip 16DL
Maritime Law (Top-Up)................................LLM variousFT

University of Nottingham
Maritime Law .... LLM 12FT 24-48PT

University of Reading
International Shipping and Finance .... MSc 12FT

Southampton Solent University
International Maritime Studies - Shipping and Logistics........ MSc
12FT 24PT
International Maritime Studies: Ship and Shipping Management
MSc 12FT 24PT
Shipping Operations..................................MSc 12-24DL

University of Stirling
Environmental Policy and Governance...........LLM 12FT/MSc 12FT

Swansea University
International Commercial and Maritime Law .... LLM 12FT 36PT
International Maritime Law .... LLM 12FT 36PT

Media law
Taught Courses

University of Brighton
Media Ethics .... MA 12FT 24PT/PGDip 12FT 24PT/
PGCert 12FT 24PT

University of Chester
Developing RPL Policy and Practice (Work Based and Integrative
Studies) ....MA 24-72PT/PGDip 24-60PT/PGCert 12-36PT
Leadership Development (Work Based and Integrative Studies)..
MA 24-72PT/MSc 24-72PT/PGDip 24-60PT/PGCert 12-36PT
Learning and Development (Work Based and Integrative
Studies) ....MA 24-72PT/MSc 24-72PT/PGDip 24-60PT/PGCert
12-36PT

University of Derby
International Protection of Human Rights and
Personal Freedom.. LLM 12FT 24PT
LLM (in an approved area of legal scholarship) ..... LLM 12FT 36PT

University of East Anglia
Media Law, Policy and Practice .... LLM 12FT 24PT
Media and International Development.................... MA 12FT 24PT

University of Greenwich
Science (Open)......................................MSc 12FT 24-36PT

Leeds Metropolitan University
Information & Technology.......MSc 12FT 24PT/PGDip 12FT 24PT/
PGCert 4FT 24PT
LLM Law (top-up)...LLM 36PT

School of Oriental and African Studies - SOAS
Law ....MA 12FT 2-36PT

University of Sheffield
Broadcast Journalism...MA 12FT/PGDip 9FT

Swansea University
Communication, Media Practice and Public Relations ....MA 12FT
24-36PT

University of Westminster
Entertainment Law.. LLM 12FT 24PT

Medical law
Taught Courses

University of Bradford
Healthcare Law ....LLM 24PT/PGDip 24PT/PGCert 12PT

University of Brighton
Medical Ethics ....MA 12FT 24PT/PGDip 12FT 24PT/PGCert 12FT
24PT

University of Bristol
Health Care Ethics and Law ....MSc 24PT/Diploma 24PT/
Cert 24PT

Cardiff University
Legal Aspects of Medical Practice .... LLM 12FT 24PT

University of Central Lancashire
Forensic and Legal Medicine........LLM 36PT/MA 36PT/PGDip 24PT
Medical Law and Bioethics ....LLM 12FT 24PT/PGDip 12FT 24PT

University of Chester
Contemporary Legal Studies ....LLM 12FT 24-36PT/PGDip 12FT
24-36PT/PGCert 12FT 12-24PT

Cranfield University
Medical Technology Regulatory Affairs ....MSc 24-60PT/PGDip
24-48PT/PGCert 36PT

De Montfort University
Medical Law and Ethics........................... PGDip 15DL/LLM 15-27DL

University of Dundee
Healthcare Law and Ethics .... LLM 36DL

University of Edinburgh
Medical Law and Ethics (Online Distance Learning) ....LLM 12FT
20 - 36PT 20 - 36DL

University of Glasgow
Animal Welfare Science, Ethics & Law.......... MSc 12FT/PGDip 9FT
Medical Law.. MML 36DL

Keele University
Medical Ethics and Law.... MA 12FT 24PT 24DL/PGDip 12PT 12DL

University of Kent
Forensic Science .... MSc 12FT
Medical Humanities .... MA 12FT 24PT
Medical Law and Ethics...............LLM 12FT 24PT/PGDip 12FT 24PT

King's College London
Medical Ethics & Law .... MA 12FT 24PT
Medical Humanities ....MSc 12FT 24PT

Lancaster University
Bioethics and Medical Law .... MA 12FT 24PT

Leeds Metropolitan University
Health Care Studies ....MA 24PT

University of Liverpool
Law, Medicine and Healthcare.................................. LLM 12FT 24PT

Law and legal studies

University of Manchester
Health Care Ethics and Law ...MA 12FT 24PT 24DL/Diploma 12FT 24PT 24DL/MSc 12FT

Middlesex University
Ethics and Law in Healthcare Practice .... MA 24PT/PGDip 18PT/ PGCert 12PT

Northumbria University
Medical Law...LLM 24DL/PGDip 18DL
Mental Health Law Policy and Practice....LLM 24DL/PGDip 18DL/ PGCert 9DL

Nottingham Trent University
Health Law .... LLM 12FT 24PT

Queen Mary, University of London
Medical Law .... LLM 12FT 24PT

University of Salford
Health Care Law.........................LLM 27DL/MA 27DL/PGDip 20DL/ PGCert 12DL

Staffordshire University
Healthcare Law and Ethics.............................. LLM 18FT 36PT

Swansea University
Healthcare Law and Ethics...MA 36PT

Teesside University
Medical Law .... LLM 12FT 24PT

University of Winchester
Medical Law and Ethics ....LLM 24PT

Medical law
Research Courses

Barts and the London School of Medicine and Dentistry
Department of Human Science and Medical Ethics...PhD/MPhil/ MA by research

Keele University
Medical Ethics .... MRes 36PT 36DL/DMedEth 48-84PT 48-84DL

University of Manchester
Bioethics and Medical Jurisprudence...................... PhD 36FT 72PT

Medical negligence
Taught Courses

Cardiff University
Legal Aspects of Medical Practice .... LLM 12FT 24PT

University of Edinburgh
Medical Law and Ethics (Online Distance Learning) ....LLM 12FT 20 - 36PT 20 - 36DL

Teesside University
Medical Law .... LLM 12FT 24PT

Mental health law
Taught Courses

University of Bradford
Mental Health Practice .... MA 12FT/PGDip 12FT
Mental Health Studies ....MA 12FT 24PT/PGCert 9PT/PGDip 9FT 21PT

University of Cumbria
Mental Health Practice: Approved Medical Health Practitioner... MA min 24FT max 60PT/PGCert 12FT/PGDip 12FT

University of Dundee
Healthcare Law and Ethics (LLM by distance learning) . LLM 36DL

Edge Hill University
Mental Health Law and Ethics ....PGCert 12FT 36PT

Leeds Metropolitan University
Mental Health Practice .... MSc 24PT
Mental Health Studies........................... PGCert 24PT/PGDip 24PT

Northumbria University
Mental Health Law......................................LLM 24DL/PGDip 18DL
Planning and Environmental Law .... LLM 24DL

Nottingham Trent University
Health Law .... LLM 12FT 24PT

Queen Mary, University of London
Mental Health: Psychological Therapies D/L option ...... MSc 12FT 24PT
Mental Health: Transcultural Mental Healthcare. MSc 12FT 24PT 24DL

Staffordshire University
Healthcare Law and Ethics.............................. LLM 18FT 36PT

Teesside University
Medical Law.. LLM 12FT 24PT

Trinity College Dublin - the University of Dublin
Dementia...MSc 12FT 24PT

Personal injury
Taught Courses

University of Chester
Contemporary Legal Studies ....LLM 12FT 24-36PT/PGDip 12FT 24-36PT/PGCert 12FT 12-24PT

Leeds Metropolitan University
Sport and Exercise Nutrition ...MSc 12FT 24PT/PGDip 12FT 24PT/ PGCert 4FT 12PT
Sport and Exercise Physiology..MSc 12FT 24PT/PGCert 4FT 12PT/ PGDip 12FT 24PT

Planning law
Taught Courses

Cardiff University
Planning Practice..PGCert 8-36PT
Planning Practice and Research.................................. MSc 12FT 24PT

University of Dundee
Spatial Planning with Marine Spatial Planning .... MSc 12FT

Leeds Metropolitan University
Town and Regional Planning.. MA 12FT 24PT
UK Planning Law & Practice ....Cert 36 (max)DL

Plymouth University
Planning... MSc 12FT

University of Reading
Corporate Real Estate ....MSc 24-72PT
Development Planning .... MSc 12FT 24PT/PGDip 12FT 24PT
Development Planning Research ......MSc 12FT 24PT/PGDip 12FT 24PT
International Planning and Sustainable Urban Management ..... MSc 12FT/PGCert 6FT/PGDip 9FT

University of Salford
Real Estate Development ....MSc 12FT 28DL/PGDip 8FT 20DL

University of Sheffield
Planning and Development..MA 12FT
Town and Regional Planning..MA 12FT

Planning law
Research Courses

University of Essex
Survey Methodology .... PhD 36FT 72PT/MPhil 24FT 48PT

Professional negligence
Taught Courses

Leeds Metropolitan University
Community Specialist Practitioner - Practice Nursing..MSc 24PT/ PGDip 24PT

Professional Skills Course
Taught Courses

University of Central Lancashire
Professional Skills Course.....................................CPD 24PT

Glasgow Caledonian University
Master of Research ....MRes 12FT

University of Kent
Advanced Child Protection..MA 24PT
Analysis and Intervention in Intellectual and Development Disabilities.....................................MSc 12FT 24PT/PGDip 12FT 24PT
Independent/Supplementary Prescribing .... PGCert 8PT
Independent/Supplementary Prescribing for Nurses (Level H) (Short Course Programme) ....PGCert 8PT/PGDip 8PT/MSc 8PT
Primary Dental Care..MSc 36PT
Primary Dental Care for Foundation Dentists............. PGCert 12FT
Professional Practice...MA 24PT/MSc 24PT
Strategic Leadership and Medical Education ......PGCert 12 - 24PT

Manchester Metropolitan University
Association of Chartered Certified Accountants Professional Qualification ....ACCA FlexiblePT

Swansea University
Enhanced Professional Practice (EPP)........MSc 36PT/PGDip 24PT/ PGCert 12PT

University of Wales Trinity Saint David
Arfer Proffesiynol........MA FlexibleFT FlexiblePT/PGDip FlexibleFT FlexiblePT/PGCert FlexibleFT FlexiblePT

University of the West of Scotland
Health Studies ....MSc 36-60PT/PGDip 24PT
Nursing ....MSc 36-48PT/PGDip 24-36PT/PGCert 12-24PT

University of the West of England, Bristol
Professional Skills Course (Law)................................PSC tbcPT

Property law
Taught Courses

Northumbria University
Graduate Diploma in Law/Common Professional Examination (GDL/CPE) ....CPE 12FT 24DL
Housing Policy and Management.............................MA 12FT
Housing Policy and Management with Professional Practice .... MA 36PT/PGDip 24PT
Laws ....MA 30-36DL

Queen Mary, University of London
Intellectual Property Law .... LLM 12FT 24PT

University of Reading
Corporate Real Estate ....MSc 24-72PT
Development Planning .... MSc 12FT 24PT/PGDip 12FT 24PT
Development Planning Research ......MSc 12FT 24PT/PGDip 12FT 24PT
Intelligent Buildings: Design, Construction and Management .... MSc 24PT
International Planning and Sustainable Urban Management ..... MSc 12FT/PGCert 6FT/PGDip 9FT
Real Estate ....MSc 12FT MSc 24-72PT
Real Estate Finance .... MSc 12FT
Rural Land and Business Management .... MSc 12FT

University of Salford
Real Estate Development ....MSc 12FT 28DL/PGDip 8FT 20DL
Real Estate and Property Management.....MSc 12FT 28DL/PGDip 8FT 20DL

University of Southampton
European and Comparative Property Law .... LLM 12FT 24PT

Property law
Research Courses

University of Aberdeen
Real Estate..PhD 36FT/MPhil 24FT

Sheffield Hallam University
Facilities and Property Management......................DBA 48PT 48DL

Scots law
Taught Courses

University of Aberdeen
Art in Scotland..MLitt 12FT 24PT

School of Advanced Study, University of London
Advanced Legislative Studies ....LLM 12FT 24PT 24DL

University of Glasgow
Contemporary Law & Practice .... LLM 12FT 24PT

Sports law
Taught Courses

De Montfort University
Sports Law and Practice.......................... PGDip 15DL/LLM 15-27DL

Leeds Metropolitan University
Leisure, Sport & Culture ....MA 12FT 24PT
Outdoor & Adventurous Activities ....MSc 12FT 24PT
Sport Coaching ....MSc 12FT 24PT
Sport, Law & Society..MA 12FT 24PT

Manchester Metropolitan University
Exercise and Sport...MSc 12FT 24-36PT
Exercise and Sport - Biomechanics ....MS 12FT 24-36PT
Exercise and Sport - Coaching Studies...............MSc 12FT 24-36PT
Exercise and Sport - Physiology ....MSc 12FT 24-36PT
Exercise and Sport - Sport Development ....MSc 12FT 24-36PT
Exercise and Sport -Psychology ....MSc 12FT 24-36PT

Nottingham Trent University
Sports Law .... LLM 12FT 24PT

Staffordshire University
LLM International Sports Law via Distance Learning ..... LLM 16DL

Sports law
Research Courses

University of Cumbria
Sports Science; Sports History/Sociology; Outdoor Studies .... MPhil 36FT 60PT 60DL/PhD 48FT 72PT 72DL

Taxation law
Taught Courses

School of Advanced Study, University of London
Taxation (Law, Administration and Practice)........... MA 12FT 24PT

Bangor University
International Commercial and Business Law................. LLM 12FT/ PGDip 9FT

University of Dundee
Energy Law and Policy ....LLM 24-60DL
Petroleum Taxation and Finance ....LLM 12FT

King's College London
International Tax ....LLM 12FT 24-48PT

Manchester Metropolitan University
Top-up LLM .... LLM 12FT 24PT

University of Reading
Rural Land and Business Management .... MSc 12FT

Tort law
Taught Courses

North East Surrey College of Technology
Acoustics and Noise Control...............................IOA Diploma 9PT
Applied Acoustics and Noise Control ....MSc 9PT

Law and legal studies

Northumbria University
Graduate Diploma in Law/Common Professional Examination
(GDL/CPE) ....CPE 12FT 24DL
Laws ....MA 30-36DL

School of Oriental and African Studies - SOAS
Law ....MA 12FT 2-36PT

Wills and probate
Research Courses

University of Greenwich
Pharmacy - Research...........................MPhil 36-72FT/PhD 36-72FT

Section sponsored by

BPP
UNIVERSITY
COLLEGE

Business and social sciences
www.prospects.ac.uk/findcourses POSTGRADUATE DIRECTORY 443

Marketing and advertising studies

Branding
Taught Courses

Bangor University
Consumer Psychology with Business............ MSc 12FT/PGDip 9FT MA 12FT
Marketing..MBA 12FT/PGDip 9FT

Bath Spa University
Design: Brand Development ....MA 12FT 24PT/PGDip 9FT 18PT/PGCert 4FT 9PT

University of Brighton
Marketing......MSc see siteFT/PGDip see siteFT/PGCert see siteFT

Brunel University
Applied Corporate Brand Management .... MSc 12FT
Design Strategy and Innovation...MA 12FT
Design and Branding Strategy ....MA 12FT
Management ....MSc 12FT
Marketing ....MSc 12FT

Cardiff Metropolitan University
Marketing...MSc 12FT 24PT

University of Central Lancashire
Chartered Institute of Marketing (Stage 1)..... CIM Diploma 12PT
Chartered Institute of Marketing (Stage 2)..... CIM Diploma 12PT
Chartered Institute of Marketing .... CIM AdvCert 12PT CIM Diploma 12PT
Fashion Brand Management .... MBA 12FT 30PT/PGDip 12FT 30PT/PGCert 12FT 30PT
Marketing Management .... MSc 12FT
Marketing and PR ....MA 12FT
Strategic Marketing Leadership (Advanced Entry) ....MA 12PT

Coventry University
Marketing...MBA 12FT 24-30PT
Strategic Marketing...................................MSc 12FT 24-30PT

University for the Creative Arts
Fashion: Promotion, Marketing and Branding...................MA 12FT
Graphic Design and Communication....................... MA 12FT 24PT
Innovation & Brand Management...MA 12FT

University of Cumbria
International Marketing Management ...MSc 12FT/PGCert 12FT/PGDip 12FT

University of Derby
Marketing Management .... MSc 12FT

University of Dundee
Design for Services ....MDes 12FT
Product Design ....MSc 12FT

ESCP Europe Business School
Master in Marketing and Creativity ...... Master in Marketing and Creativity 15FT

University of East Anglia
Brand Leadership.. MSc 12FT
Marketing.. MSc 12FT
Marketing and Management.. MSc 12FT

University of East London
Luxury Brand Management ...... MSc 12FT 24PT/PGDip 8FT 16PT/PGCert 4FT 8PT

European Business School London
Luxury Brand Management................................MA 12 - 16FT

GCU London
Brand Management .... MSc 12FT
Digital Marketing .... MSc 12FT
International Marketing .... MSc 12FT
Luxury Brand Marketing (London) .... MBA 12FT/MBA 12-15FT
Luxury Retail Management .... MSc 12FT

Glasgow Caledonian University
Digital Marketing .... MSc 12FT
Marketing.. MSc 12FT/PGDip 9FT

University of Glasgow
International Management & Design Innovation.......... MSc 12FT
International Strategic Marketing .... MSc 12FT

Goldsmiths, University of London
Brands, Communication and Culture...................... MA 12FT 24PT
Innovation in Practice...MA 12FT
Management of Innovation .... MSc 12FT

Heriot-Watt University
International Marketing..............PGDip 9FT 21PT/MSc 12FT 24PT

University of Huddersfield
International Design Marketing & Communication ....MA 12/16FT
International Fashion Management .... MA 12/16FT
International Fashion Promotion .... MA 12/16FT

Kingston University
Marketing & Brand Management ....MA 12FT

Leeds Metropolitan University
Chartered Institute of Marketing (CIM)....................Diploma 12PT
Chartered Institute of Marketing (CIM)....Professional Certificate 12PT
Marketing.. MSc 12FT

Liverpool Hope University
Marketing Management ....MSc 12FT 24PT

London Metropolitan University
Marketing... MA 12FT 24PT

Manchester Metropolitan University
Marketing Communications ....MSc 12FT 30PT/PGDip 24PT/PGCert 12PT

Northumbria University
Multidisciplinary Design Innovation .... MA 12FT/MSc 12FT

Nottingham Trent University
Branding and Identity Design .... MA 12FT/PGDip 7FT/PGCert 4FT
Fashion Marketing & Communication ....MA 12FT
Marketing.. MSc 12FT

Oxford Brookes University
Marketing ....MSc 12FT 24PT

Plymouth University
Design .... MA 12FT 24PT
Marketing Management and Strategy .... MSc 12FT

Ravensbourne
Luxury Brand Management....................................MDes 12FT 24PT

University of Roehampton
Marketing...MSc 12FT 24PT
International Management with Marketing ....PGDip 9FT 24PT

Royal Holloway, University of London
Marketing...MA 12FT

University of Salford
Marketing.......... MSc 12FT 36PT/PGDip 8FT 24PT/PGCert 4FT 9PT

Sheffield Hallam University
Global Strategic Marketing..MSc 12FT

University of Sheffield
Marketing Management Practice ....MSc 12FT

Southampton Solent University
Marketing Management .... MA 12FT 32PT

University of Southampton
Marketing Management .... MSc 12FT/PGDip 9FT

University of St Andrews
Marketing...MLitt 12FT

University of Stirling
Marketing.. MSc 12FT/PGDip 9FT

University of Strathclyde
Marketing....................MSc 12FT 24PT/PGDip 9FT 18PT

Swansea University
Marketing .... MSc 12FT

Teesside University
Marketing Management ....MSc 12FT 24PT

University of Westminster
Marketing Management ....MA 12FT

Branding
Research Courses

Birmingham City University
Marketing.............................. MPhil 24FT 36PT/PhD 24FT 36PT

Cardiff University
Marketing and Strategy............................ PhD 36-48FT possiblePT

University of Kent
Marketing.................MA by research 12FT 24PT/MPhil 24FT 36PT/PhD 36FT 60PT/New Route PhD 48FT

Newcastle University
Marketing.................................... MPhil 12FT 24PT/PhD 36FT 72PT

Campaigning
Taught Courses

Bucks New University
Advertising..MA 12FT

University of Central Lancashire
Digital Marketing (CAM)..Diploma 7.5DL

City University London
Grantmaking, Philanthropy and Social Investment ..PGDip 12PT/MSc 18PT/PGCert 6PT

Falmouth University
Creative Advertising ....MA 12FT

GCU London
Brand Management .... MSc 12FT
International Marketing.. MSc 12FT
Luxury Brand Marketing (London) .... MBA 12FT/MBA 12-15FT
Luxury Retail Management .... MSc 12FT

Glasgow Caledonian University
Digital Marketing .... MSc 12FT

Kingston University
International Political Communication, Advocacy and Campaigning.. MSc 12FT 24PT
Marketing Communications and Advertising...................MA 12FT

Political Communication, Advocacy and Campaigning...................
MSc 12FT 24PT

Nottingham Trent University
Campaigning ....MRes 12FT

Plymouth University
Marketing Management and Strategy .... MSc 12FT

University of Roehampton
Creative and Professional Writing............................ MA 12FT 24PT

Swansea University
Marketing.. MSc 12FT

West Herts College
Copywriting and Art Direction...........................PGDip 10FT

Campaigning
Research Courses

Nottingham Trent University
Campaigning...MRes 12FT

West Herts College
Advertising.. PGDip by research 8FT

E-marketing
Taught Courses

BPP Business School
Professional Marketing......................................MSc 12FT 24+PT

Bangor University
Marketing.. MBA 12FT/PGDip 9FT

Bournemouth University
Management with Marketing ....MSc 12-15FT

Bucks New University
Marketing Communications .... MA 12FT 24PT

Cardiff Metropolitan University
Marketing...MSc 12FT 24PT

University of Central Lancashire
Chartered Institute of Marketing (Stage 1)..... CIM Diploma 12PT
Chartered Institute of Marketing (Stage 2)..... CIM Diploma 12PT
Chartered Institute of Marketing .... CIM AdvCert 12PT CIM Diploma 12PT
Digital Marketing (CAM)...Diploma 7.5DL
Marketing and PR ....MA 12FT

Coventry University
Marketing...MBA 12FT 24-30PT

University of Cumbria
International Marketing Management ...MSc 12FT/PGCert 12FT/PGDip 12FT

University of Derby
Marketing Management .... MSc 12FT
Marketing and Media... MSc 12FT

ESCP Europe Business School
Master in Marketing and Creativity ...... Master in Marketing and Creativity 15FT

University of East Anglia
Brand Leadership... MSc 12FT
Marketing.. MSc 12FT
Marketing and Management.. MSc 12FT

GCU London
Brand Management .... MSc 12FT
Digital Marketing .... MSc 12FT
Luxury Brand Marketing (London) .... MBA 12FT/MBA 12-15FT
Luxury Retail Management .... MSc 12FT

Glasgow Caledonian University
Digital Marketing .... MSc 12FT
Marketing.. MSc 12FT/PGDip 9FT

University of Kent
Management (Marketing) .... MSc 12FT

Leeds Metropolitan University
Chartered Institute of Marketing (CIM)....................Diploma 12PT
Chartered Institute of Marketing (CIM)....Professional Certificate 12PT
Marketing.. MSc 12FT

London Metropolitan University
Marketing... MA 12FT 24PT

London South Bank University
Digital Marketing (Top-up 2 Units + Dissertation) ....
MSc 10FT 10PT
Digital Marketing (Top-up 3 Units + Dissertation) ....
MSc 10FT 10PT
Digital Marketing (Top-up 3 Units + Dissertation) - Distance
Learning... MSc 18FT
Marketing Management (Top-up 3 Units + Dissertation) ...... MSc 10FT 10PT

Loughborough University
Digital Media and Society..MA 12FT

Manchester Metropolitan University
Digital Marketing Communications..........MSc 30PT/PGDip 24PT/PGCert 12PT

Marketing and advertising studies

Top-up LLM .... LLM 12FT 24PT

Middlesex University
E-Marketing and Social Media .... MA 12FT 24PT

Newcastle University
E-Business .... MSc 12FT
E-Business (E-Marketing) .... MSc 12FT

Northumbria University
Mass Communication Management .... MSc 12FT 24PT
Strategic Marketing .... MSc 12FT

Nottingham Trent University
Marketing .... MSc 12FT

Oxford Brookes University
Marketing .... MSc 12FT 24PT

Plymouth University
Marketing Management and Strategy .... MSc 12FT

University of Portsmouth
Digital Marketing .... MA 12FT

University of Roehampton
Marketing .... MSc 12FT 24PT

Royal Holloway, University of London
Marketing .... MA 12FT

University of Salford
Marketing .... MSc 12FT 36PT/PGDip 8FT 24PT/PGCert 4FT 9PT
Procurement, Logistics and Supply Chain Management .... MSc 12FT 36PT/PGDip 8FT 24PT/PGCert 4FT 9PT

University of Sheffield
Marketing Management Practice .... MSc 12FT

University of South Wales
Digital Marketing .... MA 15FT 24PT

Southampton Solent University
Digital Marketing and Media .... MA 12FT
Marketing Management .... MA 12FT 32PT

University of Southampton
Digital Marketing .... MSc 12FT
Marketing Management .... MSc 12FT/PGDip 9FT

University of St Andrews
Marketing .... MLitt 12FT

University of Stirling
Marketing .... MSc 12FT/PGDip 9FT

University of Strathclyde
Marketing .... MSc 12FT 24PT/PGDip 9FT 18PT

Teesside University
Marketing Management .... MSc 12FT 24PT

University of the Highlands and Islands
Enterprise and eMarketing .... PGCert 12-24PT

E-marketing
Research Courses

Birmingham City University
Marketing .... MPhil 24FT 36PT/PhD 24FT 36PT

University of Kent
Marketing ....MA by research 12FT 24PT/MPhil 24FT 36PT/ PhD 36FT 60PT/New Route PhD 48FT

Newcastle University
Marketing .... MPhil 12FT 24PT/PhD 36FT 72PT

Event management studies
Taught Courses

University of Bedfordshire
Tourism and Event Management MSc 12-15FT 24PT/PGDip 12FT/ PGCert 12FT

Birkbeck, University of London
Creative Industries (Arts and Media)...................... MA 12FT 24PT
Sport Governance............................... PGCert 12PT 12DL
Sport Management ...... PGCert 12PT 12DL/MSc 12FT 24PT/MRes 12FT 24PT
Sport Management and Marketing.................... MSc 12FT 24PT
Sport Management and the Business of Football MSc 12FT 24PT/ MRes 12FT 24PT
Sport Marketing .... MSc 12FT 24PT

Birmingham City University
Events and Exhibition Management .... MA 12FT 24PT

Bournemouth University
Events Management .... MSc 12-15FT 24PT
Events Marketing........................... MSc 12-15FT 24PT

University of Brighton
International Event Management .... MSc 12FT 24-72PT/PGCert 12FT 24-72PT/PGDip 12FT 24-72PT

University of Central Lancashire
International Festivals and Event Management..MSc 12FT 24PT/ PGDip 12FT 24PT
International Festivals and Tourism Management........ MSc 12FT 24PT/PGDip 12FT 24PT

International Heritage and Event Management..MSc 12FT 24PT/ PGDip 12FT 24PT
International Hospitality and Event Management .... MSc 12FT 24PT/PGDip 12FT 24PT
Internship in International Tourism, Hospitality and Event Management............................ MA 12FT 24PT
Management Studies............................ DMS 18PT
Sport Business Management .... MSc 12FT up to 36PT
Sports Marketing and Business Management ..... MSc 12FT up to 36PT

University of Chester
Public Services Management (Work Based and Integrative Studies) .... MA 24-72PT/PGDip 24-60PT/PGCert 12-36PT

University of Cumbria
Events Leadership and Management....... MBA 12FT 36PT/PGCert 12FT 36PT/PGDip 12FT 36PT
Management Studies....................... GradDip 24PT/GradCert 12PT

De Montfort University
Cultural Events Management ....MA 12FT 24PT/MSc 12FT 24PT

University of Derby
Events Management .... MA 12FT 24PT

University of East Anglia
Marketing and Management................................ MSc 12FT

Edinburgh Napier University
International Event and Festival Management..... MSc 12FT 24PT
International Marketing with Tourism & Events .... MSc 12FT
Marketing with Festival and Event Management .... MSc 12FT

University of Exeter
International Tourism Management................................ MSc 12FT

Fitzwilliam Institute Group
Event Management Postgraduate Diploma with Public Relations.............................. Postgraduate Diploma 6FT
Event Management with Public Relations, Eco Events and Wedding Planning................................PGDip 6FT
Event Management .... PGDip 6DL
Public Relations .... PGDip 6DL

Glasgow Caledonian University
International Events Management......................MSc 12FT 24DL
Management..............MSc 12FT FlexiblePT/PGDip 9FT FlexiblePT/ PGCert 6FT FlexiblePT

University of Greenwich
Events Management .... MA 12FT 24PT
Events Management ....MA 12FT

Leeds Metropolitan University
Events Management - Distant Learning MSc 24PT/PGCert 12PT/ PGDip 24PT
Information & Technology.......MSc 12FT 24PT/PGDip 12FT 24PT/ PGCert 4FT 24PT
International Events Management....MSc 12FT 24PT/PGDip 12FT 24PT/PGCert unknownFT 12PT
Sport, Law & Society .... MA 12FT 24PT
Sports Event Management.... MSc 12FT 24PT/PGCert 12FT 24PT/ PGDip 12FT 24PT

London Metropolitan University
Events Marketing Management................................ MA 12FT 24PT

Manchester Metropolitan University
International Events Management....................MSc 12FT 24-60PT

Northumbria University
Arts and Media Management.......MA 12/16FT 24/28PT 24/28DL
Cultural Event Management.........MA 12/18FT 24/28PT 24/28DL
International Sport Management.................. MSc 12FT 24PT
Sport Marketing.................................. MSc 12FT 24PT

Richmond, The American International University in London
Event Management .... MSc 12FT 24PT

University of Roehampton
Post Graduate Diploma- Audiovisual Translation .... PGDip 9FT 24PT

Royal Welsh College of Music and Drama
Stage & Event Management .... MA 12FT 12PT

University of Salford
International Events Management......MSc 12FT 36PT/PGDip 8FT 24PT/PGCert 4FT 9PT
Management.... MSc 12FT 36PT/PGDip 8FT 24PT/PGCert 4FT 9PT

Sheffield Hallam University
International Events and Conference Management...... MSc 12FT

University of Sheffield
Management.. MSc 12FT
Management (Creative and Cultural Industries) .... MSc 12FT
Management (International Business)............................ MSc 12FT

University of St Andrews
Management...MLitt 12FT 24PT
Management (Human Resource Management) .... MLitt 12FT
Management and Information Technology MSc 12FT/PGDip 9FT

University of Stirling
Management.....................MSc 12FT 27PT/PGDip 9FT 21PT

University of Sunderland
Tourism and Events.............................MSc 12FT 24PT

University of Surrey
International Event Management .... MSc 12FT

University of Ulster
Event Management ....MSc 12FT 30PT/PGDip 9FT 24PT

University of West London
Fundraising and Special Events ....MA 12FT

University of the West of England, Bristol
Events Management ....MA 18FT

University of Westminster
Events and Conference Management...................... MA 12FT 24PT

University of Wolverhampton
Hospitality Management.....................MA 12FT 24-36PT

Event management studies
Research Courses

University of Cambridge
Management Studies...............................PhD 36FT

Goldsmiths, University of London
Curatorial/Knowledge ....MPhil 24FT 36PT/PhD 36-48FT 48-72PT

University of Sheffield
Management................... PhD 36FT 72PT/MPhil 24FT 48PT

International marketing
Taught Courses

BPP Business School
Professional Marketing.........................MSc 12FT 24+PT

Bangor University
Marketing.................................. MBA 12FT/PGDip 9FT

Birkbeck, University of London
International Marketing...........................MSc 12FT 24PT

University of Bradford
International Marketing................................ MSc 12FT

Brunel University
Applied Corporate Brand Management .... MSc 12FT
International Business .... MSc 12FT
Management.................................. MSc 12FT
Marketing.................................. MSc 12FT

Bucks New University
Marketing Communications .... MA 12FT 24PT

Cardiff Metropolitan University
Marketing.................................MSc 12FT 24PT

University of Central Lancashire
Global Communication Studies........................ MA 12FT 24-36PT
International Tourism Management.....................MSc 12FT 24PT/ PGDip 12FT 24PT
Marketing Management .... MSc 12FT
Marketing and PR.................................MA 12FT

Coventry University
Marketing.................................MBA 12FT 24-30PT

Cranfield University, Shrivenham
International Defence and Security Marketing..............MSc 60FT/ PGCert 36FT/PGDip 48FT

University of Cumbria
International Marketing Management ...MSc 12FT/PGCert 12FT/ PGDip 12FT

University of Derby
Marketing Management .... MSc 12FT
Marketing and Media.............................. MSc 12FT

University of East Anglia
Brand Leadership .... MSc 12FT
Entrepreneurship and Strategy .... MSc 12FT
Marketing.................................. MSc 12FT
Marketing and Management.......................... MSc 12FT

Edinburgh Napier University
Intercultural Business Communication .... MSc 12FT
International Marketing......................... MSc 12FT
International Marketing with Tourism & Events .... MSc 12FT
Marketing with Festival and Event Management .... MSc 12FT

University of Essex
International Marketing and Entrepreneurship....MSc 12FT 24PT

European Business School London
International Marketing.................................MA 12 - 16FT

GCU London
International Fashion Marketing (London)............MSc 12FT/MSc 12-15FT
International Marketing .... MSc 12FT

Glasgow Caledonian University
Digital Marketing .... MSc 12FT
Marketing.......................... MSc 12FT/PGDip 9FT

University of Glasgow
International Management & Design Innovation .... MSc 12FT
International Strategic Marketing .... MSc 12FT

Marketing and advertising studies

Goldsmiths, University of London
Design & Environment .... MA 12FT 24PT

Heriot-Watt University
International Fashion Marketing .... MSc 12FT 24PT/PGDip 9FT 21PT
International Marketing .... PGDip 9FT 21PT/MSc 12FT 24PT
Marketing .... MSc 84DL

University of Huddersfield
International Design Marketing & Communication .... MA 12/16FT
International Marketing .... MSc 12FT 36PT

King's College London
Bible and Ministry .... MA 12FT 24PT
International Marketing .... MSc 12FT

Leeds Metropolitan University
Chartered Institute of Marketing (CIM) .... Diploma 12PT
Chartered Institute of Marketing (CIM) .... Professional Certificate 12PT
International Communication .... MA 12FT
International Tourism & Hospitality Management .... MSc 12FT 24PT
Marketing .... MSc 12FT

University of Leeds
International Marketing Management .... MSc 12FT

University of Liverpool
Global Marketing (Online Degree) .... MSc 24FT 24+PT

London Metropolitan University
International Marketing Communications .... MA 12-18FT
Marketing .... MA 12FT 24PT

London South Bank University
International Marketing .... MSc 18FT 48PT
International Marketing (with Internship) .... MSc 20FT
International Tourism & Hospitality Management .... MSc 18FT 36PT

Manchester Metropolitan University
International Tourism Management .... MSc 12FT 24-60PT

Middlesex University
International Marketing .... MA 12FT 24PT

Newcastle University
Advanced International Business Management and Marketing .... MSc/MSc (Dual Award) 17FT
Cross-Cultural Communication and International Marketing ...... MA 12FT 24PT
International Marketing .... MSc 12FT

University of Northampton
International Marketing Strategy .... MA 12FT

Northumbria University
Mass Communication Management .... MSc 12FT 24PT
Strategic Marketing .... MSc 12FT

Nottingham Trent University
Management and Marketing .... MSc 12FT
Marketing .... MSc 12FT

Oxford Brookes University
International Hotel and Tourism Marketing .... MSc 12FT 24PT/MSc Sandwich Mode 24FT
Marketing .... MSc 12FT 24PT

Plymouth University
Marketing Management and Strategy .... MSc 12FT

University of Reading
Marketing and International Management .... MSc 12FT 24PT

Regent's Business School London
MA Business Management in International Travel & Tourism MA 21PT
MA Global Management (Marketing) .... MA 12FT

Robert Gordon University
International Marketing Management ..... MSc 12FT 36DL/PGDip 8FT 24DL/PGCert 4FT 12DL

University of Roehampton
International Management .... MSc 12FT 24PT
International Management with Marketing .... MSc 12FT
Marketing .... MSc 12FT 24PT

Royal Holloway, University of London
Marketing .... MA 12FT

University Campus Suffolk
Marketing Management .... MA 12FT 30PT

University of Salford
Global Management .... MSc 12FT 36PT/PGDip 8FT 24PT/PGCert 4FT 9PT
Marketing .... MSc 12FT 36PT/PGDip 8FT 24PT/PGCert 4FT 9PT

Sheffield Hallam University
Global Strategic Marketing .... MSc 12FT
International Marketing .... MSc 12FT

University of Sheffield
Global Marketing Management .... MSc 12FT/PGDip 9FT/PGCert 6FT
Marketing Management Practice .... MSc 12FT

University of South Wales
International Logistics and Supply Chain Management .... MSc 12FT 36PT

Southampton Solent University
Marketing Management .... MA 12FT 32PT

University of Southampton
Marketing Management .... MSc 12FT/PGDip 9FT

University of St Andrews
Marketing .... MLitt 12FT

University of Stirling
Marketing .... MSc 12FT/PGDip 9FT

University of Strathclyde
International Marketing .... MSc 12FT 24PT/PGDip 9FT 18PT
Marketing .... MSc 12FT 24PT/PGDip 9FT 18PT

University of Surrey
Communication and International Marketing .... MA 12FT
International Retail Marketing .... MSc 12FT

University of Sussex
International Marketing .... MSc 12FT 24PT

Swansea University
Marketing .... MSc 12FT

Teesside University
Marketing Management .... MSc 12FT 24PT

University of Warwick
Global Media and Communication ...... MA 12FT 24PT/PGDip 6FT 12PT

University of West London
Finance and Global Capital Markets .... MSc 12FT 24PT
International Investment and Arbitration Law ..... LLM 12FT 24PT

University of the West of Scotland
International Marketing .... MSc 12FT 36PT/Diploma 9FT 24PT

University of York
Global Marketing .... MSc 12FT

York St John University
Global Marketing .... MA 12FT 60PT

International marketing
Research Courses

Birmingham City University
Marketing .... MPhil 24FT 36PT/PhD 24FT 36PT

Cardiff University
Centre for Global Communications Management Research .. PhD 36FT

University of Hull
Centre for Marketing, Communications and International Strategy .... PhD 36FT 60PT/MPhil 24FT 36PT

University of Kent
Marketing .... MA by research 12FT 24PT/MPhil 24FT 36PT/PhD 36FT 60PT/New Route PhD 48FT

Newcastle University
Marketing .... MPhil 12FT 24PT/PhD 36FT 72PT

Marketing and advertising studies
Taught Courses

Aberystwyth University
Digital Marketing .... MSc 12FT 24PT
Management and Digital Business .... MSc 12FT 24PT
Management with Marketing .... MSc 12FT 24PT/PGDip 9FT 18PT
Marketing .... MSc 12FT 24PT/PGDip 9FT 21PT
Tourism Marketing .... MSc 12FT 24PT

Anglia Ruskin University
Marketing Management Practice . MSc 18FT/PGCert 18FT/PGDip 18FT
Marketing and Innovation .... MA 18FT 24PT/PGCert 18FT 24PT/PGDip 18FT 24PT

University of the Arts London - London College of Fashion
Strategic Fashion Marketing .... MA 15FT 30PT

Aston University
Market Research & Consultancy .... MSc 12FT
Marketing Management .... MSc 12FT

BPP Business School
Professional Marketing .... MSc 12FT 24+PT

Bangor University
Accounting and Finance .... MSc 12FT
Accounting and Finance - LondonCentre .... MSc 12FT
Accounting, Banking, Economics, Finance, Management Studies MPhil 24FT/PhD by taught 36FT
Banking and Finance .... MSc 12FT MA 12FT/PGDip 9FT MBA 12FT
Banking and Finance - London Centre .... MSc 12FT
Business and Finance .... MSc 12FT/PGDip 9FT MA 12FT/PGDip 9FT
Business and Marketing .... MA 12FT/PGDip 9FT
Business with Consumer Psychology .... MA 12FT/PGDip 9FT MSc 12FT/PGDip 9FT
Consumer Psychology with Business .... MSc 12FT/PGDip 9FT MA 12FT/PGDip 9FT
Finance .... MBA 12FT MA 12FT/PGDip 9FT MSc 12FT/PGDip 9FT
Finance - London Centre .... MBA 12FT MSc 12FT
International Banking and Development Finance .... MSc 12FT/PGDip 9FT
International Banking and Development Finance - London Centre .... MSc 12FT
Islamic Banking and Finance .... MA 12FT/PGDip 9FT MSc 12FT/PGDip 9FT MBA 12FT
Islamic Banking and Finance - London Centre .... MBA 12FT
Management .... MBA 12FT 36PT
Management and Finance .... MSc 12FT/MA 12FT
Marketing .... MBA 12FT/PGDip 9FT

Bath Spa University
Advertising Practice .... MA 12FT 12DL
Business and Management: Marketing .... MA 12FT 32PT

University of Bath
Management with Marketing .... MSc 12FT
Marketing .... MSc 12FT

University of Bedfordshire
Chartered Institute of Marketing (CIM) .... PGDip 12PT
Marketing Communications .... MSc 12FT
Marketing and Business Management .... MSc 12-15FT

Belfast Metropolitan College
CIM Level 3 Introductory Certificate in Marketing .... Cert 10PT
CIM Level 4 Professional Certificate in Marketing .... Cert 9PT
CIM Professional Diploma Level 6 .... CIM Diploma 9PT

Birkbeck, University of London
Creative Industries (Management) .... MSc 12FT 24PT
Digital Media Management .... PGCert 12PT
International Marketing .... MSc 12FT 24PT
Management .... MSc 12FT 24PT/MRes 12FT 24PT/PGCert 12FT 24PT
Marketing .... MSc 12FT 24PT/MRes 12FT 24PT
Marketing Communications .... MSc 12FT 24PT
Services and Retail Marketing .... MSc 12FT
Sport Management and Marketing .... MSc 12FT 24PT
Sport Marketing .... MSc 12FT 24PT

Birmingham City University
Leadership and Organisational Performance .... MSc 12FT
Multi Unit Leadership and Strategy .... MSc 12FT

University of Birmingham
Marketing .... MSc 12FT
Marketing Communications .... MSc 12FT
Strategic Marketing and Consulting .... MSc 12FT

University College Birmingham
Marketing Management (Events, Hospitality or Tourism) .... MA 15FT 21PT/PGCert 6FT 12PT/PGDip 9FT 18PT

Bournemouth University
Advertising and Marketing Communications .... MA 12FT
Events Marketing .... MSc 12-15FT 24PT

University of Bradford
International Marketing .... MSc 12FT
Marketing and Management .... MSc 12FT/PGDip 9FT
Strategic Marketing .... MSc 12FT

University of Brighton
Chartered Management Institute .... CMI Diploma see siteFT
Marketing ...... MSc see siteFT/PGDip see siteFT/PGCert see siteFT

Brunel University
Applied Corporate Brand Management .... MSc 12FT
Design Strategy and Innovation .... MA 12FT
Design and Branding Strategy .... MA 12FT
Marketing .... MSc 12FT
Sustainability, Entrepreneurship and Design (with Professional Development) .... MSc 18FT

Bucks New University
Advertising .... MA 12FT
Marketing Communications .... MA 12FT 24PT

Cardiff Metropolitan University
Marketing .... MSc 12FT 24PT

Cardiff University
Strategic Marketing .... MSc 12FT 24PT

University of Central Lancashire
Chartered Institute of Marketing (CIM) Chartered PG Diploma in Marketing (Stage 1) .... CIM Diploma 12PT
Chartered Institute of Marketing (CIM) Chartered PG Diploma in Marketing (Stage 2) .... CIM Diploma 12PT
Chartered Institute of Marketing (CIM) Professional Certificate in Marketing .... CIM AdvCert 12PT
Chartered Institute of Marketing (CIM) Professional Diploma in Marketing .... CIM Diploma 12PT
Digital Marketing (CAM) .... Diploma 7.5DL
Marketing Management .... MSc 12FT
Marketing and PR .... MA 12FT
Master of Business Administration .... MBA 12FT
Master of Business Administration - Health .... MBA 36PT
Master of Business Administration - Part-time .... MBA 36PT

Marketing and advertising studies

Sports Marketing and Business Management ..... MSc 12FT up to 36PT
Strategic Marketing Leadership (Advanced Entry) ....MA 12PT

City University London
Charity Marketing and Fundraising............PGDip 12FT/MSc 18FT
Grantmaking, Philanthropy and Social Investment..PGDip 12PT/MSc 18PT/PGCert 6PT

Cornwall College
Marketing............................LCMS 12PT/DMS 12PT/PGDip 12-36PT

Coventry University
Advertising and Marketing.. MA 12FT 24PT
International Marketing..MSc 12FT 24PT
Marketing..MBA 12FT 24-30PT
Marketing Management... MA 12FT 24PT
Strategic Marketing...MSc 12FT 24-30PT

Cranfield University
Strategic Marketing.. MSc 11FT

University for the Creative Arts
Fashion Promotion and Imaging..

University of Cumbria
International Marketing Management...MSc 12FT/PGCert 12FT/PGDip 12FT
Master of Business Administration.......................MBA 12FT 36PT

De Montfort University
Advertising and Public Relations Management... MSc 12FT up to 72PT
Marketing (CIM Professional Diploma in Marketing) ....PGDip 12PT
Marketing Management.. MSc 12FT
Strategic Marketing...MSc 12FT up to 72PT

University of Derby
Marketing Management.. MSc 12FT
Marketing and Media.. MSc 12FT

Dublin Institute of Technology
Advertising.. MSc 12FT
Marketing... MSc 12FT
Marketing (Executive) .... MSc 24PT

University of Dundee
Non-Graduating Taught Postgraduate in School of Business... PG module variableFT

Durham University
Executive MA in Marketing... MA 30DL
Marketing.. MA 18FT
Marketing Management... MSc 12FT
Strategic Marketing.. MSc 12FT

ESCP Europe Business School
Master in Marketing and Creativity ...... Master in Marketing and Creativity 15FT

University of East Anglia
Advanced Business Management...................................... MSc 12FT
Brand Leadership... MSc 12FT
Business Management .... MSc 12FT
Marketing.. MSc 12FT
Marketing and Management... MSc 12FT

University of East London
International Marketing Management .....MSc 12FT 24PT/PGDip 8FT 16PT/PGCert 4FT 8PT

Edge Hill University
Marketing and Communications.............................. MA 12FT 24PT
Master of Business Administration (Information Technology)..... MBA 12-18FT
Master of Business Administration (Marketing)........... MBA 12FT

Edinburgh Napier University
Creative Advertising ....MSc 12FT 24PT/PGDip 9FT 18PT/PGCert 4.5FT 9PT
Marketing.. MSc 12FT

University of Edinburgh
Marketing.. MSc 12FT
Marketing & Business Analysis .... MSc 12FT

University of Essex
Advertising, Marketing and the Media.................... MA 12FT 24PT

University of Exeter
Marketing.. MSc 12FT
Marketing and Financial Services...MSc 9FT

Falmouth University
Creative Advertising ....MA 12FT

GCU London
Luxury Brand Marketing (London).......... MBA 12FT/MBA 12-15FT

National University of Ireland Galway
Marketing Practice... MSc 12FT
Strategic Marketing.. MSc 12FT

Glasgow Caledonian University
Digital Marketing.. MSc 12FT
International Fashion Marketing .... MSc 12FT/PGDip 9FT
Marketing.. MSc 12FT/PGDip 9FT

University of Gloucestershire
Marketing.......................................MSc 12FT/PGDip 8FT/PGCert 4FT

Glyndwr University
Chartered Institute of Marketing (CIM)... CIM Diploma 12PT/CIM AdvCert 12PT
MSc Marketing Management ....MSc 12FT/PGCert 12FT/PGDip 12FT

Goldsmiths, University of London
Brands, Communication and Culture....................... MA 12FT 24PT
Consumer Behaviour.. MSc 12FT
Creating Social Media ....MA 12FT 24PT/MSc 12FT 24PT
Promotional Media: Public Relations, Advertising & Marketing .. MA 12FT 24PT

University of Greenwich
Strategic Marketing...MA 12FT
Strategic Marketing Communications...............................MA 12FT

Heriot-Watt University
Int'nl Business Management with Finance / HRM / Logistics / Marketing /Sustainability Mgmt. ....MSc 12FT 24PT/PGDip 9FT 21PT
International Fashion Marketing ....MSc 12FT 24PT/PGDip 9FT 21PT
International Marketing..............PGDip 9FT 21PT/MSc 12FT 24PT
Marketing..MSc 84DL

University of Hertfordshire
Marketing.. MSc 12FT
Marketing (CIM)... PGDip 9-15PT

University of Huddersfield
Marketing...MSc 12FT 24-36PT
Marketing Communications .... MSc 12FT 36PT
Marketing Management .... MSc 12FT 24PT

University of Hull
Advertising and Marketing... MSc 12FT
Marketing Management .... MSc 12FT

Imperial College London
Strategic Marketing.. MSc 12FT
Strategic Marketing Summer School ....Credit towards your degree 1FT

Keele University
Marketing......................................MA 12FT/PGDip 9FT/PGCert 9FT

University of Kent
Management (Marketing) .... MSc 12FT

Kingston University
Advanced and Strategic Marketing .... MSc 12FT
Advertising and the Creative Economy.................... MA 12FT 24PT
Communication Design and the Creative EconomyMA 12FT 24PT
Marketing.. MSc 12FT
Marketing & Brand Management..MA 12FT
Marketing Communications and Advertising...................MA 12FT
Marketing with English ....MA 12FT
Retail Management and Marketing .... MSc 12FT

Lancaster University
Advanced Marketing Management..............MSc 12FT/MRes 12FT
Management Science and Marketing Analytics .... MSc 12FT
Psychology of Advertising.. MSc 12FT 24PT

Leeds Metropolitan University
Chartered Institute of Marketing (CIM)......................Diploma 12PT
Chartered Institute of Marketing (CIM)....Professional Certificate 12PT
Contract Management ....MSc 24PT/PGDip 24PT
Marketing.. MSc 12FT
Sport Business... MA 12FT 24PT

University of Leeds
Advertising and Design.. MSc 12FT
Advertising and Marketing...MA 12FT

University of Leicester
Marketing.. MSc 12FT 24-60DL

University of Limerick
Marketing, Consumption and Society .... MSc 12FT

Liverpool Hope University
Marketing Management... MSc 12FT 24PT

Liverpool John Moores University
Entrepreneurship.. MSc 12FT 24PT
International News Journalism .... MA 12FT 24PT
Maritime Management...MBA 12FT 24PT
Mass Communications .... MA 12FT 24PT

University of Liverpool
Consumer Marketing .... MSc 12FT 24PT

London College UCK
Marketing Management.......................................PGDip 12FT 24PT

London Metropolitan University
Marketing.. MA 12FT 24PT

London South Bank University
Chartered Institute of Marketing Diploma.................. PGDip 12PT
Management in Civil Society (Marketing and Fundraising - Blended)... MSc 30PT

Management in Civil Society (Marketing and Fundraising)... MSc 30PT
Marketing (with Internship)... MSc 20FT
Marketing ....MSc 14FT MSc 26PT
Marketing Communications ....MSc 18FT 48PT
Marketing Communications (with Internship)...... MSc 20FT 48PT
Marketing Communications Top-up........................MSc 15FT 30PT
Marketing Management (Top-up 3 Units + Dissertation) ...... MSc 10FT 10PT

Loughborough University
Marketing and Management (for non-business graduates).......... MSc 12FT

Manchester Metropolitan University
Digital Marketing Communications..........MSc 30PT/PGDip 24PT/PGCert 12PT
International Creative Advertising ....MSc 12FT 24PT
Marketing Communications ....MSc 12FT 30PT/PGDip 24PT/PGCert 12PT
Marketing Management......................................MSc 12FT 24-36PT

University of Manchester
Marketing.. MSc 12FT

Middlesex University
Marketing Communications .... MA 12FT 24PT
Marketing Management .... MA 12FT 24PT
Marketing Practice, MProf ....MA 24PT

Newcastle University
Advanced Food Marketing .... MSc 12FT
Cross-Cultural Communication and International Marketing MA 12FT 24PT

University of Northampton
CIM Professional Postgraduate Diploma in Marketing............CIM Diploma 12PT
Fashion Marketing .... MA 12FT 24PT
Marketing (top-up from CIM Professional Postgraduate Diploma)..MA 12PT 12DL

Northumbria University
Business with Marketing Management........................... MSc 12FT
Mass Communication Management ....MSc 12FT 24PT
Sport Marketing...MSc 12FT 24PT
Strategic Marketing .... MSc 12FT

Norwich University of the Arts
Communication Design.. MA 12FT 24PT

Nottingham Trent University
CIM - Professional Certificate in Marketing.........CIM Professional Certificate 12PT
CIM - Professional Diploma in Marketing........ CIM Diploma 12PT
Fashion Marketing & Communication ....MA 12FT
Management and Marketing... MSc 12FT
Marketing.. MSc 12FT

University of Nottingham
Business Administration ....PGDip 9FT
Marketing.. MSc 12FT
Master of Business Administration (Executive) .... MBA 24PT
Master of Business Administration (Executive) - Corporate Social Responsibility.. MBA 24PT
Master of Business Administration (Executive) - Healthcare .... MBA 24PT
Master of Business Administration - Corporate Social Responsibility..MBA 12FT 24-48PT
Master of Business Administration - Entrepreneurship................. MBA 12FT 24-48PT
Master of Business Administration - Finance .... MBA 12FT 24-48PT
Master of Business Administration - General................ MBA 12FT 24-48PT
Master of Business Administration - Singapore.......MBA 24-48PT

The Open University
Environmental Management.........MSc variableDL/PGCert 12DL/PGDip variableDL

Oxford Brookes University
Marketing ....MSc 12FT 24PT

Plymouth University
Marketing Management and Strategy.............................. MSc 12FT

University of Portsmouth
Marketing..MA 12FT

Queen Mary, University of London
Accounting and Management.. MSc 12FT
International Business .... MSc 12FT
Management..MSc 12FT 24PT
Public Administration.. MPA 12FT 24PT

Ravensbourne
Communication Design.. MA 12FT 24PT
Luxury Brand Management...................................... MDes 12FT 24PT

University of Reading
Applied Management ....MA 36PT/PGDip 24PT
Food Economics and Marketing .... MSc 12FT
Rural Land and Business Management .... MSc 12FT

Section sponsored by
BPP UNIVERSITY COLLEGE

Business and social sciences
www.prospects.ac.uk/findcourses POSTGRADUATE DIRECTORY 447

Marketing and advertising studies

Richmond, The American International University in London
Masters in Business Administration (MBA)..........MBA 12FT 24PT

Robert Gordon University
Corporate Communication and Public Affairs .... MSc 12FT 24PT 24DL/PGDip 9FT 18PT 18DL/PGCert 6FT 12PT 12DL/ MSc 12FT 24PT 24DL

University of Roehampton
Marketing...MSc 12FT 24PT

Royal Agricultural University
Sustainable Business..MSc 12FT 24PT

Royal Holloway, University of London
Marketing...MA 12FT

University Campus Suffolk
MSc Marketing Management .... MA 12FT 30PT

University of Salford
Marketing.......... MSc 12FT 36PT/PGDip 8FT 24PT/PGCert 4FT 9PT

Sheffield Hallam University
Professional Communication.. MA 36DL/PGDip 24-36DL/PGCert 12-18DL

University of Sheffield
Global Marketing ManagementMSc 12FT/PGDip 9FT/PGCert 6FT
Marketing Management Practice ....MSc 12FT

University of South Wales
Chartered Institute of Marketing (CIM) Professional Certificate.. Cert 12PT
Chartered Institute of Marketing ....CIM PG Diploma 12PT
Chartered Institute of Marketing ....CIM Diploma 12PT
Chartered Institute of Purchasing and Supply (CIPS) Diplomas in Procurement and Supply...................Diploma in Procurement and Supply 8PT/Advanced Diploma in Procurement and Supply 8PT/ Professional Diploma in Procurement and Supply 8PT

Southampton Solent University
CIM Chartered Postgraduate Diploma in Marketing . PGDip 24PT
Digital Marketing and Media ....MA 12FT
Marketing Management .... MA 12FT 32PT

University of Southampton
Insurance Law (1 yrs)..LLM 12FT
Digital Marketing (1 yrs)...MSc 12FT
Finance (1 yrs)..MSc 12FT
Organisation Development and Facilitation ....MSc 36FT
Risk and Finance (1 yrs)..MSc 12FT
Strategy and Innovation (1 yrs)..MSc 12FT
Marketing Analytics... MSc 12FT/PGDip 9FT
Marketing Management .... MSc 12FT/PGDip 9FT

University of St Andrews
Marketing..MLitt 12FT

Staffordshire University
Marketing (CIM Porfessional Postgraduate Diploma) ....PGDip 12-24PT
Marketing (CIM Professional Certificate)..........................Cert 12PT
Marketing (CIM Professional Diploma) ......CIM Diploma 12-24PT

University of Stirling
Marketing... MSc 12FT/PGDip 9FT
Master of Business Administration .... MBA 12FT
Publishing Studies .... MLitt 12FT 27PT/PGDip 9FT 21PT MRes 12FT 27PT/PGCert 9FT 18PT
Strategic Public Relations & Communication Management .... MSc 12FT 24PT/PGDip 9FT 21PT

University of Strathclyde
Marketing...MSc 12FT 24PT/PGDip 9FT 18PT
Master in Business Administration ..... MBA 12FT 36PT 30-60DL/ PGDip 9FT 24PT 36DL

University of Sunderland
Marketing......... MA 12FT 24PT/PGDip 10FT 15PT/PGCert 7FT 7PT

University of Surrey
International Marketing Management ....MSc 12FT

Swansea University
Management (Marketing) ....MSc 12FT
Marketing...MSc 12FT

Swansea Metropolitan University
Chartered Institute of Marketing (CIM) .... PGDip 12PT

Teesside University
Marketing Management..MSc 12FT 24PT

University of Wales Trinity Saint David
Marketing................................. MBA 12FT 24PT/PGCert 12FT 24PT/ PGDip 12FT 24PT

University of Ulster
Communication, Advertising and Public Relations .... MSc 12FT 36PT/PGDip 9FT 18PT
Marketing.......................................MSc 12FT 24PT/PGDip 9FT 18PT

University of Warwick
Business (Marketing)...MSc 12FT
Marketing & Strategy..MSc 12FT

Webster Graduate School London
Marketing...MA 14FT

West Herts College
Advertising..AdvPGDip 9FT
Copywriting and Art Direction...PGDip 10FT

University of West London
Marketing...MA 12FT

University of the West of England, Bristol
Marketing...MSc 12FT 24-36PT
Marketing Communications ....MSc 12FT 24-36PT
Social Marketing..PGCert 18PT

University of Westminster
Marketing Communications ....MA 12FT
Marketing Management ....MA 12FT

University of Winchester
Marketing........MSc 12FT 24PT/PGDip 9FT 18PT/PGCert 9FT 18PT

University of Wolverhampton
Chartered Institute of Marketing: Certificate in Marketing....CIM AdvCert 12PT
Chartered Institute of Marketing: Professional Diploma in Marketing..CIM Diploma 12-24PT
Marketing.. MSc 12FT/PGCert 12PT

University of Worcester
Marketing Management .... MA 12FT 24PT

Marketing and advertising studies
Research Courses

Aberystwyth University
Management and Business ....MPhil 12FT 24PT PhD 36FT 60PT
Marketing ....MPhil 12FT 24PT PhD 36FT 60PT

Anglia Ruskin University
Business and Management .... MPhil 36FT 72PT/PhD 36FT 72PT

Bangor University
Accounting, Banking, Economics, Finance, Management Studies MPhil 24FT/PhD 36FT

Birmingham City University
Marketing...................................... MPhil 24FT 36PT/PhD 24FT 36PT

University of Birmingham
Marketing.................PhD 36FT/MPhil 24FT/MSc by research 12FT

Cardiff University
Marketing and Strategy............................. PhD 36-48FT possiblePT

De Montfort University
Marketing (Research) .... MPhil 12 - 24FT 24 - 48PT/PhD 24 - 36FT 36 - 72PT

University of East Anglia
Business Management .... PhD 36FT 72PT/MPhil 24FT 48PT

National University of Ireland Galway
College of Business, Public Policy & Law .... MBS by research 24-36FT

Goldsmiths, University of London
Management..MPhil 36FT/PhD 36FT

University of Hull
Centre for Marketing, Communications and International Strategy.. PhD 36FT 60PT/MPhil 24FT 36PT

University of Kent
Marketing................MA by research 12FT 24PT/MPhil 24FT 36PT/ PhD 36FT 60PT/New Route PhD 48FT

Lancaster University
Marketing...................................... PhD 36FT 48PT/MPhil 24FT 36PT

Manchester Metropolitan University
Marketing and Retail........PhD 48FT 90PT/MPhil 36FT 72PT/MRes 12FT 24PT/MA or MSc by Research 18FT 36PT

Newcastle University
Marketing...................................... MPhil 12FT 24PT/PhD 36FT 72PT

The Open University
Marketing.................PhD 36FT 72PT variableDL/MPhil 15FT 24PT variableDL
Social Marketing...... PhD 36FT 72PT variableDL/MPhil 15FT 24PT variableDL
Surveillance................................... MPhil 15FT 24PT/PhD 36FT 72PT

University of Portsmouth
Operations and Systems Management.......MPhil 24FT 48PT/PhD 36FT 72PT
Organisation Studies and Human Resource Management........... MPhil 24FT 48PT/PhD 36FT 72PT

Robert Gordon University
Aberdeen Business School ...PhD 12FT 36PT 36DL/MSc(Res) 12FT 36PT 36DL

Royal Welsh College of Music and Drama
Arts Management...................................MA by research 12FT 24PT

Southampton Solent University
Marketing and Leisure ....MPhil/PhD

University of Strathclyde
Marketing - Research................... PhD 33FT/MPhil 12FT/DBA 33FT

University of Surrey
Retail and Marketing................... PhD 36FT 48PT/MPhil 24FT 36PT

West Herts College
Advertising.. PGDip by research 8FT

University of the West of Scotland
Department of Management and Marketing...............PhD/MPhil

Public relations studies
Taught Courses

University of Bath
International Relations ......MA 12FT/PGDip 9FT 21PT/PGCert 4FT 16PT

University of Bedfordshire
Public Relations (PR) .... MA 12FT 24PT

Birkbeck, University of London
Marketing..MSc 12FT 24PT/MRes 12FT 24PT

Birmingham City University
Public Relations... MA 12FT 24PT

Bournemouth University
Public Relations... MA 12FT 24PT

Brunel University
Media and Public Relations... MA 12FT 24PT

Cardiff University
International Public Relations and Global Communications Management..MA 12FT

University of Central Lancashire
Chartered Institute of Marketing (CIM) Chartered PG Diploma in Marketing (Stage 1) .... CIM Diploma 12PT
Chartered Institute of Marketing (CIM) Chartered PG Diploma in Marketing (Stage 2) .... CIM Diploma 12PT
Chartered Institute of Marketing (CIM) Professional Certificate in Marketing .... CIM AdvCert 12PT
Chartered Institute of Marketing (CIM)........... CIM Diploma 12PT
International Applied Communication............................ MSc 12FT
Specialist Community Public Health Nurse - Health Visiting or School Nursing .... PGDip 12FT 24PT
Strategic Communication ....MA 24PT

De Montfort University
Advertising and Public Relations Management ... MSc 12FT up to 72PT

Dublin Institute of Technology
European Public Relations..MA 12FT
Public Relations...MA 12FT

University of East Anglia
Marketing.. MSc 12FT

University of Exeter
International Relations .... MA 12FT 24PT

Fitzwilliam Institute Group
Event Management with Public Relations Postgraduate Diploma 6FT
Event Management with Public Relations Eco Events and Wedding Planning... PGDip 6FT
Public Relations .... PGDip 6DL

National University of Ireland Galway
Public Advocacy and Activism........................ MA 12FT/PGDip 12FT

University of Glasgow
Public Policy & Management ... MSc 12FT 24PT 60BM/PGDip 9FT 21PT

Goldsmiths, University of London
Promotional Media: Public Relations, Advertising & Marketing.. MA 12FT 24PT

University of Greenwich
Public Relations..MA 24PT

King's College London
European Public Policy ....MA 12FT

Leeds Metropolitan University
Chartered Institute of Public Relations (CIPR) Advanced Certificate...CIPR Advanced Cert 12PT
Chartered Institute of Public Relations (CIPR) Diploma ....CIPR Diploma 12PT
Corporate Communications .... MSc 36PT
International Communication...MA 12FT
Public Health - Health Promotion ......MSc 12FT 30PT/PGDip 12FT 24PT/PGCert 4FT 12PT
Public Relations & Communication.....................................MA 12FT

University of Leeds
Corporate Communications and Public Relations ....MA 12FT

University of Leicester
Communications, Media and Public Relations (by Distance Learning).. MA 24FT/PGDip 20FT

University of the Arts London - London College of Communication
Public Relations...MA 12FT

Manchester Metropolitan University
Public Relations..MSc 12FT VariesPT

Marketing and advertising studies

Middlesex University
Media and Communications Management .... MA 12FT 24PT

Newcastle University
Media and Public Relations... MA 12FT 24PT

Queen Margaret University, Edinburgh
Public Relations................... MSc 12FT 24-60PT/PGDip 9FT 24-60PT

Robert Gordon University
Corporate Communication and Public Affairs .... MSc 12FT 24PT 24DL/PGDip 9FT 18PT 18DL/PGCert 6FT 12PT 12DL/ MSc 12FT 24PT 24DL

School of Oriental and African Studies - SOAS
Global Media and Postnational Communication..............MA 12FT 24-36PT
Public Policy and Management .... MSc 24DL/PGDip 12DL

Sheffield Hallam University
Corporate Communication MA 12-18FT 18-60PT 18-60DL/PGDip 8-12FT 24-36PT 24-26DL/PGCert 6FT 12-18PT 12-18DL

Professional Communication.. MA 36DL/PGDip 24-36DL/PGCert 12-18DL
Professional Communication .... MA 36DL
Public Relations.. MA 12FT 36PT

University of Stirling
Strategic Communication & Public Relations (Joint Degree).........
MSc 12FT/PGDip 9FT/PGCert 3FT
Strategic Public Relations & Communication Management ....
MSc 12FT 24PT/PGDip 9FT 21PT
Strategic Public Relations (Double Degree with Lund University)..MSc 16/21FT/PGCert 3FT
Strategic Public Relations (Online)............. MSc 30DL/PGDip 20DL

University of Sunderland
Public Relations.. MA 12FT 24-36PT

Swansea University
Communication, Media Practice and Public Relations ....MA 12FT 24-36PT

Teesside University
MA Multimedia Public Relations................................. MA 12FT 24PT

University of Ulster
Communication, Advertising and Public Relations .... MSc 12FT 36PT/PGDip 9FT 18PT

West Herts College
Public Relations...PGDip 9FT

University of Westminster
Public Relations... MA 12FT 24-48PT

Public relations studies
Research Courses

Institute for the Study of the Americas, School of Advanced Study, University of London
International Relations ....PhD 36FT/MPhil 12FT

Newcastle University
Media, Journalism and Public Relations.................. PhD 36FT 72PT

Section sponsored by

BPP
UNIVERSITY
COLLEGE

Business and social sciences
www.prospects.ac.uk/findcourses POSTGRADUATE DIRECTORY 449

Planning and surveying

Estate management
Taught Courses

University of Aberdeen
Urban Planning and Real Estate ....MSc 12FT/PGDip 12FT

Anglia Ruskin University
Professional Doctorate in the Built Environment .... DProf by taught 60DL

University of Cambridge
Real Estate Finance .... MPhil 10FT

City University London
Real Estate.. MSc 9FT 18PT
Real Estate Investment .... MSc 9-12FT

Glasgow Caledonian University
Building Services Engineering.................................MSc 12FT 24PT
Real Estate Management ....MSc 12FT 24PT

University of Glasgow
Real Estate (PgCert)...PGCert 12FT

University of Greenwich
Real Estate Development and Investment ....MSc 12FT 24PT

Heriot-Watt University
Housing and Real Estate........MSc 12FT 24PT 24-84DL/PGDip 9FT 18PT 18-84DL
MRes Courses in Urban Studies/Housing/Planning Studies/Real Estate Research... MSc(Res) 12FT
Real Estate Management and Development.........MSc 12FT 24PT 24-84DL/PGDip 9FT 21PT 24-84DL
Real Estate and Planning.......MSc 12FT 24PT 24-84DL/PGDip 9FT 21PT 24-84DL

Kingston University
Real Estate..MSc 12-24FT 24-48PT

Northumbria University
International Real Estate Management .... MSc 12FT
Real Estate Management ....MSc 12FT 36PT
Surveying/Construction programme - Real Estate Pathway.. MSc 24DL

Nottingham Trent University
International Real Estate Investment and Finance..........................
MSc 12FT 24PT

University of Reading
Corporate Real Estate ....MSc 24-72PT
Development Planning .... MSc 12FT 24PT/PGDip 12FT 24PT
Development Planning Research ......MSc 12FT 24PT/PGDip 12FT 24PT
Rural Land and Business Management .... MSc 12FT

Royal Agricultural University
International Real Estate... MSc 12FT
Property Agency and Management................................. MSc 12FT
Rural Estate Management .... MSc 12FT

University of Salford
Real Estate Development ....MSc 12FT 28DL/PGDip 8FT 20DL
Real Estate and Property Management.....MSc 12FT 28DL/PGDip 8FT 20DL

Estate management
Research Courses

Anglia Ruskin University
Copy of Professional Doctorate in the Built Environment....DProf 60DL
Professional Doctorate in Science and Technology ..... DProf 60DL

Housing studies
Taught Courses

De Montfort University
Housing Studies ....PGCert 9-18DL/PGDip 24DL/MSc 29-36DL

University of Glasgow
Housing Studies.....MSc 12FT 24PT 60BM/PGDip 9FT 18PT 48BM

University of Greenwich
Housing Management and Policy...........................MSc 12FT 24PT

Heriot-Watt University
Housing and Real Estate........MSc 12FT 24PT 24-84DL/PGDip 9FT 18PT 18-84DL

Leeds Metropolitan University
Housing, Regeneration and Urban Management MA 12FT 24PT/PGCert 12FT 12PT/PGDip 12FT 24PT
Town and Regional Planning..................................... MA 12FT 24PT

London Metropolitan University
Housing & Inclusion .... MA 12FT 24PT

London South Bank University
Housing Studies...MA 36PT

Northumbria University
Housing Policy and Management...............................MA 12FT
Housing Policy and Management with Professional Practice ....
MA 36PT/PGDip 24PT
Surveying/Construction programme - Housing Pathway....... MSc 24DL

University of Salford
Urban Design and Regeneration MSc 12FT 28PT/PGDip 8FT 20PT

Sheffield Hallam University
Housing Policy and Practice........MA 12FT 24PT/PGDip 12FT 18PT
Housing Practice...CertHE 24PT 24DL
Housing Professional Studies................... DipHE 18PT 12-18DL
Housing for Environmental Health.............................CertHE 18PT

University of Stirling
Housing Studies ....MSc 12FT/PGDip 12FT MSc 24PT/PGDip 24PT/PGCert 12PT

University of Ulster
Housing Studies..................................MSc 36PT/PGDip 24PT

University of Westminster
Housing Practice..PGCert 24PT PGDip 24PT MA 24PT

Housing studies
Research Courses

University of Birmingham
Hydrogeology.............................. PhD 36FT 72PT/MPhil 24FT 48PT

Cardiff University
Housing.. PhD 36FT 60PT

University of Dundee
Town and Regional Planning .... MPhil 24FT

Land and building surveying
Taught Courses

Anglia Ruskin University
Professional Doctorate in the Built Environment .... DProf by taught 60DL

College of Estate Management
Surveying.. MSc 40DL/PGDip 30DL

University of Central Lancashire
Building Conservation and Regeneration .... MSc 12FT 24-30PT/PGDip 6FT 12PT/PGCert 3FT 6PT
Building Services...... MSc 12FT 30PT/PGDip 6FT 12PT/PGCert 3FT 6PT

Cranfield University
Integrated Landscape Ecology MSc 12FT 60PT/PGDip 12FT 60PT/PGCert 12FT 60PT
Land Reclamation and Restoration MSc... MSc 12FT 60PT/PGCert 12FT 60PT/PGDip 12FT 60PT

University of Exeter
Engineering and Management...MSc 12FT
Surveying and Land/ Environmental Management....... MSc 12FT 24-36PT/PGDip 12FT 24-36PT

University of Glasgow
Geomatics & Management .... MSc 12FT

Kingston University
Building Surveying ....MSc 12FT 24PT

London South Bank University
Quantity Surveying .... MSc 12FT MSc 24PT

Middlesex University
Business Information Modelling Management (BIM).....MSc 12 / 24DL

Northumbria University
Real Estate Management ....MSc 12FT 36PT
Surveying (Minerals)...MSc 24DL

Nottingham Trent University
Building Surveying ....MSc 12FT 24PT

Robert Gordon University
Graduate Diploma Surveying (Quantity Surveying)..........GradDip 12FT 24DL

University of Salford
Accessibility and Inclusive Design............ MSc 32DL/PGDip 20DL/PGCert 8DL
Corporate Real Estate and Facilities Management.......MSc 28DL/PGDip 20DL/PGCert 8DL
Quantity Surveying.......................MSc 12FT 28PT/PGDip 8FT 16PT
Quantity Surveying (Mechanical and Electrical) .MSc 12FT 28DL/PGDip 8FT 16DL
Sustainable Building Design...... MSc 12FT 28PT/PGDip 8FT 20PT/PGCert 4FT 8PT

University of St Andrews
Sustainable Development................................ MSc 12FT/PGDip 9FT

Staffordshire University
Journalism.. MA 12FT 48PT

UCL - University College London
Environmental Modelling ....MSc 12FT 24PT
Mega Infrastructure Planning, Appraisal and Delivery ....
MSc 12FT 24-60PT
Surveying...MSc 12FT 24PT

University of the West of England, Bristol
Building Surveying ....MSc 24FT 36PT/GradDip 18FT 30PT

Land and building surveying
Research Courses

University of Aberdeen
Spatial Planning and Rural Surveying .... PhD 36FT/MPhil 24FT/MSc by research 12FT

Anglia Ruskin University
Copy of Professional Doctorate in the Built Environment....DProf 60PT 60DL
Professional Doctorate in Science and Technology ..... DProf 60DL

University of Glasgow
Geography and Geomatics ....PhD 36FT/MSc by research 12FT/PGDip by research 12FT/MRes 12FT

Newcastle University
Geomatics .... PhD 36FT 72PT/MPhil 12FT 24FT

University of Nottingham
Engineering and Surveying Space Geodesy...........PhD 36FT 72PT/MPhil 24FT 48PT

University of Portsmouth
Civil Engineering and Surveying.........................MPhil 24FT 48PT/PhD 36FT 72PT

UCL - University College London
Geomatic Engineering .... PhD 36FT 60PT

Land management
Taught Courses

University of Aberdeen
Land Economy (Rural Surveying) ....MSc 12FT/PGDip 12FT

Bangor University
Conservation and Land Management .... MSc 12FT/PGDip 9FT
Forestry (Distance Learning)..................... MSc 36DL/PGDip 24DL/PGCert 12DL
Forestry and Environmental Management degrees (TRANSFOR-M).. MSc 24FT
Sustainable Forest and Nature Management (SUFONAMA) (Erasmus Mundus course)... MSc 24FT

University of Birmingham
Local and Regional Economic Development..........MSc 12FT 24PT/PGDip 9FT 21PT/GradDip 9FT 21PT/GradCert 9FT 21PT

Bournemouth University
Green Economy..MSc 12DL

University of Bradford
Regeneration Project Management .... PGCert 3FT

University of Cambridge
Environmental Policy.. MPhil 10FT
Land Economy Research .... MPhil 10FT
Planning, Growth and Regeneration............................ MPhil 10FT

Cardiff University
Regeneration Studies ....MSc 12FT 24PT

University of Central Lancashire
Building Conservation and Regeneration .... MSc 12FT 24-30PT/PGDip 6FT 12PT/PGCert 3FT 6PT
Urban Environmental Management ...MSc 12FT 24PT/PGDip 9FT 18PT/PGCert 6FT 12PT

Cranfield University
Integrated Landscape Ecology MSc 12FT 60PT/PGDip 12FT 60PT/PGCert 12FT 60PT
Land Reclamation and Restoration MSc... MSc 12FT 60PT/PGCert 12FT 60PT/PGDip 12FT 60PT

University of Exeter
Food Security and Sustainable Agriculture............ MSc 12FT 24PT

University of Glasgow
City Planning & Regeneration......................MSc 12FT 24PT 60BM

Harper Adams University
International Agri-business and Food Chain Management ... MSc 12FT 48PT/PGDip 12FT 48PT/PGCert 6FT 48PT
Rural Estate and Land Management ....MSc 12FT 48PT/PGDip 12FT 48PT/PGCert 6FT 48PT

Heriot-Watt University
Sustainable Urban ManagementMSc 12FT 24PT 24-84DL/PGDip 9FT 21PT 24-84DL

Leeds Metropolitan University
Housing, Regeneration and Urban Management MA 12FT 24PT/PGCert 12FT 12PT/PGDip 12FT 24PT
International Political Economy..MA 12FT

University of Lincoln
Development and Regeneration .... MA 12FT 24PT

London Metropolitan University
Sustainable Cities...MSc 12FT 24+PT

London School of Economics and Political Science (LSE)
Economics and Management................................. MSc 10FT
Urban Policy (Double Degree)... MSc 23FT

London South Bank University
Cities and Local Development .... MSc 24PT
Urban Regeneration .... MA 13FT 30PT

Planning and surveying

University of Manchester
Urban Regeneration and Development.................. MSc 12FT 24PT

Northumbria University
Real Estate Management.. MSc 12FT 36PT

Nottingham Trent University
Urban Design and Sustainable Development............ PGCert 12PT

Oxford Brookes University
International Architectural Regeneration and Development .... MA 12FT 24PT/PGDip 6FT 18PT

University of Portsmouth
Sustainable Environmental Management............. MSc 12FT 24PT

University of Reading
Environmental Management .... MSc 12FT 24PT
Intelligent Buildings: Design, Construction and Management .... MSc 24PT
International Planning and Sustainable Urban Management ..... MSc 12FT/PGCert 6FT/PGDip 9FT
Rural Land and Business Management .... MSc 12FT
Wildlife Management and Conservation .... MSc 12FT

University of Salford
Real Estate Development ....MSc 12FT 28DL/PGDip 8FT 20DL
Real Estate and Property Management..... MSc 12FT 28DL/PGDip 8FT 20DL

Scotland's Rural College
Countryside Management........................ MSc 36DL/PGDip 24DL/ PGCert 12DL

Sheffield Hallam University
Charity Resource Management..... MSc 30PT/PGDip 18PT/PGCert 12PT
Public Rights of Way and Countryside Access Management. MSc 36DL
Urban Regeneration .... MSc 12FT 24PT

University of Sheffield
Conservation and Regeneration .... MA 12FT 24PT

Staffordshire University
Regeneration .... MA 12FT 24PT

Land management
Research Courses

University of Aberdeen
Land Economy (research degrees).......PhD 36FT 60PT/MPhil 24FT 42PT/MLE by research 12FT 24PT

Bangor University
Forest Ecology and Management........MPhil 24FT 36PT/PhD 36FT 60PT
Tropical Ecosystems .... MPhil 24FT 36PT/PhD 36FT 60PT

University of Cambridge
Biostatistics...PhD 36FT
Land Economy .... PhD 36FT 60PT
Land Economy (by thesis).. MPhil 11FT

Cranfield University
Land and Water Management .....Integrated PhD 48FT PhD 42FT

London School of Economics and Political Science (LSE)
Environmental Economics................. MPhil 36-48FT/PhD 36-48FT

Sheffield Hallam University
Countryside Research Unit..PhD/MPhil

University of the West of Scotland
Department of Land Economics.......................................PhD/MPhil

Planning and surveying
Taught Courses

Anglia Ruskin University
Conservation of Buildings.................................. MSc 12FT 24 - 30PT
Town Planning..MSc 12FT 24-30PT

University of Bradford
Regeneration Project Management .... PGCert 3FT

University of Cambridge
Planning, Growth and Regeneration.............................. MPhil 10FT

University of Central Lancashire
Building Conservation and Regeneration .... MSc 12FT 24-30PT/ PGDip 6FT 12PT/PGCert 3FT 6PT
Building Services...... MSc 12FT 30PT/PGDip 6FT 12PT/PGCert 3FT 6PT
Construction Project Management..... MSc 12FT 24PT/PGDip 6FT 12PT/PGCert 3FT 6PT

University of Dundee
Spatial Planning with Marine Spatial Planning .... MSc 12FT

University of Edinburgh
Architectural and Urban Design.. MSc 12FT

University of Exeter
Surveying and Land/ Environmental Management....... MSc 12FT 24-36PT/PGDip 12FT 24-36PT

Glasgow Caledonian University
Building Services Engineering.................................. MSc 12FT 24PT

Heriot-Watt University
MRes Courses in Urban Studies/Housing/Planning Studies/Real Estate Research .... MSc(Res) 12FT
Real Estate and Planning.......MSc 12FT 24PT 24-84DL/PGDip 9FT 21PT 24-84DL

Leeds Metropolitan University
Civil Engineering.. MSc 12FT 24PT
Contract Management ....MSc 24PT/PGDip 24PT
UK Planning Law & Practice ....Cert 36 (max)DL

University of Lincoln
Construction Project Management.................Diploma 12FT 36PT

Liverpool John Moores University
Commercial Building Surveying ....MSc 12FT 24PT/PGDip 12FT 24PT/PGCert 12FT 24PT
Commercial Property Development .... MSc 12FT 24PT
Quantity, Surveying & Commercial Management .... MSc 12FT 24PT
Sustainable Built Environment .... MSc 12FT

London Metropolitan University
Spatial Planning and Urban Design.......................... MA 12FT 30PT

London South Bank University
Building Surveying .... MSc 12FT 24PT
International Planning... MA 13.5FT 30PT
Planning Buildings for Health .... MSc 12FT MSc 24PT
Planning Policy and Practice....................................... MA 12FT 24PT
Property Development and Planning...................... MSc 12FT 24PT
Quantity Surveying .... MSc 12FT MSc 24PT
Transport Engineering and Planning....................... MSc 12FT 36PT

Newcastle University
Planning and Environment Research .... MA 12FT 24PT
Planning for Developing Countries.................................... MSc 12FT
Planning for Sustainability and Climate Change .... MSc 12FT
Spatial Planning...PGDip 9FT 21PT
Town Planning..MSc 12FT 24PT

Northumbria University
Construction Project Management...MSc 12FT 30PT/PGDip 12FT 24PT/PGCert 12FT 24PT
Surveying (Minerals)...MSc 24DL
Surveying/Construction programme - Building Surveying Pathway ....MSc 24DL
Surveying/Construction programme - Construction PathwayMSc 24DL
Surveying/Construction programme - Housing Pathway....... MSc 24DL
Surveying/Construction programme - Quantity Surveying Pathway ....MSc 24DL
Surveying/Construction programme - Real Estate Pathway.. MSc 24DL
Sustainable Development in the Built Environment ..... MSc 36PT

Nottingham Trent University
Construction Management ....MSc 12FT 24-60PT 24-60DL

University of Nottingham
Civil Engineering: Engineering Surveying .... MSc 12FT
Design ....MArch 12FT
Energy Conservation and Management.....MSc 12FT 24PT/PGDip 9FT 24PT
Part 3 Professional Practice Certificate / MArch conversion .... MArch 12FT

Oxford Brookes University
Planning .... PGDip 12FT 24PT
Spatial Planning ....MSc 12FT 24PT/PGDip 9FT 21PT
Spatial Planning Studies .... Cert 12PT
Urban Planning ....MRes 12FT 24PT
Urban Planning: Developing and Transitional Regions .... MSc 12FT 24PT

Plymouth University
Planning.. MSc 12FT

Queen's University Belfast
Planning and Regeneration ....MSc 12FT/PGDip 12FT

University of Reading
Corporate Real Estate ....MSc 24-72PT
Development Planning .... MSc 12FT 24PT/PGDip 12FT 24PT
Development Planning Research ......MSc 12FT 24PT/PGDip 12FT 24PT
International Planning and Sustainable Urban Management ..... MSc 12FT/PGCert 6FT/PGDip 9FT

Robert Gordon University
Construction Project Management. MSc 12FT 28-36PT 28-36DL/ PGDip 9FT 18-24PT 18-24DL/PGCert 4FT 9-12PT 9-12DL

Royal Agricultural University
Property Agency and Management.................................... MSc 12FT

University of Salford
Accessibility and Inclusive Design............ MSc 32DL/PGDip 20DL/ PGCert 8DL
Construction Management........MSc 12FT 24DL/PGDip 8FT 16DL
Corporate Real Estate and Facilities Management.......MSc 28DL/ PGDip 20DL/PGCert 8DL
Doctorate in the Built Environment (Professional Doctorate)....... DBEnv 60PT
Quantity Surveying........................MSc 12FT 28PT/PGDip 8FT 16PT
Quantity Surveying (Mechanical and Electrical) .... MSc 12FT 28DL/PGDip 8FT 16DL
Real Estate Development ....MSc 12FT 28DL/PGDip 8FT 20DL
Urban Design and Regeneration ....MSc 12FT 28PT/ PGDip 8FT 20PT
Urban Design and Regeneration ....MSc 12FT 28PT/ PGDip 8FT 18PT

Sheffield Hallam University
Built Environment..... MPhil 24FT 36PT/PhD by taught 24FT 60PT
Construction Management ....MSc 12FT 24-36PT

University of Sheffield
Planning and Development..MA 12FT
Urban Design.. MA 12FT 24PT
Urban Design and Planning..MA 12FT

University of South Wales
Asset Management and Development.............MSc 12FT 24-36PT
Building Information Modelling and Sustainability....... MSc 12FT 36PT

University of Strathclyde
Urban Design.... MSc 12FT 24PT/PGDip 9FT 18PT/PGCert 5FT 9PT

UCL - University College London
Built Environment: Environmental Design and Engineering......... MSc 12FT 24-60PT/PGDip 9FT
Built Environment: Heritage Science ....MRes 12FT 24-60PT/ PGCert 6FT
Built Environment: Sustainable Heritage....... MSc 12FT 24-60PT/ PGDip 9FT
International Planning......................MSc 12FT 24-60PT/PGDip 9FT
International Real Estate and Planning........... MSc 12FT 24-60PT/ PGDip 9FT
Mega Infrastructure Planning, Appraisal and Delivery .... MSc 12FT 24-60PT
Planning, Design and Development..... MSc 12FT 24-60PT/PGDip 9FT
Surveying...MSc 12FT 24PT
Urban Regeneration ....MSc 12FT 24-60PT/PGDip 9FT

University of the West of England, Bristol
Building Surveying...................MSc 24FT 36PT/GradDip 18FT 30PT

University of Westminster
Construction Commercial Management .... MSc 12FT 24PT

Planning and surveying
Research Courses

Anglia Ruskin University
Built Environment.....................................MPhil 24 - 60FT 36 - 72PT
Copy of Professional Doctorate in the Built Environment....DProf 60FT 60DL

University of Bolton
Built Environment Specialisms....PhD 36FT 72PT/PhD (via MPhil) 36FT 72PT/MPhil 24FT 36PT

University of Central Lancashire
Built Environment..........PhD 48FT 84PT/MPhil 36FT 60PT/MSc by research 24FT 36PT

City University London
Engineering Surveying Research Centre..........................PhD/MPhil

University of Dundee
Town and Regional Planning .... MPhil 24FT

Heriot-Watt University
Construction Management and Surveying PhD 36FT 48PT/MPhil 12FT 24PT

Kingston University
School of Surveying .... MA by research 12FT 24PT/ MPhil 24FT/PhD 36FT

London South Bank University
Faculty of Engineering, Science & the Built Environment.......PhD 36FT 60PT/MPhil 24FT 36PT

Loughborough University
Built Environment...PhD 36FT 60PT/MPhil 24FT 36PT/EngD 48FT

University of Manchester
Planning and Landscape..PhD 36FT

Nottingham Trent University
Surveying...PhD .FT .PT .DL/MPhil .FT .PT .DL

University of Nottingham
Building Services...PhD 12FT
Engineering and Surveying Space Geodesy...........PhD 36FT 72PT/ MPhil 24FT 48PT

Oxford Brookes University
Planning .... PhD 24-60FT 36-72PT/MPhil 24-36FT 36-48PT

University of Salford
Doctorate in the Built Environment (Professional Doctorate)....... DBEnv 60PT/DRealEst 60PT/DConsMgt 60PT
Research Centre for the Built and Human Environment
PhD 36FT 60PT 36-60DL/MPhil 36FT 60PT/MSc by research 12FT
SURFACE Inclusive Design Research Centre..........MSc by research 24DL/PhD 36FT 84PT

Section sponsored by
BPP UNIVERSITY COLLEGE

Business and social sciences
www.prospects.ac.uk/findcourses POSTGRADUATE DIRECTORY 451

Planning and surveying

University of Sheffield
City, Society and Planning: Integrated Studies.....New Route PhD 48FT

University of Southampton
Doctorate by research....PhD 36FT/MPhil 24FT

UCL - University College London
Advanced Spatial Analysis....PhD 36FT 60PT

University of the West of England, Bristol
School of the Built and Natural Environment....PhD -FT

University of Wolverhampton
Built Environment Research Unit....PhD 36FT/MPhil

Property studies
Taught Courses

University of Aberdeen
International Real Estate Markets....MSc 12FT/PGDip 12FT/PGCert 6FT
Real Estate....MSc 12FT/PGDip 9FT MBA 12FT
Real Estate Finance....MSc(Econ) 12FT/PGDip 9FT/PGCert 6FT
Urban Planning and Real Estate....MSc 12FT/PGDip 12FT

Birmingham City University
Real Estate Management.....PGCert 4FT 8PT/PGDip 4FT 8PT/MSc 4FT 8PT

College of Estate Management
Property Investment....PGDip 24DL/MSc 36DL
Real Estate....MSc 30DL
Real Estate and Construction Management....MBA 36DL

University of Cambridge
Land Economy Research....MPhil 10FT
Real Estate Finance....MPhil 10FT

Dublin Institute of Technology
Real Estate....MSc 30PT

Edinburgh Napier University
Property Management and Investment....MSc 12FT 24PT 36DL

Glasgow Caledonian University
Building Services Engineering....MSc 12FT 24PT
Real Estate Management....MSc 12FT 24PT
Sustainable Energy Technology....MSc 12FT 24PT

University of Glasgow
City Planning & Real Estate Development....MSc 12FT 24PT 60BM
Management with International Real Estate....MSc 12FT
Real Estate....MSc 12FT 24PT 60BM
Real Estate & Regeneration....MSc 12FT 24PT 60BM
Real Estate....PGCert 12FT

University of Greenwich
Real Estate Development and Investment....MSc 12FT 24PT

Heriot-Watt University
Housing and Real Estate....MSc 12FT 24PT 24-84DL/PGDip 9FT 18PT 18-84DL
MRes Courses in Urban Studies/Housing/Planning Studies/Real Estate Research....MSc(Res) 12FT
Real Estate Investment and Finance....MSc 12FT 24PT 24-84DL/PGDip 9FT 21PT 24-84DL
Real Estate Management and Development....MSc 12FT 24PT 24-84DL/PGDip 9FT 21PT 24-84DL
Real Estate and Planning....MSc 12FT 24PT 24-84DL/PGDip 9FT 21PT 24-84DL

Kingston University
Real Estate....MSc 12-24FT 24-48PT

Leeds Metropolitan University
Facilities Management....MSc 24DL

Liverpool John Moores University
Commercial Property Management....MSc 12FT 24PT/PGDip 12FT 24PT

London School of Economics and Political Science (LSE)
Development Studies....MSc 12FT 24PT
Real Estate Economics and Finance....MSc 12FT 24PT

London South Bank University
Planning Buildings for Health....MSc 12FT MSc 24PT
Property Development and Planning....MSc 12FT 24PT
Real Estate....MSc 12FT 24PT

Northumbria University
International Real Estate Management....MSc 12FT
Real Estate Management....MSc 12FT 36PT

Nottingham Trent University
International Real Estate Investment and Finance....MSc 12FT 24PT
Planning and Development....MSc 12FT 24PT
Real Estate....MSc 12FT 24PT

Oxford Brookes University
Real Estate....MSc 12FT 24PT
Real Estate Management....MSc 12FT/PGDip 9FT

University of Portsmouth
Property Development....MSc 12FT 24PT

University of Reading
Corporate Real Estate....MSc 24-72PT
Development Planning....MSc 12FT 24PT/PGDip 12FT 24PT
Development Planning Research....MSc 12FT 24PT/PGDip 12FT 24PT
International Planning and Sustainable Urban Management....MSc 12FT/PGCert 6FT/PGDip 9FT
Real Estate....MSc 12FT MSc 24-72PT
Real Estate Finance....MSc 12FT
Real Estate Investment and Finance....MSc 24-72PT

Robert Gordon University
Property Development....MSc 36DL

Royal Agricultural University
International Real Estate....MSc 12FT
Property Agency and Management....MSc 12FT
Rural Estate Management....MSc 12FT

University of Salford
Corporate Real Estate and Facilities Management....MSc 28DL/PGDip 20DL/PGCert 8DL
Real Estate Development....MSc 12FT 28DL/PGDip 8FT 20DL
Real Estate and Property Management....MSc 12FT 28DL/PGDip 8FT 20DL

Sheffield Hallam University
Real Estate....MSc 12FT 24PT
Real Estate - International....MSc 12FT

University of Sheffield
Commercial Property....MA 12FT

University of Ulster
Real Estate....MSc 12FT 36PT

UCL - University College London
International Real Estate and Planning....MSc 12FT 24-60PT/PGDip 9FT

University of the West of England, Bristol
Real Estate Management....MA 12FT 28PT/PGDip 9FT 21PT/PGCert 9FT 21PT
Real Estate Management....MA 12FT 28PT

University of Westminster
Construction Commercial Management....MSc 12FT 24PT
Property Finance....MSc 12FT 24PT
Real Estate Development....MSc 12FT 24PT

Property studies
Research Courses

University of Aberdeen
Finance....PhD 36FT/MPhil 24FT/MRes 12FT
Real Estate....PhD 36FT/MPhil 24FT

City University London
Real Estate Finance, Investment, Valuation, Management and Law....PhD/MPhil

University of Greenwich
Property/Construction by Research....MSc by research 12FT 24PT

London School of Economics and Political Science (LSE)
Development Studies....PhD 36-48FT/MPhil 36-48FT

Oxford Brookes University
Real Estate and Construction....PhD 24-60FT 36-72PT/MPhil 24-36FT 36-48PT

Sheffield Hallam University
Facilities and Property Management....DBA 48PT 48DL

Quantity surveying
Taught Courses

Glasgow Caledonian University
Quantity Surveying....MSc 12FT 24PT 24DL/PGCert 9FT 18PT/PGDip 6FT 12PT

Heriot-Watt University
Quantity Surveying....MSc 12FT 24PT 24-84DL/PGDip 9FT 21PT 24-84DL

Kingston University
Quantity Surveying....MSc 12FT 24PT

Liverpool John Moores University
Quantity, Surveying & Commercial Management....MSc 12FT 24PT

London South Bank University
Quantity Surveying....MSc 12FT MSc 24PT

Northumbria University
Surveying/Construction programme - Quantity Surveying Pathway....MSc 24DL

Nottingham Trent University
Quantity Surveying....MSc 12FT 24PT

University of Portsmouth
Quantity Surveying....MSc 12FT 24PT

University of Salford
Quantity Surveying....MSc 12FT 28PT/PGDip 8FT 16PT
Quantity Surveying (Mechanical and Electrical).MSc 12FT 28DL/PGDip 8FT 16DL

Quantity surveying
Research Courses

University of Nottingham
Engineering and Surveying Space Geodesy....PhD 36FT 72PT/MPhil 24FT 48PT
Geospatial Science....PhD 12-48FT

Town and country planning
Taught Courses

University of Aberdeen
Urban Planning and Real Estate....MSc 12FT/PGDip 12FT

Aberystwyth University
Regional and Environmental Policy....MA 12FT 24PT/PGDip 9FT 18PT

Anglia Ruskin University
Town Planning....MSc 12FT 24-30PT

Birmingham City University
Environmental Sustainability....PGCert 4FT 8PT/PGDip 4FT 8PT/MSc 4FT 8PT
Environmental Sustainability (Design and Construction)....PGCert 4FT 8PT/PGDip 4FT 8PT/MSc 4FT 8PT
Environmental and Spatial Planning...PGCert 4FT 8PT/PGDip 4FT 8PT/MA 4FT 8PT

University of Birmingham
Local and Regional Economic Development....MSc 12FT 24PT/PGDip 9FT 21PT/GradDip 9FT 21PT/GradCert 9FT 21PT
Urban Regeneration and Renewal...MSc 12FT 24PT/GradDip 9FT 21PT/GradCert 9FT 21PT/PGDip 9FT 21PT
Urban and Regional Planning (with RTPI accreditation) MSc 12FT 24PT/PGCert 6FT 12PT/PGDip 12FT 24PT

University of Brighton
Town Planning.....MSc 12FT 24PT/PGDip 12FT 24PT/PGCert 12FT 24PT

Cardiff University
European Spatial Planning, Environmental Policies and Regional Development....MSc 24FT
Planning Practice....PGCert 8-36PT
Planning Practice and Research....MSc 12FT 24PT
Sustainability, Planning and Environmental PolicyMSc 12FT 24PT
Urban Design....MA 12FT

University College Cork
Planning & Sustainable Development....MPlan 24FT

Dublin Institute of Technology
Planning and Development....MSc 24PT
Regional and Local Development....MSc 12FT
Spatial Planning....MSc 30PT

University of Dundee
Advanced Sustainable Urban Design....MSc 12FT
Spatial Planning with Environmental Assessment....MSc 12FT
Spatial Planning with Sustainable Urban Design....MSc 12FT
Spatial Planning with Urban Conservation....MSc 12FT

Edinburgh Napier University
Design (Urbanism)....MA/MDes 12FT

University of Glasgow
City & Regional Planning....MSc 12FT 24PT 60BM
City Planning & Real Estate Development....MSc 12FT 24PT 60BM
City Planning & Regeneration....MSc 12FT 24PT 60BM

Heriot-Watt University
Courses in Urban Studies/Housing/Planning Studies/Real Estate Research....MSc(Res) 12FT
Sustainable Urban ManagementMSc 12FT 24PT 24-84DL/PGDip 9FT 21PT 24-84DL
Urban Strategies and Design....MSc 12FT 24PT/PGDip 9FT 21PT
Urban and Regional Planning....MSc 12FT 24PT 24-84DL/PGDip 9FT 21PT 24-84DL

Institute of Education
Educational Planning, Economics and International Development....MA 12FT 24-48PT

Keele University
Urban Futures and Sustainable Communities....MA 12FT 24PT/PGDip 12FT 24PT/PGCert 12FT 24PT

King's College London
Cities....MA 12FT 24PT/MSc 12FT 24PT

Leeds Metropolitan University
Housing, Regeneration and Urban Management MA 12FT 24PT/PGCert 12FT 12PT/PGDip 12FT 24PT
Town and Regional Planning....MA 12FT 24PT

University of Liverpool
Environmental Management and Planning....MA 12FT 24PT
Town and Regional Planning....MA 12FT 24PT/PGDip 12FT 24PT MCD 12FT 24PT

London School of Economics and Political Science (LSE)
Local Economic Development....MSc 12FT
Regional and Urban Planning Studies....MSc 12FT 24-48PT
Urban Policy (Double Degree)....MSc 23FT

Business and social sciences
452 POSTGRADUATE DIRECTORY www.prospects.ac.uk/findcourses

Section sponsored by
BPP UNIVERSITY COLLEGE

Planning and surveying

London South Bank University
Planning Policy and Practice........ MA 12FT 24PT
Town Planning........ MA 12FT 24PT/PGDip 12FT 24PT

University of Manchester
Planning........ MPlan 12FT 24PT

Newcastle University
Planning and Environment Research........ MA 12FT 24PT
Planning for Developing Countries........ MSc 12FT
Planning for Sustainability and Climate Change........ MSc 12FT
Spatial Planning........ PGDip 9FT 21PT
Town Planning........ Diploma 12FT MSc 12FT 24PT

University of Northampton
Sustainable Urban Environments........ PGCert 6PT

Nottingham Trent University
PG Cert Planning, Urban Design and Sustainable Development . PGCert 12PT

Oxford Brookes University
Planning........ PGDip 12FT 24PT
Spatial Planning........ MSc 12FT 24PT/PGDip 9FT 21PT
Spatial Planning Studies........ Cert 12PT
Urban and Regional Regeneration........ PGCert 9FT

Plymouth University
Planning........ MSc 12FT

Queen's University Belfast
Environmental Planning........ MSc 12FT
Planning and Regeneration........ MSc 12FT/PGDip 12FT
Urban and Rural Design........ MSc 12FT/PGDip 12FT

University of Reading
Development Planning........ MSc 12FT 24PT/PGDip 12FT 24PT
Development Planning Research........ MSc 12FT 24PT/PGDip 12FT 24PT
Real Estate........ MSc 12FT
Real Estate........ MSc 24-72PT
Real Estate Finance........ MSc 12FT
Rural Land and Business Management........ MSc 12FT

University of Salford
Urban Design and Regeneration MSc 12FT 28PT/PGDip 8FT 20PT

Sheffield Hallam University
Housing Practice........ CertHE 24PT 24DL
Housing Professional Studies........ DipHE 18PT 12-18DL
Housing for Environmental Health........ CertHE 18PT
Urban and Regional Planning........ MSc 12FT 24PT
Urban and Regional Planning (Transport)........ MSc 12FT 24PT

University of Sheffield
Architecture and Town and Regional Planning........ MArch 24FT
International Development and Planning........ MA 12FT
Planning Research........ MA 12FT
Planning and Development........ MA 12FT
Town and Regional Planning........ MA 12FT
Urban Design........ MA 12FT 24PT
Urban Design and Planning........ MA 12FT

University of Stirling
Environmental Policy and Governance........ LLM 12FT/MSc 12FT

University of Strathclyde
Urban Design.... MSc 12FT 24PT/PGDip 9FT 18PT/PGCert 5FT 9PT

UCL - University College London
Building and Urban Design in Development . MSc 12FT 24-60PT/PGDip 9FT
Planning, Design and Development..... MSc 12FT 24-60PT/PGDip 9FT
Spatial Planning........ MSc 12FT 24-60PT/PGDip 9FT

University of West London
Development and Management of Sustainable Built Environment........ MSc 12FT 24PT

University of the West of England, Bristol
Town and Country Planning........ MA 12FT 28PT
Town and Country Planning Joint Distance Learning... MA TBCDL

University of Winchester
Regional and Local Archaeology. MA 12FT 24PT/PGDip 9FT 18PT/PGCert 9FT 18PT

Town and country planning
Research Courses

Cardiff University
Institute of Environment and Sustainability........ PhD 36FT/MPhil 60PT
Urban and Regional Governance........ PhD 36FT 60PT

University of Dundee
Non-Graduating Research in School of the Environment (6 months or more)........ Non-Grad 6-24FT
Non-Graduating Research in School of the Environment (less than 6 months)........ Non-Grad 1-5FT
Town and Regional Planning (MPhil)........ MPhil 24FT
Town and Regional Planning (PhD)........ PhD 36FT

Kingston University
Centre for Suburban Studies.... PhD 48FT 72PT/MPhil 24FT 48PT/MA by research 12FT 24PT

University of Liverpool
Civic Design........ PhD 36FT 60PT/MPhil 12FT 24PT

London School of Economics and Political Science (LSE)
Regional and Urban Planning........ PhD 36-48FT/MPhil 36-48FT

Oxford Brookes University
Planning........ PhD 24-60FT 36-72PT/MPhil 24-36FT 36-48PT

University of Sheffield
City, Society and Planning: Integrated Studies..... New Route PhD 48FT
Town and Regional Planning..... PhD 36FT 72PT/MPhil 24FT 48PT

UCL - University College London
Town Planning........ PhD 36FT 60PT

Transport planning
Taught Courses

Cardiff University
International Transport........ MSc 12FT 24PT
Port and Shipping Administration........ PGDip 9FT
Transport and Planning........ MSc 12FT

City University London
Transport Strategy and Systems........ MSc 12FT 24-30PT

Cranfield University
Air Transport Management........ MSc 12FT
Air Transport Management (Executive)........ MSc 24-48PT

Edinburgh Napier University
Transport Planning and Engineering........ MSc 12FT 36PT 36DL

Heriot-Watt University
Urban Strategies and Design....... MSc 12FT 24PT/PGDip 9FT 21PT

Imperial College London
Transport, also with Business Management or Sustainable Development........ MSc 12FT 24-36PT

University of Leeds
Sustainability (Transport) MSc 12FT 24-36PT/PGDip 9FT 18-24PT
Transport Planning.... MSc 12FT 24-36PT/PGDip 9-12FT 18-24PT/PGCert 3FT 6-9PT
Transport Planning and Engineering...... MSc(Eng) 12FT 24-36PT/PGDip 9FT 18-24PT/PGCert 3FT 6-9PT
Transport Planning and the Environment...... MSc 12FT 24-36PT/PGDip 9FT 18-24PT/PGCert 3FT 6-9PT

Liverpool John Moores University
Port Management........ MSc 12FT

Loughborough University
Human Factors in Transport........ MSc 12FT 24 - 36PT/PGDip 8FT 20PT

Manchester Metropolitan University
Sustainable Aviation........ MSc 12FT 12-36PT

Newcastle University
Transport Planning and Business Management........ MSc 12FT 24-48PT
Transport Planning and Engineering........ MSc 12FT 24-48PT
Transport Planning and Intelligent Transport Systems........ MSc 12FT 24PT
Transport Planning and the Environment........ MSc 12FT 24-48PT

University of Nottingham
Sustainable Bioenergy........ MRes 12-36PT

Plymouth University
Planning........ MSc 12FT

University of Reading
International Shipping and Finance........ MSc 12FT

University of Salford
Transport Engineering and Planning........ MSc 12FT 36PT

Sheffield Hallam University
Transport Planning and Management........ MSc 12FT 36PT
Urban and Regional Planning (Transport)........ MSc 12FT 24PT

Southampton Solent University
International Maritime Studies - Shipping and Logistics........ MSc 12FT 24PT
International Maritime Studies: Ship and Shipping Management MSc 12FT 24PT
Shipping Operations........ MSc 12-24DL

University of Southampton
Transportation Planning and Engineering........ MSc 12FT 24PT/PGDip 12FT

University of Surrey
Transport Planning and Practice........ MSc 12FT 72PT

UCL - University College London
Transport........ MSc 12FT 24PT

University of the West of England, Bristol
Transport Planning........ MSc 12FT 28PT

University of Westminster
International Planning and Sustainable Development... MA 12FT 24PT
Transport Planning and Management........ MSc 12FT 24PT

Transport planning
Research Courses

Arts University Bournemouth
MPhil / PhD........ MPhil 24FT/PhD 36FT

University of Central Lancashire
Politics and International studies.... MPhil 18-36FT 42-60PT/PhD 30-48FT 66-84PT/MA by research 12FT 24PT

University of Leeds
Transport Studies.... PhD 36FT 60PT/MPhil 24FT 48PT/MRes 12FT
Transport Studies - PhD, MPhil, MRes PhD 36FT 60PT/MPhil 24FT 48PT/MRes 12FT

Urban planning
Taught Courses

University of Aberdeen
Bayt al-Maqdis and Jerusalem Studies.... MLitt 12FT 24PT/PGDip 9FT 18PT

University of the Arts London - Central Saint Martins College of Art and Design
Architecture: Cities and Innovation........ MA 24FT

Birmingham City University
Environmental and Spatial Planning........ PGCert 4FT 8PT/PGDip 4FT 8PT/MA 4FT 8PT
Urban Design........ MA 12FT 24PT

University of Birmingham
International Development (Urban Development)....... MSc 12FT/PGDip 9FT
Local and Regional Economic Development........ MSc 12FT 24PT/PGDip 9FT 21PT/GradDip 9FT 21PT
Resilience and Urban Living........ MSc 12FT 24PT/MRes 12FT 24PT
Urban Regeneration and Renewal....... MSc 12FT 24PT/PGDip 9FT 21PT
Urban and Regional Planning (with RTPI accreditation) MSc 12FT 24PT/PGCert 6FT 12PT/PGDip 12FT 24PT
Urban and Regional Studies........ MSc 12FT 24PT/PGDip 9FT 21PT

University of Cambridge
Environmental Design in Architecture Option B........ PGDip 21FT

Cardiff University
European Spatial Planning, Environmental Policies and Regional Development........ MSc 24FT
International Planning and Development........ MSc 12FT
Regeneration Studies........ MSc 12FT 24PT
Urban Design........ MA 12FT

University of Central Lancashire
Building Conservation and Regeneration....... MSc 12FT 24-30PT/PGDip 6FT 12PT/PGCert 3FT 6PT
Building Services...... MSc 12FT 30PT/PGDip 6FT 12PT/PGCert 3FT 6PT
Urban Environmental Management... MSc 12FT 24PT/PGDip 9FT 18PT/PGCert 6FT 12PT

Dublin Institute of Technology
Spatial Planning........ MSc 30PT

University of Dundee
Advanced Sustainable Urban Design........ MSc 12FT
Spatial Planning with Marine Spatial Planning........ MSc 12FT
Spatial Planning with Sustainable Urban Design........ MSc 12FT
Spatial Planning with Urban Conservation........ MSc 12FT

University of East London
Architecture: Urban Design MA........ MA 12FT 24PT/PGDip 8FT 16PT/PGCert 4FT 8PT

Edinburgh Napier University
Design (Urbanism)........ MA/MDes 12FT

University of Edinburgh
Architectural and Urban Design........ MSc 12FT

University of Glasgow
City & Regional Planning........ MSc 12FT 24PT 60BM
City Planning & Real Estate Development........ MSc 12FT 24PT 60BM
City Planning & Regeneration........ MSc 12FT 24PT 60BM
Spatial Planning........ PGCert 48BM
Urban & Housing Practice........ MSc 12FT 24PT 60BM/PGDip 9FT
Urban Policy & Practice.... MSc 12FT 24PT 60BM/PGDip 9FT 18PT 48BM
Urban Regeneration........ MSc 12FT 24PT 60BM/PGDip 9FT 18PT

Goldsmiths, University of London
Photography and Urban Cultures........ MA 12FT 24PT
World Cities and Urban Life........ MA 12FT 24PT

University of Greenwich
Built Environment (Open)........ MSc 12FT 24PT
Urban Design........ MA 12FT 24PT

Heriot-Watt University
MRes Courses in Urban Studies/Housing/Planning Studies/Real Estate Research........ MSc(Res) 12FT
Sustainable Community Design. MSc 12FT 24PT 24-84DL/PGDip 9FT 21PT 24-84DL
Urban Strategies and Design....... MSc 12FT 24PT/PGDip 9FT 21PT

Section sponsored by

BPP
UNIVERSITY
COLLEGE

Business and social sciences
www.prospects.ac.uk/findcourses POSTGRADUATE DIRECTORY 453

Planning and surveying

Urban and Regional Planning .... MSc 12FT 24PT 24-84DL/
PGDip 9FT 21PT 24-84DL

Institute of Education
Educational Planning, Economics and International
Development.. MA 12FT 24-48PT

Keele University
Urban Futures and Sustainable Communities....... MA 12FT 24PT/
PGDip 12FT 24PT/PGCert 12FT 24PT

University of Kent
Architecture and Cities .... MA 12FT 24PT
Architecture and Cities (Paris option) .... MA 12FT
Architecture and Sustainable Environments .... MSc 12FT 24PT
Master of Architecture (MArch with ARB/RIBA Part 2 exemption)
MArch 24FT
Social and Public Policy: Urban Regeneration (Distance Learning,
Medway).. MA 24DL/PGDip 24DL

King's College London
Sustainable Cities.. MSc 12FT 24PT

Kingston University
Landscape and Urbanism.................................... MA 12FT 24PT
Sustainable Place Making and Urban Design .... MA 12FT 24PT

Leeds Metropolitan University
Architectural Professional Practice .... PGDip 24PT
Housing, Regeneration and Urban Management MA 12FT 24PT/
PGCert 12FT 12PT/PGDip 12FT 24PT
Town and Regional Planning.. MA 12FT 24PT
Urban DesignMA 12FT 24PT/PGDip 12FT 24PT/PGCert 12FT 24PT

University of Leeds
Culture, Creativity and Entrepreneurship... MA 12FT 24PT/PGDip
9FT 21PT/PGCert 6FT 12PT

University of Leicester
Urban Conservation..........................MA 12FT 24PT/MSc 12FT 24PT

University of Lincoln
Development and Regeneration .... MA 12FT 24PT
Planning and Urban Design..MA 12FT

Liverpool John Moores University
Architecture and Urban Design ....MA 6FT 38PT

University of Liverpool
Urban Regeneration and Management................... MSc 12FT 24PT

London Metropolitan University
Planning and Sustainable Communities................ MSc 12FT 24PT
Spatial Planning and Urban Design.......................... MA 12FT 27PT
MA 12FT 30PT
Sustainable Cities..MSc 12FT 24+PT

London School of Economics and Political Science (LSE)
City Design and Social Science.................................. MSc 12FT 24PT
Regional and Urban Planning Studies ....MSc 12FT 24-48PT
Urban Policy (Double Degree).. MSc 23FT
Urbanisation and Development................................ MSc 12FT 24PT

London South Bank University
Cities and Local Development....................................... MSc 24PT
Development and Urbanisation.................................. MSc 13FT 24PT
Urban Planning Design .... MA 12FT 24PT
Urban Regeneration .... MA 13FT 30PT

University of Manchester
Global Urban Development and Planning............. MSc 12FT 24PT

Newcastle University
Architectural Design Research ....MA 12FT
Planning and Environment Research .... MA 12FT 24PT
Planning for Developing Countries.................................. MSc 12FT
Planning for Sustainability and Climate Change........... MSc 12FT
Spatial Planning..PGDip 9FT 21PT
Urban Design........................... MA 12FT 24PT/PGDip 9FT 21PT

University of Northampton
Sustainable Urban Environments .... PGCert 6PT
Urbanism: Design and Environment......................... MSc 12FT 24PT

Nottingham Trent University
PG Cert Planning, Urban Design and Sustainable
Development..PGCert 12PT

University of Nottingham
Urban Design..MArch 12FT

Oxford Brookes University
Applied Design in Architecture ....MArchD 24FT
Planning ....PGDip 12FT 24PT
Spatial Planning ....MSc 12FT 24PT/PGDip 9FT 21PT
Spatial Planning Studies ....Cert 12PT
Urban Design .... MA 12FT 24PT/PGDip 8FT 20PT/PGCert 8PT
MRes 12FT 24PT
Urban Planning ....MRes 12FT 24PT
Urban Planning: Developing and Transitional Regions MSc 12FT
24PT
Urban and Regional Regeneration .... PGCert 9FT

Plymouth University
Master of Architecture..MArch 12FT 24PT
Planning.. MSc 12FT

University of Portsmouth
Urban Design .... MA 12FT 24PT

Queen's University Belfast
Planning and Regeneration ....MSc 12FT/PGDip 12FT
Urban and Rural Design................................MSc 12FT/PGDip 12FT

Ravensbourne
Environment Design.. MA 12FT 24PT

University of Reading
Development Planning .... MSc 12FT 24PT/PGDip 12FT 24PT
Development Planning Research ......MSc 12FT 24PT/PGDip 12FT
24PT
International Planning and Sustainable Urban Management .....
MSc 12FT/PGCert 6FT/PGDip 9FT

University of Salford
Urban Design and Regeneration MSc 12FT 28PT/PGDip 8FT 20PT

Sheffield Hallam University
Built Environment .....MPhil 24FT 36PT/PhD by taught 24FT 60PT
Urban and Regional Planning ....MSc 12FT 24PT
Urban and Regional Planning (Transport)............... MSc 12FT 24PT

University of Sheffield
Architectural Design...MA 12FT
Conservation and Regeneration .... MA 12FT 24PT
Environmental Management of Urban Land and Water ....
MSc 12FT 24PT/PGDip 9FT 18PT/PGCert 6FT 12PT
Planning and Development ....MA 12FT
Town and Regional Planning..MA 12FT
Urban Design.. MA 12FT 24PT
Urban Design and Planning..MA 12FT

University of Strathclyde
Advanced Architectural Design .... MArch 12FT 24PT/PGDip 9FT
21PT
Advanced Architectural Studies ....MSc 12FT 24PT/
PGDip 9FT 18PT
Urban Design.... MSc 12FT 24PT/PGDip 9FT 18PT/PGCert 5FT 9PT

Trinity College Dublin - the University of Dublin
Environment and Development .... MSc 12FT

UCL - University College London
Building and Urban Design in Development .... MSc 12FT
24-60PT/PGDip 9FT
Built Environment: Environmental Design and Engineering.........
MSc 12FT 24-60PT/PGDip 9FT
Built Environment: Heritage Science ....MRes 12FT 24-60PT/
PGCert 6FT

Built Environment: Sustainable Heritage .... MSc 12FT 24-60PT/
PGDip 9FT
Mega Infrastructure Planning, Appraisal and Delivery ....
MSc 12FT 24-60PT
Planning, Design and Development..... MSc 12FT 24-60PT/PGDip
9FT
Spatial Planning....................................MSc 12FT 24-60PT/PGDip 9FT
Sustainable Urbanism.......................MSc 12FT 24-60PT/PGDip 9FT
Urban Design....................................MArch 12FT 24-60PT/PGDip 9FT
Urban Development Planning ....MSc 12FT 24-60PT/PGDip 9FT
Urban Economic Development.......MSc 12FT 24-60PT/PGDip 9FT
Urban Regeneration ....MSc 12FT 24-60PT/PGDip 9FT

University of West London
Development and Management of Sustainable Built
Environment...MSc 12FT 24PT

University of the West of England, Bristol
Spatial Planning..MA TBCDL
Urban Design .... MA 18FT 27PT

University of Westminster
Urban Design Postgraduate Diploma .... PGDip 12FT 24PT
Urban and Regional Planning .... MA 12FT 24PT

Urban planning
Research Courses

University of Birmingham
Urban and Regional Studies ...... PhD 36FT 72PT/MPhil 24FT 48PT

Cardiff University
Environment................................. PhD 36FT 60PT/MPhil 36FT 60PT
Spatial Analysis... PhD 36FT 60PT
Spatial Planning and City Environments................. PhD 36FT 60PT

University of Dundee
Non-Graduating Research in School of the Environment (6
months or more)..Non-Grad 6-24FT
Non-Graduating Research in School of the Environment (less
than 6 months) .... Non-Grad 1-5FT

University of Glasgow
Urban Studies............................. PhD 36FT/MLitt by research 12FT

London School of Economics and Political Science (LSE)
Cities.. PhD 36-48FT/MPhil 36-48FT
Regional and Urban Planning .... PhD 36-48FT/MPhil 36-48FT

The Open University
Materialities, Space and Power........... PhD 36FT 72PT variableDL/
MPhil 15FT 24PT variableDL

Oxford Brookes University
Planning .... PhD 24-60FT 36-72PT/MPhil 24-36FT 36-48PT
Urban Design........ PhD 24-60FT 36-72PT/MPhil 24-36FT 36-48PT

Plymouth University
Architecture ....MRes 12FT

University of Salford
Centre for Policy Studies...PhD/MPhil

Sheffield Hallam University
Centre for Regional Economic and Social Research Applied Social
Research.. PhD 36FT 60PT
Centre for Regional Economic and Social Research Applied Social
Research.. PhD 36FT 60PT
Environment and Development ....MPhil 36FT
Environment and Development - Facilities Management.......PhD
33FT 45PT/MPhil 18FT 30PT

University of Sheffield
City, Society and Planning: Integrated Studies.....New Route PhD
48FT

Political science

European politics
Taught Courses

University of Aberdeen
European Politics and Society.....MSc 12FT 24PT/PGDip 9FT 18PT

Aberystwyth University
European Politics (Research Training)....MA 12FT
European Politics (Specialist)....MA 12FT
Modern European History (Political Culture).........MA 12FT 24PT/PGDip 9FT 18PT

Aston University
European Union and International Relations . MA 12FT 24 - 36PT
Politics and International Relations................MRes 12FT 24 - 36PT

Bangor University
Language, Policy and Planning.......MA 12FT 24-48PT/PGDip 8FT/PGCert 4FT
Policy Research and Evaluation........MA 12FT 21-30PT/PGDip 9FT 17-21PT/PGCert 5FT 12-21PT
Social Policy, Sociology....PhD by taught 36FT 60PT/MPhil 12-24FT 24-36PT

University of Bath
Contemporary European Studies ('Euromasters') and 'Euromasters' with Trans-Atlantic Track ....MA 24FT
International Relations and European Politics..... MA 12FT/PGDip 24FT/PGCert 24FT
Politics & International Studies .... MRes 12FT/PGDip 9FT/PGCert 9FT

Birkbeck, University of London
European Politics and Policy....MSc 12FT 24PT
Global Governance and Emerging Powers.............MSc 12FT 24PT
Politics....MRes 12FT 24PT

University of Birmingham
European Studies.... MA 12FT 24PT
International Relations (Terrorism and Political Violence)........MA 12FT 24PT

University of Bristol
European Governance....MSc 12FT 24PT

University of Cambridge
Politics....MPhil 10FT

Cardiff University
European Governance and Public Policy...... MSc(Econ) 12FT 24PT

University of Central Lancashire
International Relations....MA 12FT

University College Dublin
European Economic & Public Affairs.... MEconSci 12FT

University of Dundee
International Politics and Security ....MLitt 12FT/PGDip 9FT

University of East Anglia
International Relations and European Studies....... MA 12FT 24PT

University of Edinburgh
International and European Politics....MSc 12FT 24PT

University of Essex
Conflict Resolution....MA 12FT 24PT/MSc 12FT 24PT
Global and Comparative Politics ...MA 12FT 24PT/MSc 12FT 24PT
Ideology and Discourse Analysis.... MA 12FT 24PT
International Relations................. MA 12FT 24PT/MSc 12FT 24PT/MRes 12FT
International Relations and the Media.... MA 12FT 24PT
Multilevel Governance in Europe.... MA 12FT 24PT/MSc 12FT 24PT
Political Behaviour....MA 12FT 24PT/MSc 12FT 24PT
Political Economy........MA 12FT 24PT/MSc 12FT 24PT/MRes 12FT
Political Science.....MA 12FT 24PT/GradDip 12FT/MSc 12FT 24PT/MRes 12FT 24PT
Political Theory.... MA 12FT 24PT
Politics.... MA 12FT 24PT
Public Opinion and Polling.............MA 12FT 24PT/MSc 12FT 24PT

University of Exeter
European Politics.... MA 12FT 24PT

University of Glasgow
Europe and International Development....MSc 12FT
European Politics....MSc 12FT 24PT

University of Hull
Global Communication and International Politics....MA 12FT 24PT

Keele University
Masters in Politics and International Relations.....MA 12FT 24PT/MRes 12FT 24PT

University of Kent
European Public Policy (Brussels).... MA 12FT 24PT
European and Global Governance...... PGDip 12FT 24PT/MA 12FT 24PT
European and Global Governance (International Double Award) MA 24FT

King's College London
European Public Policy....MA 12FT
Russian Politics & Society....MSc 12FT 24PT

Lancaster University
European Institutions and Policy-Making....MA 12FT
Politics.................MA 12FT 24PT/MPhil 24FT/PhD by taught 24FT

University of Leeds
Politics.... MA 12FT 24PT

University of Liverpool
Research (European Union Politics).... MA 12FT 24PT

London School of Economics and Political Science (LSE)
Political Economy of Europe....MSc 12FT 24PT

London South Bank University
European Policy Studies.... MA 12FT 24PT

Loughborough University
Research methods (European and International Studies)...... MSc 12FT 24PT

University of Manchester
Political Science - European Politics & Policy.........MA 12FT 24PT/PGDip 9FT 24PT

National University of Ireland, Maynooth
European Social Policy Analysis....MA 12FT

Newcastle University
European Union Studies.... MA 12FT 24PT

University of Oxford
Global Governance and Diplomacy.... MSc 12FT
Politics: European Politics & Society .... MPhil 21FT
Russian and East European Studies.............MPhil 21FT/MSc 12FT

University of Portsmouth
European Studies.... MA 12FT 24PT

Queen's University Belfast
European Union Politics..............MA 12FT 24PT/PGDip 12FT 24PT
Irish Politics....MA 12FT 24PT/PGDip 12FT 24PT

University of Reading
Diplomacy ....MA 12FT 72PT/PGDip 12FT 72PT/PGCert 12FT 72PT
Diplomacy ....MA 12FT 24-72PT/PGCert 12FT 24-72PT/PGDip 12FT 24-72PT
International Relations ....MA (res) 12FT 24-72PT 72BM
International Relations (Strategic Studies) ......MA 12FT 24-72PT/PGDip 24-72PT/PGCert 12FT 24PT

Reseau Universitaire Transmanche
Conflict, Peace and Identity: France, Britain and Europe .... MA 15FT

Royal Holloway, University of London
European Politics....MSc 12/9FT 24/20PT

University of Sheffield
European Governance and Politics.... MA 12FT 24PT
European Health Law and Policy.... LLM 12FT 24PT
European Law, Politics and Governance....MA 12FT
European and Global Affairs....MA 24FT

University of Southampton
European Law.... LLM 12FT 24PT

University of Strathclyde
European Public Policy....MSc 12FT 24PT
International Law and Sustainable DevelopmentLLM 12FT 24PT/PGDip 9FT 21PT/PGCert 4FT 8PT

University of Surrey
European Politics.... MA 12FT 24PT
European Politics, Business and Law.... MA 12FT 24PT
European and International Politics.... MA 12FT 24PT

University of Sussex
European Politics.... MA 12FT 24PT

Swansea University
Politics.... MA 12FT 24PT

Trinity College Dublin - the University of Dublin
European Studies.... MPhil 12FT
International Politics....MSc 12FT 24PT

University of Ulster
Irish History and Society............... MA 14FT 27PT/PGDip 9FT 18PT

UCL - University College London
European Public Policy....MSc 12FT 24PT
European Studies: European Society.... MA 12FT 24PT/PGDip 9FT 18PT/PGCert 3FT 6PT
European Studies: Modern European Studies.......MA 12FT 24PT/PGDip 9FT 18PT

University of Warwick
International Politics and Europe......... MA 12FT 24PT/PGDip 9FT
Research in Politics and International Studies.......MA 12FT 24PT/PGDip 9PT

European politics
Research Courses

School of Advanced Study, University of London
Politics and International Studies.......PhD 36FT 72PT/MPhil 12FT 36PT

Bangor University
Social Policy....PhD 36FT 60PT/MPhil 12-24FT 24-36PT

University of Birmingham
European Research.... PhD 36FT 72PT/MPhil 24FT 48PT

University of Dundee
Politics.... MPhil 24FT

University of East Anglia
Cultural Politics and Contemporary Political Theory.......PhD 36FT 72PT/MPhil 24FT 48PT/MA by research 12FT 24PT
International Politics .... PhD 36FT 72PT/MPhil 24FT 48PT
Political, Social and International Studies...PhD 36FT 72PT/MPhil 24FT 48PT/MA by research 12FT 24PT
Politics and Media...........PhD 36FT 72PT/MPhil 24FT 48PT/MA by research 12FT 24PT
Public Policy and Public Management....PhD 36FT 72PT/MPhil 24FT 48PT/MA by research 12FT 24PT

University of Essex
Government.....PhD 36FT 72PT/MPhil 24FT 48PT/MA by research 12FT 24PT

University of Exeter
European Studies.... PhD 48FT 89PT/MPhil 36FT 60PT

Keele University
European Studies.... MPhil 24FT 36PT/PhD 48FT 84PT
Politics.... MPhil 24FT 36PT/PhD 48FT 84PT

King's College London
Politics Research ....MPhil 24FT 36PT/PhD 36FT 48-72PT

Kingston University
European Research Centre (ERC) ....PhD 48FT 72PT/MPhil 24FT 48PT/MA by research 12FT 24PT

London School of Economics and Political Science (LSE)
European Studies.... PhD 36-48FT/MPhil 36-48FT

Loughborough University
European Studies and International Relations.... PhD 36FT/MPhil 24FT

The Open University
Citizenship and security.... PhD 36FT 72PT variableDL/MPhil 15FT 24PT variableDL
Comparative Politics.... PhD 36FT 72PT variableDL/MPhil 15FT 24PT variableDL
Governing global security.... PhD 36FT 72PT variableDL/MPhil 15FT 24PT variableDL
Political Theory......... PhD 36FT 72PT variableDL/MPhil 15FT 24PT variableDL

University of Salford
Centre for Contemporary History & Politics....PhD/MPhil

University of Sussex
Politics Research Programme........... PhD 24-48FT 36-72PT/MPhil 12-36FT 24-48PT

UCL - University College London
East European Politics.... PhD 36FT 60PT
European Studies.... PhD 36FT 60PT

International relations
Taught Courses

University of Aberdeen
Globalization MLitt 12FT 24PT/PGDip 9FT 18PT/PGCert 6FT 12PT
International Relations................MSc 12FT 24PT/PGDip 9FT 18PT
Strategic Studies.... MLitt 12FT 24PT/PGDip 9FT 18PT

Aberystwyth University
Critical International Politics (Research Training).......... MA 12FT/PGDip 9FT
Critical International Politics (Specialist).......MA 12FT/PGDip 9FT
Democracy, Human Security and International Law.......LLM 12FT
European Politics (Research Training)....MA 12FT
European Politics (Specialist)....MA 12FT
Food & Water Security.................MSc 12FT 24PT/PGDip 9FT 18PT
Intelligence Studies....MA 12FT/PGDip 9FT
Intelligence Studies and International History (Specialist)......MA 12FT/PGDip 9FT
Intelligence and Strategic Studies (Specialist)....MA 12FT
International History (Research Training)....MA 12FT
International History (Specialist)....MA 12FT
International Politics of the Internet....MA 12FT
International Relations (Research Training)....MA 12FT
International Relations (Specialist)....MA 12FT/PGDip 9FT
International Security Studies (Research Training)..........MA 12FT
Politics, Media and Performance.... MA 12FT 24PT
Post-colonial Politics (Research Training)..... MA 12FT/PGDip 9FT/PGCert 9FT
Security Studies (Research Training)............ MA 12FT/PGDip 9FT/PGCert 9FT
Security Studies (Specialist)........ MA 12FT/PGDip 9FT/PGCert 9FT
Strategic Studies (Research Training)....MA 12FT
Strategic Studies (Specialist)....MA 12FT
War Studies (Research Training)....MA 12FT
War Studies (Specialist)....MA 12FT

Aston University
European Union and International Relations . MA 12FT 24 - 36PT
Politics and International Relations...............MRes 12FT 24 - 36PT

Section sponsored by

BPP
UNIVERSITY
COLLEGE

Business and social sciences
www.prospects.ac.uk/findcourses **POSTGRADUATE DIRECTORY 455**

Political science

University of Bath
Global Political Economy: transformations and policy analysis ...
MRes 12FT 24-36PT
International Public Policy Analysis..............MSc 12FT/PGDip 9FT/
PGCert 6FT
International Relations......MA 12FT/PGDip 9FT 21PT/PGCert 4FT
16PT
International Relations and European Politics..... MA 12FT/PGDip
24FT/PGCert 24FT
International Security ..... MA 12FT 24PT/PGDip 9FT 21PT/PGCert
4FT 16PT
Politics & International Studies .... MRes 12FT/PGDip 9FT/PGCert
9FT
Security, Conflict & Justice .... MRes 12FT 24-36PT

Birkbeck, University of London
Global Governance and Emerging Powers.............MSc 12FT 24PT
Global Politics................................MSc 12FT 24PT/MRes 12FT 24PT
International Migration and Intergration................GradCert 12PT
International Security and Global Governance ..... MSc 12FT 24PT

University of Birmingham
International Development.............................. MSc 12FT/PGDip 9FT
International Development (Conflict, Security and Development)
MSc 12FT/PGDip 9FT
International Development (International Political Economy and
Development)...MSc 12FT 24PT/PGDip 9FT
International Development (Poverty, Inequality and
Development) MSc/Graduate Diploma...... MSc 12FT 24PT 48DL/
GradDip 9FT
International Relations (Diplomacy) .... MA 12FT 24PT
International Relations (Gender)...................MA 12FT 24PT/
PGDip 9FT 18PT
International Relations (International Peacekeeping).....MA 12FT
24PT
International Relations (International Political Economy)........MA
12FT 24PT
International Relations (Research Methods)........... MA 12FT 24PT
International Relations (Security) .... MA 12FT 24PT
International Relations (Strategic Studies in the Age of Terror)....
MA 12FT 24PT
International Relations (with specialist pathways)........................
MA 12FT 24PT
International Law, Ethics and Politics...................... MA 12FT 24PT
Political Theory... MA 12FT 24PT
US Foreign Policy ....MRes 12FT 24PT

University of Bradford
African Peace and Conflict Studies .... MA 12FT 24PT
Conflict Resolution..........................MA 12FT 24PT/PGDip 9FT 21PT
Conflict, Security and Development.......MA 12FT 12-36PT/PGDip
24FT 24-36PT
International Politics and Security Studies............MA 12FT 24PT/
PGDip 9FT 21PT
Participation, Politics and Colelctive Action .... MA 12FT 24PT
Peace Studies..........................MA 12FT 24PT/PGDip 9FT 21PT

University of Bristol
Development and Security ....MSc 12FT 24PT
Gender and International Relations.........................MSc 12FT 24PT
International Development ....MSc 12FT 24PT
International Relations ....MSc 12FT 24PT
International Security ....MSc 12FT 24PT

Brunel University
Globalisation and Governance .... MA 12FT 30PT
International Relations .... MA 12FT 30PT

University of Buckingham
Global Affairs...MA 12FT
Global Affairs and Diplomacy ....MA 12FT
Security and Intelligence Studies..MA 12FT
Security, Intelligence and Diplomacy....................................MA 12FT

University of Cambridge
International Relations .... MPhil 10FT MSt 22PT

Cardiff University
International Relations .... MA 12FT 24PT
Legal and Political Aspects of International Affairs.........LLM 12FT

University of Central Lancashire
Counter Terrorism..MSc 12FT
Global Security and Justice ....MA 12FT
International Relations...MA 12FT

City University London
Global Political Economy .... MA 12FT/MA 24PT
International Politics .... MA 12FT 24PT
International Politics and Human Rights .... MA 12FT 24PT

Coventry University
Conflict Resolution Skills...PGCert 6DL
Terrorism, International Crime and Global Security...... MBA 12FT
24-30PT

Cranfield University, Shrivenham
International Defence and Security.........MSc 12FT/PGCert 12FT/
PGDip 12FT
Security Sector Management ....MSc 12FT 30PT

De Montfort University
Diplomacy and World Order.. MA 12FT 24PT

Inter-religious Relations ....MA 24PT
International Relations .... MA 12FT 24PT

University College Dublin
International Relations ....MSc 12FT/MLitt 24FT

University of Dundee
International Politics and Security ....MLitt 12FT/PGDip 9FT

Durham University
Conflict Prevention, Sustainable Peace and Security..... MSc 12FT
Defence, Development and Diplomacy............................ MSc 12FT
International Relations (East Asia).............................MA 12FT
International Relations (European).............................MA 12FT
International Relations (Middle East) ....MA 12FT
International Studies...MA 12FT
Politics and International Relations (Political Theory).....MA 12FT
Research Methods (Politics and International Relations)MA 12FT

University of East Anglia
Conflict, Governance and International Development....MA 12FT
24PT
Economics and International Relations................................MA 12FT
International Development.. MA 12FT 24PT
International Relations .... MA 12FT 24PT
International Relations and Development Studies ....
MA 12FT 24PT
International Relations and European Studies....... MA 12FT 24PT
MRes in International Development (by distance learning) MRes
24DL

University of East London
International Law and International Relations ....LLM 12FT 24PT/
PGDip 8FT 16PT/PGCert 4FT 8PT
International Relations ....MSc 12FT 24PT/PGDip 8FT 16PT/
PGCert 4FT 8PT
Terrorism Studies ....MSc 12FT 24PT/PGDip 8FT 16PT/
PGCert 4FT 8PT

Edinburgh Napier University
Advanced Security and Digital Forensics.................MSc 12FT 24PT

University of Edinburgh
Global Crime, Justice and Security.........................MSc 12FT 24PT
Global Development Challenges (Online Distance Learning).......
PGCert 12-24DL
Global Environment Challenges Certificate (Online distance
learning) ....PGCert 9DL
Global Social Change..MSc 12FT 24PT
International Relations ....MSc 12FT 24PT
International Relations of the Middle East...........MRCPsych 12FT
International Relations of the Middle East with Arabic MSc 24FT
International and European Politics ....MSc 12FT 24PT

University of Essex
Conflict Resolution.........................MA 12FT 24PT/MSc 12FT 24PT
Global and Comparative Politics ....MA 12FT 24PT/
MSc 12FT 24PT
Ideology and Discourse Analysis .... MA 12FT 24PT
International Relations ....MA 12FT 24PT/MSc 12FT 24PT/
MRes 12FT
International Relations and the Media .... MA 12FT 24PT
Multilevel Governance in Europe..MA 12FT 24PT/MSc 12FT 24PT
Political Behaviour ....MA 12FT 24PT/MSc 12FT 24PT
Political Economy ....MA 12FT 24PT/MSc 12FT 24PT/MRes 12FT
Political Science.......MA 12FT 24PT/GradDip 12FT/MSc 12FT 24PT/
MRes 12FT 24PT
Political Theory.. MA 12FT 24PT
Politics .... MA 12FT 24PT
Public Opinion and Polling..............MA 12FT 24PT/MSc 12FT 24PT

University of Exeter
Critical Global Politics.. MA 12FT 24PT
International Relations...................................... MA 12FT 24PT
International Relations of the Middle East.............. MA 12FT 24PT
Security, Conflict and Justice..................................MRes 12FT 24PT

National University of Ireland Galway
International Peace Support Operations................. LLM 12FT 24PT

University of Glasgow
Global Security.............................MSc 12FT 24PT/MRes 12FT 24PT
MRes 12FT 24PT
Human Rights & International Politics ....MRes 12FT 24PT
MSc 12FT/PGDip 9PT
International Law and Security .... LLM 12FT 24PT
International Politics (Research)...........................MRes 12FT 24PT
International Relations .... MRes 12FT 24PT MSc 12FT 24PT
Physics: Global Security ....MSc 12FT

Goldsmiths, University of London
Cultural Policy, Relations and Diplomacy................. MA 12FT 24PT
International Studies.. MA 12FT 24PT

University of Hull
Civilisation, Terrorism and Dissent .... MA 12FT 24PT
Global Communication and International Politics ....
MA 12FT 24PT
Globalisation and Governance .... MA 12FT 24PT
International Politics .... MA 12FT 24PT
Strategy and International Security .... MA 12FT 24PT

Keele University
Masters in Dialogue Studies.......................................MA 12FT

Masters in Politics and International Relations.....MA 12FT 24PT/
MRes 12FT 24PT

University of Kent
European and Global Governance ...... PGDip 12FT 24PT/MA 12FT
24PT
European and Global Governance (International Double Award)
MA 24FT
Human Rights ....MA 12FT 24PT/PGDip 12FT 24PT
International Conflict Analysis (Canterbury or Brussels) MA 12FT
24PT/PGDip 12FT 24PT
International Conflict and Security........................... MA 12FT 24PT
International Development (Brussels)...................... MA 12FT 24PT
International Law with International Relations (Brussels or
Canterbury)...................LLM 12FT 24PT/PGDip 12FT 24PT
International Relations (Brussels) ....MA 12FT 24PT/PGDip 12FT
24PT
International Relations MA (international double award)
(Canterbury, Moscow) ....MA 24FT
International Relations with International Law ....MA 12FT 24PT/
PGDip 12FT 24PT
International Security and the Politics of TerrorPGDip 12FT 24PT/
MA 12FT 24PT
Political Theory and Practices of Resistance......PGDip 12FT 24PT/
MA 12FT 24PT
Security and Terrorism ....MA 12FT 24PT/PGDip 12FT 24PT

King's College London
Conflict Resolution in Divided Societies.................. MA 12FT 24PT
Conflict, Security & Development........................... MA 12FT 24PT
Geopolitics, Territory & Security............................. MA 12FT 24PT
Intelligence & International Security....................... MA 12FT 24PT
International Conflict Studies................................... MA 12FT 24PT
International Peace & Security................................. MA 12FT 24PT
International Relations .... MA 12FT 24PT
Non-Proliferation & International Security............. MA 12FT 24PT
Science & Security .... MA 12FT 24PT
South Asia & Global Security .... MA 12FT 24PT
Terrorism, Security & Society .... MA 12FT 24PT
War Studies... MA 12FT 24PT

Kingston University
International Conflict ....MSc 12FT 24PT
International Politics and Economics .... MA 12FT 24PT
International Relations ....MSc 12FT 24PT
Nationalism ....MSc 12FT 24PT
Terrorism and Political Violence ....MSc 12FT 24PT

Lancaster University
Conflict Resolution and Peace Studies...................... MA 12FT 24PT
Conflict, Development and Security......................... MA 12FT 24PT
Diplomacy and Foreign Policy .... MA 12FT 24PT
Diplomacy and International Relations (Distance Learning) ...MA
12FT 24PT
International Law and International Relations.....LLM 12FT 24PT/
MA 12FT 24PT
International Relations .... MRes 12FT 24PT/MA 12FT 24PT
Politics ....MA 12FT 24PT/MPhil 24FT/PhD by taught 24FT
Politics and International Relations...........................PGCert 12FT 24PT

Leeds Metropolitan University
International Political Economy......................................MA 12FT
International Relations ....MA 12FT 24PT/PGCert 12PT/
PGDip 12FT 24PT
Peace & Development...................MA 12FT 24PT/PGDip 12FT 24PT

University of Leeds
Conflict, Development and Security......................... MA 12FT 24PT
Global Development... MA 12FT 24PT
Global Development and Education .... MA 12FT 24PT
Global Development and International Political Economy ......MA
12FT 24PT
International Relations .... MA 12FT 24PT
International Social Transformation......................... MA 12FT 24PT
Politics .... MA 12FT 24PT
Security and Justice .... MA 12FT 24PT
Security, Terrorism and Insurgency.......................... MA 12FT 24PT

University of Leicester
Diplomatic Studies.. MA 24DL
Globalization and Communications.....................................MA 12FT
International Relations and World Order................ MA 12FT 24PT
International Security ....MA 12FT 24PT/PGDip 12FT 24PT
Terrorism, Security and Policing ....MSc 12FT 24PT/
PGDip 12FT 24PT

University of Limerick
International Studies..MA 12FT

University of Liverpool
International Relations and Security....................... MA 12FT 24PT
Understanding Conflict .... MA 12FT 24PT

London College UCK
International Relations and Diplomacy...PGDip 12FT 18PT 24DL/
PGCert 6FT 12PT

London Metropolitan University
International Relations .... MA 12FT 24PT
International Security Studies .... MA 12FT 24PT

Political science

London School of Economics and Political Science (LSE)
Affaires Internationales and International Relations/ International Political Economy .... MSc 23FT
Diplomacy and International Strategy .... MSc 12FT
Global Politics .... MSc 12FT 24PT
History of International Relations .... MSc 12FT 24PT
International Affairs (Double Degree) .... MSc 24FT
International Employment Relations and Human Resource Management .... MSc 12FT
International Political Economy .... MSc 11FT 23PT
International Relations .... MSc 11FT 23PT
International Relations Theory .... MSc 11FT 23PT
Theory and History of International Relations .... MSc 12FT 24PT

Loughborough University
Globalization and Society .... MSc 12FT 24PT
International Relations .... MSc 12FT 24PT
Research methods (European and International Studies) .... MSc 12FT 24PT

University of Manchester
Humanitarianism and Conflict Response .... MA 12FT 24PT
International Development: Politics and Governance .... MA 12FT 24PT
International Politics .... MA 12FT 24PT/PGDip 9FT 21PT
International Politics (Research Route) .... MA 12FT 24PT/ PGDip 9FT 21PT
Peacebuilding .... MA 12FT 24PT

Middlesex University
International Relations .... MA 12FT 24PT

Newcastle University
Advanced International Business Management and Marketing .... MSc/MSc (Dual Award) 17FT
Advanced International Business and Management .... MA/MSc (Dual Award) 17FT
Cross Cultural Communications .... MA 12FT 24PT
Cross-Cultural Communication and Applied Linguistics MA 12FT 24PT
Cross-Cultural Communication and Education .... MA 12FT 24PT
Cross-Cultural Communication and International Marketing .... MA 12FT 24PT
Cross-Cultural Communication and International Relations... MA 12FT 24PT
Cross-Cultural Communication and Media Studies .... MA 12FT 24PT
International Political Economy .... MA 12FT 24PT
International Politics (Critical Geopolitics) .... MA 12FT 24PT
International Politics (Global Justice and Ethics) ... MA 12FT 24PT
International Politics (Globalisation, Poverty and Development) .... MA 12FT 24PT
International Studies .... MA 12FT 24PT
World Politics and Popular Culture .... MA 12FT 24PT

University of Northampton
International Relations .... MA 12FT 24PT/PGDip 12PT

Nottingham Trent University
International Relations ... MA 12FT 24PT/PGDip 9FT 24PT/PGCert 9FT 24PT
Politics .... MA 12FT 24PT

University of Nottingham
Diplomacy .... MA 12FT 24PT
International Law, Security and Terrorism .... MA 12FT 24PT
International Relations .... MA 12FT 24PT
International Relations (Research Track) .... MA 12FT 24PT
International Security and Terrorism .... MA 12FT 24PT
Social and Global Justice .... MA 12FT 24PT
War and Contemporary Conflict .... MA 12FT 24PT

The Open University
Conflict and Development .... PGCert variableDL

Oxford Brookes University
Humanitarian Action and Conflict (PGCert) .... PGCert 12DL
International Law and International Relations .... MA 12FT 24PT/ PGDip 8FT 20PT/PGCert 4FT 16PT
International Management and International Relations .... MSc 12FT 24PT
International Studies MA 12FT 24PT/PGDip 9FT 18PT/PGCert 9FT 18PT

University of Oxford
Development Studies .... MPhil 36FT
Diplomatic Studies Foreign Services Programme .... PGCert 9FT/ PGDip 12FT
Global Governance and Diplomacy .... MSc 12FT
Global Health Science .... MSc 12FT
International Human Rights Law .... MSt 24PT 24DL
International Relations .... MPhil 21FT
Political Theory Research .... MSc 9FT
Politics and International Relations Research .... MSc 9FT
Politics: European Politics & Society .... MPhil 21FT
Politics: Political Theory .... MPhil 21FT
Public Policy in Latin America .... MSc 12FT

Plymouth University
International Relations: Global Security and Development .... MA 12FT 24PT

University of Portsmouth
International Relations and European Studies .... MA 12FT 24PT

Queen Margaret University, Edinburgh
Conflict, Social Development and Health .... PGCert 4FT 24-48PT

Queen Mary, University of London
Global Public Health and Policy .... MSc 12FT 24-48PT
Health Systems and Global Policy .... MSc 12FT 24-48PT
International Relations .... MA 12FT 24PT/MRes 12FT 24PT

Queen's University Belfast
International Relations .... MA 12FT 24PT/PGDip 12FT 24PT
Politics .... MA 12FT 24PT
Violence, Terrorism and Security MA 12FT 24PT/PGDip 12FT 24PT

University of Reading
Diplomacy .... MA 12FT 72PT/PGDip 12FT 72PT/PGCert 12FT 72PT
Diplomacy MA 12FT 24-72PT/PGCert 12FT 24-72PT/PGDip 12FT 24-72PT
International Relations .... MA (res) 12FT 24-72PT 72BM
International Relations (Strategic Studies) .... MA 12FT 24-72PT/ PGDip 24-72PT/PGCert 12FT 24PT
Military History and Strategic Studies MA 12FT 72PT/PGDip 9FT/ PGCert 6FT

Richmond, The American International University in London
International Conflict& Security .... MA 12FT 24PT
International Relations .... MA 12FT 24PT

University of Roehampton
Human Rights and International Relations .... MA 18FT 24+PT
Human Rights and International Relations .... PGCert 10FT
Post Graduate Diploma- Human Rights and International Relations .... PGDip 12FT 24PT

Royal Holloway, University of London
Democracy, Politics and Governance .... MA 12FT 24PT
Global Politics .... MSc 12/9FT 24/20PT
International Relations .... MSc 12FT 24PT
International Relations Theory .... MSc 12/9FT 24/20PT
Political Research .... MSc 12/9FT 24/20PT
Political Theory .... MSc 12/9FT 24/20PT

University of Salford
Intelligence and Security Studies .... MA 12FT 36PT/ PGDip 9FT 20PT
International Banking and Finance .... MSc 12FT 36PT/PGDip 8FT 24PT/PGCert 4FT 9PT
International Corporate Finance MSc 12FT 36PT/PGDip 8FT 24PT/ PGCert 4FT 9PT
International Hospital and Health Service Leadership and Management .... MSc 12FT/PGDip 8FT/PGCert 4FT
Terrorism and Security .... MA 12FT 36PT 36DL/PGDip 12FT 36PT 36DL

School of Oriental and African Studies - SOAS
African Politics .... MSc 12FT 24-36PT
Development Studies with Special Reference to Central Asia MSc 12FT 24PT
Economics (with Reference to the Asia Pacific Region) .... MSc 12FT 24PT
Global Energy and Climate Policy .... MSc 12FT 24PT
International Politics .... MSc 12FT 24PT
International Studies and Diplomacy .... MA 12FT 24-36PT/PGDip 12FT 24PT
Law, Development and Globalisation .... MA 12FT 24PT
Middle East Politics .... MSc 12FT 24PT
Policy Studies .... PGCert 9FT
Political Economy of Development .... MSc 12FT 24-36PT
Politics of China .... MSc 12FT 24PT
Social Anthropology of Development .... MA 12FT 24-36PT
State, Society and Development .... MSc 12FT 24PT
Violence, Conflict and Development .... MSc 12FT 24PT

University of Sheffield
Comparative Governance and Public Policy .... MA 12FT 24PT
Contemporary Global Security .... MA 12FT 24PT
Development Economics and Policy .... MSc 12FT 24PT
European Governance and Politics .... MA 12FT 24PT
European Health Law and Policy .... LLM 12FT 24PT
European Law, Politics and Governance .... MA 12FT
Europubhealth: European Masters Programme in Public Health .... MPH 24FT
Global Justice .... MA 12FT 24PT
Global Politics and Law .... MA 12FT 24PT
Global Politics and Law (Doshisha Pathway) .... MA 24FT
Globalisation and Development .... MA 12FT 24PT
Globalising Education: Policy and Practice .... MA 12FT
International Criminology .... MA 12FT
International Political Communication .... MA 12FT
International Political Economy .... MA 12FT 24PT
International Studies .... MA 12FT 24PT
International and European Law .... LLM 12FT Up to 36PT
Political Theory .... MA 12FT 24PT
Politics .... MA 12FT 24PT
Politics with Research Methods .... MA 12FT 24PT
Politics with Research Methods .... MA 12FT 24PT
Religion, Conflict and the Media .... MA 12FT 24PT

University of Southampton
European Law .... LLM 12FT 24PT
Global Politics .... MSc 12FT 24PT/PGDip 9FT 21PT
Global Security .... MSc 12FT 24PT/PGDip 9FT 21PT
International Banking and Financial Studies MSc 12FT/PGDip 9FT

University of St Andrews
International Political Theory .... MLitt 12FT 24PT/MPhil 24FT
International Security Studies .... MLitt 12FT/PGDip 9FT
Middle East and Central Asian Security Studies .... PGDip 9FT/MLitt 12FT/MPhil 24FT
Peace and Conflict Studies .... MLitt 12FT
Terrorism Studies .... PGDip 12FT 24 -48PT 24-48DL/MLitt 12FT 24-48PT 30-66DL

Staffordshire University
International Policy and Diplomacy .... MA 12FT 30-36DL
International Policy and Diplomacy (via Distance Learning) ... MA 24-36DL
International Relations .... MA 12FT 30-36DL
International Relations (via Distance Learning) .... MA 12FT 24PT 24-36DL

University of Stirling
International Accounting & Finance .... MSc 12FT/PGDip 9FT/ PGCert 6FT
International Conflict and Co-operation .... MSc 12FT 27PT/PGDip 9FT 21PT/PGCert 3FT 9PT

University of Strathclyde
International Accounting and Finance .... MSc 12FT 24PT/ PGDip 9FT 21PT
International Banking and Finance .... MSc 12FT 24PT/PGDip 9FT 21PT
International Public Policy .... MSc 12FT 24PT
Political Research .... MSc 12FT 24PT

University of Surrey
European and International Politics .... MA 12FT 24PT
International Intervention .... MA 12FT 24PT
International Politics .... MA 12FT 24PT

University of Sussex
Conflict, Security and Development .... MA 12FT 24PT
International Relations .... MA 12FT 24PT
International Security .... MA 12FT 24PT

Swansea University
International Relations .... MA 12FT 24PT
Journalism, Media and Globalization .... MA 24FT

Trinity College Dublin - the University of Dublin
Conflict Resolution and Reconciliation .... MPhil 12FT 24PT
International Peace Studies .... MPhil 12FT 24PT
International Politics .... MSc 12FT 24PT
Political Science (Masters) .... MSc 12FT 24PT

University of the Highlands and Islands
Restorative Practice .... PGCert 12FT 24PT

University of Ulster
Peace and Conflict Studies (Applied) .... MSc 12FT 36PT/PGDip 9FT 18PT
Peace and Conflict Studies with Early Years (Applied) .... PGDip 9FT 18PT/MSc 12FT 36PT

UCL - University College London
Countering Organised Crime and Terrorism .... MSc 12FT 24-60PT/ PGDip 24PT
Global Governance and Ethics .... MSc 12FT 24PT
Identity, Culture and Power .... MA 12FT 24PT
Politics, Security and Integration .... MA 12FT 24PT
Security Studies .... MSc 12FT 24PT
Transnational Studies .... MA 12FT 24PT

University of Warwick
Double Degree with Nanyang Technological University .... MA 24FT
Double Degree with the University of Konstanz .... MA 24FT
International Political Economy .... MA 12FT 24PT/PGDip 9FT
International Relations .... MA 12FT 24PT/PGDip 9FT
International Security .... MA 12FT 24PT/PGDip 9FT

Webster Graduate School London
International Non-Governmental Organisations .... MA 14FT
International Relations .... MA 14FT

University of Westminster
International Liaison and Communication .... MA 12FT 24PT
International Relations .... MA 12FT 24PT
International Relations and Democratic Politics .... MA 12FT 24PT
International Relations and Security .... MA 12FT 24PT

University of Winchester
Reconciliation and Peacebuilding .... MA 12FT 24PT/PGDip 12FT 24PT/PGCert 12FT 24PT

University of Wolverhampton
Conflict Studies .... MA 12FT 24-36PT

University of York
International Relations .... MA 12FT 24PT/PGDip 12FT 24PT/ PGCert 6FT 12PT

International relations
Research Courses

Aberystwyth University
International Politics .... PhD 36FT

Political science

School of Advanced Study, University of London
Politics and International Studies .... PhD 36FT 72PT/MPhil 12FT 36PT

University of Bath
Global Political Economy: transformations and policy analysis (delivered collaboratively w .... MRes 12FT 24-36PT

University of Birmingham
Political Science and International Studies PhD 36FT/MPhil 24FT
US Foreign Policy .... MPhil(B) 12FT 24PT

University of Bradford
Peace Studies .... PhD 36-48FT 48-60PT/MPhil 12-24FT 24-48PT

Brunel University
Doctoral Programme in Politics, History & International Relations .... PhD 36FT 60PT/MPhil 12FT 24PT/MRes 12FT 24PT

University of Buckingham
International Affairs and Diplomacy .... MA by research 12FT

University of Cambridge
Politics and International Studies .... PhD 36FT

Canterbury Christ Church University
Politics and International Relations .... MPhil 24FT 48PT/PhD 36FT 60PT

Cardiff University
Mediatized Conflict Group .... PhD 36FT possiblePT/MPhil 24FT possiblePT

Coventry University
International Relations .... MA by research 12FT 24PT

University College Dublin
International Relations .... PhD 36FT/MLitt by research 24FT

Durham University
Government and International Affairs .... PhD 36FT

University of East Anglia
Political, Social and International Studies... PhD 36FT 72PT/MPhil 24FT 48PT/MA by research 12FT 24PT

University of Edinburgh
Politics & International Relations ..... MSc by research 12FT 24PT/PhD 36FT 72PT

University of Essex
Government..... PhD 36FT 72PT/MPhil 24FT 48PT/MA by research 12FT 24PT

University of Exeter
Strategy and Security .... MSc by research 24FT/MPhil 36FT 60PT/PhD 48FT 84PT

University of Glasgow
China in the International Arena......... MSc by research 12FT 24PT

University of Hull
Politics/International Relations/Security Studies/Legislative Studies .... PhD 36FT 60PT/MPhil 24FT 36PT

Institute for the Study of the Americas, School of Advanced Study, University of London
International Relations .... PhD 36FT/MPhil 12FT

Keele University
Politics .... MPhil 24FT 36PT/PhD 48FT 84PT
Politics and International Relations. PhD 24-48FT 48-84PT/MPhil 12-24FT 24-36PT

University of Kent
International Conflict Analysis (Brussels or Canterbury)PhD 36FT 60PT/MPhil 24FT 36PT/MA by research 12FT 24PT
International Relations (Brussels or Canterbury).PhD 36FT 60PT/MPhil 24FT 36PT/MA by research 12FT 24PT
Politcal and Social Thought .... MA by research 12FT 24PT/MPhil 24FT 36PT/PhD 36FT 60PT

King's College London
Politics Research .... MPhil 24FT 36PT/PhD 36FT 48-72PT
War Studies Research .... PhD 36FT 72PT/MPhil 24FT 48PT

Lancaster University
International Relations .... PhD 36FT 48PT/MPhil 24FT 36PT
Politics .... PhD 36FT 48PT/MPhil 24FT 36PT

University of Leeds
School of Politics and International Studies....... PhD 36+FT/MPhil 24FT/MA by research 12FT

University of Leicester
Department of Politics & International RelationsPhD 48FT/MPhil 48FT

London Metropolitan University
Dept of Law Governance and International Relations.... PhD Max 60FT Max 96PT/MPhil Max 36FT Max 54PT

London School of Economics and Political Science (LSE)
International Relations .... PhD 36-48FT/MPhil 36-48FT

Loughborough University
European Studies and International Relations .... PhD 36FT/MPhil 24FT
Politics and International Studies .... MPhil 24FT 36PT/PhD 36FT 60PT

University of Manchester
Humanitarianism and Conflict Response .... PhD 48FT 96PT

Newcastle University
Politics .... PhD 36FT 72PT/MPhil 12FT 24PT

University of Nottingham
Politics and International Relations .... MPhil 24FT 48PT/PhD 36-48FT 72-96PT/MRes 12FT 24PT
School of Politics MRes .... MRes 12FT 24PT

The Open University
Citizenship and security .. PhD 36FT 72PT variableDL/MPhil 15FT 24PT variableDL
Comparative Politics .... PhD 36FT 72PT variableDL/MPhil 15FT 24PT variableDL
Governing global security .... PhD 36FT 72PT variableDL/MPhil 15FT 24PT variableDL
International Relations .... PhD 36FT 72PT variableDL/MPhil 15FT 24PT variableDL
Political Theory......... PhD 36FT 72PT variableDL/MPhil 15FT 24PT variableDL
Politics and International Studies ...... PhD 36FT 72PT variableDL/MPhil 15FT 24PT variableDL
War, conflict and politics in Europe ... PhD 36FT 72PT variableDL/MPhil 15FT 24PT variableDL

University of Oxford
International Relations .... DPhil 48FT/MPhil 21FT

Royal Holloway, University of London
Politics and International Relations .... PhD 36FT 72PT/MPhil 24FT 48PT

School of Oriental and African Studies - SOAS
Development Studies .... PhD 36FT 48-60PT
Politics .... PhD 36FT 72PT/MPhil 24FT 36PT

University of Southampton
School of Social Sciences - Politics and International Relations .... PhD 36FT 72PT/MPhil 24FT 48PT

University of St Andrews
Cultural Identity Studies .... PhD 36FT 72PT/MPhil 12-24FT 48PT
International Relations .... PhD 36FT 72PT/MPhil 24FT 48PT

University of Surrey
Political, International and Policy Studies. PhD 33-48FT 45-96PT/MPhil 21-36FT 33-72PT

University of Sussex
International Relations Research Programme .... PhD 24-48FT 36-72PT/MPhil 12-36FT 24-48PT

Swansea University
International Relations .... MA by research 12FT 24PT/MPhil 24FT 48PT/PhD 36FT 72PT
Politics and International Relations.... PhD 36FT 72PT/MPhil 24FT 48PT

University of Ulster
Politics and International Studies .... PhD 36FT 72PT/MPhil 24FT 48PT
Transitional Justice Institute ..... PhD 36FT 72PT/MPhil 24FT 48PT

University of Warwick
Phd in Politics and International Studies .... PhD 36FT 60PT/MPhil 24FT 36PT

Middle east politics
Taught Courses

University of Bath
International Relations ...... MA 12FT/PGDip 9FT 21PT/PGCert 4FT 16PT

Birkbeck, University of London
Middle East in Global Politics: Islam, Conflict and Development. MSc 12FT 24PT
Politics .... MRes 12FT 24PT

University of Central Lancashire
Global Security and Justice .... MA 12FT
International Relations .... MA 12FT

Durham University
Arab World Studies .... MSc 24FT
International Relations (Middle East) .... MA 12FT

University of Edinburgh
Arab World Studies .... MSc 24FT
International Relations of the Middle East .... MRCPsych 12FT
International Relations of the Middle East with Arabic .... MSc 24FT

University of Exeter
International Relations of the Middle East .... MA 12FT 24PT
Middle East Politics .... MA 12FT 24PT
Middle East Studies .... MRes 12FT 24PT
Middle East and Islamic Studies .... MA 12FT 24PT

King's College London
Political Economy of the Middle East .... MA 12FT 24PT

Leeds Metropolitan University
International Relations .... MA 12FT 24PT/PGCert 12PT/PGDip 12FT 24PT

University of Leeds
Japanese Business .... MA 12FT 24PT
Security, Terrorism and Insurgency .... MA 12FT 24PT

University of Oxford
Modern Middle Eastern Studies .... MPhil 21FT

University of Reading
Diplomacy .... MA 12FT 72PT/PGDip 12FT 72PT/PGCert 12FT 72PT
Diplomacy .... MA 12FT 24-72PT/PGCert 12FT 24-72PT/PGDip 12FT 24-72PT
International Relations .... MA (res) 12FT 24-72PT 72BM
International Relations (Strategic Studies) ...... MA 12FT 24-72PT/PGDip 24-72PT/PGCert 12FT 24PT

School of Oriental and African Studies - SOAS
International Management (Middle East and North Africa).. MSc 12FT 24PT
Middle East Politics .... MSc 12FT 24PT
Near and Middle Eastern Studies .... MA 12FT 24-36PT
Turkish Studies .... MA 12FT 24PT

University of St Andrews
Middle East and Central Asian Security Studies .... PGDip 9FT/MLitt 12FT/MPhil 24FT

Swansea University
Politics .... MA 12FT 24PT

Trinity College Dublin - the University of Dublin
International Politics .... MSc 12FT 24PT

UCL - University College London
Modern Israeli Studies .... MA 12FT 24PT

Middle east politics
Research Courses

School of Advanced Study, University of London
Politics and International Studies .... PhD 36FT 72PT/MPhil 12FT 36PT

Durham University
Government and International Affairs .... PhD 36FT

University of Exeter
Arab and Islamic Studies ...... PhD 36-48FT 72PT/MPhil 24FT 48PT
Ethno-Political Studies .... MPhil 36FT 60PT/PhD 48FT 89PT
Middle East Politics .... MPhil 24FT 48PT 48DL/PhD 36FT 72PT 72DL

University of Sussex
Politics Research Programme .... PhD 24-48FT 36-72PT/MPhil 12-36FT 24-48PT

Political communication
Taught Courses

Aberystwyth University
Politics, Media and Performance .... MA 12FT 24PT

University of Bath
Global Political Economy: transformations and policy analysis ... MRes 12FT 24-36PT

Brunel University
Public Affairs & Lobbying .... MSc 15FT 30PT

Cardiff University
Legal and Political Aspects of International Affairs .... LLM 12FT
Political Communications .... MA 12FT

University of Central Lancashire
Global Communication Studies .... MA 12FT 24-36PT
MSc Internal Communication Management .... MSc 24+PT

University of Chester
Faiths and Public Policy .... MA 12FT 36PT 36DL/PGDip 12FT 24-36PT 24-36DL/PGCert 12FT 12-24PT 12-24DL

City University London
International Communications and Development .... MA 12FT 24PT
Media and Communications .... MA 12FT 24PT
Political Communication .... MA 12FT 24PT

University College Cork
Government .... MBS 12FT 24PT
Politics .... MA 12FT

Coventry University
Communication, Culture and Media .... MA 12FT 24PT
Global Journalism .... MA 12FT 24PT

Dublin Institute of Technology
Public Affairs and Political Communications .... MA 12FT

University College Dublin
Politics .... MA 12FT/MLitt 24FT

University of East Anglia
International Public Policy and Public Management ... MRes 12FT 24PT
International Relations .... MA 12FT 24PT
Media Economics .... MA 12FT
Media Law, Policy and Practice .... LLM 12FT 24PT
Media and Cultural Politics .... MA 12FT 24PT
Media, Culture and Society .... MA 12FT 24PT
Public Policy and Public Management .... MRes 12FT 24PT

University of Edinburgh
Science Communication and Public Engagement .... MSc 12FT

Political science

University of Essex
Global Project Management ...... MSc 12FT 24PT

University of Exeter
Food Security and Sustainable Agriculture ...... MSc 12FT 24PT

National University of Ireland Galway
Public Advocacy and Activism ...... MA 12FT/PGDip 12FT

Glasgow Caledonian University
Multimedia Communication ...... MSc 12FT

University of Glasgow
Political Communication ...... MSc 12FT 24PT/PGDip 9FT MRes 12FT 24PT

Goldsmiths, University of London
Media and Communications ...... MA 12FT 24PT
Political Communications ...... MA 12FT 24PT

University of Hull
Global Communication and International Politics ...... MA 12FT 24PT

University of Kent
International Relations (Brussels) ...... MA 12FT 24PT/PGDip 12FT 24PT
International Relations MA (international double award) (Canterbury, Moscow) ...... MA 24FT
International Relations with International Law ...... MA 12FT 24PT/PGDip 12FT 24PT
International Security and the Politics of Terror PGDip 12FT 24PT/MA 12FT 24PT
Peace and Conflict Studies (International Double Award) ...... MA 24FT
Political Strategy and Communication (Brussels) ...... MA 12FT 24PT
Political Theory and Practices of Resistance ...... PGDip 12FT 24PT/MA 12FT 24PT

Kingston University
International Political Communication, Advocacy and Campaigning ...... MSc 12FT 24PT
Political Communication, Advocacy and Campaigning. MSc 12FT 24PT

Leeds Metropolitan University
International Communication ...... MA 12FT
Specialist Community Public Health Nursing - Health Visiting ...... MSc 24PT/PGDip 12FT 24PT

University of Leeds
Global Development ...... MA 12FT 24PT
Global Development and Education ...... MA 12FT 24PT
Global Development and International Political Economy ...... MA 12FT 24PT
International Communications ...... MA 12FT
Political Communication ...... MA 12FT
Politics ...... MA 12FT 24PT
Politics (Political Theory) ...... MA 12FT 24PT

University of Leicester
New Media, Governance and Democracy (by Distance Learning) ...... MA 24FT/PGDip 20FT
Political Research ...... MSc 12FT 24PT/PGDip 9FT 18PT

University of Limerick
Politics ...... MA 12FT

University of Liverpool
Politics and the Mass Media.. MA 12FT 24PT/PGDip 12FT/PGCert 12FT

London School of Economics and Political Science (LSE)
Double Degree in Global Media and Communications MSc 12FT/MA 12FT
Media and Communications ...... MSc 12FT 24PT
Media and Communications (Media and Communication Governance) ...... MSc 12FT 24PT
Media, Communication and Development ...... MSc 12FT 24PT
Politics and Communication ...... MSc 12FT 24PT

Newcastle University
International Politics (Global Justice and Ethics) ... MA 12FT 24PT

Nottingham Trent University
Politics ...... MA 12FT 24PT

The Open University
Systems Thinking in Practice MSc variableDL/PGCert variableDL/PGDip variableDL

University of Oxford
Global Governance and Diplomacy ...... MSc 12FT
International Relations ...... MPhil 21FT
International Summer School in Forced Migration ...... Cert less than 1FT

Queen Mary, University of London
Health Systems and Global Policy ...... MSc 12FT 24-48PT

Queen's University Belfast
Political Psychology ...... MSc 12FT 24PT
Politics ...... MA 12FT 24PT

University of Reading
Communication for Innovation and Development ...... MSc 12FT 24PT
Diplomacy ...... MA 12FT 72PT/PGDip 12FT 72PT/PGCert 12FT 72PT
Public Policy ...... MA 12FT 24PT 72BM

Royal Holloway, University of London
New Political Communication ...... MSc 12/9FT 24/20PT
Political Research ...... MSc 12/9FT 24/20PT
Political Theory ...... MSc 12/9FT 24/20PT

University of Salford
International Relations and Globalisation ... MA 12FT 36PT 36DL/PGDip 8FT 24PT 36DL
Terrorism and Security ...... MA 12FT 36PT 36DL/PGDip 12FT 36PT 36DL

School of Oriental and African Studies - SOAS
African Politics ...... MSc 12FT 24-36PT
Anthropology of Media ...... MA 12FT 24-36PT
Asian Politics ...... MSc 12FT 24PT
Dispute and Conflict Resolution ...... MA 12FT 24PT
International Politics ...... MSc 12FT 24PT
International Studies and Diplomacy ...... MA 12FT 24-36PT/PGDip 12FT 24PT
Media in the Middle East ...... MA 12FT
Middle East Politics ...... MSc 12FT 24PT
Politics of China ...... MSc 12FT 24PT
Postcolonial Studies ...... MA 12FT 24PT
Violence, Conflict and Development ...... MSc 12FT 24PT

University of Sheffield
Comparative Governance and Public Policy ...... MA 12FT 24PT
European Governance and Politics ...... MA 12FT 24PT
European Law, Politics and Governance ...... MA 12FT
European and Global Affairs ...... MA 24FT
Global Justice ...... MA 12FT 24PT
Global Politics and Law ...... MA 12FT 24PT
Global Politics and Law (Doshisha Pathway) ...... MA 24FT
Globalisation and Development ...... MA 12FT 24PT
International Political Communication ...... MA 12FT

University of Southampton
European Law ...... LLM 12FT 24PT
Global Politics ...... MSc 12FT 24PT/PGDip 9FT 21PT
Global Security ...... MSc 12FT 24PT/PGDip 9FT 21PT

University of St Andrews
International Political Theory ...... MLitt 12FT 24PT/MPhil 24FT

University of Stirling
Strategic Communication & Public Relations (Joint Degree) ...... MSc 12FT/PGDip 9FT/PGCert 3FT
Strategic Public Relations & Communication Management ...... MSc 12FT 24PT/PGDip 9FT 21PT
Strategic Public Relations (Double Degree with Lund University) MSc 16/21FT/PGCert 3FT
Strategic Public Relations (Online) ...... MSc 30DL/PGDip 20DL

University of Surrey
International Politics ...... MA 12FT 24PT
Politics ...... MA 12FT 24PT

Swansea University
Communication, Media Practice and Public Relations ...... MA 12FT 24-36PT
Politics ...... MA 12FT 24PT

Teesside University
Mass Communications ...... MA 12FT 24PT

Trinity College Dublin - the University of Dublin
International Politics ...... MSc 12FT 24PT
Political Science (Masters) ...... MSc 12FT 24PT

University of Ulster
Political Lobbying and Public Affairs .... MSc 12FT 36PT/PGDip 9FT 24PT

UCL - University College London
Institutions, Development and Globalisation ...... MA 12FT 24PT
Politics, Security and Integration ...... MA 12FT 24PT

University of Westminster
Communication Policy ...... MA 12FT 24-48PT
International Liaison and Communication ...... MA 12FT 24PT

Political communication
Research Courses

School of Advanced Study, University of London
Politics and International Studies ...... PhD 36FT 72PT/MPhil 12FT 36PT

University of Bath
Global Political Economy: transformations and policy analysis (delivered collaboratively ...... MRes 12FT 24-36PT

University of Cambridge
Politics and International Studies ...... PhD 36FT

Cardiff University
Centre for Global Communications Management Research ...... PhD 36FT

University College Dublin
Politics ...... PhD 36FT/MLitt by research 24FT

University of East Anglia
Political, Social and International Studies ... PhD 36FT 72PT/MPhil 24FT 48PT/MA by research 12FT 24PT

Goldsmiths, University of London
Media and Communications ...... MRes 12FT 24PT

University of Kent
International Relations (Brussels or Canterbury). PhD 36FT 60PT/MPhil 24FT 36PT/MA by research 12FT 24PT

University of Liverpool
Politics ...... PhD 24-48FT 48-84PT/MPhil 12-48FT 24-72PT

Manchester Metropolitan University
Politics ... PhD 24-48FT 42-84PT 42-84DL/MPhil 18-36FT 36-72PT 36-72DL/MA by research 12-24FT 24-42PT 24-42DL

Newcastle University
Politics ...... PhD 36FT 72PT/MPhil 12FT 24PT

University of Nottingham
School of Politics ...... MRes 12FT 24PT

The Open University
Comparative Politics ...... PhD 36FT 72PT variableDL/MPhil 15FT 24PT variableDL
Political Theory ...... PhD 36FT 72PT variableDL/MPhil 15FT 24PT variableDL
Political ideas, policies and actions .... PhD 36FT 72PT variableDL/MPhil 15FT 24PT variableDL

University of Oxford
International Relations ...... DPhil 48FT/MPhil 21FT

School of Oriental and African Studies - SOAS
Politics ...... PhD 36FT 72PT/MPhil 24FT 36PT

University of Sussex
Politics Research Programme ...... PhD 24-48FT 36-72PT/MPhil 12-36FT 24-48PT

Swansea University
International Development ...... MA by research 12FT 24PT
Media and Communication Studies ... MPhil 24FT 48PT/PhD 36FT 72PT

Political science
Taught Courses

University of Aberdeen
Political Research ...... MRes 12FT

Aberystwyth University
Critical International Politics (Research Training) ...... MA 12FT/PGDip 9FT
Critical International Politics (Specialist) ...... MA 12FT/PGDip 9FT
European Politics (Research Training) ...... MA 12FT
European Politics (Specialist) ...... MA 12FT
Global Politics (Research Training) ...... MA 12FT
Global Politics (Specialist) ...... MA 12FT
Gwleidyddiaeth a Chymdeithas Cymru (Arbenigol) ...... MA 12FT 24PT/PGDip 9FT 18PT
Gwleidyddiaeth a Chymdeithas Cymru (Hyfforddiant Ymchwil) ...... MA 12FT 24PT/PGDip 9FT 18PT
Intelligence Studies ...... MA 12FT/PGDip 9FT
Intelligence Studies and International History (Specialist) ...... MA 12FT/PGDip 9FT
Intelligence and Strategic Studies (Specialist) ...... MA 12FT
International History (Research Training) ...... MA 12FT
International Politics of the Internet ...... MA 12FT
International Relations (Research Training) ...... MA 12FT
International Relations (Specialist) ...... MA 12FT/PGDip 9FT
International Security Studies (Specialist) ...... MA 12FT
Modern British History (Political Culture) ... MA 12FT 24PT/PGDip 9FT 18PT
Post-colonial Politics (Research Training) ..... MA 12FT/PGDip 9FT/PGCert 9FT
Post-colonial Politics (Specialist) ...... MA 12FT/PGDip 9FT/PGCert 9FT
Security Studies (Research Training) ...... MA 12FT/PGDip 9FT/PGCert 9FT
Security Studies (Specialist) ...... MA 12FT/PGDip 9FT/PGCert 9FT
Strategic Studies (Research Training) ...... MA 12FT
Strategic Studies (Specialist) ...... MA 12FT
Welsh Politics and Society (Research Training) ...... MA 12FT 24PT/PGDip 9FT 18PT
Welsh Politics and Society (Specialist) ...... MA 12FT 24PT/PGDip 9FT 18PT

Bangor University
Language, Policy and Planning ...... MA 12FT 24-48PT/PGDip 8FT/PGCert 4FT
Policy Research and Evaluation ...... MA 12FT 21-30PT/PGDip 9FT 17-21PT/PGCert 5FT 12-21PT
Social Policy, Sociology. PhD by taught 36FT 60PT/MPhil 12-24FT 24-36PT

University of Bath
International Public Policy Analysis ...... MSc 12FT/PGDip 9FT/PGCert 6FT
Politics & International Studies .... MRes 12FT/PGDip 9FT/PGCert 9FT

Political science

Social Policy ... MRes 12FT 24-60PT/PGDip 9FT 21PT/PGCert 4FT 16PT

Birkbeck, University of London
European Politics and Policy ... MSc 12FT 24PT
Global Governance and Emerging Powers ... MSc 12FT 24PT
Global Politics ... MSc 12FT 24PT/MRes 12FT 24PT
Government, Policy and Politics ... MSc 12FT 24PT
International Security and Global Governance ... MSc 12FT 24PT
Middle East in Global Politics: Islam, Conflict and Development. MSc 12FT 24PT
Nationalism and Ethnic Conflict ... MSc 12FT 24PT
Politics ... MRes 12FT 24PT
Public Policy and Management ... MSc 12FT 24PT/MRes 12FT 24PT
Social Research ... MSc 12FT 24PT/PGDip 12FT 24PT/PGCert 12FT 24PT
Social and Political Theory ... MSc 12FT 24PT/MRes 12FT 24PT

University of Birmingham
International Development (International Political Economy and Development) ... MSc 12FT 24PT/PGDip 9FT
International Relations (Contemporary Pacific Asia) ... MA 12FT 24PT
International Relations (Global Economic Governance) .. MA 12FT 24PT
Political Science (British Politics and the State) ... MA 12FT 24PT/PGDip 9FT 18PT
Political Science (Research Methods) ... MA 12FT 24PT
Political Science (with specialist pathways) ... MA 12FT 24PT
Social and Political Theory ... MA 12FT
US Foreign Policy ... MRes 12FT 24PT

University of Brighton
Politics and Ethics ... MA 12FT 24PT/PGDip 12FT 24PT/PGCert 12FT 24PT

University of Bristol
Social Science Research Methods (Politics/International Relations) ... MSc 12FT 24PT

Brunel University
Modern Political Thought: Violence and Revolution ... MA 12FT 30PT
Politics ... MSc 12FT 30PT

University of Buckingham
Global Affairs ... MA 12FT
Global Affairs and Diplomacy ... MA 12FT
Security and Intelligence Studies ... MA 12FT
Security, Intelligence and Diplomacy ... MA 12FT

University of Cambridge
Political Thought and Intellectual History ... MPhil 10FT

Cardiff University
Music, Culture and Politics ... MA 12FT 24PT
Political Theory ... MSc(Econ) 12FT 24PT
Politics and Public Policy ... MSc 12FT 24PT
Welsh Government and Politics ... MSc(Econ) 12FT 24PT

University of Central Lancashire
Global Security and Justice ... MA 12FT
International Relations ... MA 12FT

City University London
Global Political Economy ... MA 12FT/MA 24PT

University College Cork
Government ... MBS 12FT 24PT
Politics ... MA 12FT

Coventry University
Diplomacy, Law and Global Change ... MA 12FT 24-30PT
Peace and Reconciliation Studies ... MA 12FT 24-30DL/PGDip 9FT 18PT

University College Dublin
Nationalism and Ethno-Communal Conflict ... MSc 12FT/MLitt 24FT
Politics ... MA 12FT/MLitt 24FT

University of Dundee
International Politics and Security (MLitt) ... MLitt 12FT/PGDip 9FT

Durham University
Global Politics ... MSc 12FT

University of East Anglia
Broadcast Journalism: Theory and Practice ... MA 12FT 24PT
Conflict, Governance and International Development ... MA 12FT 24PT
Economics and International Relations ... MA 12FT
International Relations ... MA 12FT 24PT
International Security ... MA 12FT 24PT
Media and Cultural Politics ... MA 12FT 24PT
Media, Culture and Society ... MA 12FT 24PT
Philosophy, Politics and Economics of Public Choice ... MA 12FT 24PT
Politics ... MA 12FT 24PT
Public Policy and Public Management ... MRes 12FT 24PT
Social and Political Theory ... MA 12FT 24PT

University of Edinburgh
Africa and International Development ... MSc 12FT 24PT PGCert 12DL/PGCert 24DL
African Studies ... MSc 12FT 24PT
Arab World Studies ... MSc 24FT
Chinese Studies ... Master of Chinese Studies 24FT
Comparative Public Policy ... MSc 12FT 24PT
East Asian Relations ... MSc 12FT 24PT
Environmental Sustainability ... MSc 12FT 24-36PT/PGDip 9FT
Ethics ... MTh 12FT 24PT/MSc 12FT 24PT
Global Environment, Politics and Society ... MSc 12FT 24PT
Global Health Challenges (Online Distance Learning) ... PGCert 12-24DL
Global Health Policy (Online Distance Learning) ... PGCert 9-21DL
Global Health and Public Policy ... MSc 12FT 24-36PT
Health Inequalities and Public Policy ... MSc 12FT 24-36PT
Health Systems and Public Policy ... MSc 12FT 24-36PT
International Political Theory ... MSc 12FT 24PT
International Relations ... MSc 12FT 24PT
International Relations of the Middle East ... MRCPsych 12FT
International Relations of the Middle East with Arabic ... MSc 24FT
International and European Politics ... MSc 12FT 24PT
Management of Bioeconomy, Innovation and Governance ... MSc 12FT 24PT
Nationalism Studies ... MSc 12FT 24PT
Policy Studies ... MSc 12FT 24PT
Public Policy (Master of) ... MPP 15FT

University of Essex
Conflict Resolution ... MA 12FT 24PT/MSc 12FT 24PT
Ethics, Politics and Public Policy ... MA 12FT 24PT
Global and Comparative Politics ... MA 12FT 24PT/MSc 12FT 24PT
Ideology and Discourse Analysis ... MA 12FT 24PT
International RelationsMA 12FT 24PT/MSc 12FT 24PT/MRes 12FT
International Relations and the Media ... MA 12FT 24PT
Multilevel Governance in Europe .. MA 12FT 24PT/MSc 12FT 24PT
Political Behaviour ... MA 12FT 24PT/MSc 12FT 24PT
Political Economy ... MA 12FT 24PT/MSc 12FT 24PT/MRes 12FT
Political Science ... MA 12FT 24PT/GradDip 12FT/MSc 12FT 24PT/MRes 12FT 24PT
Political Theory ... MA 12FT 24PT
Politics ... MA 12FT 24PT
Politics with English for Academic Purposes ... Diploma 9FT
Public Opinion and Polling ... MA 12FT 24PT/MSc 12FT 24PT

University of Exeter
Applied Security Strategy ... MA 12FT
Critical Global Politics ... MA 12FT 24PT
Food Security and Sustainable Agriculture ... MSc 12FT 24PT
History of Political Thought ... MA 12FT 24PT
Politics ... MRes 12FT 24PT
Security, Conflict and Justice ... MRes 12FT 24PT
Social and Political Philosophy ... MA 12FT 24PT

Goldsmiths, University of London
Art & Politics ... MA 12FT 24PT
Critical Asian Studies ... MA 12FT 24PT
Cultural Studies ... MA 12FT 24PT
Global Media and Transnational Communications ... MA 12FT 24PT
Postcolonial Culture & Global Policy ... MA 12FT 24PT

University of Hull
Global Political Economy ... MA 12FT 24PT
International Law and Politics ... MA 12FT 24PT
International Politics ... MA 12FT 24PT

Keele University
Human Rights, Globalisation and Justice ... PGDip 12FT/MA 12FT 24PT

University of Kent
Comparative Politics ... MA 12FT 24PT/PGDip 12FT 24PT
European Public Policy (Brussels) ... MA 12FT 24PT
European and Global Governance ... PGDip 12FT 24PT/MA 12FT 24PT
European and Global Governance (International Double Award) MA 24FT
Human Rights ... MA 12FT 24PT/PGDip 12FT 24PT
International Conflict Analysis (Canterbury or Brussels) ... MA 12FT 24PT/PGDip 12FT 24PT
International Conflict and Security ... MA 12FT 24PT
International Development ... MSc 12FT 24PT MA 12FT 24PT
International Development (Brussels) ... MA 12FT 24PT
International Migration ... MA 12FT 24PT
International Political Economy (Brussels) ... MA 12FT 24PT
International Relations (Brussels) ... MA 12FT 24PT/PGDip 12FT 24PT
International Relations (international double award) (Canterbury, Moscow) ... MA 24FT
International Relations with International Law ... MA 12FT 24PT/PGDip 12FT 24PT
International Security and the Politics of TerrorPGDip 12FT 24PT/MA 12FT 24PT
Peace and Conflict Studies (International Double Award) ... MA 24FT
Political Sociology ... MA 12FT 24PT

Political Strategy and Communication (Brussels) ... MA 12FT 24PT
Political Theory and Practices of Resistance ... PGDip 12FT 24PT/MA 12FT 24PT
Security and Terrorism ... MA 12FT 24PT/PGDip 12FT 24PT

King's College London
Environment, Politics & Globalisation ... MA 12FT 24PT/MSc 12FT 24PT

Kingston University
Politics ... MSc 12FT 24PT

University of Leeds
Global Development and Africa ... MA 12FT 24PT
Global Development and Political Economy of International Resources ... MA 12FT 24PT
International Relations ... MA 12FT 24PT
Activism and Social Change ... MA 12FT 24PT/PGDip 12FT 24PT/PGCert 12FT 24PT
Political Communication ... MA 12FT
Politics ... MA 12FT 24PT
Politics (Parliamentary) ... MA 12FT
Politics (Political Theory) ... MA 12FT 24PT
Security, Terrorism and Insurgency ... MA 12FT 24PT

University of Leicester
International Security ... MA 12FT 24PT/PGDip 12FT 24PT
New Media, Governance and Democracy ... MA 12FT
New Media, Governance and Democracy (by Distance Learning) ... MA 24FT/PGDip 20FT
Political Research ... MSc 12FT 24PT/PGDip 9FT 18PT

University of Limerick
Europan Politics and Governance ... MA 12FT
International Studies ... MA 12FT
Politics ... MA 12FT

Liverpool Hope University
International Relations ... MA 12FT 24PT

University of Liverpool
Politics and Irish Studies ... MA 12FT 24PT
Politics and the Mass Media ... MA 12FT 24PT/PGDip 12FT/PGCert 12FT

London School of Economics and Political Science (LSE)
Comparative Politics ... MSc 12FT 24PT
Global Politics ... MSc 12FT 24PT
Political Economy of Late Development ... MSc 12FT
Political Science and Political Economy ... MSc 12FT 24PT
Political Theory ... MSc 12FT 24PT

London School of Hygiene and Tropical Medicine
Global Health Policy ... MSc 24-60DL/PGDip 12-60DL/PGCert 12-60DL

Loughborough University
International Financial and Political Relations ... MSc 12FT

University of Manchester
Political Economy ... MA 12FT 24PT/PGDip 9FT 21PT
Political Science - Democracy and Elections ... MA 12FT 24PT/PGDip 9FT 21PT
Political Science - Ethics and Political Philosophy .. MA 12FT 24PT
Political Science - Governance and Public Policy ... MA 12FT 24PT/PGDip 9FT 24PT
Political Science - Political Theory ... MA 12FT 24PT/PGDip 9FT 24PT
Politics ... MA 12FT 24PT/PGDip 9FT 21PT
Religion and Political Life ... MA 12FT 24PT

Newcastle University
International Politics (Critical Geopolitics) ... MA 12FT 24PT
International Politics (Global Justice and Ethics) ... MA 12FT 24PT
Politics (Research) ... MA 12FT 24PT
World Politics and Popular Culture ... MA 12FT 24PT

Nottingham Trent University
Politics ... MA 12FT 24PT

University of Nottingham
Critical Theory and Politics ... MA 12FT 24PT
International Relations (Advanced Research Track) ... MA 24FT 48PT
Politics (Advanced Research Track) ... MA 24FT 48PT
Politics (Research Track) ... MA 12FT 24PT
Politics and Contemporary History ... MA 12FT 24PT
Politics and Contemporary History (Research Track) ... MA 12FT 24PT

University of Oxford
Global Governance and Diplomacy ... MSc 12FT
Global Health Science ... MSc 12FT
Politics and International Relations Research ... MSc 9FT
Politics: Comparative Government ... MPhil 21FT
Politics: European Politics & Society ... MPhil 21FT
Politics: Political Theory ... MPhil 21FT

Queen Mary, University of London
Critical Theory and Global Politics ... MA 12FT 24PT
International Business and Politics ... MSc 12FT 24PT
International Public Policy ... MSc 12FT 24PT
International Relations ... MA 12FT 24PT/MRes 12FT 24PT
Law and Development ... LLM 12FT 24PT

Political science

Public Policy .... MSc 12FT 24PT/MRes 12FT 24PT

Queen's University Belfast
Comparative Ethnic Conflict .... MA 12FT 24PT/PGDip 12FT 24PT
Legislative Studies and Practice .... MA 12FT
Political Psychology .... MSc 12FT 24PT
Politics .... MA 12FT 24PT

University of Reading
Diplomacy .... MA 12FT 72PT/PGDip 12FT 72PT/PGCert 12FT 72PT
Diplomacy .... MA 12FT 24-72PT/PGCert 12FT 24-72PT/PGDip 12FT 24-72PT
Ethics & Political Theory .... MA 12FT 24PT
International Relations .... MA (res) 12FT 24-72PT 72BM
International Relations (Strategic Studies) ...... MA 12FT 24-72PT/PGDip 24-72PT/PGCert 12FT 24PT

Richmond, The American International University in London
International Development .... MA 12FT 24PT

Royal Holloway, University of London
Political Research .... MSc 12/9FT 24/20PT
Political Theory .... MSc 12/9FT 24/20PT

University of Salford
Terrorism and Security ...... MA 12FT 36PT 36DL/PGDip 12FT 36PT 36DL

School of Oriental and African Studies - SOAS
African Politics .... MSc 12FT 24-36PT
Asian Politics .... MSc 12FT 24PT
Development Studies with Special Reference to Central Asia .... MSc 12FT 24PT
International Politics .... MSc 12FT 24PT
International Studies and Diplomacy .... MA 12FT 24-36PT/PGDip 12FT 24PT
Middle East Politics .... MSc 12FT 24PT
PGDip Policy Studies .... PGCert 9FT
Political Economy of Development .... MSc 12FT 24-36PT
Politics of China .... MSc 12FT 24PT
Public Policy and Management .... MSc 24DL/PGDip 12DL
State, Society and Development .... MSc 12FT 24PT
Violence, Conflict and Development .... MSc 12FT 24PT

University of Sheffield
European Governance and Politics .... MA 12FT 24PT
European Law, Politics and Governance .... MA 12FT
Global Justice .... MA 12FT 24PT
Global Politics and Law .... MA 12FT 24PT
Global Politics and Law (Doshisha Pathway) .... MA 24FT
Globalisation and Development .... MA 12FT 24PT
Political Theory .... MA 12FT 24PT
Politics .... MA 12FT 24PT
Politics with Research Methods .... MA 12FT 24PT

University of Southampton
Citizenship and Democracy .... MSc 12FT 24PT/PGDip 9FT 21PT
Citizenship and Democracy (Research) MSc 12FT 24PT/PGDip 9FT 21PT
European Law .... LLM 12FT 24PT
Global Politics .... MSc 12FT 24PT/PGDip 9FT 21PT
Global Security .... MSc 12FT 24PT/PGDip 9FT 21PT

University of St Andrews
Peace and Conflict Studies .... MLitt 12FT

St Mary's University College, Twickenham
Religion, Politics and Conflict Resolution .. MA 24PT/PGDip 24PT/PGCert 12PT

Staffordshire University
International Policy and Diplomacy .... MA 12FT 30-36DL MA 24-36DL
International Relations .... MA 12FT 30-36DL MA 12FT 24PT 24-36DL
Terrorism, Crime and Global Security .... MA 24-60DL

University of Stirling
International Conflict and Co-operation .... MSc 12FT 27PT/PGDip 9FT 21PT/PGCert 3FT 9PT

University of Strathclyde
Political Research .... MSc 12FT 24PT

University of Surrey
European and International Politics .... MA 12FT 24PT
International Politics .... MA 12FT 24PT
Politics .... MA 12FT 24PT

University of Sussex
Corruption and Governance .... MA 12FT 24PT
Geopolitics and Grand Strategy .... MA 12FT 24PT
Governance and Development .... MA 12FT 24PT
Social and Political Thought .... MA 12FT 24PT

Swansea University
Politics .... MA 12FT 24PT

Trinity College Dublin - the University of Dublin
International Politics .... MSc 12FT 24PT
Political Science .... PhD by taught 48FT MSc 12FT 24PT

UCL - University College London
Democracy and Comparative Politics .... MSc 12FT 24PT
European Public Policy .... MSc 12FT 24PT
Identity, Culture and Power .... MA 12FT 24PT
International Master's in Economy, State and Society .... International Master's 24FT
International Public Policy .... MSc 12FT 24PT
Latin American Politics .... MSc 12FT 24PT
Legal and Political Theory .... MA 12FT 24PT
Politics, Security and Integration .... MA 12FT 24PT
The Politics and Economics of Eastern Europe .... MRes 12FT
Transnational Studies .... MA 12FT 24PT
United States Studies: History and Politics .... MA 12FT 24PT

University of Warwick
Double Degree with Nanyang Technological University. MA 24FT
Double Degree with the University of Konstanz .... MA 24FT
International Development .... MA 12FT 24PT/PGDip 9FT
International Political Economy .... MA 12FT 24PT/PGDip 9FT
International Politics and East Asia ...... MA 12FT 24PT/PGDip 9FT
Political and Legal Theory .... MA 12FT 24PT/PGDip 9FT
Public Policy .... MA 12FT 24PT/PGDip 9FT
US Foreign Policy .... MA 12FT 24PT/PGDip 9FT
Social and Political Thought .... MA 12FT 24PT/PGDip 9FT 24PT
Social and Political Thought .... MA 12FT 24PT/PGDip 12FT 24PT

University of York
Conflict, Governance and Development ..... MA 12FT 24PT/PGDip 12FT
Contemporary History and International Politics .... MA 12FT 24PT
Philosophy, Politics and Economics .... MA 12FT
Political Philosophy .... MA 12FT 24PT/PGDip 12FT
Political Philosophy: the Idea of Toleration .... MA 12FT 24PT/PGDip 12FT
Political Research .... MA 12FT
Politics, Philosophy and Economics: Economics and Development .... MA 12FT
Politics, Philosophy and Economics: Economics and Politics ... MA 12FT
Politics, Philosophy and Economics: Politics and Development.... MA 12FT
Post-war Recovery Studies .... MA 12FT/PGDip 12FT

Political science
Research Courses

University of Aberdeen
Politics and International Relations.... PhD 36FT 60PT/MPhil 24FT 48PT/MLitt by research 12FT 24PT

Aberystwyth University
International Politics .... PhD 36FT

School of Advanced Study, University of London
Politics and International Studies .... PhD 36FT 72PT/MPhil 12FT 36PT

Bangor University
Social Policy .... PhD 36FT 60PT/MPhil 12-24FT 24-36PT

Birkbeck, University of London
Politics .... PhD 24FT 36PT/MPhil 24FT 36PT

University of Birmingham
Political Science and International Studies .... PhD 36FT/MPhil 24FT
US Foreign Policy .... MPhil(B) 12FT 24PT

University of Bristol
Policy Studies .... PhD 36FT 72PT/MPhil 36FT 72PT
Sociology, Politics and International Studies .... PhD 36FT 72PT/MPhil 12FT 24PT

Brunel University
Doctoral Programme in Politics, History & International Relations .... PhD 36FT 60PT/MPhil 12FT 24PT/MRes 12FT 24PT

University of Buckingham
International Affairs and Diplomacy .... MA by research 12FT
Modern War Studies .... MA by research 12FT

University of Cambridge
Social and Political Sciences .... PhD 36FT 60PT

Canterbury Christ Church University
Politics and International Relations.... MPhil 24FT 48PT/PhD 36FT 60PT

Cardiff University
International Relations and Globalisation.. PhD 36FT 60PT/MPhil 24FT 48PT

Coventry University
Politics .... MA by research 12FT 24PT

University College Dublin
Nationalism and Ethno-communal conflict.... PhD 36FT/MLitt by research 24FT
Politics .... PhD 36FT/MLitt by research 24FT

University of Dundee
Politics .... MPhil 24FT PhD 36FT

Durham University
Politics .... PhD 36FT/MPhil 24FT/MA by research 12FT

University of East Anglia
Political, Social and International Studies... PhD 36FT 72PT/MPhil 24FT 48PT/MA by research 12FT 24PT

University of Edinburgh
African Studies .... PhD 36FT 72PT/MPhil 24FT 48PT
Canadian Studies .... PhD 36FT 72PT/MPhil 24FT 48PT
International Public Health Policy .... PhD 36FT 72PT
Politics & International Relations ..... MSc by research 12FT 24PT/PhD 36FT 72PT

University of Essex
Government..... PhD 36FT 72PT/MPhil 24FT 48PT/MA by research 12FT 24PT

European University Institute
Political and Social Sciences .... PhD 48FT

University of Exeter
Ethno-Political Studies .... MPhil 36FT 60PT/PhD 48FT 89PT
Politics .... PhD 48FT 84PT 84DL/MPhil 36FT 60PT 60DL/MA by research 12FT 24PT
Security, Conflict and Justice ..... MPhil 26FT 60PT/PhD 48FT 84PT

University of Glasgow
Politics .... PhD 36FT/MLitt by research 12FT

Goldsmiths, University of London
Political Science .... MRes 12FT 24PT
Politics .... PhD 36-48FT 48-72PT/MPhil 24FT 36PT

University of Hull
Politics/International Relations/Security Studies/Legislative Studies .... PhD 36FT 60PT/MPhil 24FT 36PT

Institute for the Study of the Americas, School of Advanced Study, University of London
Politics and International Studies of the Americas .... PhD 36FT/MPhil 12FT

University of Kent
Comparative Politics .... MA by research 12FT 24PT/MPhil 24FT 36PT/PhD 36FT 60PT
International Conflict Analysis (Brussels or Canterbury) .... PhD 36FT 60PT/MPhil 24FT 36PT/MA by research 12FT 24PT
International Relations (Brussels or Canterbury) .... PhD 36FT 60PT/MPhil 24FT 36PT/MA by research 12FT 24PT
Politcal and Social Thought .... MA by research 12FT 24PT/MPhil 24FT 36PT/PhD 36FT 60PT

Kingston University
Politics ..... PhD 48FT 72PT/MPhil 24FT 48PT/MA by research 12FT 24PT

University of Leeds
MA/MSc by ResearchMA by research 12FT 24PT/MSc by research 12FT 24PT
School of Politics and International Studies .... PhD 36+FT/MPhil 24FT/MA by research 12FT

University of Leicester
Department of Politics & International RelationsPhD 48FT/MPhil 48FT

University of Lincoln
Criminology .... MPhil 12FT 24PT/PhD 12FT 24PT

University of Liverpool
Politics .... PhD 24-48FT 48-84PT/MPhil 12-48FT 24-72PT

London School of Economics and Political Science (LSE)
Government .... PhD 36-48FT/MPhil 36-48FT
Political Science .... PhD 36-48FT/MRes 12FT

London School of Hygiene and Tropical Medicine
Public Health & Policy (Research) .... DrPH 42FT 42PT/PhD 42FT 42PT/MPhil 12FT 12PT

Loughborough University
Politics and International Studies .... MPhil 24FT 36PT/PhD 36FT 60PT

Manchester Metropolitan University
Politics ... PhD 24-48FT 42-84PT 42-84DL/MPhil 18-36FT 36-72PT 36-72DL/MA by research 12-24FT 24-42PT 24-42DL

University of Manchester
Politics .... PhD 36FT 72PT

Middlesex University
Politics and international studies ...... PhD 33FT 36PT 36DL/MPhil 18FT 30PT 30DL

Newcastle University
Politics .... PhD 36FT 72PT/MPhil 12FT 24PT

University of Nottingham
Politics and International Relations .... MPhil 24FT 48PT/PhD 36-48FT 72-96PT/MRes 12FT 24PT
School of Politics MRes .... MRes 12FT 24PT

The Open University
Comparative Politics .... PhD 36FT 72PT variableDL/MPhil 15FT 24PT variableDL
Political Theory .... PhD 36FT 72PT variableDL/MPhil 15FT 24PT variableDL
Political ideas, policies and actions.... PhD 36FT 72PT variableDL/MPhil 15FT 24PT variableDL
Politics and International Studies ...... PhD 36FT 72PT variableDL/MPhil 15FT 24PT variableDL

Political science

Oxford Brookes University
International Relations, Politics and Sociology .... PhD 24-60FT 36-72PT/MPhil 24-60FT 36-72PT

University of Oxford
Politics .... DPhil 48FT

Queen Mary, University of London
Politics .... PhD 36FT 48PT/MPhil 24FT 36PT

Queen's University Belfast
Politics, International Studies and Philosophy .....PhD 36FT 72PT/MPhil 24FT 48PT

Royal Holloway, University of London
Department of Social and Political Science....................PhD 36FT/MPhil 36FT

School of Oriental and African Studies - SOAS
Politics .... PhD 36FT 72PT/MPhil 24FT 36PT

University of Sheffield
Politics ..... PhD 36FT 72PT/MPhil 24FT 48PT/Integrated PhD 48FT

University of Surrey
Political, International and Policy Studies. PhD 33-48FT 45-96PT/MPhil 21-36FT 33-72PT

University of Sussex
Politics Research Programme .... PhD 24-48FT 36-72PT/MPhil 12-36FT 24-48PT
Social and Political Thought .... DPhil 24-48FT 36-72PT/MPhil 12-36FT 24-48PT

Swansea University
American Studies ...MA by research 12FT 24PT/MPhil 24FT 48PT/PhD 36FT 72PT
Politics and International Relations....PhD 36FT 72PT/MPhil 24FT 48PT

University of Ulster
Politics and International Studies ....PhD 36FT 72PT/MPhil 24FT 48PT

UCL - University College London
History, Politics and Economics of Eastern Europe ....PhD 36FT 60PT
Political Science... PhD 36FT 60PT

University of Warwick
Phd in Politics and International Studies ....PhD 36FT 60PT/MPhil 24FT 36PT

University of York
Politics .....PhD 36FT 72PT/MPhil 24FT 48PT/MA by research 12FT 24PT

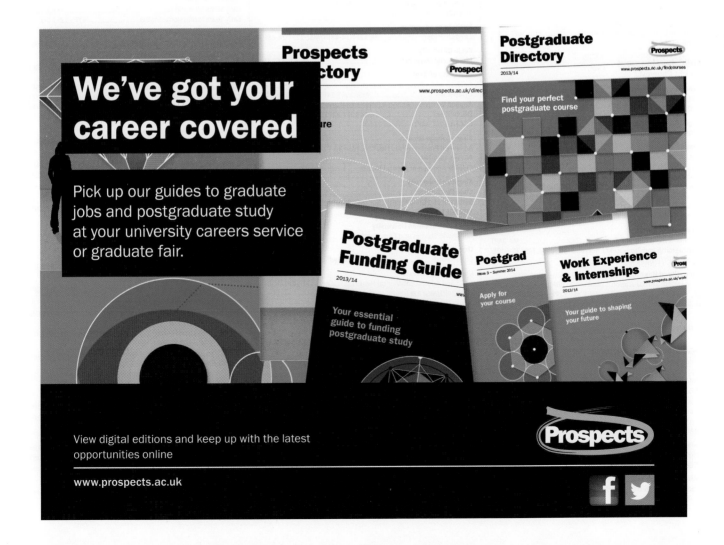

Psychology

Autism
Taught Courses

University of Aberdeen
Autism & Learning .... MEd 36PT/PGDip 14PT/PGCert 12PT

Bangor University
Applied Behaviour Analysis .... PGCert 4FT 9PT/PGDip 9FT 18PT/MSc 12FT 24PT

University of Birmingham
Autism (Adults).. PGCert 12DL/PGDip 24DL/MEd 24-72DL/MPhil 24-36DL
Autism (Children) .. PGCert 3FT 12PT 12DL/PGDip 12FT 24-48DL/MEd 12FT 24-72DL/MPhil 12FT 24-36DL

University of Central Lancashire
Personality Disorder (Practice Development) .... MSc 36-60PT/PGDip 24PT
Personality Disorder (Research) .... MSc 36-60PT/PGDip 12-24PT

University of Kent
Autism Studies ...... PGCert 12FT 24PT/PGDip 12FT 24PT/MA 12FT 24PT
Autism Studies .... PGCert 12FT 24DL/MA 12FT 24PT/PGDip 12FT 24PT

Manchester Metropolitan University
Autistic Spectrum Conditions .... MA 12-60PT

Northumbria University
Autism .... MA 36PT/PGDip 24PT/PGCert 12PT

Queen's University Belfast
Autism Spectrum Disorders .... MSc 12FT 60PT

Sheffield Hallam University
Asperger Syndrome .... PGCert 12-24PT
Autism .... CertHE 24-60PT 24-60DL MA 36PT/PGDip 24PT/PGCert 12PT

University of South Wales
Autism .... MA 12-24FT 36-60PT

University of St Andrews
Adults Support, Protection and Safeguarding .... PGCert 12DL

University of Strathclyde
Autism .... MSc 12FT 24PT/PGDip 12FT/PGCert 9FT

Autism
Research Courses

University of Nottingham
Cognitive Development and Learning .... PhD 36FT 72PT/MPhil 24FT 48PT

Child development
Taught Courses

Aberystwyth University
Childhood and Creative Development .... MA 12FT 24PT/PGDip 9FT 21PT

Anglia Ruskin University
Clinical Child Psychology .... MSc 12 - 15FT 24 - 30PT

Bangor University
Applied Behaviour Analysis .... PGCert 4FT 9PT/PGDip 9FT 18PT/MSc 12FT 24PT
Language Development .... MSc 12FT 36PT
Psychological Research .. MSc 12FT 24PT/PGDip 8FT 16PT/PGCert 4FT 8PT
Psychology .... MRes 12FT/PGCert 3FT MA 12FT 24PT/PGDip 9FT 18PT/PGCert 4FT 8PT

University of Bolton
Children's Literature and Culture .... MA 24PT
Safeguarding and Promoting Children's Welfare.... MSc 36-60PT/PGDip 24PT/PGCert 12PT

University of Brighton
Child Health and Education .... MSc 12 - 36FT 24 - 72PT/PGCert 12 - 36FT 24 - 72PT/PGDip 12 - 36FT 24 - 72PT
Child Health and Management ... MSc 12 - 36FT 24 - 72PT/PGDip 12 - 36FT 24 - 72PT/PGCert 12 - 36FT 24 - 72PT

Bucks New University
Child & Adolescent Studies .... MSc 12FT 24PT

University of Central Lancashire
Child Care Practice, PQ Specialist Award with Children, Young People, Families & Carers .... PGCert 18PT
Child Care and Welfare .... MA 12FT 24-60PT
Child Computer Interaction .... MRes 12FT 24PT
Child Health .... MSc 36PT
Neonatal Studies .... MA 60PT/PGDip 24PT/PGCert 12PT
Psychology of Child Development .... MSc 12FT 24PT/PGDip 9FT 24PT/PGCert 9FT 24PT

University of Chester
Family and Child Psychology ... MSc 12FT 24PT/PGDip 12FT 24PT/PGCert 12FT 12-24PT

University of Cumbria
Leading Intergrated Children's Services ... MSc 24 - 60PT/GradDip 12 - 36PT

University of Derby
Cognitive Behavioural Psychotherapy (Children and Adolescents) (BABCP accredited) .... MSc 24-36PT

University of Dundee
Developmental Psychology .... MSc 12FT

University of East Anglia
Child and Family Psychology .... MSc 12FT 24PT

University of East London
Child Psychoanalytic Psychotherapy Prof Doc (D. Ch. Psych. Psych.) .... DProf by taught 48FT 60PT
Child and Adolescent Primary Mental Health Care Work (M42) MA .... MA 36PT/PGDip 24PT/PGCert 12PT
Infant Mental Health (Early Years Development) M9 ... MA 36PT/PGDip 24PT/PGCert 12PT
Professional Doctorate in Educational and Child Psychology D.Ed. Ch.Psy .... DProf by taught 36FT
Psychological Therapy with Children, Young People and Families MA (M34) .... MA 36PT
Therapeutic Communication with Children .... PGCert 12PT

Edge Hill University
Integrated Children and Young People's Practice ...... MSc 36-72PT

University of Edinburgh
Applied Psychology (Healthcare) for Children and Young People. MSc 12FT
Childhood Studies .... MSc 12FT 24PT
Children & Young People's Mental Health and Psychological Practice .... MSc 12FT 24-72PT/PGCert 12-24PT/PGDip 9FT 24-48PT
Health & Social Care - Children & Young People's Mental Health: Ecological Approaches ODL .... PGCert 9DL

Glasgow Caledonian University
Sexual Health .... MSc 24-60FT On-lineDL

University of Glasgow
Child Health .... PGDip 12-24PT PGCert 12-24FT

University of Gloucestershire
Play and Playwork PGCert 12-24DL/PGDip 12-24DL/MA 24-48DL
Teacher Training PGCE (Primary) .... PGCE 12FT

Goldsmiths, University of London
Education: School-Based Explorations .... MA 24-60PT
The Science of Psychology, Genetics & Education .... MSc 12FT 24PT

Institute of Education
Child Development .... MA 12FT 24-48PT/MSc 12FT 24-48PT

Keele University
Child Social Development .... MSc 12FT 24PT

University of Kent
Analysis and Intervention in Intellectual and Development Disabilities .... MSc 12FT 24PT/PGDip 12FT 24PT
Applied Behaviour Analysis (Intellectual and Developmental Disabilities) .... MSc 12FT 24PT/PGCert 12FT 24PT/PGCert 12FT 24PT

King's College London
Advanced Practice (Child Health) .. MSc 36-72PT/PGDip 24-72PT/PGCert 12-72PT
Child & Adolescent Mental Health .... MSc 12FT 24PT

Kingston University
Child Psychology .... MSc 12FT
Maternal and Child Health: Socio-Cultural Perspectives .... MSc 12FT 24PT

Leeds Metropolitan University
Childhood Studies and Early Years .... MA 12FT 24PT

University of Leeds
Child Health .... MMedSci 36PT/PGDip 24PT

University of Leicester
Child and Adolescent Mental Health .... PGCert 12FT 12PT/PGDip 12FT 24PT/MSc 12FT 36PT

Liverpool John Moores University
Early Years (3 -7 years) .... PGCE 12FT

London Metropolitan University
Child, Adolescent and Family Mental Health .... MSc 12FT 24PT

London School of Economics and Political Science (LSE)
Anthropology and Development .... MSc 12FT 24PT
Anthropology and Development Management .... MSc 12FT 24PT

Manchester Metropolitan University
Autistic Spectrum Conditions .... MA 12-60PT

Middlesex University
Child and Family Mental Health Work .... AdvDip 12PT/PGCert 12PT
Child, Adolescent and Family Mental Health Work... AdvDip 7PT/PGCert 7PT

Newman University
Children, Young People and Families .... MA 24FT 36-48PT
Early Years Foundation Degree .... FdA 36PT
Early Years Teacher Status .... Early Years Teacher Status 6FT/Early Years Teacher Status 12FT

University of Northampton
Child and Adolescent Mental Health .... MSc 12FT 24PT/PGDip 12PT
Counselling Children and Young People .... MSc 18FT 36PT

Northumbria University
Leadership and Management in Integrated Childrens Services ... MA 36PT/PGDip 24PT/PGCert 12PT
Nursing (MNurs) Registered Nurse (Child) .... MA 24-48FT
Psychoanalytical Observational Studies .... MA 36/24PT

Nottingham Trent University
Applied Child Psychology .... MSc 12FT 24PT

University of Nottingham
Counselling Children and Young People .... MA 12FT

Oxford Brookes University
Childhood Studies .... MA 12FT 24PT/PGDip 12FT 24PT/PGCert 12FT 12PT
Children, Young People and Family Well-Being .... MSc 12-36DL/PGDip 8-36DL/PGCert 4-36DL

University of Oxford
Education (Child Development and Education) .... MSc 12FT

University of Portsmouth
Child Forensic Studies: Psychology and Law .... MSc 12/24DL

Queen Margaret University, Edinburgh
Collaborative Working: Education and Therapy ... PGCert 12-48PT

Queen Mary, University of London
Mental Health: Psychological Therapies D/L option ...... MSc 12FT 24PT

Queen's University Belfast
Atypical Child Development .... MSc 12FT

University of Roehampton
Attachment Studies .... PGCert 6FT 12PT PGDip 6-12FT 12PT

University Campus Suffolk
MA Childhood and Youth Studies .... MA 12FT 24 - 36PT

University of Salford
Child and Adolescent Mental Health .... MSc 24PT/PGDip 18PT/PGCert 9PT

Sheffield Hallam University
Early Childhood Studies .... MA 12FT 36PT/PGDip 12FT 24PT/PGCert 12FT 12PT
Early Years Education .... PGCE 12FT
Early Years Professional Status .... EYPS 12FT 6-15PT

University of Sheffield
Educational and Child Psychology .... Doctor 36FT

University of South Wales
Child Health and Welfare Studies (Online Delivery) MSc 12-48FT 36-60DL
Child and Adolescent Mental Health .... MA 12FT 36PT
Consultative Supervision .... MA 24PT/PGDip 12PT
Counselling Children and Young People .... MA 24PT
Developmental Disorders .... MSc 24-60PT

St George's, University of London
Maternal and Child Health .... MSc 12FT 24PT

University of Strathclyde
Early Childhood Studies .... MSc 24PT/PGDip 24PT/PGCert 24PT
Educational Support ...... MSc max 60PT/PGDip max 48PT/PGCert max 24PT

University of Surrey
Health Psychology .... MA 12FT 24PT

University of Sussex
Foundations of Clinical Psychology and Mental Health .... MSc 12FT 24PT

Swansea University
Childhood Studies .... MA 12FT 24PT

University of Wales Trinity Saint David
Plentyndod Cynnar .... MA 48PT/PGCert 12PT/PGDip 18PT

UCL - University College London
Child and Adolescent Mental Health ... MSc 12FT 24-60PT/PGDip 24-60PT/PGCert 12PT
International Child Health .... MSc 12FT 24-60PT/PGDip 9FT 24-60PT/PGCert 12FT 24PT
Paediatrics and Child Health: Advanced Paediatrics .... MSc 36-60PT/PGCert 12-24PT/PGDip 36-60PT
Paediatrics and Child Health: Community Child Health .... MSc 12FT 36-60PT/PGCert 12-24PT/PGDip 9FT 18-45PT

University of Warwick
Child Health .... PGA 12PT
Child Health ... MSc 12FT 24-96PT/PGDip 12FT 24PT/PGCert 12FT 24PT
Child Health Services: Management, Organisations and Data Systems .... PGA 12PT/CPDMod 1PT
Health Sciences: Child Health .... MSc 36PT/PGDip 24PT/PGCert 12PT/PGA 12PT

University of Winchester
Child Development ...... MSc 12FT 24PT/PGDip 12FT 24PT/PGCert 12FT 24PT

Business and social sciences
www.prospects.ac.uk/findcourses POSTGRADUATE DIRECTORY 463

Psychology

York St John University
Psychology of Child & Adolescent Development ... MSc 12FT 36PT

Child development
Research Courses

Aberystwyth University
Psychology (PhD) ... PhD 36FT 60PT

Bangor University
Doctorate by Research ... PhD 36FT/MPhil 24FT

University of Birmingham
Applied Educational and Child Psychology ... AppEd / Child PsyD 36FT

University College Cork
Doctor of Social Science ... DSocSci 48FT

Heriot-Watt University
Applied Psychology ... PhD 36FT 48PT/MPhil 24FT 36PT

King's College London
Child & Adolescent Psychiatry ... PhD 36FT 72PT/MPhil 36FT 72PT/MD 36FT 72PT

Liverpool School of Tropical Medicine
Child & Reproductive Health ... PhD/MPhil/MIHR

University of Liverpool
Child Health ... PhD 24-84FT/MPhil 12-48FT/MD 24-84FT

University of Nottingham
Early life nutrition and disease ... PhD 36FT 72PT/DM 24FT 48PT/MPhil 24FT 48PT

The Open University
Doctorate in Education ... EdD 36PT

Plymouth University
Behaviour ... PhD 36FT/MPhil 24FT
Developmental Disability Research & Education Group ... MPhil tbcFT
Parenting and Child Welfare ... MPhil tbcFT

Swansea University
Childhood Studies ... MPhil 12FT/PhD 36FT

UCL - University College London
Child Health ... PhD 36FT 60PT/MD(Res) 24FT
Developmental Science ... PhD 36FT 60PT

Clinical psychology
Taught Courses

Bangor University
Foundations of Clinical Neuropsychology ... MSc 12FT 24PT/PGDip 8FT 16PT/PGCert 4FT 8PT
Foundations of Clinical Psychology ... MSc 12FT 24PT/PGDip 8FT 16PT/PGCert 4FT 8PT
Psychological Research ... MSc 12FT 24PT/PGDip 8FT 16PT/PGCert 4FT 8PT
Psychology ... MRes 12FT/PGCert 3FT MA 12FT 24PT/PGDip 9FT 18PT/PGCert 4FT 8PT

University of Bath
Psychology ... MRes 12FT 24-36PT/PGDip 9FT 24-36PT/PGCert 4FT 24-36PT

University of Bedfordshire
Psychosocial Interventions ... PGCert 12FT

University of Birmingham
Clinical Psychology ... MRes 12FT 24PT

Bournemouth University
Foundations of Clinical Psychology ... MSc 10FT

University of Bradford
Health Psychology ... MSc 12FT 24PT/PGDip 12FT 24PT

Canterbury Christ Church University
Clinical Psychology ... DClinPsy by taught 36FT

Cardiff University
Clinical Psychology ... DClinPsy by taught 36FT

University of Central Lancashire
Counselling and Psychotherapy ... MSc 36PT/PGDip 24PT
Psychology ... MSc 12FT 24PT/PGDip 9FT 24PT/PGCert 9FT 24PT
Psychology of Child Development ... MSc 12FT 24PT/PGDip 9FT 24PT/PGCert 9FT 24PT
Psychology of Sport and Exercise ... MSc 12FT 24PT/PGDip 9FT 24PT/PGCert 9FT 24PT

University of Chester
Psychology (Conversion) ... MSc 12FT 24PT/PGDip 12FT 24PT

University of Chichester
Psychology of Sport and Exercise ... MSc 12-15FT 24-36PT/PGDip 9-12FT 18-24PT/PGCert 6-9FT 12-18PT

University College Cork
Behavioural & Cognitive Psychotherapy ... PGDip 18PT
Behavioural & Cognitive Psychotherapy ... MA 18PT
Integrative Psychotherapy Studies ... MA 24PT

University of Cumbria
Advanced Practice in Cognative Behaviour Therapy ... MSc 36PT/GradDip 24PT/GradCert 12PT

De Montfort University
Psychological Wellbeing ... MSc 12FT 24PT

University of Derby
Health Psychology ... MSc 12FT 24PT

University of Dundee
Psychological Therapy in Primary Care ... MSc 12FT

University of East London
Clinical and Community Psychology MSc ... MSc 12FT 24PT/PGDip 8FT 16PT/PGCert 4FT 8PT
Professional Doctorate in Applied Educational and Child Psychology ... DProf by taught 45-60PT
Professional Doctorate in Clinical Psychology ClinPsyD. DProf by taught 36FT
Professional Doctorate in Counselling Psychology ... DProf by taught 48FT

University of Edinburgh
Clinical Psychology ... DClinPsy by taught 36FT 60PT

University of Exeter
Clinical Practice ... DClinPrac 42DL
Clinical Psychology ... DClinPsy by taught 36FT
Clinical Research ... DClinRes 42BM

National University of Ireland Galway
Psychological Science (Clinical Psychology) ... DPsychSc by taught 36FT

University of Glasgow
Clinical Psychology ... DClinPsy by taught 36FT
Leadership Drugs & Alcohol Setting ... PGCert 9FT 18PT

University of Gloucestershire
Psychology in Practice ... MSc 12FT 24PT/PGAdvDip 8FT 20PT/PGCert 4FT 8PT

Goldsmiths, University of London
Cognitive and Clinical Neuroscience ... MSc 12FT 24PT
Foundations in Clinical Psychology & Health Services ... MSc 12FT

University of Hertfordshire
Clinical Psychology ... ClinPsyD by taught 36FT

Keele University
Clinical Psychological Research ... MSc 12FT 24PT
Psychology ... MSc 12FT 24PT
Psychology of Health & Well Being ... MSc 12FT 24PT

King's College London
Addiction Studies ... MSc 12FT 24PT/PGCert 12FT 24PT
Clinical Forensic Psychology ... MSc 12FT
International Programme in Addiction Studies ... MSc 12FT 24PT

Kingston University
Clinical Applications of Psychology ... MSc 12FT 24PT

Lancaster University
Clinical Psychology ... DClinPsy by taught 36FT

Leeds Metropolitan University
Psychology (conversion award) ... MSc 12FT 24PT

University of Leeds
Clinical Psychology ... DClinPsy by taught 36FT

University of Limerick
Clinical Psychology ... DClinPsy by taught 36FT

University of Liverpool
Doctor of Clinical Psychology ... DClinPsy by taught 36FT

London Metropolitan University
Addiction Psychology ... MSc 12FT 24PT

London South Bank University
Addiction Psychology & Counselling ... MSc 30PT/PGDip 24PT

University of Manchester
Clinical & Health Psychology ... MSc 12FT
Deaf Education ... PGDip 12FT 24PT

Middlesex University
Comparative Drug and Alcohol studies ... MA 24PT

Newcastle University
High Intensity Psychological Therapies ... Diploma 12FT
Psychology (Foundations in Clinical and Health Psychology) ... MSc 12FT

Newman University
Clinical Applications of Psychology ... MSc 36DL/PGDip 24-36DL/PGCert 12-24DL

Northumbria University
Health Psychology ... MSc 12FT 24PT

University of Nottingham
Doctorate in Clinical Psychology ... DClinPsy 12FT
Psychology (Conversion Course) ... PGDip 9FT

Plymouth University
Clinical Psychology ... DClinPsy by taught 36FT
Psychology ... MSc 12FT 24PT/PGDip 9FT

Queen's University Belfast
Applied Psychology (Clinical Specialism) ... MSc 24FT/PGDip 12FT 48PT

University of Reading
Clinical Aspects of Psychology ... MSc 12FT 24PT
Development and Psychopathology ... MSc 12FT 24PT/PGDip 6FT
Evidence-Based Psychological Treatments ... PGDip 12FT/PGCert 12FT
Speech and Language Therapy ... MSc 24FT

Royal Holloway, University of London
Clinical Psychology (Doctorate) ... DClinPsy by taught 36FT

University of Salford
Applied Psychology (Therapies) MSc 12FT 36PT/PGDip 8FT 24PT/PGCert 4FT 9PT

University of Sheffield
Psychology and Education ... MA 12FT

University of Southampton
Clinical Psychology ... DClinPsy by taught 36FT
Research Methods in Psychology ... MSc 12FT

University of St Andrews
Psychology ... MRes 12FT

University of Stirling
Psychological Research Methods ... MSc 12FT 24PT/PGDip 9FT 18PT
Psychological Therapy in Primary Care ... MSc 12FT
Psychology Applied to Health ... MSc 12FT 24PT/PGDip 9FT 18PT
Psychology of Faces ... MSc 12FT 24PT/PGDip 9FT 18PT

University of Strathclyde
Research Methods in Psychology ... MRes 12FT

University of Surrey
Health Psychology ... MA 12FT 24PT
Practitioner Doctorate in Clinical Psychology ... PsychD by taught 36FT

Swansea University
Abnormal and Clinical Psychology ... MSc 12FT 24PT

Teesside University
Clinical Psychology ... DClinPsy by taught 36FT
Doctorate Psychology (Top up) ... PsychD by taught 30BM

Trinity College Dublin - the University of Dublin
Clinical Psychology (Doctorate) ... D.Clin.Psych. 36FT
Clinical Supervision ... MSc 24PT

UCL - University College London
Developmental Psychology and Clinical Practice ... MSc 24FT/PGDip 12FT

University of Warwick
Clinical Psychology ... DClinPsy by taught 36FT

University of the West of Scotland
Alcohol and Drug Studies ... MSc 12FT 36PT/PGDip 11FT 36PT

University of Winchester
Psychological Research Methods ... MSc 12FT 24PT/PGCert 12FT 24PT/PGDip 12FT 24PT

University of York
Development, Disorders and Clinical Practice ... MSc 12FT

Clinical psychology
Research Courses

University of Aberdeen
Psychology ... PhD 36FT/MPhil 24FT/MSc by research 12FT/MRes 12FT

Aberystwyth University
Psychology ... MPhil 12FT 24PT PhD 36FT 60PT

Bangor University
Clinical Psychology ... DClinPsy 36FT
Doctorate by Research ... PhD 36FT/MPhil 24FT

University of Birmingham
Clinical Psychology ... MRes 12FT 24PT
Clinical Psychology Doctorate ... ClinPsyD 36FT

University of East Anglia
Doctorate Programme in Clinical Psychology ... ClinPsyD 36FT

University of Edinburgh
Clinical & Health Psychology ... PhD 36FT 72PT/MSc by research 12FT 24PT

University of Exeter
Clinical Practice ... DClinPrac 42DL
Doctorate in Clinical Psychology ... DClinPsy 36FT

Goldsmiths, University of London
Psychology ... MRes 12FT 24PT

University of Hertfordshire
Clinical Psychology - Professional Doctorate ... DClinPsy 36FT

University of Kent
Clinical Psychology of Intellectual and Developmental Disabilities ... MPhil 24FT 36PT/PhD 36FT 60PT

King's College London
Addictions ... MPhil 36FT 72PT/PhD 36FT 72PT/MD(Res) 36FT 72PT
Doctorate in Clinical Psychology ... DClinPsy 36FT

Psychology

Lancaster University
Clinical Psychology....DClinPsy 36FT

University of Liverpool
Clinical PsychologyPhD 24-48FT 48-84PT/MPhil 12-48FT 24-72PT

University of Manchester
Clinical Psychology.... MPhil 12FT 24PT/PhD 36FT 72PT
Clinical Psychology ClinPsyD....ClinPsyD 36FT

Newcastle University
Clinical Psychology....DClinPsy 36FT

University of Nottingham
Institute of Work, Health and Organisations Research Areas.... PhD 36FT 72PT/MPhil 24FT 48PT

The Open University
Psychology.... PhD 36FT 72PT variableDL/MPhil 15FT 24PT variableDL

Plymouth University
Clinical Psychology....DClinPsy 36FT

University of Roehampton
Counselling Psychology (Professional Doctorate)....PsychD 36FT 36-42PT

University of Salford
Psychology Research Group....PhD/MPhil

University of Southampton
Health Psychology Research & Professional Practice....PhD 36FT 84PT

UCL - University College London
Clinical Psychology....DClinPsy 36FT
Clinical, Educational and Health Psychology .... PhD 36FT 60PT

University of the West of Scotland
Centre for Alcohol and Drugs Studies....PhD/MPhil

Consumer psychology
Taught Courses

Bangor University
Business with Consumer Psychology....MA 12FT/PGDip 9FT MSc 12FT/PGDip 9FT
Consumer Psychology with Business.... MSc 12FT/PGDip 9FT MA 12FT/PGDip 9FT
Psychological Research ..MSc 12FT 24PT/PGDip 8FT 16PT/PGCert 4FT 8PT
Psychology....MA 12FT 24PT/PGDip 9FT 18PT/PGCert 4FT 8PT

University of Bedfordshire
Coaching Psychology.... PGDip 12FT 24PT

Heriot-Watt University
Business Psychology.... MSc 12FT 24-84PT 12-84DL/PGDip 9FT 15-48PT 9-48DL/PGCert 6FT 12-48PT 6-48DL

London Metropolitan University
Consumer Psychology.... MSc 12FT

University of Roehampton
Applied Psychological Research.... PGCert 6FT 24PT
Applied Psychological Research....PGDip 9FT 24PT

University of Worcester
Business Psychology.... MSc 36FT 72PT/PGDip 24FT 48PT/PGCert 12FT 24PT

Consumer psychology
Research Courses

Bangor University
Doctorate by Research.... PhD 36FT/MPhil 24FT

Heriot-Watt University
Applied Psychology.... PhD 36FT 48PT/MPhil 24FT 36PT

Counselling
Taught Courses

University of Aberdeen
Person Centred Counselling....PGDip 24-36PT/PGCert 24PT

University of Abertay Dundee
Counselling....MSc 24FT/PGDip 12FT/PGCert 12FT
Counselling Skills....Graduate Cetrtificate 9PT

Anglia Ruskin University
Counselling Studies....MA 24PT

Bangor University
International Social Work MA 12FT 24-30PT/PGDip 9FT 17-21PT/PGCert 5FT 12-21PT

Birkbeck, University of London
Psychodynamic Counselling and Psychotherapy.... MSc 24PT
Psychodynamic Counselling and Psychotherapy with Children and Adolescents....MSc 36PT/PGDip 36PT
Psychodynamics of Human Development....MSc 24PT/PGDip 24PT

Birmingham City University
Integrative Psychotherapy ..MSc 24PT/PGDip 18PT/PGCert 12PT/GradCert 8PT

Bradford College
Counselling in the Community....MA 16PT

University of Brighton
Humanistic Therapeutic Counselling.... PGDip 24PT/PGCert 24PT
Person-centred Counselling.... PGDip 24PT/PGCert 24PT
Psychodynamic Counselling.... PGDip 24PT/PGCert 24PT

University of Bristol
Counselling in Education....MEd 12FT 24-60PT/PGDip 12FT 24-60PT
Education: Counselling in Education....MEd 12FT 24PT/PGDip 12FT

Cardiff University
Genetic Counselling.... MSc 24FT

University of Central Lancashire
Counselling Casework Supervision.... PGCert 7PT
Counselling and Psychotherapy ....MSc 36PT/PGDip 24PT
Person-Centred Spiritual Care & Accompaniment.... PGCert 12PT
Professional Integrative Psychotherapy .... MA 36PT/PGDip 24PT

University of Chester
Clinical Counselling....MA 36PT
Counselling Studies.... MA 12FT 24PT
Counselling Supervision....PGCert 12PT
Emotional Intelligence (Work Based and Integrative Studies) MA 24-72PT/MSc 24-72PT/PGDip 24-60PT/PGCert 12-36PT
Professional Studies and Development (Work Based and Integrative Studies)...MA 24-72PT/MSc 24-72PT/PGDip 24-60PT/PGCert 12-36PT
Psychological Trauma.... MSc 24PT/PGDip 24PT/PGCert 12 - 24PT

City University London
Counselling Psychology ....PGCert 12PT DPsych 36FT

University College Cork
Behavioural & Cognitive Psychotherapy....PGDip 18PT MA 18PT
Counselling Psychology....MA 24FT
Guidance and Counselling....PGDip 12FT
Integrative Psychotherapy Studies....MA 24PT

Cornwall College
Professional Studies in Counselling.... PGDip 24PT

University of Derby
Integrative Counselling and Psychotherapy (BACP Accredited).... PGDip 30FT
Systemic Psychotherapy.... MSc 24PT

University of East Anglia
Counselling....PGDip 12FT
Counselling....MA 6FT 12PT
Focusing Oriented Psychotherapy....PGCert 12PT

University of East London
Child Psychoanalytic Psychotherapy Prof Doc (D. Ch. Psych. Psych.)....DProf by taught 48FT 60PT
Counselling Children in Schools .... MA 36PT/PGDip 24PT/PGCert 12PT
Counselling and Psychotherapy .... MA 36PT/PGDip 24PT
Couple and Individual Psychodynamic Counselling and Psychotherapy .... PGDip 24PT/PGCert 12PT
Integrative Counselling and Coaching ....PGCert 12PT
Professional Doctorate in Counselling Psychology.... DProf by taught 48FT
Psychodynamic Approaches to Working with Adolescents (M33) MA....MA 36PT/PGCert 12PT/PGDip 24PT
Psychosynthesis Counselling .... PGDip 24PT
Psychosynthesis Foundations ....GradCert 12PT
Psychosynthesis Psychotherapy ....MA 12PT
Psychosynthesis Studies ....PGCert 12PT
Theory and Skills of Psychodynamic Couple and Individual Therapeutic Communication with Children ....PGCert 12PT

University of Edinburgh
Counselling....MCouns 48PT/PGDip 36PT/PGCert 12PT
Counselling (Interpersonal Dialogue)....MCouns 24FT
Counselling Studies....MSc 12FT 24-36PT
Psychotherapy and Counselling (Interpersonal Dialogue) .... DPsychSc by taught 36FT

Glasgow Caledonian University
Counselling Psychology ...PsychD by taught 36FT 72PT/MSc 12FT 24PT
Counselling Skills in Health and Social Care....PGCert 12-24FT
Psychodynamic Counselling and Therapeutic Practice....PGDip 12-24FT

Glyndwr University
Counselling Studies with Children and Young People .... MA 30//PT

Goldsmiths, University of London
Certificate in Humanistic and Psychodynamic Counselling.... PGCert 12PT
Counselling....MA 36PT/PGDip 24PT

University of Greenwich
Therapeutic Counselling.... MSc 36PT

Heriot-Watt University
Applied Psychology....MSc 12FT 24-48PT/PGDip 9FT 15-48PT/PGCert 6FT 12-48PT
Engineering Psychology with Ergonomics.... MSc 12FT 24PT 24-84DL/PGDip 9FT 21PT 21-84DL/PGCert 6FT 18PT 18-84DL

University of Hertfordshire
Contemporary Therapeutic Counselling....MA 36PT/PGDip 36PT

Keele University
Counselling Psychology - Part Time Professional Counselling Training Route ....Cert 9PT/PGDip 12-24PT/MSc 12PT
Counselling Supervision .... PGCert 8PT
Msc in Counselling Psychology (Full time).... MSc 12FT

Leeds Metropolitan University
Counselling & Psychotherapy .... PGDip 24PT
Interpersonal & Counselling Skills....PGCert 12PT
Psychological Therapies....MA 48PT
Psychotherapy....MA 48PT

University of Leeds
Counselling Supervision ....PGCert 12FT

University of Leicester
Professional Studies (Cognitive Behavioural Therapy) .... PGCert 12PT
Professional Studies (Supervision)....PGCert 12PT
Professional Studies in Counselling and Psychotherapy....PGDip 24PT/MA 12PT
Psychodynamic Counselling and Psychotherapy ....PGDip 24PT/MA 12PT

Liverpool John Moores University
Counselling and Psychotherapeutic Practice ....MA 12PT

London Metropolitan University
Counselling Psychology .... DCounsPsych by taught 36FT 48PT

London South Bank University
Addiction Psychology & Counselling....MSc 30PT/PGDip 24PT

Manchester Metropolitan University
Psychology and Counselling.... MSc 12FT 24-36PT/PGDip 12FT 24-36PT/PGCert 12FT 24-36PT

University of Manchester
Counselling....MA 36PT
Genetic Counselling.... MSc 24FT

University of St Mark and St John
Counselling, Guidance and Support.... MA 12FT 24PT

National University of Ireland, Maynooth
Arts (School Guidance & Counselling)....HDip 12FT

Newman University
Integrative Counselling Foundation Degree.... FdA 36PT

University of Northampton
Counselling Children and Young People.... MSc 18FT 36PT
Integrative Counselling....MSc 24FT 36PT

Northumbria University
Social Work....MA 24FT

Nottingham Trent University
Professional Practice.... MA 1.5PT 3DL

University of Nottingham
Counselling....MA 12FT
Counselling Children and Young People....MA 12FT
Trauma Studies .... MA 12FT 24PT

Plymouth University
Genetic Healthcare....PGCert 24FT 24PT

Queen Mary, University of London
Trauma Sciences ....MSc 12FT 24PT

University of Roehampton
Counselling Psychology (PsychD) .... PsychD by taught 24-36FT 36-48PT
Counselling and Psychotherapy .... MSc 36PT
Integrative Counselling and Psychotherapy....MA 36PT

University of Salford
Counselling and Psychotherapy Studies (Professional Training)... MSc 36PT/PGDip 24PT

Sheffield Hallam University
Advanced Communication Skills....PGCert 4PT 4DL

University of Sheffield
Work Psychology .... MSc 12FT

University of South Wales
Consultative Supervision....MA 24PT/PGDip 12PT
Counselling (Integrative and CBT Pathways)....MA 12-48FT/PGDip 9FT/PGCert 6FT/PGCert 12PT
Counselling Children and Young People....MA 24PT
Counselling Skills.... University Certificate 12FT
Systemic Counselling .... MSc 36PT/PGDip 36PT/PGCert 24PT

Staffordshire University
Certificate in Counselling....Cert 12PT
Introduction to Basic Counselling Skills .... Introduction 2.5PT
Psychotherapeutic Counselling ....MSc 36PT/PGDip 24PT

University of Strathclyde
Counselling....MSc 12FT 24PT/PGDip 9FT 21PT

University of Surrey
Practitioner Doctorate in Psychotherapeutic and Counselling Psychology....PsychD by taught 36FT 48-60PT
Psychological Therapy: Interpersonal Psychotherapy (IPT) .... Diploma 12PT

Section sponsored by

BPP
UNIVERSITY
COLLEGE

Business and social sciences
www.prospects.ac.uk/findcourses **POSTGRADUATE DIRECTORY 465**

Psychology

Teesside University
Counselling Psychology ....DCounsPsy by taught 36FT

Trinity College Dublin - the University of Dublin
Counselling Psychology (Doctorate)......................DCounsPsych by taught 36FT

University of Ulster
Counselling and Therapeutic Communication .....MSc 12FT 36PT/PGDip 9FT 18PT

University of Warwick
Counselling Skills for Health Care Professionals .... PGA 12PT

University of the West of England, Bristol
Counselling Certificate .... Cert 24PT
Counselling Psychology .... DProf by taught 36PT

University of Worcester
Counselling .... MSc 24PT/PGDip 18PT/PGCert 12PT

York St John University
Counselling & Psychotherapy (Practitioner Route) ....MA 24PT
Counselling & Psychotherapy Studies .... MA 12FT

Counselling
Research Courses

Bangor University
Ageing and Cognitive Health .... PhD 36FT 60PT
Ageing and Dementia Studies ....MSc by research 12FT 24PT PhD 36FT 60PT/MPhil 24FT 48PT

University of Edinburgh
Counselling Studies .... PhD 36FT 72PT

University of Greenwich
Health and Social Care - Research MPhil 24FT 36-48PT/PhD 36FT 48-60PT

University of Hertfordshire
Arts Psychotherapies and Counselling in Health .PhD 36FT 72PT/MRes 12FT 24PT/MPhil 24FT 48PT

University of Leicester
Research in Counselling and Psychotherapy ......MPhil 12FT 24PT/PhD 36FT 72PT

London Metropolitan University
Counselling Psychology .... DProf 36FT 48PT

University of Manchester
Counselling Psychology ....DCounsPsych 36FT

Newman University
Psychology & Counselling.......... PhD 36FT 72PT/MPhil 24FT 48PT

The Open University
Counselling and Psychotherapy .... PhD 36FT 72PT variableDL/MPhil 15FT 24PT variableDL

University of Roehampton
Psychology............. PhD 24-48FT 36-60PT/MPhil 21-36FT 33-48PT
Psychotherapy and Counselling .... PsychD 60-72PT

York St John University
Counselling ....PhD 12-36FT/MPhil 12-36FT/MA by research 12-36FT

Dyslexia in education
Taught Courses

University of Aberdeen
Plurilingual Education...................................MEd 24PT/PGCert 12PT
Studies in Mindfulness .... MSc 36PT/PGDip 24PT/PGCert 12PT

Bath Spa University
Specific Learning Difficulties / Dyslexia ...MA 12FT 72PT/MTeach 12FT 72PT/PGCert 4FT 12PT/PGDip 9FT 24PT

University of Bristol
Education: Special and Inclusive Education .... MEd 12FT 24-60PT

University of Chester
Education: Dyslexia Research and Practice.....MA 36-72PT/PGDip 36-60PT/PGCert 12-36PT
Education: Inclusion and Marginalisation ......MA 36-72PT/PGDip 36-60PT/PGCert 12-36PT
Work Based Learning Facilitation...........................PGCert 12-36PT

Edge Hill University
Specialist Dyslexia Training for Teachers................PGCert 12-18PT

Edinburgh Napier University
Advanced Practice and Applied Education (Distance Learning)....Msc/PGDip/PGCert 36PT

University of Edinburgh
Additional Support for Learning (Learning Disabilities)..........MEd 72PT/PGDip 48PT/PGCert 24PT

National University of Ireland Galway
Special Educational Needs .... PGDip 12PT

Institute of Education
SpLD - Specific Learning Difficulties (Dyslexia)....... MA 18FT 36PT

University of Leeds
Special Educational Needs ....MA 12FT 24PT/PGDip 12FT 24PT

Liverpool John Moores University
Advanced Educational Practice (Dyslexia) ....PGCert 12PT

London Metropolitan University
Assessment for Specific Learning Difficulties in FE and HE............PGDip 12PT
Teaching Adult Dyslexic Learners in Higher and Further Education...PGCert 12PT

London South Bank University
Adult Dyslexia Diagnosis and Support (ADDS).................MA 36PT
Multi-Sensory E-Learning and Dyslexia Support....................PGCert 12-24PT
Teachers of Adults with Learning Difficulties ....PGCert 12-24PT

Manchester Metropolitan University
Specific Learning Difficulties (Further Education and Higher Education) ....MA 24-60PT/PGDip 24PT/PGCert 12PT

Northumbria University
Teaching Pupils With Dyslexia ....PGCert 12PT

University of Reading
Education (Inclusive Education).....MA 12FT 24-84PT/PGDip 12FT

University of Sheffield
Speech Difficulties ....PGDip 12FT 24PT/PGCert 12FT 24PT

University of South Wales
Diploma in Higher Education in Professional Practice
.... DipHE 48PT
SEN Specific Learning Difficulties.......................... PGDip 12FT 24PT

University of Southampton
Specific Learning Difficulties (Dyslexia)...................MSc 12FT 24PT

University of St Andrews
Adults Support, Protection and Safeguarding...........PGCert 12DL
Adults with Learning Disabilities who have Significant and Complex Needs.....................MSc 12DL/PGDip 12DL/PGCert 12DL

Staffordshire University
Journalism .... MA 12FT 48PT

Swansea University
Certificate in English Language Teaching to Adults (CELTA)... Cert 1FT 3PT

Teesside University
Promoting Inclusive Practice in Education............ PGDip 24 - 36PT

Educational psychology
Taught Courses

University of Aberdeen
Social and Educational Research ....MRes 12FT
Studies in Mindfulness .... MSc 36PT/PGDip 24PT/PGCert 12PT

Bangor University
Education Doctorate Programme .... EdD by taught 60PT
Education Studies... MA 12FT 24-60PT/MEd 12FT 24-60PT/PGDip 8FT 24-48PT/PGCert 4FT 12-24PT

Birkbeck, University of London
Educational Neuroscience...............MA 12FT 24PT/MSc 12FT 24PT

University of Birmingham
Learning Difficulties and Disabilities (Severe, Profound and Complex) .... AdvCert 12DL/PGCert 12DL/PGDip 24DL/MEd 24DL
Special Educational Needs Coordination(National Award for Special Edu. Needs Coordination) .... National Award 12-24PT

University of Bristol
Education: Psychology of Education.................. MEd 12FT 24-60PT
Education: Special and Inclusive Education .... MEd 12FT 24-60PT

Brunel University
Education (Special Educational Needs)..................... MA 12FT 24PT

Cardiff University
Educational Psychology (Doctorate)............................DEdPsy 36FT
Educational Psychology (Post-Qualification Doctorate).....DEdPsy 36PT

University of Dundee
Developmental Psychology .... MSc 12FT
Educational Psychology .... MSc 24FT

Durham University
Education .... MA 12FT 36PT
Educational Assessment...MSc 12FT 24PT

University of East London
Counselling Children in Schools ....MA 36PT/PGDip 24PT/PGCert 12PT
Professional Doctorate in Applied Educational and Child Psychology...DProf by taught 45-60PT
Professional Doctorate in Educational and Child Psychology D.Ed. Ch.Psy .... DProf by taught 36FT
Special Educational Needs ....MA 12FT 24PT/PGDip 8FT 16PT/PGCert 4FT 8PT

Edge Hill University
Special Educational Needs Coordination .... National Award 12-36DL

University of Exeter
Special Educational Needs Masters...........PGDip 12FT/MEd 12FT/PGCert 6FT

National University of Ireland Galway
Special Educational Needs .... PGDip 12PT

University of Glasgow
Professional Development in Education .... PGCert 60 maxPT

University of Gloucestershire
National Award for Special Educational Needs Continuation.......PGCert 9PT

Goldsmiths, University of London
Practice Education...............................MA 36-60PT/PGDip 36-60PT/PGCert 36-60PT
The Science of Psychology, Genetics & Education ....MSc 12FT 24PT

Institute of Education
Development Education.. MA 12FT 24PT
Developmental and Educational Psychology.........MSc 12FT 24PT
Education (Psychology).. MA 12FT 24-48PT
Joint Professional Practice: Language and Communication ....MSc 12FT 24-48PT
Psychology of Education.................MA 12FT 24PT/MSc 12FT 24PT

Keele University
Psychology...MSc 12FT 24PT

University of Kent
Developmental Psychology.................................MSc 12FT 24PT

University of Leeds
Special Educational Needs ....MA 12FT 24PT/PGDip 12FT 24PT

Liverpool John Moores University
Advanced Educational Practice (Special Educational Needs).........PGCert 12PT

Manchester Metropolitan University
Autistic Spectrum Conditions .... MA 12-60PT
Inclusive Education and Special Educational Needs ....MA 12FT 24-60PT
Emotional and Behavioural Difficulties......................PGCert 24PT
Managing Pupil Behaviour...PGCert 24PT

University of Manchester
Psychology of Education......................................MEd 12FT 24PT

University of Nottingham
Applied Educational Psychology............................DAppEdPsy 36FT
Psychology (Conversion Course)...................................PGDip 9FT
Special Needs .... MA 12FT 24-36PT

Oxford Brookes University
Education .... MA 12FT 24PT

University of Oxford
Education (Child Development and Education)............... MSc 12FT
Educational Research Methodology.....................................MSc 12FT

Plymouth University
The National Award for Special Educational Needs Co-ordination PGCert 12PT

Queen's University Belfast
Educational, Child and Adolescent Psychology DECAP. PsychD by taught 36FT
Inclusion and Special Needs Education .... DASE 12FT 60PT/MEd 12FT 60PT

University of Reading
Development and Psychopathology ...MSc 12FT 24PT/PGDip 6FT
Neuroscience of Language ....MSc 12FT 24PT

University of Roehampton
Applied Psychology in Education.......................MSc 12FT 24-36PT

University of Sheffield
Educational and Child Psychology .... Doctor 36FT
Psychology and Education ....MA 12FT

University of South Wales
Masters Gateway to SEN .30 credits at level 6 (transferable to an MA) 6PT
SEN Attention Deficit Hyperactivity Disorder (ADHD)..M level 30 credit module 3FT
SEN Developmental Co-ordination Disorder (Dyspraxia) ..PGCert 12DL
SEN Visual Impairment... PGDip 24PT
Special Educational Needs .... MA 12FT 36PT

University of Southampton
Educational Psychology ....DEdPsy 36FT
Research Methods in Psychology .... MSc 12FT

University of St Andrews
Adults Support, Protection and Safeguarding...........PGCert 12DL
Adults with Learning Disabilities who have Significant and Complex Needs.....................MSc 12DL/PGDip 12DL/PGCert 12DL

University of Stirling
Educational Research ....MSc 12FT 30PT

University of Strathclyde
Educational Psychology .... MSc 24FT
Educational Support.......MSc max 60PT/PGDip max 48PT/PGCert max 24PT
Research Methods in Psychology ....MRes 12FT

University of Sunderland
Special Needs and Inclusive Education..................... MA 12FT 36PT

Teesside University
Doctorate Psychology (Top up) .... PsychD by taught 30BM

Business and social sciences
466 POSTGRADUATE DIRECTORY www.prospects.ac.uk/findcourses

Psychology

Educational psychology
Research Courses

University of Aberdeen
Psychology..... PhD 36FT/MPhil 24FT/MSc by research 12FT/MRes 12FT

University of Birmingham
Applied Educational and Child Psychology..... AppEd / Child PsyD 36FT

University of Bristol
Educational Psychology .... DEdPsy 36FT

Cardiff University
Educational Psychology .... DEdPsy 36FT

Durham University
Education........ EdD 36FT 72PT 72DL
Education........ PhD 36FT 72PT

University of East Anglia
Counselling Studies .... PhD 36FT 72PT/MPhil 24FT 48PT/MA by research 12FT 24PT
Higher Education and Society .... PhD 36FT 72PT/MPhil 24FT 48PT/MA by research 12FT 24PT
Literacy and Development Group ....PhD 36FT 72PT/MPhil 24FT 48PT/MA by research 12FT 24PT
Mathematics Education.............PhD 36FT 72PT/MPhil 24FT 48PT/MA by research 12FT 24PT
Pedagogy and Engagement with Learning...........PhD 36FT 72PT/MPhil 24FT 48PT/MA by research 12FT 24PT
Physical Education Pedagogy Group ....PhD 36FT 72PT/MPhil 24FT 48PT/MA by research 12FT 24PT
Psychology........ PhD 36FT 72PT/MPhil 24FT 48PT
Spirituality and Religion in Education........PhD 36FT 72PT/MPhil 24FT 48PT/MA by research 12FT 24PT

University of Glasgow
Education.........PhD 36FT 60PT/MPhil 12FT 24PT/MSc by research 12FT 24PT/EdD 36-60DL

Heriot-Watt University
Applied Psychology .... PhD 36FT 48PT/MPhil 24FT 36PT

Institute of Education
Doctor in Educational Psychology .... DEdPsy 48-84PT
Four Year Route .... PhD 48FT 84PT
Professional, Educational, Child and Adolescent Psychology (DEdPsy) .... DEdPsy 36FT

University of Kent
Clinical Psychology of Intellectual and Developmental Disabilities........ MPhil 24FT 36PT/PhD 36FT 60PT

University of Manchester
Educational Psychology .... DEdPsy 72PT

Newcastle University
Applied Educational Psychology........ DAppEdPsy 36FT
Education (Clinical) .... MPhil 12FT 24PT/PhD 36FT 72PT

Oxford Brookes University
Education and Childhood Studies .... MPhil/PhD 36-60FT 48-72PT/PhD 24-60FT 36-72PT/MPhil 24-36FT 36-48PT

University of Strathclyde
Doctorate in Educational Psychology........DEdPsy 24FT

UCL - University College London
Clinical, Educational and Health Psychology .... PhD 36FT 60PT
Educational Psychology .... DEdPsy 48PT
Educational and Child Psychology ....Doctorate in Educational and Child Psychology 36FT

Ergonomics
Taught Courses

University of Aberdeen
Patient Safety: A Clinical Human Factors Approach..... MRes 12FT

University of Chester
Wellbeing in the Workplace (Work Based and Integrative Studies) .... MA 24-72PT/PGDip 24-60PT/PGCert 12-36PT

University of Derby
ErgonomicsMSc 42PT 42DL/PGDip 30PT 30DL/PGCert 18PT 18DL

University of East London
Applied Ergonomics .... PGCert 6FT 12PT

National University of Ireland Galway
Occupational Health & Safety ....MSc 12FT 24PT/HDipAppSc 12FT 24PT
Occupational Safety Engineering and Ergonomics .... MAppSci 12FT 24PT

Glyndwr University
Construction Health and Safety........NEBOSH NGC 4PT

Heriot-Watt University
Applied Psychology ....MSc 12FT 24-48PT/PGDip 9FT 15-48PT/PGCert 6FT 12-48PT
Engineering Psychology with Ergonomics.............MSc 12FT 24PT 24-84DL/PGDip 9FT 21PT 21-84DL/PGCert 6FT 18PT 18-84DL
Safety and Risk Management ....MSc 24-84DL/PGDip 21-84DL

University of Limerick
Safety and Ergonomics .... MTech 12FT

Loughborough University
Ergonomics and Human Factors...MSc 12FT 24 - 36PT/PGDip 8FT 20PT
Ergonomics for Health and Community CareMSc 12FT 24 - 36PT/PGDip 8FT 20PT
Human Factors for Inclusive Design....MSc 12FT 24 - 36PT/PGDip 8FT 20PT
Human Factors in Transport .... MSc 12FT 24 - 36PT/PGDip 8FT 20PT

University of Nottingham
Applied Ergonomics ....MSc 24-48DL/PGCert 12DL
Human Factors and Ergonomics........MSc 12FT 24-36PT
Applied Ergonomics .... PGCert 12FT 12-24DL
Workplace Health (Distance E-Learning) .... MSc 24PT

UCL - University College London
Human-Computer Interaction with Ergonomics .MSc 12FT 24PT/PGDip 9FT 24PT/PGCert 3FT 24PT

Ergonomics
Research Courses

Loughborough University
Design Ergonomics .... PhD 36FT 60PT/MPhil 24FT 36PT
Environmental Ergonomics........ PhD 36FT 60PT/MPhil 24FT 36PT
Human Factors and Complex Systems ....PhD 36FT 60PT/MPhil 24FT 36PT
User Centred Design Research.. PhD 36FT 60PT/MPhil 24FT 36PT

University of Nottingham
Human Factors........ PhD 36FT/MPhil 24FT

Forensic psychology
Taught Courses

University of Bedfordshire
Forensic Psychology........ MSc 12FT 24PT

Birmingham City University
Forensic Psychology .... MSc 12FT 24PT/PGDip 8FT 12PT/PGCert 3FT 9PT

University of Birmingham
Criminological Psychology........PGDip 12PT/MSc 24PT
Forensic Mental Health Studies..........MSc 12FT 24PT/PGDip 12FT 24PT/PGCert 12FT 24PT
Forensic Psychology Practice .... MSc 24FT 36PT

Cardiff Metropolitan University
Forensic Psychology........ MSc 12FT 24PT

University of Central Lancashire
Criminal Investigation........ MSc 12PT
Forensic Psychology .... MSc 12FT 24PT/PGDip 9FT 24PT/PGCert 9FT 24PT
Forensic Toxicology .... MSc 12FT

Coventry University
Forensic Psychology ..... MSc 12FT 24PT/PGDip 12FT 20PT/PGCert 8FT 8PT
Forensic Psychology ....MSc 12FT/PGDip 12FT/PGCert 12FT
Forensic Psychology and Crime - online . MSc 36DL/PGDip 24DL/PGCert 12DL

University of Derby
Health Psychology........ MSc 12FT 24PT

University of Dundee
Forensic Facial Identification .... MSc 12FT
Forensic Odontology .... MFOdont 12FT

Glasgow Caledonian University
Forensic Psychology..... MSc 12FT 24PT/PGDip 12FT 24PT/PGCert 12FT 12PT

University of Glasgow
Criminology .... MRes 12FT 24PT/PGDip 9FT 21PT

University of Gloucestershire
Criminology ...... PGCert 4FT 8PT/PGDip 8FT 20PT/MSc 12FT 24PT
Forensic Psychology........ MSc 12FT 24PT

Goldsmiths, University of London
The Science of Psychology, Genetics & Education .... MSc 12FT 24PT

University of Hertfordshire
Psychology (Conversion Course).. MSc 12FT 24-36PT/PGDip 12FT 24-36PT

University of Huddersfield
Investigative Psychology .... MSc 12FT

University of Kent
Forensic Psychology........ MSc 12FT 24PT

King's College London
Clinical Forensic Psychiatry........MSc 12FT 24-36PT
Clinical Forensic Psychology .... MSc 12FT
Forensic Mental Health............. MSc 12FT 24PT/PGDip 12FT 24PT
Mental Health Service & Population Research...... MSc 12FT 24PT

Kingston University
Criminological Psychology........ MA 12FT 24PT

Leeds Metropolitan University
Psychology (conversion award)........ MSc 12FT 24PT

University of Leicester
Applied Forensic Psychology........ MSc 24DL
Forensic Psychology........ MSc 12FT

University of Lincoln
Forensic Psychology .... MSc 12FT 24PT

University of Liverpool
Forensic Psychology and Criminal Investigation (Online Degree) MSc 24FT 24+PT
Investigative and Forensic Psychology........ MSc 12FT
Investigative and Forensic Psychology - London Based .... MSc 12FT

London Metropolitan University
Forensic Psychology .... MSc 12FT 24PT

London South Bank University
Forensic Mental Health Care .... MSc 36PT
International Criminal Law & Procedure................ LLM 14FT 26PT
Investigative Forensic Psychology........ MSc 12FT 24PT

Manchester Metropolitan University
Forensic Psychology........MSc 12FT 24-36PT

University of Manchester
Forensic Mental Health........MSc 36PT/PGDip 12PT

Middlesex University
Criminology with Forensic Psychology .... MSc 12FT 24PT
Forensic Psychology........ MSc 12FT 24PT

Northumbria University
Forensic Science........ MSc 12FT 36PT

Nottingham Trent University
Forensic Mental Health........ MSc 12FT 24PT
Forensic Psychology .... MSc 12FT 24PT

University of Nottingham
Criminological Psychology .... MSc 12FT 24PT
Forensic Psychology - Full Programme......... DForenPsy 36FT 72PT
Forensic Psychology - top-up programme .... DForenPsy 36FT 72PT

University of Portsmouth
Child Forensic Studies: Psychology and Law .... MSc 12/24DL
Forensic Psychology........ MSc 12FT 24PT

Queen Mary, University of London
Mental Health: Psychological Therapies D/L option ...... MSc 12FT 24PT
Mental Health: Transcultural Mental Healthcare .... MSc 12FT 24PT 24DL

Sheffield Hallam University
Forensic Criminolgy .... MSc 12FT 24PT
Forensic Pshychology........ MSc 12FT 24PT

University of Surrey
Forensic Psychology .... MA 12FT 24PT
Health Psychology........ MA 12FT 24PT

Teesside University
Forensic Psychology .... MSc 12FT 24PT

University of York
Applied Forensic Psychology........ MSc 15FT
Forensic Psychology Studies .... MSc 12FT

Forensic psychology
Research Courses

University of Birmingham
Forensic Psychology Practice Doctorate .....ForenPsyD 36FT 48PT/PhD 24FT 36PT

University of East Anglia
Doctorate Programme in Clinical Psychology..........ClinPsyD 36FT

University of Gloucestershire
Psychology and Behavioural Sciences........ MRes 12FT

University of Kent
Forensic Psychology .... PhD 36FT 60PT/MPhil 24FT 36PT/New Route PhD 48FT

King's College London
Forensic and Neurodevelopmental SciencePhD 36FT 72PT/MPhil 36FT 72PT

The Open University
Applied Psychology .... PhD 36FT 72PT variableDL/MPhil 15FT 24PT variableDL
Psychology................ PhD 36FT 72PT variableDL/MPhil 15FT 24PT variableDL

University of Roehampton
Forensic Psychology....... PsychD 36-60PT/MPhil 21-36FT 33-48PT

Health psychology
Taught Courses

Aston University
Health Psychology........ MSc 12FT
Psychology of Health and Illness........ MSc 12FT

Bangor University
Foundations of Clinical Psychology ..... MSc 12FT 24PT/PGDip 8FT 16PT/PGCert 4FT 8PT

Section sponsored by

BPP
UNIVERSITY
COLLEGE

Business and social sciences
www.prospects.ac.uk/findcourses POSTGRADUATE DIRECTORY 467

Psychology

Psychological Research .... MSc 12FT 24PT/PGDip 8FT 16PT/
PGCert 4FT 8PT
Psychology...........MA 12FT 24PT/PGDip 9FT 18PT/PGCert 4FT 8PT
Psychology.. MRes 12FT/PGCert 3FT
Public Health and Health Promotion ..MSc 12FT 24 - 60PT/PGDip
9FT

University of Bath
Health Psychology ....MSc 12FT 24PT

University of Bedfordshire
Health Psychology..MSc 12FT 24PT
Psychological Approaches to Health and Management MSc 12FT
24PT

University of Bradford
Health Psychology .... MSc 12FT 24PT/PGDip 12FT 24PT

Cardiff Metropolitan University
Health Psychology ....MSc 12FT 24PT
Health Psychology (Practitioner Programme)...PGCert 12FT 36PT

University of Central Lancashire
Health Psychology... MSc 12FT 24PT/PGDip 9FT 24PT/PGCert 9FT
24PT
Psychology.......MSc 12FT 24PT/PGDip 9FT 24PT/PGCert 9FT 24PT
Psychology of Child Development .... MSc 12FT 24PT/PGDip 9FT
24PT/PGCert 9FT 24PT
Psychology of Sport and Exercise.........MSc 12FT 24PT/PGDip 9FT
24PT/PGCert 9FT 24PT

University of Chichester
Psychology of Sport and Exercise.... MSc 12-15FT 24-36PT/PGDip
9-12FT 18-24PT/PGCert 6-9FT 12-18PT

City University London
Professional Doctorate in Health Psychology
.... DPsych 24 (min)FT 36 (min)PT

De Montfort University
Health Psychology...................................MSc 12FT 24-36PT

University of Derby
Health Psychology .... MSc 12FT 24PT

University of Dundee
Advanced Practice (Infection: Diseases, Prevention & Control) ...
MSc 36DL
Psychological Research Methods .... MSc 12FT
Psychological Therapy in Primary Care .... MSc 12FT

University of East Anglia
Clinical Science..MRes 12FT

University of Exeter
Clinical Practice.......................................DClinPrac 42DL
Clinical Psychology..................................... DClinPsy by taught 36FT
Mindfulness-based Cognitive Therapies and Approaches.............
PGCert 12PT/PGDip 24PT/MSc 24-36PT

National University of Ireland Galway
Health Psychology .... MSc 12FT

University of Hertfordshire
Health Psychology..MSc 12FT 24PT

University of Hull
Health Psychology .... MSc 12FT
Psychology and Health.................................... MSc 12FT

Keele University
Psychology of Health & Well Being ....MSc 12FT 24PT

University of Leeds
Psychological Approaches to Health ...MSc 12FT 24PT/PGDip 9FT
18PT

Liverpool John Moores University
Health Psychology...MSc 12FT 24PT

London Metropolitan University
Health Psychology........................ MSc 12FT 24PT/PGCert variousFT
Professional Doctorate 24FT 36PT
Psychology of Health ...MSc 12FT 24PT/PGDip 6-12FT 24-36PT

University of Manchester
Clinical & Health Psychology .... MSc 12FT

Middlesex University
Applied Clinical Health Psychology .... MSc 12FT 24PT
Dual Diagnosis .... MSc 36PT 36DL/AdvDip 12PT 12DL/
PGCert 12PT 12DL
Health Psychology.......................................MSc 12FT 24PT

Newcastle University
Psychology (Foundations in Clinical and Health Psychology) MSc
12FT

Northumbria University
Health Care ....Professional Doctorate 48-72PT
Health Psychology.......................................MSc 12FT 24PT
Psychology of Health and Wellbeing.......................MSc 12FT 24PT

University of Nottingham
Health Psychology.......................................MSc 12FT 24PT
Psychology and Health............... MSc 12FT 24PT/PGDip 12FT 24PT

University of Reading
Clinical Aspects of Psychology ....MSc 12FT 24PT
Development and Psychopathology ...MSc 12FT 24PT/PGDip 6FT

University of Roehampton
Stress and Health .... MSc 12FT 24PT

University of Salford
Psycho-Oncology .... MSc 36PT/PGDip 24PT/PGCert 12PT

Sheffield Hallam University
Health Psychology.. MSc 14FT 26PT 26DL

University of Sheffield
Cognitive Studies .... MA 12FT 24PT

University of South Wales
Health Psychology..MSc 12FT 24PT

University of Southampton
Cognitive Therapy for Severe Mental Health Problems........PGDip
12PT
Health Psychology...............................MSc 12FT/PGDip 12FT
Research Methods in Psychology .... MSc 12FT

University of St Andrews
Health Psychology .... MSc 12FT

Staffordshire University
Health Psychology..MSc 12FT 24PT
Professional Doctorate in Health Psychology ...... DProf by taught
24FT 48PT

University of Stirling
Health Psychology.....................MSc 12FT 24PT/PGDip 6FT 12PT
Psychology of Faces.....................MSc 12FT 24PT/PGDip 9FT 18PT

University of Strathclyde
Research Methods in Psychology .... MRes 12FT

University of Surrey
Health Psychology .... MA 12FT 24PT

Teesside University
Doctorate Psychology (Top up) .... PsychD by taught 30BM
Health Psychology..MSc 12FT 24PT

University of Ulster
Psychology (Health) .... PGDip 9-12DL/MSc 12-18DL

UCL - University College London
Health Psychology..MSc 12FT 24PT

University of the West of England, Bristol
Health Psychology .... Prof Doctortae 36PT
Psychology and Health.......................................MSc 12FT 24PT

University of Westminster
Health Psychology..MSc 12FT 24PT

Health psychology
Research Courses

Aberystwyth University
Psychology.......................MPhil 12FT 24PT PhD 36FT 60PT

Bangor University
Ageing and Cognitive Health .... PhD 36FT 60PT
Ageing and Dementia Studies ....MSc by research 12FT 24PT
PhD 36FT 60PT/MPhil 24FT 48PT
Clinical Psychology...DClinPsy 36FT
Doctorate by Research .... PhD 36FT/MPhil 24FT

University of Dundee
Psychology .... MPhil 24FT

University of East Anglia
Doctorate Programme in Clinical Psychology ....ClinPsyD 36FT

University of Edinburgh
Clinical & Health Psychology ..... PhD 36FT 72PT/MSc by research
12FT 24PT

University of Exeter
Clinical Practice.......................................DClinPrac 42DL
Doctorate in Clinical Psychology ....DClinPsy 36FT
Health and Wellbeing .... MPhil 36FT 60PT/PhD 48FT 84PT

University of Greenwich
Health and Social Care - Research MPhil 24FT 36-48PT/PhD 36FT
48-60PT

University of Nottingham
Institute of Work, Health and Organisations Research Areas........
PhD 36FT 72PT/MPhil 24FT 48PT

The Open University
Psychology................ PhD 36FT 72PT variableDL/MPhil 15FT 24PT
variableDL

University of Southampton
MPhil/PhD in Health Psychology Research & Professional
Practice... PhD 36FT 84PT

UCL - University College London
Clinical, Educational and Health Psychology .... PhD 36FT 60PT

Inclusive education
Taught Courses

University of Aberdeen
Bayt al-Maqdis and Jerusalem Studies.... MLitt 12FT 24PT/PGDip
9FT 18PT
Community Learning and Development....MSc 36PT/PGDip 24PT
Effective Teaching in Numeracy....................................PGCert 12PT

Inclusive Practice..MEd 24PT
Plurilingual Education...............................MEd 24PT/PGCert 12PT

University of Birmingham
Inclusion and Special Educational Needs...MEd 12FT 24PT 72DL/
MA 12FT 24PT 72DL/Diploma 12FT 24PT 48DL
Management of Special Education in Developing Countries MEd
12FT/PGDip 12FT/B/Phil 12FT
Special Educational Needs Coordination (National Award for
SENC).. PGCert 12/24PT

University of Bolton
Inclusive Education .... MA 12FT 24-60PT

University of Brighton
Inclusive Arts Practice ....MA 24-72PT/PGCert 24-72PT

University of Bristol
Disability Studies: Inclusive Theory and Research.......... MSc 12FT
12-60PT/PGDip 12FT 12-60PT/PGCert 12FT 12-60PT
Education: Special and Inclusive Education .... MEd 12FT 24-60PT

Brunel University
Education (Gifted Education) .... MA 12FT 24PT

University of Central Lancashire
Excellence in Leadership for Inclusion and Community..... PGCert
12-24PT

University of Chester
Education: Inclusion and Marginalisation ......MA 36-72PT/PGDip
36-60PT/PGCert 12-36PT

University College Cork
Special Educational Needs...PGDip 9FT

University of Cumbria
Collaborative Practice..MSc 36 - 60PT

University of Dundee
Advanced Practice (Practice Education) ....MSc 36DL

Edge Hill University
Special Educational Needs Coordination .... National
Award 12-36DL

University of Edinburgh
Additional Support for Learning (Inclusive Education) MEd 72PT/
PGDip 48PT/PGCert 24PT
Inclusive and Special Education............................... MSc 12FT

University of Exeter
Education Taught Doctorate......... EdD by taught 24FT 48PT 48DL
Educational Research .... MSc 12FT 24PT 12-24DL
Special Educational Needs Masters...........PGDip 12FT/MEd 12FT/
PGCert 6FT

University of Glasgow
Inclusive Education: Research, Policy & Practice...MEd 12FT 72PT
Professional Development in Education .... PGCert 60 maxPT

University of Gloucestershire
Inclusive Education .... MA 24PT/PGDip 20PT/PGCert 8PT
Teacher Training PGCE (Primary) .... PGCE 12FT
Teacher Training PGCE (Secondary)................................. PGCE 12FT

University of Hull
Inclusive Education .. MEd 18FT 36PT/AdvDip 12FT 24PT/AdvCert
6FT 12PT

Institute of Education
Change to Teach ....Change to Teach Scheme 10PT
Developing SEN Co-ordination - SENCO............PGCert 12PT 12DL
Development Education..MA 12FT 24PT
Special and Inclusive Education.................................. MA 12FT 24PT
Transnational Perspectives on Democratic Education.....30 credit
module 3FT

King's College London
Inclusive Education & Technology .... MA 12FT 24-48PT
Language, Ethnicity & Education .... MA 12FT 24-48PT

University of Leeds
Co-ordinating Inclusive Provision for Children with Learning
Difficulties...PGCert 12PT
Disability and Special Education .... MA 12FT 24PT
Provision for Children with Developmental Disorders .... PGCert
12FT
Special Educational Needs..........MA 12FT 24PT/PGDip 12FT 24PT

London Metropolitan University
Assessment for Specific Learning Difficulties in FE and HE.PGDip
12PT

London South Bank University
Teachers of Adults with Learning Difficulties ....PGCert 12-24PT

Manchester Metropolitan University
Autistic Spectrum Conditions .... MA 12-60PT
Urban Education .... MA 12FT 24 - 60PT

University of Manchester
Profound and Complex Learning Disability................ MSc 12-15FT
24-36DL/PGDip 12-15FT 18DL/PGCert 12DL

Middlesex University
Inclusive Education ....MA 36PT 36DL

University of Northampton
Special Educational Needs ....MA 24PT

Psychology

Northumbria University
Special Educational Needs and Inclusion.................PGCert 12PT

Queen's University Belfast
Inclusion and Special Needs Education .... DASE 12FT 60PT/MEd 12FT 60PT

University of Reading
Education (Inclusive Education).....MA 12FT 24-84PT/PGDip 12FT
Inclusive Education .... MA 12FT 24-60PT

University of Roehampton
Special and Inclusive Education.....................PGCert 6FT 12-24PT
PGDip 9FT 24-48PT MA 12FT 24-48PT

Sheffield Hallam University
Inclusion ....MA 12FT 36PT/PGDip 24PT

University of South Wales
SEN Developmental Co-ordination Disorder (Dyspraxia) .. PGCert 12DL
SEN Hearing Impairment .... PGDip leading to MA SEN 24PT
Special Educational Needs.............................. MA 12FT 36PT

Teeside University
Promoting Inclusive Practice in Education............ PGDip 24 - 36PT

University of Wales Trinity Saint David
Inclusive Studies...MA 12FT 24PT/PGCert 12FT 24PT/PGDip 12FT 24PT
Inclusive Studies (Neuro-diversity)....MA 12FT 24PT/PGCert 12FT 24PT/PGDip 12FT 24PT
Special Educational Needs............................GradCert 12PT

Inclusive education
Research Courses

Bath Spa University
Children and the Environment ....PhD 24 - 60FT 36 - 72PT

University of Nottingham
Cognitive Development and LearningPhD 36FT 72PT/MPhil 24FT 48PT

The Open University
Children, young people, families, and personal relationships.......
PhD 36FT 72PT/MPhil 15FT 24PT
Doctorate in Education ....EdD 36PT
Education and Educational Technology.........................EdD 36PT
variableDL/PhD 36FT 72PT variableDL/MRes 12FT/MPhil 15FT 24PT variableDL
Multimodal meaning making......PhD 36FT 72PT variableDL/EdD 36PT/MRes 12FT
Technology Enhanced Learning...PhD 36FT 72PT variableDL/EdD 36PT/MRes 12FT

Neuropsychology
Taught Courses

University of Aberdeen
Social Cognitive Neuroscience.......................MSc 12FT/PGDip 9FT/PGCert 6FT

Bangor University
Clinical and Functional Brain Imaging.........................PGCert 12PT
Foundations of Clinical Neuropsychology ....MSc 12FT 24PT/PGDip 8FT 16PT/PGCert 4FT 8PT
Neuroimaging ....MSc 12FT 24PT
Psychological Research .... MSc 12FT 24PT/PGDip 8FT 16PT/PGCert 4FT 8PT
Psychology.. MRes 12FT/PGCert 3FT
MA 12FT 24PT/PGDip 9FT 18PT/PGCert 4FT 8PT

Bath Spa University
Principles of Applied Neuropsychology......MSc 12FT 60PT/PGDip 9FT 18PT/PGCert 4FT 9PT

Birkbeck, University of London
Cognitive Neuroscience and Neuropsychology....MSc 12FT 24PT/MA 12FT 24PT
Functional Neuroimaging ....MRes 12FT 24PT

University of Birmingham
Neuropsychiatry, Clinical .... MSc 12-24FT

Bournemouth University
Lifespan Neuropsychology.................................. MSc 12FT

University of Bristol
Neuropsychology.......................................MSc 12FT 24PT

Brunel University
Functional Neuroimaging ....MSc 12FT 30PT
Neurorehabilitation.................................MSc 12FT 24PT

Bucks New University
Advancing Spinal Cord Rehabilitation and Management ...... MSc 36PT

Cardiff University
Neuorehabilitation ....MSc 18FT 36-48PT/PGDip 12FT 24PT
Neuroimaging Methods & Applications .... MSc 12FT

University of Central Lancashire
Mental Health Practice (Including approved mental health professional training).........................MA 12-60PT/PGDip 12-60PT/PGCert 12PT

Personality Disorder (Practice Development)MSc 36-60PT/PGDip 24PT
Psychology.......MSc 12FT 24PT/PGDip 9FT 24PT/PGCert 9FT 24PT
Psychology of Child Development ....MSc 12FT 24PT/PGDip 9FT 24PT/PGCert 9FT 24PT
Psychology of Sport and Exercise.........MSc 12FT 24PT/PGDip 9FT 24PT/PGCert 9FT 24PT

University of Chichester
Psychology of Sport and Exercise ... MSc 12-15FT 24-36PT/PGDip 9-12FT 18-24PT/PGCert 6-9FT 12-18PT

Coventry University
Parapsychology ....MSc 24DL

University of Dundee
Eye Movements & Cognition .... MSc 12FT
Psychological Therapy in Primary Care .... MSc 12FT

Durham University
Cognitive Neuroscience..............................MSc 12FT
Developmental Cognitive Neuroscience ....MSc 12FT

University of Edinburgh
Cognition in Science and Society.......................MSc 12FT 24PT
Human Cognitive Neuropsychology ....MSc 12FT 24PT

University of Essex
Cognitive Neuropsychology.........................MSc 12FT
Cognitive Neuroscience...............................MSc 12FT
Language and the Brain ....MSc 12FT

University of Glasgow
Applied Neuropsychology ..... MSc(MedSci) 12FT 24PT/PGDip 9FT 18PT
Brain Imaging .... MSc 12FT
Brain Sciences: From Molecules to Mind.........................MSc 12FT
Clinical Neuropsychology...... MSc(MedSci) 12FT 24PT/PGDip 9FT 18PT

Goldsmiths, University of London
Cognitive and Clinical Neuroscience ....MSc 12FT 24PT

University of Greenwich
Applied Psychology Research Methods ....MSc 12FT

Heriot-Watt University
Applied Psychology..........MSc 12FT 24-48PT/PGDip 9FT 15-48PT/PGCert 6FT 12-48PT
Engineering Psychology with Ergonomics..............MSc 12FT 24PT 24-84DL/PGDip 9FT 21PT 21-84DL/PGCert 6FT 18PT 18-84DL

University of Hertfordshire
Research Methods in Cognitive Neuropsychology ....MSc 12FT 24PT

University of Kent
Cognitive Psychology/Neuropsychology..................MSc 12FT 24PT

King's College London
Clinical Neuroscience ....MSc 12FT 24PT
Neuroimaging ....MSc 12FT
Neuroscience ....MSc 12FT 24PT

Newcastle University
High Intensity Psychological Therapies ....Diploma 12FT

Nottingham Trent University
Neuroscience ....MSc 12FT 24PT

University of Nottingham
Rehabilitation Psychology..............................MSc 12FT 24PT

University of Oxford
Neuroscience ....MSc 12FT

Plymouth University
Clinical Psychology.....................................DClinPsy by taught 36FT
Psychology.............................MSc 12FT 24PT/PGDip 9FT

Queen's University Belfast
Cognition and Culture.................................... MA 12FT 30PT

University of Reading
Cognitive Neuroscience .... MSc 12FT 20-24PT/PGDip 8-12FT 20-24PT
Neuroscience of Language ....MSc 12FT 24PT

University of Roehampton
Applied Music Psychology........................... MA 12FT 24PT
Applied Psychological Research ....MSc 12FT 24PT
Clinical Neuroscience ....MSc 12FT 24PT
Post Graduate Certificate- Clinical Neuroscience
....PGCert 6FT 24PT
Clinical Neuroscience ....PGDip 9FT 24PT

Sheffield Hallam University
Applied Cognitive Neuroscience............................MSc 12FT 24PT

University of Sheffield
Cognitive Neuroscience and Human Neuroimaging ...... MSc(Res) 12FT
Cognitive Studies............................... MA 12FT 24PT

University of Sussex
Cognitive Neuroscience.....................................MSc 12FT 24PT

Swansea University
Cognitive Neuroscience ....MSc 12FT 24PT

Trinity College Dublin - the University of Dublin
Cognitive Psychotherapy..................................MSc 24PT PGDip 12PT
Neuroscience .... MSc 12FT

UCL - University College London
Applied Paediatric Neuropsychology .... MSc 12FT
Clinical Paediatric Neuropsychology ...MSc 12FT 24PT/PGDip 9FT 18PT
Cognitive Neuroscience ......MSc 12FT 24PT/PGDip 9FT MRes 12FT
Developmental Neuroscience and Psychopathology.......MSc 24FT
Social Cognition: Research and Applications ....MSc 12FT 24PT

University of Westminster
Cognitive Rehabilitation...............................MSc 12FT 24PT

University of York
Cognitive Neuroscience ....MSc 12FT

Neuropsychology
Research Courses

Bangor University
Doctorate by Research ....PhD 36FT/MPhil 24FT

University of Birmingham
Neurophysiology .... PhD 36FT 72PT/MPhil 12FT 24PT

University of Cambridge
Brain Repair...PhD 36FT
Cognition and Brain Sciences....................... PhD 36FT 60PT

Cardiff University
Psychological Medicine and Clinical Neurosciences .....PhD 36FT/MPhil 36FT/MD 36FT

University of Dundee
Non-Graduating Research in School of Psychology (6 months or more)...Non-Grad 6-24FT
Non-Graduating Research in School of Psychology (less than 6 months)................................... Non-Grad 1-5FT

University of East Anglia
Doctorate Programme in Clinical Psychology ....ClinPsyD 36FT

University of Edinburgh
Neuroscience and Neurodegenerative Diseases (Veterinary Medicine)..PhD 36FT

Heriot-Watt University
Applied Psychology .... PhD 36FT 48PT/MPhil 24FT 36PT

University of Kent
Cognitive Psychology/Neuropsychology .... PhD 36FT 60PT

King's College London
Clinical Neuroscience .... PhD 36FT 72PT/MPhil 36FT 72PT

Lancaster University
Clinical Psychology...................................DClinPsy 36FT

Newcastle University
Neuroscience.....PhD 36FT 72PT/MD 24FT 48PT/MPhil 12FT 24PT
Neuroscience.....................................MRes 12FT

University of Nottingham
Behavioural Neuroscience.......... PhD 36FT 72PT/MPhil 24FT 48PT
Cognition and Cognitive Neuroscience ....PhD 36FT 72PT/MPhil 24FT 48PT
Rehabilitation and Ageing .... PhD 36FT 72PT

The Open University
Applied Psychology .... PhD 36FT 72PT variableDL/MPhil 15FT 24PT variableDL

University of Oxford
Neuroscience .... DPhil 48FT

Plymouth University
Centre for Brain, Cognition and Behaviour....................PhD 36FT/MPhil 24FT
Cognition..PhD 36FT/MPhil 24FT

Queen's University Belfast
Cognition and Culture............................... PhD 36FT 72PT

University of Sheffield
Neuroscience .... PhD 36FT 72PT/MPhil 24FT 48PT

University of Strathclyde
Neuroscience ....MRes 12FT

University of Sussex
Neuroscience .... PhD 24-48FT 36-72PT/MPhil 12-36FT 24-48PT

UCL - University College London
Cognitive Neuroscience.....................................PhD 36FT 60PT
Cognitive, Perceptual and Brain Sciences.............. PhD 36FT 60PT

Occupational psychology
Taught Courses

Aston University
Organisational Behaviour ....MSc 12FT 24PT
Organisational Psychology & Business.....................MSc 12FT
Work Psychology & Business.....................................MSc 12FT 24PT

Bangor University
Applied Behaviour Analysis ....PGCert 4FT 9PT/PGDip 9FT 18PT/MSc 12FT 24PT

Section sponsored by
BPP UNIVERSITY COLLEGE

Business and social sciences
www.prospects.ac.uk/findcourses POSTGRADUATE DIRECTORY 469

Psychology

Birkbeck, University of London
Career Management and Coaching.......MSc 24PT
Human Resource Development and Consultancy.......MSc 12FT 24PT
Human Resource Management.......MSc 12FT 24PT
Management Consultancy and Organisational ChangeMSc 12FT 24PT
Occupational Psychology.......MSc 12FT 24PT 12-24DL
Organizational Behaviour.......MSc 12FT 24PT 12-24DL

City University London
Organisational Behaviour.......MSc 12FT 24PT
Organisational Psychology.......MSc 12FT 24PT

University College Cork
Occupational and Organisational Psychology.......MA 12FT 24PT

De Montfort University
Psychological Wellbeing.......MSc 12FT 24PT

University of Dundee
Advanced Practice (Organisational Leadership).......MSc 36DL

University of East London
Business Psychology.......MSc 12FT 24PT/PGDip 8FT 16PT/PGCert 4FT 8PT
Consultation and the Organisation: Psychoanalytic Approaches.......MA 24PT/PGDip 24PT
Occupational Psychology Professional Doctorate.......DOccPsych by taught 36FT 60PT
Occupational and Organisational Psychology MSc.......MSc 12FT 24PT/PGDip 8FT 16PT/PGCert 4FT 8PT

University of Exeter
Social and Organisational Psychology.......MSc 12FT 24PT

University of Gloucestershire
Business Psychology.......MSc 12FT 24PT/PGDip 8FT 20PT/PGCert 4FT 8PT
Occupational Psychology.......MSc 12FT 24PT

Goldsmiths, University of London
Occupational Psychology.......MSc 12FT

Heriot-Watt University
Business Psychology.......MSc 12FT 24-84PT 12-84DL/PGDip 9FT 15-48PT 9-48DL/PGCert 6FT 12-48PT 6-48DL

University of Hertfordshire
Occupational Psychology.......MSc 12FT 24-36PT
Organisational Psychology.......MSc 12FT 24-36PT

Keele University
Psychology.......MSc 12FT 24PT

Kingston University
Business Psychology.......MSc 12FT 24PT
Occupational Psychology.......MSc 12FT 24PT

Leeds Metropolitan University
Psychology (conversion award).......MSc 12FT 24PT

University of Leicester
Occupational Psychology.......MSc 24DL
Psychology of Work.......MSc 24DL/PGDip 24DL

London Metropolitan University
Business Psychology.......MSc 12FT 24PT
Occpupational Psychology.......Professional Doctorate 24+FT
Occupational Psychology.......MSc 12FT 24PT

University of Manchester
Managerial Psychology.......MSc 12FT 24PT
Organisational Psychology.......MSc 12FT 24PT

Northumbria University
Occupational Psychology.......MSc 12FT 24PT/DProf by taught 24FT 36PT
Occupational Therapy.......Professional Doctorate 48-72PT
Occupational Therapy (Pre Registration).......MSc 24FT
Organisational Psychology.......MSc 12FT 24PT

Nottingham Trent University
Doctorate in Business Administration.......DBA by taught 36PT

University of Nottingham
Management Psychology.......MSc 12FT 24PT/PGDip 12FT
Occupational Psychology.......MSc 12FT 24PT
Psychology (Conversion Course).......PGDip 9FT
Work and Organisational Psychology.......MSc 12FT 24PT/PGDip 12FT
Workplace Health (Distance E-Learning).......MSc 24PT

University of Roehampton
Applied Psychological Research.......PGCert 6FT 24PT PGDip 9FT 24PT

Sheffield Hallam University
Organisational Psychology.......MSc 12FT 24PT

University of Sheffield
Occupational Psychology.......MSc 12FT
Work Psychology.......MSc 12FT

University of South Wales
Business Psychology.......MSc 12FT 24PT

University of Stirling
Psychology of Faces.......MSc 12FT 24PT/PGDip 9FT 18PT

University of Surrey
Occupational and Organisational Psychology.......MA 12FT 24PT

Teesside University
Doctorate Psychology (Top up).......PsychD by taught 30BM

UCL - University College London
Industrial/Organisational and Business Psychology.......MSc 12FT 24PT

University of Westminster
Business Psychology.......MSc 12FT 24PT

University of Worcester
Business / Occupational Psychology.......MSc 36FT 72PT/PGDip 24FT 48PT/PGCert 12FT 24PT
Business Psychology.......MSc 36FT 72PT/PGDip 24FT 48PT/PGCert 12FT 24PT

Occupational psychology
Research Courses

University of Aberdeen
Psychology.......PhD 36FT/MPhil 24FT/MSc by research 12FT/MRes 12FT

Aberystwyth University
Psychology.......MPhil 12FT 24PT PhD 36FT 60PT

Birkbeck, University of London
Organizational Psychology.......PhD 24FT 36PT/MPhil 24FT 36PT

Cardiff University
Work, Employment and Globalisation.......PhD 36FT possiblePT/MPhil 12FT possiblePT

University of East Anglia
Psychology.......PhD 36FT 72PT/MPhil 24FT 48PT

University of Hertfordshire
Centre for Research in Employment Studies.......PhD 36FT 72PT/MPhil 24FT 48PT/MRes 12FT 24PT

Lancaster University
Organisation, Work and Technology.......PhD 36FT 48PT/MPhil 24FT 36PT

London School of Economics and Political Science (LSE)
Employment Relations and Organisational Behaviour.......MPhil 36-48FT/PhD 36-48FT

University of Nottingham
Institute of Work, Health and Organisations Research Areas.......PhD 36FT 72PT/MPhil 24FT 48PT

The Open University
Applied Psychology.......PhD 36FT 72PT variableDL/MPhil 15FT 24PT variableDL
Psychology.......PhD 36FT 72PT variableDL/MPhil 15FT 24PT variableDL

Play therapy
Taught Courses

University of Central Lancashire
Playwriting.......MA 12FT 24PT

University of Glasgow
Primary Expressive Arts.......PGCert 12PT

University of Gloucestershire
Play and Playwork.......PGCert 12-24DL/PGDip 12-24DL/MA 24-48DL

University of Roehampton
Art Psychotherapy.......MA 24FT 36PT

University of Sheffield
Music Psychology in Education.......MA 24 PTDL

University of South Wales
Play and Therapeutic Play.......MSc 12FT 36PT 18BM

Swansea University
Developmental and Therapeutic Play.......MA 12FT 36PT/PGDip 12FT 24PT/PGCert 12FT 12PT

Play therapy
Research Courses

University of Roehampton
Arts and Play Therapies.......PhD 24-48FT 36-60PT/MPhil 21-36FT 33-48PT

Psychiatry
Taught Courses

Aston University
Psychiatric Pharmacy.......PGDip 12DL

Bangor University
Foundations of Clinical Psychology.......MSc 12FT 24PT/PGDip 8FT 16PT/PGCert 4FT 8PT

Barts and the London School of Medicine and Dentistry
Transcultural Mental health.......MSc 12FT 24PT/PGDip 12FT 24PT

Cardiff University
Psychiatry.......MSc 12FT 36PT 36DL/PGDip 12FT 24PT 24DL/PGCert 12FT 24PT 24DL

University of Central Lancashire
Child Health.......MSc 36PT
Mental Health Practice (Including approved mental health professional training).......MA 12-60PT/PGDip 12-60PT/PGCert 12PT
Personality Disorder (Practice Development).......MSc 36-60PT/PGDip 24PT
Personality Disorder (Research).......MSc 36-60PT/PGDip 12-24PT
Philosophy & Mental Health.......MA 36DL/PGDip 24DL/PGCert 12DL
Primary Care Mental Health Practice.......PGCert 12PT
Professional Integrative Psychotherapy.......MA 36PT/PGDip 24PT
Psychology.......MSc 12FT 24PT/PGDip 9FT 24PT/PGCert 9FT 24PT
Psychology of Child Development.......MSc 12FT 24PT/PGDip 9FT 24PT/PGCert 9FT 24PT
Psychology of Sport and Exercise.......MSc 12FT 24PT/PGDip 9FT 24PT/PGCert 9FT 24PT

University of Chester
Family and Child Psychology.......MSc 12FT 24PT/PGDip 12FT 24PT/PGCert 12FT 12-24PT

University of Chichester
Psychology of Sport and Exercise.......MSc 12-15FT 24-36PT/PGDip 9-12FT 18-24PT/PGCert 6-9FT 12-18PT

De Montfort University
Psychological Wellbeing.......MSc 12FT 24PT

University of Edinburgh
Children & Young People's Mental Health and Psychological Practice.......MSc 12FT 24-72PT/PGCert 12-24PT/PGDip 9FT 24-48PT
Cognitive Behaviour Therapy for Children and Young People.......PGCert 24PT

University of Glasgow
Mental Health, Global.......MSc 12FT 24PT/PGDip 9FT 18PT/PGCert 9FT 18PT

Goldsmiths, University of London
The Science of Psychology, Genetics & Education.......MSc 12FT 24PT

University of Hertfordshire
Mental Health (Primary Care).......PGCert 12PT
Mental Health Practice MSc 15FT 24-60PT/PGDip 15FT 24-60PT/PGCert 15FT 24-60PT

King's College London
Child & Adolescent Mental Health.......MSc 12FT 24PT
Clinical Forensic Psychiatry.......MSc 12FT 24-36PT
Epilepsy.......MSc 12FT 24PT
Forensic Mental Health Research.......MSc 12FT 24PT
Global Mental Health.......MSc 12FT 24PT
Health Psychology.......MSc 12FT
Mental Health Service & Population Research.......MSc 12FT 24PT
Mental Health Studies.......MSc 12FT 24PT
Mental Health in Learning Disabilities.......MSc 12FT 24PT
Organisational Psychiatry & Psychology.......MSc 12FT 24PT
Philosophy of Mental Disorder.......MSc 12FT 24PT
Psychiatric Research.......MSc 12FT 24PT
Social, Genetic & Developmental Psychiatry.......MSc 12+36FT
War & Psychiatry.......MSc 12FT 24PT/PGDip 12FT 24PT

University of Leeds
Psychiatry.......MSc 48PT

University of Leicester
Child and Adolescent Mental Health.......PGCert 12FT 12PT/PGDip 12FT 24PT/MSc 12FT 36PT

University of Liverpool
MRCPsych.......MRCPsych 12PT

London Metropolitan University
Mental Health and Wellbeing.......MA 12FT 24PT

London South Bank University
Acute and Psychiatric Intensive Care Settings.......MSc 36PT/PGDip 24PT

University of Manchester
Psychiatry.......MSc 36PT/Diploma 24PT
Psychiatry (blended learning).......MSc 36PT/PGDip 24PT

Middlesex University
Dual Diagnosis.......MSc 36PT 36DL/AdvDip 12PT 12DL/PGCert 12PT 12DL

Newcastle University
Cognitive Behavioural Therapy.......PGDip 12FT 24PT
High Intensity Psychological Therapies.......Diploma 12FT

University of Nottingham
Rehabilitation Psychology.......MSc 12FT 24PT

Queen Margaret University, Edinburgh
Cognitive Behavioural Therapy.......PGDip 24PT/PGCert 12PT

Queen Mary, University of London
Mental Health: Psychological Therapies D/L option.......MSc 12FT 24PT
Mental Health: Transcultural Mental Healthcare.......MSc 12FT 24PT 24DL

Queen's University Belfast
Cognitive Behavioural Practice.......PGCert 12PT

Psychology

Cognitive Behavioural Therapy ... PGDip 12PT

Sheffield Hallam University
Cognitive Analytic Therapy Practitioner ... MSc VAPT/PGDip VAPT

University of Southampton
Health Psychology ... MSc 12FT/PGDip 12FT

University of St Andrews
Health Psychology ... MSc 12FT

Staffordshire University
Practitioner with a Special Interest in Mental Health ... MSc 36PT

University of Stirling
Health Psychology ... MSc 12FT 24PT/PGDip 6FT 12PT
Psychological Research Methods ... MSc 12FT 24PT/PGDip 9FT 18PT

University of Sussex
Foundations of Clinical Psychology and Mental Health ... MSc 12FT 24PT

Trinity College Dublin - the University of Dublin
Child and Adolescent Psychoanalytic Psychotherapy ... MSc 24PT
Cognitive Psychotherapy ... MSc 24PT PGDip 12PT
Psychoanalytic Psychotherapy ... MSc 36PT

UCL - University College London
CYP IAPT Therapy ... PGDip 12FT
Cognitive Behavioural Therapy for Children and Young People ... MSc 24-36PT/PGDip 24PT/PGCert 12PT
Cognitive Neuroscience ... MSc 12FT 24PT/PGDip 9FT MRes 12FT
Developmental Psychology and Clinical Practice MSc 24FT/PGDip 12FT
Psychiatric Research ... MSc 24-60PT

University of Warwick
Philosophy and Ethics of Mental Health ... MSc 12FT 24PT 36DL/MA 12FT 24PT 36DL/PGA 6FT

University of Winchester
Psychological Disorders ... MSc 12FT 24PT/PGDip 12FT 24PT/PGCert 12FT 24PT

Psychiatry
Research Courses

Aberystwyth University
Psychology ... PhD 36FT 60PT

Bangor University
Clinical Psychology ... DClinPsy 36FT

Barts and the London School of Medicine and Dentistry
Department of Psychiatry ... PhD/MPhil

University of Birmingham
Psychiatry ... PhD 36FT 72PT/MPhil 12FT 24PT

University of Cambridge
Brain Repair ... PhD 36FT
Psychiatry ... PhD 36FT 60PT

University of Edinburgh
Psychiatry ... PhD 36FT 72PT/MPhil 24FT/MSc by research 12FT 24PT

King's College London
Biostatistics ... PhD 36FT 72PT/MPhil 36FT 72PT
Child & Adolescent Psychiatry ... PhD 36FT 72PT/MPhil 36FT 72PT/MD 36FT 72PT
Forensic and Neurodevelopmental Science PhD 36FT 72PT/MPhil 36FT 72PT
Health Service & Population Research Department ... PhD 36FT 72PT/MPhil 36FT 72PT/MDes by research 36FT 72PT
Psychological Medicine ... PhD 36FT 72PT/MPhil 36FT 72PT/MD (Res) 36FT 72PT
Psychosis Studies ... MPhil 36FT 72PT/PhD 36FT 72PT
Social Genetic & Developmental Psychiatry .. PhD 36FT 60-72PT/MPhil 36FT 60-72PT

University of Liverpool
Psychiatry ... PhD 24-48FT 48-84PT/MPhil 12-48FT 24-72PT/MD 24-72PT

London School of Economics and Political Science (LSE)
Social Psychology ... PhD 36-48FT/MPhil 36-48FT

University of Nottingham
Psychiatry ... PhD 36FT
Social Research in Medicines and Health ... PhD 36FT 72PT/MPhil 36FT

University of Oxford
Psychiatry ... DPhil 48FT/MSc by research 24-36FT

UCL - University College London
Cognitive Neuroscience ... PhD 36FT 60PT
Cognitive, Perceptual and Brain Sciences ... PhD 36FT 60PT

Psychology
Taught Courses

University of Aberdeen
Psychology ... MRes 12FT

University of Abertay Dundee
Psychology ... MSc 12FT/PGDip 9FT

Anglia Ruskin University
Clinical Child Psychology ... MSc 12 - 15FT 24 - 30PT
Cognitive and Clinical Neuroscience ... MSc 12 - 15FT 24 - 30PT
Research Methods in Psychology ... MSc 12 - 15FT 24 - 30PT

Bangor University
Applied Behaviour Analysis ... PGCert 4FT 9PT/PGDip 9FT 18PT/MSc 12FT 24PT
Business with Consumer Psychology ... MA 12FT/PGDip 9FT MSc 12FT/PGDip 9FT
Consumer Psychology with Business ... MSc 12FT/PGDip 9FT MA 12FT/PGDip 9FT
Foundations of Clinical Neuropsychology ... MSc 12FT 24PT/PGDip 8FT 16PT/PGCert 4FT 8PT
Foundations of Clinical Psychology ... MSc 12FT 24PT/PGDip 8FT 16PT/PGCert 4FT 8PT
Mindfulness-Based Approaches ... MSc 36PT/DipHE 24PT/CertHE 12PT
Psychological Research ... MSc 12FT 24PT/PGDip 8FT 16PT/PGCert 4FT 8PT
Psychology ... MA 12FT 24PT/PGDip 9FT 18PT/PGCert 4FT 8PT MRes 12FT/PGCert 3FT

University of Bath
Human Computer Interaction MSc ... MSc 12FT
Psychology ... MRes 12FT 24-36PT/PGDip 9FT 24-36PT/PGCert 4FT 24-36PT

University of Bedfordshire
Coaching Psychology ... PGDip 12FT 24PT
Professional Doctorate in Systemic Practice (PDSP) ... DProf by taught 36PT

Birkbeck, University of London
Cognition and Computation ... MSc 12FT 24PT/MA 12FT 24PT
Cognitive Neuroscience and Neuropsychology ... MSc 12FT 24PT/MA 12FT 24PT
Developmental Sciences ... MA 12FT 24PT/MSc 12FT 24PT
Educational Neuroscience ... MA 12FT 24PT/MSc 12FT 24PT
Functional Neuroimaging ... MRes 12FT 24PT
Psychoanalysis, History and Culture ... MA 12FT 24PT
Psychodynamic Counselling and Psychotherapy ... MSc 24PT
Psychodynamic Counselling and Psychotherapy with Children and Adolescents ... MSc 36PT/PGDip 36PT
Psychological Research Methods ... MSc 12FT 24PT
Psychology ... MSc 48PT/PGDip 36PT MRes 12FT 24PT
Psychosocial Studies ... MA 12FT 24PT

University of Birmingham
Psychological Research with Pathways ... MSc 12FT 24PT

University of Bolton
Graduate Foundation Studies in Psychology ... Certificate of Professional Development 6FT 12PT
Psychological Studies ... PGDip 12FT 18PT
Psychology ... MRes 18FT 30PT/PGDip 6FT 12PT
Psychology ... MSc 18FT 30PT/PGDip 6FT 12PT

University of Bradford
Psychology ... MSc 12FT/PGDip 12FT

University of Bristol
Philosophy of Biological and Cognitive Sciences ... MA 12FT 24PT
Research Methods in Psychology ... MSc 12FT 24PT

Brunel University
Evolutionary Psychology ... MSc 12FT 30PT
Psychology, Health & Behaviour ... MSc 12FT 30PT

Bucks New University
Applied Positive Psychology ... MSc 24PT
Psychology ... GradDip 12FT 24PT

Cardiff University
Cognitive and Behavioural Therapies ... PGDip 24PT/PGCert 24PT
Psychiatry . MSc 12FT 36PT 36DL/PGDip 12FT 24PT 24DL/PGCert 12FT 24PT 24DL
Psychology ... Diploma 9FT

University of Central Lancashire
Counselling and Psychotherapy ... MSc 36PT/PGDip 24PT
Creative Thinking ... MA 30DL
Mental Health Practice (Including approved mental health professional training) ... MA 12-60PT/PGDip 12-60PT/PGCert 12PT
Personality Disorder (Practice Development) ... MSc 36-60PT/PGDip 24PT
Personality Disorder (Research) ... MSc 36-60PT/PGDip 12-24PT
Primary Care Mental Health Practice ... PGCert 12PT
Psychology ... MSc 12FT 24PT/PGDip 9FT 24PT/PGCert 9FT 24PT
Psychology of Child Development ... MSc 12FT 24PT/PGDip 9FT 24PT/PGCert 9FT 24PT
Psychology of Sport and Exercise ... MSc 12FT 24PT/PGDip 9FT 24PT/PGCert 9FT 24PT
Social Psychology ... MSc 12FT 24PT

University of Chester
Psychology (Conversion) ... MSc 12FT 24PT/PGDip 12FT 24PT

University of Chichester
Psychology of Sport and Exercise ... MSc 12-15FT 24-36PT/PGDip 9-12FT 18-24PT/PGCert 6-9FT 12-18PT

City University London
Health Psychology ... MSc 12FT 24PT
Psychology and Health ... MSc 12FT 24PT
Research Methods and Psychology ... MSc 12FT 24PT

University College Cork
Occupational and Organisational Psychology ... MA 12FT 24PT
Psychology (Conversion Programme) ... HDip 18FT

Coventry University
Health Psychology ... MSc 12FT 24PT
Parapsychology ... MSc 24DL

University of Derby
Health Psychology ... MSc 12FT 24PT

University of Dundee
Developmental Psychology ... MSc 12FT
Non-Graduating Taught Postgraduate in School of Psychology ... PG module variableFT
Psychological Research Methods ... MSc 12FT

University of East Anglia
Child and Family Psychology ... MSc 12FT 24PT
Counselling ... PGDip 12FT MA 6FT 12PT
Focusing Oriented Psychotherapy ... PGCert 12PT
Social Science Research Methods: Psychology ... MRes 12FT 24PT

University of East London
Applied Positive Psychology (MAPP) ... MSc 12FT 24PT/PGDip 8FT 16PT/PGCert 4FT 8PT MSc 36-72DL
Applied Psychology MSc MSc 12FT 24PT/PGDip 8FT 16PT/PGCert 4FT 8PT
Coaching / Coaching Psychology MSc by distance learning .. MSc 24PT/PGDip 16PT/PGCert 8PT
Coaching Psychology ... MSc 12FT 24PT/PGDip 8FT 16PT/PGCert 4FT 8PT
Psychological Therapy with Children, Young People and Families MA (M34) ... MA 36PT
Psychology ... MSc 12FT 30PT/PGDip 8FT 16PT/PGCert 4FT 8PT
Psychosexual and Relationship Therapy ... MSc 12FT

Edge Hill University
Psychology ... MSc 12FT 24PT

University of Edinburgh
Applied Psychology (Healthcare) for Children and Young People. MSc 12FT
Children & Young People's Mental Health and Psychological Practice.. MSc 12FT 24-72PT/PGCert 12-24PT/PGDip 9FT 24-48PT
Clinical Psychology ... DClinPsy by taught 36FT 60PT
Cognition in Science and Society ... MSc 12FT 24PT
Cognitive Behaviour Therapy for Children and Young People ... PGCert 24PT
Cognitive Science ... MSc 12FT 36PT
Copy of Cognitive Science ... MSc 12FT 36PT
Counselling ... MCouns 48PT/PGDip 36PT/PGCert 12PT
Counselling (Interpersonal Dialogue) ... MCouns 24FT
Counselling Studies ... MSc 12FT 24-36PT
Evolution of Language & Cognition ... MSc 12FT 24PT
Health & Social Care - Children & Young People's Mental Health: Ecological Approaches ODL ... PGCert 9DL
History and Theory of Psychology ... MSc 12FT 24PT
Human Cognitive Neuropsychology ... MSc 12FT 24PT
Mind, Language and Embodied Cognition ... MSc 12FT 24PT
Performance Psychology . PGDip 9FT 12-48PT/MSc 12FT 24-72PT
Psychological Interventions for Children and Young People ... PGCert 12PT
Psychological Research ... MSc 12FT/PGDip 9FT
Psychology ...
Psychology of Individual Differences ...
Psychology of Language ... MSc 12FT 24PT

University of Essex
Analytical Psychology ... Prof Doc 24PT
Cognitive Neuropsychology ... MSc 12FT
Cognitive Neuroscience ... MSc 12FT
Foundations of Psychoanalytic Psychotherapy ... MA 24PT
Jungian and Post-Jungian Studies ... MA 12FT 24PT
Language and the Brain ... MSc 12FT
Psychoanalytic Psychotherapy ... Prof Doc 24PT
Psychoanalytic Social Observation ... MA 12FT 24PT
Psychoanalytic Studies ... MA 12FT 24PT
Psychodynamic Counselling ... MA 12FT 24PT
Psychodynamic Psychotherapy ... Prof Doc 24PT
Psychological Studies with English for Academic Purposes ... Diploma 9FT
Psychology ... MSc 12FT
Psychosocial Studies ... MA 12FT 24PT
Refugee Care ... MA 12FT
Research Methods in Psychology ... MSc 12FT

University of Exeter
Animal Behaviour ... MSc 12FT 24PT
Clinical Practice ... DClinPrac 42DL
Clinical Psychology ... DClinPsy by taught 36FT
Clinical Research ... DClinRes 42BM
Mindfulness-based Cognitive Therapies and Approaches PGCert 12PT/PGDip 24PT/MSc 24-36PT
Psychological Research Methods ... MSc 12FT 24PT
Psychological Therapies ... MSc 24PT

Psychology

Social and Organisational Psychology .... MSc 12FT 24PT

National University of Ireland Galway
Psychology (Conversion) ....HDip 12FT
Psychology (Full) ....HDip 24FT

Glasgow Caledonian University
Counselling Psychology ...PsychD by taught 36FT 72PT/MSc 12FT 24PT
Forensic Psychology ..... MSc 12FT 24PT/PGDip 12FT 24PT/PGCert 12FT 12PT
Life Sciences - Biological and Biomedical Sciences/Psychology/Vision Sciences .... MRes 12FT
Psychodynamic Counselling and Therapeutic Practice.........PGDip 12-24FT

University of Glasgow
Mental Health, Global....MSc 12FT 24PT/PGDip 9FT 18PT/PGCert 9FT 18PT
Psychological Science, Research Methods of.................... MSc 12FT
Psychological Studies ....MSc 12FT 24PT

University of Gloucestershire
Educational Leadership........... MEd 24PT/PGDip 20PT/PGCert 8PT
Graduate Diploma (Psychology)........................GradDip 9FT 20PT
Psychology in Practice ....MSc 12FT 24PT/PGAdvDip 8FT 20PT/PGCert 4FT 8PT

Glyndwr University
Psychology of Religion .... MSc 36PT

Goldsmiths, University of London
Consumer Behaviour.. MSc 12FT
Music, Mind and Brain ....MSc 12FT 24PT
The Science of Psychology, Genetics & Education .... MSc 12FT 24PT

University of Greenwich
Applied Psychology Research Methods .... MSc 12FT

Heriot-Watt University
Applied Psychology..........MSc 12FT 24-48PT/PGDip 9FT 15-48PT/PGCert 6FT 12-48PT
Engineering Psychology with Ergonomics.............MSc 12FT 24PT 24-84DL/PGDip 9FT 21PT 21-84DL/PGCert 6FT 18PT 18-84DL

University of Hertfordshire
Psychology (Conversion Course)........................ MSc 12FT 24-36PT/PGDip 12FT 24-36PT
Research Methods in Psychology ....MSc 12FT 24PT

Heythrop College
Psychology of Religion .... MA 12FT 24PT

University of Huddersfield
Psychology...PGDip 12FT 24PT
Psychology and Investigation..................................MSc 12FT

University of Hull
Psychology and Health....................................... MSc 12FT
Research Methods in Psychology ....MRes 12FT

Keele University
Counselling Psychology - Part Time Professional Counselling Training Route ....Cert 9PT/PGDip 12-24PT/MSc 12PT
Psychology...MSc 12FT 24PT

University of Kent
Cognitive Psychology/Neuropsychology.................MSc 12FT 24PT
Developmental Psychology..................................MSc 12FT 24PT
Forensic Psychology ....MSc 12FT 24PT
Group Processes and Intergroup Relations.............MSc 12FT 24PT
Research Methods in Psychology ....MSc 12FT 24PT
Social and Applied Psychology................................MSc 12FT 24PT

King's College London
Forensic Mental Health Research...........................MSc 12FT 24PT
Health Psychology .... MSc 12FT
Philosophy of Psychology............................... MA 12FT 24PT

Kingston University
Psychology..................................... MRes 12FT 24PT MSc 12FT 24PT

Leeds Metropolitan University
Coaching Psychology .... PGDip 24PT
Interpersonal & Counselling Skills...............................PGCert 12PT
Mental Health Practice ....MSc 24PT
Mental Health Studies............................ PGCert 24PT/PGDip 24PT
Psychological Therapies..MA 48PT
Psychology (conversion award).................................MSc 12FT 24PT
Psychology of Sport & Exercise................................... MSc 12FT
Sport and Exercise Psychology.. MSc 12FT

University of Leeds
Memory and Its Disorders...........................MSc 12FT/PGDip 12FT

University of Limerick
Clinical Psychology........................... DClinPsy by taught 36FT
Psychological Science .... MSc 12FT
Psychology...MA 12FT
Work & Organisational Psychology/Work & Organisational Behaviour.. MSc 12`FT 24PT

University of Lincoln
Developmental Psychology.. MSc 12FT
Forensic Psychology ....MSc 12FT 24PT

Liverpool Hope University
Psychology... MSc 12FT

University of Liverpool
Applied Psychology (Online Programme)........................ MSc 24FT
Research Methods in Psychology .... MSc 12FT/PGDip 6FT/PGCert 3FT

London Metropolitan University
Criminal Psychology (non-accredited) .... MSc 12FT
Graduate Conversion Programme in Psychology ....PGDip 12-24DL GradCert 6FT 12PT 6-12DL
Mental Health and Wellbeing................................. MA 12FT 24PT

London South Bank University
Psychology... PGDip 18FT 36PT

Loughborough University
Psychology........................... MRes 12FT 24PT/PGDip 9FT 20PT

Manchester Metropolitan University
Psychology and Criminology .... MSc 12FT 24-36PT/PGDip 12FT 24-36PT/PGCert 12FT 24-36PT
Psychology and Disability Studies......MSc 12FT 24PT/PGDip 12FT 24PT/PGCert 12FT 24PT
Psychology and Psychology by Research ....MSc 12FT 24-36PT

University of Manchester
Psychology..MRes 12FT 24PT

Middlesex University
Applied Psychology ....MSc 12FT 24PT
Graduate Diploma Psychology.................................PGDip 12FT
Lowenfeld Projective Play TherapyMSc 48PT/PGDip 36PT/PGCert 24PT
Psychoanalysis .... MA 12FT 24PT

Newcastle University
Cognitive Behavioural Therapy.............................PGDip 12FT 24PT
High Intensity Psychological Therapies .... Diploma 12FT
Low Intensity Psychological Therapies........................PGCert 12FT
Psychology (Foundations in Clinical and Health Psychology)........ MSc 12FT

Newman University
Clinical Applications of Psychology ... MSc 36DL/PGDip 24-36DL/PGCert 12-24DL

University of Northampton
Transpersonal Psychology and Consciousness Studies .... MSc 12FT 24PT/PGDip 12PT

Northumbria University
Health Psychology..................................... MSc 12FT 24PT
Occupational Psychology .. MSc 12FT 24PT/DProf by taught 24FT 36PT
Organisational Psychology ....MSc 12FT 24PT
Professional Practice in Sport Coaching ....MSc 12FT 24PT
Psychology...MRes 12FT
Psychology of Health and Wellbeing.......................MSc 12FT 24PT
Psychology of Sport and Exercise Behaviour..........MSc 12FT 24PT

Nottingham Trent University
Applied Child Psychology ....MSc 12FT 24PT
Professional Practice..MA 1.5PT 3DL
Psychological Research Methods ....MRes/MSc 12FT 24PT
Psychological Well-Being and Mental Health ....MSc 12FT 24PT
Psychology............................. PGDip 12FT 24PT/MSc 12FT 24PT

University of Nottingham
Brain Imaging .... MSc 12FT
Clinical Psychology..................................... DClinPsy by taught 36FT
Psychological Research Methods ....MSc 12FT 24PT
Rehabilitation Psychology..MSc 12FT 24PT

The Open University
Integrated Practice in Childhood and Youth..PGCert 12DL/PGDip variableDL

Oxford Brookes University
Developmental Psychology ....MRes 12FT 24PT
Psychology .... MSc 12FT 24PT PGCert 4FT 8PT
Rehabilitation ....MSc 12FT Up to 36PT

University of Oxford
Psychological Research .... MSc 12FT

Plymouth University
Psychological Research MethodsMSc 12FT 24PT/PGDip 9FT 24PT
Psychology.......................................MSc 12FT 24PT/PGDip 9FT

University of Portsmouth
Applied Psychology of Intellectual Disabilities......... MSc 12/24DL
Criminology and Criminal Pyschology............MSc 12FT 24/ 36DL

New School of Psychotherapy and Counselling
Certificate in Psychotherapy & Counselling.................. Cert 12PT
Counselling Psychology and Psychotherapy by Professional Studies..........DCPsych Counselling Psychology & Psychotherapy 48FT 96PT/PGCert 12FT 24PT/PGDip 24FT 48PT/MSc 24FT 48PT

Psychology

DProf in Existential Psychotherapy & Counselling by Professional Studies.... DProf by taught 48FT 96PT/MA 24FT 48PT/PGDip 24FT 48PT/PGCert 12FT 24PT
Existential Coaching ..... MA 24FT 48PT
Psychotherapy Studies ..... MSc 24FT 48PT
Professional Certificate Existential Supervision & Group Leadership ..... Professional Certificate 12PT

Queen Margaret University, Edinburgh
Cognitive Behavioural Therapy ..... PGDip 24PT/PGCert 12PT

Queen Mary, University of London
Mental Health and Law MSc 12FT 24PT 24DL/PGCert 3FT/PGDip 12FT 24PT

Queen's University Belfast
Applied Psychology (Clinical Specialism) ...MSc 24FT/PGDip 12FT 48PT
Atypical Child Development ..... MSc 12FT
Cognition and Culture ..... MA 12FT 30PT
Cognitive Behavioural Practice ..... PGCert 12PT
Cognitive Behavioural Therapy ..... PGDip 12PT
Political Psychology ..... MSc 12FT 24PT
Psychology of Performance Enhancement in Sport and Health... MSc 12FT 24PT

University of Reading
Clinical Aspects of Psychology ..... MSc 12FT 24PT
Cognitive Neuroscience ..... MSc 12FT 20-24PT/PGDip 8-12FT 20-24PT
Development and Psychopathology ...MSc 12FT 24PT/PGDip 6FT
Evidence-Based Psychological Treatments .....PGDip 12FT/PGCert 12FT
Neuroscience of Language ..... MSc 12FT 24PT
Research Methods in Psychology ..... MSc 12FT 24PT/PGDip 8FT 20PT
Speech and Language Therapy ..... MSc 24FT

University of Roehampton
Applied Psychological Research ..... MSc 12FT 24PT
Applied Psychology in Education ..... MSc 12FT 24-36PT
Attachment Studies ..... MSc 18-24FT 24-36PT
Counselling Psychology (PsychD) ..... PsychD by taught 24-36FT 36-48PT
Post Graduate Certificate- Applied Music Psychology PGCert 6FT 24PT
Stress and Health ..... PGDip 9FT 24PT

Royal Holloway, University of London
Applied Social Psychology ..... MSc 12FT
Clinical Psychology (Doctorate) ..... DClinPsy by taught 36FT

University of Salford
Media Psychology.... MSc 12FT 36PT/PGDip 8FT 24PT/PGCert 4FT 9PT
Psycho-Oncology ..... MSc 36PT/PGDip 24PT/PGCert 12PT

Sheffield Hallam University
Applied Cognitive Neuroscience ..... MSc 12FT 24PT
Asperger Syndrome ..... PGCert 12-24PT
Cognitive Analytic Therapy Practitioner ..... MSc VAPT/PGDip VAPT
Developmental Psychology ..... MSc 12FT 24-36PT
Health Psychology ..... MSc 14FT 26PT 26DL
Organisational Psychology ..... MSc 12FT 24PT
Preparation for Psychology Conversion ..... Short course 4DL
Psychology ..... MRes variousFT variousPT
Psychology ..... MSc 12FT 24-36PT

University of Sheffield
Computational Intelligence and Robotics ..... MSc 12FT
Music Psychology in Education ..... MA 24 PTDL
Occupational Psychology ..... MSc 12FT
Psychological Research ..... MSc 12FT 24PT
Psychology and Education ..... MA 12FT
Psychology for Musicians ..... MA 24 PTDL
Psychology of Music ..... MA 12FT 24PT

University of South Wales
Behaviour Analysis Supervised Practice ..... PGCert 18FT 24-36PT
Behaviour Analysis and Therapy MSc 12FT 24PT/PGCert 4FT 8PT/PGDip 8FT 16PT
Counselling Skills ..... University Certificate 12FT
Psychology by Research ..... MSc 12FT 24PT

University of Southampton
Health Psychology ..... MSc 12FT/PGDip 12FT
Research Methods in Psychology ..... MSc 12FT

University of St Andrews
Adults Support, Protection and Safeguarding ..... PGCert 12DL
Adults with Learning Disabilities who have Significant and Complex Needs ..... MSc 12DL/PGDip 12DL/PGCert 12DL
Behavioural and Neural Sciences ..... MPhil 12FT 24PT
Conversion to Psychology ..... MSc 12FT
Health Psychology ..... MSc 12FT
Psychology ..... MRes 12FT

St George's, University of London
Rehabilitation ..... MSc 12FT 24PT

Staffordshire University
Cognitive Behavioural Therapy ..... PGDip 12FT
Health Psychology ..... MSc 12FT 24PT
Health Psychology Professional Doctorate ..... PsychD by taught 24FT 48PT
Introduction to Basic Counselling Skills ..... Introduction 2.5PT
Practitioner with a Special Interest in Mental Health ... MSc 36PT
Professional Doctorate in Health Psychology ..... DProf by taught 24FT 48PT
Psychotherapeutic Counselling ..... MSc 36PT/PGDip 24PT
Terrorism, Crime and Global Security ..... MA 24-60DL

University of Stirling
Autism ..... MSc 12FT/PGCert 9FT/PGDip 9FT
Behavioural Science for Management ..... MSc 12FT/PGDip 9FT
Child Development ..... MSc 12FT 24PT/PGDip 6FT 12PT
Evolutionary Psychology ..... MSc 12FT 24PT/PGDip 9FT 18PT/PGCert 6FT 12PT
Health Psychology ..... MSc 12FT 24PT/PGDip 6FT 12PT
Measuring Perception .... MSc 12FT 24PT/PGDip 9FT 18PT/PGCert 6FT 12PT
Psychological Research Methods ..... MSc 12FT 24PT/PGDip 9FT 18PT
Psychological Therapy in Primary Care ..... MSc 12FT
Psychology Applied to Health ..... MSc 12FT 24PT/PGDip 9FT 18PT
Psychology of Faces ..... MSc 12FT 24PT/PGDip 9FT 18PT
Psychology of Sport ..... MSc 9FT 24PT/PGDip 9FT 24PT/PGCert 6FT 12PT

University of Strathclyde
Research Methods in Psychology ..... MRes 12FT

University of Sunderland
Psychological Research Methods ..... MSc 12FT
Psychological Research Methods ..... MSc 12FT
Psychology ..... MSc 12FT 24-36PT

University of Surrey
Environmental Psychology ..... MSc 12FT 24PT/PGDip 12FT 24PT
Health Psychology ..... MA 12FT 24PT
Research Methods in Psychology ..... MSc 12FT 24PT

University of Sussex
Experimental Psychology ..... MSc 12FT
Foundations of Clinical Psychology and Mental Health MSc 12FT 24PT
Psychological Methods ..... MRes 12FT 24PT
Psychological Therapy ..... PGDip 12FT 24PT

Swansea University
Abnormal and Clinical Psychology ..... MSc 12FT 24PT
Cognitive Neuroscience ..... MSc 12FT 24PT
Research Methods in Psychology ..... MSc 12FT 36PT/PGCert 12FT

Teesside University
Applied Behaviour Analysis ..... MSc 36PT
Counselling Psychology ..... DCounsPsy by taught 36FT
Doctorate Psychology (Top up) ..... PsychD by taught 30BM
Psychology ..... PGDip 12-24FT 24-36PT
Rehabilitation (Occupational Therapy) ..... MSc 36PT

Trinity College Dublin - the University of Dublin
Applied Behaviour Analysis ..... MSc 12FT PGDip 12FT
Applied Psychology ..... MSc 12FT
Clinical Psychology ..... D.Clin.Psych. 36FT
Cognitive Psychotherapy ..... MSc 24PT PGDip 12PT
Counselling Psychology ..... DCounsPsych by taught 36FT
Psychology ..... HDip 24FT
Psychology (Applied Behaviour Analysis) ..... MSc 12FT

University of Ulster
Applied Behaviour Analysis ..... MSc 24PT/PGDip 21PT
Psychology - Applied (Mental Health and Psychological Therapies) ..... MSc 12FT 24PT

UCL - University College London
Child and Adolescent Mental Health ... MSc 12FT 24-60PT/PGDip 24-60PT/PGCert 12PT
Cognitive Behavioural Therapy for Children and Young People.... MSc 24-36PT/PGDip 24PT/PGCert 12PT
Cognitive Neuroscience ..... MSc 12FT 24PT/PGDip 9FT MRes 12FT
Cognitive and Decision Sciences ..... MSc 12FT 24PT
Developmental Psychology and Clinical Practice ..... MSc 24FT/PGDip 12FT
ENT Practice (Otology) ..... MSc 12FT
Health Psychology ..... MSc 12FT 24PT
Industrial/Organisational and Business Psychology MSc ..... MSc 12FT 24PT
Language Sciences ..... MSc 12FT 24PT
Low Intensity Cognitive Behavioural Interventions ..... PGDip 9FT
Research Methods in Psychology ..... MSc 12FT 24PT

University of Warwick
Research Methods in Psychology ..... MSc 12FT

University of West London
Advanced Professional Practice ..... PGCert 24DL/PGDip 24DL
Advanced Psychosocial Interventions for Psychosis PGCert 24PT/PGDip 24PT/MSc 36PT
Health Psychology ..... MSc 12FT 24PT
Psychology ..... MPhil 36PT/PhD by taught 36PT

University of the West of Scotland
Alcohol and Drug Studies ..... MSc 48PT/Diploma 9FT 36PT/Cert 21PT

University of the West of England, Bristol
Counselling Psychology (Professional Doctorate)DProf by taught 36PT
Health Psychology ..... MSc 12FT 24PT
Psycho-Social Studies ..... MSc 24PT
Psychological Therapy (Relational Therapy) ..... MSc 24PT

University of Westminster
Psychology ..... MSc 12FT 24PT

University of Winchester
Applied Psychology ..... MSc 12FT 24PT/PGDip 12FT 24PT/PGCert 12FT 24PT
Psychological DisordersMSc 12FT 24PT/PGDip 12FT 24PT/PGCert 12FT 24PT
Psychological Research Methods ..... MSc 12FT 24PT/PGCert 12FT 24PT/PGDip 12FT 24PT
Social Psychology ..... MSc 12FT 24PT/PGDip 12FT 24PT/PGCert 12FT 24PT

University of Wolverhampton
Applied Child Psychology ..... PGCert 6PT
Counselling Psychology ..... DProf by taught 36FT
Occupational Psychology ..... MSc 18FT 36PT

University of Worcester
Applied Psychology ..... MSc 12FT 24-72PT
Psychology ..... MSc 12FT 24PT

University of York
Cognitive Neuroscience ..... MSc 12FT
Psychology ..... MRes 12FT

York St John University
Psychology of Child & Adolescent Development - MSc MSc 12FT 36PT

Psychology
Research Courses

University of Aberdeen
Psychology..... PhD 36FT/MPhil 24FT/MSc by research 12FT/MRes 12FT

Aberystwyth University
Psychology ..... MPhil 12FT 24PT PhD 36FT 60PT

Anglia Ruskin University
Applied, Social and Health Psychology ..... PhD 36FT 36-72PT
Brain and Cognition ..... PhD 24-60FT 36-72PT

Aston University
Psychology ..... PhD 36FT/MPhil 24FT

Bangor University
Ageing and Cognitive Health ..... PhD 36FT 60PT
Ageing and Dementia Studies ..... MSc by research 12FT 24PT PhD 36FT 60PT/MPhil 24FT 48PT
Clinical Psychology ..... DClinPsy 36FT
Doctorate by Research ..... PhD 36FT/MPhil 24FT

Bath Spa University
Psychology ..... PhD 24-60FT 36-72PT/MPhil 18-36FT 30-48PT

University of Bath
Psychology ..... PhD 24-48FT 36-72PT/MPhil 12-36FT 24-48PT

University of Bedfordshire
Psychology ..... MA by research 12FT 24PT/MSc by research 12FT 24PT/MPhil 24FT/PhD 36FT

Birkbeck, University of London
Psychology ..... PhD 36FT 72PT/MPhil 36FT 72PT
Psychosocial Studies ..... PhD 24FT 36PT/MPhil 24FT 36PT

University of Birmingham
Neurophysiology ..... PhD 36FT 72PT/MPhil 12FT 24PT

University of Bolton
Psychology SpecialismsPhD via MPhil 36FT 72PT/PhD 36FT 72PT/MPhil 18FT 36PT
Psychology Specialisms ..... PhD 36FT 72PT

University of Bristol
Psychology (Experimental) ..... PhD 36FT 72PT/MSc by research 12FT 24PT

Brunel University
Doctoral Programme in Psychology ..... MPhil 12FT 24PT/MRes 12FT 24PT/PhD 36FT 60PT

University of Buckingham
Psychology.... DPhil 36FT 72PT/MPhil 24FT 48PT/MSc by research 12FT 24PT

University of Cambridge
Experimental Psychology ..... MSc by research 24FT
Psychology ..... PhD 36FT

Canterbury Christ Church University
Applied Psychology ..... PhD 48FT 60PT/MPhil 24FT 48PT

University of Central Lancashire
Psychology ..... PhD 48FT 84PT/MPhil 36FT 60PT/MSc by research 24FT 36PT

De Montfort University
Psychology ..... PhD 36-48FT 48-60PT/MPhil 12-24FT 24-48PT

Psychology

University of Dundee
Non-Graduating Research in School of Psychology (6 months or more) .... Non-Grad 6-24FT
Non-Graduating Research in School of Psychology (less than 6 months) .... Non-Grad 1-5FT
Psychology (MPhil) .... MPhil 24FT
Psychology (PhD) .... PhD 36FT

Durham University
Psychology........ MA by research 12FT 24PT/MSc by research 12FT 24PT/MPhil 12FT 24PT/PhD 36FT 72PT

University of East Anglia
Psychology........ PhD 36FT 72PT/MPhil 24FT 48PT
Psychology........ PhD 36FT 72PT/MPhil 24FT 48PT

University of East London
Psychology........ PhD 2+FT/MPhil 2+FT

University of Edinburgh
Clinical & Health Psychology ..... PhD 36FT 72PT/MSc by research 12FT 24PT
Counselling Studies .... PhD 36FT 72PT
Informatics: Institute for Language, Cognition and Communication .... PhD 36FT 72PT/MPhil 24FT 48PT/MSc by research 12FT 24PT
Psychology........ PhD 36FT 72PT
MSc by research 12FT 24PT

University of Essex
Psychoanalytic Studies... PhD 36FT 72PT/MPhil 24FT 48PT/MA by research 12FT 24PT
Psychology........ PhD 36FT 72PT/MPhil 24FT 49PT
Refugee Care........ PhD 36FT 72PT/MPhil 24FT 48PT

University of Exeter
Clinical Practice........ DClinPrac 42DL
Clinical Research........ DClinRes 42DL
Doctorate in Clinical Psychology .... DClinPsy 36FT
Psychology........ PhD 48FT 84PT/MPhil 36FT 60PT

Glasgow Caledonian University
Biological and Biomedical Sciences/Psychology/Vision Sciences MRes 12FT

University of Glasgow
Psychology........ PhD 36FT

University of Gloucestershire
Psychology and Behavioural Sciences........ MRes 12FT

Goldsmiths, University of London
Psychology........ PhD 36-48FT 48-72PT/MPhil 24FT 36PT MRes 12FT 24PT MPhil 36FT/PhD 36FT

University of Greenwich
Health and Social Care - Research........ MPhil 24FT 36-48PT/PhD 36FT 48-60PT

Heriot-Watt University
Applied Psychology........ PhD 36FT 48PT/MPhil 24FT 36PT

University of Hull
Doctor of Psychology........ PsyD 12FT 24PT
Masters in Rearch Methods........ MRes 12FT
Psychology....... PhD 36FT 60PT/MPhil 24FT 36PT/MSc by research 12FT 24PT
Psychology........ MRes 12FT

Imperial College London
Neuroscience and Psychological Medicine...... PhD/MPhil/MSc by research 12FT

Keele University
Psychology........ PhD 24-48FT 48-84PT/MPhil 12-24FT 24-36PT

University of Kent
Applied Psychology........ MPhil 24FT 36PT/PhD 36FT 48PT
Cognitive Psychology/Neuropsychology........ PhD 36FT 60PT
Forensic PsychologyPhD 36FT 60PT/MPhil 24FT 36PT/New Route PhD 48FT
Psychology....... PhD 36FT 60PT/MPhil 24FT 36PT/New Route PhD 48FT/MSc by research 12FT 24PT

King's College London
Psychological Medicine....... PhD 36FT 72PT/MPhil 36FT 72PT/MD (Res) 36FT 72PT
Psychology........ PhD 36FT 72PT/MPhil 36FT 72PT/MD (Res) 36FT 72PT/DClinPsy 36FT 72PT

Kingston University
Psychology........ PhD 48FT 72PT/MPhil 24FT 48PT/MA by research 12FT 24PT

Lancaster University
Psychology........ PhD 36FT 48PT/MPhil 24FT 36PT

University of Leeds
School of Psychology...... PhD 36+FT/MPhil 24FT/MSc by research 12FT

University of Lincoln
Psychology........ MPhil 24FT 36PT/PhD 24-36FT 36-72PT

Liverpool Hope University
Postgraduate Research .... PhD 24FT 48PT/MPhil 12FT 24PT

Liverpool John Moores University
Psychology........ PhD 36FT 72PT/MPhil 24FT 48PT

University of Liverpool
Psychology........ MPhil 12-48FT 24-72PT/PhD 24-48FT 48-84PT

London Metropolitan University
Dept of Psychology ..... PhD Max 60FT Max 96PT/MPhil Max 36FT Max 54PT

Loughborough University
Masters of Research in Psychology, Human Biology.... MRes 12FT 24PT/PGDipRes 9FT 18PT
Psychology........ PhD 36FT 60PT/MPhil 24FT 36PT

Manchester Metropolitan University
Critical Psychology (by research)........ MSc by research 12FT
Faculty of Health, Psychology & Social Care .... PhD 24FT 60PT/MPhil 12FT 24PT/MA by research 12FT 24PT/MSc by research 12FT 24PT
Psychology........ PhD 24FT 36PT 36DL/MPhil 33FT 45PT 45DL MSc by research 12FT

University of Manchester
Counselling Psychology (Professional Doctorate).... DCounsPsych 36FT
Psychology........ PhD 36FT 72PT/MPhil 12FT 24PT

Middlesex University
Psychology........ PhD 36FT 60PT 60DL/MPhil 24FT 48PT 48DL

Newcastle University
Clinical Psychology........ DClinPsy 36FT
Psychology........ PhD 36FT 72PT/MPhil 12FT 24PT

Newman University
Psychology & Counselling........ PhD 36FT 72PT/MPhil 24FT 48PT

University of Northampton
Behavioural Studies........ PhD 36FT 48PT/MPhil 24FT 36PT

Nottingham Trent University
Psychology........ MPhil 24FT 48PT/PhD 48FT 96PT

University of Nottingham
Psychology Research Areas........ PhD 36FT 72PT/MPhil 24FT 48PT
School of Psychology Research AreasMPhil 12-24FT/PhD 24-36FT

The Open University
Applied Psychology........ PhD 36FT 72PT variableDL/MPhil 15FT 24PT variableDL
Applied cognitive psychology... MPhil 15FT 24PT variableDL/PhD 36FT 72PT variableDL
Forensic cognition ... MPhil 15FT 24PT variableDL/PhD 36FT 72PT variableDL
Mind, Meaning and Rationality........ PhD 36FT 72PT variableDL/MPhil 15FT 24PT variableDL
Narrative, Discursive and Psychosocial Research.. PhD 36FT 72PT variableDL/MPhil 15FT 24PT variableDL
Neuroscience and behaviour..... PhD 36FT 72PT variableDL/MPhil 15FT 24PT variableDL
Psychology........ PhD 36FT 72PT variableDL/MPhil 15FT 24PT variableDL
Value...... PhD 36FT 72PT variableDL/MPhil 15FT 24PT variableDL

Oxford Brookes University
Psychology .... PhD 24-60FT 36-72PT/MPhil 24-36FT 36-48PT

University of Oxford
Department of Experimental Psychology........ DPhil 48FT/MSc by research 24-36FT

Plymouth University
Centre for Brain, Cognition and Behaviour........ PhD 36FT/MPhil 24FT

University of Portsmouth
Psychology........ MPhil 24FT 48PT/PhD 36FT 72PT

Queen Mary, University of London
Psychology........ PhD 36FT/MPhil 24FT

Queen's University Belfast
Cognition and Culture........ PhD 36FT 72PT
Psychology........ PhD 36FT 72PT/MPhil 24FT 48PT

University of Roehampton
Psychology........ PhD 24-48FT 36-60PT/MPhil 21-36FT 33-48PT

Royal Holloway, University of London
Psychology........ PhD 36FT 72PT/M Phil 12-36FT

University of Salford
Psychology Research Group........ PhD/MPhil

University of Sheffield
Psychology........ PhD 36FT 72PT/MPhil 24FT 48PT/Integrated PhD 48FT

University of Southampton
MPhil/PhD research programme .... PhD 36FT 84PT/MPhil 36FT 84PT

University of St Andrews
Psychology........ PhD 36FT 60PT

Staffordshire University
Psychology........ PhD 36FT 72PT/MPhil 18FT 42PT

University of Stirling
Psychology........ PhD 36FT/MPhil 12FT

University of Strathclyde
Doctorate in Educational Psychology........ DEdPsy 24FT
Psychological Sciences and Health - Research..... PhD 33FT/MPhil 12FT/DEdPsy 24FT

University of Surrey
Psychology........ PhD 36FT 48PT/MPhil 24FT 36PT

University of Sussex
Cognitive Science Research Programme ... PhD 24-48FT 36-72PT/MPhil 12-36FT 24-48PT
Psychology Research Programme..... PhD 24-48FT 36-72PT/MPhil 12-36FT 24-48PT

Swansea University
Psychology........ PhD 36FT 72PT/MPhil 24FT 48PT

Teesside University
PsyD. Doctor of Psychology (Top Up Doctorate)........ PsychD 30DL
Psychology........ PhD 24FT 36PT/MPhil 18FT 30PT

University of Ulster
Psychology........ PhD 36FT 72PT/MPhil 24FT 48PT

UCL - University College London
Clinical Psychology........ DClinPsy 36FT
Clinical, Educational and Health Psychology .... PhD 36FT 60PT
Cognitive Neuroscience........ PhD 36FT 60PT
Cognitive, Perceptual and Brain Sciences........ PhD 36FT 60PT
Psychotherapy (Child and Adolescent Psychoanalytic Psychotherapy)........ DPsychotherapy 72PT

University of Warwick
Psychology....... PhD 36FT 60PT/MPhil 24FT 36PT/MSc by research 12FT 24PT

University of West London
Psychology........ PhD 36FT 72PT/MPhil 24FT 48PT

University of Worcester
Psychology........ PhD 48FT 70PT/MPhil 24FT 48PT

University of York
Psychology........ PhD 36FT 72PT/MPhil 24FT 48PT

York St John University
Health & Life Science........ PhD 12-36FT/MPhil 12-36FT/MA by research 12-36FT

Psychometrics
Research Courses

University of Cambridge
Biostatistics........ PhD 36FT

King's College London
Biostatistics........ PhD 36FT 72PT/MPhil 36FT 72PT

Psychotherapy
Taught Courses

University of Aberdeen
Pastoral Studies .... DPS 12FT 24PT

Bangor University
Applied Behaviour Analysis .... PGCert 4FT 9PT/PGDip 9FT 18PT/MSc 12FT 24PT
Foundations of Clinical Psychology ..... MSc 12FT 24PT/PGDip 8FT 16PT/PGCert 4FT 8PT
Mindfulness-Based Approaches.... MSc 36PT/DipHE 24PT/CertHE 12PT

University of Bedfordshire
Professional Doctorate in Systemic Practice (PDSP)........ DProf by taught 36PT

Birkbeck, University of London
Psychoanalysis, History and Culture........ MA 12FT 24PT
Psychodynamic Counselling and Psychotherapy .... MSc 24PT
Psychodynamic Counselling and Psychotherapy with Children and Adolescents .... MSc 36PT/PGDip 36PT

Birmingham City University
Integrative Psychotherapy ... MSc 24PT/PGDip 18PT/PGCert 12PT

University of Birmingham
Cognitive Behaviour Therapy .... MSc 33FT/PGDip 18FT
Cognitive Behaviour Therapy High Intensity........ PGDip 12FT

University of Bolton
Cognitive Behavioural Therapy........ PGDip 24PT MSc 12PT

Brunel University
Psychoanalysis and Contemporary Society .... MA 12FT 30PT

Bucks New University
Cognitive Behavioural Therapy........ MSc 12FT 24PT

Canterbury Christ Church University
Play Therapy, Practice Based........ MA 36PT

Cardiff University
Cognitive and Behavioural Therapies.... PGDip 24PT/PGCert 24PT

University of Central Lancashire
Counselling and Psychotherapy .... MSc 36PT/PGDip 24PT
Mental Health Practice (Including approved mental health professional training)........ MA 12-60PT/PGDip 12-60PT/PGCert 12PT
Professional Integrative Psychotherapy ...... MA 36PT/PGDip 24PT
Psychology....... MSc 12FT 24PT/PGDip 9FT 24PT/PGCert 9FT 24PT

Psychology

Psychology of Child Development.......MSc 12FT 24PT/PGDip 9FT 24PT/PGCert 9FT 24PT
Psychology of Sport and Exercise.........MSc 12FT 24PT/PGDip 9FT 24PT/PGCert 9FT 24PT

University of Chester
Principles in Cognitive and Behavioural Approaches: Preparation for Accreditation Training.......... MSc 12FT 24PT/PGDip 12FT 24PT
Psychological Trauma.... MSc 24PT/PGDip 24PT/PGCert 12 - 24PT

University of Chichester
Psychology of Sport and Exercise.... MSc 12-15FT 24-36PT/PGDip 9-12FT 18-24PT/PGCert 6-9FT 12-18PT

University College Cork
Behavioural & Cognitive Psychotherapy......PGDip 18PT MA 18PT
Counselling Psychology.......MA 24FT
Group Facilitation.......MA 24PT
Integrative Psychotherapy Studies ....MA 24PT PGDip 12FT

University of Cumbria
Advanced Practice in Cognative Behaviour Therapy...... MSc 36PT

De Montfort University
Psychological Wellbeing.......MSc 12FT 24PT

University of Derby
Cognitive Behavioural Psychotherapy (BABCP accredited) (incorporating PG Cert/PG Dip).......MSc 24FT 24-36PT
Cognitive Behavioural Psychotherapy (Children and Adolescents) (BABCP accredited).......MSc 24-36PT
Dance Movement Therapy/Psychotherapy.......MA 36FT
Integrative Counselling and Psychotherapy (BACP Accredited).... PGDip 30FT
Systemic Psychotherapy.......MSc 24PT

University of Dundee
Cognitive Behavioural Psychotherapy.......PGDip 8PT
Psychological Therapy in Primary Care ....MSc 12FT

Durham University
Developmental Psychopathology.......MSc 12FT

University of East Anglia
Focusing Oriented Psychotherapy.......PGCert 12PT
Occupational Therapy.......MSc 24FT

University of East London
Art Psychotherapy .... MSc 36PT/PGDip 24PT/PGCert 12PT
Child Psychoanalytic Psychotherapy Prof Doc (D. Ch. Psych. Psych.).......DProf by taught 48FT 60PT
Counselling and Psychotherapy ....MA 36PT/PGDip 24PT
Couple and Individual Psychodynamic Counselling and Psychotherapy ....PGDip 24PT/PGCert 12PT
International Humanitarian Psychosocial Consultation by Distance Learning.......MSc 36DL
Psychoanalytic Observational Studies (M7) ....MA 36PT/PGDip 24PT
Psychoanalytic Studies (M16) ....MA 12FT 24PT/PGDip 8FT 16PT/PGCert 4FT 8PT
Psychosexual and Relationship Therapy ....MSc 12FT
Psychosynthesis Counselling ....PGDip 24PT
Psychosynthesis Psychotherapy ....MA 12PT
Psychosynthesis Studies ....PGCert 12PT
Systemic Psychotherapy Prof. Doc ....DProf by taught 48PT
The Development of Couple Psychoanalytic Psychotherapy .... PGCert 12PT
Theory and Skills of Psychodynamic Couple and Individual Counselling and Psychotherapy ....GradCert 12PT
Therapeutic Communication with Children ....PGCert 12PT

Edge Hill University
Cognitive Behavioural Psychotherapy.......MSc 36-72PT

University of Edinburgh
Cognitive Behaviour Therapy for Children and Young People .... PGCert 24PT
Psychotherapy and Counselling (Interpersonal Dialogue)............ DPsychSc by taught 36FT

University of Essex
Analytical Psychology (Professional Doctorate)...... Prof Doc 24PT
Foundations of Psychoanalytic Psychotherapy ....MA 24PT
Jungian and Post-Jungian Studies ....MA 12FT 24PT
Management and Organisational Dynamics.......... MA 12FT 24PT
Psychoanalytic Psychotherapy (Professional Doctorate) Prof Doc 24PT
Psychoanalytic Social Observation ....MA 12FT 24PT
Psychoanalytic Studies.......MA 12FT 24PT
Psychoanalytic Studies with English for Academic Purposes .... Diploma 9FT
Psychodynamic Counselling.......MA 12FT 24PT
Psychodynamic Psychotherapy (Professional Doctorate) Prof Doc 24PT
Psychosocial Studies.......MA 12FT 24PT
Refugee Care.......MA 12FT

University of Exeter
Clinical Practice.......DClinPrac 42DL
Clinical Psychology.......DClinPsy by taught 36FT
Mindfulness-based Cognitive Therapies and Approaches............. PGCert 12PT/PGDip 24PT/MSc 24-36PT
Psychological Therapies.......MSc 24PT

Glasgow Caledonian University
Psychodynamic Counselling and Therapeutic Practice.........PGDip 12-24FT

Goldsmiths, University of London
Art Psychotherapy.......PGDip 24FT 36PT/MA 32FT 48PT
Certificate in Humanistic and Psychodynamic Counselling.......... PGCert 12PT

University of Greenwich
Therapeutic Counselling.......MSc 36PT

University of Hertfordshire
Cognitive Behavioural Therapy.......MSc 24PT/PGDip 24PT
Contemporary Therapeutic Counselling......MA 36PT/PGDip 36PT

King's College London
Cognitive Behavioural Therapies.. PGDip 12FT 24PT/PGCert 12FT
Cognitive Behavioural Therapy (CBT) for Psychosis... PGDip 12FT/PGCert 12FT
Family Therapy.......MSc 12FT 24PT

Leeds Metropolitan University
Art Psychotherapy Practice.......MA 24FT 36PT
Counselling & Psychotherapy.......PGDip 24PT
Psychological Therapies.......MA 48PT
Psychotherapy.......MA 48PT

University of Leeds
Psychoanalytic Observational Studies........MSc 36PT/PGDip 24PT
Systemic Family Therapy ....MSc 24PT

University of Leicester
Professional Studies (Cognitive Behavioural Therapy) .... PGCert 12PT
Professional Studies (Supervision).......PGCert 12PT
Professional Studies in Counselling and Psychotherapy......PGDip 24PT/MA 12PT
Psychodynamic Counselling and Psychotherapy .... PGDip 24PT/MA 12PT

Liverpool John Moores University
Counselling and Psychotherapeutic Practice ....MA 12PT

London South Bank University
Cognitive Behavioural Therapy (CBT).......MSc 36PT

National University of Ireland, Maynooth
Behaviour and Cognitive Therapies.......MA 12FT 24PT

Middlesex University
Lowenfeld Projective Play Therapy ....MSc 48PT/PGDip 36PT/PGCert 24PT
Psychoanalysis ....MA 12FT 24PT

Newcastle University
Cognitive Behavioural Therapy.......PGDip 12FT 24PT
High Intensity Psychological Therapies.......Diploma 12FT
Low Intensity Psychological Therapies.......PGCert 12FT

Northumbria University
Occupational Therapy..................Professional Doctorate 48-72PT
Occupational Therapy (Pre Registration).......MSc 24FT

University of Nottingham
Cognitive Behavioural Therapy....................MSc 30PT/PGDip 18PT

University of Oxford
Mindfulness Based Cognitive Therapy.......MSt 24PT

Queen Margaret University, Edinburgh
Cognitive Behavioural Therapy.............. PGDip 24PT/PGCert 12PT

Queen's University Belfast
Cognition and Culture.......MA 12FT 30PT
Cognitive Behavioural Practice.......PGCert 12PT
Cognitive Behavioural Therapy.......PGDip 12PT

University of Roehampton
Counselling and Psychotherapy ....MSc 36PT
Dance Movement Psychotherapy ....MA 24FT 36PT
Dramatherapy.......MA 24FT 36PT
Integrative Counselling and Psychotherapy.......MA 36PT
Music Therapy.......MA 24FT 36PT
Play Therapy.......MA 24FT
Applied Music Psychology.......PGCert 6FT 24PT
Stress and Health.......PGDip 9FT 24PT

Royal Holloway, University of London
Postgraduate Diploma/Certificate in Cognitive Behavioural Therapy (CBT).......PGDip 18PT/PGCert 18PT

University of Salford
Applied Psychology (Therapies) MSc 12FT 36PT/PGDip 8FT 24PT/PGCert 4FT 9PT
Cognitive Behaviour Therapy ....PGCert 12PT
Cognitive Behavioural Psychotherapy.......MSc 36PT/PGDip 24PT/PGCert 12PT
Counselling and Psychotherapy Studies (Professional Training)... MSc 36PT/PGDip 24PT
Psycho-Oncology .... MSc 36PT/PGDip 24PT/PGCert 12PT

Sheffield Hallam University
Cognitive Analytic Therapy Practitioner.... MSc VAPT/PGDip VAPT
Sexual and Relationship Psychotherapy.....MSc 48PT/PGDip 24PT

University of South Wales
Art Psychotherapy.......MA 36PT

Behaviour Analysis and Therapy MSc 12FT 24PT/PGCert 4FT 8PT/PGDip 8FT 16PT
Buddhist Studies .... PGCert 12DL/PGDip 24DL/MA 36DL
Evaluation Studies.......PGCert 9-12DL
Music Therapy.......MA 36PT
Systemic Psychotherapy.......MSc 24PT

University of Southampton
Cognitive Behavioural Therapy.......PGCert 3FT
Cognitive Therapy for Severe Mental Health Problems........PGDip 12PT

Staffordshire University
Psychotherapeutic Counselling ....MSc 36PT/PGDip 24PT

University of Surrey
Practitioner Doctorate in Psychotherapeutic and Counselling Psychology.......PsychD by taught 36FT 48-60PT
Psychological Therapy: Interpersonal Psychotherapy (IPT) .... Diploma 12PT

Swansea University
Developmental and Therapeutic Play.......MA 12FT 36PT/PGDip 12FT 24PT/PGCert 12FT 12PT

Trinity College Dublin - the University of Dublin
Child and Adolescent Psychoanalytic Psychotherapy.... MSc 24PT
Cognitive Psychotherapy.......MSc 24PT PGDip 12PT
Psychoanalytic Psychotherapy.......MSc 36PT
Psychoanalytic Studies.......MPhil 12FT

UCL - University College London
CYP IAPT Therapy.......PGDip 12FT
Cognitive Behavioural Therapy for Children and Young People.... MSc 24-36PT/PGDip 24PT/PGCert 12PT
Cognitive Neuroscience.......MSc 12FT 24PT/PGDip 9FT
Cognitive Neuroscience (MRes).......MRes 12FT
Developmental Neuroscience and Psychopathology..... MSc 24FT
Low Intensity Cognitive Behavioural Interventions......PGDip 9FT
Psychoanalytic Developmental Psychology...........MSc 12FT 24PT
Theoretical Psychoanalytic Studies.......MSc 12FT 24PT

University of West London
Clinical Hypnotherapy............PGCert 12PT/PGDip 12PT/MSc 12PT

University of the West of England, Bristol
Psychological Therapy (Cognitive Behaviour Therapy).... Diploma 24PT

University of Worcester
Psychodrama Psychotherapy.......MSc 60PT/PGDip 48PT/PGCert 24PT
Psychological Therapies.......MSc 24PT

York St John University
Counselling & Psychotherapy (Practitioner Route) ....MA 24PT
Counselling & Psychotherapy Studies ....MA 12FT

Psychotherapy
Research Courses

Bangor University
Clinical Psychology.......DClinPsy 36FT

Birkbeck, University of London
Child and Adolescent Psychotherapy...........DPsychotherapy 48PT

University of East Anglia
Occupational Therapy...........PhD 36FT 72PT/MPhil 24FT 48PT/MSc by research 12FT 24PT

University of Essex
Psychoanalytic Studies...PhD 36FT 72PT/MPhil 24FT 48PT/MA by research 12FT 24PT
Refugee Care.......PhD 36FT 72PT/MPhil 24FT 48PT

University of Exeter
Clinical Practice.......DClinPrac 42DL
Doctorate in Clinical Psychology.......DClinPsy 36FT

Goldsmiths, University of London
Art Psychotherapy...........PhD 36-48FT 48-72PT/MPhil 24FT 36PT MRes 12FT 24PT
Psychoanalytic Studies....MPhil 36-48FT 48-72PT/PhD 24FT 36PT

University of Hertfordshire
Arts Psychotherapies and Counselling in Health .PhD 36FT 72PT/MRes 12FT 24PT/MPhil 24FT 48PT

University of Leicester
Research in Counselling and Psychotherapy......MPhil 12FT 24PT/PhD 36FT 72PT

Manchester Metropolitan University
Psychoanalytical Studies (by Research).......MSc by research 12FT

The Open University
Counselling and PsychotherapyPhD 36FT 72PT variableDL/MPhil 15FT 24PT variableDL

Queen's University Belfast
Cognition and Culture.......PhD 36FT 72PT

University of Roehampton
Psychotherapy and Counselling (Professional Doctorate)............. PsychD 60-72PT

UCL - University College London
Cognitive Neuroscience.......PhD 36FT 60PT

Section sponsored by

BPP
UNIVERSITY
COLLEGE

Business and social sciences
www.prospects.ac.uk/findcourses **POSTGRADUATE DIRECTORY 475**

Psychology

Cognitive, Perceptual and Brain Sciences.............. PhD 36FT 60PT
Psychotherapy (Child and Adolescent Psychoanalytic
Psychotherapy)...DPsychotherapy 72PT

Social psychology
Taught Courses

Bangor University
Criminology and Sociology .... MA 12FT 21-30PT/PGDip 9FT
17-21PT/PGCert 5FT 12-21PT
International Social Work MA 12FT 24-30PT/PGDip 9FT 17-21PT/
PGCert 5FT 12-21PT

University of Bath
Global Political Economy: transformations and policy analysis ...
MRes 12FT 24-36PT

University of Bedfordshire
Intercultural Communication .... MA 12FT 24PT

Birkbeck, University of London
Psychodynamics of Human Development......................MSc 24PT/
PGDip 24PT
Psychosocial Studies.. MA 12FT 24PT

University of Brighton
Community Psychology ....

Brunel University
Cross-Cultural Psychology......................................MSc 12FT 30PT

Bucks New University
Community Psychology .... MSc 12FT 24PT

University of Cambridge
Modern Society and Global Transformations ....MPhil 9FT
Social Anthropology ....PhD by taught 11FT
Social and Developmental Psychology ....MPhil 9FT

University of Central Lancashire
Conflict and Violence Minimisation ....PGCert 24PT
Counselling and Psychotherapy ....MSc 36PT/PGDip 24PT
Personality Disorder (Practice Development) .... MSc 36-60PT/
PGDip 24PT
Personality Disorder (Research).......MSc 36-60PT/PGDip 12-24PT
Psychology.......MSc 12FT 24PT/PGDip 9FT 24PT/PGCert 9FT 24PT
Psychology of Child Development .... MSc 12FT 24PT/PGDip 9FT
24PT/PGCert 9FT 24PT
Psychology of Sport and Exercise ....MSc 12FT 24PT/PGDip 9FT
24PT/PGCert 9FT 24PT
Social Psychology ....MSc 12FT 24PT

University of Chester
Conflict Transformation (Work Based and Integrative Studies)....
MA 24-72PT/MSc 24-72PT/PGDip 24-60PT/PGCert 12-36PT
Family and Child Psychology ...MSc 12FT 24PT/PGDip 12FT 24PT/
PGCert 12FT 12-24PT
Psychology (Conversion)............ MSc 12FT 24PT/PGDip 12FT 24PT

University of Chichester
Psychology of Sport and Exercise .... MSc 12-15FT 24-36PT/PGDip
9-12FT 18-24PT/PGCert 6-9FT 12-18PT

City University London
Organisational Behaviour ....MSc 12FT 24PT
Organisational Psychology ....MSc 12FT 24PT
Research Methods and Psychology..........................MSc 12FT 24PT
Social Research Methods ....MSc 12FT 24PT

University College Cork
Group Facilitation...MA 24PT

University of Dundee
Developmental Psychology .... MSc 12FT
Gender, Culture and Society ....MLitt 12FT
Psychological Research Methods ....MSc 12FT

Durham University
Developmental Psychopathology ....MSc 12FT
Research Methods (Developmental Psychology) ....MA 12FT

University of East Anglia
Child and Family Psychology ....MSc 12FT 24PT
Conflicts in Intercultural Communication .... MA 12FT 24PT

University of Essex
Analytical Psychology .... Prof Doc 24PT
Foundations of Psychoanalytic Psychotherapy ....MA 24PT
Jungian and Post-Jungian Studies .... MA 12FT 24PT
Management and Organisational Dynamics........... MA 12FT 24PT
Psychoanalytic Psychotherapy (Professional Doctorate) Prof Doc
24PT
Psychoanalytic Social Observation .... MA 12FT 24PT
Psychoanalytic Studies... MA 12FT 24PT
Psychodynamic Counselling.. MA 12FT 24PT
Psychodynamic Psychotherapy .... Prof Doc 24PT
Psychology...MSc 12FT
Psychosocial Studies .... MA 12FT 24PT
Refugee Care...MA 12FT
Research Methods in Psychology ....MSc 12FT

University of Exeter
Social and Organisational Psychology ....MSc 12FT 24PT

University of Glasgow
Drugs and Alcohol Studies.......MSc 12FT 24PT/PGDip 12FT 24PT/
PGCert 12PT

University of Gloucestershire
Psychology in Practice ....MSc 12FT 24PT/PGAdvDip 8FT 20PT/
PGCert 4FT 8PT

University of Greenwich
Applied Psychology Research Methods .... MSc 12FT

Heriot-Watt University
Business Psychology .... MSc 12FT 24-84PT 12-84DL/PGDip 9FT
15-48PT 9-48DL/PGCert 6FT 12-48PT 6-48DL

University of Kent
Group Processes and Intergroup Relations............. MSc 12FT 24PT
Social and Applied Psychology..................................MSc 12FT 24PT

Kingston University
Developmental Psychology......................................MRes 12FT 24PT

Lancaster University
Developmental Psychology .... MSc 12FT 24PT
Psychological Research Methods .... MSc 12FT 24PT
Psychology of Advertising .... MSc 12FT 24PT
Social Psychology.. MSc 12FT 24PT

Leeds Metropolitan University
Mental Health Practice .... MSc 24PT
Mental Health Studies .... PGCert 24PT/PGDip 24PT

University of Leeds
International Social Transformation........................... MA 12FT 24PT

London School of Economics and Political Science (LSE)
Organisational and Social Psychology .... MSc 12FT 24PT
Social and Cultural Psychology .... MSc 12FT 24PT
Social and Public Communication .... MSc 12FT 24PT

Manchester Metropolitan University
Community Psychology/ Community Psychology (by Research)..
MSc 12FT 24-36PT/PGDip 12FT 24-36PT/PGCert 12FT 24PT

University of St Mark and St John
Creative Conflict Transformation through the Arts..........MA 20FT

Oxford Brookes University
Developmental Psychology ....MRes 12FT 24PT

University of Oxford
Evidence-Based Social Intervention................ MPhil 21FT/MSc 9FT
Sociology .... MPhil 22FT/MSc 9FT

Plymouth University
Psychology.. MSc 12FT 24PT/PGDip 9FT

Queen's University Belfast
Communication .....MSc 12FT 36PT/PGDip 12FT 24PT/PGCert 6FT
12PT/AdvPGDip 4FT 12PT

University of Roehampton
Applied Psychological Research ....PGDip 9FT 24PT

Royal Holloway, University of London
Applied Social Psychology .... MSc 12FT

University of Salford
Applied Psychology (Therapies) MSc 12FT 36PT/PGDip 8FT 24PT/
PGCert 4FT 9PT
Social Work .... MA 24FT 36PT

Sheffield Hallam University
Developmental Psychology.....................................MSc 12FT 24-36PT

University of Sheffield
Social Work...MA 24FT
Sociology .... MA 12FT 24PT

University of Southampton
Research Methods in Psychology .... MSc 12FT
Social Work.. MSc 24FT/PGDip 9FT 21PT
Sociology and Social Policy ....MSc 12FT 24PT/PGDip 9FT 21PT
Sociology and Social Research ....MSc 12FT 24PT/PGDip 9FT 21PT

University of St Andrews
Behavioural and Neural Sciences ....MPhil 12FT 24PT

University of Stirling
Behavioural Science for Management.......... MSc 12FT/PGDip 9FT
Psychology of Faces.......................MSc 12FT 24PT/PGDip 9FT 18PT
Social Work Studies.. MSc 22FT

University of Strathclyde
Research Methods in Psychology ....MRes 12FT

University of Surrey
Social Psychology .... MSc 12FT 24PT

University of Sussex
Applied Social Psychology .... MSc 12FT 24PT

UCL - University College London
Developmental Psychology and Clinical Practice..........MSc 24FT/
PGDip 12FT

York St John University
Community & Critical Social Psychology .... MSc 12FT 24PT

Social psychology
Research Courses

Bangor University
Ageing and Cognitive Health .... PhD 36FT 60PT
Ageing and Dementia Studies ....MSc by research 12FT 24PT
PhD 36FT 60PT/MPhil 24FT 48PT

Sociology ....PhD 36FT 60PT/MPhil 12-24FT 24-36PT

Bath Spa University
Psychology............. PhD 24-60FT 36-72PT/MPhil 18-36FT 30-48PT

University of Bath
Global Political Economy: transformations and policy analysis
(delivered collaboratively w .... MRes 12FT 24-36PT

Birkbeck, University of London
Child and Adolescent Psychotherapy...........DPsychotherapy 48PT
Psychosocial Studies.................... PhD 24FT 36PT/MPhil 24FT 36PT

University of Central Lancashire
Sociology, Ethnicity & Human Rights, Criminology . PhD 30-48FT
66-84PT/MPhil 18-36FT 42-60PT/MA by research 12FT 24PT

University of East Anglia
Psychology..................................... PhD 36FT 72PT/MPhil 24FT 48PT

University of Essex
Psychoanalytic Studies...PhD 36FT 72PT/MPhil 24FT 48PT/MA by
research 12FT 24PT
Psychology..................................... PhD 36FT 72PT/MPhil 24FT 49PT
Refugee Care.................................. PhD 36FT 72PT/MPhil 24FT 48PT

University of Gloucestershire
Psychology and Behavioural Sciences............................MRes 12FT

Heriot-Watt University
Applied Psychology .... PhD 36FT 48PT/MPhil 24FT 36PT

University of Kent
Social Psychology.... PhD 36FT 60PT/MPhil 24FT 36PT/New Route
PhD 48FT/MSc by research 12FT 24PT

London School of Economics and Political Science (LSE)
Social Psychology .... PhD 36-48FT/MPhil 36-48FT

Loughborough University
Social Psychology.......................... PhD 36FT 60PT/MPhil 24FT 36PT

Manchester Metropolitan University
Community Psychology (by Research) ....MSc by research 12FT

The Open University
Applied Psychology .... PhD 36FT 72PT variableDL/
MPhil 15FT 24PT variableDL
Mind, Meaning and Rationality .... PhD 36FT 72PT variableDL/
MPhil 15FT 24PT variableDL
Narrative, Discursive and Psychosocial Research ....PhD 36FT
72PT variableDL/MPhil 15FT 24PT variableDL

Plymouth University
Behaviour .... PhD 36FT/MPhil 24FT

Sports psychology
Taught Courses

Aberystwyth University
Exercise and Health Research......MSc 12FT 24PT/PGDip 9FT 21PT

Bangor University
Applied Sport Science.. MA 12FT 36PT
Applied Sport Science (Outdoor Activities)............. MA 12FT 36PT
Applied Sport Science and Outdoor Activities.......MSc 12FT 36PT
Applied Sport and Exercise Physiology ....MSc 12FT 36PT/
PGDip 8FT
Applied Sport and Exercise Psychology .... MA 12FT 36PT
MSc 12FT 36PT
Exercise Rehabilitation.................... MA 12FT 36PT MSc 12FT 36PT
Sport and Exercise Physiology..................................MRes 12FT 36PT
Sport and Exercise Psychology (BPS Accredited) ... MSc 12FT 36PT
Sport and Exercise Sciences.................................MRes 12FT 36PT

University of Bedfordshire
Physical Activity, Nutrition and Health Promotion........MSc 12FT/
PGDip 12FT/PGCert 12FT
Sports Performance ....MSc 12FT/PGDip 12FT/PGCert 12FT

Bournemouth University
Managing Sport Performance............................MSc 12-15FT 24PT

University of Brighton
Exercise and Health Science ....MSc 12FT 24PT/PGDip 12FT 24PT/
PGCert 12FT 24PT
Sport and Exercise Science.......MSc 12FT 24PT/PGDip 12FT 24PT/
PGCert 12FT 24PT

Brunel University
Sport Sciences (Sport Psychology) ....MSc 12FT 24-36PT
Sport and Exercise Psychology...........................MSc 12FT 24-48PT

Bucks New University
Health, Exercise & Wellbeing.....................................MSc 12FT 24PT

Cardiff Metropolitan University
Physical Activity and Health......... MSc 12FT 24-36PT/PGDip 12FT
24-36PT/PGCert 12FT 24-36PT
Sport & Exercise Medicine .... MSc 12FT 12-36PT/PGDip 12FT
12-36PT
Sport Psychology / Applied Sport Psychology.......MSc 12FT 36PT/
PGDip 12FT 36PT/PGCert 12FT 36PT

University of Central Lancashire
Psychology of Sport and Exercise ....MSc 12FT 24PT/PGDip 9FT
24PT/PGCert 9FT 24PT
Sport and Exercise Biomechanics.......MSc 12FT 24PT/PGDip 12FT
24PT

Business and social sciences
476 POSTGRADUATE DIRECTORY www.prospects.ac.uk/findcourses

Section sponsored by

BPP
UNIVERSITY
COLLEGE

Psychology

Sport and Exercise Physiology....................................MSc 12FT 24PT/
PGDip 12FT 24PT
Sport and Exercise Psychology...................................MSc 12FT 24PT/
PGDip 9FT 24PT/PGCert 9FT 24PT
Sport and Exercise Science........ MSc 12FT 24PT/PGDip 12FT 24PT
Sports Therapy .... MSc 18FT 36PT/PGDip 18FT 24PT
Sports Therapy Professional Practice .... MSc up to 24FT

University of Chester
Sports Sciences (with named pathways)..... MA 12FT 24PT/PGDip
12FT 24PT/PGCert 12FT 12-24PT

University of Chichester
Psychology of Sport and Exercise.... MSc 12-15FT 24-36PT/PGDip
9-12FT 18-24PT/PGCert 6-9FT 12-18PT
Sport and Exercise Physiology....................................MSc 11FT 22+PT
Sport and Exercise Psychology......................MSc 12-15FT 24-36PT

Coventry University
Sport and Exercise Nutrition .... PGCert 12 MinPT

University of Dundee
Sports and Biomechanical Medicine .... MSc 12FT
Sports and Biomechanical Medicine (with externally arranged
project).. MSc 24PT
Sports and Biomechanical Medicine (with in-house project) MSc
24PT

University of East London
Sports Psychology .... MSc 12FT 24PT/PGDip 8FT 16PT/
PGCert 4FT 8PT

Edinburgh Napier University
Sport Performance Enhancement......................MSc 12FT 24-48PT

University of Edinburgh
Performance Psychology ....PGDip 9FT 12-48PT/
MSc 12FT 24-72PT

University of Exeter
Sport and Health Sciences .... MSc 12FT 24PT

University of Glasgow
Sport & Exercise Medicine ....MSc(MedSci) 12FT 24PT
Sport & Exercise Science...MSc 12FT 24PT

University of Gloucestershire
Coaching Science ....MSc 12FT 24PT
Psychology of Sport and Exercise ....MSc 12FT 24PT
Sport and Exercise Psychology...................................MSc 12FT 24PT

University of Hull
Health Psychology.. MSc 12FT

Keele University
Psychology..MSc 12FT 24PT

Leeds Metropolitan University
Psychology of Sport & Exercise.. MSc 12FT
Sport Coaching...MSc 12FT 24PT
Sport and Exercise Biomechanics........MSc 12FT 24PT/PGCert 4FT
12PT/PGDip 12FT 24PT
Sport and Exercise Psychology .... MSc 12FT
Sport, Law & Society.. MA 12FT 24PT

University of Lincoln
Sport Science ....MSc 12FT 24PT

Liverpool John Moores University
Clinical Exercise Physiology .... MSc 12FT
Sports Physiology ....MSc 12FT 24PT/PGDip 12FT 18PT/
PGCert 6FT 12PT

London South Bank University
Applied and Interdisciplinary Sports Science .... MSc 18FT

Loughborough University
Sport and Exercise Psychology.. MSc 12FT

Manchester Metropolitan University
Biomedical Science featuring Exercise and Health options ... MSc
12FT 24-36PT
Exercise and Sport.. MA/MSc 12FT 24-36PT
Exercise and Sport - Biomechanics ....MS 12FT 24-36PT
Exercise and Sport - Coaching Studies...............MSc 12FT 24-36PT
Exercise and Sport - Physiology ....MSc 12FT 24-36PT
Exercise and Sport - Sport Development ....MSc 12FT 24-36PT
Exercise and Sport -Psychology ....MSc 12FT 24-36PT
MA Exercise and Sport- Sport Development ..... MA 12FT 24-36PT

Middlesex University
Performance Analysis...MSc 12FT 24PT

University of Northampton
Sport and Exercise Psychology...................................MSc 12FT 24PT

Northumbria University
Professional Practice in Sport Coaching ....MSc 12FT 24PT
Psychology of Sport and Exercise Behaviour..........MSc 12FT 24PT
Public Policy ....MSc 12FT 28PT
Sport Marketing..MSc 12FT 24PT
Sport and Exercise Psychology .... MSc 12FT
Strength and Conditioning ....MSc 12FT 24DL

Nottingham Trent University
MSc International Performance Analysis of Sport.......... MSc 24FT

University of Nottingham
Psychology (Conversion Course)...PGDip 9FT
Rehabilitation Psychology...MSc 12FT 24PT

University of Portsmouth
Clinical Exercise Science ....MSc 12FT 24PT
Sport and Exercise Psychology...................................MSc 12FT 24PT
Sport and Exercise Psychology (BPS accredited)....MSc 12FT 24PT

Queen's University Belfast
Psychology of Performance Enhancement in Sport and Health ...
MSc 12FT 24PT

University of Roehampton
Applied Psychological Research ....PGCert 6FT 24PT
Biomechanics .... PGDip 9FT 24-48PT
Applied Psychological Research ....PGDip 9FT 24PT
Attachment Studies .... PGDip 6-12FT 12PT
Audiovisual Translation ....PGDip 9FT 24PT
Health Sciences..PGDip 9FT 24PT
Obesity: Risks and Prevention ....PGDip 9FT 24PT
Special and Inclusive Education..................... PGDip 9FT 24-48PT
Sport Psychology .... PGDip 9FT 24-48PT
Sport and Exercise Physiology.............................PGDip 9FT 24PT
Sport and Exercise Science................................PGDip 9FT 24-48PT
Stress and Health ....PGDip 9FT 24PT
Sport and Exercise Psychology...........................MSc 12FT 24-48PT

University of Salford
Applied Psychology (Therapies) MSc 12FT 36PT/PGDip 8FT 24PT/
PGCert 4FT 9PT

Sheffield Hallam University
Leading and Managing Physical Education and Youth Sport.........
MSc 3PT
Leading and Managing Sport Development ....MSc 24PT/PGDip
16PT/PGCert 8PT

Sport and Exercise Psychology...................................MSc 12FT 24PT
Sports Engineering...MSc 12FT 24PT

Southampton Solent University
Sport and Development .... MA 24FT 12PT

St Mary's University College, Twickenham
Applied Sport Psychology.......MA 12FT 24PT/PGDip 24PT/PGCert
12PT

Staffordshire University
Applied Sport and Exercise Psychology ....PGCert 7DL/
PGDip 14DL/MSc 24DL
Sport and Exercise Psychology ....PGCert 7DL/PGDip 14DL/MSc
24DL

University of Stirling
Performance Coaching.......... MSc 24PT/PGDip 24PT/PGCert 12PT
Psychology Applied to Health .....MSc 12FT 24PT/PGDip 9FT 18PT
Psychology of Sport ...MSc 9FT 24PT/PGDip 9FT 24PT/PGCert 6FT
12PT
Sport Nutrition (International Olympic Committee Upgrade)......
MSc 6FT 12PT
Sports Coaching...............................MSc 9FT 24PT/PGDip 6FT 24PT/
PGCert 6FT 12PT

Trinity College Dublin - the University of Dublin
Exercise Physiology ....MSc 24PT/PGDip 12PT

University of Ulster
Sport and Exercise Psychology....MSc 12FT 36PT/PGDip 9FT 18PT

University of the West of England, Bristol
Sport and Exercise Psychology...................................MSc 12FT 24PT

University of Winchester
Sport and Society .MA 12FT 24PT/PGDip 12FT 24PT/PGCert 12FT
24PT

Sports psychology
Research Courses

University of Aberdeen
Psychology..... PhD 36FT/MPhil 24FT/MSc by research 12FT/MRes
12FT

Aberystwyth University
Sport & Exercise Science ....MPhil 12FT 24PT PhD 36FT 60PT

Bangor University
Sport, Health and Exercise Sciences ....MPhil 12FT/PhD 36FT

University of Cumbria
Sports Science; Sports History/Sociology; Outdoor Studies........M
Phil 36FT 60PT 60DL/PhD 48FT 72PT 72DL

University of Essex
Sports and Exercise Medicine...PhD 36FT 72PT/MPhil 24FT 48PT/
MSc by research 12FT 24PT
Sports and Exercise Science......PhD 36FT 72PT/MPhil 24FT 48PT/
MSc by research 12FT 24PT

University of Exeter
Sport and Health Sciences .... PhD 48FT 84PT/MPhil 36FT 60PT

Loughborough University
Sport and Exercise Sciences .... PhD 36FT 60PT/MPhil 24FT 36PT

Nottingham Trent University
Sport and Exercise Psychology...............................MRes 12FT 24PT

University of Stirling
Sports Studies .... PhD 36FT 72PT/MPhil 12FT 24PT

Section sponsored by

BPP
UNIVERSITY
COLLEGE

Business and social sciences
www.prospects.ac.uk/findcourses **POSTGRADUATE DIRECTORY 477**

Social sciences

African studies
Taught Courses

University of Aberdeen
Sex, Gender, Violence: Contemporary Critical Approaches .... MSc 12FT 24PT/PGDip 9FT 18PT

University of Birmingham
African Studies..MRes 12FT 24PT
African Studies.......................... MA 12FT 24PT/PGDip 9FT
Social Research (African Studies)................................ MA 12FT 24PT

University of Bradford
African Peace and Conflict Studies .... MA 12FT 24PT

University of Cambridge
African Studies...MPhil 9FT
Innovation, Strategy and Organisation ....MPhil 9FT

University of East Anglia
The Arts of Africa, Oceania and the Americas .... MA 12FT 24PT

University of Edinburgh
Africa and International Development....................MSc 12FT 24PT
Africa and International Development (Distance Learning) ....
PGCert 12DL/PGCert 24DL
African Studies ....MSc 12FT 24PT

University of Exeter
Applied Ecology .... MSc 12FT
Conservation and Biodiversity .... MSc 12FT
Evolutionary and Behavioural Ecology.............................. MSc 12FT

Goldsmiths, University of London
Contemporary African Theatre & Performance.................MA 12FT

University of Leeds
Global Development and Africa .... MA 12FT 24PT

University of Oxford
African Studies...MSc 9FT

University of Portsmouth
Francophone Africa .... MA 12FT 24PT

School of Oriental and African Studies - SOAS
African Politics..MSc 12FT 24-36PT
African Studies.. MA 12FT 24-36PT
Economics (with Reference to Africa)......................MSc 12FT 24PT
History .... MA 12FT 24PT
History: Asia/Africa .... MA 12FT 24-36PT

University of St Andrews
Social Anthropology with African Studies ....MRes 12FT

Staffordshire University
Journalism... MA 12FT 48PT

African studies
Research Courses

School of Advanced Study, University of London
Middle Eastern and African Studies ...PhD 36FT 72PT/MPhil 12FT 36PT

University of Birmingham
African Studies .... PhD 36FT 72PT/MA by research 12FT 24PT
Human Interface Technologies......................PhD 36FT/MPhil 12FT

University of East Anglia
Sainsbury Research Unit for the Arts of Africa, Oceania and the Americas ....PhD 36FT 72PT/MPhil 24FT 48PT/
MA by research 12FT 24PT

University of Edinburgh
African Studies .... PhD 36FT 72PT/MPhil 24FT 48PT

The Open University
Asian drivers and Africa ... PhD 36FT 72PT variableDL/MPhil 15FT 24PT variableDL
Empire and Postcolonial studies .... PhD 36FT 72PT variableDL/
MPhil 15FT 24PT variableDL

American studies
Taught Courses

University of Birmingham
Transatlantic Studies...................................... MA 12FT 24PT
US Foreign Policy ....MRes 12FT 24PT

University of Cambridge
American Literature..MPhil 9FT

University College Cork
English (American Literature & Film)....................................MA 12FT

University of East Anglia
American History... MA 12FT 24PT
American Literature .... MA 12FT 24PT
American Studies .... MA 12FT 24PT
American Studies and Film Studies.......................... MA 12FT 24PT
The Arts of Africa, Oceania and the Americas .... MA 12FT 24PT

University of Edinburgh
American History..MSc 12FT 24PT
American Literature ....MSc(Res) 12FT 24PT

University of Glasgow
American Studies ....MLitt 12FT 24PT

University of Hertfordshire
English Literature: Modern Literary Cultures.........MA 12FT 24PT/
PGDip 12FT 24PT/PGCert 12FT 24PT

Keele University
Humanities (American Studies)..............................MRes 12FT 24PT

University of Kent
American Studies .... MA 12FT 24PT
English and American Literature .... MA 12FT 24PT
English and American Literature (Paris option).................MA 12FT

King's College London
American Studies .... MA 12FT 24PT

University of Leeds
American Literature and Culture................................ MA 12FT 24PT

University of Leicester
American Foreign Policy ...MA 12FT 24PT 24DL/PGDip 12FT 24PT

University of Manchester
American Studies .... MA 12FT 24PT
English and American Studies .... MA 12FT 24PT

University of Nottingham
American Studies .... MA 12FT 24-48PT
American Studies (History).......................... MA 12FT 24-36PT
American Studies (Literature)......................... MA 12FT 24-36PT
American Studies (Visual Culture)..................... MA 12FT 24-48PT
American Studies with Canadian Literature ..... MA 12FT 24-36PT
American Studies with Canadian Studies.......... MA 12FT 24-36PT
American Studies with European Study............ MA 12FT 24-36PT
English and American Studies .... MA 12FT 24-36PT

University of Sheffield
English Literature (American Literature pathway). MA 12FT 24PT

UCL - University College London
United States Studies: History and Politics .... MA 12FT 24PT

American studies
Research Courses

University of Birmingham
American and Canadian Studies ....PhD 36FT 72PT/
MA by research 12FT 24PT
US Foreign Policy ....MPhil(B) 12FT 24PT

University of Central Lancashire
American StudiesPhD 18-36FT 42-60PT/MPhil 18-36FT 42-60PT/
MA by research 12FT 24PT

University of East Anglia
American Studies ....PhD 36FT 72PT/MPhil 24FT 48PT/MA by research 12FT
Sainsbury Research Unit for the Arts of Africa, Oceania and the Americas ....PhD 36FT 72PT/MPhil 24FT 48PT/
MA by research 12FT 24PT

University of Hull
American Studies .... PhD 36FT 60PT/MPhil 24FT 36PT

Institute for the Study of the Americas, School of Advanced Study, University of London
US Presidency ....PhD 36FT/MPhil 12FT
United States Studies...........................PhD 36FT/MPhil 24FT

Keele University
American Studies .... PhD 24-48FT 48-84PT/
MPhil 12-24FT 24-36PT

University of Kent
American Studies ....PhD 36FT 60PT/MPhil 24FT 36PT/MA by research 12FT 24PT

King's College London
American Studies Research.. MPhil 24FT 36PT/PhD 36FT 48-72PT

University of Leeds
American Studies ....PhD 36-42FT/MPhil 24FT/
MA by research 12FT

University of Manchester
English and American Studies ....PhD 36FT

University of Nottingham
American and Canadian Studies Research Areas.PhD 36FT 72PT/
MPhil 24FT 48PT/MRes 12FT 24PT

University of Sussex
American History and Literature ...... PhD 24-48FT 36-72PT/MPhil 12-36FT 24-48PT

Anthropology
Taught Courses

University of Aberdeen
Archaeology of the North............MSc 12FT 24PT/PGDip 9FT 18PT
Design Anthropology ....MSc 12FT 24PT/PGDip 9FT 18PT
Ethnology and Folklore ....MLitt 12FT 24PT
Materialising the Past ....MSc 12FT 24PT
People and the Environment....................................MSc 12FT 24PT
Social Anthropology of Religion ....MLitt 12FT 24PT
Social Anthropology, Ethnology and Cultural History ....
PGDip 9FT 18PT/MRes 12FT 24PT

Bangor University
Community Development .....PGCert 12PT/PGDip 24PT/MA 36PT

**Comparative Criminology and Criminal Justice .... MA 12FT 24PT/
PGDip 9FT
Criminology and Criminal Justice .... PhD by taught 36FT 72PT/
MPhil 12-24FT 24-36PT/MARes 12FT 24PT
Criminology and Sociology ....MA 12FT 21-30PT/PGDip 9FT
17-21PT/PGCert 5FT 12-21PT
Forensic Linguistics ....MSc 12FT 24PT
Language, Policy and Planning ....MA 12FT 24-48PT/PGDip 8FT/
PGCert 4FT

Birkbeck, University of London
Development Studies and Social Anthropology...MSc 12FT 24PT/
PGDip 12FT 24PT/PGCert 12PT

Bournemouth University
Biological Anthropology......................................MSc 12FT 24PT
Forensic Osteology...MSc 12FT 24PT

University of Bradford
Human Osteology and Palaeopathology ..... MSc 12FT/PGDip 9FT

University of Brighton
Tourism and Social Anthropology......................MSc 12FT 24-72PT/
PGDip 12FT 24-72PT/PGCert 12FT 24-72PT

University of Bristol
Anthropology .... MA 12FT 24PT

Brunel University
Anthropology of Childhood, Youth & Education...MSc 12FT 30PT
Anthropology of International Development and Humanitarian
Assistance...MSc 12FT 30PT
Medical Anthropology...MSc 12FT 30PT
Psychological and Psychiatric Anthropology.........MSc 12FT 30PT
Social Anthropology ....MRes 12FT 30PT

University of Cambridge
Applied Biological Anthropology .... MPhil 11FT
Social Anthropological Analysis...................................... MPhil 11FT
Social Anthropological Research .... MPhil 11FT
Social Anthropology .... PhD by taught 11FT

University of Central Lancashire
Archaeology of Death...MA 12FT

University College Cork
Human Osteoarchaeology...MA 12FT

Cranfield University
Forensic Archaeology and Anthropology ....MSc 12FT 60PT

Cranfield University, Shrivenham
Forensic Archaeology and Anthropology ....MSc 12FT 60PT

Durham University
Energy and Society.. MSc 12FT
Evolutionary Anthropology.. MSc 12FT
Evolutionary Medicine .... MSc 12FT
Medical Anthropology .... MSc 12FT
Research Methods (Anthropology)...............................MA 12FT
Socio-Cultural Anthropology.......................................MA 12FT
Sustainability, Culture and Development......................... MSc 12FT

University of East Anglia
The Arts of Africa, Oceania and the Americas .... MA 12FT 24PT
World Art Studies.. PGDip 12FT 24PT

University of East London
Anthropology ....MSc 12FT 24PT/PGDip 8FT 16PT/
PGCert 4FT 8PT
Anthropology, Human Rights and Justice ....MSc 12FT 24PT/
PGDip 8FT 16PT/PGCert 4FT 8PT

University of Edinburgh
Forensic Anthropology...MSc 12FT 24PT
Medical Anthropology...MSc 12FT 24PT
Social Anthropology ....MSc 12FT 24PT

University of Exeter
Anthrozoology....................................MA 12FT 24PT 24DL
Archaeology..MA 12FT 24PT 36DL
Experimental Archaeology...................................... MA 12FT 24PT

Goldsmiths, University of London
Anthropology and Cultural Politics........................... MA 12FT 24PT
Applied Anthropology & Community Development ....MA 12FT 24PT
Applied Anthropology and Community and Youth WorkMA 12FT 24PT
Development & Rights.. MA 12FT 24PT
Latin American Studies....................................... MA 12FT 24PT
Social Anthropology .... MA 12FT 24PT
Visual Anthropology... MA 12FT 24PT
World Cities and Urban Life................................. MA 12FT 24PT

University of Kent
Anthropology and Conservation .... MA 12FT 24PT
Anthropology of Ethnicity, Nationalism and Identity......MA 12FT 24PT
Environmental Anthropology.........MA 12FT 24PT/MSc 12FT 24PT
Evolution and Human Behaviour (taught jointly with the School
of Psychology) ....MSc 12FT 24PT
Social Anthropology .... MA 12FT 24PT
Social Anthropology and Computing...................... MA 12FT 24PT
Visual Anthropology.. MA 12FT 24PT

Section sponsored by BPP UNIVERSITY COLLEGE

Business and social sciences

478 POSTGRADUATE DIRECTORY www.prospects.ac.uk/findcourses

Social sciences

University of Liverpool
Palaeoanthropology ... MSc 12FT 24PT

London School of Economics and Political Science (LSE)
Anthropology and Development ... MSc 12FT 24PT
Anthropology and Development Management ... MSc 12FT 24PT
Law, Anthropology and Society ... MSc 12FT
Social Anthropology ... MSc 12FT 24PT

University of Manchester
Anthropological Research ... MA 12FT 24PT
Social Anthropology ... MA 12FT 24PT/PGDip 9FT 21PT
Visual Anthropology ... MA 12FT 24 (tbc)PT

The Open University
Integrated Practice in Childhood and Youth .. PGCert 12DL/PGDip variableDL

Oxford Brookes University
Primate Conservation ... MSc 12FT 24PT/PGDip 8FT 16PT 16DL/PGCert 8PT

University of Oxford
Archaeological Science ... MSt 9FT/MSc 12FT
Archaeology ... MSt 9FT/MPhil 24FT
Cognitive & Evolutionary Anthropology ... MSc 12FT
Development Studies ... MPhil 36FT
Material Anthropology & Museum Ethnography (Research Methods) ... MSc 12FT
Material Anthropology and Museum Ethnography ... MSc 12FT/MPhil 21FT
Medical Anthropology ... MPhil 24FT/MSc 12FT
Social Anthropology ... MSt 9FT/MPhil 21FT/MSc 12FT
Social Anthropology (Research Methods) ... MSc 12FT
Visual Anthropology ... MSc 12FT

Queen's University Belfast
Social Anthropology ... MA 12FT up to 36PT/GradDip 12FT 24PT

University of Reading
Research in Archaeology ... MA 12FT 24PT

University of Roehampton
Dance Anthropology ... MA 12FT 24PT
Health Sciences ... PGDip 9FT 24PT

School of Oriental and African Studies - SOAS
Anthropology of Media ... MA 12FT 24-36PT
Anthropology of Travel, Tourism and Pilgrimage ... MA 12FT 24PT
Gender Studies ... MA 12FT 24-36PT
Global Cinemas and the Transcultural ... MA 12FT 24-36PT
Law, Culture and Society ... MA 12FT 24PT
Medical Anthropology ... MA 12FT 24-36PT
Migration and Diaspora Studies ... MA 12FT 24-36PT
Social Anthropology ... MA 12FT 24-36PT
Social Anthropology of Development ... MA 12FT 24-36PT

University of Sheffield
Archaeological Materials ... MSc 12FT
Archaeology ... MA 12FT 24PT
Archaeology, Bible and Ancient Cultures ... MA 12FT 24PT
Biblical Studies Research ... MA 12FT 24PT
Biblical Studies by Distance Learning ... MA flexibleDL/PGDip flexibleDL/PGCert flexibleDL
Palaeoanthropology ... MSc 12FT
Social Research ... MA 12FT 24PT

University of St Andrews
Biblical Language and Literature ... MLitt 12FT/PGDip 9FT
Film Studies ... MLitt 12FT 24PT/PGDip 9FT
Peace and Conflict Studies ... MLitt 12FT
Social Anthropology ... MRes 12FT 24PT
Social Anthropology and Amerindian Studies ... MRes 12FT
Social Anthropology with African Studies ... MRes 12FT
Social Anthropology with Pacific Studies ... MRes 12FT

University of Sussex
Anthropology ... MA 12FT 24PT
Anthropology of Development and Social Transformation ... MA 12FT 24PT

University of Wales Trinity Saint David
Heritage Studies ... MA 12FT 24PT 12-24DL

UCL - University College London
Anthropology ... MRes 12FT
Anthropology, Environment and Development ... MSc 12FT 24PT
Culture, Materials and Design ... MA 12FT 24PT
Digital Anthropology ... MA 12FT
Human Evolution and Behaviour ... MSc 12FT 24PT
Material and Visual Culture ... MA 12FT 24PT
Medical Anthropology ... MSc 12FT 24PT
Palaeoanthropology and Palaeolithic Archaeology ... MSc 12FT 24PT
Social and Cultural Anthropology ... MSc 12FT 24PT

Anthropology
Research Courses

University of Aberdeen
Anthropology ... PhD 36FT/MPhil 24FT
Archaeology ... MSc by research 12FT/MPhil 24FT/PhD 36FT

Bangor University
Criminology and Criminal Justice ... PhD 36FT 60PT/MPhil 12-24FT 24-36PT
Sociology ... PhD 36FT 60PT/MPhil 12-24FT 24-36PT

University of Bristol
Archaeology and Anthropology ... PhD 36FT 72PT/MLitt by research 24FT 48PT/MPhil 12FT 24PT

Brunel University
Doctoral Programme in Anthropology ... MPhil 12FT 24PT/MRes 12FT 24PT/PhD 36FT 60PT

University of Cambridge
Biological Anthropological Science ... MPhil 10FT
Biological Anthropology ... PhD 36FT 60PT
Social Anthropological Research ... MPhil 12FT
Social Anthropology ... PhD 36FT

Durham University
Anthropology ... PhD 36FT
Biological Anthropology ... MSc by research 12FT
Social Anthropology ... MA by research 12FT

University of East Anglia
Sainsbury Research Unit for the Arts of Africa, Oceania and the Americas ... PhD 36FT 72PT/MPhil 24FT 48PT/MA by research 12FT 24PT

University of Edinburgh
Social Anthropology ... PhD 36FT 72PT MSc by research 12FT 24PT
Sociology and Anthropology of Health and Illness (Masters by research) ... MSc by research 12FT 24PT

University of Exeter
Archaeology ... PhD 36FT 72PT/MPhil 24FT 48PT/MA by research 12FT 24PT
Philosophy ... MA by research 12FT 24PT/MPhil 24FT 48PT/PhD 48FT 72PT

Goldsmiths, University of London
Anthropology ... MPhil 24FT 36PT/PhD 36-48FT 48-72PT MRes 12FT 24PT
Visual Anthropology ... MRes 12FT 24PT MPhil 24FT 36PT/PhD 36-48FT 48-72PT

University of Hull
Sociology and Anthropology ... PhD 36FT 60PT/MPhil 24FT 36PT

University of Kent
Anthropology .. PhD 36FT 60PT/MPhil 12FT 36PT/MA by research 12FT 24PT/MSc by research 12FT 24PT
Ethnobiology ... MSc by research 12FT 24PT/PhD 36FT 60PT

London School of Economics and Political Science (LSE)
Anthropology ... MPhil 36-48FT/PhD 36-48FT

University of Manchester
Anthropology, Media & Performance ... PhD 36FT 72PT
Ethnographic Documentary ... MPhil 12FT 24PT
Social Anthropology ... PhD 36-48FT 72-84PT
Social Anthropology with Visual Media ... PhD 48FT 84PT/MPhil 12FT 24PT

Oxford Brookes University
Anthropology and Geography ... PhD 24-60FT 36-72PT/MPhil 24-36FT 36-48PT

University of Oxford
Institute of Social and Cultural Anthropology ... DPhil 48FT

Queen's University Belfast
Social Anthropology ... PhD 36FT 72PT/MPhil 24FT 48PT

University of Roehampton
Anthropology ... PhD 24-48FT 36-60PT/MPhil 21-36FT 33-48PT

School of Oriental and African Studies - SOAS
Social Anthropology ... PhD 36FT/MPhil 24FT

University of St Andrews
Film Studies ... PhD 36FT 72-84PT/MPhil 24FT 48PT
Social Anthropology ... PhD 36FT 72PT/MPhil 12-24FT 24-48PT

University of Sussex
Social Anthropology ... PhD 24-48FT 36-72PT/MPhil 12-36FT 24-48PT

University of Wales Trinity Saint David
Anthropology ... PhD 36FT 48-72PT/MPhil 12-36FT
Archaeology ... PhD 36FT 48-72PT/MPhil 12-36FT

UCL - University College London
Anthropology ... PhD 36FT 60PT

Asia-pacific studies
Taught Courses

University of Birmingham
Contemporary Russian and East European Studies ... MSc 12FT 24PT
International Relations (Contemporary Pacific Asia) ... MA 12FT 24PT

University of Bristol
East Asian Development and the Global Economy ... MSc 12FT

University of Cambridge
Archaeology ... MPhil 11-15FT
Asian and Middle Eastern Studies ... MPhil 11FT/MPhil(A) 11FT
Modern South Asian Studies ... MPhil(A) 9FT

University of Edinburgh
Asian Religions ... MSc 12FT 24PT
South Asia and International Development ... MSc 12FT 24PT

University of Glasgow
Russian, Central & East European Studies (Erasmus Mundus International Masters) ... International Masters (double/single degree) 24FT
Russian, Central and East European Studies ... MSc 12FT 24PT/PGDip 9FT

Goldsmiths, University of London
Critical Asian Studies ... MA 12FT 24PT

King's College London
South Asia & Global Security ... MA 12FT 24PT

University of Leeds
Advanced Chinese Studies ... MA 12FT 24PT/PGDip 9FT 21PT
Asia Pacific Studies ... MA 12FT 24PT
Asia Pacific Studies (Online) ... MA 36DL
East Asian Regional Development ... MA 12FT 24PT
South East Asian Studies ... MA 12FT 24PT

University of Manchester
South Asian Studies ... MA 12FT 24PT

University of Oxford
Classical Indian Religion ... MPhil 21FT
Cuneiform Studies ... MPhil 21FT
Modern South Asian Studies ... MPhil 21FT
Oriental Studies ... MSt 9FT
Tibetan and Himalayan Studies ... MPhil 24FT

University of Roehampton
South Asian Dance Studies ... PGDip 9FT 24PT
South Asian Dance Studies ... MA 12FT 24PT

Royal Holloway, University of London
Asia Pacific Business ... MA 12FT

School of Oriental and African Studies - SOAS
Asian Politics ... MSc 12FT 24PT
Development Studies with Special Reference to Central Asia ... MSc 12FT 24PT
Economics (with Reference to South Asia) ... MSc 12FT 24PT
Economics (with Reference to the Asia Pacific Region) ... MSc 12FT 24PT
History ... MA 12FT 24PT
History: Asia/Africa ... MA 12FT 24-36PT
Languages and literatues of South East Asia ... MA 12FT 24-36PT
Pacific Asian Studies ... MA 12FT 24-36PT
South Asian Area Studies ... MA 12FT 24PT
South East Asian Studies ... MA 12FT 24-36PT

University of Sheffield
East Asian Business ... MSc 12FT
Global Politics and Law (Doshisha Pathway) ... MA 24FT

University of St Andrews
Social Anthropology with Pacific Studies ... MRes 12FT

UCL - University College London
Archaeology and Heritage of Asia ... MA 12FT 24PT

University of Warwick
MA International Politics and East Asia ... MA 12FT 24PT/PGDip 9FT

Asia-pacific studies
Research Courses

School of Advanced Study, University of London
East and South Asian Studies ... PhD 36FT 72PT/MPhil 12FT 36PT

University of Cambridge
Archaeological Research ... MPhil 12FT
Asian and Middle Eastern Studies ... PhD 48FT/MPhil(B) 11FT

University of Leeds
Department of East Asian Studies ... PhD 36+FT/MPhil 24FT/MA by research 12+FT

University of Manchester
East Asian Studies ... PhD 36FT 72PT/MPhil 12FT 24PT

The Open University
Asian drivers and Africa ... PhD 36FT 72PT variableDL/MPhil 15FT 24PT variableDL
Empire and Postcolonial studies ... PhD 36FT 72PT variableDL/MPhil 15FT 24PT variableDL

University of Oxford
Oriental Studies ... DPhil 48FT

School of Oriental and African Studies - SOAS
Languages and Cultures of South Asia ... PhD 36FT 72PT/MPhil 24FT 48PT

Australian studies
Taught Courses

University of East Anglia
The Arts of Africa, Oceania and the Americas ... MA 12FT 24PT

Section sponsored by

BPP
UNIVERSITY
COLLEGE

Business and social sciences
www.prospects.ac.uk/findcourses POSTGRADUATE DIRECTORY 479

Social sciences

UCL - University College London
Energy and Resources: Policy and Practice, Australia .... MSc 24FT 36-48PT

Australian studies
Research Courses

University of East Anglia
Sainsbury Research Unit for the Arts of Africa, Oceania and the Americas ....PhD 36FT 72PT/MPhil 24FT 48PT/ MA by research 12FT 24PT

King's College London
Menzies Centre for Australian Studies ....MPhil 24FT 36PT/PhD 36FT 48-72PT

Brazilian studies
Taught Courses

King's College London
Brazil in Global Perspective.. MA 12FT 24PT

Brazilian studies
Research Courses

King's College London
Brazilian Studies Research ... MPhil 24FT 36PT/PhD 36FT 48-72PT

Careers education
Taught Courses

University of Aberdeen
Pastoral Care, Guidance and Pupil Support ....MEd 24BM

Coventry University
Career Guidance .... PGDip 12FT 24PT

University of Derby
Education ....EdD by taught 36-72PT
Education: Guidance Studies .... MA Up to 72PT
Graduate Teacher Programme ....QTS 12FT 24PT

University of Dundee
Advanced Practice (Practice Education) ....PGCert 12DL PGDip 24DL
Diabetes Care and Education .... MSc 36-40PT PGCert 12-15PT PGDip 24-27PT
Education (Chartered Teacher)......................MEd 18PT/PGDip 9PT/ PGCert 6PT
Educational Psychology .... MSc 24FT
Global Internship Graduate Certificate (India) ....GradCert 8FT

University of East London
Career Coaching ....MA 12FT 24PT/PGDip 8FT 16PT/ PGCert 4FT 8PT

Edinburgh Napier University
Career Guidance (Top Up) ....MSc 12DL
Career Guidance and Development ....PGDip 12FT 24DL

Falmouth University
MA Creative Education............PGCHE 12PT/PGDip 12PT/MA 12PT

University of Huddersfield
Professional Studies (Guidance)............................ PGDip 12FT 24PT

University of Limerick
Guidance Counselling and Lifespan Development...........MA 24PT

London South Bank University
Careers Guidance - Add on Masters .... MSc 12PT
Careers Guidance with QCG .... PGDip 12FT 24PT

Manchester Metropolitan University
Careers Guidance and Qualification in Careers Guidance (QCG) .... PGDip 12FT 24PT
Top-up LLM.. LLM 12FT 24PT

National University of Ireland, Maynooth
Arts (School Guidance & Counselling).............................HDip 12FT

Nottingham Trent University
Career Guidance/Qualification in Careers Guidance .... Diploma 12FT 24PT
Professional Practice...................................... MA 1.5PT 3DL

Plymouth University
Clinical Education............MClinEd 36PT/PGDip 24PT/PGCert 12PT

University of Sheffield
Applied Linguistics with TESOL..................................MA 12FT 24PT/ Diploma 9FT 18PT

University of Strathclyde
Adult Guidance......................MSc 36DL/PGDip 24DL/PGCert 12DL
Education for Work and EnterprisePGDip max 48PT/PGCert max 24PT

University of Ulster
Careers Guidance ....MSc 18PT/PGDip 12FT

University of the West of Scotland
Careers Guidance .... MSc 24PT/PGDip 12FT 24PT/PGCert 24PT
Careers Guidance and Development...... MSc 24PT/Diploma 12FT 24PT/Cert 24PT

Careers education
Research Courses

University of Central Lancashire
Politics and International studies .... MPhil 18-36FT 42-60PT/PhD 30-48FT 66-84PT/MA by research 12FT 24PT
Sociology, Ethnicity & Human Rights, Criminology ....
PhD 30-48FT 66-84PT/MPhil 18-36FT 42-60PT/MA by research 12FT 24PT

University of Dundee
Education ....MPhil 24FT MSc by research 12FT PhD 36FT

University of Hertfordshire
Centre for Research in Employment Studies.........PhD 36FT 72PT/ MPhil 24FT 48PT/MRes 12FT 24PT

Celtic studies
Taught Courses

University of Aberdeen
Celtic Studies .... MLitt 12FT 24PT/PGDip 9FT 18PT
Irish and Scottish Studies.......... MLitt 12FT 24PT/PGDip 9FT 18PT

Bangor University
Archaeology.............PhD by taught 36FT 48-72PT/MPhil 12-24FT 24-48PT
Celtic Archaeology .... MA 12FT 24PT/PGDip 8FT
Celts, The / Celtiaid, Y .... MA 12FT 36PT
Cymraeg (Welsh) (Welsh medium)....... MA 12FT 24PT/PGDip 8FT
Welsh History ....PhD by taught 24-36FT 48-72PT/ MPhil 12FT 24PT

University of Cambridge
Anglo-Saxon, Norse and Celtic..MPhil 9FT

Cardiff University
Early Celtic Studies.. MA 12FT 24PT

Cliff College
Celtic Mission and SpiritualityPGCert 12PT/PGDip 12FT 24PT/MA 12-18FT 24-30PT

University College Cork
Arts (Folklore) ....HDip 9FT
Folklore...MA 12FT

University of Glasgow
Celtic Studies...MLitt 12FT 24PT

University of Oxford
Celtic Studies .... MPhil 21FT/MSt 9FT

Queen's University Belfast
Irish Translation .... MA 12FT max 31PT/PGDip 12FT max 31PT

Swansea University
Welsh.. MA 12FT 24PT
Welsh Writing in English .... MA 12FT 24PT

University of Wales Trinity Saint David
Astudiaethau Celtaidd........ MA 12FT 24PT 12-24DL/PGCert 12FT 24PT 12-24DL/PGDip 12FT 24PT 12-24DL
Celtic Studies .... MA 12FT 24PT 12-24DL/PGCert 12FT 24PT 12-24DL/PGDip 12FT 24PT 12-24DL

Celtic studies
Research Courses

University of Aberdeen
Celtic StudiesPhD 36FT 60PT/MLitt by research 12FT 24PT/MPhil 24FT 48PT

Aberystwyth University
Celtic Studies ....MPhil 12FT 24PT PhD 36FT 60PT

Bangor University
Astudiaethau Celtaidd (Celtic Studies) (Welsh medium).... MA by research 12FT/MPhil 24FT 48-60PT/PhD 24-36FT 60-72PT
Llenyddiaeth Gymraeg (Welsh Literature) (Welsh medium)..........
MPhil 24FT 48-60PT/PhD 24-36FT 60-72PT

University of Cambridge
Anglo-Saxon, Norse and Celtic..PhD 36FT

University of Edinburgh
Celtic and Scottish Studies............................PhD 36FT 72PT/ MPhil 24FT 48PT/MSc by research 12FT 24PT

University of Exeter
Cornish Studies .... PhD 36FT 72PT/MPhil 24FT 48PT

National University of Ireland Galway
College of Arts, Social Sciences & Celtic Studies ..PhD 48FT 72PT/ MLitt by research 24FT 48PT/Structured PhD 48FT 72PT

University of Glasgow
Celtic ....PhD 36FT/MPhil 12FT/MLitt by research 12FT

Queen's University Belfast
Irish and Celtic Studies............... PhD 36FT 72PT/MPhil 24FT 48PT

Swansea University
Welsh.......PhD 36FT 60PT/MPhil 12FT 24PT/MA by research 12FT 24PT

University of Ulster
Celtic Studies .... PhD 36FT 72PT/MPhil 24FT 48PT

Child protection
Taught Courses

Aberystwyth University
Childhood Studies Welfare and Rights ....MA 12FT 24PT/ PGDip 9FT 21PT

Bangor University
Implementing Evidence in Health & Social CareMRes 12FT 24PT/ PGCert 3FT 15PT

University of Bolton
Children's Literature and Culture ....MA 24FT
Safeguarding and Promoting Children's Welfare.... MSc 36-60PT/ PGDip 24PT/PGCert 12PT

Bucks New University
Child Protection and Adult Safeguarding ....MSc 12FT 24PT

University of Central Lancashire
Child Care Practice, PQ Specialist Award with Children, Young People, Families & Carers ....PGCert 18PT
Child Care and Welfare .... MA 12FT 24-60PT
Child Health .... MSc 36PT
Researching Social Care ....PGCert 12FT 24PT
Safeguarding Children ....PGCert 12PT
Social Work.. MA 24FT 36PT
Social Work (only available through employment secondment) ....PGDip 24FT 36PT
Social Work Practice (Post Qualification Specialist Award, Adults)..PGDip 3PT

University of Chester
Family and Child Psychology ...MSc 12FT 24PT/PGDip 12FT 24PT/ PGCert 12FT 12-24PT

University of East Anglia
Child and Family Psychology .... MSc 12FT 24PT
Social Work..MA 24FT

University of East London
Child Protection and Complex Childcare (M22) ....MA 36PT/ PGDip 24PT

Edinburgh Napier University
Advanced Practice in Child Protection ....MSc 12FT 36PT/ PGDip 9FT 24PT/PGCert 6FT 12PT

University of Edinburgh
Health & Social Care - Children & Young People's Mental Health: Ecological Approaches ODL...PGCert 9DL
Psychological Interventions for Children and Young People .... PGCert 12PT

University of Glasgow
Child Health ....PGCert 12-24FT PGDip 12-24PT
Childhood Practice .... PGDip 24PT

Goldsmiths, University of London
Advanced Social Work: Practice Education ....MA 24PT
Social Work..MA 24FT

University of Huddersfield
Child Welfare and Safeguarding................................. MA 12FT 36PT

Institute of Education
Social Pedagogy: Working with Children and Families ...MA 12FT 24PT

Keele University
Child Care Law and Practice..........................MA 24PT/PGDip 12PT
Social Work..MA 24FT

University of Kent
Advanced Child Protection ....MA 24PT

Leeds Metropolitan University
Social Work..MA 24FT

Liverpool Hope University
Social Work..MA 24FT

London Metropolitan University
Women and Child Abuse .... MSc 12FT 24PT

Manchester Metropolitan University
Advanced Practice and Leadership in Social Work .... MA 24-36PT

Newman University
Children, Young People and Families.................... MA 24FT 36-48PT

Northumbria University
Leadership and Management in Integrated Childrens Services ... MA 36PT/PGDip 24PT/PGCert 12PT

Oxford Brookes University
Children, Young People and Family Well-Being ....MSc 12-36DL/ PGDip 8-36DL/PGCert 4-36DL

University of Sheffield
Professional Practice with Children and Families ....MA 36PT

University of South Wales
Child Health and Welfare Studies (Online Delivery) .... MSc 12-48FT 36-60DL

University of Stirling
Applied Studies (Child Welfare and Protection) ....MSc 30PT/ PGDip 24PT/PGCert 12PT

Section sponsored by BPP UNIVERSITY COLLEGE

Business and social sciences

480 POSTGRADUATE DIRECTORY www.prospects.ac.uk/findcourses

Social sciences

University of Strathclyde
Advanced Residential Childcare ....MSc 24PT/PGDip 18PT/PGCert 9PT

University of Sussex
Effective Practice in Children's Services..... MA 60PT/PGDip 60PT/PGCert 60PT

Swansea University
Childhood Studies .... MA 12FT 24PT

Trinity College Dublin - the University of Dublin
Child Protection and Welfare .... MSc 24PT PGDip 12PT

University of the Highlands and Islands
Socio-Legal Issues of Childhood .... PGCert 12FT 24PT

University of Warwick
Child Law and Child Protection........ PGA 12PT/CPDMod 1PT

University of the West of Scotland
Child Protection .... PGCert 12PT

Child protection
Research Courses

Goldsmiths, University of London
Social Work........ PhD 36-48FT 48-72PT/MPhil 24FT 36PT

The Open University
Issues in health and social care of children, young people and families .... PhD 36FT 72PT/MPhil 15FT 24PT
Personal relationships, families, children and young people..PhD 36FT 72PT variableDL/MPhil 15FT 24PT variableDL

Plymouth University
Parenting and Child Welfare........ MPhil tbcFT

Swansea University
Childhood Studies........ MPhil 12FT/PhD 36FT

Childhood studies
Taught Courses

Aberystwyth University
Childhood Health and Well-being .... MA 12FT 24PT/PGDip 9FT 21PT
Childhood Studies Welfare and Rights .... MA 12FT 24PT/PGDip 9FT 21PT
Childhood Studies in Professional Practice........ MA 12FT
Childhood and Creative Development. MA 12FT 24PT/PGDip 9FT 21PT

Anglia Ruskin University
Children & Young People........ MSc 12FT 24PT

Bangor University
Education Doctorate Programme .... EdD by taught 60PT
Education Studies... MA 12FT 24-60PT/MEd 12FT 24-60PT/PGDip 8FT 24-48PT/PGCert 4FT 12-24PT

University of Bedfordshire
Applied Public Policy: Children's and Young People's Services MA 24PT
Applied Social Work: Children and Families........ MA 30PT
Professional Doctorate in Children and Youth People's Services (PDC&YPSL)........ DProf by taught 36PT

University College Birmingham
Childhood, Professional Studies in Childhood..... MA 24PT/PGDip 24PT/PGCert 24PT

University of Bolton
Children's Literature and Culture........ MA 24PT

Bucks New University
Child & Adolescent Studies .... MSc 12FT 24PT

Canterbury Christ Church University
Early Years........ MA 36PT

University of Central Lancashire
Child Care Practice, PQ Specialist Award with Children, Young People, Families & Carers........ PGCert 18PT
Child Care and Welfare .... MA 12FT 24-60PT
Child Computer Interaction........ MRes 12FT 24PT
Child Health........ MSc 36PT
Neonatal Studies........ MA 60PT/PGDip 24PT/PGCert 12PT
Psychology of Child Development....... MSc 12FT 24PT/PGDip 9FT 24PT/PGCert 9FT 24PT

University of Edinburgh
Childhood Studies........ MSc 12FT 24PT
Cognitive Behaviour Therapy for Children and Young People .... PGCert 24PT
Health & Social Care - Children & Young People's Mental Health: Ecological Approaches ODL........ PGCert 9DL
Psychological Interventions for Children and Young People .... PGCert 12PT

University of Glasgow
Childhood Practice .... PGDip 24PT

University of Gloucestershire
Play and Playwork .... PGCert 12-24DL/PGDip 12-24DL/MA 24-48DL

Glyndwr University
Counselling Studies with Children and Young People .... MA 30//PT

Goldsmiths, University of London
Education: School-Based Explorations........ MA 24-60PT

Institute of Education
Children's Media Culture........ 30 Credit Module 3PT
Youth Culture, Media and Education .... 30 Credit Module 3PT

King's College London
International Child Studies .... MA 12FT 24PT

Leeds Metropolitan University
Childhood Studies and Early Years........ MA 12FT 24PT

Manchester Metropolitan University
Advanced Practitioner Abuse Studies .... MA 24PT

University of St Mark and St John
Professional Practice: Children and Young People's Services...MA VariableFT

Newman University
Children, Young People and Families........ MA 24FT 36-48PT
Early Years Foundation Degree .... FdA 36PT
Early Years Teacher Status.... Early Years Teacher Status 6FT/Early Years Teacher Status 12FT

Northumbria University
Leadership and Management in Integrated Childrens Services ... MA 36PT/PGDip 24PT/PGCert 12PT
Psychoanalytical Observational Studies........ MA 36/24PT

The Open University
Childhood and Youth........ MA variableDL
Integrated Practice in Childhood and Youth........ PGCert 12DL/PGDip variableDL

Oxford Brookes University
Advanced Early Years Specialism (PGCert Advanced Educational Practice)........ PGCert 12PT
Childhood Studies .... MA 12FT 24PT/PGDip 12FT 24PT/PGCert 12FT 12PT
Children, Young People and Family Well-Being....... MSc 12-36DL/PGDip 8-36DL/PGCert 4-36DL
Nursing, Children's (Pre-registration) .... MSc 24FT 48PT/PGDip 24FT 48PT/PGCert 24FT 48PT

University of Oxford
Education (Child Development and Education)........ MSc 12FT

Plymouth University
Early Childhood Studies (IMP)........ MA 36BM
International Study of Early Childhood .... MA 24PT

Queen Margaret University, Edinburgh
Collaborative Working: Education and Therapy...PGCert 12-48PT

University of Roehampton
Children's Literature .... MA 12FT 24PT
Children's Literature .... PGDip 9FT 24PT
Children's Literature Distance Learning .... PGDip 24PT 24DL

University Campus Suffolk
Childhood and Youth Studies........ MA 12FT 24 - 36PT

University of Salford
Children's Digital Media Production .... MA 12FT/PGDip 9FT

University of Sheffield
Educational and Child Psychology .... Doctor 36FT

University of South Wales
Childhood Studies........ MA 12FT 24PT
Childhood Studies (Top Up) .... BSc 12FT 24PT

University of Strathclyde
Early Childhood Studies........ MSc 24PT/PGDip 24PT/PGCert 24PT

University of Sussex
Childhood and Youth Studies........ MA 12FT 24PT
Effective Practice in Children's Services..... MA 60PT/PGDip 60PT/PGCert 60PT

Swansea University
Developmental and Therapeutic Play........ MA 12FT 36PT/PGDip 12FT 24PT/PGCert 12FT 12PT

Trinity College Dublin - the University of Dublin
Nursing (Child Health and Well-being Strand) ..... MSc 12FT 24PT

University of the Highlands and Islands
Socio-Legal Issues of Childhood .... PGCert 12FT 24PT

UCL - University College London
Cognitive Behavioural Therapy for Children and Young People.... MSc 24-36PT/PGDip 24PT/PGCert 12PT
International Child Health........ MSc 12FT 24-60PT/PGDip 9FT 24-60PT/PGCert 12FT 24PT

Childhood studies
Research Courses

Bath Spa University
Children and the Environment .... PhD 24 - 60FT 36 - 72PT

Birkbeck, University of London
International Childhood Studies.. PhD 36FT 60-72PT/MPhil 24FT 36PT

Canterbury Christ Church University
Applied Childhood Studies........ MPhil 24FT/DPhil 36FT

The Open University
Child and Youth Studies........ PhD 36FT 72PT variableDL/MRes 12FT/EdD 36PT
Children, Young People and Families........ PhD 36FT 72PT variableDL/MPhil 15FT 24PT variableDL
Children, young people, families, and personal relationships PhD 36FT 72PT/MPhil 15FT 24PT
Issues in health and social care of children, young people and families .... PhD 36FT 72PT/MPhil 15FT 24PT
Personal life and intimacies.......PhD 36FT 72PT variableDL/MPhil 15FT 24PT variableDL
Personal relationships, families, children and young people..PhD 36FT 72PT variableDL/MPhil 15FT 24PT variableDL

Oxford Brookes University
Education and Childhood Studies .... MPhil/PhD 36-60FT 48-72PT/PhD 24-60FT 36-72PT/MPhil 24-36FT 36-48PT

University of Roehampton
Children's Literature .... PhD 24-48FT 48PT/MPhil 21-36FT 33-48PT

UCL - University College London
Developmental Science .... PhD 36FT 60PT

Chinese studies
Taught Courses

University College Cork
Contemporary Chinese Culture & Business .... MA 12FT

University of Edinburgh
Chinese Studies........ Master of Chinese Studies 24FT
Modern Chinese Cultural Studies .... MSc 12FT 24PT

University of Glasgow
Chinese Studies........ MSc 12FT 24PT
International Politics (China).. MSc 12FT 24PT/PGDip 9FT/PGCert 9FT

Goldsmiths, University of London
Critical Asian Studies........ MA 12FT 24PT

University of Greenwich
International Business in China........ MA 12FT

King's College London
China & Globalisation........ MSc 12FT 24PT
Governance in Contemporary China .... MSc 12FT 24PT

Leeds Metropolitan University
International Political Economy........ MA 12FT

University of Leeds
Advanced Chinese Studies........ MA 12FT 24PT/PGDip 9FT 21PT
Chinese........ MA 12FT/PGDip 9FT/PGCert 6FT
Chinese Business and the Asia Pacific........ MA 12FT 24PT
Chinese Studies........ MA 12FT 24PT
Chinese and Business........ MA 12FT 24PT

London School of Economics and Political Science (LSE)
China in Comparative Perspective .... MSc 12FT

University of Manchester
Chinese Business and Management........ MSc 12FT

University of Nottingham
Banking and Financial Markets in Contemporary China........ MSc 12FT
Business and Economy of Contemporary China........ MSc 12FT
Contemporary Chinese Studies .... MA 12FT
Corporate Finance in Contemporary China .... MSc 12FT
Human Geography and Chinese Studies (2 years)........ MSc 24FT
Management in Contemporary China and Emerging Markets..... MSc 12FT

University of Oxford
Chinese Studies........ MSt 9FT
Modern Chinese Studies........ MPhil 21FT
Oriental Studies........ MSt 9FT
Tibetan and Himalayan Studies .... MPhil 24FT

School of Oriental and African Studies - SOAS
Chinese Law........ MA 12FT 24PT
Chinese Literature .... MA 12FT 24-36PT
Chinese Studies........ MA 12FT 24-36PT
International Management (China) .... MSc 12FT 24-36PT
Politics of China .... MSc 12FT 24PT
Sinology .... MA 12FT 24-36PT

University of Sheffield
Chinese Studies........ MA 12FT
Teaching Chinese as a Foreign Language........ MA 12FT

UCL - University College London
Chinese Health and Humanity .... MA 12FT
Chinese Studies (Health and Humanity)........ MA 24FT

Chinese studies
Research Courses

University of Edinburgh
Chinese.. PhD 36FT 72PT/MPhil 24FT 48PT/MSc by research 12FT 24PT

Section sponsored by
BPP UNIVERSITY COLLEGE
Business and social sciences
www.prospects.ac.uk/findcourses POSTGRADUATE DIRECTORY 481

Social sciences

King's College London
Chinese Studies Research MPhil 24FT 36PT/PhD 36FT 48-72PT

University of Manchester
Chinese Studies MPhil 12FT 24PT/PhD 36FT 72PT

University of Nottingham
Contemporary Chinese Studies Research Areas PhD 36FT/MPhil 24FT/MRes 12FT

The Open University
Asian drivers and Africa PhD 36FT 72PT variableDL/MPhil 15FT 24PT variableDL

Community nursing
Taught Courses

Anglia Ruskin University
Specialist Community Public Health Nursing (Health Visiting or School Nursing) PGDip 12FT

University of Bedfordshire
Specialist Community Public Health Nursing / Specialist Community (District) Nursing MSc 12FT 24PT/PGDip 12FT 24PT

University of Birmingham
Primary and Community Care, Clinical MSc 12FT 24PT/PGDip 12FT 24PT/PGCert 12FT 24PT

University of Bolton
Community Specialist Practice (District Nursing) PGDip 12PT
Specialist Community Public Health Nursing (Health Visiting) PGDip 12FT 24PT

Bournemouth University
Public Health Nursing MSc 12FT 24-36PT

University of Brighton
Health Promotion MA 12FT 24-72PT/PGDip 12FT 24-72PT/PGCert 12FT 24-72PT
International Health Promotion MA 12FT 36PT/PGDip 12FT 36PT
Specialist Community Public Health Nursing MSc 12FT 24-72PT/PGDip 12FT 24-72PT/PGCert 12FT 24-72PT

Brunel University
Specialist Community Public Health Nursing MSc 0FT 12PT/PGDip 12FT 24PT

Bucks New University
Advanced Practice (Nursing) MSc 36PT
Community Health Care Nursing MSc 12FT 24PT
Specialist Community Public Health Nursing MSc 12FT 24PT

Canterbury Christ Church University
Community Specialist Practice PGDip 12FT 24PT
Specialist Community Public Health Nursing PGDip 12FT 24PT

Cardiff University
Specialist Community Public Health Nursing MSc 24-48FT 36-60PT/PGDip 12FT 24PT

University of Central Lancashire
Community Specialist Practitioner PGDip 12FT 24-48PT
Nursing MSc 12FT 24-60PT
Person-Centred Spiritual Care & Accompaniment PGCert 12PT

University of Chester
Nursing Studies (Work Based and Integrative Studies) MA 24-72PT/MSc 24-72PT/PGDip 24-60PT/PGCert 12-36PT

City University London
Mental Health Nursing (Graduate Entry) PGDip 24FT
Primary Care (District Nursing) MSc 12FT 24PT
Specialist Community Public Health Nurse (Health Visiting) MSc 12FT 24PT
Specialist Community Public Health Nurse (School Nursing) MSc 12FT 24PT

Coventry University
Nursing Studies MSc 15 MinFT 60 MaxPT

University of Cumbria
Community Specealist Practice Nursing PGDE 9FT 18PT
Specialist Community Public Health Nursing Practice MSc 12 - 48PT

De Montfort University
Advanced Health and Professional Practice B70076 MSc 12FT 36-72PT/PGDip 24PT/PGCert 12PT
Health and Community Studies L53072 MA 36DL/PGDip 18DL/PGCert 12DL/MA 12FT
Specialist Community Public Health Nursing MSc 36PT/PGDip 24PT

University of Derby
Community Specialist Practice MSc 12FT 24PT
Management of Long Term Conditions PGCert 12PT
Nursing (Specialist Community Public Health) MSc 12FT 24PT

University of Dundee
Advanced Practice (Physiotherapeutic Practice) MSc 36DL
Diabetes Care and Education MSc 36-40PT PGCert 12-15PT PGDip 24-27PT
Global Health and Wellbeing MSc 36DL
Health and Social Care MRes 24DL
Nursing (Masters by distance learning) MN 36DL
Nursing (Post Graduate by distance learning) (individual modules) PG module variableDL
Nursing (Post Registration by distance learning) (1 semester module) UG modules 3DL
Nursing (Post Registration by distance learning) (individual modules) Post reg modules variableDL
Palliative Care MSc 36DL
Palliative Care Research MPH 12-24FT

University of East Anglia
Advanced Practitioner (Profession) MSc 12FT 36PT
Mental Health MSc 12FT 36PT/PGDip 12FT 24PT/PGCert 12PT
Midwifery PGDip 18FT

Edinburgh Napier University
Advanced Practice in Diabetes Nursing MSc 12FT 36PT/PGDip 9FT 24PT/PGCert 6FT 12PT
Health Administration MSc 12FT 24-36PT/PGDip 9FT 18-27PT/PGCert 6FT 12-18PT

National University of Ireland Galway
Nursing (Mental Health, Community & Inpatient Acute Care) PGDip 12FT 24PT
Nursing (Practice Nursing/ Community Nursing) PGDip 12FT 24PT

Glasgow Caledonian University
Advanced Practice with Older People MSc 12FT
Advancing Practice in Primary Care MSc 24FT
Diabetes Care and Management MSc 12FT 36PT
Optimal Heart Failure Care MSc 12FT
Perinatal Mental Health MSc 12FT
Specialist Community Public Health Nursing PGDip 12FT 24PT
Telehealthcare MSc 12FT

University of Glasgow
Healthcare Chaplaincy PGCert 12PT

Glyndwr University
Community Specialist Practice Nursing MSc 12FT 24-36PT
Specialist Community Public Health Nursing MSc 12FT 24PT

University of Hertfordshire
Contemporary Nursing MSc 12FT
Specialist Community Nursing BSc Hons 12FT 24PT/MSc 12FT 24PT/PGDip 12FT 24PT
Specialist Community Public Health Nursing MSc 12FT 24PT/PGDip 12FT 24PT/BSc Hons 12FT 24PT

University of Huddersfield
Community Nursing Practice (District Nursing) MSc 18FT 30-42PT
Public Health Nursing Practice: Health Visiting/School Nursing MSc 16FT 36PT

King's College London
Advanced Practice (Diabetes Care) MSc 36-72PT/PGDip 24-72PT/PGCert 12-72PT
Advanced Practice (Nurse Practitioner/Community Matron/Case Manager) MSc 36-72PT/PGDip 24-72PT/PGCert 12-72PT
Advanced Practice (Palliative Care Nursing) MSc 36-72PT/PGDip 24-72PT/PGCert 12-72PT
Advanced Practice (Specialist Community Public Health Nursing/ Public Health/ School Nurs) MSc 36-72PT/PGDip 24-72PT/PGCert 12-72PT

Leeds Metropolitan University
Community Specialist Practitioner - Community Children's Nursing PGDip 24PT
Community Specialist Practitioner - District Nursing MSc 24PT/PGDip 12FT 24PT
Community Specialist Practitioner - Practice Nursing MSc 24PT/PGDip 24PT
Health Care Studies MA 24PT
Specialist Community Public Health Nursing - Health Visiting MSc 24PT/PGDip 12FT 24PT
Specialist Community Public Health Nursing - Occupational Health Nursing MSc 24PT/PGDip 12FT 24PT
Specialist Community Public Health Nursing - School Nursing MSc 24PT/PGDip 12FT 24PT

Liverpool John Moores University
Adult Nursing MSc 24FT 24PT
Advanced Paediatric Nurse Practitioner (APNP) in Ambulatory Care MSc 12FT 24PT

London School of Hygiene and Tropical Medicine
Public Health for Eye Care MSc 12FT 24PT

Manchester Metropolitan University
Advanced Practitioner Abuse Studies MA 24PT
Community Health MSc 12FT 24-36PT
Practice Development MSc 24-72PT
Specialist Community Public Health Nursing (Health Visiting or School Nursing) MSc 12-24FT 24-36PT/PGDip 12-24FT 24-36PT/PGCert 12-24FT 24-36PT

Northumbria University
Midwifery Professional Doctorate 48-72PT
Midwifery Studies PGDip 18FT
Nursing Professional Doctorate 48-72PT
Systemic Teaching, Training and Supervision MA 24PT

University of Nottingham
Health and Social Care MSc 12FT 24-48PT/PGCert 24-48PT/PGDip 12FT 24-48PT

Oxford Brookes University
Community Children's Nursing PGDip 12FT 24PT
Community Nursing in the Home / District Nursing PGDip 12FT 24PT
Nursing, Adult (Pre-registration) MSc 24FT 48PT/PGDip 24FT 48PT/PGCert 24FT 48PT
Nursing, Adult (Pre-registration) (Swindon) MSc 24FT 48PT/PGDip 24FT 48PT/PGCert 24FT 48PT
Nursing, Children's (Pre-registration) MSc 24FT 48PT/PGDip 24FT 48PT/PGCert 24FT 48PT
Nursing, Mental Health (Pre-registration) MA 24FT 48PT/PGDip 24FT 48PT/PGCert 24FT 48PT
Specialist Community Public Health Nursing (Health Visiting) PGDip 12FT 24-26PT
Specialist Community Public Health Nursing (School Nursing) PGDip 12FT 24-36PT

Queen Margaret University, Edinburgh
Nursing MSc 12FT 36PT/PGDip 8FT 24-36PT/PGCert 24-84PT

Queen's University Belfast
Nursing Practice DMP (Doctorate) 36FT 60PT
Nursing/Midwifery: Advanced Professional Practice MSc 24FT 60PT

Robert Gordon University
Nursing MSc 12FT 12/36DL

University of Salford
Child and Adolescent Mental Health MSc 24PT/PGDip 18PT/PGCert 9PT
Lower Limb Health, Disease and Rehabilitation PGCert 12PT
Nursing MA 36FT/PGDip 24FT/PGCert 12FT
Nursing (Education, International, Practice, Research) MSc 12FT 36PT/PGDip 9FT 24PT/PGCert 6FT 12PT
Professional Doctorate (Health and Social Care) PhD by taught 60PT

Sheffield Hallam University
Nursing Studies - Adult or Mental Health Nursing PGDip 24FT
Specialist Mental Health Practice MA 36PT/PGDip 24PT/PGCert 12PT

University of Sheffield
Advanced Nursing Studies MMedSci 36DL/Diploma 36DL/Cert 36DL
Advancing Practice MMedSci 12FT 24PT/Diploma 9FT 18PT/Cert 6FT 12PT
Long-Term Health Conditions PGCert FlexiblePT
Nursing Studies leading to professional registration as an Adult Nurse PGDip 24FT

University of South Wales
Specialist Community Public Health Nursing (Health Visiting or School Health Nursing) MSc 12FT 36PT/PGDip 12FT 24PT

University of Southampton
Doctorate in Clinical Practice DClinP 48FT 84PT/MSc 12FT 24PT/PGDip 12FT 24PT/PGCert 8FT 16PT
Nursing (Pre-registration) MSc 36FT
Nursing, Midwifery & Health Visiting MSc 12FT

Staffordshire University
Community Practice MA 12FT 48PT

University of Stirling
Advanced Practice MSc 18PT/MSc 18PT
Health Research MRes 12FT 24/36PT 24/36DL

Teesside University
Nursing MSc 12FT
Nursing (Advanced Cardiac Care) MSc 36PT
Nursing (Advanced Nurse Practitioner) MSc 36PT
Nursing (Advanced Surgical Care Practitioner) MSc 36PT
Nursing (Specialist Field) MSc 36PT

Trinity College Dublin - the University of Dublin
Nursing (Child Health and Well-being Strand) MSc 12FT 24PT
Nursing MSc 12FT 24PT
Nursing (Specialist) PGDip 24PT

University of Ulster
Specialist Community Public Health Nursing (SCPHN) PGDip 12FT 24PT

University of Warwick
Diabetes in Pregnancy PGA 12PT
Organisation and Delivery of Diabetes Care PGA 12PT/CPDMod 1PT

University of West London
Advancing Practice (Community Matron) PGCert 12PT
Nursing and Healthcare MSc 12FT
The Management of Complex and Changing Health and Social Care Needs in Clients CPPD 4PT

University of Winchester
Delivery of Primary Health Care PGCert 24PT

Section sponsored by BPP UNIVERSITY COLLEGE

Business and social sciences
482 POSTGRADUATE DIRECTORY www.prospects.ac.uk/findcourses

Social sciences

Community nursing
Research Courses

Bucks New University
Nursing .... DNursing 48-84PT

Canterbury Christ Church University
Health & Social Care (inclduing Allied Health Profs Nursing & Midwifery, & Public Health .... PhD 48FT 60PT/MPhil 24FT 48PT

Cardiff University
Nursing, Medicine, Health and Social Care .... MPhil 12FT 36PT/PhD 36FT 60PT
Primary Care and Public Health .... PhD 36FT/MPhil 36FT

University of Dundee
Nursing & Midwifery .... PhD 36FT 48FT MPhil 24FT

University of Kent
Community Care .... MPhil 24FT 36PT/PhD 36FT 60PT

University of Sheffield
Primary Medical Care and Ageing .... PhD 36FT 72PT/MPhil 24FT 48PT

University of Stirling
Nursing and Midwifery - Research .... PhD 36FT 72PT/MPhil 24FT 48PT

University of West London
Nursing .... Professional Doctorate (PD) 33FT 45PT

Community teaching
Taught Courses

University of Bedfordshire
MA Community Dance Leadership .... MA 12FT 24PT

University of Brighton
Inclusive Arts Practice .... MA 24-72PT/PGCert 24-72PT

University of Edinburgh
Community Education .... MSc 12FT 24-36PT

Goldsmiths, University of London
Applied Anthropology & Community Development .... MA 12FT 24PT

University of Sheffield
Education: Working with Communities .... MA(Ed) 12FT

University of Strathclyde
Community Care .... MSc 36PT N/ADL/PGDip 24PT/PGCert 12PT

Community teaching
Research Courses

University of Dundee
Community Learning & Development .... MPhil 24FT

Crime prevention
Taught Courses

University of Aberdeen
Sex, Gender, Violence: Contemporary Critical Approaches .... MSc 12FT 24PT/PGDip 9FT 18PT

Birkbeck, University of London
Medical Leadership .... MSc 24-60PT/PGDip 24-60PT/PGCert 24-60PT

Brunel University
Intelligence and Security Studies .... MA 12FT 30PT

University of Cambridge
Applied Criminology and Police Management .... MSt 24PT
Applied Criminology, Penology and Management .... MSt 24PT
Criminological Research .... MPhil 9FT
Criminology .... MPhil 9FT

University of Central Lancashire
Conflict and Violence Minimisation .... PGCert 24PT
Counter Terrorism .... MSc 12FT
Criminal Investigation .... MSc 12PT

University of Chester
Conflict Transformation (Work Based and Integrative Studies) .... MA 24-72PT/MSc 24-72PT/PGDip 24-60PT/PGCert 12-36PT

University of Cumbria
Leadership and Management in Policing MBA 36PT/PGDip 36PT/PGCert 36PT

University of Dundee
Advanced Practice (Infection: Diseases, Prevention & Control) ... MSc 36DL

Durham University
Conflict Prevention, Sustainable Peace and Security ..... MSc 12FT

University of Edinburgh
Criminal Law .... LLM 12FT 24PT
Criminal Law and Criminal Justice .... LLM 12FT 24PT
Criminology and Criminal Justice .... MSc 12FT 24PT
Global Crime, Justice and Security .... MSc 12FT 24PT

University of Glasgow
Drugs and Alcohol Studies .... MSc 12FT 24PT/PGDip 12FT 24PT/PGCert 12PT
Leadership Drugs & Alcohol Setting .... PGCert 9FT 18PT

Transnational Crime, Justice and Security .... MSc 12FT 24PT

Goldsmiths, University of London
Applied Anthropology & Community Development .... MA 12FT 24PT
Global Leadership .... MSc 12FT

Keele University
Ethics of Policing and Criminal Justice .... MA 12FT 24PT/PGDip 12PT

University of Leicester
Terrorism, Security and Policing .... MSc 12FT 24PT/PGDip 12FT 24PT

London Metropolitan University
Child Abuse .... PGCert variousFT
Policing, Security and Community Safety .... Professional Doctorate 48PT
Violence Against Women .... PGCert 12FT 24+PT

London School of Economics and Political Science (LSE)
Criminal Justice Policy .... MSc 12FT 24PT

London South Bank University
Crime & Litigation .... LLM 13FT 25PT
Criminology & Social Research Methods .... MSc 13FT 24PT
International Criminal Law & Procedure .... LLM 14FT 26PT

Manchester Metropolitan University
Criminology .... MA 12FT 24PT

Middlesex University
Public Protection .... MA 12FT 24PT

Nottingham Trent University
People and Physical Security .... CPD 2FT

University of Oxford
Criminology & Criminal Justice .... MSc 12FT
Criminology & Criminal Justice (Research Methods) ..... MSc 12FT
Software and Systems Security .... MSc 24-48PT

University of Portsmouth
Criminology and Community Safety .... MSc 12FT 24/ 36DL
Policing (MPA) .... MPA 24DL
Policing, Policy and Leadership .... MSc 24 / 36DL
Security Management .... MSc 12FT 24/ 36DL

Queen's University Belfast
Violence, Terrorism and Security .... MA 12FT 24PT/PGDip 12FT 24PT

University of Roehampton
Obesity: Risks and Prevention .... MSc 12FT 24PT

University of Salford
Terrorism and Security .... MA 12FT 36PT 36DL/PGDip 12FT 36PT 36DL

Sheffield Hallam University
Anti-Social Behaviour Law and Strategies .... PGCert 12PT

University of Sheffield
International Criminology .... MA 12FT

University of South Wales
International Policing .... MSc 12-60DL

University of Southampton
Crime Analysis .... MSc 12FT 24PT

University of Stirling
Criminological Research .... MRes 12FT 27PT/PGDip 9FT 21PT

University of Strathclyde
Criminal Justice and Penal Change .... MSc 12FT 24PT/LLM 12FT 24PT/PGDip 9FT

Teesside University
Criminal Investigation .... MSc 12FT 24PT

Trinity College Dublin - the University of Dublin
Drug and Alcohol Policy .... MSc 24PT

University of Ulster
Restorative Practices .... PGDip 9-15PT/MSc 24-48PT

UCL - University College London
Countering Organised Crime and Terrorism... MSc 12FT 24-60PT/PGDip 24PT
Crime Analysis (by Distance Learning) .... PGCert 12-24PT
Crime Prevention and Community Safety PGCert 9FT/PGDip 9FT 18-45PT
Crime Science .... MSc 12FT 24-60PT
Crime and Forensic Science .... MSc 12FT

University of Winchester
Reconciliation .... MA 12FT 24PT/DipHE 12FT 24PT/PGCert 12FT 24PT
Reconciliation and Peacebuilding .... MA 12FT 24PT/PGDip 12FT 24PT/PGCert 12FT 24PT

University of Worcester
Dynamics of Domestic Volence .... MA 24PT/PGDip 24PT/PGCert 12PT

Crime prevention
Research Courses

University of Bedfordshire
Crime, Society and the Media .... PhD 36FT 72PT

University of Cambridge
Criminology .... PhD 36FT 60PT

University of Hertfordshire
Centre for Community Research .... PhD 36FT 72PT/MPhil 24FT 48PT/MRes 12FT 24PT

The Open University
Policing and Criminal Justice ..... PhD 36FT 72PT variableDL/MPhil 15FT 24PT variableDL
Policing, punishment and justice .... PhD 36FT 72PT variableDL/MPhil 15FT 24PT variableDL

University of Sheffield
Criminology and Socio-Legal Studies. PhD 36FT 72PT/MPhil 24FT 48PT

UCL - University College London
Crime Science .... PhD 36FT 60PT

Criminology
Taught Courses

Aberystwyth University
Research Training .... LLM 12FT 24PT

Anglia Ruskin University
Criminology (Transnational Crime) .... MA 12FT 24PT

Bangor University
Comparative Criminology and Criminal Justice .... MA 12FT 24PT/PGDip 9FT
Criminology and Criminal Justice .... PhD by taught 36FT 72PT/MPhil 12-24FT 24-36PT/MARes 12FT 24PT
Criminology and Law .... MA 12FT
Criminology and Sociology .... MA 12FT 21-30PT/PGDip 9FT 17-21PT/PGCert 5FT 12-21PT
Forensic Linguistics .... MSc 12FT 24PT
Language Development .... MSc 12FT 36PT
Law and Criminology .... LLM 12FT

Birmingham City University
Criminology .... MA 12FT 24PT/PGDip 8FT 12PT/PGCert 3FT 9PT

University of Birmingham
Clinical Criminology .... MSc 24PT/PGDip 12PT

University of Bradford
Applied Criminal Justice Studies .... MA 24PT/PGDip 21PT/PGCert 9PT
Human Trafficking and Contemporary Slavery... MSc 24PT/PGDip 21PT/PGCert 9PT

University of Brighton
Criminology .... MA 12FT 24-72PT/PGDip 12FT 24-72PT/PGCert 12FT 24-72PT

University of Cambridge
Applied Criminology and Police Management .... MSt 24PT
Applied Criminology, Penology and Management .... MSt 24PT
Criminological Research .... MPhil 9FT
Criminology .... MPhil 9FT

Canterbury Christ Church University
Criminology and Criminal Justice .... MA 12FT 36PT

Cardiff University
Criminology and Criminal Justice .... MSc 12FT

University of Central Lancashire
Conflict and Violence Minimisation .... PGCert 24PT
Counter Terrorism .... MSc 12FT
Criminal Investigation .... MSc 12PT
Global Security and Justice .... MA 12FT

City University London
Criminology and Criminal Justice .... MA 12FT 24PT
Social Research Methods .... MSc 12FT 24PT

University of Cumbria
Leadership and Management in Policing MBA 36PT/PGDip 36PT/PGCert 36PT

De Montfort University
Criminology and Criminal Justice .... MA 24-36DL
Doctorate in criminology and criminal justice .... Doctorate 48-72PT

University of Derby
Criminal Investigation .... MSc 12FT 24PT
International and Comparative Law .... LLM 12FT 36PT

Dublin Institute of Technology
Criminology .... MA 12FT 24PT

University of Dundee
Forensic Odontology .... MFOdont 12FT
Forensic Toxicology .... MFTox 12FT

Durham University
Criminology and Criminal Justice .... MSc 12FT

University of East Anglia
Social Science Research Methods: Business .... MRes 12FT 24PT
Social Science Research Methods: Education .... MRes 12FT 24PT
Social Science Research Methods: Law .... MRes 12FT 24PT
Social Science Research Methods: Psychology .... MRes 12FT 24PT
Social Science Research Methods: Social Work ... MRes 12FT 24PT

Business and social sciences
www.prospects.ac.uk/findcourses POSTGRADUATE DIRECTORY 483

Social sciences

Edge Hill University
Criminology .... MRes 12-24FT 18-36PT

University of Edinburgh
Criminal Law .... LLM 12FT 24PT
Criminal Law and Criminal Justice .... LLM 12FT 24PT
Criminology and Criminal Justice .... MSc 12FT 24PT
Forensic Anthropology .... MSc 12FT 24PT
Global Crime, Justice and Security .... MSc 12FT 24PT

University of Essex
Criminology and Socio-Legal Research .... MA 12FT 24PT
Organised Crime, Terrorism and Security .... MSc 12FT 24PT

University of Exeter
Security, Conflict and Justice .... MRes 12FT 24PT
Socio-Legal Research .... MRes 12FT 24PT

Glasgow Caledonian University
Social Research .... MSc 12FT 24PT

University of Glasgow
Criminology .... MRes 12FT 24PT/PGDip 9FT 21PT
Criminology & Criminal Justice .... MSc 12FT 24PT/PGDip 9FT 21PT
Sociology and Research Methods .... MRes 12FT 24PT
Transnational Crime, Justice and Security .... MSc 12FT 24PT

University of Gloucestershire
Criminology ...... PGCert 4FT 8PT/PGDip 8FT 20PT/MSc 12FT 24PT

Glyndwr University
Criminology and Criminal Justice .... MA 12FT 24PT

University of Greenwich
Criminal Justice StudiesPGCert 12FT 24PT/MSc 12FT 24PT/PGDip 12FT 24PT
Criminology .... MA 12FT 24PT/PGDip 12FT 24PT
International Criminology .... MA 12FT 24PT/PGCert 12FT 24PT/PGDip 12FT 24PT

Keele University
Criminology and Criminal Justice .... MA 12FT 24PT/PGDip 12FT 24PT/PGCert 12FT 24PT/MRes 12FT 24PT

University of Kent
Criminology .... MA 12FT 24PT
Criminology with a semester abroad .... MA 12FT 24PT
Security and Terrorism .... MA 12FT 24PT/PGDip 12FT 24PT
Social and Public Policy: Criminal Justice (Distance Learning, Medway) .... MA 24DL/PGDip 24DL

Kingston University
Criminological Psychology .... MA 12FT 24PT
Criminology .... MA 12FT 24PT

Lancaster University
Criminology .... MRes 12FT 24PT

Leeds Metropolitan University
Criminology .... MSc 12FT 24PT

University of Leeds
Criminal Justice Studies .... MA 12FT 24PT
Criminal Justice Studies and Policing .... MA 12FT 24PT/PGDip 12FT 24PT
Criminal Law and Criminal Justice .... LLM 12FT 24PT
Criminological Research .... MA 12FT 24+PT
Criminology .... MA 12FT 24PT

University of Leicester
Applied Criminology .... MSc 12FT 24PT/PGDip 12FT 24PT
Clinical Criminology .... MSc 12FT 24PT/PGDip 12FT 24PT
Criminology .... MSc 12FT 24PT/PGDip 12FT 24PT
Criminology and Criminal Justice .... MSc 24DL/PGDip 18DL/PGCert 12DL
Forensic Science and Criminal Justice .... MSc 24-27DL
Security and Risk Management .... MSc 24DL/PGDip 18DL/PGCert 12DL

Liverpool Hope University
Criminal Justice .... MA 12FT 24PT/PGDip 12FT 24PT/PGCert 6FT 12PT

London Metropolitan University
Criminology .... MA 12FT 24PT
Women and Child Abuse .... MSc 12FT 24PT

London South Bank University
Crime & Litigation .... LLM 13FT 25PT
Criminology & Social Research Methods .... MSc 13FT 24PT

Manchester Metropolitan University
Criminology .... MA 12FT 24PT
Psychology and Criminology .... MSc 12FT 24-36PT/PGDip 12FT 24-36PT/PGCert 12FT 24-36PT

University of Manchester
Crime, Law and Society .... MA 12FT 24PT
Criminology & Socio-Legal Studies .... MRes 12FT 24PT

Middlesex University
Criminology .... MA 12FT 24PT
Criminology with Forensic Psychology .... MSc 12FT 24PT
Public Protection .... MA 12FT 24PT
Youth Justice, Community Safety, and Applied Criminology ... MA 12FT 24PT

University of Northampton
Criminology .... MSc 12FT 24PT/PGDip 12PT

Northumbria University
Criminology and Criminal Justice .... MA 12FT 24PT

Nottingham Trent University
Criminology .... MA 12FT 24PT
International Criminal Justice .... LLM 12FT 24PT

University of Nottingham
Criminological Psychology .... MSc 12FT 24PT
Socio-Legal and Criminological Research .... MA 12FT

The Open University
Social Policy and Criminology .... MA variableDL

University of Oxford
Criminology & Criminal Justice .... MSc 12FT
Criminology & Criminal Justice (Research Methods) ..... MSc 12FT

Plymouth University
Criminology .... MSc 12FT

University of Portsmouth
Crime Science, Investigation and Intelligence .... MSc 12FT 24PT
Criminology and Community Safety .... MSc 12FT 24/ 36DL
Criminology and Criminal Justice .... MSc 12FT 24/ 36DL
Criminology and Criminal Pyschology .... MSc 12FT 24/ 36DL

Queen's University Belfast
Criminology .... MSSc 12FT 24PT/PGDip 12FT 24PT

Sheffield Hallam University
Forensic Criminolgy .... MSc 12FT 24PT
International Criminal Justice ... MA 12FT 24PT/PGCert 6FT 12PT/PGDip 3FT 6PT Doctorate 36-60FT 48-84PT MA 12FT 24PT MA 12FT 24PT/PGDip 12PT/PGCert 6PT

University of Sheffield
Global Justice .... MA 12FT 24PT
International Criminology .... MA 12FT

University of South Wales
Criminal and Social Justice .... MA 12FT 24PT
Criminology and Criminal JusticeMSc 12FT 24PT/PGDip 4FT 8PT/PGCert 8FT 16PT

Southampton Solent University
Criminology and Criminal Justice .... MSc 12FT

University of Southampton
Crime Analysis .... MSc 12FT 24PT

University of Stirling
Applied Social Research .... MSc 12FT 30PT/PGDip 9FT 18PT
Applied Social Research (Criminology) .... MSc 12FT 30PT/PGDip 9FT 18PT
Applied Social Research .... MRes 12FT 30PT
Criminological Research .... MRes 12FT 27PT/PGDip 9FT 21PT

University of Strathclyde
Criminal Justice and Penal Change .... MSc 12FT 24PT/LLM 12FT 24PT/PGDip 9FT

University of Surrey
Criminology, Criminal Justice and Social Research .... MSc 12FT 24PT

Swansea University
Applied Criminal Justice and Criminology .... MA 12FT 36PT

Teesside University
Criminal Investigation .... MSc 12FT 24PT
Criminology .... MSc 12FT 24PT

UCL - University College London
Crime Analysis (by Distance Learning) .... PGCert 12-24PT
Crime Prevention and Community Safety .... PGCert 9FT/PGDip 9FT 18-45PT
Crime Science .... MSc 12FT 24-60PT
Crime and Forensic Science .... MSc 12FT

University of West London
Criminology and Criminal Justice .... LLM 24PT

Criminology
Research Courses

Aberystwyth University
Law & Criminology .... LLM by research 12FT 24PT MPhil 12FT 24PT PhD 36FT 60PT

Bangor University
Criminology and Criminal Justice .... PhD 36FT 60PT/MPhil 12-24FT 24-36PT

University of Bedfordshire
Crime, Society and the Media .... PhD 36FT 72PT

Birmingham City University
Social Sciences .... PhD 36FT 60PT/MPhil 36FT 60PT

University of Cambridge
Criminology .... PhD 36FT 60PT

Cardiff University
Crime, Security and Justice .... PhD 36FT possiblePT/MPhil 12FT possiblePT

University of Dundee
Forensic Medicine .... MPhil 24FT

University of Essex
Criminology ..... PhD 36FT 72PT/MPhil 24FT 48PT/MA by research 12FT 24PT
Criminology and Socio-Legal Research .... PhD 36FT 72PT/MPhil 24FT 48PT/MA by research 12FT 24PT

University of Hull
Criminology .... PhD 36FT 60PT/MPhil 24FT 36PT

Keele University
Criminology .... PhD 24-48FT 48-84PT/MPhil 12-24FT 24-36PT

University of Kent
Criminology ..... MPhil 24FT 36PT/PhD 36FT 60PT/MA by research 12FT 24PT
The Doctorate in Cultural and Global Criminology (DCGC)..... PhD 36FT 60PT

University of Leicester
Department of Criminology ...... PhD 36FT 72PT/MPhil 24FT 48PT

University of Liverpool
Criminological Research .... MRes 12FT 24PT

University of Manchester
Criminology .... PhD 36FT 72PT/MPhil 12FT 24PT

Middlesex University
Sociology and Criminology .... PhD 36FT 60PT/MPhil 24FT 48PT

Nottingham Trent University
Law .... MPhil 24FT 48PT/PhD 48FT 72PT

The Open University
Policing and Criminal Justice..... PhD 36FT 72PT variableDL/MPhil 15FT 24PT variableDL
Policing, punishment and justice....... PhD 36FT 72PT variableDL/MPhil 15FT 24PT variableDL
Social Policy and Criminology ... PhD 36FT 72PT variableDL/MPhil 15FT 24PT variableDL

University of Oxford
Legal Research .... DPhil 48FT

Queen's University Belfast
Law .... PhD 36FT 72PT/MPhil 24FT 48PT

University of Sheffield
Criminology and Socio-Legal Studies. PhD 36FT 72PT/MPhil 24FT 48PT

Swansea University
Criminology .... MPhil 24FT 48PT/PhD 36FT 72PT

UCL - University College London
Crime Science .... PhD 36FT 60PT

Critical theory
Taught Courses

Bangor University
English .... PhD by taught 36FT 72-96PT/MPhil 24FT 48-60PT

University of Brighton
Cultural and Critical Theory (Aesthetics and Cultural Theory) ...... MA 12FT 24PT/PGDip 12FT 24PT/PGCert 12FT 24PT
Cultural and Critical Theory (Globalisation, Politics and Culture) .. .. MA 12FT 24PT/PGDip 12FT 24PT/PGCert 12FT 24PT
Cultural and Critical Theory (Philosophy and Critical Theory) .... MA 12FT 24PT/PGDip 12FT 24PT/PGCert 12FT 24PT

Cardiff University
Critical and Cultural Theory .... MA 12FT 24PT

University of Derby
Systemic Thinking and Practice .... PGCert 12PT

University of Dundee
Art and Humanities .... MFA 12FT
Writing Practice & Study .... MLitt 12FT

Durham University
Studies in Poetry .... MA 12FT 24PT

University of East Anglia
Biography and Creative Non-Fiction .... MA 12FT 24PT
Creative Writing: Poetry .... MA 12FT 24PT
Creative Writing: Prose .... MA 12FT 24PT
Creative Writing: Scriptwriting .... MA 12FT 24PT
Culture and Modernity .... MA 12FT 24PT
Philosophy and Literature .... MA 12FT 24PT
Writing the Modern World .... MA 12FT 24PT

Edge Hill University
Critical Screen Practice .... MA 12FT 24PT

University of Exeter
Creative Writing .... MA 11FT 23PT
English Literary Studies .... MA 11FT 23PT

Glasgow School of Art
Writing and Criticism .... PGCert 4FT 8PT/PGDip 8FT 16PT/MLitt 12FT 24PT

University of Glasgow
Arts of China .... MLitt 12FT
Arts of Europe .... MLitt 12FT/PGDip 9FT
Creative Writing .... MFA 24FT

Goldsmiths, University of London
Creative and Cultural Industries .... GradDip 12FT

Social sciences

Critical & Creative Analysis ... MA 12FT 24PT

University of Kent
Arts Criticism ... MA 12FT 24PT
Critical Theory (taught jointly with the School of European Culture and Languages) ... MA 12FT 24PT

King's College London
Critical Methodologies ... MA 12FT 24PT

Kingston University
Aesthetics and Art Theory ... MA 12FT 24PT
Criticism, Literature, Theory ... MA 12FT 24PT
Philosophy and Contemporary Critical Theory ... MA 12FT 24PT

University of Northampton
Modern English Studies ... MA 12FT 24PT/PGDip 12PT

University of Nottingham
Critical Theory ... MA 12FT 24-36PT/PGDip 9FT 24PT MA 12FT 24-36PT
Critical Theory and Cultural Studies ... MA 12FT 24-36PT
Critical Theory and Politics ... MA 12FT 24PT
Modern Languages and Critical Theory ... MA 12FT 24PT

University of Roehampton
Film and Screen Cultures ... MA 12FT 24-36PT

School of Oriental and African Studies - SOAS
African Literature ... MA 12FT 24-36PT
Anthropology of Media ... MA 12FT 24-36PT
Anthropology of Travel, Tourism and Pilgrimage ... MA 12FT 24PT
Arabic Literature ... MA 12FT 24-36PT
Chinese Studies ... MA 12FT 24-36PT
Comparative Literature (Asia/Africa) ... MA 12FT 24-36PT
Critical Media and Cultural Studies ... MA 12FT 24-36PT
Development Studies ... MSc 12FT 24PT
Development Studies with Special Reference to Central AsiaMSc 12FT 24PT
Economics (with Reference to Africa) ... MSc 12FT 24PT
Economics (with Reference to the Asia Pacific Region) ... MSc 12FT 24PT
Ethnomusicology ... MMus 12FT 24-36PT
Gender Studies ... MA 12FT 24-36PT
Global Media and Postnational Communication ... MA 12FT 24-36PT
International Politics ... MSc 12FT 24PT
International and Comparative Legal Studies ... MA 12FT 24-36PT
Islamic Societies and Cultures ... MA 12FT 24-36PT
Islamic Studies ... MA 12FT 24-36PT
Israeli Studies ... MA 12FT 24-36PT
Japanese Studies ... MA 12FT 24-36PT
Korean Studies ... MA 12FT 24-36PT
Languages and literatues of South East Asia ... MA 12FT 24-36PT
Medical Anthropology ... MA 12FT 24-36PT
Near and Middle Eastern Studies ... MA 12FT 24-36PT
Pacific Asian Studies ... MA 12FT 24-36PT
Postcolonial Studies ... MA 12FT 24PT
Research for International Development ... MSc 12FT 24PT
Social Anthropology ... MA 12FT 24-36PT
Social Anthropology of Development ... MA 12FT 24-36PT
South Asian Area Studies ... MA 12FT 24PT
South East Asian Studies ... MA 12FT 24-36PT
State, Society and Development ... MSc 12FT 24PT
Turkish Studies ... MA 12FT 24PT

University of Sussex
Creative and Critical Writing ... MA 12FT 24PT
Critical Theory ... MA 12FT 24PT

Swansea University
International Security & Development ... MA 12FT 24PT
Literary Translation ... MA 24FT

Critical theory
Research Courses

Bangor University
Creative and Critical Writing, Film and Media, Professional Writing ... MPhil 24FT 48PT/PhD 36FT 72PT
Creative and Critical Writing, Film and Media, Professional Writing: Practice-Led Research ... MPhil 24FT 48PT/PhD 36FT 72PT

Cardiff University
Creative and Critical Writing ... PhD 36FT
Critical and Cultural Theory ... PhD 36FT/MPhil 12-24FT

University of Exeter
EnglishPhD 36-48FT 72PT/MPhil 24FT 48PT/MA by research 12FT 24PT

University of Gloucestershire
Creative Writing ... PhD 30-48FT

University of Kent
The Contemporary Novel: Practice as Research ... MA by research 12FT 24PT/PhD 36FT 60PT

Lancaster University
Ruskin Studies ... MPhil 24FT 36PT/PhD 36FT 48PT

University of Nottingham
Critical Theory and Cultural Studies ... PhD 36FT 72PT/MPhil 24FT 48PT

Cultural Studies and Critical Theory ... New Route PhD 48FT 96PT

The Open University
Environment, governance and justice ... PhD 36FT 72PT variableDL/MPhil 15FT 24PT variableDL
Modern art theory and practice ... PhD 36FT 72PT variableDL/MPhil 15FT 24PT variableDL

University of Oxford
English (to 1550) ... DPhil 48FT

Queen Mary, University of London
European Studies ... MA by research

University of Salford
Centre for Literary and Cultural Studies ... PhD/MPhil

School of Oriental and African Studies - SOAS
Art and Archaeology ... PhD 36FT/MPhil 24FT
Development Studies ... PhD 36FT 48-60PT
Economics ... PhD 36FT 72PT/MPhil 24FT 36PT
Languages and Cultures of South Asia ... PhD 36FT 72PT/MPhil 24FT 48PT
Media and Film Studies ... PhD 36-48FT
Politics ... PhD 36FT 72PT/MPhil 24FT 36PT
Social Anthropology ... PhD 36FT/MPhil 24FT

University of Sussex
English Research Programme ... PhD 24-48FT 36-72PT/MPhil 12-36FT 24-48PT
Social and Political Thought ... DPhil 24-48FT 36-72PT/MPhil 12-36FT 24-48PT

Cultural and area studies
Taught Courses

University of Aberdeen
Bayt al-Maqdis and Jerusalem Studies ... MLitt 12FT 24PT/PGDip 9FT 18PT
Ethnology and Folklore ... MLitt 12FT 24PT
Multiculturalism ... MLitt 12FT 24PT/PGDip 9FT 18PT

Aberystwyth University
Gwleidyddiaeth a Chymdeithas Cymru (Arbenigol) ... MA 12FT 24PT/PGDip 9FT 18PT
Gwleidyddiaeth a Chymdeithas Cymru (Hyfforddiant Ymchwil) ... MA 12FT 24PT/PGDip 9FT 18PT
Welsh Politics and Society (Research Training) ... MA 12FT 24PT/PGDip 9FT 18PT
Welsh Politics and Society (Specialist) ... MA 12FT 24PT/PGDip 9FT 18PT

Anglia Ruskin University
Intercultural Communication ... MA 12FT 24PT

University of Bath
International Relations ... MA 12FT/PGDip 9FT 21PT/PGCert 4FT 16PT

University of Bedfordshire
Intercultural Communication ... MA 12FT 24PT

Birkbeck, University of London
Cultural Enquiry ... MRes 12FT 24PT
Culture, Diaspora, Ethnicity ... MSc 12FT 24PT/PGDip 12FT 24PT/PGCert 12PT
Intercultural Communication for Business and Professions ... MA 12FT 24PT
Medieval Literature and Culture ... MA 12FT 24PT
Romantic Studies ... MA 12FT 24PT/PGDip 12FT 24PT/PGCert 12FT 24PT

Birmingham City University
Social Media ... MA 12FT 24PT 12-36DL

University of Birmingham
Cultural Inquiry ... MA 12FT 24PT

University of Brighton
Cultural and Critical Theory (Aesthetics and Cultural Theory) ... MA 12FT 24PT/PGDip 12FT 24PT/PGCert 12FT 24PT
Cultural and Critical Theory (Globalisation, Politics and Culture) ... MA 12FT 24PT/PGDip 12FT 24PT/PGCert 12FT 24PT
Sport and Media ... MSc 12FT 24-36PT/PGDip 12FT 24PT/PGCert 12FT 24PT
Sport and Society ... MSc 12FT 24-36PT/PGDip 12FT 24PT/PGCert 12FT 24PT

University of Bristol
Ethnicity and Multiculturalism ... MSc 12FT 24PT
Social and Cultural Theory ... MSc 12FT 24PT

Brunel University
Science, Technology and Contemporary Society ... MSc 12FT 30PT
Social and Cultural Research ... MSc 12FT 30PT

University of Cambridge
Archaeology ... MPhil 11-15FT
Modern South Asian Studies ... MPhil(A) 9FT
Polar Studies ... MPhil 9FT
Screen Media and Cultures ... MPhil 9FT
Social Anthropological Analysis ... MPhil 11FT

Cardiff Metropolitan University
Sport, Body & Society ... MA 12FT 36PT/PGDip 12FT 36PT/PGCert 9FT 36PT

Cardiff University
Critical and Cultural Theory ... MA 12FT 24PT
Music, Culture and Politics ... MA 12FT 24PT

University of Central Lancashire
Global Communication Studies ... MA 12FT 24-36PT
Religion, Culture & Society ... MA 12FT 24-36PT/PGDip 12FT 24PT/PGCert 12FT 12-24PT
Rhetoric ... MA 12FT 24PT

City University London
Global Political Economy ... MA 12FT/MA 24PT
International Communications and Development ... MA 12FT 24PT
Media and Communications ... MA 12FT 24PT

University College Cork
Arts (Folklore) ... HDip 9FT
Folklore ... MA 12FT

University of Dundee
Gender, Culture and Society ... MLitt 12FT
Scottish History ... MLitt 24-60DL MLitt 12FT

Durham University
Culture and Difference (Interdisciplinary) ... MA 12FT
International Cultural Heritage Management ... MA 12FT 24PT

University of East Anglia
American Literature ... MA 12FT 24PT
American Studies ... MA 12FT 24PT
American Studies and Film Studies ... MA 12FT 24PT
Conflicts in Intercultural Communication ... MA 12FT 24PT
Cultural Heritage and International Development ... MA 12FT 24PT
Cultural Heritage and Museum Studies ... MA 12FT 24PT
Language and Intercultural Communication ... MA 12FT 24PT
Media and Cultural Politics ... MA 12FT 24PT
Media, Culture and Society ... MA 12FT 24PT
The Arts of Africa, Oceania and the Americas ... MA 12FT 24PT

Edge Hill University
History and Culture ... MA 12FT 24PT
Popular Culture ... MA 12FT 24PT

University of Edinburgh
Cultural Studies ... MSc 12FT 24PT
Digital Media and Culture ... MSc(Res) 12FT 24PT
English Literature: Material Cultures and the History of the Book ... MSc 12FT 24PT
Environment, Culture and Society ... MSc 12FT 24PT
International Development ... MSc 12FT 24PT
International Relations ... MSc 12FT 24PT
International Relations of the Middle East ... MRCPsych 12FT
International Relations of the Middle East with Arabic ... MSc 24FT
Japanese Society and Culture ... MSc 12FT 24PT
Media, Culture & Practice ... MSc 12FT
Modern Chinese Cultural Studies ... MSc 12FT 24PT
Social and Cultural History ... MSc 12FT
Socio-Cultural Studies ...

National University of Ireland Galway
Culture & Colonialism ... MA 12FT
Ethics, Culture and Global Change ... MA 12FT 24PT

Glasgow Caledonian University
Creative and Cultural Business ... MA 12FT

University of Glasgow
Environment, Culture & Communication (Dumfries Campus) ... MLitt 12FT 24PT
Global Economy ... MSc 12FT 24PT
International Relations ... MSc 12FT 24PT MRes 12FT 24PT
Modernities: Literature, Theory & Culture ... MLitt 12FT 24PT

Goldsmiths, University of London
Anthropology and Cultural Politics ... MA 12FT 24PT
Cultural Policy and Tourism ... MA 12FT 24PT
Cultural Policy, Relations and Diplomacy ... MA 12FT 24PT
Cultural Studies ... MA 12FT 24PT
Culture Industry ... MA 12FT 24PT
Education: Culture, Language and Identity ... MA 12FT 24-60PT
Gender, Media & Culture ... MA 12FT 24PT
Global Arts ... MA 12FT 24PT
Latin American Studies ... MA 12FT 24PT
Postcolonial Culture & Global Policy ... MA 12FT 24PT
Sociocultural Linguistics ... MA 12FT 24PT

University of Huddersfield
English Language Proficiency and British Culture ... PGCert 12PT

Institute of Education
Computer Games, Culture and Education ... 30 Credit Module 3PT

Keele University
Global Media and Culture ... MA 12 - 15FT 24 - 27PT/PGDip 9-12FT 21-24PT/PGCert 9-12FT 21-24PT
Media, Communications and Culture ... MRes 12FT 24PT

University of Kent
International Political Economy (Brussels) ... MA 12FT 24PT
Postcolonial Studies ... MA 12FT 24PT
Postcolonial Studies (Paris option) ... MA 12FT

Social sciences

King's College London
Cultural & Creative Industries .... MA 12FT 24PT

Kingston University
Criticism, Literature, Theory .... MA 12FT 24PT
Language and Society .... MA 12FT 24PT

Leeds Metropolitan University
International Political Economy........ MA 12FT
International Relations .... MA 12FT 24PT/PGCert 12PT/PGDip 12FT 24PT

University of Leeds
Cultural Studies .... MA 12FT 24PT
Gender and Culture .... MA 12FT 24PT
Gender and Culture .... MA 12FT 24PT/PGDip 12FT 24PT
Postcolonial Literary and Cultural Studies........ MA 12PT

University of Leicester
New Media and Society........ MA 12FT

University of Lincoln
Media and Cultural Studies .... MRes 12FT 24PT

University of Liverpool
Cultural History........ MA 12FT 24PT
Manx Studies........ MA 12FT 24PT/PGDip 12FT

London Consortium
Humanities and Cultural Studies........ MRes 12FT

London Metropolitan University
Creative Industries .... MA 12FT 24PT

London School of Economics and Political Science (LSE)
Culture and Society........ MSc 12FT 24PT
International Political Economy........ MSc 11FT 23PT

London South Bank University
Creative Industries - Cultural Management........ MA 13FT

Loughborough University
Media And Cultural Analysis .... MA 12FT

Manchester Metropolitan University
English Studies: Contemporary Literature and Film........ MA 16FT 36PT/PGDip 12FT 24PT
Sociology and Global Change .... MA 12FT 24PT

University of Manchester
Intercultural Communication .... MA 12FT 24PT
Literature and Culture 1200-1700........ MA 12FT 24PT
Post-1900 Literatures, Theories and Cultures........ MA 12FT 24PT
Postcolonial Literatures and Cultures .... MA 12FT 24PT

Newcastle University
Cross Cultural Communications........ MA 12FT 24PT
Cross-Cultural Communication and Applied Linguistics........ MA 12FT 24PT
Cross-Cultural Communication and Education .... MA 12FT 24PT
Cross-Cultural Communication and International Marketing .... MA 12FT 24PT
Cross-Cultural Communication and Media Studies........ MA 12FT 24PT
International Politics (Global Justice and Ethics) ... MA 12FT 24PT
World Politics and Popular Culture........ MA 12FT 24PT

Northumbria University
Cultural Event Management........ MA 12/18FT 24/28PT 24/28DL
Cultural Management........ MA 12FT 24PT 22DL

Nottingham Trent University
International Relations ... MA 12FT 24PT/PGDip 9FT 24PT/PGCert 9FT 24PT

University of Nottingham
Critical Theory and Cultural Studies........ MA 12FT 24-36PT
Cultural Industries and Entrepreneurship .... MSc 12FT 24-36PT
Cultural Studies .... MA 12FT 24-36PT
Cultural Studies and Entrepreneurship .... MSc 12FT
Visual Culture........ MA 12FT 24PT

Oxford Brookes University
Food, Wine and Culture .... MA 12FT 36PT 24DL

University of Oxford
Global and Imperial History .... MSt 9FT
International Relations .... MPhil 21FT
Islamic Art and Archaeology (Research Methods)........ MSt 9FT
Jewish Studies........ MSt 9FT
Korean Studies .... MSt 9FT
Late Antique and Byzantine Studies........ MPhil 21FT/MSt 9FT
Latin American Studies........ MPhil 21FT/MSc 12FT
Migration Studies........ MSc 9FT
Social Anthropology (Research Methods)........ MSc 12FT

Plymouth University
English and Culture........ MA 12FT 24PT
History........ MA 12FT 24PT

University of Portsmouth
Literature, Culture and Identity .... MA 12FT 24PT

Queen Margaret University, Edinburgh
Arts and Cultural Management..... MA 12FT 24-84PT/PGDip 12FT 24-84PT/PGCert 12FT 24-84PT

Queen Mary, University of London
Anglo-German Cultural Relations........ MA 12FT 24PT

University of Reading
Archaeology .... MA 12FT 24PT
Law and Society .... M(Res) 12FT 24PT
Medieval Archaeology .... MA 12FT

Reseau Universitaire Transmanche
Intercultural Relations........ MA 15FT

Richmond, The American International University in London
International Relations .... MA 12FT 24PT

Royal Holloway, University of London
Cultural Geography (Research) .... MA 12FT 24PT
International Relations Theory .... MSc 12/9FT 24/20PT
Masters by Research (Comparative Literature and Culture)..... MA 12FT 24PT

University of Salford
International Relations and Globalisation... MA 12FT 36PT 36DL/PGDip 8FT 24PT 36DL
Literature, Culture and ModernityMA 12FT 36PT/PGDip 8FT 24PT

School of Oriental and African Studies - SOAS
African Literature........ MA 12FT 24-36PT
African Politics........ MSc 12FT 24-36PT
African Studies .... MA 12FT 24-36PT
Anthropology of Media........ MA 12FT 24-36PT
Anthropology of Travel, Tourism and Pilgrimage ... MA 12FT 24PT
Asian Politics........ MSc 12FT 24PT
Chinese Law .... MA 12FT 24PT
Chinese Literature .... MA 12FT 24-36PT
Chinese Studies........ MA 12FT 24-36PT
Comparative Literature (Asia/Africa)........ MA 12FT 24-36PT
Critical Media and Cultural Studies........ MA 12FT 24-36PT
Development Studies with Special Reference to Central Asia........ MSc 12FT 24PT
Dispute and Conflict Resolution........ MA 12FT 24PT
Economics (with Reference to Africa)........ MSc 12FT 24PT
Ethnomusicology........ MMus 12FT 24-36PT
Global Cinemas and the Transcultural........ MA 12FT 24-36PT
Global Creative and Cultural Industries .... MA 12FT
Global Media and Postnational Communication........ MA 12FT 24-36PT
Islamic Law........ MA 12FT 24PT
Islamic Societies and Cultures .... MA 12FT 24-36PT
Islamic Studies .... MA 12FT 24-36PT
Israeli Studies .... MA 12FT 24-36PT
Japanese Literature........ MA 12FT 24-36PT
Japanese Studies .... MA 12FT 24-36PT
Korean Literature........ MA 12FT 24-36PT
Korean Studies .... MA 12FT 24-36PT
Languages and literatues of South East Asia .... MA 12FT 24-36PT
Study of Contemporary Pakistan .... MA 12FT 24PT
Medical Anthropology .... MA 12FT 24-36PT
Middle East Politics........ MSc 12FT 24PT
Migration and Diaspora Studies........ MA 12FT 24-36PT
Near and Middle Eastern Studies........ MA 12FT 24-36PT
Pacific Asian Studies .... MA 12FT 24-36PT
Performance .... MMus 12FT 24PT
Political Economy of Development........ MSc 12FT 24-36PT
Politics of China .... MSc 12FT 24PT
Postcolonial Studies........ MA 12FT 24PT
Social Anthropology .... MA 12FT 24-36PT
Social Anthropology of Development........ MA 12FT 24-36PT
South Asian Area Studies .... MA 12FT 24PT
South East Asian Studies........ MA 12FT 24-36PT
Turkish Studies........ MA 12FT 24PT

Sheffield Hallam University
Cultural Policy and Management ..... MA 12FT 36PT/PGDip 24PT/PGCert 8PT
Cultural Studies .... MRes variousFT variousPT
History : Imperialism and Culture........ MA 36DL/PGDip 36DL/PGCert 36DL
Research Degrees - Cultural, Communication and Computing Research Institute .... MPhil 24-36FT 48-60PT/PhD by taught 36-48FT 60-72PT
Sport, Culture and Community... MA 12FT 24PT/PGDip 8FT 16PT/PGCert 4FT 8PT

University of Sheffield
Cultural Heritage Management........ MA 12FT
Cultures of the British Isles........ MA 12FT 24PT
Designing Learning Environments........ MA 12FT 24PT
Global Politics and Law .... MA 12FT 24PT
Global Politics and Law (Doshisha Pathway)........ MA 24FT
Globalisation and Development .... MA 12FT 24PT
Globalising Education: Policy and Practice .... MA 12FT
Hispanic Studies .... MA 12FT 24PT
International History........ MA 12FT 24PT
International Political Communication .... MA 12FT
International Studies........ MA 12FT 24PT
International and European Law........ LLM 12FT Up to 36PT
Latin American Studies .... MA 12FT 24PT
Management (Creative and Cultural Industries) .... MSc 12FT
Social Research........ MA 12FT 24PT

University of South Wales
Literature, Culture and Society .... MA 12FT 24PT
Social and Cultural History .... MA 12FT 24PT

University of Southampton
Film and Cultural Management .... MA 12FT 24PT
Global Politics........ MSc 12FT 24PT/PGDip 9FT 21PT
Global Security........ MSc 12FT 24PT/PGDip 9FT 21PT
International Law........ LLM 12FT 24PT
Jewish History and Culture........ MA 12FT 24PT/MRes 12FT 24PT
Social Policy and Social Research........ MSc 12FT 24PT/PGDip 9FT 21PT
Transnational Studies: Society, Culture, Language........ MA 12FT 24PT

University of St Andrews
Cultural Identity Studies........ MLitt 12FT 24PT/PGDip 9FT 18PT/MPhil 24FT
International Political Theory........ MLitt 12FT 24PT/MPhil 24FT
International Security Studies .... MLitt 12FT/PGDip 9FT
Middle East and Central Asian Security Studies. PGDip 9FT/MLitt 12FT/MPhil 24FT
Middle Eastern History & Culture.... PGDip 9FT/MLitt 12FT/MPhil 24FT
Peace and Conflict Studies........ MLitt 12FT
Social Anthropology .... MRes 12FT 24PT
Social Anthropology with African Studies .... MRes 12FT

Staffordshire University
International Relations .... MA 12FT 30-36DL
Social and Cultural Theory (via Distance Learning)........ MA 30DL

University of Stirling
International Conflict and Co-operation.... MSc 12FT 27PT/PGDip 9FT 21PT/PGCert 3FT 9PT

University of Strathclyde
Literature, Culture and Place... MLitt 12FT 24PT/PGDip 9FT 21PT/PGCert 4FT 9PT
Social Research........ MRes 12FT 24PT

Swansea University
Communication, Media Practice and Public Relations .... MA 12FT 24-36PT
International Communication & Development..... MA 12FT 24PT

Teesside University
Cultural History........ MA 12FT 24-36PT

Trinity College Dublin - the University of Dublin
Digital Humanities and Culture .... MPhil 12FT 24PT
International Politics .... MSc 12FT 24PT
Public History and Cultural Heritage........ MPhil 12FT 24PT
Texts, Contexts and Cultures .... PhD by taught 48FT

UCL - University College London
Cultural Heritage Studies........ MA 12FT 24PT
European Culture and Thought: Culture..... MA 12FT 24PT/PGDip 9FT 18PT/PGCert 3FT 6PT
European Culture and Thought: Thought... MA 12FT 24PT/PGDip 9FT 18PT/PGCert 3FT 6PT
Identity, Culture and Power........ MA 12FT 24PT
Language, Culture and History .... MA 12FT 24PT
Material and Visual Culture........ MA 12FT 24PT
Social and Cultural Anthropology........ MSc 12FT 24PT
Urban Studies........ MSc 12FT 24-60PT

University of Warwick
Comparative Cultural Studies .... MA 12FT 24PT/PGCert 3FT/PGDip 12FT
Comparative Literary and Cultural Studies........ MA 12FT 24PT
Intercultural Communication for Business and the Professions... MSc 12FT 24-48PT
International Cultural Policy and Management..... MA 12FT 24PT
Translation, Writing and Cultural Difference........ MA 12FT 24PT/PGDip 9FT 18PT

University of the West of England, Bristol
Intercultural Communication .... MA 12FT

University of Westminster
Architecture, Cultural Identity and Globalisation........ MA 12FT 24PT
Diversity and the Media .... MA 12FT
International Media Business .... MA 12FT 24PT

University of Winchester
Cultural Studies .... MA 12FT 24PT/PGDip 12FT 24PT/PGCert 12FT 24PT

University of Wolverhampton
Popular Culture........ MA 12FT 24PT

University of York
Culture and Thought after 1945 .... MA 12FT 24PT
Cultures of Empire, Resistance and Postcoloniality .... MA 12FT 24PT

Cultural and area studies

Research Courses

University of the Arts London - Central Saint Martins College of Art and Design
Cultural Studies ... PhD 24-48FT 36-96PT/MPhil 15-36FT 24-72PT

Birkbeck, University of London
Arts and Humanities .... MPhil 24FT 36PT/PhD 36-48FT 60-84PT
Humanities and Cultural Studies........ PhD 36FT/MPhil 36FT
Intercultural Communication .... New Route PhD 36FT 56PT

Section sponsored by BPP UNIVERSITY COLLEGE

Business and social sciences

486 POSTGRADUATE DIRECTORY www.prospects.ac.uk/findcourses

Social sciences

University of Cambridge
Archaeological Research .... MPhil 12FT

Canterbury Christ Church University
Media and Cultural Studies .... PhD 48FT 60PT/MPhil 24FT 48PT

Cardiff University
Area Studies .... PhD 36FT 72PT/MPhil 36FT 72PT
Centre for Global Communications Management Research ..PhD 36FT

University of East Anglia
Film, Television and Media Studies.....PhD 36FT 72PT/MPhil 24FT 48PT
Sainsbury Research Unit for the Arts of Africa, Oceania and the Americas .... PhD 36FT 72PT/MPhil 24FT 48PT/MA by research 12FT 24PT

University of Edinburgh
Cultural Studies .... PhD 36FT 72PT
Visual and Cultural Studies........ PhD 24FT 36PT/MPhil 12FT 24PT

University of Exeter
Art History and Visual Culture .... MPhil 36FT 60PT 60DL/PhD 48FT 84PT 84DL
Interdisciplinary Studies............ MPhil 36FT 60PT/PhD 48FT 84PT

Goldsmiths, University of London
Cultural Studies ....PhD 36-48FT 48-72PT/MPhil 24FT 36PT

Keele University
Cultural and Media Studies .... PhD 24-48FT 48-84PT/MPhil 12-24FT 24-36PT

University of Kent
Postcolonial StudiesMA by research 12FT 24PT/MPhil 24FT 36PT/PhD 36FT 60PT
Text and Event in Early Modern Europe (TEEME): An Erasmus Mundus Joint Doctorate .... PhD 36FT 60PT

King's College London
Culture, Media & Creative Industries Research... PhD 36FT/MPhil 36FT

Kingston University
Centre for Suburban Studies ....PhD 48FT 72PT/MPhil 24FT 48PT/MA by research 12FT 24PT
European Research Centre (ERC) ....PhD 48FT 72PT/MPhil 24FT 48PT/MA by research 12FT 24PT

Lancaster University
Cultural Research .... PhD 36FT 48PT/MPhil 24FT 36PT

University of Leeds
School of Fine Art, History of Art and Cultural Studies/CentreCATH ....PhD 36+FT/MPhil 24FT

Liverpool John Moores University
Media and Cultural Studies ..... MPhil 36FT 84PT/DPhil 36FT 84PT
Media, Critical and Creative ArtsMPhil 36FT 84PT/PhD 36FT 84PT

Manchester Metropolitan University
Communication, Cultural and Media Studies........ PhD 36FT 48PT 48DL/MPhil 18FT 36PT 36DL/MA by research 12FT 24PT 24DL
Department of Languages ....PhD 24-48FT 42-84PT 42-84DL/MPhil 18-36FT 36-72PT 36-72DL/MA by research 12-24FT 24-42PT 24-42DL
History of Art and Design ....PhD/MPhil

University of Manchester
Interdisciplinary Study of Culture .... PhD 36FT 72PT

Middlesex University
School of Humanities and Cultural Studies.......... PhD 36FT/MPhil 12-24FT/MA by research 12-24FT

University of Northampton
Literary and Cultural Studies..... PhD 36FT 48PT/MPhil 24FT 36PT

Nottingham Trent University
Communications, Cultural and Media Studies.....PhD 48FT 96PT/MPhil 36FT 72PT

University of Nottingham
Critical Theory and Cultural Studies...PhD 36FT 72PT/MPhil 24FT 48PT
Cultural Studies and Critical Theory... New Route PhD 48FT 96PT
Modern Languages and Cultures Research Areas MA by research 12FT 24PT
Visual Culture...........PhD 36FT 72PT/MPhil 24FT 48PT/MRes 12FT

The Open University
Ancient and Modern Reception of Antiquity .... PhD 36FT 72PT variableDL/MPhil 15FT 24PT variableDL
Citizenship and Governance......PhD 36FT 72PT variableDL/MPhil 15FT 24PT variableDL
Citizenship and security .... PhD 36FT 72PT variableDL/MPhil 15FT 24PT variableDL
Culture, Media and the Social...PhD 36FT 72PT variableDL/MPhil 15FT 24PT variableDL
Governing global security .... PhD 36FT 72PT variableDL/MPhil 15FT 24PT variableDL
Identities.......... PhD 36FT 72PT variableDL/MPhil 15FT 24PT variableDL
Personal life and intimacies.......PhD 36FT 72PT variableDL/MPhil 15FT 24PT variableDL
Politics of urban culture and space.... PhD 36FT 72PT variableDL/MPhil 15FT 24PT variableDL
Religion in Material, Visual and Performance Culture....PhD 36FT 72PT variableDL/MPhil 15FT 24PT variableDL
Religion, identities, cultures and citizenship.......... PhD 36FT 72PT variableDL/MPhil 15FT 24PT variableDL

University of Oxford
Institute of Social and Cultural Anthropology.......... DPhil 48FT
International Relations ....DPhil 48FT/MPhil 21FT

University of Portsmouth
Languages and Area Studies ..... MPhil 24FT 48PT/PhD 36FT 72PT

Queen's University Belfast
Geography: Society, Space and Culture ....PhD 36FT 72PT/MPhil 24FT 48PT
Past Cultural Change.......... PhD 36FT 72PT/MPhil 24FT 48PT

University of Roehampton
Media & Cultural Studies...PhD 24-48FT 36-60PT/MPhil 21-36FT 33-48PT

University of Salford
Centre for Literary and Cultural Studies ....PhD/MPhil
Social and Cultural Theory ....PhD/MPhil

School of Oriental and African Studies - SOAS
Department of Art and Archaeology ....PhD 36FT 72PT/MPhil 24FT 36PT
History .... PhD 36FT 72PT/MPhil 24FT 36PT
Languages and Cultures of South Asia ....PhD 36FT 72PT/MPhil 24FT 48PT
Media and Film Studies .... PhD 36-48FT
Music .... PhD 36FT 72PT/MPhil 24FT 36PT
Social Anthropology ....PhD 36FT/MPhil 24FT

Sheffield Hallam University
Centre for Regional Economic and Social Research Applied Social Research .... PhD 36FT 60PT

University of Southampton
Jewish History and Culture........ PhD 48FT 84PT/MPhil 48FT 84PT
Languages, Culture and Society..........PhD 36FT 72PT/MPhil 24FT 48PT
MRes Science and Heritage..........MRes 12FT

University of St Andrews
Cultural Identity Studies....... PhD 36FT 72PT/MPhil 12-24FT 48PT
Social Anthropology ....PhD 36FT 72PT/MPhil 12-24FT 24-48PT

University of Surrey
Translation Studies ....PhD 21-72FT 33-96PT/MPhil 18-33FT

University of Sussex
Media and Cultural Studies Research Programme ... PhD 24-48FT 36-72PT/MPhil 12-36FT 24-48PT
Social and Political Thought ....DPhil 24-48FT 36-72PT/MPhil 12-36FT 24-48PT

Teesside University
Cultural Studies .... PhD 24-60FT 36PT/MPhil 18FT 30PT

University of the Highlands and Islands
Gaelic and Related Studies......... PhD 36FT 72PT/MPhil 24FT 48PT

University of Warwick
Comparative and Literary Cultural Studies...........PhD 36FT 60PT/MPhil 24FT 36PT
Cultural Policy Studies ...PhD 36FT 60PT/MPhil 24FT 36PT/MA by research 12FT 24PT

Cultural geography
Taught Courses

University of Aberdeen
Transitional Justice and Reconciliation..........MSc 12FT 24PT/PGDip 9FT 18PT

University of Bath
Global Political Economy: transformations and policy analysis ... MRes 12FT 24-36PT

University of Birmingham
International Development............MSc 24-48DL/PGDip 18-48DL

University of Brighton
Cultural and Critical Theory (Aesthetics and Cultural Theory) ...... MA 12FT 24PT/PGDip 12FT 24PT/PGCert 12FT 24PT
Cultural and Critical Theory (Globalisation, Politics and Culture).........MA 12FT 24PT/PGDip 12FT 24PT/PGCert 12FT 24PT

Brunel University
Globalisation and Governance .... MA 12FT 30PT

University of Cambridge
Geographical Research.......... MPhil 12FT

Cardiff University
Geography, Policy and Practice .... MSc 12FT

University College Cork
Arts (Geography) ....HDip 9FT 18PT
European Development Studies..........MA 12FT
Sociology of Development and Globalisation ....MA 12FT

Coventry University
Global Development and International Law....MSc 12FT 24-30PT

University of East Anglia
Cultural Heritage and International Development .... MA 12FT 24PT
Globalisation, Business and Sustainable Development.......... MA 12FT 24PT

University of East London
NGO and Development Management ....MSc 12FT 24PT/PGDip 8FT 16PT/PGCert 4FT 8PT

University of Edinburgh
Cultural Studies .... MSc 12FT 24PT
Global Social Change.......... MSc 12FT 24PT

University of Exeter
Critical Human Geographies .... MRes 12FT
Energy Policy .... MSc 12FT 24PT
Environment, Energy and Resilience ....MRes 12FT 24PT
Sustainable Development.......... MSc 12FT 24PT

University of Glasgow
Equality & Human Rights .... MSc 12FT 24PT
Global Economy .... MSc 12FT 24PT

Goldsmiths, University of London
World Cities and Urban Life.......... MA 12FT 24PT

University of Kent
Anthropology and Conservation .... MA 12FT 24PT
Anthropology of Ethnicity, Nationalism and Identity......MA 12FT 24PT
Architecture and Cities .... MA 12FT 24PT
Architecture and Cities (Paris option) ....MA 12FT

King's College London
Cities ....MA 12FT 24PT/MSc 12FT 24PT
Environment, Politics & Globalisation ... MA 12FT 24PT/MSc 12FT 24PT

Leeds Metropolitan University
Urban DesignMA 12FT 24PT/PGDip 12FT 24PT/PGCert 12FT 24PT

University of Leeds
Social and Cultural Geography ..MA 12FT 24PT/PGDip 12FT 24PT

University of Leicester
European Urbanisation..........MA 12FT

University of Liverpool
Cities, Culture and Regeneration.......... MA 12FT 24PT
Geographies of Globalisation and Development... MA 12FT 24PT
Population Studies (Research Methodology)..........MA 12FT
Research Methodology (Civic Design).......... MA 12FT 24PT
Research Methodology (Lifecourse, Population and Mobility) MA 12FT 24PT

London Metropolitan University
Sustainable Cities..........MSc 12FT 24+PT

London School of Economics and Political Science (LSE)
Global Politics.......... MSc 12FT 24PT
Health, Population and Society ....MSc 12FT 24PT

London School of Hygiene and Tropical Medicine
Global Health Policy (by Distance Learning) ....MSc 24-60DL/PGDip 12-60DL/PGCert 12-60DL

Loughborough University
Globalization and Sport.......... MSc 12FT

Manchester Metropolitan University
European Urban Cultures..........MA 12FT

Newcastle University
Human Geography Research.......... MA 12FT 24PT
World Politics and Popular Culture.......... MA 12FT 24PT

University of Northampton
Integrated Urbanism .... MSc 12FT 24PT

University of Nottingham
Economy, Space and Society.......... MSc 12FT 24PT

Oxford Brookes University
Food, Wine and Culture ....MA 12FT 36PT 24DL

University of Oxford
Nature, Society and Environmental Policy.......... MSc 12FT

Queen Mary, University of London
Cities and Cultures..........MA 12FT 24PT MRes 12FT 24PT
Community Organising .... MA 12FT 24PT
Globalisation and Development .... MA 12FT 24PT MRes 12FT 24PT

Reseau Universitaire Transmanche
Intercultural Relations..........MA 15FT

Royal Holloway, University of London
Masters by Research (Comparative Literature and Culture).....MA 12FT 24PT

University of Salford
International Relations and Globalisation...MA 12FT 36PT 36DL/PGDip 8FT 24PT 36DL

School of Oriental and African Studies - SOAS
Global Media and Postnational Communication.............MA 12FT 24-36PT
Law, Development and Globalisation .... MA 12FT 24PT
Globalisation and Multinational Corporations ...... MA 12FT 24PT
Political Economy of Development..........MSc 12FT 24-36PT
Research for International Development...............MSc 12FT 24PT

Social sciences

Sheffield Hallam University
Cultural Studies ....MRes variousFT variousPT

University of Sheffield
Comparative Governance and Public Policy .... MA 12FT 24PT
Globalisation and Development .... MA 12FT 24PT
Social Research.. MA 12FT 24PT
Social and Spatial Inequalities.................................MSc 12FT 24PT

University of St Andrews
Health Geography Research ...MRes 12FT 24PT/PGDip 10FT 20PT

University of Strathclyde
Social Research..MRes 12FT 24PT

University of Sussex
Climate Change and Policy ....MSc 12FT 24PT
Global Health .... MSc 12FT
Globalisation and Development .... MA 12FT 24PT

Swansea University
Human Geography... MA 12FT 24-36PT

Teesside University
Cultural History... MA 12FT 24-36PT
Global Development & Social Research .....MSc 12FT 24PT/PGDip 12FT 24PT

Trinity College Dublin - the University of Dublin
Digital Humanities and Culture ....MPhil 12FT 24PT
Public History and Cultural Heritage.....................MPhil 12FT 24PT

University of Wales Trinity Saint David
Health, Ethics and Society................ MA 12-24DL/PGDip 12-24DL

UCL - University College London
Cultural Heritage Studies... MA 12FT 24PT
East European Studies..MRes 24FT
European Culture and Thought: Culture..... MA 12FT 24PT/PGDip 9FT 18PT/PGCert 3FT 6PT
European Culture and Thought: Thought... MA 12FT 24PT/PGDip 9FT 18PT/PGCert 3FT 6PT
Globalisation ....MSc 12FT 24PT/PGDip 9FT
Globalisation and Latin American Development............................. MSc 12FT 24PT
Identity, Culture and Power.. MA 12FT 24PT
Institutions, Development and Globalisation......... MA 12FT 24PT
Language, Culture and History .... MA 12FT 24PT
Modernity, Space and Place.. MSc 12FT
Social and Cultural Anthropology............................MSc 12FT 24PT
Urban Studies...MSc 12FT 24-60PT

University of Winchester
Managing Contemporary Global Issues...... MA 12FT 24PT/PGDip 12FT 24PT/PGCert 12FT 24PT
Managing Contemporary Global Issues with Environment and Development..MSc 12FT 24PT/PGDip 9FT 18PT/PGCert 9FT 18PT

Cultural geography
Research Courses

University of Bath
Global Political Economy: transformations and policy analysis (delivered collaboratively w............................... MRes 12FT 24-36PT

Coventry University
Cultural Geography.......................... MSc by research 12FT 24-36PT

University of Edinburgh
Cultural Studies .... PhD 36FT 72PT

University of Exeter
Environment, Energy and Resilience ....MPhil 36FT 60PT/PhD 36FT 84PT
Human Geography.........PhD 48FT 84PT/MPhil 36FT 60PT/MSc by research 12FT 24PT

University of Kent
Anthropology ..PhD 36FT 60PT/MPhil 12FT 36PT/MA by research 12FT 24PT/MSc by research 12FT 24PT

University of Leeds
Geography..PhD 36FT 60PT/MPhil 24FT

London School of Economics and Political Science (LSE)
Cities .... PhD 36-48FT/MPhil 36-48FT
Economic Geography.......................... MPhil 36-48FT/PhD 36-48FT

University of Nottingham
Cultural and Historical Geography ....PhD 36FT
New Economic Geographies...PhD 36FT

The Open University
Globalisation, Transnationalism and Social Welfare.......PhD 36FT 72PT variableDL/MPhil 15FT 24PT variableDL
Politics of urban culture and space.... PhD 36FT 72PT variableDL/MPhil 15FT 24PT variableDL

Queen's University Belfast
Geography: Society, Space and Culture.......PhD 36FT 72PT/MPhil 24FT 48PT
Past Cultural Change.................. PhD 36FT 72PT/MPhil 24FT 48PT

Swansea University
Human Geography...................... PhD 36FT 60PT/MPhil 24FT 48PT
Urban Studies...MSc by research 12FT 24PT

UCL - University College London
East European Society and National Identity......... PhD 36FT 60PT

Death studies
Taught Courses

University of Aberdeen
Divinity and Religious Studies..................................MTh 12FT 24PT

University of Central Lancashire
Archaeology of Death...MA 12FT

University of Chester
Archaeology of Death and Memory ..... MA 12FT 24 - 36PT/PGDip 12FT 24 - 36PT/PGCert 12FT 12 - 24PT

Keele University
Post Graduate Certificate End of Life Care.................. PGCert 12FT

Liverpool John Moores University
Advanced Paediatric Nurse Practitioner (APNP) in Ambulatory Care ....MSc 12FT 24PT

University of Sheffield
Religion, Conflict and the Media .... MA 12FT 24PT

University of Warwick
Palliative Care: Care of the Dying............. PGA 12PT/CPDMod 1PT

University of Winchester
Death Religion and Culture....... MA 12FT 36PT/PGDip 12FT 24PT/PGCert 12FT 24PT

Death studies
Research Courses

The Open University
Ageing and Later Life............................ PhD 36FT 72PT variableDL/MPhil 15FT 24PT variableDL
Death, Dying and Bereavement.......... PhD 36FT 72PT variableDL/MPhil 15FT 24PT variableDL

Development studies
Taught Courses

University of Aberdeen
Economics of Health... MSc 12FT/PGDip 9FT
International Health and Management.....MSc 12FT 24PT/PGDip 9FT 18PT

Aberystwyth University
Human Rights and Development..LLM 12FT

University of Bath
Economics (Development) ....MSc 12FT 24PT/PGDip 9FT 21PT/PG Cert Microeconomics (Development) 4FT/PG Cert Macroeconomics (Development) 4FT
International Development .... MRes 12FT 24-60PT/PGDip 9FT 21PT/PGCert 4FT 16PT
International Development .... MSc 12FT 24-60PT/PGDip 9FT 21PT/PGCert 4FT 16PT

Birkbeck, University of London
Development Studies...... MSc 12FT 24PT/PGDip 12-24PT/PGCert 12-24PT
Development Studies and Social Anthropology...MSc 12FT 24PT/PGDip 12FT 24PT/PGCert 12PT
International Business and Development ....MSc 12FT 24PT/MRes 12FT 24PT

University of Birmingham
Development Management (Aid Management) .MSc 12FT 24PT/PGDip 9FT 24PT
Development Management (Human Resources and Development Management).....................................MSc 12FT 24PT
Development Management (Public Economic Management and Finance)..MSc 12FT 24PT/PGDip 9FT 24PT
Development Management ....MSc 12FT 24PT/PGDip 9FT 24PT
International Development .... MSc 12FT/PGDip 9FT MSc 24-48DL/PGDip 18-48DL
International Development (Conflict, Security and Development) MSc 12FT/PGDip 9FT
International Development (Governance, State-building and Development)... MSc 12FT/PGDip 9FT
International Development (International Political Economy and Development)..MSc 12FT 24PT/PGDip 9FT
International Development (Poverty, Inequality and Development) .... MSc 12FT 24PT 48DL
Local and Regional Economic Development..........MSc 12FT 24PT/PGDip 9FT 21PT/GradDip 9FT 21PT/GradCert 9FT 21PT

University of Bradford
Development and Project Planning..... MSc 12FT 24PT/PGDip 9FT 21PT/PGCert 9PT
Economics and Finance for Development ...... MSc 12FT 24-60PT/PGDip 9FT 21PT
International Development Management ....MA 12FT 24PT/PGDip 9FT 21PT/PGCert 9PT

University of Brighton
Sport and International Development... MA 12FT 24-36PT/PGDip 12FT 24PT/PGCert 12FT 24PT
Tourism and International Development........ MSc 12FT 24-72PT/PGDip 12FT 24-72PT/PGCert 12FT 24-72PT

Brunel University
Children, Youth and International Development... MA 12FT 24PT

University of Cambridge
Development Studies...MPhil 9FT
Environment, Society and Development...........................MPhil 9FT
Materials Science.. MASt 9FT

Cardiff University
International Planning and Development........................ MSc 12FT

University of Central Lancashire
Equality and Community Leadership............................PGCert 24PT

University College Dublin
Development Studies.................. MSc 15FT 24PT/HDip 12FT 24PT

University of East Anglia
Climate Change and International Development............................ MSc 12FT 24PT
Conflict, Governance and International Development....MA 12FT 24PT
Cultural Heritage and International Development MA 12FT 24PT
Development Economics..MSc 12FT 24PT
Education and Development...................................... MA 12FT 24PT
Environment and International Development ...... MSc 12FT 24PT
Gender Analysis in International Development..... MA 12FT 24PT
Globalisation, Business and Sustainable Development..MA 12FT 24PT
Impact Evaluation for International Development .... MSc 12FT 24PT
International Development.. MA 12FT 24PT
International Relations and Development Studies MA 12FT 24PT
International Social Development............................ MA 12FT 24PT
International Development (by distance learning)......MRes 24DL
Media and International Development.................... MA 12FT 24PT
Water Security and International Development... MSc 12FT 24PT

University of East London
International Development and Health ...MSc 12FT 24PT/PGDip 8FT 16PT/PGCert 4FT 8PT
NGO and Development Management ....MSc 12FT 24PT/PGDip 8FT 16PT/PGCert 4FT 8PT

University of Edinburgh
Africa and International Development....................MSc 12FT 24PT PGCert 12DL/PGCert 24DL
Environment and Development...........MSc 12FT 24PT/PGDip 9FT
International Development..MSc 12FT 24PT
Science, Technology and International Development ... MSc 12FT 36PT/Diploma 9FT 24PT
South Asia and International Development...........MSc 12FT 24PT

University of Exeter
Food Security and Sustainable Agriculture............MSc 12FT 24PT

National University of Ireland Galway
Ethics, Culture and Global Change .... MA 12FT 24PT

Glasgow Caledonian University
International Development.. MSc 12FT

University of Glasgow
Development Studies.. MSc 12FT
Economic & Financial Sector Policies .... MSc 12FT
Europe and International Development............................ MSc 12FT
International Development.. MSc 12FT

Goldsmiths, University of London
Development & Rights.. MA 12FT 24PT

Institute of Education
Centenary Brendish Scholarships (Taught Masters Programmes) .... MA 12FT/MSc 12FT

King's College London
Emerging Economies & Inclusive Development .... MSc 12FT
Emerging Economies & International Development..... MSc 12FT
Environment & Development........MA 12FT 24PT/MSc 12FT 24PT
Political Economy of Emerging Markets........................... MSc 12FT
Tourism, Environment & Development..................MA 12FT 24PT/MSc 12FT 24PT

Lancaster University
Environment and Development (Overseas Placement) ....MRes 12FT 24PT

Leeds Metropolitan University
International Political Economy...MA 12FT
Leisure, Sport & Culture .... MA 12FT 24PT
Peace & Development.................MA 12FT 24PT/PGDip 12FT 24PT

University of Leeds
Culture, Creativity and Entrepreneurship... MA 12FT 24PT/PGDip 9FT 21PT/PGCert 6FT 12PT
Global Development... MA 12FT 24PT
Global Development and Africa .... MA 12FT 24PT
Global Development and Education .... MA 12FT 24PT
Global Development and Gender .... MA 12FT 24PT
Global Development and International Political Economy ......MA 12FT 24PT
Religious Studies and Development Studies........... MA 12FT 24PT

University of Liverpool
Humanitarian Health Programme Management..........MSc 12FT/Diploma 12FT/Cert 12FT
Humanitarian Studies.................MSc 12FT/Diploma 9FT/Cert 6FT

Section sponsored by BPP UNIVERSITY COLLEGE

Business and social sciences
488 POSTGRADUATE DIRECTORY www.prospects.ac.uk/findcourses

Social sciences

London School of Economics and Political Science (LSE)
Development Studies .... MSc 12FT 24PT
International Development .... MPA 21FT
International Development and Humanitarian Emergencies .... MSc 12FT 24PT

London School of Hygiene and Tropical Medicine
Public Health in Developing Countries .... MSc 12FT 24PT

London South Bank University
Development Studies .... MSc 12FT 24PT

Loughborough University
Globalization and Sport .... MSc 12FT

University of Manchester
Development Studies .... MA 12FT 24PT
Development Studies (Research Training) .... MA 12FT 24PT
Globalisation and Development .... MSc 12FT 24PT
ICTs for Development .... MSc 12FT 24PT
Industry, Trade and Development .... MSc 12FT 24PT
International Development: Development Management .... MA 12FT 24PT
International Development: Environment and Development MSc 12FT 24PT
International Development: Politics and Governance .... MA 12FT 24PT
International Development: Poverty, Conflict and Reconstruction .... MA 12FT 24PT
International Development: Public Policy and Management .. MA 12FT 24PT
International Development: Social Policy and Social Development .... MA 12FT 24PT
Poverty & Development .... MSc 12FT 24PT

Middlesex University
Global Governance and Public Policy .... MA 12FT 24PT

Newcastle University
International Development and Education .... MA 12FT

Northumbria University
International Development .... MSc 12FT

Nottingham Trent University
International Development .... MA 12FT 24PT/PGDip 12FT 24PT/PGCert 9FT

The Open University
Conflict and Development .... PGCert variableDL
Development Management .. MSc variableDL/PGDip variableDL/PGCert 12DL
Human Rights and Development Management .... PGCert 12DL

University of Oxford
Development Studies .... MPhil 36FT

Plymouth University
Early Childhood Studies (IMP) .... MA 36BM
International Study of Early Childhood .... MA 24PT

Queen Margaret University, Edinburgh
International Health .... MSc 12FT 60PT
Sexual and Reproductive Health MSc 12FT 60PT/PGDip 9FT 48PT/PGCert 6FT 48PT

Queen Mary, University of London
Globalisation and Development .... MRes 12FT 24PT

University of Reading
Agricultural Economics .... MSc 12FT 24PT
Applied Development Studies .... MSc 12FT 24PT
Climate Change & Development .... MSc 12FT 24PT
Communication for Innovation and Development .... MSc 12FT 24PT
Development Finance .... MSc 12FT
Environment and Development .... MSc 12FT
Social Development and Sustainable Livelihoods .... MA 12FT

University of Salford
Human Resource Management and Development .... MSc 12FT 24PT/PGDip 8FT 24PT/PGCert 4FT 9PT

School of Oriental and African Studies - SOAS
Social Anthropology of Development .... MA 12FT 24-36PT
Violence, Conflict and Development .... MSc 12FT 24PT

Schumacher College
Economics for Transition .... MA 12FT
Holistic Science .... MSc 12FT

University of Sheffield
Development Economics and Policy .... MSc 12FT 24PT
Globalisation and Development .... MA 12FT 24PT
International Development .... MA 12FT 24PT
MPH 12FT 24PT
International Development and Planning .... MA 12FT

University of Stirling
Human Resource Management and Socio Economic Development .... MSc 12FT/PGDip 9FT/PGCert 6FT

University of Sussex
Development Studies (IDS) .... MA 12FT 24PT
Environment, Development and Policy .... MA 12FT 24PT
Globalisation and Development .... MA 12FT 24PT
Governance and Development .... MA 12FT 24PT
Participation, Power and Social Change .... MA 12FT 24PT
Poverty and Development .... MA 12FT 24PT
Science, Society and Development .... MA 12FT 24PT
Social Development .... MA 12FT 24PT

Swansea University
Development and Human Rights .... MA 12FT 36PT
International Communication & Development .... MA 12FT 24PT

UCL - University College London
Development Administration and Planning .. MSc 12FT 24-60PT/PGDip 9FT
Environment and Sustainable Development . MSc 12FT 24-60PT/PGDip 9FT
Global Health and Development .... MSc 12FT 24-60PT/PGDip 9FT 24-60PT/PGCert 12-24PT
Globalisation .... MSc 12FT 24PT/PGDip 9FT
Globalisation and Latin American Development .. MSc 12FT 24PT
Risk and Disaster Reduction .... MRes 12FT 24PT PGCert 12PT

University of Westminster
International Development Management .... MA 12FT

University of York
Public Administration in International Development .... MA 12FT 24PT 12+DL/MPA 12FT/PGDip 12FT

Development studies
Research Courses

Birkbeck, University of London
Development Studies .... PhD 36FT 60-72PT/MPhil 24FT 36PT
International Childhood Studies .... PhD 36FT 60-72PT/MPhil 24FT 36PT

University of Birmingham
International Development .... MPhil 24FT/PhD 36FT

University of Bradford
Bradford Centre for International Development .... PhD 36-48FT 48-60PT/MPhil 12-24FT 24-48PT

University College Dublin
Development Studies .... PhD 36FT/MLitt by research 24FT

University of Dundee
Community Learning & Development .... MPhil 24FT

University of East Anglia
International Development: Economic Development .... PhD 36FT 72PT/MPhil 24FT 48PT
International Development: Social Development .... PhD 36FT 72PT/MPhil 24FT 48PT
International Development: Sustainable Development .... PhD 36FT 72PT/MPhil 24FT 48PT

King's College London
Development Studies with reference to Emerging Economies .... PhD 36-48FT 72-84PT

London School of Economics and Political Science (LSE)
Development Studies .... PhD 36-48FT/MPhil 36-48FT

University of Manchester
Development Policy and Management .... PhD 36FT 72PT/MPhil 12FT 24PT

The Open University
Asian drivers and Africa ... PhD 36FT 72PT variableDL/MPhil 15FT 24PT variableDL
Development Studies .... PhD 36FT 72PT variableDL/MPhil 15FT 24PT variableDL/MRes variableFT variablePT variableDL
Social technologies, innovation and development .... PhD 36FT 72PT variableDL/MPhil 15FT 24PT variableDL

University of Oxford
International Development Centre .... DPhil 48FT

University of Sussex
Development Studies .... PhD 24-48FT 36-72PT/MPhil 12-36FT 24-48PT
Development Studies (IDS) .... PhD 24-48FT 36-72PT

Swansea University
Development Studies .... PhD 36FT 60PT/MPhil 12FT 24PT
International Development .... MA by research 12FT 24PT

Disability studies
Taught Courses

University of Aberdeen
Studies in Mindfulness .... MSc 36PT/PGDip 24PT/PGCert 12PT

Bangor University
Applied Behaviour Analysis .... PGCert 4FT 9PT/PGDip 9FT 18PT/MSc 12FT 24PT
Psychological Research .. MSc 12FT 24PT/PGDip 8FT 16PT/PGCert 4FT 8PT
Psychology .... MA 12FT 24PT/PGDip 9FT 18PT/PGCert 4FT 8PT

University of Birmingham
Special Educational Needs Coordination (National Award for SENC) .... PGCert 12/24PT

University of Central Lancashire
Personality Disorder (Practice Development) MSc 36-60PT/PGDip 24PT

University of East London
Special Educational Needs MA .... MA 12FT 24PT/PGDip 8FT 16PT/PGCert 4FT 8PT

Edge Hill University
Learning Disabilities Studies .... MSc 36-72PT

Edinburgh Napier University
Advanced Practice in Intellectual Disabilities .... MSc 12FT 36PT/PGDip 9FT 24PT/PGCert 6FT 12PT
Advanced Practice in Intellectual Disabilities and Applied Education .... MSc 12FT 36PT/PGDip 9FT 24PT/PGCert 6FT 12PT

University of Edinburgh
Additional Support for Learning (Learning Disabilities) .... MEd 72PT/PGDip 48PT/PGCert 24PT

National University of Ireland Galway
International and Comparative Disability Law and Policy .... LLM 12FT 24PT

University of Glasgow
Childhood Practice .... PGDip 24PT

University of Gloucestershire
National Award for Special Educational Needs Continuation .... PGCert 9PT

Institute of Education
Habilitation and Disabilities of Sight (Children and Young People) .... GradDip 24PT/GradCert 12PT
Special and Inclusive Education CAIRO .... MA 12FT 24PT

University of Kent
Analysis and Intervention in Intellectual and Development Disabilities .... MSc 12FT 24PT/PGDip 12FT 24PT
Applied Behaviour Analysis (Intellectual and Developmental Disabilities) .... MSc 12FT 24PT/PGCert 12FT 24PT/PGCert 12FT 24PT
Autism Studies .... PGCert 12FT 24PT/PGDip 12FT 24PT/MA 12FT 24PT
Autism Studies (Distance Learning) .... PGCert 12FT 24DL/MA 12FT 24PT/PGDip 12FT 24PT
Intellectual and Developmental Disabilities .... MA 12FT 24PT/PGDip 12FT 24PT/PGCert 12FT 24PT
Intellectual and Developmental Disabilities (Distance Learning) .... MA 12FT 24PT 24DL/PGCert 12FT 24PT/PGDip 12FT 24PT

King's College London
Mental Health in Learning Disabilities .... MSc 12FT 24PT

Leeds Metropolitan University
Professional Development .... PGCert 12PT

University of Leeds
Disability Studies .... MA 12FT 24PT MA 24DL/PGDip 12DL
Disability and Global Development .... MA 12FT 24PT
Disability and Social Policy .... MA 12FT 24PT
Disability and Special Education .... MA 12FT 24PT
Disability, Ethnicity and Racism .... MA 12FT 24PT
Disability, Health and Illness .... MA 12FT 24PT

Manchester Metropolitan University
Continuing Professional, Personal and Practice Development (CP3D) .... CP3D variousFT
Psychology and Disability Studies .... MSc 12FT 24PT/PGDip 12FT 24PT/PGCert 12FT 24PT

University of Manchester
Critical Learning Disability Studies .... MA 24PT

University of Portsmouth
Applied Psychology of Intellectual Disabilities .... MSc 12/24DL

University of South Wales
Diploma in Higher Education in Professional Practice DipHE 48PT

University of Southampton
Specific Learning Difficulties (Dyslexia) .... MSc 12FT 24PT

University of St Andrews
Adults with Learning Disabilities who have Significant and Complex Needs .... MSc 12DL/PGDip 12DL/PGCert 12DL

Trinity College Dublin - the University of Dublin
Disability Studies .... MSc 12FT 24PT

Disability studies
Research Courses

Bangor University
Ageing and Cognitive Health .... PhD 36FT 60PT
Ageing and Dementia Studies .... MSc by research 12FT 24PT PhD 36FT 60PT/MPhil 24FT 48PT
Doctorate by Research .... PhD 36FT/MPhil 24FT

University of Kent
Clinical Psychology of Intellectual and Developmental Disabilities .... MPhil 24FT 36PT/PhD 36FT 60PT
Intellectual and Developmental Disabilities .... MA by research 12FT 24PT/MPhil 24FT 36PT/PhD 36FT 60PT

The Open University
Living with disability and long term conditions .... PhD 36FT 72PT variableDL/MPhil 15FT 24PT variableDL

Section sponsored by
BPP UNIVERSITY COLLEGE

Business and social sciences
www.prospects.ac.uk/findcourses POSTGRADUATE DIRECTORY 489

Social sciences

Plymouth University
Developmental Disability Research & Education Group...... MPhil tbcFT

Dutch studies
Taught Courses

UCL - University College London
Dutch Golden Age .... MA 12FT 24PT

Dutch studies
Research Courses

University of Cambridge
Old Dutch .... PhD 36FT 60PT

Environmental health
Taught Courses

University of Birmingham
Environmental Health........ MSc 12FT 72PT
Public and Environmental Health Science .... MSc 12FT

Cranfield University
Health and the Environment........ MSc 12FT 24-36PT/PGDip 12FT 24-36PT

University of Cumbria
International Health........ MSc 12FT 24PT
Public Health and Social Change....MSc 36FT 60PT/GradDip 24FT 36PT/GradCert 12FT 18PT

University of Derby
Environmental Health........ MSc 24FT 48PT 48DL
Sustainable Architecture and Healthy Environments .....MA 12FT

Dublin Institute of Technology
Environmental Health and Safety Management........ MSc 12FT 24PT

University of Dundee
Epidemiology and Global Health International Prevention Research Institute Summer School........Cert 1FT
Spatial Planning with Environmental Assessment .... MSc 12FT

Durham University
Risk, Health and Public Policy........MA 12FT

University of East Anglia
Applied Ecology and Conservation .... MSc 12FT 24PT
Climate Change .... MSc 12FT
Climate Change and International Development. MSc 12FT 24PT
Environmental Sciences........ MSc 12FT 24PT
Environmental Sciences and Humanities .... MA 12FT 24PT/MSc 12FT 24PT

University of East London
Public Health ... MSc 12FT 48PT/PGCert 4FT 8PT/PGDip 8FT 16PT

University of Edinburgh
Global Health Challenges) .... PGCert 12-24DL
Global Health Policy) ....PGCert 9-21DL
Global Health Studies) ....PGCert 36DL
Global Health and Infectious Diseases)........MSc 36DL/PGDip 24DL/PGCert 12DL
Global Health and Public Policy........MSc 12FT 24-36PT
Global Health: Non Communicable Diseases)..MSc 36DL/PGDip 24DL/PGCert 12DL
One Health........MSc 36DL/PGDip 24DL/PGCert 12DL

University of Exeter
Environment and Human Health....... PGCert 6FT/PGDip 9FT/MSc 12FT 24PT

Heriot-Watt University
Food Science, Safety and Health .... MSc 12FT 24PT 24-84DL/PGDip 9FT 21PT 24-84DL
Food and Beverage Science........MSc 12FT 24PT/PGDip 9FT 21PT

Leeds Metropolitan University
Acoustics and Noise Control........ PGDip 12PT
Environmental Health........ MSc 12FT 36PT
Public Health (Health Promotion and Environmental Health) Zambia .... MSc 36PT

London School of Hygiene and Tropical Medicine
Public Health (Environment & Health)........ MSc 12FT 24PT
Public Health (Health Economics)........ MSc 12FT 24PT

Middlesex University
Environmental Health........ MSc 12FT 24PT

North East Surrey College of Technology
Environmental Health Foundation Degree..... Foundation Degree 36PT

Royal Veterinary College
One Health (Infectious Diseases) ....PGDip 8FT

University of Salford
Environmental Acoustics...MSc 12FT 28PT 28DL/PGDip 9FT 18PT 18DL
Environmental and Public Health .... MSc 12FT 24-36PT/PGDip 8FT 24PT
Safety, Health and Environment ....MSc 12FT 36PT/PGDip 8FT 24PT

Sheffield Hallam University
Built Environment.....MPhil 24FT 36PT/PhD by taught 24FT 60PT
Housing for Environmental Health........CertHE 18PT

University of Strathclyde
Environmental Health....MSc 12FT 24PT/PGDip 9FT 18PT/PGCert 6FT 12PT

UCL - University College London
Built Environment: Environmental Design and Engineering........ MSc 12FT 24-60PT/PGDip 9FT
Built Environment: Heritage Science .... MRes 12FT 24-60PT/PGCert 6FT
Built Environment: Sustainable Heritage....... MSc 12FT 24-60PT/PGDip 9FT

University of West London
Health and Social Care Leadership........ MSc 24PT

University of the West of England, Bristol
Environmental Health........ MSc 15FT 27PT

Environmental health
Research Courses

University of East Anglia
Copy of Environmental Sciences: Geosciences and Natural Hazards .... PhD 36FT 72PT/MPhil 24FT 48PT
Environmental Sciences: Climate, Ocean and Atmospheric Sciences........ PhD 36FT 72PT/MPhil 24FT 48PT
Environmental Sciences: Resources, Sustainability and Governance........ PhD 36FT 72PT/MPhil 24FT 48PT

University of Edinburgh
Global Health .... MPhil 24FT 48PT/PhD 36FT 72PT

Middlesex University
Health or Environment DProf 24FT 60PT/MProf by research 24FT 60PT

Environmental policy
Taught Courses

University of Aberdeen
Climate Change Law and Sustainable Development......LLM 12FT 24--36PT

University of Abertay Dundee
Energy & Environmental Management .... MSc 12FT

Aberystwyth University
Remote Sensing & Geographical Information Systems (GIS) .... MSc 12FT 24PT/PGDip 9FT 18PT/PGCert 5FT 10PT
Remote Sensing and GeographyMSc 12FT 24PT/PGDip 9FT 18PT/PGCert 5FT 10PT

School of Advanced Study, University of London
Advanced Legislative Studies........LLM 12FT 24PT 24DL

Bangor University
Conservation and Land Management .... MSc 12FT/PGDip 9FT
Environmental Forestry .... MSc 12FT
Environmental Management........ MBA 12FT
Forestry and Environmental Management degrees (TRANSFOR-M)........ MSc 24FT
Marine Biology........MSc 12FT 24-36PT/PGDip 9FT
Marine Environmental Protection ....MSc 12FT 24-36PT
Physical Oceanography........MSc 12FT 24-36PT/PGDip 9FT
Rheolaeth Amgylcheddol Gynaliadwy (Sustainable Environmental Management)........MSc 12FT 24PT/MA 12FT 24PT

University of Bath
Environment, Energy & Resilience .... MRes 12FT 24-36PT

University of Bedfordshire
Environmental Management........MSc 12-18FT 36PT

Birmingham City University
Environmental Sustainability...... PGCert 4FT 8PT/PGDip 4FT 8PT/MSc 4FT 8PT
Environmental Sustainability (Design and Construction) . PGCert 4FT 8PT/PGDip 4FT 8PT/MSc 4FT 8PT

University of Birmingham
Development Management (Human Resources and Development Management)........ MSc 12FT 24PT
Environmental and Natural Resource Economics........ MSc 12FT 24PT

University of Brighton
Environmental Assessment and Management....MSc 12FT 24PT/PGCert 12FT 24PT/PGDip 12FT 24PT

University of Bristol
Climate Change Science and Policy .... MSc 12FT 24PT
Environmental Policy and Management.. MSc 12FT 24PT/PGCert 12FT 24PT/PGDip 12FT 24PT

Brunel University
Climate Change Impacts and Sustainability .... MSc 12FT 24PT
Environmental Science: Legislation and Management........ MSc 12FT 24PT

University of Cambridge
Environmental Policy........ MPhil 10FT
Land Economy Research .... MPhil 10FT

Cardiff University
Sustainability, Planning and Environmental Policy .... MSc 12FT 24PT

University of Central Lancashire
Energy and Environmental Management........MSc 12FT 24PT/PGDip 9FT 18PT/PGCert 6FT 12PT

University of Chester
Regeneration for Practitioners.....MA 12FT 24 - 72PT/PGDip 12FT 24 - 60PT/PGCert 12FT 12 - 36PT
Sustainability for Community and Business.........MSc 12FT 24PT/PGDip 12FT 24PT/PGCert 12FT 12-24PT

Cranfield University
Economics for Natural Resource & Environmental Management.. ....MSc 12FT 24-60PT/PGCert 5FT 24PT/PGDip 6FT 24PT
Environment and Public Policy.......... MSc 12FT 60PT/PGCert 12FT 60PT/PGDip 12FT 60PT
Environmental Informatics......MSc 12FT 60PT/PGDip 12FT 60PT/PGCert 12FT 60PT
Environmental Risk Management .... MSc 12FT 24-60PT/PGDip 6FT 24PT/PGCert 5FT 24PT

University of Cumbria
Leadership and Management in PolicingMBA 36PT/PGDip 36PT/PGCert 36PT

University of Dundee
Climate Change Economics and Policy .... MSc 12FT
Climate Change and Energy Law and Policy ....LLM 12FT
Energy Studies with Specialisation in Energy Policy ..... MSc 12FT
Environmental Law ....LLM 12FT
Environmental Law and Policy ....LLM 12FT
Mineral Law and Policy .... LLM 12FT LLM 60DL
Natural Resources Law and Policy .... LLM 60DL
Non-Graduating Taught Postgrad Grad School of Natural Resources Law, Policy & Management .... PG module variableFT
Petroleum Law and Policy ....LLM 12FT/PGDip 9FT LLM 24-60DL
Spatial Planning with Environmental Assessment .... MSc 12FT
Spatial Planning with Marine Spatial Planning .... MSc 12FT
Supplementary Studies in Graduate School of Natural Resources, Law, Policy and Management ....Masters Level Modules 6-9FT

University of East Anglia
Climate Change .... MSc 12FT
Climate Change and International Development........ MSc 12FT 24PT
Energy Engineering with Environmental Management .... MSc 12FT/MSc 24PT/MSc 36PT/MSc 48PT
Environment and International Development ...... MSc 12FT 24PT
Environmental Sciences........ MSc 12FT 24PT
Environmental Sciences and Humanities .... MA 12FT 24PT/MSc 12FT 24PT
Impact Evaluation for International Development .... MSc 12FT 24PT
Public Policy and Public Management........MRes 12FT 24PT

University of Edinburgh
Carbon Capture & Storage........ MSc 12FT 36PT
Carbon Finance .... MSc 12FT
Carbon Management .... MSc 12FT
Environmental Protection and Management.......MSc 12FT 24PT/PGDip 9FT
Environmental Sustainability..........MSc 12FT 24-36PT/PGDip 9FT
Global Environment Challenges Certificate (Online distance learning) ....PGCert 9DL
Global Environment and Climate Change Law...... LLM 12FT 24PT
Integrated Resource Management........ MSc 12FT

University of Exeter
Climate Change Impacts and Feedbacks........MRes 12FT 24PT
Climate Change and Risk Management........ MSc 12FT 24PT
Conservation Science and Policy .... MSc 11FT
Critical Human Geographies ....MRes 12FT
Energy Policy........ MSc 12FT 24PT
Environment, Energy and Resilience ....MRes 12FT 24PT
Sustainable Development........ MSc 12FT 24PT

National University of Ireland Galway
Economic and Environmental Modelling... MEconSci 10approxFT

University of Glasgow
Applied Carbon Management (Dumfries Campus)........ MSc 12FT 24PT
Environmental Science, Technology & Society (Dumfries Campus)........ MSc 12FT 24PT
Environmental Statistics .... MSc 12FT

Goldsmiths, University of London
Design & Environment .... MA 12FT 24PT

Heriot-Watt University
Climate Change: Impacts and Mitigation........MSc 12FT 24PT/PGDip 9FT 21PT
Climate Change: Managing The Marine Environment........ MSc 12FT 24PT/PGDip 9FT 21PT
Environmental Analysis and Assessment .... MRes 12FT 24PT/PGDip 9FT 18PT/PGCert 9FT 18PT
Marine Resource Development and Protection....MSc 12FT 24PT/PGDip 9FT 21PT

Section sponsored by BPP UNIVERSITY COLLEGE

Business and social sciences
490 POSTGRADUATE DIRECTORY www.prospects.ac.uk/findcourses

Social sciences

Institute of Education
Educational Planning, Economics and International Development .... MA 12FT 24-48PT

Keele University
Climate Change Studies - Policy, Justice and Global Politics.... MA 12FT 24PT

University of Kent
Agri-Environmental Economics and Policy .... MSc 12FT 24PT
Anthropology and Conservation .... MA 12FT 24PT
Conservation and Business .... MSc 12FT 24PT
Environmental Law and Policy..LLM 12FT 24PT/PGDip 12FT 24PT

Kingston University
Sustainability & Environmental Change .... MSc 12FT 24PT

University of Leeds
Sustainability (Climate Change) .... MSc 12FT
Sustainability (Environment and Development) .... MSc 12FT 12-48PT
Sustainability (Environmental Politics and Policy) .... MSc 12FT 12-48PT

London School of Economics and Political Science (LSE)
Environmental Economics and Climate Change ... MSc 12FT 24PT
Environmental Policy and Regulation .... MSc 12FT 24PT

London South Bank University
Management in Civil Society - Blended .... MSc 24PT

Loughborough University
Sustainable Engineering .... MSc 12FT 96PT

Middlesex University
Global Governance and Public Policy .... MA 12FT 24PT
Sustainable Environmental Management...... MA 12FT 24PT/MSc 12FT 24PT

Newcastle University
Environmental Law and Policy (Research) .... LLM 12FT 24PT
Environmental Regulation and Sustainable Development ..... LLM 12FT 24PT
Sustainable Buildings and Environments .... MSc 12FT

Nottingham Trent University
Human Security and Environmental Change......... MA 12FT 24PT/PGDip 9FT 18PT/PGCert 9FT

University of Nottingham
Economic Development and Policy Analysis .... MSc 12FT

The Open University
Science and Society........ MSc variableDL/PGDip variableDL

Oxford Brookes University
Environmental Assessment and Management .... MSc 12FT 24PT/PGDip 9FT 21PT

University of Oxford
Environmental Change & Management .... MSc 12FT
Nature, Society and Environmental Policy .... MSc 12FT
Water Science, Policy and Management .... MSc 12FT

Queen Mary, University of London
Environmental Science: Integrated Management of Freshwater Environments .... MSc 12FT 24-36PT

Queen's University Belfast
Environmental Planning .... MSc 12FT
Sustainable Design .... MSc 12FT/PGDip 9FT

Ravensbourne
Environment Design .... MA 12FT 24PT

University of Reading
Applied Development Studies .... MSc 12FT 24PT
Climate Change & Development .... MSc 12FT 24PT
Economics of Climate Change .... MSc 12FT 24PT
Environment and Development .... MSc 12FT
The Economics of Climate Change .... MSc 12FT

Robert Gordon University
Energy Management.... MSc 12FT 36DL/PGDip 8FT 24DL/PGCert 4FT 12DL
Energy and Sustainability ...MSc 42DL/PGDip 24DL/PGCert 12DL

Royal Holloway, University of London
Global Health: Pathogens and Policy .. MSc 12FT 24PT/PGDip 9FT

University of Salford
Environmental Assessment and Management....MSc 12FT 36PT/PGDip 8FT 24PT
Environmental and Public Health ..MSc 12FT 24-36PT/PGDip 8FT 24PT

School of Oriental and African Studies - SOAS
Environmental Law and Sustainable Development .... MA 12FT 24PT
Environmental Management .... MSc 12FT 24-36PT
Global Energy and Climate Policy .... MSc 12FT 24PT
MA Globalisation and Multinational Corporations MA 12FT 24PT

Schumacher College
Holistic Science .... MSc 12FT

Sheffield Hallam University
Environmental Management .... MSc 12-24FT 24-36PT
Environmental Management (International Resource and Climate Management) .... MSc 12-18FT 24-36PT
Environmental Management (Wildlife and Landscape Conservation) .... MSc 12-18FT 24-36PT
Sustainable Communities and Environments .... MSc 12-18FT 24-36PT

University of South Wales
Environmental Conservation Management .... MSc 12FT 36PT

University of Southampton
Environmental Monitoring and Assessment .... MSc 12FT 27PT
Environmental Pollution Control .... MSc 12FT 27PT

University of St Andrews
Sustainable Aquaculture . MSc 12FT 24PT/PGDip 9FT 24PT 24DL/Cert 12DL

Staffordshire University
Habitat Management and Conservation ... MSc 15FT/PGDip 12FT

University of Stirling
Environmental Policy and Governance .... LLM 12FT/MSc 12FT

University of Strathclyde
Applied Economics .... MSc 12FT 24PT 24DL/PGDip 9FT 18PT 18DL
Sustainability and Environmental Studies MSc 12FT 24PT/PGDip 9FT 18PT

University of Surrey
Environmental Strategy .... MSc 12FT 12-60PT

University of Sussex
Environment, Development and Policy .... MA 12FT 24PT

Swansea University
Environmental Dynamics and Climate Change..... MSc 12FT 36PT
Geographic Information and Climate Change......MSc 12FT 36PT/PGCert 12FT 12PT

Teesside University
Energy and Environmental Management......... MSc 12-16FT 24PT

Trinity College Dublin - the University of Dublin
Environment and Development .... MSc 12FT
Environmental Sciences .... MSc 12FT

UCL - University College London
Anthropology, Environment and Development .... MSc 12FT 24PT
Biodiversity, Evolution and Conservation MRes .... MRes 12FT
Climate Change .... MSc 12FT 24PT
Energy Demand Studies .... MRes 12FT
Energy and Resources: Policy and Practice, Australia .... MSc 24FT 36-48PT
Global Health and Development: tropEd programme .... MSc 12FT 24-60PT

University of the West of England, Bristol
Environmental Consultancy .... MSc 36-60DL

Environmental policy
Research Courses

Aberystwyth University
Earth Sciences (MPhil) .... MPhil 12FT 24PT
Earth Sciences (PhD) .... PhD 36FT 60PT
Human Geography (PhD) .... PhD 36FT 60PT

Bangor University
Biodiversity Conservation .... MPhil 24FT 36PT/PhD 36FT 60PT
Ocean Sciences .... MPhil 24FT/PhD 36FT

University of Bedfordshire
Environmental Studies .... PhD 36FT 72PT

Brunel University
Environmental Issues and Environmental Change..... MPhil 12FT/PhD 36FT

University of Cambridge
Land Economy (by thesis) .... MPhil 11FT

Cardiff University
Environment .... PhD 36FT 60PT/MPhil 36FT 60PT
Institute of Environment and Sustainability........ PhD 36FT/MPhil 60PT

Coventry University
Environmental & Climate Change......MSc by research 12FT 24PT

University of Dundee
Non-Graduating Research in Natural Resources Law, Policy and Management (6 months or more) .... Non-Grad 6-24FT
Non-Graduating Research in Natural Resources Law, Policy and Management (less than 6 mths) .... Non-Grad 1-5FT
Town and Regional Planning (MPhil) .... MPhil 24FT

University of East Anglia
Copy of Environmental Sciences: Geosciences and Natural Hazards .... PhD 36FT 72PT/MPhil 24FT 48PT
Environmental Sciences: Climate, Ocean and Atmospheric Sciences .... PhD 36FT 72PT/MPhil 24FT 48PT
Environmental Sciences: Resources, Sustainability and Governance .... PhD 36FT 72PT/MPhil 24FT 48PT

University of Exeter
Environment, Energy and Resilience ..MPhil 36FT 60PT/PhD 36FT 84PT
Human Geography.........PhD 48FT 84PT/MPhil 36FT 60PT/MSc by research 12FT 24PT

University of Gloucestershire
Sustainability .... PhD 36FT

University of Kent
Biodiversity Management .... PhD 36FT 60PT/MSc by research 12FT 24PT

London School of Economics and Political Science (LSE)
Environmental Policy and Development.........MPhil 36-48FT/PhD 36-48FT

Manchester Metropolitan University
Environmental and Geographical Sciences .... MSc by research/MPhil/PhD

Newcastle University
Energy .... PhD 36FT 72PT/MPhil 12FT 24PT
Environmental Science .... MPhil 12FT 24PT/PhD 36FT 72PT
Integrated PhD 48FT

University of Nottingham
Environmental and Geomorphological Sciences .PhD 36FT 72PT/MPhil 24FT 48PT

The Open University
Environment, governance and justicePhD 36FT 72PT variableDL/MPhil 15FT 24PT variableDL
Geography .... PhD 36FT 72PT variableDL/MPhil 15FT 24PT variableDL
Political ideas, policies and actions.... PhD 36FT 72PT variableDL/MPhil 15FT 24PT variableDL

Oxford Brookes University
Impact Assessment .... MPhil/PhD 36-60FT 48-72PT/PhD 24-60FT 36-72PT/MPhil 24-36FT 36-48PT

Queen's University Belfast
Environmental Change .... PhD 36FT 72PT/MPhil 24FT 48PT

Sheffield Hallam University
Centre for Regional Economic and Social Research Applied Social Research .... PhD 36FT 60PT
Environment and Development .... MPhil 36PT
Environment and Development - Facilities Management.......PhD 33FT 45PT/MPhil 18FT 30PT

Swansea University
Environmental Sustainability .... MSc by research 12FT 24PT
Sustainable Resources .... MSc by research 12FT

Ethnicity studies
Taught Courses

University of Aberdeen
Multiculturalism .... MLitt 12FT 24PT/PGDip 9FT 18PT

Birkbeck, University of London
Culture, Diaspora, Ethnicity.....MSc 12FT 24PT/PGDip 12FT 24PT/PGCert 12PT
Nationalism and Ethnic Conflict .... MSc 12FT 24PT

University of Bristol
Ethnicity and Multiculturalism .... MSc 12FT 24PT

University of Central Lancashire
Advancing Equality, Diversity and Inclusion .... MA 12FT 36PT/PGDip 12FT 36PT/PGCert 12FT 24PT

University of Cumbria
Equality and Diversity Management .... MA 12FT 48PT

University College Dublin
Nationalism and Ethno-Communal ConflictMSc 12FT/MLitt 24FT

University of Glasgow
Equality & Human Rights .... MSc 12FT 24PT

Goldsmiths, University of London
Black British Writing, Drama and Performance...... MA 12FT 24PT

University of Kent
Anthropology of Ethnicity, Nationalism and Identity......MA 12FT 24PT

University of Leeds
Disability, Ethnicity and Racism .... MA 12FT 24PT
Race and Resistance .... MA 12FT 24PT
Racism and Ethnicity Studies .... MA 12FT 24PT

University of Oxford
Material Anthropology & Museum Ethnography (Research Methods) .... MSc 12FT

Queen's University Belfast
Comparative Ethnic Conflict.......MA 12FT 24PT/PGDip 12FT 24PT

University of Roehampton
Media, Culture and Identity .... PGDip 9FT 24PT

School of Oriental and African Studies - SOAS
Critical Media and Cultural Studies .... MA 12FT 24-36PT
Dispute and Conflict Resolution .... MA 12FT 24PT
Ethnomusicology .... MMus 12FT 24-36PT
Global Cinemas and the Transcultural .... MA 12FT 24-36PT
Islamic Societies and Cultures .... MA 12FT 24-36PT
Korean Studies .... MA 12FT 24-36PT
Medical Anthropology .... MA 12FT 24-36PT

Section sponsored by

BPP
UNIVERSITY
COLLEGE

Business and social sciences
www.prospects.ac.uk/findcourses **POSTGRADUATE DIRECTORY 491**

Social sciences

Migration and Diaspora Studies............................ MA 12FT 24-36PT
Pacific Asian Studies... MA 12FT 24-36PT
Performance ....MMus 12FT 24PT
Social Anthropology .... MA 12FT 24-36PT
South Asian Area Studies .... MA 12FT 24PT
South East Asian Studies.. MA 12FT 24-36PT
Turkish Studies.. MA 12FT 24PT

Trinity College Dublin - the University of Dublin
Race, Ethnicity, Conflict.. MPhil 12FT

University of Warwick
Islam in Contemporary Society...............................MA 12FT
Social Research with Specialism in Race and Ethnic Studies ...MA 12FT 24PT/PGDip 9FT 24PT

University of the West of Scotland
Professional Practice in Race Equality............. Level 1 module 4PT

Ethnicity studies
Research Courses

Cardiff University
Race, Representation and Cultural Identity Group..........PhD 36FT possiblePT/MPhil 24FT possiblePT

University College Dublin
Nationalism and Ethno-communal conflict.... PhD 36FT/MLitt by research 24FT

University of Exeter
Ethno-Political Studies................ MPhil 36FT 60PT/PhD 48FT 89PT

Institute for the Study of the Americas, School of Advanced Study, University of London
Race and Ethnicity..PhD 36FT/MPhil 12FT

The Open University
Citizenship and Governance......PhD 36FT 72PT variableDL/MPhil 15FT 24PT variableDL
Religion in Material, Visual and Performance Culture....PhD 36FT 72PT variableDL/MPhil 15FT 24PT variableDL
Religion, identities, cultures and citizenship.......... PhD 36FT 72PT variableDL/MPhil 15FT 24PT variableDL

University of Oxford
Institute of Social and Cultural Anthropology.............. DPhil 48FT

School of Oriental and African Studies - SOAS
Languages and Cultures of South Asia ....PhD 36FT 72PT/MPhil 24FT 48PT
Social Anthropology ....PhD 36FT/MPhil 24FT

University of Warwick
Ethnic Relations .... MPhil 24FT 36PT/PhD 36FT 60PT

European studies
Taught Courses

University of Aberdeen
Bayt al-Maqdis and Jerusalem Studies.... MLitt 12FT 24PT/PGDip 9FT 18PT
European Politics and Society .....MSc 12FT 24PT/PGDip 9FT 18PT
Modern Thought ....MLitt 12FT 24PT

Anglia Ruskin University
Intercultural Communication .... MA 12FT 24PT

Bangor University
European Languages and Cultures .... MA 12FT 24PT

University of Bath
Contemporary European Studies ('Euromasters') and 'Euromasters' with Trans-Atlantic Track ....MA 24FT
Politics & International Studies .... MRes 12FT/PGDip 9FT/PGCert 9FT

Birkbeck, University of London
International Business and the European Union .MSc 12FT 24PT/MRes 12FT 24PT

University of Bristol
European Literatures .... MA 12FT 24PT

University of Cambridge
European Literature and Culture..MPhil 9FT
Modern European History... MPhil 10FT

Cardiff University
European Studies .... MA 12FT 24PT

University of Central Lancashire
International Relations ....MA 12FT

University College Dublin
European Studies ....MA 12FT

University of East Anglia
International Relations and European Studies....... MA 12FT 24PT
Modern European History... MA 12FT 24PT

University of Essex
Continental Philosophy .... MA 12FT 24PT

University of Exeter
European Languages and Cultures ....MA 12FT 24PT/MRes 12FT 24PT
European Politics .... MA 12FT 24PT

University of Glasgow
European Studies: Cultures, Societies & Languages.... MLitt 12FT 24PT
Russian, Central & East European Studies (Erasmus Mundus International Masters) ....International Masters (double/single degree) 24FT
Russian, Central and East European Studies ....MSc 12FT 24PT/PGDip 9FT

Institute of Education
European Masters: Lifelong Learning Policy and Management.... MA 12FT

University of Kent
Comparative Literature.. MA 12FT 24PT
Comparative Literature (Paris option).....................................MA 12FT
Modern European Literature .... MA 12FT 24PT

King's College London
European Studies...MA 12FT
Middle East & Mediterranean Studies...................... MA 12FT 24PT

Lancaster University
European Institutions and Policy-Making.....................MA 12FT

Leeds Metropolitan University
English: Contemporary Literatures .... MA 12FT 24PT

London Metropolitan University
Comparative European Social Studies .... MA 12FT 24PT

London School of Economics and Political Science (LSE)
European Studies (Double Degree)..................MSc 12FT/MSc 12FT
European Studies (Research)....................................MSc 12FT 24PT
European Studies: Ideas and Identities ....MSc 12FT 24PT
Global Studies: A European Perspective........................MA 24FT

Manchester Metropolitan University
European Urban Cultures...MA 12FT

Newcastle University
European Union Studies.. MA 12FT 24PT

University of Nottingham
American Studies with European Study.............. MA 12FT 24-36PT

University of Oxford
Classical Armenian Studies...MSt 9FT
Russian and East European Studies..............MPhil 21FT/MSc 12FT

University of Portsmouth
European Studies .... MA 12FT 24PT
International Relations and European Studies....... MA 12FT 24PT

Queen's University Belfast
European Union Politics...............MA 12FT 24PT/PGDip 12FT 24PT

Royal Holloway, University of London
European Politics ....MSc 12/9FT 24/20PT

University of Sheffield
Crossways European Humanities (Mundus) ....MA 24FT

University of St Andrews
Central and East European Studies....MLitt 12FT 24PT/PGDip 9FT 18PT

University of Sussex
Contemporary European Studies .... MA 12FT 24PT

Trinity College Dublin - the University of Dublin
European Studies .... MPhil 12FT

UCL - University College London
Central and South-East European Studies............... MA 12FT 24PT
East European Studies...MRes 24FT
European Public Policy ....MSc 12FT 24PT
European Studies: European Society.... MA 12FT 24PT/PGDip 9FT 18PT/PGCert 3FT 6PT
European Studies: Modern European Studies ....MA 12FT 24PT/PGDip 9FT 18PT
Institutions, Development and Globalisation......... MA 12FT 24PT
Russian and East European Literature and Culture MA 12FT 24PT

European studies
Research Courses

Aberystwyth University
European Languages ....MPhil 12FT 24PT
French ....MPhil 12FT 24PT
German ....MPhil 12FT 24PT
Spanish .... PhD 36FT 60PT

School of Advanced Study, University of London
Italian or Comparative/Interdisciplinary Studies .PhD 36FT 60PT/MPhil 12FT 24PT

Aston University
Languages and European Studies ......PhD 36FT 60PT 60DL/MPhil 24FT 48PT 48DL
Languages and European Studies ......PhD 36FT 60PT 60DL/MPhil 24FT 48PT 48DL
School of Languages and European Studies......... PhD 36FT/MPhil 24FT/MSc by research 12FT

Bangor University
French..PhD 36FT/MPhil 12FT
German ....PhD 36FT/MPhil 12FT
Spanish ....MPhil 12FT/PhD 36FT

University of Bath
Politics, Languages and International Studies........... PhD 24-48FT 36-72PT/MPhil 12-36FT 24-48PT

University of Birmingham
Integrated Studies in European Languages and Cultures..............MPhil(B) 12FT 24PT/PhD 48FT 96PT
Modern European History........................MPhil(B) 12FT 24PT
Russian and East European Studies....PhD 36FT 72PT/MPhil 24FT 48PT/MA by research 12FT 24PT

University of Bradford
Department of Languages and European Studies.... PhD 36-48FT 48-60PT/MPhil 12-24FT 24-48PT

University College Dublin
European Studies .... PhD 36FT/MLitt by research 24FT

University of Exeter
European Studies .... PhD 48FT 89PT/MPhil 36FT 60PT

University of Glasgow
Russian and East European Studies.................... PhD 36FT/MLitt by research 12FT

Keele University
European Studies .... MPhil 24FT 36PT/PhD 48FT 84PT

University of Kent
Comparative Literature.............PhD 36FT 60PT/MPhil 24FT 36PT/MA by research 12FT 24PT
Text and Event in Early Modern Europe (TEEME): An Erasmus Mundus Joint Doctorate.................................. PhD 36FT 60PT

King's College London
European Studies Research............ PhD 36FT 48-72PT/MPhil 36FT 48-72PT
Middle East & Mediterranean Studies Research.............PhD 36FT 48-72PT/MPhil 24FT 36PT

Kingston University
European Studies ....PhD 48FT 72PT/MPhil 24FT 48PT/MA by research 12FT 24PT

Lancaster University
European Languages and Cultures .....PhD 36FT 48PT/MPhil 24FT 36PT

Loughborough University
European Studies .... PhD 36FT 60PT/MPhil 24FT 36PT

University of Nottingham
Southeast European Studies .... MA by research 12FT 24PT

The Open University
Citizenship and security .. PhD 36FT 72PT variableDL/MPhil 15FT 24PT variableDL
Governing global security .... PhD 36FT 72PT variableDL/MPhil 15FT 24PT variableDL
Policing and Criminal Justice.....PhD 36FT 72PT variableDL/MPhil 15FT 24PT variableDL

Queen Mary, University of London
European Studies .... MA by research

University of Salford
European Studies Research Institute ....PhD/MPhil

University of St Andrews
Cultural Identity Studies....... PhD 36FT 72PT/MPhil 12-24FT 48PT

University of Sussex
Contemporary European Studies ..... PhD 24-48FT 36-72PT/MPhil 12-36FT 24-48PT

UCL - University College London
East European Society and National Identity......... PhD 36FT 60PT
European Studies .... PhD 36FT 60PT
History, Politics and Economics of Eastern Europe PhD 36FT 60PT
Languages and Culture of Eastern Europe............. PhD 36FT 60PT

University of Warwick
European Cinema...................MPhil 24FT 48PT/PhD 36-48FT 60PT

University of the West of Scotland
Centre for Contemporary European Studies ....PhD/MPhil

Forensics
Taught Courses

Anglia Ruskin University
Forensic Science...MSc 12 - 15FT 24 - 30PT

Bournemouth University
Forensic Osteology...MSc 12FT 24PT
Forensic Toxicology by Research ....MSc 12FT 24PT

University of Central Lancashire
Criminal Investigation ....MSc 12PT
DNA Profiling...MSc 12FT 24PT
Document Analysis...MSc 12FT 24PT
Fire Investigation ....MSc 12FT/PGDip 9FT/PGCert 6FT
Fire Scene Investigation..MSc 24-36PT
Forensic Anthropology ..... MSc 12FT/PGDip 6FT 12PT/PGCert 3FT 6PT
Forensic Medicine and Bioethics ....MSc 36PT/PGDip 24PT
Forensic Psychology MSc 12FT 24PT/PGDip 9FT 24PT/PGCert 9FT 24PT
Forensic Toxicology .... MSc 12FT

Business and social sciences
492 POSTGRADUATE DIRECTORY www.prospects.ac.uk/findcourses

Section sponsored by
BPP
UNIVERSITY
COLLEGE

Social sciences

Forensic and Legal Medicine........LLM 36PT/MA 36PT/PGDip 24PT

Cranfield University
Safety and Accident Investigation - Air Transport ....MSc 24-36PT
Safety and Accident Investigation - Rail...MSc 36PT/PGDip 36PT/PGCert 36PT

Cranfield University, Shrivenham
Forensic Archaeology and Anthropology .... MSc 12FT 60PT
Forensic Ballistics......................MSc 12FT 60PT/PGDip 12FT 60PT/PGCert 12FT 60PT
Forensic Engineering and Science........MSc 12FT 60PT/PGDip 7FT 36PT/PGCert 7FT 36PT
Forensic Explosives and Explosion Investigation .MSc 12FT 60PT/PGDip 60PT/PGCert 12FT 60PT
Forensic Investigation ....MSc 12FT 60PT/PGDip 12FT 60PT/PGCert 12FT 60PT

University of Dundee
Anatomy and Advanced Forensic Anthropology .... MSc 12FT
Forensic Art ....MSc 12FT MSc 48PT
Forensic Facial Identification .... MSc 12FT
Forensic Medicine ....MFM 12FT
Forensic Odontology ....MFOdont 12FT
Forensic Toxicology ....MFTox 12FT

University of East Anglia
Forensic Linguistics and Translation .... MA 12FT 24PT

University of Edinburgh
Forensic Anthropology...MSc 12FT 24PT

University of Glasgow
Forensic Toxicology...................................MSc(MedSci) 12FT

University of Huddersfield
Forensic Podiatry ....PGCert 18-24BM

University of Hull
Analytical and Forensic Chemistry.................... MSc 12FT

King's College London
Forensic Mental Health.............. MSc 12FT 24PT/PGDip 12FT 24PT
Forensic Science ....MSc 12FT/MRes 15FT

Kingston University
Forensic Analysis...................................... MSc 12FT

University of Leicester
Forensic Science and Criminal Justice.........................MSc 24-27DL

London Metropolitan University
Forensic Science..................................MSc 12FT 24PT

London South Bank University
Forensic Science.......................................MSc 12FT 24PT

University of Manchester
Biomedical and Forensic Studies in Egyptology ....MSc 12FT 24PT

Northumbria University
Forensic Science.......................................MSc 12FT 36PT

Nottingham Trent University
Forensic Science and Technology ....MSc 12FT 24PT

Queen Mary, University of London
Forensic Medical Sciences...................................MSc 12FT 24-60PT

Sheffield Hallam University
Forensic Accounting.................................MSc 12FT 24PT
Forensic Engineering ....MSc 12FT 24PT
Forensic Science ....MSc 12FT 24PT

University of South Wales
Analytical and Forensic Science.............................. MSc 24FT

Staffordshire University
Forensic Science via Distance Learning.....MSc 12-18FT 12/36DL/PGDip 12-18FT

University of Strathclyde
Forensic Science.........................MSc 12FT/PGDip 9FT/PGCert 9FT

Swansea University
Applied Analytical Science (LCMS).....MSc 12FT 36PT/PGDip 12FT 36PT

Teesside University
Criminal Investigation....................................MSc 12FT 24PT
Forensic Radiography .... PGCert 12PT 12DL MSc 36PT 36DL
Forensic Science .... MSc 12 or 16FT 24PT MSc 12FT 24PT

UCL - University College London
Crime Analysis (by Distance Learning)...................PGCert 12-24PT
Crime Prevention and Community Safety ....PGCert 9FT/PGDip 9FT 18-45PT
Crime and Forensic Science .... MSc 12FT

University of the West of England, Bristol
Advanced Forensic Analysis...................................MSc 12FT 24PT

University of Wolverhampton
Fire Scene Investigation.............................MSc 12FT 24PT
Forensic Genetics and Human Identification.........MSc 12FT 24PT
Forensic Mark Comparison in collaboration with West Midlands Police..MSc 12FT 24PT

Forensics
Research Courses

University of Central Lancashire
Forensic and Investigative Science......PhD 48FT 84PT/MPhil 36FT 60PT/MD 48PT/MSc by research 24FT 36PT

University of Dundee
Forensic Medicine ....MPhil 24FT MSc by research 12FT PhD 36FT

University of Lincoln
Forensic Science.... MSc by research 12FT 24PT/MPhil 18FT 36PT/PhD 33FT 60PT

Teesside University
Forensic Science .... PhD 24FT 36PT/MPhil 18FT 30PT

UCL - University College London
Crime Science .... PhD 36FT 60PT

French studies
Taught Courses

University of Aberdeen
Modern Thought ....MLitt 12FT 24PT

Birkbeck, University of London
Comparative Literature.. MA 12FT 24PT
Modern Languages: Combined Language StudiesMA 12FT 24PT/MRes 12FT 24PT/PGDip 12FT 24PT
Modern Languages: French Studies .....MA 12FT 24PT/MRes 12FT 24PT/PGDip 12FT 24PT/PGCert 12PT
World Cinema...MA 12FT 24PT

University College Cork
French ....HDip 9FT 18PT MA 12FT
French (French & Comparative Literature).......................MA 12FT
French - Linguistics...MA 12FT
French Creativity/Literature & Film...................................MA 12FT
Translation Studies (French) ....MA 12FT

National University of Ireland Galway
French ....MA 12FT

University of London Institute in Paris
Paris Studies: History and Culture .... MA 12FT 24PT

University of Kent
Modern French Studies (Paris option)...................................MA 12FT
Modern French Studies: Writing, Theory and Visual Culture...MA 12FT 24PT

King's College London
French Literature & Culture ....MA 12FT 24PT

National University of Ireland, Maynooth
French..MA 12FT

University of Nottingham
20th and 21st Century French Thought .... MA 12FT 24-36PT
Early Modern French Studies................................. MA 12FT 24-36PT
Francophone and Postcolonial Studies.............. MA 12FT 24-36PT
French Culture and Politics .... MA 12FT 24-36PT
Twentieth and Twenty-First Century French Thought .....MA 12FT 24-36PT

University of Reading
Franco-British History .... MA (Res) 12FT 24-60PT
French Studies ....MA (Res) 12FT

Royal Holloway, University of London
French.. MA 12FT 24PT

University of Sheffield
French Studies (Research Track)................................. MA 12FT 24PT

University of St Andrews
French Language Studies..........MLitt 12FT 24PT/PGDip 9FT 24PT/MPhil 24FT
French Studies........MLitt 12FT 24PT/PGDip 9FT 24PT/MPhil 24FT

UCL - University College London
French and Francophone Studies .... MA 12FT 24PT

University of Warwick
French Culture and Thought.......................................MA 12FT 24PT

French studies
Research Courses

University of Aberdeen
French.......................PhD 36FT 60PT/MLitt by research 12FT 24PT

School of Advanced Study, University of London
French or Comparative/Interdisciplinary Studies PhD 36FT 60PT/MPhil 12FT 24PT

Aston University
Citizenship and Culture in Modern France .. MA by research 12FT 24PT

Bangor University
French..PhD 36FT/MPhil 12FT

University of Birmingham
French Studies........ PhD 36FT 72PT/MLitt by research 24FT 48PT/MA by research 12FT 24PT

University of Bristol
French..PhD 36FT 72PT/MLitt by research 24FT 48PT/MPhil 12FT 24PT

University of Cambridge
French..PhD 36FT 60PT

Durham University
Modern Languages and Cultures ....PhD 36FT 72PT/MA by research 12FT 24PT

University of Edinburgh
French.... PhD 36FT 72PT/MPhil 24FT 48PT/MSc by research 12FT 24PT

University of Exeter
French Studies.............................. PhD 36FT 60PT/MPhil 48FT 89PT

University of London Institute in Paris
French and Comparative Studies.........PhD 36FT 72PT/MPhil 24FT 48PT

University of Kent
French......PhD 36FT 60PT/MPhil 24FT 36PT/MA by research 12FT 24PT

King's College London
French Research ....PhD 36FT 48-72PT/MPhil 24FT 36PT

University of Leeds
Department of French..... PhD 36+FT/MPhil 24FT/MA by research 12+FT

University of Liverpool
French.................... PhD 24-48FT 48-84PT/MPhil 12-48FT 48-72PT

University of Manchester
French Studies.............................. PhD 36FT 72PT/MPhil 12FT 24PT

Nottingham Trent University
French.................................... PhD 48FT 96PT/MPhil 36FT 72PT

University of Nottingham
French.............. MRes 12FT 24PT/MPhil 24FT 48PT/PhD 36FT 72PT MA by research 12FT 24PT

Queen's University Belfast
French Studies.............................. PhD 36FT 72PT/MPhil 24FT 48PT

Royal Holloway, University of London
French...PhD 36FT

University of St Andrews
French Language Studies..........PhD 36FT 72PT/DLang 36FT 72PT/MPhil 12-24FT 48PT
French Studies........................ PhD 36FT 72PT/MPhil 12-24FT 48PT

UCL - University College London
French... PhD 36FT 60PT

University of Warwick
French Studies...........................PhD 36FT 60PT/MPhil 24FT 36PT/MA by research 12FT 24PT

Funeral studies
Taught Courses

University of Central Lancashire
Archaeology of Death...MA 12FT

University of Winchester
Funeral Celebrancy...PGCert 12PT

Gender studies
Taught Courses

University of Aberdeen
Philosophical Research..................................MLitt 12FT 24PT
Sex, Gender, Violence: Contemporary Critical Approaches .... MSc 12FT 24PT/PGDip 9FT 18PT

Bangor University
Women's Studies......................MA 24PT/PGDip 24PT/PGCert 12PT

Birkbeck, University of London
Culture, Diaspora, Ethnicity.....MSc 12FT 24PT/PGDip 12FT 24PT/PGCert 12PT
Gender, Sexuality and Culture . MA 12FT 24PT/PGDip 12FT 24PT/PGCert 12FT 24PT
Gender, Sexuality and SocietyMSc 12FT 24PT/PGCert 12FT 24PT/PGDip 12FT 24PT
Japanese Cultural Studies/Japanese Creative Industries Studies.. MA 12FT 24PT

University of Birmingham
Gender Studies...MRes 12FT 24PT
International Relations (Gender)............................MA 12FT 24PT/PGDip 9FT 18PT

University of Bristol
Gender and International Relations ....MSc 12FT 24PT

University of Cambridge
Social Anthropological Analysis................................... MPhil 11FT

University of Dundee
Gender, Culture and Society ....MLitt 12FT

University of East Anglia
Gender Analysis in International Development..... MA 12FT 24PT
International Social Development............................ MA 12FT 24PT
Media and International Development................... MA 12FT 24PT

University of Edinburgh
Gender History...MSc 12FT 24PT

Social sciences

National University of Ireland Galway
Gender, Globalisation and Rights ... MA 12FT 24PT

Glasgow Caledonian University
Sexual Health ... MSc 24-60FT On-lineDL
Social Research (Policy Analysis) ... MSc 12FT 24PT

University of Glasgow
Equality & Human Rights ... MSc 12FT 24PT

Goldsmiths, University of London
Development & Rights ... MA 12FT 24PT
Gender, Media & Culture ... MA 12FT 24PT
Social Anthropology ... MA 12FT 24PT

University of Hull
Gender Research ... MSc 12FT 24PT

Institute of Education
Education, Gender and International Development ... MA 12FT 24-48PT

Keele University
Gender Sexuality and Law ... PGDip 12FT 12PT/LLM 12FT 24PT

University of Leeds
Disability and Gender ... MA 12FT 24PT
Gender Studies ... MA 12FT 24PT/PGDip 12FT 24PT
Gender Studies (Research Methods) .. MA 12FT 24PT/PGDip 12FT 24PT
Gender and Culture ... MA 12FT 24PT PGDip 12FT 24PT
Gender and Management ... MA 12FT 24PT/PGDip 12FT 24PT
Gender, Sexuality and Queer Theory ... MA 12FT 24PT/PGDip 12FT 24PT PGDip 12FT 24PT/MA 12FT 24PT
Global Development and Gender ... MA 12FT 24PT
Global Genders ... PGDip 12FT 24PT/MA 12FT 24PT

London School of Economics and Political Science (LSE)
Gender ... MSc 12FT 24PT
Gender, Development and Globalisation ... MSc 12FT 24PT
Gender, Media and Culture ... MSc 12FT 24PT
Gender, Policy and Inequalities ... MSc 12FT 24PT

London South Bank University
Gender & Sexuality ... MA 12FT 24PT

University of Manchester
Gender, Sexuality and Culture ... MA 12FT 24PT/PGDip 12FT

University of Nottingham
MATILDA Women's and Gender History (European Master) ... MA 24FT

University of Reading
Applied Development Studies ... MSc 12FT 24PT

University of Roehampton
Religion and Gender ... MA 12FT 24PT PGDip 12FT 24PT

School of Oriental and African Studies - SOAS
Gender Studies ... MA 12FT 24-36PT

University of Sheffield
European Gender Studies ... MA 12FT 24PT

University of St Andrews
Mediaeval Studies ... MLitt 12FT/PGDip 9FT
Women, Writing and Gender .. MLitt 12FT 24PT/PGDip 9FT 24PT/MPhil 24FT

University of Sussex
Gender Studies ... MA 12FT 24PT
Gender and Development ... MA 12FT 24PT
Gender and Media Studies ... MA 12FT 24PT
Sexual Dissidence in Literature and Culture ... MA 12FT 24PT

Swansea University
Gender and Culture ... MA 12FT 24-36PT

Trinity College Dublin - the University of Dublin
Gender and Women's Studies ... MPhil 12FT 24PT

University of Ulster
Gender, Conflict and Human Rights ... LLM 12FT 24PT

UCL - University College London
Gender, Society and Representation ... MA 12FT 24PT

University of Warwick
Social Research with Specialism in Interdisciplinary Gender Studies ... MA 12FT 24PT/PGDip 9FT 24PT

University of York
European Gender and Equality Studies (Egales) ... MA 24FT/PGAdvDip 18FT

Gender studies
Research Courses

Birkbeck, University of London
Gender and Sexuality Studies ... PhD 36FT 60PT/MPhil 24FT 36PT

University of Birmingham
Gender Studies ... MRes 12FT 24PT

Coventry University
Geographies of Gender ... MSc by research 12FT 24-36PT

University of Hull
Gender Studies ... PhD 36FT 60PT/MPhil 24FT 36PT
Social Policy and Gender Studies ... PhD 36FT 60PT/MPhil 24FT 36PT

University of Leeds
Gender Studies ... MPhil 24FT/PhD 36+FT

London School of Economics and Political Science (LSE)
Gender ... PhD 36-48FT/MPhil 36-48FT

The Open University
Citizenship and Governance ... PhD 36FT 72PT variableDL/MPhil 15FT 24PT variableDL
Gender in the Humanities ... PhD 36FT 72PT variableDL/MPhil 15FT 24PT variableDL
Narrative, Discursive and Psychosocial Research ... PhD 36FT 72PT variableDL/MPhil 15FT 24PT variableDL
Political Theory ... PhD 36FT 72PT variableDL/MPhil 15FT 24PT variableDL

University of Sussex
Gender Studies Research Programme ... PhD 24-48FT 36-72PT/MPhil 12-36FT 24-48PT

UCL - University College London
Gender Studies ... PhD 36FT 60PT

German studies
Taught Courses

Birkbeck, University of London
Comparative Literature ... MA 12FT 24PT
Modern Languages: Combined Language Studies MA 12FT 24PT/MRes 12FT 24PT/PGDip 12FT 24PT
Modern Languages: German Studies ... MA 12FT 24PT/MRes 12FT 24PT/PGDip 12FT 24PT/PGCert 12PT
World Cinema ... MA 12FT 24PT

University of Birmingham
German Studies, Contemporary ... MRes 12FT 24PT

University College Cork
Arts (German) ... HDip 9FT 18PT
German Studies ... MA 12FT 24PT

National University of Ireland Galway
German Literature/ Language ... MA 12FT

University of Kent
Modern German and Comparative Literature ... MA 12FT 24PT

National University of Ireland, Maynooth
German ... MA 12FT 24PT

University of Nottingham
Modern and Contemporary German Studies ... MA 12FT 24-36PT

Queen Mary, University of London
Anglo-German Cultural Relations ... MA 12FT 24PT

University of Reading
German Studies ... MA (Res) 12FT 24PT

Royal Holloway, University of London
Research (German) ... MA 12FT 24PT

University of Sheffield
Germanic Studies (Programme Track) ... MA 12FT 24PT
Germanic Studies (Research Track) ... MA 12FT 24PT

University of St Andrews
German Studies ... MLitt 12FT 24PT/PGDip 9FT 24PT/MPhil 24FT

UCL - University College London
German History ... MA 12FT 24PT/PGDip 9FT 18PT/PGCert 3FT 6PT
German Studies ... MA 12FT 24PT/PGDip 9FT 18PT/PGCert 3FT 6PT

University of Warwick
German Cultural Studies ... MA 12FT 24PT/PGDip 9FT 21PT/PGCert 3-6FT 6PT

German studies
Research Courses

University of Aberdeen
German ... PhD 36FT 60PT/MLitt by research 12FT 24PT/MPhil 24FT

Aberystwyth University
German ... MPhil 12FT 24PT

School of Advanced Study, University of London
Germanic and/or Romance Studies ... PhD 36FT 60PT/MPhil 12FT 24PT PhD 36FT 60PT/MPhil 36FT 60PT
Germanic or Comparative/Interdisciplinary Studies ... PhD 36FT 60PT/MPhil 12FT 24PT

Bangor University
German ... PhD 36FT/MPhil 12FT

University of Birmingham
Contemporary German Studies ... MRes 12FT 24PT
German Studies (Social Sciences) ... PhD 36FT 72PT/MPhil 24FT 48PT
German Studies ... PhD 36FT 72PT/MA by research 12FT 24PT

University of Bristol
German ... PhD 36FT 72PT/MLitt by research 24FT 48PT/MPhil 12FT 24PT

University of Cambridge
German ... PhD 36FT 60PT

University of Edinburgh
German ... PhD 36FT 72PT/MPhil 24FT 48PT/MSc by research 12FT 24-36PT

University of Exeter
German Studies ... PhD 48FT 84PT/MPhil 36FT 60PT

University of Kent
German Literature ... PhD 36FT 60PT/MPhil 24FT 36PT/MA by research 12FT 24PT
German and Comparative Literature ... PhD 36FT 60PT

King's College London
German Research ... PhD 36FT 48-72PT/MPhil 24FT 36PT

University of Leeds
German ... PhD 36+FT/MPhil 24FT/MA by research 12+FT

University of Liverpool
German ... PhD 24-48FT 48-84PT/MPhil 12-48FT 24-72PT

University of Manchester
German Studies ... PhD 36FT 72PT/MPhil 12FT 24PT

Nottingham Trent University
German ... PhD 48FT 96PT/MPhil 36FT 72PT

University of Nottingham
German ... MA by research 12FT 24-36PT MPhil 12-36FT 24-72PT/PhD 24-48FT 48-96PT

Queen Mary, University of London
German ... PhD 36FT 72PT/MPhil 24FT 48PT

Royal Holloway, University of London
German ... PhD 36FT/MPhil 24FT/MA by research 12FT

University of St Andrews
German Studies ... PhD 36FT 72PT/DLang 36FT 72PT/MPhil 12-24FT 48PT

University of Ulster
German ... PhD 36FT 72PT/MPhil 24FT 48PT

UCL - University College London
German ... PhD 36FT 60PT

University of Warwick
German Studies ... PhD 36-48FT 60PT

Gerontology
Taught Courses

University of Bradford
Dementia Studies ... MSc 24-36DL/PGDip 12-24DL/PGCert 9-12DL

Brunel University
Ageing Studies ... PGCert 12PT/PGDip 24PT/MSc 36PT

Cardiff University
Ageing, Health and Disease ... MSc 24PT/PGDip 12FT/PGCert 12PT

University of East London
Long Term Conditions in Adults ... PGCert 5FT 12 - 36PT

University of Edinburgh
Cognitive Ageing Research Methods for Medical Scientists (online distance learning) ... PGCert 12PT 12DL
Dementia: International Experience, Policy and Practice (Online Distance Learning) ... MSc 24DL/PGDip 21DL/PGCert 9DL

National University of Ireland Galway
Nursing (Gerontology) ... PGDip 12FT 24PT

Glasgow Caledonian University
Life Sciences - Biological and Biomedical Sciences/Psychology/Vision Sciences ... MRes 12FT

Keele University
Geriatric Medicine ... MSc 24PT/PGDip 16PT
Gerontology ... MA 12FT 24PT/PGDip 12PT

King's College London
Advanced Care in Dementia ... MSc 12FT 24PT
Ageing & Society ... MA 12FT/MSc 12FT/PGDip 12FT/PGCert 12FT
Gerontology ... MSc 12FT 24PT/PGDip 12FT 24PT/PGCert 12FT 24PT
Public Policy & Ageing ... MA 12FT 24PT/PGCert 12FT 24PT/PGDip 12FT 24PT
Research Methods for Social Science & Health ... PGCert 3FT 24PT

University Campus Suffolk
Science of Healthy Ageing ... MSc 12FT

University of Salford
Geriatric Medicine ... MSc 48-60PT/PGDip 24-60PT/PGCert 12-60PT

University of South Wales
Care of the Older Person ... MSc 24 - 72DL

University of Southampton
Gerontology ... MSc 12FT 24PT/PGDip 9FT 21PT MSc 12DL/PGDip 9DL

Staffordshire University
Ageing, Mental Health and Dementia ... MSc 36DL

Social sciences

University of Stirling
Dementia Studies.................... MSc 36PT/PGDip 24PT/PGCert 12PT
Health and Wellbeing of the Older Person...................... MSc 24FT

Swansea University
Ageing Studies .... MSc 12FT 36PT/PGDip 12FT 24PT/PGCert 12FT 12PT

Trinity College Dublin - the University of Dublin
Dementia...MSc 12FT 24PT
Gerontological Nursing...MSc 24PT

University of Ulster
Interdisciplinary Dementia Studies ....PGDip 24DL/MSc 36DL

University of West London
Anti-ageing and Lifespan Medicine................................PGDip 24DL

University of Worcester
Applied Psychology ....MSc 12FT 24-72PT

Gerontology
Research Courses

Bangor University
Ageing and Cognitive Health .... PhD 36FT 60PT
Ageing and Dementia Studies ....MSc by research 12FT 24PT PhD 36FT 60PT/MPhil 24FT 48PT

University of Edinburgh
Geriatric Medicine.........PhD 36FT 72PT/MPhil 24FT 48PT/MSc by research 12FT 24PT
Pathology.........PhD 36FT 72PT/MPhil 24FT/MSc by research 12FT 24PT

Keele University
Social Policy, Sociology, and Social Gerontology .... PhD 24-48FT 48-84PT/MPhil 12-24FT 24-36PT

King's College London
Age-Related Diseases (Wolfson Centre for)................ PhD 36-48FT 48-72PT/MPhil 36-48FT 36-48PT/MDS by research 36-48FT 36-48PT
Gerontology Research .... PhD 36FT 72PT/MPhil 36FT 72PT
Old Age Psychiatry & Dementia MPhil 36FT 72PT/PhD 36FT 72PT
Wolfson Centre for Age Related Diseases . PhD 36-48FT 48-72PT/MPhil 36-48FT 48-72PT/MD (Res) 36-48FT 48-72PT

Lancaster University
Biomedical and Life Sciences..... PhD 36FT 48PT/MPhil 24FT 36PT

Newcastle University
Ageing ....MPhil 12FT 24PT/PhD 36FT 72PT/MD 24FT 48PT
Ageing and Health ....MRes 12FT

The Open University
Ageing and Later Life .... PhD 36FT 72PT variableDL/ MPhil 15FT 24PT variableDL

Plymouth University
Preventive and Supportive Care ....MPhil TBCFT

University of Sheffield
Primary Medical Care and Ageing.......PhD 36FT 72PT/MPhil 24FT 48PT

University of Southampton
School of Social Sciences - Gerontology ......PhD 36FT 72PT/MPhil 24FT 48PT

St George's, University of London
Clinical Developmental Sciences.........PhD 36FT 84PT/MPhil 24FT 48PT/MDRes 24PT

University of the West of Scotland
Centre for Gerontology and Health Studies ....PhD/MPhil/MSc by research 12FT

Health teaching
Taught Courses

University of Aberdeen
Social and Educational Research ....MRes 12FT

Anglia Ruskin University
Medical & Healthcare Education ....MSc 12FT 36PT

University of Bedfordshire
Physical Activity, Nutrition and Health Promotion........MSc 12FT/ PGDip 12FT/PGCert 12FT

Birmingham City University
Practice Teacher Preparations ....PGCert 12DL

University of Birmingham
Physiotherapy (pre-registration) ....MSc 24FT

University of Bolton
Advanced Practice (Health and Social Care)....................MSc 24PT
Teaching and Learning.. MA 12FT 60PT
Teaching and Learning for Professional Practice........PGCert 12PT

Bournemouth University
Education Practice................... MA 31FT/PGDip 24FT/PGCert 12FT

University of Bradford
Health Professional Educator........................PGDip 18PT/MSc 60PT

University of Brighton
Clinical Education............................MA 36 - 72PT/PGDip 36 - 72PT

Health Promotion............MA 12FT 24-72PT/PGDip 12FT 24-72PT/ PGCert 12FT 24-72PT
Health Promotion and Education......................MA 12FT 24 - 72PT/ PGDip 12FT 24 - 72PT
Health Promotion and Management...MA 12FT 24 - 72PT/PGDip 12FT 24 - 72PT
Health and Education.MSc 12FT 24 - 72PT/PGDip 12FT 24 - 72PT
Health and Social Care Education...........................PGCert 12 - 18PT
International Health Promotion..........................MA 12FT 36PT/ PGDip 12FT 36PT
Physiotherapy and Education....... MSc 12 - 24FT 24 - 72PT/PGDip 12 - 24FT 24 - 72PT/PGCert 12 - 24FT 24 - 72PT
Teaching in Clinical Settings.................................PGCert 12 - 24PT

University of Bristol
Teaching and Learning for Health Professionals ....MSc 12 - 24FT/ Diploma 12 - 36FT/Cert 12 - 36FT

Brunel University
Health Promotion and Public Health ....MSc 12FT 36PT n/aDL

Canterbury Christ Church University
Health Promotion and Public Health .... MSc 12FT 36PT
Health and Social Care (14-19) PGCE .... PGCE(QTS) 12FT

University of Central Lancashire
Applied Public Health: Health Improvement ....PGCert 12PT
Health & Social Care Education......................................PGCert 12PT
Health Informatics.......................................MSc 33PT/PGDip 24PT
Health and Social Care Education ....PGCert 12PT
Integrated Healthcare by elearning.....MSc 36-48PT/PGDip 24PT/ PGCert 12PT

University of Chester
Health and Social Care - Professional Education...MEd 24 - 72PT/ PGDip 24 - 60PT/PGCert 12 - 36PT
Weight ManagementMSc 12FT 24 - 48PT/PGDip 12FT 24 - 48PT/ PGCert 12FT 12 - 24PT
Weight Management (Taught in Dublin, Ireland) .. MSc 24-48PT/ PGDip 24-48PT/PGCert 12-24PT

Durham University
Medical Education...MSc 12FT 24PT

University of East Anglia
Clinical Education..............MClinEd 12FT 36PT/PGDip 12FT 24PT/ PGCert 12PT
Clinical Science...MRes 12FT

University of East London
Health Promotion ... MSc 12FT 24PT/PGDip 8FT 16PT/PGCert 4FT 8PT
e-Health .... MSc 12FT 24PT/PGDip 8FT 16PT/PGCert 4FT 8PT

Edge Hill University
Teaching and Learning in Clinical Practice...................PGCert 12PT

University of Exeter
Bioarchaeology ....MSc 12FT 24PT

National University of Ireland Galway
Health Promotion........................MA 12FT 24PT/PGDip 12FT 24PT
Health Sciences (Clinical Education) ...... MHSc 12FT/PGDip 12FT/ PGCert 12FT
Health Services Research........................... MHSc 24PT/PGDip 24PT

Glasgow Caledonian University
Healthcare Education...MSc 12FT 36PT

University of Glasgow
Health Professions Education .... MSc(MedSci) 12FT 36PT 36DL/ DHPE 48FT 72PT

University of Gloucestershire
Physical Activity and Health...... MSc 12FT 24PT/PGDip 8FT 20PT/ PGCert 4FT 8PT
Sports Coaching...MSc 12FT 24PT

Glyndwr University
Professional Education. MSc 12FT 24-60PT/PGDip 24FT 24-36PT/ PGCert 6FT 12PT
Professional Education........... MSc 12FT 24-60PT/DipMedEd 24FT 24-36PT/CertMedEd 6FT 12PT

Goldsmiths, University of London
Higher Specialist Social Work: Practice Education...... PGDip 24PT
Practice Education............................... MA 36-60PT/PGDip 36-60PT PGCert 36-60PT

Imperial College London
Health Policy.. MScD 24PT

Institute of Education
Centenary Brendish Scholarships (Taught Masters Programmes) MA 12FT/MSc 12FT
Education, Health Promotion and International Development.... MA 12FT 24-48PT

King's College London
Health Promotion...MSc 12FT 24-48PT
Health Studies..PGCert 12FT 24PT

Leeds Metropolitan University
Health & Social Care Chaplaincy...................................PGCert 12PT
Health Care Studies ....MA 24PT
Public Health (Health Promotion and Environmental Health) Zambia ....MSc 36PT

Public Health - Health Promotion ......MSc 12FT 30PT/PGDip 12FT 24PT/PGCert 4FT 12PT

London School of Economics and Political Science (LSE)
Health, Community and Development ....MSc 12FT 24PT

London School of Hygiene and Tropical Medicine
Public Health for Eye Care ....MSc 12FT 24PT

London South Bank University
Public Health and Health Promotion ....MSc 12-18FT 24-36PT

University of Northampton
Practice Education................................MSc 12FT 24PT/PGCert 12PT

Northumbria University
Family Therapy and Systemic Practice .... MA 36PT/PGDip 24PT/ PGCert 12PT
Health and Social Care Quality Provision.....................PGCert 12FT

University of Nottingham
Health Communication by Web Based Distance Learning.......MA 24-48DL
Practice Teacher in Health and Social Care ....PGCert 12-24PT
Psychology and Health............... MSc 12FT 24PT/PGDip 12FT 24PT

Oxford Brookes University
Higher Professional Education..... MSc 12FT 12-36PT/PGDip 12FT 24PT/PGCert 12FT 18PT
Medical & Dental Education (a collaborative programme with Oxford PGMDE)... PGCert 9PT

University of Roehampton
Obesity: Risks and Prevention...................................MSc 12FT 24PT
Obesity: Risks and Prevention..................................PGCert 6FT 12PT
Obesity: Risks and Prevention...................................PGDip 9FT 24PT

University Campus Suffolk
Health and Social Care Practice ...... MA 60PT/PGCert 36PT/PGDip 48PT

Sheffield Hallam University
Health Care Education (including teacher status for health professionals)...MSc variablePT
Healthcare Education............MSc VAPT/PGDip VAPT/PGCert VAPT
Leading and Managing Physical Education and Youth Sport......... MSc 3PT
Leading and Managing Sport Development ....MSc 24PT/PGDip 16PT/PGCert 8PT

University of South Wales
Education for Health and Social Care Professionals......MSc 12PT/ PGCert 12PT

University of Southampton
Health Education and Promotion...........................MSc 12FT 24PT

University of Surrey
Learning and Teaching for Professional Practice...... PGCert 12PT/ PGDip 24PT/MSc 36PT/Practice Teacher 4PT

Swansea University
Public Health & Health Promotion ....MSc 12FT 36PT

Trinity College Dublin - the University of Dublin
Clinical Health Sciences Education (PG. Dip.)............... PGDip 12PT

University of Ulster
Health Promotion and Public Health ... MSc 12FT 27-36PT/PGDip 9FT 18PT/PGCert 4-9FT 9-18PT

University of Warwick
Patient and Public Involvement in Healthcare ....PGA 12PT/ CPDMod 1PT
Theory & Practical Techniques of Self Management ....PGA 12PT/ CPDMod 1PT

University of West London
Employment Law...LLM 12FT 24PT

University of Winchester
Education: Early Years, School, College and Workplace Educators' Pathway .... MA(Ed) up to 60PT

Health teaching
Research Courses

Bucks New University
Education... Professional Doctorate 48PT

Cardiff University
Nursing, Medicine, Health and Social Care ....MPhil 12FT 36PT/ PhD 36FT 60PT

University of Chester
Health and Social Care...DProf 24-84PT

University of Gloucestershire
Sport and Exercise................PhD 30-48FT 48-84PT/MPhil 18-36FT 30-60PT/MSc by research 12-24FT 18-36PT

Liverpool School of Tropical Medicine
Child & Reproductive Health................................. PhD/MPhil/MIHR

University of Nottingham
Education and Technology for Health...............................PhD 36FT

University of Sheffield
Health and Related Research..... PhD 36FT 72PT/MPhil 24FT 48PT

Section sponsored by
BPP UNIVERSITY COLLEGE

Business and social sciences
www.prospects.ac.uk/findcourses POSTGRADUATE DIRECTORY 495

Social sciences

Himalayan studies
Taught Courses

University of Oxford
Tibetan and Himalayan Studies .... MPhil 24FT

Housing studies
Taught Courses

De Montfort University
Housing Studies ....PGCert 9-18DL/PGDip 24DL/MSc 29-36DL

University of Glasgow
Housing Studies..... MSc 12FT 24PT 60BM/PGDip 9FT 18PT 48BM

University of Greenwich
Housing Management and Policy............................ MSc 12FT 24PT

Heriot-Watt University
Housing and Real Estate........MSc 12FT 24PT 24-84DL/PGDip 9FT 18PT 18-84DL

Leeds Metropolitan University
Housing, Regeneration and Urban Management MA 12FT 24PT/ PGCert 12FT 12PT/PGDip 12FT 24PT
Town and Regional Planning...................................... MA 12FT 24PT

London Metropolitan University
Housing & Inclusion .... MA 12FT 24PT

London South Bank University
Housing Studies...MA 36PT

Northumbria University
Housing Policy and Management...MA 12FT
Housing Policy and Management with Professional Practice .... MA 36PT/PGDip 24PT
Surveying/Construction programme - Housing Pathway....... MSc 24DL

University of Salford
Urban Design and Regeneration ....MSc 12FT 28PT/ PGDip 8FT 20PT MSc 12FT 28PT/PGDip 8FT 18PT

Sheffield Hallam University
Housing Policy and Practice........MA 12FT 24PT/PGDip 12FT 18PT
Housing Practice...CertHE 24PT 24DL
Housing Professional Studies.......................... DipHE 18PT 12-18DL
Housing for Environmental Health...............................CertHE 18PT

University of Stirling
Housing Studies ....MSc 12FT/PGDip 12FT MSc 24PT/PGDip 24PT/PGCert 12PT

University of Ulster
Housing Studies...MSc 36PT/PGDip 24PT

University of Westminster
Housing Practice...PGCert 24PT PGDip 24PT MA 24PT

Housing studies
Research Courses

University of Birmingham
Hydrogeology................................ PhD 36FT 72PT/MPhil 24FT 48PT

Cardiff University
Housing... PhD 36FT 60PT

University of Dundee
Town and Regional Planning .... MPhil 24FT

Human rights
Taught Courses

University of Aberdeen
Criminal Justice...LLM 12FT 24-36PT
Criminal Justice and Human Rights .... LLM 12FT 36PT
Human Rights ....LLM 12FT 24-36PT
Human Rights & Criminal Justice ....LLM 12FT 24-36PT
International Law ....LLM 12FT 24-36PT

Aberystwyth University
Climate Change and Human Rights....................................LLM 12FT
Democracy, Human Security and International Law.......LLM 12FT
Human Rights and Development...LLM 12FT
Human Rights and Humanitarian Law...............................LLM 12FT LLM 36DL
International Commercial Law and Human Rights.........LLM 12FT 24PT/PGDip 9FT 21PT
Rights, Gender and International Law ....LLM 12FT

School of Advanced Study, University of London
Human Rights .... MA 12FT 24PT

Bangor University
Criminology and Law...MA 12FT
International Law - specialising in International Criminal&International Human Rights Law ....LLM 12FT
Law..PhD by taught 36FT/MPhil 24FT
Law and Criminology...LLM 12FT

University of Bath
Security, Conflict & Justice .... MRes 12FT 24-36PT

Birkbeck, University of London
Constitutional Politics, Law and Theory .... LLM 12FT 24PT
Human Rights ....MA 12FT 24PT/LLM 12FT 24PT
Law (General).. LLM 12FT 24PT

Birmingham City University
International Human Rights........ PGDip 6-8FT 12-16PT/LLM 12FT 24PT

University of Birmingham
Human Rights and Human Values.MSc 12FT 24-48PT/PGDip 9FT 36PT/PGCert 4FT 24PT

University of Bradford
Conflict, Security and Development.......MA 12FT 12-36PT/PGDip 24FT 24-36PT

University of Bristol
Human Rights Law... LLM 12FT 24PT

Brunel University
International Human Rights Law....................LLM 12FT/PGDip 9FT

Cardiff University
Human Rights ....LLM 12FT

University of Central Lancashire
Global Security and Justice..MA 12FT

City University London
Human Rights .... MA 12FT 24PT
International Politics and Human Rights .... MA 12FT 24PT

De Montfort University
International Human Rights Law......... PGDip 15DL/LLM 15-27DL

University College Dublin
Human Rights ....MSc 12FT/MLitt 24FT

University of Dundee
International Criminal Justice & Human Rights ....LLM 12FT
International Law ....LLM 12FT

Durham University
Conflict Prevention, Sustainable Peace and Security..... MSc 12FT

University of East London
Anthropology, Human Rights and Justice ....MSc 12FT 24PT/ PGDip 8FT 16PT/PGCert 4FT 8PT
Human Rights ...LLM 12FT 24PT/PGDip 8FT 16PT/PGCert 4FT 8PT

Edge Hill University
International Justice and Human Rights Law........ LLM 12FT 24PT

University of Edinburgh
Global Crime, Justice and Security...........................MSc 12FT 24PT
International Law .... LLM 12FT 24PT

University of Essex
Human Rights and Arts .... MA 12FT 24PT
Human Rights and Cultural Diversity .... MA 12FT 24PT
Human Rights and Research Methods...................... MA 12FT 24PT
International Human Rights Law.......................................LLM 12FT
International Human Rights and Humanitarian Law.....LLM 12FT
Theory and Practice of Human Rights .... MA 12FT 24PT
UK Human Rights and Public Law............................ LLM 12FT 24PT

University of Exeter
International Human Rights Law............................. LLM 12FT 24PT
Security, Conflict and Justice..................................MRes 12FT 24PT

National University of Ireland Galway
Gender, Globalisation and Rights............................. MA 12FT 24PT
Human Rights Law (Cross-border).......................................LLM 12FT
Human Rights and Criminal Justice (Cross Border).........LLM 12FT
International Human Rights Law............................. LLM 12FT 24PT

Glasgow Caledonian University
Citizenship and Human Rights by Learning Contract...MSc 12FT/ PGDip 12FT/PGCert 12FT

University of Glasgow
Equality & Human Rights...MRes 12FT 24PT MSc 12FT 24PT
Human Rights & International Politics ....MRes 12FT 24PT
Human Rights and International Politics..... MSc 12FT/PGDip 9FT
International Law and Security.................................. LLM 12FT 24PT
Transnational Crime, Justice and Security ....MSc 12FT 24PT

Goldsmiths, University of London
Development & Rights... MA 12FT 24PT

University of Hull
International Human Rights Law............................. LLM 12FT 24PT
International Law .... LLM 12FT 24PT

Keele University
Human Rights, Globalisation and Justice ... PGDip 12FT/MA 12FT 24PT
Law and Society......... LLM 12FT 24- 48PT/PGDip 12-48PT/PGCert 12-24PT

University of Kent
Human Rights ....MA 12FT 24PT/PGDip 12FT 24PT
International Criminal Justice...PGDip 12FT 24PT/LLM 12FT 24PT

Kingston University
Human Rights .... MA 12FT 24PT
Human Rights and Genocide Studies .....Joint European MA 18FT

Lancaster University
International Human Rights and Terrorism Law... LLM 12FT 24PT

University of Leeds
International and European Human Rights Law... LLM 12FT 24PT
Security and Justice .... MA 12FT 24PT

University of Leicester
International Human Rights Law.............................. LLM 12FT 24PT

University of Limerick
Human Rights in Criminal Justice..................... MA 12FT/LLM 12FT

University of Lincoln
Globalising Justice .... MA 12FT 24PT
Journalism, War and International Human Rights.......................... MA 12FT 24PT

University of Liverpool
Humanitarian Studies..................MSc 12FT/Diploma 9FT/Cert 6FT
International Human Rights Law............................. LLM 12FT 24PT

London School of Economics and Political Science (LSE)
Human Rights ....MSc 12FT 24PT

London South Bank University
Human Rights & Development .... LLM 16FT 28PT
International Human Rights & Development......... LLM 16FT 28PT
International Refugee Law and Policy.................PGCert 16FT 28PT

University of Manchester
Human Rights ....MA 12FT 24PT/PGDip 9FT 21PT
Humanitarianism and Conflict Response .... MA 12FT 24PT

Middlesex University
Human Rights and Business..MA 24PT/PGCert 12PT/PGDip 15PT
Minorities, Rights and the Law................................. LLM 12FT 24PT

Northumbria University
Information Rights Law and Practice.......LLM 24DL/PGDip 18DL/ PGCert 9DL

Nottingham Trent University
Human Rights .... LLM 12FT 24PT
International Criminal Justice................................... LLM 12FT 24PT

University of Nottingham
Global Citizenship, Identities and Human Rights .... MA 12FT 24PT
Human Rights Law.. LLM 12FT 24-48PT
International Criminal Justice Law and Armed Conflict.................. LLM 12FT 24-48PT
Social and Global Justice .... MA 12FT 24PT

The Open University
Human Rights and Development Management........PGCert 12DL

Oxford Brookes University
Development and Emergency Practice ....MA 12FT 24PT/ PGDip 9FT 21PT/PGCert 3-9FT 9PT
Humanitarian Action and Conflict ....PGCert 12DL
International Human Rights LawLLM 12FT 24PT/PGDip 9FT 18PT

University of Oxford
Criminology & Criminal Justice... MSc 12FT
International Human Rights Law.............................MSt 24PT 24DL
Refugee and Forced Migration Studies.................................MSc 9FT

Queen Mary, University of London
Human Rights Law.......................................LLB graduate entry 12FT

Queen's University Belfast
Human Rights Law... LLM 12FT 24PT
Human Rights Law (Cross-Border).......................................LLM 12FT
Human Rights and Criminal Justice ....LLM 12FT 24PT/MSSc 12FT 24PT
Human Rights and Criminal Justice (Cross-Border).........LLM 12FT

University of Reading
Advanced Legal Studies .... LLM 12FT 24PT
International Law and World Order ...LLM 12FT 24PT/PGDip 9FT/ PGCert 6FT

Richmond, The American International University in London
International Conflict& Security .... MA 12FT 24PT

University of Roehampton
Human Rights .... MA 18FT 24+PT
Human Rights Practice: Erasmus Mundus..........................MA 24FT
Human Rights and International Relations.......... MA 18FT 24+PT
Human Rights ....PGCert 10FT 12+PT PGDip 12FT 24+PT
Human Rights and International Relations................. PGCert 10FT PGDip 12FT 24PT

School of Oriental and African Studies - SOAS
Human Rights Law.. MA 12FT 24PT

Sheffield Hallam University
International Criminal Justice........... MA 12FT 24PT/PGDip 12PT/ PGCert 6PT

University of Sheffield
Global Justice .... MA 12FT 24PT

University of Southampton
International Law .... LLM 12FT 24PT

University of St Andrews
Peace and Conflict Studies...MLitt 12FT

University of Strathclyde
Criminal Justice and Penal Change........MSc 12FT 24PT/LLM 12FT 24PT/PGDip 9FT
Human Rights Law...LLM 12FT 24PT/PGDip 9FT 21PT/PGCert 9FT

Business and social sciences
496 POSTGRADUATE DIRECTORY www.prospects.ac.uk/findcourses

Section sponsored by
BPP
UNIVERSITY
COLLEGE

Social sciences

University of Surrey
International Intervention .... MA 12FT 24PT
LLM Justice .... LLM 12FT 24PT

University of Sussex
Conflict, Security and Development........................... MA 12FT 24PT
Criminal Law and Criminal Justice..................... LLM 12FT 24PT
Human Rights .... MA 12FT 24PT
International Criminal Law........................ LLM 12FT 24PT

Swansea University
Development and Human Rights........................ MA 12FT 36PT
International Security & Development .... MA 12FT 24PT

University of Ulster
Gender, Conflict and Human Rights........................ LLM 12FT 24PT
Human Rights Law and Transational Justice.......... LLM 12FT 24PT

UCL - University College London
Human Rights .... MA 12FT 24PT
Transnational Studies.................................... MA 12FT 24PT

University of Warwick
International Development Law and Human Rights ......LLM 12FT 24PT/PGDip 9FT

University of York
Applied Human Rights............ MA 12FT 24PT/Diploma 12FT 24PT
International Human Rights Law & Practice.........LLM 12FT 24PT/PGDip 12FT 24PT

Human rights
Research Courses

School of Advanced Study, University of London
International Human Rights..........................PhD 36FT/MPhil 12FT

University of Central Lancashire
Sociology, Ethnicity & Human Rights, Criminology ....
PhD 30-48FT 66-84PT/MPhil 18-36FT 42-60PT/MA by research 12FT 24PT

University College Dublin
Human Rights .... PhD 36FT/MLitt by research 24FT

University of Dundee
Non-Graduating Research in School of Humanities (6 months or more) ....Non-Grad 6-24FT
Non-Graduating Research in School of Humanities (less than 6 months)... Non-Grad 1-5FT
Non-Graduating Research in School of Law (6 months or more).. Non-Grad 6-24FT
Non-Graduating Research in School of Law (less than 6 months) Non-Grad 1-5FT

University of Essex
Human Rights .... MPhil 24FT 48PT/PhD 36FT 72PT
Human Rights and Research MethodsPhD 36FT 72PT/MPhil 24FT 48PT

Kingston University
Helen Bamber Centre for the Study of Rights and Conflict.....PhD 48FT 72PT/MPhil 24FT 48PT/MA by research 12FT 24PT

University of Manchester
Humanitarianism and Conflict Response .... PhD 48FT 96PT

University of Nottingham
School of Law Research Areas .. PhD 36FT/MPhil 24FT/MRes 24FT

University of Salford
Research Opportunities at Salford Law School...Salford Centre of Legal Research 36DL

School of Oriental and African Studies - SOAS
Development Studies....................................PhD 36FT 48-60PT

University of Sussex
Human Rights Research ProgrammePhD 24-48FT 36-72PT/MPhil 12-36FT 24-48PT

Indian studies
Taught Courses

Goldsmiths, University of London
Critical Asian Studies..................................... MA 12FT 24PT

University of Greenwich
International Business in India .... MBA 12FT 36PT

King's College London
Contemporary India.................................MRes 12FT 24PT
Modern India .... MA 12FT 24PT

University of Oxford
Contemporary India....................................MSc 9FT

School of Oriental and African Studies - SOAS
Economics (with Reference to South Asia) .... MSc 12FT 24PT
South Asian Area Studies.......................... MA 12FT 24PT

Indian studies
Research Courses

King's College London
Contemporary India Research.............MPhil 24FT 36PT/PhD 36FT 48-72PT

Industrial relations
Taught Courses

Birmingham City University
Public Relations.................................. MA 12FT 24PT

Brunel University
Human Resource Management and Employment Relations......... MSc 12FT

University of Cambridge
Industrial Systems, Manufacturing and Management .... MPhil 9FT

University of Central Lancashire
International Relations..MA 12FT

University of East Anglia
Employment Law.................... LLM 12FT 24PT/PGCert 12FT
Industrial Economics.................................... MSc 12FT

National University of Ireland Galway
Industrial Relations & Human Resource Management........ MSc 9 approxFT

University of Hertfordshire
Human Resource Management and Employment Relations...MA 12FT 24PT/PGCert 12FT 24PT/PGDip 12FT 24PT

Keele University
Industrial Relations and Employment LawMA 24PT/PGDip 18PT/PGCert 18PT

Leeds Metropolitan University
Specialist Community Public Health Nursing - Health Visiting .... MSc 24PT/PGDip 12FT 24PT

University of Leicester
Industrial Relations and Workplace Learning ....MSc 24-36DL/GradDip 18DL/PGCert 12DL

London School of Economics and Political Science (LSE)
Management, Organisations and Governance .... MSc 12FT

University of Manchester
International Human Resource Management and Comparative Industrial Relations... MSc 12FT

Nottingham Trent University
Employment Law... LLM 12FT 24PT

University of Nottingham
Public Procurement Law and Policy .... PGDip 21PT/LLM 24PT/PGCert 12-21PT

Ruskin College
International Labour and Trade Union Studies........ MA 12FT 24PT

University of Salford
Industrial and Commercial Combustion Engineering .MSc 36DL/PGDip 12DL/PGCert 12DL

School of Oriental and African Studies - SOAS
Labour, Social Movements and Development ,....... MSc 12FT 24PT
MA Globalisation and Multinational Corporations........................ MA 12FT 24PT

University of Warwick
Certificate in Employment Research .... CER 12PT
Industrial Relations & Managing Human Resources ....MA 12FT 24PT
International Employment Relations........................ MA 12FT 24PT
Social Research with Specialism in Comparative Labour Studies... MA 12FT 24PT

University of Westminster
Public Relations.. MA 12FT 24-48PT

Industrial relations
Research Courses

Cardiff University
Work, Employment and Globalisation......... PhD 36FT possiblePT/MPhil 12FT possiblePT

University of Hertfordshire
Centre for Research in Employment Studies.........PhD 36FT 72PT/MPhil 24FT 48PT/MRes 12FT 24PT

Keele University
Employment policy and Equalities .... PhD 24-48FT 48-96PT/MPhil 12-24FT 24-36PT

University of Kent
Industrial Relations.... PhD 36FT 60PT/MA by research 12FT 24PT

Lancaster University
Organisation, Work and Technology ..PhD 36FT 48PT/MPhil 24FT 36PT

London Metropolitan University
Dept of Law Governance and International Relations.... PhD Max 60FT Max 96PT/MPhil Max 36FT Max 54PT

London School of Economics and Political Science (LSE)
Employment Relations and Organisational Behaviour .... MPhil 36-48FT/PhD 36-48FT

University of Salford
Institute for Materials ResearchPhD 36FT/MSc by research 12FT/MPhil 12FT

School of Oriental and African Studies - SOAS
Development Studies.............................PhD 36FT 48-60PT
Economics.................................. PhD 36FT 72PT/MPhil 24FT 36PT
Politics .... PhD 36FT 72PT/MPhil 24FT 36PT

University of Warwick
Employment Research .... PhD 36FT 60PT

IPLDP
Taught Courses

Anglia Ruskin University
International Social Welfare and Social Policy.......MSc 12FT 24PT

University of Bolton
Safeguarding and Promoting Children's Welfare.... MSc 36-60PT/PGDip 24PT/PGCert 12PT

University of Cumbria
Leadership and Management in PolicingMBA 36PT/PGDip 36PT/PGCert 36PT

University of East Anglia
Water Security and International Development ... MSc 12FT 24PT

Edinburgh Napier University
Advanced Security and Digital Forensics.................MSc 12FT 24PT

University of Leicester
Terrorism, Security and Policing ....MSc 12FT 24PT/PGDip 12FT 24PT

Queen Margaret University, Edinburgh
Conflict, Social Development and Health ......PGCert 4FT 24-48PT

University of Salford
Intelligence and Security Studies MA 12FT 36PT/PGDip 9FT 20PT

University of St Andrews
International Security Studies ....MLitt 12FT/PGDip 9FT

IPLDP
Research Courses

The Open University
Policing, punishment and justice....... PhD 36FT 72PT variableDL/MPhil 15FT 24PT variableDL

Irish gaelic
Taught Courses

Aberystwyth University
Irish/Gwyddeleg .... MA 12FT 24PT

University College Cork
Modern Irish .... MA 12FT 24PT

Dublin Institute of Technology
Applied Irish/Ghaeilge Fheidhmeach ....MA 24PT

National University of Ireland Galway
Ateangaireacht Chomhdhála..........................MA 12FT/PGDip 9FT
Nua-Ghaeilge ....MA 12FT
Old and Middle Irish ....MA 12FT

National University of Ireland, Maynooth
sa Nua-Ghaeilge (Modern Irish) ....MA 12FT

Trinity College Dublin - the University of Dublin
Old Irish...PGDip 12FT

University of Ulster
Modern Irish .... MA 27PT/PGDip 18PT

Irish studies
Taught Courses

University of Aberdeen
Transitional Justice and Reconciliation...................MSc 12FT 24PT/PGDip 9FT 18PT

University College Cork
Contemporary Migration and Diaspora Studies ....MA 12FT

National University of Ireland Galway
Irish Studies .... MA 12FT 24PT
Nua-Ghaeilge..MA 12FT
Old and Middle Irish ....MA 12FT

University of Liverpool
Irish Studies ....MA 12FT 24PT/PGDip 12PT
Politics and Irish Studies.............................. MA 12FT 24PT

National University of Ireland, Maynooth
Culture, Religion and Society in Modern Ireland..............MA 12FT

Queen's University Belfast
Irish Studies ....MA 12FT max 31PT
Irish Translation ....MA 12FT max 31PT/PGDip 12FT max 31PT

University of Roehampton
Media, Culture and Identity.................................PGDip 9FT 24PT

St Mary's University College, Twickenham
Irish Studies .... MA 12FT 24PT

Trinity College Dublin - the University of Dublin
Conflict Resolution and Reconciliation...........MPhil 12FT 24PT
Early Irish .... MPhil 12FT
European Employment Studies ....MSc 12FT 24PT
Irish Art History.. MPhil 12FT

Section sponsored by

BPP
UNIVERSITY
COLLEGE

Business and social sciences
www.prospects.ac.uk/findcourses POSTGRADUATE DIRECTORY 497

Social sciences

Irish Writing..MPhil 12FT/PGDip 9FT
Old Irish...PGDip 12FT

University of Ulster
Modern Irish...MA 27PT/PGDip 18PT

Irish studies
Research Courses

Aberystwyth University
Celtic Studies ....MPhil 12FT 24PT PhD 36FT 60PT

University of Liverpool
Irish Studies .... PhD 24-48FT 48-84PT/MPhil 12-48FT 24-72PT

Queen's University Belfast
Irish Studies .... PhD 36FT 72PT/MPhil 24FT 48PT
Irish and Celtic Studies................ PhD 36FT 72PT/MPhil 24FT 48PT

St Mary's University College, Twickenham
Sociology/Irish Studies .... PhD 36FT 72PT/MPhil 24FT 48PT

Islamic studies
Taught Courses

University of Aberdeen
Bayt al-Maqdis and Jerusalem Studies.... MLitt 12FT 24PT/PGDip 9FT 18PT
Islamic Studies .... MLitt 12FT 24PT/PGDip 9FT 18PT

Bangor University
Accounting, Banking, Economics, Finance, Management Studies MPhil 24FT/PhD by taught 36FT
Islamic Banking and Finance .... MBA 12FT

Birkbeck, University of London
Middle East in Global Politics: Islam, Conflict and Development.
MSc 12FT 24PT

University of Birmingham
Islamic Studies ...PGDip 8FT 16PT/MA 12FT 24PT/PGCert 3FT 6PT

Cardiff University
Islam in Contemporary Britain........ MA 12FT 24PT/Diploma 36PT
Religious Studies: Asian Religions............................. MA 12FT 24PT

University of East London
Islamic and Middle Eastern Studies LLM.... LLM 12FT 24PT/PGDip 8FT 16PT/PGCert 4FT 8PT

University of Edinburgh
Islamic and Middle Eastern Studies........................... MSc 12FT 24PT

University of Exeter
Islamic Studies .... MA 12FT 24PT
Middle East and Islamic Studies.................................. MA 12FT 24PT

Islamic College for Advanced Studies
Islam and the West: A Comparative Study ..MA 12FT 24PT 36DL/PGDip 12FT 24PT
Islam and the West: A Comparative Study - via Distance
Learning..MA 12FT 24PT 36-48DL
Islamic Finance........MSc 12FT 24PT 24DL/PGDip 12FT 24PT 24DL
Islamic Studies ....MA 12FT 24PT 12-36DL

Markfield Institute of Higher Education
Islamic Banking, Finance and Management.........MA 12FT 24PT/PGDip 12FT 24PT/PGCert 6FT 12PT
Islamic StudiesMA 12FT 24PT/PGDip 12FT 24PT/PGCert 6FT 12PT
Muslim Community Studies..... MA 12FT 24PT/PGDip 12FT 24PT/PGCert 6FT 12PT

Newcastle University
Finance and Law with Islamic Finance................................ MSc 12FT

University of Oxford
Islamic Art and Archaeology (Research Methods) ....MSt 9FT
Islamic Studies and History .... MPhil 21FT
Study of Religion...MSt 12FT

Queen Mary, University of London
Islam and the West .... MA 12FT 24PT

University of Salford
Islamic Banking and FInance..... MSc 12FT 36PT/PGDip 8FT 24PT/PGCert 4FT 9PT

School of Oriental and African Studies - SOAS
Islamic Societies and Cultures .... MA 12FT 24-36PT
Islamic Studies .... MA 12FT 24-36PT
Religions .... MA 12FT 24-36PT

University of St Andrews
Middle East and Central Asian Security Studies........... PGDip 9FT/MLitt 12FT/MPhil 24FT
Middle Eastern History & Culture....PGDip 9FT/MLitt 12FT/MPhil 24FT

University of Wales Trinity Saint David
Islamic Studies ....MA 12FT 24PT 12-60DL/PGCert 12FT 24PT 12-60DL/PGDip 12FT 24PT 12-60DL

UCL - University College London
Archaeology of the Arab and Islamic World.......................MA 24FT
Archaeology of the Middle East.................................. MA 12FT 24PT

University of Warwick
Applied Social Research with Specialism in Islam in
Contemporary Societies........................... MA 12FT/MA 24PT
Islam in Contemporary Society.................................MA 12FT

Islamic studies
Research Courses

University of Birmingham
Islam and Christian/Muslim Relations ....PhD 36FT 72PT 48DL/MPhil 12FT 24PT
Islamic Studies .... MPhil(B) 12FT 24PT 24DL

University of Edinburgh
Islamic and Middle Eastern Studies........... PhD 36FT 72PT/MSc by research 12FT 24PT/MPhil 24FT 48PT

University of Exeter
Arab and Islamic Studies...... PhD 36-48FT 72PT/MPhil 24FT 48PT
Kurdish Studies........MPhil 36FT 60PT 60DL/PhD 48FT 84PT 84DL
Palestine Studies .....MPhil 36FT 60PT 60DL/PhD 48FT 84PT 84DL

Prince's School of Traditional Arts
Visual Islamic and Traditional Arts... PhD 24-36FT 36-72PT/MPhil 12FT 24PT

School of Oriental and African Studies - SOAS
Study of Religions........................ PhD 36FT 72PT/MPhil 24FT 36PT

University of Wales Trinity Saint David
Islamic Studies .... PhD 36FT 48-72PT/MPhil 12-36FT

Italian studies
Taught Courses

University College Cork
Arts (Italian) ....HDip 9FT 18PT
Italian ....MA 12FT

University of Reading
Italian Studies ....MA (Res) 12FT 24PT
Modern Italian History ....MA (Res) 12FT 24PT
The City of Rome .... MA(Res) 12FT 24PT 60BM

Royal Holloway, University of London
Italian .... MA 12FT 24PT

University of St Andrews
Italian Studies ....MLitt 12FT 24PT/PGDip 9FT 24PT/MPhil 24FT

University of Warwick
Italian Studies: Culture and Communication .... MA 12FT 24PT

Italian studies
Research Courses

School of Advanced Study, University of London
Italian or Comparative/Interdisciplinary Studies.PhD 36FT 60PT/MPhil 12FT 24PT

Bangor University
Italian ....MPhil 12FT/PhD 36FT

University of Birmingham
Italian Studies .... PhD 36FT 72PT/MLitt by research 24FT 48PT/MPhil 12FT 24PT

University of Bristol
Italian .. PhD 36FT 72PT/MLitt by research 24FT 48PT/MPhil 12FT 24PT

University of Cambridge
Italian .... PhD 36FT 60PT

University of Exeter
Italian Studies .... PhD 48FT 84PT/MPhil 36FT 60PT

University of Kent
Italian ......PhD 36FT 60PT/MPhil 24FT 36PT/MA by research 12FT 24PT

University of Manchester
Italian Studies .... PhD 36FT 72PT/MPhil 12FT 24PT

Royal Holloway, University of London
Italian .... PhD 36FT 72PT/MPhil 24FT 48PT

University of St Andrews
Italian Studies .... PhD 36FT 72PT/MPhil 24FT 48PT

Swansea University
Italian .... PhD 36FT 72PT/MPhil 24FT 48PT

UCL - University College London
Italian .... PhD 36FT 60PT

University of Warwick
Italian ......PhD 36FT 60PT/MPhil 24FT 48PT/MA by research 12FT 24PT

Japanese studies
Taught Courses

Birkbeck, University of London
Japanese Cultural Studies/Japanese Creative Industries Studies.
MA 12FT 24PT

University of Cambridge
Human Evolutionary Studies... MPhil 11FT
Innovation, Strategy and Organisation ....MPhil 9FT

University of Edinburgh
Japanese Society and Culture ....MSc 12FT 24PT

Goldsmiths, University of London
Critical Asian Studies .... MA 12FT 24PT

University of Leeds
Japanese Business................................... MA 12FT 24PT
Japanese Studies .... MA 12FT 24PT

University of Oxford
Japanese Studies..MSt 10FT
Modern Japanese Studies ....MPhil 24FT/MSc 12FT
Oriental Studies ....MSt 9FT

School of Oriental and African Studies - SOAS
International Management (Japan) ....MSc 12FT 24-36PT
Japanese Literature........................... MA 12FT 24-36PT
Japanese Studies .... MA 12FT 24-36PT
Religions .... MA 12FT 24-36PT
Religions: Japanese Religions Pathway........... MA 12FT 24-36PT

University of Sheffield
Japanese Studies ....MA 12FT

Japanese studies
Research Courses

University of Edinburgh
Japanese PhD 36FT 72PT/MPhil 24FT 48PT/MSc by research 12FT 24PT

University of Manchester
Japanese Studies .... PhD 36FT 72PT/MPhil 12FT 24PT

Jewish studies
Taught Courses

University of Aberdeen
Jewish Studies............................ MLitt 12FT 24PT/PGDip 9FT 18PT

King's College London
Jewish Studies .... MA 12FT 24PT

University of Manchester
Jewish Studies... MA 12FT 24PT

Oxford Centre for Hebrew and Jewish Studies
MSt in Jewish Studies...MSt 9FT

University of Oxford
Jewish Studies ....MSt 9FT
Jewish Studies in the Graeco-Roman Period ....MPhil 21FT/MSt 9FT
Judaism and Christianity in the Graeco-Roman World ....
MPhil 21FT
Modern Jewish Studies........................... MPhil 21FT/MSt 9FT
Study of Religion...MSt 12FT
Yiddish Studies...MSt 9FT

Queen Mary, University of London
European Jewish History............................... MA 12FT 24PT

Royal Holloway, University of London
Holocaust Studies .... MA 12FT 24PT

School of Oriental and African Studies - SOAS
Israeli Studies .... MA 12FT 24-36PT
Religions .... MA 12FT 24-36PT

University of Southampton
Jewish History and Culture.......... MA 12FT 24PT/MRes 12FT 24PT

UCL - University College London
Hebrew and Jewish Studies.................................. MA 12FT 24PT
Holocaust Studies .... MA 12FT 24PT
Jewish History .... MA 12FT 24PT

Jewish studies
Research Courses

University of Birmingham
Jewish and Holocaust Studies .. PhD 36FT 72PT/MPhil 12FT 24PT

School of Oriental and African Studies - SOAS
Study of Religions........................ PhD 36FT 72PT/MPhil 24FT 36PT

University of Southampton
Jewish History and Culture........ PhD 48FT 84PT/MPhil 48FT 84PT

UCL - University College London
Hebrew and Jewish Studies.................................. PhD 36FT 60PT
Jewish History .... PhD 36FT 60PT

Latin american studies
Taught Courses

Birkbeck, University of London
Politics...MRes 12FT 24PT
Spanish, Portuguese and Latin American Cultural Studies ......MA 12FT 24PT/MRes 12FT 24PT
World Cinema... MA 12FT 24PT

University of Cambridge
Latin American Studies ....MPhil 9FT

University College Cork
Arts (Hispanic Studies)...HDip 9FT 18PT
Hispanic Studies .... MA 12FT 24PT

University of Essex
Curating Latin American Art................................... MA 12FT 24PT

Goldsmiths, University of London
Latin American Studies .... MA 12FT 24PT

Social sciences

King's College London
Spanish, Portuguese & Latin American Studies ..... MA 12FT 24PT

University of Liverpool
Latin American Studies (by Directed Research) ...... MA 12FT 24PT

Newcastle University
Latin American Interdisciplinary Studies .... MA 12FT 24PT

University of Oxford
Latin American Studies ....MPhil 21FT/MSc 12FT
Public Policy in Latin America.. MSc 12FT

University of Sheffield
Latin American Studies.. MA 12FT 24PT

University of St Andrews
Social Anthropology and Amerindian Studies............... MRes 12FT
Spanish and Latin American Studies................... MLitt 12FT 24PT/
PGDip 9FT 24PT

Swansea University
Politics .... MA 12FT 24PT

UCL - University College London
Caribbean and Latin American Studies .... MA 12FT 24PT
Globalisation and Latin American Development .. MSc 12FT 24PT
Latin American Politics...MSc 12FT 24PT
Latin American Studies .... MA 12FT 24PT

Latin american studies
Research Courses

University of Cambridge
Latin American Studies...PhD 36FT

University of Exeter
Hispanic Studies .... PhD 48FT 84PT/MPhil 36FT 60PT
Latin American Studies.............. MPhil 36FT 60PT/PhD 48FT 84PT

Institute for the Study of the Americas, School of Advanced Study, University of London
Democratisation..................................PhD 36FT/MPhil 12FT
Globalisation, Social Justice, and Environmental Change........PhD 36FT/MPhil 12FT
History of Latin America..............................PhD 36FT/MPhil 24FT
Human Rights, Transitional Justice and Memory PhD 36FT/MPhil 12FT
International Relations..................................PhD 36FT/MPhil 12FT
Latin America Studies....................................PhD 36FT/MPhil 12FT
Political Economy ....PhD 36FT/MPhil 12FT

King's College London
Spanish, Portuguese & Latin American Studies Research ....PhD 36FT 84-96PT/MPhil 24FT 36PT

University of Liverpool
Latin American Studies....... PhD 24-48FT 48-84PT/MPhil 12-48FT 24-72PT

University of Manchester
Latin American Cultural Studies...............................PhD 36FT 72PT/ MPhil 12FT 24PT

University of St Andrews
Spanish and Latin American Studies............PhD 36FT 72PT/MPhil 12-24FT 48PT

University of Sussex
American History and Literature ...... PhD 24-48FT 36-72PT/MPhil 12-36FT 24-48PT
Politics Research Programme .... PhD 24-48FT 36-72PT/MPhil 12-36FT 24-48PT

UCL - University College London
Spanish and Latin American Studies........................ PhD 36FT 60PT

Local governance
Taught Courses

School of Advanced Study, University of London
Advanced Legislative Studies ....LLM 12FT 24PT 24DL

University of the Arts London - Central Saint Martins College of Art and Design
Architecture: Cities and Innovation.....................................MA 24FT

Bangor University
Language, Policy and Planning ....MA 12FT 24-48PT/PGDip 8FT/ PGCert 4FT

University of Bath
Global Political Economy: transformations and policy analysis ... MRes 12FT 24-36PT

Birkbeck, University of London
Global Governance and Emerging Powers.............. MSc 12FT 24PT

University of Birmingham
Development Management ....MSc 12FT 24PT/PGDip 9FT 24PT
Local Policy and Politics...MSc 12FT 24PT
Local and Regional Economic Development..........MSc 12FT 24PT/ PGDip 9FT 21PT
Public Management (with specialist pathways) ..MSc 12FT 24PT/ PGDip 12FT 24PT/PGCert 12FT 15PT
Social Research (Local Government and Public Policy) ....MA 12FT 24PT

University of Cambridge
Politics .... MPhil 10FT

Cardiff University
Governance and Devolution...LLM 12FT

University of Central Lancashire
Advancing Equality, Diversity and Inclusion .... MA 12FT 36PT/ PGDip 12FT 36PT/PGCert 12FT 24PT
Equality and Community Leadership..........................PGCert 24PT

University of Chester
Conflict Transformation (Work Based and Integrative Studies) ....
MA 24-72PT/MSc 24-72PT/PGDip 24-60PT/PGCert 12-36PT

University College Cork
Government.. MBS 12FT 24PT

University of Dundee
Advanced Practice (Clinical Governance) ....MSc 36DL

University of East Anglia
Conflict, Governance and International Development....MA 12FT 24PT

University of East London
NGO and Development Management....................MSc 12FT 24PT/ PGDip 8FT 16PT/PGCert 4FT 8PT

University of Exeter
Applied Ecology .... MSc 12FT

London School of Economics and Political Science (LSE)
Local Economic Development .... MSc 12FT
Political Science and Political Economy .... MSc 12FT 24PT

Northumbria University
Public Administration .... MPA 12FT 24PT

University of Oxford
Global Governance and Diplomacy .... MSc 12FT

Queen's University Belfast
Legislative Studies and Practice...MA 12FT

University of Reading
Law ....M (Res) 12FT 24PT/PGDip 9FT/PGCert 9FT
Public Policy .... MA 12FT 24PT 72BM

University of Salford
Intelligence and Security Studies..............................MA 12FT 36PT/ PGDip 9FT 20PT

School of Oriental and African Studies - SOAS
Asian Politics..MSc 12FT 24PT
Chinese Law...MA 12FT 24PT
Development Studies with Special Reference to Central Asia....... MSc 12FT 24PT
Environmental Law and Sustainable Development
.... MA 12FT 24PT
Global Energy and Climate Policy ....MSc 12FT 24PT
Human Rights Law ....MA 12FT 24PT
International Politics ....MSc 12FT 24PT
International Studies and Diplomacy ....MA 12FT 24-36PT/PGDip 12FT 24PT
Islamic Law..MA 12FT 24PT
Middle East Politics...MSc 12FT 24PT
Near and Middle Eastern Studies......................... MA 12FT 24-36PT
PGDip Policy Studies .... PGCert 9FT
Political Economy of Development....................MSc 12FT 24-36PT
Politics of China ....MSc 12FT 24PT
State, Society and Development ....MSc 12FT 24PT
Turkish Studies ....MA 12FT 24PT
Violence, Conflict and Development.......................MSc 12FT 24PT

University of Sheffield
Globalisation and Development .... MA 12FT 24PT

University of Stirling
Environmental Policy and Governance...........LLM 12FT/MSc 12FT

University of Sussex
Corruption and Governance .... MA 12FT 24PT

UCL - University College London
Urban Economic Development........MSc 12FT 24-60PT/PGDip 9FT

Local governance
Research Courses

University of Bath
Global Political Economy: transformations and policy analysis (delivered collaboratively w................................. MRes 12FT 24-36PT

University of Birmingham
Local Government Studies .... PhD 36FT 72PT/MPhil 24FT 48PT

London School of Economics and Political Science (LSE)
Government.. PhD 36-48FT/MPhil 36-48FT

School of Oriental and African Studies - SOAS
Development Studies...PhD 36FT 48-60PT

London studies
Taught Courses

Queen Mary, University of London
London Studies... MA 12FT 24PT

University of Westminster
Creative Writing: Writing the City............................ MA 12FT 24PT

Middle east studies
Taught Courses

Durham University
Arab World Studies .... MSc 24FT

University of East London
Islamic and Middle Eastern Studies .... LLM 12FT 24PT/PGDip 8FT 16PT/PGCert 4FT 8PT

University of Edinburgh
Arab World Studies .... MSc 24FT
Islamic and Middle Eastern Studies......................... MSc 12FT 24PT

University of Exeter
Islamic Studies .... MA 12FT 24PT
Middle East Politics..MA 12FT 24PT
Middle East Studies...MRes 12FT 24PT
Middle East and Islamic Studies............................. MA 12FT 24PT

University of Leeds
Middle Eastern and Islamic Studies .... MA 12FT 24PT

University of Oxford
Islamic Studies and History .... MPhil 21FT
Medieval Arabic Thought .... MPhil 21FT
Modern Middle Eastern Studies .... MPhil 21FT

University of Reading
Research in Archaeology.. MA 12FT 24PT

University of Salford
Terrorism and Security ......MA 12FT 36PT 36DL/PGDip 12FT 36PT 36DL

School of Oriental and African Studies - SOAS
Arabic Literature ....MA 12FT 24-36PT
Economics (with reference to the Middle East).....MSc 12FT 24PT
International Management (Middle East and North Africa).. MSc 12FT 24PT
Israeli Studies ....MA 12FT 24-36PT
Middle East Politics..MSc 12FT 24PT
Near and Middle Eastern Studies .... MA 12FT 24-36PT
Turkish Studies .... MA 12FT 24PT

University of St Andrews
Iranian Studies ....PGDip 9FT/MLitt 12FT/MPhil 24FT
Middle Eastern History & Culture....PGDip 9FT/MLitt 12FT/MPhil 24FT

UCL - University College London
Archaeology of the Middle East................................ MA 12FT 24PT
Modern Israeli Studies .... MA 12FT 24PT

Middle east studies
Research Courses

School of Advanced Study, University of London
Middle Eastern and African Studies ...PhD 36FT 72PT/MPhil 12FT 36PT

Durham University
Government and International Affairs ....PhD 36FT
Middle Eastern Studies ......PhD 36FT/MPhil 24FT/MA by research 12FT

University of Edinburgh
Islamic and Middle Eastern Studies........... PhD 36FT 72PT/MSc by research 12FT 24PT/MPhil 24FT 48PT

University of Exeter
Arab and Islamic Studies ...... PhD 36-48FT 72PT/MPhil 24FT 48PT
Ethno-Political Studies............... MPhil 36FT 60PT/PhD 48FT 89PT
Kurdish Studies ....MPhil 36FT 60PT 60DL/PhD 48FT 84PT 84DL
Middle East Politics......................................MPhil 24FT 48PT 48DL/ PhD 36FT 72PT 72DL
Palestine Studies .....MPhil 36FT 60PT 60DL/PhD 48FT 84PT 84DL

University of Leeds
Department of Arabic and Middle Eastern Studies.....PhD 36+FT/ MPhil 12+FT/MA by research 12+FT

University of Manchester
Arab World Studies .... PhD 36FT 72PT
Middle Eastern Studies............... PhD 36FT 72PT/MPhil 12FT 24PT

Migration studies
Taught Courses

Birkbeck, University of London
Culture, Diaspora, Ethnicity.....MSc 12FT 24PT/PGDip 12FT 24PT/ PGCert 12PT

University of Birmingham
New Migration and Social Policy.........MA 12FT 24PT/PGDip 12FT 24PT/PGCert 6FT 12PT

University of Bradford
Human Trafficking and Contemporary Slavery...MSc 24PT/PGDip 21PT/PGCert 9PT

City University London
Global Migration .... MA 12FT 24PT

Section sponsored by
BPP UNIVERSITY COLLEGE

Business and social sciences
www.prospects.ac.uk/findcourses POSTGRADUATE DIRECTORY 499

Social sciences

University College Cork
Contemporary Migration and Diaspora Studies ....MA 12FT

University of Edinburgh
Diaspora and Migration History...............................MSc 12FT 24PT

University of Kent
International Migration... MA 12FT 24PT

University of Liverpool
Research Methodology (Civic Design)...................... MA 12FT 24PT

Middlesex University
Minorities, Rights and the Law .... LLM 12FT 24PT

University of Oxford
International Summer School in Forced Migration Cert less than 1FT
Migration Studies...MSc 9FT
Refugee and Forced Migration Studies................................MSc 9FT

School of Oriental and African Studies - SOAS
Dispute and Conflict Resolution................................ MA 12FT 24PT
Labour, Social Movements and Development .... MSc 12FT 24PT
Law, Culture and Society .... MA 12FT 24PT
Law, Development and Globalisation .... MA 12FT 24PT
Migration and Diaspora Studies.......................... MA 12FT 24-36PT
Pacific Asian Studies .... MA 12FT 24-36PT
South Asian Area Studies .... MA 12FT 24PT
South East Asian Studies .... MA 12FT 24-36PT
Violence, Conflict and Development........................ MSc 12FT 24PT

University of Sussex
Migration Studies... MA 12FT 24PT

UCL - University College London
Global Migration .... MSc 12FT 24PT/PGDip 12FT 24PT

Migration studies
Research Courses

The Open University
Citizenship and Governance......PhD 36FT 72PT variableDL/MPhil 15FT 24PT variableDL

School of Oriental and African Studies - SOAS
Languages and Cultures of South Asia ....PhD 36FT 72PT/MPhil 24FT 48PT
Media and Film Studies .... PhD 36-48FT

University of Sussex
Migration Studies... PhD 24-48FT 36-72PT/MPhil 12-36FT 24-48PT

Modern greek studies
Taught Courses

University of Aberdeen
Sociolinguistics .... MLitt 12FT 24PT/PGDip 9FT 21PT

King's College London
Modern Greek Studies (Interdisciplinary) .... MA 12FT 24PT
Modern Greek Studies (Literature) .... MA 12FT 24PT
Modern Greek Studies (Sociolinguistics)................. MA 12FT 24PT

University of Oxford
Greek and/or Latin Languages and Literature ..... MPhil 21FT/MSt 9FT

University of St Andrews
Greek ....PGDip 9FT 18PT/MLitt 12FT 24PT
Greek and Latin......................................PGDip 9FT/MLitt 12FT 24PT

Modern greek studies
Research Courses

University of Birmingham
Modern Greek Studies ....MPhil(B) 12FT 24PT

University of Cambridge
Modern Greek .... PhD 36FT 60PT

King's College London
Byzantine & Modern Greek Studies Research PhD 36FT 48-72PT/MPhil 36FT 48-72PT

Portuguese studies
Taught Courses

Birkbeck, University of London
Comparative Literature.. MA 12FT 24PT
Spanish, Portuguese and Latin American Cultural Studies ......MA 12FT 24PT/MRes 12FT 24PT

University College Cork
Arts (Hispanic Studies)...HDip 9FT 18PT
Hispanic Studies .... MA 12FT 24PT

University of Sheffield
Hispanic Studies .... MA 12FT 24PT

University of St Andrews
Spanish and Latin American Studies.................... MLitt 12FT 24PT/PGDip 9FT 24PT

Portuguese studies
Research Courses

University of Bristol
Hispanic, Portuguese and Latin American Studies..........PhD 36FT 72PT/MLitt by research 24FT 48PT/MPhil 12FT 24PT

University of Cambridge
Portuguese .... PhD 36FT 60PT

University of Leeds
Department of Spanish and Portuguese PhD 36+FT/MPhil 24FT/MA by research 12+FT

University of Manchester
Latin American Cultural Studies..............................PhD 36FT 72PT/MPhil 12FT 24PT
Portuguese Studies...................... PhD 36FT 72PT/MPhil 12FT 24PT

University of Nottingham
Hispanic & Latin American Studies .... MA by research 12FT PhD 36-48FT/MPhil 36-48FT
Portuguese and Lusophone StudiesPhD 36-48FT/MPhil 24-48FT/MRes 12FT 24PT

Queen's University Belfast
Spanish and Portuguese Studies.............................PhD 36FT 72PT/MPhil 24FT 48PT

Practice teaching award
Taught Courses

University of Aberdeen
Social and Educational Research ....MRes 12FT

Anglia Ruskin University
Masters of Teaching and Learning...

Bournemouth University
Advanced Practice .... MSc 12PT
Education Practice................... MA 31FT/PGDip 24FT/PGCert 12FT
Professional Practice................Dr Professional Practice up to 48PT

University of Cambridge
Advanced Subject Teaching .... MSt 24PT

University of Central Lancashire
Doctorate in Education .... EdD by taught 60PT
Education (Research)...............MA 24PT/PGDip 24PT/PGCert 24PT
Education and History...MA 24PT
Education and Religion in Society.......................................MA 24PT
Practice Teacher .... PGCert 6PT
Professional Practice in EducationMEd 24-60PT/PGCert 24-60PT/PGDip 24-60PT

University of Chester
Coach-Mentoring and Facilitation in Organisations (Work Based and Integrative Studies)............MA 24-72PT/MSc 24-72PT/PGDip 24-60PT/PGCert 12-36PT
Dental Practice Management (Work Based and Integrative Studies) ....MA 24-72PT/PGDip 24-60PT/PGCert 12-36PT
Developing RPL Policy and Practice (Work Based and Integrative Studies) ....MA 24-72PT/PGDip 24-60PT/PGCert 12-36PT
Education and Teaching Studies (Work Based and Integrative Studies) ....MA 24-72PT/MSc 24-72PT/PGDip 24-60PT/PGCert 12-36PT
Education: Creativity and Education for the Professions..........MA 24-72PT/PGDip 24-60PT/PGCert 12-36PT
Leadership Development (Work Based and Integrative Studies).. MA 24-72PT/MSc 24-72PT/PGDip 24-60PT/PGCert 12-36PT
Leading RPL Policy and Practice (Work Based and Integrative Studies) ....MA 24-72PT/PGDip 24-60PT/PGCert 12-36PT
Learning and Development (Work Based and Integrative Studies) ....MA 24-72PT/MSc 24-72PT/PGDip 24-60PT/PGCert 12-36PT
Nursing Studies (Work Based and Integrative Studies).............MA 24-72PT/MSc 24-72PT/PGDip 24-60PT/PGCert 12-36PT
Personal Leadership Development (Work Based and Integrative Studies) ....MA 24-72PT/PGDip 24-60PT/PGCert 12-36PT
Professional Studies and Development (Work Based and Integrative Studies)...MA 24-72PT/MSc 24-72PT/PGDip 24-60PT/PGCert 12-36PT

University of Cumbria
Education..MA 36PT

University of Derby
Interprofessional Practice Education.......................PGCert 12-18PT

University of Dundee
Practice Education...PGCert 12DL

University of East Anglia
Advanced Educational Practice.......................... MA 36PT/MA 48PT

University of Gloucestershire
National Award for Special Educational Needs Continuation .... PGCert 9PT

Goldsmiths, University of London
Advanced Social Work: Practice Education ....MA 24PT

Kingston University
Child Centred Interprofessional Practice............................MA 24PT

University of Liverpool
Advanced Science..........MSc 12FT 24PT/PGDip 12FT/PGCert 12FT

Manchester Metropolitan University
Continuing Professional, Personal and Practice Development (CP3D)... CP3D variousFT
National Award for Special Needs Co-ordinators National Award 12PT

Sheffield Hallam University
Doctorate in Education .... Doctorate 48PT
Integrated Working..................MA 36PT/PGDip 24PT/PGCert 12PT

University of Wales Trinity Saint David
Education......MA 12FT 48PT/PGDip 12FT 48PT/PGCert 12FT 48PT
Professional Practice.............MA FlexibleFT FlexiblePT FlexibleDL/PGDip FlexibleFT FlexiblePT/PGCert FlexibleFT FlexiblePT
Technology Enhanced Learning........................... PGCert 24PT 24DL

Practice teaching award
Research Courses

University of Nottingham
EPSRC AstraZeneca Doctoral Training Centre in Targeted Therapeutics... PhD 48FT 72PT

Oxford Brookes University
Doctorate of Education - Professional Doctorate...... EdD 60-84PT

University of Portsmouth
Professional Doctorate in Education ....EdD 48PT

University of Southampton
Integrated PhD in Education ....Integrated PhD 36FT

Primary care
Taught Courses

University of Aberdeen
Primary Care ....MSc 48-60PT

Barts and the London School of Medicine and Dentistry
Primary Care .... MSc 12FT 24PT/PGDip 12FT 24PT

University of Bath
Primary Care .... MSc 96PT/PGDip 72PT/PGCert 48PT

Birmingham City University
Advanced Healthcare (Nursing, Midwifery or Primary Care)......... PGDip 12PT/MSc 24PT

University of Birmingham
Advancing Practice.....................MSc 13FT 72PT/PGDip 10FT 48PT/PGCert 3FT
Clinical Primary and Community Care........MSc 12FT 60PT/PGDip 12FT 60PT/PGCert 12FT 60PT
Primary and Community Care, Clinical.......MSc 12FT 24PT/PGDip 12FT 24PT/PGCert 12FT 24PT

University of Central Lancashire
Evidence Based Practice..PGCert 12PT
Excellence in Leadership for Inclusion and Community..... PGCert 12-24PT
General Practice..........MSc 36-60PT/PGDip 24-60PT/PGCert 12PT
Health & Social Care Education.......................................PGCert 12PT
Health Informatics..MSc 33PT/PGDip 24PT
Health and Social Care Education ....PGCert 12PT
Research for Professional Practice ... Professional Doctorate 24PT

University of Chester
Health and Social Care - Advanced Practice .... MSc 24 - 72PT/PGDip 24 - 60PT/PGCert 12 - 36PT

City University London
Primary Care ....MSc 12FT 24PT
Primary Care (Advanced Nurse Practitioner)..........MSc 12FT 24PT
Primary Care (District Nursing).................................MSc 12FT 24PT
Primary Care (Long Term Conditions).......................MSc 12FT 24PT

University of Derby
Community Specialist Practice ....MSc 12FT 24PT

University of Dundee
Primary Care ....MSc 36-60PT
Psychological Therapy in Primary Care .... MSc 12FT

National University of Ireland Galway
Health Sciences (Clinical Primary Care) PGDip 12PT/PGCert 12PT
Health Sciences (Primary Care).. PGDip 12PT

Glasgow Caledonian University
Diagnostic Imaging..MSc 12-24FT
Musculoskeletal Management.......................................MSc 36-72PT
Radiatiotherapy and Oncology ....MSc 12-24FT

University of Glasgow
Primary Care ..... MPC 12FT 24-60PT/PGDip 12FT 24-36PT/PGCert 24PT

University of Greenwich
Independent and Supplementary Prescribing / Supplementary Prescribing...PGCert 8DL

University of Kent
Primary Dental Care...MSc 36PT
Primary Dental Care for Foundation Dentists............PGCert 12FT

King's College London
Primary Health Care ....MSc 12FT 24PT

Leeds Metropolitan University
Environmental Health..MSc 12FT 36PT

Social sciences

Health Care Studies .... MA 24PT

University of Leeds
Primary Care Education .... PGCert 12-24PT
Primary Health Care ..... MMedSci 30PT/PGDip 24PT/PGCert 12PT

University of Liverpool
Diploma in International Community Health Care ... Diploma 3FT

London South Bank University
Primary Care .... MSc 12FT up to 72PT
Primary Care and Mental Health .... PGCert 12PT

Manchester Metropolitan University
Community Health .... MSc 12FT 24-36PT

University of Manchester
Primary Care .... MRes 12 - 60DL

University of Northampton
Community Practice .... MSc 24-60PT/PGDip 12PT

The Open University
Advancing Professional Practice .... MSc variableDL

Queen Mary, University of London
International Primary Health Care .... MSc 12FT 24-48PT

University of Roehampton
Health Sciences .... MSc 12FT 24PT

University of Salford
Public Health .... MSc 12FT 36PT/PGDip 8FT 24PT/PGCert 9PT

Sheffield Hallam University
Cardiovascular Medicine for Primary Care Physicians .... PGDip 24PT/PGCert 12PT

University of Sheffield
Public Health .... MPH 12FT 24-36PT
Public Health (Health Services Research) .... MPH 12FT 24-36PT
Public Health (Management and Leadership) .... MPH 12FT 24-36PT

University of South Wales
Community Health Studies .... BSc 24-36PT/MSc 36PT

St George's, University of London
Physician Assistant Studies .... PGDip 24FT

University of Stirling
Psychological Therapy in Primary Care .... MSc 12FT

Swansea University
Advanced Practice in Health Care .... MSc 36PT/PGDip 24PT
Advanced Practice in Health Care - Infection Control ... MSc 36PT/PGDip 24PT

University of Ulster
Primary Care and General Practice .... MSc 36DL

University of Warwick
Diabetes in Pregnancy .... PGA 12PT
Patient and Public Involvement in Healthcare .... PGA 12PT/CPDMod 1PT
Sexual Health in Primary Care .... PGA 12PT

University of the West of England, Bristol
Community Practice .... MSc 12FT 60PT

University of Winchester
Delivery of Primary Health Care .... PGCert 24PT

University of Wolverhampton
Primary Health Care Practice .... MSc 12PT

Primary care
Research Courses

University of Aberdeen
General Practice and Primary Care .... PhD 36FT/MD 24FT/MSc by research 12FT

Barts and the London School of Medicine and Dentistry
Department of General Practice and Primary Care .... PhD/MPhil/MSc by research/MD

University of Birmingham
Primary Care Clinical Sciences.... PhD 36FT 72PT/MSc by research 12FT 24PT

University of Cambridge
Public Health and Primary Care .... PhD 36FT 60PT

Cardiff University
Primary Care and Public Health .... PhD 36FT/MPhil 36FT

University of Central Lancashire
Healthcare/Public Health .... MSc by research 12FT 24PT/MPhil 24FT 36-48PT/PhD 36FT 60PT/MD 36FT 60PT

University of Cumbria
Public Health and Primary Care PhD 48FT 72PT 72DL/MPhil 36FT 36PT 36DL

University of East Anglia
Nursing .... PhD 36FT 72PT/MPhil 24FT 48PT/MSc by research 12FT 24PT

University of Edinburgh
General Practice .... PhD 36FT 72PT/MPhil 24FT 36PT/MSc by research 12FT 24PT

University of Hertfordshire
Centre for Research in Primary and Community Care .... PhD 36FT 72PT/MPhil 24FT 48PT/MRes 12FT 24PT/DHRes 36FT 72PT

Imperial College London
Primary Care and Population Health Science .... PhD/MPhil

King's College London
Health & Social Care (Research Division) .... PhD 36FT 48-72PT/MPhil 36FT 48-72PT/DHC 36FT 48-72PT

University of Liverpool
Primary Care .... MPhil 12-48FT 24-72PT/PhD 24-48FT 48-84PT/MD 24-72PT

University of Nottingham
Epidemiology and Public Health .... PhD 36FT 72PT/MPhil 24FT 48PT
Primary Care .... PhD 36FT

University of Oxford
Primary Health Care .... DPhil 48FT/MSc by research 24-36FT
Public Health .... DPhil 48FT/MSc by research 24FT

University of Roehampton
Health Sciences.... PhD 24-48FT 36-60PT/MPhil 21-36FT 36-60PT

University of Sheffield
Primary Medical Care and Ageing .... PhD 36FT 72PT/MPhil 24FT 48PT

St George's, University of London
Community Health Sciences .... PhD 36FT 72PT/MPhil 24FT 48PT/MD(Res) 24 minFT 48 minPT

UCL - University College London
Primary Health Care and Population Sciences ...... PhD 36FT 60PT/MD(Res) 24FT 24PT

Public health
Taught Courses

University of Aberdeen
Global Health .... MSc 12FT 24-36PT/PGDip 9FT/PGCert 4FT
Health Services and Public Health Research .... MSc 12FT 24PT/PGDip 9FT 21PT
Human Nutrition and Metabolism .... MSc 12FT/PGDip 8FT
Public Health Nutrition .... MSc 12FT 24PT/PGDip 9FT 18PT

Anglia Ruskin University
Public Health .... MSc 12FT 24PT

Bangor University
Health Science .... MSc 12FT 24 - 60PT/PGDip 9FT
Health Studies/Health Science, Nursing, Midwifery, Radiography and Allied Health Professio... PhD by taught 36FT 48-60PT/MPhil 24FT 36PT
Health and Social Care Leadership .... MSc 12FT 24 - 60PT/PGDip 9FT
Public Health and Health Promotion .... MSc 12FT 24 - 60PT/PGDip 9FT
Risk Management in Health and Social Care ...... MSc 36PT/PGDip 24PT/PGCert 12PT

University of Bedfordshire
Advanced Practice .... MSc 24PT/PGCert 24PT/PGDip 24PT
Enhancing Quality Through Patient Safety .... MSc 12FT 24PT/PGCert 12FT 24PT/PGDip 12FT 24PT
Health Studies .... MSc 24PT/PGCert 24PT/PGDip 24PT
Leadership in Healthcare Practice .... MSc 24PT
Public Health .... MSc 12FT 24PT 12-24DL

Birkbeck, University of London
Health and Disease .... MSc 24PT

Birmingham City University
Health and Social Care .... PGDip 12PT/MSc 24PT
Health and Social Care (Leadership) .... PGDip 12PT/PGDip 36PT
Public Health .... PGDip 12PT/MSc 24PT

University of Birmingham
Public Health .... MPH 12FT 24PT/PGDip 12FT 24PT/PGCert 9FT 12PT
Public Health (Health Technology Assessment) .... MPH 12FT 24PT/PGDip 12FT 24PT/PGCert 9FT 12PT
Public Health - Statement of Extra Accredited Learning (SEAL) .... MSc 12FT 60PT

University of Bolton
Community Specialist Practice (District Nursing) .... PGDip 12PT

Bournemouth University
Public Health .... MSc 12FT 36PT
Public Health Nursing .... MSc 12FT 24-36PT

University of Brighton
Health .... MSc 12FT 24-72PT/PGDip 12FT 24-72PT/PGCert 12FT 24-72PT
Health and Education. MSc 12FT 24 - 72PT/PGDip 12FT 24 - 72PT
Public Health .... MSc 12 - 36FT 24 - 72PT/PGCert 12 - 36FT 24 - 72PT/PGDip 12 - 36FT 24 - 72PT
Specialist Community Public Health Nursing MSc 12FT 24-72PT/PGDip 12FT 24-72PT/PGCert 12FT 24-72PT

Brunel University
Health Promotion and Public Health .... MSc 12FT 36PT n/aDL
Specialist Community Public Health Nursing .... MSc 0FT 12PT/PGDip 12FT 24PT

Bucks New University
Specialist Community Public Health Nursing .... MSc 12FT 24PT

University of Cambridge
Epidemiology .... MPhil 12FT
Public Health .... MPhil 12FT

Canterbury Christ Church University
Health Promotion and Public Health .... MSc 12FT 36PT

Cardiff Metropolitan University
Applied Public Health .... MSc 12FT 24PT/PGDip 12FT 24PT

Cardiff University
Public Health .... MPH 12FT

University of Central Lancashire
Advanced Practice (Health and Social Care) .... MSc 24PT
Advanced Stroke Practice ...... MSc 36FT 60PT/PGDip 24PT/PGCert 12PT
Allied Health Practice .... MSc up to 60PT
Allied Health Practice; (Occupational Therapy).. MSc 36PT/PGDip 24PT/PGCert 12PT
Applied Public Health .... MSc 15FT 24PT/PGDip 12FT 24PT
Applied Public Health: Health Improvement .... PGCert 12PT
Applied Public Health: Health Protection .... PGCert 4FT 12PT
Arts-Health Analysis .... PGCert 6PT
Cancer Biology and Therapy .... MSc 12FT
Community Specialist Practitioner .... PGDip 12FT 24-48PT
Health & Social Care Education .... PGCert 12PT
Health Improvement: Settings Approaches .... PGCert 12PT
Health Informatics .... MSc 33PT/PGDip 24PT
Health and Social Care Education .... PGCert 12PT
Integrated Healthcare by elearning..... MSc 36-48PT/PGDip 24PT/PGCert 12PT
Research Methods in Health and Social Care .... PGCert 36PT
Research for Professional Practice ... Professional Doctorate 24PT
Researching Social Care .... PGCert 12FT 24PT
Sexual Health Studies .... MSc 60PT/PGDip 60PT/PGCert 24PT
Specialist Community Public Health Nurse - Health Visiting or School Nursing .... PGDip 12FT 24PT

University of Chester
Health and Social Care - Global Health .... MSc 12FT 24 - 72PT/PGDip 12FT 24 - 60PT/PGCert 12FT 12 - 36PT
Health and Social Care - Health Improvement and WellbeingMSc 12FT 24 - 72PT/PGDip 12FT 24 - 60PT/PGCert 12FT 12 - 36PT
Health and Social Care - Public Health .... MSc 12FT 24 - 72PT/PGDip 12FT 24 - 60PT/PGCert 12FT 12 - 36PT
Public Health Nutrition .... MSc 12FT 24 - 72PT/PGDip 12FT 24 - 60PT/PGCert 12FT 12 - 36PT
Public Services Management (Work Based and Integrative Studies) .... MA 24-72PT/PGDip 24-60PT/PGCert 12-36PT
Weight ManagementMSc 12FT 24 - 48PT/PGDip 12FT 24 - 48PT/PGCert 12FT 12 - 24PT
Weight Management (Taught in Dublin, Ireland) .. MSc 24-48PT/PGDip 24-48PT/PGCert 12-24PT

University of Chichester
Management (Health and Social Care Services) .... MA 27PT/PGDip 18PT/PGCert 12PT

University College Cork
Occupational Health .... MSc 24PT
Public Health .... MA 12FT 60PT

Cranfield University
Health and the Environment .... MSc 12FT 24-36PT/PGDip 12FT 24-36PT

University of Cumbria
Advanced Practice in Health and Social Care .... MSc 24 - 60PT
Community Specialist Practice Nursing .... PGDE 9FT 18PT
International Health .... MSc 12FT 24PT
Leadership in Health and Social Care .... MBA 12FT 36PT/PGDip 12FT 36PT/PGCert 12FT 36PT
Public Health and Social Change .... MSc 36FT 60PT
Specialist Community Public Health Nursing Practice .... MSc 12 - 48PT

De Montfort University
Specialist Community Public Health Nursing ..... MSc 36PT/PGDip 24PT

University of Derby
Community Specialist Practice .... MSc 12FT 24PT
Management of Long Term Conditions .... PGCert 12PT
Nursing (Specialist Community Public Health) ..... MSc 12FT 24PT

University of Dundee
Epidemiology and Global Health International Prevention Research Institute Summer School .... Cert 1FT
Global Health and Wellbeing .... MSc 36DL
Non-Graduating Taught Postgraduate in Medical School .... PG module variableFT
Public Health .... MPH 12-24FT
Quality Improvement .... MSc 36DL PGCert 12DL PGDip 24DL

Durham University
Public Policy and Health .... PGCert 10PT MSc 12FT 24PT
Risk, Health and Public Policy .... MA 12FT

Section sponsored by

BPP
UNIVERSITY
COLLEGE

Business and social sciences
www.prospects.ac.uk/findcourses **POSTGRADUATE DIRECTORY 501**

Social sciences

University of East Anglia
Clinical Science..MRes 12FT
International Social Development.............................. MA 12FT 24PT

University of East London
Public Health ... MSc 12FT 48PT/PGCert 4FT 8PT/PGDip 8FT 16PT

Edge Hill University
Public Health ....PGCert 6FT 15PT

University of Edinburgh
Global Health Challenges (Online Distance Learning) .... PGCert 12-24DL
Global Health Policy (Online Distance Learning) ...PGCert 9-21DL
Global Health Studies (online distance learning) ......PGCert 36DL
Global Health and Infectious Diseases (Online Distance Learning).................................MSc 36DL/PGDip 24DL/PGCert 12DL
Global Health and Public Policy ....MSc 12FT 24-36PT
Global Health: Non Communicable Diseases (online distance learning) ....MSc 36DL/PGDip 24DL/PGCert 12DL
Health Inequalities and Public Policy ....MSc 12FT 24-36PT
Integrated Service Improvement: Health and Social Care...... MSc 24-36PT/PGDip 20PT/PGCert 12PT
Public Health ....MPH 12FT 24-36PT
Public Health Policy...........................MSc(Res) 12FT 24-36PT

University of Essex
Adult Nursing.. MSc 24FT
Advanced Musculoskeletal Assessment....MSc 24-60PT/Diploma 18-60PT/Cert 12-60PT
Clinical Psychology .... Prof Doc 24PT
Counselling Psychology .... Prof Doc 24PT
Health Care Management ....Diploma 18-60PT/MSc 24-60PT
Health Care Practice .... MSc 24-60PT/PGCert 18-60PT/PGDip 18-60PT
Health Research ....MA 12FT 24PT/MSc 12FT 24PT
Health Services Management ....Prof Doc 48-84PT
Health and Organisational Research......................MSc 12FT 24PT
Infection Control....MSc 24-60PT/Diploma 18-60PT/Cert 12-60PT
Medical and Clinical Education.. MSc 24-60PT/Diploma 18-60PT/ Cert 12-60PT
Mental Health Nursing...................................... MSc 24FT
Nursing .... Prof Doc 48-84PT
Occupational Therapy ....MSc 24FT Prof Doc 48-84PT
Physiotherapy..............................MSc 24FT Prof Doc 48-84PT
Psychological Wellbeing Practitioner (Low-Intensity Therapy) ..... PGCert 18-60PT
Public Health .... MA 12FT 24-60PT
Public Health (Health Visiting) ....Prof Doc 48-84PT
Public Health Management........ MSc 24-60PT/Diploma 18-60PT/ Cert 12-60PT
Social Care Education ....Prof Doc 48-84PT
Social Care Practice Management .... Prof Doc 48-84PT
Social Services Management ....Prof Doc 48-84PT
Speech and Language Therapy .... MSc 24FT

GCU London
Public Health with Social Action .... MSc 12FT

National University of Ireland Galway
Nursing (Public Health Nursing).........................PGDip 12FT

Glasgow Caledonian University
Advanced Practice with Older People .... MSc 12FT
Advancing Practice in Primary Care........................ MSc 24FT
Medical Ultrasound ....MSc 12-24FT
Optimal Heart Failure Care .... MSc 12FT
Perinatal Mental Health .... MSc 12FT
Public Health ....PGCert 6DL/PGDip 12DL/MSc 24DL
Public Health with Social Action .... MSc 12FT
Specialist Community Public Health Nursing.... PGDip 12FT 24PT
Telehealthcare.. MSc 12FT

University of Glasgow
Global Health ....MSc 12FT 24PT
Mental Health, Global....MSc 12FT 24PT/PGDip 9FT 18PT/PGCert 9FT 18PT
Public Health .... MPH 12FT 24-36PT/PGDip 9FT 18-33PT/ PGCert 5FT 10PT
Translational Medicine......................................MRes 12FT

University of Gloucestershire
Physical Activity and Health ...... MSc 12FT 24PT/PGDip 8FT 20PT/ PGCert 4FT 8PT

Heriot-Watt University
Biotechnology...................MSc 12FT 24PT/PGDip 9FT 20PT
Food Science, Safety and Health .... MSc 12FT 24PT 24-84DL/ PGDip 9FT 21PT 24-84DL

University of Huddersfield
Public Health Nursing Practice: Health Visiting/School Nursing.. MSc 16FT 36PT

Imperial College London
Masters of Public Health ....MPH 12FT

King's College London
Advanced Practice (Specialist Community Public Health Nursing/ Public Health/ School Nurs)............MSc 36-72PT/PGDip 24-72PT/PGCert 12-72PT
Health & Society..............................MSc 12FT 24-48PT
Health Studies......................................PGCert 12FT 24PT

Public Health ....MPH 12FT 24PT/MSc 12FT 24PT

Leeds Metropolitan University
Community Specialist Practitioner - District Nursing...MSc 24PT/ PGDip 12FT 24PT
Dietetics...PGDip 24FT
Environmental Health ....MSc 12FT 36PT
Health & Social Care Chaplaincy.................................PGCert 12PT
Public Health (Health Promotion and Environmental Health) Zambia .... MSc 36PT
Public Health - Health Promotion ......MSc 12FT 30PT/PGDip 12FT 24PT/PGCert 4FT 12PT
Specialist Community Public Health Nursing - Occupational Health Nursing .... MSc 24PT/PGDip 12FT 24PT

University of Leeds
International Health....................PGCert 3FT/PGDip 9FT/MSc 12FT
Public Health...............MPH 12FT 24-48PT/PGDip 12FT 24-48PT
Public Health (International)...... PGCert 3FT/PGDip 9FT/MA 12FT

Liverpool John Moores University
International Public Health.......................................MSc 12FT 24PT
Public Health .... MSc 12FT

University of Liverpool
International Public Health....MSc 12FT/Diploma 12FT/Cert 12FT
Master of Public Health (Online Degree) .... MPH 24FT 24+PT
Master of Public Health - London Based ....MPH 12FT 24-72PT
Public Health ....MPH 12FT 24-72PT/PGDip 12FT 24-72PT/PGCert 12FT 24-72PT

London College UCK
Leadership and Management in the Health and Social Care Sector... PGDip 12FT 24PT

London Metropolitan University
Human Nutrition (Public Health/Sports)...............MSc 12FT 24PT
Public Health ....MSc 12FT 24PT

London School of Economics and Political Science (LSE)
Global Health ....MSc 12FT 24PT
Health Policy, Planning and Financing....................MSc 12FT 24PT
Health, Community and Development ....MSc 12FT 24PT
Health, Population and Society ....MSc 12FT 24PT

London School of Hygiene and Tropical Medicine
Demography & Health..MSc 12FT 24PT
Epidemiology...MSc 12FT 24PT
MSc 24 - 60DL/PGDip 12 - 60DL/PGCert 12-60DL
Global Health Policy (by Distance Learning) MSc 24-60DL/PGDip 12-60DL/PGCert 12-60DL
Medical Statistics ....MSc 12FT 24PT
Nutrition for Global Health ....MSc 12FT 24PT
Public Health ....MSc 12FT 24PT
Public Health (Environment & Health)...................MSc 12FT 24PT
Public Health (Health Economics)......................MSc 12FT 24PT
Public Health (Health Promotion)......................MSc 12FT 24PT
Public Health (Health Services Management)........ MSc 12FT 24PT
Public Health (Health Services Research)................MSc 12FT 24PT
Public Health (by Distance Learning) ....MSc 24 - 60DL/PGDip 12 - 60DL/PGCert 12-60DL
Public Health in Developing Countries ....MSc 12FT 24PT
Reproductive & Sexual Health Research ....MSc 12FT 24PT

London South Bank University
Public Health and Health Promotion ....MSc 12-18FT 24-36PT

Loughborough University
Physical Activity and Health ....MSc 12FT 24-96PT/PGDip up to 60PT/PGCert up to 36PT

University of Manchester
Community Pharmacy Public Health Services.....MSc 36PT 36DL/ PGDip 24PT 24DL/PGCert 12PT 12DL
Dental Public Health...... MDPH 12-60DL/PGDip 12-60DL/PGCert 12-60DL MRes 12-60DL/PGCert 12-60DL/PGDip 12-60DL
Global Health ....PGCert 12FT 12DL/PGDip 12DL
Public Health .... MRes 12FT 24-PT
PGCert 12DL/PGDip 48DL/MPH 12-60DL

Newcastle University
Public Health and Health Services Research .. MSc 12FT 24-36PT/ PGDip 9FT 21PT/PGCert 9PT

University of Northampton
Public Health .... MSc 12FT 24PT

Northumbria University
Public Health ....MPH 36PT/PGDip 24PT/PGCert 12PT

Nottingham Trent University
Public Health .... MA 12FT 24PT

University of Nottingham
Applied Epidemiology.....................................MSc 12FT 24PT
Master of Public Health ....MPH 12FT 24PT
Public Health ....MPH 12FT 24PT
Public Health (International Health).....................MPH 12FT 24PT

Oxford Brookes University
Infection Prevention and Control ..... MSc 12FT Up to 36PT/PGDip 9FT Up to 36PT/PGCert 4FT Up to 36PT
Public Health ....MSc 12FT Up to 36PT

University of Oxford
Global Health Science .... MSc 12FT

Medical Anthropology ....MPhil 24FT/MSc 12FT

Peninsula College of Medicine and Dentistry
Infection Prevention & Control....................................PGCert 12PT

Queen Margaret University, Edinburgh
International Health..MSc 12FT 60PT
Public Health Nutrition... MSc 12FT 24-60PT/PGDip 9FT 24-60PT
Public Health Practice...MSc 12FT 48PT
Sexual and Reproductive HealthMSc 12FT 60PT/PGDip 9FT 48PT/ PGCert 6FT 48PT

Queen Mary, University of London
Global Public Health and Policy.........................MSc 12FT 24-48PT
Health Systems and Global Policy.......................MSc 12FT 24-48PT
International Primary Health Care.....................MSc 12FT 24-48PT

Queen's University Belfast
Public Health .... MPH 12FT

Robert Gordon University
Health Improvement and Health Promotion...................MSc 24DL

Royal Holloway, University of London
Global Health: Pathogens and Policy ..MSc 12FT 24PT/PGDip 9FT

University of Salford
Environmental and Public Health ..MSc 12FT 24-36PT/PGDip 8FT 24PT
Health Care Law.......................LLM 27DL/MA 27DL/PGDip 20DL/ PGCert 12DL
International Hospital and Health Service Leadership and Management.................................MSc 12FT/PGDip 8FT/PGCert 4FT
Lower Limb Health, Disease and Rehabilitation.........PGCert 12PT
Occupational Safety and Health MSc 12FT 36PT/PGDip 8FT 24PT
Public Health ....MSc 12FT 36PT/PGDip 8FT 24PT/PGCert 9PT

Sheffield Hallam University
Health and Society..MRes 12FT 36PT
Nutrition with Public Health Management .... MSc 12FT
Public Health .... MA 18FT 36PT

University of Sheffield
Dental Public Health......................... MDPH 12FT MClinDent 24FT
Europubhealth: European Masters Programme in Public Health. MPH 24FT
Health Economics and Decision Modelling ......MSc 12FT 24-36PT
International Development (Masters in Public Health)MPH 12FT 24PT
Long-Term Health Conditions ....PGCert FlexiblePT
Public Health ....MPH 12FT 24-36PT
Public Health (Health Services Research).........MPH 12FT 24-36PT
Public Health (Management and Leadership) .... MPH 12FT 24-36PT
Statistics with Medical Applications ....MSc 12FT 24-36 PTDL

University of South Wales
Public Health ....MSc 12FT 24PT
Specialist Community Public Health Nursing (Health Visiting or School Health Nursing).............. MSc 12FT 36PT/PGDip 12FT 24PT

University of Southampton
Advanced Clinical Practice ....MSc 12FT 24PT/PGDip 12FT/PGCert 12FT
Gerontology.......................MSc 12FT 24PT/PGDip 9FT 21PT
Gerontology (Distance Learning) ....MSc 12DL/PGDip 9DL
Health Informatics .... MSc 24DL/PGDip 16DL
Health Psychology.................................MSc 12FT/PGDip 12FT
Public Health Practice...MSc 12FT 24PT/PGDip 12FT/PGCert 12FT
Management of Diabetes ....MSc 15FT 24PT/PGDip 12FT 18PT/ PGCert 6FT 6PT
Public Health NutritionMSc 12FT 36PT/PGDip 12FT 24PT/PGCert 12FT 12PT

University of St Andrews
Health Geography Research ...MRes 12FT 24PT/PGDip 10FT 20PT
Health Psychology... MSc 12FT
Medicine..MRes 12FT 24PT

St Mary's University College, Twickenham
Nutrition and Physical Activity for Public Health............ MSc 12FT

Staffordshire University
Physical Activity and Public Health (Distance Learning) .... PGCert 24-60DL/PGDip 24-60DL/MSc 24-60DL
Public Health (Distance Learning)..........PGCert 7DL/PGDip 14DL/ MPH 24DL
Public Health (Health Informatics) ....PGCert 8PT/PGDip 16PT/ MPH 24PT

University of Stirling
Health Psychology..........................MSc 12FT 24PT/PGDip 6FT 12PT
Health Research.............................MRes 12FT 24/36PT 24/36DL
Health and Wellbeing of the Older Person...................... MSc 24FT

University of Strathclyde
Analysis of Medicines...........MSc 36DL/PGDip 24DL/PGCert 12DL
Health History....MSc 12FT 24PT/PGDip 9FT 18PT/PGDip 9FT 9PT

University of Sunderland
Health and Social Care Research ....MSc 12FT 24PT
Public Health .... MSc 12FT

University of Surrey
Health and Social Care ....MSc 12FT 24PT
Public Health Practice................. PGDip 12FT 24PT/MSc 12FT 24PT

Social sciences

University of Sussex
Global Health .... MSc 12FT

Swansea University
Public Health & Health Promotion .... MSc 12FT 36PT
Public Health and Partnerships in Care .... MSc 12FT 36PT

Teesside University
Evidence-based Medicine .... MSc 24 or 36PT 24 or 36DL
Evidence-based Medicine (Anaesthesia) ...... MSc 24 or 36PT 24 or 36DL
Evidence-based Practice .... MSc 24 or 36PT 24 or 36DL
Health & Social Care Sciences (Public Health) .... MSc 18FT 36PT
Public Health .... MSc 18FT 36PT 36DL

Trinity College Dublin - the University of Dublin
Global Health .... MSc 12FT 24PT
Healthcare Infection Management .... MSc 24PT

University of Wales Trinity Saint David
Health, Ethics and Society .... MA 12-24DL/PGDip 12-24DL

University of the Highlands and Islands
Health and Wellbeing .... MA 36PT yesDL/PGDip 36PT/PGCert 36PT

University of Ulster
Health Promotion and Public Health ... MSc 12FT 27-36PT/PGDip 9FT 18PT/PGCert 4-9FT 9-18PT
Specialist Community Public Health Nursing (SCPHN) .... PGDip 12FT 24PT

UCL - University College London
Clinical and Public Health Nutrition .... MSc 12FT/PGDip 9FT/PGCert 3FT
Clinical and Public Health Nutrition: Eating Disorders .... MSc 12FT/PGDip 9FT/PGCert 3FT
Dental Public Health .... MSc 12FT 24PT
Evidence-Based Healthcare .. MSc 12FT 24-48PT/PGDip 24-48PT/PGCert 24-48PT
Global Health and Development: tropEd programme .. MSc 12FT 24-60PT
Health and Society: Social Epidemiology ... MSc 12FT 24PT/PGDip 9FT 18PT
Healthcare Associated Infection Control .... MSc 24-60PT/PGDip 24-60PT
Infection and Immunity .. MSc 12FT 24-60PT/PGDip 9FT 24-60PT/PGCert 3FT 6-24PT
Paediatrics and Child Health: Community Child Health .... MSc 12FT 36-60PT/PGCert 12-24PT/PGDip 9FT 18-45PT
Sexually Transmitted Infections and HIV .... MSc 12FT 24-60PT/PGDip 9FT 18-45PT

University of Warwick
Health Sciences: Public Health ...... MSc 36PT/PGDip 24PT/PGCert 12PT/PGA 12PT
International Health Policy .... PGA 12PT/cpdmod 1PT
Public Health (MPH) .... MPH 12FT 24-36PT

University of the West of England, Bristol
Public Health .... MSc 16FT 30PT/PGDip 24PT/PGCert 12PT
Public Health (Specialist Community Public Health Nursing) Health Visiting/School Nursing .... PGDip 36FT 48PT

University of Westminster
Public Health Nutrition .... MSc 12FT

University of Wolverhampton
Public Health (MPH) .... MPH 12FT 24PT

University of Worcester
Advancing Practice .... MA 36FT 72PT/PGDip 24FT 48PT/PGCert 12FT 24PT

University of York
Masters in Public Health .... MPH 12FT 24PT

Public health
Research Courses

University of Aberdeen
Public Health .... PhD 36FT/MSc by research 12FT

Bangor University
Health Services Research .... PhD 36FT 60PT/MPhil 24FT 48PT MSc by research 12FT 24PT
Health Studies/Health Science, Nursing, Midwifery, Radiography & Allied Health Professions .... MPhil 24FT 36PT/PhD 36FT 48-60PT

University of Bath
Health .... MPhil 12FT 24PT/PhD 36FT 72PT
Health and Wellbeing .... MRes 12FT 24-36PT

University of Birmingham
Public Health and Epidemiology .... PhD 36FT 72PT/MPhil 12FT 24PT

University of Bristol
Social and Community Medicine .... PhD 36FT 72PT/MSc by research 12FT 24PT/MD 24-60PT

Brunel University
Public Health .... DrPH 36FT

University of Cambridge
Epidemiology .... PhD 36FT
Public Health and Primary Care .... PhD 36FT 60PT

Canterbury Christ Church University
Health & Social Care (inclduing Allied Health Profs Nursing & Midwifery, & Public Health .... PhD 48FT 60PT/MPhil 24FT 48PT

Cardiff University
Applied Clinical Research and Public HealthPhD 36FT possiblePT/MScD by research 12FT possiblePT/MPhil 12FT possiblePT
Primary Care and Public Health .... PhD 36FT/MPhil 36FT

University of Central Lancashire
Healthcare/Public Health .... MSc by research 12FT 24PT/MPhil 24FT 36-48PT/PhD 36FT 60PT/MD 36FT 60PT

University of Cumbria
Public Health and Primary Care .... PhD 48FT 72PT 72DL/MPhil 36FT 36PT 36DL
Rehabilitation and Public Health .... PhD 48FT 72PT 72DL/MPhil 36FT 60PT 60DL

University of Dundee
Social Dimensions of Health Institute .... MPhil 24FT PhD 36FT

University of Edinburgh
Global Health .... MPhil 24FT 48PT/PhD 36FT 72PT
International Public Health Policy .... PhD 36FT 72PT
Public Health Policy .... MSc by research 12FT 24-36PT
Public Health Sciences .... MPhil 24FT 48PT/PhD 36FT 72PT/MSc by research 12FT 24PT

University of Essex
Clinical Psychology .... PhD 72PT/MPhil 48PT
Health Studies .... PhD 72PT/MPhil 48PT/MSc by research 24PT
Nursing Studies .... PhD 72PT/MPhil 48PT/MSc by research 24PT
Occupational Therapy ...... PhD 72PT/MPhil 48PT/MSc by research 24PT
Physiotherapy .... PhD 72PT/MPhil 48PT/MSc by research 24PT
Public Health .... PhD 72PT/MPhil 48PT/MSc by research 24PT
Social Policy .... PhD 72PT/MPhil 48PT/MSc by research 24PT
Speech and Language Therapy .... PhD 72PT/MPhil 48PT/MSc by research 24PT

University of Greenwich
Research in Health and Social Care .... MSc by research 24PT

Heriot-Watt University
Applied Psychology .... PhD 36FT 48PT/MPhil 24FT 36PT

King's College London
Health & Social Care (Research Division) .... PhD 36FT 48-72PT/MPhil 36FT 48-72PT/DHC 36FT 48-72PT
Health Service & Population Research Department .... PhD 36FT 72PT/MPhil 36FT 72PT/MDes by research 36FT 72PT
Women's Health (Research Division) ...... MPhil 36-48FT 48-72PT/PhD 36-48FT 48-72PT/MDes by research 36-48FT 48-72PT

Lancaster University
Health Research .... PhD 36FT 48PT/MPhil 24FT 36PT

University of Leeds
Nuffield Institute for Health .... PhD 36+FT/MPhil 24FT/MA by research 12+FT

University of Liverpool
Epidemiology .... MPhil 12FT/PhD 36FT
Epidemiology and Population Health .... MPhil 12FT/PhD 36FT
Global Health .... MPhil 12FT/PhD 36FT/MD 24FT
Infection and Global Health (Medical) .... MPhil 12FT/PhD 36FT/MD 24FT
Public Health .... PhD 24-48FT 48-84PT/MPhil 12-48FT 24-72PT/MD 24-72FT

London School of Hygiene and Tropical Medicine
Epidemiology & Population Health (Research) .. DrPH 42FT 42PT/PhD 42FT 42PT/MPhil 12FT 12PT
Public Health & Policy (Research) .... DrPH 42FT 42PT/PhD 42FT 42PT/MPhil 12FT 12PT

University of Manchester
Dental Public Health/Community Dentistry .... PhD 36FT 72PT/MPhil 12FT 24PT

Newcastle University
Public Health, Epidemiology and Health Services Research .... MPhil 12FT 24PT/PhD 36FT 72PT/MD 24FT 48PT

University of Nottingham
Epidemiology and Public Health .... PhD 36FT 72PT/MPhil 24FT 48PT
Risk Analysis, Social Processes and Health .... MPhil 36FT/PhD 24FT
Social Research in Medicines and Health .... PhD 36FT 72PT/MPhil 36FT

University of Oxford
Primary Health Care .... DPhil 48FT/MSc by research 24-36FT
Public Health .... DPhil 48FT/MSc by research 24FT

Queen's University Belfast
Public Health ... PhD 36FT 72PT/MD 24FT 48PT/MPhil 24FT 48PT/MCh by research 12FT 24PT

University of Salford
Health Informatics .... PhD 36FT 60PT/MSc by research 24PT
Health and Social Care Research .... PhD/MPhil/MSc by research 12FT
Psychology Research Group .... PhD/MPhil

University of Sheffield
Primary Medical Care and Ageing .... PhD 36FT 72PT/MPhil 24FT 48PT
Public Health: Integrated Studies .... New Route PhD 48FT

University of Surrey
Medicine and Health ..... PhD 36FT 48PT/MPhil 24FT 36PT/MSc by research 12FT

UCL - University College London
Epidemiology and Public Health .... PhD 36FT 60PT
Infection and Immunity .... PhD 36FT 60PT
Infection and Population Health .... PhD 36FT 60PT/MD(Res) 24FT 24PT

Refugee care
Taught Courses

University of East London
International Social Welfare with Refugee Studies MA .. MA 12FT 24PT/PGDip 8FT 16PT/PGCert 4FT 8PT
Refugee Studies .... MA 12FT 24PT/PGDip 8FT 16PT/PGCert 4FT 8PT
Refugee Studies and Community Development .... MA 12FT 24PT/PGDip 8FT 16PT/PGCert 4FT 8PT

University of Essex
Foundations of Psychoanalytic Psychotherapy .... MA 24PT
Refugee Care .... MA 12FT

National University of Ireland Galway
International Peace Support Operations .... LLM 12FT 24PT

University of Limerick
Peace and Development Studies .... MA 12FT

London School of Economics and Political Science (LSE)
International Development and Humanitarian Emergencies MSc 12FT 24PT

London South Bank University
International Human Rights & Development .... LLM 16FT 28PT
International Refugee Law and Policy .... PGCert 16FT 28PT
Refugee Studies .... MSc 12FT MSc 24PT

Oxford Brookes University
Development and Emergency Practice .... MA 12FT 24PT/PGDip 9FT 21PT/PGCert 3-9FT 9PT

University of Surrey
International Intervention .... MA 12FT 24PT

University of Sussex
Conflict, Security and Development .... MA 12FT 24PT

Refugee care
Research Courses

University of Essex
Refugee Care .... PhD 36FT 72PT/MPhil 24FT 48PT

Rural development
Taught Courses

University of Aberdeen
Sustainable Rural Development .... MSc 12FT 24PT/PGDip 9FT 18PT

Aberystwyth University
Food & Water Security .... MSc 12FT 24PT/PGDip 9FT 18PT

University of Chester
Sustainability for Community and Business .... MSc 12FT 24PT/PGDip 12FT 24PT/PGCert 12FT 12-24PT

University of Cumbria
Sustainable Uplands .... MSc 12FT 24PT/GradDip 6FT 12PT/GradCert 3FT 6PT

University College Dublin
Development Studies .... MSc 15FT 24PT/HDip 12FT 24PT

University of East Anglia
Agriculture and Rural Development .... MA 12FT 24PT
Environment and International Development ...... MSc 12FT 24PT

University of Exeter
Food Security and Sustainable Agriculture .... MSc 12FT 24PT

University of Gloucestershire
Sustainable Environments .... MSc 12FT 24PT 18DL/PGDip 9FT 20PT 12DL/PGCert 4FT 8PT 6DL

Harper Adams University
Farm and Agri-business Management .... MSc 12FT 48PT/PGDip 12FT 48PT/PGCert 6FT 48PT
International Agri-business and Food Chain Management ... MSc 12FT 48PT/PGDip 12FT 48PT/PGCert 6FT 48PT
Rural Estate and Land Management .... MSc 12FT 48PT/PGDip 12FT 48PT/PGCert 6FT 48PT

University of Kent
Conservation and Rural Development .... MSc 12FT 24PT

Leeds Metropolitan University
International Political Economy .... MA 12FT

Section sponsored by

BPP
UNIVERSITY
COLLEGE

Business and social sciences
www.prospects.ac.uk/findcourses POSTGRADUATE DIRECTORY 503

Social sciences

London Metropolitan University
Planning and Sustainable Communities.................MSc 12FT 24PT

London School of Economics and Political Science (LSE)
Development Studies.....................................MSc 12FT 24PT

University of Manchester
International Development: Economics and Management of
Rural Development ....MSc 12FT 24PT

Newcastle University
Food and Rural Development Research ....MSc 12FT 24PT

University of Oxford
Development Studies.................................... MPhil 36FT

Queen's University Belfast
Leadership for Sustainable Rural Development .... MSc 12FT
Urban and Rural Design.................................MSc 12FT/PGDip 12FT

University of Reading
Agricultural Development Economics ....MSc 12FT 24PT
Agricultural Economics ....MSc 12FT 24PT
Agriculture and Development ....MSc 12FT 24PT
Applied Development Studies ....MSc 12FT 24PT
Communication for Innovation and Development .... MSc 12FT 24PT
Rural Land and Business Management ....MSc 12FT
Social Development and Sustainable Livelihoods ....MA 12FT

Royal Agricultural University
International Rural Development ....MSc 15FT 24PT

University of Salford
Real Estate Development ....MSc 12FT 28DL/PGDip 8FT 20DL

Schumacher College
Sustainable Horticulture and Food Production...............MSc 12FT

Sheffield Hallam University
Sustainable Communities and Environments ....MSc 12-18FT 24-36PT

University of Sheffield
Planning and Development...............................MA 12FT

Staffordshire University
Regeneration .... MA 12FT 24PT

University of Sussex
Innovation and Sustainability for International Development.....
MSc 12FT 24PT

University of the Highlands and Islands
Managing Sustainable Rural Development...........MSc 24FT 36PT/
PGDip 12FT 24PT/PGCert 12FT 24PT

UCL - University College London
Anthropology, Environment and Development ....MSc 12FT 24PT

University of Worcester
Sustainable Development Advocacy (Professional Practice) ...MA 12FT 36PT

Rural development
Research Courses

Aberystwyth University
IBERS - Rural Sciences .... PhD 36FT 60PT

Coventry University
Rural Change .... MSc by research 12FT 24-36PT

University College Dublin
Development Studies................ PhD 36FT/MLitt by research 24FT

University of Dundee
Town and Regional Planning .... MPhil 24FT

University of East Anglia
International Development: Economic Development ....PhD 36FT 72PT/MPhil 24FT 48PT
International Development: Social DevelopmentPhD 36FT 72PT/MPhil 24FT 48PT
International Development: Sustainable Development................
PhD 36FT 72PT/MPhil 24FT 48PT

University of Gloucestershire
Countryside and Community ....
PhD 30-48FT 48-84PT/MPhil 18-36FT 30-60PT/MSc by research 12-24FT 18-36PT/MA by research 12-24FT 18-36PT

Harper Adams University
Precision Farming (MRes is Subject to Validation)...... MRes 12FT/
MPhil 24FT/PhD 38FT
Rural Affairs Management............................MPhil 24FT/PhD 38FT

London School of Economics and Political Science (LSE)
Development Studies........................ PhD 36-48FT/MPhil 36-48FT

University of the Highlands and Islands
Sustainability Studies... MPhil 24FT 48PT/PhD 36FT 72PT/MSc by research 12FT 24PT

Russian and slavonic studies
Taught Courses

University of Birmingham
Russian and East European Studies.......................... MA 12FT 24PT

University of Bristol
Russian History .... MA 12FT 24PT

University of Cambridge
Russian Studies...MPhil 9FT

University of Glasgow
Russian, Central & East European Studies.......... MRes 12FT 24PT/
PGDip 9FT
Russian, Central & East European Studies (Erasmus Mundus
International Masters) ....International Masters (double/single
degree) 24FT
Russian, Central and East European Studies ....MSc 12FT 24PT/
PGDip 9FT

Keele University
Humanities (Russian Studies) ....MRes 12FT 24PT

King's College London
Russian Politics & Society.............................MSc 12FT 24PT

University of Nottingham
Slavonic Studies (by research)...........................MA 12FT

University of Oxford
Russian and East European Studies.............MPhil 21FT/MSc 12FT
Slavonic Studies .... MPhil 24FT/MSt 9FT

University of St Andrews
Central and East European Studies....MLitt 12FT 24PT/PGDip 9FT 18PT
Russian Studies .... MLitt 12FT 24PT/PGDip 9FT 24PT

UCL - University College London
East European Studies...............................MRes 24FT
Russian Studies.. MA 12FT 24PT
Russian and East European Literature and CultureMA 12FT 24PT
The Politics and Economics of Eastern Europe..............MRes 12FT

Russian and slavonic studies
Research Courses

University of Birmingham
Russian and East European Studies....PhD 36FT 72PT/MPhil 24FT 48PT/MA by research 12FT 24PT

University of Bristol
Russian and Czech.PhD 36FT 72PT/MLitt by research 24FT 48PT/MPhil 12FT 24PT

University of Cambridge
Slavonic Studies.. PhD 36FT 60PT

University of Edinburgh
Russian .. PhD 36FT 72PT/MPhil 24FT 48PT/MSc by research 12FT 24PT
Russian Studies (Masters by Research)........MSc by research 12FT 24/36PT

University of Exeter
Russian Studies........................... PhD 36FT 72PT/MPhil 24FT 48PT

University of Glasgow
Russian and East European Studies.. PhD 36FT/MLitt by research 12FT
Slavonic Studies .....PhD 36FT/MPhil 12FT/MLitt by research 12FT

Keele University
Russian .... PhD 24-48FT 48-84PT/MPhil 12-24FT 24-36PT

King's College London
Russian & Eurasian Studies .... PhD 48FT 96PT

University of Leeds
Department of Russian and Slavonic Studies ....PhD 36+FT/MPhil 24FT/MA by research 12+FT

University of Manchester
Polish Studies .... PhD 36FT 72PT/MPhil 12FT 24PT
Russian Studies .... PhD 36FT 72PT/MPhil 12FT 24PT

University of Nottingham
Russian Studies...............................MA by research 12FT 24PT
Russian and Slavonic Studies .... PhD 36FT 72PT/MPhil 24FT 48PT
Slavonic Studies ....MA by research 12FT 24PT

Queen Mary, University of London
Russian ....PhD/MPhil

University of St Andrews
Russian Studies............PhD 36FT 72PT/DLang 36FT 72PT/MPhil 12-24FT 48PT

UCL - University College London
East European Economics ....PhD 36FT 60PT
East European Politics ....PhD 36FT 60PT
East European Society and National Identity.........PhD 36FT 60PT
Russian.. PhD 36FT 60PT

Scandinavian studies
Taught Courses

University of Aberdeen
Scandinavian Studies .... MLitt 12FT 24PT/PGDip 9FT 18PT

University of Edinburgh
Scandinavian Studies ....MSc(Res) 12FT 24PT

University of Reading
Research in Archaeology.............................. MA 12FT 24PT

UCL - University College London
Scandinavian Studies (Medieval and West Norse) ....
MA 12FT 24PT

Scandinavian studies
Research Courses

University of Edinburgh
Scandinavian Studies ....PhD 36FT 72PT/MPhil 24FT 48PT/MSc by research 12FT 24PT
Scandinavian Studies (Masters by Research) ....MSc by research 12FT 24/36PT

UCL - University College London
Scandinavian Studies .... PhD 36FT 60PT

Scottish gaelic
Taught Courses

University of Aberdeen
Gaelic Medium Education ....PGCert 12PT

University of St Andrews
Reformation Studies....... MLitt 12FT 24PT/MPhil 24FT/PGDip 9FT 24PT

University of the Highlands and Islands
Orkney and Shetland Studies..........MLitt 12FT 24PT/PGCert 12FT 24PT/PGDip 12FT 24PT

Scottish studies
Taught Courses

University of Aberdeen
Art in Scotland ....MLitt 12FT 24PT
Ethnology and Folklore ....MLitt 12FT 24PT

University College Cork
Arts (Folklore) ....HDip 9FT
Folklore...MA 12FT

University of Dundee
Scottish History .... MLitt 24-60DL MLitt 12FT

University of Edinburgh
Scottish Art and Visual Culture 1750-2000MSc 12FT 24PT/PGDip 9FT 18PT
Scottish Ethnology...
Scottish History.......................MSc 12FT 24PT MSc(Res) 12FT 24PT
Scottish Studies ....MSc 12FT 24PT

Goldsmiths, University of London
Global Arts .... MA 12FT 24PT

University of St Andrews
National Trust for Scotland Studies.......................MPhil 24FT 48PT
Reformation Studies....... MLitt 12FT 24PT/MPhil 24FT/PGDip 9FT 24PT

University of the Highlands and Islands
History of the Highlands and Islands....... MLitt 12FT 24PT/PGDip 12FT 24PT/PGCert 12FT 24PT
Material Culture and the Environment ...PGDip 0FT 24PT/PGCert 0FT 12PT/MA 0FT 36PT
Orkney and Shetland Studies..........MLitt 12FT 24PT/PGCert 12FT 24PT/PGDip 12FT 24PT

Scottish studies
Research Courses

University of Aberdeen
Irish and Scottish Studies...PhD 36FT

University of Edinburgh
Celtic and Scottish Studies........PhD 36FT 72PT/MPhil 24FT 48PT/MSc by research 12FT 24PT
Scottish Ethnology ....MSc by research 12FT 24PT
Scottish Ethnology (Masters by Research)..........................MSc by research 12FT 24/36PT
Scottish History..............PhD 36FT 72PT/MPhil 24FT 48PT/MSc by research 12FT 24PT
Scottish History (Masters by Research) ....MSc by research 12FT 24PT

University of St Andrews
National Trust of Scotland Studies ....MPhil 12-24FT 24-48PT

Social policy
Taught Courses

Anglia Ruskin University
International Social Welfare and Social Policy.......MSc 12FT 24PT

Aston University
Social Research and Social Change...................MA 12FT 24 - 36PT

Bangor University
Comparative Criminology and Criminal Justice ....MA 12FT 24PT/PGDip 9FT
Criminology and Criminal Justice .... PhD by taught 36FT 72PT/MPhil 12-24FT 24-36PT/MARes 12FT 24PT
Health and Social Care Leadership................... MSc 12FT 24 - 60PT/PGDip 9FT
Implementing Evidence in Health & Social Care ....
MRes 12FT 24PT/PGCert 3FT 15PT

Social sciences

International Social Work......................................MA 12FT 24-30PT/ PGDip 9FT 17-21PT/PGCert 5FT 12-21PT
Language, Policy and Planning.......MA 12FT 24-48PT/PGDip 8FT/ PGCert 4FT
Policy Research and Evaluation........ MA 12FT 21-30PT/PGDip 9FT 17-21PT/PGCert 5FT 12-21PT
Public Health and Health Promotion ..MSc 12FT 24 - 60PT/PGDip 9FT
Risk Management in Health and Social Care......MSc 36PT/PGDip 24PT/PGCert 12PT
Social Policy, Sociology...........................PhD by taught 36FT 60PT/ MPhil 12-24FT 24-36PT
Social Research and Social Policy........... MA 12FT 24PT/PGDip 9FT
Social Work..MA 24FT

University of Bath
European Social Policy.........MRes 12FT 24-60PT/PGDip 9FT 21PT/ PGCert 4FT 16PT
Wellbeing and Human Development ....MSc 12FT 30PT/ PGDip 9FT 21PT/PGCert 4FT

University of Bedfordshire
Applied Public Policy: Children's and Young People's Services....... MA 24PT

University of Birmingham
New Migration and Social Policy.........MA 12FT 24PT/PGDip 12FT 24PT/PGCert 6FT 12PT
Policy into Practice ....MA 12FT 24PT/PGDip 12FT
Policy into Practice (with Integrated Placement)..............MA 21FT
Social Policy...................................MA 12FT 24PT/PGDip 9FT 18PT
Social Research (Local Government and Public Policy) ....MA 12FT 24PT
Social Research (Social Policy) ......MA 12FT 24PT/PGDip 9FT 18PT

University of Bradford
Public Policy and Programme Management ....MSc 12FT 24PT/ PGDip 9FT 21PT/PGCert 9PT

University of Bristol
Policy Research...MSc 12FT 12-60PT/Diploma 12FT 12-60PT/Cert 12FT 12-60PT
Public Policy ....MSc 12FT 24PT

Cardiff University
Politics and Public Policy...MSc 12FT 24PT

University of Central Lancashire
Advancing Equality, Diversity and Inclusion ....MA 12FT 36PT/

PGDip 12FT 36PT/PGCert 12FT 24PT
Counter Terrorism..MSc 12FT
Criminal Investigation..MSc 12PT
Equality and Community Leadership..........................PGCert 24PT
Social Policy.................................. MA 15FT 24-60PT/PGDip /FT /PT
Social Work.. MA 24FT 36PT
Social Work (only available through employment secondment).. PGDip 24FT 36PT
Social Work Practice (Post Qualification Specialist Award, Adults)..PGDip 3PT

University of Chester
Faiths and Public Policy....................................MA 12FT 36PT 36DL/ PGDip 12FT 24-36PT 24-36DL/PGCert 12FT 12-24PT 12-24DL

City University London
Food and Nutrition Policy..MSc 12FT 24PT
Social Research Methods....................................MSc 12FT 24PT

University of Cumbria
Leadership and Management in Policing MBA 36PT/PGDip 36PT/ PGCert 36PT
Leadership in Equality and Diversity ....MBA 12FT 36PT

University of Dundee
Social Research Methods (Population and Welfare) ...... MSc 12FT

Durham University
Social Research Methods (Social Policy) .... MA 12FT 24PT

University of East Anglia
Social Science Research Methods: Business.........MRes 12FT 24PT
Social Science Research Methods: Education......MRes 12FT 24PT
Social Science Research Methods: Law..................MRes 12FT 24PT
Social Science Research Methods: Psychology ....MRes 12FT 24PT
Social Science Research Methods: Social Work ...MRes 12FT 24PT

University of Edinburgh
Comparative Public Policy ....MSc 12FT 24PT
Health Systems and Public Policy......................MSc 12FT 24-36PT
Social Research................................MSc 12FT 24PT/PGDip 9FT 21PT

Glasgow Caledonian University
Social Research...MSc 12FT 24PT
Social Research (Policy Analysis)..............................MSc 12FT 24PT

University of Glasgow
Sociology and Research Methods.........................MRes 12FT 24PT

University of Huddersfield
Child Welfare and Safeguarding............................... MA 12FT 36PT

University of Hull
European Union Governance ....MA 12FT

Institute of Education
Inspection and Regulation ....MA 24PT

University of Kent
Civil Society, NGO and Nonprofit Studies ... PGDip 12FT 24PT/MA 12FT 24PT
Criminology .... MA 12FT 24PT
Criminology with a semester abroad..................... MA 12FT 24PT
Health Services Research..MSc 12FT 24PT
International Social Policy.. MA 12FT 24PT
Methods of Social Research...................................... MA 12FT 24PT
Social and Public Policy (Distance Learning, Medway) . MA 24DL/ PGDip 24DL
Social and Public Policy: Commissioning (Distance Learning, Medway)..MA 24DL/PGDip 24DL
Social and Public Policy: Criminal Justice (Distance Learning, Medway)...MA 24DL/PGDip 24DL
Social and Public Policy: Urban Regeneration (Distance Learning, Medway)...MA 24DL/PGDip 24DL

King's College London
European Public Policy ....MA 12FT

Kingston University
Applied Social Research Methods .... MA 12FT 24PT

University of Leeds
Disability and Global Development.......................... MA 12FT 24PT
Disability and Social Policy....................................... MA 12FT 24PT
Disability, Health and Illness .... MA 12FT 24PT
International Social Transformation....................... MA 12FT 24PT
Social Research (ESRC recognised) .... MA 12FT 24PT
Social and Political Thought .... MA 12FT 24PT
Social and Public Policy... MA 12FT 24PT

University of Liverpool
Research Methodology (Sociology and Social Policy) ......MA 12FT 24PT

London Metropolitan University
Organising for Social and Community Development ... MSc 12FT 24PT
Researching Work (Professional Doctorate) .... Professional Doctorate 48PT

London School of Economics and Political Science (LSE)
Gender, Policy and Inequalities.................................MSc 12FT 24PT

Section sponsored by
BPP UNIVERSITY COLLEGE

Business and social sciences
www.prospects.ac.uk/findcourses POSTGRADUATE DIRECTORY 505

Social sciences

International Health Policy........MSc 12FT 24PT
Public and Economic Policy........MPA 21FT
Social Policy........MSc 12FT 24PT
Social Policy (Research)........MSc 12FT 24PT
Social Policy and Development........MSc 12FT

London South Bank University
Development and Urbanisation........MSc 13FT 24PT
European Policy Studies........MA 12FT 24PT
Social Policy and Social Research Methods........MSc 12FT 28PT

National University of Ireland, Maynooth
European Social Policy Analysis........MA 12FT

Northumbria University
Health and Social Care Quality Provision........PGCert 12FT

University of Nottingham
Public Policy........MA 12FT 24-48PT/PGDip 9FT 24PT
Research Methods (Public Policy)........MA 12FT 24PT
Research Methods (Social Policy)........PGDip 12FT 24PT

The Open University
Social Policy and Criminology........MA variableDL

University of Oxford
Comparative Social Policy........MSc 12FT/MPhil 24FT
Evidence-Based Social Intervention........MPhil 21FT/MSc 9FT
Global Governance and Diplomacy........MSc 12FT

Queen Mary, University of London
International Public Policy........MSc 12FT 24PT
Public Administration........MPA 12FT 24PT

Queen's University Belfast
Social Research Methods (by research)........MRes 12FT 24PT/Diploma 12FT 24PT

University of Reading
Law........M (Res) 12FT 24PT/PGDip 9FT/PGCert 9FT
Public Policy........MA 12FT 24PT 72BM

Richmond, The American International University in London
International Development........MA 12FT 24PT

University of Salford
Strength and Conditioning.. MSc 36PT/PGDip 24PT/PGCert 12PT

Sheffield Hallam University
Social Sciences........MPhil 36FT 84PT MA 12FT 24PT
Sociology, Planning and Policy........MRes variousFT variousPT

University of Sheffield
European Gender Studies........MA 12FT 24PT
Global and International Social Policy........MA 12FT 24PT
Social Research........MA 12FT 24PT
Social and Spatial Inequalities........MSc 12FT 24PT

University of Southampton
Social Policy and Social Research MSc 12FT 24PT/PGDip 9FT 21PT
Sociology and Social Policy........MSc 12FT 24PT/PGDip 9FT 21PT
Sociology and Social Research....MSc 12FT 24PT/PGDip 9FT 21PT

University of Stirling
Applied Social Research........MSc 12FT 30PT/PGDip 9FT 18PT
Housing Studies........MSc 12FT/PGDip 12FT

University of Strathclyde
Social Research........MRes 12FT 24PT

Swansea University
Public Policy........MA 12FT 24PT

Trinity College Dublin - the University of Dublin
Applied Social Research........MSc 12FT
Economic Policy Studies........MSc 24PT

UCL - University College London
Economic Policy........MSc 12FT
Public Policy........MSc 12FT 24PT

University of Warwick
International Cultural Policy and Management..... MA 12FT 24PT
Political and Legal Theory........MA 12FT 24PT/PGDip 9FT
Public Policy........MA 12FT 24PT/PGDip 9FT
Social Research with Specialism in Social Policy... MA 12FT 24PT/PGDip 9FT 24PT

University of the West of Scotland
Alcohol and Drug Studies........MSc 48PT/Diploma 9FT 36PT/Cert 21PT
Professional Practice in Race Equality........Level 1 module 4PT

University of Wolverhampton
Voluntary and Public Sectors........MA 12FT 24PT

University of Worcester
Social Work........MA 24FT

University of York
Comparative Applied Social and Public Policy, Evaluation and Research........MPA 21FT
Comparative and International Social Policy........MA 12FT 24PT
Social Policy........MRes 12FT 24PT MA 12FT 24PT

Social policy
Research Courses

Bangor University
Criminology and Criminal Justice PhD 36FT 60PT/MPhil 12-24FT 24-36PT
Social Policy........PhD 36FT 60PT/MPhil 12-24FT 24-36PT

University of Bath
Social and Policy Sciences .. PhD 24-48FT 36-72PT/MPhil 12-36FT 24-48PT

University of Bedfordshire
Social Policy and Administration.MA by research 12FT 24PT/MSc by research 12FT 24PT/MPhil 24FT/PhD 36FT

University of Birmingham
Applied Social Research Doctorate........SocScD 36FT 72PT
Integrated Study (Social Sciences)........PhD 48FT 48PT

University of Bristol
Social Science (Policy Studies Doctorate)........DSocSci 36FT 96PT

University of Chester
Higher Degrees by Research........MPhil 12 - 48FT 24 - 72PT/PhD 24 - 48FT 48 - 84PT

De Montfort University
Public Policy (Research). MPhil 12 - 24FT 24 - 48PT/PhD 24 - 36FT 36 - 72PT

University of Dundee
Social Dimensions of Health Institute........MPhil 24FT PhD 36FT
Town and Regional Planning (MPhil)........MPhil 24FT

University of Edinburgh
Social Policy........PhD 36FT 72PT/MPhil 24FT 48PT
Social Policy (Masters by Research)....MSc by research 12FT 24PT

University of Hertfordshire
Centre for Community Research........PhD 36FT 72PT/MPhil 24FT 48PT/MRes 12FT 24PT

University of Hull
Social Policy........PhD 36FT 60PT/MPhil 24FT 36PT
Social Policy and Gender Studies........PhD 36FT 60PT/MPhil 24FT 36PT

Institute for the Study of the Americas, School of Advanced Study, University of London
Social Policy........PhD 36FT/MPhil 12FT

University of Kent
Criminology.....MPhil 24FT 36PT/PhD 36FT 60PT/MA by research 12FT 24PT
Personal Social Services........MPhil 24FT 36PT/PhD 36FT 60PT/MA by research 12FT 24PT
Social Policy...... PhD 36FT 60PT/MPhil 24FT 36PT/MA by research 12FT 24PT
The Doctorate in Cultural and Global Criminology (DCGC).....PhD 36FT 60PT

King's College London
Interdisciplinary Policy Studies..... MPhil 36FT 48-84PT/PhD 36FT 48-84PT

University of Liverpool
Social Research........MRes 12FT 24PT
Sociology and Social Policy........PhD 24-48FT 48-84PT/MPhil 12-48FT 48-72PT

London School of Economics and Political Science (LSE)
Social Policy........PhD 36-48FT/MPhil 36-48FT

Loughborough University
Social Policy and Administration........PhD 36FT 60PT/MPhil 24FT 36PT

Middlesex University
Social Policy........MPhil 12FT 24PT 24DL/PhD 36FT 60PT 60DL

Newcastle University
Sociology........PhD 36FT 72PT/MPhil 12FT 24PT

University of Nottingham
Social Policy and Administration........MA by research 12FT 24PT
Sociology and Social Policy........PhD 36FT 72PT
Sociology and Social Policy Research Areas PhD 24-36FT 48-72PT/MPhil 12-24FT 36-48PT

The Open University
Globalisation, Transnationalism and Social Welfare.......PhD 36FT 72PT variableDL/MPhil 15FT 24PT variableDL
Personal relationships, families, children and young people..PhD 36FT 72PT variableDL/MPhil 15FT 24PT variableDL
Public Leadership and Social Enterprise........PhD 36FT 72PT variableDL/MPhil 15FT 24PT variableDL
Social Policy and Criminology ...PhD 36FT 72PT variableDL/MPhil 15FT 24PT variableDL
Social divisions, social identities and welfare........PhD 36FT 72PT variableDL/MPhil 15FT 24PT variableDL
The changing nature of contemporary and historical welfare...... PhD 36FT 72PT variableDL/MPhil 15FT 24PT variableDL

University of Oxford
Social Intervention........DPhil 48FT
Social Policy........DPhil 48FT

Plymouth University
Social Exclusion, Diversity and Disadvantage........MPhil tbcFT
Social Sciences...... PhD 24-48FT 36-72PT/MPhil 12-36FT 24-48PT

Robert Gordon University
Aberdeen Business School ...PhD 12FT 36PT 36DL/MSc(Res) 12FT 36PT 36DL

University of Salford
Centre for Policy Studies........PhD/MPhil

Sheffield Hallam University
Centre for Regional Economic and Social Research Applied Social Research........PhD 36FT 60PT

University of Southampton
School of Social Sciences - Social Policy.......PhD 36FT 72PT/MPhil 24FT 48PT

Swansea University
Social Policy........PhD 36FT 60PT/MPhil 12FT 24PT
Urban Studies........MSc by research 12FT 24PT

Teesside University
Social Policy.. PhD 24FT 36PT/MPhil 18FT 30PT/DProf 24FT 36PT/MProf by research 18FT 30PT

University of Ulster
Social Policy and Adminstration........PhD 36FT 72PT/MPhil 24FT 48PT

University of Westminster
Health Sciences........DProf 48-96PT

University of York
Social Policy and Social Work .... PhD 36FT 72PT/MPhil 24FT 48PT

Social psychology
Taught Courses

Bangor University
Criminology and Sociology........MA 12FT 21-30PT/PGDip 9FT 17-21PT/PGCert 5FT 12-21PT
International Social Work MA 12FT 24-30PT/PGDip 9FT 17-21PT/PGCert 5FT 12-21PT

University of Bath
Global Political Economy: transformations and policy analysis ... MRes 12FT 24-36PT

University of Bedfordshire
Intercultural Communication........MA 12FT 24PT

Birkbeck, University of London
Psychodynamics of Human Development........MSc 24PT/PGDip 24PT
Psychosocial Studies........MA 12FT 24PT GradCert 8PT

University of Brighton
Community Psychology........

Brunel University
Cross-Cultural Psychology........MSc 12FT 30PT

Bucks New University
Community Psychology........MSc 12FT 24PT

University of Cambridge
Modern Society and Global Transformations........MPhil 9FT
Social Anthropology........PhD by taught 11FT
Social and Developmental Psychology........MPhil 9FT

University of Central Lancashire
Conflict and Violence Minimisation........PGCert 24PT
Counselling and Psychotherapy........MSc 36PT/PGDip 24PT
Personality Disorder (Practice Development)........MSc 36-60PT/PGDip 24PT
Personality Disorder (Research).......MSc 36-60PT/PGDip 12-24PT
Psychology.......MSc 12FT 24PT/PGDip 9FT 24PT/PGCert 9FT 24PT
Psychology of Child Development.......MSc 12FT 24PT/PGDip 9FT 24PT/PGCert 9FT 24PT
Psychology of Sport and Exercise........MSc 12FT 24PT/PGDip 9FT 24PT/PGCert 9FT 24PT
Social Psychology........MSc 12FT 24PT

University of Chester
Conflict Transformation (Work Based and Integrative Studies).... MA 24-72PT/MSc 24-72PT/PGDip 24-60PT/PGCert 12-36PT
Family and Child Psychology ...MSc 12FT 24PT/PGDip 12FT 24PT/PGCert 12FT 12-24PT
Psychology (Conversion)........MSc 12FT 24PT/PGDip 12FT 24PT

University of Chichester
Psychology of Sport and Exercise.... MSc 12-15FT 24-36PT/PGDip 9-12FT 18-24PT/PGCert 6-9FT 12-18PT

City University London
Organisational Behaviour........MSc 12FT 24PT
Organisational Psychology........MSc 12FT 24PT
Research Methods and Psychology........MSc 12FT 24PT
Social Research Methods........MSc 12FT 24PT

University College Cork
Group Facilitation........MA 24PT

University of Dundee
Developmental Psychology........MSc 12FT
Gender, Culture and Society........MLitt 12FT
Psychological Research Methods........MSc 12FT

Section sponsored by BPP UNIVERSITY COLLEGE

Business and social sciences
506 POSTGRADUATE DIRECTORY www.prospects.ac.uk/findcourses

Social sciences

Durham University
Developmental Psychopathology .... MSc 12FT
Research Methods (Developmental Psychology) .... MA 12FT

University of East Anglia
Child and Family Psychology .... MSc 12FT 24PT
Conflicts in Intercultural Communication .... MA 12FT 24PT

University of Essex
Analytical Psychology .... Prof Doc 24PT
Foundations of Psychoanalytic Psychotherapy .... MA 24PT
Jungian and Post-Jungian Studies .... MA 12FT 24PT
Management and Organisational Dynamics .... MA 12FT 24PT
Psychoanalytic Psychotherapy .... Prof Doc 24PT
Psychoanalytic Social Observation .... MA 12FT 24PT
Psychoanalytic Studies .... MA 12FT 24PT
Psychodynamic Counselling .... MA 12FT 24PT
Psychodynamic Psychotherapy .... Prof Doc 24PT
Psychology .... MSc 12FT/GradDip 12FT
Psychosocial Studies .... MA 12FT 24PT
Refugee Care .... MA 12FT
Research Methods in Psychology .... MSc 12FT

University of Exeter
Social and Organisational Psychology .... MSc 12FT 24PT

Glasgow Caledonian University
Psychology (Conversion) .... GradDip 12FT

University of Glasgow
Drugs and Alcohol Studies .... MSc 12FT 24PT/PGDip 12FT 24PT/PGCert 12PT

University of Gloucestershire
Psychology in Practice .... MSc 12FT 24PT/PGAdvDip 8FT 20PT/PGCert 4FT 8PT

University of Greenwich
Applied Psychology Research Methods .... MSc 12FT

Heriot-Watt University
Business Psychology .... MSc 12FT 24-84PT 12-84DL/PGDip 9FT 15-48PT 9-48DL/PGCert 6FT 12-48PT 6-48DL

University of Kent
Group Processes and Intergroup Relations .... MSc 12FT 24PT
Social and Applied Psychology .... MSc 12FT 24PT

Kingston University
Developmental Psychology .... MRes 12FT 24PT

Lancaster University
Developmental Psychology .... MSc 12FT 24PT
Psychological Research Methods .... MSc 12FT 24PT
Psychology of Advertising .... MSc 12FT 24PT
Social Psychology .... MSc 12FT 24PT

Leeds Metropolitan University
Mental Health Practice .... MSc 24PT
Mental Health Studies .... PGCert 24PT/PGDip 24PT

University of Leeds
International Social Transformation .... MA 12FT 24PT

London School of Economics and Political Science (LSE)
Organisational and Social Psychology .... MSc 12FT 24PT
Social and Cultural Psychology .... MSc 12FT 24PT
Social and Public Communication .... MSc 12FT 24PT

Manchester Metropolitan University
Community Psychology/ Community Psychology (by Research).. MSc 12FT 24-36PT/PGDip 12FT 24-36PT/PGCert 12FT 24PT

University of St Mark and St John
Creative Conflict Transformation through the Arts .... MA 20FT

Oxford Brookes University
Developmental Psychology .... MRes 12FT 24PT

University of Oxford
Evidence-Based Social Intervention .... MPhil 21FT/MSc 9FT
Sociology .... MPhil 22FT/MSc 9FT

Plymouth University
Psychology .... MSc 12FT 24PT/PGDip 9FT

Queen's University Belfast
Communication .... MSc 12FT 36PT/PGDip 12FT 24PT/PGCert 6FT 12PT/AdvPGDip 4FT 12PT

University of Roehampton
Applied Psychological Research .... PGDip 9FT 24PT

Royal Holloway, University of London
Applied Social Psychology .... MSc 12FT

University of Salford
Applied Psychology (Therapies) MSc 12FT 36PT/PGDip 8FT 24PT/PGCert 4FT 9PT
Social Work .... MA 24FT 36PT

Sheffield Hallam University
Developmental Psychology .... MSc 12FT 24-36PT

University of Sheffield
Social Work .... MA 24FT
Sociology .... MA 12FT 24PT

University of Southampton
Research Methods in Psychology .... MSc 12FT
Social Work .... MSc 24FT/PGDip 9FT 21PT
Sociology and Social Policy .... MSc 12FT 24PT/PGDip 9FT 21PT
Sociology and Social Research .... MSc 12FT 24PT/PGDip 9FT 21PT

University of St Andrews
Behavioural and Neural Sciences .... MPhil 12FT 24PT

University of Stirling
Behavioural Science for Management .... MSc 12FT/PGDip 9FT
Psychology of Faces .... MSc 12FT 24PT/PGDip 9FT 18PT
Social Work Studies .... MSc 22FT

University of Strathclyde
Research Methods in Psychology .... MRes 12FT

University of Surrey
Social Psychology .... MSc 12FT 24PT

University of Sussex
Applied Social Psychology .... MSc 12FT 24PT

UCL - University College London
Developmental Psychology and Clinical Practice .... MSc 24FT/PGDip 12FT

York St John University
Community & Critical Social Psychology .... MSc 12FT 24PT

Social psychology
Research Courses

Bangor University
Ageing and Cognitive Health .... PhD 36FT 60PT
Ageing and Dementia Studies .... MSc by research 12FT 24PT PhD 36FT 60PT/MPhil 24FT 48PT
Sociology .... PhD 36FT 60PT/MPhil 12-24FT 24-36PT

Bath Spa University
Psychology .... PhD 24-60FT 36-72PT/MPhil 18-36FT 30-48PT

University of Bath
Global Political Economy: transformations and policy analysis.... MRes 12FT 24-36PT

Birkbeck, University of London
Child and Adolescent Psychotherapy .... DPsychotherapy 48PT
Psychosocial Studies .... PhD 24FT 36PT/MPhil 24FT 36PT

University of Central Lancashire
Sociology, Ethnicity & Human Rights, Criminology .... PhD 30-48FT 66-84PT/MPhil 18-36FT 42-60PT/MA by research 12FT 24PT

University of East Anglia
Psychology .... PhD 36FT 72PT/MPhil 24FT 48PT

University of Essex
Psychoanalytic Studies... PhD 36FT 72PT/MPhil 24FT 48PT/MA by research 12FT 24PT
Psychology .... PhD 36FT 72PT/MPhil 24FT 49PT
Refugee Care .... PhD 36FT 72PT/MPhil 24FT 48PT

University of Gloucestershire
Psychology and Behavioural Sciences .... MRes 12FT

Heriot-Watt University
Applied Psychology .... PhD 36FT 48PT/MPhil 24FT 36PT

University of Kent
Social Psychology.... PhD 36FT 60PT/MPhil 24FT 36PT/New Route PhD 48FT/MSc by research 12FT 24PT

London School of Economics and Political Science (LSE)
Social Psychology .... PhD 36-48FT/MPhil 36-48FT

Loughborough University
Social Psychology .... PhD 36FT 60PT/MPhil 24FT 36PT

Manchester Metropolitan University
Community Psychology (by Research) .... MSc by research 12FT

The Open University
Applied Psychology .... PhD 36FT 72PT variableDL/MPhil 15FT 24PT variableDL
Mind, Meaning and Rationality .... PhD 36FT 72PT variableDL/MPhil 15FT 24PT variableDL
Narrative, Discursive and Psychosocial Research.. PhD 36FT 72PT variableDL/MPhil 15FT 24PT variableDL

Plymouth University
Behaviour .... PhD 36FT/MPhil 24FT

Social sciences
Taught Courses

University of Aberdeen
Sex, Gender, Violence: Contemporary Critical Approaches.... MSc 12FT 24PT/PGDip 9FT 18PT
Social Research .... MRes 12FT 24PT

Aston University
Social Research and Social Change .... MA 12FT 24 - 36PT

Bangor University
Community Development .... PGCert 12PT/PGDip 24PT/MA 36PT
Comparative Criminology and Criminal Justice.... MA 12FT 24PT/PGDip 9FT
Criminology and Criminal Justice .... PhD by taught 36FT 72PT/MPhil 12-24FT 24-36PT/MARes 12FT 24PT
Health and Social Care Leadership .... MSc 12FT 24 - 60PT/PGDip 9FT
Implementing Evidence in Health & Social Care .... MRes 12FT 24PT/PGCert 3FT 15PT
International Social Work MA 12FT 24-30PT/PGDip 9FT 17-21PT/PGCert 5FT 12-21PT
Language, Policy and Planning .... MA 12FT 24-48PT/PGDip 8FT/PGCert 4FT
Policy Research and Evaluation .... MA 12FT 21-30PT/PGDip 9FT 17-21PT/PGCert 5FT 12-21PT
Social Policy, Sociology .... PhD by taught 36FT 60PT/MPhil 12-24FT 24-36PT
Social Research and Social Policy .... MA 12FT 24PT/PGDip 9FT
Social Work .... MA 24FT

University of Bath
Social Policy .... MRes 12FT 24-60PT/PGDip 9FT 21PT/PGCert 4FT 16PT

Birkbeck, University of London
Education, Power and Social Change.. MSc 12FT 24PT/PGDip 6FT 15PT/PGCert 3FT 6PT

University of Birmingham
Health Research - Academic Clinical Fellows (ACF) Framework.... MRes 24PT
Social Research .... MA 12FT 24PT
Social Research (Business) .... MA 12FT 24PT
Social Research (Education) .... MA 12FT 24PT

University of Brighton
Applied Social and Community Research........
Health .... MSc 12FT 24-72PT/PGDip 12FT 24-72PT/PGCert 12FT 24-72PT
Health and Education. MSc 12FT 24 - 72PT/PGDip 12FT 24 - 72PT
Research Methodology .... PGDip 12FT 24PT/PGCert 12FT 24PT

University of Bristol
Social Science Research Methods (Politics/International Relations) .... MSc 12FT 24PT

Bucks New University
Applied Positive Psychology .... MSc 24PT

University of Cambridge
Applied Criminology, Penology and Management .... MSt 24PT
Criminological Research .... MPhil 9FT
Criminology .... MPhil 9FT
Social Anthropological Research .... MPhil 11FT
Social Anthropology .... PhD by taught 11FT

Cardiff University
Social Science Research Methods .... MSc 12FT 24PT

University of Central Lancashire
Community Leadership .... MA 12FT 36PT/PGDip 12FT 24PT
Global Security and Justice .... MA 12FT
Social Policy .... MA 15FT 24-60PT/PGDip /FT /PT

University of Chester
Action Research and Appreciative Inquiry (Work Based and Integrative Studies)... MSc 24-72PT/MA 24-72PT/PGDip 24-60PT/PGCert 12-36PT

City University London
Social Research Methods .... MSc 12FT 24PT

University of Cumbria
International Health .... MSc 12FT 24PT/GradDip 6FT 12PT/GradCert 3FT 6PT
Leadership in Equality and Diversity .... MBA 12FT 36PT
Management and Leadership in Health and Social Care .... MSc 36PT/PGDip 48PT/PGCert 12PT
Social Work .... MA 24FT/PGDip 24FT

University of Dundee
Gender, Culture and Society .... MLitt 12FT
Social Research Methods .... MSc 12FT

Durham University
Community and Youth Work .... MA 12FT 24PT

University of East Anglia
Education .... MA 12FT
Education and Development .... MA 12FT 24PT
Environment and International Development .... MSc 12FT 24PT
Impact Evaluation for International Development .... MSc 12FT 24PT
International Development .... MA 12FT 24PT
International Social Development .... MA 12FT 24PT
Legal Studies .... GradDip 12FT
International Development (by distance learning) .... MRes 24DL
Social Science Research Methods: Business .... MRes 12FT 24PT
Social Science Research Methods: Education .... MRes 12FT 24PT
Social Science Research Methods: Law .... MRes 12FT 24PT
Social Science Research Methods: Psychology .... MRes 12FT 24PT
Social Science Research Methods: Social Work .... MRes 12FT 24PT

University of East London
Narrative Research (Postgraduate Associate Certificate) by distance learning .... Postgraduate Associate Certificate 5DL MA 12FT 24PT/PGDip 8FT 16PT/PGCert 4FT 8PT
Research .... MRes 12FT 24PT

University of Edinburgh
Africa and International Development .... MSc 12FT 24PT
Africa and International Development (Distance Learning) .... PGCert 12DL/PGCert 24DL

Section sponsored by BPP UNIVERSITY COLLEGE

Business and social sciences
www.prospects.ac.uk/findcourses POSTGRADUATE DIRECTORY 507

Social sciences

African Studies ... MSc 12FT 24PT
American History ... MSc 12FT 24PT
Arab World Studies ... MSc 24FT
Celtic and Scottish Studies ... MSc 12FT 24PT
Childhood Studies ... MSc 12FT 24PT
Children & Young People's Mental Health and Psychological Practice.. MSc 12FT 24-72PT/PGCert 12-24PT/PGDip 9FT 24-48PT
Cognition in Science and Society ... MSc 12FT 24PT
Forensic Anthropology ... MSc 12FT 24PT
Global Development Challenges (Online Distance Learning)........ PGCert 12-24DL
Global Environment Challenges Certificate (Online distance learning) ... PGCert 9DL
Global Environment, Politics and Society ... MSc 12FT 24PT
Global Health Challenges (Online Distance Learning) .... PGCert 12-24DL
Global Health Policy (Online Distance Learning) ... PGCert 9-21DL
Global Health Studies (online distance learning) ...... PGCert 36DL
Global Health and Infectious Diseases (Online Distance Learning) ... MSc 36DL/PGDip 24DL/PGCert 12DL
Global Health and Public Policy ... MSc 12FT 24-36PT
Global Health: Non Communicable Diseases (online distance learning) ... MSc 36DL/PGDip 24DL/PGCert 12DL
Global Social Change ... MSc 12FT 24PT
Health Inequalities and Public Policy ... MSc 12FT 24-36PT
Health Systems and Public Policy ... MSc 12FT 24-36PT
Interdisciplinary Creative Practices ... MSc 12FT 24PT
International Development ... MSc 12FT 24PT
Medical Anthropology ... MSc 12FT 24PT
Nationalism Studies ... MSc 12FT 24PT
Policy Studies ... MSc 12FT 24PT
Public Policy ... MPP 15FT
Science Communication and Public Engagement ... MSc 12FT
Science and Technology in Society ... MSc 12FT 36PT/Diploma 9FT 36PT
Science, Technology and International Development ... MSc 12FT 36PT/Diploma 9FT 24PT
Social Research ... MSc 12FT 24PT/PGDip 9FT 21PT
Social and Cultural History ... MSc 12FT

University of Essex
Advertising, Marketing and the Media ... MA 12FT 24PT
Criminology and Socio-Legal Research ... MA 12FT 24PT
Longitudinal Social Research ... MA 12FT 24PT
Organised Crime, Terrorism and Security ... MSc 12FT 24PT
Sociological Research ... MA 12FT 24PT
Sociology ... MA 12FT 24PT/PGCert 9FT
Sociology and Management ... MA 12FT 24PT
Survey Methods for Social Research ... MSc 12FT 24PT

University of Exeter
Anthrozoology ... MA 12FT 24PT 24DL
History and Philosophy of Biology ... MA 12FT 24PT
Philosophy and Sociology of Science ... MA 12FT 24PT
Politics ... MRes 12FT 24PT
Science and Technology Studies ... MRes 12FT 24PT

National University of Ireland Galway
Life Course Studies ... PGDip 12PT/MA 24PT

Glasgow Caledonian University
Social Research ... MSc 12FT 24PT
Social Research (Policy Analysis) ... MSc 12FT 24PT

University of Glasgow
Environment, Culture & Communication (Dumfries Campus) ..... MLitt 12FT 24PT
Russian for Social Sciences ... PGDip 12FT/PGCert 9FT
Social Science Research ... MSc 12FT 24PT/PGDip 9FT 21PT
Sociology and Research Methods ... MRes 12FT 24PT
Young People, Social Inclusion & Change ... MSc 12FT 24PT

University of Hull
Applied Social Research ... MSc 12FT 24PT

Institute of Education
Policy Analysis and Evaluation ... MSc 12FT 24PT

Keele University
Social Science Research Methods.... MRes 12FT 24PT/PGDip 12FT 24PT/PGCert 12FT 24PT
Social Work ... Professional Doctorate 60-84PT

University of Kent
Anthropology of Ethnicity, Nationalism and Identity...... MA 12FT 24PT
Civil Society, NGO and Nonprofit Studies ... PGDip 12FT 24PT/MA 12FT 24PT
Environmental Social Science ... MSc 12FT 24PT
Methods of Social Research ... MA 12FT 24PT

King's College London
Complex Systems Modelling - From Biomedical and Natural to Economic and Social Sciences ... MSc 12FT 24PT
Education, Policy & Society ... MA 12FT 24-72PT

Kingston University
Law joint masters degree (with Criminology or Human Rights) .. LLM 12FT 24PT/MA 12FT 24PT
Professional Education and Training ... MA 36PT/PGDip 24PT

University of Limerick
Gender, Culture & Society ... MA 12FT 24PT

Sociology (Youth, Communtiy and Social Regeneration) .... MA 12FT 24PT
Sociology (Applied Research) ... MA 12FT 24PT

University of Lincoln
Advanced Professional Practice in Social Work ... MSc 0PT
Globalising Justice ... MA 12FT 24PT

Liverpool Hope University
Peace Studies ... MA 12FT 24PT
Research Methods ... MSc 12FT

Liverpool John Moores University
Critical Social Science ... MRes 12FT
Social Work ... MA 24FT/PGDip 24FT

University of Liverpool
Population Studies ... MA 12FT 24PT

London Metropolitan University
Comparative European Social Studies ... MA 12FT 24PT
Managing Equality and Diversity ... MA 12FT 24PT

London School of Economics and Political Science (LSE)
City Design and Social Science ... MSc 12FT 24PT
Population and Development ... MSc 12FT 24-28PT

London School of Hygiene and Tropical Medicine
Demography & Health ... MSc 12FT 24PT
Global Health Policy (by Distance Learning) ... MSc 24-60DL/PGDip 12-60DL/PGCert 12-60DL
Health Policy, Planning and Financing ... MSc 12FT 24PT
Nutrition for Global Health ... MSc 12FT 24PT
One Health ... MSc 12FT 24PT
Public Health ... MSc 12FT 24PT
Public Health (Health Promotion) ... MSc 12FT 24PT
Public Health (Health Services Management) ... MSc 12FT 24PT
Public Health (Health Services Research) ... MSc 12FT 24PT
Public Health (Public Health) ... MSc 12FT 24PT
Public Health (by Distance Learning) ... MSc 24 - 60DL/PGDip 12 - 60DL/PGCert 12-60DL
Public Health for Eye Care ... MSc 12FT 24PT
Public Health in Developing Countries ... MSc 12FT 24PT
Reproductive & Sexual Health Research ... MSc 12FT 24PT

Manchester Metropolitan University
Exercise and Sport - Biomechanics ... MS 12FT 24-36PT

University of Manchester
Global Health ... PGCert 12FT 12DL/PGDip 12DL
Social Research Methods and Statistics ..... MSc 12FT 24PT/PGDip 9FT 24PT

National University of Ireland, Maynooth
Applied Social Studies ... MA 12FT 24PT

Middlesex University
Social Science Research Methods ... MSc 12FT 24PT

Newcastle University
Social Science and Health Research..... MSc 12FT 24PT/PGDip 9FT 18PT
Sociology ... MA 12FT 24PT
Sociology and Social Research ... MA 12FT 24PT

Northumbria University
Social Sciences ... MRes 12FT 24PT

Nottingham Trent University
Sociology ... MA 12FT 24PT

University of Nottingham
Research Methods Science and Technology Studies .... MA 12FT 24PT
Science, Technology and Society .... MA (by research) 12FT 24PT

The Open University
Science ... MSc variableDL
Science and Society ... MSc variableDL/PGDip variableDL
Systems Thinking in Practice MSc variableDL/PGCert variableDL/PGDip variableDL

Oxford Brookes University
Humanities and Social Sciences ... MSc 21-24FT/MA 21-24FT

Oxford Centre for Hebrew and Jewish Studies
Jewish Studies ... MSt 9FT

University of Oxford
Economic and Social History ... MPhil 21FT/MSc 12FT
Educational Research Methodology ... MSc 12FT
Social Science of the Internet ... MSc 10FT
Sociology ... MPhil 22FT/MSc 9FT

Plymouth University
Social Research Methods ... MSc 12FT 24PT

Queen's University Belfast
Applied Social Studies ... MSc 36PT/PGDip 24PT/PGCert 12PT
Childhood Studies ... DChild (Doctorate) 48-72PT
Educational Leadership ... MSc 12FT up to 60PT
Sociology ... MA 12FT 24PT/PGDip 24PT

University of Reading
Applied Linguistics ... MA 12FT 24-48PT/PGCert 12FT/PGDip 12FT
Applied Linguistics - Research Pathway ... MA (Res) 12FT 24-72PT
Human Geography ... MSc(Res) 12FT 24PT

University of Roehampton
Human Rights ... MA 18FT 24+PT
Human Rights and International Relations ... MA 18FT 24+PT
Social Research Methods ... MA 12FT 24PT

Royal Holloway, University of London
Cultural Geography (Research) ... MA 12FT 24PT

University of Salford
Advanced Practice (Health and Social Care) .... MSc 24PT/PGDip 18PT/PGCert 12PT
Counselling and Psychotherapy Studies (Professional Training)... MSc 36PT/PGDip 24PT
Social Media ... MA 9FT/PGDip 9FT
Social Work ... MA 24FT 36PT

School of Oriental and African Studies - SOAS
African Studies ... MA 12FT 24-36PT
Anthropology of Media ... MA 12FT 24-36PT
Chinese Studies ... MA 12FT 24-36PT
Critical Media and Cultural Studies ... MA 12FT 24-36PT
Development Studies ... MSc 12FT 24PT
Development Studies with Special Reference to Central Asia....... MSc 12FT 24PT
Gender Studies ... MA 12FT 24-36PT
Global Cinemas and the Transcultural ... MA 12FT 24-36PT
Global Creative and Cultural Industries ... MA 12FT
Islamic Societies and Cultures ... MA 12FT 24-36PT
Islamic Studies ... MA 12FT 24-36PT
Israeli Studies ... MA 12FT 24-36PT
Japanese Studies ... MA 12FT 24-36PT
Korean Studies ... MA 12FT 24-36PT
Labour, Social Movements and Development ... MSc 12FT 24PT
Law, Culture and Society ... MA 12FT 24PT
Study of Contemporary Pakistan ... MA 12FT 24PT
Medical Anthropology ... MA 12FT 24-36PT
Migration and Diaspora Studies ... MA 12FT 24-36PT
Near and Middle Eastern Studies ... MA 12FT 24-36PT
Pacific Asian Studies ... MA 12FT 24-36PT
Performance ... MMus 12FT 24PT
Postcolonial Studies ... MA 12FT 24PT
Public Policy and Management (Distance Learning).... MSc 24DL/PGDip 12DL
Social Anthropology ... MA 12FT 24-36PT
Social Anthropology of Development ... MA 12FT 24-36PT
South Asian Area Studies ... MA 12FT 24PT
State, Society and Development ... MSc 12FT 24PT

Schumacher College ...
Holistic Science ... MSc 12FT

Sheffield Hallam University
Business ... MRes 12FT 36PT
Cultural Studies ... MRes variousFT variousPT
Social Sciences ... MPhil 36FT 84PT MA 12FT 24PT
Sociology, Planning and Policy ... MRes variousFT variousPT

University of Sheffield
Social Research ... MA 12FT 24PT
Social Science and Oral Health ... MSc 12FT 24PT
Social Scientific Biblical Studies ... MA 12FT 24PT
Social Work ... MA 24FT
Sociology ... MA 12FT 24PT
Web Journalism ... MA 12FT/PGDip 9FT

University of South Wales
Social and Cultural History ... MA 12FT 24PT
Working for Children & Young People: Youth Work ... MA 12-24FT 36-60PT
Youth and Community Work ... PGDip 12FT 24PT

University of Southampton
Demography ... MSc 12FT 24PT/PGDip 9FT
Professional Studies ... MSc 30PT/PGCert 12PT/PG Cert in Management and Leadership 12-24 PTDL
Social Policy and Social Research MSc 12FT 24PT/PGDip 9FT 21PT
Social Statistics ... MSc 12-24FT 24PT/PGDip 9FT 21PT
Social Work ... MSc 24FT/PGDip 9FT 21PT
Sociology and Social Policy .... MSc 12FT 24PT/PGDip 9FT 21PT
Sociology and Social Research .... MSc 12FT 24PT/PGDip 9FT 21PT

Staffordshire University
Community Practice ... MA 12FT 48PT
Regeneration ... MA 24FT 60PT
Regeneration ... MA 12FT 24PT
Social Welfare Law, Policy and Advice Practice ... MA 28DL
Terrorism, Crime and Global Security ... MA 24-60DL

University of Stirling
Applied Social Research ... MSc 12FT 30PT/PGDip 9FT 18PT
Applied Social Research (Criminology) ... MSc 12FT 30PT/PGDip 9FT 18PT
Applied Social Research ... MRes 12FT 30PT
Applied Studies (Child Welfare and Protection) .... MSc 30PT/PGDip 24PT/PGCert 12PT
Counselling & Psychotherapy ... MSc 12FT/PGDip 9FT
Dementia Studies and Gerontology .... MSc 36PT/PGDip 24PT/PGCert 12PT
Housing Studies ... MSc 12FT/PGDip 12FT MSc 24PT/PGDip 24PT/PGCert 12PT
Social Enterprise ... MSc 12FT/PGDip 9FT/PGCert 6FT

Social sciences

Social Work Studies ... MSc 22FT

University of Strathclyde
Autism ... MSc 12FT 24PT/PGDip 12FT/PGCert 9FT
Education for Work and Enterprise ... PGDip max 48PT/PGCert max 24PT
Research Methodology in Business and Management ... MRes 12FT 24PT/PGDip 9FT 21PT/PGCert 4FT 9PT
Social Research ... MRes 12FT 24PT

University of Sussex
Social Research Methods ... MSc 12FT 24PT/PGDip 12FT 24PT/PGCert 9FT 18PT

Swansea University
Ageing Studies ... MSc 12FT 36PT/PGDip 12FT 24PT/PGCert 12FT 12PT
Social Research Methods ... MSc 12FT 24PT

Teesside University
Criminology (Contemporary Drug Issues) ... MSc 12FT 24PT
Cultural History ... MA 12FT 24-36PT
Social Research Methods ... MSc 12FT 24PT/PGDip 12FT 24PT

UCL - University College London
Cultural Heritage Studies ... MA 12FT 24PT

University of Warwick
Access and Equality in Health Care ... PGA 12PT/CPDMod 1PT

University of the West of Scotland
Alcohol and Drug Studies ... MSc 12FT 36PT/PGDip 11FT 36PT

University of the West of England, Bristol
Psycho-Social Studies ... MSc 24PT

University of Westminster
Communication ... MA 12FT 24PT
Diversity and the Media ... MA 12FT
Global Media ... MA 12FT
International Media Business ... MA 12FT 24PT
Social Media ... MA 12FT 24PT

University of Wolverhampton
Human Sciences ... MRes 12FT 24PT

University of York
Applied Human Rights ... MA 12FT 24PT/Diploma 12FT 24PT
Comparative and International Social Policy ... MA 12FT 24PT
Women's Studies (Social Research) ... MA 12FT 24PT

Social sciences
Research Courses

University of Aberdeen
Sociology ... PhD 36FT 60PT/MPhil 24FT/MRes 12FT

Anglia Ruskin University
English Language and Intercultural Communication MPhil 24FT/PhD 36FT
English Language and Linguistics ... MPhil 24FT/PhD 36FT

Bangor University
Criminology and Criminal Justice ... PhD 36FT 60PT/MPhil 12-24FT 24-36PT
Social Policy ... PhD 36FT 60PT/MPhil 12-24FT 24-36PT

University of Bath
Social and Policy Sciences .. PhD 24-48FT 36-72PT/MPhil 12-36FT 24-48PT

Birmingham City University
Social Sciences ... PhD 36FT 60PT/MPhil 36FT 60PT

University of Birmingham
Integrated Study (Business and Management) ... PhD 48FT
PhD Integrated Study (Social Sciences) ... PhD 48FT

University of Bradford
Department of Social Sciences and Humanities ... PhD 36-48FT 48-60PT/MPhil 12-24FT 24-48PT

University of Brighton
Applied Social Sciences Division ... PhD 24-60FT 36-72PT/MPhil 18-36FT 30-48PT

University of Buckingham
Anthropology ... MA by research 12FT

University of Cambridge
Social and Political Sciences ... PhD 36FT 60PT

Cardiff University
Culture, Transformation and Subjectivity ... PhD 36FT 60PT/MPhil 12FT
Knowledge, Science and Technology ... PhD 36FT possiblePT/MPhil 12FT possiblePT
Methods and Methodology ... PhD 36FT

University of Central Lancashire
Education, Deaf Studies ... PhD 18-36FT 42-60PT/MPhil 18-36FT 42-60PT/MA by research 12FT 24PT

University of Chester
Higher Degrees by Research ... MPhil 12 - 48FT 24 - 72PT/PhD 24 - 48FT 48 - 84PT

University College Cork
Doctor of Social Science ... DSocSci 48FT

Coventry University
School of Health and Social Sciences ... PhD/MPhil

De Montfort University
Health and Applied Social Sciences PhD 24 - 36FT 48 -72PT/MPhil 12 - 24FT 24 - 48PT

University of Dundee
Social Work ... MPhil 24FT

Durham University
Applied Social Sciences ... MA by research 12FT 24PT/MProf by research 12FT 24PT/MPhil 24FT 48PT/PhD 36FT 72PT

University of East Anglia
Pedagogy and Engagement with Learning ... PhD 36FT 72PT/MPhil 24FT 48PT/MA by research 12FT 24PT

University of Edinburgh
African Studies ... PhD 36FT 72PT/MPhil 24FT 48PT
Canadian Studies ... PhD 36FT 72PT/MPhil 24FT 48PT
Celtic and Scottish Studies PhD 36FT 72PT/MPhil 24FT 48PT/MSc by research 12FT 24PT
Global Health ... MPhil 24FT 48PT/PhD 36FT 72PT
Interdisciplinary Social Sciences in Health ... PhD 36FT 72PT
International Public Health Policy ... PhD 36FT 72PT
Medical Anthropology ... MSc by research 12FT 24PT
Population Health Sciences ... PhD 36FT 72PT/MPhil 24FT 48PT/MSc by research 12FT 24PT
Science and Technology Studies ... PhD 36FT 72PT MSc by research 12FT 24PT
Science, Technology and Innovation Studies ... MSc by research 12FT 24PT/PhD 36FT 72PT

University of Essex
Applied Social and Economic Research ... PhD 36FT 72PT/MPhil 24FT 48PT
Criminology ... PhD 36FT 72PT/MPhil 24FT 48PT/MA by research 12FT 24PT
Criminology and Socio-Legal Research ... PhD 36FT 72PT/MPhil 24FT 48PT/MA by research 12FT 24PT
Health Research ... PhD 36FT 72PT/MPhil 24FT 48PT
Sociological Research ... PhD 36FT 72PT/MPhil 24FT 48PT/MA by research 12FT 24PT
Sociology ... PhD 36FT 72PT/MPhil 24FT 48PT/MA by research 12FT 24PT
Survey Methodology ... PhD 36FT 72PT/MPhil 24FT 48PT

European University Institute
Political and Social Sciences ... PhD 48FT

University of Exeter
Health and Wellbeing ... MPhil 36FT 60PT/PhD 48FT 84PT
Politics ... PhD 48FT 84PT 84DL/MPhil 36FT 60PT 60DL/MA by research 12FT 24PT
Sociology ... PhD 36FT 72PT 72DL/MPhil 24FT 48PT 48DL

National University of Ireland Galway
College of Arts, Social Sciences & Celtic Studies .. PhD 48FT 72PT/MLitt by research 24FT 48PT/Structured PhD 48FT 72PT

University of Gloucestershire
Social and Policy Sciences ... PhD 30-48FT 48-84PT/MPhil 18-36FT 30-60PT/MSc by research 12-24FT 18-36PT/MA by research 12-24FT 18-36PT

University of Hull
Social Justice ... PhD 36FT 60PT/MPhil 24FT 36PT

Institute of Education
Educational and Social Research ... MRes 12FT 24PT

Keele University
Environmental Social Sciences ... PhD 24-48FT 48-84PT/MPhil 12-24FT 24-36PT
Ethics ... PhD 24-48FT 48-84PT/MPhil 12-24FT 24-36PT
European Studies ... MPhil 24FT 36PT/PhD 48FT 84PT
Philosophy ... PhD 24-48FT 48-84PT/MPhil 12-24FT 24-36PT
Politics ... MPhil 24FT 36PT/PhD 48FT 84PT
Sociology ... PhD 24-48FT 48-84PT/MPhil 12-24FT 24-36PT

University of Kent
Anthropology .. PhD 36FT 60PT/MPhil 12FT 36PT/MA by research 12FT 24PT/MSc by research 12FT 24PT
Environmental Social Science .. PhD 36FT 60PT/MPhil 24FT 36PT/MSc by research 12FT 24PT
Socio-Legal Studies ... PhD 36FT 60PT/MPhil 24FT 36PT/LLM by research 12FT 24PT

King's College London
Social Science, Health & Medicine Research ... MPhil 24FT 48PT/PhD 36FT 48-72PT

Lancaster University
Applied Social Science ... PhD 36FT 48PT/MPhil 24FT 36PT

University of Leicester
Doctorate of Social Science (Work & Employment) DSocSci 42DL/MSocSci by research 36DL

University of Lincoln
Social Policy ... MPhil 12-48FT/PhD 12-48FT
Social Sciences ... MPhil 12-48FT/PhD 24-48FT

Liverpool Hope University
Postgraduate Research ... PhD 24FT 48PT/MPhil 12FT 24PT

Liverpool John Moores University
Health and Applied Social Sciences ... PDNurs 36FT 48PT/PDMidw 36FT 48PT/PDHSci 36FT 48PT

London Metropolitan University
Dept of Applied Social Studies ... PhD Max 60FT Max 96PT/MPhil Max 36FT Max 54PT

London School of Economics and Political Science (LSE)
Philosophy, Logic and Scientific Method ... PhD 36-48FT/MPhil 36-48FT
Social Research Methods ... MPhil 36-48FT/PhD 36-48FT

London School of Hygiene and Tropical Medicine
Epidemiology & Population Health (Research) .. DrPH 42FT 42PT/PhD 42FT 42PT/MPhil 12FT 12PT
Public Health & Policy (Research) ... DrPH 42FT 42PT/PhD 42FT 42PT/MPhil 12FT 12PT

Manchester Metropolitan University
Department of Humanities and Applied Social Studies ... MA by research
Humanities and Applied Social Studies ... PhD 36FT 54PT/MPhil 24FT 36PT/MA by research 12FT 24PT

University of Manchester
Social Change ... PhD 36FT 72PT

University of Nottingham
Social Sciences Research Methodology ... MPhil 24FT 48PT/PhD 36-48FT 72-96PT

The Open University
Health, Social Work and Social Care ... PhD 36FT 72PT variableDL/MPhil 15FT 24PT variableDL
Materialities, Space and Power ... PhD 36FT 72PT variableDL/MPhil 15FT 24PT variableDL
Personal life and intimacies ... PhD 36FT 72PT variableDL/MPhil 15FT 24PT variableDL
Social technologies, innovation and development ... PhD 36FT 72PT variableDL/MPhil 15FT 24PT variableDL

University of Oxford
Information, Communication and the Social Sciences ... DPhil 48FT

University of Portsmouth
Social, Historical and Literary Studies ... MPhil 24FT 48PT/PhD 36FT 72PT

University of Roehampton
Business & Management ... PhD 24-48FT 36-60PT/MPhil 21-36FT 33-48PT

Royal Holloway, University of London
Department of Social and Political Science ... PhD 36FT/MPhil 36FT

University of Salford
Social Sciences ... MRes 12FT 24PT

School of Oriental and African Studies - SOAS
Development Studies ... PhD 36FT 48-60PT
Languages and Cultures of South Asia ... PhD 36FT 72PT/MPhil 24FT 48PT
Media and Film Studies ... PhD 36-48FT
Social Anthropology ... PhD 36FT/MPhil 24FT

Sheffield Hallam University
Social Science and Law ... PhD/MPhil

Southampton Solent University
Social Science Research Centre ... PhD/MPhil

University of Southampton
Economics ... PhD 36-48FT 84PT/MPhil 24-48FT 84PT
School of Social Sciences - Demography ... PhD 36FT 72PT/MPhil 24FT 48PT
School of Social Sciences - Gerontology ... PhD 36FT 72PT/MPhil 24FT 48PT
School of Social Sciences - Social Statistics ... PhD 36FT 72PT/MPhil 24FT 48PT

St Mary's University College, Twickenham
Sociology/Irish Studies ... PhD 36FT 72PT/MPhil 24FT 48PT

University of Strathclyde
Applied Social Sciences - Research ... PhD 33FT/MPhil 12FT
Government and Public Policy - Research ... PhD 33FT/MPhil 12FT

University of Sussex
Science and Technology Policy Studies ... PhD 24-48FT 36-72PT/MPhil 12-36FT 24-48PT

University of Ulster
Media Studies ... PhD 36FT 72PT/MPhil 24FT 48PT

University of Warwick
Health and Social Studies .. PhD 36FT 60PT/MPhil 24FT 36PT/MA by research 12FT 24PT

University of the West of Scotland
Department of Applied Social Studies ... PhD/MPhil

University of the West of England, Bristol
School of Humanities, Languages and Social Sciences ... PhD -FT

University of Westminster
Social Sciences, Humanities and Languages ... MPhil 18-36FT 30-60PT

Business and social sciences
www.prospects.ac.uk/findcourses POSTGRADUATE DIRECTORY 509

Social sciences

University of Wolverhampton
School of Humanities, Languages and Social Sciences MPhil/PhD
Sociology and Applied Social Studies .... PhD/MPhil

University of Worcester
Social Work and Social Policy .... PhD 48FT 70PT/MPhil 24FT 48PT

University of York
Language and Communication .... PhD 36FT 72PT/MPhil 24FT 48PT

Social work and community studies
Taught Courses

University of Aberdeen
Community Learning and Development....MSc 36PT/PGDip 24PT
Social and Educational Research .... MRes 12FT

Anglia Ruskin University
Advanced Practice .... MSc 12FT 24PT

Bangor University
Community Development .....PGCert 12PT/PGDip 24PT/MA 36PT
Comparative Criminology and Criminal Justice....MA 12FT 24PT/PGDip 9FT
Criminology and Criminal Justice........ PhD by taught 36FT 72PT/MPhil 12-24FT 24-36PT/MARes 12FT 24PT
Health and Social Care Leadership........ MSc 12FT 24 - 60PT/PGDip 9FT
Implementing Evidence in Health & Social Care MRes 12FT 24PT/PGCert 3FT 15PT
International Social Work MA 12FT 24-30PT/PGDip 9FT 17-21PT/PGCert 5FT 12-21PT
Social Work........ MA 24FT

University of Bath
Research in Health Practice .... MSc 24-60PT/PGDip 24-60PT/PGCert 12-60PT

University of Bedfordshire
Applied Social Work: Children and Families........ MA 30PT
Applied Social Work: Practice Education........ MA 30PT
Social Work........ MSc 24FT

Birmingham City University
Health and Social Care........ PGDip 12PT/MSc 24PT
Health and Social Care (Leadership)........PGDip 12PT/PGDip 36PT

University of Birmingham
Leadership and Management for Social Care...... MA 36PT/PGDip 24PT
Leadership and Management for Social Work..... PGDip 18PT/MA 36PT
Social Research (Social Work and Professional Practice).MA 12FT 24PT/PGDip 9FT 18PT
Special Educational Needs Coordination (National Award for SENC)........ PGCert 12/24PT

University of Bolton
Health and Social Care.... MSc 36-60PT/PGDip 24PT/PGCert 12PT
Leadership in Health and Social Care..MSc 36-60PT/PGDip 24PT/PGCert 12PT

Bradford College
Counselling in the Community........ MA 16PT

University of Bradford
Health and Social Care Management........MSc 24-36PT/PGDip 12-24PT/PGCert 9-12PT

University of Brighton
Advanced Social Work........
Advanced Social Work and Management........
Community Psychology........
Community Specialist Practice.. MSc 12FT 24 - 36PT/PGDip 12FT 24 - 36PT
Professional Development in Health and Social Care........ MSc 24 - 36PT/PGCert 24 - 36PT/PGDip 24 - 36PT
Social Work........MSc 24FT/PGDip 24FT/PGCert 24FT

Canterbury Christ Church University
Interprofessional Health and Social Care........MSc 12FT 24-72PT

Cardiff Metropolitan University
Youth & Community Work........MSc 36PT/PGDip 24PT

University of Central Lancashire
Advancing Equality, Diversity and Inclusion ....MA 12FT 36PT/PGDip 12FT 36PT/PGCert 12FT 24PT
Child Care and Welfare .... MA 12FT 24-60PT
Child Health........ MSc 36PT
Community Engagement........ MA 24PT/PGDip 18PT/PGCert 9PT
Community Leadership........MA 12FT 36PT/PGDip 12FT 24PT
Counselling Casework Supervision........ PGCert 7PT
Education and History........ MA 24PT
Equality and Community Leadership........ PGCert 24PT
Excellence in Leadership for Inclusion and Community..... PGCert 12-24PT
Health & Social Care Education........ PGCert 12PT
Health Informatics........MSc 33PT/PGDip 24PT
Health and Social Care Education .... PGCert 12PT
Research Methods in Health and Social Care........ PGCert 36PT
Researching Social Care .... PGCert 12FT 24PT
Social Policy........ MA 15FT 24-60PT/PGDip /FT /PT
Social Work........ MA 24FT 36PT
Social Work (only available through employment secondment).. PGDip 24FT 36PT
Social Work Practice (Post Qualification Specialist Award, Adults) PGDip 3PT
Sport, Policy and Community Development .... MA 12FT 24PT

University of Chester
Dental Practice Management (Work Based and Integrative Studies) .... MA 24-72PT/PGDip 24-60PT/PGCert 12-36PT
Education: Leadership and Management..... MA 24 - 72PT/PGDip 24 - 60PT/PGCert 12 - 36PT
Leadership Development (Work Based and Integrative Studies).. MA 24-72PT/MSc 24-72PT/PGDip 24-60PT/PGCert 12-36PT
Leadership and Management (Work Based and Integrative Studies) ....MA 24-72PT/MSc 24-72PT/PGDip 24-60PT/PGCert 12-36PT
Learning and Development (Work Based and Integrative Studies) ....MA 24-72PT/MSc 24-72PT/PGDip 24-60PT/PGCert 12-36PT
Personal Leadership Development (Work Based and Integrative Studies) .... MA 24-72PT/PGDip 24-60PT/PGCert 12-36PT
Transpersonal Leadership (Work Based and Integrative Studies). MA 24-72PT/MSc 24-72PT/PGDip 24-60PT/PGCert 12-36PT

University College Cork
Social Work........ MSW 24FT

Coventry University
Community Cohesion Management by Work Based Learning...... MA 12PT
Health Studies........ MSc 15FT 30 - 48PT

University of Cumbria
Equality and Diversity Management .... MA 12FT 48PT
Leadership in Health and Social Care........ MBA 12FT 36PT/PGDip 12FT 36PT/PGCert 12FT 36PT
Management and Leadership in Health and Social Care........ MSc 36PT/PGDip 48PT/PGCert 12PT
Social Work........ MA 24FT/PGDip 24FT
Youth and Community Work........ PGDip 12FT 24PT

De Montfort University
Health and Community Studies .... MA 36DL/PGDip 18DL/PGCert 12DL/MA 12FT
Theory and Practice of Parenting ....PGCert 12PT/PGDip 24PT/MSc 25PT/MSc 36PT
Youth Work and Community Development with Professional Qualification ....MA 24-36DL/PGDip 18DL
Youth and Community Development Studies........MA 24-36DL/PGDip 18DL/PGCert 12DL
Youth work , Health and community Development....... MSc 24PT 36DL

Dublin Institute of Technology
Child, Family and Community Studies........ MA 12FT 24PT

University of Dundee
Augmentative and Alternative Communications .... MSc 12FT
Gender, Culture and Society .... MLitt 12FT
Social Research Methods .... MSc 12FT
Social Research Methods (Population and Welfare) ...... MSc 12FT

Durham University
Managing Community Practice........ MA 12FT 24PT
Managing Youth Work Practice .... MA 12FT 24PT

University of East Anglia
Advanced Professional Practice and Planning..... MA 60PT/PGDip 60PT
Social Science Research Methods: Psychology....MRes 12FT 24PT
Social Science Research Methods: Social Work...MRes 12FT 24PT

University of East London
Approved Mental Health Practice (AMHP) ....PGDip 8FT
Child and Adolescent Primary Mental Health Care Work ....MA 36PT/PGDip 24PT/PGCert 12PT

Edinburgh Napier University
Health & Social Welfare Law........ LLM 12FT 24PT
Managerial Leadership .... MSc 12FT

University of Edinburgh
Advanced Social Work Studies (Mental Health)........PGCert 12PT
Community Education ....MSc 12FT 24-36PT
Health & Social Care - Children & Young People's Mental Health: Ecological Approaches ODL........ PGCert 9DL

National University of Ireland Galway
Community Development .... MA 24FT
Life Course Studies........ PGDip 12PT/MA 24PT

Glasgow Caledonian University
Counselling Skills in Health and Social Care........PGCert 12-24FT
Health and Social Care (Social Work) ....MSc 12-24FT 12-72PT
Mental Health Social Work (Mental Health Officer)........ PGCert 12PT
Social Enterprise .... PGCert 6PT
Social Work........MSc 24FT/PGDip 24FT

University of Glasgow
Advanced Community Development........MSc 24DL
Community Learning & Development........MEd 12FT 24PT/PGDip 9FT 18PT
Drugs and Alcohol Studies.......MSc 12FT 24PT/PGDip 12FT 24PT/PGCert 12PT
Leadership Drugs & Alcohol Setting (PgCert) ..... PGCert 9FT 18PT
Organisational Leadership (Oman)........MSc 24PT/PGDip 18PT/PGCert 12PT
Young People, Social Inclusion & Change .... MSc 12FT 24PT

University of Gloucestershire
Work with Children, Young People, their Families and Carers MSc 12FT 24PT

Goldsmiths, University of London
Advanced Social Work: Practice Education .... MA 24PT
Applied Anthropology and Community and Youth Work MA 12FT 24PT
Global Leadership........ MSc 12FT
Higher Specialist Social Work: Practice Education...... PGDip 24PT
Photography and Urban Cultures .... MA 12FT 24PT
Social Work........ MA 24FT

University of Greenwich
Professional Practice in Health & Social Care........ MA 12FT 24PT 27DL/PGDip 12FT 24PT 27DL

University of Huddersfield
Child Welfare and Safeguarding........ MA 12FT 36PT
Health and Social Care .... MSc 12FT 36PT
Social Work........ MSc 24FT
Youth and Community Work, Professional Studies........MA 24PT

University of Hull
Community and Youth Work .... MA 12FT 24PT
Social Work........ MA 24FT

Keele University
Social Work........ MA 24FT

University of Kent
Advanced Child Protection........ MA 24PT
Intellectual and Developmental Disabilities........MA 12FT 24PT/PGDip 12FT 24PT/PGCert 12FT 24PT
Intellectual and Developmental Disabilities (Distance Learning) MA 12FT 24PT 24DL/PGCert 12FT 24PT/PGDip 12FT 24PT

Kingston University
Professional Education and Training........MA 36PT/PGDip 24PT

Leeds Metropolitan University
Advanced Practice .... MSc 36PT/PGDip 24PT/PGCert 12PT
Biomedical Sciences........MSc 12FT unknownPT
Community Specialist Practitioner - District Nursing...MSc 24PT/PGDip 12FT 24PT
Environmental Health........ MSc 12FT 36PT
Health & Social Care Chaplaincy........ PGCert 12PT
Health Care Studies .... MA 24PT
Mental Health Practice .... MSc 24PT
Mental Health Studies .... PGCert 24PT/PGDip 24PT
Psychotherapy .... MA 48PT
Social Work........ MA 24FT
Youth & Community Development Studies........ MA 12FT 24PT
Youth Work & Community Development (JNC) PGDip 12FT 24PT

University of Leeds
International Social Transformation........ MA 12FT 24PT

University of Leicester
Civil Society .... MA 12FT 24PT
Social Work........ MA 22FT

University of Lincoln
Social Work........ MSc 12FT 24PT

Liverpool Hope University
Social Work........ MA 24FT

Liverpool School of Tropical Medicine
Community Health .... MCommH 12FT/PGDip 8FT/PGCert 4FT

London College UCK
Leadership and Management in the Health and Social Care Sector........ PGDip 12FT 24PT

London Metropolitan University
Organisation and Community Development........ MSc 12FT 24PT
Social Work........ MA 24FT

London School of Economics and Political Science (LSE)
Health, Community and Development .... MSc 12FT 24PT

Manchester Metropolitan University
Advanced Practice and Leadership in Social Work .... MA 24-36PT
Social Work........ MA 24FT/PGDip 12FT
Youth and Community Work (Initial Qualification) .... MA 12FT 24PT

University of Manchester
Health and Social Care...... MRes HSC 12-24DL/PGCert Res 24DL/PGDip Res 12-24DL

University of St Mark and St John
Community and Youth Work........ PGDip 12FT
Counselling, Guidance and Support........ MA 12FT 24PT
Youth and Community Work......PGDip 12FT 24PT/MA 12FT 24PT

National University of Ireland, Maynooth
Applied Social Studies .... MA 12FT 24PT
Community Work .... HDip 12FT

Section sponsored by BPP UNIVERSITY COLLEGE

Business and social sciences
510 POSTGRADUATE DIRECTORY www.prospects.ac.uk/findcourses

Social sciences

Middlesex University
Leading and Developing Public and Community Services, ... PGCert 12PT/AdvDip 12PT
Youth Justice, Community Safety, and Applied Criminology...MA 12FT 24PT

Newman University
Youth and Community Work..........MA 36PT/PGDip 24PT

University of Northampton
Youth and Community Work..........MA 12FT

Northumbria University
Education in Professional Practice..........MSc 36PT/PGDip 24PT/PGCert 12PT
Family Therapy and Systemic Practice....... MA 36PT/PGDip 24PT/PGCert 12PT
Health Care..........Professional Doctorate 48-72PT
Leadership and Management in Integrated Childrens Services... MA 36PT/PGDip 24PT/PGCert 12PT
Midwifery..........Professional Doctorate 48-72PT
Midwifery Studies..........PGDip 18FT
Social Care..........Professional Doctorate 48-72PT
Social Work..........MA 24FT

The Open University
Advancing Professional Practice..........MSc variableDL

Oxford Brookes University
Community Children's Nursing..........PGDip 12FT 24PT
Community Nursing in the Home / District Nursing.......... PGDip 12FT 24PT
Health and Social Care, Student Designed Award.......... MA 12FT 60PT/MSc 12FT 60PT/PGDip 12FT 48PT/PGCert 36PT
Higher Professional Education..... MSc 12FT 12-36PT/PGDip 12FT 24PT/PGCert 12FT 18PT
Management in Health and Social Care .... MSc 12FT 30-36PT/PGCert 12FT 12PT/PGDip 12FT 12-18PT
Social Work..........MA 24FT 36-60PT/PGDip 18FT Up to 60PT

University of Oxford
Evidence-Based Social Intervention.......... MPhil 21FT/MSc 9FT
Sociology..........MPhil 22FT/MSc 9FT

Plymouth University
Social Work..........MA 24FT

University of Portsmouth
Leadership in Health and Wellbeing..........MSc 36PT

New School of Psychotherapy and Counselling
Counselling Psychology and Psychotherapy by Professional Studies DCPsych Counselling Psychology & Psychotherapy 48FT 96PT/PGCert 12FT 24PT/PGDip 24FT 48PT/MSc 24FT 48PT
Existential Psychotherapy & Counselling by Professional Studies DProf by taught 48FT 96PT/MA 24FT 48PT/PGDip 24FT 48PT/PGCert 12FT 24PT
Existential Coaching..........MA 24FT 48PT
Psychotherapy Studies..........MSc 24FT 48PT
Professional Certificate Existential Supervision & Group Leadership..........Professional Certificate 12PT

Robert Gordon University
Social Work..........MSc 27FT/PGDip 24FT

University of Roehampton
Education Leadership and Management..........MA 12FT 24+PT

Royal Holloway, University of London
Leadership & Management in Health..........MSc 12FT 24PT
Social Work..........MSc 24FT

University Campus Suffolk
Community Leadership..........MA 12FT
Health and Social Care Practice...... MA 60PT/PGCert 36PT/PGDip 48PT

University of Salford
Counselling and Psychotherapy Studies (Professional Training)... MSc 36PT/PGDip 24PT
Health and Social Care..........PhD by taught 60PT
Social Work..........MA 24FT 36PT

Sheffield Hallam University
Advanced Professional Development.......MSc VAFT/PGDip VAFT/PGCert VAFT
Anti-Social Behaviour Law and Strategies..........PGCert 12PT
Health and Social Care Leadership..........MSc 36PT/PGDip 24PT/PGCert 12PT
Social Work..........MRes 12FT 36PT

University of Sheffield
Education: Working with Communities..........MA(Ed) 12FT
Professional Practice with Children and Families..........MA 36PT
Social Research..........MA 12FT 24PT
Social Work..........MA 24FT
Sociology..........MA 12FT 24PT

University of South Wales
Care of the Older Person (Distance Learning)..........MSc 24 - 72DL
Community Regeneration..........MSc 12FT 24PT/PGCert 4FT 8PT/PGDip 8FT 16PT
Community and Partnerships..........MSc 12FT 12-60DL
Post-Qualifying Social Work..........BSc 38PT

University of Southampton
Public Health Practice...MSc 12FT 24PT/PGDip 12FT/PGCert 12FT
Social Policy and Social Research..........MSc 12FT 24PT/PGDip 9FT 21PT
Social Work..........MSc 24FT/PGDip 9FT 21PT
Sociology and Social Policy..........MSc 12FT 24PT/PGDip 9FT 21PT
Sociology and Social Research....MSc 12FT 24PT/PGDip 9FT 21PT

University of St Andrews
Adults Support, Protection and Safeguarding..........PGCert 12DL

St George's, University of London
Clinical Practice..........MRes 12FT 24PT

Staffordshire University
Community Practice..........MA 12FT 48PT
Health by Negotiated Learning..........MSc 36PT

University of Stirling
Applied Studies (Child Welfare and Protection)..........MSc 30PT/PGDip 24PT/PGCert 12PT
Applied Studies (Management and Leadership in Social Services)..........MSc 30PT/PGDip 24PT/PGCert 12PT
Professional Learning and Leadership..........MSc 36PT
Social Work Studies..........MSc 22FT

University of Strathclyde
Community Care........MSc 36PT N/ADL/PGDip 24PT/PGCert 12PT
School Leadership and Management (SQH)..........PGDip 12FT
Social Research..........MRes 12FT 24PT
Social Work..........MA 24FT/PGDip 24FT
Social Work Management.......MSc 24PT/PGDip 14PT/PGCert 8PT

University of Sunderland
Health and Social Care Research..........MSc 12FT 24PT

University of Surrey
Health and Social Care..........MSc 12FT 24PT

University of Sussex
Gender and Development..........MA 12FT 24PT
Leadership and Management in Integrated Children's Services... MA 60PT/PGDip 60PT/PGCert 60PT

Swansea University
Social Work..........MSc 48FT

Teesside University
Doctor of Health and Social Care..........DProf by taught 72PT
Leadership in Health and Social Care..........PGCert 12PT
Transformational Leadership in Health and Social Care MSc 36PT

Trinity College Dublin - the University of Dublin
Drug and Alcohol Policy..........MSc 24PT
Social Work (M.S.W.)..........MSW 24FT
Social Work Research..........MPhil 24PT

University of the Highlands and Islands
Professional Development.....MA 36PT/PGCert 12PT/PGDip 24PT
Restorative Practice..........PGCert 12FT 24PT

University of Ulster
Community Youth Work..........MSc 36PT/PGDip 24PT
Education (Primary)..........PGCE 9FT
Health and Wellbeing..........PGDip 12-36PT/MSc 12-36PT

UCL - University College London
Paediatrics and Child Health: Community Child Health.......... MSc 12FT 36-60PT/PGCert 12-24PT/PGDip 9FT 18-45PT
Social Development Practice..........MSc 12FT 24-60PT/PGDip 9FT

University of West London
Advancing Practice..........MSc 24PT
The Management of Complex and Changing Health and Social Care Needs in Clients..........CPPD 4PT

University of the West of England, Bristol
Health and Social Care..........DProf by taught 60PT

University of Winchester
Social Research in Education..........MRes 12FT 24PT

University of Worcester
Dynamics of Domestic Volence...... MA 24PT/PGDip 24PT/PGCert 12PT
MBA in Executive Leadership & Management (Health & Social Care)..........MBA 12FT 36PT
Social Work..........MA 24FT
Social Work and Community Studies..........MA 12FT 24-36PT
Systemic Youth Work..........MA 24PT/PGDip 24PT/PGCert 12PT

York St John University
Professional Health and Social Care Studies..........MSc 12-48PT

Social work and community studies
Research Courses

Anglia Ruskin University
Applied, Social and Health Psychology..........PhD 36FT 36-72PT

Bangor University
Ageing and Cognitive Health..........PhD 36FT 60PT
Ageing and Dementia Studies..........MSc by research 12FT 24PT PhD 36FT 60PT/MPhil 24FT 48PT
Criminology and Criminal Justice..........PhD 36FT 60PT/MPhil 12-24FT 24-36PT

Birkbeck, University of London
Community, Youth and Voluntary Sector....PhD 24FT 36PT/MPhil 24FT 36PT

University of Bristol
Social Sciences..........PhD 48FT

Cardiff University
Health, Wellbeing and Social Care..... PhD 36FT possiblePT/MPhil 12FT possiblePT

University of Central Lancashire
Social Work.......MSc by research 12FT 24PT/MPhil 24FT 36-48PT/PhD 36FT 60PT/MD 36FT 60PT

University of Chester
Health and Social Care..........DProf 24-84PT

University College Cork
Doctor of Social Science..........DSocSci 48FT

University of Dundee
Community Learning & Development..........MPhil 24FT
Social Work..........MPhil 24FT PhD 36FT

University of Gloucestershire
Health..........PhD 30-48FT

Goldsmiths, University of London
Community and Youth Work... PhD 36-48FT 48-72PT/MPhil 24FT 36PT
Social Work..........PhD 36-48FT 48-72PT/MPhil 24FT 36PT

University of Greenwich
Research in Health and Social Care..........MSc by research 24PT

University of Hertfordshire
Centre for Community Research..........PhD 36FT 72PT/MPhil 24FT 48PT/MRes 12FT 24PT
Centre for Research in Primary and Community Care....PhD 36FT 72PT/MPhil 24FT 48PT/MRes 12FT 24PT/DHRes 36FT 72PT

Keele University
Social Work.......... PhD 24-48FT 48-84PT/MPhil 12-24FT 24-36PT

University of Kent
Community Care..........MPhil 24FT 36PT/PhD 36FT 60PT
Intellectual and Developmental Disabilities..........MA by research 12FT 24PT/MPhil 24FT 36PT/PhD 36FT 60PT
Mental Health (Social and Community Care)....MPhil 24FT 36PT/PhD 36FT 60PT
Personal Social Services..........MPhil 24FT 36PT/PhD 36FT 60PT/MA by research 12FT 24PT

Liverpool John Moores University
Professional Doctorate..........MPhil 36FT 84PT

Manchester Metropolitan University
Faculty of Health, Psychology & Social Care .... PhD 24FT 60PT/MPhil 12FT 24PT/MA by research 12FT 24PT/MSc by research 12FT 24PT
Master of Research Education and Society..........MRes 12FT 24PT

The Open University
Children, young people, families, and personal relationships....... PhD 36FT 72PT/MPhil 15FT 24PT
Personal relationships, families, children and young people..PhD 36FT 72PT variableDL/MPhil 15FT 24PT variableDL
Public Leadership and Social Enterprise..........PhD 36FT 72PT variableDL/MPhil 15FT 24PT variableDL
Social divisions, social identities and welfare........ PhD 36FT 72PT variableDL/MPhil 15FT 24PT variableDL
The changing nature of contemporary and historical welfare .... PhD 36FT 72PT variableDL/MPhil 15FT 24PT variableDL

University of Oxford
Social Intervention..........DPhil 48FT

Plymouth University
Parenting and Child Welfare..........MPhil tbcFT

Royal Holloway, University of London
Health and Social Care..........MPhil 24FT

University of Salford
Health and Social Care Research.......PhD/MPhil/MSc by research 12FT

University of Southampton
School of Social Sciences - Gerontology......PhD 36FT 72PT/MPhil 24FT 48PT

St George's, University of London
Community Health Sciences....PhD 36FT 72PT/MPhil 24FT 48PT/MD(Res) 24 minFT 48 minPT

University of Sussex
Education Research Programme...... PhD 24-48FT 36-72PT/MPhil 12-36FT 24-48PT/EdD 48PT
Social Work and Social Care Research Programme... PhD 24-48FT 36-72PT/MPhil 12-36FT 24-48PT

University of the West of England, Bristol
School of Health and Social Care..........PhD TBCFT

Social work studies
Taught Courses

Anglia Ruskin University
Social Work..........MA 24FT

Social sciences

Bangor University
Comparative Criminology and Criminal Justice .... MA 12FT 24PT/PGDip 9FT
Criminology and Criminal Justice .... PhD by taught 36FT 72PT/MPhil 12-24FT 24-36PT/MARes 12FT 24PT
International Social Work MA 12FT 24-30PT/PGDip 9FT 17-21PT/PGCert 5FT 12-21PT
Social Research and Social Policy.......... MA 12FT 24PT/PGDip 9FT
Social Work.................... MA 24FT

University of Bath
Social Work.................... MRes 12FT/PGDipRes 9FT/PGCert 5FT

University of Bedfordshire
Applied Social Work: Children and Families.................... MA 30PT
Applied Social Work: Practice Education.................... MA 30PT
Social Work.................... MSc 24FT

University of Birmingham
Managing Integration for Health and Well-being MSc 12FT 24PT/PGDip 12FT 24PT
Social Work.................... MA 24FT

Bournemouth University
Social Work.................... MA 24FT

University of Bradford
Social Work.................... MA 24FT

University of Brighton
Social Work.................... MSc 24FT/PGDip 24FT/PGCert 24FT

University of Bristol
Social Work.................... MSc 24FT
Social Work Research......MSc 12FT 24-60PT/PGDip 12FT 24-60PT

Brunel University
Enabling the Learning And Assessment of Others .... Portfolio route optional 3PT
Social Work Post-qualifying framework.................... PGCert 18FT
Social Work.................... MA 24FT 24BM

Bucks New University
Social Work.................... MSc 24FT

Canterbury Christ Church University
Social Work.................... MA 24FT 36PT

Cardiff University
Post Qualifying Social Work.................... MSc 36PT
Social Work.................... MA 24FT/PGDip 21PT

University of Central Lancashire
Counselling Casework Supervision.................... PGCert 7PT
Person-Centred Spiritual Care & Accompaniment.... PGCert 12PT
Research Methods in Health and Social Care.............. PGCert 36PT
Researching Social Care.................... PGCert 12FT 24PT
Social Policy.................... MA 15FT 24-60PT/PGDip /FT /PT
Social Work.................... MA 24FT 36PT
Social Work (only available through employment secondment).. PGDip 24FT 36PT
Social Work Practice (Post Qualification Specialist Award, Adults) PGDip 3PT

University of Chester
Health and Social Care - Social Work............ MA 24FT/PGDip 24FT
Nursing Studies (Work Based and Integrative Studies)............. MA 24-72PT/MSc 24-72PT/PGDip 24-60PT/PGCert 12-36PT

University College Cork
Social Work.................... MSW 24FT

Cornwall College
Social Work.................... PGDip 24FT

University of Cumbria
Leadership in Health and Social Care.................... MBA 12FT 36PT/PGDip 12FT 36PT/PGCert 12FT 36PT
Management and Leadership in Health and Social Care........ MSc 36PT/PGDip 48PT/PGCert 12PT
Social Work.................... MA 24FT/PGDip 24FT
Youth and Community Work.................... PGDip 12FT 24PT

De Montfort University
Masters in Research (Social Work) .... MRes 12FT 24PT/PGDip 24-48PT/PGCert 12-24PT

University of Dundee
Social Work .... MSc 22FT

Durham University
Social Research Methods (Social Work).................... MA 12FT 24PT
Social Work.................... MSW 24FT
Social Work Studies.................... MA 12FT

University of East Anglia
Social Work.................... MA 24FT

University of East London
Consolidating Social Work Practice and Enabling Others .... PGCert 4FT 8PT
International Social Welfare and Community Development .... MA 12FT 24PT/PGDip 8FT 16PT/PGCert 4FT 8PT
Social Work MA.................... MA 24FT

Edge Hill University
Practice Education.................... MA 12FT 36PT

University of Edinburgh
Advanced Social Work Studies (Mental Health).........PGCert 12PT
Social Work (MSW).................... MSW 21FT

National University of Ireland Galway
Social Work.................... MA 24FT

Glasgow Caledonian University
Mental Health Social Work (Mental Health Officer) .... PGCert 12PT
Social Work.................... MSc 24FT/PGDip 24FT

University of Glasgow
Young People, Social Inclusion & Change .... MSc 12FT 24PT

Goldsmiths, University of London
Social Work.................... MA 24FT

University of Greenwich
Higher Specialist Social Work PGDip / Advanced Social Work MA.................... PGDip 24PT/MA 12PT
Specialist Social Work (Children and Families / Working with Adults).................... GradDip 24PT

University of Hertfordshire
Social Work.................... MSc 24FT

University of Huddersfield
Child Welfare and Safeguarding.................... MA 12FT 36PT
Health & Social Care (Approved Mental Health Practice)....... MSc 36PT
Social Work.................... MSc 24FT

University of Hull
Social Work.................... MA 24FT

Keele University
Social Work.................... MA 24FT

University of Kent
Advanced Child Protection.................... MA 24PT

Kingston University
Social Work.................... MSW 24FT/PGDip 24FT

Lancaster University
Social Work.................... MA 24FT/PGDip 21FT

Leeds Metropolitan University
Community Specialist Practitioner - Practice Nursing..MSc 24PT/PGDip 24PT
Social Work.................... MA 24FT

University of Leicester
Social Work.................... MA 22FT

University of Lincoln
Social Work.................... MSc 12FT 24PT

Liverpool Hope University
Social Work.................... MA 24FT

London Metropolitan University
Social Work.................... MA 24FT

London South Bank University
Social Work.................... MSc 24FT

University of Manchester
Social Work.................... MA 24FT

Middlesex University
Comparative Drug and Alcohol studies.................... MA 24PT
Social Work.................... MA 24FT

Newman University
Youth and Community Work.................... MA 36PT/PGDip 24PT

Northumbria University
Social Care.................... Professional Doctorate 48-72PT
Social Work.................... MA 24FT

Nottingham Trent University
Professional Practice.................... MA 1.5PT 3DL

University of Nottingham
Health and Social Care..........MSc 12FT 24-48PT/PGCert 24-48PT/PGDip 12FT 24-48PT
Research Methods (Social Work).................... MA 12FT 24PT
Social Work....... MA 22FT/PGDip 22FT MSW 12FT 24PT/MSW Adv 32PT

The Open University
Advancing Professional Practice.................... MSc variableDL

Oxford Brookes University
Social Work .... MA 24FT 36-60PT/PGDip 18FT Up to 60PT

University of Oxford
Comparative Social Policy.................... MSc 12FT/MPhil 24FT
Sociology.................... MPhil 22FT/MSc 9FT

University of Portsmouth
Social Work.................... MSc 24FT

Robert Gordon University
Social Work.................... MSc 27FT/PGDip 24FT

Royal Holloway, University of London
Social Work.................... MSc 24FT

University of Salford
Professional Doctorate (Health and Social Care) ... PhD by taught 60PT
Social Work.................... MA 24FT 36PT

Sheffield Hallam University
Advanced Professional Development .... MSc VAFT/PGDip VAFT/PGCert VAFT
Social Work.................... MRes 12FT 36PT

University of Sheffield
Professional Practice with Children and Families .... MA 36PT
Social Research.................... MA 12FT 24PT
Social Work.................... MA 24FT
Sociology .... MA 12FT 24PT
Work Psychology .... MSc 12FT

University of Southampton
Health and Rehabilitation........MSc 12FT 24PT/PGDip 12FT 24PT/PGCert 8FT 16PT
Leadership and Management Health and Social Care... MSc 12FT 48PT
Professional Studies.................. MSc 30PT/PGCert 12PT/PG Cert in Management and Leadership 12-24 PTDL
Social Policy and Social Research MSc 12FT 24PT/PGDip 9FT 21PT
Social Work.................... MSc 24FT/PGDip 9FT 21PT
Sociology and Social Policy .... MSc 12FT 24PT/PGDip 9FT 21PT
Sociology and Social Research .... MSc 12FT 24PT/PGDip 9FT 21PT

University of Stirling
Applied Social Research .... MSc 12FT 30PT/PGDip 9FT 18PT
Psychology of Faces.................... MSc 12FT 24PT/PGDip 9FT 18PT
Social Work Studies.................... MSc 22FT

University of Strathclyde
Social Research.................... MRes 12FT 24PT

University of Sussex
Social Work.................... MA 24FT

Swansea University
Social Work.................... MSc 48FT

Trinity College Dublin - the University of Dublin
Social Work (M.S.W.) .... MSW 24FT
Social Work Research.................... MPhil 24PT

University of Ulster
Social Work - Professional Development . MSc 24-60PT 24-60DL/PGDip 16-24PT 16-24DL

University of Warwick
Social Work.................... MA 24FT

University of the West of England, Bristol
Social Work Studies (Specialist Social Work with Adults) GradDip 60PT

University of Westminster
Leading and Managing Health and Social Care (Advanced Professional Practice) .... MSc 24PT
Leading and Managing Health and Social Care (Advanced Professional Practice) .... PGDip 12PT
Leading and Managing Health and Social Care (Advanced Professional Practice).................... PGCert 12PT

University of Wolverhampton
Social Work.................... MA 24FT

University of Worcester
Social Work and Community Studies.................. MA 12FT 24-36PT

University of York
Social Work.................... MRes 12FT 24PT MA 24FT

Social work studies
Research Courses

Bangor University
Criminology and Criminal Justice .... PhD 36FT 60PT/MPhil 12-24FT 24-36PT

Bucks New University
Social Work.................... Professional Doctorate 48-84PT

Cardiff University
Social Work (Professional Doctorate).................... DSW 60-84PT

University College Cork
Doctor of Social Science.................... DSocSci 48FT

University of East Anglia
Psychology.................... PhD 36FT 72PT/MPhil 24FT 48PT
Social Work.................... PhD 36FT 72PT/MPhil 24FT 48PT

University of Edinburgh
Social Work..... MPhil 24FT 48PT/PhD 36FT 72PT/MSc by research 12FT 24PT

University of Glasgow
Social Work.................... PhD 36FT/MLitt by research 12FT

Goldsmiths, University of London
Social Work.................... PhD 36-48FT 48-72PT/MPhil 24FT 36PT

University of Greenwich
Research in Health and Social Care.............. MSc by research 24PT

University of Hull
Social Work.................... PhD 36FT 60PT/MPhil 24FT 36PT

University of Kent
Personal Social Services............ MPhil 24FT 36PT/PhD 36FT 60PT/MA by research 12FT 24PT

Section sponsored by BPP UNIVERSITY COLLEGE

Business and social sciences

512 POSTGRADUATE DIRECTORY www.prospects.ac.uk/findcourses

Social sciences

Social Work........ PhD 36FT 60PT/MPhil 24FT 36PT

University of Leicester
Social Work........ PhD 24FT 36PT/MPhil 24FT 36PT

University of Manchester
Social Work... MPhil 12FT 24PT 12-24DL/PhD 36FT 72PT 36-72DL

University of Nottingham
Social Work........ PhD 36-48FT/MPhil 24FT

The Open University
Health, Social Work and Social Care.. PhD 36FT 72PT variableDL/MPhil 15FT 24PT variableDL
Social divisions, social identities and welfare........ PhD 36FT 72PT variableDL/MPhil 15FT 24PT variableDL

University of Oxford
Social Intervention........ DPhil 48FT

Plymouth University
Social Exclusion, Diversity and Disadvantage........ MPhil tbcFT

University of Portsmouth
Health Sciences and Social Work........ MPhil 24FT 48PT/PhD 36FT 72PT/MD 24FT 48PT
Professional Doctorate in Social Work........ DSW 48PT

Queen's University Belfast
Sociology, Social Policy and Social Work...... PhD 36FT 72PT/MPhil 24FT 48PT

Sheffield Hallam University
Division of Nursing and Social Work........ PhD/MPhil

University of Southampton
School of Social Sciences - Social Work Studies.... PhD 48FT 84PT/MPhil 24FT 36PT

University of York
Social Policy and Social Work .... PhD 36FT 72PT/MPhil 24FT 48PT

Sociology
Taught Courses

University of Aberdeen
Cultural Sociology........ MSc 12FT 24PT/PGDip 9FT 18PT
Sociology .... MSc 12FT 24PT/PGDip 9FT 18PT/PGCert 6FT 12PT
Sociology of Peace Processes........ MSc 12FT 24PT
Transitional Justice and Reconciliation........ MSc 12FT 24PT/PGDip 9FT 18PT

Anglia Ruskin University
Sociology .... MA 12FT 24PT

Aston University
Social Research and Social Change........ MA 12FT 24 - 36PT

Bangor University
Comparative Criminology and Criminal Justice.... MA 12FT 24PT/PGDip 9FT
Criminology and Criminal Justice .... PhD by taught 36FT 72PT/MPhil 12-24FT 24-36PT/MARes 12FT 24PT
Criminology and Sociology........ MA 12FT 21-30PT/PGDip 9FT 17-21PT/PGCert 5FT 12-21PT
Policy Research and Evaluation........ MA 12FT 21-30PT/PGDip 9FT 17-21PT/PGCert 5FT 12-21PT
Social Policy, Sociology........ PhD by taught 36FT 60PT/MPhil 12-24FT 24-36PT
Social Research and Social Policy........ MA 12FT 24PT/PGDip 9FT

University of Bath
Business and Community .... MSc 12FT 24-60PT/PGDip 9FT 21PT/PGCert 4FT
Sociology .... MRes 12FT 24-60PT/PGDip 9FT 21PT/PGCert 4FT 16PT

Birkbeck, University of London
International Migration and Intergration........ GradCert 12PT
Social Research.... MSc 12FT 24PT/PGDip 12FT 24PT/PGCert 12FT 24PT

University of Birmingham
Social Research (Sociology)........ MA 12FT
Social and Political Theory .... MA 12FT

University of Brighton
Sport and Media..... MSc 12FT 24-36PT/PGDip 12FT 24PT/PGCert 12FT 24PT
Sport and Society ... MSc 12FT 24-36PT/PGDip 12FT 24PT/PGCert 12FT 24PT

University of Bristol
Contemporary Identities .... MSc 12FT 24PT/Diploma 12FT 24PT
Social Science Research Methods (Sociology)........ MSc 12FT 24PT
Social and Cultural Theory .... MSc 12FT 24PT
Socio-Legal Studies .... MSc 12FT 24PT
Sociology .... MSc 12FT 24PT

Brunel University
Medicine, Bioscience and Society........ MSc 12FT 30PT
Science, Technology and Contemporary Society... MSc 12FT 30PT
Social and Cultural Research .... MSc 12FT 30PT
Sociology of Health and Illness........ MSc 12FT 30PT

University of Cambridge
Applied Criminology, Penology and Management........ MSt 24PT
Criminological Research .... MPhil 9FT
Criminology .... MPhil 9FT
Modern Society and Global Transformations .... MPhil 9FT
Social Anthropological Research .... MPhil 11FT
Social Anthropology .... PhD by taught 11FT

University of Central Lancashire
Advancing Equality, Diversity and Inclusion .... MA 12FT 36PT/PGDip 12FT 36PT/PGCert 12FT 24PT
Community Leadership........ MA 12FT 36PT/PGDip 12FT 24PT
Counter Terrorism........ MSc 12FT
Equality and Community Leadership........ PGCert 24PT
Global Security and Justice .... MA 12FT
Religion, Culture & Society . MA 12FT 24-36PT/PGDip 12FT 24PT/PGCert 12FT 12-24PT
Social Policy........ MA 15FT 24-60PT/PGDip /FT /PT
Social Work........ MA 24FT 36PT
Social Work (only available through employment secondment).. PGDip 24FT 36PT
Social Work Practice (Post Qualification Specialist Award, Adults)........ PGDip 3PT

University of Chester
Sociology of Sport and Exercise........ MSc 12FT 24PT/PGDip 12FT 24PT/PGCert 12FT 12-24PT

City University London
Social Research Methods........ MSc 12FT 24PT
Sociology .... MA 12FT 24PT

University College Cork
Arts (Sociology)........ HDip 9FT
Sociology........ MA 12FT
Sociology of Development and Globalisation .... MA 12FT

University of Cumbria
Equality and Diversity Management .... MA 12FT 48PT

University of Dundee
Social Research Methods .... MSc 12FT

Durham University
Social Research Methods (Sociology)........ MA 12FT 24PT

University of East Anglia
Gender Analysis in International Development..... MA 12FT 24PT
Media, Culture and Society........ MA 12FT 24PT
Social and Political Theory .... MA 12FT 24PT

University of Edinburgh
Global Social Change........ MSc 12FT 24PT
Social Research........ MSc 12FT 24PT/PGDip 9FT 21PT
Socio-Cultural Studies........

University of Essex
Advertising, Marketing and the Media........ MA 12FT 24PT
Criminology and Socio-Legal Research........ MA 12FT 24PT
Longitudinal Social Research........ MA 12FT 24PT
Organised Crime, Terrorism and Security........ MSc 12FT 24PT
Sociological Research .... MA 12FT 24PT
Sociology .... MA 12FT 24PT/PGCert 9FT
Sociology and Management .... MA 12FT 24PT
Survey Methods for Social Research........ MSc 12FT 24PT

University of Exeter
Ethics, Religion and Society .... MA 12FT 24PT
History and Philosophy of Biology........ MA 12FT 24PT
Philosophy and Sociology of Science........ MA 12FT 24PT
Science and Technology Studies........ MRes 12FT 24PT
Social and Political Philospohy........ MA 12FT 24PT
Socio-Legal Research .... MRes 12FT 24PT
Theology........ MA 12FT 24PT

University of Glasgow
Drugs and Alcohol Studies....... MSc 12FT 24PT/PGDip 12FT 24PT/PGCert 12PT
Global Health .... MSc 12FT 24PT
Sociology .... MSc 12FT 24PT
Sociology and Research Methods........ MRes 12FT 24PT

University of Gloucestershire
Educational Leadership........ MEd 24PT/PGDip 20PT/PGCert 8PT

Goldsmiths, University of London
Critical & Creative Analysis........ MA 12FT 24PT
Culture Industry........ MA 12FT 24PT
Digital Sociology........ MA 12FT 24PT/MSc 12FT 24PT
Social Anthropology .... MA 12FT 24PT
Social Entrepreneurship........ MA 12FT 24PT/PGDip 6FT 12PT
Social Research........ MA 12FT 24PT
Sociocultural Linguistics........ MA 12FT 24PT
Visual Sociology........ MA 12FT 24PT

Institute of Education
Social Justice and Education........ MA 12FT 24-48PT
Sociology of Education........ MA 12FT 24-48PT

University of Kent
Civil Society, NGO and Nonprofit Studies ... PGDip 12FT 24PT/MA 12FT 24PT
Medical Humanities .... MA 12FT 24PT
Methods of Social Research........ MA 12FT 24PT
Political Sociology........ MA 12FT 24PT
Security and Terrorism .... MA 12FT 24PT/PGDip 12FT 24PT
Social Anthropology .... MA 12FT 24PT
Social and Public Policy (Distance Learning, Medway) . MA 24DL/PGDip 24DL
Social and Public Policy: Commissioning (Distance Learning, Medway)........ MA 24DL/PGDip 24DL
Social and Public Policy: Criminal Justice (Distance Learning, Medway)........ MA 24DL/PGDip 24DL
Social and Public Policy: Urban Regeneration (Distance Learning, Medway)........ MA 24DL/PGDip 24DL
Sociology .... MA 12FT 24PT

King's College London
Health & Society........ MSc 12FT 24-48PT

Lancaster University
Environment, Culture and Society........ MA 12FT 24PT
Sociological Research .... MA 12FT 24PT
Sociology .... MA 12FT 24PT/MPhil 24FT/PhD by taught 24FT

University of Leeds
MA in Activism and Social Change ..... MA 12FT 24PT/PGDip 12FT 24PT/PGCert 12FT 24PT
Social Research (ESRC recognised)........ MA 12FT 24PT
Social and Political Thought .... MA 12FT 24PT
Social and Public Policy .... MA 12FT 24PT

University of Leicester
Civil Society........ MA 12FT 24PT
Contemporary Sociology .... MA 12FT 24PT
New Media and Society (by Distance Learning).. MA 24FT/PGDip 20FT

University of Limerick
History of the Family........ MA 12FT 24PT 12/24DL
Sociology (Applied Research) .... MA 12FT 24PT

University of Liverpool
Research Methodology (Sociology and Social Policy) ...... MA 12FT 24PT

London School of Economics and Political Science (LSE)
Culture and Society........ MSc 12FT 24PT
Diploma in Sociology........ Diploma 12FT 24PT
Political Sociology........ MSc 12FT 24PT
Social Research Methods........ MSc 12FT 24PT
Sociology .... MSc 12FT 24PT

London South Bank University
Social Research Methods........ MSc 12FT 24PT

Loughborough University
Sociology of Sport .... MSc 12FT

Manchester Metropolitan University
Applied Social Studies (Sociology) ...... MA 12FT 24PT/PGDip 12PT
Sociology and Global Change .... MA 12FT 24PT

University of Manchester
Social Change........ MA 12FT/PGDip 9FT
Sociological Research .... MSc 12FT 24PT
Sociology .... MA 12FT 24PT/PGDip 9FT 21PT

Newcastle University
Sociology .... MA 12FT 24PT
Sociology and Social Research .... MA 12FT 24PT

Nottingham Trent University
Sociology .... MA 12FT 24PT

University of Nottingham
International Social Policy........ MA 12FT 24-48PT
Research Methods Sociology........ MA 12FT 24PT

The Open University
Integrated Practice in Childhood and Youth.. PGCert 12DL/PGDip variableDL

University of Oxford
Migration Studies........ MSc 9FT
Nature, Society and Environmental Policy........ MSc 12FT
Sociology .... MPhil 22FT/MSc 9FT

Queen Margaret University, Edinburgh
Social Justice, Development and Health .... MSc 12FT 60PT/PGDip 8FT/PGCert 4FT

Queen's University Belfast
Interprofessional Health and Social Care Management........ MSc 24-36PT
Social Research Methods (by research) MRes 12FT 24PT/Diploma 12FT 24PT
Sociology .... MA 12FT 24PT/PGDip 24PT

University of Reading
Law and Society (M Res) .... M(Res) 12FT 24PT

University of Roehampton
Human Rights .... MA 18FT 24+PT
Human Rights and International Relations........ MA 18FT 24+PT
Human Rights .... PGCert 10FT 12+PT PGDip 12FT 24+PT

Royal Holloway, University of London
Medical Sociology .... MSc 12FT 24PT

University of Salford
Intelligence and Security Studies........ MA 12FT 36PT/PGDip 9FT 20PT
Literature, Culture and Modernity........ MA 12FT 36PT/PGDip 8FT 24PT
Media Psychology.... MSc 12FT 36PT/PGDip 8FT 24PT/PGCert 4FT 9PT
Social Media........ MA 9FT/PGDip 9FT

Section sponsored by
BPP UNIVERSITY COLLEGE

Business and social sciences
www.prospects.ac.uk/findcourses POSTGRADUATE DIRECTORY 513

Social sciences

Social Work.......... MA 24FT 36PT

School of Oriental and African Studies - SOAS
Social Anthropology .... MA 12FT 24-36PT
Social Anthropology of Development.......... MA 12FT 24-36PT
State, Society and Development .... MSc 12FT 24PT

Sheffield Hallam University
Sociology, Planning and Policy.......... MRes variousFT variousPT

University of Sheffield
European Gender Studies.......... MA 12FT 24PT
Global Justice .... MA 12FT 24PT
Global Politics and Law.......... MA 12FT 24PT
Global Politics and Law (Doshisha Pathway).......... MA 24FT
Global and International Social Policy .... MA 12FT 24PT
Globalisation and Development .... MA 12FT 24PT
Social Research.......... MA 12FT 24PT
Social Work.......... MA 24FT
Sociology .... MA 12FT 24PT

University of Southampton
Citizenship and Democracy.......... MSc 12FT 24PT/PGDip 9FT 21PT
Citizenship and Democracy (Research).......... MSc 12FT 24PT/PGDip 9FT 21PT
Global Politics.......... MSc 12FT 24PT/PGDip 9FT 21PT
Global Politics (Research) .... MSc 12FT 24PT/PGDip 9FT 21PT
Global Security.......... MSc 12FT 24PT/PGDip 9FT 21PT
Social Policy and Social Research MSc 12FT 24PT/PGDip 9FT 21PT
Social Work.......... MSc 24FT/PGDip 9FT 21PT
Sociology and Social Policy .... MSc 12FT 24PT/PGDip 9FT 21PT
Sociology and Social Research .... MSc 12FT 24PT/PGDip 9FT 21PT

University of Stirling
Applied Social Research .... MSc 12FT 30PT/PGDip 9FT 18PT
Applied Social Research (Criminology) .... MSc 12FT 30PT/PGDip 9FT 18PT
Applied Social Research .... MRes 12FT 30PT
Applied Social Research Doctorate .... PhD by taught 48-96PT
Media Research.......... MRes 12FT/PGDip 9FT
Social Work Studies.......... MSc 22FT

University of Strathclyde
Literature, Culture and Place... MLitt 12FT 24PT/PGDip 9FT 21PT/PGCert 4FT 9PT
Social Research.......... MRes 12FT 24PT

University of Sussex
Anthropology of Development and Social Transformation...... MA 12FT 24PT
Participation, Power and Social Change.......... MA 12FT 24PT
Social and Political Thought .... MA 12FT 24PT

Teesside University
Criminology (Contemporary Drug Issues).......... MSc 12FT 24PT

Trinity College Dublin - the University of Dublin
Applied Social Research .... MSc 12FT

University of Ulster
Social Research Skills with Specialisms .. MSc 24DL/PGDip 16DL/PGCert 8DL

UCL - University College London
Identity, Culture and Power.......... MA 12FT 24PT
Social Development Practice.......... MSc 12FT 24-60PT/PGDip 9FT

University of Warwick
Applied Social Research with Specialism in Islam in Contemporary Societies.......... MA 12FT/MA 24PT
Comparative Labour Studies .... MA 12FT 24PT/PGDip 9FT 24PT
Philosophy and Social Theory.......... MA 12FT 24PT
Social Research.......... MA 12FT 24PT/PGDip 9FT 24PT
Social Research with Specialism in Comparative Labour Studies.......... MA 12FT 24PT
Social Research with Specialism in Interdisciplinary Gender Studies.......... MA 12FT 24PT/PGDip 9FT 24PT
Social Research with Specialism in Race and Ethnic Studies ... MA 12FT 24PT/PGDip 9FT 24PT
Social Research with Specialism in Social Policy ... MA 12FT 24PT/PGDip 9FT 24PT
Social Research with Specialism in Sport, Politics and Society MA 12FT 24PT/PGDip 9FT 24PT
Social Research with Specialism in the Sociology of Education.... MA 12FT 24PT/PGDip 9FT 24PT
Social Research with Specialism in the Sociology of Health..... MA 12FT 24PT/PGDip 9FT 24PT
Social and Political Thought .... MA 12FT 24PT/PGDip 9FT 24PT
Sociology .... MA 12FT 24PT/PGDip 12FT 24PT
Sociology of Education.......... MA 12FT 24PT/PGDip 9FT 24PT

University of York
Eighteenth Century Studies: Representations and Contexts 1750-1850.......... MA 12FT 24PT
Social Media and Interactive Technologies.......... MSc 12FT
Social Research.......... MA 12FT 24PT

Sociology
Research Courses

Anglia Ruskin University
Social Sciences (Sociology, Criminology)..... PhD 36FT 72PT/MPhil 24FT 48PT

Bangor University
Criminology and Criminal Justice PhD 36FT 60PT/MPhil 12-24FT 24-36PT
Social Policy.......... PhD 36FT 60PT/MPhil 12-24FT 24-36PT
Sociology .... PhD 36FT 60PT/MPhil 12-24FT 24-36PT

Birkbeck, University of London
Politics .... PhD 24FT 36PT/MPhil 24FT 36PT

University of Birmingham
Sociology .... PhD 36FT 72PT/MPhil 24FT 48PT

University of Bristol
Social Science (Policy Studies Doctorate).......... DSocSci 36FT 96PT

Brunel University
Doctoral Programme in Sociology & Communications........ MPhil 12FT 24PT/MRes 12FT 24PT/PhD 36FT 60PT

University of Cambridge
Social and Political Sciences .... PhD 36FT 60PT

Canterbury Christ Church University
Sociology .... PhD 36FT 60PT/MPhil 24FT 48PT

City University London
Department of Sociology.......... PhD/MPhil

University of Cumbria
Sports Science; Sports History/Sociology; Outdoor Studies .... MPhil 36FT 60PT 60DL/PhD 48FT 72PT 72DL

University of Dundee
Economics .... MPhil 24FT MSc by research 12FT
Social Work .... MPhil 24FT

University of Edinburgh
Socio-Cultural Studies .... MSc by research 12FT 36PT/PGDip by research 9FT 36PT
SociologyPhD 36FT 72PT/MPhil 24FT 48PT/MSc by research 12FT 24PT
Sociology and Anthropology of Health and Illness (Masters by research).......... MSc by research 12FT 24PT

University of Essex
Applied Social and Economic Research........ PhD 36FT 72PT/MPhil 24FT 48PT
Criminology ..... PhD 36FT 72PT/MPhil 24FT 48PT/MA by research 12FT 24PT
Criminology and Socio-Legal Research........ PhD 36FT 72PT/MPhil 24FT 48PT/MA by research 12FT 24PT
Health Research.......... PhD 36FT 72PT/MPhil 24FT 48PT
Sociological Research ..... PhD 36FT 72PT/MPhil 24FT 48PT/MA by research 12FT 24PT
Sociology .... PhD 36FT 72PT/MPhil 24FT 48PT/MA by research 12FT 24PT
Survey Methodology .... PhD 36FT 72PT/MPhil 24FT 48PT

University of Exeter
Philosophy........ MA by research 12FT 24PT/MPhil 24FT 48PT/PhD 48FT 72PT
Sociology .... PhD 36FT 72PT 72DL/MPhil 24FT 48PT 48DL

University of Glasgow
Sociology, Anthropology and Applied Social Sciences.. PhD 36FT/MLitt by research 12FT

Goldsmiths, University of London
Sociology .... MRes 36FT PhD 36-48FT 48-72PT/MPhil 24FT 36PT
Visual Sociology.......... MPhil 24FT 36PT/PhD 36-48FT 48-72PT

University of Hull
Sociology and Anthropology..... PhD 36FT 60PT/MPhil 24FT 36PT

Institute for the Study of the Americas, School of Advanced Study, University of London
Political Sociology.......... PhD 36FT/MPhil 12FT
Social Policy.......... PhD 36FT/MPhil 12FT

University of Kent
Ethnobiology .... MSc by research 12FT 24PT/PhD 36FT 60PT
Politcal and Social Thought .... MA by research 12FT 24PT/MPhil 24FT 36PT/PhD 36FT 60PT
Social Policy...... PhD 36FT 60PT/MPhil 24FT 36PT/MA by research 12FT 24PT
Social Work.......... PhD 36FT 60PT/MPhil 24FT 36PT
Sociology PhD 36FT 60PT/MPhil 24FT 36PT/MA by research 12FT 24PT

King's College London
Politics Research .... MPhil 24FT 36PT/PhD 36FT 48-72PT

Kingston University
Sociology .... PhD 48FT 72PT/MPhil 24FT 48PT/MA by research 12FT 24PT

Lancaster University
Applied Social Science.......... PhD 36FT 48PT/MPhil 24FT 36PT
Science Studies .... PhD 36FT 48-60PT/MPhil 24FT 36PT
Sociology .... PhD 36FT 48PT/MPhil 24FT 36PT

University of Leeds
Sociology and Social Policy Research Opportunities... PhD 36+FT/MPhil 24FT/MA by research 12FT

University of Leicester
Department of Sociology .... PhD 36FT 72PT 72DL

University of Liverpool
Social Research.......... MRes 12FT 24PT
Sociology and Social Policy .... PhD 24-48FT 48-84PT/MPhil 12-48FT 48-72PT

London Metropolitan University
Dept of Applied Social Studies.... PhD Max 60FT Max 96PT/MPhil Max 36FT Max 54PT

London School of Economics and Political Science (LSE)
Social Psychology.......... PhD 36-48FT/MPhil 36-48FT
Sociology .... PhD 36-48FT/MPhil 36-48FT

Loughborough University
Sociology .... PhD 36FT 60PT/MPhil 24FT 36PT/MRes 12FT 24PT

Manchester Metropolitan University
Department of Sociology.......... PhD 24-48FT 42-84PT 42-84DL/MPhil 18-36FT 36-72PT 36-72DL/MA by research 12-24FT 24-42PT 24-42DL
Education and Society.......... MRes 12FT

University of Manchester
Social Statistics .... PhD 36FT 48-72PT
Sociology .... PhD 36FT 72PT

Middlesex University
Sociology and Criminology........ PhD 36FT 60PT/MPhil 24FT 48PT

Newcastle University
Sociology .... PhD 36FT 72PT/MPhil 12FT 24PT

University of Northampton
Sociology .... PhD/MPhil

University of Nottingham
Sociology and Social Policy .... PhD 36FT 72PT
Sociology and Social Policy Research AreasPhD 24-36FT 48-72PT/MPhil 12-24FT 36-48PT

The Open University
Children, young people, families, and personal relationships....... PhD 36FT 72PT/MPhil 15FT 24PT
Citizenship and Governance...... PhD 36FT 72PT variableDL/MPhil 15FT 24PT variableDL
Culture, Media and the Social... PhD 36FT 72PT variableDL/MPhil 15FT 24PT variableDL
Globalisation, Transnationalism and Social Welfare....... PhD 36FT 72PT variableDL/MPhil 15FT 24PT variableDL
IdentitiesPhD 36FT 72PT variableDL/MPhil 15FT 24PT variableDL
Personal life and intimacies....... PhD 36FT 72PT variableDL/MPhil 15FT 24PT variableDL
Political ideas, policies and actions.... PhD 36FT 72PT variableDL/MPhil 15FT 24PT variableDL
Social divisions, social identities and welfare........ PhD 36FT 72PT variableDL/MPhil 15FT 24PT variableDL
Sociology .... PhD 36FT 72PT variableDL/MPhil 15FT 24PT variableDL
The social life of methods .... PhD 36FT 72PT variableDL/MPhil 15FT 24PT variableDL

University of Oxford
Institute of Social and Cultural Anthropology.......... DPhil 48FT
Sociology .... DPhil 48FT

Plymouth University
Social Exclusion, Diversity and Disadvantage.......... MPhil tbcFT

University of Salford
Social and Cultural Theory .... PhD/MPhil

School of Oriental and African Studies - SOAS
Social Anthropology .... PhD 36FT/MPhil 24FT

University of Sheffield
Sociological Studies .... PhD 36FT 72PT/MPhil 24FT 48PT

University of Southampton
Languages, Culture and Society.......... PhD 36FT 72PT/MPhil 24FT 48PT
School of Social Sciences - SociologyPhD 24-48FT 36-84PT/MPhil 12-48FT 24-84PT

St Mary's University College, Twickenham
Sociology/Irish Studies .... PhD 36FT 72PT/MPhil 24FT 48PT

University of Surrey
Sociology .... PhD 36FT 48PT 48DL/MPhil 24FT 36PT 36DL/Integrated PhD 12FT

University of Sussex
Social and Political Thought .... DPhil 24-48FT 36-72PT/MPhil 12-36FT 24-48PT
Sociology Research Programme .... PhD 24-48FT 36-72PT/MPhil 12-36FT 24-48PT

Teesside University
Sociology ..... PhD 24FT 36PT/MPhil 18FT 30PT/MProf by research 18FT 30PT/DProf 24FT 36PT

University of Warwick
Sociology PhD 36FT 60PT/MPhil 24FT 36PT/MA by research 12FT 24PT

University of Wolverhampton
Sociology and Applied Social Studies.......... PhD/MPhil

Social sciences

University of York
Language and Communication ....PhD 36FT 72PT/ MPhil 24FT 48PT
Sociology .... PhD 36FT 72PT/MPhil 24FT 48PT
Sociology by Research ....MA by research 12FT 24PT

Spanish studies
Taught Courses

University of Aberdeen
Latin American Studies .... MLitt 12FT
Modern Thought ....MLitt 12FT 24PT

Birkbeck, University of London
World Cinema... MA 12FT 24PT

University College Cork
Arts (Hispanic Studies).................................HDip 9FT 18PT
Hispanic Studies .... MA 12FT 24PT

National University of Ireland Galway
Spanish...MA 12FT

University of Kent
Hispanic and Comparative Literature .... MA 12FT 24PT
Modern Hispanic Studies ....MA 24PT

King's College London
Spanish, Portuguese & Latin American Studies ..... MA 12FT 24PT

Royal Holloway, University of London
MA by Research (Hispanic Studies)........................... MA 12FT 24PT

University of Sheffield
Catalan Studies.. MA 12FT 24PT
Hispanic Studies .... MA 12FT 24PT
Latin American Studies .... MA 12FT 24PT

University of St Andrews
Spanish and Latin American Studies ..... MLitt 12FT 24PT/ PGDip 9FT 24PT

UCL - University College London
Hispanic Studies .... MA 12FT 24PT

Spanish studies
Research Courses

University of Aberdeen
Hispanic Studies .... PhD 36FT 60PT/MLitt by research 12FT 24PT/ MPhil 24FT

Aberystwyth University
Spanish .... PhD 36FT 60PT

Bangor University
Spanish................................MPhil 12FT/PhD 36FT

University of Birmingham
Hispanic Studies .... PhD 36FT 72PT/MPhil 12FT 24PT

University of Bristol
Hispanic, Portuguese and Latin American Studies..........PhD 36FT 72PT/MLitt by research 24FT 48PT/MPhil 12FT 24PT

University of Cambridge
Spanish... PhD 36FT 60PT

University of Edinburgh
Hispanic Studies.........PhD 36FT 72PT/MPhil 24FT 48PT/MSc by research 12FT 24PT

University of Exeter
Hispanic Studies .... PhD 48FT 84PT/MPhil 36FT 60PT

University of Glasgow
Hispanic Studies ....PhD 36FT/MPhil 12FT/MLitt by research 12FT

University of Kent
Hispanic Studies ....PhD 36FT 60PT/MPhil 24FT 36PT/MA by research 12FT 24PT

King's College London
Spanish, Portuguese & Latin American Studies Research ....PhD 36FT 84-96PT/MPhil 24FT 36PT

University of Leeds
Department of Spanish and Portuguese PhD 36+FT/MPhil 24FT/ MA by research 12+FT

University of Liverpool
Hispanic Studies .. PhD 24-72FT 48-84PT/MPhil 12-48FT 24-72PT

University of Manchester
Latin American Cultural Studies.........................PhD 36FT 72PT/ MPhil 12FT 24PT
Spanish Studies......................... PhD 36FT 72PT/MPhil 12FT 24PT

Nottingham Trent University
Spanish................................ PhD 48FT 96PT/MPhil 36FT 72PT

University of Nottingham
Hispanic & Latin American Studies .... MA by research 12FT
Hispanic and Latin American Studies ....PhD 36-48FT/MPhil 36-48FT

Queen Mary, University of London
Hispanic Studies ....PhD 36FT 48PT/MPhil

Queen's University Belfast
Spanish and Portuguese Studies...............................PhD 36FT 72PT/ MPhil 24FT 48PT

Royal Holloway, University of London
Hispanic Studies .... PhD 24FT/MPhil 12FT

University of St Andrews
Spanish and Latin American Studies...........PhD 36FT 72PT/MPhil 12-24FT 48PT

Swansea University
Hispanic Studies .... PhD 36FT 72PT/MPhil 24FT 48PT

UCL - University College London
Spanish and Latin American Studies....................... PhD 36FT 60PT

Viking studies
Taught Courses

University of Cambridge
Anglo-Saxon, Norse and Celtic..............................MPhil 9FT

University of Edinburgh
Viking Studies..MSc 12FT 24PT

University of Nottingham
Viking and Anglo Saxon Studies...........................MA 12FT 24-36PT

Welsh studies
Taught Courses

University of Aberdeen
Ethnology and Folklore ....MLitt 12FT 24PT

Aberystwyth University
Welsh Politics and Society (Research Training)......MA 12FT 24PT/ PGDip 9FT 18PT
Welsh Politics and Society (Specialist)....................MA 12FT 24PT/ PGDip 9FT 18PT

Bangor University
Celtic Archaeology .... MA 12FT 24PT/PGDip 8FT
Celts, The / Celtiaid, Y..................................... MA 12FT 36PT
Cymraeg (Welsh) (Welsh medium)....... MA 12FT 24PT/PGDip 8FT
Welsh History ....PhD by taught 24-36FT 48-72PT/ MPhil 12FT 24PT

Cardiff University
Welsh and Celtic Studies .... MA 12FT 24PT

University College Cork
Arts (Folklore) ....HDip 9FT
Folklore...MA 12FT

University of Wales Trinity Saint David
Astudiaethau Celtaidd .... MA 12FT 24PT 12-24DL/PGCert 12FT 24PT 12-24DL/PGDip 12FT 24PT 12-24DL

Welsh studies
Research Courses

Aberystwyth University
Welsh Literature ....MPhil 12FT 24PT PhD 36FT 60PT

Bangor University
Astudiaethau Celtaidd (Celtic Studies) (Welsh medium).... MA by research 12FT/MPhil 24FT 48-60PT/PhD 24-36FT 60-72PT
Llenyddiaeth Gymraeg (Welsh Literature) (Welsh medium)MPhil 24FT 48-60PT/PhD 24-36FT 60-72PT

University of Wales Trinity Saint David
Bilingualism and MultilingualismPhD 12FT 24PT/MA by research 12FT 24PT
Centre for Bilingualism and Welsh Studies .... PhD 36FT/MPhil 12-24FT
Welsh.. PhD 36-60FT/MPhil 12-36FT

Women's studies
Taught Courses

Bangor University
Women's Studies.....................MA 24PT/PGDip 24PT/PGCert 12PT

University of Brighton
Women's Health and Education.............. MSc 12 - 36FT 24 - 72PT/ PGCert 12 - 36FT 24 - 72PT/PGDip 12 - 36FT 24 - 72PT

University College Cork
Women's Studies...MA 12FT

University of Dundee
Gender, Culture and Society ....MLitt 12FT

University of East Anglia
Gender Analysis in International Development..... MA 12FT 24PT

Goldsmiths, University of London
Gender, Media & Culture .... MA 12FT 24PT

King's College London
Advanced Practice (Women's Healthcare).....MSc 36-72PT/PGDip 24-72PT/PGCert 12-72PT

Lancaster University
Gender and Women's Studies............. MA 12FT 24PT/MPhil 24FT/ PhD by taught 24FT
Gender and Women's Studies and English.............. MA 12FT 24PT
Gender and Women's Studies and Sociology.......... MA 12FT 24PT
Gender and Women's studies (With Pathways) ..... MA 12FT 24PT

University of Leeds
Gender and Culture ....MA 12FT 24PT/PGDip 12FT 24PT

Global Genders ....MA 12FT 24PT/PGDip 12FT 24PT

London Metropolitan University
Women and Child Abuse.......................................MSc 12FT 24PT

University of Nottingham
MATILDA Women's and Gender History (European Master)....MA 24FT

University of Oxford
Women's Studies...MSt 9FT

Ruskin College
Women's Studies .... MA 12FT 24PT

University of St Andrews
Women, Writing and Gender .... MLitt 12FT 24PT/ PGDip 9FT 24PT/MPhil 24FT

Swansea University
Gender and Culture .... MA 12FT 24-36PT

Trinity College Dublin - the University of Dublin
Gender and Women's Studies...........................MPhil 12FT 24PT

UCL - University College London
Gender, Society and Representation .... MA 12FT 24PT

University of West London
Women, Mental Health and Childbearing: Developing the Service .... CPPD 4PT 4DL

University of York
Women's Studies .... MA 12FT 24PT
Women's Studies (Humanities) .... MA 12FT 24PT
Women's Studies (Social Research) .... MA 12FT 24PT
Women, Violence and Conflict................................ MA 12FT 24PT

Women's studies
Research Courses

Cardiff University
Feminist Media Studies ....PhD 36FT possiblePT/MPhil 24FT possiblePT

Lancaster University
Women's Studies......................... PhD 36FT 48PT/MPhil 24FT 36PT

University of Nottingham
Social Sciences Research Methodology ....MPhil 24FT 48PT/PhD 36-48FT 72-96PT

UCL - University College London
Gender Studies .... PhD 36FT 60PT

University of York
Women's Studies.............PhD 36FT 72PT/MPhil 24FT 48PT/MA by research 12FT 24PT

Youth studies
Taught Courses

University of Aberdeen
People and the Environment..................................MSc 12FT 24PT

Anglia Ruskin University
Children & Young People...................................MSc 12FT 24PT

University of Bedfordshire
Applied Public Policy: Children's and Young People's Services.......MA 24PT
Applied Social Work: Children and Families ....MA 30PT
Children and Youth People's Services (PDC&YPSL) .... DProf by taught 36PT

University College Birmingham
Childhood, Professional Studies in Childhood..... MA 24PT/PGDip 24PT/PGCert 24PT

University of Bolton
Children's Literature and Culture ....MA 24PT

Brunel University
Children, Youth and International Development... MA 12FT 24PT
Youth and Community Studies....................................MA 24-36DL

Bucks New University
Child & Adolescent Studies .... MSc 12FT 24PT

Cardiff Metropolitan University
Youth & Community Work...........................MSc 36PT/PGDip 24PT

University of Central Lancashire
Social Work.. MA 24FT 36PT
Social Work (only available through employment secondment)..PGDip 24FT 36PT
Social Work Practice (Post Qualification Specialist Award, Adults) PGDip 3PT

University of Cumbria
Leading Intergrated Children's Services .... MSc 24 - 60PT
Youth and Community Work.................................. PGDip 12FT 24PT

De Montfort University
Youth Work and Community Development with Professional Qualification L53075 ....MA 24-36DL/PGDip 18DL
Youth and Community Development Studies ....MA 24-36DL/ PGDip 18DL/PGCert 12DL
Youth work , Health and community Development....... MSc 24PT 36DL

Social sciences

Durham University
Managing Youth Work Practice .... MA 12FT 24PT

University of East London
Youth & Community Work ....MA 12FT 24PT/PGDip 8FT 16PT/
PGCert 4FT 8PT
Youth and Community Studies ....MA 12FT 24PT/
PGDip 8FT 16PT/PGCert 4FT 8PT

Edge Hill University
Integrated Children and Young People's Practice......MSc 36-72PT

University of Edinburgh
Cognitive Behaviour Therapy for Children and Young People ....
PGCert 24PT
Health & Social Care - Children & Young People's Mental Health:
Ecological Approaches ODL..PGCert 9DL
Psychological Interventions for Children and Young People ....
PGCert 12PT

Glasgow Caledonian University
Sexual Health .... MSc 24-60FT On-lineDL

University of Glasgow
Young People, Social Inclusion & Change ....MSc 12FT 24PT

University of Gloucestershire
Work with Children, Young People, their Families and Carers.......
MSc 12FT 24PT

Glyndwr University
Counselling Studies with Children and Young People ....
MA 30//PT

Goldsmiths, University of London
Anthropology and Cultural Politics.............................. MA 12FT 24PT
Applied Anthropology & Community Development ....MA 12FT
24PT
Applied Anthropology and Community and Youth Work ....
MA 12FT 24PT

University of Huddersfield
Education and Youth Work Studies... MA 12FT 36PT/PGDip 24PT/
PGCert 12PT
Youth and Community Work......................................Diploma 12FT
Youth and Community Work, Professional Studies..........MA 24PT

University of Hull
Community and Youth Work .... MA 12FT 24PT

Institute of Education
Social Pedagogy: Working with Children and Families ...MA 12FT
24PT

King's College London
Youth Ministry.. MA 12FT 24-48PT

Leeds Metropolitan University
Professional Development..PGCert 12PT
Youth & Community Development Studies............ MA 12FT 24PT
Youth Work & Community Development (JNC) ....
PGDip 12FT 24PT

London School of Economics and Political Science (LSE)
Anthropology and Development Management....MSc 12FT 24PT
Development Studies...MSc 12FT 24PT

Manchester Metropolitan University
Youth and Community Work (Initial Qualification).........................
MA 12FT 24PT

University of St Mark and St John
Community and Youth Work...PGDip 12FT
Professional Practice: Children and Young People's Services...MA
VariableFT
Youth and Community Work......PGDip 12FT 24PT/MA 12FT 24PT

Middlesex University
Youth Justice, Community Safety, and Applied Criminology...MA
12FT 24PT

Newman University
Children, Young People and Families................... MA 24FT 36-48PT
Youth and Community Work.........................MA 36PT/PGDip 24PT

University of Northampton
Youth and Community Work..MA 12FT

The Open University
Childhood and Youth.. MA variableDL
Integrated Practice in Childhood and Youth..PGCert 12DL/PGDip
variableDL

University of Roehampton
Attachment Studies...MSc 18-24FT 24-36PT

University Campus Suffolk
MA Childhood and Youth Studies .... MA 12FT 24 - 36PT

Sheffield Hallam University
Youth Work.. GradDip 12FT 24PT

University of South Wales
Working for Children & Young People: Youth Work
.... MA 12-24PT 36-60PT
Youth and Community Work................................. PGDip 12FT 24PT

University of Sussex
Childhood and Youth Studies..................................... MA 12FT 24PT
Effective Practice in Children's Services..... MA 60PT/PGDip 60PT/
PGCert 60PT

Teesside University
Professional Qualification in Youth Work (NYA Validated) ..... MSc
12FT 24PT/PGDip 12FT 24PT

University of Wales Trinity Saint David
Youth and Community Work.....MA 12FT 36PT 36DL/PGDip 12FT
36PT/PGCert 12FT 36PT

University of Ulster
Community Youth Work ....MSc 36PT/PGDip 24PT

Youth studies
Research Courses

Birkbeck, University of London
Community, Youth and Voluntary Sector ....PhD 24FT 36PT/MPhil
24FT 36PT

University College Cork
Doctor of Social Science..DSocSci 48FT

University of Dundee
Community Learning & Development .... MPhil 24FT

Goldsmiths, University of London
Community and Youth Work... PhD 36-48FT 48-72PT/MPhil 24FT
36PT

University of Hertfordshire
Centre for Community Research ....PhD 36FT 72PT/MPhil 24FT
48PT/MRes 12FT 24PT

London School of Economics and Political Science (LSE)
Development Studies........................... PhD 36-48FT/MPhil 36-48FT

The Open University
Child and Youth Studies...PhD 36FT 72PT variableDL/MRes 12FT/
EdD 36PT
Children, Young People and Families...................... PhD 36FT 72PT
variableDL/MPhil 15FT 24PT
Children, young people, families, and personal relationships.......
PhD 36FT 72PT/MPhil 15FT 24PT
Issues in health and social care of children, young people and
families .... PhD 36FT 72PT/MPhil 15FT 24PT
Personal relationships, families, children and young people.........
PhD 36FT 72PT variableDL/MPhil 15FT 24PT variableDL

University of Roehampton
Anthropology .... PhD 24-48FT 36-60PT/MPhil 21-36FT 33-48PT

University of Sheffield
Criminology and Socio-Legal Studies.....................PhD 36FT 72PT/
MPhil 24FT 48PT

Sports science

Golf
Taught Courses

University of Birmingham
Golf Coaching .... AdvCert 12-36PT

Horse riding
Research Courses

Anglia Ruskin University
Equine Research Anglia... MPhil 18 - 36FT 30-48PT/PhD 24 - 60FT 30 - 48PT

Leisure management
Taught Courses

University of Bedfordshire
Community Sport Management ...... MA 12FT 24PT/PGCert 12FT/PGDip 12FT
International Tourism Management.... MSc 12-15FT 24PT/PGDip 12FT/PGCert 12FT
Sport Development Management....... MA 12-15FT/PGCert 12FT/PGDip 12FT
Sport Tourism Management .... MSc 12FT 24PT/PGDip 12FT/PGCert 12FT
Tourism and Environmental Management .... MSc 12-15FT 24PT/PGDip 12FT/PGCert 12FT
Tourism and Event ManagementMSc 12-15FT 24PT/PGDip 12FT/PGCert 12FT

University of Brighton
Sport and International Development... MA 12FT 24-36PT/PGDip 12FT 24PT/PGCert 12FT 24PT

Cardiff Metropolitan University
Events Management ... MSc 12FT 24PT/PGDip 12FT 36PT/PGCert 24FT 24PT
Sport Management and LeadershipMA 24-46PT/PGDip 24-46PT/PGCert 24-46PT

University of Central Lancashire
Adventure Sport Coaching .... MA 12FT
International Festivals and Event Management .. MSc 12FT 24PT/PGDip 12FT 24PT
International Festivals and Tourism Management......... MSc 12FT 24PT/PGDip 12FT 24PT
International Heritage and Attraction Management .... MSc 12FT 24PT/PGDip 12FT 24PT
International Heritage and Event Management.. MSc 12FT 24PT/PGDip 12FT 24PT
International Hospitality and Event Management .... MSc 12FT 24PT/PGDip 12FT 24PT
International Hospitality and Tourism Management .... MSc 12FT 24PT/PGDip 12FT 24PT
International Tourism Management .... MSc 12FT 24PT/PGDip 12FT 24PT
International Tourism and Attraction Management ..... MSc 12FT 24PT/PGDip 12FT 24PT
Internship in International Tourism, Hospitality and Event Management .... MA 12FT 24PT
Management Studies .... DMS 18PT
Marketing and PR .... MA 12FT
Physical Education and School Sport .... MA 12FT 24PT
Sport Business Management .... MSc 12FT up to 36PT
Sport, Policy and Community Development .... MA 12FT 24PT
Sports Marketing and Business Management ..... MSc 12FT up to 36PT
Sports Therapy Professional Practice .... MSc up to 24FT

University College Cork
Food Business .... MSc 24FT

University of Cumbria
Events Leadership and Management .... MBA 12FT 36PT/PGCert 12FT 36PT/PGDip 12FT 36PT
Greening Outdoor Practice .... PGCert 24-36PT
Outdoor and Experiential Learning .... MA 12FT 24-36PT/GradDip 12FT 24PT

University of Derby
International Hospitality Management ...... MA 12FT 36PT/PGDip 12FT/PGCert 9FT
International Spa Management .... MA 36FT
Marketing Management .... MSc 12FT

University of Edinburgh
Sport and Recreation Business ManagementPGDip 9FT 24-48PT/MSc 12FT 24-72PT

University of Exeter
International Tourism Management .... MSc 12FT

Glasgow Caledonian University
International Sports Management .... MSc 12FT

University of Gloucestershire
MBA Hospitality .... MBA 12FT

Leeds Metropolitan University
Leisure, Sport & Culture .... MA 12FT 24PT
Multi Unit Leadership .... MSc 12FT 24PT
Outdoor & Adventurous Activities .... MSc 12FT 24PT
Sport Business .... MA 12FT 24PT
Sport, Law & Society .... MA 12FT 24PT

London Metropolitan University
Sport Management .... MA 12FT 24PT

Manchester Metropolitan University
Food Safety .... MSc 12FT 24-60PT
Food and Nutrition .... MSc 12FT 24-60PT
International Food Management .... MSc 12FT 24-60PT

Northumbria University
Sport Marketing .... MSc 12FT 24PT

Nottingham Trent University
Sport and Leisure Management .... MRes 12FT 24PT

Regent's Business School London
Business Management in International Travel & Tourism .... MA 21PT

Sheffield Hallam University
Sport Business Management .... MSc 12FT 24PT/PGDip 8FT 16PT/PGCert 4FT 8PT

University of Stirling
Psychology of Sport ... MSc 9FT 24PT/PGDip 9FT 24PT/PGCert 6FT 12PT

University of Sunderland
Applied Management .... MSc 24PT

University of Wales Trinity Saint David
Heritage Tourism .... MA 12-24FT 18-48PT/PGDip 9FT 18-36PT/PGCert 9FT 18PT

University of the Highlands and Islands
Interpretation: Management and Practice...... PGCert 12FT 24PT/PGDip 12FT 24PT/MSc 12FT 24PT

University of Ulster
Sport Management .... MSc 12FT 24PT

University of the West of England, Bristol
Sports Management .... MA 18FT

Leisure management
Research Courses

University of Bolton
Leisure and Sport Specialisms..... MPhil 18FT 24 - 42PT/PhD 36FT 60 - 72PT

University of Brighton
Chelsea School Research Division .... PhD 24-60FT 36-72PT/MPhil 18-36FT 30-48PT

University of Cambridge
Management Studies .... PhD 36FT

Canterbury Christ Church University
Sport Science, Tourism Studies .... PhD 48FT 60PT/MPhil 24FT 48PT

Liverpool John Moores University
Professional Doctorate .... MPhil 36FT 84PT

Sheffield Hallam University
Countryside Research Unit .... PhD/MPhil
School of Leisure and Food Management .... PhD/MPhil

Southampton Solent University
Marketing and Leisure .... MPhil/PhD

Sports science
Taught Courses

University of Aberdeen
Molecular Nutrition .... MSc 12FT/PGDip 9FT/PGDip 4FT

Aberystwyth University
Exercise and Health Research...... MSc 12FT 24PT/PGDip 9FT 21PT

Anglo-European College of Chiropractic
BSc/MSc Chiropractic .... MSc 30DL/PGDip 24DL/PGCert 12DL
MSc Medical Ultrasound .... MSc 36PT

Bangor University
Applied Sport Science .... MA 12FT 36PT MSc 12FT 36PT
Applied Sport Science (Outdoor Activities) .... MA 12FT 36PT MSc 12FT 36PT
Applied Sport and Exercise Physiology .... MA 12FT 36PT MSc 12FT 36PT/PGDip 8FT
Applied Sport and Exercise Psychology .... MA 12FT 36PT MSc 12FT 36PT
Exercise Rehabilitation .... MA 12FT 36PT MSc 12FT 36PT
Sport and Exercise Physiology .... MRes 12FT 36PT
Sport and Exercise Psychology .... MRes 12FT 36PT
Sport and Exercise Psychology (BPS Accredited) ... MSc 12FT 36PT
Sport and Exercise Sciences .... MRes 12FT 36PT

University of Bath
Sport and Exercise Medicine .... MSc 36-60PT/PGDip 24-48PT
Sports Physiotherapy..... MSc 36FT Up to 60DL/PGDip 24FT Up to 60DL/PGCert 12FT Up to 60DL

University of Bedfordshire
Clinical Exercise Physiology .. MSc 12FT/PGCert 12FT/PGDip 12FT
Community Sport Management ...... MA 12FT 24PT/PGCert 12FT/PGDip 12FT
Molecular and Cellular Exercise Physiology .... MSc 12FT
Physical Activity, Nutrition and Health Promotion........ MSc 12FT/PGDip 12FT/PGCert 12FT
Physical Education and Sport Pedagogy..... MA 12FT 24PT/PGCert 12FT/PGDip 12FT
Sport Development Management .... MA 12-15FT/PGCert 12FT/PGDip 12FT
Sport Tourism Management .... MSc 12FT 24PT/PGDip 12FT/PGCert 12FT
Sport and Exercise Rehabilitation .... MSc 12FT 24-72PT
Sports Performance .... MSc 12FT/PGDip 12FT/PGCert 12FT

University of Birmingham
AdCert in Golf Coaching .... AdvCert 12PT
Exercise and Sport (Sciences) .... MSc 12FT 24PT
Exercise and Sports Medicine (Football)..... MSc 13FT 72PT/PGDip 10FT 48PT
Physical Education and Sport Pedagogy MSc............ MSc 24-72FT
Sports Coaching .... MSc 24-48PT/PGDip 24PT

University of Bolton
Strength and Conditioning .... MSc 36PT

Bournemouth University
Managing Sport Performance .... MSc 12-15FT 24PT
Sport Management .... MSc 12-15FT 24PT

University of Brighton
Applied Exercise Physiology..... MSc 12FT 24PT/PGDip 12FT 24PT/PGCert 12FT 24PT
Exercise and Health Science .... MSc 12FT 24PT/PGDip 12FT 24PT/PGCert 12FT 24PT
Sport and Exercise Science....... MSc 12FT 24PT/PGDip 12FT 24PT/PGCert 12FT 24PT
Sport and International Development... MA 12FT 24-36PT/PGDip 12FT 24PT/PGCert 12FT 24PT

University of Bristol
Nutrition, Physical Activity and Public Health .... MSc 12FT 24PT

Brunel University
Sport Sciences .... MSc 12FT 24PT
Sport Sciences (Human Performance) .... MSc 12FT 24PT
Sport Sciences (Sport Psychology) .... MSc 12FT 24-36PT

Cardiff Metropolitan University
Performance Analysis... MSc 12FT 24-36PT/PGDip 12FT 24-36PT/PGCert 12FT 24-36PT
Physical Activity and Health......... MSc 12FT 24-36PT/PGDip 12FT 24-36PT/PGCert 12FT 24-36PT
Physical Education and Sport .... MA 24PT
Sport & Exercise Medicine .... MSc 12FT 12-36PT/PGDip 12FT 12-36PT
Sport Coaching .... MSc 12FT 36PT/PGDip 12FT 36PT
Sport Management and LeadershipMA 24-46PT/PGDip 24-46PT/PGCert 24-46PT
Sport and Exercise Science .... MSc 12FT 24-36PT/PGDip 12FT 24-36PT/PGCert 9FT 24-36PT
Sport, Body & Society .... MA 12FT 36PT/PGDip 12FT 36PT/PGCert 9FT 36PT
Strength and Conditioning .... MSc 12FT 24-60PT

Cardiff University
Sports and Exercise Physiotherapy ...... MSc 12FT 24PT/PGDip 9FT 18PT

University of Central Lancashire
Adventure Sport Coaching .... MA 12FT
Psychology of Sport and Exercise......... MSc 12FT 24PT/PGDip 9FT 24PT/PGCert 9FT 24PT
Sport Business Management .... MSc 12FT up to 36PT
Sport and Exercise Biomechanics....... MSc 12FT 24PT/PGDip 12FT 24PT
Sport and Exercise Physiology.. MSc 12FT 24PT/PGDip 12FT 24PT
Sport and Exercise Psychology.. MSc 12FT 24PT/PGDip 9FT 24PT/PGCert 9FT 24PT
Sport and Exercise Science........ MSc 12FT 24PT/PGDip 12FT 24PT
Sport, Policy and Community Development .... MA 12FT 24PT
Sports Coaching .... MA 12FT 24PT/PGDip 12FT 24PT
Sports Marketing and Business Management ..... MSc 12FT up to 36PT
Sports Therapy .... MSc 18FT 36PT/PGDip 18FT 24PT
Sports Therapy Professional Practice .... MSc up to 24FT

University of Chester
Exercise and Nutrition Science .. MSc 12FT 24 - 48PT/PGDip 12FT 24 - 48PT/PGCert 12FT 12 - 24PT
Exercise and Nutrition Science (Taught in Dublin, Ireland) .... MSc 24 - 48PT/PGDip 24 - 48PT/PGCert 12 - 24PT
Sociology of Sport and Exercise.......... MSc 12FT 24PT/PGDip 12FT 24PT/PGCert 12FT 12-24PT
Sports Sciences (with named pathways)..... MA 12FT 24PT/PGDip 12FT 24PT/PGCert 12FT 12-24PT

University of Chichester
Psychology of Sport and Exercise.... MSc 12-15FT 24-36PT/PGDip 9-12FT 18-24PT/PGCert 6-9FT 12-18PT
Sport and Exercise Biomechanics......... MSc 12FT 24PT/PGDip 9FT 18PT/PGCert 9FT 12PT
Sport and Exercise Physiology .... MSc 11FT 22+PT
Sport and Exercise Psychology .... MSc 12-15FT 24-36PT

Sports science

Coventry University
International Sport Management..........................MBA 12FT 24PT
Sport and Exercise Nutrition...................................PGCert 12 MinPT

University of Cumbria
Sport Coaching and Sport Development.................MA 12FT 24PT

De Montfort University
Sport History and Culture...MA 12-24DL

University of Dundee
Sports and Biomechanical Medicine.................................MSc 12FT
Sports and Biomechanical Medicine (with externally arranged
project)...MSc 24PT
Sports and Biomechanical Medicine (with in-house project) MSc
24PT

University of East London
Exercise Science and Health MSc.........MSc 12FT 24PT/PGDip 8FT
16PT/PGCert 4FT 8PT
Sports Science MRes..MRes 12FT 24PT

Edge Hill University
Applied Sport and Exercise Science..........................MSc 12FT 24PT
Coach Education...MRes 12FT 24PT
Physical Education and School Sport....................MRes 12FT 24PT
Sport and Exercise..MRes 12FT 24PT
Sports Development...MRes 12FT 24PT
Sports Studies..MRes 12FT 24PT

Edinburgh Napier University
Sport Performance Enhancement......................MSc 12FT 24-48PT

University of Edinburgh
Dance Science and Education.....MSc 12FT 72PT/PGDip 9FT 48PT
Physical Activity for Health........MSc 12FT 72PT/PGCert 24-48PT/
PGDip 9FT 48PT
Strength and Conditioning..............PGDip 9FT 24-48PT/MSc 12FT
24-72PT
Swimming Science...PGCert 24PT

University of Essex
Cardiac Rehabilitation...MSc 12FT 24PT

University of Exeter
Paediatric Exercise and Health...................................MSc 12FT 24PT
Sport and Health Sciences...MSc 12FT 24PT

National University of Ireland Galway
Sports & Exercise Physiotherapy..MSc 24PT
Sports and Exercise Medicine..MSc 24PT

Glasgow Caledonian University
International Sports Management...................................MSc 12FT

University of Glasgow
Exercise Science............................MRes 12FT 24PT/PGDip 8FT 18PT
Sport & Exercise Medicine...........................MSc(MedSci) 12FT 24PT
Sport & Exercise Science...MSc 12FT 24PT
Sports Nutrition...PGCert 4FT

University of Gloucestershire
Applied Sport and Exercise Sciences...MSc 12FT 24PT/PGDip 8FT
20PT/PGCert 4FT 8PT
Coaching Science...MSc 12FT 24PT
Physical Activity and Health......MSc 12FT 24PT/PGDip 8FT 20PT/
PGCert 4FT 8PT
Sports Coaching...MSc 12FT 24PT
Sports Development.MA 12FT 24PT/PGDip 8FT 20PT/PGCert 4FT
8PT
Sports Strength and Conditioning...........................MSc 12FT 24PT
Sports and Christian Outreach (Sports Ministry)...MA 12FT 24PT

University of Kent
Sports Science for Optimal Performance.................MSc 12FT 24PT
Sports Therapy and Rehabilitation....MSc 12FT 24PT/PGDip 12FT
24PT

Kingston University
Exercise for Health...MSc 12FT 24PT
Physiotherapy (pre-registration)...MSc 24FT

Leeds Metropolitan University
Sport Coaching...MSc 12FT 24PT
Sport and Exercise Nutrition...MSc 12FT 24PT/PGDip 12FT 24PT/
PGCert 4FT 12PT
Sport and Exercise Physiology..MSc 12FT 24PT/PGCert 4FT 12PT/
PGDip 12FT 24PT
Sport and Exercise Science........MSc 12FT 36PT/PGCert 4FT 12PT/
PGDip 12FT 24PT
Sport, Law & Society...MA 12FT 24PT

Leeds Trinity University
Health and Wellbeing...........MSc 24PT 24DL/PGCert 12PT 12DL/
PGDip 24PT 24DL

University of Limerick
Education Physical Education..............Professional Diploma 12FT
Sports Performance..MSc 12FT 24PT

University of Lincoln
Sport Science...MSc 12FT 24PT

Liverpool Hope University
Health, Exercise and Nutrition......................MSc 12-15FT 24-36PT/
PGDip 12FT 24PT/PGCert 6FT 12PT

Liverpool John Moores University
Clinical Exercise Physiology...MSc 12FT
Sport and Exercise Biomechanics...........................MSc 12FT 24PT
Sports Physiology MSc, PgDip, PgCert........MSc 12FT 24PT/PGDip
12FT 18PT/PGCert 6FT 12PT

University of Liverpool
Football Industries...MBA 12FT 24PT

London Metropolitan University
Human Nutrition (Public Health/Sports)................MSc 12FT 24PT
Sport Management...MA 12FT 24PT

London South Bank University
Applied and Interdisciplinary Sports Science..................MSc 18FT

Loughborough University
Exercise Physiology..MSc 12FT
Globalization and Sport..MSc 12FT
International Sports Management MBA......................MBA 24BM
Physical Activity and Health........MSc 12FT 24-96PT/PGDip up to
60PT/PGCert up to 36PT
Sociology of Sport...MSc 12FT
Sport Coaching....MSc 12FT 24-96PT/PGDip 8FT 24-96PT/PGCert
12-96PT
Sport Management..MSc 12FT 24PT
Sport and Exercise Nutrition...MSc 12FT
Sport and Exercise Psychology...MSc 12FT
Sports Biomechanics...MSc 12FT
Sports and Exercise Science..MSc 12FT

Manchester Metropolitan University
Biomedical Science featuring Exercise and Health options...MSc
12FT 24-36PT
Exercise and Sport.............................MA/MSc 12FT 24-36PT
Exercise and Sport - Coaching Studies...............MSc 12FT 24-36PT
Exercise and Sport - Physiology...........................MSc 12FT 24-36PT
Exercise and Sport - Sport Development.........MSc 12FT 24-36PT
Exercise and Sport -Psychology..........................MSc 12FT 24-36PT

University of St Mark and St John
Applied Sports Development................................MA 12FT 24-48PT
Elite Performance in Applied Sport Development...........MA 12FT
24-48PT
Management in Applied Sport Development...MA 12FT 24-48PT
Outdoor Learning in Applied Sport Development...........MA 12FT
24-48PT
Physical Activity and Health in Applied Sport Development...MA
12FT 24-48PT

Physical Education in Applied Sport Development..........MA 12FT
24-48PT
Sport Science in Applied Sport Development...MA 12FT 24-48PT

Middlesex University
Performance Analysis..MSc 12FT 24PT
Sports and Exercise Science...MSc 12FT 24PT
Strength & Conditioning...MSc 12FT 24PT

Newman University
Physical Education and Sports Studies..................MA 24PT 24DL/
MSc 24PT 24DL

University of Northampton
Sport and Exercise Performance...............................MSc 12FT 24PT

Northumbria University
Clinical Exercise Physiology..MSc 12FT 36PT
Exercise Science...MRes 12FT 24PT
International Sport Management.................................MSc 12FT 24PT
Sport...DProf by taught 24FT 36PT
Sport Marketing..MSc 12FT 24PT
Sport and Exercise Psychology......................................MSc 12FT
Strength and Conditioning...MSc 12FT 24DL

Nottingham Trent University
International Performance Analysis of Sport.................MSc 24PT
Sport Science...MRes 12FT 24PT
Sport and Leisure Management...............................MRes 12FT 24PT

University of Nottingham
Sports and Exercise Medicine...MSc 12FT 24PT/PGDip 12FT 24PT

Oxford Brookes University
Applied Sport & Exercise Nutrition.....MSc 12FT 24PT/PGDip 8FT
20PT

University of Portsmouth
Clinical Exercise Science...MSc 12FT 24PT
Sports Management...MSc 12FT 24PT
Sports Performance..MSc 12FT 24PT

Robert Gordon University
Sports Biomechanics..MSc 12FT

University of Roehampton
Biomechanics...MSc 12FT 24-48PT
Health Sciences...MSc 12FT 24PT
Obesity: Risks and Prevention..................................MSc 12FT 24PT
PGCert 6FT 12PT PGDip 9FT 24PT
Sport and Exercise Physiology...........................PGDip 9FT 24-48PT

Sports science

Sport and Exercise Science.................... PGDip 9FT 24-48PT
Sport and Exercise Physiology............................MSc 12FT 24-48PT
Sport and Exercise Science................................ MRes 12FT 24-48PT
MSc 12FT 24-48PT

University of Salford
Sports Injury Rehabilitation. MSc 36PT/PGDip 24PT/PGCert 12PT

Sheffield Hallam University
Leading and Managing Physical Education and Youth Sport........
MSc 3PT
Leading and Managing Sport Development ....MSc 24PT/PGDip
16PT/PGCert 8PT
Nutrition with Public Health Management .... MSc 12FT
Physical Activity for Health........ MSc 12FT 24PT/PGDip 6FT 12PT/
PGCert 4FT 8PT
Sport and Exercise Psychology................................. MSc 12FT 24PT
Sport and Exercise Science......... MSc 12FT 24PT/PGDip 8FT 16PT/
PGCert 4FT 8PT
Sport and Health Management ....MSc 12FT/PGDip 8FT/
PGCert 4FT
Sport, Culture and Community...MA 12FT 24PT/PGDip 8FT 16PT/
PGCert 4FT 8PT
Sports Engineering....................................... MSc 12FT 24PT

University of South Wales
Performance Coaching......................................MSc 12FT 24-36PT
Sport, Health and Exercise Science ....MSc 12FT 24-36PT
Sports Coaching.....................................MSc 12-18FT 24 - 36PT
Youth Sport Coaching.....................................MSc 12FT 24-36PT

Southampton Solent University
Sport and Development .... MA 24FT 12PT

St Mary's University College, Twickenham
Applied Sport Science................. MSc 12FT 24PT/PGDip 12FT 24PT
Strength and Conditioning .... MSc 12FT

Staffordshire University
Applied Sport and Exercise Psychology (Distance Learning)..........
PGCert 7DL/PGDip 14DL/MSc 24DL
Applied Sport and Exercise Science .... PGCert 12FT 7DL/PGDip
14DL/MSc 24DL
Physical Activity and Public Health (Distance Learning) .... PGCert
24-60DL/PGDip 24-60DL/MSc 24-60DL
Sport and Exercise Psychology (Distance Learning) ..PGCert 7DL/
PGDip 14DL/MSc 24DL

University of Stirling
Performance Coaching.......... MSc 24PT/PGDip 24PT/PGCert 12PT
Sport Management ...MSc 9FT 24PT/PGDip 9FT 24PT/PGCert 6FT
12PT
Sport Nutrition (International Olympic Committee Upgrade)......
MSc 6FT 12PT
Sports Coaching............................MSc 9FT 24PT/PGDip 6FT 24PT/
PGCert 6FT 12PT

University of Sunderland
Sport and Exercise Sciences.. MSc 12FT 24PT

Teesside University
Movement Science and Rehabilitation.....................MSc 12FT 24PT
Sport and Exercise... MSc 12FT 24PT
Sports Therapy.. MSc 18FT 36PT
Strength & Conditioning..MSc 12FT 24PT

Trinity College Dublin - the University of Dublin
Sports and Exercise Medicine.. MSc 12FT

University of Ulster
Physical Activity and Public Health............................MSc 12FT 36PT
Sport & Exercise Medicine.. MSc 12FT 36PT
Sport Management .... MSc 12FT 24PT
Sport and Exercise Nutrition ..... PGDip 18PT 9DL/MSc 22PT 12DL
Sports Development and Coaching.....MSc 12FT 36PT/PGDip 9FT
18PT

UCL - University College London
Sports Medicine, Exercise and Health.. MSc 12FT 24-60PT/PGDip
9FT

University of the West of England, Bristol
Sports Management...MA 18FT

University of Westminster
International Public Health Nutrition.....................MSc 12FT 24PT
Sport and Exercise Nutrition .... MSc 12FT

University of Winchester
Applied Sport and Exercise Science ...MSc 12FT 24PT/PGDip 12FT
24PT/PGCert 12FT 24PT

University of Worcester
Applied Sport Science..MSc 12FT 36PT
European Basketball Coaching Science ....MSc 12FT/PGDip 9FT/
PGCert 6FT
Sports Coaching.. MSc 12FT 24PT/PGDip 6-12FT 12-24PT/PGCert
6-12FT 12-24PT

Sports Management. MSc 12FT 24-36PT/PGDip 6-12FT 12-24PT/
PGCert 6-12FT 12-24PT

Sports science
Research Courses

University of Aberdeen
Nutrition and Health........ PhD 36FT/MPhil 24FT/MSc by research
12FT

Aberystwyth University
Sport and Exercise Science ....MPhil 12FT 24PT PhD 36FT 60PT

Bangor University
Sport, Health and Exercise Sciences ....MPhil 12FT/PhD 36FT

Barts and the London School of Medicine and Dentistry
Department of Sports Medicine............................PhD/MPhil/FRCS

University of Bath
Sport and Exercise Science............................ PhD 24-48FT 36-72PT/
MPhil 12-36FT 24-48PT

University of Birmingham
Exercise and Sport Sciences ....MRes 12FT
Sport and Exercise Sciences...........................PhD 36FT 72PT 36DL

University of Bolton
Leisure and Sport Specialisms..... MPhil 18FT 24 - 42PT/PhD 36FT
60 - 72PT

University of Brighton
Chelsea School Research Division .... PhD 24-60FT 36-72PT/MPhil
18-36FT 30-48PT

University of Bristol
Policy Studies.................................. PhD 36FT 72PT/MPhil 36FT 72PT

Brunel University
School of Sport and Education.PhD 36FT 72PT/MPhil 12FT 24PT/
EdD 48FT 72PT

Cardiff Metropolitan University
Sport ....PhD 12-60FT 12-60PT

University of Chichester
Centre for Sports Science, Physical Education and Recreation
Studies.................................PhD 36-48FT 84PT/MPhil 24-36FT 84PT

Coventry University
Exercise Physiology .... MSc by research 12FT 24-36PT

University of Cumbria
Sports Science; Sports History/Sociology; Outdoor Studies..........
MPhil 36FT 60PT 60DL/PhD 48FT 72PT 72DL

De Montfort University
International Centre for Sports History and Culture........................
PhD 36-48FT 48-72PT/MPhil 12-24FT 24-48PT

University of East Anglia
Physical Education Pedagogy Group ..PhD 36FT 72PT/MPhil 24FT
48PT/MA by research 12FT 24PT

University of East London
Research Programmes..PhD/MPhil

University of Essex
Sports and Exercise Medicine...PhD 36FT 72PT/MPhil 24FT 48PT/
MSc by research 12FT 24PT
Sports and Exercise Science......PhD 36FT 72PT/MPhil 24FT 48PT/
MSc by research 12FT 24PT

University of Exeter
Sport and Health Sciences .... PhD 48FT 84PT/MPhil 36FT 60PT

University of Glasgow
Sports Medicine and Science................. PhD 36FT/MSc(MedSci) by
research 12FT

University of Gloucestershire
Sport and Exercise................PhD 30-48FT 48-84PT/MPhil 18-36FT
30-60PT/MSc by research 12-24FT 18-36PT

University of Kent
Sport, Exercise Science and Sports Therapy........MPhil 24FT 36PT/
PhD 36FT 60PT
Sport, Exercise and Health Science .. Professional Doctorate 72PT

University of Leeds
Exercise and Health ....PhD 36+FT/MPhil 24FT/MSc by research
12FT
Sport and Exercise Sciences...........PhD 36+FT/MPhil 24FT/MSc by
research 12FT

University of Lincoln
Sport Coaching ...MA by research 12FT 24-48PT/MSc by research
12FT 24-48PT
Sport Development ....MA by research 12FT 24-48PT/MSc by
research 12FT 24-48PT
Sport and Exercise Science...... MSc by research 12FT 24PT/MA by
research 12FT 24PT
Sport and Physical Education........ MA by research 12FT 24-48PT/
MSc by research 12FT 24-48PT
Sports Science ....MA by research 12FT 24-48PT/MSc by research
12FT 24-48PT
Sport and Exercise Science........... MPhil 18FT 30PT/PhD 24-36FT
36-48PT

Section sponsored by

BPP
UNIVERSITY
COLLEGE

Business and social sciences
www.prospects.ac.uk/findcourses **POSTGRADUATE DIRECTORY 519**

Sports science

Liverpool Hope University
Postgraduate Research .... PhD 24FT 48PT/MPhil 12FT 24PT

Loughborough University
Sport and Exercise Sciences....... PhD 36FT 60PT/MPhil 24FT 36PT

Manchester Metropolitan University
Exercise and Sport Science....... PhD/MPhil/MSc by research 12FT

Newman University
Physical Education and Sports Studies ....PhD 36FT 72PT/MPhil 24FT 48PT

Nottingham Trent University
Exercise Physiology ....MRes 12FT 24PT
Performance Analysis...MRes 12FT 24PT
Performance Nutrition...MRes 12FT 24PT

University of Nottingham
Sports and Exercise Medicine.......DM 36FT 72PT/PhD 36FT 72PT/ MPhil 24FT 48PT

Oxford Brookes University
Health & Biomedical Sciences - Human Health & Performance Research Group .... PhD 24-60FT 36-72PT/ MPhil 24-36FT 36-48PT

University of Portsmouth
Sport and Exercise Science......... MPhil 24FT 48PT/PhD 36FT 72PT

University of Roehampton
Health Sciences.... PhD 24-48FT 36-60PT/MPhil 21-36FT 36-60PT
Sport & Exercise Sciences...PhD 24-48FT 36-60PT/MPhil 21-36FT 33-48PT

Sheffield Hallam University
Faculty of Health and Wellbeing ....PhD/MPhil

University of Stirling
Sports Studies .... PhD 36FT 72PT/MPhil 12FT 24PT

Swansea University
Sports Science ....MPhil 24FT 48PT/PhD 36FT 72PT/ MSc by research 12FT 24PT

University of Ulster
Sports Related Studies .... PhD 36FT 72PT/MPhil 24FT 48PT

University of Wolverhampton
Sport ....MRes 12FT 24PT

University of Worcester
Socio-Cultural Studies of Sport and Exercise ....MRes 12FT 24PT
Sport and Exercise Science......... PhD 48FT 70PT/MPhil 24FT 48PT

York St John University
Health & Life Science..............PhD 12-36FT/MPhil 12-36FT/MA by research 12-36FT

Sports surface technology
Taught Courses

Leeds Metropolitan University
Sport Coaching...MSc 12FT 24PT

Northumbria University
Sport Marketing... MSc 12FT 24PT

University of Stirling
Psychology of Sport ...MSc 9FT 24PT/PGDip 9FT 24PT/PGCert 6FT 12PT

Sports surface technology
Research Courses

University of Nottingham
Biophysics and Surface Analysis..........PhD 36FT 72PT/MPhil 24FT 36PT/MRes 12FT

Sports therapy
Taught Courses

Bangor University
Applied Sport Science........................ MA 12FT 36PT MSc 12FT 36PT
Applied Sport Science (Outdoor Activities).............. MA 12FT 36PT
Applied Sport Science and Outdoor Activities....... MSc 12FT 36PT
Applied Sport and Exercise Physiology ....MSc 12FT 36PT/ PGDip 8FT
Applied Sport and Exercise Physiology .... MA 12FT 36PT MSc 12FT 36PT
Applied Sport and Exercise Psychology .... MA 12FT 36PT
Exercise Rehabilitation...................... MSc 12FT 36PT MA 12FT 36PT
Occupational Therapy ....MSc 24FT/PGDip 24FT
Sport and Exercise Physiology...............................MRes 12FT 36PT
Sport and Exercise Psychology...............................MRes 12FT 36PT
Sport and Exercise Psychology (BPS Accredited) ...MSc 12FT 36PT
Sport and Exercise Sciences.....................................MRes 12FT 36PT

Barts and the London School of Medicine and Dentistry
Sports Medicine...................................MSc 12FT 24PT/PGDip 8FT

University of Bath
Sport and Exercise Medicine ....MSc 36-60PT/PGDip 24-48PT

University of Bedfordshire
Sport and Exercise Rehabilitation ....MSc 12FT 24-72PT

University of Birmingham
Exercise and Sports Medicine (Football).....MSc 13FT 72PT/PGDip 10FT 48PT

University of Bradford
Sports Physiotherapy... PGCert 6FT 18PT

University of Brighton
Sports Injury Management........... MSc 12FT 24-36PT/PGDip 12FT 24-36PT/PGCert 12FT 24PT

Bucks New University
Advancing Spinal Cord Rehabilitation and Management ...... MSc 36PT
Health, Exercise & Wellbeing .... MSc 12FT 24PT

Cardiff Metropolitan University
Sport & Exercise Medicine .... MSc 12FT 12-36PT/PGDip 12FT 12-36PT

University of Central Lancashire
Psychology of Sport and Exercise ....MSc 12FT 24PT/PGDip 9FT 24PT/PGCert 9FT 24PT
Sports Therapy .... MSc 18FT 36PT/PGDip 18FT 24PT
Sports Therapy Professional Practice .... MSc up to 24FT

University of Chichester
Psychology of Sport and Exercise .... MSc 12-15FT 24-36PT/PGDip 9-12FT 18-24PT/PGCert 6-9FT 12-18PT

Coventry University
Sport and Exercise Nutrition .... PGCert 12 MinPT

University of Dundee
Sports and Biomechanical Medicine (MSc Full time in-house)..... MSc 12FT
Sports and Biomechanical Medicine (MSc Part time with externally arranged project).. MSc 24PT
Sports and Biomechanical Medicine (MSc Part time with in-house project) .... MSc 24PT

University of East Anglia
Physiotherapy .... MSc 24FT

University of East London
Sports Rehabilitation ....PGCert 5FT 12 - 36PT
Strength and Conditioning MSc ....MSc 12FT 24PT/ PGDip 8FT 16PT/PGCert 4FT 8PT

Edge Hill University
Football Rehabilitation .... MSc 24PT
Sports Therapy ....MRes 12FT 24PT

University of Exeter
Sport and Exercise Medicine .... MSc 12FT 24PT

National University of Ireland Galway
Sports and Exercise Medicine.. MSc 24PT

University of Glasgow
Evidence Based Medicine & Education.............. MSc (ClinSci) 12FT
Sport & Exercise Medicine ....MSc(MedSci) 12FT 24PT
Sports Nutrition .... PGCert 4FT

University of Gloucestershire
Sports Therapy .... MSc 12FT 24PT

University of Kent
Sports Therapy and Rehabilitation ....MSc 12FT 24PT/PGDip 12FT 24PT

Leeds Metropolitan University
Sport Coaching...MSc 12FT 24PT
Sport and Exercise Biomechanics........MSc 12FT 24PT/PGCert 4FT 12PT/PGDip 12FT 24PT
Sport, Law & Society... MA 12FT 24PT
Sports Therapy ....MSc 12FT 24PT

University of Lincoln
Sport Science ....MSc 12FT 24PT

Liverpool John Moores University
Clinical Exercise Physiology .... MSc 12FT
Sports Physiology ....MSc 12FT 24PT/PGDip 12FT 18PT/ PGCert 6FT 12PT

London Metropolitan University
Sports Rehabilitation and Therapy ....MSc 12FT 24+PT
Sports Therapy ....MSc 12FT 24+PT

Loughborough University
Sports Biomechanics .... MSc 12FT

Manchester Metropolitan University
Biomedical Science featuring Exercise and Health options ... MSc 12FT 24-36PT
Exercise and Sport- Sport Development............. MA 12FT 24-36PT

Middlesex University
Sports Massage Therapy and Rehabilitation..........MSc 12FT 24PT

University of Northampton
Sports Therapy .... MSc 12FT 24PT

Northumbria University
Clinical Exercise Physiology .... MSc 12FT 36PT
Sport Marketing..MSc 12FT 24PT

University of Nottingham
Rehabilitation Psychology...MSc 12FT 24PT
Sports and Exercise Medicine... MSc 12FT 24PT/PGDip 12FT 24PT

University of Portsmouth
Clinical Exercise Science .... MSc 12FT 24PT

Queen Mary, University of London
Sport and Exercise Medicine ....MSc 12FT/PGDip 12FT 24PT

University of Roehampton
Biomechanics .... PGDip 9FT 24-48PT

University of Salford
Sports Injury Rehabilitation.........................MSc 36PT/PGDip 24PT/ PGCert 12PT
Trauma and Orthopaedics .... MSc 12FT 36PT/PGDip 8FT 24PT/ PGCert 4FT 9PT

Sheffield Hallam University
Sport Injury Management and Therapy .....MSc 12FT 24PT/PGDip 8FT 16PT/PGCert 4FT 8PT
Sport and Exercise Psychology.................................MSc 12FT 24PT

University of Southampton
Health and Rehabilitation........MSc 12FT 24PT/PGDip 12FT 24PT/ PGCert 8FT 16PT
Physiotherapy .... MSc 24FT

St Mary's University College, Twickenham
Applied Sport Psychology.......MA 12FT 24PT/PGDip 24PT/PGCert 12PT
Applied Sport and Exercise Physiology .... MA 12FT 24PT/PGDip 12PT/PGCert 12PT
Nutrition and Physical Activity for Public Health............ MSc 12FT

Staffordshire University
Applied Sport and Exercise Science ....PGCert 12FT 7DL/PGDip 14DL/MSc 24DL
Sport and Exercise Psychology (Distance Learning) ..PGCert 7DL/ PGDip 14DL/MSc 24DL

University of Stirling
Psychology of Sport ....MSc 9FT 24PT/PGDip 9FT 24PT/ PGCert 6FT 12PT
Sport Nutrition (International Olympic Committee Upgrade)...... MSc 6FT 12PT

Teesside University
Advanced Clinical Practice (Manipulative Therapy) .... MSc 36PT
Advanced Clinical Practice (Neurolgical Rehabilitation)MSc 36PT
Advanced Sports Therapy and Rehabilitation Science... MSc 12FT 24PT
Movement Science and Rehabilitation....................MSc 12FT 24PT
Sports Therapy ....MSc 18FT 36PT

Trinity College Dublin - the University of Dublin
Sports and Exercise Medicine.. MSc 12FT

UCL - University College London
Sports Medicine, Exercise and Health.. MSc 12FT 24-60PT/PGDip 9FT

University of Worcester
Sports Therapy .... MSc 12FT

Sports therapy
Research Courses

Bangor University
Sport, Health and Exercise Sciences ....MPhil 12FT/PhD 36FT

Barts and the London School of Medicine and Dentistry
Department of Sports Medicine............................PhD/MPhil/FRCS

University of East Anglia
Physiotherapy ....PhD 36FT 72PT/MPhil 24FT 48PT/ MSc by research 12FT 24PT

University of Kent
Sport, Exercise Science and Sports Therapy........MPhil 24FT 36PT/ PhD 36FT 60PT

University of Nottingham
Sports and Exercise Medicine.......DM 36FT 72PT/PhD 36FT 72PT/ MPhil 24FT 48PT

University of Stirling
Sports Studies .... PhD 36FT 72PT/MPhil 12FT 24PT

Swimming
Taught Courses

University of Edinburgh
Swimming Science...PGCert 24PT

Yoga
Taught Courses

Bucks New University
Health, Exercise & Wellbeing ....MSc 12FT 24PT

University of Central Lancashire
Advanced Legal Practice ....LLM 12FT 24PT/PGDip 12FT

University of Roehampton
Biomechanics .... PGDip 9FT 24-48PT

Teacher training and education

Adult and continuing education

Taught Courses

University of Aberdeen
Effective Teaching in Numeracy....PGCert 12PT
Plurilingual Education....MEd 24PT/PGCert 12PT
Teaching Qualification in Further Education....PGCert 12PT

Anglia Ruskin University
Learning and Teaching (Higher Education)....MA 12FT 36PT/PGCert 36PT/PGDip 36PT

Bangor University
Education Doctorate Programme (EdD)....EdD by taught 60PT
Education Studies... MA 12FT 24-60PT/MEd 12FT 24-60PT/PGDip 8FT 24-48PT/PGCert 4FT 12-24PT

University of Bedfordshire
Post-Compulsory Education....PGCE 24PT/CertEd 24PT

Birmingham City University
Post-Compulsory Education and Training....PGCE 12FT 24PT

University of Bolton
Teaching and Learning in Higher Education....PGCert 18PT

University of Bradford
Higher Education Practice....PGCert 12PT
Training and Development....MEd 36DL/PGDip 24DL

University of Brighton
Post-Compulsory Education....PGCE 12 - 48FT 24 - 60PT/CertEd 12 - 48FT 24 - 60PT/Cert 12 - 48FT 24 - 60PT

Canterbury Christ Church University
Lifelong Education and Professional Practice....MA 24PT

Cardiff Metropolitan University
Post Compulsory Education and Training...PGCE 24-60PT/CertEd 24-60PT

Cardiff University
Education (PCET)....PGCE 12FT PGCE 24PT

University of Central Lancashire
Education (Lifelong Learning)....PGCert 12FT 24PT/PGCE 12FT 24PT
Practice Teacher....PGCert 6PT
Professional Practice in EducationMEd 24-60PT/PGCert 24-60PT/PGDip 24-60PT

University of Chester
Work Based Learning Facilitation....PGCert 12-36PT

City University London
Academic Practice....MSc 12FT 24PT/PGDip 12FT/PGCert 9FT

University College Cork
Education....PGDE 9FT
Education (Sc)....MA(Ed) 24PT
Masters in Education (Modular)....MA(Ed) 12FT

Cornwall College
Education....PGCE 21PT

University of Cumbria
Learning and Teaching in Higher Education....PGCert 18PT

University Centre Doncaster
Education In-Service....PGCE 24PT
Education Pre-Service....PGCE 12FT

Dublin Institute of Technology
Third Level Learning and TeachingPGCert 9PT/PGDip 9PT/MA 9PT

University of Dundee
Advanced Practice (Practice Education)....MSc 36DL
Teaching Qualification (Further Education)....TQFE 9PT 36DL
Teaching in Higher Education (CertTHE)....PGCert 24PT

University of East Anglia
Adult Literacy, Lifelong Learning & Development....MA 12FT
Advanced Educational Practice....MA 36PT/MA 48PT
Mathematics Education....MA 12FT

University of East London
Learning and Teaching in Higher Education....MA 36PT/PGDip 24PT/PGCert 12PT

Edge Hill University
Post-Compulsory Education and Training (DTLLS)....PGCE 24PT

Edinburgh Napier University
Advanced Practice and Applied Education (Distance Learning)....Msc/PGDip/PGCert 36PT
Blended and Online Education....MSc 12-24PT/PGDip 9-18PT/PGCert 6-12PT

University of Edinburgh
Research-Informed Science Education (Online Distance Learning)....PGCert 21PT 21DL

Falmouth University
Creative Education....PGCHE 12PT/PGDip 12PT/MA 12PT

National University of Ireland Galway
Teaching and Learning in Higher Education....Cert ModularPT/Diploma ModularPT/MA ModularPT

Glasgow Caledonian University
Health and Social Care Education....MSc 12FT

Glasgow School of Art
Learning and Teaching (Creative Practices)....PGCert 4FT 8PT
Supervision (Creative Practices)....PGCert 4FT 8PT

University of Glasgow
Adult & Continuing Education....MSc 12FT 24PT
Learning and Teaching in Higher Education....MEd 36DL/PGDip 24DL
Teaching Adults....MSc 12FT 24PT/PGDip 9FT 18PT

University of Gloucestershire
Academic Practice....PGCert 9PT

Glyndwr University
Professional Development in Higher Education (PGCPD)....GradCert 12PT

Goldsmiths, University of London
Higher Specialist Social Work: Practice Education....PGDip 24PT
Management of Learning & Teaching in Higher Education....MA 12FT 24-60PT

University of Greenwich
Adult Literacy for Subject Specialists/ESOL for Subject Specialists....Professional Development Certificate 1PT
Higher Education....MA 12FT 24PT/PGDip 24PT/PGCert 12PT
Level 5 Diploma in teaching ESOL/Literacy/Numeracy....Cert 12PT
Post-compulsory Education / Lifelong Learning..PGCE 12FT 24PT

University of Huddersfield
Higher Education Practice....MA 36PT/PGDip 24PT/PGCert 12PT
Teacher Training (Lifelong Learning) pre-service....PGCE 12FT

ifs School of Finance
Higher Education....PGCert 12PT 12DL

Institute of Education
Adult Literacy, Language and Numeracy (inc. PG Cert Adult Literacy and ESOL Teaching)....MA 24-48PT/PGCert 12PT
Higher and Professional Education....MA 12FT 24-48PT
Lifelong Learning....MA 12FT 24-48PT
Post-Compulsory PGCE: In-service....PGCE 24PT
Post-Compulsory PGCE: Literacy and ESOL... PGCE 12-24PT/PGCE 12FT
Post-Compulsory PGCE: Mathematics with Numeracy... Diploma 24PT/Diploma 12FT
Post-Compulsory PGCE: Pre-service FT....PGCE 12FT
Post-Compulsory PGCE: Pre-service PT....PGCE 24PT
Teaching and Learning in Higher and Professional Education....MA 12FT 24-48PT

Keele University
Learning and Teaching in Higher Education....MA

Kingston University
Design with Learning and Teaching in Higher Education....MA 12FT 24PT
Professional Education and Training....MA 36PT/PGDip 24PT

London Metropolitan University
Learning and Teaching in Higher Education....MA 12-72PT/PGCert 12-36PT
Teaching Adult Dyslexic Learners in Higher and Further Education....PGCert 12PT

London South Bank University
Training the Teacher Trainers....PGCert 12-24PT

Manchester Metropolitan University
Education (Post-compulsory Education and Training..PGCE 12FT

National University of Ireland, Maynooth
Adult & Community Education....MA 12FT 24PT
Arts (Adult Guidance & Counselling)....HDip 12FT
Arts (Application of Information and Communication Technology in Education)....HDip 12FT
Education....HDip 12FT

Middlesex University
Lifelong Learning....MA 12FT 24PT 36DL

Newcastle University
Education: International Perspectives....MA 12FT

Newman University
Education....MA 36PT

Northumbria University
Academic Practice ..DProf by taught 24PT/MA 36PT/PGDip 24PT/PGCert 12PT
Advanced Practice in Post Compulsory Education and Training...PGCert 12PT
Advanced Practice in Post Compulsory Education and Training (Literacy)....PGCert 12PT
Advanced Practice in Post Compulsory Education and Training (Numeracy)....PGCert 12PT
Post Compulsory Education and Training....PGCE 24PT/CertEd 12PT

Norwich City College of Further and Higher Education
Post-compulsory Education....PGCE 10FT

Nottingham Trent University
PGCE/ProfGCE/CertEd: Lifelong Learning Sector (Pre-Service)....PGCE 10FT/ProfGCE 10FT/CertEd 10FT

University of Nottingham
International Higher Education....MA 12FT 24PT

The Open University
Academic Practice....PGCert 24DL

Oxford Brookes University
Education....MA 12FT 24PT
Education (Delivered at Solihull College)....MA 12FT 24PT
Education, Post-compulsory - Certificate in Education/PGCE....PGCE 12FT 24PT
Education: Artist Teacher Scheme (PGCert Advanced Educational Practice)....PGCert 12PT
Education: Gifted and Talented Education (PGCert Advanced Educational Practice)....PGCert 12PT
Education: National Award for Senco Co-ordination (PGCert Advanced Educational Practice)....PGCert 12PT

University of Oxford
Educational Studies (Higher Education)....MSc 12FT

Plymouth University
Post Compulsory Education & Training...PGCE 12FT 24PT/CertEd 12FT 24PT

University of Portsmouth
Learning and Teaching....MA 24PT
Post Compulsory Education....PGCE (Postgraduate) 12FT 24PT/PGCE (Professional) 12FT 24PT

Queen Margaret University, Edinburgh
Professional and Higher Education....PGCert 12-24PT

Queen's University Belfast
Education....EdD by taught 36-72FT 48-96PT
Educational Studies....MEd 12FT 60PT
Educational, Child and Adolescent Psychology DECAP....PsychD by taught 36FT

University of Roehampton
Education....PGCert 6FT 24PT
English Education....PGCert 6FT 12+PT

Rose Bruford College
PG Certificate in Learning and Teaching in Higher Education (Theatre & Performing Arts)....PGCHE 12PT

University Campus Suffolk
PGCE Lifelong Learning Sector....PGCE 12FT 24PT

Sheffield Hallam University
Education....MRes variousFT variousPT
Education - Research Degree....MPhil 24FT 36PT/PhD by taught 36-48FT 48-84PT
Education for International Students....MA 12FT/MSc 12FT
Learning and Teaching in Higher Education....PGCert 12PT
Post Compulsory Education and Training...MA 12FT 36PT/PGDip 24PT/PGCert 12PT

University of Sheffield
Applied Professional Studies in Education....MA 24-36DL
Education....MA 12FT
Psychology and Education....MA 12FT

University of South Wales
Developing Professional Practice in Higher Education..Cert 12FT
Leadership and Management (PCET)....MA 24 - 60PT

University of Southampton
Education Practice and Innovation....MSc 12FT 24PT

St Mary's University College, Twickenham
Education: Leading Innovation and ChangeMA 12FT 24PT/PGDip 24PT/PGCert 12PT
Education: Pedagaogy and Professional practice in Physical Education....MA 36PT/PGDip 24PT/PGCert 12PT
Education: Pedagogy and Professional Values and Practice (International students)....MA 10FT

Staffordshire University
Higher and Professional Education....PGCHE 9PT

University of Stirling
Educational Research....MSc 12FT 30PT
Professional Learning and Leadership....MSc 36PT
Teaching Qualification in Adult Education (TQAE)....PGCert 12PT
Teaching Qualification in Further Education (TQFE)..PGCert 12FT

University of Strathclyde
Adult Guidance....MSc 36DL/PGDip 24DL/PGCert 12DL
Advanced Academic Studies....PGDip 18PT/PGCert 10PT
Education....EdD by taught 36-72PT/MEd 24-36PT 24-36DL

University of Sunderland
Advancing Pedagogy....MA 24PT
PG/CE in Post Compulsory Education and Training (PCET)...PGCE 12FT 24PT/CertEd 12FT 24PT

Swansea Metropolitan University
Education....MA(Ed) 24 - 60PT

Teesside University
Education (Doctorate)....EdD by taught 48FT 72PT
Educational Studies....MA 12FT 24PT

University of Ulster
Education (Further)....PGCE 9PT

Teacher training and education

University of Warwick
Learning in Practice.. PGA 12PT/CPDMod 1PT

University of the West of England, Bristol
Education: PGCE Post-Compulsory Education and Training
(PCET) .... PGCE 12FT

University of Westminster
Higher Education................................. MA 24DL PGCert 24DL

University of Winchester
Research Degree Supervision ....PGCert up to 36PT

University of Worcester
Higher Education ....MA 24PT/PGDip 18PT/PGCert 12PT
Teaching & Learning in Higher Education....................PGCert 48PT

Adult and continuing education
Research Courses

Birkbeck, University of London
Education/Lifelong Learning ..... MPhil 24FT 36PT/PhD 24FT 36PT

City University London
Department of Continuing Education ....PhD/MPhil

University of East Anglia
Applied Research in Education............PhD 36FT 72PT/MPhil 24FT
48PT/MA by research 12FT 24PT
Counselling Studies ....PhD 36FT 72PT/MPhil 24FT 48PT/MA by
research 12FT 24PT
Higher Education and Society ....PhD 36FT 72PT/MPhil 24FT
48PT/MA by research 12FT 24PT
Literacy and Development Group ....PhD 36FT 72PT/MPhil 24FT
48PT/MA by research 12FT 24PT
Mathematics Education PhD 36FT 72PT/MPhil 24FT 48PT/MA by
research 12FT 24PT
Pedagogy and Engagement with Learning............PhD 36FT 72PT/
MPhil 24FT 48PT/MA by research 12FT 24PT
Physical Education Pedagogy Group ....PhD 36FT 72PT/
MPhil 24FT 48PT/MA by research 12FT 24PT
Spirituality and Religion in Education....................PhD 36FT 72PT/
MPhil 24FT 48PT/MA by research 12FT 24PT

University of Glasgow
Education.........PhD 36FT 60PT/MPhil 12FT 24PT/MSc by research
12FT 24PT/EdD 36-60DL

Keele University
Education............... PhD 24-48FT 48-84PT/MPhil 12-24FT 24-36PT

King's College London
Higher Education Research .. MPhil 24FT 36PT/PhD 36FT 48-72PT

University of Leeds
Lifelong Learning & Continuing Education.... PhD 36FT 48PT/EdD
36FT 48PT

National University of Ireland, Maynooth
Adult Education ....PhD 36FT/MLitt by research 24FT

Newcastle University
Education (Clinical) .... MPhil 12FT 24PT/PhD 36FT 72PT

University of Nottingham
CELE Research Staff and Interests ....PhD 36FT 72PT/MPhil 24FT
48PT
Cognitive Development and Learning ....PhD 36FT 72PT/
MPhil 24FT 48PT

The Open University
Doctorate in Education ....EdD 36PT

Oxford Brookes University
Education and Childhood Studies .... MPhil/PhD 36-60FT
48-72PT/PhD 24-60FT 36-72PT/MPhil 24-36FT 36-48PT

University of Portsmouth
Education and Continuing Studies .....MPhil 24FT 48PT/PhD 36FT
72PT

Queen's University Belfast
Education.. PhD 36FT 72PT/MPhil 24FT 48PT

University of Salford
Higher Education Research ....PhD/MPhil

Sheffield Hallam University
Education................................ PhD 48FT 84PT/MPhil 48FT 84PT

Swansea University
Adult and Continuing Education............................PhD 36FT 60PT/
MPhil 12FT 36PT

Art and design teaching
Taught Courses

University of Aberdeen
Community Learning and Development....MSc 36PT/PGDip 24PT

Bangor University
Secondary Education... PGCE 12FT

Birmingham City University
Artist Teacher Scheme Short Course .... Short Course 4PT
Arts and Education.. MA 12FT 24PT
Secondary Education (Art & Design)......................PGCE(QTS) 12FT

University of Brighton
(Secondary) Art and Design .... PGCE 12FT 16PT

Ethics of Art and Design .... MA 12FT 24PT/PGDip 12FT 24PT/
PGCert 12FT 24PT

Canterbury Christ Church University
Applied Art and Design (14-19) PGCE .... PGCE(QTS) 12FT
Art and Design (11-18) PGCE................................ PGCE(QTS) 12FT

University of Central Lancashire
Transdisciplinary Design............................... MA 12FT 24PT

University of Chester
Education: Creativity and Education for the Professions.........MA
24-72PT/PGDip 24-60PT/PGCert 12-36PT

University for the Creative Arts
Learning and Teaching in the Creative Arts ....PGCert 12FT

University of Derby
Art and Design: Applied Practice and Theories (ADAPT)................
MA 17FT 34PT

Edge Hill University
Secondary Applied Art and Design (Age Phase 14-19) with QTS..
PGCE 12FT

University of Exeter
Creative Arts in Education.....PGCert 12FT/PGDip 12FT/MEd 12FT

Glasgow School of Art
Learning and Teaching (Creative Practices) ....PGCert 4FT 8PT
Supervision (Creative Practices)................................PGCert 4FT 8PT

University of Glasgow
Art, Style & Design: Renaissance to Modernism..........MLitt 12FT/
PGDip 12FT

Goldsmiths, University of London
Artist Teachers & Contemporary Practices ...... MA 36PT/MA 12FT
Design Education................................... MA 12FT 24-36PT
Fine Art...................... MFA 24FT 36ft&ptPT/MFA 48PT/PGDip 12FT
Participatory and Community Arts.. PGCert 12FT 24-60PT/PGDip
12FT 24-60PT/MA 12FT 24-60PT

Institute of Education
Art and Design .... PGCE 16PT
Art and Design in Education.. MA 12FT 24PT

King's College London
Education in Arts & Cultural Settings .... MA 12FT 24-48PT

Kingston University
Design with Learning and Teaching in Higher Education
.... MA 12FT 24PT
Fine Art with Learning and Teaching in Higher Education ....MA
12FT 24PT

Leeds Metropolitan University
Art & Design... MA 12FT 24PT

Liverpool John Moores University
Art and Design - Traditional (11-16), Applied (14-19) ....
PGCE 12FT

Manchester Metropolitan University
Secondary Education with QTS............................... PGCE(QTS) 12FT

University of St Mark and St John
PGCE 14-19 Diploma Creative and Media...................... PGCE 12FT
PGCE Secondary Art and Design............................... PGCE 12FT

National University of Ireland, Maynooth
Arts (Adult Guidance & Counselling)................................HDip 12FT

Middlesex University
PGCE Secondary Art and Design................................... PGCE 12FT

Northumbria University
Secondary Education (Art, Craft and Design) PGCE...... PGCE 12FT

University of Nottingham
Creative and Professional Practice in Arts and Education ....MA
24PT

University of Reading
Art & Design (Secondary Teaching) .... PGCE 10FT

University of Roehampton
Art, Craft and Design Education.................................. MA 12FT 24PT
Art, Craft and Design Education .... PGCert 6FT 24PT
Art, Craft and Design Education ....PGDip 9FT 24PT

University of Salford
Art and Design: Contemporary Fine Art................. MA 12FT 36PT/
PGDip 8FT 24PT
Art and Design: Creative Education...... MA 12FT 24PT/PGDip 8FT
15PT
Art and Design: Product Design .. MA 12FT 24PT/PGDip 9FT 15PT

Sheffield Hallam University
Design and Technology Education .... MA 36PT/PGDip 24PT/
PGCert 12PT
Design and Technology Education ....INSET courses variousPT

Art and design teaching
Research Courses

Bath Spa University
Arts Education.................................PhD 24 - 60FT 36 - 72PT

Glasgow School of Art
Art and Design .... PhD 36FT 60PT/MPhil 12FT 24PT

Goldsmiths, University of London
Art...MPhil 24FT 36PT/PhD 36-48FT 48-72PT
Art Practice & Learning...MPhil 24FT 36PT/PhD 36-48FT 48-72PT

Oxford Brookes University
Arts ....MPhil/PhD 36-60FT 48-72PT/PhD 24-60FT 36-72PT/
MPhil 24-36FT 36-48PT

Autism
Taught Courses

University of Aberdeen
Autism & Learning.................MEd 36PT/PGDip 14PT/PGCert 12PT

Bangor University
Applied Behaviour Analysis ....PGCert 4FT 9PT/PGDip 9FT 18PT/
MSc 12FT 24PT

University of Birmingham
Autism (Adults)..PGCert 12DL/PGDip 24DL/MEd 24-72DL/MPhil
24-36DL
Autism (Children) ..PGCert 3FT 12PT 12DL/PGDip 12FT 24-48DL/
MEd 12FT 24-72DL/MPhil 12FT 24-36DL

University of Central Lancashire
Personality Disorder (Practice Development) .... MSc 36-60PT/
PGDip 24PT
Personality Disorder (Research).......MSc 36-60PT/PGDip 12-24PT

University of Kent
Autism Studies......PGCert 12FT 24PT/PGDip 12FT 24PT/MA 12FT
24PT
Autism Studies (Distance Learning) .... PGCert 12FT 24DL/
MA 12FT 24PT/PGDip 12FT 24PT

Manchester Metropolitan University
Autistic Spectrum Conditions .... MA 12-60PT

Northumbria University
Autism..........................MA 36PT/PGDip 24PT/PGCert 12PT

Queen's University Belfast
Autism Spectrum Disorders.....................................MSc 12FT 60PT

Sheffield Hallam University
Asperger Syndrome...PGCert 12-24PT
Autism.............................MA 36PT/PGDip 24PT/PGCert 12PT

University of South Wales
Autism..MA 12-24FT 36-60PT

University of St Andrews
Adults Support, Protection and Safeguarding............PGCert 12DL

University of Strathclyde
Autism................................MSc 12FT 24PT/PGDip 12FT/PGCert 9FT

Autism
Research Courses

University of Nottingham
Cognitive Development and Learning ....PhD 36FT 72PT/
MPhil 24FT 48PT

Biology teaching
Taught Courses

Anglia Ruskin University
Postgraduate Certificate in Education: Secondary Science with
Biology .... PGCE 12FT

Bangor University
Secondary Education.. PGCE 12FT

University of Brighton
(Secondary) Biology .... PGCE 12FT 16PT

Brunel University
Secondary Education (Science: Biology) with recommendation
for QTS..PGCert 12FT 24PT

University of Chester
Education: PGCE Secondary Science with Biology Enhancement
PGCE(QTS) 12FT

University of Derby
Conservation Biology...MSc 12FT 36PT

University of East London
Secondary Science: Biology: Postgraduate Certificate in
Education.. PGCE 12FT

Edge Hill University
Secondary Science (Biology) (Age Phase 11-16) with QTS.... PGCE
12FT 36PT

Glasgow Caledonian University
Life Sciences - Biological and Biomedical Sciences/Psychology/
Vision Sciences...MRes 12FT

Imperial College London
Conservation Science .... MSc 12FT

Liverpool John Moores University
Science - Biology, Chemistry, Physics (11-16) , Applied Chemistry
or Physics (14-19) PGCE .... PGCE 12FT

Teacher training and education

Biology teaching
Research Courses

University of Aberdeen
Biological Science....MSc by research 12FT/MPhil 24FT/PhD 36FT

Business studies teaching
Taught Courses

Canterbury Christ Church University
Applied Business Studies (14-19) PGCE................ PGCE(QTS) 12FT

Edge Hill University
Secondary Business Education (Age Phase 14-19) with QTS PGCE 12FT 36PT

University of Exeter
Finance..GradDip 9FT

Gloucestershire SCITT Consortium
PGCE in Business Education..................................... PGCE(QTS) 12FT

Leeds Metropolitan University
Doctorate of Business Administration................................DBA 48PT

University of Manchester
PGCE Secondary Business Education................................ PGCE 10FT

Middlesex University
PGCE Secondary Business Studies .... PGCE 10FT

University of Portsmouth
Business Studies...........................PGCE (Postgraduate) 12FT/PGCE (Professional) 12FT

Sheffield Hallam University
Secondary Business Education................................ PGCE(QTS) 12FT

Southampton Solent University
Business Studies .... MA 24-72PT 24-72DL

University of Sunderland
PGCE Business Education - Secondary (1 year).... PGCE(QTS) 12FT
PGCE Business Education 2 years........................... PGCE(QTS) 12FT

Business studies teaching
Research Courses

University of Aberdeen
Finance.. PhD 36FT/MPhil 24FT/MRes 12FT

Careers education
Taught Courses

University of Aberdeen
Pastoral Care, Guidance and Pupil Support...................MEd 24BM

Coventry University
Career Guidance .... PGDip 12FT 24PT

University of Derby
Education..EdD by taught 36-72PT
Education: Guidance Studies ....MA Up to 72PT
Graduate Teacher Programme ....QTS 12FT 24PT

University of Dundee
Advanced Practice (Practice Education) ....PGCert 12DL
Advanced Practice (Practice Education) ....PGDip 24DL
Diabetes Care and Education ....MSc 36-40PT
Diabetes Care and Education ....PGCert 12-15PT
Diabetes Care and Education ....PGDip 24-27PT
Education (Chartered Teacher)......................MEd 18PT/PGDip 9PT/PGCert 6PT
Educational Psychology .... MSc 24FT
Global Internship Graduate Certificate (India).........GradCert 8FT

University of East London
Career Coaching ....MA 12FT 24PT/PGDip 8FT 16PT/PGCert 4FT 8PT

Edinburgh Napier University
Career Guidance (Top Up) ....MSc 12DL
Career Guidance and Development ....PGDip 12FT 24DL

Falmouth University
Creative Education..................PGCHE 12PT/PGDip 12PT/MA 12PT

University of Huddersfield
Professional Studies (Guidance)........................... PGDip 12FT 24PT

University of Limerick
Guidance Counselling and Lifespan Development...........MA 24PT

London South Bank University
Careers Guidance - Add on Masters .... MSc 12PT
Careers Guidance with QCG .... PGDip 12FT 24PT

Manchester Metropolitan University
Careers Guidance and Qualification in Careers Guildance (QCG). PGDip 12FT 24PT

National University of Ireland, Maynooth
Arts (School Guidance & Counselling).............................HDip 12FT

Nottingham Trent University
Career Guidance/Qualification in Careers Guidance....... Diploma 12FT 24PT
Professional Practice.. MA 1.5PT 3DL

Plymouth University
Clinical Education...........MClinEd 36PT/PGDip 24PT/PGCert 12PT

University of Strathclyde
Adult Guidance.....................MSc 36DL/PGDip 24DL/PGCert 12DL
Education for Work and Enterprise..................... PGDip max 48PT/PGCert max 24PT

University of Ulster
Careers Guidance ....MSc 18PT/PGDip 12FT

University of the West of Scotland
Careers Guidance .... MSc 24PT/PGDip 12FT 24PT/PGCert 24PT
Careers Guidance and Development...... MSc 24PT/Diploma 12FT 24PT/Cert 24PT

Careers education
Research Courses

University of Central Lancashire
Politics and International studies .... MPhil 18-36FT 42-60PT/PhD 30-48FT 66-84PT/MA by research 12FT 24PT
Sociology, Ethnicity & Human Rights, Criminology .... PhD 30-48FT 66-84PT/MPhil 18-36FT 42-60PT/MA by research 12FT 24PT

University of Dundee
Education (MPhil).......................MPhil 24FT MSc by research 12FT PhD 36FT

University of Hertfordshire
Centre for Research in Employment Studies.........PhD 36FT 72PT/MPhil 24FT 48PT/MRes 12FT 24PT

Chemistry teaching
Taught Courses

Anglia Ruskin University
Postgraduate Certificate in Education: Secondary Science with Chemistry .... PGCE 12FT

Bangor University
Secondary Education .... PGCE 12FT

University of Bedfordshire
Chemistry Enhancement...PGCE 6FT

Birmingham City University
Secondary Education (Science with Chemistry) .... PGCE 12FT

University of Brighton
(Secondary) Chemistry..PGCE 12FT 16PT

Brunel University
Secondary Education (Science: Chemistry) with recommendation for QTS ....PGCert 12FT 24PT

University of Chester
Education: PGCE Secondary Science with Biology Enhancement... .... PGCE(QTS) 12FT
Education: PGCE Secondary Science with Chemistry Enhancement .... PGCE(QTS) 12FT

University of East London
Secondary Science: Chemistry: Postgraduate Certificate in Education... PGCE 12FT

Edge Hill University
Secondary Science (Chemistry) (Age Phase 11-16) with QTS .... PGCE 12FT 36PT

University of Manchester
PGCE Secondary Chemistry... PGCE 10FT

University of Portsmouth
Science with Chemistry ....PGCE (Postgraduate) 12FT/PGCE (Professional) 12FT

Chemistry teaching
Research Courses

Keele University
Chemistry .... PhD 36FT 60PT/MPhil 12FT 24PT

Citizenship teaching
Taught Courses

University of Aberdeen
Divinity and Religious Studies...................................MTh 12FT 24PT

Canterbury Christ Church University
Citizenship (11-18) PGCE... PGCE(QTS) 12FT

University of Central Lancashire
Education and History...MA 24PT

University of Cumbria
Society, Health and Development Education..........GradCert 18PT

Glasgow Caledonian University
Citizenship and Human Rights by Learning Contract...MSc 12FT/PGDip 12FT/PGCert 12FT
Social Enterprise .... PGCert 6PT

Glasgow School of Art
Design and Citizenship .... MDes 12FT 24PT/PGDip 9FT 21PT/PGCert 4FT 9PT

Institute of Education
Humanities Education (Citizenship/History/Religious Education) MA 12FT 24-48PT

London Metropolitan University
PGCE Secondary Citizenship... PGCE 12FT

Middlesex University
PGCE Secondary Citizenship... PGCE 10FT

Newman University
PGCE Secondary Citizenship.................................. PGCE(QTS) 12FT

University of Nottingham
Global Citizenship, Identities and Human Rights.. MA 12FT 24PT

Sheffield Hallam University
Secondary Citizenship.. PGCE 48PT

University of South Wales
Education for Sustainable Development and Global Citizenship. MA 12FT 36PT

University of Ulster
Peace and Conflict Studies with Early Years (Applied)..PGDip 9FT 18PT/MSc 12FT 36PT

University of York
Global and International Citizenship Education - Institute for Effective Education ....MA 12FT

Citizenship teaching
Research Courses

Manchester Metropolitan University
Master of Research Education and Society...........MRes 12FT 24PT

The Open University
Citizenship and Governance......PhD 36FT 72PT variableDL/MPhil 15FT 24PT variableDL

Classics teaching
Taught Courses

University of Bristol
Classical Reception.. MA 12FT 24PT

University of St Andrews
Classical Studies ....PGDip 9FT/MLitt 12FT 24PT
Latin ....PGDip 12-24FT 24PT/MLitt 12FT 24PT

Classics teaching
Research Courses

University of St Andrews
Classics...PhD 36FT 72PT/MPhil 24FT

Coaching and mentoring
Taught Courses

University of Aberdeen
Coaching... PGCert 6-8PT

Bangor University
Applied Sport Science.. MA 12FT 36PT
Applied Sport Science..MSc 12FT 36PT
Applied Sport Science (Outdoor Activities)............. MA 12FT 36PT
Applied Sport Science and Outdoor Activities....... MSc 12FT 36PT
Applied Sport and Exercise Physiology.................... MA 12FT 36PT
Applied Sport and Exercise PhysiologyMSc 12FT 36PT/PGDip 8FT
Applied Sport and Exercise Psychology .... MA 12FT 36PT
Applied Sport and Exercise Psychology .... MSc 12FT 36PT
Exercise Rehabilitation.. MA 12FT 36PT
Exercise Rehabilitation..MSc 12FT 36PT
Sport and Exercise Physiology................................MRes 12FT 36PT
Sport and Exercise Psychology...............................MRes 12FT 36PT
Sport and Exercise Psychology (BPS Accredited)... MSc 12FT 36PT
Sport and Exercise Sciences....................................MRes 12FT 36PT

University of Birmingham
AdCert in Golf Coaching ....AdvCert 12PT
Golf Coaching..AdvCert 12-36PT
Sports Coaching.. MSc 24-48PT/PGDip 24PT

University of Bradford
Training and Development ....MEd 36DL/PGDip 24DL

University of Brighton
Masters in Teaching and Learning (MTL).. PGDip 12-36PT/PGCert 12-36PT
Post-Compulsory Education ....PGCE 12 - 48FT 24 - 60PT/CertEd 12 - 48FT 24 - 60PT/Cert 12 - 48FT 24 - 60PT

University of Central Lancashire
Adventure Sport Coaching...MA 12FT
Sports Coaching............................MA 12FT 24PT/PGDip 12FT 24PT

Central School of Speech and Drama, University of London
Actor Training and Coaching .... MA 12FT 24PT

University of Chester
Business and Personal Coaching (Work Based and Integrative Studies) ....MA 24-72PT/PGDip 24-60PT/PGCert 12-36PT
Coach-Mentoring and Facilitation in Organisations (Work Based and Integrative Studies)............MA 24-72PT/MSc 24-72PT/PGDip 24-60PT/PGCert 12-36PT
Coaching Skills & Practice (Work Based and Integrative Studies) MA 24-72PT/MSc 24-72PT/PGDip 24-60PT/PGCert 12-36PT
Coaching Supervision (Work Based and Integrative Studies)..MA 24-72PT/PGDip 24-60PT/PGCert 12-36PT

Teacher training and education

Coaching for Internal Business Solutions and Team Development (WBIS).......................MA 24-72PT/PGDip 24-60PT/PGCert 12-36PT
Education: Inclusion and Marginalisation......MA 36-72PT/PGDip 36-60PT/PGCert 12-36PT
Emotional Intelligence (Work Based and Integrative Studies) MA 24-72PT/MSc 24-72PT/PGDip 24-60PT/PGCert 12-36PT
Executive Coaching (Work Based and Integrative Studies) ......MA 24-72PT/MSc 24-72PT/PGDip 24-60PT/PGCert 12-36PT
Facilitation (Work Based and Integrative Studies)....MA 24-72PT/MSc 24-72PT/PGDip 24-60PT/PGCert 12-36PT
Mentoring (Work Based and Integrative Studies).....MA 24-72PT/MSc 24-72PT/PGDip 24-60PT/PGCert 12-36PT
Neuro Linguistic Programming (Work Based and Integrative Studies) ....MA 24-72PT/MSc 24-72PT/PGDip 24-60PT/PGCert 12-36PT

University of Cumbria
Development Training............. MA 24DL/PGDip 15DL/PGCert 9DL
Sport Coaching and Sport Development .... MA 12FT 24PT

University of Derby
Leadership Coaching ....MA 36PT

University of East London
Coaching / Coaching Psychology ....MSc 24PT/PGDip 16PT/PGCert 8PT
Coaching Psychology .....MSc 12FT 24PT/PGDip 8FT 16PT/PGCert 4FT 8PT
Emotional Factors in Learning and Teaching: Counselling Aspects in Education (D1) MAMA 36PT/PGDip 24PT/PGCert 12PT
Integrative Counselling and Coaching PG CertificatePGCert 12PT
Theatre Directing ......MA 12FT 24PT/PGDip 8FT 16PT/PGCert 4FT 8PT

Edinburgh Napier University
Advanced Practice and Applied Education (Distance Learning)....Msc/PGDip/PGCert 36PT

Falmouth University
Creative Education ....PGCHE 12PT/PGDip 12PT/MA 12PT

University of Gloucestershire
Postgraduate Certificate in Mentoring and Coaching PGCert 8PT
Sports Coaching..MSc 12FT 24PT
Work with Children, Young People, their Families and CarersMSc 12FT 24PT

Goldsmiths, University of London
Higher Specialist Social Work: Practice Education...... PGDip 24PT

Heriot-Watt University
Business Psychology........ MSc 12FT 24-84PT 12-84DL/PGDip 9FT 15-48PT 9-48DL/PGCert 6FT 12-48PT 6-48DL

University of Hertfordshire
Leading Learning ....MA 12FT 24PT/MEd 12FT 24PT/PGDip 12FT 24PT/PGCert 12FT 24PT

University of Huddersfield
Leadership in Education and Public Services........... MA 12FT 36PT

University of Hull
Mentoring in Education................................... MEd 36-60PT

Institute of Education
Postgraduate Certificate in Coaching and Mentoring........ PGCert 12PT

Leeds Metropolitan University
Coaching Psychology.. PGDip 24PT
Coaching Supervision .... PGDip 24PT
Executive & Business Coaching.................. MA 12PT/PGCert 12PT
Sport Coaching...MSc 12FT 24PT

University of Limerick
Educational Mentoring ..... PGCert 12PT/GradDip 24PT/MEd 36PT

Liverpool John Moores University
Advanced Educational Practice (Mentoring and Coaching) ....PGCert 12PT

Manchester Metropolitan University
Coaching and Mentoring......................PGCert 24-60PT/Cert 12PT
Exercise and Sport.......................................MSc 12FT 24-36PT
Exercise and Sport - Biomechanics ....MS 12FT 24-36PT
Exercise and Sport - Coaching Studies...............MSc 12FT 24-36PT
Exercise and Sport - Physiology ....MSc 12FT 24-36PT
Exercise and Sport - Sport Development ....MSc 12FT 24-36PT
Exercise and Sport -Psychology ....MSc 12FT 24-36PT
Practice Development ....MSc 24-72PT

Newcastle University
Coaching and Mentoring for Teacher Development .... PGCert 12FT

Nottingham Trent University
Professional Coaching Practice......................................PGCert 12PT

University of Nottingham
Mentoring and Coaching...PGCert 12PT 6DL

Oxford Brookes University
Coaching and Mentoring Practice ....MA 24-60PT/PGDip 24-60PT/PGCert 12PT
Coaching and Mentoring Practice (Delivered in Hong Kong)........MA 24-60PT
Coaching and Mentoring Supervision .... PGCert 9PT

University of Portsmouth
Coaching and Development ....PGCert 12PT PGDip 12PT MSc 12PT

Queen Margaret University, Edinburgh
Collaborative Working: Education and Therapy ...PGCert 12-48PT

Sheffield Hallam University
Coaching and Mentoring.........MSc 30PT/PGDip 15PT/PGCert 7PT
Mentoring ....PGCert 12PT

University of Sunderland
Coaching for Organisational Excellence ....MA 18PT

Trinity College Dublin - the University of Dublin
Development Practice .... MSc 24FT

University of the West of England, Bristol
Leadership and Management (Coaching and Mentoring)...... MSc 12FT

University of Wolverhampton
Coaching and Mentoring...MA 24PT

Coaching and mentoring
Research Courses

Bangor University
Sport, Health and Exercise Sciences.............MPhil 12FT/PhD 36FT

University of East Anglia
Counselling Studies ....PhD 36FT 72PT/MPhil 24FT 48PT/MA by research 12FT 24PT
Higher Education and Society..PhD 36FT 72PT/MPhil 24FT 48PT/MA by research 12FT 24PT
Literacy and Development Group ....PhD 36FT 72PT/MPhil 24FT 48PT/MA by research 12FT 24PT
Mathematics Education.........PhD 36FT 72PT/MPhil 24FT 48PT/MA by research 12FT 24PT
Pedagogy and Engagement with Learning............PhD 36FT 72PT/MPhil 24FT 48PT/MA by research 12FT 24PT
Physical Education Pedagogy Group ....PhD 36FT 72PT/MPhil 24FT 48PT/MA by research 12FT 24PT
Spirituality and Religion in Education....................PhD 36FT 72PT/MPhil 24FT 48PT/MA by research 12FT 24PT

Heriot-Watt University
Applied Psychology .... PhD 36FT 48PT/MPhil 24FT 36FT

Oxford Brookes University
Doctorate in Coaching and Mentoring - Professional Doctorate.. DCaM 36-60PT

Community teaching
Taught Courses

University of Bedfordshire
Community Dance Leadership................................... MA 12FT 24PT

University of Brighton
Inclusive Arts Practice ....MA 24-72PT/PGCert 24-72PT

University of Edinburgh
Community Education ....MSc 12FT 24-36PT

Goldsmiths, University of London
Applied Anthropology & Community Development ....MA 12FT 24PT

University of Sheffield
Education: Working with Communities...................... MA(Ed) 12FT

University of Strathclyde
Community Care........MSc 36PT N/ADL/PGDip 24PT/PGCert 12PT

Dance teaching
Taught Courses

University of Bedfordshire
Dance Performance & Choreography .... MA 12FT 24PT
Secondary Education Dance .... PGCE 12FT

University of Brighton
(Secondary) Dance ....PGCE 12FT 16PT

University of Central Lancashire
Dance and Somatic Well-being.......MA 24PT/PGDip 24PT/PGCert 24PT

University of Chester
Education: Creativity and Education for the Professions..........MA 24-72PT/PGDip 24-60PT/PGCert 12-36PT

Middlesex University
Professional Practice (Dance Technique Pedagogy) ....MA 16PT
Professional Practice in Dance Technique Pedagogy........MA 18PT

University of Roehampton
Choreography ....MFA 24FT 48PT
Community Dance .... MA 12FT 24-36PT
Dance Studies... MA 12FT 24PT
Choreography and Performance ....MRes 12FT 24PT

Deaf teaching
Taught Courses

University of Birmingham
Multisensory Impairment (Deafblindness) ...PGCert 12DL/PGDip 24DL/MEd 36-72DL
Teachers of Children with Hearing Impairment........... MEd 36DL/PGDip 24DL

University of Bristol
Deafhood Studies.......................................MPhil 12FT 60PT

University of Central Lancashire
Child Care Practice, PQ Specialist Award with Children, Young People, Families & Carers...PGCert 18PT

University of Edinburgh
Additional Support for Learning (Deaf Education) ....MEd 72PT/PGDip 48PT/PGCert 24PT

University of Hertfordshire
Education of Deaf Children..PGDip 12FT 24PT/PGCert 12FT 24PT

University of Leeds
Deaf Education (Teacher of the Deaf Qualification)........................MA 12FT 24PT

University of Manchester
Deaf Education...................................... MSc 36PT/PGDip 12FT 24PT
Deaf Education.............................MSc 36PT/PGDip 12FT 24PT 24DL

Newcastle University
Evidence Based Practice in Communication Disorders.. MSc 12FT 24PT/PGDip 24PT/PGCert 12PT

University of Reading
Speech and Language Therapy .... MSc 24FT

University of Sheffield
Professional Practice with Children and Families ....MA 36PT

University of South Wales
SEN Hearing Impairment .... PGDip leading to MA SEN 24PT

Deaf teaching
Research Courses

University of Bristol
Deaf Studies.................................. PhD 36FT 72PT/MPhil 36FT 72PT

UCL - University College London
Speech, Hearing and Phonetic Sciences.................. PhD 36FT 60PT

Design and technology teaching
Taught Courses

Birmingham City University
Secondary Education (Design & Technology: Food & Textiles)......PGCE(QTS) 12FT

University of Brighton
(Secondary) Design and Technology.......................PGCE 12FT 16PT
(Secondary) Design and Technology (2 year).................. PGCE 24FT

Canterbury Christ Church University
Design and Technology (11-18) PGCE ....PGCE(QTS) 12FT
Design and Technology (7-14) PGCE.......................PGCE(QTS) 12FT

University of Chichester
Secondary Design and Technology ....PGCE(QTS) 9.5FT

University of East London
Secondary Design and Technology (Food & Textiles) ....PGCE 12FT

Edge Hill University
Secondary Design and Technology (Age Phase 11-16) with QTS ..PGCE 12FT 36PT

Gloucestershire SCITT Consortium
PGCE in Design and Technology ....PGCE 12FT

Goldsmiths, University of London
Design Education...MA 12FT 24-36PT

Liverpool John Moores University
Design and Technology (PGCE) ....PGCE 12FT
Engineering... PGCE 12FT

University of Manchester
PGCE Secondary Design & Technology ....PGCE 10FT

Northumbria University
Secondary Education (Design and Technology SCITT)
.... PGCE 12FT

Sheffield Hallam University
Design and Technology Education ....INSET courses variousPT
Design and Technology Education .... MA 36PT/PGDip 24PT/PGCert 12PT
Secondary Design and Technology .... PGCE 12FT
Secondary Design and Technology .... PGCE(QTS) 12FT
Secondary Design and Technology (Textiles) .... PGCE(QTS) 12FT
Secondary Design and Technology - Food Technology....................PGCE 12FT

University of South Wales
Secondary Design and Technology .... PGCE 12FT

Business and social sciences

524 POSTGRADUATE DIRECTORY www.prospects.ac.uk/findcourses

Section sponsored by

BPP
UNIVERSITY
COLLEGE

Teacher training and education

University of Sunderland
PGCE Design and Technology - (Food and Textiles) 18months......
PGCE(QTS) 18FT
PGCE Design and Technology - Secondary Education 1 year.........
PGCE(QTS) 12FT
PGCE Design and Technology Education 2 year... PGCE(QTS) 24FT

Design and technology teaching
Research Courses

Bath Spa University
Educational Innovation and Technology .... PhD 24 - 60FT
36 - 72PT

Goldsmiths, University of London
Design ....MRes 12FT 24PT

The Open University
Education research in design ....PhD 36FT 72PT variableDL/MPhil
15FT 24PT variableDL

Drama teaching
Taught Courses

University of Aberdeen
Plurilingual Education.....................................MEd 24PT/PGCert 12PT

Birmingham City University
Secondary Education (Drama)................................... PGCE(QTS) 12FT

University of Birmingham
Shakespeare and Education.......................MA 12FT 24PT 24-72DL/
PGDip 12FT 24PT 24-72DL

Central School of Speech and Drama, University of London
PG Certificate in Applied Theatre with Young People
....PGCert 12FT
PGCE Drama...PGCE(QTS) 12FT
Voice Studies .... MA 12FT/MFA 24FT

University of Chester
Education: Creativity and Education for the Professions..........MA
24-72PT/PGDip 24-60PT/PGCert 12-36PT
Education: PGCE Secondary Drama........................ PGCE(QTS) 12FT
Education: Singing in the Curriculum...................PGCert 12 - 36PT

Edge Hill University
Secondary English (Age Phase 11-16) with QTS ..PGCE 12FT 36PT

University of Glasgow
Primary Expressive Arts ....PGCert 12FT

King's College London
Creative Arts in the Classroom .... MA 12FT 24-48PT

Middlesex University
PGCE Secondary Drama... PGCE 12FT

University of Nottingham
Creative and Professional Practice in Arts and Education ....MA
24PT

University of Reading
Drama (Secondary Teaching).................................... PGCE 10FT

University of Wales Trinity Saint David
Drama and Education: Context and Practice .... MA 24PT/PGDip
12PT/PGCert 12PT

University of Warwick
Drama and Theatre Education ..... MA 12FT 24-48PT/PGDip 12FT/
PGCert 12FT/PGA 3FT

Drama teaching
Research Courses

Bath Spa University
Arts Education..PhD 24 - 60FT 36 - 72PT

University of Exeter
Drama.. PhD 48FT 89PT/MPhil 36FT 60PT

Queen's University Belfast
Drama Studies.............................. PhD 36FT 72PT/MPhil 24FT 48PT

Dyslexia in education
Taught Courses

University of Aberdeen
Plurilingual Education.................................MEd 24PT/PGCert 12PT
Studies in Mindfulness .... MSc 36PT/PGDip 24PT/PGCert 12PT

Bath Spa University
Specific Learning Difficulties / Dyslexia ....MA 12FT 72PT/MTeach
12FT 72PT/PGCert 4FT 12PT/PGDip 9FT 24PT

University of Bristol
Education: Special and Inclusive Education .... MEd 12FT 24-60PT

University of Chester
Education: Dyslexia Research and Practice.....MA 36-72PT/PGDip
36-60PT/PGCert 12-36PT
Education: Inclusion and Marginalisation ......MA 36-72PT/PGDip
36-60PT/PGCert 12-36PT
Work Based Learning Facilitation............................PGCert 12-36PT

Edge Hill University
Specialist Dyslexia Training for Teachers................PGCert 12-18PT

Edinburgh Napier University
Advanced Practice and Applied Education (Distance Learning)....
Msc/PGDip/PGCert 36PT

University of Edinburgh
Additional Support for Learning (Learning Disabilities)..........MEd
72PT/PGDip 48PT/PGCert 24PT

National University of Ireland Galway
Special Educational Needs .... PGDip 12PT

Institute of Education
SpLD - Specific Learning Difficulties (Dyslexia)....... MA 18FT 36PT

University of Leeds
Special Educational Needs ....MA 12FT 24PT/PGDip 12FT 24PT

Liverpool John Moores University
Advanced Educational Practice (Dyslexia) ....PGCert 12PT

London Metropolitan University
Assessment for Specific Learning Difficulties in FE and HE...........
PGDip 12PT
Teaching Adult Dyslexic Learners in Higher and Further
Education..PGCert 12PT

London South Bank University
Adult Dyslexia Diagnosis and Support (ADDS)..................MA 36PT
Multi-Sensory E-Learning and Dyslexia Support..PGCert 12-24PT
Teachers of Adults with Learning Difficulties ....PGCert 12-24PT

Manchester Metropolitan University
Specific Learning Difficulties (Further Education and Higher
Education) ....MA 24-60PT/PGDip 24PT/PGCert 12PT

Northumbria University
Teaching Pupils With Dyslexia ....PGCert 12PT

University of Reading
Education (Inclusive Education).....MA 12FT 24-84PT/PGDip 12FT

University of Sheffield
Speech Difficulties .... PGDip 12FT 24PT/PGCert 12FT 24PT

University of South Wales
SEN Specific Learning Difficulties.........................PGDip 12FT 24PT

University of Southampton
Specific Learning Difficulties (Dyslexia)...................MSc 12FT 24PT

University of St Andrews
Adults Support, Protection and Safeguarding............PGCert 12DL
Adults with Learning Disabilities who have Significant and
Complex Needs......................MSc 12DL/PGDip 12DL/PGCert 12DL

Teesside University
Promoting Inclusive Practice in Education............ PGDip 24 - 36PT

E-learning studies
Taught Courses

Birkbeck, University of London
Learning Technologies..MSc 12FT 24PT

University of Bolton
E-Learning for Educationalists .... MA 12FT 24-60PT

Bucks New University
Technology Enhanced Learning..................... MSc 12FT 24PT 12DL

University of Chester
Learning and Development (Work Based and Integrative
Studies) ....MA 24-72PT/MSc 24-72PT/PGDip 24-60PT/PGCert
12-36PT

Dublin Institute of Technology
Applied E Learning .... MSc 24PT

University of East London
e-Health MSc.... MSc 12FT 24PT/PGDip 8FT 16PT/PGCert 4FT 8PT

Edinburgh Napier University
Advanced Practice and Applied Education (Distance Learning)....
Msc/PGDip/PGCert 36PT
Blended and Online Education ....MSc 12-24PT/PGDip 9-18PT/
PGCert 6-12PT

University of Glasgow
Learning and Teaching in Higher Education.......MEd 36DL/PGDip
24DL

Glyndwr University
Learning & Technology ....MSc 36FT/PGDip 24FT/PGCert 12FT

University of Hertfordshire
E-Learning Technology...MSc 12-16FT

University of Huddersfield
Technology Enhanced Learning ....MSc 12FT 36PT

University of Hull
E-Learning (Education) (via the internet)...... MEd 30-108PT 36DL

King's College London
ICT Education .... MA 12FT 24-48PT

Newcastle University
E-Business .... MSc 12FT
E-Business (E-Marketing) .... MSc 12FT

The Open University
Academic Practice ....PGCert 24DL
Online and Distance Education .... MA variableDL/PGDip
variableDL/PGCert variableDL

University of Oxford
Educational Studies (E-learning) .... MSc 12FT

University of Southampton
Authoring and Researching eLearning and eTeaching ....
PCES 12DL

University of Wales Trinity Saint David
Technology Enhanced Learning .... PGCert 24PT 24DL

University of York
Human-Centred Interactive Technologies .... MSc 12FT

E-learning studies
Research Courses

Bath Spa University
Educational Innovation and Technology .PhD 24 - 60FT 36 - 72PT

University of Nottingham
Cognitive Development and Learning ....PhD 36FT 72PT/
MPhil 24FT 48PT

The Open University
Education and Educational Technology.......EdD 36PT variableDL/
PhD 36FT 72PT variableDL/MRes 12FT/MPhil 15FT 24PT
variableDL
Educational Dialogue ....PhD 36FT 72PT variableDL/EdD 36PT/
MRes 12FT
Educational studies..............PhD 36FT 72PT/EdD 36PT/MRes 12FT
Language Learning and Teaching....... PhD 36FT 72PT variableDL/
MRes 12FT/EdD 36PT
Multimodal meaning making......PhD 36FT 72PT variableDL/EdD
36PT/MRes 12FT
Technology Enhanced Learning ...PhD 36FT 72PT variableDL/EdD
36PT/MRes 12FT
Technology, communication and education .... PhD 36FT 72PT
variableDL/MPhil 15FT 24PT variableDL

Early childhood education
Taught Courses

University of Aberdeen
Early Years Education...PGCert 12DL
Enhanced Professional Practice ....MSc 24PT/PGDip 12PT

Anglia Ruskin University
Early Childhood Professional Studies....................... MA 12FT 36PT

Bangor University
Applied Behaviour Analysis ....PGCert 4FT 9PT/PGDip 9FT 18PT/
MSc 12FT 24PT
Education........ PhD by taught 36FT 48-60PT/MPhil 24FT 36-48PT
Education Doctorate Programme (EdD) .... EdD by taught 60PT
Education Studies... MA 12FT 24-60PT/MEd 12FT 24-60PT/PGDip
8FT 24-48PT/PGCert 4FT 12-24PT

University of Bedfordshire
Primary Education with Early years .... PGCE 12FT

University College Birmingham
Childhood, Professional Studies in Childhood ..... MA 24PT/PGDip
24PT/PGCert 24PT
Early Years PGCE..PGCE 12FT

University of Chester
Early Childhood......MA 24-72PT/PGDip 24-60PT/PGCert 12-36PT
Early Years Practice with Early Years Professional Status (EYPS) ...
PGCert 12FT
Education: PGCE Early Years .... PGCE(QTS) 12FT

University of Cumbria
Leading Intergrated Children's Services ....MSc 24 - 60PT

University of Derby
Education...EdD by taught 36-72PT
PGCE Primary... PGCE 12FT

University of Dundee
Education (Chartered Teacher).....................MEd 18PT/PGDip 9PT/
PGCert 6PT
Educational Psychology .... MSc 24PT

University of East Anglia
Early Childhood Studies...MA 36PT

University of East London
Early Childhood Studies ....MA 12FT 24PT/PGDip 8FT 16PT/
PGCert 4FT 8PT

Edge Hill University
Early Years with QTS... PGCE 12FT

University of Glasgow
Childhood Practice .... PGDip 24PT

University of Gloucestershire
Teacher Training PGCE (Primary) .... PGCE 12FT

Goldsmiths, University of London
Education (Primary) .... PGCE 12FT
Education: School-Based Explorations......................... MA 24-60PT

University of Hertfordshire
Early Years....MA 12FT 24PT/PGDip 12FT 24PT/PGCert 12FT 24PT

University of Huddersfield
Early Childhood Studies.................................... MA 12FT 36PT
Early Childhood Studies with EYPS .... PGCert 12FT 6PT

Section sponsored by

BPP
UNIVERSITY
COLLEGE

Business and social sciences
www.prospects.ac.uk/findcourses POSTGRADUATE DIRECTORY 525

Teacher training and education

Early Years Professional Status Graduate Entry Pathway........EYPS 12FT

University of Hull
Early Childhood Studies...................................MEd 12FT 24PT

Institute of Education
Early Years Education............................... MA 12FT 24-48PT
Sociology of Childhood and Children's Rights .. MA 12FT 24-48PT

Leeds Metropolitan University
Childhood Studies and Early Years........................... MA 12FT 24PT
Early Childhood Education - PGCE .... PGCE 12FT

Liverpool John Moores University
Early Years (3 -7 years).. PGCE 12FT

London Metropolitan University
Early Years and Primary Education........................... PGCE 12FT

Manchester Metropolitan University
Childhood Studies and Practice in the Early Years ....
MA 12FT 60PT
Early Years Professional Status (EYPS) ...EYP Full Training Pathway 15PT

University of St Mark and St John
Postgraduate Certificate Early Years...........................PGCert 12FT

Middlesex University
Early Years Professional Studies...........................PGCert 12FT
PGCE Early Years... PGCE 12FT
PGCE Primary Education.................................. PGCE 12FT

Newcastle University
Education: International Perspectives ....MA 12FT

Newman University
Children, Young People and Families.................. MA 24FT 36-48PT
Early Years Foundation Degree ....FdA 36PT
Early Years Teacher Status .... Early Years Teacher Status 6FT/Early Years Teacher Status 12FT
Education...MA 36PT

Northumbria University
Early Years and Primary (Flexible) PGCE .... PGCE 12-24DL

Oxford Brookes University
Advanced Early Years Specialism (PGCert Advanced Educational Practice)...PGCert 12PT
Childhood Studies MA 12FT 24PT/PGDip 12FT 24PT/PGCert 12FT 12PT
Children, Young People and Family Well-Being ....MSc 12-36DL/ PGDip 8-36DL/PGCert 4-36DL
Education .... MA 12FT 24PT
Education (Delivered at Solihull College) .... MA 12FT 24PT
Education: Artist Teacher Scheme (PGCert Advanced Educational Practice) ....PGCert 12PT
Education: Gifted and Talented Education (PGCert Advanced Educational Practice)...PGCert 12PT
Education: National Award for Senco Co-ordination (PGCert Advanced Educational Practice)..........................PGCert 12PT

University of Oxford
Education (Child Development and Education)............... MSc 12FT

Queen's University Belfast
Education...EdD by taught 36-72FT 48-96PT
Educational Studies ....MEd 12FT 60PT

University of Reading
Education (Early Years) ....MA 12FT 24-84PT/PGDip 12FT
Primary Teaching (Early Years)................................PGCE 10FT

University of Roehampton
Early Childhood Studies.. MA 12FT 24PT
Early Childhood Studies................................PGCert 12FT 24PT PGDip 12FT 24PT

University Campus Suffolk
Childhood and Youth Studies............................ MA 12FT 24 - 36PT

Sheffield Hallam University
Early Childhood Studies MA 12FT 36PT/PGDip 12FT 24PT/PGCert 12FT 12PT
Early Years Education.. PGCE 12FT
Early Years Professional Status .... EYPS 12FT 6-15PT
Education...MRes variousFT variousPT
Education - Research Degree...... MPhil 24FT 36PT/PhD by taught 36-48FT 48-84PT
Education for International Students .... MA 12FT/MSc 12FT

University of Sheffield
Early Childhood Education ....MA 24-36DL

University of South Wales
Early Years.. MA 12FT 36PT

St Mary's University College, Twickenham
Education: Leading Innovation and Change...........MA 12FT 24PT/ PGDip 24PT/PGCert 12PT
Education: Pedagaogy and Professional practice in Physical Education.................................MA 36PT/PGDip 24PT/PGCert 12PT
Education: Pedagogy and Professional Values and Practice (International students) ....MA 10FT

University of Strathclyde
Early Childhood Studies........ MSc 24PT/PGDip 24PT/PGCert 24PT

University of Sussex
Effective Practice in Children's Services..... MA 60PT/PGDip 60PT/ PGCert 60PT

Swansea Metropolitan University
Education..MA(Ed) 24 - 60PT

Teesside University
Education (Doctorate) ....EdD by taught 48FT 72PT
Educational Studies .... MA 12FT 24PT

University of Wales Trinity Saint David
Early Years Education...............MA 48PT/PGDip 18PT/PGCert 12PT
Plentyndod Cynnar................MA 48PT/PGCert 12PT/PGDip 18PT

University of the Highlands and Islands
Socio-Legal Issues of Childhood ....PGCert 12FT 24PT

University of Worcester
Early Childhood........................ MA 6FT 24-36PT/PGDip 12FT 24PT/ PGCert 12FT 12PT

Early childhood education
Research Courses

Bangor University
Education...........................PhD 36FT 60-72PT/MPhil 24FT 36-48PT

University of Dundee
Education ....MPhil 24FT MSc by research 12FT PhD 36FT

Goldsmiths, University of London
Art Practice & Learning...MPhil 24FT 36PT/PhD 36-48FT 48-72PT

Heriot-Watt University
Applied Psychology .... PhD 36FT 48PT/MPhil 24FT 36PT

Newcastle University
Education (Clinical) .... MPhil 12FT 24PT/PhD 36FT 72PT

The Open University
Educational studies.............. PhD 36FT 72PT/EdD 36PT/MRes 12FT
Issues in health and social care of children, young people and families .... PhD 36FT 72PT/MPhil 15FT 24PT

Oxford Brookes University
Education and Childhood Studies .... MPhil/PhD 36-60FT 48-72PT/PhD 24-60FT 36-72PT/MPhil 24-36FT 36-48PT

Queen's University Belfast
Education.................................. PhD 36FT 72PT/MPhil 24FT 48PT

Sheffield Hallam University
Education.............................. PhD 48FT 84PT/MPhil 48FT 84PT

Economics teaching
Taught Courses

University of Aberdeen
Economics.. MSc 12FT

Institute of Education
Economics of Education...... MSc 12FT 24-48PT/MA 12FT 24-48PT

University of Surrey
Economics... MA 12FT 24PT

University of Sussex
Economics.................................... MSc 12FT 24PT/GradDip 9FT

Education management
Taught Courses

University of Aberdeen
Advanced Educational Studies.. MEd 12FT 24PT 48DL/PGDip 9FT 18PT 36DL
Advanced Professional Studies......MEd 12FT/PGDip 12FT/PGCert 12FT
Community Learning and Development....MSc 36PT/PGDip 24PT
Effective Teaching in Numeracy.....................................PGCert 12PT
Leadership in Professional Contexts.................................MSc 24PT
Learning and Development (Primary)...........................PGCert 12PT

Bath Spa University
Education Studies...MA 12FT

Birkbeck, University of London
Education, Power and Social Change .. MSc 12FT 24PT/PGDip 6FT 15PT/PGCert 3FT 6PT
Higher Education (PGCE) ....PGCert 12PT

University of Birmingham
Management of Special Education in Developing Countries .... MEd 12FT 24PT/PGDip 12FT 24PT
Professional Studies.....MEd 12FT 24PT/PGDip 12FT 24PT/PGCert 3FT 12PT/AdvCert 3FT 12PT
School Improvement and Educational Leadership.... MA 12-24FT 24-48PT/PGDip 24-48PT/PGCert 12-24PT

University of Bolton
Educational Management .... MA 12FT 24-60PT

University of Brighton
Doctorate in Education ....MA 48PT/MSc 48PT
Education (International Education) ....MA 12FT 36PT/ PGDip 24PT/PGCert 12PT
Education (Leadership and Management) MA.... MA 24PT/PGDip 24PT/PGCert 12PT
Professional Education Studies.......................................PGCert 12PT

University of Bristol
Education: Educational Leadership, Policy & Development...MEd 12FT 24-60PT

Brunel University
Education (Educational Management)..................... MA 12FT 24PT

University of Buckingham
Educational Leadership..MEd 18FT

Bucks New University
Leadership & Management in the Public Sector.............MA 24PT

Canterbury Christ Church University
Leadership and Management for Learning ....MA 36PT
Literacy and Learning..MA 36PT

University of Chester
Education and Teaching Studies (Work Based and Integrative Studies) ....MA 24-72PT/MSc 24-72PT/PGDip 24-60PT/PGCert 12-36PT
Education: Leadership and Management.....MA 24 - 72PT/PGDip 24 - 60PT/PGCert 12 - 36PT
Educational Leadership (Work Based and Integrative Studies)..... MA 24-72PT/MSc 24-72PT/PGDip 24-60PT/PGCert 12-36PT
Leadership Development (Work Based and Integrative Studies) ....MA 24-72PT/MSc 24-72PT/PGDip 24-60PT/PGCert 12-36PT
Leadership and Management (Work Based and Integrative Studies) ....MA 24-72PT/MSc 24-72PT/PGDip 24-60PT/PGCert 12-36PT
Learning and Development (Work Based and Integrative Studies) ....MA 24-72PT/MSc 24-72PT/PGDip 24-60PT/PGCert 12-36PT
Personal Leadership Development (Work Based and Integrative Studies) ....MA 24-72PT/PGDip 24-60PT/PGCert 12-36PT
Transpersonal Leadership (Work Based and Integrative Studies) ....MA 24-72PT/MSc 24-72PT/PGDip 24-60PT/PGCert 12-36PT

University College Cork
Educational Administration.. PGDip 24PT

University of Derby
Education...EdD by taught 36-72PT

University Centre Doncaster
Education In-Service..PGCE 24PT
Education Pre-Service...PGCE 12FT
Education, Innovation & Enterprise .... MA 12FT 24PT

University of Dundee
Advanced Practice (Organisational Leadership) ....MSc 36DL
Education (Chartered Teacher)....................MEd 18PT/PGDip 9PT/ PGCert 6PT
Educational Psychology .... MSc 24FT

Durham University
Education... MA 12FT 36PT

University of East Anglia
Adult Literacy, Lifelong Learning & Development ....MA 12FT
Advanced Educational Practice......................... MA 36PT/MA 48PT
Education...MA 12FT
Mathematics Education...MA 12FT
Social Science Research Methods: Psychology ....MRes 12FT 24PT
Social Science Research Methods: Social Work ...MRes 12FT 24PT

University of East London
Creative Leadership in Education MA ....MA 24PT/PGCert 16PT/ PGDip 8PT

Edge Hill University
Management of International Higher Education ....MA 24PT

Edinburgh Napier University
Managerial Leadership .... MSc 12FT

University of Edinburgh
Developing Educational Leadership and Learning.....PGCert 24PT
Educational Leadership and Management (including the Scottish Qualification for Headship Diploma) ... PGDip 27PT/MEd 33PT/PGCert 15PT

University of Exeter
Education Taught Doctorate......... EdD by taught 24FT 48PT 48DL
Educational Research ....MSc 12FT 24PT 12-24DL
Professional Studies...MEd 36PT

National University of Ireland Galway
Education: Master of..MEd 12PT
Professional Education Studies... PGDip 12PT
Professional Education Studies [School Planning]...... PGDip 12PT

Glasgow Caledonian University
Health and Social Care Education .... MSc 12FT

University of Glasgow
Community Learning & Development..................MEd 12FT 24PT/ PGDip 9FT 18PT
International Management and Leadership .... MSc 12FT
Learning and Teaching in Higher Education.......MEd 36DL/PGDip 24DL
Middle Leadership & Management in Schools (Inservice Programme)...PGCert 24+PT
Organisational Leadership..................................MSc 12FT 24PT
Organisational Leadership (Oman)............MSc 24PT/PGDip 18PT/ PGCert 12PT
Professional Development in Education .... PGCert 60 maxPT

Teacher training and education

School Leadership & Management (Scottish Qualification for Headship) (inservice programme)................................... PGDip 24PT

University of Gloucestershire
Educational Leadership........... MEd 24PT/PGDip 20PT/PGCert 8PT

Glyndwr University
Education................................ PGCE 12FT 24-36PT/CertEd 24-36PT
Professional Education........... MSc 12FT 24-60PT/DipMedEd 24FT 24-36PT/CertMedEd 6FT 12PT

Goldsmiths, University of London
Education: School-Based Explorations.......................... MA 24-60PT
Global Leadership.. MSc 12FT

University of Hertfordshire
Leading Learning.......MA 12FT 24PT/MEd 12FT 24PT/PGDip 12FT 24PT/PGCert 12FT 24PT

University of Huddersfield
Action Research for Education........ MA 36PT/PGDip 24PT/PGCert 12PT
Leadership in Education and Public Services........... MA 12FT 36PT
Learning & Development Managment.................... MA 12FT 36PT
Professional Work-Based Learning Suite............................MA 36PT

University of Hull
Education......................MEd 12FT 24-72PT/AdvDip 12FT 24-72PT/AdvCert 6FT 12-36PT
Leadership and Learning ....MEd 12FT 24PT

Institute of Education
Development Education.. MA 12FT 24PT
Educational Leadership (International) ....MBA 24-48PT
Educational Planning, Economics and International Development .... MA 12FT 24-48PT
European Masters: Lifelong Learning Policy and Management.... MA 12FT
Harris Academy Leadership ....MA 24PT
Higher Education Management...MBA 24PT
Intensive Course in Education Management Information Systems (EMIS)... Intensive Course 3FT
Leadership .... MA 12FT 24-48PT
Lifelong Learning: Policy and Management.... European Master's 24FT
National Professional Qualification for Headship (NPQH)............. Headship Qualification 4-18DL
School Effectiveness and School Improvement................................ MA 12FT 24-48PT

Keele University
Education MBA......... MBA 28PT 28DL/DBA by taught 20PT 20DL/PGCert 15PT
Educational Leadership, Management and Learning ....MA 24PT/PGDip 18PT/Cert 10PT
Leadership and Management ....PGCert 12PT

University of Kent
Higher Education..........................PGDip 12FT 24PT/MA 12FT 24PT
Higher Education (PGCHE)... PGCHE 24FT

King's College London
Education Management....................................... MA 12FT 24-48PT
Further Education Management.......................MBA 12FT 24-48PT

Lancaster University
Human Resources and Consulting....................................MA 12FT
Management Learning and Leadership.................... MA 12FT 24PT

Leeds Metropolitan University
Leadership & Management.........................MSc 36PT/PGDip 36PT
Multi Unit Leadership ....MSc 12FT 24PT
Professional Development ....PGCert 12PT

University of Leeds
International Educational Management..... MA 12FT/PGDip 12FT

University of Leicester
Educational Leadership...MSc 24-48DL

Liverpool John Moores University
Advanced Educational Practice (Leadership and Management)... PGCert 12PT

Loughborough University
Management and Leadership (Higher Education Administration) MSc 30PT/PGDip 18PT

Manchester Metropolitan University
Doctor of Education...................................EdD by taught 48-72PT
Education Business Management ....MSc 24-72PT
Education Studies... MA 12FT 24PT
Educational Leadership and Management................MSc 36-60PT
Management and Leadership ....Cert 6PT
Teaching and Learning....................................... MA 12-18PT

University of Manchester
Educational Leadership and Improvement......................MA 24PT
Educational Leadership and School Improvement ....MA 12FT
Educational Leadership and School Improvement (Inclusive Education) MA...MA 12FT

National University of Ireland, Maynooth
Educational Management ....HDip 12FT

Middlesex University
Education, MA .....MA 36PT 36DL/PGCert 12PT 12DL/PGDip 24PT 24DL

Education: Leadership, Management and Change........................ MA 18FT 24PT

Northumbria University
Education with Leadership ....MEd 12FT

Nottingham Trent University
Doctorate in Business Administration ....DBA by taught 36PT

University of Nottingham
Educational Leadership and Management............MA 12FT 24PT/PGDip 9FT 18PT/PGCert 6FT 12PT
International Higher Education .... MA 12FT 24PT

University of Oxford
Education (Child Development and Education)............... MSc 12FT

University of Reading
Education (Leadership and Management)........MA 12FT 24-84PT/PGDip 12FT

University of Roehampton
Education... MA 12FT 24PT
Education Leadership and Management ....MA 12FT 24+PT PGCert 6FT 12+PT PGDip 9FT 18+PT

Sheffield Hallam University
Advanced Professional Development ....MSc VAFT/PGDip VAFT/PGCert VAFT
Leadership and Management in Education...........MSc 12FT 36PT/PGDip 12FT 24PT/PGCert 12FT 12PT

University of Sheffield
Applied Professional Studies in Education.................MA 24-36DL
Education...MA 12FT

University of South Wales
Leadership and Management (Education) .... MA 12FT 36PT
Leadership and Management (FE/PCET)................... MA 36- 60PT
Leadership and Management (Health Promotion & Education).. MA 36-60PT

University of Southampton
Education Management and Leadership.................MSc 12FT 24PT

St Mary's University College, Twickenham
Catholic School Leadership: Principles and Practice........MA 12FT 36PT/PGDip 24PT/PGCert 12PT

University of Stirling
Educational Leadership and Educational Leadership (SQH)... MSc 36PT/PGDip 15PT/PGCert 6PT
Professional Learning and Leadership .... MSc 36PT

University of Strathclyde
Education...............EdD by taught 36-72PT/MEd 24-36PT 24-36DL
Management and Leadership in Education........... MSc max 60PT/PGDip max 48PT/PGCert max 24PT
School Leadership and Management (SQH)..................PGDip 12FT

Trinity College Dublin - the University of Dublin
Master in Education (M.Ed.) .... MSc 12FT 24/36PT

University of Warwick
Educational Studies .... MA 12FT 24-48PT

University of West London
Management Studies (Health and Social Care) - Top up................. MA 12PT

Education management
Research Courses

Bath Spa University
Education Policy in Practice ....PhD 24 - 60FT 36 - 72PT

University of Bath
Higher Education Management ....DBA 36-96PT

Birkbeck, University of London
Education/Lifelong Learning ..... MPhil 24FT 36PT/PhD 24FT 36PT

University of Birmingham
Leaders and Leadership in Education .... EdD 36FT 72PT

University of Dundee
Education .... MPhil 24FT
MSc by research 12FT PhD 36FT

Durham University
Education.......................................EdD 36FT 72PT 72DL
Education..PhD 36FT 72PT

University of East Anglia
Applied Research in Education.PhD 36FT 72PT/MPhil 24FT 48PT/MA by research 12FT 24PT
Counselling Studies ....PhD 36FT 72PT/MPhil 24FT 48PT/MA by research 12FT 24PT
Higher Education and Society..PhD 36FT 72PT/MPhil 24FT 48PT/MA by research 12FT 24PT
Literacy and Development Group ....PhD 36FT 72PT/MPhil 24FT 48PT/MA by research 12FT 24PT
Pedagogy and Engagement with Learning............PhD 36FT 72PT/MPhil 24FT 48PT/MA by research 12FT 24PT
Physical Education Pedagogy Group ....PhD 36FT 72PT/MPhil 24FT 48PT/MA by research 12FT 24PT
Spirituality and Religion in Education.....................PhD 36FT 72PT/MPhil 24FT 48PT/MA by research 12FT 24PT

Keele University
Education Professional Doctorate.... EdD 48-84PT 48-84DL/MRes 24-36PT 24-36DL

University of Kent
Higher Education.. PhD 36FT 60PT

London Metropolitan University
Education...EdD 60PT

University of Nottingham
Educational Leadership..EdD 48PT

The Open University
Doctorate in Education ....EdD 36PT
Educational studies.............PhD 36FT 72PT/EdD 36PT/MRes 12FT
Language Policy ....PhD 36FT 72PT variableDL/EdD 36PT/MRes 12FT

University of Southampton
Doctorate in Education EdD........................... EdD 36FT 48PT

University of Warwick
Education..........MA by research 12FT 24PT/MSc by research 12FT 24PT/MPhil 24FT 36PT/PhD 36FT 60PT

Education research
Taught Courses

University of Aberdeen
Social and Educational Research ....MRes 12FT

Anglia Ruskin University
Education... MA 36 - 60PT

Bangor University
Education........ PhD by taught 36FT 48-60PT/MPhil 24FT 36-48PT
Education Doctorate Programme (EdD) .... EdD by taught 60PT
Education Studies... MA 12FT 24-60PT/MEd 12FT 24-60PT/PGDip 8FT 24-48PT/PGCert 4FT 12-24PT

Bath Spa University
Education Studies..MA 12FT

University of Bedfordshire
Education...............................MA 36-72PT/PGDip 12FT

Birmingham City University
Education...................MA 36PT/PGDip 24PT/PGCert 12PT

University of Birmingham
International Studies in Education .... MEd 12FT 72PT/MA 12FT 72PT/Diploma 12FT 48PT/Cert 6FT 24PT
International Studies in Education (Education and Development)......................MA 12FT 24/72PT/MEd 12FT 24/72PT
Learning and Learning Contexts EdD ....EdD by taught 36FT 72PT
Professional Studies.....MEd 12FT 24PT/PGDip 12FT 24PT/PGCert 3FT 12PT/AdvCert 3FT 12PT
School Improvement and Educational Leadership .... MA 12-24FT 24-48PT/PGDip 24-48PT/PGCert 12-24PT
Social Research (Education) .... MA 12FT 24PT

University of Bradford
Higher Education Practice...PGCert 12PT

University of Brighton
Doctorate in Education ....MA 48PT/MSc 48PT
Education (International Education) ....MA 12FT 36PT/PGDip 24PT/PGCert 12PT
Education MA (Higher Education)..MA 24PT/PGDip 24PT/PGCert 12PT
Ethics of EducationMA 12FT 24PT/PGDip 12FT 24PT/PGCert 12FT 24PT
Professional Doctorate in Education ....EdD by taught 60-96PT
Professional Education Studies......................................PGCert 12PT

University of Bristol
Education - Science and Education ....MSc 12FT 60PT
Education, Technology and Society...MSc 12FT 24-60PT/Diploma 12FT 24-60PT/PGCert 12FT 24-60PT
Educational Research ....MSc 12FT 36-60PT

Brunel University
Education (Science, Maths and Technology) .... MA 12FT 24PT

Bucks New University
Education...MA 24PT
Learning and Teaching in Higher Education.........PGCert 12-24PT

Canterbury Christ Church University
Educational Studies ....MA 36PT
Post Compulsory Education.......................................PCES 12FT

Cardiff Metropolitan University
Post Compulsory Education and Training ...PGCE 24-60PT/CertEd 24-60PT

Cardiff University
Education... MSc 12FT

University of Chester
Education: Leadership and Management.....MA 24 - 72PT/PGDip 24 - 60PT/PGCert 12 - 36PT
Research Methods.... MSc 12FT 24 - 72PT/PGDip 12FT 24 - 60PT/PGCert 12FT 12 - 36PT

University of Chichester
Education.............................MA(Ed) 30PT/PGDip 24PT/PGCert 12PT

Section sponsored by
BPP UNIVERSITY COLLEGE

Business and social sciences
www.prospects.ac.uk/findcourses POSTGRADUATE DIRECTORY 527

Teacher training and education

University College Cork
Masters in Education (Modular) .... MA(Ed) 12FT
Teaching & Learning in Higher Education .... PGCert 9PT

University for the Creative Arts
Learning and Teaching in the Creative Arts .... PGCert 12PT

University of Cumbria
Development Training .... MA 24DL/PGDip 15DL/PGCert 9DL

De Montfort University
Education Practice .... MA 12FT 24PT

University of Derby
Education .... EdD by taught 36-72PT
Education: Guidance Studies .... MA Up to 72PT
Graduate Teacher Programme .... QTS 12FT 24PT

University of Dundee
Advanced Practice (Practice Education) .... MSc 36DL
Education (Chartered Teacher) .... MEd 18PT/PGDip 9PT/PGCert 6PT
Educational Psychology .... MSc 24FT

Durham University
Education .... MA 12FT 36PT
Intercultural Education and Internationalisation .. MA 12FT 36PT
Research Methods (Education) .... MA 12FT 24PT

University of East Anglia
Adult Literacy, Lifelong Learning & Development .... MA 12FT
Advanced Educational Practice .... MA 36PT/MA 48PT
Clinical Education..MClinEd 12FT 36PT/PGDip 12FT 24PT/PGCert 12PT
Education .... MA 12FT
Education and Development .... MA 12FT 24PT
Mathematics Education .... MA 12FT

Edge Hill University
Early Mathematics Intervention .... PGCert 12PT/MA 24-60PT
Education .... MA 12FT 60PT
MRes Qualitative Educational Research .... MRes 18-36DL

University of Exeter
Education Taught Doctorate .... EdD by taught 24FT 48PT 48DL
Educational Research .... MSc 12FT 24PT 12-24DL

University of Glasgow
Inter-Professional Science Education & Communication .... MSc 12FT 24PT/PGDip 9FT 21PT/PGCert 9FT 21PT
Primary Expressive Arts .... PGCert 12PT
Professional Development in Education .... PGCert 60 maxPT

Glyndwr University
Education .... PGCE 12FT 24-36PT/CertEd 24-36PT

Goldsmiths, University of London
Multilingualism, Linguistics and Education .... MA 12FT 24PT
Practice Education .... MA 36-60PT/PGDip 36-60PT/PGCert 36-60PT

Institute of Education
Comparative Education .... MA 12FT 24-48PT
Curriculum, Pedagogy and Assessment .... MA 12FT 24-48PT
Educational Assessment .... MA 12FT 24-48PT/PGDip 24FT 36-60PT 24-60DL/PGCert 24FT 36-60PT 24-60DL
Effective Learning and Teaching .... MA 12FT 24-48PT
English, Globalization and Language Policy (formerly World Englishes) .... MA 12FT 24-48PT
Research for Public Policy and Practice ..MSc 12FT 24PT/30 credit module 4FT
Sociology of Education .... MA 12FT 24-48PT
Systematic reviews for Policy and Practice (Module) .... Masters Module 4PT

University of Kent
Higher Education .... PGDip 12FT 24PT/MA 12FT 24PT
Higher Education (PGCHE) .... PGCHE 24FT

King's College London
Academic Practice in Higher Education ..... MA 24PT/PGDip 18PT/PGCert 24PT
Assessment in Education .... MA 12FT 24-48PT
English in Education .... MA 12FT 24-48PT

Kingston University
Doctor of Education .... EdD by taught 60-72PT
Professional Studies in Education .... MA 24PT/PGCert 6PT/PGDip 12PT

Leeds Metropolitan University
Research Methodology .... PGCert

University of Leeds
Educational Research Methods .... MSc 12FT 24PT/PGDip 12FT 24PT

University of Leicester
International Education .... MA 12FT 24DL

Liverpool John Moores University
Education and Society .... MRes 12FT 24PT

Manchester Metropolitan University
Language Education .... MA 12-36PT

University of Manchester
Educational Research .... MSc 12FT 24PT

Newcastle University
Education Research .... MA 12FT 24PT

University of Northampton
Education .... MA 12FT 36PT/PGDip 24PT/PGCert 12PT

Norwich City College of Further and Higher Education
Post-compulsory Education .... PGCE 10FT

Nottingham Trent University
Education .... PGCert 12PT/PGDip 24PT/MA 36PT

University of Nottingham
Education .... MA 12FT 24-48PT/PGDip 18FT 36PT/PGCert 6FT 12PT
Education (Flexible) ..... MA 24PT 24DL/PGDip 18DL/PGCert 12DL
English Language Education .... MRes 12FT

The Open University
Academic Practice .... PGCert 24DL
Education .... PGCert variableDL/MEd variableDL
Integrated Practice in Childhood and Youth..PGCert 12DL/PGDip variableDL
Online and Distance Education .... MA variableDL/PGDip variableDL/PGCert variableDL
Professional Studies in Education .... PGDip variableDL/PGCert 12DL

Oxford Brookes University
Education .... MA 12FT 24PT

University of Oxford
Education (Child Development and Education) .... MSc 12FT
Education (Comparative and International Education). MSc 12FT
Educational Research Methodology .... MSc 12FT
Educational Studies (Comparative and International Education) .... MSc 12FT
Educational Studies (E-learning) .... MSc 12FT
Educational Studies (Higher Education) .... MSc 12FT

Queen's University Belfast
Educational Studies .... MEd 12FT 60PT
Educational, Child and Adolescent Psychology DECAP .... PsychD by taught 36FT

University of Reading
Inclusive Education .... MA 12FT 24-60PT
Music Education .... MA 12FT 24-60PT/PGDip 12FT 24-60PT
Primary Teaching (Early Years) .... PGCE 10FT
Primary Teaching (Primary Years) .... PGCE 10FT

University of Roehampton
Applied Music Education .... MA 12FT 24PT
Art, Craft and Design Education .... MA 12FT 24PT
Education .... MA 12FT 24PT PGCert 6FT 24PT PGDip 9FT 24PT

Sheffield Hallam University
Education - Research Degree ...... MPhil 24FT 36PT/PhD by taught 36-48FT 48-84PT
Post Compulsory Education and Training ... MA 12FT 36PT/PGDip 24PT/PGCert 12PT
Teaching English for Academic Purposes .... PGCert 12FT

University of Sheffield
Educational Research .... MA 12FT
International Health Technology Assessment ..... MSc 24-60 PTDL

University of South Wales
Education .... MA 12FT 36PT
Educational PracticeMSc 24FT 36-60PT/PGDip variedFT variedPT/PGCert variedFT variedPT
ICT and Education .... MA 12FT 36PT

Southampton Solent University
Research .... PGCert 12PT
Research Methods .... PGCert 12PT

University of Southampton
Applied Linguistics for Language Teaching .... MA 12FT 24PT
Education Practice and Innovation .... MSc 12FT 24PT
Education for Health Professionals ...... MSc 12FT 24PT/PGDip 9FT 18PT/PGCert 5PT

University of Stirling
Educational Research .... MSc 12FT 30PT

University of Strathclyde
Educational Support ...... MSc max 60PT/PGDip max 48PT/PGCert max 24PT

University of Sunderland
Teaching and Learning with ICT .... MA 12FT 36PT

Teesside University
Education (Doctorate) .... EdD by taught 48FT 72PT
Educational Studies .... MA 12FT 24PT

University of Ulster
Education with Specialisms .... PGDip 12-36PT 12-36DL/MEd 12-36PT 12-36DL

UCL - University College London
Lifelong Health and Wellbeing .... MRes 12FT

University of Warwick
Educational Studies .... MA 12FT 24-48PT
English Language Teaching (with a Specialism in ICT and Multimedia) .... MA 12FT 24-48PT

University of Winchester
Education Studies .... MA 12FT 24PT/PGDip 12FT 24PT/PGCert 12FT 24PT
Social Research in Education .... MRes 12FT 24PT

University of York
Applied Linguistics for Language Teaching .... MA 12FT
Education .... MA 12FT 24PT

Education research
Research Courses

University of Aberdeen
Education .... PhD 36FT/MPhil 24FT/EdD 36FT

Aberystwyth University
Education .... MPhil 12FT 24PT PhD 36FT 60PT

Bangor University
Education .... PhD 36FT 60-72PT/MPhil 24FT 36-48PT

Bath Spa University
Children and the Environment .... PhD 24 - 60FT 36 - 72PT
Education Policy in Practice .... PhD 24 - 60FT 36 - 72PT
Educational Innovation and Technology .... PhD 24 - 60FT 36 - 72PT

University of Bath
Education .... PhD 24-48FT 36-72PT/MPhil 12-36FT 24-48PT

Birkbeck, University of London
Education/Lifelong Learning ..... MPhil 24FT 36PT/PhD 24FT 36PT

Birmingham City University
Education .... EdD 48 - 72PT

University of Birmingham
Education and Learning PhD with Integrated Study ..... Integrated PhD 48FT 72PT
Educational Studies .... MRes 12FT 24PT

University of Bolton
Educational Organisations and Learning Technology Specialisms .... MPhil 18FT 30 - 36PT/PhD 36FT 60 - 72PT

University of Brighton
Education and Languages Research Division .... PhD 24-60FT 36-72PT/MPhil 18-36FT 30-48PT

University of Bristol
Education .... EdD 48FT 96PT PhD 36FT 72PT/MPhil 12FT 24PT

Canterbury Christ Church University
Education .... PhD 48FT 60PT/MPhil 24FT 48PT

Cardiff Metropolitan University
Education .... PhD 12-60FT

Cardiff University
Education (Professional Doctorate) .... EdD 60-84PT

University of Chester
Education .... EdD 24-84PT

University of Cumbria
Research Degrees .... MPhil 24 - 36FT 36 - 60PT/PhD 24 - 48FT 48 - 96PT

University of Dundee
Education .... MPhil 24FT MSc by research 12FT PhD 36FT

Durham University
Education .... EdD 36FT 72PT 72DL PhD 36FT 72PT

University of East Anglia
Applied Research in Education. PhD 36FT 72PT/MPhil 24FT 48PT/MA by research 12FT 24PT
Counselling Studies .... PhD 36FT 72PT/MPhil 24FT 48PT/MA by research 12FT 24PT
Higher Education and Society .. PhD 36FT 72PT/MPhil 24FT 48PT/MA by research 12FT 24PT
Literacy and Development Group .... PhD 36FT 72PT/MPhil 24FT 48PT/MA by research 12FT 24PT
Pedagogy and Engagement with Learning .... PhD 36FT 72PT/MPhil 24FT 48PT/MA by research 12FT 24PT
Physical Education Pedagogy Group .... PhD 36FT 72PT/MPhil 24FT 48PT/MA by research 12FT 24PT
Spirituality and Religion in Education .... PhD 36FT 72PT/MPhil 24FT 48PT/MA by research 12FT 24PT

University of Edinburgh
Education .... PhD 36FT 72PT/MPhil 24FT 48PT

Institute of Education
Associate of the Institute of Education .... Associate 12FT 24PT
Doctor in Education (EdD) .... EdD 48-84PT
Dual Doctor in Education (EdD) Award .... EdD 48-84PT
Educational and Social Research .... MRes 12FT 24PT

Keele University
Education .... PhD 24-48FT 48-84PT/MPhil 12-24FT 24-36PT

University of Kent
Higher Education .... PhD 36FT 60PT

King's College London
Doctorate in Education/Professional Studies .. EdD 36-72PT/DrPS 36-72PT

Lancaster University
Education and Social Justice .... PhD 48PT

Business and social sciences
528 POSTGRADUATE DIRECTORY www.prospects.ac.uk/findcourses

Section sponsored by

BPP
UNIVERSITY
COLLEGE

Teacher training and education

Educational Research .... PhD 36FT 48PT/MPhil 24FT 48PT
Higher Education: Research, Evaluation and Enhancement ...PhD 48PT

University of Leeds
School of Education ...PhD 36+FT/EdD 36+FT/MPhil 24FT/MEd by research 24+FT

Manchester Metropolitan University
Education and Society...MRes 12FT

University of Manchester
Education EdD ....EdD 72PT

Newcastle University
Education (Clinical) .... MPhil 12FT 24PT/PhD 36FT 72PT

University of Nottingham
CELE Research Staff and Interests ....PhD 36FT 72PT/MPhil 24FT 48PT
Learning Sciences Research Institute .... PhD 36FT 72PT
School of Education .... PhD 24-48FT/MPhil 12-24FT/EdD 12-24FT MRes 12FT 24PT

The Open University
Academic and Professional Communication Literacies..PhD 36FT 72PT variableDL/EdD 36PT variableDL/MRes 12FT
Doctorate in Education ....EdD 36PT
Education.....................................MRes 12FT variablePT variableDL
Education and Educational Technology.......EdD 36PT variableDL/PhD 36FT 72PT variableDL/MRes 12FT/MPhil 15FT 24PT variableDL
Education research in design ....PhD 36FT 72PT variableDL/MPhil 15FT 24PT variableDL
Educational Dialogue .... PhD 36FT 72PT variableDL/EdD 36PT/MRes 12FT
Educational studies.............. PhD 36FT 72PT/EdD 36PT/MRes 12FT
English... PhD 36FT 72PT variableDL/MPhil 15FT 24PT variableDL
Language Learning and Teaching....... PhD 36FT 72PT variableDL/MRes 12FT/EdD 36PT
Language Policy ....PhD 36FT 72PT variableDL/EdD 36PT/MRes 12FT
Multimodal meaning making......PhD 36FT 72PT variableDL/EdD 36PT/MRes 12FT
STEM Education and engagement....... PhD 36FT 72PT variableDL
Technology Enhanced Learning ...PhD 36FT 72PT variableDL/EdD 36PT/MRes 12FT
Technology, communication and education .... PhD 36FT 72PT variableDL/MPhil 15FT 24PT variableDL

Oxford Brookes University
Education and Childhood Studies .... MPhil/PhD 36-60FT 48-72PT/PhD 24-60FT 36-72PT/MPhil 24-36FT 36-48PT

Plymouth University
The Institute for Science Education...............PhD 36FT/MPhil 24FT

University of Portsmouth
Professional Doctorate in Education ....EdD 48PT

University of Roehampton
Education (Professional Doctorate)..................................EdD 72PT
Language Testing and Assessment.. PhD 24-48FT 36-60PT/MPhil 21-36FT 33-48PT

University of Southampton
Research Methodology ....MPhil 12FT 24PT

University of Ulster
Education......................MPhil 24FT 48PT/PhD 36FT 72PT 60DL/EdD 24FT 48PT

UCL - University College London
Educational and Child Psychology . Doctorate in Educational and Child Psychology 36FT

University of Warwick
Education..........MA by research 12FT 24PT/MSc by research 12FT 24PT/MPhil 24FT 36PT/PhD 36FT 60PT

University of Worcester
Education.. PhD 48FT 70PT/MPhil 24FT 48PT

University of York
Education - Institute for Effective Education.........PhD 36FT 72PT/MPhil 24FT 48PT
Education - Institute for Effective Education........................... MA by research 12FT 24PT

Educational psychology
Taught Courses

University of Aberdeen
Social and Educational Research ....MRes 12FT
Studies in Mindfulness .... MSc 36PT/PGDip 24PT/PGCert 12PT

Bangor University
Education Doctorate Programme (EdD) .... EdD by taught 60PT
Education Studies... MA 12FT 24-60PT/MEd 12FT 24-60PT/PGDip 8FT 24-48PT/PGCert 4FT 12-24PT

Birkbeck, University of London
Educational Neuroscience...............MA 12FT 24PT/MSc 12FT 24PT

University of Birmingham
Learning Difficulties and Disabilities (Severe, Profound and Complex) .... AdvCert 12DL/PGCert 12DL/PGDip 24DL/MEd 24DL

Special Educational Needs Coordination(National Award for Special Edu. Needs Coordination) .... National Award 12-24PT

University of Bristol
Education: Psychology of Education.................. MEd 12FT 24-60PT
Education: Special and Inclusive Education .... MEd 12FT 24-60PT

Brunel University
Education (Special Educational Needs).................... MA 12FT 24PT

Cardiff University
Educational Psychology (Doctorate)..........................DEdPsy 36FT
Educational Psychology (Post-Qualification Doctorate).....DEdPsy 36PT

University of Dundee
Developmental Psychology .... MSc 12FT
Educational Psychology .... MSc 24FT

Durham University
Education.. MA 12FT 36PT
Educational Assessment..MSc 12FT 24PT

University of East London
Counselling Children in Schools .... MA 36PT/PGDip 24PT/PGCert 12PT
Professional Doctorate in Applied Educational and Child Psychology........................DProf by taught 45-60PT
Professional Doctorate in Educational and Child Psychology .... DProf by taught 36FT
Special Educational Needs ....MA 12FT 24PT/PGDip 8FT 16PT/PGCert 4FT 8PT

University of Exeter
Special Educational Needs Masters...........PGDip 12FT/MEd 12FT/PGCert 6FT

National University of Ireland Galway
Special Educational Needs...................................... PGDip 12PT

University of Glasgow
Professional Development in Education .... PGCert 60 maxPT

University of Gloucestershire
National Award for Special Educational Needs Continuation....... PGCert 9PT

Goldsmiths, University of London
Practice Education..............................MA 36-60PT/PGDip 36-60PT/PGCert 36-60PT
The Science of Psychology, Genetics & Education ....MSc 12FT 24PT

Institute of Education
Development Education .... MA 12FT 24PT
Developmental and Educational Psychology ....MSc 12FT 24PT
Education (Psychology)..MA 12FT 24-48PT
Joint Professional Practice: Language and Communication .. MSc 12FT 24-48PT
Psychology of Education.................MA 12FT 24PT/MSc 12FT 24PT

Keele University
Psychology...MSc 12FT 24PT

University of Kent
Developmental Psychology....................................MSc 12FT 24PT

University of Leeds
Special Educational Needs ....MA 12FT 24PT/PGDip 12FT 24PT

Liverpool John Moores University
Advanced Educational Practice (Special Educational Needs).........PGCert 12PT

Manchester Metropolitan University
Autistic Spectrum Conditions .... MA 12-60PT
Inclusive Education and Special Educational Needs ....MA 12FT 24-60PT
Emotional and Behavioural Difficulties......................PGCert 24PT
Managing Pupil Behaviour......................................PGCert 24PT

University of Manchester
Psychology of Education..MEd 12FT 24PT

University of Nottingham
Applied Educational Psychology..........................DAppEdPsy 36FT
Psychology (Conversion Course).......................................PGDip 9FT
Special Needs .... MA 12FT 24-36PT

Oxford Brookes University
Education .... MA 12FT 24PT

University of Oxford
Education (Child Development and Education).............. MSc 12FT
Educational Research Methodology.................................MSc 12FT

Plymouth University
The National Award for Special Educational Needs Co-ordination ....PGCert 12PT

Queen's University Belfast
Educational, Child and Adolescent Psychology DECAP................... PsychD by taught 36FT
Inclusion and Special Needs Education .... DASE 12FT 60PT/MEd 12FT 60PT

University of Reading
Development and Psychopathology ...MSc 12FT 24PT/PGDip 6FT
Neuroscience of Language .... MSc 12FT 24PT

University of Roehampton
Applied Psychology in Education..........................MSc 12FT 24-36PT

University of Sheffield
Educational and Child Psychology .... Doctor 36FT
Psychology and Education ....MA 12FT

University of South Wales
SEN Developmental Co-ordination Disorder (Dyspraxia) .. PGCert 12DL
SEN Visual Impairment.. PGDip 24PT
Special Educational Needs .... MA 12FT 36PT

University of Southampton
Educational Psychology ....DEdPsy 36FT
Research Methods in Psychology ....MSc 12FT

University of St Andrews
Adults Support, Protection and Safeguarding...........PGCert 12DL
Adults with Learning Disabilities who have Significant and Complex Needs ....MSc 12DL/PGDip 12DL/PGCert 12DL

University of Stirling
Educational Research .... MSc 12FT 30PT

University of Strathclyde
Educational Psychology .... MSc 24FT
Educational Support......MSc max 60PT/PGDip max 48PT/PGCert max 24PT
Research Methods in Psychology ....MRes 12FT

University of Sunderland
Special Needs and Inclusive Education .... MA 12FT 36PT

Teesside University
Doctorate Psychology (Top up) .... PsychD by taught 30BM

University of Wales Trinity Saint David
Special Educational Needs......................................GradCert 12PT

Educational psychology
Research Courses

University of Aberdeen
Psychology..... PhD 36FT/MPhil 24FT/MSc by research 12FT/MRes 12FT

University of Birmingham
Applied Educational and Child Psychology..... AppEd / Child PsyD 36FT

University of Bristol
Educational Psychology ....DEdPsy 36FT

Cardiff University
Educational Psychology ....DEdPsy 36FT

Durham University
Education..................................EdD 36FT 72PT 72DL PhD 36FT 72PT

University of East Anglia
Counselling Studies ....PhD 36FT 72PT/MPhil 24FT 48PT/MA by research 12FT 24PT
Higher Education and Society..PhD 36FT 72PT/MPhil 24FT 48PT/MA by research 12FT 24PT
Literacy and Development Group ....PhD 36FT 72PT/MPhil 24FT 48PT/MA by research 12FT 24PT
Pedagogy and Engagement with Learning...........PhD 36FT 72PT/MPhil 24FT 48PT/MA by research 12FT 24PT
Physical Education Pedagogy Group ..PhD 36FT 72PT/MPhil 24FT 48PT/MA by research 12FT 24PT
Psychology..................................... PhD 36FT 72PT/MPhil 24FT 48PT
Spirituality and Religion in Education....................PhD 36FT 72PT/MPhil 24FT 48PT/MA by research 12FT 24PT

University of Glasgow
Education.........PhD 36FT 60PT/MPhil 12FT 24PT/MSc by research 12FT 24PT/EdD 36-60DL

Heriot-Watt University
Applied Psychology .... PhD 36FT 48PT/MPhil 24FT 36PT

Institute of Education
Doctor in Educational Psychology (DEdPsy) ....DEdPsy 48-84PT
Four Year Route (Integrated MPhil/PhD)................ PhD 48FT 84PT
Professional, Educational, Child and Adolescent Psychology (DEdPsy)...DEdPsy 36FT

University of Kent
Clinical Psychology of Intellectual and Developmental Disabilities...................................... MPhil 24FT 36PT/PhD 36FT 60PT

University of Manchester
Educational Psychology .... DEdPsy 72PT

Newcastle University
Applied Educational Psychology...........................DAppEdPsy 36FT
Education (Clinical) .... MPhil 12FT 24PT/PhD 36FT 72PT

Oxford Brookes University
Education and Childhood Studies .... MPhil/PhD 36-60FT 48-72PT/PhD 24-60FT 36-72PT/MPhil 24-36FT 36-48PT

University of Strathclyde
Doctorate in Educational Psychology...........................DEdPsy 24FT

UCL - University College London
Clinical, Educational and Health Psychology .... PhD 36FT 60PT
Educational Psychology ....DEdPsy 48PT

Teacher training and education

Educational and Child Psychology ....Doctorate in Educational and Child Psychology 36FT

English language teaching
Taught Courses

University of Aberdeen
English Linguistics for Advanced Teachers of English (ELATE).......
MLitt 12FT 24PT/PGDip 9FT 18PT

Anglia Ruskin University
Applied Linguistics and TESOL (Teaching English to Speakers of Other Languages)..................MA 12FT 24PT 12-24DL
Postgraduate Certificate in Education: Secondary (English) PGCE 12FT

University of Bedfordshire
ELT Management .... MA 12FT 24PT
Secondary Education English .... PGCE 12FT

Birkbeck, University of London
Language Teaching .... MA 12FT 24PT
Teaching English to Speakers of Other Languages (TESOL)......MA 12FT 24PT

University of Bolton
Policy and Practice in Basic Skills (ESOL)........... MA 12FT 24 - 60PT

University of Brighton
(Secondary) English.................................PGCE 12FT 16PT
English Language Teaching......MA 12FT 24PT/PGCert 12FT 24PT/ PGDip 12FT 24PT

Brunel University
Secondary Education (English) with recommendation for QTS.....
PGCert 12FT 24PT

University of Cambridge
Advanced Subject Teaching .... MSt 24PT

Canterbury Christ Church University
English with Drama and Media (11-18) PGCE ..... PGCE(QTS) 12FT 60DL
English with Drama and Media (7-14) PGCE....... PGCE(QTS) 12FT
Teaching English as an Additional Language ....MA 36PT

University of Central Lancashire
Interpreting & Translation ....MA 12FT
Teaching English to Speakers of Other Languages (TESOL) with Applied Linguistics .... MA 12FT 24-60PT 24-60DL

University of Chester
Education: Teaching and Learning MA 24 - 72PT/PGDip 24-60PT/ PGCert 12-36PT

University of Chichester
Secondary English .... PGCE(QTS) 9.5FT

Coventry University
English Language Teaching........................... MA 12FT 30PT

University of Cumbria
TESOL (Teaching English to Speakers of Other Languages)......MA 12FT

De Montfort University
English Language Teaching........................... MA 12FT 24PT

University of East London
English Language Teaching (ELT) MA......................MA 12FT 24PT/ PGDip 8FT 16PT/PGCert 4FT 8PT
English Language Teaching MA by distance learning......................
MA 24-72PT
Primary with English as an Additional Language PGCEPGCE 12FT
Secondary English Postgraduate Certificate in Education (PGCE): PGCE 12FT
Secondary English Professional Graduate Certificate in Education (PGCE).. PGCE 12FT

Edge Hill University
Primary English Education with QTS .... PGCE 12FT
Secondary English (Age Phase 11-16) with QTS ..PGCE 12FT 36PT

University of Edinburgh
Language Teaching ....MSc 12FT 24PT/PGDip 9FT 21PT

University of Essex
Teaching English as a Foreign Language .... MA 12FT 24PT

University of Glasgow
English Language & English Linguistics: Applied..MSc 12FT 24PT
English Language Teaching.............................MEd 12FT 72PT
English Language and English Linguistics..............MSc 12FT 24PT
TESOL: Teaching of English to Speakers of Other Languages MSc 12FT 24PT

University of Hertfordshire
Practice of English Language Teaching (The) ....MA 12FT

Institute of Education
English Education................................... MA 12FT 24PT

University of Kent
Linguistics................................... MA 12FT 24PT

King's College London
English in Education .... MA 12FT 24-48PT

Kingston University
Education: English Language Teaching........ MA 12FT/PGDip 12FT

Lancaster University
English Language (By distance) .... MA 36DL
TESOL (Teaching English to Speakers of Other Languages) Hong Kong...MA 24PT

Leeds Metropolitan University
English Language Teaching........MA 12FT 24PT 24DL/PGDip 12FT 24PT
English Language Teaching & Professional Practice/Cambridge Delta...PGCert 12FT 24PT

University of Leeds
English as an Additional Language and Education........ MA 36PT/ PGDip 36PT
Linguistics and English Language Teaching............. MA 12FT 24PT

Manchester Metropolitan University
Education Studies (English Language Teaching) .... MA 12FT 24PT

University of Manchester
PGCE Secondary English .... PGCE 10FT

University of St Mark and St John
PGCE Secondary English .... PGCE 12FT

Middlesex University
PGCE Secondary English .... PGCE 12FT

Newman University
PGCE Primary with English as an Additional Language ....
PGCE(QTS) 12FT
PGCE Secondary English .... PGCE(QTS) 12FT

Northumbria University
Applied Linguistics - TESOL .... MA 12FT 36PT

Nottingham Trent University
English Language Teaching............................ MA 12FT 24PT

University of Nottingham
Applied Linguistics and English Language Teaching ....MA 12FT 24-36PT
Applied Linguistics and English Language Teaching by web-based distance learning.................................. MA 24-48DL
Digital Technologies for Language Teaching (Distance Learning)... MA 24DL
English Language Education..........................MRes 12FT
PGCE Secondary - English.......................... PGCE 12FT
Teaching English to Speakers of Other Languages (TESOL)......MA 12FT 24PT/PGDip 9FT 18PT 18DL
Teaching English to Speakers of Other Languages (TESOL) by web-based distance learning.............................. MA 36DL

Oxford Brookes University
Education (TESOL) .... MA 12FT/MA 24-36PT

University of Portsmouth
English........PGCE (Postgraduate) 12FT/PGCE (Professional) 12FT

University of Reading
Education (English Education) ....MA 12FT 24-84PT/PGDip 12FT
Education (English Language Teaching) ....MA 12FT 24-84PT/ PGDip 12FT
English (Secondary Teaching)........................ PGCE 10FT
English Language Teaching .MA 12FT 24PT 24-48DL/PGDip 12FT 24PT/PGCert 12FT 24PT

University of Roehampton
English Education....................PGCert 6FT 12+PT PGDip 9FT 18+PT

University of Salford
TESOL and Applied Linguistics ..... MA 12FT 36PT/PGDip 9FT 24PT

Sheffield Hallam University
English........................MPhil 36FT 84PT/PhD by taught 36FT 84PT
English Language Teaching..............................MA 12FT
English Language and Linguistics .... MA 12FT 24-72PT
Secondary English .... PGCE 12FT

University of Sheffield
English Language Studies .... MA 12FT 24PT

University of Southampton
English Language Teaching.........MA 12FT 24PT/PGCert 12DL/MA 28DL

University of St Andrews
Business and English (Diploma) ....Diploma 9FT
English Studies.............................. PGDip 9FT/MLitt 12FT

St Mary's University College, Twickenham
Applied Linguistics and English Language Teaching........MA 12FT 24PT/PGDip 12FT 24PT/PGCert 6FT 12FT

University of Stirling
English Language and Linguistics ......MLitt 12FT 27PT/PGDip 9FT 21PT/PGCert 3FT 9PT
Teaching English to Speakers of other Languages (TESOL) and Computer Assisted Language Learning......MSc 12FT 24PT/PGDip 9FT 18PT/PGCert 6FT 12FT

University of Sunderland
PGCE English Secondary Education .... PGCE(QTS) 12FT
Teaching English to Speakers of Other Languages...........................
MA 12FT 36FT 18DL

University of Sussex
English Language Teaching.........MA 12FT 24PT/PGDip 12FT 24PT

Swansea University
Certificate in English Language Teaching to Adults (CELTA)... Cert 1FT 3PT
English Language Studies .... MA 12FT 24-36PT
English Literature .... MA 12FT 24-36PT

Trinity College Dublin - the University of Dublin
English Language Teaching........................MPhil 12FT/PGDip 12FT

University of Warwick
English Language Teaching............MA 12FT 24-48PT/PGDip 12FT 24-48PT
English Language Teaching (Studies and Methods).........MA 12FT
English Language Teaching (with a Specialism in English for Specific Purposes)........................... MA 12FT 24-48PT
English Language Teaching (with a Specialism in English to Young Learners) .... MA 12FT 24-48PT
English Language Teaching (with a Specialism in ICT and Multimedia)............................... MA 12FT 24-48PT
English Language Teaching (with a Specialism in Testing and Assessment)........................... MA 12FT 24-48PT

English language teaching
Research Courses

Birkbeck, University of London
Language Teaching .... New Route PhD 36FT 56PT
Teaching English to Speakers of Other Languages (TESOL)....New Route PhD 36FT 56PT

University of Cambridge
English and Applied Linguistics ....PhD 36FT

University of Central Lancashire
Translation, English as a Foreign Language, Learning & Teaching Methodology, Language.....PhD 30-48FT 66-84PT/MPhil 18-36FT 42-60PT/MA by research 12FT 24PT

University of Essex
English Language Teaching........PhD 36FT 60PT 48DL/MPhil 24FT 48PT

University of Kent
English Language and Linguistics ...... MA by research 12FT 24PT/ MPhil 24FT 36PT/PhD 36-48FT 60-72PT

Newcastle University
English Language and/or Linguistics....................MLitt by research 12FT 24PT
Linguistics and English Language .... Integrated PhD 48FT 72PT

Newman University
English............................... PhD 36FT 72PT/MPhil 24FT 48PT

University of Roehampton
English Language & Linguistics........ PhD 24-48FT 36-60PT/MPhil 21-36FT 33-48PT

University of Southampton
Integrated PhD in Applied Linguistics/English Language Teaching...............................Integrated PhD 60FT

University of Warwick
Applied Linguistics/English Language Teaching ..PhD 36FT 60PT/ MPhil 24FT 36PT

English literature teaching
Taught Courses

Anglia Ruskin University
Postgraduate Certificate in Education: Secondary (English) PGCE 12FT

University of Bedfordshire
Secondary Education English .... PGCE 12FT

University of Birmingham
Shakespeare and Education.....................MA 12FT 24PT 24-72DL/ PGDip 12FT 24PT 24-72DL

University of Brighton
(Secondary) English.................................PGCE 12FT 16PT

Brunel University
Secondary Education (English) with recommendation for QTS.....
PGCert 12FT 24PT

University of Cambridge
Advanced Subject Teaching .... MSt 24PT

Canterbury Christ Church University
English with Drama and Media (11-18) PGCE ..... PGCE(QTS) 12FT 60DL
English with Drama and Media (7-14) PGCE....... PGCE(QTS) 12FT

University of Chester
Education: Teaching and Learning MA 24 - 72PT/PGDip 24-60PT/ PGCert 12-36PT

University of Chichester
Secondary English .... PGCE(QTS) 9.5FT

Edge Hill University
Primary English Education with QTS .... PGCE 12FT
Secondary English (Age Phase 11-16) with QTS ..PGCE 12FT 36PT

Institute of Education
English Education................................... MA 12FT 24PT

Teacher training and education

King's College London
Medieval English: Sex, Gender & Culture .... MA 12FT 24PT

University of Manchester
PGCE Secondary English .... PGCE 10FT

University of St Mark and St John
PGCE Secondary English .... PGCE 12FT

Middlesex University
PGCE Secondary English .... PGCE 12FT

Newman University
PGCE Primary with English as an Additional Language
.... PGCE(QTS) 12FT
PGCE Secondary English .... PGCE(QTS) 12FT

Northumbria University
English Literature ....MRes 12FT 24PT

University of Nottingham
English Literature .... MA 12FT 24-36PT
PGCE Secondary - English... PGCE 12FT

University of Portsmouth
English.........PGCE (Postgraduate) 12FT/PGCE (Professional) 12FT

University of Reading
Education (English Education) ....MA 12FT 24-84PT/PGDip 12FT
English (Secondary Teaching)... PGCE 10FT

University of Roehampton
English Education....................PGCert 6FT 12+PT PGDip 9FT 18+PT

Sheffield Hallam University
Secondary English .... PGCE 12FT

University of St Andrews
English Studies...PGDip 9FT/MLitt 12FT

University of Sunderland
PGCE English Secondary Education .... PGCE(QTS) 12FT

Swansea University
English Literature .... MA 12FT 24-36PT

Environmental science teaching
Taught Courses

University of Bradford
Analytical Sciences....... MSc 12FT 60PT/PGDip 12FT 60PT/PGCert 12FT 60PT

University of Chester
Driving Assessment and Outdoor Mobility (Work Based and Integrative Studies)............................MA 24-72PT/PGDip 24-60PT/ PGCert 12-36PT

University of Cumbria
Greening Outdoor Practice ....PGCert 24-36PT
Outdoor and Experiential Learning .... MA 12FT 24-36PT/GradDip 12FT 24PT

University of Edinburgh
Outdoor Environmental and Sustainability Education.. MSc 15FT 72PT/PGDip 12FT 48PT/PGCert 24PT

Goldsmiths, University of London
Practice Education...............................MA 36-60PT/PGDip 36-60PT/ PGCert 36-60PT

Heriot-Watt University
Environmental Analysis and Assessment .... MRes 12FT 24PT/ PGDip 9FT 18PT/PGCert 9FT 18PT

Institute of Education
Science Education....................................... MA 12FT 24-48PT

London South Bank University
Education for Sustainability ....MSc 60DL MSc 16FT 60PT

Newcastle University
Environmental Regulation and Sustainable Development .....LLM 12FT 24PT

University of Nottingham
Sustainable Bioenergy (MRes) ....MRes 12-36PT

Plymouth University
Learning for Sustainability....................................MSc 12FT 24PT

Robert Gordon University
Instrumental Analytical Sciences: Environmental Analysis ... MSc 12FT 36PT/PGDip 9FT 24PT

School of Oriental and African Studies - SOAS
Environmental Law and Sustainable Development........................
MA 12FT 24PT

Sheffield Hallam University
Science Education...PGCert 12DL

Environmental science teaching
Research Courses

King's College London
Analytical & Environmental Sciences ... MPhil 36-48FT 72PT/PhD 36-48FT 72PT

Geography teaching
Taught Courses

University of Brighton
(Secondary) Geography...PGCE 12FT 16PT

Canterbury Christ Church University
Geography (11-18) PGCE .... PGCE(QTS) 12FT
Geography (7-14) PGCE .... PGCE(QTS) 12FT

University College Cork
Geography (Coastal Management Systems)......................MA 12FT

Edge Hill University
Secondary Geography (Age Phase 11-16) with QTS ..... PGCE 12FT

University of Glasgow
Education (Primary/Secondary)................................PGDE 10FT

Institute of Education
Geography in Education .... MA 12FT 24-48PT 12-24DL

Leeds Metropolitan University
Multi Unit Leadership .... MSc 12FT 24PT

University of St Mark and St John
PGCE Secondary Geography with ICT............................ PGCE 12FT

Middlesex University
PGCE Secondary Geography .... PGCE 12FT

Newman University
PGCE Secondary Citizenship.................................. PGCE(QTS) 12FT

University of Nottingham
PGCE Secondary - Geography....................................... PGCE 12FT

University of Portsmouth
Geography..PGCE (Postgraduate) 12FT/PGCE (Professional) 12FT

University of Sunderland
PGCE Geography Education.. PGCE(QTS) 12FT

Geography teaching
Research Courses

University of Cambridge
Geography.. PhD 36FT 60PT

London School of Economics and Political Science (LSE)
Economic Geography........................... MPhil 36-48FT/PhD 36-48FT

Oxford Brookes University
Anthropology and Geography .... PhD 24-60FT 36-72PT/MPhil 24-36FT 36-48PT

Graduate Teacher Programme
Taught Courses

Bangor University
Education........ PhD by taught 36FT 48-60PT/MPhil 24FT 36-48PT
Primary Education .... PGCE 12FT

University of Bedfordshire
Graduate Teacher Programme (GTP) ....GTP 12FT

University of Dundee
Teaching Qualification (Further Education).............TQFE 9PT 36DL

Loughborough University
Postgraduate Diploma/Certificate in Education with QTS ..PGDip 12FT 36PT/PGCert 12FT 36PT

Titan Partnership Ltd
Graduate Teacher Programme (11-16) .... PGCE(QTS) 10FT

Graduate Teacher Programme
Research Courses

Bangor University
Education..........................PhD 36FT 60-72PT/MPhil 24FT 36-48PT

Health teaching
Taught Courses

University of Aberdeen
Social and Educational Research ....MRes 12FT

Anglia Ruskin University
Medical & Healthcare Education .... MSc 12FT 36PT

University of Bedfordshire
Physical Activity, Nutrition and Health Promotion........MSc 12FT/ PGDip 12FT/PGCert 12FT

Birmingham City University
Practice Teacher Preparations ....PGCert 12DL

University of Birmingham
Physiotherapy (pre-registration) .... MSc 24FT

University of Bolton
Advanced Practice (Health and Social Care)..................... MSc 24PT
Teaching and Learning .... MA 12FT 60PT
Teaching and Learning for Professional Practice........PGCert 12PT

Bournemouth University
Education Practice................... MA 31FT/PGDip 24FT/PGCert 12FT

University of Bradford
Health Professional Educator......................PGDip 18PT/MSc 60PT

University of Brighton
Clinical Education............................MA 36 - 72PT/PGDip 36 - 72PT
Health Promotion............MA 12FT 24-72PT/PGDip 12FT 24-72PT/ PGCert 12FT 24-72PT
Health Promotion and EducationMA 12FT 24 - 72PT/PGDip 12FT 24 - 72PT
Health Promotion and Management...............MA 12FT 24 - 72PT/ PGDip 12FT 24 - 72PT
Health and Education.................................. MSc 12FT 24 - 72PT/ PGDip 12FT 24 - 72PT
Health and Social Care Education ....PGCert 12 - 18PT
International Health Promotion...............................MA 12FT 36PT/ PGDip 12FT 36PT
Physiotherapy and Education....... MSc 12 - 24FT 24 - 72PT/PGDip 12 - 24FT 24 - 72PT/PGCert 12 - 24FT 24 - 72PT
Teaching in Clinical Settings..................................PGCert 12 - 24PT

University of Bristol
Teaching and Learning for Health Professionals....MSc 12 - 24FT/ Diploma 12 - 36FT/Cert 12 - 36FT

Brunel University
Health Promotion and Public Health ....MSc 12FT 36PT n/aDL

Canterbury Christ Church University
Health Promotion and Public Health ....MSc 12FT 36PT
Health and Social Care (14-19) PGCE .... PGCE(QTS) 12FT

University of Central Lancashire
Applied Public Health: Health Improvement..............PGCert 12PT
Health & Social Care Education......................................PGCert 12PT
Health Informatics.................................MSc 33PT/PGDip 24PT
Health and Social Care Education ....PGCert 12PT
Integrated Healthcare by elearning.....MSc 36-48PT/PGDip 24PT/ PGCert 12PT

University of Chester
Health and Social Care - Professional Education...MEd 24 - 72PT/ PGDip 24 - 60PT/PGCert 12 - 36PT
Weight ManagementMSc 12FT 24 - 48PT/PGDip 12FT 24 - 48PT/ PGCert 12FT 12 - 24PT
Weight Management (Taught in Dublin, Ireland) .. MSc 24-48PT/ PGDip 24-48PT/PGCert 12-24PT

Durham University
Medical Education... MSc 12FT 24PT

University of East Anglia
Clinical Education..MClinEd 12FT 36PT/PGDip 12FT 24PT/PGCert 12PT
Clinical Science.. MRes 12FT

University of East London
Health Promotion MSc...MSc 12FT 24PT/PGDip 8FT 16PT/PGCert 4FT 8PT
e-Health MSc... MSc 12FT 24PT/PGDip 8FT 16PT/PGCert 4FT 8PT

Edge Hill University
Teaching and Learning in Clinical Practice...................PGCert 12PT

University of Exeter
Bioarchaeology .... MSc 12FT 24PT

National University of Ireland Galway
Health Promotion........................MA 12FT 24PT/PGDip 12FT 24PT
Health Sciences (Clinical Education) ...... MHSc 12FT/PGDip 12FT/ PGCert 12FT
Health Services Research........................ MHSc 24PT/PGDip 24PT

Glasgow Caledonian University
Healthcare Education..................................... MSc 12FT 36PT

University of Glasgow
Health Professions Education .... MSc(MedSci) 12FT 36PT 36DL/ DHPE 48FT 72PT

University of Gloucestershire
Physical Activity and Health...... MSc 12FT 24PT/PGDip 8FT 20PT/ PGCert 4FT 8PT
Sports Coaching.. MSc 12FT 24PT

Glyndwr University
Professional Education. MSc 12FT 24-60PT/PGDip 24FT 24-36PT/ PGCert 6FT 12PT
Professional Education........... MSc 12FT 24-60PT/DipMedEd 24FT 24-36PT/CertMedEd 6FT 12PT

Goldsmiths, University of London
Higher Specialist Social Work: Practice Education...... PGDip 24PT
Practice Education. MA 36-60PT/PGDip 36-60PT/PGCert 36-60PT

Imperial College London
MSc in Health Policy .... MScD 24PT

Institute of Education
Centenary Brendish Scholarships (Taught Masters Programmes)
MA 12FT/MSc 12FT
Education, Health Promotion and International Development....
MA 12FT 24-48PT

King's College London
Health Promotion..............................MSc 12FT 24-48PT
Health Studies.................................PGCert 12FT 24PT

Leeds Metropolitan University
Health & Social Care Chaplaincy....................................PGCert 12PT
Health Care Studies ....MA 24PT

Teacher training and education

Public Health (Health Promotion and Environmental Health)
Zambia .... MSc 36PT
Public Health - Health Promotion ......MSc 12FT 30PT/PGDip 12FT
24PT/PGCert 4FT 12PT

London School of Economics and Political Science (LSE)
Health, Community and Development .... MSc 12FT 24PT

London School of Hygiene and Tropical Medicine
Public Health for Eye Care .... MSc 12FT 24PT

University of Northampton
Practice Education .... MSc 12FT 24PT/PGCert 12PT

Northumbria University
Family Therapy and Systemic Practice .... MA 36PT/PGDip 24PT/
PGCert 12PT
Health and Social Care Quality Provision .... PGCert 12FT

University of Nottingham
Health Communication by Web Based Distance Learning .... MA
24-48DL
Practice Teacher in Health and Social Care .... PGCert 12-24PT
Psychology and Health .... MSc 12FT 24PT/PGDip 12FT 24PT

Oxford Brookes University
Higher Professional Education ..... MSc 12FT 12-36PT/PGDip 12FT
24PT/PGCert 12FT 18PT
Medical & Dental Education (a collaborative programme with
Oxford PGMDE) .... PGCert 9PT

University of Roehampton
Obesity: Risks and Prevention .... MSc 12FT 24PT
Post Graduate Certificate- Obesity: Risks and Prevention . PGCert
6FT 12PT
Obesity: Risks and Prevention .... PGDip 9FT 24PT

University Campus Suffolk
MA Health and Social Care PracticeMA 60PT/PGCert 36PT/PGDip
48PT

Sheffield Hallam University
Health Care Education (including teacher status for health
professionals) .... MSc variablePT
Healthcare Education .... MSc VAPT/PGDip VAPT/PGCert VAPT
Leading and Managing Physical Education and Youth Sport. MSc
3PT
Leading and Managing Sport Development .... MSc 24PT/PGDip
16PT/PGCert 8PT

University of South Wales
Education for Health and Social Care Professionals ...... MSc 12PT/
PGCert 12PT

University of Southampton
Health Education and Promotion .... MSc 12FT 24PT

University of Surrey
Learning and Teaching for Professional Practice ...... PGCert 12PT/
PGDip 24PT/MSc 36PT/Practice Teacher 4PT

Swansea University
Public Health & Health Promotion .... MSc 12FT 36PT

Trinity College Dublin - the University of Dublin
Clinical Health Sciences Education (PG. Dip.) .... PGDip 12PT

University of Ulster
Health Promotion and Public Health ... MSc 12FT 27-36PT/PGDip
9FT 18PT/PGCert 4-9FT 9-18PT

University of Warwick
Patient and Public Involvement in HealthcarePGA 12PT/CPDMod
1PT
Theory & Practical Techniques of Self Management ....PGA 12PT/
CPDMod 1PT

University of West London
Employment Law .... LLM 12FT 24PT

University of Winchester
Education: Early Years, School, College and Workplace Educators'
Pathway .... MA(Ed) up to 60PT

Health teaching
Research Courses

Bucks New University
Education .... Professional Doctorate 48PT

Cardiff University
Nursing, Medicine, Health and Social Care (PhD) .... MPhil 12FT
36PT/PhD 36FT 60PT

University of Chester
Health and Social Care .... DProf 24-84PT

University of Gloucestershire
Sport and Exercise .... PhD 30-48FT 48-84PT/MPhil 18-36FT
30-60PT/MSc by research 12-24FT 18-36PT

Liverpool School of Tropical Medicine
Child & Reproductive Health .... PhD/MPhil/MIHR

University of Nottingham
Education and Technology for Health .... PhD 36FT

University of Sheffield
Health and Related Research..... PhD 36FT 72PT/MPhil 24FT 48PT

History teaching
Taught Courses

University of Cambridge
Advanced Subject Teaching .... MSt 24PT

Canterbury Christ Church University
History (11-18) PGCE .... PGCE(QTS) 12FT
History (7-14) PGCE .... PGCE(QTS) 12FT

University of Central Lancashire
Education and History ....MA 24PT

University of Chichester
Secondary History .... PGCE(QTS) 9.5FT

University of Dundee
History (MLitt) ....MLitt 12FT

Edge Hill University
Secondary History (Age Phase 11-16) with QTS .... PGCE 12FT

Goldsmiths, University of London
History .... MA 12FT 24PT

Institute of Education
Humanities Education (Citizenship/History/Religious Education)
MA 12FT 24-48PT

University of Nottingham
PGCE Secondary - History .... PGCE 12FT

University of Reading
History (Secondary Teaching) .... PGCE 10FT

University of St Andrews
Book History .... MLitt 12FT 24PT/MPhil 24FT/PGDip 9FT

History teaching
Research Courses

University of Dundee
History .... MPhil 24FT

Goldsmiths, University of London
History ....MRes 12FT 24PT

Home economics teaching
Taught Courses

Birmingham City University
Secondary Education (Design & Technology: Food & Textiles) ......
PGCE(QTS) 12FT

University of Glasgow
Art History: Dress & Textile Histories.....................MLitt 12FT 24PT

Heriot-Watt University
Food and Beverage Science ....MSc 12FT 24PT/PGDip 9FT 21PT

Sheffield Hallam University
Secondary Design and Technology - Food Technology.....................
PGCE 12FT

University of Sunderland
PGCE Design and Technology - (Food and Textiles) 18months ......
PGCE(QTS) 18FT

ICT teaching
Taught Courses

Anglia Ruskin University
Postgraduate Certificate in Education: Secondary Information
and Communication Technology .... PGCE 12FT

University of Bedfordshire
Secondary Education 14-19 Applied ICT .... PGCE 12FT

Brunel University
Secondary Education (Information and Communication
Technology) with recommendation for QTS .... PGCert 12FT

Canterbury Christ Church University
Information and Communication Technology (11-18) PGCE ....
PGCE(QTS) 12FT
Information and Communication Technology (7-14) PGCE ....
PGCE(QTS) 12FT

Chiltern Training Group
ICT .... PGCE 12FT

University of East London
Secondary Information Communication Technology
Postgraduate Certificate in Education (PGCE .... PGCE 12FT
Secondary Information Communication Technology Professional
Graduate Certificate in Education .... PGCE 12FT

Edge Hill University
Secondary Computer Science and Information Technology
Education (Age Phase 11-16) with QTS.................PGCE 12FT 36FT

Edinburgh Napier University
Strategic ICT Leadership .... MSc 24PT

Gloucestershire SCITT Consortium
PGCE in ICT .... PGCE 12FT

Institute of Education
Education and Technology .... MA 12FT 24-48PT

King's College London
ICT Education .... MA 12FT 24-48PT

Leeds Metropolitan University
Information & Technology .... MSc 12FT 24PT/PGDip 12FT 24PT/
PGCert 4FT 24PT

University of Leeds
ICT and Education .... MA 12FT 24PT
ICT and Education (Distance Learning) .... MA 24DL

Liverpool John Moores University
Applied ICT PGCE .... PGCE(QTS) 20FT
Secondary ICT (11-16) PGCE .... PGCE 12FT

University of Manchester
Digital Technologies, Communication and Education .... MA
12FT 27PT 36DL/PGDip 9FT 20PT 21-36DL/PGCert 12PT 9-21DL/
TESOL 12FT 24PT
Educational Technology and TESOL ....MA 12FT 27PT 36DL

University of St Mark and St John
PGCE Secondary Geography with ICT........................... PGCE 12FT
PGCE Secondary ICT .... PGCE 12FT

National University of Ireland, Maynooth
Arts (Application of Information and Communication
Technology in Education) ....HDip 12FT

Middlesex University
PGCE Secondary Information Communication Technology ....
PGCE 12FT

Newman University
PGCE Secondary Computer Science and ICT......... PGCE(QTS) 12FT

University of Nottingham
Learning, Technology and Education/Learning, Technology and
Education (online) ....MA 12FT 24-48PT/MA 24DL

University of Portsmouth
Computer Science ....PGCE (Postgraduate) 12FT/PGCE
(Professional) 12FT

University of Reading
ICT (Secondary Teaching) .... PGCE 10FT

Sheffield Hallam University
Information Technology .... PGCE 12FT 60PT
Secondary Information and Communication Technology (ICT) ....
PGCE(QTS) 12FT

University of South Wales
ICT and Education .... MA 12FT 36PT

University of Sunderland
PGCE ICT Secondary Education 2 year................... PGCE(QTS) 24FT
Teaching and Learning with ICT .... MA 12FT 36PT

University of Warwick
English Language Teaching (with a Specialism in ICT and
Multimedia) .... MA 12FT 24-48PT

West Midlands Consortium
ICT.. PGCE(QTS) 10FT

ICT teaching
Research Courses

Bath Spa University
Educational Innovation and Technology .... PhD 24 - 60FT
36 - 72PT

The Open University
Technology, communication and education .... PhD 36FT 72PT
variableDL/MPhil 15FT 24PT variableDL

Inclusive education
Taught Courses

University of Aberdeen
Community Learning and Development ....MSc 36PT/PGDip 24PT
Effective Teaching in Numeracy......................................PGCert 12PT
Inclusive Practice ....MEd 24PT
Plurilingual Education...................................MEd 24PT/PGCert 12PT

University of Birmingham
Inclusion and Special Educational Needs...MEd 12FT 24PT 72DL/
MA 12FT 24PT 72DL/Diploma 12FT 24PT 48DL
Management of Special Education in Developing Countries ....
MEd 12FT/PGDip 12FT/B/Phil 12FT
Special Educational Needs Coordination (National Award for
SENC) ....PGCert 12/24PT

University of Bolton
Inclusive Education .... MA 12FT 24-60PT

University of Brighton
Inclusive Arts Practice .... MA 24-72PT/PGCert 24-72PT

University of Bristol
Disability Studies: Inclusive Theory and Research .... MSc 12FT
12-60PT/PGDip 12FT 12-60PT/PGCert 12FT 12-60PT
Education: Special and Inclusive Education .... MEd 12FT 24-60PT

Brunel University
Education (Gifted Education) .... MA 12FT 24PT

Section sponsored by BPP UNIVERSITY COLLEGE

Business and social sciences

532 POSTGRADUATE DIRECTORY www.prospects.ac.uk/findcourses

Teacher training and education

University of Central Lancashire
Excellence in Leadership for Inclusion and Community..... PGCert 12-24PT

University of Chester
Education: Inclusion and Marginalisation ...... MA 36-72PT/PGDip 36-60PT/PGCert 12-36PT

University College Cork
Special Educational Needs .... PGDip 9FT

University of Cumbria
Collaborative PracticeMSc 36 - 60PT/GradDip 24 - 36PT/GradCert 12 - 24PT

University of Dundee
Advanced Practice (Practice Education) .... MSc 36DL

Edge Hill University
Special Educational Needs Coordination .... National Award 12-36DL

University of Edinburgh
Additional Support for Learning (Inclusive Education) MEd 72PT/PGDip 48PT/PGCert 24PT
Inclusive and Special Education .... MSc 12FT

University of Exeter
Education Taught Doctorate......... EdD by taught 24FT 48PT 48DL
Educational Research .... MSc 12FT 24PT 12-24DL
Special Educational Needs Masters........... PGDip 12FT/MEd 12FT/PGCert 6FT

University of Glasgow
Inclusive Education: Research, Policy & Practice...MEd 12FT 72PT
Professional Development in Education .... PGCert 60 maxPT

University of Gloucestershire
Inclusive Education .... MA 24PT/PGDip 20PT/PGCert 8PT
Teacher Training PGCE (Primary) .... PGCE 12FT
Teacher Training PGCE (Secondary) .... PGCE 12FT

University of Hull
Inclusive Education .. MEd 18FT 36PT/AdvDip 12FT 24PT/AdvCert 6FT 12PT

Institute of Education
Change to Teach .... Change to Teach Scheme 10PT
Developing SEN Co-ordination - SENCO .... PGCert 12PT 12DL
Development Education .... MA 12FT 24PT
Special and Inclusive Education .... MA 12FT 24PT

King's College London
Inclusive Education & Technology .... MA 12FT 24-48PT
Language, Ethnicity & Education .... MA 12FT 24-48PT

University of Leeds
Co-ordinating Inclusive Provision for Children with Learning Difficulties .... PGCert 12PT
Disability and Special Education .... MA 12FT 24PT
Provision for Children with Developmental Disorders .... PGCert 12FT
Special Educational Needs .... MA 12FT 24PT/PGDip 12FT 24PT

London Metropolitan University
Assessment for Specific Learning Difficulties in FE and HE........... PGDip 12PT

London South Bank University
Teachers of Adults with Learning Difficulties ....PGCert 12-24PT

Manchester Metropolitan University
Autistic Spectrum Conditions .... MA 12-60PT
Urban Education .... MA 12FT 24 - 60PT

University of Manchester
Profound and Complex Learning Disability............... MSc 12-15FT 24-36DL/PGDip 12-15FT 18DL/PGCert 12DL

Middlesex University
Inclusive Education .... MA 36PT 36DL

University of Northampton
Special Educational Needs .... MA 24PT

Northumbria University
Special Educational Needs and Inclusion .... PGCert 12PT

Queen's University Belfast
Inclusion and Special Needs Education .... DASE 12FT 60PT/MEd 12FT 60PT

University of Reading
Education (Inclusive Education)..... MA 12FT 24-84PT/PGDip 12FT
Inclusive Education .... MA 12FT 24-60PT

University of Roehampton
Special and Inclusive Education... PGCert 6FT 12-24PT PGDip 9FT 24-48PT MA 12FT 24-48PT

Sheffield Hallam University
Inclusion .... MA 12FT 36PT/PGDip 24PT

University of South Wales
SEN Developmental Co-ordination Disorder (Dyspraxia) .. PGCert 12DL
SEN Hearing Impairment .... PGDip leading to MA SEN 24PT
Special Educational Needs .... MA 12FT 36PT

Teesside University
Promoting Inclusive Practice in Education........... PGDip 24 - 36PT

University of Wales Trinity Saint David
Inclusive Studies ... MA 12FT 24PT/PGCert 12FT 24PT/PGDip 12FT 24PT
Inclusive Studies (Neuro-diversity).... MA 12FT 24PT/PGCert 12FT 24PT/PGDip 12FT 24PT
Special Educational Needs .... GradCert 12PT

Inclusive education
Research Courses

Bath Spa University
Children and the Environment .... PhD 24 - 60FT 36 - 72PT

University of Nottingham
Cognitive Development and Learning .... PhD 36FT 72PT/MPhil 24FT 48PT

The Open University
Children, young people, families, and personal relationships....... PhD 36FT 72PT/MPhil 15FT 24PT
Doctorate in Education .... EdD 36PT
Education and Educational TechnologyEdD 36PT variableDL/PhD 36FT 72PT variableDL/MRes 12FT/MPhil 15FT 24PT variableDL
Multimodal meaning making...... PhD 36FT 72PT variableDL/EdD 36PT/MRes 12FT
Technology Enhanced Learning ... PhD 36FT 72PT variableDL/EdD 36PT/MRes 12FT

International education
Taught Courses

Bangor University
Education Doctorate Programme (EdD) .... EdD by taught 60PT
Education Studies... MA 12FT 24-60PT/MEd 12FT 24-60PT/PGDip 8FT 24-48PT/PGCert 4FT 12-24PT

University of Bedfordshire
Education (International) .... PGCE 15FT

Birmingham City University
International Education............... MA 12FT/PGDip 8FT/PGCert 3FT

University of Birmingham
International Studies in Education .... MEd 12FT 72PT/MA 12FT 72PT/Diploma 12FT 48PT/Cert 6FT 24PT
International Studies in Education (Education and Development)........ MA 12FT 24/72PT/MEd 12FT 24/72PT
Management of Special Education in Developing Countries .... MEd 12FT/PGDip 12FT/B/Phil 12FT

Canterbury Christ Church University
School Development .... MA 24PT

University of Derby
Education .... EdD by taught 36-72PT

University of Dundee
Education (Chartered Teacher)........ MEd 18PT/PGDip 9PT/PGCert 6PT
Educational Psychology .... MSc 24FT

Durham University
Education (International Postgraduate Programme).......MA 36PT
PGCE Primary (International) .... PGCE 12FT
PGCE Secondary (International) .... PGCE 12FT

University of East Anglia
Education .... MA 12FT
Education and Development .... MA 12FT 24PT
International Social Development .... MA 12FT 24PT

Edge Hill University
Management of International Higher Education ....MA 24PT

University of Glasgow
Professional Development in Education .... PGCert 60 maxPT

Glyndwr University
Education .... PGCE 12FT 24-36PT/CertEd 24-36PT
Professional Education........... MSc 12FT 24-60PT/DipMedEd 24FT 24-36PT/CertMedEd 6FT 12PT

University of Huddersfield
International Education .... MA 12FT

Institute of Education
Education and International Development....... MA 12FT 24-48PT 12-24DL
Education, Gender and International Development .... MA 12FT 24-48PT
Education, Health Promotion and International Development.... MA 12FT 24-48PT

Leeds Metropolitan University
Doctorate of Business Administration .... DBA 48PT
Professional Development .... PGCert 12PT

University of Leeds
International Educational Management..... MA 12FT/PGDip 12FT

University of Leicester
International Education .... MA 12FT 24DL

University of Manchester
Education (International) .... MA 12FT

Northumbria University
Education with Curriculum Development .... MEd 12FT
Education with Leadership .... MEd 12FT
Education with Teaching and Learning .... MEd 12FT

University of Nottingham
International Higher Education .... MA 12FT 24PT

Oxford Brookes University
Education (TESOL) .... MA 12FT/MA 24-36PT

University of Oxford
Education (Comparative and International Education) .... MSc 12FT
Educational Studies (Comparative and International Education) .... MSc 12FT

School of Oriental and African Studies - SOAS
Research for International Development .... MSc 12FT 24PT

Sheffield Hallam University
Education for International Students .... MA 12FT/MSc 12FT

University of Sheffield
Globalising Education: Policy and Practice .... MA 12FT

University of South Wales
Education for Sustainable Development and Global Citizenship. MA 12FT 36PT

University of Stirling
Educational Research .... MSc 12FT 30PT

University of Sussex
International Education and Development............ MA 12FT 24PT

University of York
Global and International Citizenship Education - Institute for Effective Education .... MA 12FT

International education
Research Courses

University of Central Lancashire
Politics and International studies .... MPhil 18-36FT 42-60PT/PhD 30-48FT 66-84PT/MA by research 12FT 24PT

University of Dundee
Education .... MPhil 24FT MSc by research 12FT PhD 36FT

University of East Anglia
International Development: Economic Development....PhD 36FT 72PT/MPhil 24FT 48PT
International Development: Sustainable Development .... PhD 36FT 72PT/MPhil 24FT 48PT

University of Glasgow
Education.........PhD 36FT 60PT/MPhil 12FT 24PT/MSc by research 12FT 24PT/EdD 36-60DL

Institute of Education
Doctor in Education (EdD) International Programme .... EdD 48-84PT

Keele University
Education.............. PhD 24-48FT 48-84PT/MPhil 12-24FT 24-36PT

Islamic education
Taught Courses

Markfield Institute of Higher Education
Islamic Education .... MEd 12FT/PGDip 12FT/PGCert 6FT

School of Oriental and African Studies - SOAS
Islamic Societies and Cultures .... MA 12FT 24-36PT
Islamic Studies .... MA 12FT 24-36PT

Jewish education
Taught Courses

University of Aberdeen
Jewish Studies .... MLitt 12FT 24PT/PGDip 9FT 18PT
Plurilingual Education .... MEd 24PT/PGCert 12PT

University of Oxford
Modern Jewish Studies .... MPhil 21FT/MSt 9FT

Law teaching
Taught Courses

Manchester Metropolitan University
LLM (Master of Laws) .... LLM 12FT 24PT

University of Warwick
Legal Education .... LLM 12FT 24+PT/PGDip 9FT

Leisure and tourism teaching
Taught Courses

Aberystwyth University
Management and Tourism Management.............. MSc 12FT 24PT

Canterbury Christ Church University
Leisure and Tourism (14-19) PGCE .... PGCE(QTS) 12FT

University of Derby
International Spa Management .... MA 36FT

School of Oriental and African Studies - SOAS
Anthropology of Travel, Tourism and Pilgrimage ... MA 12FT 24PT

Teacher training and education

Literacy and numeracy
Taught Courses

University of Aberdeen
Adult Literacies Development.....MEd 12BM/PGDip 9BM/PGCert 6BM
Effective Teaching in Numeracy.......................................PGCert 12PT

University of Bolton
Policy and Practice in Basic Skills (Literacy) ..... MA 12FT 24 - 60PT
Policy and Practice in Basic Skills Education (Numeracy)...............
MA 12FT 24-60PT

University of Chester
Education: Dyslexia Research and Practice.....MA 36-72PT/PGDip 36-60PT/PGCert 12-36PT

University of East Anglia
Adult Literacy, Lifelong Learning & Development ....MA 12FT
Education and Development...MA 12FT 24PT

University of East London
Literacy and Education .... MA 24PT/PGDip 16PT/PGCert 8PT

University of Glasgow
Childrens's Literature & Literacies .... MEd 12FT 24-36PT

Institute of Education
Adult Literacy, Language and Numeracy (inc. PG Cert Adult Literacy and ESOL Teaching) .... MA 24-48PT/PGCert 12PT
Joint Professional Practice: Language and Communication .. MSc 12FT 24-48PT
Literacy Learning and Literacy Difficulties (Academic Route)..MA 12FT 24PT
Post-Compulsory PGCE: Literacy and ESOL... PGCE 12-24PT/PGCE 12FT
Reading Recovery And Literacy Leadership (formerly LLLD prof route)..MA 12FT
Reading Recovery in Primary Literacy Leadership (RRiPLLe) ....30 Credit Module 8PT

Manchester Metropolitan University
Practice Development...MSc 24-72PT
Teaching of Reading/......................................PGDip 12-36PT

Northumbria University
Advanced Practice in Post Compulsory Education and Training (Literacy) ....PGCert 12PT
Advanced Practice in Post Compulsory Education and Training (Numeracy) ....PGCert 12PT
Post Compulsory Education and Training (Literacy) ....PGCE 24PT/CertEd 12PT

University of South Wales
Adult Literacy/ Adult Numeracy/ ESOL .... Level 5 Certificate in Teaching 12PT
Adult Literacy/ Adult Numeracy/ ESOL ....PGCE 24FT/Certificate of Education 24FT
Post-compulsory Education and Training Adult Literacy / Adult Numeracy / ESOL.......................................PGCE 24PT/CertEd 24PT

Literacy and numeracy
Research Courses

Newcastle University
Education........................... PhD 36FT 72PT/MPhil 12FT 24PT

University of Nottingham
CELE Research Staff and Interests ....PhD 36FT 72PT/MPhil 24FT 48PT

Lower primary education studies
Taught Courses

Bangor University
Education........ PhD by taught 36FT 48-60PT/MPhil 24FT 36-48PT
Primary Education..PGCE 12FT

Bath Spa University
PGCE Primary and Early Years...................................PGCE 12FT 20PT

University of Bedfordshire
Primary Education with Early years...................................PGCE 12FT

Canterbury Christ Church University
Primary Education (3 -7) PGCE.....................PGCE(QTS) 12FT 20PT

University of Cumbria
Leading Intergrated Children's Services ....MSc 24 - 60PT

University of Derby
Education...EdD by taught 36-72PT
PGCE Primary..PGCE 12FT

University of Dundee
Education (Chartered Teacher).....................MEd 18PT/PGDip 9PT/PGCert 6PT
Educational Psychology .... MSc 24FT

University of East Anglia
Primary Teacher Training (3 to 9 years) Foundation Stage/Key Stage One...PGCE(QTS) 12FT
Primary Teacher Training (5 to 11 years) General Class Teacher with Modern Foreign Languages: French...............PGCE(QTS) 12FT
Primary Teacher Training (5 to 11 years) General Class Teacher with Modern Foreign Languages: German...........PGCE(QTS) 12FT

Primary Teacher Training (5 to 11 years) General Class Teacher with Modern Foreign Languages: Spanish .... PGCE(QTS) 12FT
Primary Teacher Training (5 to 11 years) Key Stage One/Lower Key Stage Two...PGCE(QTS) 12FT
Primary Teacher Training (5 to 11 years) Key Stage Two.................
PGCE(QTS) 12FT

Edge Hill University
Early Years with QTS.. PGCE 12FT

University of Gloucestershire
Teacher Training PGCE (Primary) .... PGCE 12FT

University of Hertfordshire
Early Years.....MA 12FT 24PT/PGDip 12FT 24PT/PGCert 12FT 24PT

University of Huddersfield
Early Childhood Studies.................................... MA 12FT 36PT
Early Childhood Studies with EYPS ....PGCert 12FT 6PT
Early Years Professional Status Graduate Entry Pathway........EYPS 12FT

University of Hull
Early Childhood Studies...................................MEd 12FT 24PT

University of Leeds
PGCE Primary..PGCE 12FT

Liverpool John Moores University
Early Years (3 -7 years).................................PGCE 12FT

London Metropolitan University
Early Years and Primary Education.......................PGCE 12FT

Middlesex University
PGCE Early Years....................................... PGCE 12FT
PGCE Primary Education................................ PGCE 12FT

Newman University
Early Years Foundation Degree ....FdA 36PT
Early Years Teacher Status ....Early Years Teacher Status 6FT/Early Years Teacher Status 12FT
PGCE Primary.. PGCE(QTS) 12FT
PGCE Primary with English as an Additional Language
.... PGCE(QTS) 12FT
PGCE Primary with Modern Foreign Languages................................
PGCE(QTS) 12FT

Nottingham Trent University
PGCE Primary.........................PGCE(QTS) 10FT/ProfGCE(QTS) 10FT

University of Reading
Education (Early Years).....................MA 12FT 24-84PT/PGDip 12FT
Education (Primary Education) ......MA 12FT 24-84PT/PGDip 12FT

Sheffield Hallam University
Early Years Education.................................... PGCE 12FT
Early Years Professional Status .... EYPS 12FT 6-15PT

St Mary's University College, Twickenham
PGCE Primary Education..PGCE 12FT 18PT

University of Ulster
Education (Primary).....................................PGCE 9FT

Lower primary education studies
Research Courses

Bangor University
Education..........................PhD 36FT 60-72PT/MPhil 24FT 36-48PT

University of Dundee
Education ....MPhil 24FT MSc by research 12FT PhD 36FT

Maths teaching
Taught Courses

Anglia Ruskin University
Postgraduate Certificate in Education: Secondary Mathematics .... PGCE 12FT

Bangor University
Secondary Education .... PGCE 12FT

University of Bedfordshire
Mathematics Enhancement ....PGCE 6FT
Secondary Education Mathematics.................................. PGCE 12FT

Birmingham City University
Secondary Education (Mathematics) .... PGCE(QTS) 12FT

University of Birmingham
Postgraduate Diploma Secondary Education (QTS) - Mathematics (two year route)............................... PGCE(QTS) 24FT

Bradford College
Education (Secondary Mathematics) ....PGCert 12FT

University of Brighton
(Secondary) Mathematics ....PGCE 12FT 16PT
(Secondary) Physics with Mathematics................PGCE 12FT 16PT

Teacher training and education

University of Bristol
Education: Mathematics in Education............. MEd 12FT 24-60PT
Mathematics Education................................... MEd 12FT 24-60PT

Brunel University
Secondary Education (Mathematics) with recommendation for
QTS .... PGCert 12FT 24PT

Canterbury Christ Church University
Mathematics (11-18) PGCE....................................... PGCE(QTS) 12FT
Mathematics (7-14) PGCE .... PGCE(QTS) 12FT

University of Chester
Education: PGCE Secondary Mathematics............ PGCE(QTS) 12FT
Education: Teaching and Learning MA 24 - 72PT/PGDip 24-60PT/
PGCert 12-36PT

University of Chichester
Mathematics Education....MA 30-34PT/PGDip 24PT/PGCert 12PT
Secondary Mathematics........................PGCE(QTS) 9.5FT 60 maxPT

Durham University
Mathematics Education....................................... MSc 12FT 36PT
Teaching A-Level Mathematics ....PGCert 12PT

University of East Anglia
Mathematics Education...MA 12FT
Mathematics with Mathematics Education.................... MSc 12FT

University of East London
Physics with Mathematics PGCE .... PGCE 12FT
Secondary Mathematics: Postgraduate Certificate in Education .
PGCE 12FT
Secondary Mathematics: Professional Graduate Certificate in
Education (PGCE).. PGCE 12FT
Secondary Physics with Mathematics (PGCE)............... PGCE 12FT

Edge Hill University
Mathematics Specialist Teacher Programme.................MaST 24PT
Primary Mathematics Education with QTS.................... PGCE 12FT
Primary Mathematics Specialist with QTS.................... PGCE 12FT
Secondary Mathematics (Age Phase 11-16) with QTS....................
PGCE 12FT 36PT
Secondary Physics with Mathematics (Age Phase 11-19) with
QTS .... PGCE 12FT
Specialist Primary Mathematics Practice.................... MA 36-60PT

University of Glasgow
Education (Primary/Secondary).................................PGDE 10FT

Institute of Education
Mathematics Development Programme for Teachers (MDPT)......
H/M level credits 12PT
Mathematics Education................................MA 12FT 24-48PT 48DL
Post-Compulsory PGCE: Mathematics with Numeracy... Diploma
24PT/Diploma 12FT
Teaching Advanced Mathematics .... PGCert 15FT

King's College London
Mathematics Education.. MA 12FT 24-72PT

University of Leeds
Mathematics Education..............MA 12FT 24PT/PGDip 12FT 24PT

Liverpool John Moores University
Secondary Mathematics PGCE.................................... PGCE 12FT

London Metropolitan University
Mathematics ....MSc 12FT 24-48PT
PGCE Secondary Mathematics.. PGCE 12FT

London South Bank University
Graduate Teacher Programme Secondary Mathematics
(11-16).. QTS 12FT
PGCE Secondary Mathematics (11-16 Year Olds) PGCE(QTS) 12FT

University of Manchester
PGCE Secondary Mathematics .... PGCE 10FT
PGCE Secondary Physics with Maths.......................... PGCE 10FT

University of St Mark and St John
PGCE Secondary Mathematics .... PGCE 12FT

Middlesex University
PGCE Secondary Mathematics .... PGCE 12FT

Newman University
PGCE Secondary Mathematics................................ PGCE(QTS) 12FT

University of Nottingham
PGCE Secondary - Mathematics .... PGCE 12FT 24PT

University of Portsmouth
Mathematics .... PGCE (Postgraduate) 12FT/PGCE (Professional)
12FT

University of Reading
Mathematics (Secondary Teaching)................................ PGCE 10FT

Sheffield Hallam University
Secondary Mathematics.....................................PGCE 12FT 24PT
Secondary Mathematics .... PGCE(QTS) 12FT

University of Sunderland
Mathematics Enhancement Course (Followed by the 1 year
PGCE)... PGCE(QTS) 18FT
PGCE Mathematics Secondary Education 1 year PGCE(QTS) 12FT
PGCE Mathematics Secondary Education 2 year PGCE(QTS) 24FT

University of Sussex
Mathematics .... MSc 12FT

Maths teaching
Research Courses

Kingston University
Mathematical Education Group .... PhD 48FT/MPhil 24FT

The Open University
Mathematics .... PhD 36FT 72PT variableDL/MPhil 15FT 24PT
variableDL
Mathematics Education... PhD 36FT 72PT variableDL/MPhil 15FT
24PT variableDL

Media studies teaching
Taught Courses

University of Aberdeen
Creative Writing.......................... MLitt 12FT 24PT/PGDip 9FT 21PT

University of Bradford
Professional Media Practice.. MA 12FT 24PT

Central School of Speech and Drama, University of London
PGCE Media Studies.. PGCE(QTS) 12FT

Glasgow School of Art
Supervision (Creative Practices)................................PGCert 4FT 8PT

Goldsmiths, University of London
Media and Communications..GradDip 12FT

Institute of Education
Media, Culture and Education .... MA 12FT 24-48PT

London South Bank University
Media Education..MA 24PT

University of St Mark and St John
PGCE 14-19 Diploma Creative and Media...................... PGCE 12FT

University of Nottingham
Creative and Professional Practice in Arts and Education ....MA
24PT

Queen Mary, University of London
Trauma Sciences .... MSc 12FT 24PT

University of Roehampton
English Education... PGDip 9FT 18+PT
International Management with Marketing ....PGDip 9FT 24PT
Media, Culture and Identity.................................PGDip 9FT 24PT

Swansea University
Communication, Media Practice and Public Relations ....MA 12FT
24-36PT
English Language Studies .... MA 12FT 24-36PT

Media studies teaching
Research Courses

Bath Spa University
Arts Education.......................................PhD 24 - 60FT 36 - 72PT

University of Manchester
Anthropology, Media & Performance .... PhD 36FT 72PT

Medical teaching
Taught Courses

University of Aberdeen
Community Learning and Development....MSc 36PT/PGDip 24PT
Social and Educational Research .... MRes 12FT

Anglia Ruskin University
Medical & Healthcare Education ....MSc 12FT 36PT

Bangor University
Medical Education Practice..PGCert 12FT

University of Bedfordshire
Academic and Clinical Education (BSO).......................PGCert 12PT
Medical Education............................ MA 24-60PT/PGCert 24-60PT/
PGDip 24-60PT
Medical Education Leadership ....PGCert 12-36PT
Medical Stimulation ....PGCert 12-36PT

Birmingham City University
Practice Teacher Preparations ....PGCert 12DL

University of Birmingham
Education for Health Professionals.......PGCert 12PT/PGDip 24PT/
MEd 36PT

University of Bolton
Teaching and Learning for Professional Practice........PGCert 12PT

University of Brighton
Clinical Education...... PGCert 24PT MA 36 - 72PT/PGDip 36 - 72PT
Health and Social Care Education ....PGCert 12 - 18PT
Medical Education...PGCert 12PT
Teaching in Clinical Settings....................................PGCert 12 - 24PT

University of Bristol
Teaching and Learning for Health Professionals ....MSc 12 - 24FT/
Diploma 12 - 36FT/Cert 12 - 36FT

Cardiff University
Medical Education...MSc 12FT 24PT
Medical Education (e-Learning).... PGCert 12FT/PGDip 12FT/MSc
12FT

University of Central Lancashire
Enhancing Learning, Teaching and Assessing in Multi-
professional Practice ....Uni Cert 3PT
Nursing ....MSc 12FT 24-60PT
Research for Professional Practice ... Professional Doctorate 24PT

University of Chester
Health and Social Care - Education for Postgraduate Medical
Practice... MA 24 - 72PT

University of Dundee
Advanced Practice (Clinical Governance) ....MSc 36DL
Medical Education (MMedEd)............................... MMedEd 12FT
Oral Cancer .... MRes 12FT
Orthodontics .... MSc 36PT

Durham University
Medical Education.. MSc 12FT 24PT

University of East Anglia
Clinical Education..MClinEd 12FT 36PT/PGDip 12FT 24PT/PGCert
12PT

Edge Hill University
Clinical Education .... MA 24-60PT
Teaching and Learning in Clinical Practice....................PGCert 12PT
Workplace-based Postgraduate Medical Education............ PGCert
12-36DL

Edinburgh Napier University
Advanced Practice and Applied Education (Distance Learning)....
Msc/PGDip/PGCert 36PT

University of Edinburgh
Clinical Education (Online Distance learning) ...MSc 36DL/PGDip
24PT 24DL/PGCert 12PT 12DL
Medical Sciences...MMedSci 12FT

National University of Ireland Galway
Nursing (Education)...PGDip 12FT

Glasgow Caledonian University
Medical Ultrasound ....MSc 12-24FT
Professional Doctorate for Health, Social Care Sector and
Nursing Professionals... DProf by taught 48FT

University of Glasgow
Leadership Drugs & Alcohol Setting .... PGCert 9FT 18PT

Glyndwr University
Professional Education........... MSc 12FT 24-60PT/DipMedEd 24FT
24-36PT/CertMedEd 6FT 12PT

Goldsmiths, University of London
Practice Education.............................MA 36-60PT/PGDip 36-60PT/
PGCert 36-60PT

University of Hertfordshire
Health and Medical Education. MA 15FT 60PT/PGDip 15FT 60PT/
PGCert 15FT 60PT
Supervision of Midwives .... PGCert 1BM

Institute of Education
Clinical Education .... MA 12FT 24PT

Keele University
Medical Education....................... MA 60PT/PGDip 60PT/Cert 60PT

University of Kent
Strategic Leadership and Medical Education ......PGCert 12 - 24PT

King's College London
Clinical Nursing for International Students....... MSc 12FT/PGCert
12FT
Clinical Pedagogy ....MA 24PT/PGDip 18PT/PGCert 12PT
Education for Healthcare Professionals......MSc 12FT 36PT/PGDip
12FT 36PT

Leeds Metropolitan University
Professional Development...PGCert 12PT

University of Leeds
Clinical Education...MEd 36PT/PGCert 12PT

Liverpool John Moores University
Adult Nursing .... MSc 24FT 24PT

University of Manchester
Medical Education..........................MSc 12-36PT/PGCert 12-36PT/
PGDip 12-36PT

Newcastle University
Clinical Education........... MClinEd 12FT 12-24PT/PGDip 12-24PT/
PGCert 12PT
Medical Sciences. .... MSc 12FT

Northumbria University
Education in Professional Practice ....MSc 36PT/PGDip 24PT/
PGCert 12PT
Nursing ....Professional Doctorate 48-72PT
Systemic Teaching, Training and Supervision ....MA 24PT

University of Nottingham
Medical Education.. MMedSci 12FT 24PT

Oxford Brookes University
Medical & Dental Education (a collaborative programme with
Oxford PGMDE)..PGCert 9PT

Teacher training and education

Peninsula College of Medicine and Dentistry
Clinical Education Research/Clinical Education Practice.... PGCert 12PT/PGDip 24PT/MClinEd 36PT

Plymouth University
Clinical Education............MClinEd 36PT/PGDip 24PT/PGCert 12PT
Simulation and Patient Safety.. MSc 36FT

Queen Mary, University of London
Health Systems and Global Policy......................MSc 12FT 24-48PT

Queen's University Belfast
Clinical Education..........MMedSci 36PT/PGDip 24PT/PGCert 12PT

Robert Gordon University
Advanced Clinical Practice ... MSc 36PT/PGDip 24PT/PGCert 12PT

University Campus Suffolk
Clinical Effectiveness... MA Max 60FT
Healthcare Education..............MA 18PT/PGCert 18PT/PGDip 18PT

University of Salford
Nursing (Education, International, Practice, Research) ....
MSc 12FT 36PT/PGDip 9FT 24PT/PGCert 6FT 12PT
Professional Doctorate (Health and Social Care) ... PhD by taught 60PT

Sheffield Hallam University
Clinical Education.................. MSc 24PT/PGDip 24PT/PGCert 12PT
Health Care Education (including teacher status for health professionals) ....MSc variablePT
Healthcare Education............MSc VAPT/PGDip VAPT/PGCert VAPT

University of Sheffield
Europubhealth: European Masters Programme in Public Health. MPH 24FT
Medical Education..PGCert 12-24PT

University of South Wales
Education for Health and Social Care Professionals......MSc 12PT/ PGCert 12PT

University of Southampton
Education for Health Professionals...... MSc 12FT 24PT/PGDip 9FT 18PT/PGCert 5PT

St George's, University of London
Clinical Practice..MRes 12FT 24PT

Staffordshire University
Advanced Clinical Practice ....PGCert 12PT/PGDip 24PT/MSc 36PT
Medical Education.................. MSc 36PT/PGCert 24PT/PGDip 12PT

University of Stirling
Psychological Therapy in Primary Care .... MSc 12FT

University of Surrey
Learning and Teaching for Professional Practice...... PGCert 12PT/ PGDip 24PT/MSc 36PT/Practice Teacher 4PT

Teesside University
Advanced Clinical Practice (Cardiac Care) .... MSc 36PT
Advanced Clinical Practice (Management of Long-term Health Conditions)... MSc 36PT
Advanced Clinical Practice (Manipulative Therapy) .... MSc 36PT
Advanced Clinical Practice (Neurolgical Rehabilitation) .... MSc 36PT
Clinical Research..MRes 18FT 36PT
Doctor of Health and Social Care .... DProf by taught 72PT

University of Ulster
Education (Primary)..PGCE 9FT
Education for Nurses and Midwives............................PGCert 12PT

UCL - University College London
Medical Education ...... MSc 36PT/PGDip 24PT/PGCert 12PT

University of Warwick
Learning in Practice..................................... PGA 12PT/CPDMod 1PT
Medical Education................PGA 12PT/MA 36-96PT/MSc 36-96PT

University of Winchester
Education: Early Years, School, College and Workplace Educators' Pathway .... MA(Ed) up to 60PT
Medical Education..MA 36PT

Medical teaching
Research Courses

University of Dundee
Dental School (Clinical 4 year PhD)..............................PhD 48FT
Dental School (Clinical 5 year PhD)..............................PhD 60FT
Dental School (Clinical MDSc by research) ....MDSc by research 12FT
Dental School (Non-clinical MDSc by research)..............MDSc by research 12FT

University of Edinburgh
Medical Sciences............PhD 36FT 72PT/MPhil 24FT 36PT/MSc by research 12FT 24PT
Medical Sciences (MMedSci) ......MMedSci by research 12FT 24PT

King's College London
Medical Education (Research Division). MPhil 36FT 48-72PT/PhD 36FT 48-72PT

University of Liverpool
Medical Education................MPhil 12-48FT 48-72PT/PhD 24-48FT 48-84PT/MD 24-72FT

Newcastle University
Clinical Linguistics and Evidence Based Practice (Research) .. MSc by research 12FT 24PT/PGDip by research 8FT 16PT

University of Nottingham
Education and Technology for Health ....PhD 36FT

UCL - University College London
Medical Education.. PhD 36FT 60PT

Modern languages teaching
Taught Courses

Anglia Ruskin University
Postgraduate Certificate in Education: Secondary Modern Languages .... PGCE 12FT

University of Bedfordshire
Secondary Education Modern Languages......................PGCE 12FT

Birkbeck, University of London
Language Teaching .... MA 12FT 24PT

University of Birmingham
Secondary Education (QTS) - French/Spanish/German........PGDip 9-12FT

University of Brighton
(Secondary) Modern Foreign Languages ....PGCE 12FT 16PT
Media Assisted Language Teaching...MA 12FT 24PT/PGCert 12FT 24PT/PGDip 12FT 24PT

University of Bristol
Modern Languages .... MA 12FT 24PT

Canterbury Christ Church University
French with Masters 1 (11-18) PGCE...................... PGCE(QTS) 12FT
Modern Foreign Languages (11-18) PGCE .... PGCE(QTS) 12FT
Modern Foreign Languages (7-14) PGCE............... PGCE(QTS) 12FT
Primary Education - Primary Languages (5-11) PGCE .. PGCE(QTS) 12FT

University of Central Lancashire
Interpreting & Translation ....MA 12FT

University of Chester
Education: PGCE Secondary Modern Languages French................ PGCE(QTS) 12FT
Education: PGCE Secondary Modern Languages French with German .... PGCE(QTS) 12FT
Education: PGCE Secondary Modern Languages French with Spanish... PGCE(QTS) 12FT
Education: PGCE Secondary Modern Languages German .... PGCE(QTS) 12FT
Education: PGCE Secondary Modern Languages German with French... PGCE(QTS) 12FT
Education: PGCE Secondary Modern Languages German with Spanish.. PGCE(QTS) 12FT
Education: PGCE Secondary Modern Languages Spanish.............. PGCE(QTS) 12FT
Education: PGCE Secondary Modern Languages Spanish with French... PGCE(QTS) 12FT
Education: PGCE Secondary Modern Languages Spanish with German .... PGCE(QTS) 12FT

University of Chichester
Primary Education: Modern Languages .... PGCE(QTS) 9.5FT
Secondary Modern Foreign Languages................. PGCE(QTS) 9.5FT

University of East London
Postgraduate Certificate in Education (Primary) with Modern Foreign Languages .... PGCE 12FT
Professional Graduate Certificate in Education (Primary) with Modern Foreign Languages .... PGCE 12FT

Edge Hill University
Primary Modern Languages Education with QTS.......... PGCE 12FT
Secondary Modern Languages (Age Phase 11-16) with QTS.......... PGCE 12FT 36PT

University of Edinburgh
Language Teaching ....MSc 12FT 24PT/PGDip 9FT 21PT

University of Glasgow
Education (Primary/Secondary)...............................PGDE 10FT
Learning and Teaching of Modern Languages in the Primary School ....PGCert 15PT

Goldsmiths, University of London
Education (Primary with Modern Languages) .... PGCE 12FT

University of Greenwich
Management of Language Learning..................................MA 12FT

King's College London
Modern Foreign Languages Education .... MA 12FT 24-72PT

University of Limerick
Languages ....GradDip 9FT

Liverpool John Moores University
Modern Languages: French, Spanish, German, French & Spanish or French & German .... PGCE 10FT

London Metropolitan University
PGCE Secondary Modern Languages................................PGCE 12FT

University of Manchester
PGCE Primary (Modern Language)..............................PGCE 10FT

PGCE Secondary Modern Languages..............................PGCE 10FT

University of St Mark and St John
PGCE Primary with a Primary Languages Specialism (French or Spanish).. PGCE 12FT
PGCE Secondary Modern Foreign Languages................ PGCE 12FT

Middlesex University
PGCE Secondary Modern Foreign Languages................ PGCE 10FT

Newman University
PGCE Primary with Modern Foreign Languages.. PGCE(QTS) 12FT
PGCE Secondary Modern Foreign Languages....... PGCE(QTS) 12FT

University of Nottingham
PGCE Secondary - Modern Languages ....PGCE 12FT 24PT

Oxford Brookes University
Education (PGCE) - Primary......................................PGCE 10FT

University of Oxford
General Linguistics and Comparative Philology.. MPhil 21FT/MSt 9FT
Modern Languages .... MPhil 21FT/MSt 9FT

University of Portsmouth
Modern Foreign Languages: French and German.................. PGCE (Postgraduate) 12FT/PGCE (Professional) 12FT
Modern Foreign Languages: French and Italian .... PGCE (Postgraduate) 12FT/PGCE (Professional) 12FT
Modern Foreign Languages: French and Mandarin .... PGCE (Postgraduate) 12FT/PGCE (Professional) 12FT
Modern Foreign Languages: French and Spanish .... PGCE (Postgraduate) 12FT/PGCE (Professional) 12FT
Modern Foreign Languages: German and French .... PGCE (Postgraduate) 12FT/PGCE (Professional) 12FT
Modern Foreign Languages: Spanish and French .... PGCE (Postgraduate) 12FT/PGCE (Professional) 12FT

University of Reading
Education (English Language Teaching) ....MA 12FT 24-84PT/ PGDip 12FT
French (Conversion Course) (Secondary) .... PGCE 24FT
Modern Languages (Secondary Teaching) .... PGCE 10FT
Primary Teaching with French Specialism .... PGCE 10FT

Sheffield Hallam University
Secondary Modern Foreign Languages............................ PGCE 12FT
Secondary Modern Languages................................ PGCE(QTS) 12FT

University of Sheffield
Germanic Studies (Research Track) .... MA 12FT 24PT

University of St Andrews
German Studies .....MLitt 12FT 24PT/PGDip 9FT 24PT/MPhil 24FT
Italian Studies ....MLitt 12FT 24PT/PGDip 9FT 24PT/MPhil 24FT
Language and Linguistics.........MLitt 12FT 24PT/PGDip 9FT 18PT/ MPhil 24FT

Modern languages teaching
Research Courses

School of Advanced Study, University of London
Modern Languages (French, German, Italian and Spanish) .... MRes 12FT 24PT

University of Bristol
German ....PhD 36FT 72PT/MLitt by research 24FT 48PT/ MPhil 12FT 24PT

Newcastle University
Modern Languages .... PhD 36FT 72PT/MPhil 12FT 24PT
MLitt by research 12FT 24PT

The Open University
Language Learning and Teaching....... PhD 36FT 72PT variableDL/ MRes 12FT/EdD 36PT

University of Southampton
Modern Languages .... PhD 48FT 84PT/MPhil 48FT 84PT

University of St Andrews
Italian Studies .... PhD 36FT 72PT/MPhil 24FT 48PT
Language and Linguistics.........PhD 36FT 72PT/DLang 36FT 72PT/ MPhil 24FT 48PT

Music teaching
Taught Courses

Bangor University
Secondary Education .... PGCE 12FT

Birmingham City University
Secondary Education (Instrumental Music) .... PGCE 12FT
Secondary Education (Music)................................ PGCE(QTS) 12FT

Canterbury Christ Church University
Music (11-18) PGCE .... PGCE(QTS) 12FT
Music (7-14) PGCE... PGCE(QTS) 12FT

University of Chester
Education: Singing in the Curriculum...................PGCert 12 - 36PT

Edge Hill University
Secondary Music (Age Phase 11-16) with QTS.....PGCE 12FT 36PT

Gloucestershire SCITT Consortium
PGCE in Music.. PGCE 12FT

Section sponsored by BPP UNIVERSITY COLLEGE

Business and social sciences
536 POSTGRADUATE DIRECTORY www.prospects.ac.uk/findcourses

Teacher training and education

Goldsmiths, University of London
Music ..... GradDip 12FT

Institute of Education
Music - PGCE - part-time ..... PGCE 16PT
Music Education ..... MA 12FT 24-48PT
TLHPE MUSIC PATHWAY (instrumental and vocal teaching) ..... Professional Cert. 12PT

Kingston University
Music Education ..... MA 12FT 24PT

Loughborough University
Art & the Public Sphere ..... MA 12FT 24PT

Middlesex University
PGCE Secondary Music ..... PGCE 12FT

University of Reading
Education (Music Education) ..... MA 12FT 24-84PT/PGDip 12FT
Instrumental Teaching ..... PGDip 24-48PT
Music (Secondary Teaching) ..... PGCE 10FT
Music Education ..... MA 12FT 24-60PT/PGDip 12FT 24-60PT
Music Teaching in Professional Practise ..... MA 12FT 36PT/PGDip 24FT 48PT

University of Roehampton
Applied Music Education ..... MA 12FT 24PT
Applied Music Education ..... PGCert 6FT 24PT PGDip 9FT 24-48PT

Royal Holloway, University of London
Advanced Musical Studies ..... MMus 12FT 24PT

University of Salford
Creative Writing: Innovation and Experiment ..... MA 12FT 36PT/PGDip 8FT 24PT/PGCert 4FT 12PT

School of Oriental and African Studies - SOAS
Music and Development ..... MA 12FT 24PT

Trinity Laban Conservatoire of Music and Dance
PGCE 'Musicians In Education' ..... PGCE 12FT

Music teaching
Research Courses

University of Aberdeen
Music ..... PhD 36FT/MPhil 24FT

Outdoor activities teaching
Taught Courses

University of Aberdeen
Social and Educational Research ..... MRes 12FT

Bangor University
Secondary Education ..... PGCE 12FT

University of Central Lancashire
Adventure Sport Coaching ..... MA 12FT
Physical Education and School Sport ..... MA 12FT 24PT
Physiotherapy Professional Practice ..... MSc 12FT up to 60PT

University of Chester
Driving Assessment and Outdoor Mobility (Work Based and Integrative Studies) ..... MA 24-72PT/PGDip 24-60PT/PGCert 12-36PT

University of Cumbria
Development Training ..... MA 24DL/PGDip 15DL/PGCert 9DL
Greening Outdoor Practice ..... PGCert 24-36PT
Outdoor and Experiential Learning ..... MA 12FT 24-36PT/GradDip 12FT 24PT

University of Edinburgh
Outdoor Education ..... MSc 15FT 72PT/PGDip 12FT 48PT/PGCert 24PT
Outdoor Environmental and Sustainability Education.. MSc 15FT 72PT/PGDip 12FT 48PT/PGCert 24PT

Leeds Metropolitan University
Outdoor & Adventurous Activities ..... MSc 12FT 24PT

Manchester Metropolitan University
Maker Teacher ..... MA 24-60PT

University of Nottingham
Creative and Professional Practice in Arts and Education ..... MA 24PT

University of Roehampton
Art, Craft and Design Education ..... PGCert 6FT 24PT PGDip 9FT 24PT

University of Stirling
Performance Coaching ..... MSc 24PT/PGDip 24PT/PGCert 12PT
Sports Coaching ..... MSc 9FT 24PT/PGDip 6FT 24PT/PGCert 6FT 12PT

University of Wales Trinity Saint David
Outdoor Education ..... MA 12FT 24PT 12-24DL/PGDip 12FT 24PT 12-24DL/PGCert 12FT 24PT 12-24DL

University of Worcester
Outdoor Education ..... MA 24FT 48PT

Outdoor activities teaching
Research Courses

University of Chichester
Centre for Sports Science, Physical Education and Recreation Studies ..... PhD 36-48FT 84PT/MPhil 24-36FT 84PT

Overseas Trained Teacher Programme
Taught Courses

University of Aberdeen
Chartered Teacher Programme ..... MEd 5-60PT/PGDip 5-60PT/PGCert 5-60PT

University of Cumbria
Development Training ..... MA 24DL/PGDip 15DL/PGCert 9DL

University of Liverpool
Advanced Science ..... MSc 12FT 24PT/PGDip 12FT/PGCert 12FT

Manchester Metropolitan University
LLM (Master of Laws) ..... LLM 12FT 24PT

Physical education teaching
Taught Courses

Bangor University
Secondary Education ..... PGCE 12FT

University of Bedfordshire
Physical Education and Sport Pedagogy ..... MA 12FT 24PT/PGCert 12FT/PGDip 12FT
Secondary Education Physical Education ..... PGCE 12FT

University of Brighton
(Secondary) Physical Education ..... PGCE 12FT 16PT
(Secondary) Physics ..... PGCE 12FT 16PT

Brunel University
Secondary Education (Physical Education) with recommendation for QTS ..... PGCert 12FT

Canterbury Christ Church University
Physical Education (11-18) PGCE ..... PGCE 12FT

Cardiff Metropolitan University
Physical Education and Sport ..... MA 24PT

University of Central Lancashire
Physical Education and School Sport ..... MA 12FT 24PT

University of Chester
Education: Creativity and Education for the Professions ..... MA 24-72PT/PGDip 24-60PT/PGCert 12-36PT
Education: PGCE Secondary Physical Education.. PGCE(QTS) 12FT

University of Chichester
Secondary Physical Education ..... PGCE(QTS) 9.5FT

University of East London
Secondary Physical Education: Postgraduate Certificate in Education ..... PGCE 12FT
Secondary Physical Education: Professional Graduate Certificate in Education ..... PGCE 12FT

Edge Hill University
Physical Education and School Sport ..... MRes 12FT 24PT
Secondary Physical Education (Age Phase 11-16) with QTS ..... PGCE 12FT

University of Edinburgh
Physical Education, 3-14 ..... PGDE 24FT

University of Glasgow
Education (Primary/Secondary) ..... PGDE 10FT
Primary Physical Education (inservice programme)..PGCert 15PT

Leeds Metropolitan University
Secondary Physical Education ..... PGCE 12FT

Liverpool John Moores University
Physical Education PGCE ..... PGCE 12FT

London Metropolitan University
PGCE Secondary Physical Education ..... PGCE 12FT

University of St Mark and St John
PGCE Secondary Physical Education ..... PGCE 12FT

Middlesex University
PGCE Secondary Physical Education ..... PGCE 10FT

Newman University
PGCE Secondary Physical Education ..... PGCE(QTS) 12FT

Northumbria University
Primary Education PGCE ..... PGCE 12FT
Secondary Education (Physical Education SCITT) ..... PGCE 12FT

University of Reading
PE (Secondary Teaching) ..... PGCE 10FT

University of Roehampton
PGCE Primary (Full-time) ..... PGCE 12FT

Sheffield Hallam University
Leading and Managing Physical Education and Youth Sport ..... MSc 3PT
Leading and Managing Sport Development ..... MSc 24PT/PGDip 16PT/PGCert 8PT
Secondary Physical Education ..... PGCE 12FT

University of Wales Trinity Saint David
Physical Education ..... MA 12FT 24PT/PGCert 12FT 24PT/PGDip 12FT 24PT
Physical Education with Secondary QTS (international students only) ..... MA 12FT 24PT/PGDip 12FT 24PT

University of Ulster
Education (Primary) ..... PGCE 9FT

West Midlands Consortium
Physical Education ..... PGCE(QTS) 10FT

Physical education teaching
Research Courses

University of Chichester
Centre for Sports Science, Physical Education and Recreation Studies ..... PhD 36-48FT 84PT/MPhil 24-36FT 84PT

Physics teaching
Taught Courses

University of Aberdeen
Enhanced Professional Practice ..... MSc 24PT/PGDip 12PT
Plurilingual Education ..... MEd 24PT/PGCert 12PT

Anglia Ruskin University
Postgraduate Certificate in Education: Secondary Science with Physics ..... PGCE 12FT

Birmingham City University
Secondary Education (Science with Physics) ..... PGCE 12FT

University of Brighton
(Secondary) Physics with Mathematics ..... PGCE 12FT 16PT

Brunel University
Secondary Education (Science: Physics) with recommendation for QTS ..... PGCert 12FT 24PT

University of Chester
Education: PGCE Secondary Science with Biology Enhancement ..... PGCE(QTS) 12FT
Education: PGCE Secondary Science with Physics Enhancement ..... PGCE(QTS) 12FT

University of East London
Physics with Mathematics PGCE ..... PGCE 12FT
Secondary Science: Physics (Professional Graduate Certificate in Education) ..... PGCE 12FT
Secondary Science: Physics: Postgraduate Certificate in Education ..... PGCE 12FT

Edge Hill University
Secondary Physics with Mathematics (Age Phase 11-19) with QTS ..... PGCE 12FT
Secondary Science (Physics) (Age Phase 11-16) with QTS..... PGCE 12FT 36PT

Liverpool John Moores University
Science - Biology, Chemistry, Physics (11-16) , Applied Chemistry or Physics (14-19) PGCE ..... PGCE 12FT

University of Manchester
PGCE Secondary Physics ..... PGCE 10FT
PGCE Secondary Physics with Maths ..... PGCE 10FT

Physics teaching
Research Courses

University of Cambridge
Physics ..... PhD 36FT 60PT/MPhil 12FT

Practice teaching award
Taught Courses

University of Aberdeen
Social and Educational Research ..... MRes 12FT

Anglia Ruskin University
Masters of Teaching and Learning .....

Bournemouth University
Advanced Practice ..... MSc 12PT
Education Practice ..... MA 31FT/PGDip 24FT/PGCert 12FT
Professional Practice ..... Dr Professional Practice up to 48PT

University of Cambridge
Advanced Subject Teaching ..... MSt 24PT

University of Central Lancashire
Doctorate in Education ..... EdD by taught 60PT
Education (Research) ..... MA 24PT/PGDip 24PT/PGCert 24PT
Education and History ..... MA 24PT
Education and Religion in Society ..... MA 24PT
Practice Teacher ..... PGCert 6PT
Professional Practice in Education MEd 24-60PT/PGCert 24-60PT/PGDip 24-60PT

University of Chester
Coach-Mentoring and Facilitation in Organisations (Work Based and Integrative Studies) ..... MA 24-72PT/MSc 24-72PT/PGDip 24-60PT/PGCert 12-36PT
Dental Practice Management (Work Based and Integrative Studies) ..... MA 24-72PT/PGDip 24-60PT/PGCert 12-36PT
Developing RPL Policy and Practice (Work Based and Integrative Studies) ..... MA 24-72PT/PGDip 24-60PT/PGCert 12-36PT

Section sponsored by
BPP UNIVERSITY COLLEGE

Business and social sciences
www.prospects.ac.uk/findcourses POSTGRADUATE DIRECTORY 537

Teacher training and education

Education and Teaching Studies (Work Based and Integrative Studies) .... MA 24-72PT/MSc 24-72PT/PGDip 24-60PT/PGCert 12-36PT
Education: Creativity and Education for the Professions .... MA 24-72PT/PGDip 24-60PT/PGCert 12-36PT
Leadership Development (Work Based and Integrative Studies).. MA 24-72PT/MSc 24-72PT/PGDip 24-60PT/PGCert 12-36PT
Leading RPL Policy and Practice (Work Based and Integrative Studies) .... MA 24-72PT/PGDip 24-60PT/PGCert 12-36PT
Learning and Development (Work Based and Integrative Studies) .... MA 24-72PT/MSc 24-72PT/PGDip 24-60PT/PGCert 12-36PT
Nursing Studies (Work Based and Integrative Studies) .... MA 24-72PT/MSc 24-72PT/PGDip 24-60PT/PGCert 12-36PT
Personal Leadership Development (Work Based and Integrative Studies) .... MA 24-72PT/PGDip 24-60PT/PGCert 12-36PT
Professional Studies and Development (Work Based and Integrative Studies)... MA 24-72PT/MSc 24-72PT/PGDip 24-60PT/PGCert 12-36PT

University of Cumbria
Education .... MA 36PT

University of Derby
Interprofessional Practice Education .... PGCert 12-18PT

University of Dundee
Practice Education .... PGCert 12DL

University of East Anglia
Advanced Educational Practice .... MA 36PT/MA 48PT

University of Gloucestershire
National Award for Special Educational Needs Continuation .... PGCert 9PT

Goldsmiths, University of London
Advanced Social Work: Practice Education .... MA 24PT

Kingston University
Child Centred Interprofessional Practice .... MA 24PT

University of Liverpool
Advanced Science .... MSc 12FT 24PT/PGDip 12FT/PGCert 12FT

Manchester Metropolitan University
National Award for Special Needs Co-ordinators National Award 12PT

Sheffield Hallam University
Doctorate in Education .... Doctorate 48PT
Integrated Working .... MA 36PT/PGDip 24PT/PGCert 12PT

University of Wales Trinity Saint David
Education...... MA 12FT 48PT/PGDip 12FT 48PT/PGCert 12FT 48PT
Professional Practice .... MA FlexibleFT FlexiblePT FlexibleDL/PGDip FlexibleFT FlexiblePT/PGCert FlexibleFT FlexiblePT
Technology Enhanced Learning .... PGCert 24PT 24DL

Practice teaching award
Research Courses

University of Nottingham
EPSRC AstraZeneca Doctoral Training Centre in Targeted Therapeutics .... PhD 48FT 72PT

Oxford Brookes University
Doctorate of Education - Professional Doctorate...... EdD 60-84PT

University of Portsmouth
Professional Doctorate in Education .... EdD 48PT

University of Southampton
Integrated PhD in Education .... Integrated PhD 36FT

Primary education studies
Taught Courses

Anglia Ruskin University
Early Childhood Professional Studies .... MA 12FT 36PT

Bangor University
Education........ PhD by taught 36FT 48-60PT/MPhil 24FT 36-48PT
Education Doctorate Programme (EdD) .... EdD by taught 60PT
Education Studies... MA 12FT 24-60PT/MEd 12FT 24-60PT/PGDip 8FT 24-48PT/PGCert 4FT 12-24PT
Primary Education .... PGCE 12FT

Bath Spa University
PGCE Primary and Early Years .... PGCE 12FT 20PT

University College Birmingham
Childhood, Professional Studies in Childhood..... MA 24PT/PGDip 24PT/PGCert 24PT
Early Years PGCE .... PGCE 12PT

Canterbury Christ Church University
Primary Education (3 -7) PGCE .... PGCE(QTS) 12FT 20PT

University of Central Lancashire
Education (Research) .... MA 24PT/PGDip 24PT/PGCert 24PT
Education and History .... MA 24PT
Education and Religion in Society .... MA 24PT
Practice Teacher .... PGCert 6PT
Professional Practice in EducationMEd 24-60PT/PGCert 24-60PT/PGDip 24-60PT

University of Chester
Education: Primary Graduate Teacher Programme .... QTS 12FT

University of Chichester
Primary Education: Early Years .... PGCE(QTS) 9.5FT 19PT
Primary Education: Modern Languages .... PGCE(QTS) 9.5FT

University of Cumbria
Education .... MA 36PT

University of Derby
Education .... EdD by taught 36-72PT
PGCE Primary .... PGCE 12FT

University of Dundee
Education (Chartered Teacher) .... MEd 18PT/PGDip 9PT/PGCert 6PT
Educational Psychology .... MSc 24FT
Primary Education (PGDE) .... PGDE 11FT

Durham University
Education (Primary) .... PGCE 12FT
PGCE Primary (International) .... PGCE 12FT
Practice of Education .... PGCert 12PT

University of East Anglia
Early Childhood Studies .... MA 36PT
Primary Teacher Training (3 to 9 years) Foundation Stage/Key Stage One .... PGCE(QTS) 12FT
Primary Teacher Training (5 to 11 years) General Class Teacher with Modern Foreign Languages: French.............. PGCE(QTS) 12FT
Primary Teacher Training (5 to 11 years) General Class Teacher with Modern Foreign Languages: German .... PGCE(QTS) 12FT
Primary Teacher Training (5 to 11 years) General Class Teacher with Modern Foreign Languages: Spanish .... PGCE(QTS) 12FT
Primary Teacher Training (5 to 11 years) Key Stage One/Lower Key Stage Two .... PGCE(QTS) 12FT
Primary Teacher Training (5 to 11 years) Key Stage Two................. PGCE(QTS) 12FT

University of Glasgow
Childhood Practice .... PGDip 24PT
Primary Expressive Arts .... PGCert 12PT
Professional Practice with PGDE .... MEd 18PT

Glyndwr University
Education .... MA 12FT 24-36PT
PGCE 12FT 24-36PT/CertEd 24-36PT

Goldsmiths, University of London
Practice Education .... MA 36-60PT/PGDip 36-60PT/PGCert 36-60PT

Institute of Education
Primary Education (Policy and Practice) .... MA 12FT 24-48PT
Sociology of Childhood and Children's Rights .. MA 12FT 24-48PT

Leeds Metropolitan University
Early Childhood Education - PGCE .... PGCE 12FT
Primary Education .... PGCE 12FT

Leeds Trinity University
Education .... PGCert 6PT/PGDip 18PT/MA 24PT

University of Leeds
PGCE Primary .... PGCE 12FT

Liverpool John Moores University
Early Years (3 -7 years) .... PGCE 12FT

London Metropolitan University
Early Years and Primary Education .... PGCE 12FT

Newman University
Children, Young People and Families .... MA 24FT 36-48PT
PGCE Primary .... PGCE(QTS) 12FT
PGCE Primary with English as an Additional Language .... PGCE(QTS) 12FT
PGCE Primary with Modern Foreign Languages.. PGCE(QTS) 12FT

Northumbria University
Early Years and Primary (Flexible) PGCE .... PGCE 12-24DL

Nottingham Trent University
PGCE Primary .... PGCE(QTS) 10FT/ProfGCE(QTS) 10FT

Oxford Brookes University
Advanced Early Years Specialism (PGCert Advanced Educational Practice) .... PGCert 12PT
Childhood Studies .... MA 12FT 24PT/PGDip 12FT 24PT/PGCert 12FT 12PT
Children, Young People and Family Well-Being .... MSc 12-36DL/PGDip 8-36DL/PGCert 4-36DL

University of Reading
Education (Early Years) .... MA 12FT 24-84PT/PGDip 12FT
Education (Primary Education) ...... MA 12FT 24-84PT/PGDip 12FT

University Campus Suffolk
Childhood and Youth Studies .... MA 12FT 24 - 36PT
PGCE (Suffolk and Norfolk Primary SCITT) .... PGDE 12FT

University of Sheffield
Education .... MA 12FT

St Mary's University College, Twickenham
PGCE Primary Education .... PGCE 12FT 18PT

University of Strathclyde
Early Childhood Studies........ MSc 24PT/PGDip 24PT/PGCert 24PT
Education .... EdD by taught 36-72PT/MEd 24-36PT 24-36DL

University of Ulster
Education (Primary) .... PGCE 9FT

Primary education studies
Research Courses

Bangor University
Education .... PhD 36FT 60-72PT/MPhil 24FT 36-48PT

University of Dundee
Education .... MPhil 24FT MSc by research 12FT PhD 36FT

Keele University
Education .... PhD 24-48FT 48-84PT/MPhil 12-24FT 24-36PT

The Open University
Doctorate in Education .... EdD 36PT
Educational studies .... PhD 36FT 72PT/EdD 36PT/MRes 12FT

Primary school teaching
Taught Courses

University of Aberdeen
Learning and Development (Primary) .... PGCert 12PT
Primary Education .... PGDE 9FT 24PT 24DL
Professional Learning and Development (Primary) ..... PGCert 3PT

Anglia Ruskin University
Postgraduate Certificate in Education: Primary .... PGCE 12FT

Bangor University
Education........ PhD by taught 36FT 48-60PT/MPhil 24FT 36-48PT
Primary Education .... PGCE 12FT

Bath Spa University
PGCE Primary and Early Years .... PGCE 12FT 20PT

University of Bedfordshire
Education KS2/3 Middle Years .... PGCE 12FT
Primary Education .... PGCE 12FT
Primary Education with Early years .... PGCE 12FT

Birmingham City University
Primary and Early Years Education .... PGCE(QTS) 12FT 24PT

University of Birmingham
Postgraduate Diploma Primary Education (PGCE Advanced) General Primary or Early Years .... PGCE(QTS) 12FT

University College Birmingham
Early Years PGCE .... PGCE 12PT

Bishop Grosseteste University College Lincoln
Primary PGCE .... PGCE 12FT

University of Brighton
Primary Education (3-7 years) .... PGCE 12FT
Primary Education (5-11 years) .... PGCE 12FT

Brunel University
Primary Education (5 to 11 Years) with recommendation for QTS PGCert 12FT

Canterbury Christ Church University
Modern Foreign Languages (7-14) PGCE .... PGCE(QTS) 12FT
Primary Education (5-11) PGCE .... PGCE(QTS) 12FT 20PT
Primary Education - Primary Languages (5-11) PGCE .. PGCE(QTS) 12FT

Cardiff Metropolitan University
Primary Teaching .... PGCE 12FT

University of Chester
Education: PGCE Early Years .... PGCE(QTS) 12FT
Education: PGCE Primary .... PGCE(QTS) 12FT

University of Chichester
Primary: Generalist Route .... PGCE(QTS) 9.5FT
Primary: Generalist Route (Flexible) .... PGCE(QTS) 18PT

University College Cork
Teaching of Science in the Primary School .... PGDip 24PT

Cumbria Primary Teacher Training
Primary 5-11 Initial Teacher Training PGCE(QTS) 12FT/PGCE 12FT

University of Dundee
Primary Education (PGDE) .... PGDE 11FT

Durham University
Education (Primary) .... PGCE 12FT

University of East Anglia
Primary Teacher Training (3 to 9 years) Foundation Stage/Key Stage One .... PGCE(QTS) 12FT
Primary Teacher Training (5 to 11 years) General Class Teacher with Modern Foreign Languages: French .... PGCE(QTS) 12FT
Primary Teacher Training (5 to 11 years) General Class Teacher with Modern Foreign Languages: German .... PGCE(QTS) 12FT
Primary Teacher Training (5 to 11 years) General Class Teacher with Modern Foreign Languages: Spanish .... PGCE(QTS) 12FT
Primary Teacher Training (5 to 11 years) Key Stage One/Lower Key Stage Two .... PGCE(QTS) 12FT
Primary Teacher Training (5 to 11 years) Key Stage Two .... PGCE(QTS) 12FT

University of East London
Postgraduate Certificate in Education (Primary) with Modern Foreign Languages .... PGCE 12FT

Teacher training and education

Primary Early Years 3-7 .... PGCE TBCFT
Primary Teacher Training/Postgraduate Certificate in Education PGCE - (Primary) .... PGCE 12FT
Primary with English as an Additional Language PGCEPGCE 12FT
Professional Graduate Certificate in Education (Primary) .... PGCE 12FT
Professional Graduate Certificate in Education (Primary) with Modern Foreign Languages .... PGCE 12FT

Edge Hill University
Primary Mathematics Education with QTS .... PGCE 12FT
Primary Mathematics Specialist with QTS .... PGCE 12FT
Primary Modern Languages Education with QTS .... PGCE 12FT
Primary Science Education with QTS .... PGCE 12FT
Specialist Primary Mathematics Practice .... MA 36-60PT

University of Glasgow
Education (Primary/Secondary) .... PGDE 10FT
Learning and Teaching of Modern Languages in the Primary School .... PGCert 15PT
Primary Physical Education (inservice programme) .. PGCert 15PT

University of Gloucestershire
Teacher Training PGCE (Primary) .... PGCE 12FT

Goldsmiths, University of London
Education (Primary with Modern Languages) .... PGCE 12FT
Education (Primary) .... PGCE 12FT

University of Greenwich
Primary Education .... PGCE 12FT 24PT

University of Hertfordshire
Primary Education (PGCE) .... PGCE 12FT 24PT

Kingston University
Primary Teaching leading to Qualified Teacher Status (QTS) .... PGCE 12FT

Leeds Metropolitan University
Early Childhood Education - PGCE .... PGCE 12FT
Primary Education .... PGCE 12FT

University of Leeds
PGCE Primary .... PGCE 12FT

Liverpool John Moores University
Early Years (3 -7 years) .... PGCE 12FT

London Metropolitan University
Early Years Practice .... PGCert variousFT
Early Years and Primary Education .... PGCE 12FT

London South Bank University
Early Years (3-7) PGCE with QTS .... PGCE(QTS) 12FT
Graduate Teacher Programme Primary/Early Years .... QTS 12FT
PGCE Primary (5-11 Year Olds) .... PGCE(QTS) 12FT 24PT

Manchester Metropolitan University
Education Studies .... MA 12FT 24PT
Primary Education with QTS .... PGCE 12FT
Teaching and Learning .... MA 12-18PT

University of Manchester
PGCE Primary .... PGCE 10FT
PGCE Primary (Modern Language) .... PGCE 10FT

University of St Mark and St John
PGCE Primary .... PGCE 12FT
PGCE Primary with a Primary Languages Specialism (French or Spanish) .... PGCE 12FT

Middlesex University
PGCE Early Years .... PGCE 12FT
PGCE Primary Education .... PGCE 12FT

Newcastle University
Postgraduate Certificate in Education (PGCE) - Primary .... PGCE 10FT

Newman University
PGCE Primary .... PGCE(QTS) 12FT
PGCE Primary with English as an Additional Language .... PGCE(QTS) 12FT
PGCE Primary with Modern Foreign Languages.. PGCE(QTS) 12FT

Northumbria University
Early Years and Primary (Flexible) PGCE .... PGCE 12-24DL
Primary Education PGCE .... PGCE 12FT

Nottingham Trent University
PGCE Primary .... PGCE(QTS) 10FT/ProfGCE(QTS) 10FT

University of Nottingham
PGCE Primary - School Based Initial Teacher Training (SCITT) .... PGCE 12FT

Oxford Brookes University
Education (PGCE) - Primary .... PGCE 10FT

Plymouth University
Primary .... PGCE 12FT
Primary - Early Years Education (5-11 or 3-7) .... PGCE 12FT

University of Reading
Education (Primary Education) ......MA 12FT 24-84PT/PGDip 12FT
Primary Teaching (Early Years) .... PGCE 10FT
Primary Teaching (Primary Years) .... PGCE 10FT
Primary Teaching with French Specialism .... PGCE 10FT

University of Roehampton
PGCE Primary (Full-time) .... PGCE 12FT
PGCE Primary (Part-time) .... PGCE 24PT

University Campus Suffolk
PGCE (Suffolk and Norfolk Primary SCITT) .... PGDE 12FT

Sheffield Hallam University
Primary Education (5-11) .... PGCE 12FT

University of Sheffield
Education .... MA 12FT
PGCE .... PGCE 9FT
Postgraduate Certificate in Education .... PGCE 9FT

University of Southampton
PGCE (Primary) .... PGCE 12FT
Post Graduate Certificate in Education in Post Compulsory Education & Training .... PGCE 24PT

St Mary's University College, Twickenham
PGCE Primary Education .... PGCE 12FT 18PT

University of Strathclyde
Education .... EdD by taught 36-72PT/MEd 24-36PT 24-36DL
Primary Education .... PGDE 10FT 21PT

University of Sunderland
PGCE Primary Education (5-11) .... PGCE(QTS) 12FT

Swansea Metropolitan University
PGCE Primary with Qualified Teacher Status .... PGCE(QTS) 10FT

Thames Primary SCITT Consortium
Key Stage One; Key Stage Two .... PGCE 10FT

Titan Partnership Ltd
Primary SCITT .... PGCE(QTS) 10FT

University of Ulster
Education (Primary) .... PGCE 9FT

University of the West of Scotland
Primary Education .... PGDE 9FT

University of the West of England, Bristol
Education: PGCE Primary .... PGCE 10FT

University of Winchester
PGCE Primary .... PGCE 12FT 24PT

University of Wolverhampton
Primary Education .... PGCE 12FT

University of Worcester
Postgraduate Certificate in Education - PGCE - Primary........ PGCE 12FT

York St John University
Education (Primary) .... PGCE 12FT 24PT

Primary school teaching
Research Courses

Bangor University
Education .... PhD 36FT 60-72PT/MPhil 24FT 36-48PT

Psychology teaching
Taught Courses

Anglia Ruskin University
Clinical Child Psychology .... MSc 12 - 15FT 24 - 30PT

Canterbury Christ Church University
Psychology (14-19) PGCE .... PGCE(QTS) 12FT

Glyndwr University
Teaching of Psychology .... MSc 36PT

Keele University
Psychology .... MSc 12FT 24PT

Leeds Metropolitan University
Psychology (conversion award) .... MSc 12FT 24PT

University of Nottingham
Psychological Therapies .... PGCert 12PT
Rehabilitation Psychology .... MSc 12FT 24PT

University of Salford
Applied Psychology (Therapies) MSc 12FT 36PT/PGDip 8FT 24PT/PGCert 4FT 9PT

University of St Andrews
Conversion to Psychology .... MSc 12FT

Teesside University
Doctorate Psychology (Top up) .... PsychD by taught 30BM

Psychology teaching
Research Courses

University of Aberdeen
Psychology..... PhD 36FT/MPhil 24FT/MSc by research 12FT/MRes 12FT

University of East Anglia
Psychology .... PhD 36FT 72PT/MPhil 24FT 48PT

Religious education
Taught Courses

University of Aberdeen
Divinity and Religious Studies .... MTh 12FT 24PT
Practical Theology .... MTh 12FT 24PT
Religion and Politics .... MSc 12FT 24PT
Religion and Society .... MSc 12FT 24PT/PGDip 9FT 18PT/PGCert 6FT 12PT
Theology and Religious Studies .... MTh 12FT 24PT

Bangor University
Philosophy and Religion .... MA 12FT 36PT MRes 12FT 36PT

University of Brighton
(Secondary) Religious Studies .... PGCE 12FT 16PT

Canterbury Christ Church University
Religion in Education .... MA 24PT
Religious Education (11-18) PGCE .... PGCE(QTS) 12FT
Religious Education (7-14) PGCE .... PGCE(QTS) 12FT

University of Central Lancashire
Education and History .... MA 24PT
Education and Religion in Society .... MA 24PT
Religion, Culture & Society . MA 12FT 24-36PT/PGDip 12FT 24PT/PGCert 12FT 12-24PT

University of Chester
Education: PGCE Secondary Religious Education .... PGCE(QTS) 12FT
Faiths and Public PolicyMA 12FT 36PT 36DL/PGDip 12FT 24-36PT 24-36DL/PGCert 12FT 12-24PT 12-24DL
Practical and Contextual Theology .... MA 12FT 36PT 36DL/PGDip 12FT 24 - 36PT 24 - 36DL/PGCert 12FT 12 - 24PT 12 - 24DL
Religious Studies ....MA 12FT 36PT 36DL/PGDip 12FT 24 - 36PT 24 - 36DL/PGCert 12FT 12 - 24PT 12 - 24DL
Theology ..MA 12FT 36PT 36DL/PGDip 12FT 24 - 36PT 24 - 36DL/PGCert 12FT 12 - 24PT 12 - 24DL

University of Chichester
Secondary Religious Education .... PGCE(QTS) 9.5FT

University College Cork
Teaching of Religious Education .... PGDip 24PT

University of Cumbria
Theology .... MA 12FT 36PT/PGDip 6FT 24PT/PGCert 3FT 12PT

Edge Hill University
Secondary Religious Education (Age Phase 11-16) with QTS .... PGCE 12FT 36PT

University of Edinburgh
Science and Religion .... MSc 12FT

University of Exeter
Theology .... MA 12FT 24PT

University of Glasgow
Education (Primary/Secondary) .... PGDE 10FT
Healthcare Chaplaincy .... PGCert 12PT
Religion, Education and Culture .... MEd 24 - 36PT
Religion, Theology & Culture ......MLitt 12FT 24PT/MTh 12FT 24PT
Religious Education by Distance Learning .... PGCert 24DL

University of Gloucestershire
Sports and Christian Outreach (Sports Ministry)... MA 12FT 24PT
Theology .... MTh 24PT

Heythrop College
Abrahamic Religions .... MA 12FT 24PT
Biblical Studies .... MA 24FT 12PT
Christian Theology .... MA 24FT 12PT
Philosophy and Religion .... MA 12FT 24PT

University of Hull
Theology .... MA 12FT 24PT

Institute of Education
Humanities Education (Citizenship/History/Religious Education) .... MA 12FT 24-48PT

King's College London
Bible and Ministry .... MA 12FT 24PT
Christianity & the Arts .... MA 12FT 24PT
Religious Education .... MA 12FT 24 - 72PT
Theology & Religious Studies .... GradDip 12FT 24PT

Leeds Metropolitan University
Health & Social Care Chaplaincy .... PGCert 12PT

University of Leeds
Theology and Pastoral Studies .... MA 12FT 24PT
Theology or Religious Studies and Development Studies .... MA 12FT 24PT

University of St Mark and St John
PGCE Secondary Religious Education .... PGCE 12FT

Newman University
PGCE Secondary Religious Education .... PGCE(QTS) 12FT

University of Oxford
Applied Theology .... MTh 12FT 48PT/PGDip 12FT 48PT
Eastern Christian Studies .... MPhil 21FT
Study of Religion .... MSt 12FT
Theology .... MPhil 21FT/MSt 9FT/PGDip 12FT

Section sponsored by
BPP UNIVERSITY COLLEGE

Business and social sciences
www.prospects.ac.uk/findcourses POSTGRADUATE DIRECTORY 539

Teacher training and education

School of Oriental and African Studies - SOAS
Religions .... MA 12FT 24-36PT

Sheffield Hallam University
Secondary Religious Education .... PGCE 12FT

University of Sheffield
Archaeology, Bible and Ancient Cultures .... MA 12FT 24PT
Ministry and Biblical Studies .... MA 12FT 24PT
Ministry and Theology .... MA 12FT 24PT
Religion, Conflict and the Media .... MA 12FT 24PT
Social Scientific Biblical Studies .... MA 12FT 24PT

University of South Wales
Religious Education .... MA 12FT 36PT
Religious Education Professional Development .... Professional Development 24PT/MA 12FT 24 - 36PT

University of St Andrews
Scripture and Theology .... MLitt 12FT 24PT/PGDip 9FT 18PT
Systematic and Historical Theology .... PGDip 9FT/MLitt 12FT

University of Wales Trinity Saint David
Ancient Religions .... MA 24PT 24DL
Christian Theology .... MTh 12FT 24PT
Church History .... MTh 12FT 24PT 12-24DL
Study of Religions .... MA 12FT 24PT/PGCert 12FT 24PT/PGDip 12FT 24PT

University of Warwick
Religions and Education .... MA 24-48DL

University of Winchester
PGCE Secondary Religious Education .... PGCE 18-36PT

York St John University
Education (Secondary RE) Postgraduate Certificate .... PGCE(QTS) 12FT

Religious education
Research Courses

Bangor University
Theology and Religious Studies .... MPhil 24FT 36PT/PhD 24-36FT 60PT

University of Bristol
Theology and Religious StudiesPhD 36FT 72PT/MLitt by research 24FT 48PT/MPhil 12FT 24PT

University of Cambridge
Theology and Religious Studies .... PhD 36FT 60PT
Theology and Religious Studies .... MLitt by research 24FT

Canterbury Christ Church University
Religious Studies or Theology ... PhD 48FT 60PT/MPhil 24FT 48PT

University of Chester
Theology and Religious Studies .... DProf 24 - 48FT 24 - 84PT

University of Chichester
Theology .... PhD 36FT 84PT/DPhil 24FT 84PT

University of Exeter
Theology and Religion .... PhD 48FT 84PT 48DL/MPhil 36FT 60PT 36DL/MA by research 12FT 24PT

Heythrop College
Pastoral Theology .... MRes 12FT 24PT

University of Wales Trinity Saint David
Religious Studies .... PhD 36FT 48-72PT 36-72DL/MPhil 12FT 18-24PT 12-24DL

Science teaching
Taught Courses

University of Bedfordshire
Secondary Education Science with Chemistry, Physics or Biology .... PGCE 12FT

Bradford College
Education (Secondary Science) .... PGCert 12FT

University of Bristol
Education - Science and Education .... MSc 12FT 60PT

Brunel University
Secondary Education (Science: Biology) with recommendation for QTS .... PGCert 12FT 24PT
Secondary Education (Science: Chemistry) with recommendation for QTS .... PGCert 12FT 24PT
Secondary Education (Science: Physics) with recommendation for QTS .... PGCert 12FT 24PT

Canterbury Christ Church University
Science (11-18) PGCE .... PGCE(QTS) 12FT
Science (7-14) PGCE .... PGCE(QTS) 12FT

Cardiff University
Science, Media and Communication .... MSc 12FT

University of Chester
Education: Secondary Graduate Teacher Programme .... QTS 12FT
Education: Teaching and Learning MA 24 - 72PT/PGDip 24-60PT/PGCert 12-36PT

University of Chichester
Secondary Science .... PGCE(QTS) 9.5FT

University College Cork
Education (Sc) .... MA(Ed) 24PT
Teaching of Science in the Primary School .... PGDip 24PT

Durham University
Science Education .... MSc 12FT 36PT

Edge Hill University
Primary Science Education with QTS .... PGCE 12FT

University of Edinburgh
Science Communication and Public Engagement .... MSc 36DL/PGDip 24DL/PGCert 12DL

Institute of Education
Science Education .... MA 12FT 24-48PT

University of Kent
Science, Communication and Society .... MSc 12FT 24PT

King's College London
Science Education .... MA 12FT 24-72PT

University of Leeds
Science Education .... MA 12FT 24PT

Liverpool John Moores University
Engineering .... PGCE 12FT
Science - Biology, Chemistry, Physics (11-16) , Applied Chemistry or Physics (14-19) PGCE .... PGCE 12FT

London Metropolitan University
PGCE Secondary Science with Biology/Chemistry/Physics .. PGCE 12-24FT

Manchester Metropolitan University
Science, Technology, Engineering and Maths (STEM) .... MSc 24-72PT

University of Manchester
PGCE Secondary Biology .... PGCE 10FT

University of St Mark and St John
PGCE Secondary Science .... PGCE 12FT

Middlesex University
PGCE Secondary Science .... PGCE 10FT

Newman University
PGCE Secondary Science .... PGCE(QTS) 12FT

University of Nottingham
PGCE Secondary - Science .... PGCE 12FT 24PT

The Open University
Science and Society .... MSc variableDL/PGDip variableDL

University of Portsmouth
Science with Biology .... PGCE (Postgraduate) 12FT/PGCE (Professional) 12FT
Science with Physics .... PGCE (Postgraduate) 12FT/PGCE (Professional) 12FT

University of Reading
Science (Secondary Teaching) .... PGCE 10FT

Sheffield Hallam University
Science Education .... PGCert 12DL
Secondary Science .... PGCE 12FT

University of Sunderland
PGCE Science Secondary Education 1 year .... PGCE(QTS) 12FT
PGCE Science Secondary Education 2 year .... PGCE(QTS) 24FT

University of York
Science Education .... MA 12FT

Science teaching
Research Courses

Bath Spa University
Early Scientific Learning .... PhD 24 - 60FT 36 - 72PT

University of Glasgow
Science Education .... PhD 36FT 48PT/MSc by research 12FT

Secondary education studies
Taught Courses

University of Aberdeen
Secondary Education .... PGDip 9FT 24PT 24DL

Anglia Ruskin University
Postgraduate Certificate in Education: Secondary (English) PGCE 12FT
Postgraduate Certificate in Education: Secondary Information and Communication Technology .... PGCE 12FT
Postgraduate Certificate in Education: Secondary Mathematics .... PGCE 12FT
Postgraduate Certificate in Education: Secondary Modern Languages .... PGCE 12FT
Postgraduate Certificate in Education: Secondary Science with Biology .... PGCE 12FT
Postgraduate Certificate in Education: Secondary Science with Chemistry .... PGCE 12FT
Postgraduate Certificate in Education: Secondary Science with Physics .... PGCE 12FT

Bangor University
Education Doctorate Programme (EdD) .... EdD by taught 60PT
Education Studies... MA 12FT 24-60PT/MEd 12FT 24-60PT/PGDip 8FT 24-48PT/PGCert 4FT 12-24PT
Secondary Education .... PGCE 12FT

Bath Spa University
PGCE Secondary .... PGCE 10FT

Birmingham City University
Secondary Education (Art & Design) .... PGCE(QTS) 12FT
Secondary Education (Instrumental Music) .... PGCE 12FT
Secondary Education (Music) .... PGCE(QTS) 12FT
Secondary Education (Science with Chemistry) .... PGCE 12FT
Secondary Education (Science with Physics) .... PGCE 12FT

Cardiff Metropolitan University
Secondary Teaching .... PGCE 12FT

University of Central Lancashire
Education (Research) .... MA 24PT/PGDip 24PT/PGCert 24PT
Education and History .... MA 24PT
Education and Religion in Society .... MA 24PT
Practice Teacher .... PGCert 6PT
Professional Practice in EducationMEd 24-60PT/PGCert 24-60PT/PGDip 24-60PT

University of Chichester
Secondary ICT .... PGCE(QTS) 9.5FT 5 maxPT
Secondary Science .... PGCE(QTS) 9.5FT

University of Cumbria
Education .... MA 36PT

University of Derby
Education .... EdD by taught 36-72PT
PGCE Primary .... PGCE 12FT

University of Dundee
Education (Chartered Teacher) .... MEd 18PT/PGDip 9PT/PGCert 6PT
Educational Psychology .... MSc 24FT
Secondary Education (PGDE) .... PGDE 9FT 18PT

Durham University
Education (Secondary) .... PGCE 12FT
PGCE Secondary (International) .... PGCE 12FT
Practice of Education .... PGCert 12PT

University of East Anglia
Secondary Teacher Training (11-16 years) with post-16 enhancement experience: English .... PGCE(QTS) 12FT
Secondary Teacher Training (11-16 years) with post-16 enhancement experience: Geography .... PGCE(QTS) 12FT
Secondary Teacher Training (11-16 years) with post-16 enhancement experience: History .... PGCE(QTS) 12FT
Secondary Teacher Training (11-16 years) with post-16 enhancement experience: Mathematics .... PGCE(QTS) 12FT
Secondary Teacher Training (11-16 years) with post-16 enhancement experience: Modern Foreign Languages .... PGCE(QTS) 12FT
Secondary Teacher Training (11-16 years) with post-16 enhancement experience: Physical Education .... PGCE(QTS) 12FT
Secondary Teacher Training (11-16 years) with post-16 enhancement experience: Science (Biology) .... PGCE(QTS) 12FT
Secondary Teacher Training (11-16 years) with post-16 enhancement experience: Science (Chemistry) .. PGCE(QTS) 12FT
Secondary Teacher Training (11-16 years) with post-16 enhancement experience: Science (Physics) .... PGCE(QTS) 12FT

University of East London
Secondary Design and Technology (Food & Textiles) Postgraduate Certificate in Education .... PGCE 12FT
Secondary Design and Technology (Food & Textiles) Professional Graduate Certificate in Education .... PGCE 12FT
Secondary English Postgraduate Certificate in Education (PGCE): PGCE 12FT
Secondary English Professional Graduate Certificate in Education (PGCE) .... PGCE 12FT
Secondary Information Communication Technology Postgraduate Certificate in Education (PGCE .... PGCE 12FT
Secondary Information Communication Technology Professional GRaduate Certificate in Educat .... PGCE 12FT
Secondary Mathematics: Postgraduate Certificate in Education .... PGCE 12FT
Secondary Mathematics: Professional Graduate Certificate in Education (PGCE) .... PGCE 12FT
Secondary Modern Languages Postgraduate Certificate in Education (PGCE): .... PGCE 12FT
Secondary Modern Languages: Professional Graduate Certificate in Education (PGCE): .... PGCE 12FT
Secondary Physical Education: Postgraduate Certificate in Education .... PGCE 12FT
Secondary Physical Education: Professional Graduate Certificate in Education .... PGCE 12FT
Secondary Physics with Mathematics (PGCE) .... PGCE 12FT
Secondary Science: Biology :Professional Graduate Certificate in Education .... PGCE 12FT
Secondary Science: Biology: Postgraduate Certificate in Education .... PGCE 12FT
Secondary Science: Chemistry (Professional Graduate Certificate in Education) .... PGCE 12FT
Secondary Science: Chemistry: Postgraduate Certificate in Education .... PGCE 12FT

Teacher training and education

Secondary Science: Physics (Professional Graduate Certificate in Education)... PGCE 12FT
Secondary Science: Physics: Postgraduate Certificate in Education... PGCE 12FT

University of Gloucestershire
Teacher Training PGCE (Secondary)................................... PGCE 12FT

Glyndwr University
Education................................. PGCE 12FT 24-36PT/CertEd 24-36PT MA 12FT 24-36PT

Goldsmiths, University of London
Education (Secondary) .... PGCE 12FT

University of Greenwich
Secondary Education .... PGCE 12FT

University of Hertfordshire
Secondary Education (PGCE) .... PGCE 12FT 24PT

Keele University
PGCE (Secondary Education) .... PGCE(QTS) 12FT

Kent and Medway Training
PGCE 11-18 .... PGCE(QTS) 10FT

Leeds Trinity University
Education................................. PGCert 6PT/PGDip 18PT/MA 24PT

University of Leeds
PGCE Secondary .... PGCE 10FT

University of Leicester
Secondary PGCE .... PGCE 12FT

Liverpool John Moores University
Secondary ICT (11-16) PGCE .... PGCE 12FT
Secondary Mathematics PGCE........................ PGCE 12FT

London South Bank University
PGCE Secondary Mathematics (11-16 Year Olds)...........................
PGCE(QTS) 12FT

Loughborough University
Education with Qualified Teacher Status (QTS) ..... MSc 12FT 36PT
Postgraduate Diploma/Certificate in Education with QTS..PGDip 12FT 36PT/PGCert 12FT 36PT

Newman University
PGCE Secondary Citizenship................................... PGCE(QTS) 12FT
PGCE Secondary Computer Science and ICT......... PGCE(QTS) 12FT
PGCE Secondary English .... PGCE(QTS) 12FT
PGCE Secondary Mathematics................................... PGCE(QTS) 12FT
PGCE Secondary Modern Foreign Languages....... PGCE(QTS) 12FT
PGCE Secondary Physical Education....................... PGCE(QTS) 12FT
PGCE Secondary Religious Education.................... PGCE(QTS) 12FT
PGCE Secondary Science..................................... PGCE(QTS) 12FT

North London Consortium
Secondary Education .... PGCE 11FT

University of Nottingham
PGCE Secondary - English................................... PGCE 12FT

Plymouth University
Secondary Education .... PGCE 12FT

University of Reading
Art & Design (Secondary Teaching) .... PGCE 10FT
French (Conversion Course) (Secondary)......................... PGCE 24FT
History (Secondary Teaching)............................... PGCE 10FT
ICT (Secondary Teaching)..................................... PGCE 10FT
Mathematics (Secondary Teaching)....................... PGCE 10FT
Modern Languages (Secondary Teaching) .... PGCE 10FT
Music (Secondary Teaching) .... PGCE 10FT
PE (Secondary Teaching) .... PGCE 10FT
Science (Secondary Teaching)................................... PGCE 10FT

Robert Owen Society
Secondary PGCE School Centred Initial Teacher Education .. PGCE 10FT/PGCE(QTS) 10FT/QTS 10FT
Secondary PGCE School Centred Initial Teacher Education .. PGCE 10FT/QTS 10FT/PGCE(QTS) 10FT

Sheffield Hallam University
Secondary Business Education................................... PGCE(QTS) 12FT
Secondary Design and Technology .... PGCE(QTS) 12FT
Secondary Design and Technology .... PGCE 12FT
Secondary Design and Technology (Textiles) .... PGCE(QTS) 12FT
Secondary Design and Technology - Food Technology....................
PGCE 12FT
Secondary English .... PGCE 12FT
Secondary Infromation and Communication Technology (ICT) ....
PGCE(QTS) 12FT
Secondary Mathematics............................... PGCE(QTS) 12FT
Secondary Mathematics.............................PGCE 12FT 24PT
Secondary Modern Foreign Languages......................... PGCE 12FT
Secondary Modern Languages.........................PGCE(QTS) 12FT
Secondary Physical Education................................... PGCE 12FT
Secondary Religious Education .... PGCE 12FT
Secondary Science.. PGCE 12FT

University of Sheffield
Education...MA 12FT
PGCE ....PGCE 9FT
Postgraduate Certificate in Education ....PGCE 9FT

University of Southampton
PGCE (Secondary) .... PGCE 12FT
Post Graduate Certificate in Education in Post Compulsory Education & Training... PGCE 24PT

St Mary's University College, Twickenham
PGCE Secondary Education .... PGCE 12FT

St Thomas High School
Secondary Education (11-18) ....PGCE 9FT

University of Strathclyde
Education................EdD by taught 36-72PT/MEd 24-36PT 24-36DL
Secondary Education .... PGDE 10FT 21PT N/ADL

Swansea Metropolitan University
PGCE Secondary with QTS.............................. PGCE(QTS) 10FT

University of the West of Scotland
Secondary Education .... PGDE 9FT

Secondary education studies
Research Courses

University of Dundee
Education ....MPhil 24FT MSc by research 12FT PhD 36FT

The Open University
Doctorate in Education ....EdD 36PT
Educational studies.............PhD 36FT 72PT/EdD 36PT/MRes 12FT

Social science teaching
Taught Courses

Bangor University
Social Work...MA 24FT

University of Bedfordshire
Applied Social Work: Practice Education ....MA 30PT

University of Central Lancashire
Education and History...MA 24FT

Glasgow Caledonian University
Social Research... MSc 12FT 24PT

Goldsmiths, University of London
Humanities and Social Sciences ....GradDip 12FT

Institute of Education
Science Education.. MA 12FT 24-48PT

Social science teaching
Research Courses

University of Birmingham
Integrated Study (Social Sciences) .... PhD 48FT 48PT

University of Cambridge
Social and Political Sciences .... PhD 36FT 60PT

Speech and language teaching
Taught Courses

University of Birmingham
Speech and Language Difficulties....... PGCert 12DL/PGDip 24DL/MEd 36DL

Canterbury Christ Church University
Speech and Language Therapy ....PGDip 24FT

University of Central Lancashire
British Sign Language/English Interpreting and Translation...MA 36PT PGDip 24PT
Interpreting & Translation ....MA 12FT

University of Dundee
Augmentative and Alternative Communications .... MSc 12FT

University of East London
Secondary Modern Languages Postgraduate Certificate in Education (PGCE):... PGCE 12FT
Secondary Modern Languages: Professional Graduate Certificate in Education (PGCE): .... PGCE 12FT

University of Edinburgh
Language Teaching ....MSc 12FT 24PT/PGDip 9FT 21PT

University of Greenwich
Speech and Language Therapy ....PGDip 24FT

University of Kent
Linguistics.. MA 12FT 24PT

Manchester Metropolitan University
Teaching.. MA 24-60PT

University of St Mark and St John
Advanced Speech and Language Therapy: Peninsula Postgraduate Health Institute .... MSc 36PT
Speech and Language Therapy .... MSc 36PT

Northumbria University
Applied Linguistics - TESOL .... MA 12FT 36PT
Teaching Pupils With Dyslexia ....PGCert 12PT

University of Sheffield
Computer Science with Speech and Language Processing..... MSc 12FT
Language and Communication Impairment in Children ....
PGDip 24 PTDL/PGCert 12 PTDL

Speech Difficulties .... PGDip 12FT 24PT/PGCert 12FT 24PT

Trinity College Dublin - the University of Dublin
Clinical Speech and Language Studies.................... MSc 12FT 24PT

UCL - University College London
Speech, Language and Cognition............................MRes 12FT 24PT

Speech and language teaching
Research Courses

King's College London
Language, Discourse & Communication.....MPhil 24FT 36PT/PhD 36FT 48-72PT

The Open University
Multimodal meaning making......PhD 36FT 72PT variableDL/EdD 36PT/MRes 12FT

UCL - University College London
Cognitive, Perceptual and Brain Sciences................. PhD 36FT 60PT
Developmental Science .... PhD 36FT 60PT

Teacher training
Taught Courses

University of Aberdeen
Chartered Teacher Programme...........MEd 5-60PT/PGDip 5-60PT/PGCert 5-60PT
Pastoral Care, Guidance and Pupil Support ....MEd 24BM
Secondary Education ....PGDip 9FT 24PT 24DL
Teaching Qualification in Further Education..............PGCert 12PT

Aberystwyth University
Postgraduate Certificate in Education (Secondary) (Teacher Training).. PGCE 10FT

Arthur Terry School
Teacher Training .... PGCE(QTS) 12FT

Bangor University
Education........ PhD by taught 36FT 48-60PT/MPhil 24FT 36-48PT
Secondary Education .... PGCE 12FT

Bath Spa University
PGCE Secondary... PGCE 10FT

University of Bath
Education...... MA 12FT 24-96PT/PGDip 24FT 24-60PT/PGCE 24FT 24-60PT
Professional / Postgraduate Certificate in Education ....
PGCE 10FT

University of Bedfordshire
Secondary Education Dance .... PGCE 12FT
Secondary Education English .... PGCE 12FT

Billericay Educational Consortium
School Centred Initial Teacher Training .... PGCE 12FT

University of Birmingham
Postgraduate Diploma Secondary Education (QTS) (via 13 subject routes) .... PGCE(QTS) 12FT
Postgraduate Diploma Secondary Education (QTS) - French/Spanish/German ....PGDip 9-12FT

Bishop Grosseteste University College Lincoln
PGCE Primary (Flexible route) ....PGCE 3FT 3-36PT
Secondary PGCE .... PGCE 12FT

University of Bolton
Professional Graduate Diploma in Education (PGDE)..PGDE 12FT 24PT

University of Brighton
Post-Compulsory Education ....PGCE 12 - 48FT 24 - 60PT/CertEd 12 - 48FT 24 - 60PT/Cert 12 - 48FT 24 - 60PT

University of Bristol
Postgraduate Certificate in Education .... PGCE 12FT

University of Buckingham
Independent Postgraduate Certificate of Education (PGCE) PGCE 12FT

Canterbury Christ Church University
Applied Art and Design (14-19) PGCE .... PGCE(QTS) 12FT
Applied Business Studies (14-19) PGCE................. PGCE(QTS) 12FT
Design and Technology (7-14) PGCE..................... PGCE(QTS) 12FT
Health and Social Care (14-19) PGCE .... PGCE(QTS) 12FT
Leisure and Tourism (14-19) PGCE .... PGCE(QTS) 12FT

Cardiff Metropolitan University
Secondary Teaching .... PGCE 12FT

University of Central Lancashire
Practice Teacher .... PGCert 6PT

University of Chester
Early Childhood......MA 24-72PT/PGDip 24-60PT/PGCert 12-36PT
Early Years Practice with Early Years Professional Status (EYPS) ...
PGCert 12FT
Education: PGCE Early Years .... PGCE(QTS) 12FT
Education: PGCE Primary.................................. PGCE(QTS) 12FT
Education: PGCE Secondary Drama........................ PGCE(QTS) 12FT
Education: PGCE Secondary Mathematics............ PGCE(QTS) 12FT
Education: PGCE Secondary Modern Languages French...............
PGCE(QTS) 12FT

Business and social sciences
www.prospects.ac.uk/findcourses POSTGRADUATE DIRECTORY 541

Teacher training and education

Education: PGCE Secondary Modern Languages French with German ... PGCE(QTS) 12FT
Education: PGCE Secondary Modern Languages French with Spanish ... PGCE(QTS) 12FT
Education: PGCE Secondary Modern Languages German ... PGCE(QTS) 12FT
Education: PGCE Secondary Modern Languages German with French ... PGCE(QTS) 12FT
Education: PGCE Secondary Modern Languages German with Spanish ... PGCE(QTS) 12FT
Education: PGCE Secondary Modern Languages Spanish ... PGCE(QTS) 12FT
Education: PGCE Secondary Modern Languages Spanish with French ... PGCE(QTS) 12FT
Education: PGCE Secondary Modern Languages Spanish with German ... PGCE(QTS) 12FT
Education: PGCE Secondary Physical Education.. PGCE(QTS) 12FT
Education: PGCE Secondary Religious Education PGCE(QTS) 12FT
Education: PGCE Secondary Science with Biology Enhancement PGCE(QTS) 12FT
Education: PGCE Secondary Science with Chemistry Enhancement ... PGCE(QTS) 12FT
Education: PGCE Secondary Science with Physics Enhancement ... PGCE(QTS) 12FT
Education: Secondary Graduate Teacher Programme ... QTS 12FT

Chiltern Training Group
Post Graduate Certificate of Education ... PGCE 12FT

De Montfort University
Education Practice ... MA 12FT 24PT

University of Derby
Education ... EdD by taught 36-72PT
Education: Guidance Studies ... MA Up to 72PT
Graduate Teacher Programme ... QTS 12FT 24PT

University Centre Doncaster
Education In-Service ... PGCE 24PT
Education Pre-Service ... PGCE 12FT

University of Dundee
Education (Chartered Teacher) ... MEd 18PT/PGDip 9PT/PGCert 6PT
Educational Psychology ... MSc 24FT
Teaching Qualification (Further Education) ... TQFE 9PT 36DL

Durham University
PGCE Primary (International) ... PGCE 12FT
PGCE Secondary (International) ... PGCE 12FT

University of East Anglia
Primary Teacher Training (3 to 9 years) Foundation Stage/Key Stage One ... PGCE(QTS) 12FT
Primary Teacher Training (5 to 11 years) General Class Teacher with Modern Foreign Languages: French ... PGCE(QTS) 12FT
Primary Teacher Training (5 to 11 years) General Class Teacher with Modern Foreign Languages: German ... PGCE(QTS) 12FT
Primary Teacher Training (5 to 11 years) General Class Teacher with Modern Foreign Languages: Spanish ... PGCE(QTS) 12FT
Primary Teacher Training (5 to 11 years) Key Stage One/Lower Key Stage Two ... PGCE(QTS) 12FT
Primary Teacher Training (5 to 11 years) Key Stage Two ... PGCE(QTS) 12FT
Secondary Teacher Training (11-16 years) with post-16 enhancement experience: English ... PGCE(QTS) 12FT
Secondary Teacher Training (11-16 years) with post-16 enhancement experience: Geography ... PGCE(QTS) 12FT
Secondary Teacher Training (11-16 years) with post-16 enhancement experience: History ... PGCE(QTS) 12FT
Secondary Teacher Training (11-16 years) with post-16 enhancement experience: Mathematics ... PGCE(QTS) 12FT
Secondary Teacher Training (11-16 years) with post-16 enhancement experience: Modern Foreign Languages ... PGCE(QTS) 12FT
Secondary Teacher Training (11-16 years) with post-16 enhancement experience: Physical Education ... PGCE(QTS) 12FT
Secondary Teacher Training (11-16 years) with post-16 enhancement experience: Science (Biology) ... PGCE(QTS) 12FT
Secondary Teacher Training (11-16 years) with post-16 enhancement experience: Science (Chemistry) ... PGCE(QTS) 12FT
Secondary Teacher Training (11-16 years) with post-16 enhancement experience: Science (Physics) ... PGCE(QTS) 12FT

University of East London
Secondary Teacher Training: Postgraduate Certificate in Education PGCE (Secondary) ... PGCE 9FT
Transpersonal and Integrative Supervision PG Cert ... PGCert 12PT

University of Edinburgh
Outdoor Education ... MSc 15FT 72PT/PGDip 12FT 48PT/PGCert 24PT
Outdoor Environmental and Sustainability Education.. MSc 15FT 72PT/PGDip 12FT 48PT/PGCert 24PT
Physical Education, 3-14 ... PGDE 24FT
Professional Graduate Diploma in Education (Primary) ... PGDE 12FT
Professional Graduate Diploma in Education (Secondary) ... PGDE 12FT

Research-Informed Science Education (Online Distance Learning) ... PGCert 21PT 21DL

Essex Primary Schools Training Group
Teacher Training ... PGCE 12FT

University of Exeter
Creative Arts in Education ... PGCert 12FT/PGDip 12FT/MEd 12FT
Education Taught Doctorate ... EdD by taught 24FT 48PT 48DL
Educational Research ... MSc 12FT 24PT 12-24DL
Teaching English to Speakers of Other Languages Masters ... PGDip 12FT/MEd 12FT 60PT/PGCert 6FT
Teaching English to Speakers of Other Languages Masters (Summer Course) ... MEd 36PT

National University of Ireland Galway
Education (Professional Diploma) ... Professional Diploma 12FT

University of Glasgow
English Language & English Linguistics: Applied.. MSc 12FT 24PT
Professional Development in Education ... PGCert 60 maxPT

University of Gloucestershire
Teacher Training PGCE (Primary) ... PGCE 12FT
Teacher Training PGCE (Secondary) ... PGCE 12FT

Glyndwr University
Learning & Technology ... MSc 36FT/PGDip 24FT/PGCert 12FT
Professional Development in Higher Education ... PGCHE 12PT
Professional Education ... MSc 12FT 24-60PT/DipMedEd 24FT 24-36PT/CertMedEd 6FT 12PT

Goldsmiths, University of London
Education (Primary) ... PGCE 12FT
Education (Secondary) ... PGCE 12FT
Education (Secondary) Flexible Programme ... PGCE 12-24PT

Grand Union Training Partnership
Secondary PGCE ... PGCE 10FT

University of Greenwich
Secondary Education ... PGCE 12FT

University of Hertfordshire
Secondary Education (PGCE) ... PGCE 12FT 24PT

University of Huddersfield
Action Research for Education ... MA 36PT/PGDip 24PT/PGCert 12PT
Teacher Training (Lifelong Learning) in-service ... PGCE 24PT
Teacher Training, PGCE with QTS ... PGCE(QTS) 12FT

Hull College
PGCE ... PGCE 12FT 24PT

Institute of Education
Bilingual Learners ... MA 12FT 24PT
Change to Teach ... Change to Teach Scheme 10PT
Masters in Teaching and Learning (MTL) ... MA 36PT
Masters in Teaching and Learning (MTL) Transfer Programme ... MA 24PT
Post-Compulsory PGCE: Pre-service PT ... PGCE 24PT
TEACH CANADA PGCE ... PGCE Teach Canada 12FT
TEACH FIRST ... MA 24PT
Teaching & Learning in Higher Education -Professional Certificate ... Professional Certificate 12PT
Teaching (MTeach) ... MTeach 24-36PT/MTeach 24-36DL

Keele University
Creative and Critical Practice in Educational Settings ... MA 24PT/PGDip 15PT/PGCert 6PT
PGCE (Secondary Education) ... PGCE(QTS) 12FT

Kingston University
Secondary Teaching leading to Qualified Teacher Status ... PGCE 12FT

Leeds Trinity University
Secondary Education ... PGCE 8FT

University of Leeds
PGCE Primary ... PGCE 12FT
PGCE Secondary ... PGCE 10FT
Teaching ... MA 36PT

University of Leicester
Secondary PGCE ... PGCE 12FT

London South Bank University
Certificate in Management ... CM 12PT
Educations (QTLS) ... PGCert 12PT
Learning and Teaching in Post-Compulsory Education ... MA 24FT 36PT

Loughborough University
Education with Qualified Teacher Status (QTS) ... MSc 12FT 36PT
Postgraduate Diploma/Certificate in Education with QTS ..PGDip 12FT 36PT/PGCert 12FT 36PT

Manchester Metropolitan University
Education Secondary ... MA 12FT 36-60PT

University of St Mark and St John
Graduate Teacher Programme ... Graduate Teacher Programme 12FT
Masters in Teaching and Learning ...
PGCE Primary ... PGCE 12FT
PGCE Primary with a Primary Languages Specialism (French or Spanish) ... PGCE 12FT

National University of Ireland, Maynooth
Education ... HDip 12FT

Mid Essex SCITT Consortium
Mid Essex SCITT ... PGCE 12FT
PGCE ... PGCE 12FT
PGCE- Secondary Education ... PGCE 10FT

Newcastle University
Education Research ... MA 12FT 24PT
Education: International Perspectives ... MA 12FT
Innovative Pedagogy and Curriculum ... PGCert 12FT
Postgraduate Certificate in Education (PGCE) - Secondary... PGCE 10FT
Practitioner Enquiry ... MEd 24-36PT

Newman University
Education ... MA 36PT
PGCE Primary ... PGCE(QTS) 12FT
PGCE Primary with English as an Additional Language PGCE(QTS) 12FT
PGCE Primary with Modern Foreign Languages.. PGCE(QTS) 12FT
PGCE Secondary Citizenship ... PGCE(QTS) 12FT
PGCE Secondary Computer Science and ICT ... PGCE(QTS) 12FT
PGCE Secondary English ... PGCE(QTS) 12FT
PGCE Secondary Mathematics ... PGCE(QTS) 12FT
PGCE Secondary Modern Foreign Languages ... PGCE(QTS) 12FT
PGCE Secondary Physical Education ... PGCE(QTS) 12FT
PGCE Secondary Religious Education ... PGCE(QTS) 12FT
PGCE Secondary Science ... PGCE(QTS) 12FT
Teaching and Learning Support Assistants Foundation Degree ... FdA 36PT

N.E. Essex Coastal Confederation
11-18 Secondary ... PGCE(QTS) 10FT
Education ... PGCE(QTS) 10FT

North London Consortium
Secondary Education ... PGCE 11FT

Northumbria University
Post Compulsory Education and Training (Literacy) ... PGCE 24PT/CertEd 12PT

Norwich City College of Further and Higher Education
Learning and Teaching ... PGCert 12PT/PGDip 24PT/MA 36PT
Post-compulsory Education ... PGCE 10FT

Nottingham Trent University
PGCE Primary ... PGCE(QTS) 10FT/ProfGCE(QTS) 10FT
PGCE Secondary ... PGCE(QTS) 10FT/ProfGCE(QTS) 10FT

University of Nottingham
PGCE Primary - School Based Initial Teacher Training (SCITT) ... PGCE 12FT
PGCE Secondary - English ... PGCE 12FT

The Open University
Education PGCE ... PGCE 12FT 12 - 36PT

Oxford Brookes University
Education ... MA 12FT 24PT
Education (Delivered at Solihull College) ... MA 12FT 24PT
Education (PGCE) - Secondary ... PGCE 12FT
Education (TESOL) ... MA 12FT/MA 24-36PT
Education: Artist Teacher Scheme (PGCert Advanced Educational Practice) ... PGCert 12PT
Education: Gifted and Talented Education (PGCert Advanced Educational Practice) ... PGCert 12PT
Education: National Award for Senco Co-ordination (PGCert Advanced Educational Practice) ... PGCert 12PT

Plymouth University
Primary ... PGCE 12FT

Queen Margaret University, Edinburgh
Professional and Higher Education ... PGCert 12-24PT

Queen's University Belfast
Education ... EdD by taught 36-72FT 48-96PT
Education: Postgraduate Certificate in Education (PGCE) ... PGCE 12FT
Educational Studies ... MEd 12FT 60PT
Educational, Child and Adolescent Psychology DECAP ... PsychD by taught 36FT

University of Reading
Music Teaching in Professional Practise ... MA 12FT 36PT/PGDip 24FT 48PT

Robert Owen Society
Secondary PGCE School Centred Initial Teacher Education .. PGCE 10FT/PGCE(QTS) 10FT/QTS 10FT

University of Roehampton
Education ... MA 12FT 24PT
Education Leadership and Management ... MA 12FT 24+PT
PGCE Secondary ... PGCE 12FT
Applied Music Education ... PGCert 6FT 24PT
Art, Craft and Design Education ... PGCert 6FT 24PT
Education ... PGCert 6FT 24PT
Education Leadership and Management ... PGCert 6FT 12+PT
English Education ... PGCert 6FT 12+PT
Special and Inclusive Education ... PGCert 6FT 12-24PT
Applied Music Education ... PGDip 9FT 24-48PT
Art, Craft and Design Education ... PGDip 9FT 24PT

Teacher training and education

Education .... PGDip 9FT 24PT
Education Leadership and Management .... PGDip 9FT 18+PT
English Education .... PGDip 9FT 18+PT
Special and Inclusive Education .... PGDip 9FT 24-48PT

University Campus Suffolk
Learning and Teaching .... MA TBCFT TBCPT
PGCE (North East Essex Coastal Confederation) .... PGCE 12FT
PGCE (Suffolk and Norfolk Primary SCITT) .... PGDE 12FT
PGCE Lifelong Learning Sector .... PGCE 12FT 24PT

Sheffield Hallam University
Doctorate in Education .... Doctorate 48PT
Education .... MRes variousFT variousPT
Education - Research Degree ...... MPhil 24FT 36PT/PhD by taught 36-48FT 48-84PT
Education for International Students .... MA 12FT/MSc 12FT
Integrated Working .... MA 36PT/PGDip 24PT/PGCert 12PT
Learning and Teaching .. MA 12FT 36PT/PGDip 24PT/PGCert 12PT
Learning and Teaching in Higher Education .... PGCert 12PT
Post Compulsory Education and Training ... MA 12FT 36PT/PGDip 24PT/PGCert 12PT
Post-compulsory Education and Training (PCET) ..... Diploma 24PT
Secondary Business Education .... PGCE(QTS) 12FT
Secondary Citizenship .... PGCE 48PT
Secondary Design and Technology .... PGCE(QTS) 12FT
Secondary Design and Technology .... PGCE 12FT
Secondary Design and Technology (Textiles) .... PGCE(QTS) 12FT
Secondary Design and Technology - Food Technology PGCE 12FT
Secondary English .... PGCE 12FT
Secondary Infromation and Communication Technology (ICT) .... PGCE(QTS) 12FT
Secondary Mathematics .... PGCE(QTS) 12FT
Secondary Mathematics .... PGCE 12FT 24PT
Secondary Modern Foreign Languages .... PGCE 12FT
Secondary Modern Languages .... PGCE(QTS) 12FT
Secondary Physical Education .... PGCE 12FT
Secondary Religious Education .... PGCE 12FT
Secondary Science .... PGCE 12FT

University of Sheffield
Applied Linguistics with TESOL .... MA 12FT 24PT/ Diploma 9FT 18PT
PGCE .... PGCE 9FT
Postgraduate Certificate in Education .... PGCE 9FT

University of South Wales
Diploma in Higher Education in Professional PracticeDipHE 48PT
Post-compulsory Education .... PGCE 12FT
Post-compulsory Education and TrainingPGCE 24PT/CertEd 24PT
Post-compulsory Education and Training Adult Literacy / Adult Numeracy / ESOL .... PGCE 24PT/CertEd 24PT

University of Southampton
PGCE (Primary) .... PGCE 12FT
PGCE (Secondary) .... PGCE 12FT
Post Graduate Certificate in Education in Post Compulsory Education & Training .... PGCE 24PT
Specific Learning Difficulties (Dyslexia) .... MSc 12FT 24PT

St Mary's University College, Twickenham
Education: Leading Innovation and Change .... MA 12FT 24PT/ PGDip 24PT/PGCert 12PT
Education: Pedagogy and Professional practice in Physical Education .... MA 36PT/PGDip 24PT/PGCert 12PT
Education: Pedagogy and Professional Values and Practice (International students) .... MA 10FT
PGCE Primary Education .... PGCE 12FT 18PT
PGCE Secondary Education .... PGCE 12FT

St Thomas High School
Secondary Education (11-18) .... PGCE 9FT

University of Strathclyde
Primary Education .... PGDE 10FT 21PT
Secondary Education .... PGDE 10FT 21PT N/ADL

University of Sunderland
PGCE (Secondary Education) .... PGCE 12FT

University of Sussex
Postgraduate Certificate in Education (PGCE) .... PGCE 12FT

Swansea Metropolitan University
Education .... MA(Ed) 24 - 60PT
PGCE Secondary with QTS .... PGCE(QTS) 10FT
Post-Graduate Certificate in Education .... PCET 24 - 36PT
Professional Development, Education and Training (PDET) ..... MA 36 - 60PT

Teesside University
Education .... MA 12FT 24PT
Education (Doctorate) .... EdD by taught 48FT 72PT
Educational Studies .... MA 12FT 24PT
Professional Studies in Education .... PGDip 24 -36PT
Promoting Inclusive Practice in Education .... PGDip 24 - 36PT

Titan Partnership Ltd
Primary SCITT .... PGCE(QTS) 10FT
Secondary SCITT (11-16 years) .... PGCE 10FT/PGCE(QTS) 10FT

Trinity College Dublin - the University of Dublin
Education .... PGDip 12FT

Trinity Laban Conservatoire of Music and Dance
PGCE 'Musicians In Education' .... PGCE 12FT

University of Wales Trinity Saint David
Professional Development .... PGDip 36PT/PGCert 36PT

University of the Highlands and Islands
Chartered Teacher .... PGCert 20PT/PGDip 40PT/MSc 60PT

University of Ulster
Education (Post Primary) .... PGCE 12FT

Wandsworth Primary School Consortium
Postgraduate Certificate in Education .... PGCE 10FT

University of Warwick
Postgraduate Certificate in Education (PGCE) .... PGCE 12FT

West Midlands Consortium
Secondary Education .... PGCE 12FT

University of the West of Scotland
Chartered Teacher & CPD for School Teachers... MSc VARIABLEPT/ PGDip VARIABLEPT/PGCert VARIABLEPT
Secondary Education .... PGDE 9FT

University of the West of England, Bristol
Education: PGCE Secondary (12 subject options) .... PGCE 10FT

University of Worcester
Postgraduate Certificate in Education - PGCE - Secondary... PGCE 12FT

University of York
Teaching English to Young Learners (by distance) - Institute for Effective Education .... MA 24DL

Teacher training
Research Courses

University of Aberdeen
Education .... PhD 36FT/MPhil 24FT/EdD 36FT

Bangor University
Education .... PhD 36FT 60-72PT/MPhil 24FT 36-48PT

University of Bolton
Education Specialisms ..... PhD 36FT 72PT/MPhil 12-24FT 36-48PT

University of Dundee
Education .... MPhil 24FT MSc by research 12FT PhD 36FT

Newcastle University
Education (Clinical) .... MPhil 12FT 24PT/PhD 36FT 72PT

Oxford Brookes University
Doctorate of Education - Professional Doctorate ...... EdD 60-84PT
Education and Childhood Studies .... MPhil/PhD 36-60FT 48-72PT/PhD 24-60FT 36-72PT/MPhil 24-36FT 36-48PT

Queen's University Belfast
Education .... PhD 36FT 72PT/MPhil 24FT 48PT

University of Salford
Higher Education Research .... PhD/MPhil

Sheffield Hallam University
Education .... PhD 48FT 84PT/MPhil 48FT 84PT

University of Southampton
Integrated PhD in Education .... Integrated PhD 36FT

York St John University
Education Studies .... MA by research 12FT 24PT/PhD 36FT 72PT

Teacher training and education
Taught Courses

University of Aberdeen
Community Learning and Development .... MSc 36PT/PGDip 24PT
Studies in Mindfulness .... MSc 36PT/PGDip 24PT/PGCert 12PT

Bangor University
Education .... PhD by taught 36FT 48-60PT/MPhil 24FT 36-48PT
Medical Education Practice .... PGCert 12FT
Primary Education .... PGCE 12FT

Bath Spa University
Education: International Education .... MA 15FT
Education: Leadership and Management .... MA 15FT
Education: Learning Technology .... MA 15FT
Education:Early Childhood Studies .... MA 12FT
Professional Master's Programme ... MA 12FT 72PT/MTeach 12FT 72PT/PGDip 12FT 48PT/PGCert 4FT 12PT

University of Bath
Education .... MRes 12FT 24PT

University of Bedfordshire
Advanced Professional Certificate in Education .... AdvCert 6PT
Education .... MA 36-72PT/PGDip 12FT
Postgraduate Certificates in Education .... PGCert 12PT

Birkbeck, University of London
Higher Education (PGCE) .... PGCert 12PT

Birmingham City University
Arts and Education .... MA 12FT 24PT

University College Birmingham
Early Years PGCE .... PGCE 12PT

Bishop Grosseteste University College Lincoln
Education .... MA 24PT
Postgraduate Professional Studies in Education ...... PGCert 12PT/ PGDip 24-72PT

University of Bolton
E-Learning for Educationalists .... MA 12FT 24-60PT
Professional Development .... MEd 12FT 24-60PT
Teaching and Learning .... MA 12FT 60PT
Technical and Vocational Education .... MA 12FT 24-60PT/ MEd 12FT 24-60PT

Bradford College
Education .... MEd 24-30PT

University of Brighton
Education .... MA 24PT/PGDip 24PT/PGCert 12PT
Education (International Education) MA 12FT 36PT/PGDip 24PT/ PGCert 12PT
Education MA (Higher Education).. MA 24PT/PGDip 24PT/PGCert 12PT
Masters in Teaching and Learning (MTL).. PGDip 12-36PT/PGCert 12-36PT
Podiatry and Education .... MSc 12 - 24FT 24 - 72PT/PGCert 12FT 24PT/PGDip 12 - 24FT 24 - 48PT
Professional Doctorate in Education .... EdD by taught 60-96PT

Brunel University
Education .... MA 12FT 24PT

University of Buckingham
Secondary PGCE with Teachers' Standards .... PGCE 12FT
Educational Leadership .... MEd 18FT
Independent Postgraduate Certificate of Education (PGCE) PGCE 12FT
Middle Leadership .... PGCert 12FT
Primary PGCE with Teachers' Standards .... PGCE 12FT

Bucks New University
Education .... MA 24PT

University of Cambridge
Education .... MPhil 12FT 24PT

Canterbury Christ Church University
Enabling Learning (SEN) .... MA 36PT/PGDip 24PT/PGCert 12PT

Cardiff Metropolitan University
Education .... MA(Ed) 12FT 36-60PT/PGDip 12FT/PGCert 12FT

Cardiff University
Education .... MSc 12FT

University of Central Lancashire
Doctorate in Education .... EdD by taught 60PT
Education (Research) .... MA 24PT/PGDip 24PT/PGCert 24PT
Education and History .... MA 24PT
Education and Religion in Society .... MA 24PT
Professional Practice in EducationMEd 24-60PT/PGCert 24-60PT/ PGDip 24-60PT

University of Chester
Education: Creativity and Education for the Professions .... MA 24-72PT/PGDip 24-60PT/PGCert 12-36PT
Education: Dyslexia Research and Practice ..... MA 36-72PT/PGDip 36-60PT/PGCert 12-36PT
Education: Leadership and Management ..... MA 24 - 72PT/PGDip 24 - 60PT/PGCert 12 - 36PT
Education: Primary Graduate Teacher Programme .... QTS 12FT
Education: Singing in the Curriculum .... PGCert 12 - 36PT
Education: Teaching and Learning MA 24 - 72PT/PGDip 24-60PT/ PGCert 12-36PT
Work Based and Integrative StudiesMA 24 - 72PT/MSc 24 - 72PT/ PGDip 24 - 60PT/PGCert 12 - 36PT

City University London
Professional Development (Through Work-Based Learning) ... MA 12-36FT 12-72PT

University College Cork
Education .... PGDE 9FT
Education (Sc) .... MA(Ed) 24PT
Masters in Education (Modular) .... MA(Ed) 12FT
Special Educational Needs .... PGDip 9FT
Teaching & Learning in Higher Education .... PGCert 9PT
Teaching of Religious Education .... PGDip 24PT
Teaching of Science in the Primary School .... PGDip 24PT

University of Cumbria
Education .... MA 36PT/PGDip 24PT/PGCert 12PT

Cumbria Primary Teacher Training
Primary 5-11 Initial Teacher Training .... PGCE(QTS) 12FT/ PGCE 12FT

University Centre Doncaster
Education In-Service .... PGCE 24PT
Education Pre-Service .... PGCE 12FT

University of Dundee
Applied Professional Studies .... MSc 30PT/Diploma 20PT/ Cert 10PT
Pre-Sessional Programme for Postgraduates (4 weeks) ... Cert 1FT
Primary Education (PGDE) .... PGDE 11FT
Secondary Education (PGDE) .... PGDE 9FT 18PT
Teaching Qualification (Further Education) .... TQFE 9PT 36DL

Teacher training and education

Durham University
Educational Assessment - International .... MSc 36DL
Technology Enhanced Learning .... MSc 12FT 36PT

University of East Anglia
Adult Literacy, Lifelong Learning & Development .... MA 12FT
Advanced Educational Practice .... MA 36PT/MA 48PT
Education .... MA 12FT
Primary Teacher Training (3 to 9 years) Foundation Stage/Key Stage One .... PGCE(QTS) 12FT
Primary Teacher Training (5 to 11 years) General Class Teacher with Modern Foreign Languages: French .... PGCE(QTS) 12FT
Primary Teacher Training (5 to 11 years) General Class Teacher with Modern Foreign Languages: German .... PGCE(QTS) 12FT
Primary Teacher Training (5 to 11 years) General Class Teacher with Modern Foreign Languages: Spanish .... PGCE(QTS) 12FT
Primary Teacher Training (5 to 11 years) Key Stage One/Lower Key Stage Two .... PGCE(QTS) 12FT
Primary Teacher Training (5 to 11 years) Key Stage Two .... PGCE(QTS) 12FT
Secondary Teacher Training (11-16 years) with post-16 enhancement experience: English .... PGCE(QTS) 12FT
Secondary Teacher Training (11-16 years) with post-16 enhancement experience: Geography .... PGCE(QTS) 12FT
Secondary Teacher Training (11-16 years) with post-16 enhancement experience: History .... PGCE(QTS) 12FT
Secondary Teacher Training (11-16 years) with post-16 enhancement experience: Mathematics .... PGCE(QTS) 12FT
Secondary Teacher Training (11-16 years) with post-16 enhancement experience: Modern Foreign LanguagesPGCE(QTS) 12FT
Secondary Teacher Training (11-16 years) with post-16 enhancement experience: Physical Education .... PGCE(QTS) 12FT
Secondary Teacher Training (11-16 years) with post-16 enhancement experience: Science (Biology) .... PGCE(QTS) 12FT
Secondary Teacher Training (11-16 years) with post-16 enhancement experience: Science (Chemistry) .. PGCE(QTS) 12FT
Secondary Teacher Training (11-16 years) with post-16 enhancement experience: Science (Physics) .... PGCE(QTS) 12FT

University of East London
Doctor of Education EdD .... DProf by taught 36FT 45PT
Education .... MA 24PT/PGDip 16PT/PGCert 8PT
Teaching and Learning (MTL) .... MA 36PT

University of Edinburgh
Additional Support for Learning (Bilingual Learners) .. MEd 72PT/PGDip 48PT/PGCert 24PT
Additional Support for Learning (Deaf Education) .... MEd 72PT/PGDip 48PT/PGCert 24PT
Additional Support for Learning (Inclusive Education) MEd 72PT/PGDip 48PT/PGCert 24PT
Additional Support for Learning (Learning Disabilities) .... MEd 72PT/PGDip 48PT/PGCert 24PT
Additional Support for Learning (Pupil Support)MEd 72PT/PGDip 48PT/PGCert 24PT
Additional Support for Learning (Specific Learning Difficulties)... MEd 72PT/PGDip 48PT/PGCert 24PT
Additional Support for Learning (Visual Impairment). MEd 72PT/PGDip 48PT/PGCert 24PT
Community Education .... MSc 12FT 24-36PT
Dance Science and Education ..... MSc 12FT 72PT/PGDip 9FT 48PT
Developing Educational Leadership and Learning..... PGCert 24PT
Digital Education (Online Distance Learning) .... MSc 12-72DL/PGCert 12-24DL/PGDip 12-48DL
Education .... MSc 12FT 24-36PT
Education (MSc Educational Research)MSc Educational Research 12FT 24-36PT
Education: Language, Theory, Practice & LiteracyMSc 12FT 72PT/PGDip 9FT 48PT/PGCert 4FT 24PT
Educational Leadership and Management (including the Scottish Qualification for Headship Diploma)... PGDip 27PT/MEd 33PT/PGCert 15PT
Inclusive and Special Education .... MSc 12FT
Language Teaching .... MSc 12FT 24PT/PGDip 9FT 21PT
Outdoor Education....... MSc 15FT 72PT/PGDip 12FT 48PT/PGCert 24PT
Outdoor Environmental and Sustainability Education.. MSc 15FT 72PT/PGDip 12FT 48PT/PGCert 24PT
Physical Activity for Health........ MSc 12FT 72PT/PGCert 24-48PT/PGDip 9FT 48PT
Physical Education, 3-14 .... PGDE 24FT
Professional Graduate Diploma in Education (Primary)........ PGDE 12FT
Professional Graduate Diploma in Education (Secondary)... PGDE 12FT
Research-Informed Science Education (Online Distance Learning) .... PGCert 21PT 21DL

University of Exeter
Education Taught Doctorate......... EdD by taught 24FT 48PT 48DL
Educational Research .... MSc 12FT 24PT 12-24DL
Professional Studies .... MEd 36PT
Special Educational Needs Masters .... PGDip 12FT/MEd 12FT/PGCert 6FT
Technology, Creativity and Thinking .... MEd 12FT 24PT/PGCert 12FT/PGDip 12FT

University of Glasgow
Academic Practice .... PGCert 24PT
Doctorate in Education (Research) .... EdD by taught 60DL
Educational Studies .... MSc 12FT 24PT
English Language & English Linguistics: Applied.. MSc 12FT 24PT
Inter-Professional Science Education & Communication .... MSc 12FT 24PT/PGDip 9FT 21PT/PGCert 9FT 21PT
Professional Learning & Enquiry .... MEd modularBM

University of Gloucestershire
Professional Studies .... MA 24PT/PGDip 20PT/PGCert 8PT
Teacher Training PGCE (Primary) .... PGCE 12FT
Teacher Training PGCE (Secondary) .... PGCE 12FT

Glyndwr University
Education .... PGCE 12FT 24-36PT/CertEd 24-36PT
Education .... MA 12FT 24-36PT
Professional Development (Education). .... GradCert 12-48PT/GradDip 24-48PT
Professional Development in Higher Education .... PGCHE 12PT

Goldsmiths, University of London
Education: Culture, Language and Identity .... MA 12FT 24-60PT
Writer/Teacher .... MA 12FT 24PT

University of Greenwich
Doctorate in Education .... PhD by taught 36PT
Education .... MA 24-36PT

University of Hertfordshire
Education .... EdD by taught 60PT
MA 12FT 24PT/PGDip 12FT 24PT/PGCert 12FT 24PT

Heythrop College
Philosophy in Education .... MA 12FT 24PT

University of Huddersfield
Education .... MA 12FT 36PT/PGDip 24PT/PGCert 12PT
Education and Youth Work Studies... MA 12FT 36PT/PGDip 24PT/PGCert 12PT
Vocational Education and Training .... MA 12FT 36PT

University of Hull
Education MEd 12FT 24-72PT/AdvDip 12FT 24-72PT/AdvCert 6FT 12-36PT

Institute of Education
Advanced Educational Practice Programme...... MA 24FT 36-60PT 24-60DL/PGDip 24FT 36-60PT 24-60DL/PGCert 24FT 36-60PT 24-60DL
Centenary Brendish Scholarships (Taught Masters Programmes) .... MA 12FT/MSc 12FT
Centenary Scholarships (Taught Masters Programmes)MA 12FT/MSc 12FT
Commonwealth Shared Scholarship .... MA 12FT
Erasmus-Doctoral School .... PhD by taught 3-9FT
History of Education .... MA 12FT 24-48PT
Leading Inquiry Based Professional Learning Communities .... GradCert 6FT
Policy Studies in Education .... MA 12FT 24-48PT
Post-Compulsory PGCE: In-service .... PGCE 24PT
QTS Self-Funded Route .... QTS 12FT
Social Justice and Education .... MA 12FT 24-48PT
Special Course Masters Level - Freestanding Module.... 15/30/60 Credit Module 1-12PT
Teaching and Learning in Higher and Professional Education....... MA 12FT 24-48PT
iPGCE .... iPGCE 6PT

University of Kent
Higher Education .... PGDip 12FT 24PT/MA 12FT 24PT
Higher Education (PGCHE) .... PGCHE 24FT

King's College London
Academic Practice in Higher Education..... MA 24PT/PGDip 18PT/PGCert 24PT
Creative Arts in the Classroom .... MA 12FT 24-48PT
Doctorate in Education/Professional Studies . EdD by taught min 48PT/DrPS min 48PT
Education & Professional Studies .... MA 12FT 24-48PT
Education, Policy & Society .... MA 12FT 24-72PT
Master's in Teaching & Learning ....
Postgraduate/Professional Certificate in Education .... PGCE 9FT

Kingston University
Doctor of Education .... EdD by taught 60-72PT
Professional Education and Training .... MA 36PT/PGDip 24PT

Leeds Metropolitan University
Artist Teachers in Art & Design .... MA 24PT

University of Leeds
Education .... MA 12FT 24PT

University of Leicester
Educational Studies .... PGCert 12PT

University of Limerick
Education Business .... Professional Diploma 12FT
Education Mathematics Teaching....... Professional Diploma 12FT
Education Music .... Professional Diploma 12FT
Education Physical Education .... Professional Diploma 12FT
Education Technology .... Professional Diploma 18FT
Educational Mentoring..... PGCert 12PT/GradDip 24PT/MEd 36PT
Guidance Counselling and Lifespan Development .... MA 24PT
Integrative Psychotherapy .... GradDip 18FT/MA 18FT
Mathematics for teaching .... Professional Diploma 24PT
Teaching, Learning and Scholarship .... Specialist Diploma 12FT

Liverpool Hope University
Academic Practice .... MA 36PT
Education........ MA 12FT 36PT/PGDip 12FT 24PT/PGCert 6FT 12PT
Education & Biology .... MA 36PT
Education & Computer Science .... MA 36PT
Education & English Language .... MA 36PT
Education & English Literature .... MA 36PT
Education & Geography .... MA 36PT
Education & Mathematics .... MA 36PT
Education & Music .... MA 36PT
Education (Children and Young People) .... MA 12FT 36PT
Education (Disability Studies) .... MA 12FT 36PT
Education (Early Childhood) .... MA 12FT 36PT
Education (International Perspective) .... MA 12FT 36PT
Education (Leadership and Management) .... MA 12FT 36PT
Education (Music Education) .... MA 12FT 36PT
Education (Religious Education) .... MA 12FT 36PT
Education (Special Educational Needs) .... MA 12FT 36PT
Education (Teaching and Learning) .... MA 12FT 36PT

Liverpool John Moores University
Advanced Educational Practice .... PGCert 12PT
MA 24PT/PGCert 12PT
Doctor of Education .... EdD by taught 36FT

London Metropolitan University
Education .... MA 12FT 24PT
Learning and Teaching in Higher Education .... MA 12-72PT/PGCert 12-36PT

London South Bank University
Education .... MA 30PT
Educations (QTLS) .... PGCert 12PT

Manchester Metropolitan University
Professional Studies .... MA 12FT 36-60PT
Secondary Education with QTS .... PGCE (QTS) 12FT
Science, Technology, Engineering and Maths (STEM) .... MSc 24-72PT

University of St Mark and St John
Graduate Teacher Programme .... Graduate Teacher Programme 12FT
Masters in Teaching and Learning ....
PGCE 14-19 Diploma Creative and Media .... PGCE 12FT
PGCE Primary .... PGCE 12FT
PGCE Primary with a Primary Languages Specialism (French or Spanish) .... PGCE 12FT
Professional Development for Teachers ..... PGCert variableFT/MA variableFT

National University of Ireland, Maynooth
Master of Education (Bi annual) .... MA 24FT

Newcastle University
Education Research .... MA 12FT 24PT
Education: International Perspectives .... MA 12FT
Innovative Pedagogy and Curriculum .... PGCert 12FT
Practitioner Enquiry .... MEd 24-36PT

Newman University
Early Years Foundation Degree .... FdA 36PT
Early Years Teacher Status .... Early Years Teacher Status 6FT/Early Years Teacher Status 12FT
Education .... MA 36PT
PGCE Primary .... PGCE(QTS) 12FT
PGCE Primary with English as an Additional Language .... PGCE(QTS) 12FT
PGCE Primary with Modern Foreign Languages.. PGCE(QTS) 12FT
PGCE Secondary Citizenship .... PGCE(QTS) 12FT
PGCE Secondary Computer Science and ICT .... PGCE(QTS) 12FT
PGCE Secondary English .... PGCE(QTS) 12FT
PGCE Secondary Mathematics .... PGCE(QTS) 12FT
PGCE Secondary Modern Foreign Languages .... PGCE(QTS) 12FT
PGCE Secondary Physical Education .... PGCE(QTS) 12FT
PGCE Secondary Religious Education .... PGCE(QTS) 12FT
PGCE Secondary Science .... PGCE(QTS) 12FT
Teaching and Learning Support Assistants Foundation Degree ... FdA 36PT

Northumbria University
Advanced Practice in Post Compulsory Education and Training ... PGCert 12PT
Advanced Practice in Post Compulsory Education and Training (Literacy) .... PGCert 12PT
Advanced Practice in Post Compulsory Education and Training (Numeracy) .... PGCert 12PT
Education .... PGCert 12PT/PGDip 24PT/MA 36PT
Education Studies .... MA 12FT
Post Compulsory Education and Training (Literacy) .... PGCE 24PT/CertEd 12PT
Primary Education PGCE .... PGCE 12FT
Secondary Education (Art, Craft and Design) PGCE...... PGCE 12FT
Secondary Education (Design and Technology SCITT) .... PGCE 12FT
Secondary Education (Physical Education SCITT) PGCEPGCE 12FT
Special Educational Needs and Inclusion .... PGCert 12PT

Business and social sciences
544 POSTGRADUATE DIRECTORY www.prospects.ac.uk/findcourses

Section sponsored by

BPP
UNIVERSITY
COLLEGE

Teacher training and education

Teaching Pupils With Dyslexia ....PGCert 12PT

Norwich City College of Further and Higher Education
Learning and Teaching ....PGCert 12PT/PGDip 24PT/MA 36PT
Post-compulsory Education.. PGCE 10FT

Nottingham Trent University
Doctorate in Business Administration............DBA by taught 36PT
PGCE Primary..........................PGCE(QTS) 10FT/ProfGCE(QTS) 10FT

University of Nottingham
Educational Leadership and Management (by distance
learning) ....MA 24DL
International Student Advice and Support.................PGCert 12PT
Teaching Chinese to Speakers of Other Languages (TCSOL) ....MA
12FT 24PT

The Open University
Academic Practice ....PGCert 24DL
Online and Distance Education .... MA variableDL/PGDip
variableDL/PGCert variableDL
Professional Studies in EducationPGDip variableDL/PGCert 12DL

Oxford Brookes University
Education .... MA 12FT 24PT
Education (Delivered at Solihull College) .... MA 12FT 24PT
Education (TESOL) .... MA 12FT/MA 24-36PT
Education: Artist Teacher Scheme (PGCert Advanced Educational
Practice)..PGCert 12PT
Education: Gifted and Talented Education (PGCert Advanced
Educational Practice)..PGCert 12PT
Education: National Award for Senco Co-ordination (Advanced
Educational Practice)..PGCert 12PT
Education: Postgraduate Certificate in Advanced Educational
Practice (PGCert)..PGCert 12-18PT

University of Oxford
Educational Studies (Comparative and International
Education) .... MSc 12FT

Plymouth University
Education (International Masters Programme)... MA 60PT/PGDip
60PT/PGCert 60PT
Post Compulsory Education & Training ... PGCE 12FT 24PT/CertEd
12FT 24PT
Primary.. PGCE 12FT
Primary - Early Years Education (5-11 or 3-7)................. PGCE 12FT
Professional Doctorate in Education (EdD) .... EdD by taught 60PT
Secondary Education .... PGCE 12FT

University of Portsmouth
Educational Leadership and Management............. MSc 12FT 24PT

New School of Psychotherapy and Counselling
Existential Coaching .... MA 24FT 48PT

Queen Margaret University, Edinburgh
Professional and Higher Education.........................PGCert 12-24PT

Queen Mary, University of London
Applied Linguistics for English Language TeachingMA 12FT 24PT

Queen's University Belfast
Education...EdD by taught 36-72FT 48-96PT
Educational Studies ....MEd 12FT 60PT
Educational, Child and Adolescent Psychology DECAP. PsychD by
taught 36FT

University of Reading
Art & Design (Secondary Teaching) .... PGCE 10FT
Drama (Secondary Teaching).. PGCE 10FT
Education (Early Years) ....MA 12FT 24-84PT/PGDip 12FT
Education (English Education) ....MA 12FT 24-84PT/PGDip 12FT
Education (English Language Teaching) ....MA 12FT 24-84PT/
PGDip 12FT
Education (Generic) .... MA 12FT 24-84PT
Education (Inclusive Education).....MA 12FT 24-84PT/PGDip 12FT
Education (Leadership and Management)........MA 12FT 24-84PT/
PGDip 12FT
Education (Music Education)..........MA 12FT 24-84PT/PGDip 12FT
English (Secondary Teaching) .... PGCE 10FT
French (Conversion Course) (Secondary) .... PGCE 24FT
History (Secondary Teaching) .... PGCE 10FT
Instrumental Teaching ....PGDip 24-48PT
Mathematics (Secondary Teaching).................................. PGCE 10FT
Modern Languages (Secondary Teaching) .... PGCE 10FT
Music (Secondary Teaching) .... PGCE 10FT
PE (Secondary Teaching) .... PGCE 10FT
Primary Teaching with French Specialism...................... PGCE 10FT
Science (Secondary Teaching).. PGCE 10FT

Robert Owen Society
Secondary PGCE School Centred Initial Teacher Education ....
PGCE 10FT/PGCE(QTS) 10FT/QTS 10FT

Royal Veterinary College
Veterinary Education - PG Associate (PT) .... PG Associateship
6-24PT

University Campus Suffolk
Learning and Teaching ....MA TBCFT TBCPT
PGCE (North East Essex Coastal Confederation) .... PGCE 12FT
PGCE (Suffolk and Norfolk Primary SCITT)....................PGDE 12FT
PGCE Lifelong Learning Sector ....PGCE 12FT 24PT

Sheffield Hallam University
Doctorate in Education .... Doctorate 48PT
Early Years Education.. PGCE 12FT
Early Years Professional Status .... EYPS 12FT 6-15PT
Education...MRes variousFT variousPT
Education - Research Degree....... MPhil 24FT 36PT/PhD by taught
36-48FT 48-84PT
Education for International Students .... MA 12FT/MSc 12FT
Integrated Working..................MA 36PT/PGDip 24PT/PGCert 12PT
Learning and Teaching ..MA 12FT 36PT/PGDip 24PT/PGCert 12PT
Learning and Teaching in Higher Education...............PGCert 12PT
Post Compulsory Education and Training ... MA 12FT 36PT/PGDip
24PT/PGCert 12PT
Secondary Business Education................................PGCE(QTS) 12FT
Secondary Design and Technology .... PGCE(QTS) 12FT
Secondary Design and Technology .... PGCE 12FT
Secondary Design and Technology (Textiles) .... PGCE(QTS) 12FT
Secondary Design and Technology - Food Technology PGCE 12FT
Secondary English .... PGCE 12FT
Secondary Infromation and Communication Technology (ICT) ....
PGCE(QTS) 12FT
Secondary Mathematics..PGCE(QTS) 12FT
Secondary Mathematics..PGCE 12FT 24PT
Secondary Modern Foreign Languages .... PGCE 12FT
Secondary Modern Languages........................... PGCE(QTS) 12FT
Secondary Physical Education .... PGCE 12FT
Secondary Religious Education .... PGCE 12FT
Secondary Science .... PGCE 12FT
Technology Enhanced Learning, Innovation and Change....... MSc
36PT/PGDip 24PT/PGCert 12PT

University of Sheffield
Applied Professional Studies in Education..................MA 24-36DL
Education..MA 12FT
Educational Research ....MA 12FT
Globalising Education: Policy and Practice ....MA 12FT
PGCE ....PGCE 9FT
Postgraduate Certificate in Education ....PGCE 9FT

University of South Wales
Post-compulsory Education and Training Adult Literacy / Adult
Numeracy / ESOL...........................PGCE 24PT/CertEd 24PT
Returning and Supply Teachers Course University Certificate 6FT
Teaching English to Young Learners (TEYL) .... MA 12FT 24PT

University of Southampton
Authoring and Researching eLearning and eTeaching ....
PCES 12DL
Dissertation through Flexible Study........MA(Ed) 12FT 24PT 24DL
Educational Psychology ....DEdPsy 36FT
PGCE (Primary)... PGCE 12FT
PGCE (Secondary) .... PGCE 12FT
Post Graduate Certificate in Education in Post Compulsory
Education & Training.. PGCE 24PT
Specific Learning Difficulties (Dyslexia)..................MSc 12FT 24PT

St Mary's University College, Twickenham
Education: Leading Innovation and Change..........MA 12FT 24PT/
PGDip 24PT/PGCert 12PT
Education: Pedagogy and Professional practice in Physical
Education...........................MA 36PT/PGDip 24PT/PGCert 12PT
Education: Pedagogy and Professional Values and Practice ....MA
24PT/PGDip 24PT/PGCert 12PT
Education: Pedagogy and Professional Values and Practice
(International students) ....MA 10FT
PGCE Primary Education.......................................PGCE 12FT 18PT
PGCE Secondary Education .... PGCE 12FT

St Thomas High School
Secondary Education (11-18) ....PGCE 9FT

Staffordshire University
Design and Technology..PGCE 9FT
Doctorate in Education (EdD) .... EdD by taught 48PT
Early Childhood ....MA 24PT
Economics and Business...PGCE 9FT
Education (Education Leadership).. MA 36FT/PGCert 24FT/PGDip
12FT
Education (Negotiated)..........MA 36PT/PGCert 24PT/PGDip 12PT
Higher and Professional Education..............................PGCHE 9PT
Primary (General) ....PGCE 9FT

University of Stirling
Education: Professional Enquiry....MSc 36PT/PGDip 27PT/PGCert
12PT
Educational Leadership and Educational Leadership (SQH)... MSc
36PT/PGDip 15PT/PGCert 6PT
Educational Research ....MSc 12FT 30PT
Professional Learning and Leadership .... MSc 36PT
Teaching English to Speakers of Other Languages (on-line).. MSc
36PT
Teaching English to Speakers of other Languages (TESOL) and
Computer Assisted Language Learning......MSc 12FT 24PT/PGDip
9FT 18PT/PGCert 6FT 12PT
Teaching Qualification in Adult Education (TQAE).....PGCert 12PT
Teaching Qualification in Further Education (TQFE)..PGCert 12PT
Teaching of English to Speakers of Other Languages (TESOL)MSc
12FT 24PT/PGDip 9FT 18PT/PGCert 6FT 12PT

Teaching of English to Speakers of Other Languages (TESOL) and
Applied Linguistics ....MSc 12FT 24PT/PGDip 9FT 18PT/
PGCert 6FT 12PT

University of Strathclyde
Advanced Professional Studies......MSc 24PT/PGDip 24PT/PGCert
12PT
Education...............EdD by taught 36-72PT/MEd 24-36PT 24-36DL
Educational Psychology ....MSc 24FT
Philosophy with Children ....PGCert 24PT
Primary Education..PGDE 10FT 21PT
Supporting Bilingual Learners.................................PGCert 24PT
Supporting Teacher Learning ....PGCert 24PT

University of Sunderland
Advanced Professional Practice (Primary)..................MA 12FT
Copy of Advanced Professional Practice (Secondary).......MA 12FT

University of Sussex
Education Studies.........................MA 12FT 24PT/PGDip 12FT 24PT

Swansea Metropolitan University
Education..MA(Ed) 24 - 60PT
PGCE Secondary with QTS....................................... PGCE(QTS) 10FT
Post-Graduate Certificate in Education ....PCET 24 - 36PT
Professional Development, Education and Training (PDET) .....MA
36 - 60PT

Teesside University
Education (Doctorate) ....EdD by taught 48FT 72PT
Educational Studies .... MA 12FT 24PT
Professional Studies in Education .... PGDip 24 -36PT
Promoting Inclusive Practice in Education............ PGDip 24 - 36PT

Titan Partnership Ltd
Primary SCITT ....PGCE(QTS) 10FT

Trinity College Dublin - the University of Dublin
Professional Diploma in Education................................PGDip 12FT

Trinity Laban Conservatoire of Music and Dance
PGCE 'Musicians In Education' ....PGCE 12FT

University of Warwick
Childhood in Society...MA 12FT 24-36PT
Drama Education and English Language Teaching (ELT) .MA 12FT
24-36PT
Educational Assessment................................MA 12FT 24-36PT
Educational Innovation..MA 24-48PT

University of the West of England, Bristol
Education..MA 48PT
Education (Professional Doctorate) .... EdD by taught 48PT

University of Winchester
Doctor of Education (EdD)......................EdD by taught 36FT 84PT

University of Wolverhampton
Education...MA 12FT 24PT

University of Worcester
Education......MA 18FT 36PT/PGDip 12FT 24PT/PGCert 12FT 12PT
Leading Early Years Practice....................................PGCert 6FT 12PT
Mentoring in Early Childhood ....PGCert 6FT 12PT
National Award SENCo (NASC) PG Cert Education (Special
Educational Needs Coordination) ....PGCert 12PT

University of York
Applied Linguistics for Language Teaching.........................MA 12FT

York St John University
Practitioner Research: Improving Professional Practice..MA 24PT

Teacher training and education
Research Courses

Anglia Ruskin University
Professional Doctorate in Education .... EdD 36FT 36 - 72PT

Bangor University
Education.............................PhD 36FT 60-72PT/MPhil 24FT 36-48PT

Bath Spa University
Education...PhD 24 - 60FT 36 - 72PT

University of Bath
Education...EdD 24-60FT 36-96PT

Birmingham City University
Education... EdD 48 - 72PT

University of Birmingham
Education... PhD 36FT 72PT/MA by research 12FT 24PT/EdD 36FT
48PT

Brunel University
School of Sport and Education.. PhD 36FT 72PT/MPhil 12FT 24PT
School of Sport and Education.PhD 36FT 72PT/MPhil 12FT 24PT/
EdD 48FT 72PT

University of Cambridge
Education... PhD 36FT 60PT

University of Central Lancashire
Education, Deaf Studies.......PhD 18-36FT 42-60PT/MPhil 18-36FT
42-60PT/MA by research 12FT 24PT
Politics and International studies .... MPhil 18-36FT 42-60PT/PhD
30-48FT 66-84PT/MA by research 12FT 24PT

Section sponsored by

BPP
UNIVERSITY
COLLEGE

Business and social sciences
www.prospects.ac.uk/findcourses **POSTGRADUATE DIRECTORY 545**

Teacher training and education

Sociology, Ethnicity & Human Rights, Criminology ....
PhD 30-48FT 66-84PT/MPhil 18-36FT 42-60PT/MA by research
12FT 24PT

University of Chester
Education.. EdD 24-84PT

University of Cumbria
Department of Education ....PhD 48FT 72PT 72DL/
MPhil 36FT 60PT 60DL

University of Dundee
Community Learning & Development (PhD) ....PhD 36FT

University of Edinburgh
Education........................... PhD 36FT 72PT/MPhil 24FT 48PT
Education (Doctor of)..EdD 60PT

University of Exeter
Education...........PhD 48FT 84PT/MPhil 24FT 48PT/EdD 48FT 84PT

University of Glasgow
Education.........PhD 36FT 60PT/MPhil 12FT 24PT/MSc by research
12FT 24PT/EdD 36-60DL

University of Gloucestershire
Education..............PhD 30-48FT 48-84PT/MPhil 18-36FT 30-60PT/
MA by research 12-24FT 18-36PT

Goldsmiths, University of London
Education.......................PhD 36-48FT 48-72PT/MPhil 24FT 36PT

University of Greenwich
Doctorate in Education .... EdD appr. 60PT

University of Hertfordshire
Education...................MRes 12FT/MPhil 24FT 48PT/PhD 36FT 72PT
Education (Professional Doctorate).....................................EdD 60PT

University of Hull
Education.. MEd by research 12FT
Education/Educational Studies ......PhD 36FT/MPhil 24FT/MEd by
research 12FT/EdD 36FT

Institute of Education
Dual Doctor in Education (EdD) Award........................ EdD 48-84PT
Education and related areas (PhD / MPhil)............... PhD 36-48FT
48-84PT/MPhil 24-36FT 36-60PT
PhD ESRC Studentship .... ESRC Studentship 36-48FT 48-84PT
Post-doctoral Research................... Post-doctoral Research 3-12FT

Keele University
Education.............. PhD 24-48FT 48-84PT/MPhil 12-24FT 24-36PT

University of Kent
Higher Education .... PhD 36FT 60PT

King's College London
Education & Professional Studies Research ... PhD 36FT 48-84PT/
MPhil 36FT 48-84PT/EdD 36FT 48-84PT

Kingston University
Education..................... PhD 48FT 72PT/MA by research 12FT 24PT

University of Leicester
Doctor of Education....................................... EdD 36FT 60PT
PhD in Research in Education.................................. PhD 36FT 72PT

Liverpool John Moores University
Professional Doctorate.......................................MPhil 36FT 84PT

London Metropolitan University
Dept of Education ....PhD Max 60FT Max 96PT/MPhil Max 36FT
Max 54PT/EdD MaxPT

London South Bank University
Professional Doctorate in Education .... EdD 48-84PT

Manchester Metropolitan University
Institute of Education ...... MA by research 24FT 60PT/MPhil 60FT
72PT/PhD 72FT 96PT/MSc by research 12FT 60PT
Master of Research Education and Society...........MRes 12FT 24PT

University of Manchester
Education PhD.. PhD 36FT 72PT

Middlesex University
School of Lifelong Learning and Education...... PhD/MPhil/DProf/
MProf by research

Newcastle University
Education... PhD 36FT 72PT/MPhil 12FT 24PT
Education (Clinical) .... MPhil 12FT 24PT/PhD 36FT 72PT
Education, Doctor of..EdD 36-60FT 72-96PT

University of Northampton
School of Education ....PhD 36FT/MPhil 24FT

Nottingham Trent University
Education.. PhD 48FT 96PT/MPhil 36FT 72PT

The Open University
Inquiry-based science learning............. PhD 36FT 72PT variableDL
Online science experimentation .... PhD 36FT 72PT variableDL
Physics education....MPhil 15FT 24PT variableDL/PhD 36FT 72PT
variableDL
Technology, communication and education .... PhD 36FT 72PT
variableDL/MPhil 15FT 24PT variableDL
e-assessment..PhD 36FT 72PT variableDL

Oxford Brookes University
Doctorate of Education - Professional Doctorate...... EdD 60-84PT

Education and Childhood Studies (MPhil/PhD)............MPhil/PhD
36-60FT 48-72PT/PhD 24-60FT 36-72PT/MPhil 24-36FT 36-48PT

University of Oxford
Educational Studies .... DPhil 48FT

Plymouth University
Education.. PhD 48FT 72PT/MPhil 36FT 48PT

Queen's University Belfast
Education.. PhD 36FT 72PT/MPhil 24FT 48PT

University of Roehampton
Education.............. PhD 24-48FT 36-60PT/MPhil 21-36FT 33-48PT

University of Salford
Higher Education Research ....PhD/MPhil

Sheffield Hallam University
Education.............................. PhD 48FT 84PT/MPhil 48FT 84PT
Learning and Teaching Institute.......................................PhD/MPhil

University of Southampton
Doctorate in Education EdD.................................... EdD 36FT 48PT
Education............................... MPhil 12FT 24PT/PhD 24FT 36PT
Integrated PhD in Education ....Integrated PhD 36FT

University of Stirling
Education... PhD 36FT/MPhil 12FT

University of Strathclyde
Education - Research ....PhD 33FT/MPhil 12FT/EdD 36FT 48PT

Swansea Metropolitan University
Faculty of Education ....PhD/MPhil

University of Wales Trinity Saint David
Centre for Theology and Education ....PhD/MPhil

University of Warwick
Educational Development Appraisal and Research.........PhD 36FT
60PT/MPhil 24FT 36PT

University of the West of Scotland
Department of Education ....PhD/MPhil

University of the West of England, Bristol
Faculty of Creative Arts, Humanities and Education.......... PhD .FT

University of Westminster
Negotiated Education related title ....DProf 36-60DL
Westminster Exchange.................................MPhil 18-36FT 30-60PT

University of Worcester
Doctor of Education (EdD)...EdD 36PT
Education........................... PhD 48FT 70PT/MPhil 24FT 48PT

University of York
Education - Institute for Effective Education.........PhD 36FT 72PT/
MPhil 24FT 48PT
Education - Institute for Effective Education......................... MA by
research 12FT 24PT

Teaching conversion qualification
Taught Courses

University of East Anglia
Primary Teacher Training (3 to 9 years) Foundation Stage/Key
Stage One.. PGCE(QTS) 12FT
Primary Teacher Training (5 to 11 years) General Class Teacher
with Modern Foreign Languages: French............ PGCE(QTS) 12FT
Primary Teacher Training (5 to 11 years) General Class Teacher
with Modern Foreign Languages: German........... PGCE(QTS) 12FT
Primary Teacher Training (5 to 11 years) General Class Teacher
with Modern Foreign Languages: Spanish .... PGCE(QTS) 12FT
Primary Teacher Training (5 to 11 years) Key Stage One/Lower
Key Stage Two.. PGCE(QTS) 12FT
Primary Teacher Training (5 to 11 years) Key Stage Two..................
PGCE(QTS) 12FT
Secondary Teacher Training (11-16 years) with post-16
enhancement experience: English .... PGCE(QTS) 12FT
Secondary Teacher Training (11-16 years) with post-16
enhancement experience: Geography .... PGCE(QTS) 12FT
Secondary Teacher Training (11-16 years) with post-16
enhancement experience: History .... PGCE(QTS) 12FT
Secondary Teacher Training (11-16 years) with post-16
enhancement experience: Mathematics .... PGCE(QTS) 12FT
Secondary Teacher Training (11-16 years) with post-16
enhancement experience: Modern Foreign Languages..................
PGCE(QTS) 12FT
Secondary Teacher Training (11-16 years) with post-16
enhancement experience: Physical Education .... PGCE(QTS) 12FT
Secondary Teacher Training (11-16 years) with post-16
enhancement experience: Science (Biology) .... PGCE(QTS) 12FT
Secondary Teacher Training (11-16 years) with post-16
enhancement experience: Science (Chemistry) .. PGCE(QTS) 12FT
Secondary Teacher Training (11-16 years) with post-16
enhancement experience: Science (Physics)........ PGCE(QTS) 12FT

TEFL training
Taught Courses

University of Aberdeen
English Linguistics for Advanced Teachers of English (ELATE)........
MLitt 12FT 24PT/PGDip 9FT 18PT

Anglia Ruskin University
Applied Linguistics and TESOL (Teaching English to Speakers of
Other Languages)..MA 12FT 24PT 12-24DL

Aston University
Certificate in Advanced Studies in English Language Teaching
(ELT).. Cert 6-12PT
TESOL and Translation Studies........................... MA 12FT 24 -36PT
Teaching English to Speakers of Other Languages (TESOL)......MA
12FT 24 -36PT
Applied Linguistics ....MSc 24 - 36DL
Teaching English to Speakers of Other Languages (TESOL).... MSc
24 - 60PT

University of Bath
Teaching English to Speakers of Other Languages (TESOL)......MA
12FT 24-60PT/DELTA 12FT

University of Bedfordshire
Applied Linguistics (TEFL)... MA 12FT 24PT
Certificate in ELT.....................................Cert 12PT/Cert 1BM
ELT Management.. MA 12FT 24PT

Belfast Metropolitan College
Cambridge ESOL Level 5 Certificate in Teaching English to
Speakers of Other Languages (CELTA) ....Cert 5PT

Birkbeck, University of London
Teaching English to Speakers of Other Languages (TESOL)......MA
12FT 24PT

University of Birmingham
Teaching English as a Foreign Language (TEFL)MA 12FT 24-72PT/
PGDip 12FT 24PT/PGCert 6FT 12PT
Teaching English as a Second/Foreign Language... MA 12FT 30DL

University of Bolton
Policy and Practice in Basic Skills (ESOL)........... MA 12FT 24 - 60PT

University of Bradford
TESOL and Applied Linguistics ...MEd 24PT/PGDip 20PT/MA 24PT

University of Brighton
English Language Teaching......MA 12FT 24PT/PGCert 12FT 24PT/
PGDip 12FT 24PT
Media Assisted Language Teaching...MA 12FT 24PT/PGCert 12FT
24PT/PGDip 12FT 24PT
Teaching English to Speakers of Other LanguagesMA 12FT 24PT/
PGDip 12FT 24PT/PGCert 12FT 24PT

University of Bristol
Education - Teaching English to Speakers of Other Languages
(TESOL) ....MSc 12FT 24-60PT

Canterbury Christ Church University
TESOL.. MA 12FT 60PT
Teaching English as an Additional Language....................MA 36PT

University of Central Lancashire
Teaching English to Speakers of Other Languages (TESOL) with
Applied Linguistics .... MA 12FT 24-60PT 24-60DL

Coventry University
English Language Teaching.. MA 12FT 30PT

University of Cumbria
TESOL (Teaching English to Speakers of Other Languages)......MA
12FT

De Montfort University
English Language Teaching.. MA 12FT 24PT

Durham University
Applied Linguistics for TESOL ....MA 12FT

Edinburgh Napier University
Intercultural Communication with TESOL .... MSc 12FT

University of Edinburgh
Teaching English to Speakers of Other Languages (TESOL).... MSc
12FT 72PT/PGDip 9FT 48PT/PGCert 4FT 24PT

University of Essex
Cambridge Certificate in English Language Teaching to Adults ...
GradCert 9FT
Teaching English as a Foreign Language .... MA 12FT 24PT
Teaching English to Speakers of Other Languages MA 12FT 24PT

University of Exeter
Education Taught Doctorate......... EdD by taught 24FT 48PT 48DL
Educational Research ....MSc 12FT 24PT 12-24DL
Teaching English to Speakers of Other Languages Masters..........
PGDip 12FT/MEd 12FT 60PT/PGCert 6FT
Teaching English to Speakers of Other Languages Masters
(Summer Course)...MEd 36PT

National University of Ireland Galway
Teaching English as a Foreign Language (TEFL) .... HDip 12PT/Cert
12PT

University of Glasgow
English Language & English Linguistics: Applied.. MSc 12FT 24PT

Glyndwr University
Advanced English for Speakers of Other Languages........MA 12FT
24PT/PGDip 12FT 24PT/PGCert 12FT 24PT

University of Greenwich
Level 5 Diploma in teaching ESOL/Literacy/Numeracy.................
Cert 12PT

Teacher training and education

University of Hertfordshire
Practice of English Language Teaching (The) ....MA 12FT

University of Huddersfield
Teaching English to Speakers of Other Languages (TESOL)......MA 12FT

University of Hull
TESOL .... MA 12FT 24PT
TESOL with Translation Studies .... MA 12FT 24PT
Translation Studies with TESOL .... MA 12FT 24PT

Institute of Education
Teaching of English to Speakers of Other Languages ......MA 12FT 24-48PT 24-48DL

King's College London
Modern Foreign Languages Education .... MA 12FT 24-72PT

Lancaster University
TESOL (Teaching English to Speakers of Other Languages)......MA 24PT
TESOL (Teaching English to Speakers of Other Languages) Hong Kong...MA 24PT
TESOL (Teaching English to Speakers of Other Languages) by distance...MA 30PT
Teaching English as a Foreign Language .... MA 12FT 24PT

Leeds Metropolitan University
English Language Teaching & Professional Practice/Cambridge Delta ....PGCert 12FT 24PT

University of Leeds
TESOL...............................MA 12FT 24PT/PGDip 12FT 24PT
TESOL Studies.................................MA 12FT 24PT/PGDip 12FT 24PT
TESOL Teacher Education...MA 12FT 24PT/MEd 12FT 24PT/PGDip 12FT 24PT
TESOL for Young Learners ....MA 12FT 24PT/PGDip 12FT 24PT

University of Leicester
Applied Linguistics and TESOL ...MA 12FT 24PT 30DL/PGCert 4FT 8PT 12DL

University of Limerick
Languages ....GradDip 9FT

University of Liverpool
Cambridge ESOL CELTA...CELTA 1FT
Teaching English to Speakers of Other Languages (TESOL)......MA 12FT

London Metropolitan University
TESOL and Applied Linguistics ....MA 12FT 24+PT

Manchester Metropolitan University
Teaching English as a Foreign Language .... MA 12FT 24PT

University of Manchester
Educational Technology and TESOL ....MA 12FT 27PT 36DL
TESOL..MA 12FT 27PT 36DL

Newcastle University
Applied Linguistics and TESOL .... MA 12FT 24PT

Northumbria University
TESOL..MA 12FT

Nottingham Trent University
Teaching Adult ESOL..PGCE 10PT

University of Nottingham
Teaching English for Academic Purposes by Distance Learning....MA 24-48DL

Teaching English to Speakers of Other Languages (TESOL)......MA 12FT 24PT/PGDip 9FT 18PT 18DL
Teaching English to Speakers of Other Languages (TESOL) by web-based distance learning..MA 36DL

University of Oxford
English Language ....MSt 9FT

University of Portsmouth
Applied Linguistics and TESOL .... MA 12FT 24PT
Applied Linguistics and TESOL (DL)............................ MA 36DL

Queen's University Belfast
TESOL (Teaching English to Speakers of Other Languages (Masters)......................................MSc 12FT up to 60PT
TESOL (Teaching English to Speakers of Other Languages) (Doctorate)......................................EdD (Doctorate) 36-72FT

University of Roehampton
Applied Linguistics and TESOL ..... MA 12FT 24PT/PGDip 9FT 18PT

University of Salford
TESOL and Applied Linguistics ..... MA 12FT 36PT/PGDip 9FT 24PT

Sheffield Hallam University
TESOL..MA 24-36DL
Teaching English to Speakers of Other Languages (TESOL)......MA 24-36DL/Diploma 12-48FT/Cert 10DL

University of Sheffield
Teaching Chinese as a Foreign Language...........................MA 12FT

University of South Wales
Teaching English as an Additional Language.......... MA 12FT 36PT
Teaching English to Speakers of Other Languages (TESOL).....MA 12FT 36PT
Teaching English to Young Learners (TEYL) .... MA 12FT 24PT

University of Southampton
English Language Teaching.........MA 12FT 24PT/PGCert 12DL/MA 28DL
English Language Teaching Innovation ....PGDip 4PT

University of Stirling
Teaching English to Speakers of Other Languages (on-line).. MSc 36PT
Teaching English to Speakers of other Languages (TESOL) and Computer Assisted Language Learning......MSc 12FT 24PT/PGDip 9FT 18PT/PGCert 6FT 12PT
Teaching of English to Speakers of Other Languages (TESOL).......MSc 12FT 24PT/PGDip 9FT 18PT/PGCert 6FT 12PT
Teaching of English to Speakers of Other Languages (TESOL) and Applied Linguistics ..MSc 12FT 24PT/PGDip 9FT 18PT/PGCert 6FT 12PT
Translation Studies with TESOL MSc 12FT 27PT/PGDip 9FT 21PT/PGCert 9FT 9PT

University of Sunderland
Teaching English to Speakers of Other Languages...........................MA 12FT 36PT 18DL

Swansea University
Chinese-English Translation and Language Teaching......MA 12FT
English Literature .... MA 12FT 24-36PT
Teaching English as a Foreign Language (TEFL) .....MA 12FT 36PT/PGDip 12FT 24PT

University of Wales Trinity Saint David
English (TEFL)...............................MA 12FT 24PT/PGCert 12FT 24PT/PGDip 12FT 24PT

University of Ulster
Teaching of English to Speakers of Other Languages (TESOL).......MA 4FT 12PT/PGDip 9FT 18PT

University of Warwick
English Language Teaching (Studies and Methods).........MA 12FT
English Language Teaching (with a Specialism in Testing and Assessment).. MA 12FT 24-48PT

University of Westminster
Teaching English to Speakers of Other Languages (TESOL)......MA 12FT 24PT
Teaching English to Speakers of other Languages and Creative Writing .... MA 12FT 24PT

University of York
Teaching English to Speakers of Other Languages (TESOL) -Institute for Effective Education ....MA 12FT

TEFL training
Research Courses

Birkbeck, University of London
Teaching English to Speakers of Other Languages (TESOL)....New Route PhD 36FT 56PT

University of Central Lancashire
Translation, English as a Foreign Language, Learning & Teaching Methodology, Language......PhD 30-48FT 66-84PT/MPhil 18-36FT 42-60PT/MA by research 12FT 24PT

University of East Anglia
Language and Communication Studies ......PhD 36FT 72PT/MPhil 24FT 48PT/MA by research 12FT 24PT

University of Essex
English Language Teaching........PhD 36FT 60PT 48DL/MPhil 24FT 48PT

Newcastle University
TESOL and Cross-Cultural Communication ....MPhil 12FT 24PT/ PhD 36FT 72PT

The Open University
Language Learning and Teaching....... PhD 36FT 72PT variableDL/ MRes 12FT/EdD 36PT

Visually impaired teaching
Taught Courses

University of South Wales
SEN Visual Impairment.................................... PGDip 24PT

Welsh teaching
Taught Courses

Bangor University
Primary Education... PGCE 12FT
Secondary Education... PGCE 12FT

Welsh teaching
Research Courses

Aberystwyth University
Welsh Literature ....MPhil 12FT 24PT

Section sponsored by

BPP
UNIVERSITY
COLLEGE

Business and social sciences
www.prospects.ac.uk/findcourses **POSTGRADUATE DIRECTORY 547**

Tourism, hospitality and event management

Airport management
Taught Courses

Bucks New University
Air Transport Management ....MSc 15FT 27PT

City University London
Air Safety Management.................................MSc 12FT 36PT
Air Transport Management ....MSc 12FT 36PT

Cranfield University
Air Transport Management .... MSc 12FT
Air Transport Management (Executive)......................MSc 24-48PT
Airport Planning and Management .... MSc 12FT
Airport Planning and Management MSc - Executive..... MSc 36PT

University of West London
Airline and Airport Management............................... MA 12FT 24PT

University of Westminster
Air Transport Planning and Management ....MSc 12FT 24PT

Ecotourism
Taught Courses

Bangor University
Biodiversity Conservation .... PhD by taught 36FT 60PT/
MPhil 24FT 36PT

University of Bedfordshire
Tourism and Environmental Management .... MSc 12-15FT 24PT/
PGDip 12FT/PGCert 12FT

University of Birmingham
Development Management (Human Resources and
Development Management)...MSc 12FT 24PT

Bournemouth University
Tourism Management...MSc 12-15FT 24PT
Tourism Management and Marketing.............. MSc 12/15FT 24PT

Edinburgh Napier University
Ecotourism ....MSc 12FT 24-48PT/PGDip 9FT 18-36PT/PGCert 6FT
12-24PT

University of Exeter
Tourism, Development and Policy........ MSc 12FT 24PT/PGDip 9FT

University of Kent
Conservation and Tourism ....MSc 12FT 24PT

London Metropolitan University
International Sustainable Tourism Management.............MA 12FT

Oxford Brookes University
Tourism: Environment and Development ....MSc 12FT 24PT/
PGDip 9FT 21PT/PGCert 9PT

School of Oriental and African Studies - SOAS
Anthropology of Travel, Tourism and Pilgrimage ... MA 12FT 24PT
Environmental Law and Sustainable Development ....
MA 12FT 24PT

University of Wales Trinity Saint David
Heritage Tourism ....MA 12-24FT 18-48PT/PGDip 9FT 18-36PT/
PGCert 9FT 18PT

UCL - University College London
Built Environment: Sustainable Heritage .... MSc 12FT 24-60PT/
PGDip 9FT

Ecotourism
Research Courses

University of Southampton
Science and Heritage..MRes 12FT

Event management studies
Taught Courses

University of Bedfordshire
Tourism and Event ManagementMSc 12-15FT 24PT/PGDip 12FT/
PGCert 12FT

Birkbeck, University of London
Creative Industries (Arts and Media)........................ MA 12FT 24PT
Sport Governance.. PGCert 12PT 12DL
Sport Management ...... PGCert 12PT 12DL/MSc 12FT 24PT/MRes
12FT 24PT
Sport Management and Marketing........................... MSc 12FT 24PT
Sport Management and the Business of FootballMSc 12FT 24PT/
MRes 12FT 24PT
Sport Marketing... MSc 12FT 24PT

Birmingham City University
Events and Exhibition Management......................... MA 12FT 24PT

Bournemouth University
Events Management ....MSc 12-15FT 24PT
Events Marketing..MSc 12-15FT 24PT

University of Brighton
International Event Management ....MSc 12FT 24-72PT/PGCert
12FT 24-72PT/PGDip 12FT 24-72PT

University of Central Lancashire
International Festivals and Event Management ..MSc 12FT 24PT/
PGDip 12FT 24PT

International Festivals and Tourism Management......... MSc 12FT
24PT/PGDip 12FT 24PT
International Heritage and Event Management..MSc 12FT 24PT/
PGDip 12FT 24PT
International Hospitality and Event Management .... MSc 12FT
24PT/PGDip 12FT 24PT
Internship in International Tourism, Hospitality and Event
Management... MA 12FT 24PT
Management Studies.. DMS 18PT
Sport Business Management .... MSc 12FT up to 36PT
Sports Marketing and Business Management ..... MSc 12FT up to
36PT

University of Chester
Public Services Management (Work Based and Integrative
Studies) ....MA 24-72PT/PGDip 24-60PT/PGCert 12-36PT

University of Cumbria
Events Leadership and Management....... MBA 12FT 36PT/PGCert
12FT 36PT/PGDip 12FT 36PT

De Montfort University
Cultural Events Management ....MA 12FT 24PT/MSc 12FT 24PT

University of Derby
Events Management .... MA 12FT 24PT

University of East Anglia
Marketing and Management....................................... MSc 12FT

Edinburgh Napier University
International Event and Festival Management..... MSc 12FT 24PT
International Marketing with Tourism & Events .... MSc 12FT
Marketing with Festival and Event Management .... MSc 12FT

University of Exeter
International Tourism Management .... MSc 12FT

Fitzwilliam Institute Group
Event Management Postgraduate Diploma with Public Relations
Postgraduate Diploma 6FT
Event Management with Public Relations, Eco Events and
Wedding Planning..PGDip 6FT
Event Management (PG Dip. Event Man.) by Distance Learning ..
PGDip 6DL
Public Relations (PG Dip. PR) by Distance Learning ...... PGDip 6DL

Glasgow Caledonian University
International Events Management.........................MSc 12FT 24DL
Management.............MSc 12FT FlexiblePT/PGDip 9FT FlexiblePT/
PGCert 6FT FlexiblePT

University of Greenwich
Events Management .... MA 12FT 24PT

Leeds Metropolitan University
Events Management - Distant Learning MSc 24PT/PGCert 12PT/
PGDip 24PT
Information & Technology ....MSc 12FT 24PT/PGDip 12FT 24PT/
PGCert 4FT 24PT
International Events Management....MSc 12FT 24PT/PGDip 12FT
24PT/PGCert unknownFT 12PT
Sport, Law & Society.. MA 12FT 24PT
Sports Event Management .... MSc 12FT 24PT/PGCert 12FT 24PT/
PGDip 12FT 24PT

London Metropolitan University
Events Marketing Management................................. MA 12FT 24PT

Manchester Metropolitan University
International Events Management......................MSc 12FT 24-60PT

Northumbria University
Arts and Media Management.......MA 12/16FT 24/28PT 24/28DL
Cultural Event Management ....MA 12/18FT 24/28PT 24/28DL
International Sport Management...........................MSc 12FT 24PT
Sport Marketing..MSc 12FT 24PT

Richmond, The American International University in London
Event Management ....MSc 12FT 24PT

University of Roehampton
Audiovisual Translation ....PGDip 9FT 24PT

Royal Welsh College of Music and Drama
Stage & Event Management .... MA 12FT 12PT

University of Salford
International Events Management......MSc 12FT 36PT/PGDip 8FT
24PT/PGCert 4FT 9PT
Management.... MSc 12FT 36PT/PGDip 8FT 24PT/PGCert 4FT 9PT

Sheffield Hallam University
International Events and Conference Management ...... MSc 12FT

University of Sheffield
Management... MSc 12FT
Management (Creative and Cultural Industries) .... MSc 12FT
Management (International Business)............................ MSc 12FT

University of St Andrews
Management...MLitt 12FT 24PT
Management (Human Resource Management) .... MLitt 12FT
Management and Information Technology ....MSc 12FT/
PGDip 9FT

University of Stirling
Management.......................MSc 12FT 27PT/PGDip 9FT 21PT

University of Sunderland
Tourism and Events..MSc 12FT 24PT

University of Surrey
International Event Management .... MSc 12FT

University of Ulster
Event Management ....MSc 12FT 30PT/PGDip 9FT 24PT

University of West London
Event Management ....GradDip 12FT
Fundraising and Special Events ....MA 12FT

University of the West of England, Bristol
Events Management ....MA 18FT

University of Westminster
Events and Conference Management...................... MA 12FT 24PT

University of Wolverhampton
Hospitality Management.......................................MA 12FT 24-36PT

Event management studies
Research Courses

University of Cambridge
Management Studies...PhD 36FT

Goldsmiths, University of London
Curatorial/Knowledge ....MPhil 24FT 36PT/PhD 36-48FT 48-72PT

University of Sheffield
Management................................ PhD 36FT 72PT/MPhil 24FT 48PT

Heritage centre management
Taught Courses

Bath Spa University
Curatorial Practice.....MA 12FT 24PT/PGDip 9FT 18PT/PGCert 4FT
9PT
Heritage Management ... MA 12FT 24PT/PGDip 9FT 18PT/PGCert
4FT

University of Birmingham
Heritage Management ....MA 12FT 24DL/PGDip 3FT
Heritage and Identity .... PGCert 30DL/PGDip 30DL/MA 30DL

Bishop Grosseteste University College Lincoln
Heritage Education .... MA 12FT 24PT

University of Central Lancashire
International Heritage and Attraction Management .... MSc 12FT
24PT/PGDip 12FT 24PT
International Heritage and Event Management..MSc 12FT 24PT/
PGDip 12FT 24PT

Durham University
Conservation of Archaeological and Museum Objects
(Dissertation)... MA 24FT 36PT
Conservation of Archaeological and Museum Objects
(Professional Practice) .... MA 24FT 36PT

University of East Anglia
Cultural Heritage and International Development ....
MA 12FT 24PT
Cultural Heritage and Museum Studies .... MA 12FT 24PT
Museum Studies...MA 12FT

University of East London
Heritage Studies MA....................MA 12FT 24PT/PGCert 8FT 16PT/
PGDip 4FT 8PT

University of Glasgow
Museum Studies...MSc 12FT 24PT

University of Kent
Heritage Management (Athens) ....MA 12FT

King's College London
Eighteenth-Century Studies .... MA 12FT 24PT

Kingston University
Heritage (Contemporary Practice) .... MA 12FT 24PT
Museums and Galleries and the Creative EconomyMA 12FT 24PT

University of Leeds
Art Gallery and Museum Studies .... MA 12FT 24PT

University of Leicester
Art Museum and Gallery Studies ....MA 12FT/PGDip 9FT
Country House ....MA 24-48DL
Interpretation, Representation and Heritage ....MA 24DL/PGCert
18DL
Learning and Visitor Studies in Museums and Galleries...........MA
24DL/PGCert 18DL

University of Lincoln
Conservation Studies.. GradDip 12FT 24PT

Newcastle University
Art Museum and Gallery Practice .... MPrac 24FT 48PT
Art Museum and Gallery Studies (with specialist pathways in:
Curatorship, and Education).......... MA 12FT 24PT/PGDip 9FT 18PT
Heritage Practice...MHPrac 24FT 48PT
Heritage Studies (specialist pathways in: Education and
Interpretation, and Management)........ MA 12FT 24PT/PGDip 9FT
18PT
Museum Practice...MPrac 24FT 48PT
Museum Studies......PGCert 18PT MA 12FT 24PT/PGDip 9FT 18PT

Tourism, hospitality and event management

Northumbria University
Cultural Heritage Management ...MA 12/18FT 24/28PT 24/28DL

Norwich University of the Arts
Curation .... MA 12FT 24PT

Nottingham Trent University
Museum and Heritage Management .... MA 12FT 24PT/
PGDip 19FT 21PT

Queen Margaret University, Edinburgh
Arts and Cultural Management.....MA 12FT 24-84PT/PGDip 12FT
24-84PT/PGCert 12FT 24-84PT

Queen's University Belfast
Heritage Science.............................MSc 12FT 24PT/PGDip 7FT 14PT

University of Salford
Art and Design: Museum and Heritage Interpretation...MA 12FT
24PT/PGDip 8FT 15PT

University of Sheffield
Cultural Heritage Management .... MA 12FT
Cultures of the British Isles.............................. MA 12FT 24PT

University of St Andrews
Museum and Gallery Studies... MLitt 12FT 24PT/PGDip 9FT 18PT
National Trust for Scotland Studies...................... MPhil 24FT 48PT

St Mary's University College, Twickenham
Charity Management .... PGCert 12PT/PGDip 24PT/MA 12FT 24PT

University of Sussex
International Trade Law.................................... LLM 12FT 24PT

University of Wales Trinity Saint David
Heritage Studies..............................MA 12FT 24PT 12-24DL

University of Ulster
Cultural Heritage and Museum Studies.................. MA 12FT 36PT
Cultural Management....MSc 12FT 30PT/PGDip 9FT 18PT/PGCert
4FT 8PT

UCL - University College London
Built Environment: Heritage Science MRes 12FT 24-60PT/PGCert
6FT
Built Environment: Sustainable Heritage .... MSc 12FT 24-60PT/
PGDip 9FT
Conservation...................MSc 12FT/PGDip 9FT/PGCert 3FT
Conservation for Archaeology and Museums.................. MSc 24FT
Museum Studies.................................... MA 12FT 24PT
Museum and Gallery Practice .... MA 12FT 24PT

University of Westminster
Museums, Galleries and Contemporary Culture.... MA 12FT 24PT

University of Winchester
Cultural Heritage and Resource Management ...... MA 12FT 24PT/
PGDip 9FT 18PT/PGCert 5FT 10PT

University of York
Cultural Heritage Management .... MA 12FT 36PT
Digital Heritage ....MSc 12FT 24PT/PGDip 9FT
Stained Glass Conservation and Heritage Management...............
MA 24FT

Heritage centre management
Research Courses

City University London
Arts Policy and Management............................PhD/MPhil
Department of Arts Policy and Management...............PhD/MPhil

University of Glasgow
Education.........PhD 36FT 60PT/MPhil 12FT 24PT/MSc by research
12FT 24PT/EdD 36-60DL

Newcastle University
Museum, Gallery and Heritage Studies.......PhD 36FT 72PT/MPhil
12FT 24PT

The Open University
Heritage .... PhD 36FT 72PT variableDL/MPhil 15FT 24PT
variableDL

University of Southampton
Science and Heritage...MRes 12FT

University of St Andrews
Museum and Gallery Studies.... PhD 36FT 72PT/MPhil 24FT 48PT

Hotel and catering management
Taught Courses

Bath Spa University
Travel and Nature Writing..................................MA 12FT 24PT 12DL

University of Bedfordshire
International Tourism Management.... MSc 12-15FT 24PT/PGDip
12FT/PGCert 12FT
Tourism and Environmental Management .... MSc 12-15FT 24PT/
PGDip 12FT/PGCert 12FT

University College Birmingham
Hospitality Management.............MA 12FT 24PT/PGDip 9FT 18PT/
PGCert 5FT 9PT
Hospitality with Tourism Management .....MSc 12FT 24PT/PGDip
12FT 24PT
Professional Hospitality and Tourism Management..... MA 30DL/
PGDip 24DL/PGCert 12DL

Tourism Business Administration ....MA 12FT 24PT 18-30DL/
PGDip 9FT 18PT 24DL/PGCert 5FT 9PT 12DL
Tourism Destination Management ...... MA 12FT 24PT/PGDip 9FT
12PT
UCB MBA / MBA (Hospitality and Tourism pathway) ... MBA 12FT

Bournemouth University
Hotel and Food Services Management..............MSc 12-15FT 24PT

Cardiff Metropolitan University
Hospitality Management ....MSc 24FT 36PT/PGDip 18FT 36PT/
PGCert 9FT 36PT

University of Central Lancashire
International Hospitality and Event Management .... MSc 12FT
24PT/PGDip 12FT 24PT
International Hospitality and Tourism Management.... MSc 12FT
24PT/PGDip 12FT 24PT
International Tourism Management......................MSc 12FT 24PT/
PGDip 12FT 24PT
International Tourism and Attraction Management ..... MSc 12FT
24PT/PGDip 12FT 24PT
Internship in International Tourism, Hospitality and Event
Management... MA 12FT 24PT

University College Cork
Food Business .... MSc 24FT

University of Derby
International Hospitality Management ...... MA 12FT 36PT/PGDip
12FT/PGCert 9FT
International Spa Management....................................MA 36FT

Dublin Institute of Technology
Hospitality Management.........................MSc 12FT 24PT

Edinburgh Napier University
International Human Resource Management.............. MSc 12FT
Tourism and Hospitality Management.................... MSc 12FT 24PT

University of Exeter
International Tourism Management .... MSc 12FT

Glasgow Caledonian University
International Tourism Management..MSc 12FT 24PT FlexibleDL/
PGDip 9FT

University of Glasgow
Management with Human Resources............................ MSc 12FT

University of Gloucestershire
MBA Hospitality.. MBA 12FT

University of Huddersfield
International Hospitality Management .... MSc 12FT 24PT

Leeds Metropolitan University
International Hospitality Management......MSc 12FT 24PT/PGDip
12FT 24PT/PGCert 4FT 12PT
International Tourism & Hospitality Management....... MSc 12FT
24PT
Multi Unit Leadership .... MSc 12FT 24PT

University of Lincoln
Hospitality and Tourism Services Management .... MSc 12FT

London College UCK
Hospitality and Tourism Management......PGDip 12FT 24PT 24DL

Manchester Metropolitan University
Hospitality Management......................MSc 12FT 24-60PT
International Tourism Management...............MSc 12FT 24-60PT

Middlesex University
International Tourism and Hospitality Management......MA 12FT
24PT

Northumbria University
Business with Hospitality and Tourism Management... MSc 12FT

Oxford Brookes University
International Hospitality and Tourism Management ... MSc 12FT
24PT/MSc-Sandwich Mode 24FT
International Hotel and Tourism Management ..MSc 12FT 24PT/
MSc-Sandwich Mode 24FT

Plymouth University
Tourism and Hospitality Management.......MSc 12FT/PGDip 12FT

Queen Margaret University, Edinburgh
International Management and Leadership with Hospitality
.... MSc 12FT 24PT/PGDip 9FT 18PT/PGCert 3FT 6PT
Hospitality Management............. MBA 12FT 24-84PT/PGDip 12FT
24-84PT/PGCert 12FT 24-84PT

Regent's Business School London
Business Management in International Travel & Tourism ....MA
21PT

Robert Gordon University
International Tourism and Hospitality Management....... MSc 12FT
36PT/PGDip 9FT 24PT/PGCert 6FT 12PT

University of Roehampton
International Management....................................MSc 12FT 24PT

School of Oriental and African Studies - SOAS
Anthropology of Travel, Tourism and Pilgrimage ... MA 12FT 24PT

Sheffield Hallam University
International Hospitality Management (full time) ....
MSc 12FT 36DL
International Hospitality and Tourism Management.... MSc 12FT

St Mary's University College, Twickenham
International Tourism Development .... MA 12FT 24PT

University of Strathclyde
International Hospitality and Tourism Management.... MSc 12FT
24PT/PGDip 9FT 21PT

University of Sunderland
Tourism and Hospitality .... MSc 12FT 24PT

University of Surrey
International Hotel Management .... MSc 12FT
Master of Business Administration (MBA) .... MBA 12FT

Swansea Metropolitan University
MBA (International Tourism)...........................MBA 12FT 24 - 48PT

University of Ulster
International Hotel and Tourism Management .... MSc 12FT 30PT

University of West London
Gastronomy and Food Management...................... MA 12FT 24PT
Hospitality Management.............................. MA 12FT 24PT

University of Wolverhampton
Hospitality Management....................................MA 12FT 24-36PT

Hotel and catering management
Research Courses

Manchester Metropolitan University
Research in Hospitality and Tourism Management ....
PhD VariableFT VariablePT/MPhil VariableFT VariablePT/MSc by
research 12FT 24PT

Oxford Brookes University
Hospitality, Leisure and Tourism Management .... PhD 24-60FT
36-72PT/MPhil 24-36FT 36-48PT

Robert Gordon University
Aberdeen Business School ...PhD 12FT 36PT 36DL/MSc(Res) 12FT
36PT 36DL

University of Surrey
Hospitality................................ PhD 36FT 48PT/MPhil 24FT 36PT

University of West London
London School of Hospitality & Tourism.....PhD 36FT 72PT/MPhil
24FT 48PT

Tourism, hospitality and event management
Taught Courses

Aberystwyth University
Management and Tourism Management...............MSc 12FT 24PT
Tourism Marketing..MSc 12FT 24PT

Anglia Ruskin University
International Sustainable Tourism Management.. MA 18FT 24PT
Sustainability: Working for Positive Change....MSc 12FT 24-30PT

University of Bedfordshire
International Tourism Management.... MSc 12-15FT 24PT/PGDip
12FT/PGCert 12FT
International Tourism and Hospitality Management.............. MSc
12-18FT/PGDip 6FT/PGCert 6FT
Sport Tourism Management ....MSc 12FT 24PT/PGDip 12FT/
PGCert 12FT
Tourism and Event ManagementMSc 12-15FT 24PT/PGDip 12FT/
PGCert 12FT

University College Birmingham
Hospitality with Tourism Management .....MSc 12FT 24PT/PGDip
12FT 24PT
Professional Hospitality and Tourism Management..... MA 30DL/
PGDip 24DL/PGCert 12DL
Tourism Business Administration MA 12FT 24PT 18-30DL/PGDip
9FT 18PT 24DL/PGCert 5FT 9PT 12DL
Tourism Destination Management ...... MA 12FT 24PT/PGDip 9FT
12PT
UCB MBA / MBA (Hospitality and Tourism pathway) ... MBA 12FT

Bournemouth University
International Hospitality and Tourism Management.............. MSc
12-15FT 24PT
Sustainable Tourism Planning................MSc 12-15FT 24PT
Tourism Management....................................MSc 12-15FT 24PT
Tourism Management and Marketing.............. MSc 12/15FT 24PT

University of Brighton
International Hospitality Management .... MSc 12FT 24-72PT/
PGDip 12FT 24-72PT/PGCert 12FT 24-72PT
International Tourism Management.... MSc 12FT 24-72PT/PGDip
12FT 24-72PT/PGCert 12FT 24-72PT
Tourism and International Development........ MSc 12FT 24-72PT/
PGDip 12FT 24-72PT/PGCert 12FT 24-72PT
Tourism and Social Anthropology..................... MSc 12FT 24-72PT/
PGDip 12FT 24-72PT/PGCert 12FT 24-72PT

Cardiff Metropolitan University
Hospitality Management ....MSc 24FT 36PT/PGDip 18FT 36PT/
PGCert 9FT 36PT

Tourism, hospitality and event management

Tourism Management...............MSc 24FT 36PT/PGDip 18FT 36PT/
PGCert 9FT 36PT

University of Central Lancashire
International Festivals and Tourism Management......... MSc 12FT
24PT/PGDip 12FT 24PT
International Heritage and Attraction Management.... MSc 12FT
24PT/PGDip 12FT 24PT
International Hospitality and Tourism Management.... MSc 12FT
24PT/PGDip 12FT 24PT
International Tourism Management......................MSc 12FT 24PT/
PGDip 12FT 24PT
International Tourism and Attraction Management ..... MSc 12FT
24PT/PGDip 12FT 24PT
Internship in International Tourism, Hospitality and Event
Management.. MA 12FT 24PT

Coventry University
International Tourism Management..................MSc 12FT 24-30PT

University of Cumbria
Events Leadership and Management....... MBA 12FT 36PT/PGCert
12FT 36PT/PGDip 12FT 36PT

University of Derby
International Hospitality Management...... MA 12FT 36PT/PGDip
12FT/PGCert 9FT
Tourism Management..... MA 12FT 24PT/PGDip 12FT/PGCert 9FT

Dublin Institute of Technology
Tourism Management...MSc 12FT 24PT

Edinburgh Napier University
Heritage and Cultural Tourism Management........ MSc 12FT 24PT
International Marketing with Tourism & Events .... MSc 12FT
International Tourism Management.... MSc 12FT 24-36PT/PGDip
9FT 24-36PT
Tourism and Hospitality Management.....................MSc 12FT 24PT

University of Exeter
International Tourism Management................................. MSc 12FT
Tourism Studies .... MRes 12FT
Tourism, Development and Policy........MSc 12FT 24PT/PGDip 9FT

Glasgow Caledonian University
International Events Management..........................MSc 12FT 24DL
International Tourism Management..MSc 12FT 24PT FlexibleDL/
PGDip 9FT

University of Glasgow
Tourism, Heritage & Development.........................MLitt 12FT 24PT

University of Gloucestershire
MBA Hospitality.. MBA 12FT

Goldsmiths, University of London
Cultural Policy and Tourism .... MA 12FT 24PT

University of Greenwich
International Tourism Management................... MA 12FT 24-48PT

University of Hertfordshire
International Tourism and Hospitality Management.... MSc 12FT
24-30PT/PGDip 12FT 24-30PT/PGCert 12FT 24-30PT

University of Huddersfield
International Hospitality Management .... MSc 12FT 24PT

University of Kent
Conservation and Tourism .... MSc 12FT 24PT

King's College London
Tourism, Environment & Development....................MA 12FT 24PT/
MSc 12FT 24PT

Leeds Metropolitan University
International Tourism & Hospitality Management........ MSc 12FT
24PT
Responsible Tourism Management ..MSc 12FT 36PT 36DL/PGDip
12FT 24PT 24DL/PGCert 4FT 24PT 24DL

University of Limerick
International Tourism.. MA 12FT 24PT

University of Lincoln
International Tourism Management................... MSc 12FT 24PT

London College UCK
Hospitality and Tourism Management......PGDip 12FT 24PT 24DL

London South Bank University
International Tourism & Hospitality Management........ MSc 18FT
36PT

Manchester Metropolitan University
Environmental Public Health .... MSc 12FT 24PT
Food Innovation ....MSc 12FT 24PT
Hospitality Management.......................MSc 12FT 24-60PT
International Events Management....................MSc 12FT 24-60PT
International Tourism Management..................MSc 12FT 24-60PT

Middlesex University
International Tourism and Hospitality Management......MA 12FT
24PT

Newcastle University
Art Museum and Gallery Studies (with specialist pathways in:
Curatorship, and Education)......... MA 12FT 24PT/PGDip 9FT 18PT
Heritage Practice ....MHPrac 24FT 48PT

University of Northampton
International Tourism & Hospitality ManagementMA 12FT 24PT

Northumbria University
Business with Hospitality and Tourism Management... MSc 12FT
Cultural Event Management ....MA 12/18FT 24/28PT 24/28DL

Oxford Brookes University
International Hospitality and Tourism Management ... MSc 12FT
24PT/MSc-Sandwich Mode 24FT
International Hotel and Tourism Marketing ....MSc 12FT 24PT/
MSc Sandwich Mode 24FT
Tourism: Environment and Development .MSc 12FT 24PT/PGDip
9FT 21PT/PGCert 9PT

Plymouth University
International Hospitality Management .... MSc 12FT/PGDip 6FT
Tourism and Hospitality Management.......MSc 12FT/PGDip 12FT

Queen Margaret University, Edinburgh
MBA - Hospitality Management MBA 12FT 24-84PT/PGDip 12FT
24-84PT/PGCert 12FT 24-84PT

Royal Agricultural University
Sustainable Business......................................MSc 12FT 24PT
Sustainable Rural Tourism..MSc 12FT 24PT

Royal Welsh College of Music and Drama
Stage & Event Management .... MA 12FT 12PT

Sheffield Hallam University
International Hospitality and Tourism Management.... MSc 12FT
International Tourism Management.................................. MSc 12FT

University of Sunderland
Tourism and Events...MSc 12FT 24PT
Tourism and Hospitality ....MSc 12FT 24PT

University of Surrey
Tourism Development... MSc 12FT
Tourism Management .... MSc 12FT
Tourism Marketing... MSc 12FT

Swansea Metropolitan University
MBA (International Tourism)...........................MBA 12FT 24 - 48PT

University of Wales Trinity Saint David
Tourism Management............... MBA 12-24FT 18-48PT/PGDip 9FT
18-36PT/PGCert 9FT 18-36PT

University of the Highlands and Islands
Interpretation: Management and Practice...... PGCert 12FT 24PT/
PGDip 12FT 24PT/MSc 12FT 24PT

University of Ulster
Coastal and Marine Tourism........................ MSc 30DL/PGDip 20DL
International Hotel and Tourism Management .... MSc 12FT 30PT
International Tourism Development.......................MSc 12FT 30PT

University of West London
Tourism Management... MA 12FT 24PT

University of the West of England, Bristol
International Tourism Management............MSc 12-18FT 24-36PT

University of Westminster
Tourism Management .... MA 12FT 24PT

Tourism, hospitality and event management
Research Courses

Manchester Metropolitan University
Research in Hospitality and Tourism Management ....
PhD VariableFT VariablePT/MPhil VariableFT VariablePT/MSc by
research 12FT 24PT

Oxford Brookes University
Hospitality, Leisure and Tourism Management .... PhD 24-60FT
36-72PT/MPhil 24-36FT 36-48PT

Royal Welsh College of Music and Drama
Arts Management....................................MA by research 12FT 24PT

University of Surrey
Tourism .... PhD 36FT 48PT/MPhil 24FT 36PT

University of West London
London School of Hospitality & Tourism.....PhD 36FT 72PT/MPhil
24FT 48PT

Accounting 368

Higher education institutions A-Z

This section provides contact information for all higher education institutions in the UK and Ireland. You should always refer to each institution's website and prospectus for detailed information, including current fee levels and specific contacts. Institutions are listed in alphabetical order, although colleges of the University of the Arts London are listed under 'A'. Colleges of the University of London are listed under the respective college names. This index includes some further education colleges that provide postgraduate-level qualifications validated by another institution

A

University of Aberdeen
Postgraduate Admissions Office
King's College, Aberdeen AB24 3FX
01224 273506
pgadmissions@abdn.ac.uk
www.abdn.ac.uk

University of Abertay Dundee
Student Recruitment Office
Kydd Building, Dundee DD1 1HG
01382 308643
institute@abertay.ac.uk
www.abertay.ac.uk

Aberystwyth University
Postgraduate Admissions Office
Student Welcome Centre, Penglais
Aberystwyth, Ceredigion SY23 3FB
01970 622270
pg-admissions@aber.ac.uk
www.aber.ac.uk

Anglia Ruskin University
Bishop Hall Lane
Chelmsford CM1 1SQ
0845 271 3333
answers@anglia.ac.uk
www.anglia.ac.uk
See profile on page 22

Anglo-European College of Chiropractic
13-15 Parkwood Road
Bournemouth BH5 2DF
01202 436200
admissions@aecc-chiropractic.ac.uk
www.aecc.ac.uk

ARK Schools
65 Kingsway, London WC28 6TD
020 3116 0800
info@arkonline.org
www.arkschools.org

University of the Arts London: Camberwell College of Arts
Peckham Road, London SE5 8UF
020 7514 6302
info@camberwell.arts.ac.uk
www.camberwell.arts.ac.uk

University of the Arts London: Central Saint Martins College of Art and Design
Southampton Row, London WC1B 4AP
020 7514 7022
info@csm.arts.ac.uk
www.csm.arts.ac.uk

University of the Arts London: Chelsea College of Art and Design
16 John Islip Street, London SW1P 4JU
020 7514 7751
info@chelsea.arts.ac.uk
www.chelsea.arts.ac.uk

University of the Arts London: London College of Communication
Elephant and Castle, London SE1 6SB
020 7514 6569
info@lcc.arts.ac.uk
www.lcc.arts.ac.uk

University of the Arts London: London College of Fashion
20 John Princes Street
London W1G 0BJ
020 7514 7344
enquiries@fashion.arts.ac.uk
www.fashion.arts.ac.uk

University of the Arts London: Wimbledon College of Art
Merton Hall Road, London SW19 3QA
020 7514 9641
info@wimbledon.arts.ac.uk
www.wimbledon.arts.ac.uk

Aston University
Aston Triangle, Birmingham B4 7ET
0121 204 3000
registry@aston.ac.uk
www.aston.ac.uk

B

Bangor University
Postgraduate Admissions Office
Academic Registry
Bangor University
Bangor LL57 2DG
01248 383762
postgraduate@bangor.ac.uk
www.bangor.ac.uk
See profile on page 23

Barts and The London School of Medicine and Dentistry
Queen Mary, University of London
Mile End Road, London E1 4NS
020 7882 3377
pgsmd@qmul.ac.uk
www.smd.qmul.ac.uk

University of Bath
Graduate Office, Bath BA2 7AY
01225 383692
www.bath.ac.uk/ask-admissions
www.bath.ac.uk
See profile on page 22

University of Bath School of Management
Bath BA2 7AY
01225 386742
recep@management.bath.ac.uk
www.bath.ac.uk/management

Bath Spa University
Newton Park, Newton St Loe
Bath BA2 9BN
01225 875875
enquiries@bathspa.ac.uk
www.bathspa.ac.uk
See profile on page 24

University of Bedfordshire
Park Square, Luton LU1 3JU
0844 848 2234
Contact via www.beds.ac.uk/howtoapply/ask
www.beds.ac.uk
See profile on page 25

Belfast Metropolitan College
Brunswick Street, Belfast BT2 7GX
028 90 265265
central_admissions@belfastmet.ac.uk
www.belfastmet.ac.uk

Billericay Educational Consortium
School Centred Initial Teacher Training
C/O Oakfield Primary School
Scott Drive, Wickford SS12 9PW
01268 570944
bscitt@rmplc.co.uk
www.billericayscitt.com

Birkbeck, University of London
Malet Street, Bloomsbury
London WC1E 7HX
0845 601 0174
info@bbk.ac.uk
www.bbk.ac.uk

University of Birmingham
Edgbaston, Birmingham B15 2TT
0121 414 3344
pgadmissions@contacts.bham.ac.uk
www.bham.ac.uk

University College Birmingham
Summer Row, Birmingham B3 1JB
0121 243 0116
admissions@ucb.ac.uk
www.ucb.ac.uk

Birmingham City University
Franchise Street, Perry Barr
Birmingham B42 2SU
0121 331 5595
choices@bcu.ac.uk
www.bcu.ac.uk
See profile on page 24

Bishop Grosseteste University College Lincoln
Newport, Lincoln LN1 3DY
01522 527347
info@bishopg.ac.uk
www.bishopg.ac.uk

University of Bolton
Deane Road, Bolton BL3 5AB
01204 903903
enquiries@bolton.ac.uk
www.bolton.ac.uk

Arts University Bournemouth
Wallisdown, Poole BH12 5HH
01202 533011
general@aib.ac.uk
www.aucb.ac.uk

Bournemouth University
Fern Barrow, Talbot Campus
Poole BH12 5BB
08456 501 501 (UK callers only)
01202 961916
askbuenquiries@bournemouth.ac.uk
www.bournemouth.ac.uk
See profile on page 22

BPP University College
(BPP Business School
& BPP Law School)
Admissions and Enquiries
Aldine House, Aldine Place
142-144 Uxbridge Road
London W12 8AW
0845 077 5566
admissions@bpp.com
www.bpp.com

University of Bradford
Richmond Road, Bradford BD7 1DP
0800 073 1225
course-enquiries@bradford.ac.uk
www.brad.ac.uk

Bradford College
Great Horton Road, Bradford BD7 1AY
01274 433333
admissions@bradfordcollege.ac.uk
www.bradfordcollege.ac.uk

University of Brighton
Mithras House, Lewes Road
Brighton BN2 4AT
01273 644644
enquiries@brighton.ac.uk
www.brighton.ac.uk

University of Bristol
Postgraduate Recruitment
and Admissions Office
Students' Union Building
Queen's Road, Clifton, Bristol BS8 1LN
0117 954 5735
pg-admissions@bristol.ac.uk
www.bris.ac.uk

**University of the
West of England: Bristol**
Frenchay Campus, Coldharbour Lane
Bristol BS16 1QY
0117 328 3333
admissions@uwe.ac.uk
www.uwe.ac.uk

**British Institute of
Technology & E-commerce**
Avicenna House, 258-262 Romford
Road
London E7 9HZ
020 8552 3071
admissions@bite.ac.uk
www.bite.ac.uk

Brunel University London
Admissions Office, Uxbridge UB8 3PH
01895 265265
admissions@brunel.ac.uk
www.brunel.ac.uk

University of Buckingham
Admissions Office, Hunter Street
Buckingham MK18 1EG
01280 820313
info@buckingham.ac.uk
www.buckingham.ac.uk

Bucks New University
Queen Alexandra Road
High Wycombe HP11 2JZ
0800 0565 660 (UK)
+44 1494 522141 (overseas)
advice@bucks.ac.uk
www.bucks.ac.uk
See profile on page 27

C

University of Cambridge
The Old Schools, Trinity Lane
Cambridge, CB2 1TN
01223 760606
admissions@gradstudies.cam.ac.uk
www.cam.ac.uk

**Canterbury Christ Church
University**
Student Recruitment
(Postgraduate Admissions)
North Holmes Road
Canterbury CT1 1QU
01227 782900
admissions@canterbury.ac.uk
www.canterbury.ac.uk

Cardiff University
Postgraduate Recruitment Office
Student Recruitment and
Web Division, Deri House
2-4 Park Grove, Cardiff CF10 3PA
029 2087 0084
postgradenquiries@cardiff.ac.uk
www.cardiff.ac.uk
See profile on page 27

**Cardiff Metropolitan University
(UWIC)**
Admissions, Western Avenue
Cardiff CF5 2YB
029 2041 6044
courses@uwic.ac.uk
www.cardiffmet.ac.uk

**University of Central
Lancashire (UCLan)**
Preston, PR1 2HE
01772 892 400
cenquiries@uclan.ac.uk
www.uclan.ac.uk
See profile on page 28

**Central School of Speech and
Drama, University of London**
Eton Avenue, London NW3 3HY
020 7722 8183
enquiries@cssd.ac.uk
www.cssd.ac.uk

University of Chester
Parkgate Road, Chester CH1 4BJ
01244 512 456
PGCE 01244 512 527
postgrad@chester.ac.uk
www.chester.ac.uk

University of Chichester
Bishop Otter Campus, College Lane
Chichester PO19 6PE
01243 816002
admissions@chi.ac.uk
www.chi.ac.uk

Chiltern Training Group
Challney High School for Boys
and Community College
Stoneygate Road, Luton LU4 9TJ
01582 493680
info@chilterntraininggroup.org
www.chilterntraininggroup.org

Christie's Education London
153 Great Titchfield Street
London W1W 5BD
020 7665 4350
education@christies.com
www.christieseducation.com

City Lit
Keeley Street
Covent Garden
London WC2B 4BA
020 7492 2600
infoline@city.ac.uk
www.citylit.ac.uk

City University London
Northampton Square
London EC1V 0HB
020 7040 5060
enquiries@city.ac.uk
www.city.ac.uk
See profile on pages 30-31

City & Guilds of London Art School
124 Kennington Park Road
London SE11 4DJ
020 7735 2306
info@CityandGuildsArtSchool.ac.uk
www.CityandGuildsArtSchool.ac.uk

Cliff College
Calver, Hope Valley S32 3XG
01246 584200
admin@cliffcollege.ac.uk
www.cliffcollege.ac.uk

University College Cork (UCC)
Cork, Ireland
www.ucc.ie
+353 21 490 3000

Cornwall College
Trevenson Road, Pool
Redruth TR15 3RD
0845 223 2567
enquiries@cornwall.ac.uk
www.cornwall.ac.uk

Courtauld Institute of Art
Somerset House, Strand
London WC2R 0RN
020 7872 0220
pgadmissions@courtauld.ac.uk
www.courtauld.ac.uk

Coventry University
Priory Street, Coventry CV1 5FB
024 7615 2222
studentenquiries@coventry.ac.uk
www.coventry.ac.uk

Cranfield University
Cranfield, MK43 0AL
01234 750111
info@cranfield.ac.uk
www.cranfield.ac.uk

Cranfield University, Shrivenham
Royal Military College of Science
Shrivenham, Swindon SN6 8LA
01793 785400
academicreg@cranfield.ac.uk
www.cranfield.ac.uk/cds

University for the Creative Arts
New Dover Road, Canterbury
Kent CT1 3AN
01252 892883
admissions@ucreative.ac.uk
www.ucreative.ac.uk

University of Cumbria
Fusehill Street
Carlisle CA1 2HH
01228 616234
postgraduateadmissions@
cumbria.ac.uk
www.cumbria.ac.uk
See profile on page 32

**Cumbria Primary
Teacher Training**
CPTT Centre, High Street
Workington CA14 4ES
01900 325060
enquiries@cptt.org.uk
www.cptt.ac.uk

D

De Montfort University, Leicester
The Gateway, Leicester LE1 9BH
08459 454647 (UK)
+44 116 257 7513 (International)
enquiry@dmu.ac.uk/
international@dmu.ac.uk
www.dmu.ac.uk

University of Derby
Kedleston Road, Derby DE22 1GB
01332 590500
askadmissions@derby.ac.uk
www.derby.ac.uk

University Centre Doncaster
High Melton, Doncaster DN5 7SZ
0800 358 7474
he@don.ac.uk
www.don.ac.uk

Dublin City University
The Registry, Dublin 9, Ireland
+353-1-7005566
registry@dcu.ie
www.dcu.ie

University College Dublin
Belfield, Dublin 4, Ireland
+353-1-7164022/4043
graduatestudies@ucd.ie
www.ucd.ie

Dublin Institute of Technology
143-149 Rathmines Road, Dublin 6
+353-1-4023434
postgraduate@dit.ie
www.dit.ie

University of Dundee
Admissions and Student
Recruitment, Nethergate
Dundee DD1 4HN
01382 383838
postgrad-admissions@
dundee.ac.uk
www.dundee.ac.uk
See profile on page 29

Durham University
Graduate School
Mountjoy Research Centre
Block 2, Stockton Road
Durham DH1 3UP
0191 334 6492
pg.admissions@durham.ac.uk
www.durham.ac.uk

E

University of East Anglia
The Admissions Office
The Registry, Norwich NR4 7TJ
01603 591515
admissions@uea.ac.uk
www.uea.ac.uk
See profile on inside-back cover

University of East London
Docklands Campus, University Way
London E16 2RD
020 8223 3333
study@uel.ac.uk
www.uel.ac.uk

Edge Hill University
St Helens Road, Ormskirk L39 4QP
01695 575171
enquiries@edgehill.ac.uk
www.edgehill.ac.uk

The University of Edinburgh
Old College, South Bridge
Edinburgh EH8 9YL
0131 650 2160
postgrad@ed.ac.uk
www.ed.ac.uk/studying/postgraduate

The University of Edinburgh Business School
29 Buccleuch Place
Edinburgh EH8 9JS
Taught course enquiries:
0131 650 9663
hssug@ed.ac.uk
Research course enquiries:
0131 651 5337
phd@business-school.ed.ac.uk
www.business-school.ed.ac.uk
See profile on page 33

Edinburgh Napier University
Craiglockhart Campus
219 Collinton Road
Edinburgh EH14 1DJ
08455 203050
pgadmissions@napier.ac.uk
www.napier.ac.uk

University of Essex
Wivenhoe Park
Colchester CO4 3SQ
01206 872719
pgadmit@essex.ac.uk
www.essex.ac.uk
See profile on page 34

Essex Primary Schools Training Group
Harlow Centre, Partridge Road
Harlow, Essex CM18 6TE
01279 400139
info@essexteachertraining.co.uk
www.essexteachertraining.co.uk

College of Estate Management
Whiteknights, Reading
Berkshire RG6 6AW
0800 019 9697 (UK)
0118 921 4696 (International)
courses@cem.ac.uk
www.cem.ac.uk

European Business School London, Regent's College
Regent's Park, Inner Circle
London NW1 4NS
020 7487 7505
ebsl@regents.ac.uk
www.ebslondon.ac.uk

ESCP Europe Business School
527 Finchley Road, London NW3 7BG
0207 443 8800
info.uk@escpeurope.eu
www.escpeurope.eu

University of Exeter
Mail Room, The Old Library
Prince of Wales Road, Exeter EX4 4SB
01392 263316
pg-ad@exeter.ac.uk
www.exeter.ac.uk

F

Falmouth University
Admissions Office
Woodlane, Falmouth TR11 4RH
01326 211077
admissions@falmouth.ac.uk
www.falmouth.ac.uk

Farnborough College of Technology
Boundary Road
Farnborough GU14 6SB
01252 405555
info@farn-ct.ac.uk
www.farn-ct.ac.uk

Fitzwilliam Institute
Temple Court, Temple Road
Blackrock, Co. Dublin, Ireland
+353 1 283 4579
info@fitzwilliaminstitute.ie
www.fitzwilliaminstitute.ie

Forum for the Future
Overseas House
19-23 Ironmonger Row
London EC1V 3QN
020 7324 3630
info@forumforthefuture.org.uk
www.forumforthefuture.org.uk

G

NUI Galway
University Road, Galway, Ireland
+353 091 495 999
postgrad@nuigalway.ie
www.nuigalway.ie

GCU London
40 Fashion Street, Spitalfields
London, E1 6PX
0203 369 3000
enquiries@gculondon.ac.uk
www.gculondon.ac.uk

University of Glasgow
International and
Postgraduate Admissions
Student Services, The Fraser Building
65 Hillhead Street, Glasgow G12 8QF
0141 330 4045
pgadmissions@admin.gla.ac.uk
www.gla.ac.uk

Glasgow Caledonian University
City Campus
70 Cowcaddens Road
Glasgow G4 0BA
0141 331 3000
helpline@gcal.ac.uk (UK)
international@gcal.ac.uk
(International)
www.gcal.ac.uk

The Glasgow School of Art
167 Renfrew Street, Glasgow G3 6RQ
0141 353 4500
info@gsa.ac.uk
www.gsa.ac.uk

University of Gloucestershire
Recruitment Office
Hardwick Administration Centre
St Paul's Road, Cheltenham GL50 4BS
01242 714500
postgrad@glos.ac.uk
www.glos.ac.uk

Gloucestershire SCITT Consortium
St Peter's High School, Stroud Road
Tuffley, Gloucester GL4 0DD
01452 509208
www.gitep.co.uk

Glyndwr University
Plas Coch, Mold Road
Wrexham LL11 2AW
01978 293439
sid@glyndwr.ac.uk
www.glyndwr.ac.uk

Goldsmiths, University of London
Goldsmiths College, Lewisham Way
London SE14 6NW
020 7919 7060
admissions@gold.ac.uk
www.goldsmiths.ac.uk
See profile on page 37

Grand Union Training Partnership
Sponne School
Brackley Road, Towcester
Northamptonshire NN12 6DJ
01327 350284 ext. 253
www.gutp.org.uk

University of Greenwich
Old Royal Naval College, Park Row
Greenwich, London SE10 9LS
0800 005 006
courseinfo@greenwich.ac.uk
www.cms.gre.ac.uk

Griffith College Dublin
166-174 South Circular Road, Dublin 8
+353 1 415 0400
admissions@gcd.ie
www.gcd.ie

Grimsby Institute of Further & Higher Education
Nuns Corner, Grimsby,
North East Lincolnshire DN34 5BQ
0800 315002
infocent@grimsby.ac.uk
www.grimsby.ac.uk

H

Harper Adams University
Newport, Shropshire TF10 8NB
01952 815000
admissions@harper-adams.ac.uk
www.harper-adams.ac.uk
See profile on page 27

Heriot-Watt University
John Muir Building, Riccarton
Edinburgh EH14 4AS
0131 451 3729
pgadmissions@hw.ac.uk
www.hw.ac.uk

University of Hertfordshire
College Lane, Hatfield AL10 9AB
01707 284000
admissions@herts.ac.uk
www.herts.ac.uk

Heythrop College
University of London, Kensington
Square
London W8 5HN
020 7795 6600
enquiries@heythrop.ac.uk
www.heythrop.ac.uk

Holborn College
Woolwich Road, London SE7 8LN
020 8317 6000
admissions@holborncollege.ac.uk
www.holborncollege.ac.uk

University of Huddersfield
Student Admissions
and Records Office
Queensgate, Huddersfield HD1 3DH
01484 473969
admissionsandrecords@hud.ac.uk
www.hud.ac.uk

University of Hull
Cottingham Road, Hull HU6 7RX
01482 466850
pgstudy@hull.ac.uk
www.hull.ac.uk

University of Hull: Scarborough Campus
Filey Road, Scarborough YO11 3AZ
01723 362392
scarborough.campus@hull.ac.uk
www.hull.ac.uk/scarborough

Hull College
Learner Support Services
Queen's Gardens (Chesters Building)
Hull HU1 3DG
01482 598744
info@hull-college.ac.uk
www.hull-college.ac.uk

I

Imperial College London
Exhibition Road, London SW7 2AZ
020 7589 5111
www.imperial.ac.uk

Inchbald School of Design
Interior Design, 7 Eaton Gate
London SW1W 9BA
020 7730 5508
interiors@inchbald.co.uk
www.inchbald.co.uk

**Institute of Advanced Legal
Studies, School of Advanced Study**
University of London
Charles Clore House
17 Russell Square, London WC1B 5DR
020 7862 5800
ials@sas.ac.uk
www.sas.ac.uk/ials

The Institute of Cancer Research
123 Old Brompton Road
London SW7 3RP
020 7352 8133
www.icr.ac.uk

**Institute of Historical Research,
School of Advanced Study**
University of London, Senate House,
Malet Street, London WC1E 7HU
020 7862 8740
Ihr.reception@sas.ac.uk
www.ihr.sas.ac.uk

**Institute of Commonwealth
Studies, School of Advanced Study**
University of London, 2nd Floor
Southblock, Senate House
Malet Street, London, WC1E 7HU
020 7862 8844
ics@sas.ac.uk
www.commonwealth.sas.ac.uk

**Institute of Education,
University of London**
20 Bedford Way, London WC1H 0AL
+44 (0)20 7612 6000
info@ioe.ac.uk
www.ioe.ac.uk

**Institute of English Studies,
School of Advanced Study**
University of London, Room NG18
Senate House, Malet Street
London WC1E 7HU
020 7862 8680
cmps@sas.ac.uk
www.ies.sas.ac.uk

**Institute of Germanic & Romance
Studies, School of Advanced Study**
University of London, Senate House
Malet Street, London WC1E 7HU
020 7862 8677
igrs@sas.ac.uk
www.igrs.sas.ac.uk

**University of London
Institute in Paris**
11 Rue de Constantine
75430, Paris Cedex 07
010 33 1 44 11 73 83
www.bip.lon.ac.uk

**Institute for the Study
of the Americas, School
of Advanced Study**
University of London, Senate House
Malet Street, London WC1E 7HU
020 7862 8870
americas@sas.ac.uk
www.sas.ac.uk/ilas

**Institute for System Level
Integration (iSLI)**
Heriot-Watt University Research Park
Research Avenue North
Edinburgh EH14 4AP
+ 44 (0) 131 510 0670
info@sli-institute.ac.uk
www.sli-institute.ac.uk

**Islamic College
for Advanced Studies**
133 High Road, Willesden
London NW10 2SW
020 8451 9993
info@islamic-college.ac.uk
www.islamic-college.ac.uk

J

Jewish Primary Schools
SCITT Consortium
Bet Meir, 44A Albert Road
Hendon, London NW4 2SJ
020 8457 9706

K

Keele University
Postgraduate Office
Keele ST5 5BG
01782 734472/734370
postgrad@keele.ac.uk
www.keele.ac.uk
See profile on page 36

University of Kent
Information, Recruitment
& Admissions Office
The Registry, Canterbury CT2 7NZ
01227 827272
recruitment@kent.ac.uk
www.ukc.ac.uk

Kent and Medway Training
c/o The Leigh Technology Academy
Green Street Green Road
Dartford DA1 1QE
01322 620518
bsm@leighacademy.org.uk
www.kmtraining.org.uk

King's College London
The Strand, London WC2R 2LS
020 7836 5454
www.kcl.ac.uk

Kingston University London
Applicant Services (Postgraduate)
River House, 53-57 High Street
Kingston Upon Thames KT1 1LQ
020 8417 9000
aps@kingston.ac.uk
www.kingston.ac.uk
See profile on page 36

L

**Trinity Laban Conservatoire
of Music and Dance**
Creekside, London, SE8 3DZ
020 8305 4444
info@trinitylaban.ac.uk
www.trinitylaban.ac.uk

Lancaster University
Postgraduate Admissions Office
University House
Lancaster LA1 4YW
01524 592032
pgadmissions@lancaster.ac.uk
www.lancs.ac.uk

The College of Law
Braboeuf Manor, St Catherines
Guildford GU3 1HA
01483 216000
admissions@lawcol.co.uk
www.college-of-law.co.uk

University of Leeds
Course Enquiry Team
Leeds LS2 9JT
0113 243 1751
ask@leeds.ac.uk
www.leeds.ac.uk

Leeds Metropolitan University
Civic Quarter, Calverley Street
Leeds LS1 3HE
0113 812 3113
course-enquiries@leedsmet.ac.uk
www.lmu.ac.uk
See profile on page 39

Leeds College of Music
3 Quarry Hill, Leeds LS2 7PD
0113 222 3416
Enquiries.assistant@lcm.ac.uk
www.lcm.ac.uk

University of Leicester
University Road, Leicester LE1 7RH
0116 252 2298
www.le.ac.uk

Leeds Trinity University College
(previously Leeds Trinity and All
Saints)
Brownberrie Lane, Horsforth
Leeds LS18 5HD
0113 283 7123
admissions@leedstrinity.ac.uk
www.leedstrinity.ac.uk

University of Limerick
County Limerick
+353 (0) 61 202700
postgradadmissions@ul.ie
www.ul.ie

University of Lincoln
Brayford Pool, Lincoln LN6 7TS
01522 882000
www.lincoln.ac.uk

University of Liverpool
Student Recruitment
and Admissions Office
Foundation Building, Brownlow Hill
Liverpool L69 7ZX
0151 794 5927
pgrecruitment@liv.ac.uk
www.liv.ac.uk

**Liverpool School
of Tropical Medicine**
The Registry, Pembroke Place
Liverpool L3 5QA
0151 705 3100
www.liv.ac.uk/lstm

Liverpool Hope University
Postgraduate Admissions
Hope Park, Liverpool L16 9JD
0151 291 3000
postgraduate@hope.ac.uk
www.hope.ac.uk
See profile on page 40

**Liverpool John Moores
University**
The Recruitment Team
Roscoe Court, 4-6 Rodney Street
Liverpool L1 2TZ
0151 231 5090
courses@livjm.ac.uk
www.livjm.ac.uk
See profile on page 38

London Business School
Regent's Park, London NW1 4SA
020 7000 7000
www.london.edu

The London College, UCK
Victoria Gardens, Notting Hill Gate
London W11 3PE
0207 243 4000
admissions@lcuck.ac.uk
www.lcuck.ac.uk

**The London Consortium
Institute of Contemporary Arts**
12 Carlton House Terrace
London SW1Y 5AH
020 7836 7558
loncon@ica.org.uk
www.londonconsortium.com

**London Contemporary
Dance School**
The Place, 17 Duke's Road
London WC1H 9PY
020 7121 1000
www.theplace.org.uk/lcds

London Metropolitan University
166-220 Holloway Road
London N7 8DB
020 7133 4202
admissions@londonmet.ac.uk
www.londonmet.ac.uk

**London School of Economics
and Political Science (LSE)**
Houghton Street
London WC2A 2AE
020 7955 7160
www.lse.ac.uk/graduate
See profile on page 41

London School of Hygiene & Tropical Medicine
Keppell Street, London WC1E 7HT
020 7299 4646
registry@lshtm.ac.uk
www.lshtm.ac.uk

London South Bank University
90 London Road, London SE1 6LN
020 7815 6100
Course.enquiry@lsbu.ac.uk
www.lsbu.ac.uk

Loughborough University
Ashby Road
Loughborough LE11 3TU
01509 263171
www.lboro.ac.uk
See profile on page 42

Luther King House Theological College
Brighton Grove, Manchester M14 5JP
0161 249 2504
registrar@lkh.co.uk
www.ptem.org.uk

M

The University of Manchester
Oxford Road, Manchester M13 9PL
0161 275 4740
pg-admissions@manchester.ac.uk
www.manchester.ac.uk
See profile on page 43

Manchester Metropolitan University
All Saints Campus, Oxford Road
Manchester M15 6BH
0161 247 2000
enquiries@mmu.ac.uk
www.mmu.ac.uk
See profile on pages 44-45

University College Plymouth St Mark & St John
Derriford Road, Plymouth PL6 8BH
01752 636890
admissions@marjon.ac.uk
www.marjon.ac.uk

The Markfield Institute of Higher Education
Ratby Lane, Markfield LE67 9SY
01530 244922
www.mihe.org.uk

NUI Maynooth
Maynooth, Co. Kildare, Ireland
01 708 6000
admissions@nuim.ie
www.nuim.ie

Mid Essex SCITT Consortium
c/o Shenfield High School, Alexander Lane, Shenfield, Brentwood CM15 8RY
01277 249288
itt@shenfield.essex.sch.uk
www.midessexscitt.org

Middlesex University London
The Burroughs, Hendon
London N14 4YZ
020 8411 5555
enquiries@mdx.ac.uk
www.mdx.ac.uk
See profile on page 38

N

North East Surrey
College of Technology
Reigate Road, Ewell, Epsom KT17 3DS
020 8394 1731
info@nescot.ac.uk
www.nescot.ac.uk

Newcastle University
PG Admissions, Kings Gate
Newcastle Upon Tyne NE1 7RU
0191 222 5503
pgadmissions@ncl.ac.uk
www.ncl.ac.uk
See profile on page 46

Newman University College
Bartley Green, Birmingham B32 3NT
0121 476 1181
admissions@newman.ac.uk
www.newman.ac.uk

University of Wales, Newport
Caerleon Campus
Lodge Road, Caerleon
Newport NP18 3QT
01633 432432
uic@newport.ac.uk
www.newport.ac.uk

N.E. Essex Coastal Confederation SCITT and DRB
Clacton County High School
Walton Road, Clacton on Sea CO15 6DZ
01255 431949
teach@coastalscitt.co.uk
www.coastalscitt.co.uk

London North Consortium
Middlesex University, Trent Park
Bramley Road, London N14 4YZ
lonoco@mdx.ac.uk
www.lonoco.co.uk

University of Northampton
Park Campus, Boughton Green Road
Northampton NN2 7AL
01604 735500
study@northampton.ac.uk
www.northampton.ac.uk

Northumbria University
Ellison Building, Ellison Place
Newcastle upon Tyne NE1 8ST
0191 243 7420
er.admissions@northumbria.ac.uk
www.northumbria.ac.uk

City College Norwich
Ipswich Road, Norwich NR2 2LJ
01603 773311
information@ccn.ac.uk
www.ccn.ac.uk

Norwich University of the Arts
Francis House, 3-7 Redwell Street
Norwich NR2 4SN
01603 610561
info@nsad.ac.uk
www.nsad.ac.uk

The University of Nottingham
University Park
Nottingham NG7 2RD
0115 951 5559
postgraduate-enquiries@
nottingham.ac.uk
www.nottingham.ac.uk
See profiles on pages 3 & 49

Nottingham Trent University
Burton Street, Nottingham NG1 4BU
0115 848 4200
www.ntu.ac.uk
See profile on page 50

O

The Open University
Student Registration & Enquiry Service
The Open University, PO Box 197
Milton Keynes MK7 6BJ
0845 300 60 90
www.open.ac.uk

University of Oxford
University Offices, Wellington Square
Oxford OX1 2JD
01865 270000
www.ox.ac.uk

Oxford Brookes University
Headington Campus,
Oxford OX3 0BP
01865 484848
query@brookes.ac.uk
www.brookes.ac.uk
See profiles on pages 36 & 47

Oxford Centre for Hebrew and Jewish Studies
Yarnton Manor, Church Lane
Yarnton, Oxford OX5 1PY
01865 377946
enquiries@ochjs.ac.uk
www.ochjs.ac.uk

P

Peninsula College of Medicine and Dentistry
The John Bull Building
Tamar Science Park, Research Way
Plymouth, Devon PL6 8BU
01752 437444
info@pcmd.ac.uk
www.pcmd.ac.uk

Plymouth College of Art
Tavistock Place, Plymouth
Devon PL4 8AT
01752 203434
enquiries@plymouthart.ac.uk
www.plymouthart.ac.uk

Plymouth University
Drake Circus, Plymouth PL4 8AA
01752 585858
prospectus@plymouth.ac.uk
www.plymouth.ac.uk
See profiles on page 51 & outside-back cover

University of Portsmouth
Academic Registry
University House
Winston Churchill Avenue
Portsmouth PO1 2UP
023 9284 8484
infocentre@port.ac.uk
www.port.ac.uk
See profile on page 50

The Prince's Drawing School
19-22 Charlotte Road
London EC2A 3SG
020 7613 8522
registrar@princesdrawingschool.org
www.princesdrawingschool.org

The Prince's School of Traditional Arts
V.I.T.A. Programme
19-22 Charlotte Road
London EC2A 3SG
020 7613 8500
ririko.suzuki@psta.org.uk
www.psta.org.uk

Q

Queen Margaret University, Edinburgh
Edinburgh
Musselburgh EH21 6UU
0131 474 0000
admissions@qmu.ac.uk
www.qmuc.ac.uk

Queen Mary, University of London
Mile End Road, London E1 4NS
020 7882 5511
admissions@qmul.ac.uk
www.qmul.ac.uk

Queen's University Belfast
Postgraduate Office
Research and Regional Services
Lanyon North, Belfast, BT7 1NN
028 9097 2585
pg.office@qub.ac.uk
www.qub.ac.uk

R

Ravensbourne
(formally Ravensbourne College of Design and Communication)
6 Penrose Way, London SE10 0EW
020 3040 35000
info@rave.ac.uk
www.rave.ac.uk

University of Reading
Whiteknights, P.O. Box 217
Reading RG6 6AH
0118 378 8618
student.recruitment@
reading.ac.uk
www.reading.ac.uk
See profile on page 52

Regent's University London
Regent's College, Inner Circle
Regent's Park, London NW1 4NS
020 7487 7505
excel@regents.ac.uk
www.rbslondon.ac.uk
See profile on pages 54-55

Richmond, The American International University in London
Queen's Road
Richmond-upon-Thames
TW10 6JP
0208 332 9000
enroll@richmond.ac.uk
www.richmond.ac.uk
See profile on page 53

Robert Gordon University
Schoolhill, Aberdeen AB10 1FR
01224 262132
PostgraduateAdmissions@rgu.ac.uk
www.rgu.ac.uk

Robert Owen Society
Robert Owen House, 18 Burgess Street
Leominster, Herefordshire HR6 8DE
01568 615510
admin@robertowen.org
www.robertowen.org

The University of Roehampton
Erasmus House, Roehampton Lane
London SW15 5PU
020 8392 3000
enquiries@roehampton.ac.uk
www.roehampton.ac.uk

Rose Bruford College
Lamorbey Park, Burnt Oak Lane
Sidcup, Kent DA15 9DF
020 8308 2600
enquiries@bruford.ac.uk
www.bruford.ac.uk

Royal Academy of Music
Marylebone Road, London NW1 5HT
020 7873 7393
registry@ram.ac.uk
www.ram.ac.uk

Royal Agricultural University
Stroud Road, Cirencester GL7 6JS
01285 652531
admissions@rac.ac.uk
www.rac.ac.uk

Royal College of Art
Kensington Gore, London SW7 2EU
020 7590 4444
admissions@rca.ac.uk
www.rca.ac.uk

Royal College of Music
Prince Consort Road, London SW7 2BS
020 7589 3643
admissions@rcm.ac.uk
www.rcm.ac.uk

Royal College of Nursing Institute
20 Cavendish Square
London W1G 0RN
020 7647 3700
www.rcn.org.uk

Royal Conservatoire of Scotland
100 Renfrew Street, Glasgow G2 3DB
0141 332 4101
www.rcs.ac.uk

Royal Holloway, University of London
Egham Hill, Egham TW20 0EX
01784 443355
admissions@rhul.ac.uk
www.rhul.ac.uk
See profile on page 56

Royal Northern College of Music
124 Oxford Road
Manchester M13 9RD
0161 907 5200
info@rncm.ac.uk
www.rncm.ac.uk

Royal Veterinary College
University of London
Royal College Street, London NW1 0TU
020 7468 5134
graduateschool@rvc.ac.uk
www.rvc.ac.uk

Royal Welsh College of Music & Drama
Castle Grounds, Cathays Park
Cardiff CF10 3ER
029 2034 2854
admissions@rwcmd.ac.uk
www.rwcmd.ac.uk

S

University of Salford
Course Enquiries Service
Faraday House, The Crescent
Salford M5 4WT
0161 295 4545
course-enquiries@salford.ac.uk
www.salford.ac.uk

School of Oriental and African Studies (SOAS)
University of London
Thornhaugh Street, Russell Square
London WC1H 0XG
020 7637 2388
masteradmissions@soas.ac.uk
www.soas.ac.uk

The School of Pharmacy, University of London
29/39 Brunswick Square
London WC1N 1AX
020 7753 5800
registry@pharmacy.ac.uk
www.ulsop.ac.uk

Schumacher College
The Adminstrator, Schumacher College, The Old Postern
Dartington, Totnes TQ9 6EA
01803 865 934
admin@schumachercollege.org.uk
www.schumachercollege.org.uk

Scottish Agricultural College
Student Recruitment and Admissions Office
SAC Ayr Campus, Auchincruive Estates, Ayr KA6 5HW
0800 269453
recruitment@sac.co.uk
www.sac.ac.uk

The University of Sheffield
The Admissions Service
Student Services Department
9 Northumberland Street
Sheffield S10 2TT
0114 222 8030
www.shef.ac.uk

Sheffield Hallam University
City Campus, Howard Street
Sheffield S1 1WB
0114 225 5555
enquiries@shu.ac.uk
www.shu.ac.uk

Sotheby's Institute of Art
30 Bedford Square, London WC1B 3EE
020 7462 3232
info@sothebysinstitute.com
www.sothebysinstitute.com

University of South Wales
Enquiry and Admissions Unit
Trefforest, Pontypridd CF37 1DL
08456 434030 (UK)
+44 (0)1443 654450 (International)
applications@glam.ac.uk
www.glam.ac.uk
See profile on page 35

University of Southampton
University Road, Highfield
Southampton, SO17 1BJ
023 8059 5000
admissions@soton.ac.uk
www.southampton.ac.uk

Southampton Solent University
East Park Terrace
Southampton SO14 0YN
023 8031 9000
ask@solent.ac.uk
www.solent.ac.uk

Spurgeon's College
South Norwood Hill, London SE25 6DJ
020 8653 0850
enquiries@spurgeons.ac.uk
www.spurgeons.ac.uk

Staffordshire University
College Road, Stoke on Trent ST4 2DE
01782 292753
admissions@staffs.ac.uk
www.staffs.ac.uk

University of St Andrews
Postgraduate Admissions
Applications Centre, St Katharine's West 16 The Scores
St Andrews KY16 9AX
01334 476161
pgadmissions@st-andrews.ac.uk
www.st-and.ac.uk
See profile on page 57

St George's, University of London
Cranmer Terrace
Tooting SW17 0RE
020 8672 9944
www.sghms.ac.uk

University of Stirling
Stirling FK9 4LA
01786 466655
Graduate.admissions@stir.ac.uk
www.stir.ac.uk

St Loye's Foundation
Brittany House, New North Road
Exeter EX4 4EP
01392 255428
info@stloyes.ac.uk
www.stloyesfoundation.org.uk

St Mary's University College
Waldegrave Road, Strawberry Hill
Twickenham TW1 4SX
020 8240 4027
pgadmit@smuc.ac.uk
www.smuc.ac.uk

University of Strathclyde
16 Richmond Street
Glasgow G1 1XQ
0141 552 4400
enquiries@mis.strath.ac.uk
www.strath.ac.uk

St Thomas High School
Hatherleigh Road, St Thomas
Exeter EX2 9JU
01392 424717/254336

University of Sunderland
The Gateway, City Campus
Chester Road, Sunderland SR3 1SD
0191 515 3000
student-helpline@sunderland.ac.uk
www.sunderland.ac.uk

University of Surrey
Guildford GU2 7XH
0800 980 3200
pg-enquiries@surrey.ac.uk
www.surrey.ac.uk

University of Sussex
Sussex House, Brighton BN1 9RH
01273 876787
pg.enquiries@sussex.ac.uk
www.sussex.ac.uk

Swansea University
Singleton Park, Swansea SA2 8PP
01792 205678
www.swan.ac.uk
See profile on page 58

Swansea Metropolitan University
Mount Pleasant, Swansea SA1 6ED
01792 481010
enquiry@smu.ac.uk
www.smu.ac.uk

T

**TASMAC London
– School of Business**
1-3 Valley Drive, Kingsbury
London NW9 9NG
0208 206 0066
info@tasmac.org.uk
www.tasmac.org.uk

Teesside University
Graduate Research School
Middlesbrough, Tees Valley TS1 3BA
01642 218121
enquiries@tees.ac.uk
www.tees.ac.uk

**Thames Primary
SCITT Consortium**
Runwell Primary School
Canewdon Gardens, Runwell
Mickford, Essex SS11 7BJ
01268 570215
www.thamesprimaryconsortium.com

Titan Partnership Ltd
St George's Post 16 Centre
Great Hampton Row
Birmingham B19 3JG
0121 2124567
enquiry@titan.org.uk
www.titan.org.uk

**Trinity College Dublin,
The University of Dublin**
College Green, Dublin 2
+353 1 896 1000
gradinfo@tcd.ie
www.tcd.ie

Trinity College of Music
King Charles Court
Old Royal Naval College
Greenwich SE10 9JF
020 8305 4444
enquiries@tcm.ac.uk
www.tcm.ac.uk

**University of Wales Trinity Saint
David Carmarthen Campus**
Registry, Carmarthen SA31 3EP
01267 676716
registrycc@tsd.ac.uk
www.tsd.ac.uk

**University of Wales Trinity Saint
David Lampeter Campus**
Registry, Ceredigion SA48 7ED
01570 424831
registrylc@tsd.ac.uk
www.tsd.ac.uk

U

University College London (UCL)
Gower Street, London WC1E 6BT
020 7679 7742
admissions@ucl.ac.uk
www.ucl.ac.uk

UHI Millennium Institute
Executive Office, 12b Ness Walk
Inverness IV3 5SQ
0845 272 3600
www.uhi.ac.uk

**University Campus
Suffolk (UCS)**
Waterfront Building
Neptune Quay, Ipswich IP4 1QJ
01473 338833
info@ucs.ac.uk
www.ucs.ac.uk

University of Ulster
Cromore Rd, Coleraine BT52 1SA
08 700 400 700
www.ulster.ac.uk
See profile on page 59

W

Wandsworth Primary
School Consortium
Swaffield Primary School
St Ann's Hill, London SW18 2SA
020 88741442
www.scitt.co.uk

**Warburg Institute,
School of Advanced Study**
University of London, Woburn Square
London WC1H 0AB
020 7862 8949
SAS.Registry@sas.ac.uk
www.sas.ac.uk/warburg

The University of Warwick
Coventry CV4 7AL
024 7652 4585
pgadmissions@warwick.ac.uk
www.warwick.ac.uk

Webster Graduate School
Regent's College Inner Circle
Regent's Park, London NW1 4NS
020 7487 7452
webster@regents.ac.uk
www.webster.ac.uk

West Herts College
Watford Campus, Hempstead Road
Watford WD17 3EZ
01923 812345
admissions@westherts.ac.uk
www.westherts.ac.uk

University of West London
St Mary's Road, Ealing
London W5 5RF
0800 036 8888
courses@uwl.ac.uk
www.uwl.ac.uk
See profile on page 60

West Midlands Consortium
Thomas Telford School, Old Park
Telford TF3 4NW
01952 200000
wmc@ttsonline.net

University of the West of Scotland
Paisley Campus, High Street
Paisley PA1 2BE
0141 848 3000
info@uws.ac.uk
www.uws.ac.uk

University of Westminster
Headquarters Building
309 Regent Street, London W1B 2UW
020 7915 5511
course-enquiries@westminster.ac.uk
www.westminster.ac.uk

The University of Winchester
Winchester SO22 4NR
01962 827234
course.enquiries@
winchester.ac.uk
www.winchester.ac.uk
See profile on page 61

University of Wolverhampton
Wulfruna Street
Wolverhampton WV1 1LY
01902 321000
admissions@wlv.ac.uk
www.wolverhampton.ac.uk

University of Worcester
Henwick Grove
Worcester WR2 6AJ
01905 855000
www.worcester.ac.uk

Writtle College
Chelmsford, Essex CM1 3RR
01245 424200
info@writtle.ac.uk
www.writtle.ac.uk

Y

The University of York
The Graduate Schools Office
University of York
Haslington, York YO10 5DD
+44 (0) 1904 324000
pg-admissions@york.ac.uk
www.york.ac.uk
See profile on page 46

York St John University
Lord Mayors Walk, York, YO31 7EX
01904 624624
admissions@yorksj.ac.uk
www.yorksj.ac.uk

Subject index

This index is designed to aid your search for postgraduate taught courses and research opportunities which are listed alphabetically, by institution, under each relevant subject area. Listings start from page 77 of this directory. You can also search online at www.prospects.ac.uk/findcourses

Advertisers index

Acronyms and abbreviations

This list includes terms that you will see during your search for a course, research opportunity or funding

AI	Artificial Intelligence
ACU	Association of Commonwealth Universities
AGCAS	Association of Graduate Careers Advisory Services
AHRC	Arts and Humanities Research Council
APEL	Accreditation of Prior Experiential Learning
APL	Accreditation of Prior Learning
ARELS	Association of Recognised English Language Services
BBSRC	Biotechnology and Biological Sciences Research Council
BIS	Department for Business, Innovation and Skills
BPTC	Bar Professional Training Course
BVC	Bar Vocational Course
CASE	Co-operative Awards in Science and Engineering
CATS	Credit Accumulation and Transfer Scheme
CDL	Career Development Loans
COSHEP	Committee of Scottish Higher Education Principals
CPD	Continuing Professional Development
CPE	Common Professional Examination
CQSW	Certificate of Qualification in Social Work
DARDNI	Department of Agriculture & Rural Development, Northern Ireland
DBA	Doctorate of Business Administration
DENI	Department of Education Northern Ireland
DfID	Department for International Development
DL	Distance Learning
DLitt	Doctor of Literature
DPhil	Doctor of Philosophy
DTI	Department of Trade and Industry
EC	European Community
EdD	Doctor of Education
EEA	European Economic Area
EFL	English as a Foreign Language
ELT	English Language Teaching
EPSRC	Engineering and Physical Sciences Research Council
ESF	European Social Fund
ESOL	English for Speakers of Other Languages
ESRC	Economic and Social Research Council
EU	European Union
EYPS	Early Years Professional Status
FE	Further Education
FCO	Foreign and Commonwealth Office
FT	Full Time
FTE	Full-time Equivalent
GDL	Graduate Diploma in Law
GRAs	Graduate Research Assistantships
GSCC	General Social Care Council
GTAs	Graduate Teaching Assistantships
GTTR	Graduate Teacher Training Register
HE	Higher Education
HECSU	Higher Education Careers Services Unit
HEFCE	Higher Education Funding Council for England
HEFCW	Higher Education Funding Council for Wales
HEI	Higher Education Institution
HNC	Higher National Certificate
HND	Higher National Diploma
HVAC	Heating, Ventilating and Air Conditioning
ICT	Information and Communication Technologies
IET	The Institution of Engineering and Technology
IELTS	International English Language Testing System
IChemE	Institution of Chemical Engineers
IMechE	Institution of Mechanical Engineers
ITT	Initial Teacher Training
KTP	Knowledge Transfer Partnerships
LEA	Local Education Authority
LLB	Bachelor of Laws
LLM	Master of Laws
LPC	Legal Practice Course
MArch	Master of Architecture
MA	Master of Arts
MBA	Master of Business Administration
MEd	Master of Education
MEng	Master of Engineering
MLitt	Master of Literature
MMus	Master of Music
Mod	Modular degree/module
MPhil	Master of Philosophy
MPA	Master of Public Administration
MRC	Medical Research Council
MRes	Masters by Research
MSc	Master of Science
MSocSci	Master of Social Science
NATO	North Atlantic Treaty Organisation
NERC	Natural Environment Research Council
NGO	Non-Governmental Organisation
NHS	National Health Service
NIHEC	Northern Ireland Higher Education Council
NPC	National Postgraduate Committee
NQT	Newly Qualified Teacher
NUS	National Union of Students
OECD	Organisation for Economic Co-operation and Development
ORSAS	Overseas Research Students Awards Scheme
PCDL	Professional and Career Development Loans
PGCE	Postgraduate Certificate in Education
PGCert	Postgraduate Certificate
PGDE	Postgraduate Diploma in Education
PGDip	Postgraduate Diploma
PhD	Doctor of Philosophy
PT	Part Time
QAA	Quality Assurance Agency for Higher Education
QTS	Qualified Teacher Status
QUANGO	Quasi-Autonomous Non-Governmental Organisation
RAE	Research Assessment Exercise
RIBA	Royal Institute of British Architects
RICS	Royal Institute of Chartered Surveyors
SAAS	Students Awards Agency for Scotland
SCOTCAT	Scottish Credit Accumulation and Transfer Scheme
SFC	Scottish Funding Council
SSS	Scottish Studentship Scheme
STEM	Science, Technology, Engineering and Maths
STFC	Science and Technology Facilities Council
TEFL	Teaching English as a Foreign Language
TESOL	Teachers of English to Speakers of Other Languages
TOEFL	Test of English as a Foreign Language
TQA	Teaching Quality Assessment
UCAS	University and Colleges Admissions Service for the UK
UKCGE	UK Council for Graduate Education
UKCISA	UK Council for International Student Affairs
UN	United Nations
UUK	Universities UK
WHO	World Health Organisation